Beginning & Intermediate Algebra

Third Edition

Julie Miller
Daytona State College

Molly O'Neill
Daytona State College

Nancy Hyde
Broward College—Professor Emeritus

McGraw Hill

Connect
Learn
Succeed™

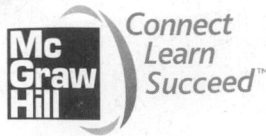

BEGINNING AND INTERMEDIATE ALGEBRA, THIRD EDITION

Published by McGraw-Hill, a business unit of The McGraw-Hill Companies, Inc., 1221 Avenue of the Americas, New York, NY 10020. Copyright © 2011 by The McGraw-Hill Companies, Inc. All rights reserved. Previous editions © 2008 and 2004. No part of this publication may be reproduced or distributed in any form or by any means, or stored in a database or retrieval system, without the prior written consent of The McGraw-Hill Companies, Inc., including, but not limited to, in any network or other electronic storage or transmission, or broadcast for distance learning.

Some ancillaries, including electronic and print components, may not be available to customers outside the United States.

This book is printed on acid-free paper.

1 2 3 4 5 6 7 8 9 0 WDQ/WDQ 1 0 9 8 7 6 5 4 3 2 1 0

ISBN 978–0–07–338421–4
MHID 0–07–338421–6

ISBN 978–0–07–729627–8 (Annotated Instructor's Edition)
MHID 0–07–729627–3

Vice President, Editor-in-Chief: *Marty Lange*
Vice President, EDP: *Kimberly Meriwether David*
Vice-President New Product Launches: *Michael Lange*
Editorial Director: *Stewart K. Mattson*
Executive Editor: *David Millage*
Senior Developmental Editor: *Emilie J. Berglund*
Senior Marketing Manager: *Victoria Anderson*
Lead Project Manager: *Peggy J. Selle*
Senior Production Supervisor: *Sherry L. Kane*
Lead Media Project Manager: *Stacy A. Patch*

Senior Designer: *Laurie B. Janssen*
(USE) Cover Image: © *James Balog/Gettyimages.*
Cover Illustration: *Imagineering Media Services, Inc.. Mosaic Royalty-Free images: Alamy, Brand X Images, Comstock, Corbis, Digital Vision, Getty Images, Imagestate, Photodisc, PunchStock, SuperStock.*
Lead Photo Research Coordinator: *Carrie K. Burger*
Supplement Producer: *Mary Jane Lampe*
Compositor: *Aptara, Inc.*
Typeface: *10/12 Times Ten Roman*
Printer: *World Color Press Inc.*

All credits appearing on page or at the end of the book are considered to be an extension of the copyright page.

Photo Credits: Page 1: © Getty images/Blend Images RF; p. 2: © Photodisc/Getty RF; p. 47: © Ryan McVay/Getty Images RF; p. 50(top): © BrandX/Jupiter RF; p. 50(bottom): © U.S. Air Force; p. 58(left): © Vol. 44/Corbis RF; p. 58(right): © Comstock images/Alamy; p. 70: © RF/Corbis; p. 71: © C. Borland/PhotoLink/Getty Images RF; p. 130: © Corbis RF; p. 131: © Keith Eng; p. 133(top): © Vol. 44/Corbis RF; p. 133(bottom): © Corbis/age fotostock RF; p. 134: © Comstock Images/Masterfile RF; p. 135: © BrandX/Punchstock RF; p. 137: © Stockbyte/Getty Images RF; p. 138: © BananaStock/JupiterImages RF; p. 139: © Comstock/Alamy RF; p. 141(left): © Creatas/PictureQuest RF; p. 141(right): © BananaStock/Punchstock RF; p. 142(left): © Comstock/PunchStock RF; p. 142(right): © Image100/Corbis RF; p. 151: © Corbis RF; p. 153: © BananaStock/PunchStock RF; p. 155: © Adam Gault/Getty RF; p. 156: © BananaStock/PictureQuest RF; p. 158(left): © Comstock/Jupiter Images RF; p. 158(top right): © The McGraw-Hill Companies, Inc./Jill Braaten, photographer ; p. 158(bottom right): © Getty RF; p. 161: © Dennis MacDonald/Alamy RF; p. 175: © Corbis RF; p. 197: © Getty RF; p. 222: © Getty RF; p. 225: © Vol. 107/Corbis RF; p. 226: © Erica Simone Leeds; p. 251: Julie Miller; p. 253: © PNC/Getty RF; p. 254: © Getty RF; p. 301: © Burke/Triolo/Brand X Pictures RF; p. 305: © Stockbyte/Punchstock Images RF; p. 309(left): © Corbis RF; p. 309(right): © S. Solum/PhotoLink/Getty Images RF; p. 310(top left): © The McGraw-Hill Companies, Inc./Jill Braaten, photographer; p. 310(top right): © Steve Mason/Getty Images RF; p. 310(bottom), p. 323: © PhotoDisc/Getty RF; p. 333: © Vol. 132/Corbis RF; p. 335: © The McGraw-Hill Companies, Inc./Jill Braaten, photographer; p. 349: © BrandX/Alamy RF; p. 369: © Getty RF; p. 408: © Alberto Fresco/Alamy RF; p. 409: © Brand X Photography/Veer RF; p. 467: © The McGraw-Hill Companies, Inc./Jill Braaten, photographer; p. 471: © IT Stock Free/Alamy RF; p. 483: © Ryan McVay/Getty RF; p. 494(top): © Corbis RF; p. 494(bottom): © Jeff Maloney/Getty Images RF; p. 527: © PhotoLink/Getty; p. 540: © Brand X Pictures/PunchStock RF; p. 545: © Getty Images RF; p. 547: © Duncan Smith/Getty Images RF; p. 549: © PhotoLink/Getty RF; p. 558: © PhotoDisc/Getty RF; p. 559: © BananaStock/PunchStock RF; p. 570: © Digital Vision/Getty Images RF; p. 610(left): © Sean justice/Corbis RF; p. 610(right): © BananaStock/PunchStock RF; p. 611: © Patrick Clark/Getty Images RF; p. 619: © Vol. 59/Corbis RF; p. 634: © The McGraw-Hill Companies, Inc./Dr. Al Telser, photographer; p. 635: © BrandX/Punchstock/Getty RF; p. 662: © The McGraw-Hill Companies, Inc./John Thoeming, photographer; p. 686: © Corbis RF; p. 739: © Jonnie Miles/Getty RF; p. 745: © Vol. 145/Corbis RF; p. 749: © Image Source RF; p. 783: © Corbis RF; p. 797: © Hisham Ibrahim/Corbis RF; p. 822: © Royalty-Free/CORBIS; p. 826: © The McGraw-Hill Companies, Inc./Jill Braaten, photographer; p. 833: © Medioimages/Superstock RF; p. 834: © Photodisc/Getty Images RF; p. 855: © Corbis RM; p. 872: © PhotoDisc/Getty RF; p. 944(bottom): © Royalty-Free/CORBIS; p. 933(top): © Getty Images/Photodisc RF; p. 1011: © Steve Mason/Getty Images RF; p. A-23: © R. Morley/PhotoLink/Getty RF.

Library of Congress Cataloging-in-Publication Data

Miller, Julie, 1962-
 Beginning and intermediate algebra / Julie Miller, Molly O'Neill. — 3rd ed. / Nancy Hyde ; with contributions by Mitchel Levy.
 p. cm.
 Includes index.
 ISBN 978–0–07–338421–4 — ISBN 0–07–338421–6 (hard copy : alk. paper) 1. Algebra—Textbooks. I. O'Neill, Molly, 1953- II. Hyde, Nancy. III. Title.

QA152.3.M57 2011
512.9—dc22
                         2009031496

www.mhhe.com

Letter from the Authors

Dear Colleagues,

We originally embarked on this textbook project because we were seeing a lack of student success in our developmental math sequence. In short, we were not getting the results we wanted from our students with the materials and textbooks that we were using at the time. The primary goal of our project was to create teaching and learning materials that would get better results.

At Daytona State College, our students were instrumental in helping us develop the clarity of writing; the step-by-step examples; and the pedagogical elements, such as Avoiding Mistakes, Concept Connections, and Problem Recognition Exercises, found in our textbooks. They also helped us create the content for the McGraw-Hill video exercises that accompany this text. Using our text with a course redesign at Daytona State College, our student success rates in developmental courses have improved by 20% since 2006 (for further information, see *The Daytona Beach News Journal,* December 18, 2006). We think you will agree that these are the kinds of results we are all striving for in developmental mathematics courses.

This project has been a true collaboration with our Board of Advisors and colleagues in developmental mathematics around the country. We are sincerely humbled by those of you who adopted the first edition and the over 400 colleagues around the country who partnered with us providing valuable feedback and suggestions through reviews, symposia, focus groups, and being on our Board of Advisors. You partnered with us to create materials that will help students get better results. For that we are immeasurably grateful.

As an author team, we have an ongoing commitment to provide the best possible text materials for instructors and students. With your continued help and suggestions we will continue the quest to help all of our students get better results.

Sincerely,

Julie Miller
julie.miller.math@gmail.com

Molly O'Neill
molly.s.oneill@gmail.com

Nancy Hyde
nhyde@montanasky.com

About the Authors

Julie Miller

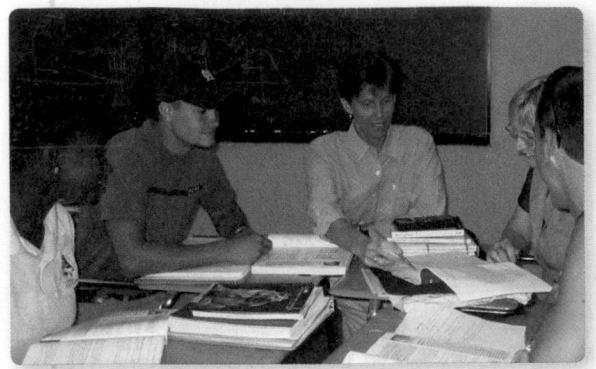

Julie Miller has been on the faculty in the School of Mathematics at Daytona State College for 20 years, where she has taught developmental and upper-level courses. Prior to her work at DSC, she worked as a software engineer for General Electric in the area of flight and radar simulation. Julie earned a bachelor of science in applied mathematics from Union College in Schenectady, New York, and a master of science in mathematics from the University of Florida. In addition to this textbook, she has authored several course supplements for college algebra, trigonometry, and precalculus, as well as several short works of fiction and nonfiction for young readers.

"My father is a medical researcher, and I got hooked on math and science when I was young and would visit his laboratory. I can remember using graph paper to plot data points for his experiments and doing simple calculations. He would then tell me what the peaks and features in the graph meant in the context of his experiment. I think that applications and hands-on experience made math come alive for me and I'd like to see math come alive for my students."

—Julie Miller

Molly O'Neill

Molly O'Neill is also from Daytona State College, where she has taught for 22 years in the School of Mathematics. She has taught a variety of courses from developmental mathematics to calculus. Before she came to Florida, Molly taught as an adjunct instructor at the University of Michigan–Dearborn, Eastern Michigan University, Wayne State University, and Oakland Community College. Molly earned a bachelor of science in mathematics and a master of arts and teaching from Western Michigan University in Kalamazoo, Michigan. Besides this textbook, she has authored several course supplements for college algebra, trigonometry, and precalculus and has reviewed texts for developmental mathematics.

"I differ from many of my colleagues in that math was not always easy for me. But in seventh grade I had a teacher who taught me that if I follow the rules of mathematics, even I could solve math problems. Once I understood this, I enjoyed math to the point of choosing it for my career. I now have the greatest job because I get to do math every day and I have the opportunity to influence my students just as I was influenced. Authoring these texts has given me another avenue to reach even more students."

—Molly O'Neill

Nancy Hyde served as a full-time faculty member of the Mathematics Department at Broward College for 24 years. During this time she taught the full spectrum of courses from developmental math through differential equations. She received a bachelor of science degree in math education from Florida State University and a master's degree in math education from Florida Atlantic University. She has conducted workshops and seminars for both students and teachers on the use of technology in the classroom. In addition to this textbook, she has authored a graphing calculator supplement for *College Algebra*.

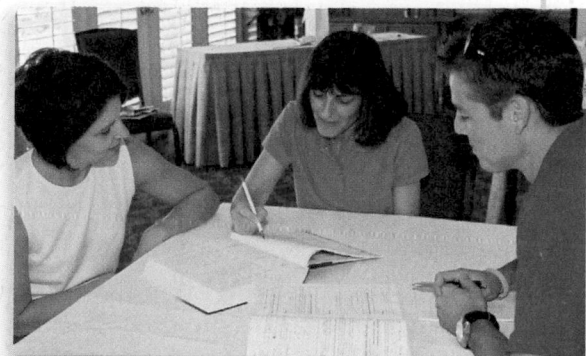

"I grew up in Brevard County, Florida, with my father working at Cape Canaveral. I was always excited by mathematics and physics in relation to the space program. As I studied higher levels of mathematics I became more intrigued by its abstract nature and infinite possibilities. It is enjoyable and rewarding to convey this perspective to students while helping them to understand mathematics."

—Nancy Hyde

*D*edication

To Susan and Jim Conway
 —*Julie Miller*

To Nora, Stu, and Jonathan
 —*Molly O'Neill*

To Kristine
 —*Nancy Hyde*

Get Better Results with Miller/O'Neill/Hyde

About the Cover

A mosaic is made up of pieces placed together to create a unified whole. Similarly, a beginning and intermediate algebra course provides an array of topics that together create a solid mathematical foundation for the developmental mathematics student.

The Miller/O'Neill/Hyde developmental mathematics series helps students see the whole picture through better pedagogy and supplemental materials. In this *Beginning and Intermediate Algebra* textbook, Julie Miller, Molly O'Neill, and Nancy Hyde focused their efforts on guiding students successfully through core topics, building mathematical proficiency, and getting better results!

"We originally embarked on this textbook project because we were seeing a lack of student success in courses beyond our developmental sequence. We wanted to build a better bridge between developmental algebra and higher level math courses. Our goal has been to develop pedagogical features to help students achieve better results in mathematics."

—Julie Miller, Molly O'Neill, Nancy Hyde

How Will Miller/O'Neill/Hyde Help Your Students *Get Better Results?*

Better Clarity, Quality, and Accuracy

Julie Miller, Molly O'Neill, and Nancy Hyde know what students need to be successful in mathematics. Better results come from clarity in their exposition, quality of step-by-step worked examples, and accuracy of their exercises sets; but it takes more than just great authors to build a textbook series to help students achieve success in mathematics. Our authors worked with a strong mathematical team of instructors from around the country to ensure that the clarity, quality, and accuracy you expect from the Miller/O'Neill/Hyde series was included in this edition.

> "I think the level of rigor is perfect for my students. I have examined other textbooks that would have been placed at the extremes of a continuum. This book is, in the words of Goldilocks, 'just right.'"
> —Angie McCombs, *Illinois State University*

Better Exercise Sets!

Comprehensive sets of exercises are available for every student level. Julie Miller, Molly O'Neill, and Nancy Hyde worked with a board of advisors from across the country to offer the appropriate depth and breadth of exercises for your students. **Problem Recognition Exercises** were created to improve student performance while testing.

Our practice exercise sets help students progress from skill development to conceptual understanding. Student tested and instructor approved, the Miller/O'Neill/Hyde exercise sets will help your student *get better results*.

- ▶ **Problem Recognition Exercises**
- ▶ **Skill Practice Exercises**
- ▶ **Study Skills Exercises**
- ▶ **Mixed Exercises**
- ▶ **Expanding Your Skills Exercises**

> "Plenty of exercises covering all concepts. The mixed exercises help students to realize they have to be aware of the difference between types of problems. The quality of exercises range from basic to more difficult concepts with a good transition between the two, and they are relevant to the concepts taught in the section."
> —Natalie Weaver, *Daytona State College*

Better Step-By-Step Pedagogy!

Intermediate Algebra provides enhanced step-by-step learning tools to help students *get better results*.

- ▶ **Worked Examples** provide an "easy-to-understand" approach, clearly guiding each student through a step-by-step approach to master each practice exercise for better comprehension.

- ▶ **TIPs** offer students extra cautious direction to help improve understanding through hints and further insight.

- ▶ **Avoiding Mistakes** boxes alert students to common errors and provide practical ways to avoid them. Both of these learning aids will help students get better results by showing how to work through a problem using a clearly defined step-by-step methodology that has been class tested and student approved.

> "MOH gives a more detailed explanation of the material. MOH leaves no stone unturned."
> —Joseph Kazimir, *East Los Angeles College*

> "The textbook does a good job of warning students of possible errors and commonly made mistakes per section. Students seem to appreciate the fact that they have been warned and they are able to prevent the mistakes from happening."
> —Alberto Guerra, *Saint Phillips College*

Formula for Student Success

Step-by-Step Worked Examples

► Do you get the feeling that there is a disconnection between your students' class work and homework?

► Do your students have trouble finding worked examples that match the practice exercises?

► Do you prefer that your students see examples in the textbook that match the ones you use in class?

Miller/O'Neill/Hyde's *Worked Examples* offer a clear, concise methodology that replicates the mathematical processes used in the authors' classroom lectures!

"The MOH text does an excellent job of providing numerous in-depth examples on the topic. They are easy to follow and flow well."

—Melanie Largin, *Georgia Highlands College*

Classroom Examples: pp. 362–363, Exercises 36, 38, and 42

Example 4 Simpl... ...g Expressions with Negative Exponents

Simplify. Assume tha... $x \neq 0$.

a. $(5x)^{-3}$ **b.** $5x^{-3}$ **c.** $-5x^{-3}$

Solution:

a. $(5x)^{-3} = \left(\dfrac{1}{5x}\right)^3$ Take the reciprocal of th... of the exponent.

$= \dfrac{(1)^3}{(5x)^3}$ Apply the exponen... parentheses.

$= \dfrac{1}{125x^3}$ Simplify.

b. $5x^{-3} = 5 \cdot x^{-3}$ Note that the exponent, ...

$= 5 \cdot \dfrac{1}{x^3}$ Rewrite x^{-3} as $\dfrac{1}{x^3}$.

$= \dfrac{5}{x^3}$ Multiply.

c. $-5x^{-3} = -5 \cdot x^{-3}$ Note that the exponent, -3, applies only to x, and that -5 is a coefficient.

$\dfrac{1}{...}$ ... $^{-3}$ as $\dfrac{1}{x^3}$.

...$w \neq 0$.

$-2w^{-4}$

"Good clear worked examples with a clear step-by-step approach to solving them. This is a good idea as many of our students benefit from having a clear list of steps and the reason behind each step being used. This allows them to see why the method works."

—Donald Robertson, *Olympic College*

"The worked examples illustrate the mechanics very well. I often find myself saying, "If you need more help, the textbook has a very nice example on page [x]." It would have been difficult to improve upon them. Again, the text and tips included with these examples often include things I have said to my own students, so I feel like the authors "gel" with my approach to teaching."

—Angie McCombs, *Illinois State University*

To ensure that the classroom experience also matches the examples in the text and the practice exercises, we have included references to even-numbered exercises to be used as Classroom Examples. These exercises are highlighted in the Practice Exercises at the end of each section.

Better Learning Tools

Chapter Openers

Tired of students not being prepared? The Miller/O'Neill/Hyde *Chapter Openers* help students get better results through engaging *Puzzles and Games* that introduce the chapter concepts and ask "Are You Prepared?"

"I liked how the MOH puzzle asked questions that made use of many of the concepts students will encounter in the chapter."

—Michelle Jackson,
Bowling Green Community College at WKU

Chapter 6

This chapter is devoted to factoring polynomials for the purpose of solving equations.

Are You Prepared?

Along the way, we will need the skill of recognizing perfect squares and perfect cubes. A perfect square is a number that is a square of a rational number. For example, 49 is a perfect square because $49 = 7^2$. We also will need to recognize perfect cubes. A perfect cube is a number that is a cube of a rational number. For example, 125 is a perfect cube because $125 = 5^3$.

To complete the puzzle, first answer the questions and fill in the appropriate box. Then fill the grid so that every row, every column, and every 2 × 3 box contains the digits 1 through 6.

- **A.** What number squared is 1?
- **B.** What number squared is 16?
- **C.** What number cubed is 1?
- **D.** What number squared is 36?
- **E.** What number squared is 25?
- **F.** What number cubed is 64?
- **G.** What number cubed is 8?
- **H.** What number cubed is 27?
- **I.** What number squared is 4?
- **J.** What number squared is 9?

"The puzzle allows the students to provide input and achieve a small measure of success at the outset of the chapter. This should help to ease their anxiety and increase their self-efficacy."

—David Clutts, *Southeast Kentucky Community & Technical College*

TIP and Avoiding Mistakes Boxes

TIP and Avoiding Mistakes boxes have been created based on the authors' classroom experiences—they have also been integrated into the **Worked Examples.** These pedagogical tools will help students get better results by learning how to work through a problem using a clearly defined step-by-step methodology.

Example 10 Factoring by Grouping

Factor by grouping. $ax + ay - x - y$

Solution:

$ax + ay - x - y$ **Step 1:** Identify and factor out the GCF from all four terms. In this case, the GCF is 1.

$= ax + ay - x - y$ Group the first pair of terms and the second pair of terms.

$= a(x + y) - 1(x + y)$ **Step 2:** Factor out a from the first pair of terms. Factor out -1 from the second pair of terms. (This causes sign changes within the second parentheses.) The terms in parentheses now match.

$= (x + y)(a - 1)$ **Step 3:** Factor out the common binomial factor.

Check: $(x + y)(a - 1) = x(a) + x(-1) + y(a) + y(-1)$
$= ax - x + ay - y$ ✔

Skill Practice Factor by grouping.
15.

Avoiding Mistakes

In step 2, the expression $a(x + y) - (x + y)$ is not yet factored completely because it is a *difference*, not a product. To factor the expression, you must carry it one step further.

$a(x + y) - 1(x + y)$
$= (x + y)(a - 1)$

The factored form must be represented as a product.

"Without question, Avoiding Mistakes is the most helpful for me in the classroom."
—Joseph Howe, *St. Charles Community College*

Avoiding Mistakes Boxes:

Avoiding Mistakes boxes are integrated throughout the textbook to alert students to common errors and how to avoid them.

"I really like the Avoiding Mistakes and the TIPS in the margins. I so often find when I'm reading them, that they are word-for-word what I've been saying for 15 years."

—Angie Russell, *Wenatchee Valley College*

"These elements are excellent. I went from section to section looking for specific tips, and found every one of them in the text."

—Tim Chappell, *Longview Community College*

TIP Boxes

Teaching tips are usually revealed only in the classroom. Not anymore! TIP boxes offer students helpful hints and extra direction to help improve understanding and further insight.

TIP: Notice that the sign of each term is changed when finding the opposite of a polynomial.

Better Exercise Sets! Better Practice! Better Results!

▶ Do your students have trouble with problem solving?

▶ Do you want to help students overcome math anxiety?

▶ Do you want to help your students improve performance on math assessments?

Problem Recognition Exercises

Problem Recognition Exercises present a collection of problems that look similar to a student upon first glance, but are actually quite different in the manner of their individual solutions. Students sharpen critical thinking skills and better develop their "solution recall" to help them distinguish the method needed to solve an exercise—an essential skill in developmental mathematics.

Problem Recognition Exercises, tested in a developmental mathematics classroom, were created to improve student performance while testing.

"Provides a good opportunity to compare and contrast the different types of problems and the approaches to solving them."

—Elsie Newman, *Owens Community College*

Problem Recognition Exercises

Comparing Rational Equations and Rational Expressions

Often adding or subtracting rational expressions is confused with solving rational equations. When adding rational expressions, we combine the terms to simplify the expression. When solving an equation, we clear the fractions and find numerical solutions, if possible. Both processes begin with finding the LCD, but the LCD is used differently in each process. Compare these two examples.

Example 1:

Add. $\dfrac{4}{x} + \dfrac{x}{3}$ (The LCD is $3x$.)

$$= \dfrac{3}{3} \cdot \left(\dfrac{4}{x}\right) + \left(\dfrac{x}{3}\right) \cdot \dfrac{x}{x}$$

$$= \dfrac{12}{3x} + \dfrac{x^2}{3x}$$

$$= \dfrac{12 + x^2}{3x} \quad \text{The answer is a rational expression.}$$

Example 2:

Solve. $\dfrac{4}{x} + \dfrac{x}{3} = -\dfrac{8}{3}$ (The LCD is $3x$.)

$$\dfrac{3x}{1}\left(\dfrac{4}{x} + \dfrac{x}{3}\right) = \dfrac{3x}{1}\left(-\dfrac{8}{3}\right)$$

$$12 + x^2 = -8x$$

$$x^2 + 8x + 12 = 0$$

$$(x + 2)(x + 6) = 0$$

$$x + 2 = 0 \text{ or } x + 6 = 0$$

$$x = -2 \text{ or } x = -6 \quad \text{The answer is the set } \{-2, -6\}.$$

For Exercises 1–20, solve the equation or simplify the expression by combining the terms.

1. $\dfrac{y}{2y + 4} - \dfrac{2}{y^2 + 2y}$

2. $\dfrac{1}{x + 2} + 2 = \dfrac{x + 11}{x + 2}$

3. $\dfrac{5t}{2} - \dfrac{t - 2}{3} = 5$

4. $3 - \dfrac{2}{a - 5}$

5. $\dfrac{7}{6p^2} + \dfrac{2}{9p} + \dfrac{1}{3p^2}$

6. $\dfrac{3b}{b + 1} - \dfrac{2b}{b - 1}$

9. $\dfrac{1}{x - 6} - \dfrac{3}{^2 - 6x} = \dfrac{4}{x}$

"The PREs are a great addition to the text. These exercises are great: they require critical thinking, address appropriate content, and are at a fitting level of difficulty."

—Richard Hobbs, *Mission College*

"Love these!!!!"

—Vicki McMillian, *Ocean County College*

Get Better Results

Student Centered Applications!

The Miller/O'Neill/Hyde Board of Advisors partnered with our authors to bring the *best applications* from every region in the country! These applications include real data and topics that are more relevant and interesting to today's student.

47. The amount of pollution entering the atmosphere over a given time varies directly as the number of people living in an area. If 80,000 people cause 56,800 tons of pollutants, how many tons enter the atmosphere in a city with a population of 500,000?

Group Activities!

Each chapter concludes with a Group Activity to promote classroom discussion and collaboration—helping students not only to solve problems but to explain their solutions for better mathematical mastery. Group Activities are great for instructors and adjuncts—bringing a more interactive approach to teaching mathematics! All required materials, activity time, and suggested group sizes are provided in the end-of-chapter material. Activities include Computing Body Mass Index, Computing Monthly Mortgage Payments, Deciphering a Coded Message and more!

Group Activity

Computing Monthly Mortgage Payments

Materials: A calculator

Estimated Time: 15–20 minutes

Group Size: 3

When a person borrows money to buy a house, the bank usually requires a down payment of between 0% and 20% of the cost of the house. The bank then issues a loan for the remaining balance on the house. The loan to buy a house is called a *mortgage*. Monthly payments are made to pay off the mortgage over a period of years.

A formula to calculate the monthly payment, P, for a loan is given by the complex fraction:

$$P = \frac{\dfrac{Ar}{12}}{1 - \dfrac{1}{\left(1 + \dfrac{r}{12}\right)^{12t}}}$$

where
- P is the monthly payment
- A is the original amount of the mortgage
- r is the annual interest rate written as a decimal
- t is the term of the loan in years

Suppose a person wants to buy a $200,000 house. The bank requires a down payment of 20%, and the loan issued for 30 years at 7.5% interest for 30 years.

1. Find the amount of the down payment. _____

2. Find the amount of the mortgage. _____

3. Find the monthly payment (to the nearest cent). _____

"A great idea, and beneficial when you have, as our school, multiple part-timers teaching sections. Brings an aspect of useful uniformity to the different sections."

—Don York, *Danville Area Community College*

uestion 3 by the total text of the problem.

oan for the house? _____

6. What was the total amount paid to the bank (include the down payment). _____

"This is another useful feature of this textbook and I like the idea of giving our students the opportunity to work together and to communicate with each other in a "mathematical way". The group activity topics are an excellent feature.

—Donald Robertson, *Olympic College*

Dynamic Math Animations

The Miller/O'Neill/Hyde author team has developed a series of Flash animations to illustrate difficult concepts where static images and text fall short. The animations leverage the use of on-screen movement and morphing shapes to enhance conceptual learning. For example, one animation "cuts" a triangle into three pieces and rotates the pieces to show that the sum of the angular measures equals 180° (below).

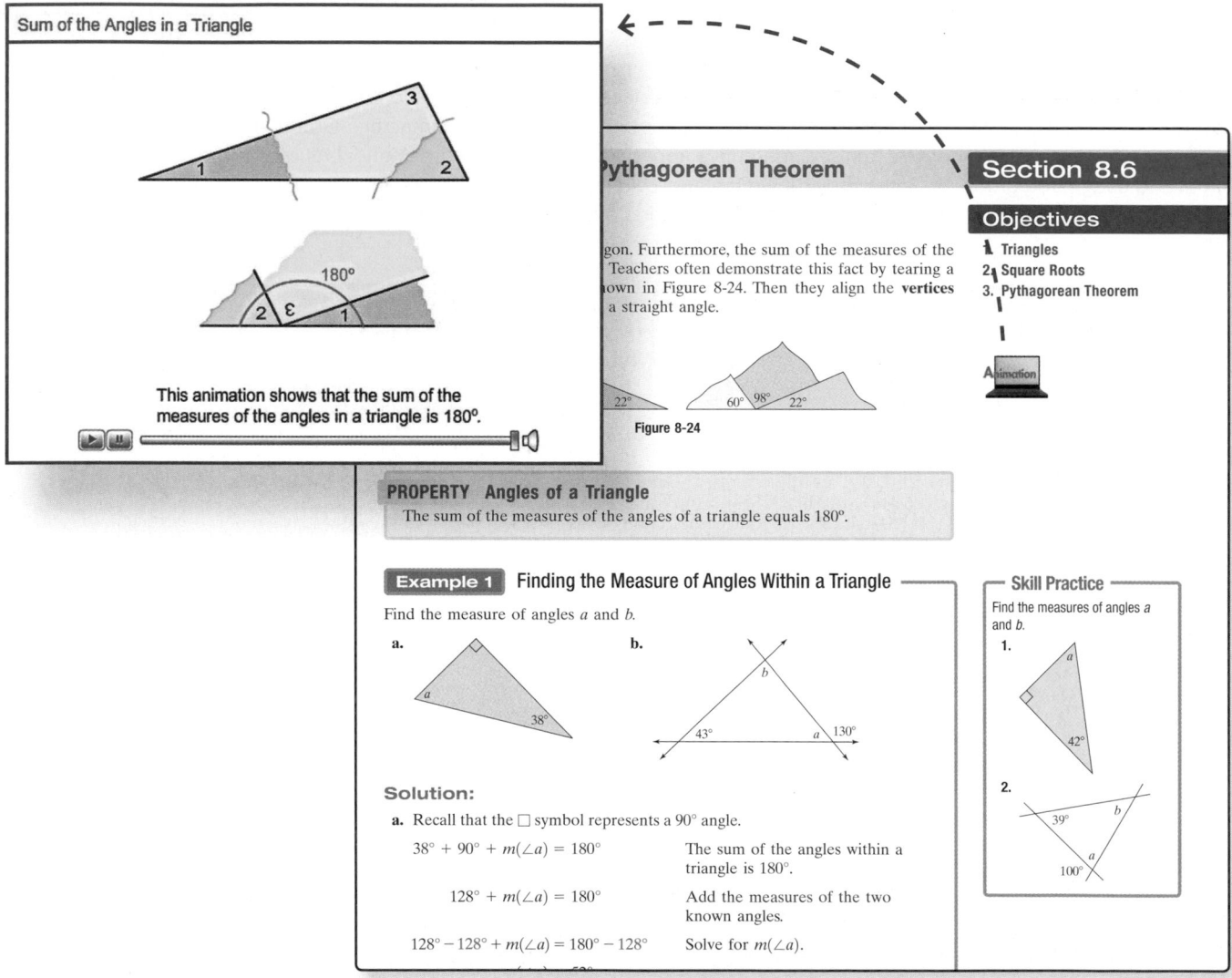

Through their classroom experience, the authors recognize that such media assets are great teaching tools for the classroom and excellent for online learning. The Miller/O'Neill/Hyde animations are interactive and quite diverse in their use. Some provide a virtual laboratory for which an application is simulated and where students can collect data points for analysis and modeling. Others provide interactive question-and-answer sessions to test conceptual learning. For word problem applications, the animations ask students to estimate answers and practice "number sense."

Get Better Results

The animations were created by the authors based on over 75 years of combined teaching experience! To facilitate the use of the animations, the authors have placed icons in the text to indicate where animations are available. Students and instructors can access these assets online in MathZone or ALEKS.

Modeling Using a Linear Equation in Two Variables

x Time (hr)	y Height (in.)
1	7.5
1.4	10.5
1.8	13.5
2.7	20.25
3.6	27
4.4	33
5.3	39.75
6.1	45.75

Animate

60 in.
40 in.   **Get data point**
20 in.
0 in.   Click here

Click on the "*Get data point*" button several times.

Copyright © 2009 Julie Miller

2. Graphing Linear Equations i

In the introduction to this section, we found $x + y = 4$. If we graph these solutions, notice Figure 9-9.)

Equation: $x + y = 4$

Several solutions: $(2, 2)$

$(1, 3)$

$(4, 0)$

$(-1, 5)$

The equation actually has infinitely many soluti This is because there are infinitely many comb tions of x and y whose sum is 4. The graph o solutions to this equation makes up the line shown each end indicate that the line extends infinitely. This is called the *graph of the equation*.

The graph of a linear equation is a line. Therefore, we need to plot at least two points and then draw the line between them. This is demonstrated in Example 4.

Skill Practice

Graph the equation.

7. $-x + y = 4$

Example 4   Graphing a Linear Equation

Graph the equation. $-x + y = 2$

Solution:

We will find three ordered pairs that are solutions to $-x + y = 2$. To find the ordered pairs, choose arbitrary values for x or y, such as those shown in the table. Then complete the table.

x	y	
3		⟶ (3,)
	−2	⟶ (, −2)
−1		⟶ (−1,)

Complete: $(3,)$

$-x + y = 2$

$-(3) + y = 2$

$-3 + 3 + y = 2 + 3$

$y = 5$

Complete: $(, -2)$

$-x + y = 2$

$-x + (-2) = 2$

$-x - 2 + 2 = 2 + 2$

$-x = 4$

$x = -4$

Complete: $(-1,)$

$-x + y = 2$

$-(-1) + y = 2$

$1 + y = 2$

$1 - 1 + y = 2 - 1$

$y = 1$

Answer

7.

$-x + y = 4$

Get Better Results

Experience Student Success!

ALEKS® ALEKS is a unique online math tool that uses adaptive questioning and artificial intelligence to correctly place, prepare, and remediate students . . . all in one product! Institutional case studies have shown that **ALEKS has improved pass rates by over 20% versus traditional online homework, and by over 30% compared to using a text alone.**

By offering each student an individualized learning path, ALEKS directs students to work on the math topics that they are ready to learn. Also, to help students keep pace in their course, instructors can correlate ALEKS to their textbook or syllabus in seconds.

To learn more about how ALEKS can be used to boost student performance, please visit **www.aleks.com/highered/math** or contact your McGraw-Hill representative.

Easy Graphing Utility!
Students can answer graphing problems with ease!

ALEKS Pie
Each student is given her or his own individualized learning path.

Course Calendar
Instructors can schedule assignments and reminders for students.

With ALEKS®

New ALEKS Instructor Module

Enhanced Functionality and Streamlined Interface Help to Save Instructor Time

ALEKS® The new ALEKS Instructor Module features enhanced functionality and a streamlined interface based on research with ALEKS instructors and homework management instructors. Paired with powerful assignment-driven features, textbook integration, and extensive content flexibility, the new ALEKS Instructor Module simplifies administrative tasks and makes ALEKS more powerful than ever.

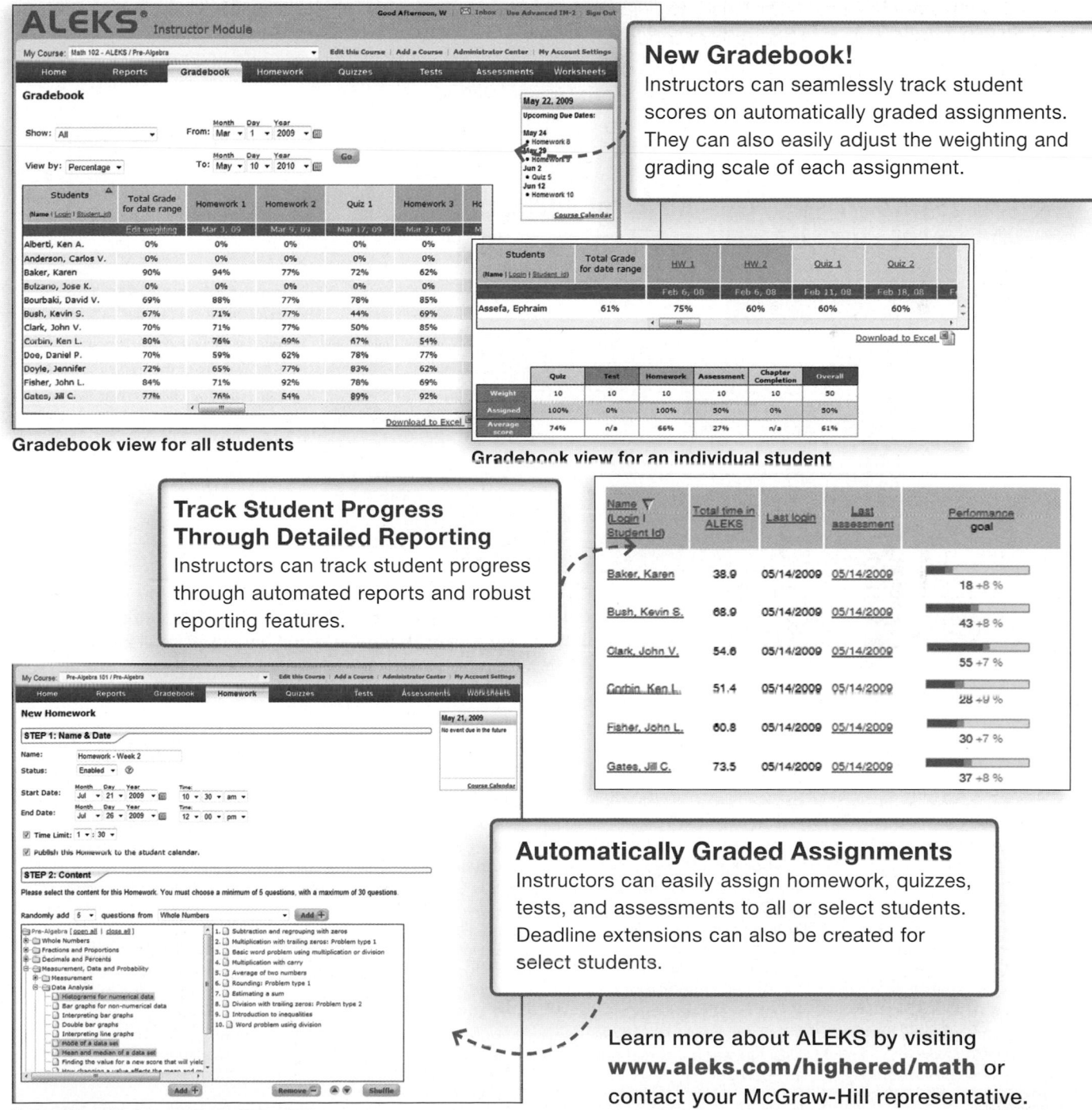

Gradebook view for all students

Gradebook view for an individual student

New Gradebook!
Instructors can seamlessly track student scores on automatically graded assignments. They can also easily adjust the weighting and grading scale of each assignment.

Track Student Progress Through Detailed Reporting
Instructors can track student progress through automated reports and robust reporting features.

Automatically Graded Assignments
Instructors can easily assign homework, quizzes, tests, and assessments to all or select students. Deadline extensions can also be created for select students.

Select topics for each assignment

Learn more about ALEKS by visiting **www.aleks.com/highered/math** or contact your McGraw-Hill representative.

360° Development Process

McGraw-Hill's 360° Development Process is an ongoing, never-ending, market-oriented approach to building accurate and innovative print and digital products. It is dedicated to continual large-scale and incremental improvement that is driven by multiple customer-feedback loops and checkpoints. This is initiated during the early planning stages of our new products, and intensifies during the development and production stages—then begins again upon publication, in anticipation of the next edition.

A key principle in the development of any mathematics text is its ability to adapt to teaching specifications in a universal way. The only way to do so is by contacting those universal voices—and learning from their suggestions. We are confident that our book has the most current content the industry has to offer, thus pushing our desire for accuracy to the highest standard possible. In order to accomplish this, we have moved through an arduous road to production. Extensive and open-minded advice is critical in the production of a superior text.

Here is a brief overview of the initiatives included in the *Beginning and Intermediate Algebra*, 360° Development Process:

Board of Advisors

A hand-picked group of trusted teachers active in the *Beginning and Intermediate Algebra* course served as chief advisors and consultants to the author and editorial team with regards to manuscript development. The

Board of Advisors reviewed parts of the manuscript; served as a sounding board for pedagogical, media, and design concerns; consulted on organizational changes; and attended a focus group to confirm the manuscript's readiness for publication.

Would you like to inquire about becoming a BOA member?
If so, email the editor, David Millage at david_millage@mcgraw-hill.com.

Prealgebra
Vanetta Grier-Felix, *Seminole State College of Florida*
Teresa Hasenauer, *Indian River State College*
Shelbra Jones, *Wake Technical Community College*
Nicole Lloyd, *Lansing Community College*
Kausha Miller, *Bluegrass Community and Technical College*
Linda Schott, *Ozarks Technical Community College*
Renee Sundrud, *Harrisburg Area Community College*

Beginning Algebra
Anabel Darini, *Suffolk County Community College*
Sabine Eggleston, *Edison State College*
Brandie Faulkner, *Tallahassee Community College*
Kelli Hammer, *Broward College–South*
Joseph Howe, *St. Charles Community College*
Laura Iossi, *Broward College–Central*
DiDi Quesada, *Miami Dade College*

Intermediate Algebra
Connie Buller, *Metropolitan Community College*
Nancy Carpenter, *Johnson County Community College*
Pauline Chow, *Harrisburg Area Community College*
Donna Gerken, *Miami Dade College*
Gayle Krzemien, *Pikes Peak Community College*
Judy McBride, *Indiana University–Purdue University at Indianapolis*
Patty Parkison, *Ball State University*

Beginning and Intermediate Algebra
Annette Burden, *Youngstown State University*
Lenore Desilets, *DeAnza College*
Gloria Guerra, *St. Philip's College*
Julie Turnbow, *Collin County Community College*
Suzanne Williams, *Central Piedmont Community College*
Janet Wyatt, *Metropolitan Community College–Longview*

Get Better Results

Better Development!

Question: How do you build a better developmental mathematics textbook series?

Answer: Employ a developmental mathematics instructor from the classroom to become a McGraw-Hill editor!

Emilie Berglund joined the developmental mathematics team at McGraw-Hill, bringing her extensive classroom experience to the Miller/O'Neill/Hyde textbook series. A former developmental mathematics instructor at Utah Valley State College, Ms. Berglund has won numerous teaching awards and has served as the beginning algebra course coordinator for the department. Ms. Berglund's experience teaching developmental mathematics students from the Miller/O'Neill/Hyde translates into more well-developed pedagogy throughout the textbook series and can be seen in everything from the updated Worked Examples to the Exercise Sets.

Listening to You . . .

This textbook has been reviewed by over 300 teachers across the country. Our textbook is a commitment to your students, providing a clear explanation, a concise writing style, step-by-step learning tools, and the best exercises and applications in developmental mathematics. **How do we know? You told us so!**

Teachers *Just Like You* are saying great things about the Miller/O'Neill/Hyde developmental mathematics series:

> "As we matched MOH against many other Intermediate Algebra books, the reading level and writing style, combined with the appropriate use of color and good "looks" of the pages, made this book rise to the top."
> —Connie Buller, *Metropolitan Community College*

> "I think the level of rigor is perfect for my students. I have examined other textbooks that would have been placed at the extremes of a continuum. This book is, in the words of Goldilocks, "just right.""
> —Angie McCombs, *Illinois State University*

> "I believe that MOH has separated and grouped the content into sections that will make it easier for students to digest."
> —Gayle Krzemien, *Pikes Peak Community College*

Acknowledgments and Reviewers

The development of this textbook series would never have been possible without the creative ideas and feedback offered by many reviewers. We are especially thankful to the following instructors for their careful review of the manuscript.

Symposia

Every year McGraw-Hill conducts general mathematics symposia that are attended by instructors from across the country. These events provide opportunities for editors from McGraw-Hill to gather information about the needs and challenges of instructors teaching these courses. This information helped to create the book plan for *Beginning and Intermediate Algebra.* A forum is also offered for the attendees to exchange ideas and experiences with colleagues they otherwise might not have met.

Advisors Symposium—Barton Creek, Texas

Connie Buller, *Metropolitan Community College*
Pauline Chow, *Harrisburg Area Community College*
Anabel Darini, *Suffolk County Community College*
Maria DeLucia, *Middlesex County College*
Sabine Eggleston, *Edison State College*
Brandie Faulkner, *Tallahassee Community College*
Vanetta Grier-Felix, *Seminole State College of Florida*
Gloria Guerra, *St. Philip's College*
Joseph Howe, *St. Charles Community College*
Laura Iossi, *Broward College–Central*

Gayle Krzemien, *Pikes Peak Community College*
Nicole Lloyd, *Lansing Community College*
Judy McBride, *Indiana University–Purdue University at Indianapolis*
Kausha Miller, *Bluegrass Community and Technical College*
Patty Parkison, *Ball State University*
Linda Schott, *Ozarks Technical and Community College*
Renee Sundrud, *Harrisburg Area Community College*
Janet Wyatt, *Metropolitan Community College–Longview*

Napa Valley Symposium

Antonio Alfonso, *Miami Dade College*
Lynn Beckett-Lemus, *El Camino College*
Kristin Chatas, *Washtenaw Community College*
Maria DeLucia, *Middlesex County College*
Nancy Forrest, *Grand Rapids Community College*
Michael Gibson, *John Tyler Community College*
Linda Horner, *Columbia State College*
Matthew Hudock, *St. Philip's College*

Judith Langer, *Westchester Community College*
Kathryn Lavelle, *Westchester Community College*
Scott McDaniel, *Middle Tennessee State University*
Adelaida Quesada, *Miami Dade College*
Susan Shulman, *Middlesex County College*
Stephen Toner, *Victor Valley College*
Chariklia Vassiliadis, *Middlesex County College*
Melanie Walker, *Bergen Community College*

Myrtle Beach Symposium

Patty Bonesteel, *Wayne State University*
Zhixiong Chen, *New Jersey City University*
Latonya Ellis, *Bishop State Community College*
Bonnie Filer, *Tubaugh University of Akron*
Catherine Gong, *Citrus College*

Marcia Lambert, *Pitt Community College*
Katrina Nichols, *Delta College*
Karen Stein, *The University of Akron*
Walter Wang, *Baruch College*

Get Better Results

La Jolla Symposium

Darryl Allen, *Solano Community College*
Yvonne Aucoin, *Tidewater Community College–Norfolk*
Sylvia Carr, *Missouri State University*
Elizabeth Chu, *Suffolk County Community College*
Susanna Crawford, *Solano Community College*
Carolyn Facer, *Fullerton College*

Terran Felter, *California State University–Bakersfield*
Elaine Fitt, *Bucks County Community College*
John Jerome, *Suffolk County Community College*
Sandra Jovicic, *The University of Akron*
Carolyn Robinson, *Mt. San Antonio College*
Carolyn Shand-Hawkins, *Missouri State University*

Class Tests

Multiple class tests provided the editorial team with an understanding of how content and the design of a textbook impact a student's homework and study habits in the general mathematics course area.

Special *"thank you"* to our Manuscript Class-Testers

Manuscript Review Panels

Over 200 teachers and academics from across the country reviewed the various drafts of the manuscript to give feedback on content, design, pedagogy, and organization. This feedback was summarized by the book team and used to guide the direction of the text.

Reviewers of Miller/O'Neill/Hyde Developmental Mathematics Series

Max Aeschbacher, *Utah Valley University*
Ali Ahmad, *Dona Ana Community College*
James Alsobrook, *Southern Union State Community College*
Lisa Angelo, *Bucks County Community College*
Peter Arvanites, *Rockland Community College*
Holly Ashton, *Pikes Peak Community College*
Tony Ayers, *Collin County Community College–Plano*
Tom Baker, *South Plains College*
Lynn Beckett-Lemus, *El Camino College*
Chris Bendixen, *Lake Michigan College*
Mary Benson, *Pensacola Junior College*
Vickie Berry, *Northeastern Oklahoma A&M College*
Abraham Biggs, *Broward College–South*
Erika Blanken, *Daytona State College*
Andrea Blum, *Suffolk County Community College*
Steven Boettcher, *Estrella Mountain Community College*
Gabriele Booth, *Daytona State College*
Charles Bower, *Saint Philip's College*
Cherie Bowers, *Santa Ana College*
Lee Brendel, *Southwestern Illinois College*
Ellen Brook, *Cuyahoga Community College*
Debra Bryant, *Tennessee Tech University*
Robert Buchanan, *Pensacola Junior College*
Gail Butler, *Erie Community College–North*

Susan Caldiero, *Consumnes River College*
Kimberly Caldwell, *Volunteer State Community College*
Jose Castillo, *Broward College–South*
Chris Chappa, *Tyler Junior College*
Timothy Chappell, *Penn Valley Community College*
Dianna Cichocki, *Erie Community College–South*
William Clarke, *Pikes Peak Community College*
David Clutts, *Southeast Kentucky Community & Technical College*
De Cook, *Okaloosa-Walton College*
Susan Costa, *Broward College–Central*
Mark Crawford, *Waubonsee Community College*
Patrick Cross, *University of Oklahoma*
Imad Dakka, *Oakland Community College–Royal Oak*
Shirley Davis, *South Plains College*
Nelson De La Rosa, *Miami Dade College*
Mary Dennison, *University of Nebraska at Omaha*
Donna Densmore , *Bossier Parish Community College*
David DeSario, *Georgetown College*
Michael Divinia, *San Jose City College*
Dennis Donohue, *College of Southern Nevada*
Jay Driver, *South Plains College*
Laura Dyer, *Southwestern Illinois College*
Sabine Eggleston, *Edison State College*
Mike Everett, *Santa Ana College*

Reviewers of the Miller/O'Neill/Hyde Developmental Mathematics Series

Elizabeth Farber, *Bucks County Community College*
Nerissa Felder, *Polk Community College*
Rhoderick Fleming, *Wake Technical Community College*
Carol Ford, *Copiah-Lincoln Community College–Wesson*
Marion Foster, *Houston Community College–Southeast*
Kevin Fox, *Shasta College*
Matt Gardner, *North Hennepin Community College*
Sunshine Gibbons, *Southeast Missouri State University*
Antonnette Gibbs, *Broward College–North*
Barry Gibson, *Daytona State College*
Jeremiah Gilbert, *San Bernardino Valley College*
Sharon Giles, *Grossmont College*
Elizabeth Gore, *Georgia Highlands College*
Brent Griffin, *Georgia Highlands College*
Albert Guerra, *Saint Philip's College*
Lucy Gurrola, *Dona Ana Community College*
Elizabeth Hamman, *Cypress College*
Mark Harbison, *Sacramento City College*
Pamela Harden, *Tennessee Tech University*
Sherri Hardin, *East Tennessee State University*
Cynthia Harris, *Triton College*
Christie Heinrich, *Broward College–North*
Linda Henderson, *Ocean County College*
Rodger Hergert, *Rock Valley College*
Max Hibbs, *Blinn College*
Terry Hobbs, *Maple Woods Community College*
Richard Hobbs, *Mission College*
Michelle Hollis, *Bowling Green Community College at WKU*
Kathy Holster, *South Plains College*
Mark Hopkins, *Oakland Community College–Auburn Hills*
Robert Houston, *Rose State College*
Steven Howard, *Rose State College*
Joe Howe, *St. Charles Community College*
Glenn Jablonski, *Triton College*
Michelle Jackson, *Bowling Green Community College at WKU*
Pamela Jackson, *Oakland Community College–Orchard Ridge*
Thomas Jay, *Houston Community College–Northwest*
Michael Jones, *Suffolk County Community College*
Diane Joyner, *Wayne Community College*
Maryann Justinger, *Erie Community College–South*
Cheryl Kane, *University of Nebraska–Lincoln*
Susan Kautz, *Lone Star College–CyFair*
Joseph Kazimir, *East Los Angeles College*
Eliane Keane, *Miami Dade College*
Mandy Keiner, *Iowa Western Community College*
Maria Kelly, *Reedley College*

Brianna Killian, *Daytona State College*
Harriet Kiser, *Georgia Highlands College*
Daniel Kleinfelter, *College of the Desert*
Linda Kuroski, *Erie Community College*
Catherine LaBerta, *Erie Community College–North*
Debra Landre, *San Joaquin Delta College*
Cynthia Landrigan, *Erie Community College–South*
Melanie Largin, *Georgia Highlands College*
Betty Larson, *South Dakota State University*
Kathryn Lavelle, *Westchester Community College*
Karen Lee, *Oakland Community College–Southfield*
Paul Lee, *St. Philip's College*
Richard Leedy, *Polk Community College*
Julie Letellier, *University of Wisconsin–Whitewater*
Nancy Leveille, *University of Houston–Downtown*
Janna Liberant, *Rockland Community College*
Joyce Lindstrom, *St. Charles Community College*
John Linnen, *Ferris State University*
Mark Littrell, *Rio Hondo College*
Linda Lohman, *Jefferson Community & Technical College*
Tristan Londre, *Metropolitan Community College–Blue River*
Wanda Long, *St. Charles Community College*
Yixia Lu, *South Suburban College*
Shawna Mahan, *Pikes Peak Community College*
Vincent Manatsa, *Georgia Highlands College*
Dorothy Marshall, *Edison State College*
Melvin Mays, *Metropolitan Community College*
William Mays, *Salem Community College*
Angela McCombs, *Illinois State University*
Paul Mccombs, *Rock Valley College*
Robert McCullough, *Ferris State University*
Raymond McDaniel, *Southern Illinois University Edwardsville*
Jamie McGill, *East Tennessee State University*
Vicki McMillian, *Ocean County College*
Lynette Meslinsky, *Erie Community College–City*
Gabrielle Michaelis, *Cumberland County College*
John Mitchell, *Clark College*
Chris Mizell, *Okaloosa-Walton College*
Daniel Munton, *Santa Rosa Junior College*
Revathi Narasimhan, *Kean Community College*
Michael Nasab, *Long Beach City College*
Elsie Newman, *Owens Community College*
Charles Odion, *Houston Community College*
Jean Olsen, *Pikes Peak Community College*
Jason Pallett, *Metropolitan Community College–Longview*
Alan Papen, *Ozarks Technical Community College*

Reviewers of the Miller/O'Neill/Hyde Developmental Mathematics Series

Victor Pareja, *Daytona State College*

Linda Parrish, *Brevard College*

Mari Peddycoart, *Lone Star College–Kingwood*

Joanne Peeples, *El Paso Community College*

Matthew Pitassi, *Rio Hondo College*

Froozen Pourboghrat-Afiat, *College of Southern Nevada*

Jay Priester, *Horry-Georgetown Technical College*

Gail Queen, *Shelton State Community College*

Adelaida Quesada, *Miami Dade College*

Jill Rafael, *Sierra College*

Janice Rech, *University of Nebraska at Omaha*

George Reed, *Angelina College*

Pamelyn Reed, *Lone Star College–CyFair*

Andrea Reese, *Daytona State College*

Donna Riedel, *Jefferson Community & Technical College*

Donald Robertson, *Olympic College*

Cosmin Roman, *The Ohio State University*

Tracy Romesser, *Erie Community College*

Suzanne Rosenberger, *Harrisburg Area Community College*

Connie Rost, *South Louisiana Community College*

Richard Rupp, *Del Mar College*

Angela Russell, *Wenatchee Valley College*

Kristina Sampson, *Lone Star College–CyFair*

Jenell Sargent, *Tennessee Tech University*

Vicki Schell, *Pensacola Junior College*

Linda Schott, *Ozarks Technical Community College*

Rebecca Schuering, *Metropolitan Community College–Blue River*

Christyn Senese, *Triton College*

Alicia Serfaty De Markus, *Miami Dade College*

Angie Shreckhise, *Ozarks Technical Community College*

Abdallah Shuaibi, *Harry S Truman College*

Julia Simms, *Southern Illinois University Edwardsville*

Azar Sioshansi, *San Jose City College*

Leonora Smook, *Suffolk County Community College*

Carol St. Denis, *Okaloosa-Walton College*

Andrew Stephan, *St. Charles Community College*

Sean Stewart, *Owens Community College*

Arcola Sullivan, *Copiah-Lincoln Community College*

Nader Taha, *Kent State University*

Michael Tiano, *Suffolk County Community College*

Roy Tucker, *Palo Alto College*

Clairie Vassiliadis, *Middlesex County College*

Rieken Venema, *University of Alaska Anchorage*

Sherry Wallin, *Sierra College*

Kathleen Wanstreet, *Southern Illinois University Edwardsville*

Natalie Weaver, *Daytona State College*

Greg Wheaton, *Kishwaukee College*

Deborah Wolfson, *Suffolk County Community College*

Rick Woodmansee, *Sacramento City College*

Kevin Yokoyama, *College of the Redwoods*

Donald York, *Danville Area Community College*

Vivian Zabrocki, *Montana State University–Billings*

Ruth Zasada, *Owens Community College*

Loris Zucca, *Kingwood College*

Diane Zych, *Erie Community College–North*

Special thanks go to Brandie Faulkner for preparing the *Instructor's Solutions Manual* and the *Student's Solution Manual* and to Carrie Green, Rebecca Hubiak, and Hal Whipple for their work ensuring accuracy. Many thanks to Cindy Reed for her work in the video series, and to Kelly Jackson for advising us on the Instructor Notes.

Finally, we are forever grateful to the many people behind the scenes at McGraw-Hill without whom we would still be on page 1. To our developmental editor (and math instructor extraordinaire), Emilie Berglund, thanks for your day-to-day support and understanding of the world of developmental mathematics. To David Millage, our executive editor and overall team captain, thanks for keeping the train on the track. Where did you find enough hours in the day? To Torie Anderson and Sabina Navsariwala, we greatly appreciate your countless hours of support and creative ideas promoting all of our efforts. To our director of development and champion, Kris Tibbetts, thanks for being there in our time of need. To Pat Steele, where would we be without your watchful eye over our manuscript? To our publisher, Stewart Mattson, we're grateful for your experience and energizing new ideas. Thanks for believing in us. To Jeff Huettman and Amber Bettcher, we give our greatest appreciation for the exciting technology so critical to student success, and to Peggy Selle, thanks for keeping watch over the whole team as the project came together.

Most importantly, we give special thanks to all the students and instructors who use *Beginning and Intermediate Algebra* in their classes.

Get Better Results

A COMMITMENT TO ACCURACY

You have a right to expect an accurate textbook, and McGraw-Hill invests considerable time and effort to make sure that we deliver one. Listed below are the many steps we take to make sure this happens.

Our Accuracy Verification Process

First Round

Step 1: Numerous **college math instructors** review the manuscript and report on any errors that they may find. Then the authors make these corrections in their final manuscript.

Second Round

Step 2: Once the manuscript has been typeset, the **authors** check their manuscript against the first page proofs to ensure that all illustrations, graphs, examples, exercises, solutions, and answers have been correctly laid out on the pages, and that all notation is correctly used.

Step 3: An outside, **professional mathematician** works through every example and exercise in the page proofs to verify the accuracy of the answers.

Step 4: A **proofreader** adds a triple layer of accuracy assurance in the first pages by hunting for errors, then a second, corrected round of page proofs is produced.

Third Round

Step 5: The **author team** reviews the second round of page proofs for two reasons: (1) to make certain that any previous corrections were properly made, and (2) to look for any errors they might have missed on the first round.

Step 6: A **second proofreader** is added to the project to examine the new round of page proofs to double check the author team's work and to lend a fresh, critical eye to the book before the third round of paging.

Fourth Round

Step 7: A **third proofreader** inspects the third round of page proofs to verify that all previous corrections have been properly made and that there are no new or remaining errors.

Step 8: Meanwhile, in partnership with **independent mathematicians,** the text accuracy is verified from a variety of fresh perspectives:

- The **test bank authors** check for consistency and accuracy as they prepare the computerized test item file.
- The **solutions manual author** works every exercise and verifies his/her answers, reporting any errors to the publisher.
- A **consulting group of mathematicians,** who write material for the text's MathZone site, notifies the publisher of any errors they encounter in the page proofs.
- A video production company employing **expert math instructors** for the text's videos will alert the publisher of any errors it might find in the page proofs.

Final Round

Step 9: The **project manager,** who has overseen the book from the beginning, performs a **fourth proofread** of the textbook during the printing process, providing a final accuracy review.

➡ What results is a mathematics textbook that is as accurate and error-free as is humanly possible, and our authors and publishing staff are confident that our many layers of quality assurance have produced textbooks that are the leaders in the industry for their integrity and correctness.

1st Round:
Author's Manuscript

↓

✓ Multiple Rounds of Review by College Math Instructors

↓

2nd Round:
Typeset Pages

↓

Accuracy Checks by:
✓ Authors
✓ Professional Mathematician
✓ 1st Proofreader

↓

3rd Round:
Typeset Pages

↓

Accuracy Checks by:
✓ Authors
✓ 2nd Proofreader

↓

4th Round:
Typeset Pages

↓

Accuracy Checks by:
✓ 3rd Proofreader
✓ Test Bank Author
✓ Solutions Manual Author
✓ Consulting Mathematicians for MathZone site
✓ Math Instructors for text's video series

↓

Final Round:
Printing

↓

✓ Accuracy Check by 4th Proofreader

Brief Contents

Contents

Study Tips

In taking a course in algebra, you are making a commitment to yourself, your instructor, and your classmates. Following some or all of the study tips presented here can help you be successful in this endeavor. The features of this text that will assist you are printed in blue.

1. Before the Course

1. Purchase the necessary materials for the course before the course begins or on the first day.
2. Obtain a three-ring binder to keep and organize your notes, homework, tests, and any other materials acquired in the class. We call this type of notebook a portfolio.
3. Arrange your schedule so that you have enough time to attend class and to do homework. A common rule is to set aside at least 2 hours for homework for every hour spent in class. That is, if you are taking a 4-credit-hour course, plan on at least 8 hours a week for homework. A 4-credit-hour course will then take *at least* 12 hours each week—about the same as a part-time job. If you experience difficulty in mathematics, plan for more time.
4. Communicate with your employer and family members the importance of your success in this course so that they can support you.
5. Be sure to find out the type of calculator (if any) that your instructor requires.

2. During the Course

1. Read the section in the text *before* the lecture to familiarize yourself with the material and terminology. Write a one-sentence preview of what the section is about.
2. Attend every class, and be on time. Be sure to bring any materials that are needed for class such as graph paper, a ruler, or a calculator.
3. Take notes in class. Write down all of the examples that the instructor presents. Read the notes after class, and add any comments to make your notes clearer to you. Use a tape recorder to record the lecture if the instructor permits the recording of lectures.
4. Ask questions in class.
5. Read the section in the text *after* the lecture, and pay special attention to the Tip boxes and Avoiding Mistakes boxes.
6. After you read an example, try the accompanying Skill Practice problem. The skill practice problem mirrors the example and tests your understanding of what you have read.

7. Do homework every night. Even if your class does not meet every day, you should still do some work every night to keep the material fresh in your mind.

8. Check your homework with the answers that are supplied in the back of this text. Correct the exercises that do not match, and circle or star those that you cannot correct yourself. This way you can easily find them and ask your instructor, tutor, online tutor, or math lab staff the next day.

9. Write the definition and give an example of each Key Term found at the beginning of the Practice Exercises.

10. The Problem Recognition Exercises are located in most chapters. These provide additional practice distinguishing among a variety of problem types. Sometimes the most difficult part of learning mathematics is retaining all that you learn. These exercises are excellent tools for retention of material.

11. Form a study group with fellow students in your class, and exchange phone numbers. You will be surprised by how much you can learn by talking about mathematics with other students.

12. If you use a calculator in your class, read the Calculator Connections boxes to learn how and when to use your calculator.

13. Ask your instructor where you might obtain extra help if necessary.

3. Preparation for Exams

1. Look over your homework. Pay special attention to the exercises you have circled or starred to be sure that you have learned that concept.

2. Read through the Summary at the end of the chapter. Be sure that you understand each concept and example. If not, go to the section in the text and reread that section.

3. Give yourself enough time to take the Chapter Test uninterrupted. Then check the answers. For each problem you answered incorrectly, go to the Review Exercises and do all of the problems that are similar.

4. To prepare for the final exam, complete the Cumulative Review Exercises at the end of each chapter, starting with Chapter 2. If you complete the cumulative reviews after finishing each chapter, then you will be preparing for the final exam throughout the course. The Cumulative Review Exercises are another excellent tool for helping you retain material.

4. Where to Go for Help

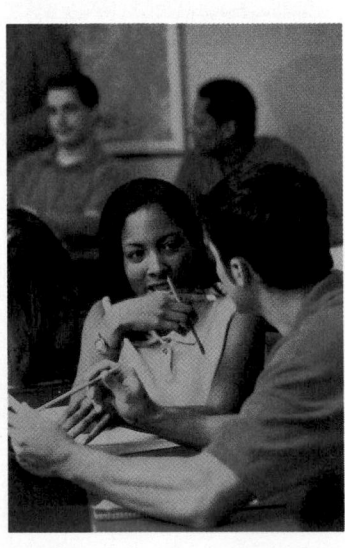

1. At the first sign of trouble, see your instructor. Most instructors have specific office hours set aside to help students. Don't wait until after you have failed an exam to seek assistance.

2. Get a tutor. Most colleges and universities have free tutoring available. There may also be an online tutor available.

3. When your instructor and tutor are unavailable, use the Student Solutions Manual for step-by-step solutions to the odd-numbered problems in the exercise sets.

4. Work with another student from your class.

5. Work on the computer. Many mathematics tutorial programs and websites are available on the Internet, including the website that accompanies this text.

Group Activity

Becoming a Successful Student

Materials: Computer with Internet access

Estimated Time: 15 minutes

Group Size: 4

Good time management, good study skills, and good organization will help you be successful in this course. Answer the following questions and compare your answers with your group members.

Answers will vary.

1. To motivate yourself to complete a course, it is helpful to have clear reasons for taking the course. List your goals for taking this course and discuss them with your group.

2. For the following week, write down the times each day that you plan to study math.

Monday	Tuesday	Wednesday	Thursday	Friday	Saturday	Sunday

3. Write down the date of your next math test. _____

4. Taking 12 credit-hours is the equivalent of a full-time job. Often students try to work too many hours while taking classes at school.

   a. Write down the number of hours you work per week and the number of credit-hours you are taking this term.

   number of hours worked per week _____

   number of credit-hours this term _____

   b. The table gives a recommended limit to the number of hours you should work for the number of credit-hours you are taking at school. (Keep in mind that other responsibilities in your life such as your family might also make it necessary to limit your hours at work even more.) How do your numbers from part (a) compare to those in the table? Are you working too many hours?

Number of Credit-Hours	Maximum Number of Hours of Work per Week
3	40
6	30
9	20
12	10
15	0

5. Look through Chapter 2 and find the page number corresponding to each feature in that chapter. Discuss with your group members how you might use each feature.

   Problem Recognition Exercises: page _____

   Chapter Summary: page _____

   Chapter Review Exercises: page _____

   Chapter Test: page _____

   Cumulative Review Exercises: page _____

6. Look at the Skill Practice exercises. For example, find Skill Practice exercises 1 and 2 in Section 1.1. Where are the answers to these exercises located? Discuss with your group members how you might use the Skill Practice exercises.

7. Discuss with your group members places where you can go for extra help in math. Then write down three of the suggestions.

   _____

   _____

   _____

8. Do you keep an organized notebook for this class? Can you think of any suggestions that you can share with your group members to help them keep their materials organized?

9. Do you think that you have math anxiety? Read the following list for some possible solutions. Check the activities that you can realistically try to help you overcome this problem.

   _____ Read a book on math anxiety.

   _____ Search the Web for tips on handling math anxiety.

   _____ See a counselor to discuss your anxiety.

   _____ See your instructor to inform him or her about your situation.

   _____ Evaluate your time management to see if you are trying to do too much. Then adjust your schedule accordingly.

10. Some students favor different methods of learning over others. For example, you might prefer:

    - Learning through listening and hearing.
    - Learning through seeing images, watching demonstrations, and visualizing diagrams and charts.
    - Learning by experience through a hands-on approach.
    - Learning through reading and writing.

    Most experts believe that the most effective learning comes when a student engages in *all* of these activities. However, each individual is different and may benefit from one activity more than another. You can visit a number of different websites to determine your "learning style." Try doing a search on the Internet with the key words *"learning styles assessment."* Once you have found a suitable website, answer the questionnaire and the site will give you feedback on what method of learning works best for you.

The Set of Real Numbers

1

Chapter 1

In Chapter 1, we present operations on fractions and real numbers. The skills that you will learn in this chapter are particularly important as you continue in algebra.

Are You Prepared?

This puzzle will refresh your skills with whole numbers and the order of operations. Fill in each blank box with one of the four basic operations, $+$, $-$, $\times$, or $\div$ so that the statement is true both going across and going down. Pay careful attention to the order of operations.

18	+	2	+	10	=	30
÷		+		−		÷
3	×	4	−	7	−	5
−		+		+		÷
2	×	0	+	6	=	6
=		=		=		=
4	+	6	−	9	=	1

Section 1.1 | Fractions

1. Basic Definitions

The study of algebra involves many of the operations and procedures used in arithmetic. Therefore, we begin this text by reviewing the basic operations of addition, subtraction, multiplication, and division on fractions and mixed numbers.

We begin with the numbers used for counting:

the **natural numbers**: 1, 2, 3, 4, . . .

and

the **whole numbers**: 0, 1, 2, 3, . . .

Whole numbers are used to count the number of whole units in a quantity. A fraction is used to express part of a whole unit. If a child gains $2\frac{1}{2}$ lb, the child has gained two whole pounds plus a portion of a pound. To express the additional half pound mathematically, we may use the fraction, $\frac{1}{2}$.

DEFINITION **A Fraction and Its Parts**

Fractions are numbers of the form $\frac{a}{b}$, where $\frac{a}{b} = a \div b$ and b does not equal zero.

In the fraction $\frac{a}{b}$, the **numerator** is a, and the **denominator** is b.

The denominator of a fraction indicates how many equal parts divide the whole. The numerator indicates how many parts are being represented. For instance, suppose Jack wants to plant carrots in $\frac{2}{5}$ of a rectangular garden. He can divide the garden into five equal parts and use two of the parts for carrots (Figure 1-1).

5 equal parts

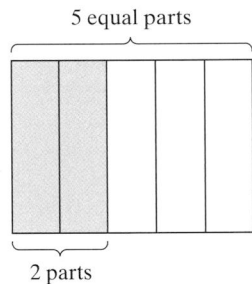

2 parts

Figure 1-1

The shaded region represents $\frac{2}{5}$ of the garden.

Instructor Note: Tell the students that the word "improper" does not imply that there is anything wrong with a fraction.

DEFINITION **Proper Fractions, Improper Fractions, and Mixed Numbers**

1. If the numerator of a fraction is less than the denominator, the fraction is a **proper fraction**. A proper fraction represents a quantity that is less than a whole unit.
2. If the numerator of a fraction is greater than or equal to the denominator, then the fraction is an **improper fraction**. An improper fraction represents a quantity greater than or equal to a whole unit.
3. A **mixed number** is a whole number added to a proper fraction.

Proper Fractions: $\dfrac{3}{5}$ ⬡ $\dfrac{1}{8}$ ⬡

Improper Fractions: $\dfrac{7}{5}$ ⬡ ⬡ $\dfrac{8}{8}$ ⬡

Mixed Numbers: $1\frac{1}{5}$ ⬡ ⬡ $2\frac{3}{8}$ ⬡ ⬡ ⬡

2. Prime Factorization

To perform operations on fractions it is important to understand the concept of a factor. For example, when the numbers 2 and 6 are multiplied, the result (called the **product**) is 12.

$$2 \times 6 = 12$$

factors   product

The numbers 2 and 6 are said to be **factors** of 12. (In this context, we refer only to natural number factors.) The number 12 is said to be factored when it is written as the product of two or more natural numbers. For example, 12 can be factored in several ways:

$$12 = 1 \times 12 \qquad 12 = 2 \times 6 \qquad 12 = 3 \times 4 \qquad 12 = 2 \times 2 \times 3$$

A natural number greater than 1 that has only two factors, 1 and itself, is called a **prime number**. The first several prime numbers are 2, 3, 5, 7, 11, and 13. A natural number greater than 1 that is not prime is called a **composite number**. That is, a composite number has factors other than itself and 1. The first several composite numbers are 4, 6, 8, 9, 10, 12, 14, 15, and 16.

Example 1   **Writing a Natural Number as a Product of Prime Factors**

Classroom Example: p. 19, Exercise 36

Write each number as a product of prime factors.

a. 12   **b.** 30

Solution:

a. $12 = 2 \times 2 \times 3$ Divide 12 by prime numbers until only prime numbers are obtained.   Or use a factor tree

$$\begin{array}{r} 2)\overline{12} \\ 2)\overline{6} \\ 3 \end{array}$$

b. $30 = 2 \times 3 \times 5$

$$\begin{array}{r} 2)\overline{30} \\ 3)\overline{15} \\ 5 \end{array}$$

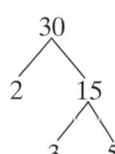

Skill Practice Write the number as a product of prime factors.

1. 40   **2.** 60

Answers

1. $2 \times 2 \times 2 \times 5$
2. $2 \times 2 \times 3 \times 5$

3. Simplifying Fractions to Lowest Terms

The process of factoring numbers can be used to reduce or simplify fractions to lowest terms. A fractional portion of a whole can be represented by infinitely many fractions. For example, Figure 1-2 shows that $\frac{1}{2}$ is equivalent to $\frac{2}{4}, \frac{3}{6}, \frac{4}{8}$, and so on.

      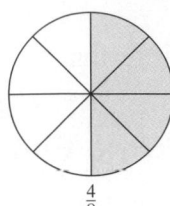

$$\frac{1}{2} \qquad \frac{2}{4} \qquad \frac{3}{6} \qquad \frac{4}{8}$$

Figure 1-2

The fraction $\frac{1}{2}$ is said to be in **lowest terms** because the numerator and denominator share no common factor other than 1.

To simplify a fraction to lowest terms, we use the following important principle.

PROPERTY   Fundamental Principle of Fractions

Suppose that a number, c, is a common factor in the numerator and denominator of a fraction. Then

$$\frac{a \times c}{b \times c} = \frac{a}{b} \times \frac{c}{c} = \frac{a}{b} \times 1 = \frac{a}{b}$$

To simplify a fraction, we begin by factoring the numerator and denominator into prime factors. This will help identify the common factors.

Classroom Example: p. 19, Exercise 44

Example 2   Simplifying a Fraction to Lowest Terms

Simplify $\frac{45}{30}$ to lowest terms.

Solution:

$$\frac{45}{30} = \frac{3 \times 3 \times 5}{2 \times 3 \times 5} \qquad \text{Factor the numerator and denominator.}$$

$$= \frac{3}{2} \times \frac{3}{3} \times \frac{5}{5} \qquad \text{Apply the fundamental principle of fractions.}$$

$$= \frac{3}{2} \times 1 \times 1 \qquad \text{Any nonzero number divided by itself is 1.}$$

$$= \frac{3}{2} \qquad \text{Any number multiplied by 1 is itself.}$$

Instructor Note: Students often confuse writing a fraction in lowest terms with writing a mixed number. The fraction $\frac{3}{2}$ is in lowest terms.

Skill Practice   Simplify to lowest terms.

3. $\frac{20}{50}$

Answer

3. $\frac{2}{5}$

In Example 2, we showed numerous steps to reduce fractions to lowest terms. However, the process is often simplified. Notice that the same result can be obtained by dividing out the greatest common factor from the numerator and denominator. (The **greatest common factor** is the largest factor that is common to both numerator and denominator.)

$$\frac{45}{30} = \frac{3 \times 15}{2 \times 15}$$ The greatest common factor of 45 and 30 is 15.

$$= \frac{3 \times \overset{1}{\cancel{15}}}{2 \times \underset{1}{\cancel{15}}}$$ The symbol ╱ is often used to show that a common factor has been divided out.

$$= \frac{3}{2}$$ Notice that "dividing out" the common factor of 15 has the same effect as dividing the numerator and denominator by 15. This is often done mentally.

$$\frac{\overset{3}{\cancel{45}}}{\underset{2}{\cancel{30}}} = \frac{3}{2}$$ ⟵ 45 divided by 15 equals 3.
         ⟵ 30 divided by 15 equals 2.

Example 3   **Simplifying a Fraction to Lowest Terms**

Simplify $\frac{14}{42}$ to lowest terms.

Solution:

$$\frac{14}{42} = \frac{1 \times 14}{3 \times 14}$$ The greatest common factor of 14 and 42 is 14.

$$= \frac{1 \times \overset{1}{\cancel{14}}}{3 \times \underset{1}{\cancel{14}}}$$

$$= \frac{1}{3}$$ $\dfrac{\overset{1}{\cancel{14}}}{\underset{3}{\cancel{42}}} = \dfrac{1}{3}$ ⟵ 14 divided by 14 equals 1.
         ⟵ 42 divided by 14 equals 3.

Skill Practice Simplify to lowest terms.

4. $\dfrac{32}{12}$

Classroom Example: p. 19, Exercise 48

Avoiding Mistakes

In Example 3, the common factor 14 in the numerator and denominator simplifies to 1. It is important to remember to write the factor of 1 in the numerator. The simplified form of the fraction is $\frac{1}{3}$.

4. Multiplying Fractions

PROCEDURE   **Multiplying Fractions**

If b is not zero and d is not zero, then

$$\frac{a}{b} \times \frac{c}{d} = \frac{a \times c}{b \times d}$$

To multiply fractions, multiply the numerators and multiply the denominators.

Answer

4. $\dfrac{8}{3}$

Classroom Example: p. 19, Exercise 58

$\frac{1}{4}$ of $\frac{1}{2} = \frac{1}{8}$

Figure 1-3

Example 4 **Multiplying Fractions**

Multiply the fractions: $\frac{1}{4} \times \frac{1}{2}$

Solution:

$$\frac{1}{4} \times \frac{1}{2} = \frac{1 \times 1}{4 \times 2} = \frac{1}{8}$$ Multiply the numerators. Multiply the denominators.

Notice that the product $\frac{1}{4} \times \frac{1}{2}$ represents a quantity that is $\frac{1}{4}$ of $\frac{1}{2}$. Taking $\frac{1}{4}$ of a quantity is equivalent to dividing the quantity by 4. One-half of a pie divided into four pieces leaves pieces that each represent $\frac{1}{8}$ of the pie (Figure 1-3).

Skill Practice Multiply.

5. $\frac{2}{7} \times \frac{3}{4}$

Classroom Example: p. 19, Exercise 62

Example 5 **Multiplying Fractions**

Multiply the fractions.

a. $\frac{7}{10} \times \frac{15}{14}$ **b.** $\frac{2}{13} \times \frac{13}{2}$ **c.** $5 \times \frac{1}{5}$

Solution:

a. $\frac{7}{10} \times \frac{15}{14} = \frac{7 \times 15}{10 \times 14}$ Multiply the numerators. Multiply the denominators.

$$= \frac{\overset{3}{\cancel{105}}}{\underset{4}{\cancel{140}}}$$ Divide out the common factor, 35.

$$= \frac{3}{4}$$

TIP: The same result can be obtained by dividing out common factors *before* multiplying.

$$\frac{\overset{1}{\cancel{7}}}{\underset{2}{\cancel{10}}} \times \frac{\overset{3}{\cancel{15}}}{\underset{2}{\cancel{14}}} = \frac{3}{4}$$

b. $\frac{2}{13} \times \frac{13}{2} = \frac{2 \times 13}{13 \times 2} = \frac{\overset{1}{\cancel{2}} \times \overset{1}{\cancel{13}}}{\underset{1}{\cancel{13}} \times \underset{1}{\cancel{2}}} = \frac{1}{1} = 1$ ⟵ Multiply $1 \times 1 = 1$. ⟵ Multiply $1 \times 1 = 1$.

Instructor Note: You can also show multiplication of fractions using shading: the overlapped portion is the product.

$\frac{1}{2} \times \frac{1}{3} = \frac{1}{6}$ $\frac{1}{2}$ $\frac{1}{3}$

c. $5 \times \frac{1}{5} = \frac{5}{1} \times \frac{1}{5}$ The whole number 5 can be written as $\frac{5}{1}$.

$$= \frac{\overset{1}{\cancel{5}} \times 1}{1 \times \underset{1}{\cancel{5}}} = \frac{1}{1} = 1$$ Multiply and simplify to lowest terms.

Skill Practice Multiply.

6. $\frac{8}{9} \times \frac{3}{4}$ **7.** $\frac{4}{5} \times \frac{5}{4}$ **8.** $10 \times \frac{1}{10}$

Answers

5. $\frac{3}{14}$ **6.** $\frac{2}{3}$ **7.** 1 **8.** 1

5. Dividing Fractions

Before we divide fractions, we need to know how to find the reciprocal of a fraction. Notice from Example 5 that $\frac{2}{13} \times \frac{13}{2} = 1$ and $5 \times \frac{1}{5} = 1$. The numbers $\frac{2}{13}$ and $\frac{13}{2}$ are said to be reciprocals because their product is 1. Likewise the numbers 5 and $\frac{1}{5}$ are reciprocals.

DEFINITION   The Reciprocal of a Number

Two nonzero numbers are **reciprocals** of each other if their product is 1. Therefore, the reciprocal of the fraction

$$\frac{a}{b} \text{ is } \frac{b}{a} \qquad \text{because} \qquad \frac{a}{b} \times \frac{b}{a} = 1$$

Number	Reciprocal	Product
$\frac{2}{15}$	$\frac{15}{2}$	$\frac{2}{15} \times \frac{15}{2} = 1$
$\frac{1}{8}$	$\frac{8}{1}$ (or equivalently 8)	$\frac{1}{8} \times 8 = 1$
$6 \left(\text{or equivalently } \frac{6}{1}\right)$	$\frac{1}{6}$	$6 \times \frac{1}{6} = 1$

To understand the concept of dividing fractions, consider a pie that is half-eaten. Suppose the remaining half must be divided among three people, that is, $\frac{1}{2} \div 3$. However, dividing by 3 is equivalent to taking $\frac{1}{3}$ of the remaining $\frac{1}{2}$ of the pie (Figure 1-4).

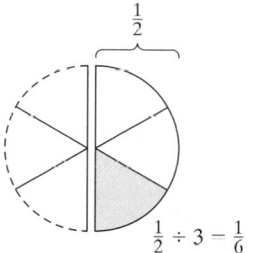

$$\frac{1}{2} \div 3 = \frac{1}{2} \times \frac{1}{3} = \frac{1}{6}$$

$$\frac{1}{2} \div 3 = \frac{1}{6}$$

Figure 1-4

This example illustrates that dividing two numbers is equivalent to multiplying the first number by the reciprocal of the second number.

PROCEDURE   Dividing Fractions

Let a, b, c, and d be numbers such that b, c, and d are not zero. Then,

multiply

$$\frac{a}{b} \div \frac{c}{d} = \frac{a}{b} \times \frac{d}{c}$$

reciprocal

To divide fractions, multiply the first fraction by the reciprocal of the second fraction.

Classroom Examples: p. 19, Exercises 60 and 64

Example 6 Dividing Fractions

Divide the fractions.

a. $\dfrac{8}{5} \div \dfrac{3}{10}$ **b.** $\dfrac{12}{13} \div 6$

Solution:

a. $\dfrac{8}{5} \div \dfrac{3}{10} = \dfrac{8}{5} \times \dfrac{10}{3}$ Multiply by the reciprocal of $\frac{3}{10}$, which is $\frac{10}{3}$.

$= \dfrac{8 \times \overset{2}{\cancel{10}}}{\underset{1}{\cancel{5}} \times 3} = \dfrac{16}{3}$ Multiply and simplify to lowest terms.

b. $\dfrac{12}{13} \div 6 = \dfrac{12}{13} \div \dfrac{6}{1}$ Write the whole number 6 as $\frac{6}{1}$.

$= \dfrac{12}{13} \times \dfrac{1}{6}$ Multiply by the reciprocal of $\frac{6}{1}$, which is $\frac{1}{6}$.

$= \dfrac{\overset{2}{\cancel{12}} \times 1}{13 \times \underset{1}{\cancel{6}}} = \dfrac{2}{13}$ Multiply and simplify to lowest terms.

Skill Practice Divide.

9. $\dfrac{12}{25} \div \dfrac{8}{15}$ **10.** $\dfrac{1}{4} \div 2$

6. Adding and Subtracting Fractions

PROCEDURE   Adding and Subtracting Fractions

Two fractions can be added or subtracted if they have a common denominator. Let a, b, and c be numbers such that b does not equal zero. Then,

$$\frac{a}{b} + \frac{c}{b} = \frac{a+c}{b} \qquad \text{and} \qquad \frac{a}{b} - \frac{c}{b} = \frac{a-c}{b}$$

To add or subtract fractions with the same denominator, add or subtract the numerators and write the result over the common denominator.

Classroom Examples: p. 20, Exercises 78 and 80

Example 7 Adding and Subtracting Fractions with the Same Denominator

Add or subtract as indicated.

a. $\dfrac{1}{12} + \dfrac{7}{12}$ **b.** $\dfrac{13}{5} - \dfrac{3}{5}$

Answers

9. $\dfrac{9}{10}$ **10.** $\dfrac{1}{8}$

Solution:

a. $\dfrac{1}{12} + \dfrac{7}{12} = \dfrac{1+7}{12}$ Add the numerators.

$= \dfrac{8}{12}$

$= \dfrac{2}{3}$ Simplify to lowest terms.

b. $\dfrac{13}{5} - \dfrac{3}{5} = \dfrac{13-3}{5}$ Subtract the numerators.

$= \dfrac{10}{5}$ Simplify.

$= 2$ Simplify to lowest terms.

Skill Practice Add or subtract as indicated.

11. $\dfrac{2}{3} + \dfrac{5}{3}$ **12.** $\dfrac{5}{8} - \dfrac{1}{8}$

> **TIP:** The sum $\frac{1}{12} + \frac{7}{12}$ can be visualized as the sum of the pink and blue sections of the figure.

In Example 7, we added and subtracted fractions with the same denominators. To add or subtract fractions with different denominators, we must first become familiar with the idea of a least common multiple between two or more numbers. The **least common multiple (LCM)** of two numbers is the smallest whole number that is a multiple of each number. For example, the LCM of 6 and 9 is 18.

    multiples of 6:   6, 12, 18, 24, 30, 36, …

    multiples of 9:   9, 18, 27, 36, 45, 54, …

Listing the multiples of two or more given numbers can be a cumbersome way to find the LCM. Therefore, we offer the following method to find the LCM of two numbers.

PROCEDURE   Finding the LCM of Two Numbers

    Step 1   Write each number as a product of prime factors.

    Step 2   The LCM is the product of unique prime factors from *both* numbers. Use repeated factors the maximum number of times they appear in *either* factorization.

Animation

Example 8   Finding the LCM of Two Numbers

Find the LCM of 9 and 15.

Classroom Example: p. 20, Exercise 82

Solution:

	3's	5's
9 =	③ × ③	
15 =	3 ×	⑤

For the factors of 3 and 5, we circle the greatest number of times each occurs. The LCM is the product.

LCM = 3 × 3 × 5 = 45

Skill Practice Find the LCM.

13. 10 and 25

Answers

11. $\dfrac{7}{3}$ **12.** $\dfrac{1}{2}$ **13.** 50

To add or subtract fractions with *different* denominators, we must first write each fraction as an equivalent fraction with a common denominator. A common denominator may be *any* common multiple of the denominators. However, we will use the least common denominator. The **least common denominator (LCD)** of two or more fractions is the LCM of the denominators of the fractions. The following steps outline the procedure to write a fraction as an equivalent fraction with a common denominator.

> **PROCEDURE** Writing Equivalent Fractions
>
> To write a fraction as an equivalent fraction with a common denominator, multiply the numerator and denominator by the factors from the common denominator that are missing from the denominator of the original fraction.
>
> *Note:* Multiplying the numerator and denominator by the *same* nonzero quantity will not change the value of the fraction.

Classroom Examples: p. 20,
Exercises 86 and 90

Example 9   Writing Equivalent Fractions and Subtracting Fractions

a. Write each of the fractions $\frac{1}{9}$ and $\frac{1}{15}$ as an equivalent fraction with the LCD as its denominator.

b. Subtract $\frac{1}{9} - \frac{1}{15}$.

Solution:

From Example 8, we know that the LCM for 9 and 15 is 45. Therefore, the LCD of $\frac{1}{9}$ and $\frac{1}{15}$ is 45.

a. $\frac{1}{9} = \frac{}{45}$ $\frac{1 \times 5}{9 \times 5} = \frac{5}{45}$ So, $\frac{1}{9}$ is equivalent to $\frac{5}{45}$.

What number must we multiply 9 by to get 45?   Multiply numerator and denominator by 5.

$\frac{1}{15} = \frac{}{45}$ $\frac{1 \times 3}{15 \times 3} = \frac{3}{45}$ So, $\frac{1}{15}$ is equivalent to $\frac{3}{45}$.

What number must we multiply 15 by to get 45?   Multiply numerator and denominator by 3.

b. $\frac{1}{9} - \frac{1}{15}$

$= \frac{5}{45} - \frac{3}{45}$ Write $\frac{1}{9}$ and $\frac{1}{15}$ as equivalent fractions with the same denominator.

$= \frac{2}{45}$ Subtract.

Skill Practice

14. Write each of the fractions $\frac{5}{8}$ and $\frac{5}{12}$ as an equivalent fraction with the LCD as its denominator.

15. Subtract. $\dfrac{5}{8} - \dfrac{5}{12}$

Example 10 **Adding and Subtracting Fractions**

Classroom Example: p. 20, Exercise 98

Simplify. $\dfrac{5}{12} + \dfrac{3}{4} - \dfrac{1}{2}$

Solution:

$\dfrac{5}{12} + \dfrac{3}{4} - \dfrac{1}{2}$

To find the LCD, we have:

LCD = $2 \times 2 \times 3 = 12$

	2's	3's
12 =	(2 × 2)	③
4 =	2 × 2	
2 =	2	

$= \dfrac{5}{12} + \dfrac{3 \times 3}{4 \times 3} - \dfrac{1 \times 6}{2 \times 6}$

Write each fraction as an equivalent fraction with the LCD as its denominator.

$= \dfrac{5}{12} + \dfrac{9}{12} - \dfrac{6}{12}$

$= \dfrac{5 + 9 - 6}{12}$

Add and subtract the numerators.

$= \dfrac{\overset{2}{\cancel{8}}}{\underset{3}{\cancel{12}}}$

Simplify to lowest terms.

$= \dfrac{2}{3}$

Skill Practice Add.

16. $\dfrac{2}{3} + \dfrac{1}{2} + \dfrac{5}{6}$

---

7. Operations on Mixed Numbers

Recall that a mixed number is a whole number added to a fraction. The number $3\frac{1}{2}$ represents the sum of three wholes plus a half, that is, $3\frac{1}{2} = 3 + \frac{1}{2}$. For this reason, any mixed number can be converted to an improper fraction by using addition.

$$3\tfrac{1}{2} = 3 + \dfrac{1}{2} = \dfrac{6}{2} + \dfrac{1}{2} = \dfrac{7}{2}$$

Answers

14. $\dfrac{5}{8} = \dfrac{15}{24}$ and $\dfrac{5}{12} = \dfrac{10}{24}$ **15.** $\dfrac{5}{24}$

16. 2

> **TIP:** A shortcut to writing a mixed number as an improper fraction is to multiply the whole number by the denominator of the fraction. Then add this value to the numerator of the fraction, and write the result over the denominator.
>
> $3\frac{1}{2}$ ⟶ Multiply the whole number by the denominator: $3 \times 2 = 6$
> Add the numerator: $6 + 1 = 7$
> Write the result over the denominator: $\frac{7}{2}$

To add, subtract, multiply, or divide mixed numbers, we will first write the mixed number as an improper fraction.

Classroom Example: p. 21, Exercise 114

Example 11   Operations on Mixed Numbers

Subtract. $5\frac{1}{3} - 2\frac{1}{4}$

Solution:

$5\frac{1}{3} - 2\frac{1}{4}$

$= \dfrac{16}{3} - \dfrac{9}{4}$ Write the mixed numbers as improper fractions.

$= \dfrac{16 \times 4}{3 \times 4} - \dfrac{9 \times 3}{4 \times 3}$ The LCD is 12. Multiply numerators and denominators by the missing factors from the denominators.

$= \dfrac{64}{12} - \dfrac{27}{12}$

$= \dfrac{37}{12}$ or $3\dfrac{1}{12}$ Subtract the fractions.

Skill Practice Subtract.

17. $2\frac{3}{4} - 1\frac{1}{3}$

> **TIP:** An improper fraction can also be written as a mixed number. Both answers are acceptable. Note that
>
> $$\frac{37}{12} = \frac{36}{12} + \frac{1}{12} = 3 + \frac{1}{12}, \text{ or } 3\frac{1}{12}$$
>
> This can easily be found by dividing.
>

Answer

17. $\dfrac{17}{12}$ or $1\dfrac{5}{12}$

Example 12   Operations on Mixed Numbers

Classroom Example: p. 20, Exercise 110

Divide. $7\dfrac{1}{2} \div 3$

Solution:

$7\dfrac{1}{2} \div 3$

$= \dfrac{15}{2} \div \dfrac{3}{1}$ Write the mixed number and whole number as fractions.

$= \dfrac{\overset{5}{\cancel{15}}}{2} \times \dfrac{1}{\underset{1}{\cancel{3}}}$ Multiply by the reciprocal of $\frac{3}{1}$, which is $\frac{1}{3}$.

$= \dfrac{5}{2}$ or $2\dfrac{1}{2}$ The answer may be written as an improper fraction or as a mixed number.

> **Avoiding Mistakes**
>
> Remember that when dividing (or multiplying) fractions, a common denominator is not necessary.

Skill Practice Divide.

18. $5\dfrac{5}{6} \div 3\dfrac{2}{3}$

Answer

18. $\dfrac{35}{22}$ or $1\dfrac{13}{22}$

Section 1.1   Practice Exercises

Boost *your* GRADE at ALEKS.com!

ALEKS version 3.0

- Practice Problems
- Self-Tests
- NetTutor

- e-Professors
- Videos

For additional exercises, see Classroom Activities 1.1A–1.1E in the *Instructor's Resource Manual* at www.mhhe.com/moh.

Study Skills Exercises

1. To enhance your learning experience, we provide study skills that focus on eight areas: learning about your course, using your text, taking notes, doing homework, taking an exam (test and math anxiety), managing your time, recognizing your learning style, and studying for the final exam.

    Each activity requires only a few minutes and will help you pass this course and become a better math student. Many of these skills can be carried over to other disciplines and help you become a model college student. To begin, write down the following information:

    a. Instructor's name

    b. Instructor's office number

    c. Instructor's telephone number

    d. Instructor's e-mail address

    e. Instructor's office hours

    f. Days of the week that the class meets

    g. The room number in which the class meets

    h. Is there a lab requirement for this course? How often must you attend lab and where is it located?

2. Define the key terms.

    a. natural numbers

    b. whole numbers

    c. fractions

    d. numerator

    e. denominator

    f. proper fraction

    g. improper fraction

    h. mixed number

    i. product

    j. factors

    k. prime number

    l. composite number

    m. lowest terms

    n. greatest common factor

    o. reciprocal

    p. least common multiple (LCM)

    q. least common denominator (LCD)

 Writing   Translating Expression   Geometry   Scientific Calculator   Video   NS&E

Concept 1: Basic Definitions

For Exercises 3–10, identify the numerator and denominator of each fraction. Then determine if the fraction is a proper fraction or an improper fraction.

3. $\dfrac{7}{8}$ Numerator: 7; denominator: 8; proper

4. $\dfrac{2}{3}$ Numerator: 2; denominator: 3; proper

5. $\dfrac{9}{5}$ Numerator: 9; denominator: 5; improper

6. $\dfrac{5}{2}$ Numerator: 5; denominator: 2; improper

7. $\dfrac{6}{6}$ Numerator: 6; denominator: 6; improper

8. $\dfrac{4}{4}$ Numerator: 4; denominator: 4; improper

9. $\dfrac{12}{1}$ Numerator: 12; denominator: 1; improper

10. $\dfrac{5}{1}$ Numerator: 5; denominator: 1; improper

For Exercises 11–18, write a proper or improper fraction associated with the shaded region of each figure.

11. $\dfrac{3}{4}$

12. $\dfrac{4}{5}$

13. $\dfrac{4}{3}$

14. $\dfrac{5}{4}$

15. $\dfrac{1}{6}$

16. $\dfrac{1}{8}$

17. $\dfrac{2}{2}$

18. 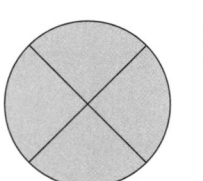 $\dfrac{4}{4}$

For Exercises 19–22, write both an improper fraction and a mixed number associated with the shaded region of each figure.

19. $\dfrac{5}{2}$ or $2\frac{1}{2}$

20. $\dfrac{5}{3}$ or $1\frac{2}{3}$

21. $\dfrac{6}{2}$ or 3

22. $\dfrac{6}{3}$ or 2

23. Explain the difference between the set of whole numbers and the set of natural numbers.   The set of whole numbers includes the number 0 and the set of natural numbers does not.

24. Explain the difference between a proper fraction and an improper fraction.   A proper fraction represents a number less than one unit. An improper fraction represents a number greater than or equal to a whole unit.

25. Write a fraction that simplifies to $\frac{1}{2}$. (Answers may vary.)   For example: $\dfrac{2}{4}$

26. Write a fraction that simplifies to $\frac{1}{3}$. (Answers may vary.)   For example: $\dfrac{2}{6}$

Concept 2: Prime Factorization

For Exercises 27–34, identify each number as either a prime number or a composite number.

27. 5 Prime **28.** 9 Composite **29.** 4 Composite **30.** 2 Prime

31. 39 Composite **32.** 23 Prime **33.** 53 Prime **34.** 51 Composite

For Exercises 35–42, write each number as a product of prime factors. **(See Example 1.)**

35. 36 $2 \times 2 \times 3 \times 3$ **36.** 70 $2 \times 5 \times 7$ **37.** 42 $2 \times 3 \times 7$ **38.** 35 5×7

39. 110 $2 \times 5 \times 11$ **40.** 136 $2 \times 2 \times 2 \times 17$ **41.** 135 $3 \times 3 \times 3 \times 5$ **42.** 105 $3 \times 5 \times 7$

Concept 3: Simplifying Fractions to Lowest Terms

For Exercises 43–54, simplify each fraction to lowest terms. **(See Examples 2–3.)**

43. $\frac{3}{15}$ $\frac{1}{5}$ **44.** $\frac{8}{12}$ $\frac{2}{3}$ **45.** $\frac{6}{16}$ $\frac{3}{8}$ **46.** $\frac{12}{20}$ $\frac{3}{5}$

47. $\frac{42}{48}$ $\frac{7}{8}$ **48.** $\frac{35}{80}$ $\frac{7}{16}$ **49.** $\frac{48}{64}$ $\frac{3}{4}$ **50.** $\frac{32}{48}$ $\frac{2}{3}$

51. $\frac{110}{176}$ $\frac{5}{8}$ **52.** $\frac{70}{120}$ $\frac{7}{12}$ **53.** $\frac{150}{200}$ $\frac{3}{4}$ **54.** $\frac{119}{210}$ $\frac{17}{30}$

Concepts 4–5: Multiplying and Dividing Fractions

For Exercises 55–56, determine if the statement is true or false. If it is false, rewrite as a true statement.

55. When multiplying or dividing fractions, it is necessary to have a common denominator.
False: When adding or subtracting fractions, it is necessary to have a common denominator.

56. When dividing two fractions, it is necessary to multiply the first fraction by the reciprocal of the second fraction. True

Animation

For Exercises 57–68, multiply or divide as indicated. **(See Examples 4–6.)**

57. $\frac{10}{13} \times \frac{26}{15}$ $\frac{4}{3}$ or $1\frac{1}{3}$ **58.** $\frac{15}{28} \times \frac{7}{9}$ $\frac{5}{12}$ **59.** $\frac{3}{7} \div \frac{9}{14}$ $\frac{2}{3}$ **60.** $\frac{7}{25} \div \frac{1}{5}$ $\frac{7}{5}$ or $1\frac{2}{5}$

61. $\frac{9}{10} \times 5$ $\frac{9}{2}$ or $4\frac{1}{2}$ **62.** $\frac{3}{7} \times 14$ 6 **63.** $\frac{12}{5} \div 4$ $\frac{3}{5}$ **64.** $\frac{20}{6} \div 5$ $\frac{2}{3}$

65. $\frac{5}{2} \times \frac{10}{21} \times \frac{7}{5}$ $\frac{5}{3}$ or $1\frac{2}{3}$ **66.** $\frac{55}{9} \times \frac{18}{32} \times \frac{24}{11}$ $\frac{15}{2}$ or $7\frac{1}{2}$ **67.** $\frac{9}{100} \div \frac{13}{1000}$ $\frac{90}{13}$ or $6\frac{12}{13}$ **68.** $\frac{1000}{17} \div \frac{10}{3}$ $\frac{300}{17}$ or $17\frac{11}{17}$

69. Gus decides to save $\frac{1}{3}$ of his pay each month. If his monthly pay is $2112, how much will he save each month? $704

70. Stephen's take-home pay is $4200 a month. If he budgeted $\frac{1}{4}$ of his pay for rent, how much is his rent? $1050

71. On a college basketball team, one-third of the team graduated with honors. If the team has 12 members, how many graduated with honors?
4 graduated with honors.

72. Shontell had only enough paper to print out $\frac{3}{5}$ of her book report before school. If the report is 10 pages long, how many pages did she print out?
6 pages

73. Natalie has 4 yd of material with which she can make holiday aprons. If it takes $\frac{1}{2}$ yd of material per apron, how many aprons can she make?   8 aprons

74. There are 4 cups of oatmeal in a box. If each serving is $\frac{1}{3}$ of a cup, how many servings are contained in the box?   12 servings

75. Gail buys 6 lb of mixed nuts to be divided into decorative jars that will each hold $\frac{3}{4}$ lb of nuts. How many jars will she be able to fill?   8 jars

76. Troy has a $\frac{7}{8}$-in. nail that he must hammer into a board. Each strike of the hammer moves the nail $\frac{1}{16}$ in. into the board. How many strikes of the hammer must he make to drive the nail completely into the board?   Troy must make 14 strikes.

Concept 6: Adding and Subtracting Fractions

For Exercises 77–80, add or subtract as indicated. **(See Example 7.)**

77. $\frac{5}{14} + \frac{1}{14}$ $\frac{3}{7}$

78. $\frac{9}{5} + \frac{1}{5}$ 2

79. $\frac{17}{24} - \frac{5}{24}$ $\frac{1}{2}$

80. $\frac{11}{18} - \frac{5}{18}$ $\frac{1}{3}$

For Exercises 81–84, find the least common multiple for each list of numbers. **(See Example 8.)**

81. 6, 15   30

82. 12, 30   60

83. 20, 8, 4   40

84. 24, 40, 30   120

For Exercises 85–100, add or subtract as indicated. **(See Examples 9–10.)**

85. $\frac{1}{8} + \frac{3}{4}$ $\frac{7}{8}$

86. $\frac{3}{16} + \frac{1}{2}$ $\frac{11}{16}$

87. $\frac{3}{8} - \frac{3}{10}$ $\frac{3}{40}$

88. $\frac{12}{35} - \frac{1}{10}$ $\frac{17}{70}$

89. $\frac{7}{26} - \frac{2}{13}$ $\frac{3}{26}$

90. $\frac{11}{24} - \frac{5}{16}$ $\frac{7}{48}$

91. $\frac{7}{18} + \frac{5}{12}$ $\frac{29}{36}$

92. $\frac{3}{16} + \frac{9}{20}$ $\frac{51}{80}$

93. $\frac{3}{4} - \frac{1}{20}$ $\frac{7}{10}$

94. $\frac{1}{6} - \frac{1}{24}$ $\frac{1}{8}$

95. $\frac{5}{12} + \frac{5}{16}$ $\frac{35}{48}$

96. $\frac{3}{25} + \frac{8}{35}$ $\frac{61}{175}$

97. $\frac{1}{6} + \frac{3}{4} - \frac{5}{8}$ $\frac{7}{24}$

98. $\frac{1}{2} + \frac{2}{3} - \frac{5}{12}$ $\frac{3}{4}$

99. $\frac{4}{7} + \frac{1}{2} + \frac{3}{4}$ $\frac{51}{28}$ or $1\frac{23}{28}$

100. $\frac{9}{10} + \frac{4}{5} + \frac{3}{4}$ $\frac{49}{20}$ or $2\frac{9}{20}$

Concept 7: Operations on Mixed Numbers

For Exercises 101–118, perform the indicated operations. **(See Examples 11–12.)**

101. $3\frac{1}{5} \times \frac{7}{8}$ $\frac{14}{5}$ or $2\frac{4}{5}$

102. $2\frac{1}{2} \times \frac{4}{5}$ 2

103. $4\frac{3}{5} \div \frac{1}{10}$ 46

104. $2\frac{4}{5} \div \frac{7}{11}$ $\frac{22}{5}$ or $4\frac{2}{5}$

105. $3\frac{1}{5} \times 2\frac{7}{8}$ $\frac{46}{5}$ or $9\frac{1}{5}$

106. $2\frac{1}{2} \times 1\frac{4}{5}$ $\frac{9}{2}$ or $4\frac{1}{2}$

107. $1\frac{2}{9} \div 7\frac{1}{3}$ $\frac{1}{6}$

108. $2\frac{2}{5} \div 1\frac{2}{7}$ $\frac{28}{15}$ or $1\frac{13}{15}$

109. $1\frac{2}{9} \div 6$ $\frac{11}{54}$

110. $2\frac{2}{5} \div 2$ $\frac{6}{5}$ or $1\frac{1}{5}$

111. $2\frac{1}{8} + 1\frac{3}{8}$ $\frac{7}{2}$ or $3\frac{1}{2}$

112. $1\frac{3}{14} + 1\frac{1}{14}$ $\frac{16}{7}$ or $2\frac{2}{7}$

113. $3\frac{1}{2} - 1\frac{7}{8}$ $\frac{13}{8}$ or $1\frac{5}{8}$

114. $5\frac{1}{3} - 2\frac{3}{4}$ $\frac{31}{12}$ or $2\frac{7}{12}$

115. $1\frac{1}{6} + 3\frac{3}{4}$ $\frac{59}{12}$ or $4\frac{11}{12}$

116. $4\frac{1}{2} + 2\frac{2}{3}$ $\frac{43}{6}$ or $7\frac{1}{6}$

117. $1 - \frac{7}{8}$ $\frac{1}{8}$

118. $2 - \frac{3}{7}$ $\frac{11}{7}$ or $1\frac{4}{7}$

119. A board $26\frac{3}{8}$ in. long must be cut into three pieces of equal length. Find the length of each piece. $8\frac{19}{24}$ in.

$26\frac{3}{8}$ in.

120. A futon, when set up as a sofa, measures $3\frac{5}{6}$ ft wide. When it is opened to be used as a bed, the width is increased by $1\frac{3}{4}$ ft. What is the total width of this bed? $5\frac{7}{12}$ ft

$3\frac{5}{6}$ ft x

121. A plane trip from Orlando to Detroit takes $2\frac{3}{4}$ hr. If the plane traveled for $1\frac{1}{6}$ hr, how much time remains for the flight? $1\frac{7}{12}$ hr

122. Antonio bought $3\frac{3}{4}$ lb of smoked turkey for sandwiches. If he made 10 sandwiches, how much turkey did he put in each sandwich? $\frac{3}{8}$ lb

123. José ordered two seafood platters for a party. One platter has $1\frac{1}{2}$ lb of shrimp, and the other has $\frac{3}{4}$ lb of shrimp. How many pounds of shrimp does he have altogether? $2\frac{1}{4}$ lb

124. Ayako took a trip to the store $5\frac{1}{2}$ mi away. If she rode the bus for $4\frac{5}{6}$ mi and walked the rest of the way, how far did she have to walk? $\frac{2}{3}$ mi

125. If Tampa, Florida averages $6\frac{1}{4}$ in. of rain during each summer month, how much total rain would be expected in June, July, August, and September?   25 in.

126. Pete started working out and found that he lost approximately $\frac{3}{4}$ in. off his waistline every month. How much would he lose around his waist in 6 months? $\frac{9}{2}$ in. or $4\frac{1}{2}$ in.

Sets of Numbers and the Real Number Line   Section 1.2

1. The Set of Real Numbers

The numbers we work with on a day-to-day basis are all part of the set of **real numbers**. The real numbers encompass zero, all positive, and all negative numbers, including those represented by fractions and decimal numbers. The set of real numbers can be represented graphically on a horizontal number line with a point labeled as 0. Positive real numbers are graphed to the right of 0, and negative real numbers are graphed to the left of 0. Zero is neither positive nor negative. Each point on the number line corresponds to exactly one real number. For this reason, this number line is called the *real number line* (Figure 1-5).

Concepts

1. The Set of Real Numbers
2. Inequalities
3. Opposite of a Real Number
4. Absolute Value of a Real Number

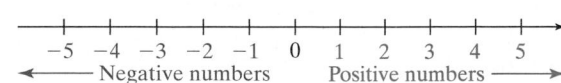

Negative numbers ← | → Positive numbers

Figure 1-5

 Writing   Translating Expression   Geometry   Scientific Calculator   Video   NS&E

Example 1   **Plotting Points on the Real Number Line**

Plot the numbers on the real number line.

a. -3 **b.** $\dfrac{3}{2}$ **c.** -4.7 **d.** $\dfrac{16}{5}$

Solution:

a. Because -3 is negative, it lies three units to the left of 0.

b. The fraction $\frac{3}{2}$ can be expressed as the mixed number $1\frac{1}{2}$, which lies half-way between 1 and 2 on the number line.

c. The negative number -4.7 lies $\frac{7}{10}$ units to the left of -4 on the number line.

d. The fraction $\frac{16}{5}$ can be expressed as the mixed number $3\frac{1}{5}$, which lies $\frac{1}{5}$ unit to the right of 3 on the number line.

Skill Practice Plot the numbers on the real number line.

1. $\{-1, \frac{3}{4}, -2.5, \frac{10}{3}\}$

In mathematics, a well-defined collection of elements is called a **set**. "Well-defined" means the set is described in such a way that it is clear whether an element is in the set. The symbols { } are used to enclose the elements of the set. For example, the set {A, B, C, D, E} represents the set of the first five letters of the alphabet.

Several sets of numbers are used extensively in algebra and are *subsets* (or part) of the set of real numbers.

DEFINITION   **Natural Numbers, Whole Numbers, and Integers**

The set of **natural numbers** is $\{1, 2, 3, \ldots\}$
The set of **whole numbers** is $\{0, 1, 2, 3, \ldots\}$
The set of **integers** is $\{\ldots -3, -2, -1, 0, 1, 2, 3, \ldots\}$

Notice that the set of whole numbers includes the natural numbers. Therefore, every natural number is also a whole number. The set of integers includes the set of whole numbers. Therefore, every whole number is also an integer.

Fractions are also among the numbers we use frequently. A number that can be written as a fraction whose numerator is an integer and whose denominator is a nonzero integer is called a *rational number*.

DEFINITION   **Rational Numbers**

The set of **rational numbers** is the set of numbers that can be expressed in the form $\frac{p}{q}$, where both p and q are integers and q does not equal 0.

Answer

1.

We also say that a rational number $\frac{p}{q}$ is a *ratio* of two integers, p and q, where q is not equal to zero.

Classroom Examples: p. 30, Exercises 10 and 12

Example 2   Identifying Rational Numbers

Show that the following numbers are rational numbers by finding an equivalent ratio of two integers.

a. $\dfrac{-2}{3}$ **b.** -12 **c.** 0.5 **d.** $0.\overline{6}$

Solution:

a. The fraction $\frac{-2}{3}$ is a rational number because it can be expressed as the ratio of -2 and 3.

b. The number -12 is a rational number because it can be expressed as the ratio of -12 and 1, that is, $-12 = \frac{-12}{1}$. In this example, we see that an integer is also a rational number.

c. The terminating decimal 0.5 is a rational number because it can be expressed as the ratio of 5 and 10. That is, $0.5 = \frac{5}{10}$. In this example, we see that a terminating decimal is also a rational number.

d. The repeating decimal $0.\overline{6}$ is a rational number because it can be expressed as the ratio of 2 and 3. That is, $0.\overline{6} = \frac{2}{3}$. In this example, we see that a repeating decimal is also a rational number.

Skill Practice Show that each number is rational by finding an equivalent ratio of two integers.

2. $\dfrac{3}{7}$ **3.** -5 **4.** 0.3 **5.** $0.\overline{3}$

TIP: A rational number can be represented by a terminating decimal or by a repeating decimal.

Some real numbers, such as the number π, cannot be represented by the ratio of two integers. These numbers are called irrational numbers and in decimal form are nonterminating, nonrepeating decimals. The value of π, for example, can be approximated as $\pi \approx 3.1415926535897932$. However, the decimal digits continue forever with no repeated pattern. Another example of an irrational number is $\sqrt{3}$ (read as "the positive square root of 3"). The expression $\sqrt{3}$ is a number that when multiplied by itself is 3. There is no rational number that satisfies this condition. Thus, $\sqrt{3}$ is an irrational number.

DEFINITION   Irrational Numbers

The set of **irrational numbers** is a subset of the real numbers whose elements cannot be written as a ratio of two integers.

Note: An irrational number cannot be written as a terminating decimal or as a repeating decimal.

Answers
2. Ratio of 3 and 7
3. Ratio of −5 and 1
4. Ratio of 3 and 10
5. Ratio of 1 and 3

The set of real numbers consists of both the rational and the irrational numbers. The relationship among these important sets of numbers is illustrated in Figure 1-6:

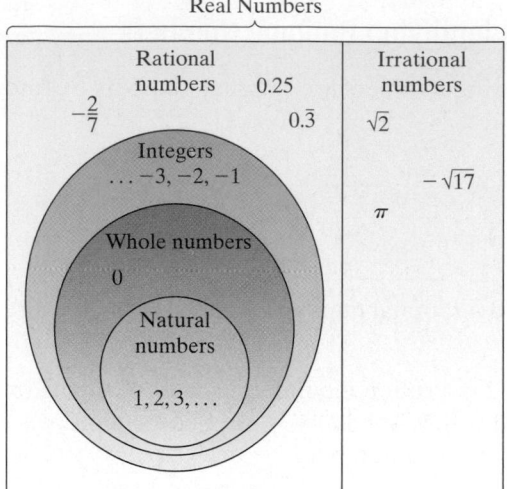

Figure 1-6

Classroom Examples: p. 30, Exercises 32 and 34

Example 3 **Classifying Numbers by Set**

Check the set(s) to which each number belongs. The numbers may belong to more than one set.

	Natural Numbers	Whole Numbers	Integers	Rational Numbers	Irrational Numbers	Real Numbers
5						
$\frac{-47}{3}$						
1.48						
$\sqrt{7}$						
0						

Solution:

	Natural Numbers	Whole Numbers	Integers	Rational Numbers	Irrational Numbers	Real Numbers
5	✔	✔	✔	✔ (ratio of 5 and 1)		✔
$\frac{-47}{3}$				✔ (ratio of −47 and 3)		✔
1.48				✔ (ratio of 148 and 100)		✔
$\sqrt{7}$					✔	✔
0		✔	✔	✔ (ratio of 0 and 1)		✔

Skill Practice Identify the sets to which each number belongs. Choose from: natural numbers, whole numbers, integers, rational numbers, irrational numbers, real numbers.

6. -4 **7.** $0.\overline{7}$ **8.** $\sqrt{13}$ **9.** 12 **10.** 0

2. Inequalities

The relative size of two real numbers can be compared using the real number line. Suppose a and b represent two real numbers. We say that a is less than b, denoted $a < b$, if a lies to the left of b on the number line.

$a < b$

We say that a is greater than b, denoted $a > b$, if a lies to the right of b on the number line.

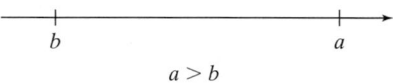

$a > b$

Table 1-1 summarizes the relational operators that compare two real numbers a and b.

Table 1-1

Mathematical Expression	Translation	Example
$a < b$	a is less than b.	$2 < 3$
$a > b$	a is greater than b.	$5 > 1$
$a \leq b$	a is less than or equal to b	$4 \leq 4$
$a \geq b$	a is greater than or equal to b.	$10 \geq 9$
$a = b$	a is equal to b.	$6 = 6$
$a \neq b$	a is not equal to b.	$7 \neq 0$
$a \approx b$	a is approximately equal to b.	$2.3 \approx 2$

The symbols $<$, $>$, $\leq$, $\geq$, and $\neq$ are called *inequality signs*, and the expressions $a < b, a > b, a \leq b, a \geq b$, and $a \neq b$ are called **inequalities**.

Example 4   **Ordering Real Numbers**

The average temperatures (in degrees Celsius) for selected cities in the United States and Canada in January are shown in Table 1-2.

Table 1-2

City	Temp (°C)
Prince George, British Columbia	-12.5
Corpus Christi, Texas	13.4
Parkersburg, West Virginia	-0.9
San Jose, California	9.7
Juneau, Alaska	-5.7
New Bedford, Massachusetts	-0.2
Durham, North Carolina	4.2

Classroom Example: p. 31, Exercise 38

Answers

6. Integers, rational numbers, real numbers
7. Rational numbers, real numbers
8. Irrational numbers, real numbers
9. Natural numbers, whole numbers, integers, rational numbers, real numbers
10. Whole numbers, integers, rational numbers, real numbers

Plot a point on the real number line representing the temperature of each city. Compare the temperatures between the following cities, and fill in the blank with the appropriate inequality sign: $<$ or $>$.

Solution:

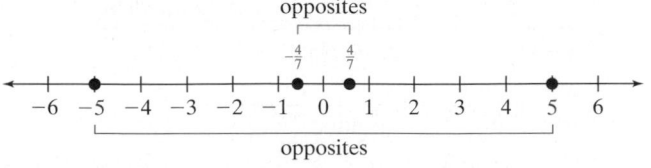

a. Temperature of San Jose $\boxed{<}$ temperature of Corpus Christi

b. Temperature of Juneau $\boxed{>}$ temperature of Prince George

c. Temperature of Parkersburg $\boxed{<}$ temperature of New Bedford

d. Temperature of Parkersburg $\boxed{>}$ temperature of Prince George

Skill Practice Fill in the blanks with the appropriate inequality sign: $<$ or $>$.

11. -11 _____ 20 **12.** -3 _____ -6

13. 0 _____ -9 **14.** -6.2 _____ -1.8

3. Opposite of a Real Number

To gain mastery of any algebraic skill, it is necessary to know the meaning of key definitions and key symbols. Two important definitions are the *opposite* of a real number and the *absolute value* of a real number.

> **DEFINITION** **The Opposite of a Real Number**
>
> Two numbers that are the same distance from 0 but on opposite sides of 0 on the number line are called **opposites** of each other. Symbolically, we denote the opposite of a real number a as $-a$.

Classroom Examples: p. 31, Exercises 40 and 42

Example 5 Finding the Opposite of a Real Number

a. Find the opposite of 5.   b. Find the opposite of $-\frac{4}{7}$.

Solution:

a. The opposite of 5 is -5.   b. The opposite of $-\frac{4}{7}$ is $\frac{4}{7}$.

opposites

$$\overset{-\frac{4}{7} \quad \frac{4}{7}}{\underset{-6\ -5\ -4\ -3\ -2\ -1\ \ 0\ \ 1\ \ 2\ \ 3\ \ 4\ \ 5\ \ 6}{\longleftrightarrow}}$$

opposites

Skill Practice Find the opposite.

15. 224   **16.** -3.4

Answers

11. $<$ **12.** $>$ **13.** $>$
14. $<$ **15.** -224 **16.** 3.4

Example 6 Finding the Opposite of a Real Number

Classroom Example: p. 31, Exercise 50

a. Evaluate $-(0.46)$.   **b.** Evaluate $-\left(-\dfrac{11}{3}\right)$.

Solution:

a. $-(0.46) = -0.46$ The expression $-(0.46)$ represents the opposite of 0.46.

b. $-\left(-\dfrac{11}{3}\right) = \dfrac{11}{3}$ The expression $-(-\frac{11}{3})$ represents the opposite of $-\frac{11}{3}$.

Skill Practice Evaluate.

17. $-(2.8)$ **18.** $-\left(-\dfrac{1}{5}\right)$

4. Absolute Value of a Real Number

The concept of absolute value will be used to define the addition of real numbers in Section 1.4.

Instructor Note: Remind students that because absolute value is a measure of *distance* it will always be nonnegative. We don't measure distance with negative numbers.

> **DEFINITION Informal Definition of the Absolute Value of a Real Number**
>
> The **absolute value** of a real number a, denoted $|a|$, is the distance between a and 0 on the number line.
>
> *Note:* The absolute value of any real number is positive or zero.

For example, $|3| = 3$ and $|-3| = 3$.

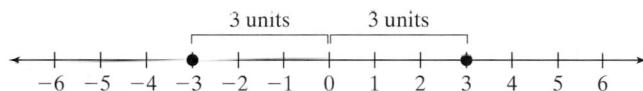

Example 7 Finding the Absolute Value of a Real Number

Classroom Examples: p. 31, Exercises 56 and 60

Evaluate the absolute value expressions.

a. $|-4|$ **b.** $\left|\frac{1}{2}\right|$ **c.** $|-6.2|$ **d.** $|0|$

Solution:

a. $|-4| = 4$ -4 is 4 units from 0 on the number line.

b. $\left|\frac{1}{2}\right| = \frac{1}{2}$ $\frac{1}{2}$ is $\frac{1}{2}$ unit from 0 on the number line.

Answers

17. -2.8 **18.** $\dfrac{1}{5}$

c. $|-6.2| = 6.2$ −6.2 is 6.2 units from 0 on the number line.

d. $|0| = 0$ 0 is 0 units from 0 on the number line.

Skill Practice Evaluate.

19. $|-99|$ **20.** $\left|\dfrac{7}{8}\right|$ **21.** $|-1.4|$ **22.** $|1|$

The absolute value of a number a is its distance from 0 on the number line. The definition of $|a|$ may also be given symbolically depending on whether a is negative or nonnegative.

> **DEFINITION   Absolute Value of a Real Number**
>
> Let a be a real number. Then
>
> **1.** If a is nonnegative (that is, $a \geq 0$), then $|a| = a$.
>
> **2.** If a is negative (that is, $a < 0$), then $|a| = -a$.

This definition states that if a is a nonnegative number, then $|a|$ equals a itself. If a is a negative number, then $|a|$ equals the opposite of a. For example:

$|9| = 9$ Because 9 is positive, then $|9|$ equals the number 9 itself.

$|-7| = 7$ Because −7 is negative, then $|-7|$ equals the opposite of −7, which is 7.

Classroom Examples: p. 32, Exercises 82 and 88

Example 8   Comparing Absolute Value Expressions

Determine if the statements are true or false.

a. $|3| \leq 3$ **b.** $-|5| = |-5|$

Solution:

a. $|3| \leq 3$ $|3| \overset{?}{\leq} 3$ Simplify the absolute value.

                       $3 \overset{?}{\leq} 3$ True

b. $-|5| = |-5|$ $-|5| \overset{?}{=} |-5|$ Simplify the absolute values.

                         $-5 \overset{?}{=} 5$ False

Skill Practice Answer true or false.

23. $-|4| > |-4|$ **24.** $|-17| = 17$

Answers

19. 99   **20.** $\dfrac{7}{8}$

21. 1.4   **22.** 1

23. False   **24.** True

Calculator Connections

Topic: Approximating Irrational Numbers on a Calculator

Scientific and graphing calculators approximate irrational numbers by using rational numbers in the form of terminating decimals. For example, consider approximating π and $\sqrt{3}$.

Scientific Calculator:

Enter: $\boxed{\pi}$ or $\boxed{2^{nd}}$ $\boxed{\pi}$ Result: $\boxed{3.141592654}$

Enter: 3 $\boxed{\sqrt{\ }}$ Result: $\boxed{1.732050808}$

Graphing Calculator:

Enter: $\boxed{2^{nd}}$ $\boxed{\pi}$ $\boxed{ENTER}$

Enter: $\boxed{2^{nd}}$ $\boxed{\sqrt{\ }}$ 3 $\boxed{ENTER}$

```
π
        3.141592654
√(3)
        1.732050808
```

Note that when writing approximations, we use the symbol, $\approx$.

$$\pi \approx 3.141592654 \quad \text{and} \quad \sqrt{3} \approx 1.732050808$$

Calculator Exercises

Use a calculator to approximate the irrational numbers. Remember to use the appropriate symbol, $\approx$, when expressing answers.

1. $\sqrt{12}$ **2.** $\sqrt{99}$ **3.** $4 \cdot \pi$ **4.** $\sqrt{\pi}$
≈ 3.464101615 ≈ 9.949874371 ≈ 12.56637061 ≈ 1.772453851

Section 1.2 Practice Exercises

Study Skills Exercises

1. Look over the notes that you took today. Do you understand what you wrote? If there were any rules, definitions, or formulas, highlight them so that they can be easily found when studying for the test. You may want to begin by highlighting the order of operations.

2. Define the key terms.

a. real numbers   b. set   c. natural numbers   d. whole numbers

e. integers   f. rational numbers   g. irrational numbers   h. inequality

i. opposite   j. absolute value

Review Exercises

For Exercises 3–6, simplify.

3. $4\frac{1}{2} - 1\frac{5}{6}$ $2\frac{2}{3}$ **4.** $4\frac{1}{2} \times 1\frac{5}{6}$ $8\frac{1}{4}$ **5.** $4\frac{1}{2} \div 1\frac{5}{6}$ $2\frac{5}{11}$ **6.** $4\frac{1}{2} + 1\frac{5}{6}$ $6\frac{1}{3}$

Concept 1: The Set of Real Numbers

7. Plot the numbers on the real number line: $\{1, -2, -\pi, 0, -\frac{5}{2}, 5.1\}$ **(See Example 1.)**

8. Plot the numbers on the real number line: $\{3, -4, \frac{1}{8}, -1.7, -\frac{4}{3}, 1.75\}$

For Exercises 9–24, describe each number as (a) a terminating decimal, (b) a repeating decimal, or (c) a nonterminating, nonrepeating decimal. Then classify the number as a rational number or as an irrational number. **(See Example 2.)**

9. 0.29   a; rational

10. 3.8   a; rational

11. $\frac{1}{9}$ b; rational

12. $\frac{1}{3}$ b; rational

13. $\frac{1}{8}$ a; rational

14. $\frac{1}{5}$ a; rational

15. 2π c; irrational

16. 3π c; irrational

17. -0.125 a; rational

18. -3.24 a; rational

19. -3 a; rational

20. -6 a; rational

21. $0.\overline{2}$ b; rational

22. $0.\overline{6}$ b; rational

23. $\sqrt{6}$ c; irrational

24. $\sqrt{10}$ c; irrational

25. List three numbers that are real numbers but not rational numbers.
For example: $\pi, -\sqrt{2}, \sqrt{3}$

26. List three numbers that are real numbers but not irrational numbers.
For example: $-\frac{1}{2}, 5, 0.\overline{3}$

27. List three numbers that are integers but not natural numbers.
For example: $-4, -1, 0$

28. List three numbers that are integers but not whole numbers.
For example: $-5, -2, -1$

29. List three numbers that are rational numbers but not integers.   For example: $-\frac{3}{4}, \frac{1}{2}, 0.206$

For Exercises 30–36, let $A = \{-\frac{3}{2}, \sqrt{11}, -4, 0.\overline{6}, 0, \sqrt{7}, 1\}$ **(See Example 3.)**

30. Are all of the numbers in set A real numbers?
Yes

31. List all of the rational numbers in set A. $-\frac{3}{2}, -4, 0.\overline{6}, 0, 1$

32. List all of the whole numbers in set A.
0, 1

33. List all of the natural numbers in set A.   1

34. List all of the irrational numbers in set A.
$\sqrt{11}, \sqrt{7}$

35. List all of the integers in set A. $-4, 0, 1$

36. Plot the real numbers from set A on a number line. (*Hint:* $\sqrt{11} \approx 3.3$ and $\sqrt{7} \approx 2.6$)

Concept 2: Inequalities

37. The LPGA Samsung World Championship of women's golf scores for selected players are given in the table. Compare the scores and fill in the blank with the appropriate inequality sign: $<$ or $>$.
(See Example 4.)

   a. Kane's score ___>___ Pak's score.

   b. Sorenstam's score ___>___ Davies' score.

   c. Pak's score ___<___ McCurdy's score.

   d. Kane's score ___>___ Davies' score.

LPGA Golfers	Final Score with Respect to Par
Annika Sorenstam	7
Laura Davies	−4
Lorie Kane	0
Cindy McCurdy	3
Se Ri Pak	−8

 Writing   Translating Expression   Geometry   Scientific Calculator   Video   NS&E

38. The elevations of selected cities in the United States are shown in the figure. Compare the elevations and fill in the blank with the appropriate inequality sign: $<$ or $>$. (A negative number indicates that the city is below sea level.)

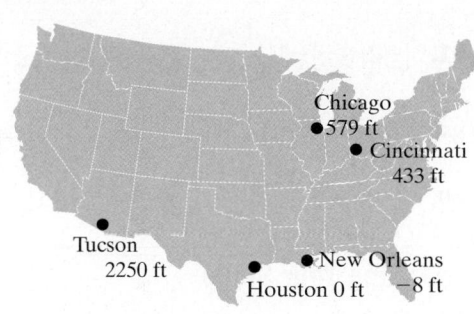

   a. Elevation of Tucson ___$>$___ elevation of Cincinnati.

   b. Elevation of New Orleans ___$<$___ elevation of Chicago.

   c. Elevation of New Orleans ___$<$___ elevation of Houston.

   d. Elevation of Chicago ___$>$___ elevation of Cincinnati.

Concept 3: Opposite of a Real Number

For Exercises 39–46, find the opposite of each number. **(See Example 5.)**

39. 18 -18 **40.** 2 -2 **41.** -6.1 6.1   **42.** -2.5 2.5

43. $-\dfrac{5}{8}$ $\dfrac{5}{8}$ **44.** $-\dfrac{1}{3}$ $\dfrac{1}{3}$ **45.** $\dfrac{7}{3}$ $-\dfrac{7}{3}$ **46.** $\dfrac{1}{9}$ $-\dfrac{1}{9}$

The opposite of a is denoted as $-a$. For Exercises 47–54, simplify. **(See Example 6.)**

47. $-(-3)$ 3   **48.** $-(-5.1)$ 5.1   **49.** $-\left(\dfrac{7}{3}\right)$ $-\dfrac{7}{3}$ **50.** $-(-7)$ 7

51. $-(-8)$ 8   **52.** $-(36)$ -36 **53.** $-(72.1)$ -72.1 **54.** $-\left(\dfrac{9}{10}\right)$ $-\dfrac{9}{10}$

Concept 4: Absolute Value of a Real Number

For Exercises 55–66, simplify. **(See Example 7.)**

55. $|-2|$ 2   **56.** $|-7|$ 7   **57.** $|-1.5|$ 1.5   **58.** $|-3.7|$ 3.7

59. $-|-1.5|$ -1.5 **60.** $-|-3.7|$ -3.7 **61.** $\left|\dfrac{3}{2}\right|$ $\dfrac{3}{2}$ **62.** $\left|\dfrac{7}{4}\right|$ $\dfrac{7}{4}$

63. $-|10|$ -10 **64.** $-|20|$ -20 **65.** $-\left|-\dfrac{1}{2}\right|$ $-\dfrac{1}{2}$ **66.** $-\left|-\dfrac{11}{3}\right|$ $-\dfrac{11}{3}$

For Exercises 67–68, answer true or false. If a statement is false, explain why.

67. If n is positive, then $|n|$ is negative.
False, $|n|$ is never negative.

68. If m is negative, then $|m|$ is negative.
False, $|m|$ is never negative.

For Exercises 69–92, determine if the statements are true or false. Use the real number line to justify the answer. **(See Example 8.)**

69. $5 > 2$ True   **70.** $8 < 10$ True   **71.** $6 < 6$ False   **72.** $19 > 19$ False

73. $-7 \geq -7$ True   **74.** $-1 \leq -1$ True   **75.** $\dfrac{3}{2} \leq \dfrac{1}{6}$ False   **76.** $-\dfrac{1}{4} \geq -\dfrac{7}{8}$ True

77. $-5 > -2$ False   **78.** $6 < -10$ False   **79.** $8 \neq 8$ False   **80.** $10 \neq 10$ False

81. $|-2| \geq |-1|$ True   **82.** $|3| \leq |-1|$ False   **83.** $\left|-\dfrac{1}{9}\right| = \left|\dfrac{1}{9}\right|$ True   **84.** $\left|-\dfrac{1}{3}\right| = \left|\dfrac{1}{3}\right|$ True

85. $|7| \neq |-7|$ False   **86.** $|-13| \neq |13|$ False   **87.** $-1 < |-1|$ True   **88.** $-6 < |-6|$ True

89. $|-8| \geq |8|$ True   **90.** $|-11| \geq |11|$ True   **91.** $|-2| \leq |2|$ True   **92.** $|-21| \leq |21|$ True

Expanding Your Skills

93. For what numbers, a, is $-a$ positive?
For all $a < 0$

94. For what numbers, a, is $|a| = a$?
For all $a \geq 0$

Section 1.3   Exponents, Square Roots, and the Order of Operations

Concepts

1. Evaluating Algebraic Expressions
2. Exponential Expressions
3. Square Roots
4. Order of Operations
5. Translations

1. Evaluating Algebraic Expressions

A **variable** is a symbol or letter such as x, y, and z, used to represent an unknown number. **Constants** are values that do not vary such as the numbers 3, -1.5, $\frac{2}{7}$, and π. An algebraic **expression** is a collection of variables and constants under algebraic operations. For example, $\frac{3}{x}$, $y + 7$, and $t - 1.4$ are algebraic expressions.

The symbols used to show the four basic operations of addition, subtraction, multiplication, and division are summarized in Table 1-3.

Table 1-3

Operation	Symbols	Translation
Addition	$a + b$	**sum** of a and b a plus b b added to a b more than a a increased by b the total of a and b
Subtraction	$a - b$	**difference** of a and b a minus b b subtracted from a a decreased by b b less than a a less b
Multiplication	$a \times b$, $a \cdot b$, $a(b)$, $(a)b$, $(a)(b)$, ab (*Note:* From this point forward we will seldom use the notation $a \times b$ because the symbol, $\times$, might be confused with the variable, x.)	**product** of a and b a times b a multiplied by b
Division	$a \div b$, $\dfrac{a}{b}$, a/b, $b\,\overline{)a}$	**quotient** of a and b a divided by b b divided into a ratio of a and b a over b a per b

 Writing   Translating Expression   Geometry   Scientific Calculator   Video   NS&E

The value of an algebraic expression depends on the values of the variables within the expression.

Classroom Examples: p. 40, Exercises 10 and 12

| **Example 1** | **Evaluating Algebraic Expressions** |

Evaluate the algebraic expression when $p = 4$ and $q = \frac{3}{4}$.

a. $100 - p$ **b.** pq

Solution:

a. $100 - p$

$100 - (\ \ )$ When substituting a number for a variable, use parentheses.

$= 100 - (4)$ Substitute $p = 4$ in the parentheses.

$= 96$ Subtract.

b. pq

$= (\ \ )(\ \ )$ When substituting a number for a variable, use parentheses.

$= (4)\left(\dfrac{3}{4}\right)$ Substitute $p = 4$ and $q = \frac{3}{4}$.

$= \dfrac{\overset{1}{\cancel{4}}}{1} \cdot \dfrac{3}{\underset{1}{\cancel{4}}}$ Write the whole number as a fraction.

$= \dfrac{3}{1}$ Multiply fractions.

$= 3$ Simplify.

Skill Practice Evaluate the algebraic expressions when $x = 5$ and $y = 2$.

1. $20 - y$ **2.** xy

2. Exponential Expressions

In algebra, repeated multiplication can be expressed using exponents. The expression, $4 \cdot 4 \cdot 4$ can be written as

exponent

4^3

base

In the expression 4^3, 4 is the base, and 3 is the exponent, or power. The exponent indicates how many factors of the base to multiply.

TIP: A number or variable with no exponent shown implies that there is an exponent of 1. That is, $b = b^1$.

DEFINITION Definition of b^n

Let b represent any real number and n represent a positive integer. Then,

$$b^n = \underbrace{b \cdot b \cdot b \cdot b \cdot \ldots b}_{n \text{ factors of } b}$$

b^n is read as "b to the nth power."

b is called the **base**, and n is called the **exponent**, or **power**.

b^2 is read as "b squared," and b^3 is read as "b cubed."

The exponent, n, is the number of times the base, b, is used as a factor.

Classroom Examples: p. 41, Exercises 34 and 36

Example 2 Evaluating Exponential Expressions

Translate the expression into words and then evaluate the expression.

a. 2^5 **b.** 5^2 **c.** $\left(\dfrac{3}{4}\right)^3$ **d.** 1^6

Solution:

a. The expression 2^5 is read as "two to the fifth power."
$2^5 = (2)(2)(2)(2)(2) = 32$

b. The expression 5^2 is read as "five to the second power" or "five, squared."
$5^2 = (5)(5) = 25$

c. The expression $\left(\frac{3}{4}\right)^3$ is read as "three-fourths to the third power" or "three-fourths, cubed."

$$\left(\frac{3}{4}\right)^3 = \left(\frac{3}{4}\right)\left(\frac{3}{4}\right)\left(\frac{3}{4}\right) = \frac{27}{64}$$

d. The expression 1^6 is read as "one to the sixth power."
$1^6 = (1)(1)(1)(1)(1)(1) = 1$

Skill Practice Evaluate.

3. 4^3 **4.** 2^4 **5.** $\left(\dfrac{2}{3}\right)^2$ **6.** $(1)^7$

3. Square Roots

The inverse operation to squaring a number is to find its **square roots**. For example, finding a square root of 9 is equivalent to asking "what number(s) when squared equals 9?" The symbol, $\sqrt{\ }$ (called a *radical sign*), is used to find the *principal* square root of a number. By definition, the principal square root of a number is nonnegative. Therefore, $\sqrt{9}$ is the nonnegative number that when squared equals 9. Hence, $\sqrt{9} = 3$ because 3 is nonnegative and $(3)^2 = 9$.

Classroom Examples: p. 41, Exercises 44 and 52

Example 3 Evaluating Square Roots

Evaluate the square roots.

Answers

3. 64 **4.** 16 **5.** $\dfrac{4}{9}$ **6.** 1

a. $\sqrt{64}$ **b.** $\sqrt{121}$ **c.** $\sqrt{0}$ **d.** $\sqrt{\dfrac{4}{9}}$

Solution:

a. $\sqrt{64} = 8$ Because $(8)^2 = 64$

b. $\sqrt{121} = 11$ Because $(11)^2 = 121$

c. $\sqrt{0} = 0$ Because $(0)^2 = 0$

d. $\sqrt{\dfrac{4}{9}} = \dfrac{2}{3}$ Because $\dfrac{2}{3} \cdot \dfrac{2}{3} = \dfrac{4}{9}$

Skill Practice Evaluate.

7. $\sqrt{81}$ **8.** $\sqrt{100}$ **9.** $\sqrt{1}$ **10.** $\sqrt{\dfrac{9}{25}}$

A perfect square is a number whose square root is a rational number. If a number is not a perfect square, its square root is an irrational number that can be approximated on a calculator.

> **TIP:** To simplify square roots, it is advisable to become familiar with the following perfect squares and square roots.
>
> $0^2 = 0 \longrightarrow \sqrt{0} = 0$ $7^2 = 49 \longrightarrow \sqrt{49} = 7$
>
> $1^2 = 1 \longrightarrow \sqrt{1} = 1$ $8^2 = 64 \longrightarrow \sqrt{64} = 8$
>
> $2^2 = 4 \longrightarrow \sqrt{4} = 2$ $9^2 = 81 \longrightarrow \sqrt{81} = 9$
>
> $3^2 = 9 \longrightarrow \sqrt{9} = 3$ $10^2 = 100 \longrightarrow \sqrt{100} = 10$
>
> $4^2 = 16 \longrightarrow \sqrt{16} = 4$ $11^2 = 121 \longrightarrow \sqrt{121} = 11$
>
> $5^2 = 25 \longrightarrow \sqrt{25} = 5$ $12^2 = 144 \longrightarrow \sqrt{144} = 12$
>
> $6^2 = 36 \longrightarrow \sqrt{36} = 6$ $13^2 = 169 \longrightarrow \sqrt{169} = 13$

4. Order of Operations

When algebraic expressions contain numerous operations, it is important to evaluate the operations in the proper order. Parentheses ( ), brackets [ ], and braces { } are used for grouping numbers and algebraic expressions. It is important to recognize that operations must be done within parentheses and other grouping symbols first. Other grouping symbols include absolute value bars, radical signs, and fraction bars.

PROCEDURE Order of Operations

Step 1 Simplify expressions within parentheses and other grouping symbols first. These include absolute value bars, fraction bars, and radicals. If imbedded parentheses are present, start with the innermost parentheses.

Step 2 Evaluate expressions involving exponents, radicals, and absolute values.

Step 3 Perform multiplication or division in the order that they occur from left to right.

Step 4 Perform addition or subtraction in the order that they occur from left to right.

Instructor Note: Radical signs act as grouping symbols. $\sqrt{30 + 6} = \sqrt{(30 + 6)}$. Perform the operations inside the radical first, then apply the square root.

Answers

7. 9   **8.** 10   **9.** 1   **10.** $\dfrac{3}{5}$

Classroom Examples: p. 41,
Exercises 58 and 64

Example 4 Applying the Order of Operations

Simplify the expressions.

a. $17 - 3 \cdot 2 + 2^2$ **b.** $\dfrac{1}{2}\left(\dfrac{5}{6} - \dfrac{3}{4}\right)$

Solution:

a. $17 - 3 \cdot 2 + 2^2$

$= 17 - 3 \cdot 2 + 4$ Simplify exponents.

$= 17 - 6 + 4$ Multiply before adding or subtracting.

$= 11 + 4$ Add or subtract from left to right.

$= 15$

b. $\dfrac{1}{2}\left(\dfrac{5}{6} - \dfrac{3}{4}\right)$ Subtract fractions within the parentheses.

$= \dfrac{1}{2}\left(\dfrac{10}{12} - \dfrac{9}{12}\right)$ The least common denominator is 12.

$= \dfrac{1}{2}\left(\dfrac{1}{12}\right)$

$= \dfrac{1}{24}$ Multiply fractions.

Skill Practice Simplify the expressions.

11. $14 - 3 \cdot 2 + 3^2$ **12.** $\dfrac{13}{4} - \dfrac{1}{4}(10 - 2)$

Classroom Examples: p. 41,
Exercises 72 and 76

Example 5 Applying the Order of Operations

Simplify the expressions.

a. $25 - 12 \div 3 \cdot 4$ **b.** $6.2 - |-2.1| + \sqrt{15 - 6}$

c. $28 - 2[(6 - 3)^2 + 4]$

Solution:

a. $25 - 12 \div 3 \cdot 4$ Multiply or divide in order from left to right.

$= 25 - 4 \cdot 4$ Notice that the operation $12 \div 3$ is performed first (not $3 \cdot 4$).

$= 25 - 16$ Multiply $4 \cdot 4$ before subtracting.

$= 9$ Subtract.

b. $6.2 - |-2.1| + \sqrt{15 - 6}$

$= 6.2 - |-2.1| + \sqrt{9}$ Simplify within the square root.

$= 6.2 - (2.1) + 3$ Simplify the absolute value and square root.

$= 4.1 + 3$ Add or subtract from left to right.

$= 7.1$ Add.

Avoiding Mistakes

In Example 5(a), division is performed before multiplication because it occurs first as we read from left to right.

Answers

11. 17   **12.** $\dfrac{5}{4}$

c. $28 - 2[(6 - 3)^2 + 4]$

$= 28 - 2[(3)^2 + 4]$ Simplify within the inner parentheses first.

$= 28 - 2[(9) + 4]$ Simplify exponents.

$= 28 - 2[13]$ Add within the square brackets.

$= 28 - 26$ Multiply before subtracting.

$= 2$ Subtract.

Skill Practice Simplify the expressions.

13. $1 + 2 \cdot 3^2 \div 6$ **14.** $|-20| - \sqrt{20 - 4}$ **15.** $60 - 5[(7 - 4) + 2^2]$

5. Translations

Example 6 **Translating from English Form to Algebraic Form**

Classroom Examples: p. 42, Exercises 88 and 98

Translate each English phrase to an algebraic expression.

a. The quotient of x and 5

b. The difference of p and the square root of q

c. Seven less than n

d. Seven less n

e. Eight more than the absolute value of w

f. x subtracted from 18

Solution:

a. $\dfrac{x}{5}$ or $x \div 5$ The quotient of x and 5

b. $p - \sqrt{q}$ The difference of p and the square root of q

c. $n - 7$ Seven less than n

d. $7 - n$ Seven less n

e. $|w| + 8$ Eight more than the absolute value of w

f. $18 - x$ x subtracted from 18

> **Avoiding Mistakes**
>
> Recall that "*a* less than *b*" is translated as $b - a$. Therefore, the statement "seven less than *n*" must be translated as $n - 7$, not $7 - n$.

Instructor Note: Show students that 7 less than x would not be written $7 < x$. This expression would be worded as 7 *is* less than x.

Skill Practice Translate each English phrase to an algebraic expression.

16. The product of 6 and y

17. The difference of the square root of t and 7

18. Twelve less than x

19. Twelve less x

20. One more than two times x

21. Five subtracted from the absolute value of w.

Answers

13. 4	**14.** 16	**15.** 25
16. $6y$	**17.** $\sqrt{t} - 7$	
18. $x - 12$	**19.** $12 - x$	
20. $2x + 1$	**21.** $|w| - 5$	

Classroom Examples: p. 42,
Exercises 100 and 106

Example 7   Translating from English Form to Algebraic Form

Translate each English phrase into an algebraic expression. Then evaluate the expression for $a = 6$, $b = 4$, and $c = 20$.

  a. The product of a and the square root of b

  b. Twice the sum of b and c

  c. The difference of twice a and b

Solution:

  a. The product of a and the square root of b

$$a\sqrt{b}$$

$= ()\sqrt{()}$	Use parentheses to substitute a number for a variable.
$= (6)\sqrt{(4)}$	Substitute $a = 6$ and $b = 4$.
$= 6 \cdot 2$	Simplify the radical first.
$= 12$	Multiply.

  b. Twice the sum of b and c

$2(b + c)$	To compute "twice the sum of b and c," it is necessary to take the sum first and then multiply by 2. To ensure the proper order, the sum of b and c must be enclosed in parentheses. The proper translation is $2(b + c)$.
$= 2(() + ())$	Use parentheses to substitute a number for a variable.
$= 2((4) + (20))$	Substitute $b = 4$ and $c = 20$.
$= 2(24)$	Simplify within the parentheses first.
$= 48$	Multiply.

  c. The difference of twice a and b

$2a - b$	
$= 2() - ()$	Use parentheses to substitute a number for a variable.
$= 2(6) - (4)$	Substitute $a = 6$ and $b = 4$.
$= 12 - 4$	Multiply first.
$= 8$	Subtract.

Skill Practice Translate each English phrase to an algebraic expression. Then evaluate the expression for $x = 3$, $y = 9$, $z = 10$.

  22. The quotient of the square root of y and x.

  23. One-half the sum of x and y.

  24. The difference of z and twice x.

Answers

22. $\dfrac{\sqrt{y}}{x}$; 1   **23.** $\dfrac{1}{2}(x + y)$; 6

24. $z - 2x$; 4

Calculator Connections

Topic: Evaluating Exponential Expressions on a Calculator

On a calculator, we enter exponents greater than the second power by using the key labeled $\boxed{y^x}$ or $\boxed{\wedge}$. For example, evaluate 2^4 and 10^6:

Scientific Calculator:

Enter: 2 $\boxed{y^x}$ 4 $\boxed{=}$ **Result:** [16]

Enter: 10 $\boxed{y^x}$ 6 $\boxed{=}$ **Result:** [1000000]

Graphing Calculator:

```
2^4
              16
10^6
         1000000
```

Topic: Applying the Order of Operations on a Calculator

Most calculators also have the capability to enter several operations at once. However, it is important to note that fraction bars and radicals require user-defined parentheses to ensure that the proper order of operations is followed. For example, evaluate the following expressions on a calculator:

a. $130 - 2(5 - 1)^3$ **b.** $\dfrac{18 - 2}{11 - 9}$ **c.** $\sqrt{25 - 9}$

Scientific Calculator:

Enter: 130 $\boxed{-}$ 2 $\boxed{\times}$ $\boxed{(}$ 5 $\boxed{-}$ 1 $\boxed{)}$ $\boxed{y^x}$ 3 $\boxed{=}$ **Result:** [2]

Enter: $\boxed{(}$ 18 $\boxed{-}$ 2 $\boxed{)}$ $\boxed{\div}$ $\boxed{(}$ 11 $\boxed{-}$ 9 $\boxed{)}$ $\boxed{=}$ **Result:** [8]

Enter: $\boxed{(}$ 25 $\boxed{-}$ 9 $\boxed{)}$ $\boxed{\sqrt{}}$ **Result:** [4]

Graphing Calculator:

```
130-2*(5-1)^3
              2
(18-2)/(11-9)
              8
√(25-9)
              4
```

Calculator Exercises

Simplify each expression without the use of a calculator. Then enter the expression into the calculator to verify your answer.

1. $\dfrac{4 + 6}{8 - 3}$ 2

2. $110 - 5(2 + 1) - 4$ 91

3. $100 - 2(5 - 3)^3$ 84

4. $3 + (4 - 1)^2$ 12

5. $(12 - 6 + 1)^2$ 49

6. $3 \cdot 8 - \sqrt{32 + 2^2}$ 18

7. $\sqrt{18 - 2}$ 4

8. $(4 \cdot 3 - 3 \cdot 3)^3$ 27

9. $\dfrac{20 - 3^2}{26 - 2^2}$ 0.5

Section 1.3 Practice Exercises

Boost *your* GRADE at
ALEKS.com!

ALEKS®
version 3.0

- Practice Problems
- Self-Tests
- NetTutor
- e-Professors
- Videos

For additional exercises, see Classroom Activities
1.3A–1.3C in the *Instructor's Resource Manual*
at www.mhhe.com/moh.

Study Skills Exercises

1. Sometimes you may run into a problem with homework or you find that you are having trouble keeping up with the pace of the class. A tutor can be a good resource.

   a. Does your college offer tutoring?

   b. Is it free?

   c. Where would you go to sign up for a tutor?

2. Define the key terms.

   a. variable   b. constant   c. expression   d. sum

   e. difference   f. product   g. quotient   h. base

   i. exponent   j. power   k. square root   l. order of operations

Review Exercises

3. Which of the following are rational numbers? $-4, 5.\overline{6}, \sqrt{29}, 0, \pi, 4.02, \dfrac{7}{9}$ $-4, 5.\overline{6}, 0, 4.02, \dfrac{7}{9}$

4. Evaluate. $|-56|$ 56   5. Evaluate. $|9.2|$ 9.2   6. Evaluate. $-|-14|$ -14

7. Find the opposite of 19. -19 8. Find the opposite of -34.2.   34.2

Concept 1: Evaluating Algebraic Expressions

For Exercises 9–16, evaluate each expression given the values $c = 6$ and $d = \dfrac{2}{3}$. **(See Example 1.)**

9. $c - 3$ 3   **10.** $3c$ 18   11. cd 4   **12.** $c \div d$ 9

13. $5 + 6d$ 9   14. $\dfrac{1}{12}c + 1$ $\dfrac{3}{2}$ 15. $\dfrac{1}{c} + d$ $\dfrac{5}{6}$ 16. $c - 6d$ 2

Concept 2: Exponential Expressions

For Exercises 17–22, write each product using exponents.

17. $\dfrac{1}{6} \cdot \dfrac{1}{6} \cdot \dfrac{1}{6} \cdot \dfrac{1}{6}$ $\left(\dfrac{1}{6}\right)^4$ 18. $10 \cdot 10 \cdot 10 \cdot 10 \cdot 10 \cdot 10$ 10^6 19. $a \cdot a \cdot a \cdot b \cdot b$ $a^3 b^2$

20. $7 \cdot x \cdot x \cdot y \cdot y$ $7x^2 y^2$ 21. $5c \cdot 5c \cdot 5c \cdot 5c \cdot 5c$ $(5c)^5$ 22. $3 \cdot w \cdot z \cdot z \cdot z \cdot z$ $3wz^4$

23. a. For the expression $5x^3$, what is the base for the exponent 3? x

   b. Does 5 have an exponent? If so, what is it?   Yes, 1

24. a. For the expression $2y^4$, what is the base for the exponent 4? y

   b. Does 2 have an exponent? If so, what is it?   Yes, 1

 Writing   Translating Expression   Geometry   Scientific Calculator   Video   NS&E

For Exercises 25–32, write each expression in expanded form using the definition of an exponent.

25. x^3 $x \cdot x \cdot x$

26. y^4 $y \cdot y \cdot y \cdot y$

27. $(2b)^3$ $2b \cdot 2b \cdot 2b$

28. $(8c)^2$ $8c \cdot 8c$

29. $10y^5$ $10 \cdot y \cdot y \cdot y \cdot y \cdot y$

30. x^2y^3 $x \cdot x \cdot y \cdot y \cdot y$

31. $2wz^2$ $2 \cdot w \cdot z \cdot z$

32. $3a^3b$ $3 \cdot a \cdot a \cdot a \cdot b$

For Exercises 33–40, simplify each expression. **(See Example 2.)**

33. 6^2 36

34. 5^3 125

35. $\left(\dfrac{1}{7}\right)^2$ $\dfrac{1}{49}$

36. $\left(\dfrac{1}{2}\right)^5$ $\dfrac{1}{32}$

37. $(0.2)^3$ 0.008

38. $(0.8)^2$ 0.64

39. 2^6 64

40. 13^2 169

Concept 3: Square Roots

For Exercises 41–52, simplify the square roots. **(See Example 3.)**

41. $\sqrt{81}$ 9

42. $\sqrt{64}$ 8

43. $\sqrt{4}$ 2

44. $\sqrt{9}$ 3

45. $\sqrt{144}$ 12

46. $\sqrt{49}$ 7

47. $\sqrt{16}$ 4

48. $\sqrt{36}$ 6

49. $\sqrt{\dfrac{1}{9}}$ $\dfrac{1}{3}$

50. $\sqrt{\dfrac{1}{64}}$ $\dfrac{1}{8}$

51. $\sqrt{\dfrac{25}{81}}$ $\dfrac{5}{9}$

52. $\sqrt{\dfrac{49}{100}}$ $\dfrac{7}{10}$

Concept 4: Order of Operations

For Exercises 53–82, use the order of operations to simplify each expression. **(See Examples 4–5.)**

53. $8 + 2 \cdot 6$ 20

54. $7 + 3 \cdot 4$ 19

55. $(8 + 2) \cdot 6$ 60

56. $(7 + 3) \cdot 4$ 40

57. $4 + 2 \div 2 \cdot 3 + 1$ 8

58. $5 + 12 \div 2 \cdot 6 - 1$ 40

59. $81 - 4 \cdot 3 + 3^2$ 78

60. $100 - 25 \cdot 2 - 5^2$ 25

61. $\dfrac{1}{4} \cdot \dfrac{2}{3} - \dfrac{1}{6}$ 0

62. $\dfrac{3}{4} \cdot \dfrac{2}{3} + \dfrac{2}{3}$ $\dfrac{7}{6}$

63. $\left(\dfrac{11}{6} - \dfrac{3}{8}\right) \cdot \dfrac{4}{5}$ $\dfrac{7}{6}$

64. $\left(\dfrac{9}{8} - \dfrac{1}{3}\right) \cdot \dfrac{3}{4}$ $\dfrac{19}{32}$

65. $3[5 + 2(8 - 3)]$ 45

66. $2[4 + 3(6 - 4)]$ 20

67. $10 + |-6|$ 16

68. $18 + |-3|$ 21

69. $21 - |8 - 2|$ 15

70. $12 - |6 - 1|$ 7

71. $2^2 + \sqrt{9} \cdot 5$ 19

72. $3^2 + \sqrt{16} \cdot 2$ 17

73. $\sqrt{9 + 16} - 2$ 3

74. $\sqrt{36 + 13} - 5$ 2

75. $[4^2 \cdot (6 - 4) \div 8] + [7 \cdot (8 - 3)]$ 39

76. $(18 \div \sqrt{4}) \cdot \{[(9^2 - 1) \div 2] - 15\}$ 225

77. $48 - 13 \cdot 3 + \lfloor(50 - 7 \cdot 5) + 2\rfloor$ 26

78. $80 \div 16 \cdot 2 + (6^2 - |-2|)$ 44

79. $\dfrac{7 + 3(8 - 2)}{(7 + 3)(8 - 2)}$ $\dfrac{5}{12}$

80. $\dfrac{16 - 8 \div 4}{4 + 8 \div 4 - 2}$ $\dfrac{7}{2}$

81. $\dfrac{15 - 5(3 \cdot 2 - 4)}{10 - 2(4 \cdot 5 - 16)}$ $\dfrac{5}{2}$

82. $\dfrac{5(7 - 3) + 8(6 - 4)}{4[7 + 3(2 \cdot 9 - 8)]}$ $\dfrac{9}{37}$

83. The area of a rectangle is given by $A = lw$, where l is the length of the rectangle and w is the width. Find the area for the rectangle shown.   57,600 ft²

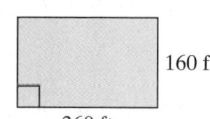

160 ft

360 ft

84. The perimeter of a rectangle is given by $P = 2l + 2w$. Find the perimeter for the rectangle shown.   1040 ft

85. The area of a trapezoid is given by $A = \frac{1}{2}(b_1 + b_2)h$, where b_1 and b_2 are the lengths of the two parallel sides and h is the height. A window is in the shape of a trapezoid. Find the area of the trapezoid with dimensions shown in the figure. 21 ft^2

86. The volume of a rectangular solid is given by $V = lwh$, where l is the length of the box, w is the width, and h is the height. Find the volume of the box shown in the figure. 1000 yd^3

Concept 5: Translations

For Exercises 87–98, write each English phrase as an algebraic expression. **(See Example 6.)**

87. The product of 3 and x $3x$

88. The sum of b and 6 $b + 6$

89. The quotient of x and 7 $\frac{x}{7}$ or $x \div 7$

90. Four divided by k $\frac{4}{k}$ or $4 \div k$

91. The difference of 2 and a $2 - a$

92. Three subtracted from t $t - 3$

93. x more than twice y $2y + x$

94. Nine decreased by the product of 3 and p $9 - 3p$

95. Four times the sum of x and 12 $4(x + 12)$

96. Twice the difference of x and 3 $2(x - 3)$

97. Q less than 3 $3 - Q$

98. Fourteen less than t $t - 14$

For Exercises 99–106, write the English phrase as an algebraic expression. Then evaluate each expression for $x = 4$, $y = 2$, and $z = 10$. **(See Example 7.)**

99. Two times y cubed $2y^3$; 16

100. Three times z squared $3z^2$; 300

101. The absolute value of the difference of z and 8 $|z - 8|$; 2

102. The absolute value of the difference of x and 3 $|x - 3|$; 1

103. The product of 5 and the square root of x $5\sqrt{x}$; 10

104. The square root of the difference of z and 1 $\sqrt{z - 1}$; 3

105. The value x subtracted from the product of y and z $yz - x$; 16

106. The difference of z and the product of x and y $z - xy$; 2

Expanding Your Skills

For Exercises 107–110, use the order of operations to simplify each expression.

107. $\dfrac{\sqrt{\frac{1}{9}} + \frac{2}{3}}{\sqrt{\frac{4}{25}} + \frac{3}{5}}$ 1

108. $\dfrac{5 - \sqrt{9}}{\sqrt{\frac{4}{9}} + \frac{1}{3}}$ 2

109. $\dfrac{|-2|}{|-10| - |2|}$ $\frac{1}{4}$

110. $\dfrac{|-4|^2}{2^2 + \sqrt{144}}$ 1

111. Some students use the following common memorization device (mnemonic) to help them remember the order of operations: the acronym PEMDAS or **P**lease **E**xcuse **M**y **D**ear **A**unt **S**ally to remember **P**arentheses, **E**xponents, **M**ultiplication, **D**ivision, **A**ddition, and **S**ubtraction. The problem with this mnemonic is that it suggests that multiplication is done before division and similarly, it suggests that addition is performed before subtraction. Explain why following this acronym may give incorrect answers for the expressions:

   a. $36 \div 4 \cdot 3$
   $36 \div 4 \cdot 3$ Division must be performed before multiplication.
   $= 9 \cdot 3$
   $= 27$

   b. $36 - 4 + 3$
   $36 - 4 + 3$ Subtraction must be performed before addition.
   $= 32 + 3$
   $= 35$

112. If you use the acronym **P**lease **E**xcuse **M**y **D**ear **A**unt **S**ally to remember the order of operations, what must you keep in mind about the last four operations?   Multiplication or division is performed in order from left to right. Addition or subtraction is performed in order from left to right.

113. Explain why the acronym **P**lease **E**xcuse **D**r. **M**ichael **S**mith's **A**unt could also be used as a memory device for the order of operations.   This is acceptable, provided division and multiplication are performed in order from left to right, and subtraction and addition are performed in order from left to right.

 Writing   Translating Expression   Geometry   Scientific Calculator   Video   NS&E

Addition of Real Numbers

1. Addition of Real Numbers and the Number Line

Concepts

1. Addition of Real Numbers and the Number Line
2. Addition of Real Numbers
3. Translations
4. Applications Involving Addition of Real Numbers

Adding real numbers can be visualized on the number line. To add a positive number, move to the right on the number line. To add a negative number, move to the left on the number line. The following example may help to illustrate the process.

On a winter day in Detroit, suppose the temperature starts out at 5 degrees Fahrenheit (5°F) at noon, and then drops 12° two hours later when a cold front passes through. The resulting temperature can be represented by the expression $5° + (-12°)$. On the number line, start at 5 and count 12 units to the left (Figure 1-7). The resulting temperature at 2:00 P.M. is $-7°$F.

Figure 1-7

Example 1 **Using the Number Line to Add Real Numbers**

Use the number line to add the numbers.

a. $-5 + 2$ **b.** $-1 + (-4)$ **c.** $7 + (-4)$

Classroom Examples: p. 48, Exercises 10 and 12

Solution:

a. $-5 + 2 = -3$

Start at -5, and count 2 units to the right.

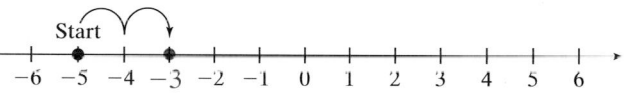

b. $-1 + (-4) = -5$

Start at -1, and count 4 units to the left.

TIP: Note that we move to the left on the number line when we add a negative number. We move to the right when we add a positive number.

c. $7 + (-4) = 3$

Start at 7, and count 4 units to the left.

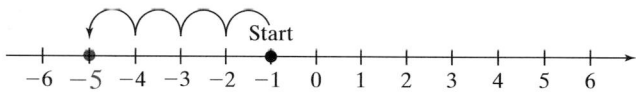

Skill Practice Use the number line to add the numbers.

1. $-2 + 4$ **2.** $-2 + (-3)$ **3.** $5 + (-6)$

Answers
1. 2 **2.** -5 **3.** -1

2. Addition of Real Numbers

When adding large numbers or numbers that involve fractions or decimals, counting units on the number line can be cumbersome. Study the following example to determine a pattern for adding two numbers with the *same* sign.

$1 + 4 = 5$

$-1 + (-4) = -5$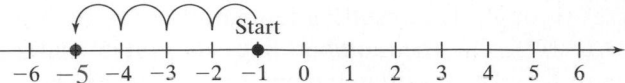

> **PROCEDURE**   **Adding Numbers with the *Same* Sign**
>
> To add two numbers with the *same* sign, add their absolute values and apply the common sign.

Study the following example to determine a pattern for adding two numbers with *different* signs.

$1 + (-4) = -3$

Instructor Note: Memory Device:
Same Sign ⇒ Sum
Different Sign ⇒ Difference

$-1 + 4 = 3$

> **PROCEDURE**   **Adding Numbers with *Different* Signs**
>
> To add two numbers with *different* signs, subtract the smaller absolute value from the larger absolute value. Then apply the sign of the number having the larger absolute value.

Classroom Examples: pp. 49,
Exercises 22 and 52

Example 2   **Adding Real Numbers with the Same Sign**

Add.

a. $-12 + (-14)$ **b.** $-8.8 + (-3.7)$ **c.** $-\dfrac{4}{3} + \left(-\dfrac{6}{7}\right)$

Solution:

a. $-12 + (-14)$

$= -(12 + 14)$

common sign is negative

$= -26$

First find the absolute value of the addends. $|-12| = 12$ and $|-14| = 14$.

Add their absolute values and apply the common sign (in this case, the common sign is negative).

The sum is -26.

b. $-8.8 + (-3.7)$ First find the absolute value of the addends.
                                    $|-8.8| = 8.8$ and $|-3.7| = 3.7$.

$= -(8.8 + 3.7)$ Add their absolute values and apply the common
                                    sign (in this case, the common sign is negative).

common sign is negative

$= -12.5$ The sum is -12.5.

c. $-\dfrac{4}{3} + \left(-\dfrac{6}{7}\right)$ The least common denominator (LCD) is 21.

$= -\dfrac{4 \cdot 7}{3 \cdot 7} + \left(-\dfrac{6 \cdot 3}{7 \cdot 3}\right)$ Write each fraction with the LCD.

$= -\dfrac{28}{21} + \left(-\dfrac{18}{21}\right)$ Find the absolute value of the addends.

$$\left|-\dfrac{28}{21}\right| = \dfrac{28}{21} \text{ and } \left|-\dfrac{18}{21}\right| = \dfrac{18}{21}.$$

$= -\left(\dfrac{28}{21} + \dfrac{18}{21}\right)$ Add their absolute values and apply the common
                                    sign (in this case, the common sign is negative).

common sign is negative

$= -\dfrac{46}{21}$ The sum is $-\dfrac{46}{21}$.

Skill Practice Add.

4. $-5 + (-25)$ **5.** $-14.8 + (-9.7)$ **6.** $-\dfrac{1}{2} + \left(-\dfrac{5}{8}\right)$

Example 3 **Adding Real Numbers with Different Signs**

Classroom Examples: pp. 48–49, Exercises 20 and 32

Add.   **a.** $12 + (-17)$ **b.** $-8 + 8$

Solution:

a. $12 + (-17)$ First find the absolute value of the addends.
                          $|12| = 12$ and $|-17| = 17$.

The absolute value of -17 is greater than the absolute
value of 12. Therefore, the sum is negative.

$= -(17 - 12)$ Next, subtract the smaller absolute value from the
                          larger absolute value.

Apply the sign of the number with the larger absolute value.

$= -5$

b. $-8 + 8$ First find the absolute value of the addends.
                          $|-8| = 8$ and $|8| = 8$.

$= (8 - 8)$ The absolute values are equal. Therefore, their
                          difference is 0. The number zero is neither positive
$= 0$ nor negative.

Skill Practice Add.

7. $-15 + 16$ **8.** $6 + (-6)$

Answers

4. -30 **5.** -24.5 **6.** $-\dfrac{9}{8}$

7. 1 **8.** 0

Classroom Examples: p. 49, Exercises 46 and 54

Example 4 **Adding Real Numbers with Different Signs**

Add. **a.** $-10.6 + 20.4$ **b.** $\dfrac{2}{15} + \left(-\dfrac{4}{5}\right)$

Solution:

a. $-10.6 + 20.4$

First find the absolute value of the addends.
$|-10.6| = 10.6$ and $|20.4| = 20.4$.

The absolute value of 20.4 is greater than the absolute value of -10.6. Therefore, the sum is positive.

$= +(20.4 - 10.6)$

Next, subtract the smaller absolute value from the larger absolute value.

Apply the sign of the number with the larger absolute value.

$= 9.8$

b. $\dfrac{2}{15} + \left(-\dfrac{4}{5}\right)$

The least common denominator is 15.

$= \dfrac{2}{15} + \left(-\dfrac{4 \cdot 3}{5 \cdot 3}\right)$

Write each fraction with the LCD.

$= \dfrac{2}{15} + \left(-\dfrac{12}{15}\right)$

Find the absolute value of the addends.

$\left|\dfrac{2}{15}\right| = \dfrac{2}{15}$ and $\left|-\dfrac{12}{15}\right| = \dfrac{12}{15}$.

The absolute value of $-\frac{12}{15}$ is greater than the absolute value of $\frac{2}{15}$. Therefore, the sum is negative.

$= -\left(\dfrac{12}{15} - \dfrac{2}{15}\right)$

Next, subtract the smaller absolute value from the larger absolute value.

Apply the sign of the number with the larger absolute value.

$= -\dfrac{10}{15}$

Subtract.

$= -\dfrac{2}{3}$

Simplify to lowest terms. $-\dfrac{\overset{2}{\cancel{10}}}{\underset{3}{\cancel{15}}} = -\dfrac{2}{3}$

Skill Practice Add.

9. $27.3 + (-18.1)$ **10.** $-\dfrac{9}{10} + \dfrac{2}{5}$

3. Translations

Classroom Examples: p. 50, Exercises 86 and 88

Example 5 **Translating Expressions Involving the Addition of Real Numbers**

Write each English phrase as an algebraic expression. Then simplify the result.

a. The sum of $-12, -8, 9,$ and -1

b. Negative three-tenths added to $-\frac{7}{8}$

c. The sum of -12 and its opposite

Answers

9. 9.2 **10.** $-\dfrac{1}{2}$

Solution:

a. The sum of $-12, -8, 9,$ and -1

$\underbrace{-12 + (-8)} + 9 + (-1)$

$= \underbrace{-20 + 9} + (-1)$ Add from left to right.

$= \underbrace{-11 + (-1)}$

$= -12$

b. Negative three-tenths added to $-\frac{7}{8}$

$-\frac{7}{8} + \left(-\frac{3}{10}\right)$

$= -\frac{35}{40} + \left(-\frac{12}{40}\right)$ The common denominator is 40.

$= -\frac{47}{40}$ The numbers have the same signs. Add their absolute values and keep the common sign. $-\left(\frac{35}{40} + \frac{12}{40}\right)$.

c. The sum of -12 and its opposite

$-12 + (12)$

$= 0$ Add.

Skill Practice Write as an algebraic expression, and simplify the result.

11. The sum of $-10, 4,$ and -6 **12.** Negative 2 added to $-\frac{1}{2}$

13. -60 added to its opposite

4. Applications Involving Addition of Real Numbers

Example 6   Adding Real Numbers in Applications

a. A running back on a football team gains 4 yd. On the next play, the quarterback is sacked and loses 13 yd. Write a mathematical expression to describe this situation and then simplify the result.

b. A student has $120 in her checking account. After depositing her paycheck of $215, she writes a check for $255 to cover her portion of the rent and another check for $294 to cover her car payment. Write a mathematical expression to describe this situation and then simplify the result.

Solution:

a. $4 + (-13)$ The loss of 13 yd can be interpreted as adding -13 yd.

$= -9$ The football team has a net loss of 9 yd.

b. $\underbrace{120 + 215} + (-255) + (-294)$ Writing a check is equivalent to adding a negative amount to the bank account.

$= \underbrace{335 + (-255)} + (-294)$ Use the order of operations. Add from left to right.

$= 80 + (-294)$

$= -214$ The student has overdrawn her account by $214.

Answers

11. $-10 + 4 + (-6); -12$

12. $-\frac{1}{2} + (-2); -\frac{5}{2}$

13. $60 + (-60); 0$

Skill Practice

14. GE stock was priced at $32.00 per share at the beginning of the month. After the first week, the price went up $2.15 per share. At the end of the second week it went down $3.28 per share. Write a mathematical expression to describe the price of the stock and find the price of the stock at the end of the 2-week period.

Answer

14. 32.00 + 2.15 + (−3.28); $30.87 per share

Section 1.4 Practice Exercises

Boost *your* GRADE at ALEKS.com!

• Practice Problems   • e-Professors   For additional exercises, see Classroom Activities
• Self-Tests   • Videos   1.4A–1.4B in the *Instructor's Resource Manual*
• NetTutor   at www.mhhe.com/moh.

Study Skills Exercise

1. It is very important to attend class every day. Math is cumulative in nature, and you must master the material learned in the previous class to understand today's lesson. Because this is so important, many instructors have an attendance policy that may affect your final grade. Write down the attendance policy for your class.

Review Exercises

Plot the points in set A on a number line. Then for Exercises 2–7 place the appropriate inequality ($<, >$) between the numbers.

$$A = \left\{ -2, \frac{3}{4}, -\frac{5}{2}, 3, \frac{9}{2}, 1.6, 0 \right\}$$

2. $-2 \;\square\; 0$ $<$

3. $\dfrac{9}{2} \;\square\; \dfrac{3}{4}$ $>$

4. $-2 \;\square\; -\dfrac{5}{2}$ $>$

5. $0 \;\square\; -\dfrac{5}{2}$ $>$

6. $\dfrac{3}{4} \;\square\; 1.6$ $<$

7. $\dfrac{3}{4} \;\square\; -\dfrac{5}{2}$ $>$

8. Evaluate the expressions.

  a. $-(-8)$ 8 **b.** $-|-8|$ -8

Concept 1: Addition of Real Numbers and the Number Line

For Exercises 9–16, add the numbers using the number line. **(See Example 1.)**

9. $-2 + (-4)$ -6

10. $-3 + (-5)$ -8

11. $-7 + 10$ 3

12. $-2 + 9$ 7

13. $6 + (-3)$ 3

14. $8 + (-2)$ 6

15. $2 + (-5)$ -3

16. $7 + (-3)$ 4

Concept 2: Addition of Real Numbers

For Exercises 17–70, add. **(See Examples 2–4.)**

17. $-19 + 2$ -17

18. $-25 + 18$ -7

19. $-4 + 11$ 7

20. $-3 + 9$ 6

 Writing   Translating Expression   Geometry   Scientific Calculator   Video   NS&E

21. $-16 + (-3)$ $_{-19}$ **22.** $-12 + (-23)$ $_{-35}$ **23.** $-2 + (-21)$ $_{-23}$ **24.** $-13 + (-1)$ $_{-14}$

25. $0 + (-5)$ $_{-5}$ **26.** $0 + (-4)$ $_{-4}$ **27.** $-3 + 0$ $_{-3}$ **28.** $-8 + 0$ $_{-8}$

29. $-16 + 16$ $_0$ **30.** $11 + (-11)$ $_0$ **31.** $41 + (-41)$ $_0$ **32.** $-15 + 15$ $_0$

33. $4 + (-9)$ $_{-5}$ **34.** $6 + (-9)$ $_{-3}$ **35.** $7 + (-2) + (-8)$ $_{-3}$ **36.** $2 + (-3) + (-6)$ $_{-7}$

37. $-17 + (-3) + 20$ $_0$ **38.** $-9 + (-6) + 15$ $_0$

39. $-3 + (-8) + (-12)$ $_{-23}$ **40.** $-8 + (-2) + (-13)$ $_{-23}$

41. $-42 + (-3) + 45 + (-6)$ $_{-6}$ **42.** $36 + (-3) + (-8) + (-25)$ $_0$

43. $-5 + (-3) + (-7) + 4 + 8$ $_{-3}$ **44.** $-13 + (-1) + 5 + 2 + (-20)$ $_{-27}$

45. $23.81 + (-2.51)$ $_{21.3}$ **46.** $-9.23 + 10.53$ $_{1.3}$ **47.** $-\dfrac{2}{7} + \dfrac{1}{14}$ $_{-\frac{3}{14}}$ **48.** $-\dfrac{1}{8} + \dfrac{5}{16}$ $_{\frac{3}{16}}$

49. $\dfrac{2}{3} + \left(-\dfrac{5}{6}\right)$ $_{-\frac{1}{6}}$ **50.** $\dfrac{1}{2} + \left(-\dfrac{3}{4}\right)$ $_{-\frac{1}{4}}$ **51.** $-\dfrac{7}{8} + \left(-\dfrac{1}{16}\right)$ $_{-\frac{15}{16}}$ **52.** $-\dfrac{1}{9} + \left(-\dfrac{4}{3}\right)$ $_{-\frac{13}{9}}$

53. $-\dfrac{1}{4} + \dfrac{3}{10}$ $_{\frac{1}{20}}$ **54.** $-\dfrac{7}{6} + \dfrac{7}{8}$ $_{-\frac{7}{24}}$ **55.** $-2.1 + \left(-\dfrac{3}{10}\right)$ $_{-2.4 \text{ or } -\frac{12}{5}}$ **56.** $-8.3 + \left(-\dfrac{9}{10}\right)$ $_{-9.2 \text{ or } -\frac{46}{5}}$

57. $\dfrac{3}{4} + (-0.5)$ $_{\frac{1}{4} \text{ or } 0.25}$ **58.** $-\dfrac{3}{2} + 0.45$ $_{-\frac{21}{20} \text{ or } -1.05}$ **59.** $8.23 + (-8.23)$ $_0$ **60.** $-7.5 + 7.5$ $_0$

61. $-\dfrac{7}{8} + 0$ $_{-\frac{7}{8}}$ **62.** $0 + \left(-\dfrac{21}{22}\right)$ $_{-\frac{21}{22}}$ **63.** $-\dfrac{3}{2} + \left(-\dfrac{1}{3}\right) + \dfrac{5}{6}$ $_{-1}$ **64.** $-\dfrac{7}{8} + \dfrac{7}{6} + \dfrac{7}{12}$ $_{\frac{7}{8}}$

65. $-\dfrac{2}{3} + \left(-\dfrac{1}{9}\right) + 2$ $_{\frac{11}{9}}$ **66.** $-\dfrac{1}{4} + \left(-\dfrac{3}{2}\right) + 2$ $_{\frac{1}{4}}$ **67.** $-47.36 + 24.28$ $_{-23.08}$ **68.** $-0.015 + (0.0026)$ $_{-0.0124}$

69. $-0.000617 + (-0.0015)$ $_{-0.002117}$ **70.** $-5315.26 + (-314.89)$ $_{-5630.15}$

71. State the rule for adding two numbers with different signs. To add two numbers with different signs, subtract the smaller absolute value from the larger absolute value and apply the sign of the number with the larger absolute value.

72. State the rule for adding two numbers with the same signs. To add two numbers with the same sign, add their absolute values and apply the common sign.

For Exercises 73–80, evaluate each expression for $x = -3$, $y = -2$, and $z = 16$.

73. $x + y + \sqrt{z}$ $_{-1}$ **74.** $2z + x + y$ $_{27}$ **75.** $y + 3\sqrt{z}$ $_{10}$ **76.** $-\sqrt{z} + y$ $_{-6}$

77. $|x| + |y|$ $_5$ **78.** $z + x + |y|$ $_{15}$ **79.** $-x + y$ $_1$ **80.** $x + (-y) + z$ $_{15}$

Concept 3: Translations

For Exercises 81–90, write each English phrase as an algebraic expression. Then simplify the result. **(See Example 5.)**

81. The sum of -6 and -10 $_{-6 + (-10); -16}$ **82.** The sum of -3 and 5 $_{-3 + 5; 2}$

83. Negative three increased by 8 $_{-3 + 8; 5}$ **84.** Twenty-one increased by 4 $_{21 + 4; 25}$

85. Seventeen more than -21 $-21 + 17; -4$

86. Twenty-four more than -7 $-7 + 24; 17$

87. Three times the sum of -14 and 20 $3(-14 + 20); 18$

88. Two times the sum of 6 and -10 $2(6 + (-10)); -8$

89. Five more than the sum of -7 and -2
$(-7 + (-2)) + 5; -4$

90. Negative six more than the sum of 4 and -1
$(4 + (-1)) + (-6); -3$

Concept 4: Applications Involving Addition of Real Numbers

91. The temperature in Minneapolis, Minnesota, began at $-5°F$ ($5°$ below zero) at 6:00 A.M. By noon, the temperature had risen $13°$, and by the end of the day, the temperature had dropped $11°$ from its noontime high. Write an expression using addition that describes the change in temperatures during the day. Then evaluate the expression to give the temperature at the end of thc day.
$-5 + 13 + (-11); -3°F$

92. The temperature in Toronto, Ontario, Canada, began at $4°F$. A cold front went through at noon, and the temperature dropped $9°$. By 4:00 P.M., the temperature had risen $2°$ from its noontime low. Write an expression using addition that describes the changes in temperature during the day. Then evaluate the expression to give the temperature at the end of the day. $4 + (-9) + 2; -3°F$

93. During a football game, the Nebraska Cornhuskers lost 2 yd, gained 6 yd, and then lost 5 yd. Write an expression using addition that describes the team's total loss or gain and evaluate the expression. **(See Example 6.)**
$-2 + 6 + (-5); -1$ yd or 1-yd loss

94. During a football game, the University of Oklahoma's team gained 3 yd, lost 5 yd, and then gained 14 yd. Write an expression using addition that describes the team's total loss or gain and evaluate the expression.
$3 + (-5) + 14; 12$-yd gain

95. Yoshima has $52.23 in her checking account. She writes a check for groceries for $52.95. **(See Example 6.)**

   a. Write an addition problem that expresses Yoshima's transaction. $52.23 + (-52.95)$

   b. Is Yoshima's account overdrawn? Yes

96. Mohammad has $40.02 in his checking account. He writes a check for a pair of shoes for $40.96.

   a. Write an addition problem that expresses Mohammad's transaction. $40.02 + (-40.96)$

   b. Is Mohammad's account overdrawn? Yes

97. The table gives the golf scores for Tiger Woods for the four rounds of the U.S. Open held in the summer of 2008. Find his total score. -1

Tiger Woods	
Round 1	+1
Round 2	−3
Round 3	−1
Round 4	+2

98. A company that has been in business for 5 years has the following profit and loss record.

   a. Write an expression using addition to describe the company's profit/loss activity.
   $-50,000 + (-32,000) + (-5000) + 13,000 + 26,000$

   b. Evaluate the expression from part (a) to determine the company's net profit or loss.
   $-\$48,000$

Year	Profit/Loss ($)
1	−50,000
2	−32,000
3	−5000
4	13,000
5	26,000

Subtraction of Real Numbers

1. Subtraction of Real Numbers

In Section 1.4, we learned the rules for adding real numbers. Subtraction of real numbers is defined in terms of the addition process. For example, consider the following subtraction problem and the corresponding addition problem:

$$6 - 4 = 2 \quad \Leftrightarrow \quad 6 + (-4) = 2$$

In each case, we start at 6 on the number line and move to the left 4 units. That is, adding the opposite of 4 produces the same result as subtracting 4. This is true in general. To subtract two real numbers, add the opposite of the second number to the first number.

Concepts

1. Subtraction of Real Numbers
2. Translations
3. Applications Involving Subtraction
4. Applying the Order of Operations

PROCEDURE   Subtracting Real Numbers

If a and b are real numbers, then $a - b = a + (-b)$.

$$\left.\begin{array}{l} 10 - 4 = 10 + (-4) = 6 \\ -10 - 4 = -10 + (-4) = -14 \end{array}\right\} \quad \text{Subtracting 4 is the same as adding } -4.$$

$$\left.\begin{array}{l} 10 - (-4) = 10 + (4) = 14 \\ 10 - (-4) = 10 + (4) = 6 \end{array}\right\} \quad \text{Subtracting } -4 \text{ is the same as adding 4.}$$

Example 1   **Subtracting Integers**

Subtract the numbers.

a. $4 - (-9)$ **b.** $-6 - 9$ **c.** $-11 - (-5)$ **d.** $7 - 10$

Solution:

a. $4 - (-9)$

$= 4 + (9) = 13$

Change subtraction to addition.   Take the opposite of -9.

b. $-6 - 9$

$= -6 + (-9) = -15$

Change subtraction to addition.   Take the opposite of 9.

c. $-11 - (-5)$

$= -11 + (5) = -6$

Change subtraction to addition.   Take the opposite of -5.

d. $7 - 10$

$= 7 + (-10) = -3$

Change subtraction to addition.   Take the opposite of 10.

Classroom Examples: p. 57, Exercises 16, 18, and 20

Skill Practice Subtract.

1. $1 - (-3)$ **2.** $-2 - 2$ **3.** $-6 - (-11)$ **4.** $8 - 15$

Answers

1. 4   **2.** -4 **3.** 5   **4.** -7

Classroom Examples: p. 57, Exercises 46 and 48

Example 2 Subtracting Real Numbers

a. $\dfrac{3}{20} - \left(-\dfrac{4}{15}\right)$ **b.** $-2.3 - 6.04$

Solution:

a. $\dfrac{3}{20} - \left(-\dfrac{4}{15}\right)$ The least common denominator is 60.

$= \dfrac{9}{60} - \left(-\dfrac{16}{60}\right)$ Write equivalent fractions with the LCD.

$= \dfrac{9}{60} + \left(\dfrac{16}{60}\right)$ Rewrite subtraction in terms of addition.

$= \dfrac{25}{60}$ Add.

$= \dfrac{\overset{5}{\cancel{25}}}{\underset{12}{\cancel{60}}}$ Simplify to lowest terms.

$= \dfrac{5}{12}$

b. $-2.3 - 6.04$

$-2.3 + (-6.04)$ Rewrite subtraction in terms of addition.

-8.34 Add.

Skill Practice Subtract.

5. $\dfrac{1}{6} - \left(-\dfrac{7}{12}\right)$ **6.** $-7.5 - 1.5$

2. Translations

Classroom Examples: p. 57, Exercises 64 and 70

Example 3 Translating Expressions Involving Subtraction

Write an algebraic expression for each English phrase and then simplify the result.

a. The difference of -7 and -5

b. 12.4 subtracted from -4.7

c. -24 decreased by the sum of -10 and 13

d. Seven-fourths less than one-third

Solution:

a. The difference of -7 and -5

$-7 - (-5)$

$= -7 + (5)$ Rewrite subtraction in terms of addition.

$= -2$ Simplify.

Answers

5. $\dfrac{3}{4}$ **6.** -9

b. 12.4 subtracted from -4.7

$-4.7 - 12.4$

$= -4.7 + (-12.4)$ Rewrite subtraction in terms of addition.

$= -17.1$ Simplify.

c. -24 decreased by the sum of -10 and 13

$-24 - (-10 + 13)$

$= -24 - (3)$ Simplify inside parentheses.

$= -24 + (-3)$ Rewrite subtraction in terms of addition.

$= -27$ Simplify.

d. Seven-fourths less than one-third

$\dfrac{1}{3} - \dfrac{7}{4}$

$= \dfrac{1}{3} + \left(-\dfrac{7}{4}\right)$ Rewrite subtraction in terms of addition.

$= \dfrac{4}{12} + \left(-\dfrac{21}{12}\right)$ The common denominator is 12.

$= -\dfrac{17}{12}$

TIP: Recall that "*b* subtracted from *a*" is translated as $a - b$. In Example 3(b), -4.7 is written first and then 12.4.

TIP: Parentheses must be used around the sum of -10 and 13 so that -24 is decreased by the entire quantity $(-10 + 13)$.

Skill Practice Write an algebraic expression for each phrase and then simplify.

7. 8 less than -10

8. -7.2 subtracted from -8.2

9. 10 more than the difference of -2 and 3

10. Two-fifths decreased by four-thirds

3. Applications Involving Subtraction

Example 4   **Using Subtraction of Real Numbers in an Application**

During one of his turns on *Jeopardy*, Harold selected the category "Show Tunes." He got the $200, $600, and $1000 questions correct, but he got the $400 and $800 questions incorrect. Write an expression that determines Harold's score. Then simplify the expression to find his total winnings for that category.

Classroom Example: p. 58, Exercise 72

Solution:

$200 + 600 + 1000 - 400 - 800$

$= 200 + 600 + 1000 + (-400) + (-800)$ Add the positive numbers. Add the negative numbers.

$= 1800 + (-1200)$

$= 600$ Harold won $600.

Skill Practice

11. During Harold's first round on *Jeopardy*, he got the $100, $200, and $400 questions correct but he got the $300 and $500 questions incorrect. Determine Harold's score for this round.

Answers

7. $-10 - 8; -18$

8. $-8.2 - (-7.2); -1$

9. $(-2 - 3) + 10; 5$

10. $\dfrac{2}{5} - \dfrac{4}{3}; -\dfrac{14}{15}$

11. -100, Harold lost $100.

Classroom Example: p. 58,
Exercise 74

Example 5 Using Subtraction of Real Numbers in an Application

The highest recorded temperature in North America was 134°F, recorded on July 10, 1913, in Death Valley, California. The lowest temperature of −81°F was recorded on February 3, 1947, in Snag, Yukon, Canada.

Find the difference between the highest and lowest recorded temperatures in North America.

Solution:

$134 - (-81)$

$= 134 + (81)$ Rewrite subtraction in terms of addition.

$= 215$ Add.

The difference between the highest and lowest temperatures is 215°F.

Skill Practice

12. The record high temperature for the state of Montana occurred in 1937 and was 117°F. The record low occurred in 1954 and was −70°F. Find the difference between the highest and lowest temperatures.

4. Applying the Order of Operations

Classroom Examples: pp. 58–59,
Exercises 86 and 92

Example 6 Applying the Order of Operations

Simplify the expressions.

a. $-6 + \{10 - [7 - (-4)]\}$ **b.** $5 - \sqrt{35 - (-14)} - 2$

Solution:

a. $-6 + \{10 - [7 - (-4)]\}$ Work inside the inner brackets first.

$= -6 + \{10 - [7 + (4)]\}$ Rewrite subtraction in terms of addition.

$= -6 + \{10 - (11)\}$ Simplify the expression inside braces.

$= -6 + \{10 + (-11)\}$ Rewrite subtraction in terms of addition.

$= -6 + (-1)$ Add within the braces.

$= -7$ Add.

b. $5 - \sqrt{35 - (-14)} - 2$ Work inside the radical first.

$= 5 - \sqrt{35 + (14)} - 2$ Rewrite subtraction in terms of addition.

$= 5 - \sqrt{49} - 2$ Add within the radical sign.

$= 5 - 7 - 2$ Simplify the radical.

$= 5 + (-7) + (-2)$ Rewrite subtraction in terms of addition.

$= -2 + (-2)$ Add from left to right.

$= -4$

Skill Practice Simplify the expressions.

13. $-11 - \{8 - [2 - (-3)]\}$ **14.** $(12 - 5)^2 + \sqrt{4 - (-21)}$

Answers

12. 187°F   **13.** −14   **14.** 54

Example 7   **Applying the Order of Operations**

Simplify the expressions.

a. $\left(-\dfrac{5}{8} - \dfrac{2}{3}\right) - \left(\dfrac{1}{8} + 2\right)$ b. $-6 - |7 - 11| + (-3 + 7)^2$

Classroom Examples: p. 59, Exercises 90 and 94

Solution:

a. $\left(-\dfrac{5}{8} - \dfrac{2}{3}\right) - \left(\dfrac{1}{8} + 2\right)$ Work inside the parentheses first.

$= \left[-\dfrac{5}{8} + \left(-\dfrac{2}{3}\right)\right] - \left(\dfrac{1}{8} + 2\right)$ Rewrite subtraction in terms of addition.

$= \left[-\dfrac{15}{24} + \left(-\dfrac{16}{24}\right)\right] - \left(\dfrac{1}{8} + \dfrac{16}{8}\right)$ Get a common denominator in each parentheses.

$= \left(-\dfrac{31}{24}\right) - \left(\dfrac{17}{8}\right)$ Add fractions in each parentheses.

$= \left(-\dfrac{31}{24}\right) + \left(-\dfrac{17}{8}\right)$ Rewrite subtraction in terms of addition.

$= -\dfrac{31}{24} + \left(-\dfrac{51}{24}\right)$ Get a common denominator.

$= -\dfrac{82}{24}$ Add.

$= -\dfrac{41}{12}$ Simplify to lowest terms.

b. $-6 - |7 - 11| + (-3 + 7)^2$ Simplify within absolute value bars and parentheses first.

$= -6 - |7 + (-11)| + (-3 + 7)^2$ Rewrite subtraction in terms of addition.

$= -6 - |-4| + (4)^2$

$= -6 - (4) + 16$ Simplify absolute value and exponent.

$= -6 + (-4) + 16$ Rewrite subtraction in terms of addition.

$= -10 + 16$ Add from left to right.

$= 6$

Skill Practice Simplify the expressions.

15. $\left(-1 + \dfrac{1}{4}\right) - \left(\dfrac{3}{4} - \dfrac{1}{2}\right)$

16. $4 - 2|6 + (-8)| + (4)^2$

Answers

15. -1 16. 16

Calculator Connections

Topic: Operations with Signed Numbers on a Calculator

Most calculators can add, subtract, multiply, and divide signed numbers. It is important to note, however, that the key used for the negative sign is different from the key used for subtraction. On a scientific calculator, the +/- key or +o- key is used to enter a negative number or to change the sign of an existing number. On a graphing calculator, the (-) key is used. These keys should not be confused with the – key which is used for subtraction. For example, try simplifying the following expressions.

a. $-7 + (-4) - 6$ **b.** $-3.1 - (-0.5) + 1.1$

Scientific Calculator:

Enter: 7 +o- + (4 +o-) – 6 =   **Result:** $\boxed{-17}$

Enter: 3.1 +o- – (0.5 +o-) + 1.1 =   **Result:** $\boxed{-1.5}$

Graphing Calculator:

```
-7+(-4)-6
              -17
-3.1-(-0.5)+1.1
              -1.5
```

Calculator Exercises

Simplify the expression without the use of a calculator. Then use the calculator to verify your answer.

1. $-8 + (-5)$ -13 **2.** $4 + (-5) + (-1)$ -2 **3.** $627 - (-84)$ 711 **4.** $-0.06 - 0.12$
                                    -0.18

5. $-3.2 + (-14.5)$ -17.7 **6.** $-472 + (-518)$ -990 **7.** $-12 - 9 + 4$ -17 **8.** $209 - 108 + (-63)$
                                          38

Section 1.5   Practice Exercises

Boost *your* GRADE at ALEKS.com!

ALEKS version 3.0

- Practice Problems
- Self-Tests
- NetTutor
- e-Professors
- Videos

For additional exercises, see Classroom Activities 1.5A–1.5C in the *Instructor's Resource Manual* at www.mhhe.com/moh.

Study Skills Exercise

1. Some instructors allow the use of calculators. What is your instructor's policy regarding calculators in class, on the homework, and on tests?

Helpful Hint: If you are not permitted to use a calculator on tests, it is a good idea to do your homework in the same way, without a calculator.

Review Exercises

↔ For Exercises 2–5, write each English phrase as an algebraic expression.

2. The square root of 6 $\sqrt{6}$ **3.** The square of x x^2

4. Negative seven increased by 10 $-7 + 10$ **5.** Two more than $-b$ $-b + 2$

For Exercises 6–8, simplify the expression.

6. $4^2 - 6 \div 2$ 13 **7.** $1 + 36 \div 9 \cdot 2$ 9 **8.** $14 - |10 - 6|$ 10

Concept 1: Subtraction of Real Numbers

For Exercises 9–14, fill in the blank to make each statement correct.

9. $5 - 3 = 5 +$ ____−3____

10. $8 - 7 = 8 +$ ____−7____

11. $-2 - 12 = -2 +$ ____−12____

12. $-4 - 9 = -4 +$ ____−9____

13. $7 - (-4) = 7 +$ ____4____

14. $13 - (-4) = 13 +$ ____4____

For Exercises 15–60, simplify. **(See Examples 1–2.)**

15. $3 - 5$ -2

16. $9 - 12$ -3

17. $3 - (-5)$ 8

18. $9 - (-12)$ 21

19. $-3 - 5$ -8

20. $-9 - 12$ -21

21. $-3 - (-5)$ 2

22. $-9 - (-5)$ -4

23. $23 - 17$ 6

24. $14 - 2$ 12

25. $23 - (-17)$ 40

26. $14 - (-2)$ 16

27. $-23 - 17$ -40

28. $-14 - 2$ -16

29. $-23 - (-23)$ 0

30. $-14 - (-14)$ 0

31. $-6 - 14$ -20

32. $-9 - 12$ -21

33. $-7 - 17$ -24

34. $-8 - 21$ -29

35. $13 - (-12)$ 25

36. $20 - (-5)$ 25

37. $-14 - (-9)$ -5

38. $-21 - (-17)$ -4

39. $-\dfrac{6}{5} - \dfrac{3}{10}$ $-\dfrac{3}{2}$

40. $-\dfrac{2}{9} - \dfrac{5}{3}$ $-\dfrac{17}{9}$

41. $\dfrac{3}{8} - \left(-\dfrac{4}{3}\right)$ $\dfrac{41}{24}$

42. $\dfrac{7}{10} - \left(-\dfrac{5}{6}\right)$ $\dfrac{23}{15}$

43. $\dfrac{1}{2} - \dfrac{1}{10}$ $\dfrac{2}{5}$

44. $\dfrac{2}{7} - \dfrac{3}{14}$ $\dfrac{1}{14}$

45. $-\dfrac{11}{12} - \left(-\dfrac{1}{4}\right)$ $-\dfrac{2}{3}$

46. $-\dfrac{7}{8} - \left(-\dfrac{1}{6}\right)$ $-\dfrac{17}{24}$

47. $6.8 - (-2.4)$ 9.2

48. $7.2 - (-1.9)$ 9.1

49. $3.1 - 8.82$ -5.72

50. $1.8 - 9.59$ -7.79

51. $-4 - 3 - 2 - 1$ -10

52. $-10 - 9 - 8 - 7$ -34

53. $6 - 8 - 2 - 10$ -14

54. $20 - 50 - 10 - 5$ -45

55. $-36.75 - 14.25$ -51

56. $-84.21 - 112.16$ -196.37

57. $-112.846 + (-13.03) - 47.312$ -173.188

58. $-96.473 + (-36.02) - 16.617$ -149.11

59. $0.085 - (-3.14) + 0.018$ 3.243

60. $0.00061 - (-0.00057) + 0.0014$ 0.00258

Concept 2: Translations

For Exercises 61–70, write each English phrase as an algebraic expression. Then evaluate the expression. **(See Example 3.)**

61. Six minus -7 $6 - (-7); 13$

62. Eighteen minus -1 $18 - (-1); 19$

63. Eighteen subtracted from 3 $3 - 18; -15$

64. Twenty-one subtracted from 8 $8 - 21; -13$

65. The difference of -5 and -11 $-5 - (-11); 6$

66. The difference of -2 and -18 $-2 - (-18); 16$

67. Negative thirteen subtracted from -1
$-1 - (-13); 12$

68. Negative thirty-one subtracted from -19
$-19 - (-31); 12$

69. Twenty less than -32 $-32 - 20; -52$

70. Seven less than -3 $-3 - 7; -10$

Concept 3: Applications Involving Subtraction

71. On the game, *Jeopardy*, Jasper selected the category "The Last." He got the first four questions correct (worth $200, $400, $600, and $800) but then missed the last question (worth $1000). Write an expression that determines Jasper's score. Then simplify the expression to find his total winnings for that category.
(See Example 4.) $200 + 400 + 600 + 800 - 1000$; $1000

72. On Courtney's turn in *Jeopardy*, she chose the category "Birds of a Feather." She already had $1200 when she selected a Double Jeopardy question. She wagered $500 but guessed incorrectly (therefore she lost $500). On her next turn, she got the $800 question correct. Write an expression that determines Courtney's score. Then simplify the expression to find her total winnings for that category.
$1200 - 500 + 800$; $1500

73. In Ohio, the highest temperature ever recorded was 113°F and the lowest was −39°F. Find the difference between the highest and lowest temperatures. (*Source: Information Please Almanac*) **(See Example 5.)**   152°F

74. On a recent winter day at the South Pole, the temperature was −52°F. On the same day in Springfield, Missouri, it was a pleasant summer temperature of 75°F. What was the difference in temperature?   The difference in the temperature was 127°F.

75. The highest mountain in the world is Mt. Everest, located in the Himalayas. Its height is 8848 meters (m). The lowest recorded depth in the ocean is located in the Marianas Trench in the Pacific Ocean. Its "height" relative to sea level is −11,033 m. Determine the difference in elevation, in meters, between the highest mountain in the world and the deepest ocean trench. (*Source: Information Please Almanac*)   19,881 m

76. The lowest point in North America is located in Death Valley, California, at an elevation of −282 ft. The highest point in North America is Mt. McKinley, Alaska, at an elevation of 20,320 ft. Find the difference in elevation, in feet, between the highest and lowest points in North America. (*Source: Information Please Almanac*)   20,602 ft

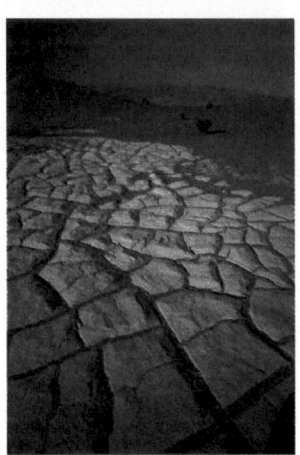

Concept 4: Applying the Order of Operations

For Exercises 77–96, perform the indicated operations. **(See Examples 6–7.)**

77. $6 + 8 - (-2) - 4 + 1$ 13

78. $-3 - (-4) + 1 - 2 - 5$ −5

79. $-1 - 7 + (-3) - 8 + 10$ −9

80. $13 - 7 + 4 - 3 - (-1)$ 8

81. $2 - (-8) + 7 + 3 - 15$ 5

82. $8 - (-13) + 1 - 9$ 13

83. $-6 + (-1) + (-8) + (-10)$ −25

84. $-8 + (-3) + (-5) + (-2)$ −18

85. $-4 - \{11 - [4 - (-9)]\}$ −2

86. $15 - \{25 + 2[3 - (-1)]\}$ −18

87. $-\dfrac{13}{10} + \dfrac{8}{15} - \left(-\dfrac{2}{5}\right)$ $-\dfrac{11}{30}$

88. $\dfrac{11}{14} - \left(-\dfrac{9}{7}\right) - \dfrac{3}{2}$ $\dfrac{4}{7}$

89. $\left(\dfrac{2}{3} - \dfrac{5}{9}\right) - \left(\dfrac{4}{3} - (-2)\right)$ $-\dfrac{29}{9}$ **90.** $\left(-\dfrac{9}{8} - \dfrac{1}{4}\right) - \left(-\dfrac{5}{6} + \dfrac{1}{8}\right)$ $-\dfrac{2}{3}$ **91.** $\sqrt{29 + (-4)} - 7$ -2

92. $8 - \sqrt{98 + (-3) + 5}$ -2 **93.** $|10 + (-3)| - |-12 + (-6)|$ **94.** $|6 - 8| + |12 - 5|$ 9
-11

95. $\dfrac{3 - 4 + 5}{4 + (-2)}$ 2 **96.** $\dfrac{12 - 14 + 6}{6 + (-2)}$ 1

For Exercises 97–104, evaluate each expression for $a = -2$, $b = -6$, and $c = -1$.

97. $(a + b) - c$ -7 **98.** $(a - b) + c$ 3 **99.** $a - (b + c)$ 5 **100.** $a + (b - c)$ -7

101. $(a - b) - c$ 5 **102.** $(a + b) + c$ -9 **103.** $a - (b - c)$ 3 **104.** $a + (b + c)$ -9

Problem Recognition Exercises

Addition and Subtraction of Real Numbers

1. State the rule for adding two negative numbers.
Add their absolute values and apply a negative sign.

2. State the rule for adding a negative number to a positive number. Subtract the smaller absolute value from the larger absolute value. Apply the sign of the number with the larger absolute value.

For Exercises 3–32, perform the indicated operations.

3. $65 - 24$ 41 **4.** $42 - 29$ 13 **5.** $13 - (-18)$ 31 **6.** $22 - (-24)$ 46

7. 4.8 6.1 1.3 **8.** 3.5 7.1 3.6 **9.** $4 + (-20)$ 16 **10.** $5 + (-12)$ 7

11. $\dfrac{1}{3} - \dfrac{5}{12}$ $-\dfrac{1}{12}$ **12.** $\dfrac{3}{8} - \dfrac{1}{12}$ $\dfrac{7}{24}$ **13.** $-32 - 4$ -36 **14.** $-51 - 8$ -59

15. $-6 + (-6)$ -12 **16.** $-25 + (-25)$ -50 **17.** $-4 - \left(-\dfrac{5}{6}\right)$ $-\dfrac{19}{6}$ **18.** $-2 - \left(-\dfrac{2}{5}\right)$ $-\dfrac{8}{5}$

19. $-60 + 55$ -5 **20.** $-55 + 23$ -32 **21.** $-18 - (-18)$ 0 **22.** $-3 - (-3)$ 0

23. $-3.5 - 4.2$ -7.7 **24.** $-6.6 - 3.9$ -10.5 **25.** $-\dfrac{9}{5} + \left(-\dfrac{1}{3}\right)$ $-\dfrac{32}{15}$ **26.** $-\dfrac{7}{8} + \left(-\dfrac{1}{4}\right)$ $-\dfrac{9}{8}$

27. $-14 + (-2) - 16$ -32 **28.** $-25 + (-6) - 15$ -46 **29.** $-4.2 + 1.2 + 3.0$ 0 **30.** $-4.6 + 8.6 + (-4.0)$ 0

31. $-10 - 8 - 6 - 4 - 2$ -30 **32.** $-100 - 90 - 80 - 70 - 60$ -400

 Writing   Translating Expression   Geometry   Scientific Calculator   Video   NS&E

Concepts

1. Multiplication of Real Numbers
2. Exponential Expressions
3. Division of Real Numbers
4. Order of Operations

1. Multiplication of Real Numbers

Multiplication of real numbers can be interpreted as repeated addition. For example:

$$3(4) = 4 + 4 + 4 = 12 \qquad \text{Add 3 groups of 4.}$$

$$3(-4) = -4 + (-4) + (-4) = -12 \qquad \text{Add 3 groups of } -4.$$

These results suggest that the product of a positive number and a negative number is *negative*. Consider the following pattern of products.

$$
\begin{aligned}
4 \times \ \ 3 &= \ \ 12 \\
4 \times \ \ 2 &= \ \ \ \ 8 \\
4 \times \ \ 1 &= \ \ \ \ 4 \\
4 \times \ \ 0 &= \ \ \ \ 0 \\
4 \times -1 &= \ \ -4 \\
4 \times -2 &= \ \ -8 \\
4 \times -3 &= -12
\end{aligned}
$$

The pattern decreases by 4 with each row.

Thus, the product of a positive number and a negative number must be *negative* for the pattern to continue.

Now suppose we have a product of two negative numbers. To determine the sign, consider the following pattern of products.

$$
\begin{aligned}
-4 \times \ \ 3 &= -12 \\
-4 \times \ \ 2 &= \ \ -8 \\
-4 \times \ \ 1 &= \ \ -4 \\
-4 \times \ \ 0 &= \ \ \ \ 0 \\
-4 \times -1 &= \ \ \ \ 4 \\
-4 \times -2 &= \ \ \ \ 8 \\
-4 \times -3 &= \ \ 12
\end{aligned}
$$

The pattern increases by 4 with each row.

Thus, the product of two negative numbers must be *positive* for the pattern to continue.

From the first four rows, we see that the product increases by 4 for each row. For the pattern to continue, it follows that the product of two negative numbers must be *positive*.

We now summarize the rules for multiplying real numbers.

PROCEDURE   Multiplying Real Numbers

- The product of two real numbers with the *same* sign is positive.

  Examples: $(5)(6) = 30$

   $(-4)(-10) = 40$

- The product of two real numbers with *different* signs is negative.

  Examples: $(-2)(5) = -10$

   $(4)(-9) = -36$

- The product of any real number and zero is zero.

  Examples: $(8)(0) = 0$

   $(0)(-6) = 0$

Example 1 Multiplying Real Numbers

Classroom Examples: p. 67, Exercises 8 and 14

Multiply the real numbers.

a. $-8(-4)$ b. $-2.5(-1.7)$ c. $-7(10)$

d. $\dfrac{1}{2}(-8)$ e. $0(-8.3)$ f. $-\dfrac{2}{7}\left(-\dfrac{7}{2}\right)$

Solution:

a. $-8(-4) = 32$ *Same* signs. Product is positive.

b. $-2.5(-1.7) = 4.25$ *Same* signs. Product is positive.

c. $-7(10) = -70$ *Different* signs. Product is negative.

d. $\dfrac{1}{2}(-8) = -4$ *Different* signs. Product is negative.

e. $0(-8.3) = 0$ The product of any real number and zero is zero.

f. $-\dfrac{2}{7}\left(-\dfrac{7}{2}\right) = \dfrac{14}{14}$ *Same* signs. Product is positive.

$\qquad\qquad = 1$ Simplify.

Skill Practice Multiply.

1. $-9(-3)$ 2. $-1.5(-1.5)$ 3. $-6(4)$

4. $\dfrac{1}{3}(-15)$ 5. $0(-4.1)$ 6. $-\dfrac{5}{9}\left(-\dfrac{9}{5}\right)$

Observe the pattern for repeated multiplications.

$$(-1)(-1) \qquad \underline{(-1)(-1)}(-1) \qquad \underline{(-1)(-1)}(-1)(-1) \qquad \underline{(-1)(-1)}(-1)(-1)(-1)$$

$$= 1 \qquad\qquad = (1)(-1) \qquad\quad = \underline{(1)(-1)}(-1) \qquad\quad = \underline{(1)(-1)}(-1)(-1)$$

$$\qquad\qquad\qquad = -1 \qquad\qquad = (-1)(-1) \qquad\qquad = \underline{(-1)(-1)}(-1)$$

$$\qquad\qquad\qquad\qquad\qquad\qquad = 1 \qquad\qquad\qquad = (1)(-1)$$

$$\qquad\qquad\qquad\qquad\qquad\qquad\qquad\qquad\qquad = -1$$

The pattern demonstrated in these examples indicates that

- The product of an even number of negative factors is positive.
- The product of an odd number of negative factors is negative.

2. Exponential Expressions

Recall that for any real number b and any positive integer, n:

$$b^n = \underbrace{b \cdot b \cdot b \cdot b \cdot \ldots b}_{n \text{ factors of } b}$$

Answers

1. 27   2. 2.25   3. -24

4. -5 5. 0   6. 1

Be particularly careful when evaluating exponential expressions involving negative numbers. An exponential expression with a negative base is written with parentheses around the base, such as $(-2)^4$.

To evaluate $(-2)^4$, the base -2 is used as a factor four times:

$$(-2)^4 = (-2)(-2)(-2)(-2) = 16$$

If parentheses are *not* used, the expression -2^4 has a different meaning:

- The expression -2^4 has a base of 2 (not -2) and can be interpreted as $-1 \cdot 2^4$.

$$-2^4 = -1(2)(2)(2)(2) = -16$$

- The expression -2^4 can also be interpreted as the opposite of 2^4.

$$-2^4 = -(2 \cdot 2 \cdot 2 \cdot 2) = -16$$

Classroom Examples: p. 68,
Exercises 16, 18, 20, and 22

TIP: The following expressions are translated as:

$-(-3)$ opposite of negative 3
-3^2 opposite of 3 squared
$(-3)^2$ negative 3, squared

Example 2   Evaluating Exponential Expressions

Simplify.

a. $(-5)^2$ **b.** -5^2 **c.** $\left(-\dfrac{1}{2}\right)^3$ **d.** -0.4^3

Solution:

a. $(-5)^2 = (-5)(-5) = 25$ Multiply two factors of -5.

b. $-5^2 = -1(5)(5) = -25$ Multiply -1 by two factors of 5.

c. $\left(-\dfrac{1}{2}\right)^3 = \left(-\dfrac{1}{2}\right)\left(-\dfrac{1}{2}\right)\left(-\dfrac{1}{2}\right) = -\dfrac{1}{8}$ Multiply three factors of $-\dfrac{1}{2}$.

d. $-0.4^3 = -1(0.4)(0.4)(0.4) = -0.064$ Multiply -1 by three factors of 0.4.

Skill Practice Simplify.

7. $(-7)^2$ **8.** -7^2 **9.** $\left(-\dfrac{2}{3}\right)^3$ **10.** -0.2^3

Avoiding Mistakes

The negative sign is not part of the base unless it is in parentheses with the base. Thus, in the expression -5^2, the exponent applies only to 5 and not to the negative sign.

3. Division of Real Numbers

Two numbers are *reciprocals* if their product is 1. For example, $-\frac{2}{7}$ and $-\frac{7}{2}$ are reciprocals because $-\frac{2}{7}\left(-\frac{7}{2}\right) = 1$. Symbolically, if a is a nonzero real number, then the reciprocal of a is $\frac{1}{a}$ because $a \cdot \frac{1}{a} = 1$. This definition also implies that a number and its reciprocal have the same sign.

DEFINITION   The Reciprocal of a Real Number

Let a be a nonzero real number. Then, the **reciprocal** of a is $\frac{1}{a}$.

Recall that to subtract two real numbers, we add the opposite of the second number to the first number. In a similar way, division of real numbers is defined in terms of multiplication. To divide two real numbers, we multiply the first number by the reciprocal of the second number.

Answers

7. 49   **8.** -49

9. $-\dfrac{8}{27}$ **10.** -0.008

DEFINITION Division of Real Numbers

Let a and b be real numbers such that $b \neq 0$. Then, $a \div b = a \cdot \frac{1}{b}$.

Consider the quotient $10 \div 5$. The reciprocal of 5 is $\frac{1}{5}$, so we have

multiply

$$10 \div 5 = 2 \qquad \text{or equivalently,} \qquad 10 \cdot \frac{1}{5} = 2$$

reciprocal

Because division of real numbers can be expressed in terms of multiplication, then the sign rules that apply to multiplication also apply to division.

PROCEDURE Dividing Real Numbers

- The quotient of two real numbers with the *same* sign is positive.

  Examples: $24 \div 4 = 6$
  $-36 \div -9 = 4$

- The quotient of two real numbers with *different* signs is negative.

  Examples: $100 \div (-5) = -20$
  $-12 \div 4 = -3$

Example 3 **Dividing Real Numbers**

Divide the real numbers.

a. $200 \div (-10)$ **b.** $\dfrac{-48}{16}$ **c.** $\dfrac{-6.25}{-1.25}$ **d.** $\dfrac{9}{-5}$

Classroom Examples: p. 68, Exercises 24 and 26

Solution:

a. $200 \div (-10) = -20$ *Different* signs. Quotient is negative.

b. $\dfrac{-48}{16} - -3$ *Different* signs. Quotient is negative.

c. $\dfrac{-6.25}{-1.25} = 5$ *Same* signs. Quotient is positive.

d. $\dfrac{-9}{-5} = \dfrac{9}{5}$ *Same* signs. Quotient is positive.

Because 5 does not divide into 9 evenly the answer can be left as a fraction.

TIP: If the numerator and denominator of a fraction are both negative, then the quotient is positive. Therefore, $\frac{-9}{-5}$ can be simplified to $\frac{9}{5}$.

Skill Practice Divide.

11. $-14 \div 7$ **12.** $\dfrac{-18}{3}$ **13.** $\dfrac{-7.6}{-1.9}$ **14.** $\dfrac{-7}{-3}$

Answers

11. -2 **12.** -6 **13.** 4 **14.** $\dfrac{7}{3}$

Classroom Examples: pp. 68–69, Exercises 30 and 82

Example 4 Dividing Real Numbers

Divide the real numbers.

a. $15 \div -25$ **b.** $-\dfrac{3}{14} \div \dfrac{9}{7}$

Solution:

a. $15 \div -25$ *Different* signs. Quotient is negative.

$= \dfrac{15}{-25}$

$= -\dfrac{3}{5}$

TIP: If the numerator and denominator of a fraction have opposite signs, then the quotient will be negative. Therefore, a fraction has the same value whether the negative sign is written in the numerator, in the denominator, or in front of the fraction.

$$\dfrac{-3}{5} = \dfrac{3}{-5} = -\dfrac{3}{5}$$

b. $-\dfrac{3}{14} \div \dfrac{9}{7}$ *Different* signs. Quotient is negative.

$= -\dfrac{3}{14} \cdot \dfrac{7}{9}$ Multiply by the reciprocal of $\frac{9}{7}$ which is $\frac{7}{9}$.

$= -\dfrac{\overset{1}{3}}{\underset{2}{14}} \cdot \dfrac{\overset{1}{7}}{\underset{3}{9}}$ Divide out common factors.

$= -\dfrac{1}{6}$ Multiply the fractions.

Skill Practice Divide.

15. $12 \div (-18)$ **16.** $\dfrac{3}{4} \div \left(-\dfrac{9}{16}\right)$

Multiplication can be used to check any division problem. If $\frac{a}{b} = c$, then $bc = a$ (provided that $b \neq 0$). For example:

$$\dfrac{8}{-4} = -2 \; \rightarrow \; \underline{\text{Check:}} \quad (-4)(-2) = 8 \; ✔$$

This relationship between multiplication and division can be used to investigate division problems involving the number zero.

1. The quotient of 0 and any nonzero number is 0. For example:

$$\dfrac{0}{6} = 0 \qquad \text{because } 6 \cdot 0 = 0 \; ✔$$

Instructor Note: Memory Device: Zero under the line, division undefined.

2. The quotient of any nonzero number and 0 is undefined. For example:

$$\dfrac{6}{0} = ?$$

Finding the quotient $\frac{6}{0}$ is equivalent to asking, "What number times zero will equal 6?" That is, $(0)(?) = 6$. No real number satisfies this condition. Therefore, we say that division by zero is undefined.

3. The quotient of 0 and 0 cannot be determined. Evaluating an expression of the form $\frac{0}{0} = ?$ is equivalent to asking, "What number times zero will equal 0?" That is, $(0)(?) = 0$. Any real number will satisfy this requirement; however, expressions involving $\frac{0}{0}$ are usually discussed in advanced mathematics courses.

Answers

15. $-\dfrac{2}{3}$ **16.** $-\dfrac{4}{3}$

PROPERTY Division Involving Zero

Let a represent a nonzero real number. Then,

1. $\dfrac{0}{a} = 0$ **2.** $\dfrac{a}{0}$ is undefined

---

4. Order of Operations

Example 5 Applying the Order of Operations

Simplify. $-8 + 8 \div (-2) \div (-6)$

Classroom Example: p. 69, Exercise 100

Solution:

$-8 + 8 \div (-2) \div (-6)$

$= -8 + (-4) \div (-6)$ Perform division before addition.

$= -8 + \dfrac{4}{6}$ The quotient of -4 and -6 is positive $\frac{4}{6}$ or $\frac{2}{3}$.

$= -\dfrac{8}{1} + \dfrac{2}{3}$ Write -8 as a fraction.

$= -\dfrac{24}{3} + \dfrac{2}{3}$ Get a common denominator.

$= -\dfrac{22}{3}$ Add.

Skill Practice Simplify.

17. $-36 + 36 \div (-4) \div (-3)$

Example 6 Applying the Order of Operations

Simplify. $\dfrac{24 - 2[-3 + (5 - 8)]^2}{2|-12 + 3|}$

Classroom Example: p. 69, Exercise 114

Solution:

$\dfrac{24 - 2[-3 + (5 - 8)]^2}{2|-12 + 3|}$ Simplify numerator and denominator separately.

$= \dfrac{24 - 2[-3 + (-3)]^2}{2|-9|}$ Simplify within the inner parentheses and absolute value.

$= \dfrac{24 - 2[-6]^2}{2(9)}$ Simplify within brackets, [ ]. Simplify the absolute value.

$= \dfrac{24 - 2(36)}{2(9)}$ Simplify exponents.

$= \dfrac{24 - 72}{18}$ Perform multiplication before subtraction.

$= \dfrac{-48}{18}$ or $-\dfrac{8}{3}$ Simplify to lowest terms.

Answer

17. -33

Skill Practice Simplify.

18. $\dfrac{100 - 3[-1 + (2 - 6)^2]}{|20 - 25|}$

Classroom Example: p. 69, Exercise 116

Example 7 Evaluating Algebraic Expressions

Given $y = -6$, evaluate the expressions.

  a. y^2 **b.** $-y^2$

Solution:

a. y^2

$= (\quad)^2$ When substituting a number for a variable, use parentheses.

$= (-6)^2$ Substitute $y = -6$.

$= 36$ Square -6, that is, $(-6)(-6) = 36$.

b. $-y^2$

$= -(\quad)^2$ When substituting a number for a variable, use parentheses.

$= -(-6)^2$ Substitute $y = -6$.

$= -(36)$ Square -6.

$= -36$ Multiply by -1.

Skill Practice Given $a = -7$, evaluate the expressions.

19. a^2 **20.** $-a^2$

Answers

18. 11   **19.** 49   **20.** −49

Calculator Connections

Topic: Evaluating Exponential Expressions with Positive and Negative Bases

Be particularly careful when raising a negative number to an even power on a calculator. For example, the expressions $(-4)^2$ and -4^2 have different values. That is, $(-4)^2 = 16$ and $-4^2 = -16$. Verify these expressions on a calculator.

Scientific Calculator:

To evaluate $(-4)^2$

Enter: (4 +○-) x^2 **Result:** | 16 |

To evaluate -4^2 on a scientific calculator, it is important to square 4 first and then take its opposite.

Enter: 4 x^2 +○-   **Result:** | −16 |

Graphing Calculator:

```
(-4)²
            16
-4²
           -16
```

The graphing calculator allows for several methods of denoting the multiplication of two real numbers. For example, consider the product of −8 and 4.

Calculator Exercises

Simplify the expression without the use of a calculator. Then use the calculator to verify your answer.

1. $-6(5)$ $\quad$ −30 $\qquad$ **2.** $\dfrac{-5.2}{2.6}$ $\quad$ −2 $\qquad$ **3.** $(-5)(-5)(-5)(-5)$ $\quad$ 625 $\qquad$ **4.** $(-5)^4$ $\quad$ 625 $\qquad$ **5.** -5^4 $\quad$ −625

6. -2.4^2 $\quad$ −5.76 $\qquad$ **7.** $(-2.4)^2$ $\quad$ 5.76 $\qquad$ **8.** $(-1)(-1)(-1)$ $\quad$ −1 $\qquad$ **9.** $\dfrac{-8.4}{-2.1}$ $\quad$ 4 $\qquad$ **10.** $90 \div (-5)(2)$ −36

Section 1.6 Practice Exercises

Study Skills Exercises

1. Look through Section 1.6, and write down a page number that contains:

    a. An Avoiding Mistakes box _____

    b. A Tip box _____

    c. A key term (shown in bold) _____

2. Define the key term **reciprocal of a real number**.

Review Exercises

For Exercises 3–6, determine if the expression is true or false.

3. $6 + (-2) > -5 + 6$ $\quad$ True $\qquad\qquad$ **4.** $|-6| + |-14| \le |-3| + |-17|$ $\quad$ True

5. $\sqrt{36} - |-6| > 0$ $\quad$ False $\qquad\qquad$ **6.** $\sqrt{9} + |-3| \le 0$ $\quad$ False

Concept 1: Multiplication of Real Numbers

For Exercises 7–14, multiply the real numbers. **(See Example 1.)**

7. $8(-7)$ $\quad$ −56 $\qquad$ **8.** $(-3) \cdot 4$ $\quad$ −12 $\qquad$ **9.** $(-11)(-13)$ $\quad$ 143 $\qquad$ **10.** $(-5)(-26)$ $\quad$ 130

11. $(-2.2)(5.8)$ $\quad$ −12.76 $\qquad$ **12.** $(9.1)(-4.5)$ $\quad$ −40.95 $\qquad$ **13.** $\left(-\dfrac{2}{3}\right)\left(-\dfrac{9}{8}\right)$ $\quad$ $\dfrac{3}{4}$ $\qquad$ **14.** $\left(-\dfrac{5}{4}\right)\left(-\dfrac{12}{25}\right)$ $\quad$ $\dfrac{3}{5}$

 Writing   Translating Expression   Geometry   Scientific Calculator   Video   NS&E

Concept 2: Exponential Expressions

For Exercises 15–22, simplify the exponential expressions. **(See Example 2.)**

15. $(-6)^2$ 36

16. $(-10)^2$ 100

17. -6^2 −36

18. -10^2 −100

19. $\left(-\dfrac{3}{5}\right)^3$ $-\dfrac{27}{125}$

20. $\left(-\dfrac{5}{2}\right)^3$ $-\dfrac{125}{8}$

21. $(-0.2)^4$ 0.0016

22. $(-0.1)^4$ 0.0001

Concept 3: Division of Real Numbers

For Exercises 23–30, divide the real numbers. **(See Examples 3–4.)**

23. $\dfrac{54}{-9}$ −6

24. $\dfrac{-27}{3}$ −9

25. $\dfrac{-15}{-17}$ $\dfrac{15}{17}$

26. $\dfrac{-21}{-16}$ $\dfrac{21}{16}$

27. $\dfrac{-14}{-7}$ 2

28. $\dfrac{-21}{-3}$ 7

29. $\dfrac{13}{-65}$ $-\dfrac{1}{5}$

30. $\dfrac{7}{-77}$ $-\dfrac{1}{11}$

For Exercises 31–38, show how multiplication can be used to check the division problems.

31. $\dfrac{14}{-2} = -7$
$(-2)(-7) = 14$

32. $\dfrac{-18}{-6} = 3$
$(-6)(3) = -18$

33. $\dfrac{0}{-5} = 0$
$-5 \cdot 0 = 0$

34. $\dfrac{0}{-4} = 0$
$-4 \cdot 0 = 0$

35. $\dfrac{6}{0}$ is undefined
No number multiplied by zero equals 6.

36. $\dfrac{-4}{0}$ is undefined
No number multiplied by zero equals −4.

37. $-24 \div (-6) = 4$
$(-6)(4) = -24$

38. $-18 \div 2 = -9$
$(2)(-9) = -18$

Mixed Exercises

For Exercises 39–82, multiply or divide as indicated.

 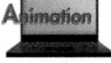

39. $2 \cdot 3$ 6

40. $8 \cdot 6$ 48

41. $2(-3)$ −6

42. $8(-6)$ −48

43. $(-24) \div 3$ −8

44. $(-52) \div 2$ −26

45. $(-24) \div (-3)$ 8

46. $(-52) \div (-2)$ 26

47. $-6 \cdot 0$ 0

48. $-8 \cdot 0$ 0

49. $-18 \div 0$ Undefined

50. $-42 \div 0$ Undefined

51. $0\left(-\dfrac{2}{5}\right)$ 0

52. $0\left(-\dfrac{1}{8}\right)$ 0

53. $0 \div \left(-\dfrac{1}{10}\right)$ 0

54. $0 \div \left(\dfrac{4}{9}\right)$ 0

55. $\dfrac{-9}{6}$ $-\dfrac{3}{2}$

56. $\dfrac{-15}{10}$ $-\dfrac{3}{2}$

57. $\dfrac{-30}{-100}$ $\dfrac{3}{10}$

58. $\dfrac{-250}{-1000}$ $\dfrac{1}{4}$

59. $\dfrac{26}{-13}$ −2

60. $\dfrac{52}{-4}$ −13

61. $1.72(-4.6)$ −7.912

62. $361.3(-14.9)$ −5383.37

63. $-0.02(-4.6)$ 0.092

64. $-0.06(-2.15)$ 0.129

65. $\dfrac{14.4}{-2.4}$ −6

66. $\dfrac{50.4}{-6.3}$ −8

67. $\dfrac{-5.25}{-2.5}$ 2.1

68. $\dfrac{-8.5}{-27.2}$ 0.3125

69. $(-3)^2$ 9

70. $(-7)^2$ 49

71. -3^2 −9

72. -7^2 −49

73. $\left(-\dfrac{4}{3}\right)^3$ $-\dfrac{64}{27}$

74. $\left(-\dfrac{1}{5}\right)^3$ $-\dfrac{1}{125}$

75. $2.8(-5.1)$ -14.28 **76.** $(7.21)(-0.3)$ -2.163 ⊚ **77.** $(-6.8) \div (-0.02)$ 340 **78.** $(-12.3) \div (-0.03)$ 410

79. $\left(-\dfrac{2}{15}\right)\left(\dfrac{25}{3}\right)$ $-\dfrac{10}{9}$ **80.** $\left(-\dfrac{5}{16}\right)\left(\dfrac{4}{9}\right)$ $-\dfrac{5}{36}$ **81.** $\left(-\dfrac{7}{8}\right) \div \left(-\dfrac{9}{16}\right)$ $\dfrac{14}{9}$ ⊚ **82.** $\left(-\dfrac{22}{23}\right) \div \left(-\dfrac{11}{3}\right)$ $\dfrac{6}{23}$

Concept 4: Order of Operations

For Exercises 83–114, perform the indicated operations. **(See Examples 5–6.)**

83. $(-2)(-5)(-3)$ -30

84. $(-6)(-1)(-10)$ -60

85. $(-8)(-4)(-1)(-3)$ 96

86. $(-6)(-3)(-1)(-5)$ 90

87. $100 \div (-10) \div (-5)$ 2

88. $150 \div (-15) \div (-2)$ 5

89. $-12 \div (-6) \div (-2)$ -1

90. $-36 \div (-2) \div 6$ 3

91. $\dfrac{2}{5} \cdot \dfrac{1}{3} \cdot \left(-\dfrac{10}{11}\right)$ $-\dfrac{4}{33}$

92. $\left(-\dfrac{9}{8}\right) \cdot \left(-\dfrac{2}{3}\right) \cdot \left(1\dfrac{5}{12}\right)$ $\dfrac{17}{16}$

93. $\left(1\dfrac{1}{3}\right) \div 3 \div \left(-\dfrac{7}{9}\right)$ $-\dfrac{4}{7}$

94. $-\dfrac{7}{8} \div \left(3\dfrac{1}{4}\right) \div (-2)$ $\dfrac{7}{52}$

95. $12 \div (-2)(4)$ -24

96. $(-6) \cdot 7 \div (-2)$ 21

97. $\left(-\dfrac{12}{5}\right) \div (-6) \cdot \left(-\dfrac{1}{8}\right)$ $-\dfrac{1}{20}$

98. $10 \cdot \dfrac{1}{3} \div \dfrac{25}{6}$ $\dfrac{4}{5}$

99. $8 - 2^3 \cdot 5 + 3 - (-6)$ -23

100. $-14 \div (-7) - 8 \cdot 2 + 3^3$ 13

⊚ **101.** $-(2 - 8)^2 \div (-6) \cdot 2$ 12

102. $-(3 - 5)^2 \cdot 6 \div (-4)$ 6

103. $\dfrac{6(-4) - 2(5 - 8)}{-6 - 3 - 5}$ $\dfrac{9}{7}$

104. $\dfrac{3(-4) - 5(9 - 11)}{-9 - 2 - 3}$ $\dfrac{1}{7}$

105. $\dfrac{-4 + 5}{(-2) \cdot 5 + 10}$ Undefined

106. $\dfrac{-3 + 10}{2(-4) + 8}$ Undefined

107. $-4 - 3[2 - (-5 + 3)] - 8 \cdot 2^2$ -48

108. $-6 - 5[-4 - (6 - 12)] + (-5)^2$ 9

109. $-|-1| - |5|$ -6

110. $-|-10| - |6|$ -16

111. $\dfrac{|2 - 9| - |5 - 7|}{10 - 15}$ -1

112. $\dfrac{|-2 + 6| - |3 - 5|}{13 - 11}$ 1

113. $\dfrac{6 - 3[2 - (6 - 8)]^2}{-2|2 - 5|}$ 7

⊚ **114.** $\dfrac{12 - 4[-6 - (5 - 8)]^2}{4|6 - 10|}$ $-\dfrac{3}{2}$

For Exercises 115–120, evaluate the expression for $x = -2$, $y = -4$, and $z = 6$. **(See Example 7.)**

115. $-x^2$ -4

116. x^2 4

117. $4(2x - z)$ -40

118. $6(3x + y)$ -60

119. $\dfrac{3x + 2y}{y}$ $\dfrac{7}{2}$

⊚ **120.** $\dfrac{2z - y}{x}$ -8

121. Is the expression $\dfrac{10}{5x}$ equal to 10/5x? Explain.
No. The first expression is equivalent to $10 \div (5x)$. The second is $10 \div 5 \cdot x$.

122. Is the expression $10/(5x)$ equal to $\dfrac{10}{5x}$? Explain.
Yes, the parentheses indicate that the divisor is the quantity $5x$.

For Exercises 123–130, write each English phrase as an algebraic expression. Then evaluate the expression.

123. The product of -3.75 and 0.3
$-3.75(0.3)$; -1.125

124. The product of -0.4 and -1.258
$(-0.4)(-1.258)$; 0.5032

125. The quotient of $\dfrac{16}{5}$ and $\left(-\dfrac{8}{9}\right)$ $\dfrac{16}{5} \div \left(-\dfrac{8}{9}\right)$; $-\dfrac{18}{5}$

126. The quotient of $\left(-\dfrac{3}{14}\right)$ and $\dfrac{1}{7}$ $-\dfrac{3}{14} \div \dfrac{1}{7}$; $-\dfrac{3}{2}$

 Writing Translating Expression Geometry Scientific Calculator ⊚ Video NS&E

127. The number -0.4 plus the quantity
6 times -0.42 $-0.4 + 6(-0.42); -2.92$

128. The number 0.5 plus the quantity -2 times 0.125
$0.5 + (-2)(0.125); 0.25$

129. The number $-\frac{1}{4}$ minus the quantity
6 times $-\frac{1}{3}$ $-\frac{1}{4} - 6\left(-\frac{1}{3}\right); \frac{7}{4}$

130. Negative five minus the quantity $\left(-\frac{5}{6}\right)$ times $\frac{3}{8}$
$-5 - \left(-\frac{5}{6}\right)\frac{3}{8}; -\frac{75}{16}$

131. For 3 weeks, Jim pays \$2 a week for lottery tickets. Jim has one winning ticket for \$3. Write an expression that describes his net gain or loss. How much money has Jim won or lost? $3(-2) + 3 = -3$; loss of \$3

132. Stephanie pays \$2 a week for 6 weeks for lottery tickets. Stephanie has one winning ticket for \$5. Write an expression that describes her net gain or loss. How much money has Stephanie won or lost?

$-2(6) + 5 = -7$; loss of \$7

133. Evaluate the expressions in parts (a) and (b).

   a. $-4 - 3 - 2 - 1$ -10

   b. $-4(-3)(-2)(-1)$ 24

   c. Explain the difference between the operations in parts (a) and (b).   In part (a), we subtract; in part (b), we multiply.

134. Evaluate the expressions in parts (a) and (b).

   a. $-10 - 9 - 8 - 7$ -34

   b. $-10(-9)(-8)(-7)$ 5040

   c. Explain the difference between the operations in parts (a) and (b).
In part (a), we subtract; in part (b), we multiply.

Problem Recognition Exercises

Adding, Subtracting, Multiplying, and Dividing Real Numbers

Perform the indicated operations.

1.   **a.** $-8 - (-4)$ -4 **b.** $-8(-4)$ 32
   c. $-8 + (-4)$ -12 **d.** $-8 \div (-4)$ 2

2.   **a.** $12 + (-2)$ 10 **b.** $12 - (-2)$ 14
   c. $12(-2)$ -24 **d.** $12 \div (-2)$ -6

3.   **a.** $-36 + 9$ -27 **b.** $-36(9)$ -324
   c. $-36 \div 9$ -4 **d.** $-36 - 9$ -45

4.   **a.** $27 - (-3)$ 30 **b.** $27 + (-3)$ 24
   c. $27(-3)$ -81 **d.** $27 \div (-3)$ -9

5.   **a.** $-5(-10)$ 50 **b.** $-5 + (-10)$ -15
   c. $-5 \div (-10)$ $\frac{1}{2}$ **d.** $-5 - (-10)$ 5

6.   **a.** $-20 \div 4$ -5 **b.** $-20 - 4$ -24
   c. $-20 + 4$ -16 **d.** $-20(4)$ -80

7.   **a.** $-4(-16)$ 64 **b.** $-4 - (-16)$ 12
   c. $-4 \div (-16)$ $\frac{1}{4}$ **d.** $-4 + (-16)$ -20

8.   **a.** $-21 \div 3$ -7 **b.** $-21 - 3$ -24
   c. $-21(3)$ -63 **d.** $-21 + 3$ -18

9.   **a.** $80(-5)$ -400 **b.** $80 - (-5)$ 85
   c. $80 \div (-5)$ -16 **d.** $80 + (-5)$ 75

10. **a.** $-14 - (-21)$ 7 **b.** $-14(-21)$ 294
   c. $-14 \div (-21)$ $\frac{2}{3}$ **d.** $-14 + (-21)$ -35

Properties of Real Numbers and Simplifying Expressions

1. Commutative Properties of Real Numbers

Concepts

When getting dressed, it makes no difference whether you put on your left shoe first and then your right shoe, or vice versa. This example illustrates a process in which the order does not affect the outcome. Such a process or operation is said to be *commutative*.

In algebra, the operations of addition and multiplication are commutative because the order in which we add or multiply two real numbers does not affect the result. For example:

$$10 + 5 = 5 + 10 \quad \text{and} \quad 10 \cdot 5 = 5 \cdot 10$$

1. **Commutative Properties of Real Numbers**
2. **Associative Properties of Real Numbers**
3. **Identity and Inverse Properties of Real Numbers**
4. **Distributive Property of Multiplication over Addition**
5. **Algebraic Expressions**

PROPERTY   Commutative Properties of Real Numbers

If a and b are real numbers, then

1. $a + b = b + a$ **commutative property of addition**

2. $ab = ba$ **commutative property of multiplication**

It is important to note that although the operations of addition and multiplication are commutative, subtraction and division are *not* commutative. For example:

$$\underbrace{10 - 5}_{5} \neq \underbrace{5 - 10}_{-5} \quad \text{and} \quad \underbrace{10 \div 5}_{2} \neq \underbrace{5 \div 10}_{\frac{1}{2}}$$

Example 1   **Applying the Commutative Property of Addition**

Use the commutative property of addition to rewrite each expression.

a. $-3 + (-7)$ **b.** $3x^3 + 5x^4$

Solution:

a. $-3 + (-7) = -7 + (-3)$

b. $3x^3 + 5x^4 = 5x^4 + 3x^3$

Skill Practice Use the commutative property of addition to rewrite each expression.

1. $-5 + 9$ **2.** $7y + x$

Classroom Example: p. 81, Exercise 16

Recall that subtraction is not a commutative operation. However, if we rewrite $a - b$, as $a + (-b)$, we can apply the commutative property of addition. This is demonstrated in Example 2.

Answers

1. $9 + (-5)$ **2.** $x + 7y$

Classroom Example: p. 81, Exercise 24

Example 2 Applying the Commutative Property of Addition

Rewrite the expression in terms of addition. Then apply the commutative property of addition.

a. $5a - 3b$ **b.** $z^2 - \dfrac{1}{4}$

Solution:

a. $5a - 3b$

$= 5a + (-3b)$ Rewrite subtraction as addition of $-3b$.

$= -3b + 5a$ Apply the commutative property of addition.

b. $z^2 - \dfrac{1}{4}$

$= z^2 + \left(-\dfrac{1}{4}\right)$ Rewrite subtraction as addition of $-\frac{1}{4}$.

$= -\dfrac{1}{4} + z^2$ Apply the commutative property of addition.

Skill Practice Rewrite each expression in terms of addition. Then apply the commutative property of addition.

3. $8m - 2n$ **4.** $\dfrac{1}{3}x - \dfrac{3}{4}$

Classroom Example: p. 81, Exercise 22

Example 3 Applying the Commutative Property of Multiplication

Use the commutative property of multiplication to rewrite each expression.

a. $12(-6)$ **b.** $x \cdot 4$

Solution:

a. $12(-6) = -6(12)$

b. $x \cdot 4 = 4 \cdot x$ (or simply $4x$)

Skill Practice Use the commutative property of multiplication to rewrite each expression.

5. $-2(5)$ **6.** $y \cdot 6$

2. Associative Properties of Real Numbers

The associative property of real numbers states that the manner in which three or more real numbers are grouped under addition or multiplication will not affect the outcome. For example:

$$(5 + 10) + 2 = 5 + (10 + 2) \qquad \text{and} \qquad (5 \cdot 10)2 = 5(10 \cdot 2)$$
$$15 + 2 = 5 + 12 \qquad\qquad\qquad\qquad (50)2 = 5(20)$$
$$17 = 17 \qquad\qquad\qquad\qquad\qquad 100 = 100$$

Answers

3. $8m + (-2n); -2n + 8m$

4. $\dfrac{1}{3}x + \left(-\dfrac{3}{4}\right); -\dfrac{3}{4} + \dfrac{1}{3}x$

5. $5(-2)$ **6.** $6y$

> **PROPERTY** **Associative Properties of Real Numbers**
>
> If a, b, and c represent real numbers, then
>
> **1.** $(a + b) + c = a + (b + c)$ **associative property of addition**
>
> **2.** $(ab)c = a(bc)$ **associative property of multiplication**

Example 4   **Applying the Associative Property**

Classroom Examples: p. 81, Exercises 28 and 30

Use the associative property of addition or multiplication to rewrite each expression. Then simplify the expression if possible.

a. $(y + 5) + 6$ **b.** $4(5z)$ **c.** $-\dfrac{3}{2}\left(-\dfrac{2}{3}w\right)$

Solution:

a. $(y + 5) + 6$

    $= y + (5 + 6)$ Apply the associative property of addition.

    $= y + 11$ Simplify.

b. $4(5z)$

    $= (4 \cdot 5)z$ Apply the associative property of multiplication.

    $= 20z$ Simplify.

c. $-\dfrac{3}{2}\left(-\dfrac{2}{3}w\right)$

    $-\left[-\dfrac{3}{2}\left(-\dfrac{2}{3}\right)\right]w$ Apply the associative property of multiplication.

    $= 1w$ Simplify.

    $= w$

Note: In most cases, a detailed application of the associative property will not be shown. Instead, the process will be written in one step, such as

$$(y + 5) + 6 = y + 11, \quad 4(5z) = 20z \quad \text{and} \quad -\dfrac{3}{2}\left(-\dfrac{2}{3}w\right) = w$$

Skill Practice Use the associative property of addition or multiplication to rewrite each expression. Simplify if possible.

7. $(x + 4) + 3$ **8.** $-2(4x)$ **9.** $\dfrac{5}{4}\left(\dfrac{4}{5}t\right)$

3. Identity and Inverse Properties of Real Numbers

The number 0 has a special role under the operation of addition. Zero added to any real number does not change the number. Therefore, the number 0 is said to be the *additive identity* (also called the *identity element of addition*). For example:

$$-4 + 0 = -4 \qquad 0 + 5.7 = 5.7 \qquad 0 + \dfrac{3}{4} = \dfrac{3}{4}$$

Answers

7. $x + (4 + 3)$; $x + 7$
8. $(-2 \cdot 4)x$; $-8x$
9. $\left(\dfrac{5}{4} \cdot \dfrac{4}{5}\right)t$; t

The number 1 has a special role under the operation of multiplication. Any real number multiplied by 1 does not change the number. Therefore, the number 1 is said to be the *multiplicative identity* (also called the *identity element of multiplication*). For example:

$$(-8)1 = -8 \qquad 1(-2.85) = -2.85 \qquad 1\left(\frac{1}{5}\right) = \frac{1}{5}$$

PROPERTY   **Identity Properties of Real Numbers**

If a is a real number, then

   1. $a + 0 = 0 + a = a$ **identity property of addition**

   2. $a \cdot 1 = 1 \cdot a = a$ **identity property of multiplication**

The sum of a number and its opposite equals 0. For example, $-12 + 12 = 0$. For any real number, a, the opposite of a (also called the *additive inverse* of a) is $-a$ and $a + (-a) = -a + a = 0$. The inverse property of addition states that the sum of any number and its additive inverse is the identity element of addition, 0. For example:

Number	Additive Inverse (Opposite)	Sum
9	-9	$9 + (-9) = 0$
-21.6	21.6	$-21.6 + 21.6 = 0$
$\dfrac{2}{7}$	$-\dfrac{2}{7}$	$\dfrac{2}{7} + \left(-\dfrac{2}{7}\right) = 0$

If b is a nonzero real number, then the reciprocal of b (also called the *multiplicative inverse* of b) is $\frac{1}{b}$. The inverse property of multiplication states that the product of b and its multiplicative inverse is the identity element of multiplication, 1. Symbolically, we have $b \cdot \frac{1}{b} = \frac{1}{b} \cdot b = 1$. For example:

Number	Multiplicative Inverse (Reciprocal)	Product
7	$\dfrac{1}{7}$	$7 \cdot \dfrac{1}{7} = 1$
3.14	$\dfrac{1}{3.14}$	$3.14\left(\dfrac{1}{3.14}\right) = 1$
$-\dfrac{3}{5}$	$\dfrac{5}{3}$	$-\dfrac{3}{5}\left(-\dfrac{5}{3}\right) = 1$

PROPERTY   **Inverse Properties of Real Numbers**

If a is a real number and b is a nonzero real number, then

   1. $a + (-a) = -a + a = 0$ **inverse property of addition**

   2. $b \cdot \dfrac{1}{b} = \dfrac{1}{b} \cdot b = 1$ **inverse property of multiplication**

4. Distributive Property of Multiplication over Addition

The operations of addition and multiplication are related by an important property called the **distributive property of multiplication over addition**. Consider the expression $6(2 + 3)$. The order of operations indicates that the sum $2 + 3$ is evaluated first, and then the result is multiplied by 6:

$$6(2 + 3)$$
$$= 6(5)$$
$$= 30$$

Notice that the same result is obtained if the factor of 6 is multiplied by each of the numbers 2 and 3, and then their products are added:

$6(2 + 3)$ The factor of 6 is distributed to the numbers 2 and 3.

$= 6(2) + 6(3)$

$=\ \ 12 + 18$

$=\ \ \ \ 30$

The distributive property of multiplication over addition states that this is true in general.

> **TIP:** The mathematical definition of the distributive property is consistent with the everyday meaning of the word *distribute*. To distribute means to "spread out from one to many." In the mathematical context, the factor a is distributed to both b and c in the parentheses.

PROPERTY **Distributive Property of Multiplication over Addition**

If a, b, and c are real numbers, then

$$a(b + c) = ab + ac \qquad \text{and} \qquad (b + c)a = ab + ac$$

Example 5 **Applying the Distributive Property**

Apply the distributive property: $2(a + 6b + 7)$

Classroom Example: p. 82, Exercise 48

Solution:

$2(a + 6b + 7)$

$-\ 2(a + 6b + 7)$

$= 2(a) + 2(6b) + 2(7)$ Apply the distributive property.

$= 2a + 12b + 14$ Simplify.

Skill Practice Apply the distributive property.

10. $7(x + 4y + z)$

Answer

10. $7x + 28y + 7z$

Because the difference of two expressions $a - b$ can be written in terms of addition as $a + (-b)$, the distributive property can be applied when the operation of subtraction is present within the parentheses. For example:

$$5(y - 7)$$
$$= 5[y + (-7)] \qquad \text{Rewrite subtraction as addition of } -7.$$
$$= 5[y + (-7)] \qquad \text{Apply the distributive property.}$$
$$= 5(y) + 5(-7)$$
$$= 5y + (-35), \text{ or } 5y - 35 \qquad \text{Simplify.}$$

Classroom Example: p. 82, Exercise 60

| Example 6 | Applying the Distributive Property |

Use the distributive property to rewrite each expression.

a. $-(-3a + 2b + 5c)$ **b.** $-6(2 - 4x)$

Solution:

a. $-(-3a + 2b + 5c)$

$$= -1(-3a + 2b + 5c) \qquad \begin{array}{l}\text{The negative sign preceding the} \\ \text{parentheses can be interpreted as} \\ \text{taking the opposite of the} \\ \text{quantity that follows or as}\end{array}$$

$$= -1(-3a + 2b + 5c) \qquad -1(-3a + 2b + 5c)$$

$$= -1(-3a) + (-1)(2b) + (-1)(5c) \qquad \text{Apply the distributive property.}$$

$$= 3a + (-2b) + (-5c) \qquad \text{Simplify.}$$

$$= 3a - 2b - 5c$$

> **TIP:** Notice that a negative factor preceding the parentheses changes the signs of all the terms to which it is multiplied.
>
> $$-1(-3a + 2b + 5c)$$
> $$= +3a - 2b - 5c$$

b. $-6(2 - 4x)$

$$= -6[2 + (-4x)] \qquad \text{Change subtraction to addition of } -4x.$$

$$= -6[2 + (-4x)] \qquad \begin{array}{l}\text{Apply the distributive property. Notice that} \\ \text{multiplying by } -6 \text{ changes the signs of all}\end{array}$$
$$= -6(2) + (-6)(-4x) \qquad \text{terms to which it is applied.}$$

$$= -12 + 24x \qquad \text{Simplify.}$$

Skill Practice Use the distributive property to rewrite each expression.

11. $-(12x + 8y - 3z)$ **12.** $-6(-3a + 7b)$

Note: In most cases, the distributive property will be applied without as much detail as shown in Examples 5 and 6. Instead, the distributive property will be applied in one step.

$$2(a + 6b + 7) \qquad\qquad -(3a + 2b + 5c) \qquad\qquad -6(2 - 4x)$$
$$1\text{ step} = 2a + 12b + 14 \qquad 1\text{ step} = -3a - 2b - 5c \qquad 1\text{ step} = -12 + 24x$$

Answers
11. $-12x - 8y + 3z$
12. $18a - 42b$

5. Algebraic Expressions

A term is a constant or the product or quotient of constants and variables. An algebraic expression is the sum of one or more terms. For example, the expression

$$-7x^2 + xy - 100 \quad \text{or} \quad -7x^2 + xy + (-100)$$

consists of the terms $-7x^2$, xy, and -100.

The terms $-7x^2$ and xy are **variable terms** and the term -100 is called a **constant term**. It is important to distinguish between a term and the factors within a term. For example, the quantity xy is one term, and the values x and y are factors within the term. The constant factor in a term is called the *numerical coefficient* (or simply **coefficient**) of the term. In the terms $-7x^2$, xy, and -100, the coefficients are -7, 1, and -100, respectively.

Terms are *like* terms if they each have the same variables and the corresponding variables are raised to the same powers. For example:

Like Terms	Unlike Terms	
$-3b$ and $5b$	$-5c$ and $7d$	(different variables)
$9p^2q^3$ and p^2q^3	$4p^2q^3$ and $8p^3q^2$	(different powers)
$5w$ and $2w$	$5w$ and 2	(different variables)

Example 7   **Identifying Terms, Factors, Coefficients and *Like* Terms**

Classroom Examples: p. 83, Exercises 82 and 84

a. List the terms of the expression $5x^2 - 3x + 2$.

b. Identify the coefficient of the term $6yz^3$.

c. Which of the pairs are *like* terms: $8b, 3b^2$ or $4c^2d, -6c^2d$?

Solution:

a. The terms of the expression $5x^2 - 3x + 2$ are $5x^2$, $-3x$, and 2.

b. The coefficient of $6yz^3$ is 6.

c. $4c^2d$ and $-6c^2d$ are *like* terms.

Skill Practice

13. List the terms in the expression. $4xy - 9x^7 + 15$
14. Identify the coefficients of each term in the expression. $2a - b + c - 80$
15. Which of the pairs are *like* terms? $5x^3, 5x$ or $-7x^2, 11x^2$

Two terms can be added or subtracted only if they are *like* terms. To add or subtract *like* terms, we use the distributive property as shown in Example 8.

Answers

13. $4xy$, $-9x^2$, 15
14. 2, -1, 1, -80
15. $-7x^2$ and $11x^2$ are *like* terms.

Classroom Example: p. 83,
Exercise 90

Example 8 **Using the Distributive Property to Add and Subtract *Like* Terms**

Add or subtract as indicated.

a. $7x + 2x$ **b.** $-2p + 3p - p$

Solution:

a. $7x + 2x$

$$= (7 + 2)x \qquad \text{Apply the distributive property.}$$

$$= 9x \qquad \text{Simplify.}$$

b. $-2p + 3p - p$

$$= -2p + 3p - 1p \qquad \text{Note that } -p \text{ equals } -1p.$$

$$= (-2 + 3 - 1)p \qquad \text{Apply the distributive property.}$$

$$= (0)p \qquad \text{Simplify.}$$

$$= 0$$

Skill Practice Simplify by adding *like* terms.

16. $8x + 3x$ **17.** $-6a + 4a + a$

Although the distributive property is used to add and subtract *like* terms, it is tedious to write each step. Observe that adding or subtracting *like* terms is a matter of adding or subtracting the coefficients and leaving the variable factors unchanged. This can be shown in one step, a shortcut that we will use throughout the text. For example:

$$7x + 2x = 9x \qquad -2p + 3p - 1p = 0p = 0 \qquad -3a - 6a = -9a$$

Classroom Examples: p. 83,
Exercises 92 and 94

Instructor Note: Ask students why $2x^2 + 3x^2$ is not $5x^4$.

Example 9 **Combining *Like* Terms**

Simplify by combining *like* terms.

a. $3yz + 5 - 2yz + 9$ **b.** $1.2w^3 + 5.7w^3$

Solution:

a. $3yz + 5 - 2yz + 9$

$$= 3yz - 2yz + 5 + 9 \qquad \text{Arrange } like \text{ terms together. Notice that constants such as 5 and 9 are } like \text{ terms.}$$

$$= 1yz + 14 \qquad \text{Combine } like \text{ terms.}$$

$$= yz + 14$$

b. $1.2w^3 + 5.7w^3$

$$= 6.9w^3 \qquad \text{Combine } like \text{ terms.}$$

Skill Practice Simplify by combining *like* terms.

18. $4pq - 7 + 5pq - 8$ **19.** $8.3x^2 + 5.1x^2$

Answers

16. $11x$ **17.** $-a$
18. $9pq - 15$ **19.** $13.4x^2$

When we apply the distributive property, the parentheses are removed. Sometimes this is referred to as *clearing parentheses*. In Examples 10 and 11, we clear parentheses and combine *like* terms.

Example 10 Clearing Parentheses and Combining *Like* Terms

Simplify by *clearing parentheses* and combining *like* terms. $5 - 2(3x + 7)$

Solution:

$5 - 2(3x + 7)$ The order of operations indicates that we must perform multiplication before subtraction.

It is important to understand that a factor of -2 (not 2) will be multiplied to all terms within the parentheses. To see why this is so, we may rewrite the subtraction in terms of addition.

$= 5 + (-2)(3x + 7)$ Change subtraction to addition.

$= 5 + (-2)(3x + 7)$ A factor of -2 is to be distributed to terms in the parentheses.

$= 5 + (-2)(3x) + (-2)(7)$ Apply the distributive property.

$= 5 + (-6x) + (-14)$ Simplify.

$= (-6x) + 5 + (-14)$ Arrange *like* terms together.

$= -6x + (-9)$ Combine *like* terms.

$= -6x - 9$ Simplify by changing addition of the opposite to subtraction.

Skill Practice Clear the parentheses and combine *like* terms.

20. $9 - 5(2x - 7)$

Classroom Example: p. 83, Exercise 104

Example 11 Clearing Parentheses and Combining *Like* Terms

Simplify by clearing parentheses and combining *like* terms.

a. $\dfrac{1}{4}(4k + 2) - \dfrac{1}{2}(6k + 1)$ **b.** $-(4s - 6t) - (3t + 5s) - 2s$

Solution:

a. $\dfrac{1}{4}(4k + 2) - \dfrac{1}{2}(6k + 1)$

$= \dfrac{4}{4}k + \dfrac{2}{4} - \dfrac{6}{2}k - \dfrac{1}{2}$ Apply the distributive property. Notice that a factor of $-\frac{1}{2}$ is distributed through the second parentheses and changes the signs.

$= k + \dfrac{1}{2} - 3k - \dfrac{1}{2}$ Simplify fractions.

$= k - 3k + \dfrac{1}{2} - \dfrac{1}{2}$ Arrange *like* terms together.

$= -2k + 0$ Combine *like* terms.

$= -2k$

Classroom Examples: p. 83, Exercises 108 and 116

Answer

20. $-10x + 44$

b. $-(4s - 6t) - (3t + 5s) - 2s$

$$= -1(4s - 6t) - 1(3t + 5s) - 2s$$ Notice that a factor of -1 is distributed through each parentheses.

$$= -4s + 6t - 3t - 5s - 2s$$ Apply the distributive property.

$$= -4s - 5s - 2s + 6t - 3t$$ Arrange *like* terms together.

$$= -11s + 3t$$ Combine *like* terms.

Skill Practice   Clear the parentheses and combine *like* terms.

21. $\dfrac{1}{2}(8x + 4) + \dfrac{1}{3}(3x - 9)$ **22.** $-4(x + 2y) - (2x - y) - 5x$

Classroom Example: p. 83, Exercise 124

Example 12   Clearing Parentheses and Combining *Like* Terms

Simplify by clearing parentheses and combining *like* terms.

$$-7a - 4[3a - 2(a + 6)] - 4$$

Solution:

$$-7a - 4[3a - 2(a + 6)] - 4$$

$$= -7a - 4[3a - 2a - 12] - 4$$ Apply the distributive property to clear the innermost parentheses.

$$= -7a - 4[a - 12] - 4$$ Simplify within brackets by combining *like* terms.

$$= -7a - 4a + 48 - 4$$ Apply the distributive property to clear the brackets.

$$= -11a + 44$$ Combine *like* terms.

> **Avoiding Mistakes**
>
> First clear the innermost parentheses and combine *like* terms within the brackets. Then use the distributive property to clear the brackets.

Skill Practice   Clear the parentheses and combine *like* terms.

23. $6 - 5[-2y - 4(2y - 5)]$

Answers
21. $5x - 1$ **22.** $-11x - 7y$
23. $50y - 94$

Section 1.7   Practice Exercises

Study Skills Exercises

1. Write down the page number(s) for the Chapter Summary for this chapter. Describe one way in which you can use the Summary found at the end of each chapter.

 Writing   Translating Expression   Geometry   Scientific Calculator   Video   NS&E

2. Define the key terms.

    a. commutative property of addition

    b. commutative property of multiplication

    c. associative property of addition

    d. associative property of multiplication

    e. identity property of addition

    f. identity property of multiplication

    g. inverse property of addition

    h. inverse property of multiplication

    i. distributive property of multiplication over addition

    j. variable term

    k. constant term

    l. coefficient

    m. *like* terms

Review Exercises

For Exercises 3–14, perform the indicated operations.

3. $(-6) + 14$ 8

4. $(-2) + 9$ 7

5. $-13 - (-5)$ -8

6. $-1 - (-19)$ 18

7. $18 \div (-4)$ $-\dfrac{9}{2}$ or -4.5

8. $-27 \div 5$ $-\dfrac{27}{5}$ or -5.4

9. $-3 \cdot 0$ 0

10. $0(-15)$ 0

11. $\dfrac{1}{2} + \dfrac{3}{8}$ $\dfrac{7}{8}$

12. $\dfrac{25}{21} - \dfrac{6}{7}$ $\dfrac{1}{3}$

13. $\left(-\dfrac{3}{5}\right)\left(\dfrac{4}{27}\right)$ $-\dfrac{4}{45}$

14. $\left(-\dfrac{11}{12}\right) \div \left(-\dfrac{5}{4}\right)$ $\dfrac{11}{15}$

Concept 1: Commutative Properties of Real Numbers

For Exercises 15–22, rewrite each expression using the commutative property of addition or the commutative property of multiplication. **(See Examples 1 and 3.)**

15. $5 + (-8)$ $-8 + 5$

16. $7 + (-2)$ $-2 + 7$

17. $8 + x$ $x + 8$

18. $p + 11$ $11 + p$

19. $5(4)$ $4(5)$

20. $10(8)$ $8(10)$

21. $x(-12)$ $-12x$

22. $y(-23)$ $-23y$

For Exercises 23–26, rewrite each expression using addition. Then apply the commutative property of addition. **(See Example 2.)**

23. $x - 3$
    $x + (-3); -3 + x$

24. $y - 7$
    $y + (-7); -7 + y$

25. $4p - 9$
    $4p + (-9); -9 + 4p$

26. $3m - 12$
    $3m + (-12); -12 + 3m$

Concept 2: Associative Properties of Real Numbers

For Exercises 27–38, use the associative property of addition or multiplication to rewrite each expression. Then simplify the expression if possible. **(See Example 4.)**

27. $(x + 4) + 9$
    $x + (4 + 9); x + 13$

28. $-3 + (5 + z)$
    $(-3 + 5) + z; 2 + z$

29. $-5(3x)$ $(\,5 \cdot 3)x; -15x$

30. $12(4z)$ $(\,12 \cdot 4)z; -48z$

31. $\dfrac{6}{11}\left(\dfrac{11}{6}x\right)$ $\left(\dfrac{6}{11} \cdot \dfrac{11}{6}\right)x; x$

32. $\dfrac{3}{5}\left(\dfrac{5}{3}x\right)$ $\left(\dfrac{3}{5} \cdot \dfrac{5}{3}\right)x; x$

33. $-4\left(-\dfrac{1}{4}t\right)$ $\left(-4 \cdot -\dfrac{1}{4}\right)t; t$

34. $-5\left(-\dfrac{1}{5}w\right)$ $\left(-5 \cdot -\dfrac{1}{5}\right)w; w$

35. $-8 + (2 + y)$
    $(-8 + 2) + y; -6 + y$

36. $[x + (-5)] + 7$
    $x + (-5 + 7); x + 2$

37. $-5(2x)$
    $(-5 \cdot 2)x; -10x$

38. $-10(6t)$
    $(-10 \cdot 6)t; -60t$

Concept 3: Identity and Inverse Properties of Real Numbers

39. What is another name for multiplicative inverse?
    Reciprocal

40. What is another name for additive inverse?
    Opposite

41. What is the additive identity?   0

42. What is the multiplicative identity?   1

 Writing   Translating Expression   Geometry   Scientific Calculator   Video   NS&E

Concept 4: Distributive Property of Multiplication over Addition

For Exercises 43–62, use the distributive property to clear parentheses. **(See Examples 5–6.)**

43. $6(5x + 1)$
$30x + 6$

44. $2(x + 7)$
$2x + 14$

45. $-2(a + 8)$
$-2a - 16$

46. $-3(2z + 9)$
$-6z - 27$

47. $3(5c - d)$
$15c - 3d$

48. $4(w - 13z)$
$4w - 52z$

49. $-7(y - 2)$
$-7y + 14$

50. $-2(4x - 1)$
$-8x + 2$

51. $-\dfrac{2}{3}(x - 6)$ $-\dfrac{2}{3}x + 4$

52. $-\dfrac{1}{4}(2b - 8)$ $-\dfrac{1}{2}b + 2$

53. $\dfrac{1}{3}(m - 3)$ $\dfrac{1}{3}m - 1$

54. $\dfrac{2}{5}(n - 5)$ $\dfrac{2}{5}n - 2$

55. $-(2p + 10)$
$-2p - 10$

56. $-(7q + 1)$
$-7q - 1$

57. $-2(-3w - 5z + 8)$
$6w + 10z - 16$

58. $-4(-7a - b - 3)$
$28a + 4b + 12$

59. $4(x + 2y - z)$
$4x + 8y - 4z$

60. $-6(2a - b + c)$
$-12a + 6b - 6c$

61. $-(-6w + x - 3y)$
$6w - x + 3y$

62. $-(-p - 5q - 10r)$
$p + 5q + 10r$

Mixed Exercises

For Exercises 63–70, use the associative property or distributive property to clear parentheses.

63. $2(3 + x)$ $6 + 2x$

64. $5(4 + y)$ $20 + 5y$

65. $4(6z)$ $24z$

66. $8(2p)$ $16p$

67. $-2(7x)$ $-14x$

68. $3(-11t)$ $-33t$

69. $-4(1 + x)$ $-4 - 4x$

70. $-9(2 + y)$ $-18 - 9y$

For Exercises 71–79, match each statement with the property that describes it.

71. $6 \cdot \dfrac{1}{6} = 1$ b

a. Commutative property of addition

72. $7(4 \cdot 9) = (7 \cdot 4)9$ f

b. Inverse property of multiplication

73. $2(3 + k) = 6 + 2k$ i

c. Commutative property of multiplication

74. $3 \cdot 7 = 7 \cdot 3$ c

d. Associative property of addition

75. $5 + (-5) = 0$ g

e. Identity property of multiplication

76. $18 \cdot 1 = 18$ e

f. Associative property of multiplication

77. $(3 + 7) + 19 = 3 + (7 + 19)$ d

g. Inverse property of addition

78. $23 + 6 = 6 + 23$ a

h. Identity property of addition

79. $3 + 0 = 3$ h

i. Distributive property of multiplication over addition

Concept 5: Algebraic Expressions

For Exercises 80–83, for each expression list the terms and their coefficients. **(See Example 7.)**

80. $3xy - 6x^2 + y - 17$

Term	Coefficient
$3xy$	3
$-6x^2$	-6
y	1
-17	-17

81. $2x - y + 18xy + 5$

Term	Coefficient
$2x$	2
$-y$	-1
$18xy$	18
5	5

 Writing   Translating Expression   Geometry   Scientific Calculator   Video   NS&E

82. $x^4 - 10xy + 12 - y$

Term	Coefficient
x^4	1
$-10xy$	-10
12	12
$-y$	-1

83. $-x + 8y - 9x^2y - 3$

Term	Coefficient
$-x$	-1
$8y$	8
$-9x^2y$	-9
-3	-3

84. Explain why $12x$ and $12x^2$ are not *like* terms.
The exponents on x are different.

85. Explain why $3x$ and $3xy$ are not *like* terms.
The variable factors are different.

86. Explain why $7z$ and $\sqrt{13}z$ are *like* terms.
The variables are the same and raised to the same power.

87. Explain why πx and $8x$ are *like* terms.
The variables are the same and raised to the same power.

88. Write three different *like* terms.
For example, $5y, -2y, y$

89. Write three terms that are not *like*.
For example: $5y, -2x, 6$

For Exercises 90–98, simplify by combining *like* terms. **(See Examples 8–9.)**

90. $5k - 10k$ $-5k$

91. $-4p - 2p$ $-6p$

92. $-7x^2 + 14x^2$ $7x^2$

93. $2y^2 - 5y^2 - 3y^2$ $-6y^2$

94. $2ab + 5 + 3ab - 2$ $5ab + 3$

95. $8x^3y + 3 - 7 - x^3y$
$7x^3y - 4$

96. $\frac{1}{4}a + b - \frac{3}{4}a - 5b$ $-\frac{1}{2}a - 4b$

97. $\frac{2}{5} + 2t - \frac{3}{5} + t - \frac{6}{5}$ $3t - \frac{7}{5}$

98. $2.8z - 8.1z + 6 - 15.2$
$-5.3z - 9.2$

For Exercises 99–126, simplify by clearing parentheses and combining *like* terms. **(See Examples 10–12.)**

99. $-3(2x - 4) + 10$
$-6x + 22$

100. $-2(4a + 3) - 14$
$-8a - 20$

101. $4(w + 3) - 12$ $4w$

102. $5(2r + 6) - 30$ $10r$

103. $5 - 3(x - 4)$
$-3x + 17$

104. $4 - 2(3x + 8)$
$-6x - 12$

105. $-3(2t + 4) + 8(2t - 4)$
$10t - 44$

106. $-5(5y + 9) + 3(3y + 6)$
$-16y - 27$

107. $2(w - 5) - (2w + 8)$
-18

108. $6(x + 3) - (6x - 5)$ 23

109. $-\frac{1}{3}(6t + 9) + 10$
$-2t + 7$

110. $-\frac{3}{4}(8 + 4q) + 7$
$-3q + 1$

111. $10(5.1a - 3.1) + 4$
$51a - 27$

112. $100(-3.14p - 1.05) + 212$
$-314p + 107$

113. $-4m + 2(m - 3) + 2m$ -6

114. $-3b + 4(b + 2) - 8b$
$-7b + 8$

115. $\frac{1}{2}(10q - 2) + \frac{1}{3}(2 - 3q)$
$4q - \frac{1}{3}$

116. $\frac{1}{5}(15 - 4p) - \frac{1}{10}(10p + 5)$
$-\frac{9}{5}p + \frac{5}{2}$

117. $7n - 2(n - 3) - 6 + n$ $6n$

118. $8k - 4(k - 1) + 7 - k$
$3k + 11$

119. $6(x + 3) - 12 - 4(x - 3)$
$2x + 18$

120. $5(y - 4) + 3 - 6(y - 7)$
$-y + 25$

121. $6.1(5.3z - 4.1) - 5.8$
$32.33z - 30.81$

122. $-3.6(1.7q - 4.2) + 14.6$
$-6.12q + 29.72$

123. $6 + 2[-8 - 3(2x + 4)] + 10x$
$-2x - 34$

124. $-3 + 5[-3 - 4(y + 2)] - 8y$
$-28y - 58$

125. $1 - 3[2(z + 1) - 5(z - 2)]$
$9z - 35$

126. $1 - 6[3(2t + 2) - 8(t + 2)]$
$12t + 61$

Expanding Your Skills

For Exercises 127–134, determine if the expressions are equivalent. If two expressions are not equivalent, state why.

127. $3a + b, b + 3a$
Equivalent

128. $4y + 1, 1 + 4y$
Equivalent

129. $2c + 7, 9c$
Not equivalent. The terms are not *like* terms and cannot be combined.

130. $5z + 4, 9z$
Not equivalent. The terms are not *like* terms and cannot be combined.

131. $5x - 3, 3 - 5x$
Not equivalent; subtraction is not commutative.

132. $6d - 7, 7 - 6d$
Not equivalent; subtraction is not commutative.

133. $5x - 3, -3 + 5x$
Equivalent

134. $8 - 2x, -2x + 8$
Equivalent

 Writing   Translating Expression   Geometry   Scientific Calculator   Video   NS&E

135. As a small child in school, the great mathematician Karl Friedrich Gauss (1777–1855) was said to have found the sum of the integers from 1 to 100 mentally:

$$1 + 2 + 3 + 4 + \cdots + 99 + 100$$

Rather than adding the numbers sequentially, he added the numbers in pairs:

$$(1 + 99) + (2 + 98) + (3 + 97) + \cdots + 100$$

a. Use this technique to add the integers from 1 to 10.   55

$$1 + 2 + 3 + 4 + 5 + 6 + 7 + 8 + 9 + 10$$

b. Use this technique to add the integers from 1 to 20.   210

Group Activity

Evaluating Formulas Using a Calculator

Materials: A calculator

Estimated Time: 15 minutes

Group Size: 2

In this chapter, we learned one of the most important concepts in mathematics—the order of operations. The proper order of operations is required whenever we evaluate any mathematical expression. The following formulas are taken from applications from science, math, statistics, and business. These are just some samples of what you may encounter as you work your way through college.

For Exercises 1–8, substitute the given values into the formula. Then use a calculator and the proper order of operations to simplify the result. Round to three decimal places if necessary.

1. $F = \dfrac{9}{5}C + 32$ (biology) $C = 35$ $F = 95$

2. $V = \dfrac{nRT}{P}$ (chemistry) $n = 1.00, R = 0.0821, T = 273.15, P = 1.0$ $V = 22.426$

3. $R = k\left(\dfrac{L}{r^2}\right)$ (electronics) $k = 0.05, L = 200, r = 0.5$ $R = 40$

4. $m = \dfrac{y_2 - y_1}{x_2 - x_1}$ (mathematics) $x_1 = -8.3, x_2 = 3.3, y_1 = 4.6, y_2 = -9.2$ $m = -1.190$

5. $z = \dfrac{\bar{x} - \mu}{\dfrac{\sigma}{\sqrt{n}}}$ (statistics) $\bar{x} = 69, \mu = 55, \sigma = 20, n = 25$ $z = 3.5$

6. $S = R\left[\dfrac{(1 + i)^n - 1}{i}\right]$ (finance) $R = 200, i = 0.08, n = 30$ $S = 22{,}656.642$

7. $x = \dfrac{-b + \sqrt{b^2 - 4ac}}{2a}$ (mathematics) $a = 2, b = -7, c = -15$ $x = 5$

8. $h = \dfrac{1}{2}gt^2 + v_0 t + h_0$ (physics) $g = -32, t = 2.4, v_0 = 192, h_0 = 288$ $h = 656.64$

 Writing   Translating Expression   Geometry   Scientific Calculator   Video   NS E

Chapter 1 Summary

Section 1.1 Fractions

Key Concepts	Examples
Simplifying Fractions	**Example 1**

Simplifying Fractions

Divide the numerator and denominator by their greatest common factor.

Example 1

$$\frac{60}{84} = \frac{5 \times \overset{1}{\cancel{12}}}{7 \times \underset{1}{\cancel{12}}} = \frac{5}{7}$$

Multiplication of Fractions

$$\frac{a}{b} \times \frac{c}{d} = \frac{a \times c}{b \times d}$$

Example 2

$$\frac{25}{108} \times \frac{27}{40} = \frac{\overset{5}{\cancel{25}}}{\underset{4}{\cancel{108}}} \times \frac{\overset{1}{\cancel{27}}}{\underset{8}{\cancel{40}}}$$

$$= \frac{5 \times 1}{4 \times 8} = \frac{5}{32}$$

Division of Fractions

$$\frac{a}{b} \div \frac{c}{d} = \frac{a}{b} \times \frac{d}{c}$$

Example 3

$$\frac{95}{49} \div \frac{65}{42} = \frac{\overset{19}{\cancel{95}}}{\underset{7}{\cancel{49}}} \times \frac{\overset{6}{\cancel{42}}}{\underset{13}{\cancel{65}}}$$

$$= \frac{19 \times 6}{7 \times 13} = \frac{114}{91}$$

Addition and Subtraction of Fractions

$$\frac{a}{b} + \frac{c}{b} = \frac{a + c}{b} \quad \text{and} \quad \frac{a}{b} - \frac{c}{b} = \frac{a - c}{b}$$

Example 4

$$\frac{8}{9} + \frac{2}{15} = \frac{8 \times 5}{9 \times 5} + \frac{2 \times 3}{15 \times 3}$$

$$= \frac{40}{45} + \frac{6}{45} = \frac{46}{45}$$

The least common denominator (LCD) of 9 and 15 is 45.

To perform operations on mixed numbers, convert to improper fractions.

Example 5

$$2\frac{5}{6} - 1\frac{1}{3} = \frac{17}{6} - \frac{4}{3}$$

The LCD is 6.

$$= \frac{17}{6} - \frac{4 \times 2}{3 \times 2} = \frac{17}{6} - \frac{8}{6}$$

$$= \frac{9}{6}$$

$$= \frac{3}{2} \text{ or } 1\frac{1}{2}$$

Section 1.2 Sets of Numbers and the Real Number Line

Key Concepts

Natural numbers: $\{1, 2, 3, \ldots\}$

Whole numbers: $\{0, 1, 2, 3, \ldots\}$

Integers: $\{\ldots -3, -2, -1, 0, 1, 2, 3, \ldots\}$

Rational numbers: The set of numbers that can be expressed in the form $\frac{p}{q}$, where p and q are integers and q does not equal 0. In decimal form, rational numbers are terminating or repeating decimals.

Irrational numbers: A subset of the real numbers whose elements cannot be written as a ratio of two integers. In decimal form, irrational numbers are nonterminating, nonrepeating decimals.

Real numbers: The set of both the rational numbers and the irrational numbers.

$a < b$	"a is less than b."
$a > b$	"a is greater than b."
$a \le b$	"a is less than or equal to b."
$a \ge b$	"a is greater than or equal to b."

Two numbers that are the same distance from zero but on opposite sides of zero on the number line are called **opposites**. The opposite of a is denoted $-a$.

The **absolute value** of a real number, a, denoted $|a|$, is the distance between a and 0 on the number line.

If $a \ge 0$, $|a| = a$

If $a < 0$, $|a| = -a$

Examples

Example 1

-5, 0, and 4 are integers.

$-\dfrac{5}{2}$, -0.5, and $0.\overline{3}$ are rational numbers.

$\sqrt{7}$, $-\sqrt{2}$, and π are irrational numbers.

Example 2

All real numbers can be located on the real number line.

Example 3

$5 < 7$	"5 is less than 7."
$-2 > -10$	"-2 is greater than -10."
$y \le 3.4$	"y is less than or equal to 3.4."
$x \ge \frac{1}{2}$	"x is greater than or equal to $\frac{1}{2}$."

Example 4

5 and -5 are opposites.

Example 5

$|7| = 7$

$|-7| = 7$

Section 1.3 Exponents, Square Roots, and the Order of Operations

Key Concepts

A **variable** is a symbol or letter used to represent an unknown number.

A **constant** is a value that is not variable.

An algebraic **expression** is a collection of variables and constants under algebraic operations.

$$b^n = \underbrace{b \cdot b \cdot b \cdot b \cdot \ldots b}_{n \text{ factors of } b}$$ b is the **base**, n is the **exponent**

$\sqrt{x}$ is the positive **square root** of x.

The Order of Operations

1. Simplify expressions within parentheses and other grouping symbols first.
2. Evaluate expressions involving exponents, radicals, and absolute values.
3. Perform multiplication or division in the order that they occur from left to right.
4. Perform addition or subtraction in the order that they occur from left to right.

Examples

Example 1

Variables: x, y, z, a, b

Constants: $2, -3, \pi$

Expressions: $2x + 5, 3a + b^2$

Example 2

$5^3 = 5 \cdot 5 \cdot 5 = 125$

Example 3

$\sqrt{49} = 7$

Example 4

$10 + 5(3 - 1)^2 - \sqrt{5 - 1}$

$= 10 + 5(2)^2 - \sqrt{4}$ Work within grouping symbols.

$= 10 + 5(4) - 2$ Simplify exponents and radicals.

$= 10 + 20 - 2$ Perform multiplication.

$= 30 - 2$ Add and subtract, left to right

$= 28$

Section 1.4 Addition of Real Numbers

Key Concepts

Addition of Two Real Numbers

Same Signs.   Add the absolute values of the numbers and apply the common sign to the sum.

Different Signs.   Subtract the smaller absolute value from the larger absolute value. Then apply the sign of the number having the larger absolute value.

Examples

Example 1

$-3 + (-4) = -7$

$-1.3 + (-9.1) = -10.4$

Example 2

$-5 + 7 = 2$

$\dfrac{2}{3} + \left(-\dfrac{7}{3}\right) = -\dfrac{5}{3}$

Section 1.5   Subtraction of Real Numbers

Key Concepts

Subtraction of Two Real Numbers

Add the opposite of the second number to the first number. That is,

$$a - b = a + (-b)$$

Examples

Example 1

$$7 - (-5) = 7 + (5) = 12$$

$$-3 - 5 = -3 + (-5) = -8$$

$$-11 - (-2) = -11 + (2) = -9$$

Section 1.6   Multiplication and Division of Real Numbers

Key Concepts

Multiplication and Division of Two Real Numbers

Same Signs

Product is positive.

Quotient is positive.

Different Signs

Product is negative.

Quotient is negative.

The **reciprocal** of a nonzero number a is $\frac{1}{a}$.

Multiplication and Division Involving Zero

The product of any real number and 0 is 0.

The quotient of 0 and any nonzero real number is 0.

The quotient of any nonzero real number and 0 is undefined.

Examples

Example 1

$$(-5)(-2) = 10 \qquad \frac{-20}{-4} = 5$$

Example 2

$$(-3)(7) = -21 \qquad \frac{-4}{8} = -\frac{1}{2}$$

Example 3

The reciprocal of -6 is $-\frac{1}{6}$.

Example 4

$$4 \cdot 0 = 0$$

$$0 \div 4 = 0$$

$$4 \div 0 \text{ is undefined.}$$

Section 1.7 Properties of Real Numbers and Simplifying Expressions

Key Concepts

Properties of Real Numbers

Commutative Properties

$a + b = b + a$

$ab = ba$

Associative Properties

$(a + b) + c = a + (b + c)$

$(ab)c = a(bc)$

Identity Properties

$0 + a = a$

$1 \cdot a = a$

Inverse Properties

$a + (-a) = 0$

$b \cdot \dfrac{1}{b} = 1$ for $b \neq 0$

Distributive Property of Multiplication over Addition

$a(b + c) = ab + ac$

A **term** is a constant or the product or quotient of constants and variables. The **coefficient** of a term is the numerical factor of the term.

Like **terms** have the same variables, and the corresponding variables have the same powers.

Terms can be added or subtracted if they are *like* terms. Sometimes it is necessary to clear parentheses before adding or subtracting *like* terms.

Examples

Example 1

$(-5) + (-7) = (-7) + (-5)$

$3 \cdot 8 = 8 \cdot 3$

Example 2

$(2 + 3) + 10 = 2 + (3 + 10)$

$(2 \cdot 4) \cdot 5 = 2 \cdot (4 \cdot 5)$

Example 3

$0 + (-5) = -5$

$1(-8) = -8$

Example 4

$1.5 + (-1.5) = 0$

$6 \cdot \dfrac{1}{6} = 1$

Example 5

$-2(x - 3y) = (-2)x + (-2)(-3y)$

$\qquad\qquad = -2x + 6y$

Example 6

$-2x$ is a term with coefficient -2.

yz^2 is a term with coefficient 1.

$3x$ and $-5x$ are *like* terms.

$4a^2b$ and $4ab$ are not *like* terms.

Example 7

$-2w - 4(w - 2) + 3$

$= -2w - 4w + 8 + 3$ Clear parentheses.

$= -6w + 11$ Combine *like* terms.

Chapter 1   Review Exercises

Section 1.1

For Exercises 1–4, identify as a proper or improper fraction.

1. $\dfrac{14}{5}$ **2.** $\dfrac{1}{6}$ **3.** $\dfrac{3}{3}$ **4.** $\dfrac{7}{1}$

Improper   Proper   Improper   Improper

5. Write 112 as a product of primes. $2 \times 2 \times 2 \times 2 \times 7$

6. Simplify. $\dfrac{84}{70}$ $\dfrac{6}{5}$

For Exercises 7–12, perform the indicated operations.

7. $\dfrac{2}{9} + \dfrac{3}{4}$ $\dfrac{35}{36}$ **8.** $\dfrac{7}{8} - \dfrac{1}{16}$ $\dfrac{13}{16}$ **9.** $\dfrac{21}{24} \times \dfrac{16}{49}$ $\dfrac{2}{7}$

10. $\dfrac{68}{34} \div \dfrac{20}{12}$ $\dfrac{6}{5}$ or $1\dfrac{1}{5}$ **11.** $5\dfrac{1}{3} \div 1\dfrac{7}{9}$ 3 **12.** $3\dfrac{4}{5} - 2\dfrac{1}{10}$ $\dfrac{17}{10}$ or $1\dfrac{7}{10}$

13. The surface area of the Earth is approximately 510 million km². If water covers about $\dfrac{7}{10}$ of the surface, how many square kilometers of the Earth is covered by water?   357 million km²

Section 1.2

14. Given the set $\{7, \frac{1}{3}, -4, 0, -\sqrt{3}, -0.\overline{2}, \pi, 1\}$,

   a. List the natural numbers.   7, 1

   b. List the integers.   7, −4, 0, 1

   c. List the whole numbers.   7, 0, 1

   d. List the rational numbers. $7, \frac{1}{3}, -4, 0, -0.\overline{2}, 1$

   e. List the irrational numbers. $-\sqrt{3}, \pi$

   f. List the real numbers. $7, \frac{1}{3}, -4, 0, -\sqrt{3}, -0.\overline{2}, \pi, 1$

For Exercises 15–18, determine the absolute value.

15. $\left|\dfrac{1}{2}\right|$ **16.** $|-6|$ **17.** $|-\sqrt{7}|$ **18.** $|0|$

$\dfrac{1}{2}$ 6 $\sqrt{7}$ 0

For Exercises 19–27, identify whether the inequality is true or false.

19. $-6 > -1$ **20.** $0 < -5$ **21.** $-10 \leq 0$

False   False   True

22. $5 \neq -5$ **23.** $7 \geq 7$ **24.** $7 \geq -7$

True   True   True

25. $0 \leq -3$ False   **26.** $-\dfrac{2}{3} \leq -\dfrac{2}{3}$ **27.** $|-3| > -|3|$

                     True   True

Section 1.3

↔ For Exercises 28–33, write each English phrase as an algebraic expression.

28. The product of x and $\dfrac{2}{3}$ $x \cdot \dfrac{2}{3}$ or $\dfrac{2}{3}x$

29. The quotient of 7 and y $\dfrac{7}{y}$ or $7 \div y$

30. The sum of 2 and $3b$ $2 + 3b$

31. The difference of a and 5 $a - 5$

32. Two more than $5k$ $5k + 2$

33. Seven less than $13z$ $13z - 7$

For Exercises 34–37, evaluate each expression for $x = 8$, $y = 4$, and $z = 1$.

34. $x - 2y$ 0   **35.** $x^2 - y$ 60

36. $\sqrt{x + z}$ 3   **37.** $\sqrt{x + 2y}$ 4

For Exercises 38–43, simplify the expressions.

38. 6^3 216   **39.** 15^2 225   **40.** $\sqrt{36}$ 6

41. $\dfrac{1}{\sqrt{100}}$ $\dfrac{1}{10}$ **42.** $\left(\dfrac{1}{4}\right)^2$ $\dfrac{1}{16}$ **43.** $\left(\dfrac{3}{2}\right)^3$ $\dfrac{27}{8}$

For Exercises 44–47, perform the indicated operations.

44. $15 - 7 \cdot 2 + 12$ **45.** $|-11| + |5| - (7 - 2)$

13   11

46. $4^2 - (5 - 2)^2$ **47.** $22 - 3(8 \div 4)^2$

7   10

Section 1.4

For Exercises 48–60, add.

48. $-6 + 8$ 2   **49.** $14 + (-10)$ 4

50. $21 + (-6)$ 15   **51.** $-12 + (-5)$ −17

52. $\dfrac{2}{7} + \left(-\dfrac{1}{9}\right)$ $\dfrac{11}{63}$ **53.** $\left(-\dfrac{8}{11}\right) + \left(\dfrac{1}{2}\right)$ $-\dfrac{5}{22}$

54. $\left(-\dfrac{1}{10}\right) + \left(-\dfrac{5}{6}\right)$ $-\dfrac{14}{15}$ **55.** $\left(-\dfrac{5}{2}\right) + \left(-\dfrac{1}{5}\right)$ $-\dfrac{27}{10}$

56. $-8.17 + 6.02$ −2.15   **57.** $2.9 + (-7.18)$ −4.28

 Writing   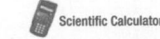 Translating Expression   Geometry   Scientific Calculator   Video   NS&E

58. $13 + (-2) + (-8)$ 3 **59.** $-5 + (-7) + 20$ 8

60. $2 + 5 + (-8) + (-7) + 0 + 13 + (-1)$ 4

61. Under what conditions will the expression $a + b$ be negative? When a and b are both negative or when a and b have different signs and the number with the larger absolute value is negative.

62. Richard's checkbook was overdrawn by $45 (that is, his balance was -45). He deposited $117 but then wrote a check for $80. Was the deposit enough to cover the check? Explain.
No. He is still overdrawn by $8.

Section 1.5

For Exercises 63–75, subtract.

63. $13 - 25$ -12
64. $31 - (-2)$ 33

65. $-8 - (-7)$ -1
66. $-2 - 15$ -17

67. $\left(-\dfrac{7}{9}\right) - \dfrac{5}{6}$ $-\dfrac{29}{18}$
68. $\dfrac{1}{3} - \dfrac{9}{8}$ $-\dfrac{19}{24}$

69. $7 - 8.2$ -1.2
70. $-1.05 - 3.2$ -4.25

71. $-16.1 - (-5.9)$ -10.2
72. $7.09 - (-5)$ 12.09

73. $\dfrac{11}{2} - \left(-\dfrac{1}{6}\right) - \dfrac{7}{3}$ $\dfrac{10}{3}$
74. $-\dfrac{4}{5} - \dfrac{7}{10} - \left(-\dfrac{13}{20}\right)$ $\dfrac{17}{20}$

75. $6 - 14 - (-1) - 10 - (-21) - 5$ -1

76. Under what conditions will the expression $a - b$ be negative? If $a < b$

For Exercises 77–81, write an algebraic expression and simplify.

77. -18 subtracted from -7
$-7 - (-18)$; 11

78. The difference of -6 and 41
$-6 - 41$; -47

79. Seven decreased by 13
$7 - 13$; -6

80. Five subtracted from the difference of 20 and -7
$(20 - (-7)) - 5$; 22

81. The sum of 6 and -12, decreased by 21
$(6 + (-12)) - 21$; -27

82. In Nevada, the highest temperature ever recorded was 125°F and the lowest was -50°F. Find the difference between the highest and lowest temperatures. (*Source: Information Please Almanac*)
175°F

Section 1.6

For Exercises 83–100, multiply or divide as indicated.

83. $10(-17)$ -170
84. $(-7)13$ -91

85. $(-52) \div 26$ -2
86. $(-48) \div (-16)$ 3

87. $\dfrac{7}{4} \div \left(-\dfrac{21}{2}\right)$ $-\dfrac{1}{6}$
88. $\dfrac{2}{3}\left(-\dfrac{12}{11}\right)$ $-\dfrac{8}{11}$

89. $-\dfrac{21}{5} \cdot 0$ 0
90. $\dfrac{3}{4} \div 0$ Undefined

91. $0 \div (-14)$ 0
92. $(-0.45)(-5)$ 2.25

93. $\dfrac{-21}{14}$ $-\dfrac{3}{2}$
94. $\dfrac{-13}{-52}$ $\dfrac{1}{4}$

95. $(5)(-2)(3)$ -30
96. $(-6)(-5)(15)$ 450

97. $\left(-\dfrac{1}{2}\right)\left(\dfrac{7}{8}\right)\left(-\dfrac{4}{7}\right)$ $\dfrac{1}{4}$
98. $\left(\dfrac{12}{13}\right)\left(-\dfrac{1}{6}\right)\left(\dfrac{13}{14}\right)$ $-\dfrac{1}{7}$

99. $40 \div 4 \div (-5)$ -2
100. $\dfrac{10}{11} \div \dfrac{7}{11} \div \dfrac{5}{9}$ $\dfrac{18}{7}$

For Exercises 101–106, perform the indicated operations.

101. $9 - 4[-2(4 - 8) - 5(3 - 1)]$ 17

102. $\dfrac{8(-3) - 6}{-7 - (-2)}$ 6
103. $\dfrac{2}{3} - \left(\dfrac{3}{8} + \dfrac{5}{6}\right) \div \dfrac{5}{3}$ $\dfrac{7}{8}$ (?)

104. $5.4 - (0.3)^2 \div 0.09$ 4.4
105. $\dfrac{5 - [3 \cdot 120(-4)^2]}{36 \div (-2)(3)}$ $-\dfrac{1}{3}$

106. $|-8 + 5| - \sqrt{5^2 - 3^2}$ -1

For Exercises 107–110, evaluate each expression given the values $x = 4$ and $y = -9$.

107. $3(x + 2) \div y$ -2
108. $\sqrt{x} - y$ 11

109. $-xy$ 36
110. $3x + 2y$ -6

111. In statistics, the formula $x = \mu + z\sigma$ is used to find cutoff values for data that follow a bell-shaped curve. Find x if $\mu = 100$, $z = -1.96$, and $\sigma = 15$. 70.6

For Exercises 112–118, answer true or false. If a statement is false, explain why.

112. If n is positive, then $-n$ is negative.   True

113. If m is negative, then m^4 is negative.   False, any nonzero real number raised to an even power is positive.

114. If m is negative, then m^3 is negative.   True

115. If $m > 0$ and $n > 0$, then $mn > 0$.   True

116. If $p < 0$ and $q < 0$, then $pq < 0$.   False, the product of two negative numbers is positive.

117. A number and its reciprocal have the same signs.   True

118. A nonzero number and its opposite have different signs.   True

Section 1.7

For Exercises 119–126, answers may vary.

119. Give an example of the commutative property of addition. For example: $2 + 3 = 3 + 2$

120. Give an example of the associative property of addition. For example: $(2 + 3) + 4 = 2 + (3 + 4)$

121. Give an example of the inverse property of addition. For example: $5 + (-5) = 0$

122. Give an example of the identity property of addition. For example: $7 + 0 = 7$

123. Give an example of the commutative property of multiplication. For example: $5 \cdot 2 = 2 \cdot 5$

124. Give an example of the associative property of multiplication. For example: $(8 \cdot 2)10 = 8(2 \cdot 10)$

125. Give an example of the inverse property of multiplication. For example: $3 \cdot \dfrac{1}{3} = 1$

126. Give an example of the identity property of multiplication. For example: $8 \cdot 1 = 8$

127. Explain why $5x - 2y$ is the same as $-2y + 5x$. $5x - 2y = 5x + (-2y)$, then use the commutative property of addition.

128. Explain why $3a - 9y$ is the same as $-9y + 3a$. $3a - 9y = 3a + (-9y)$, then use the commutative property of addition.

129. List the terms of the expression:
$3y + 10x - 12 + xy$
$3y, 10x, -12, xy$

130. Identify the coefficients for the terms listed in Exercise 129.
$3, 10, -12, 1$

For Exercises 131–132, simplify by combining *like* terms.

131. $3a + 3b - 4b + 5a - 10$
$8a - b - 10$

132. $-6p + 2q + 9 - 13q - p + 7$
$-7p - 11q + 16$

For Exercises 133–134, use the distributive property to clear the parentheses.

133. $-2(4z + 9)$
$-8z - 18$

134. $5(4w - 8y + 1)$
$20w - 40y + 5$

For Exercises 135–140, simplify each expression.

135. $2p - (p + 5) + 3$ $p - 2$

136. $6(h + 3) - 7h - 4$ $-h + 14$

137. $\dfrac{1}{2}(-6q) + q - 4\left(3q + \dfrac{1}{4}\right)$ $-14q - 1$

138. $0.3b + 12(0.2 - 0.5b)$ $-5.7b + 2.4$

139. $-4[2(x + 1) - (3x + 8)]$ $4x + 24$

140. $5[(7y - 3) + 3(y + 8)]$ $50y + 105$

Chapter 1   Test

1. Simplify. $\dfrac{135}{36}$ $\dfrac{15}{4}$

2. Add and subtract. $\dfrac{5}{4} - \dfrac{5}{12} + \dfrac{2}{3}$ $\dfrac{3}{2}$

3. Divide. $4\dfrac{1}{12} \div 1\dfrac{1}{3}$ $3\dfrac{1}{16}$

4. Subtract. $4\dfrac{1}{4} - 1\dfrac{7}{8}$ $2\dfrac{3}{8}$

5. Is $0.\overline{315}$ a rational number or an irrational number? Explain your reasoning. Rational, all repeating decimals are rational numbers.

 Writing   Translating Expression   Geometry   Scientific Calculator   Video   NS&E

6. Plot the points on a number line: $|3|$, 0, -2, 0.5, $\left|-\frac{3}{2}\right|$, $\sqrt{16}$.

$$-2 \qquad 0 \quad \left|-\frac{3}{2}\right| \quad |3| \quad \sqrt{16}$$
$$0\,0.5$$

7. Use the number line in Exercise 6 to identify whether the statements are true or false.

a. $|3| < -2$ False   **b.** $0 \le \left|-\dfrac{3}{2}\right|$ True

c. $-2 < 0.5$ True   **d.** $|3| \ge \left|-\dfrac{3}{2}\right|$ True

8. Use the definition of exponents to expand the expressions:

a. $(4x)^3$ $(4x)(4x)(4x)$ **b.** $4x^3$ $4 \cdot x \cdot x \cdot x$

9. a. Write the expression as an English phrase: $2(a - b)$. (Answers may vary.)
Twice the difference of a and b
b. Write the expression as an English phrase: $2a - b$. (Answers may vary.)
b subtracted from twice a

10. Write the phrase as an algebraic expression: "The quotient of the square root of c and the square of d."
$\dfrac{\sqrt{c}}{d^2}$ or $\sqrt{c} \div d^2$

For Exercises 11–25, perform the indicated operations.

11. $18 + (-12)$ 6 **12.** $-15 - (-3)$ -12

13. $21 - (-7)$ 28 **14.** $-\dfrac{1}{8} + \left(-\dfrac{3}{4}\right)$ $-\dfrac{7}{8}$

15. $-10.06 - (-14.72)$ 4.66 **16.** $-14 + (-2) - 16$ -32

17. $-84 \div 7$ -12 **18.** $38 \div 0$ Undefined

19. $7(-4)$ -28 **20.** $-22 \cdot 0$ 0

21. $(-16)(-2)(-1)(-3)$ 96 **22.** $\dfrac{2}{5} \div \left(-\dfrac{7}{10}\right) \cdot \left(-\dfrac{7}{6}\right)$ $\dfrac{2}{3}$

23. $(8 - 10) \cdot \dfrac{3}{2} + (-5)$ -8

24. $8 - [(2 - 4) - (8 - 9)]$ 9

25. $\dfrac{\sqrt{5^2 - 4^2}}{|-12 + 3|}$ $\dfrac{1}{3}$

26. The average high temperature in January for Nova Scotia, Canada, is $-1.2°C$. The average low is $-10.7°C$. Find the difference between the average high and the average low.
The difference is $9.5°C$.

27. In the third quarter of a football game, a quarterback made a 5-yd gain, a 2-yd gain, a 10-yd loss, and then a 4-yd gain.

a. Write an expression using addition to describe the quarterback's movement.
$5 + 2 + (-10) + 4$
b. Evaluate the expression from part (a) to determine the quarterback's gain or loss in yards.   He gained 1 yd.

28. Identify the property that justifies each statement.

a. $6(-8) = (-8)6$ **b.** $5 + 0 = 5$
Commutative property of multiplication   Identity property of addition
c. $(2 + 3) + 4 = 2 + (3 + 4)$
Associative property of addition

d. $\dfrac{1}{7} \cdot 7 = 1$ **e.** $8[7(-3)] = (8 \cdot 7)(-3)$
Inverse property of multiplication   Associative property of multiplication

For Exercises 29–33, simplify each expression.

29. $-5x - 4y + 3 - 7x + 6y - 7$ $-12x + 2y - 4$

30. $-3(4m + 8p - 7)$ $-12m - 24p + 21$

31. $3k - 20 + (-9k) + 12$ $-6k - 8$

32. $4(p - 5) - (8p + 3)$ $-4p - 23$

33. $\dfrac{1}{2}(12p - 4) + \dfrac{1}{3}(2 - 6p)$ $4p - \dfrac{4}{3}$

For Exercises 34–37, evaluate each expression given the values $x = 4$ and $y = -3$ and $z = -7$.

34. $y^2 - x$ 5 **35.** $3x - 2y$ 18

36. $y(x - 2)$ 6 **37.** $-y^2 - 4x + z$ 32

For Exercises 38–40, write each English statement as an algebraic expression. Then simplify the expression.

38. Subtract -4 from 12 $12 - (-4)$; 16

39. Find the difference of 6 and 8 $6 - 8$; -2

40. The quotient of 10 and -12 $\dfrac{10}{-12}$; $-\dfrac{5}{6}$

Linear Equations and Inequalities

2

CHAPTER OUTLINE

Chapter 2

In Chapter 2, we learn how to solve linear equations and inequalities in one variable.

Are You Prepared?

One of the skills we need involves multiplying by fractions and decimals. The following set of problems will review that skill. For help with multiplying fractions, see Section 1.1. For help with multiplying decimals, see Section A.1 in the appendix.

   Simplify each expression and fill in the blank with the correct answer written as a word. Then fill the word into the puzzle. The words will fit in the puzzle according to the number of letters each word has.

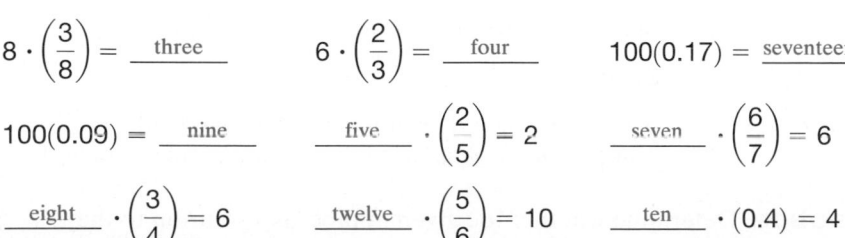

$8 \cdot \left(\dfrac{3}{8}\right) = \underline{\text{three}}$ $6 \cdot \left(\dfrac{2}{3}\right) = \underline{\text{four}}$ $100(0.17) = \underline{\text{seventeen}}$

$100(0.09) = \underline{\text{nine}}$ $\underline{\text{five}} \cdot \left(\dfrac{2}{5}\right) = 2$ $\underline{\text{seven}} \cdot \left(\dfrac{6}{7}\right) = 6$

$\underline{\text{eight}} \cdot \left(\dfrac{3}{4}\right) = 6$ $\underline{\text{twelve}} \cdot \left(\dfrac{5}{6}\right) = 10$ $\underline{\text{ten}} \cdot (0.4) = 4$

Concepts

1. Definition of a Linear Equation in One Variable
2. Addition and Subtraction Properties of Equality
3. Multiplication and Division Properties of Equality
4. Translations

1. Definition of a Linear Equation in One Variable

An *equation* is a statement that indicates that two quantities are equal. The following are equations.

$$x = 5 \qquad y + 2 = 12 \qquad -4z = 28$$

All equations have an equal sign. Furthermore, notice that the equal sign separates the equation into two parts, the left-hand side and the right-hand side. A **solution to an equation** is a value of the variable that makes the equation a true statement. Substituting a solution into an equation for the variable makes the right-hand side equal to the left-hand side.

Equation	Solution	Check	
$x = 5$	5	$x = 5$ $\downarrow$ $5 = 5$ ✔	Substitute 5 for x. Right-hand side equals left-hand side.
$y + 2 = 12$	10	$y + 2 = 12$ $\downarrow$ $10 + 2 = 12$ ✔	Substitute 10 for y. Right-hand side equals left-hand side.
$-4z = 28$	-7	$-4z = 28$ $\downarrow$ $-4(-7) = 28$ ✔	Substitute -7 for z. Right-hand side equals left-hand side.

Avoiding Mistakes

Be sure to notice the difference between solving an equation versus simplifying an expression. For example, $2x + 1 = 7$ is an equation, whose solution is 3, while $2x + 1 + 7$ is an expression that simplifies to $2x + 8$.

Classroom Examples: p. 106, Exercises 10 and 14

Example 1 Determining Whether a Number Is a Solution to an Equation

Determine whether the given number is a solution to the equation.

a. $4x + 7 = 5$; $-\frac{1}{2}$ **b.** $-6w + 14 = 4$; 3

Solution:

a. $\qquad 4x + 7 = 5$

$4\left(-\frac{1}{2}\right) + 7 \stackrel{?}{=} 5$ Substitute $-\frac{1}{2}$ for x.

$-2 + 7 \stackrel{?}{=} 5$ Simplify.

$5 \stackrel{?}{=} 5$ ✔ Right-hand side equals the left-hand side. Thus, $-\frac{1}{2}$ *is a solution* to the equation $4x + 7 = 5$.

b. $-6w + 14 = 4$

$-6(3) + 14 \stackrel{?}{=} 4$ Substitute 3 for w.

$-18 + 14 \stackrel{?}{=} 4$ Simplify.

$-4 \neq 4$ Right-hand side does not equal left-hand side. Thus, 3 *is not a solution* to the equation $-6w + 14 = 4$.

Skill Practice Determine whether the given number is a solution to the equation.

1. $4x - 1 = 7$; 3 **2.** $-2y + 5 = 9$; -2

Answers

1. No **2.** Yes

The set of all solutions to an equation is called the **solution set** and is written with set braces. For example, the solution set for Example 1(a) is $\{-\frac{1}{2}\}$.

In the study of algebra, you will encounter a variety of equations. In this chapter, we will focus on a specific type of equation called a linear equation in one variable.

DEFINITION   Linear Equation in One Variable

Let a and b be real numbers such that $a \neq 0$. A **linear equation in one variable** is an equation that can be written in the form

$$ax + b = 0$$

Notice that a linear equation in one variable has only one variable. Furthermore, because the variable has an implied exponent of 1, a linear equation is sometimes called a *first-degree equation*.

Linear Equation in One Variable	*Not* a Linear Equation in One Variable
$2x + 3 = 0$	$4x^2 + 8 = 0$ (exponent for x is not 1)
$\frac{1}{5}a + \frac{2}{7} = 0$	$\frac{3}{4}a + \frac{5}{8}b = 0$ (more than one variable)

2. Addition and Subtraction Properties of Equality

If two equations have the same solution set, then the equations are equivalent. For example, the following equations are equivalent because the solution set for each equation is $\{6\}$.

Equivalent Equations	Check the Solution 6
$2x - 5 = 7 \longrightarrow$	$2(6) - 5 \overset{?}{=} 7 \Rightarrow 12 - 5 \overset{?}{=} 7 \checkmark$
$2x = 12 \longrightarrow$	$2(6) \overset{?}{=} 12 \Rightarrow \quad 12 \overset{?}{=} 12 \checkmark$
$x = 6 \longrightarrow$	$6 \overset{?}{=} 6 \Rightarrow \quad 6 \overset{?}{=} 6 \checkmark$

To solve a linear equation, $ax + b = 0$, the goal is to find *all* values of x that make the equation true. One general strategy for solving an equation is to rewrite it as an equivalent but simpler equation. This process is repeated until the equation can be written in the form $x = $ number. We call this "isolating the variable." The addition and subtraction properties of equality help us isolate the variable.

PROPERTY   Addition and Subtraction Properties of Equality

Let a, b, and c represent algebraic expressions.

1. **Addition property of equality:**   If $\qquad a = b,$
   then $\quad a + c = b + c$

2. ***Subtraction property of equality:**   If $\qquad a = b,$
   then $\quad a - c = b - c$

*The subtraction property of equality follows directly from the addition property, because subtraction is defined in terms of addition.

If $\quad a + (-c) = b + (-c)$

then, $\quad a - c = b - c$

The addition and subtraction properties of equality indicate that adding or subtracting the same quantity on each side of an equation results in an equivalent equation. This is true because if two equal quantities are increased or decreased by the same amount, then the resulting quantities will also be equal (Figure 2-1).

Figure 2-1

Classroom Examples: p. 106,
Exercises 16 and 18

Example 2   **Applying the Addition and Subtraction Properties of Equality**

Solve the equations.

a. $p - 4 = 11$ **b.** $w + 5 = -2$

Solution:

In each equation, the goal is to isolate the variable on one side of the equation. To accomplish this, we use the fact that the sum of a number and its opposite is zero and the difference of a number and itself is zero.

a. $p - 4 = 11$

$p - 4 + 4 = 11 + 4$ To isolate p, add 4 to both sides $(-4 + 4 = 0)$.

$p + 0 = 15$ Simplify.

$p = 15$ Check by substituting $p = 15$ into the original equation.

Check: $p - 4 = 11$

$15 - 4 \stackrel{?}{=} 11$

The solution set is {15}. $11 \stackrel{?}{=} 11$ ✔   True

b. $w + 5 = -2$

$w + 5 - 5 = -2 - 5$ To isolate w, subtract 5 from both sides. $(5 - 5 = 0)$.

$w + 0 = -7$ Simplify.

$w = -7$ Check by substituting $w = -7$ into the original equation.

Check: $w + 5 = -2$

$-7 + 5 \stackrel{?}{=} -2$

The solution set is {−7}. $-2 \stackrel{?}{=} -2$ ✔   True

Skill Practice Solve the equations.

3. $v - 7 = 2$ **4.** $x + 4 = 4$

Answers
3. {9}   **4.** {0}

| **Example 3** | **Applying the Addition and Subtraction Properties of Equality** |

Classroom Examples: p. 106, Exercises 30 and 32

Solve the equations.

a. $\dfrac{9}{4} = q - \dfrac{3}{4}$ **b.** $-1.2 + z = 4.6$

Solution:

a. $\dfrac{9}{4} = q - \dfrac{3}{4}$

$\dfrac{9}{4} + \dfrac{3}{4} = q - \dfrac{3}{4} + \dfrac{3}{4}$ To isolate q, add $\frac{3}{4}$ to both sides $(-\frac{3}{4} + \frac{3}{4} = 0)$.

$\dfrac{12}{4} = q + 0$ Simplify.

$3 = q$ or equivalently, $q = 3$

> **TIP:** The variable may be isolated on either side of the equation.

Check: $\dfrac{9}{4} = q - \dfrac{3}{4}$

$\dfrac{9}{4} \overset{?}{=} 3 - \dfrac{3}{4}$ Substitute $q = 3$.

$\dfrac{9}{4} \overset{?}{=} \dfrac{12}{4} - \dfrac{3}{4}$ Common denominator

The solution set is {3}. $\dfrac{9}{4} \overset{?}{=} \dfrac{9}{4}$ ✔ True

b. $-1.2 + z = 4.6$

$-1.2 + 1.2 + z = 4.6 + 1.2$ To isolate z, add 1.2 to both sides.

$0 + z = 5.8$

$z = 5.8$ Check: $-1.2 + z = 4.6$

$-1.2 + 5.8 \overset{?}{=} 4.6$ Substitute $z = 5.8$.

The solution set is {5.8}. $4.6 \overset{?}{=} 4.6$ ✔ True

Skill Practice Solve the equations.

5. $\dfrac{1}{4} = a - \dfrac{2}{3}$ **6.** $-8.1 + w = 11.5$

3. Multiplication and Division Properties of Equality

Adding or subtracting the same quantity to both sides of an equation results in an equivalent equation. In a similar way, multiplying or dividing both sides of an equation by the same nonzero quantity also results in an equivalent equation. This is stated formally as the multiplication and division properties of equality.

Answers

5. $\left\{\dfrac{11}{12}\right\}$ **6.** {19.6}

PROPERTY Multiplication and Division Properties of Equality

Let a, b, and c represent algebraic expressions.

1. **Multiplication property of equality:**   If $\quad a = b,$
   then $\quad ac = bc$

2. ***Division property of equality:***   If $\quad a = b$
   then $\quad \dfrac{a}{c} = \dfrac{b}{c}$ (provided $c \neq 0$)

*The division property of equality follows directly from the multiplication property because division is defined as multiplication by the reciprocal.

If $\quad a \cdot \dfrac{1}{c} = b \cdot \dfrac{1}{c} \quad (c \neq 0)$

then, $\quad \dfrac{a}{c} = \dfrac{b}{c}$

To understand the multiplication property of equality, suppose we start with a true equation such as $10 = 10$. If both sides of the equation are multiplied by a constant such as 3, the result is also a true statement (Figure 2-2).

$10 = 10$

$3 \cdot 10 = 3 \cdot 10$

$30 = 30$

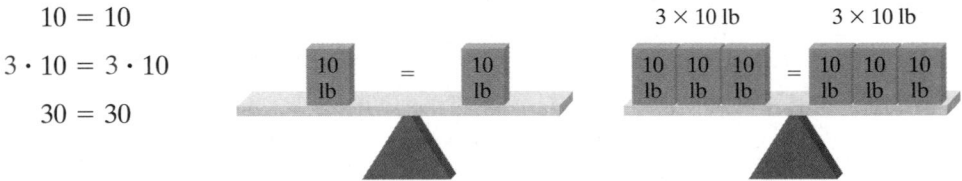

Figure 2-2

Similarly, if both sides of the equation are divided by a nonzero real number such as 2, the result is also a true statement (Figure 2-3).

$10 = 10$

$\dfrac{10}{2} = \dfrac{10}{2}$

$5 = 5$

Figure 2-3

TIP: The product of a number and its reciprocal is always 1. For example:

$\dfrac{1}{5}(5) = 1$

$-\dfrac{7}{2}\left(-\dfrac{2}{7}\right) = 1$

To solve an equation in the variable x, the goal is to write the equation in the form $x = $ number. In particular, notice that we desire the coefficient of x to be 1. That is, we want to write the equation as $1x = $ number. Therefore, to solve an equation such as $5x = 15$, we can multiply both sides of the equation by the reciprocal of the x-term coefficient. In this case, multiply both sides by the reciprocal of 5, which is $\frac{1}{5}$.

$$5x = 15$$

$$\frac{1}{5}(5x) = \frac{1}{5}(15) \qquad \text{Multiply by } \frac{1}{5}.$$

$$1x = 3 \qquad \text{The coefficient of the } x\text{-term is now 1.}$$

$$x = 3$$

The division property of equality can also be used to solve the equation $5x = 15$ by dividing both sides by the coefficient of the x-term. In this case, divide both sides by 5 to make the coefficient of x equal to 1.

$$5x = 15$$

$$\frac{5x}{5} = \frac{15}{5} \qquad \text{Divide by 5.}$$

$$1x = 3 \qquad \text{The coefficient of the } x\text{-term is now 1.}$$

$$x = 3$$

> **TIP:** The quotient of a nonzero real number and itself is always 1. For example:
>
> $$\frac{5}{5} = 1$$
>
> $$\frac{-3.5}{-3.5} = 1$$

Example 4 Applying the Division Property of Equality

Solve the equations using the division property of equality.

a. $12x = 60$ **b.** $48 = -8w$ **c.** $-x = 8$

Classroom Examples: p. 106, Exercises 38 and 50

Solution:

a. $12x = 60$

$$\frac{12x}{12} = \frac{60}{12} \qquad \text{To obtain a coefficient of 1 for the } x\text{-term,}$$
$$\text{divide both sides by 12.}$$

$$1x = 5 \qquad \text{Simplify.}$$

$$x = 5 \qquad \underline{\text{Check:}} \quad 12x = 60$$

$$12(5) \stackrel{?}{=} 60$$

The solution set is $\{5\}$. $\qquad 60 \stackrel{?}{=} 60 \checkmark \quad$ True

b. $48 = -8w$

$$\frac{48}{-8} = \frac{-8w}{-8} \qquad \text{To obtain a coefficient of 1 for the } w\text{-term, divide}$$
$$\text{both sides by } -8.$$

$$-6 = 1w \qquad \text{Simplify.}$$

$$-6 = w \qquad \underline{\text{Check:}} \ 48 = -8w$$

$$48 \stackrel{?}{=} -8(-6)$$

The solution set is $\{-6\}$. $\qquad 48 \stackrel{?}{=} 48 \checkmark \quad$ True

c. $-x = 8 \qquad$ Note that $-x$ is equivalent to $-1 \cdot x$.

$$-1x = 8$$

$$\frac{-1x}{-1} = \frac{8}{-1} \qquad \text{To obtain a coefficient of 1 for the } x\text{-term, divide}$$
$$\text{by } -1.$$

$$x = -8 \qquad \underline{\text{Check:}} \ -x = 8$$

$$-(-8) \stackrel{?}{=} 8$$

The solution set is $\{-8\}$. $\qquad 8 \stackrel{?}{=} 8 \checkmark \quad$ True

> **TIP:** In Example 4(c), we could also have *multiplied* both sides by -1 to create a coefficient of 1 on the x-term.
>
> $$-x = 8$$
>
> $$(-1)(-x) = (-1)8$$
>
> $$x = -8$$

Skill Practice Solve the equations.

7. $4x = -20$ **8.** $100 = -4p$ **9.** $-y = -11$

Classroom Example: p. 106, Exercise 46

Example 5 Applying the Multiplication Property of Equality

Solve the equation by using the multiplication property of equality.

$$-\frac{2}{9}q = \frac{1}{3}$$

Solution:

$$-\frac{2}{9}q = \frac{1}{3}$$

$$\left(\frac{9}{2}\right)\left(-\frac{2}{9}q\right) = \frac{1}{3}\left(\frac{9}{2}\right) \qquad \text{To obtain a coefficient of 1 for the } q\text{-term,}$$
$$\text{multiply by the reciprocal of } -\frac{2}{9}, \text{ which is } -\frac{9}{2}.$$

$$1q = -\frac{9}{6} \qquad \text{The product of a number and its reciprocal is 1.}$$

$$1q = -\frac{3}{2} \qquad \text{Simplify.}$$

$$q = -\frac{3}{2} \qquad \underline{\text{Check:}} \quad -\frac{2}{9}q = \frac{1}{3}$$

$$-\frac{2}{9}\left(-\frac{3}{2}\right) \stackrel{?}{=} \frac{1}{3}$$

The solution set is $\left\{-\frac{3}{2}\right\}$. $\qquad \frac{1}{3} \stackrel{?}{=} \frac{1}{3}$ ✔ True

Skill Practice Solve the equation.

10. $-\frac{2}{3}a = \frac{1}{4}$

TIP: When applying the multiplication or division property of equality to obtain a coefficient of 1 for the variable term, we will generally use the following convention:

- If the coefficient of the variable term is expressed as a fraction, we will usually multiply both sides by its reciprocal, as in Example 5.
- If the coefficient of the variable term is an integer or decimal, we will divide both sides by the coefficient itself, as in Example 6.

Classroom Example: p. 106, Exercise 52

Example 6 Applying the Division Property of Equality

Solve the equation by using the division property of equality.

$$-3.43 = -0.7z$$

Solution:

$$-3.43 = -0.7z$$

$$\frac{-3.43}{-0.7} = \frac{-0.7z}{-0.7} \qquad \text{To obtain a coefficient of 1 for the } z\text{-term,}$$
$$\text{divide by } -0.7.$$

$$4.9 = 1z \qquad \text{Simplify.}$$

$$4.9 = z$$

Answer

10. $\left\{-\frac{3}{8}\right\}$

$z = 4.9$ <u>Check:</u> $-3.43 = -0.7z$

$$-3.43 \overset{?}{=} -0.7(4.9)$$

The solution set is $\{4.9\}$. $-3.43 \overset{?}{=} -3.43$ ✔   True

Skill Practice Solve the equation.

11. $6.82 = 2.2w$

Example 7 **Applying the Multiplication Property of Equality**

Solve the equation by using the multiplication property of equality.

$$\frac{d}{6} = -4$$

Classroom Example: p. 106, Exercise 42

Solution:

$$\frac{d}{6} = -4$$

$$\frac{1}{6}d = -4 \qquad\qquad \frac{d}{6} \text{ is equivalent to } \frac{1}{6}d.$$

$$\frac{6}{1} \cdot \frac{1}{6}d = -4 \cdot \frac{6}{1} \qquad \text{To obtain a coefficient of 1 for the } d\text{-term,} \\ \text{multiply by the reciprocal of } \frac{1}{6}, \text{ which is } \frac{6}{1}.$$

$$1d = -24 \qquad\qquad \text{Simplify.}$$

$$d = -24 \qquad\qquad \underline{\text{Check:}} \; \frac{d}{6} = -4$$

$$\frac{-24}{6} \overset{?}{=} 4$$

The solution set is $\{-24\}$. $-4 \overset{?}{=} -4$ ✔   True

Instructor Note: Remind students that dividing by a number is the same as multiplying by its reciprocal. Thus, $\frac{d}{6} = \frac{1}{6}d$

Skill Practice Solve the equation.

12. $\dfrac{x}{5} = -8$

It is important to distinguish between cases where the addition or subtraction properties of equality should be used to isolate a variable versus those in which the multiplication or division property of equality should be used. Remember the goal is to isolate the variable term and obtain a coefficient of 1. Compare the equations:

$$5 + x = 20 \qquad \text{and} \qquad 5x = 20$$

In the first equation, the relationship between 5 and x is addition. Therefore, we want to reverse the process by subtracting 5 from both sides. In the second equation, the relationship between 5 and x is multiplication. To isolate x, we reverse the process by dividing by 5 or equivalently, multiplying by the reciprocal, $\frac{1}{5}$.

$$5 + x = 20 \qquad\qquad \text{and} \qquad 5x = 20$$

$$5 - 5 + x = 20 - 5 \qquad\qquad \frac{5x}{5} = \frac{20}{5}$$

$$x = 15 \qquad\qquad\qquad x = 4$$

Answers
11. $\{3.1\}$ **12.** $\{-40\}$

4. Translations

We have already practiced writing an English sentence as a mathematical equation. Recall from Section 1.3 that several key words translate to the algebraic operations of addition, subtraction, multiplication, and division.

Classroom Examples: p. 106, Exercises 60 and 62

Example 8 Translating to a Linear Equation

Write an algebraic equation to represent each English sentence. Then solve the equation.

a. The quotient of a number and 4 is 6.

b. The product of a number and 4 is 6.

c. Negative twelve is equal to the sum of -5 and a number.

d. The value 1.4 subtracted from a number is 5.7.

Solution:

For each case we will let x represent the unknown number.

a. The quotient of a number and 4 is 6.

> **Avoiding Mistakes**
> Do not confuse the word "and" with sum. "And" identifies which numbers are being affected by one of the four basic operations.

$$\frac{x}{4} = 6$$

$$4 \cdot \frac{x}{4} = 4 \cdot 6 \qquad \text{Multiply both sides by 4.}$$

$$\frac{4}{1} \cdot \frac{x}{4} = 4 \cdot 6$$

$$x = 24 \qquad \text{Check:} \quad \frac{24}{4} \stackrel{?}{=} 6 \; ✔ \quad \text{True}$$

The number is 24.

b. The product of a number and 4 is 6.

$$4x = 6$$

$$\frac{4x}{4} = \frac{6}{4} \qquad \text{Divide both sides by 4.}$$

$$x = \frac{3}{2} \qquad \text{Check:} \quad 4\left(\frac{3}{2}\right) \stackrel{?}{=} 6 \; ✔ \quad \text{True}$$

The number is $\frac{3}{2}$.

c. Negative twelve is equal to the sum of -5 and a number.

$$-12 = -5 + x$$

$$-12 + 5 = -5 + 5 + x \qquad \text{Add 5 to both sides.}$$

$$-7 = x \qquad\qquad \text{Check:} \quad -12 \stackrel{?}{=} -5 + (-7) \; ✔ \quad \text{True}$$

The number is -7.

d. The value 1.4 subtracted from a number is 5.7.

$$x - 1.4 = 5.7$$

$$x - 1.4 + 1.4 = 5.7 + 1.4 \qquad \text{Add 1.4 to both sides.}$$

$$x = 7.1 \qquad \text{Check: } 7.1 - 1.4 \overset{?}{=} 5.7 \ ✔ \quad \text{True}$$

The number is 7.1.

Skill Practice Write an algebraic equation to represent each English sentence. Then solve the equation.

13. The quotient of a number and -2 is 8.
14. The product of a number and -3 is -24.
15. The sum of a number and 6 is -20.
16. 13 is equal to 5 subtracted from a number.

Answers

13. $\dfrac{x}{-2} = 8$; The number is -16.
14. $-3x = -24$; The number is 8.
15. $y + 6 = -20$; The number is -26.
16. $13 = x - 5$; The number is 18.

Section 2.1   Practice Exercises

Study Skills Exercises

1. After getting a test back, it is a good idea to correct the test so that you do not make the same errors again. One recommended approach is to use a clean sheet of paper, and divide the paper down the middle vertically as shown. For each problem that you missed on the test, rework the problem correctly on the left-hand side of the paper. Then give a written explanation on the right-hand side of the paper. To reinforce the correct procedure, do four more problems of that type.

Take the time this week to make corrections from your last test.

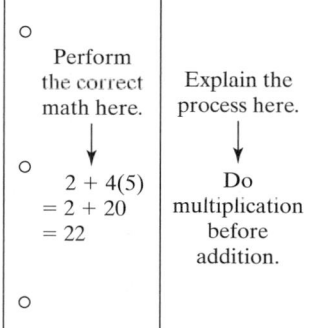

2. Define the key terms.

 a. linear equation in one variable   **b. solution to an equation**

 c. solution set   **d. addition property of equality**

 e. subtraction property of equality   **f. multiplication property of equality**

 g. division property of equality

Concept 1: Definition of a Linear Equation in One Variable

For Exercises 3–6, identify the following as either an expression or an equation.

3. $x - 4 + 5x$ **4.** $8x + 2 = 7$ **5.** $9 = 2x - 4$ **6.** $3x^2 + x = -3$
 Expression   Equation   Equation   Equation

7. Explain how to determine if a number is a solution to an equation.
 Substitute the value into the equation and determine if the right-hand side is equal to the left-hand side.

8. Explain why the equations $6x = 12$ and $x = 2$ are *equivalent equations*.
 They are equivalent equations because their solution sets are the same. The solution set is {2} in both cases.

For Exercises 9–14, determine whether the given number is a solution to the equation. **(See Example 1.)**

9. $x - 1 = 5$; 4   No   **10.** $x - 2 = 1$; -1 No   **11.** $5x = -10$; -2 Yes

12. $3x = 21$; 7   Yes   **13.** $3x + 9 = 3$; -2 Yes   **14.** $2x - 1 = -3$; -1 Yes

Concept 2: Addition and Subtraction Properties of Equality

For Exercises 15–34, solve each equation using the addition or subtraction property of equality. Be sure to check your answers. **(See Examples 2–3.)**

15. $x + 6 = 5$ $\{-1\}$ **16.** $x - 2 = 10$ $\{12\}$ **17.** $q - 14 = 6$ $\{20\}$ **18.** $w + 3 = -5$ $\{-8\}$

19. $2 + m = -15$ $\{-17\}$ **20.** $-6 + n = 10$ $\{16\}$ **21.** $-23 = y - 7$ $\{-16\}$ **22.** $-9 = -21 + b$ $\{12\}$

23. $4 + c = 4$ $\{0\}$ **24.** $-13 + b = -13$ $\{0\}$ **25.** $4.1 = 2.8 + a$ $\{1.3\}$ **26.** $5.1 = -2.5 + y$ $\{7.6\}$

27. $5 = z - \dfrac{1}{2}$ $\left\{\dfrac{11}{2}\right\}$ or $\left\{5\dfrac{1}{2}\right\}$ **28.** $-7 = p + \dfrac{2}{3}$ $\left\{-\dfrac{23}{3}\right\}$ or $\left\{-7\dfrac{2}{3}\right\}$ **29.** $x + \dfrac{5}{2} = \dfrac{1}{2}$ $\{-2\}$ **30.** $\dfrac{7}{3} = x - \dfrac{2}{3}$ $\{3\}$

31. $-6.02 + c = -8.15$ $\{-2.13\}$ **32.** $p + 0.035 = -1.12$ $\{-1.155\}$ **33.** $3.245 + t = -0.0225$ $\{-3.2675\}$ **34.** $-1.004 + k = 3.0589$ $\{4.0629\}$

Concept 3: Multiplication and Division Properties of Equality

For Exercises 35–54, solve each equation using the multiplication or division property of equality. Be sure to check your answers. **(See Examples 4–7.)**

35. $6x = 54$ $\{9\}$ **36.** $2w = 8$ $\{4\}$ **37.** $12 = -3p$ $\{-4\}$ **38.** $6 = -2q$ $\{-3\}$

39. $-5y = 0$ $\{0\}$ **40.** $-3k = 0$ $\{0\}$ **41.** $-\dfrac{y}{5} = 3$ $\{-15\}$ **42.** $-\dfrac{z}{7} = 1$ $\{-7\}$

43. $\dfrac{4}{5} = -t$ $\left\{-\dfrac{4}{5}\right\}$ **44.** $-\dfrac{3}{7} = -h$ $\left\{\dfrac{3}{7}\right\}$ **45.** $\dfrac{2}{5}a = -4$ $\{-10\}$ **46.** $\dfrac{3}{8}b = -9$ $\{-24\}$

47. $-\dfrac{1}{5}b = -\dfrac{4}{5}$ $\{4\}$ **48.** $-\dfrac{3}{10}w = \dfrac{2}{5}$ $\left\{-\dfrac{4}{3}\right\}$ **49.** $-41 = -x$ $\{41\}$ **50.** $32 = -y$ $\{-32\}$

51. $3.81 = -0.03p$ $\{-127\}$ **52.** $2.75 = -0.5q$ $\{-5.5\}$ **53.** $5.82y = -15.132$ $\{-2.6\}$ **54.** $-32.3x = -0.4522$ $\{0.014\}$

Concept 4: Translations

For Exercises 55–66, write an algebraic equation to represent each English sentence. (Let x represent the unknown number.) Then solve the equation. **(See Example 8.)**

55. The sum of negative eight and a number is forty-two. $-8 + x = 42$; The number is 50.

56. The sum of thirty-one and a number is thirteen. $31 + x = 13$; The number is -18.

57. The difference of a number and negative six is eighteen. $x - (-6) = 18$; The number is 12.

58. The sum of negative twelve and a number is negative fifteen. $-12 + x = -15$; The number is -3.

59. The product of a number and seven is the same as negative sixty-three. $x \cdot 7 = -63$ or $7x = -63$; The number is -9.

60. The product of negative three and a number is the same as twenty-four. $-3x = 24$; The number is -8.

61. The value 3.2 subtracted from a number is 2.1. $x - 3.2 = 2.1$; The number is 5.3.

62. The value -3 subtracted from a number is 4. $x - (-3) = 4$; The number is 1.

63. The quotient of a number and twelve is one-third. $\frac{x}{12} = \frac{1}{3}$; The number is 4.

64. Eighteen is equal to the quotient of a number and two. $18 = \frac{x}{2}$; The number is 36.

65. The sum of a number and $\frac{5}{8}$ is $\frac{13}{8}$.
$x + \frac{5}{8} = \frac{13}{8}$; The number is 1.

66. The difference of a number and $\frac{2}{3}$ is $\frac{1}{3}$.
$x - \frac{2}{3} = \frac{1}{3}$; The number is 1.

Mixed Exercises

For Exercises 67–94, solve each equation using the appropriate property of equality.

67. $a - 9 = 1$ {10}

68. $b - 2 = -4$ {−2}

69. $-9x = 1$ $\left\{-\frac{1}{9}\right\}$

70. $-2k = -4$ {2}

71. $-\frac{2}{3}h = 8$ {−12}

72. $\frac{3}{4}p = 15$ {20}

73. $\frac{2}{3} + t = 8$ $\left\{\frac{22}{3}\right\}$

74. $\frac{3}{4} + y = 15$ $\left\{\frac{57}{4}\right\}$

75. $\frac{r}{3} = -12$ {−36}

76. $\frac{d}{-4} = 5$ {−20}

77. $k + 16 = 32$ {16}

78. $-18 = -9 + t$ {−9}

79. $16k = 32$ {2}

80. $-18 = -9t$ {2}

81. $7 = -4q$ $\left\{-\frac{7}{4}\right\}$

82. $-3s = 10$ $\left\{-\frac{10}{3}\right\}$

83. $-4 + q = 7$ {11}

84. $s - 3 = 10$ {13}

85. $-\frac{1}{3}d = 12$ {−36}

86. $-\frac{2}{5}m = 10$ {−25}

87. $4 = \frac{1}{2} + z$ $\left\{\frac{7}{2}\right\}$

88. $3 = \frac{1}{4} + p$ $\left\{\frac{11}{4}\right\}$

89. $1.2y = 4.8$ {4}

90. $4.3w = 8.6$ {2}

91. $4.8 = 1.2 + y$ {3.6}

92. $8.6 = w - 4.3$ {12.9}

93. $0.0034 = y - 0.405$
{0.4084}

94. $-0.98 = m + 1.0034$
{−1.9834}

For Exercises 95–102, determine if the equation is a linear equation in one variable. Answer yes or no.

95. $4p + 5 = 0$ Yes

96. $3x - 5y = 0$ No

97. $4 + 2a^2 = 5$ No

98. $-8t = 7$ Yes

99. $x - 4 = 9$ Yes

100. $2x^3 + y = 0$ No

101. $19b = -3$ Yes

102. $13 + x = 19$ Yes

Expanding Your Skills

For Exercises 103–108, construct an equation with the given solution set. Answers will vary.

103. {6} For example: $y + 9 = 15$

104. {2} For example: $1 + x = 3$

105. {−4} For example: $2p = -8$

106. {−10} For example: $-4t = 40$

107. {0} For example: $5a + 5 = 5$

108. {1} For example: $6k + 1 = 7$

For Exercises 109–112, simplify by collecting the *like* terms. Then solve the equation.

109. $5x - 4x + 7 = 8 - 2$ {−1}

110. $2 + 3 = 2y + 1 - y$ {4}

111. $6p - 3p = 15 + 6$ {7}

112. $12 - 20 = 2t + 2t$ {−2}

Section 2.2   Solving Linear Equations

Concepts

1. **Linear Equations Involving Multiple Steps**
2. **Procedure for Solving a Linear Equation in One Variable**
3. **Conditional Equations, Identities, and Contradictions**

Classroom Example: p. 115, Exercise 14

1. Linear Equations Involving Multiple Steps

In Section 2.1, we studied a one-step process to solve linear equations by using the addition, subtraction, multiplication, and division properties of equality. In Example 1, we solve the equation $-2w - 7 = 11$. Solving this equation will require multiple steps. To understand the proper steps, always remember that the ultimate goal is to isolate the variable. Therefore, we will first isolate the *term* containing the variable before dividing both sides by -2.

Example 1 Solving a Linear Equation

Solve the equation. $-2w - 7 = 11$

Solution:

$$-2w - 7 = 11$$

$$-2w - 7 + 7 = 11 + 7 \qquad \text{Add 7 to both sides of the equation. This isolates the } w\text{-term.}$$

$$-2w = 18$$

$$\frac{-2w}{-2} = \frac{18}{-2} \qquad \text{Next, apply the division property of equality to obtain a coefficient of 1 for } w. \text{ Divide by } -2 \text{ on both sides.}$$

$$w = -9$$

Check:

$$-2w - 7 = 11$$

$$-2(-9) - 7 \stackrel{?}{=} 11 \qquad \text{Substitute } w = -9 \text{ in the original equation.}$$

$$18 - 7 \stackrel{?}{=} 11$$

$$11 \stackrel{?}{=} 11 \checkmark \qquad \text{True.}$$

The solution set is $\{-9\}$.

Skill Practice Solve the equation.

1. $-5y - 5 = 10$

Classroom Example: p. 115, Exercise 22

Example 2 Solving a Linear Equation

Solve the equation. $2 = \frac{1}{5}x + 3$

Solution:

$$2 = \frac{1}{5}x + 3$$

$$2 - 3 = \frac{1}{5}x + 3 - 3 \qquad \text{Subtract 3 from both sides. This isolates the } x\text{-term.}$$

$$-1 = \frac{1}{5}x \qquad \text{Simplify.}$$

Answer

1. $\{-3\}$

$$5(-1) = 5 \cdot \left(\frac{1}{5}x\right)$$

Next, apply the multiplication property of equality to obtain a coefficient of 1 for x.

$$-5 = 1x$$

$$-5 = x$$ Simplify. The answer checks in the original equation.

The solution set is $\{-5\}$.

Skill Practice Solve the equation.

2. $2 = \frac{1}{2}a - 7$

In Example 3, the variable x appears on both sides of the equation. In this case, apply the addition or subtraction property of equality to collect the variable terms on one side of the equation and the constant terms on the other side. Then use the multiplication or division property of equality to get a coefficient equal to 1.

Example 3   **Solving a Linear Equation**

Classroom Example: p. 115, Exercise 30

Solve the equation. $6x - 4 = 2x - 8$

Solution:

$$6x - 4 = 2x - 8$$

$$6x - 2x - 4 = 2x - 2x - 8$$ Subtract $2x$ from both sides leaving $0x$ on the right-hand side.

$$4x - 4 = 0x - 8$$ Simplify.

$$4x - 4 = -8$$ The x-terms have now been combined on one side of the equation.

$$4x - 4 + 4 = -8 + 4$$

$$4x = -4$$ Add 4 to both sides of the equation. This combines the constant terms on the *other* side of the equation.

$$\frac{4x}{4} = \frac{-4}{4}$$ To obtain a coefficient of 1 for x, divide both sides of the equation by 4.

$$x = -1$$ The answer checks in the original equation.

The solution set is $\{-1\}$.

Skill Practice Solve the equation.

3. $10x - 3 = 4x - 2$

Answers

2. $\{18\}$ **3.** $\left\{\frac{1}{6}\right\}$

> **TIP:** It is important to note that the variable may be isolated on either side of the equation. We will solve the equation from Example 3 again, this time isolating the variable on the right-hand side.
>
> $$6x - 4 = 2x - 8$$
>
> $$6x - 6x - 4 = 2x - 6x - 8 \qquad \text{Subtract } 6x \text{ on both sides.}$$
>
> $$0x - 4 = -4x - 8$$
>
> $$-4 = -4x - 8$$
>
> $$-4 + 8 = -4x - 8 + 8 \qquad \text{Add } 8 \text{ to both sides.}$$
>
> $$4 = -4x$$
>
> $$\frac{4}{-4} = \frac{-4x}{-4} \qquad \text{Divide both sides by } -4.$$
>
> $$-1 = x \quad \text{or equivalently } x = -1$$

2. Procedure for Solving a Linear Equation in One Variable

In some cases, it is necessary to simplify both sides of a linear equation before applying the properties of equality. Therefore, we offer the following steps to solve a linear equation in one variable.

PROCEDURE   **Solving a Linear Equation in One Variable**

Step 1   Simplify both sides of the equation.
- Clear parentheses
- Combine *like* terms

Step 2   Use the addition or subtraction property of equality to collect the variable terms on one side of the equation.

Step 3   Use the addition or subtraction property of equality to collect the constant terms on the other side of the equation.

Step 4   Use the multiplication or division property of equality to make the coefficient of the variable term equal to 1.

Step 5   Check your answer.

Classroom Example: p. 115, Exercise 44

Example 4   **Solving a Linear Equation**

Solve the equation. $-2(p - 3) = 7 + 3$

Solution:

$$-2(p - 3) = 7 + 3$$

$$-2p + 6 = 10 \qquad \textbf{Step 1:} \quad \text{Simplify both sides of the equation by clearing parentheses and combining } like \text{ terms.}$$

$$\textbf{Step 2:} \quad \text{The variable terms are already on one side.}$$

$$-2p + 6 - 6 = 10 - 6 \qquad \textbf{Step 3:} \quad \text{Subtract 6 from both sides to collect the constant terms on the other side.}$$

$$-2p = 4$$

$$\frac{-2p}{-2} = \frac{4}{-2}$$

Step 4: Divide both sides by -2 to obtain a coefficient of 1 for p.

$$p = -2$$

Step 5: <u>Check</u>:

$$-2(p - 3) = 7 + 3$$

$$-2(-2 - 3) \overset{?}{=} 7 + 3$$

$$-2(-5) \overset{?}{=} 10$$

The solution set is $\{-2\}$.

$$10 \overset{?}{=} 10 \;✔\;\; \text{True}$$

Skill Practice Solve the equation.

4. $12 + 2 = 7(3 - y)$

| **Example 5** | **Solving a Linear Equation** |

Solve the equation. $2.2y - 8.3 = 6.2y + 12.1$

Classroom Example: p. 115, Exercise 46

Solution:

$$2.2y - 8.3 = 6.2y + 12.1$$

Step 1: The right- and left-hand sides are already simplified.

$$2.2y \;\; 2.2y - 8.3 = 6.2y - 2.2y + 12.1$$

$$-8.3 = 4y + 12.1$$

Step 2: Subtract $2.2y$ from both sides to collect the variable terms on one side of the equation.

TIP: In Examples 5 and 6 we collected the variable terms on the right side to avoid negative coefficients on the variable term.

$$-8.3 - 12.1 = 4y + 12.1 - 12.1$$

$$-20.4 = 4y$$

Step 3: Subtract 12.1 from both sides to collect the constant terms on the other side.

$$\frac{-20.4}{4} = \frac{4y}{4}$$

$$-5.1 = y$$

Step 4: To obtain a coefficient of 1 for the y-term, divide both sides of the equation by 4.

$$y - -5.1$$

Step 5: <u>Check</u>:

$$2.2y - 8.3 = 6.2y + 12.1$$

$$2.2(-5.1) - 8.3 \overset{?}{=} 6.2(-5.1) + 12.1$$

$$-11.22 - 8.3 \overset{?}{=} -31.62 + 12.1$$

The solution set is $\{-5.1\}$.

$$-19.52 \overset{?}{=} -19.52 \;✔\;\; \text{True}$$

Skill Practice Solve the equation.

5. $1.5t + 2.3 = 3.5t - 1.9$

Answers

4. $\{1\}$ **5.** $\{2.1\}$

Classroom Example: p. 115,
Exercise 50

Example 6   Solving a Linear Equation

Solve the equation. $2 + 7x = 5 + 6(x + 3) + 2x$

Solution:

$$2 + 7x = 5 + 6(x + 3) + 2x$$

$2 + 7x = 5 + 6x + 18 + 2x$	**Step 1:** Clear parentheses on the right.
$2 + 7x = 8x + 23$	Combine *like* terms.
$2 + 7x - 7x = 8x - 7x + 23$	**Step 2:** Subtract $7x$ from both sides.
$2 = x + 23$	Simplify.
$2 - 23 = x + 23 - 23$	**Step 3:** Subtract 23 from both sides.
$-21 = x$	**Step 4:** Because the coefficient of the x term is already 1, there is no need to apply the multiplication or division property of equality.
$x = -21$	

The solution set is $\{-21\}$.   **Step 5:**   The check is left to the reader.

Skill Practice Solve the equation.

6. $4(2y - 1) + y = 6y + 3 - y$

Classroom Example: p. 115,
Exercise 54

Example 7   Solving a Linear Equation

Solve the equation. $9 - (z - 3) + 4z = 4z - 5(z + 2) - 6$

Solution:

$$9 - (z - 3) + 4z = 4z - 5(z + 2) - 6$$

$9 - z + 3 + 4z = 4z - 5z - 10 - 6$	**Step 1:** Clear parentheses.
$12 + 3z = -z - 16$	Combine *like* terms.
$12 + 3z + z = -z + z - 16$	**Step 2:** Add z to both sides.
$12 + 4z = -16$	
$12 - 12 + 4z = -16 - 12$	**Step 3:** Subtract 12 from both sides.
$4z = -28$	
$\dfrac{4z}{4} = \dfrac{-28}{4}$	**Step 4:** Divide both sides by 4.
$z = -7$	**Step 5:** The check is left for the reader.

> **Avoiding Mistakes**
>
> When distributing a negative number through a set of parentheses, be sure to change the signs of every term within the parentheses.

The solution set is $\{-7\}$.

Skill Practice Solve the equation.

7. $10 - (x + 5) + 3x = 6x - 5(x - 1) - 3$

Answers

6. $\left\{\dfrac{7}{4}\right\}$ 7. $\{-3\}$

3. Conditional Equations, Identities, and Contradictions

The solutions to a linear equation are the values of x that make the equation a true statement. A linear equation has one unique solution. Some types of equations, however, have no solution while others have infinitely many solutions.

I. Conditional Equations

An equation that is true for some values of the variable but false for other values is called a **conditional equation**. The equation $x + 4 = 6$, for example, is true on the condition that $x = 2$. For other values of x, the statement $x + 4 = 6$ is false.

II. Contradictions

Some equations have no solution, such as $x + 1 = x + 2$. There is no value of x, that when increased by 1 will equal the same value increased by 2. If we tried to solve the equation by subtracting x from both sides, we get the contradiction $1 = 2$. This indicates that the equation has no solution. An equation that has no solution is called a **contradiction**. The solution set is the empty set. We express this as $\{\ \}$.

> **TIP:** The empty set is also called the null set and can be expressed by the symbol $\varnothing$.

$$x + 1 = x + 2$$
$$x - x + 1 = x - x + 2$$
$$1 = 2 \quad \text{(Contradiction)} \qquad \text{Solution set: } \{\ \}$$

III. Identities

An equation that has all real numbers as its solution set is called an **identity**. For example, consider the equation, $x + 4 = x + 4$. Because the left- and right-hand sides are equal, any real number substituted for x will result in equal quantities on both sides. If we subtract x from both sides of the equation, we get the identity $4 = 4$. In such a case, the solution is the set of all real numbers.

$$x + 4 = x + 4$$
$$x - x + 4 = x - x + 4$$
$$4 = 4 \quad \text{(Identity)} \qquad \text{Solution set: } \text{The set of real numbers.}$$

Example 8 **Identifying Conditional Equations, Contradictions, and Identities**

Classroom Examples: p. 116, Exercises 60, 62, and 64

Solve the equation. Identify each equation as a conditional equation, a contradiction, or an identity.

a. $4k - 5 = 2(2k - 3) + 1$ **b.** $2(b - 4) = 2b - 7$ **c.** $3x + 7 = 2x - 5$

Solution:

a.
$$4k - 5 = 2(2k - 3) + 1$$

$4k - 5 = 4k - 6 + 1$	Clear parentheses.
$4k - 5 = 4k - 5$	Combine *like* terms.
$4k - 4k - 5 = 4k - 4k - 5$	Subtract $4k$ from both sides.
$-5 = -5$ (Identity)	

> **TIP:** In Example 8(a), we could have stopped at the step $4k - 5 = 4k - 5$ because the expressions on the left and right are identical.

This is an identity. Solution set: The set of real numbers.

b. $2(b - 4) = 2b - 7$

   $2b - 8 = 2b - 7$ Clear parentheses.

   $2b - 2b - 8 = 2b - 2b - 7$ Subtract $2b$ from both sides.

   $-8 = -7$ (Contradiction)

This is a contradiction. Solution set: { }

c. $3x + 7 = 2x - 5$

   $3x - 2x + 7 = 2x - 2x - 5$ Subtract $2x$ from both sides.

   $x + 7 = -5$ Simplify.

   $x + 7 - 7 = -5 - 7$ Subtract 7 from both sides.

   $x = -12$ (Conditional equation)

This is a conditional equation. The solution set is $\{-12\}$. (The equation is true only on the condition that $x = -12$.)

Skill Practice Solve the equation. Identify the equation as a conditional equation, a contradiction, or an identity.

Answers

8. The set of real numbers; identity
9. { }; contradiction
10. {2}; conditional equation

8. $4(2t + 1) - 1 = 8t + 3$ **9.** $3x - 5 = 4x + 1 - x$

10. $6(v - 2) = 2v - 4$

Section 2.2 Practice Exercises

Study Skills Exercises

1. Several strategies are given here about taking notes. Which would you do first to help make the most of note-taking? Put them in order of importance to you by labeling them with the numbers 1–6.

_____ Read your notes after class and complete any abbreviations or incomplete sentences.

_____ Highlight important terms and definitions.

_____ Review your notes from the previous class.

_____ Bring pencils (more than one) and paper to class.

_____ Sit in class where you can clearly read the board and hear your instructor.

_____ Turn off your cell phone and keep it off your desk to avoid distraction.

2. Define the key terms.

   a. conditional equation   **b. contradiction**   **c. identity**

Review Exercises

For Exercises 3–6, simplify each expression by clearing parentheses and combining *like* terms.

3. $5z + 2 - 7z - 3z$ $-5z + 2$ **4.** $10 - 4w + 7w - 2 + w$ $4w + 8$

5. $-(-7p + 9) + (3p - 1)$ $10p - 10$ **6.** $8y - (2y + 3) - 19$ $6y - 22$

 Writing   Translating Expression   Geometry   Scientific Calculator   Video   NS&E

7. Explain the difference between simplifying an expression and solving an equation.
To simplify an expression, clear parentheses and combine *like* terms. To solve an equation, use the addition, subtraction, multiplication, and division properties of equality to isolate the variable and determine the solution set.

For Exercises 8–12, solve each equation using the addition, subtraction, multiplication, or division property of equality.

8. $5w = -30$ $\{-6\}$

9. $-7y = 21$ $\{-3\}$

10. $x + 8 = -15$ $\{-23\}$

11. $z - 23 = -28$ $\{-5\}$

12. $-\dfrac{9}{8} = -\dfrac{3}{4}k$ $\left\{\dfrac{3}{2}\right\}$

Concept 1: Linear Equations Involving Multiple Steps

For Exercises 13–36, solve each equation using the steps outlined in the text. **(See Examples 1–3.)**

13. $6z + 1 = 13$ $\{2\}$

14. $5x + 2 = -13$ $\{-3\}$

15. $3y - 4 = 14$ $\{6\}$

16. $-7w - 5 = -19$ $\{2\}$

17. $-2p + 8 = 3$ $\left\{\dfrac{5}{2}\right\}$

18. $2b - \dfrac{1}{4} - 5$ $\left\{\dfrac{21}{8}\right\}$

19. $0.2x + 3.1 = -5.3$ $\{-42\}$

20. $-1.8 + 2.4a = -6.6$ $\{-2\}$

21. $\dfrac{5}{8} = \dfrac{1}{4} - \dfrac{1}{2}p$ $\left\{-\dfrac{3}{4}\right\}$

22. $\dfrac{6}{7} = \dfrac{1}{7} + \dfrac{5}{3}r$ $\left\{\dfrac{3}{7}\right\}$

23. $7w - 6w + 1 = 10 - 4$ $\{5\}$

24. $5v - 3 - 4v = 13$ $\{16\}$

25. $11h - 8 - 9h = -16$ $\{-4\}$

26. $6u - 5 - 8u = -7$ $\{1\}$

27. $3a + 7 = 2a - 19$ $\{-26\}$

28. $6b - 20 = 14 + 5b$ $\{34\}$

29. $-4r - 28 = -58 - r$ $\{10\}$

30. $-6x - 7 = -3 - 8x$ $\{2\}$

31. $-2z - 8 = -z$ $\{-8\}$

32. $-7t + 4 = 6t$ $\{4\}$

33. $\dfrac{5}{6}x + \dfrac{2}{3} - \dfrac{1}{6}x - \dfrac{5}{3}$ $\left\{-\dfrac{7}{3}\right\}$

34. $\dfrac{3}{7}x - \dfrac{1}{4} = -\dfrac{4}{7}x - \dfrac{5}{4}$ $\{-1\}$

35. $3y - 2 = 5y - 2$ $\{0\}$

36. $4 + 10t = -8t + 4$ $\{0\}$

Concept 2: Procedure for Solving a Linear Equation in One Variable

For Exercises 37–58, solve each equation using the steps outlined in the text. **(See Examples 4–7.)**

37. $4q + 14 = 2$ $\{-3\}$

38. $6 = 7m - 1$ $\{1\}$

39. $-9 = 4n - 1$ $\{-2\}$

40. $-\dfrac{1}{2} - 4x = 8$ $\left\{-\dfrac{17}{8}\right\}$

41. $3(2p - 4) = 15$ $\left\{\dfrac{9}{2}\right\}$

42. $4(t + 15) = 20$ $\{-10\}$

43. $6(3x + 2) - 10 = -4$ $\left\{-\dfrac{1}{3}\right\}$

44. $4(2k + 1) - 1 = 5$ $\left\{\dfrac{1}{4}\right\}$

45. $3.4x - 2.5 = 2.8x + 3.5$ $\{10\}$

46. $5.8w + 1.1 = 6.3w + 5.6$ $\{-9\}$

47. $17(s + 3) = 4(s - 10) + 13$ $\{-6\}$

48. $5(4 + p) = 3(3p - 1) - 9$ $\{8\}$

49. $6(3t - 4) + 10 = 5(t - 2) - (3t + 4)$ $\{0\}$

50. $-5y + 2(2y + 1) = 2(5y - 1) - 7$ $\{1\}$

51. $5 - 3(x + 2) = 5$ $\{-2\}$

52. $1 - 6(2 - h) = 7$ $\{3\}$

53. $3(2z - 6) - 4(3z + 1) = 5 - 2(z + 1)$ $\left\{-\dfrac{25}{4}\right\}$

54. $-2(4a + 3) - 5(2 - a) = 3(2a + 3) - 7$ $\{-2\}$

 Writing   Translating Expression   Geometry   Scientific Calculator   Video   NS&E

55. $-2[(4p + 1) - (3p - 1)] = 5(3 - p) - 9$ $\left\{\dfrac{10}{3}\right\}$ **56.** $5 - (6k + 1) = 2[(5k - 3) - (k - 2)]$ $\left\{\dfrac{3}{7}\right\}$

57. $3(-0.9n + 0.5) = -3.5n + 1.3$ {−0.25} **58.** $7(0.4m - 0.1) = 5.2m + 0.86$ {−0.65}

Concept 3: Conditional Equations, Identities, and Contradictions

For Exercises 59–64, solve each equation. Identify as a conditional equation, an identity, or a contradiction. **(See Example 8.)**

59. $2(k - 7) = 2k - 13$
{ }; contradiction

60. $5h + 4 = 5(h + 1) - 1$
The set of real numbers; identity

61. $7x + 3 = 6(x - 2)$
{−15}; conditional equation

62. $3y - 1 = 1 + 3y$
{ }; contradiction

63. $3 - 5.2p = -5.2p + 3$
The set of real numbers; identity

64. $2(q + 3) = 4q + q - 9$
{5}; conditional equation

65. A conditional linear equation has (choose one): One solution, no solution, or infinitely many solutions. One solution

66. An equation that is a contradiction has (choose one): One solution, no solution, or infinitely many solutions. No solution

67. An equation that is an identity has (choose one): One solution, no solution, or infinitely many solutions. Infinitely many solutions

68. If the only solution to a linear equation is 5, then is the equation a conditional equation, an identity, or a contradiction? Conditional equation

Mixed Exercises

For Exercises 69–92, solve each equation.

69. $4p - 6 = 8 + 2p$ {7}

70. $\dfrac{1}{2}t - 2 = 3$ {10}

71. $2k - 9 = -8$ $\left\{\dfrac{1}{2}\right\}$

72. $3(y - 2) + 5 = 5$ {2}

73. $7(w - 2) = -14 - 3w$ {0}

74. $0.24 = 0.4m$ {0.6}

75. $2(x + 2) - 3 = 2x + 1$
The set of real numbers

76. $n + \dfrac{1}{4} = -\dfrac{1}{2}$ $\left\{-\dfrac{3}{4}\right\}$

77. $0.5b = -23$ {−46}

78. $3(2r + 1) = 6(r + 2) - 6$
{ }

79. $8 - 2q = 4$ {2}

80. $\dfrac{x}{7} - 3 = 1$ {28}

81. $2 - 4(y - 5) = -4$ $\left\{\dfrac{13}{2}\right\}$

82. $4 - 3(4p - 1) = -8$ $\left\{\dfrac{5}{4}\right\}$

83. $0.4(a + 20) = 6$ {−5}

84. $2.2r - 12 = 3.4$ {7}

85. $10(2n + 1) - 6 = 20(n - 1) + 12$
{ }

86. $\dfrac{2}{5}y + 5 = -3$ {−20}

87. $c + 0.123 = 2.328$ {2.205}

88. $4(2z + 3) = 8(z - 3) + 36$
The set of real numbers

89. $\dfrac{4}{5}t - 1 = \dfrac{1}{5}t + 5$ {10}

90. $6g - 8 = 4 - 3g$ $\left\{\dfrac{4}{3}\right\}$

91. $8 - (3q + 4) = 6 - q$ {−1}

92. $6w - (8 + 2w) = 2(w - 4)$ {0}

Expanding Your Skills

93. Suppose the solution set to the equation $x + a = 10$ is {−5}. Find the value of a.
$a = 15$

94. Suppose the solution set to the equation $x + a = -12$ is {6}. Find the value of a.
$a = -18$

95. Suppose the solution set to the equation $ax = 12$ is {3}. Find the value of a.
$a = 4$

96. Suppose the solution set to the equation $ax = 49.5$ is {11}. Find the value of a.
$a = 4.5$

97. Write an equation that is an identity.
Answers may vary.
For example: $5x + 2 = 2 + 5x$

98. Write an equation that is a contradiction.
Answers may vary.
For example: $4x - 3 = 4x + 1$

 Writing Translating Expression Geometry Scientific Calculator Video NS E

Linear Equations: Clearing Fractions and Decimals | Section 2.3

1. Linear Equations with Fractions

Linear equations that contain fractions can be solved in different ways. The first procedure, illustrated here, uses the method outlined in Section 2.2.

$$\frac{5}{6}x - \frac{3}{4} = \frac{1}{3}$$

$$\frac{5}{6}x - \frac{3}{4} + \frac{3}{4} = \frac{1}{3} + \frac{3}{4} \qquad \text{To isolate the variable term, add } \frac{3}{4} \text{ to both sides.}$$

$$\frac{5}{6}x = \frac{4}{12} + \frac{9}{12} \qquad \text{Find the common denominator on the right-hand side.}$$

$$\frac{5}{6}x = \frac{13}{12} \qquad \text{Simplify.}$$

$$\frac{6}{5}\left(\frac{5}{6}x\right) = \frac{\overset{1}{\cancel{6}}}{5}\left(\frac{13}{\cancel{12}_2}\right) \qquad \text{Multiply by the reciprocal of } \frac{5}{6}, \text{ which is } \frac{6}{5}.$$

$$x = \frac{13}{10} \qquad \text{The solution set is } \left\{\frac{13}{10}\right\}.$$

Sometimes it is simpler to solve an equation with fractions by eliminating the fractions first by using a process called **clearing fractions**. To clear fractions in the equation $\frac{5}{6}x - \frac{3}{4} = \frac{1}{3}$, we can apply the multiplication property of equality to multiply both sides of the equation by the least common denominator (LCD). In this case, the LCD of $\frac{5}{6}x$, $-\frac{3}{4}$, and $\frac{1}{3}$ is 12. Because each denominator in the equation is a factor of 12, we can simplify common factors to leave integer coefficients for each term.

Example 1   Solving a Linear Equation by Clearing Fractions

Solve the equation by clearing fractions first. $\dfrac{5}{6}x - \dfrac{3}{4} = \dfrac{1}{3}$

Solution:

$$\frac{5}{6}x - \frac{3}{4} = \frac{1}{3}$$

$$12\left(\frac{5}{6}x - \frac{3}{4}\right) = 12\left(\frac{1}{3}\right) \quad \text{Multiply both sides of the equation by the LCD, 12.}$$

$$\frac{\overset{2}{\cancel{12}}}{1}\left(\frac{5}{\cancel{6}}x\right) - \frac{\overset{3}{\cancel{12}}}{1}\left(\frac{3}{\cancel{4}}\right) = \frac{\overset{4}{\cancel{12}}}{1}\left(\frac{1}{\cancel{3}}\right) \quad \text{Apply the distributive property (recall that } 12 = \frac{12}{1}).$$

$$2(5x) - 3(3) = 4(1) \quad \text{Simplify common factors to clear the fractions.}$$

$$10x - 9 = 4$$

$$10x - 9 + 9 = 4 + 9 \quad \text{Add 9 to both sides.}$$

$$10x = 13$$

$$\frac{10x}{10} = \frac{13}{10} \quad \text{Divide both sides by 10.}$$

$$x = \frac{13}{10} \quad \text{The solution set is } \left\{\frac{13}{10}\right\}.$$

Concepts

1. **Linear Equations with Fractions**
2. **Linear Equations with Decimals**

Classroom Example: p. 122, Exercise 18

TIP: Recall that the multiplication property of equality indicates that multiplying both sides of an equation by a nonzero constant results in an equivalent equation.

TIP: The fractions in this equation can be eliminated by multiplying both sides of the equation by *any* common multiple of the denominators. These include 12, 24, 36, 48, and so on. We chose 12 because it is the *least* common multiple.

Skill Practice Solve the equation by clearing fractions.

1. $\dfrac{2}{5}y + \dfrac{1}{2} = -\dfrac{7}{10}$

In this section, we combine the process for clearing fractions and decimals with the general strategies for solving linear equations. To solve a linear equation, it is important to follow the steps listed below.

PROCEDURE Solving a Linear Equation in One Variable

Step 1 Simplify both sides of the equation.
- Clear parentheses
- Consider clearing fractions and decimals (if any are present) by multiplying both sides of the equation by a common denominator of all terms.
- Combine *like* terms

Step 2 Use the addition or subtraction property of equality to collect the variable terms on one side of the equation.

Step 3 Use the addition or subtraction property of equality to collect the constant terms on the other side of the equation.

Step 4 Use the multiplication or division property of equality to make the coefficient of the variable term equal to 1.

Step 5 Check your answer.

Classroom Example: p. 122, Exercise 32

Example 2 Solving a Linear Equation Containing Fractions

Solve the equation. $\dfrac{1}{3}(x + 7) - \dfrac{1}{2}(x + 1) = 4$

Solution:

$$\dfrac{1}{3}(x + 7) - \dfrac{1}{2}(x + 1) = 4$$

$$\dfrac{1}{3}x + \dfrac{7}{3} - \dfrac{1}{2}x - \dfrac{1}{2} = 4 \qquad \text{Clear parentheses.}$$

$$6\left(\dfrac{1}{3}x + \dfrac{7}{3} - \dfrac{1}{2}x - \dfrac{1}{2}\right) = 6(4) \qquad \begin{array}{l}\text{The LCD of}\\ \dfrac{1}{3}x, \dfrac{7}{3}, -\dfrac{1}{2}x, -\dfrac{1}{2} \text{ and } \dfrac{4}{1} \text{ is 6.}\end{array}$$

$$\dfrac{\overset{2}{\cancel{6}}}{1} \cdot \dfrac{1}{\cancel{3}}x + \dfrac{\overset{2}{\cancel{6}}}{1} \cdot \dfrac{7}{\cancel{3}} + \dfrac{\overset{3}{\cancel{6}}}{1}\left(-\dfrac{1}{\cancel{2}}x\right) + \dfrac{\overset{3}{\cancel{6}}}{1}\left(-\dfrac{1}{\cancel{2}}\right) = 6(4) \qquad \begin{array}{l}\text{Apply the distributive}\\ \text{property.}\end{array}$$

Answer

1. $\{-3\}$

$$2x + 14 - 3x - 3 = 24$$

$$-x + 11 = 24 \qquad \text{Combine } like \text{ terms.}$$

$$-x + 11 - 11 = 24 - 11 \qquad \text{Subtract 11.}$$

$$-x = 13$$

$$\frac{-x}{-1} = \frac{13}{-1} \qquad \text{Divide by } -1.$$

$$x = -13 \qquad \text{The check is left to the reader.}$$

The solution set is $\{-13\}$.

Skill Practice Solve the equation.

2. $\dfrac{1}{5}(z + 1) + \dfrac{1}{4}(z + 3) - 2$

TIP: In Example 2 both parentheses and fractions are present within the equation. In such a case, we recommend that you clear parentheses first. Then clear the fractions.

Example 3 Solving a Linear Equation Containing Fractions

Solve the equation. $\qquad \dfrac{x - 2}{5} - \dfrac{x - 4}{2} = 2$

Classroom Example: p. 122, Exercise 32

Solution:

$$\frac{x - 2}{5} - \frac{x - 4}{2} = \frac{2}{1} \qquad \text{The LCD of } \tfrac{x-2}{5}, \tfrac{x-4}{2}, \text{ and } \tfrac{2}{1} \text{ is 10.}$$

$$10\left(\frac{x - 2}{5} - \frac{x - 4}{2}\right) = 10\left(\frac{2}{1}\right) \qquad \text{Multiply both sides by 10.}$$

$$\overset{2}{\cancel{10}} \cdot \left(\frac{x - 2}{\cancel{5}}\right) - \overset{5}{\cancel{10}} \cdot \left(\frac{x - 4}{\cancel{2}}\right) - \frac{10}{1} \cdot \left(\frac{2}{1}\right) \qquad \text{Apply the distributive property.}$$

$$2(x - 2) - 5(x - 4) = 20 \qquad \text{Clear fractions.}$$

$$2x - 4 - 5x + 20 = 20 \qquad \text{Apply the distributive property.}$$

$$-3x + 16 = 20 \qquad \text{Simplify both sides of the equation.}$$

$$-3x + 16 - 16 = 20 - 16 \qquad \text{Subtract 16 from both sides.}$$

$$-3x = 4$$

$$\frac{-3x}{-3} = \frac{4}{-3} \qquad \text{Divide both sides by } -3.$$

$$x = -\frac{4}{3} \qquad \text{The check is left to the reader.}$$

The solution set is $\left\{-\dfrac{4}{3}\right\}$.

Avoiding Mistakes

In Example 3, several of the fractions in the equation have two terms in the numerator. It is important to enclose these fractions in parentheses when clearing fractions. In this way, we will remember to use the distributive property to multiply the factors shown in blue with both terms from the numerator of the fractions.

Skill Practice Solve the equation.

3. $\dfrac{x + 1}{4} + \dfrac{x + 2}{6} = 1$

Answers

2. $\left\{\dfrac{7}{3}\right\}$ **3.** $\{1\}$

2. Linear Equations with Decimals

The same procedure used to clear fractions in an equation can be used to **clear decimals**. For example, consider the equation

$$2.5x + 3 = 1.7x - 6.6$$

Recall that any terminating decimal can be written as a fraction. Therefore, the equation can be interpreted as

$$\frac{25}{10}x + 3 = \frac{17}{10}x - \frac{66}{10}$$

A convenient common denominator of all terms is 10. Therefore, we can multiply the original equation by 10 to clear decimals. The result is

$$25x + 30 = 17x - 66$$

Multiplying by the appropriate power of 10 moves the decimal points so that all coefficients become integers.

Classroom Example: p. 122, Exercise 40

> **TIP:** Notice that multiplying a decimal number by 10 has the effect of moving the decimal point one place to the right. Similarly, multiplying by 100 moves the decimal point two places to the right, and so on.

Example 4 Solving a Linear Equation Containing Decimals

Solve the equation by clearing decimals. $2.5x + 3 = 1.7x - 6.6$

Solution:

$$2.5x + 3 = 1.7x - 6.6$$

$$10(2.5x + 3) = 10(1.7x - 6.6)$$ Multiply both sides of the equation by 10.

$$25x + 30 = 17x - 66$$ Apply the distributive property.

$$25x - 17x + 30 = 17x - 17x - 66$$ Subtract $17x$ from both sides.

$$8x + 30 = -66$$

$$8x + 30 - 30 = -66 - 30$$ Subtract 30 from both sides.

$$8x = -96$$

$$\frac{8x}{8} = \frac{-96}{8}$$ Divide both sides by 8.

$$x = -12$$ The check is left to the reader.

The solution set is $\{-12\}$.

Skill Practice Solve the equation.

4. $1.2w + 3.5 = 2.1 + w$

Example 5 **Solving a Linear Equation Containing Decimals**

Solve the equation by clearing decimals. $0.2(x + 4) - 0.45(x + 9) = 12$

Classroom Example: p. 122, Exercise 46

Solution:

$$0.2(x + 4) - 0.45(x + 9) = 12$$

$0.2x + 0.8 - 0.45x - 4.05 = 12$	Clear parentheses first.
$100(0.2x + 0.8 - 0.45x - 4.05) = 100(12)$	Multiply both sides by 100.
$20x + 80 - 45x - 405 = 1200$	Apply the distributive property.
$-25x - 325 = 1200$	Simplify both sides.
$-25x - 325 + 325 = 1200 + 325$	Add 325 to both sides.
$-25x = 1525$	
$\dfrac{-25x}{-25} = \dfrac{1525}{-25}$	Divide both sides by -25.
$x = -61$	The check is left to the reader.

The solution set is $\{-61\}$.

TIP: The terms with the most digits following the decimal point are $-0.45x$ and -4.05. Each of these is written to the hundredths place. Therefore, we multiply both sides by 100.

Skill Practice Solve the equation.

5. $0.25(x + 2) - 0.15(x + 3) = 4$

Answer

5. $\{39.5\}$

Section 2.3 Practice Exercises

Boost *your* GRADE at ALEKS.com!

ALEKS
version 3.0

- Practice Problems
- Self-Tests
- NetTutor
- e-Professors
- Videos

For additional exercises, see Classroom Activities 2.3A–2.3B in the *Instructor's Resource Manual* at www.mhhe.com/moh.

Study Skills Exercises

1. Instructors vary in what they emphasize on tests. For example, test material may come from the textbook, notes, handouts, or homework. What does your instructor emphasize?

2. Define the key terms.

    a. clearing fractions   **b.** clearing decimals

Review Exercises

For Exercises 3–6, solve each equation.

3. $5(x + 2) - 3 = 4x + 5$ $\{-2\}$

4. $-2(2x - 4x) = 6 + 18$ $\{6\}$

5. $3(2y + 3) - 4(-y + 1) = 7y - 10$ $\{-5\}$

6. $-(3w + 4) + 5(w - 2) - 3(6w - 8) = 10$ $\{0\}$

7. Solve the equation and describe the solution set. $7x + 2 = 7(x - 12)$ $\{\ \}$

8. Solve the equation and describe the solution set. $2(3x - 6) = 3(2x - 4)$ The set of real numbers

 Writing   Translating Expression   Geometry   Scientific Calculator   Video   NS&E

Concept 1: Linear Equations with Fractions

For Exercises 9–14, determine which of the values could be used to clear fractions or decimals in the given equation.

9. $\dfrac{2}{3}x - \dfrac{1}{6} = \dfrac{x}{9}$

Values: 6, 9, 12, 18, 24, 36   18, 36

10. $\dfrac{1}{4}x - \dfrac{2}{7} = \dfrac{1}{2}x + 2$

Values: 4, 7, 14, 21, 28, 42   28

11. $0.02x + 0.5 = 0.35x + 1.2$

Values: 10; 100; 1000; 10,000

100; 1000; 10,000

12. $0.003 - 0.002x = 0.1x$

Values: 10; 100; 1000; 10,000

1000; 10,000

13. $\dfrac{1}{6}x + \dfrac{7}{10} = x$

Values: 3, 6, 10, 30, 60

30, 60

14. $2x - \dfrac{5}{2} = \dfrac{x}{3} - \dfrac{1}{4}$

Values: 2, 3, 4, 6, 12, 24

12, 24

For Exercises 15–36, solve each equation. **(See Examples 1–3.)**

15. $\dfrac{1}{2}x + 3 = 5$ {4}

16. $\dfrac{1}{3}y - 4 = 9$ {39}

17. $\dfrac{2}{15}z + 3 = \dfrac{7}{5}$ {−12}

18. $\dfrac{1}{6}y + 2 = \dfrac{5}{12}$ $\left\{-\dfrac{19}{2}\right\}$

19. $\dfrac{1}{3}q + \dfrac{3}{5} = \dfrac{1}{15}q - \dfrac{2}{5}$

$\left\{-\dfrac{15}{4}\right\}$

20. $\dfrac{3}{7}x - 5 = \dfrac{24}{7}x + 7$

{−4}

21. $\dfrac{12}{5}w + 7 = 31 - \dfrac{3}{5}w$

{8}

22. $-\dfrac{1}{9}p - \dfrac{5}{18} = -\dfrac{1}{6}p + \dfrac{1}{3}$

{11}

23. $\dfrac{1}{4}(3m - 4) - \dfrac{1}{5} = \dfrac{1}{4}m + \dfrac{3}{10}$

{3}

24. $\dfrac{1}{25}(20 - t) = \dfrac{4}{25}t - \dfrac{3}{5}$

{7}

25. $\dfrac{1}{6}(5s + 3) = \dfrac{1}{2}(s + 11)$

{15}

26. $\dfrac{1}{12}(4n - 3) = \dfrac{1}{4}(2n + 1)$

{−3}

27. $\dfrac{2}{3}x + 4 = \dfrac{2}{3}x - 6$

{ }

28. $-\dfrac{1}{9}a + \dfrac{2}{9} = \dfrac{1}{3} - \dfrac{1}{9}a$

{ }

29. $\dfrac{1}{6}(2c - 1) = \dfrac{1}{3}c - \dfrac{1}{6}$

The set of real numbers

30. $\dfrac{3}{2}b - 1 = \dfrac{1}{8}(12b - 8)$

The set of real numbers

31. $\dfrac{2x + 1}{3} + \dfrac{x - 1}{3} = 5$ {5}

32. $\dfrac{4y - 2}{5} - \dfrac{y + 4}{5} = -3$ {−3}

33. $\dfrac{3w - 2}{6} = 1 - \dfrac{w - 1}{3}$ {2}

34. $\dfrac{z - 7}{4} = \dfrac{6z - 1}{8} - 2$ $\left\{\dfrac{3}{4}\right\}$

35. $\dfrac{x + 3}{3} - \dfrac{x - 1}{2} = 4$ {−15}

36. $\dfrac{5y - 1}{2} - \dfrac{y + 4}{5} = 1$ {1}

Concept 2: Linear Equations with Decimals

For Exercises 37–54, solve each equation. **(See Examples 4–5.)**

37. $9.2y - 4.3 = 50.9$
{6}

38. $-6.3x + 1.5 = -4.8$
{1}

39. $21.1w + 4.6 = 10.9w + 35.2$
{3}

40. $0.05z + 0.2 = 0.15z - 10.5$
{107}

41. $0.2p - 1.4 = 0.2(p - 7)$
The set of real numbers

42. $0.5(3q + 87) = 1.5q + 43.5$
The set of real numbers

43. $0.20x + 53.60 = x$
{67}

44. $z + 0.06z = 3816$
{3600}

45. $0.15(90) + 0.05p = 0.10(90 + p)$
{90}

46. $0.25(60) + 0.10x = 0.15(60 + x)$
{120}

47. $0.40(y + 10) - 0.60(y + 2) = 2$
{4}

48. $0.75(x - 2) + 0.25(x + 4) = 0.5$
{1}

49. $0.4x + 0.2 = -3.6 - 0.6x$
{−3.8}

50. $0.12x + 3 - 0.8x = 0.22x - 0.6$
{4}

51. $0.06(x - 0.5) = 0.06x + 0.01$
{ }

52. $0.125x = 0.025(5x + 1)$
{ }

53. $-3.5x + 1.3 = -0.3(9x - 5)$
{−0.25}

54. $x + 4 = 2(0.4x + 1.3)$
{−7}

Mixed Exercises

For Exercises 55–64, solve each equation.

55. $0.2x - 1.8 = -3$ $\quad${−6}

56. $9.8h + 2 = 3.8h + 20$ $\quad${3}

57. $\dfrac{1}{4}(x + 4) = \dfrac{1}{5}(2x + 3)$ $\quad\left\{\dfrac{8}{3}\right\}$ or $\left\{2\dfrac{2}{3}\right\}$

58. $\dfrac{2}{3}(y - 1) = \dfrac{3}{4}(3y - 2)$ $\quad\left\{\dfrac{10}{19}\right\}$

59. $0.3(x + 6) - 0.7(x + 2) = 4$ $\quad${−9}

60. $0.05(2t - 1) - 0.03(4t - 1) = 0.2$ $\quad${−11}

61. $\dfrac{2k + 5}{4} = 2 - \dfrac{k + 2}{3}$ $\quad\left\{\dfrac{1}{10}\right\}$

62. $\dfrac{3d - 4}{6} + 1 = \dfrac{d + 1}{8}$ $\quad\left\{-\dfrac{5}{9}\right\}$

63. $\dfrac{1}{8}v + \dfrac{2}{3} = \dfrac{1}{6}v + \dfrac{3}{4}$ $\quad${−2}

64. $\dfrac{2}{5}z - \dfrac{1}{4} = \dfrac{3}{10}z + \dfrac{1}{2}$ $\quad\left\{\dfrac{15}{2}\right\}$

Expanding Your Skills

For Exercises 65–68, solve each equation.

65. $\dfrac{1}{2}a + 0.4 = -0.7 - \dfrac{3}{5}a$ $\quad${−1}

66. $\dfrac{3}{4}c - 0.11 = 0.23(c - 5)$ $\quad${−2}

67. $0.8 + \dfrac{7}{10}b = \dfrac{3}{2}b - 0.8$ $\quad${2}

68. $0.78 - \dfrac{1}{25}h = \dfrac{3}{5}h - 0.5$ $\quad${2}

Problem Recognition Exercises

Equations vs. Expressions

The concept of solving equations is often confused with simplifying expressions. They may both begin with clearing parentheses and combining like terms, but an equation will result with a solution set and an expression will remain an expression. An equation can be identified by the presence of an equals sign ($=$). Compare these two examples.

Example 1

Solve the equation.

$4(x - 3) + 15 = -13$

$4x - 12 + 15 = -13$

$4x + 3 = -13$

$4x = -16$

$x = -4$ $\quad$ The solution set is {−4}.

Example 2

Simplify the expression.

$4(x - 3) + 15$

$4x - 12 + 15$

$4x + 3$ $\qquad$ This expression is simplified.

For Exercises 1–30, identify each exercise as an expression or an equation. Then simplify the expression or solve the equation.

1. $2b + 23 - 6b - 5$
Expression; $-4b + 18$

2. $10p - 9 + 2p - 3 + 8p - 18$
Expression; $20p - 30$

3. $\frac{y}{4} = -2$ Equation; $\{-8\}$

4. $-\frac{x}{2} = 7$ Equation; $\{-14\}$

5. $3(4h - 2) - (5h - 8) = 8 - (2h + 3)$ Equation; $\left\{\frac{1}{3}\right\}$

6. $7y - 3(2y + 5) = 7 - (10 - 10y)$
Equation; $\left\{-\frac{4}{3}\right\}$

7. $3(8z - 1) + 10 - 6(5 + 3z)$
Expression; $6z - 23$

8. $-5(1 - x) - 3(2x + 3) + 5$
Expression; $-x - 9$

9. $6c + 3(c + 1) = 10$
Equation; $\left\{\frac{7}{9}\right\}$

10. $-9 + 5(2y + 3) = -7$
Equation; $\left\{-\frac{13}{10}\right\}$

11. $0.5(2a - 3) - 0.1 = 0.4(6 + 2a)$
Equation; $\{20\}$

12. $0.07(2v - 4) = 0.1(v - 4)$
Equation; $\{-3\}$

13. $-\frac{5}{9}w + \frac{11}{12} = \frac{23}{36}$ Equation; $\left\{\frac{1}{2}\right\}$

14. $\frac{3}{8}t - \frac{5}{8} = \frac{1}{2}t + \frac{1}{8}$
Equation; $\{-6\}$

15. $\frac{3}{4}x + \frac{1}{2} - \frac{1}{8}x + \frac{5}{4}$
Expression; $\frac{5}{8}x + \frac{7}{4}$

16. $\frac{7}{3}(6 - 12t) + \frac{1}{2}(4t + 8)$
Expression; $-26t + 18$

17. $2z - 7 = 2(z - 13)$
Equation; $\{\ \}$

18. $-6x + 2(x + 1) = -2(2x + 3)$
Equation; $\{\ \}$

19. $\frac{2x - 1}{4} + \frac{3x + 2}{6} = 2$
Equation; $\left\{\frac{23}{12}\right\}$

20. $\frac{w - 4}{6} - \frac{3w - 1}{2} = -1$
Equation; $\left\{\frac{5}{8}\right\}$

21. $4b - 8 - b = -3b + 2(3b - 4)$
Equation; The set of real numbers

22. $-k - 41 - 2 - k = -2(20 + k) - 3$
Equation; The set of real numbers

23. $\frac{4}{3}(6y - 3) = 0$
Equation; $\left\{\frac{1}{2}\right\}$

24. $\frac{1}{2}(2c - 4) + 3 = \frac{1}{3}(6c + 3)$
Equation; $\{0\}$

25. $3(x + 6) - 7(x + 2) - 4(1 - x)$
Expression; 0

26. $-10(2k + 1) - 4(4 - 5k) + 25$
Expression; -1

27. $3 - 2[4a - 5(a + 1)]$
Expression; $2a + 13$

28. $-9 - 4[3 - 2(q + 3)]$
Expression; $8q + 3$

29. $4 + 2[8 - (6 + x)] = -2(x - 1) - 4 + x$
Equation; $\{10\}$

30. $-1 - 5[2 + 3(w - 2)] = 5(w + 4)$ Equation; $\left\{-\frac{1}{20}\right\}$

Section 2.4   Applications of Linear Equations: Introduction to Problem Solving

Concepts

1. **Problem-Solving Strategies**
2. **Translations Involving Linear Equations**
3. **Consecutive Integer Problems**
4. **Applications of Linear Equations**

1. Problem-Solving Strategies

Linear equations can be used to solve many real-world applications. However, with "word problems," students often do not know where to start. To help organize the problem-solving process, we offer the following guidelines:

 Writing   Translating Expression   Geometry   Scientific Calculator   Video   NS&E

Problem-Solving Flowchart for Word Problems

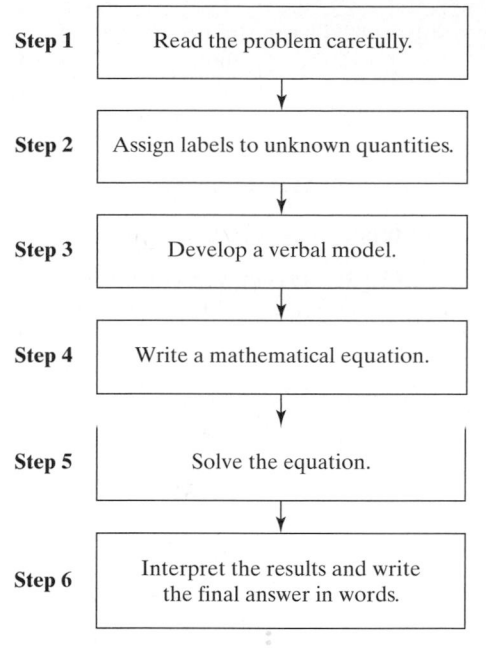

Step 1 | Read the problem carefully.
- Familiarize yourself with the problem. Identify the unknown, and if possible, estimate the answer.

Step 2 | Assign labels to unknown quantities.
- Identify the unknown quantity or quantities. Let x or another variable represent one of the unknowns. Draw a picture and write down relevant formulas.

Step 3 | Develop a verbal model.
- Write an equation in *words*.

Step 4 | Write a mathematical equation.
- Replace the verbal model with a mathematical equation using x or another variable.

Step 5 | Solve the equation.
- Solve for the variable using the steps for solving linear equations.

Step 6 | Interpret the results and write the final answer in words.
- Once you have obtained a numerical value for the variable, recall what it represents in the context of the problem. Can this value be used to determine other unknowns in the problem? Write an answer to the word problem in *words*.

Instructor Note: Remind students that x is a convenient variable, but any letter can be used. For example, for an unknown width use w.

> **Avoiding Mistakes**
>
> Once you have reached a solution to a word problem, verify that it is reasonable in the context of the problem.

2. Translations Involving Linear Equations

We have already practiced translating an English sentence to a mathematical equation. Recall from Section 1.3 that several key words translate to the algebraic operations of addition, subtraction, multiplication, and division.

Example 1   Translating to a Linear Equation

The sum of a number and negative eleven is negative fifteen. Find the number.

Classroom Example: p. 131, Exercise 10

Solution:

	Step 1: Read the problem.
Let x represent the unknown number.	**Step 2:** Label the unknown.
$\underset{\downarrow}{\text{the sum of}} \quad \underset{\downarrow}{\text{is}}$ $(\text{a number}) + (-11) = (-15)$	**Step 3:** Develop a verbal model.
$x + (-11) = -15$	**Step 4:** Write an equation.
$x + (-11) + 11 = -15 + 11$	**Step 5:** Solve the equation.
$x = -4$	
The number is -4.	**Step 6:** Write the final answer in words.

Skill Practice

1. The sum of a number and negative seven is 12. Find the number.

Classroom Example: p. 132,
Exercise 14

Example 2   Translating to a Linear Equation

Forty less than five times a number is fifty-two subtracted from the number. Find the number.

Solution:

Step 1:   Read the problem.

Let x represent the unknown number.   Step 2:   Label the unknown.

$$\underbrace{\left(\begin{array}{c} 5 \text{ times} \\ \text{a number} \end{array} \right)}_{5x} \overset{\text{less than}}{\downarrow} (40) \overset{\text{is}}{\underset{=}{\downarrow}} \underbrace{\left(\begin{array}{c} \text{the} \\ \text{number} \end{array} \right)}_{x} \overset{\text{subtracted from}}{\underset{-}{\downarrow}} (52)$$

Step 3:   Develop a verbal model.

$$5x \quad - \quad 40 \quad = \quad x \quad - \quad 52$$

Step 4:   Write an equation.

$$5x - 40 = x - 52$$

Step 5:   Solve the equation.

$$5x - x - 40 = x - x - 52$$

$$4x - 40 = -52$$

$$4x - 40 + 40 = -52 + 40$$

$$4x = -12$$

$$\frac{4x}{4} = \frac{-12}{4}$$

$$x = -3$$

The number is -3.   Step 6:   Write the final answer in words.

Avoiding Mistakes

It is important to remember that subtraction is not a commutative operation. Therefore, the order in which two real numbers are subtracted affects the outcome. The expression "forty less than five times a number" must be translated as: $5x - 40$ (not $40 - 5x$). Similarly, "fifty-two subtracted from the number" must be translated as: $x - 52$ (not $52 - x$).

Skill Practice

2. Thirteen more than twice a number is 5 more than the number. Find the number.

Classroom Example: p. 132,
Exercise 18

Example 3   Translating to a Linear Equation

Twice the sum of a number and six is two more than three times the number. Find the number.

Solution:

Step 1:   Read the problem.

Let x represent the unknown number.   Step 2:   Label the unknown.

$$\overset{\text{twice}}{\underset{\downarrow}{2}} \; \overset{\text{the sum}}{\underset{\downarrow}{(x+6)}} \; \overset{\text{is}}{\underset{=}{\downarrow}} \; \overset{\text{2 more than}}{\underset{\underset{\underset{\text{a number}}{\text{three times}}}{\uparrow}}{3x+2}}$$

Step 3:   Develop a verbal model.

Step 4:   Write an equation.

Answer

2. The number is -8.

$$2(x + 6) = 3x + 2$$ **Step 5:** Solve the equation.

$$2x + 12 = 3x + 2$$

$$2x - 2x + 12 = 3x - 2x + 2$$

$$12 = x + 2$$

$$12 - 2 = x + 2 - 2$$

$$10 = x$$

The number is 10.   **Step 6:** Write the final answer in words.

Skill Practice

3. Three times the sum of a number and eight is 4 more than the number. Find the number.

3. Consecutive Integer Problems

The word *consecutive* means "following one after the other in order without gaps." The numbers 6, 7, and 8 are examples of three **consecutive integers**. The numbers $-4, -2, 0,$ and 2 are examples of **consecutive even integers**. The numbers 23, 25, and 27 are examples of **consecutive odd integers**.

Notice that any two consecutive integers differ by 1. Therefore, if x represents an integer, then $(x + 1)$ represents the next larger consecutive integer (Figure 2-4).

Consecutive integers differ by 1 unit.

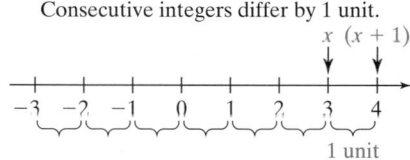

Figure 2-4

Any two consecutive even integers differ by 2. Therefore, if x represents an even integer, then $(x + 2)$ represents the next consecutive larger even integer (Figure 2-5).

Consecutive even integers differ by 2 units.

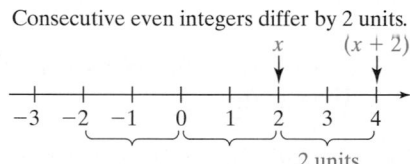

Figure 2-5

Likewise, any two consecutive odd integers differ by 2. If x represents an odd integer, then $(x + 2)$ is the next larger odd integer (Figure 2-6).

Consecutive odd integers differ by 2 units.

Figure 2-6

Answer

3. The number is -10.

Classroom Example: p. 132, Exercise 22

Example 4 Solving an Application Involving Consecutive Integers

The sum of two consecutive odd integers is -188. Find the integers.

Solution:

In this example we have two unknown integers. We can let x represent either of the unknowns.

	Step 1: Read the problem.
Suppose x represents the first odd integer.	**Step 2:** Label the variables.

Then $(x + 2)$ represents the second odd integer.

$$\left(\begin{array}{c}\text{First}\\\text{integer}\end{array}\right) + \left(\begin{array}{c}\text{second}\\\text{integer}\end{array}\right) = (\text{total})$$

Step 3: Write an equation in words.

$$x + (x + 2) = -188$$

Step 4: Write a mathematical equation.

$$x + (x + 2) = -188$$
$$2x + 2 = -188$$

Step 5: Solve for x.

$$2x + 2 - 2 = -188 - 2$$
$$2x = -190$$
$$\frac{2x}{2} = \frac{-190}{2}$$
$$x = -95$$

The first integer is $x = -95$.

Step 6: Interpret the results and write the answer in words.

The second integer is $x + 2 = -95 + 2 = -93$.

The two integers are -95 and -93.

TIP: With word problems, it is advisable to check that the answer is reasonable.

The numbers -95 and -93 are consecutive odd integers. Furthermore, their sum is -188 as desired.

Skill Practice

4. The sum of two consecutive even integers is 66. Find the integers.

Classroom Example: p. 132, Exercise 30

Example 5 Solving an Application Involving Consecutive Integers

Ten times the smallest of three consecutive integers is twenty-two more than three times the sum of the integers. Find the integers.

Solution:

	Step 1: Read the problem.
Let x represent the first integer.	**Step 2:** Label the variables.

$x + 1$ represents the second consecutive integer.

$x + 2$ represents the third consecutive integer.

Answer

4. The integers are 32 and 34.

$$\begin{pmatrix} 10 \text{ times} \\ \text{the first} \\ \text{integer} \end{pmatrix} = \begin{pmatrix} 3 \text{ times} \\ \text{the sum of} \\ \text{the integers} \end{pmatrix} + 22$$

Step 3: Write an equation in words.

$$10x = 3\underbrace{[(x) + (x + 1) + (x + 2)]}_{\text{the sum of the integers}} + 22$$

Step 4: Write a mathematical equation.

$$10x = 3(x + x + 1 + x + 2) + 22$$

Step 5: Solve the equation.

$$10x = 3(3x + 3) + 22$$

Clear parentheses.

$$10x = 9x + 9 + 22$$

Combine *like* terms.

$$10x = 9x + 31$$

$$10x - 9x = 9x - 9x + 31$$

$$x = 31$$

Isolate the *x*-terms on one side.

The first integer is $x = 31$.

The second integer is $x + 1 = 31 + 1 = 32$.

The third integer is $x + 2 = 31 + 2 = 33$.

Step 6: Interpret the results and write the answer in words.

The three integers are 31, 32, and 33.

Skill Practice

5. Five times the smallest of three consecutive integers is 17 less than twice the sum of the integers. Find the integers.

4. Applications of Linear Equations

Example 6   Using a Linear Equation in an Application

A carpenter cuts a 6-ft board into two pieces. One piece must be three times as long as the other. Find the length of each piece.

Classroom Example: p. 133, Exercise 32

Solution:

In this problem, one piece must be three times as long as the other. Thus, if x represents the length of one piece, then $3x$ can represent the length of the other.

Step 1: Read the problem completely.

x represents the length of the smaller piece. $3x$ represents the length of the longer piece.

Step 2: Label the unknowns. Draw a figure.

Answer

5. The integers are 11, 12, and 13.

$$\left(\begin{matrix}\text{Length of}\\\text{one piece}\end{matrix}\right) + \left(\begin{matrix}\text{length of}\\\text{other piece}\end{matrix}\right) = \left(\begin{matrix}\text{total length}\\\text{of the board}\end{matrix}\right)$$

Step 3: Set up a verbal equation.

$$x \quad + \quad 3x \quad = \quad 6$$

Step 4: Write an equation.

$$4x = 6$$

Step 5: Solve the equation.

$$\frac{4x}{4} = \frac{6}{4}$$

$$x = 1.5$$

The smaller piece is $x = 1.5$ ft.

Step 6: Interpret the results.

The longer piece is $3x$ or $3(1.5 \text{ ft}) = 4.5$ ft.

> **TIP:** The variable can represent either unknown. In Example 6, if we let x represent the length of the longer piece of board, then $\frac{1}{3}x$ would represent the length of the smaller piece. The equation would become $x + \frac{1}{3}x = 6$. Try solving this equation and interpreting the result.

Skill Practice

6. A plumber cuts a 96-in. piece of pipe into two pieces. One piece is five times longer than the other piece. How long is each piece?

Classroom Example: p. 133, Exercise 38

Example 7   Using a Linear Equation in an Application

The hit movie *The Dark Knight* set a record for grossing the most money during its opening weekend. This amount surpassed the previous record set by the movie *Spider-Man 3* by $4.2 million. The revenue from these two movies was $306.4 million. How much revenue did each movie bring in during its opening weekend?

Solution:

In this example, we have two unknowns. The variable x can represent *either* quantity. However, the revenue from *The Dark Knight* is given in terms of the revenue for *Spider-Man 3*.

Step 1: Read the problem.

Let x represent the revenue for *Spider-Man 3*.

Step 2: Label the variables.

Then $x + 4.2$ represents the revenue for *The Dark Knight*.

$$\left(\begin{matrix}\text{Revenue from}\\\text{Spider-Man 3}\end{matrix}\right) + \left(\begin{matrix}\text{revenue from}\\\text{The Dark Knight}\end{matrix}\right) = \left(\begin{matrix}\text{total}\\\text{revenue}\end{matrix}\right)$$

Step 3: Write an equation in words.

$$x \quad + \quad (x + 4.2) \quad = 306.4$$

Step 4: Write an equation.

$$2x + 4.2 = 306.4$$

Step 5: Solve the equation.

$$2x = 302.2$$

$$x = 151.1$$

- Revenue from *Spider-Man 3*: $x = 151.1$
- Revenue from *The Dark Knight*: $x + 4.2 = 151.1 + 4.2 = 155.3$

Answer

6. One piece is 80 in. and the other is 16 in.

The revenue from *Spider-Man 3* was $151.1 million for its opening weekend. The revenue for *The Dark Knight* was $155.3 million.

Skill Practice

7. There are 40 students in an algebra class. There are 4 more women than men. How many women and how many men are in the class?

Answer

7. There are 22 women and 18 men.

Section 2.4 Practice Exercises

Boost *your* GRADE at ALEKS.com!

 ALEKS® version 3.0

- Practice Problems
- Self-Tests
- NetTutor
- e-Professors
- Videos

For additional exercises, see Classroom Activities 2.4A–2.4C in the *Instructor's Resource Manual* at www.mhhe.com/moh.

Study Skills Exercises

1. After doing a section of homework, check the odd-numbered answers in the back of the text. Choose a method to identify the exercises that gave you trouble (i.e., circle the number or put a star by the number). List some reasons why it is important to label these problems.

2. Define the key terms.

   a. consecutive integers   **b. consecutive even integers**   **c. consecutive odd integers**

Concept 2: Translations Involving Linear Equations

For Exercises 3–8, write an expression representing the unknown quantity.

3. In a math class, the number of students who received an "A" in the class was 5 more than the number of students who received a "B." If x represents the number of "B" students, write an expression for the number of "A" students. $x + 5$

4. At a recent motorcycle rally, the number of men exceeded the number of women by 216. If x represents the number of women, write an expression for the number of men. $x + 216$

5. Anna is three times as old as Jake. If x represents Jake's age, write an expression for Anna's age. $3x$

6. Rebecca downloaded twice as many songs as Nigel. If x represents the number of songs downloaded by Nigel, write an expression for the number downloaded by Rebecca. $2x$

7. Sidney made $20 more than three times Casey's weekly salary. If x represents Casey's weekly salary, write an expression for Sidney's weekly salary. $3x + 20$

8. David scored 26 points less than twice the number of points Rich scored in a video game. If x represents the number of points scored by Rich, write an expression representing the number of points scored by David. $2x - 26$

For Exercises 9–18, use the problem-solving flowchart on page 125. **(See Examples 1–3.)**

9. Six less than a number is −10. Find the number.
The number is −4.

10. Fifteen less than a number is 41. Find the number.   The number is 56.

11. Twice the sum of a number and seven is eight. Find the number.   The number is −3.

12. Twice the sum of a number and negative two is sixteen. Find the number.   The number is 10.

 Writing   Translating Expression   Geometry   Scientific Calculator   Video   NS&E

13. A number added to five is the same as twice the number. Find the number.
The number is 5.

14. Three times a number is the same as the difference of twice the number and seven. Find the number.   The number is −7.

15. The sum of six times a number and ten is equal to the difference of the number and fifteen. Find the number.   The number is −5.

16. The difference of fourteen and three times a number is the same as the sum of the number and negative ten. Find the number.
The number is 6.

17. If the difference of a number and four is tripled, the result is six more than the number. Find the number.   The number is 9.

18. Twice the sum of a number and eleven is twenty-two less than three times the number. Find the number.   The number is 44.

Concept 3: Consecutive Integer Problems

19. a. If x represents the smallest of three consecutive integers, write an expression to represent each of the next two consecutive integers. $x + 1, x + 2$

b. If x represents the largest of three consecutive integers, write an expression to represent each of the previous two consecutive integers. $x − 1, x − 2$

20. a. If x represents the smallest of three consecutive odd integers, write an expression to represent each of the next two consecutive odd integers. $x + 2, x + 4$

b. If x represents the largest of three consecutive odd integers, write an expression to represent each of the previous two consecutive odd integers. $x − 2, x − 4$

For Exercises 21–30, use the problem-solving flowchart from page 125. **(See Examples 4–5.)**

21. The sum of two consecutive integers is −67. Find the integers.   The integers are −34 and −33.

22. The sum of two consecutive odd integers is 52. Find the integers.   The integers are 25 and 27.

23. The sum of two consecutive odd integers is 28. Find the integers.   The integers are 13 and 15.

24. The sum of three consecutive even integers is 66. Find the integers.   The integers are 20, 22, and 24.

25. The perimeter of a pentagon (a five-sided polygon) is 80 in. The five sides are represented by consecutive integers. Find the measures of the sides.   The sides are 14 in., 15 in., 16 in., 17 in., and 18 in.

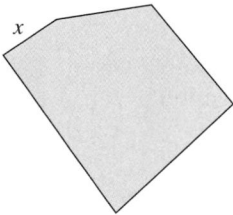

26. The perimeter of a triangle is 96 in. The lengths of the sides are represented by consecutive integers. Find the measures of the sides.   The sides are 31 in., 32 in., and 33 in.

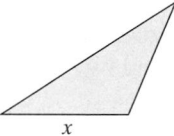

27. The sum of three consecutive even integers is 48 more than twice the smallest of the three integers. Find the integers.   The integers are 42, 44, and 46.

28. The sum of three consecutive odd integers is 89 more than twice the largest integer. Find the integers.   The integers are 91, 93, and 95.

29. Eight times the sum of three consecutive odd integers is 210 more than ten times the middle integer. Find the integers.   The integers are 13, 15, and 17.

30. Five times the sum of three consecutive even integers is 140 more than ten times the smallest. Find the integers.   The integers are 22, 24, and 26.

Concept 4: Applications of Linear Equations

For Exercises 31–42, use the problem-solving flowchart (page 125) to solve the problems.

31. A board is 86 cm in length and must be cut so that one piece is 20 cm longer than the other piece. Find the length of each piece. **(See Example 6.)**

The lengths of the pieces are 33 cm and 53 cm.

32. A rope is 54 in. in length and must be cut into two pieces. If one piece must be twice as long as the other, find the length of each piece.

The lengths of the pieces are 18 in. and 36 in.

33. Karen's age is 12 years more than Clarann's age. The sum of their ages is 58. Find their ages.

Karen's age is 35, and Clarann's age is 23.

34. Maria's age is 15 years less than Orlando's age. The sum of their ages is 29. Find their ages.

Maria's age is 7, and Orlando's age is 22.

35. For a recent year, 31 more Democrats than Republicans were in the U.S. House of Representatives. If the total number of representatives in the House from these two parties was 433, find the number of representatives from each party.

There were 201 Republicans and 232 Democrats.

36. For a recent year, the number of men in the U.S. Senate totaled 4 more than five times the number of women. Find the number of men and the number of women in the Senate given that the Senate has 100 members.

There were 84 men and 16 women.

37. Approximately 5.816 million people watch *The Oprah Winfrey Show*. This is 1.118 million more than watch *The Dr. Phil Show*. How many watch *The Dr. Phil Show*? (*Source: Neilson Media Research*) **(See Example 7.)**

4.698 million watch *The Dr. Phil Show*.

38. Two of the largest Internet retailers are e-Bay and Amazon.com. Recently, the estimated U.S. sales of e-Bay were $0.1 billion less than twice the sales of Amazon.com. Given the total sales of $5.6 billion, determine the sales of e-Bay and Amazon.com. e-Bay's sales were $3.7 billion and Amazon.com's sales were $1.9 billion.

39. The longest river in Africa is the Nile. It is 2455 km longer than the Congo River, also in Africa. The sum of the lengths of these rivers is 11,195 km. What is the length of each river? The Congo River is 4370 km long, and the Nile River is 6825 km.

Nile

Congo

40. The average depth of the Gulf of Mexico is three times the depth of the Red Sea. The difference between the average depths is 1078 m. What is the average depth of the Gulf of Mexico and the average depth of the Red Sea? The average depth of the Red Sea is 539 m and that of the Gulf of Mexico is 1617 m.

41. Asia and Africa are the two largest continents in the world. The land area of Asia is approximately 14,514,000 km² larger than the land area of Africa. Together their total area is 74,644,000 km². Find the land area of Asia and the land area of Africa. The area of Africa is 30,065,000 km². The area of Asia is 44,579,000 km².

42. Mt. Everest, the highest mountain in the world, is 2654 m higher than Mt. McKinley, the highest mountain in the United States. If the sum of their heights is 15,042 m, find the height of each mountain. Mt. McKinley is 6194 m high. Mt. Everest is 8848 m high.

Mixed Exercises

43. A group of hikers walked from Hawk Mt. Shelter to Blood Mt. Shelter along the Appalachian Trail, a total distance of 20.5 mi. It took 2 days for the walk. The second day the hikers walked 4.1 mi less than they did on the first day. How far did they walk each day? They walked 12.3 mi on the first day and 8.2 mi on the second.

 Writing   Translating Expression   Geometry   Scientific Calculator   Video   NS&E

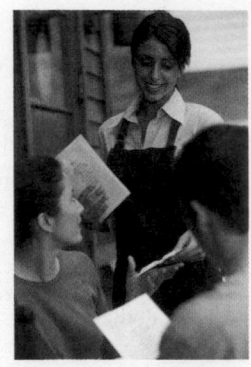

44. $120 is to be divided among three restaurant servers. Angie made $10 more than Marie. Gwen, who went home sick, made $25 less than Marie. How much money should each server get?   Marie made $45, Angie made $55, and Gwen made $20.

45. A 4-ft piece of PVC pipe is cut into three pieces. The longest piece is 12 in. longer than twice the shortest piece. The middle piece is 12 in. more than the shortest piece. How long is each piece?   The pieces are 6 in., 18 in., and 24 in.

46. A 6-ft piece of copper wire must be cut into three pieces. The shortest piece is 16 in. less than the middle piece. The longest piece is twice as long as the middle piece. How long is each piece?   The pieces are 6 in., 22 in., and 44 in.

47. Three consecutive integers are such that three times the largest exceeds the sum of the two smaller integers by 47. Find the integers.
The integers are 42, 43, and 44.

48. Four times the smallest of three consecutive odd integers is 236 more than the sum of the other two integers. Find the integers.   The integers are 121, 123, and 125.

49. In a recent year, the estimated earnings for Jennifer Lopez was $2.5 million more than half of the earnings for the band U2. If the total earnings were $106 million, what were the earnings for Jennifer Lopez and U2? (*Source: Forbes*)   Jennifer Lopez made $37 million, and U2 made $69 million.

50. Two of the longest-running TV series are *Gunsmoke* and *The Simpsons. Gunsmoke* ran 97 fewer episodes than twice the number of *The Simpsons*. If the total number of episodes is 998, how many of each show was produced?   There are 633 episodes of *Gunsmoke* and 365 episodes of *The Simpsons*.

51. Five times the difference of a number and three is four less than four times the number. Find the number.   The number is 11.

52. Three times the difference of a number and seven is one less than twice the number. Find the number.   The number is 20.

53. The sum of the page numbers on two facing pages in a book is 941. What are the page numbers?
The page numbers are 470 and 471.

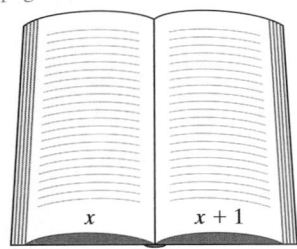

54. Three raffle tickets are represented by three consecutive integers. If the sum of the three integers is 2,666,031, find the numbers.   The ticket numbers are 888,676; 888,677; and 888,678.

55. If three is added to five times a number, the result is forty-three more than the number. Find the number.   The number is 10.

56. If seven is added to three times a number, the result is thirty-one more than the number.   The number is 12.

57. The deepest point in the Pacific Ocean is 676 m more than twice the deepest point in the Arctic Ocean. If the deepest point in the Pacific is 10,920 m, how many meters is the deepest point in the Arctic Ocean?   The deepest point in the Arctic Ocean is 5122 m.

58. The area of Greenland is 201,900 km^2 less than three times the area of New Guinea. What is the area of New Guinea if the area of Greenland is 2,175,600 km^2?   The area of New Guinea is 792,500 km^2.

59. The sum of twice a number and $\frac{3}{4}$ is the same as the difference of four times the number and $\frac{1}{8}$. Find the number.   The number is $\frac{7}{16}$.

60. The difference of a number and $-\frac{11}{12}$ is the same as the difference of three times the number and $\frac{1}{6}$. Find the number.   The number is $\frac{13}{24}$.

61. The product of a number and 3.86 is equal to 7.15 more than the number. Find the number.   The number is 2.5.

62. The product of a number and 4.6 is 33.12 less than the number. Find the number.   The number is −9.2.

Applications Involving Percents

1. Basic Percent Equations

In Section A.1 in the appendix, we define the word *percent* as meaning "per hundred."

Percent	Interpretation
63% of homes have a computer	63 out of 100 homes have a computer.
5% sales tax	5¢ in tax is charged for every 100¢ in merchandise.
15% commission	$15 is earned in commission for every $100 sold.

Concepts

1. **Basic Percent Equations**
2. **Applications Involving Simple Interest**
3. **Applications Involving Discount and Markup**

Percents come up in a variety of applications in day-to-day life. Many such applications follow the basic percent equation.

$$\text{Amount} = (\text{percent})(\text{base}) \qquad \text{Basic percent equation}$$

In Example 1, we apply the basic percent equation to compute sales tax.

Example 1 Computing Sales Tax

A new digital camera costs $429.95.

  a. Compute the sales tax if the tax rate is 4%.

  b. Determine the total cost, including tax.

Solution:

  a. Let x represent the amount of tax.

   Amount = (percent) · (base)

   Sales tax = (tax rate)(price of merchandise)

   $x = (0.04)(\$429.95)$

   $x = \$17.198$

   $x = \$17.20$

   The tax on the merchandise is $17.20.

Step 1: Read the problem.

Step 2: Label the variable.

Step 3: Write a verbal equation. Apply the percent equation to compute sales tax.

Step 4: Write a mathematical equation.

Step 5: Solve the equation.

   Round to the nearest cent.

Step 6: Interpret the results.

Classroom Example: p. 140, Exercise 18

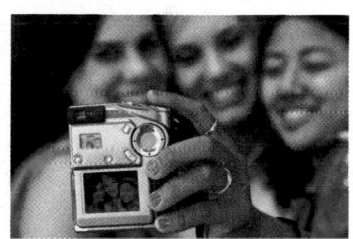

Avoiding Mistakes

Be sure to use the decimal form of a percent within an equation.

$$4\% = 0.04$$

  b. The total cost is found by:

   total cost = cost of merchandise + amount of tax

   Therefore the total cost is $429.95 + $17.20 = $447.15.

Skill Practice

1. Find the amount of tax on a portable CD player that sells for $89. Assume the tax rate is 6%.
2. Find the total cost including tax.

In Example 2, we solve a problem in which the percent is unknown.

Classroom Example: p. 140, Exercise 22

Example 2   Finding an Unknown Percent

A group of 240 college men were asked what intramural sport they most enjoyed playing. The results are in the graph. What percent of the men surveyed preferred tennis?

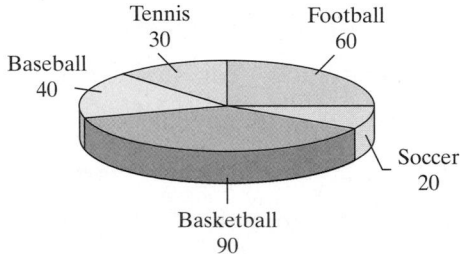

Tennis 30   Football 60   Baseball 40   Soccer 20   Basketball 90

Solution:

Step 1: Read the problem.

Let x represent the unknown percent.   **Step 2:** Label the variable.

The problem can be rephrased as:

30 is what percent of 240?   **Step 3:** Write an equation in words.

$$30 = x \cdot 240$$ **Step 4:** Write a mathematical equation.

$$30 = 240x$$ **Step 5:** Solve the equation.

$$\frac{30}{240} = \frac{240x}{240}$$ Divide both sides by 240.

$$0.125 = x$$

$$0.125 \times 100\% = 12.5\%$$ **Step 6:** Interpret the results. Change the value of x to a percent by multiplying by 100%.

In this survey, 12.5% of men prefer tennis.

Skill Practice   Refer to the graph in Example 2.

3. What percent of the men surveyed prefer basketball as their favorite intramural sport?

Answers

1. The amount of tax is $5.34.
2. The total cost is $94.34.
3. 37.5% of the men surveyed prefer basketball.

Example 3	Solving a Percent Equation with an Unknown Base

Classroom Example: p. 140, Exercise 24

Andrea spends 20% of her monthly paycheck on rent each month. If her rent payment is $750, what is her monthly paycheck?

Solution:

	Step 1:	Read the problem.
Let x represent the amount of Andrea's monthly paycheck.	**Step 2:**	Label the variables.

The problem can be rephrased as:

$750 is 20% of what number?	**Step 3:**	Write an equation in words.
$\downarrow\ \ \downarrow\ \ \downarrow\ \ \ \downarrow\ \ \ \downarrow$		
$750 = 0.20\ \cdot\ \ x$	**Step 4:**	Write a mathematical equation.
$750 = 0.20x$	**Step 5:**	Solve the equation.
$\dfrac{750}{0.20} = \dfrac{0.20x}{0.20}$		Divide both sides by 0.20.
$3750 = x$		

Andrea's monthly paycheck is $3750.	**Step 6:**	Interpret the results.

Skill Practice

4. In order to pass an exam, a student must answer 70% of the questions correctly. If answering 42 questions correctly results in a 70% score, how many questions are on the test?

2. Applications Involving Simple Interest

One important application of percents is in computing simple interest on a loan or on an investment.

   Simple interest is interest that is earned on principal (the original amount of money invested in an account). The following formula is used to compute simple interest:

$$\begin{pmatrix} \text{Simple} \\ \text{interest} \end{pmatrix} = \begin{pmatrix} \text{principal} \\ \text{invested} \end{pmatrix} \begin{pmatrix} \text{annual} \\ \text{interest rate} \end{pmatrix} \begin{pmatrix} \text{time} \\ \text{in years} \end{pmatrix}$$

This formula is often written symbolically as $I = Prt$.

Answer

4. There are 60 questions on the test.

For example, to find the simple interest earned on $2000 invested at 7.5% interest for 3 years, we have

$$I = Prt$$

$$\text{Interest} = (\$2000)(0.075)(3)$$

$$= \$450$$

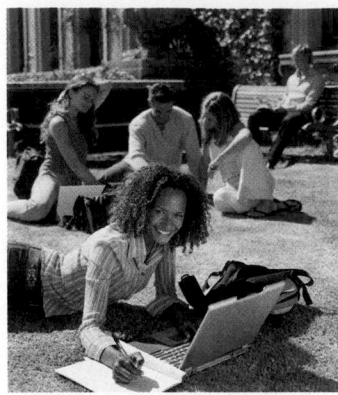

Avoiding Mistakes

The interest is computed on the original principal, P, not on the total amount $4340. That is, the interest is $P(0.06)(4)$, not ($4340)(0.06)(4).

Example 4   **Applying Simple Interest**

Jorge wants to save money for his daughter's college education. If Jorge needs to have $4340 at the end of 4 years, how much money would he need to invest at a 6% simple interest rate?

Solution:

	Step 1: Read the problem.
Let P represent the original amount invested.	**Step 2:** Label the variables.

$$\left(\begin{array}{c}\text{Original}\\\text{principal}\end{array}\right) + (\text{interest}) = (\text{total})$$

Step 3: Write an equation in words.

$$(P) \quad + \quad (Prt) \quad = (\text{total})$$

$$P \quad + \quad P(0.06)(4) = 4340$$

Step 4: Write a mathematical equation.

$$P + 0.24P = 4340$$

$$1.24P = 4340$$

Step 5: Solve the equation.

$$\frac{1.24P}{1.24} = \frac{4340}{1.24}$$

$$P = 3500$$

The original investment should be $3500.

Step 6: Interpret the results and write the answer in words.

Skill Practice

5. Cassandra invested some money in her bank account, and after 10 years at 4% simple interest, it has grown to $7700. What was the initial amount invested?

3. Applications Involving Discount and Markup

Applications involving percent increase and percent decrease are abundant in many real-world settings. Sales tax, for example, is essentially a markup by a state or local government. It is important to understand that percent increase or decrease is always computed on the original amount given.

In Example 5, we illustrate an example of percent decrease in an application where merchandise is discounted.

Answer

5. The initial investment was $5500.

Example 5 **Applying Percents to a Discount Problem**

After a 38% discount, a used treadmill costs $868 on e-Bay. What was the original cost of the treadmill?

Classroom Example: p. 141, Exercise 36

Solution:

	Step 1:	Read the problem.
Let x be the original cost of the treadmill.	**Step 2:**	Label the variables.
$\left(\begin{array}{c}\text{Original}\\\text{cost}\end{array}\right) - (\text{discount}) = \left(\begin{array}{c}\text{sale}\\\text{price}\end{array}\right)$	**Step 3:**	Write an equation in words.
$x \quad - \quad 0.38(x) \quad = \quad 868$	**Step 4:**	Write a mathematical equation. The discount is a percent of the *original* amount.

$x - 0.38x = 868$	**Step 5:**	Solve the equation.
$0.62x = 868$		Combine *like* terms.
$\dfrac{0.62x}{0.62} = \dfrac{868}{0.62}$		Divide by 0.62.
$x = 1400$		

The original cost of the treadmill was $1400.	**Step 6:**	Interpret the result.

Skill Practice

6. An iPod is on sale for $151.20. This is after a 20% discount. What was the original cost of the iPod?

Answer

6. The iPod originally cost $189.

Section 2.5 Practice Exercises

Boost *your* GRADE at ALEKS.com!

ALEKS® version 3.0

• Practice Problems
• Self-Tests
• NetTutor

• e-Professors
• Videos

For additional exercises, see Classroom Activities 2.5A–2.5D in the *Instructor's Resource Manual* at www.mhhe.com/moh.

Study Skills Exercises

1. It is always helpful to read the material in a section and make notes before it is presented in class. Writing notes ahead of time will free you to listen more in class and to pay special attention to the concepts that need clarification. Refer to your class syllabus and identity the next two sections that will be covered in class. Then determine a time when you can read these sections before class.

2. Define the key term **simple interest**.

Review Exercises

For Exercises 3–4, use the steps for problem solving to solve these applications.

3. Find two consecutive integers such that three times the larger is the same as 45 more than the smaller.
   The integers are 21 and 22.

4. The height of the Great Pyramid of Giza is 17 m more than twice the height of the pyramid found in Saqqara. If the difference in their heights is 77 m, find the height of each pyramid.
   The pyramid at Saqqara is 60 m high, and the Great Pyramid is 137 m high.

 Writing Translating Expression Geometry Scientific Calculator Video

Concept 1: Basic Percent Equations

For Exercises 5–16, find the missing values.

5. 45 is what percent of 360? 12.5%

6. 338 is what percent of 520? 65%

7. 544 is what percent of 640? 85%

8. 576 is what percent of 800? 72%

9. What is 0.5% of 150? 0.75

10. What is 9.5% of 616? 58.52

11. What is 142% of 740? 1050.8

12. What is 156% of 280? 436.8

13. 177 is 20% of what number? 885

14. 126 is 15% of what number? 840

15. 275 is 12.5% of what number? 2200

16. 594 is 45% of what number? 1320

17. A Craftsman drill is on sale for $99.99. If the sales tax rate is 7%, how much will Molly have to pay for the drill? **(See Example 1.)** Molly will have to pay $106.99.

18. Patrick purchased four new tires that were regularly priced at $94.99 each, but are on sale for $20 off per tire. If the sales tax rate is 6%, how much will be charged to Patrick's VISA card? Patrick will have to pay $317.96.

For Exercises 19–22, use the graph showing the distribution for leading forms of cancer in men. (*Source:* Centers for Disease Control)

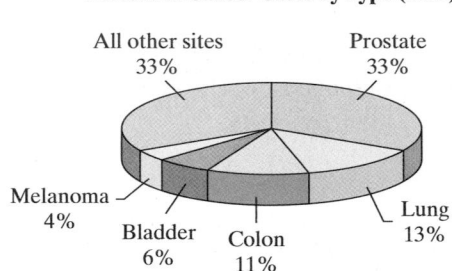

Percent of Cancer Cases by Type (Men)

19. If there are 700,000 cases of cancer in men in the United States, approximately how many are prostate cancer?
Approximately 231,000 cases

20. Approximately how many cases of lung cancer would be expected in 700,000 cancer cases among men in the United States?
Approximately 91,000 cases

21. There were 14,000 cases of cancer of the pancreas diagnosed out of 700,000 cancer cases. What percent is this? **(See Example 2.)** 2%

22. There were 21,000 cases of leukemia diagnosed out of 700,000 cancer cases. What percent is this? 3%

23. Javon is in a 28% tax bracket for his federal income tax. If the amount of money that he paid for federal income tax was $23,520, what was his taxable income? **(See Example 3.)**
Javon's taxable income was $84,000.

24. In a recent survey of college-educated adults, 155 indicated that they regularly work more than 50 hr a week. If this represents 31% of those surveyed, how many people were in the survey?
There were 500 people in the survey.

Concept 2: Applications Involving Simple Interest

25. Aidan is trying to save money and has $1800 to set aside in some type of savings account. He checked his bank one day, and found that the rate for a 12-month CD had an annual percentage yield (APY) of 4.25%. The interest rate on his savings account was 2.75% APY. How much more simple interest would Aidan earn if he invested in a CD for 12 months rather than leaving the $1800 in a regular savings account?
Aidan would earn $27 more in the CD.

26. How much interest will Roxanne have to pay if she borrows $2000 for 2 years at a simple interest rate of 4%?
Roxanne will have to pay $160.

27. Bob borrowed money for 1 year at 5% simple interest. If he had to pay back a total of $1260, how much did he originally borrow? **(See Example 4.)** Bob borrowed $1200.

28. Mike borrowed some money for 2 years at 6% simple interest. If he had to pay back a total of $3640, how much did he originally borrow? Mike borrowed $3250.

29. If $1500 grows to $1950 after 5 years, find the simple interest rate.   The rate is 6%.

30. If $9000 grows to $10,440 in 2 years, find the simple interest rate.   The rate is 8%.

31. Perry is planning a vacation to Europe in 2 years. How much should he invest in a certificate of deposit that pays 3% simple interest to get the $3500 that he needs for the trip? Round to the nearest dollar.   Perry needs to invest $3302.

32. Sherica invested in a mutual fund and at the end of 20 years she has $14,300 in her account. If the mutual fund returned an average yield of 8%, how much did she originally invest?   Sherica invested $5500.

Concept 3: Applications Involving Discount and Markup

33. A Pioneer car CD/MP3 player costs $170. Best Buy has it on sale for 12% off with free installation.

   a. What is the discount on the CD/MP3 player?
   $20.40
   b. What is the sale price? $149.60

34. A laptop computer, originally selling for $899, is on sale for 10% off.

   a. What is the discount on the laptop? $89.90

   b. What is the sale price? $809.10

35. A Sony digital camera is on sale for $400. This price is 15% off the original price. What was the original price? Round to the nearest cent. **(See Example 5.)**   The original price was $470.59.

36. The *Star Wars: Episode III* DVD is on sale for $18. If this represents an 18% discount rate, what was the original price of the DVD?   The original price was $21.95.

37. The original price of an Audio Jukebox was $250. It is on sale for $220. What percent discount does this represent?   The discount rate is 12%.

38. During the holiday season, the Xbox 360 sold for $425.00 in stores. This product was in such demand that it sold for $800 online. What percent markup does this represent? (Round to the nearest whole percent.)   The markup rate is 88%.

39. In one area, the cable company marked up the monthly cost by 6%. The new cost is $63.60 per month. What was the cost before the increase?   The original cost was $60.

40. A doctor ordered a dosage of medicine for a patient. After 2 days, she increased the dosage by 20% and the new dosage came to 18 cc. What was the original dosage?   The original dosage was 15 cc.

Mixed Exercises

41. Sun Lei bought a laptop computer for $1800. The total cost, including tax, came to $1890. What is the tax rate?   The tax rate is 5%.

42. Jamie purchased a compact disk and paid $18.26. If the disk price is $16.99, what is the sales tax rate (round to the nearest tenth of a percent)?   The tax rate is 7.5%.

43. To discourage tobacco use and to increase state revenue, several states tax tobacco products. One year, the state of New York increased taxes on tobacco, resulting in a 32% increase in the retail price of a pack of cigarettes. If the new price of a pack of cigarettes is $6.86, what was the cost before the increase in tax?   The original cost was $5.20 per pack.

44. A hotel room rented for 5 nights costs $706.25 including 13% in taxes. Find the original price of the room (before tax) for the 5 nights. Then find the price per night.   The 5 nights (without tax) costs $625. The price per night is $125.

 Writing   Translating Expression   Geometry   Scientific Calculator   Video   NS&E

45. Deon purchased a house and sold it for a 24% profit. If he sold the house for $260,400, what was the original purchase price? The original price was $210,000.

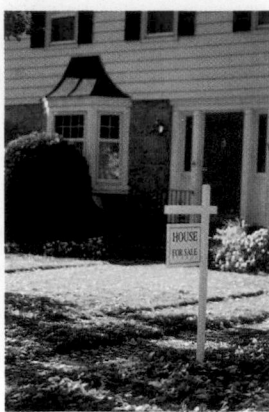

46. To meet the rising cost of energy, the yearly membership at a YMCA had to be increased by 12.5% from the past year. The yearly membership fee is currently $450. What was the cost of membership last year? The cost was $400.

47. Alina earns $1600 per month plus a 12% commission on pharmaceutical sales. If she sold $25,000 in pharmaceuticals one month, what was her salary that month? Alina made $4600 that month.

48. Dan sold a beachfront home for $650,000. If his commission rate is 4%, what did he earn in commission? Dan earned $26,000.

49. Diane sells women's sportswear at a department store. She earns a regular salary and, as a bonus, she receives a commission of 4% on all sales over $200. If Diane earned an extra $25.80 last week in commission, how much merchandise did she sell over $200? Diane sold $645 over $200 worth of merchandise.

50. For selling software, Tom received a bonus commission based on sales over $500. If he received $180 in commission for selling a total of $2300 worth of software, what is his commission rate? Tom's commission rate is 10%.

Section 2.6 Formulas and Applications of Geometry

Concepts

1. **Literal Equations and Formulas**
2. **Geometry Applications**

1. Literal Equations and Formulas

Literal equations are equations that contain several variables. A formula is a literal equation with a specific application. For example, the perimeter of a triangle (distance around the triangle) can be found by the formula $P = a + b + c$, where a, b, and c are the lengths of the sides (Figure 2-7).

$$P = a + b + c$$
$$= 5 \text{ ft} + 7 \text{ ft} + 8 \text{ ft}$$
$$= 20 \text{ ft}$$

Figure 2-7

In this section, we will learn how to rewrite formulas to solve for a different variable within the formula. Suppose, for example, that the perimeter of a triangle is known and two of the sides are known (say, sides a and b). Then the third side, c, can be found by subtracting the lengths of the known sides from the perimeter (Figure 2-8).

$b = 7$ ft

$a = 5$ ft

$c = ?$

If the perimeter is 20 ft, then
$c = P - a - b$
$= 20$ ft $- 5$ ft $- 7$ ft
$= 8$ ft

Figure 2-8

To solve a formula for a different variable, we use the same properties of equality outlined in the earlier sections of this chapter. For example, consider the two equations $2x + 3 = 11$ and $wx + y = z$. Suppose we want to solve for x in each case:

$2x + 3 = 11$		$wx + y = z$	
$2x + 3 - 3 = 11 - 3$	Subtract 3.	$wx + y - y = z - y$	Subtract y.
$2x = 8$		$wx = z - y$	
$\dfrac{2x}{2} = \dfrac{8}{2}$	Divide by 2.	$\dfrac{wx}{w} = \dfrac{z - y}{w}$	Divide by w.
$x = 4$		$x = \dfrac{z - y}{w}$	

The equation on the left has only one variable and we are able to simplify the equation to find a numerical value for x. The equation on the right has multiple variables. Because we do not know the values of w, y, and z, we are not able to simplify further. The value of x is left as a formula in terms of w, y, and z.

Example 1 **Solving for an Indicated Variable**

Solve for the indicated variable.

a. $d = rt$ for t **b.** $5x + 2y = 12$ for y

Solution:

a. $d = rt$ for t The goal is to isolate the variable t.

$\dfrac{d}{r} = \dfrac{rt}{r}$ Because the relationship between r and t is multiplication, we reverse the process by dividing both sides by r.

$\dfrac{d}{r} = t$, or equivalently $t = \dfrac{d}{r}$

b. $5x + 2y = 12$ for y The goal is to solve for y.

$5x - 5x + 2y = 12 - 5x$ Subtract $5x$ from both sides to isolate the y-term.

$2y = -5x + 12$ $-5x + 12$ is the same as $12 - 5x$.

$\dfrac{2y}{2} = \dfrac{-5x + 12}{2}$ Divide both sides by 2 to isolate y.

$y = \dfrac{-5x + 12}{2}$

Classroom Examples: p. 149, Exercises 16 and 24

Avoiding Mistakes

In the expression $\dfrac{-5x + 12}{2}$ do not try to divide the 2 into the 12. The divisor of 2 is dividing the entire quantity, $-5x + 12$ (not just the 12).

We may, however, apply the divisor to each term individually in the numerator. That is,

$y = \dfrac{-5x + 12}{2}$ can be written in several different forms. Each is correct.

$$y = \frac{-5x + 12}{2} \quad \text{or} \quad y = \frac{-5x}{2} + \frac{12}{2} \quad \Rightarrow \quad y = -\frac{5}{2}x + 6$$

Skill Practice Solve for the indicated variable.

1. $A = lw$ for l 2. $-2a + 4b = 7$ for a

Classroom Example: p. 149, Exercise 36

Example 2   Solving for an Indicated Variable

The formula $C = \frac{5}{9}(F - 32)$ is used to find the temperature, C, in degrees Celsius for a given temperature expressed in degrees Fahrenheit, F. Solve the formula $C = \frac{5}{9}(F - 32)$ for F.

Solution:

$$C = \frac{5}{9}(F - 32)$$

$$C = \frac{5}{9}F - \frac{5}{9} \cdot 32 \qquad \text{Clear parentheses.}$$

$$C = \frac{5}{9}F - \frac{160}{9} \qquad \text{Multiply: } \frac{5}{9} \cdot \frac{32}{1} = \frac{160}{9}.$$

$$9(C) = 9\left(\frac{5}{9}F - \frac{160}{9}\right) \qquad \text{Multiply by the LCD to clear fractions.}$$

$$9C = \frac{9}{1} \cdot \frac{5}{9}F - \frac{9}{1} \cdot \frac{160}{9} \qquad \text{Apply the distributive property.}$$

$$9C = 5F - 160 \qquad \text{Simplify.}$$

$$9C + 160 = 5F - 160 + 160 \qquad \text{Add 160 to both sides.}$$

$$9C + 160 = 5F$$

$$\frac{9C + 160}{5} = \frac{5F}{5} \qquad \text{Divide both sides by 5.}$$

$$\frac{9C + 160}{5} = F$$

The answer may be written in several forms:

$$F = \frac{9C + 160}{5} \quad \text{or} \quad F = \frac{9C}{5} + \frac{160}{5} \quad \Rightarrow \quad F = \frac{9}{5}C + 32$$

Skill Practice Solve for the indicated variable.

3. $y = \dfrac{1}{3}(x - 7)$ for x.

Answers

1. $l = \dfrac{A}{w}$

2. $a = \dfrac{7 - 4b}{-2}$ or $a = \dfrac{4b - 7}{2}$

3. $x = 3y + 7$

2. Geometry Applications

In Section A.2, we review numerous facts and formulas relating to geometry. There are also geometry formulas on the inside back cover of the text for quick reference.

Example 3	Solving a Geometry Application Involving Perimeter

Classroom Example: p. 149, Exercise 46

The length of a rectangular lot is 1 m less than twice the width. If the perimeter is 190 m, find the length and width.

Solution:

Step 1: Read the problem.

Let x represent the width of the rectangle.　　**Step 2:** Label the variables.

Then $2x - 1$ represents the length.

x

$2x - 1$

$$P = 2l + 2w$$ 　　**Step 3:** Perimeter formula

$$190 = 2(2x - 1) + 2(x)$$ 　　**Step 4:** Write an equation in terms of x.

$$190 = 4x - 2 + 2x$$ 　　**Step 5:** Solve for x.

$$190 = 6x - 2$$

$$192 = 6x$$

$$\frac{192}{6} = \frac{6x}{6}$$

$$32 = x$$

The width is $x = 32$.　　**Step 6:** Interpret the results and write the answer in words.

The length is $2x - 1 = 2(32) - 1 = 63$.

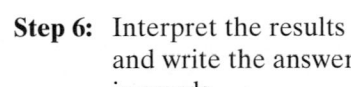
The width of the rectangular lot is 32 m and the length is 63 m.

Skill Practice

4. The length of a rectangle is 10 ft less than twice the width. If the perimeter is 178 ft find the length and width.

Recall some facts about angles.

- Two angles are complementary if the sum of their measures is 90°.
- Two angles are supplementary if the sum of their measures is 180°.
- The sum of the measures of the angles within a triangle is 180°.
- Vertical angles are equal in measure.

Answer

4. The length is 56 ft, and the width is 33 ft.

Classroom Example: p. 150,
Exercise 50

Example 4 **Solving a Geometry Application Involving
Complementary Angles**

Two complementary angles are drawn such that one angle is 4° more than seven times the other angle. Find the measure of each angle.

Solution:

| | **Step 1:** | Read the problem. |

Let x represent the measure of one angle.   **Step 2:** Label the variables.

Then $7x + 4$ represents the measure of the other angle.

The angles are complementary, so their sum must be 90°.

$$\left(\begin{array}{c}\text{Measure of} \\ \text{first angle}\end{array}\right) + \left(\begin{array}{c}\text{measure of} \\ \text{second angle}\end{array}\right) = 90°$$ **Step 3:** Create a verbal equation.

$$x \quad + \quad 7x + 4 \quad = 90$$ **Step 4:** Write a mathematical equation.

$$8x + 4 = 90$$ **Step 5:** Solve for x.

$$8x = 86$$

$$\frac{8x}{8} = \frac{86}{8}$$

$$x = 10.75$$

One angle is $x = 10.75$.   **Step 6:** Interpret the results and write the answer in words.

The other angle is $7x + 4 = 7(10.75) + 4 = 79.25$.

The angles are 10.75° and 79.25°.

Skill Practice

5. Two complementary angles are constructed so that one measures 1° less than six times the other. Find the measures of the angles.

Classroom Example: p. 150,
Exercise 58

Example 5 **Solving a Geometry Application Involving
Angles in a Triangle**

One angle in a triangle is twice as large as the smallest angle. The third angle is 10° more than seven times the smallest angle. Find the measure of each angle.

Solution:

| | **Step 1:** | Read the problem. |

Let x represent the measure of the smallest angle.   **Step 2:** Label the variables.

Then $2x$ and $7x + 10$ represent the measures of the other two angles.

The sum of the angles must be 180°.

Answer

5. The angles are 13° and 77°.

$$\left(\begin{matrix}\text{Measure of} \\ \text{first angle}\end{matrix}\right) + \left(\begin{matrix}\text{measure of} \\ \text{second angle}\end{matrix}\right) + \left(\begin{matrix}\text{measure of} \\ \text{third angle}\end{matrix}\right) = 180°$$

Step 3: Create a verbal equation.

$$x \quad + \quad 2x \quad + \quad (7x + 10) \ = 180$$

Step 4: Write a mathematical equation.

$$x + 2x + 7x + 10 = 180$$

Step 5: Solve for x.

$$10x + 10 = 180$$

$$10x = 170$$

$$x = 17$$

Step 6: Interpret the results and write the answer in words.

The smallest angle is $x = 17$.

The other angles are $2x = 2(17) = 34$

$$7x + 10 = 7(17) + 10 = 129$$

The angles are $17°, 34°,$ and $129°$.

Skill Practice

6. In a triangle, the measure of the first angle is $80°$ greater than the measure of the second angle. The measure of the third angle is twice that of the second. Find the measures of the angles.

Example 6   **Solving a Geometry Application Involving Circumference**

Classroom Example: p. 151, Exercise 66

The distance around a circular garden is 188.4 ft. Find the radius to the nearest tenth of a foot (Figure 2-9). Use 3.14 for π.

Solution:

$$C = 2\pi r \qquad \text{Use the formula for the circumference of a circle.}$$

$$188.4 = 2\pi r \qquad \text{Substitute 188.4 for } C.$$

$$\frac{188.4}{2\pi} = \frac{2\pi r}{2\pi} \qquad \text{Divide both sides by } 2\pi.$$

$$\frac{188.4}{2\pi} = r$$

$$r \approx \frac{188.4}{2(3.14)}$$

$$= 30.0$$

TIP: The symbol $\approx$ means "is approximately equal to."

The radius is approximately 30.0 ft.

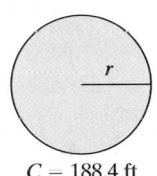

$C = 188.4$ ft

Figure 2-9

Skill Practice

7. The circumference of a drain pipe is 12.5 cm. Find the radius. Round to the nearest tenth of a centimeter.

Answers

6. The angles are $25°, 50°,$ and $105°$.
7. The radius is 2.0 cm.

Calculator Connections

Topic: Using the π Key on a Calculator

In Example 6 we could have obtained a more accurate result if we had used the π key on the calculator.

Note that parentheses are required to divide 188.4 by the quantity 2π. This guarantees that the calculator follows the implied order of operations. Without parentheses, the calculator would divide 188.4 by 2 and then multiply the result by π.

Scientific Calculator

Enter: 188.4 ÷ (2 × π) =   **Result:** 29.98479128 correct

Enter: 188.4 ÷ 2 × π =   **Result:** 295.938028 incorrect

Graphing Calculator

188.4/(2π)
              29.98479128 ← Correct
188.4/2π
              295.938028 ← Incorrect

Calculator Exercises

Approximate the expressions with a calculator. Round to three decimal places if necessary.

1. $\dfrac{880}{2\pi}$ 140.056

2. $\dfrac{1600}{\pi(4)^2}$ 31.831

3. $\dfrac{20}{5\pi}$ 1.273

4. $\dfrac{10}{7\pi}$ 0.455

Section 2.6 Practice Exercises

Study Skills Exercises

1. A good technique for studying for a test is to choose four problems from each section of the chapter and write the problems along with the directions on a 3 × 5 card. On the back of the card, put the page number where you found that problem. Then shuffle the cards and test yourself on the procedure to solve each problem. If you find one that you do not know how to solve, look at the page number and do several of that type. Write four problems you would choose for this section.

2. Define the key term **literal equation**.

Review Exercises

For Exercises 3–8, solve the equation.

3. $3(2y + 3) - 4(-y + 1) = 7y - 10$ $\{-5\}$

4. $-(3w + 4) + 5(w - 2) - 3(6w - 8) = 10$ $\{0\}$

5. $\dfrac{1}{2}(x - 3) + \dfrac{3}{4} = 3x - \dfrac{3}{4}$ $\{0\}$

6. $\dfrac{5}{6}x + \dfrac{1}{2} = \dfrac{1}{4}(x - 4)$ $\left\{-\dfrac{18}{7}\right\}$

7. $0.5(y + 2) - 0.3 = 0.4y + 0.5$ $\{-2\}$

8. $0.25(500 - x) + 0.15x = 75$ $\{500\}$

 Writing   Translating Expression   Geometry   Scientific Calculator Video NS&E

Concept 1: Literal Equations and Formulas

For Exercises 9–40, solve for the indicated variable. **(See Examples 1–2.)**

9. $P = a + b + c$ for a
$a = P - b - c$

10. $P = a + b + c$ for b
$b = P - a - c$

11. $x = y - z$ for y
$y = x + z$

12. $c + d = e$ for d
$d = e - c$

13. $p = 250 + q$ for q
$q = p - 250$

14. $y = 35 + x$ for x
$x = y - 35$

15. $A = bh$ for b $b = \dfrac{A}{h}$

16. $d = rt$ for r $r = \dfrac{d}{t}$

17. $PV = nrt$ for t $t = \dfrac{PV}{nr}$

18. $P_1V_1 = P_2V_2$ for V_1 $V_1 = \dfrac{P_2V_2}{P_1}$

19. $x - y = 5$ for x $x = 5 + y$

20. $x + y = -2$ for y $y = -2 - x$

21. $3x + y = -19$ for y
$y = -3x - 19$

22. $x - 6y = -10$ for x
$x = 6y - 10$

23. $2x + 3y = 6$ for y
$y = \dfrac{-2x + 6}{3}$ or $y = -\dfrac{2}{3}x + 2$

24. $7x + 3y = 1$ for y
$y = \dfrac{-7x + 1}{3}$ or $y = -\dfrac{7}{3}x + \dfrac{1}{3}$

25. $-2x - y = 9$ for x
$x = \dfrac{y + 9}{-2}$ or $x = -\dfrac{1}{2}y - \dfrac{9}{2}$

26. $3x - y = -13$ for x
$x = \dfrac{y - 13}{3}$ or $x = \dfrac{1}{3}y - \dfrac{13}{3}$

27. $4x - 3y = 12$ for y
$y = \dfrac{-4x + 12}{-3}$ or $y = \dfrac{4}{3}x - 4$

28. $6x - 3y = 4$ for y
$y = \dfrac{-6x + 4}{-3}$ or $y = 2x - \dfrac{4}{3}$

29. $ax + by = c$ for y
$y = \dfrac{-ax + c}{b}$ or $y = -\dfrac{a}{b}x + \dfrac{c}{b}$

30. $ax + by = c$ for x
$x = \dfrac{-by + c}{a}$ or $x = -\dfrac{b}{a}y + \dfrac{c}{a}$

31. $A = P(1 + rt)$ for t
$t = \dfrac{A - P}{Pr}$ or $t = \dfrac{A}{Pr} - \dfrac{1}{r}$

32. $P = 2(L + w)$ for L
$L = \dfrac{P - 2w}{2}$ or $L = \dfrac{P}{2} - w$

33. $a = 2(b + c)$ for c
$c = \dfrac{a - 2b}{2}$ or $c = \dfrac{a}{2} - b$

34. $3(x + y) = z$ for x
$x = \dfrac{z - 3y}{3}$ or $x = \dfrac{z}{3} - y$

35. $Q = \dfrac{x + y}{2}$ for y
$y = 2Q - x$

36. $Q = \dfrac{a - b}{2}$ for a
$a = 2Q + b$

37. $M = \dfrac{a}{S}$ for a
$a = MS$

38. $A = \dfrac{1}{3}(a + b + c)$ for c
$c = 3A - a - b$

39. $P = I^2R$ for R $R = \dfrac{P}{I^2}$

40. $F = \dfrac{GMm}{d^2}$ for m $m = \dfrac{Fd^2}{GM}$

Concept 2: Geometry Applications

For Exercises 41–62, use the problem-solving flowchart (page 125) from Section 2.4.

41. The perimeter of a rectangular garden is 24 ft. The length is 2 ft more than the width. Find the length and the width of the garden. **(See Example 3.)**
The length is 7 ft, and the width is 5 ft.

42. In a small rectangular wallet photo, the width is 7 cm less than the length. If the border (perimeter) of the photo is 34 cm, find length and width.
The length is 12 cm, and the width is 5 cm.

43. The length of a rectangular parking area is four times the width. The perimeter is 300 yd. Find the length and width of the parking area. The length is 120 yd and the width is 30 yd.

44. The width of Jason's workbench is $\frac{1}{2}$ the length. The perimeter is 240 in. Find the length and the width of the workbench. The length is 80 in. and the width is 40 in.

45. A builder buys a rectangular lot of land such that the length is 5 m less than two times the width. If the perimeter is 590 m, find the length and the width. The length is 195 m, and the width is 100 m.

46. The perimeter of a rectangular pool is 140 yd. If the length is 20 yd less than twice the width, find the length and the width.
The length is 40 yd, and the width is 30 yd.

$2w - 5$

w

$2w - 20$

w

47. A triangular parking lot has two sides that are the same length and the third side is 5 m longer. If the perimeter is 71 m, find the lengths of the sides. The sides are 22 m, 22 m, and 27 m.

48. The perimeter of a triangle is 16 ft. One side is 3 ft longer than the shortest side. The third side is 1 ft longer than the shortest side. Find the lengths of all the sides. The sides are 4 ft, 5 ft, and 7 ft.

49. Sometimes memory devices are helpful for remembering mathematical facts. Recall that the sum of two complementary angles is 90°. That is, two complementary angles when added together form a right angle or "corner." The words *Complementary* and *Corner* both start with the letter "*C*." Derive your own memory device for remembering that the sum of two supplementary angles is 180°. "Adjacent supplementary angles form a straight angle." The words *Supplementary* and *Straight* both begin with the same letter.

$$x° + y° = 90°$$

Complementary angles form a "Corner"

$$x° + y° = 180°$$

Supplementary angles . . .

50. Two angles are complementary. One angle is 20° less than the other angle. Find the measures of the angles.
The angles are 55° and 35°.

51. Two angles are complementary. One angle is 4° less than three times the other angle. Find the measures of the angles. **(See Example 4.)** The angles are 23.5° and 66.5°.

52. Two angles are supplementary. One angle is three times as large as the other angle. Find the measures of the angles. The angles are 45° and 135°.

53. Two angles are supplementary. One angle is 6° more than four times the other. Find the measures of the two angles. The angles are 34.8° and 145.2°.

54. Refer to the figure. The angles, $\angle a$ and $\angle b$, are vertical angles.

a. If the measure of $\angle a$ is 32°, what is the measure of $\angle b$?

b. What is the measure of the supplement of $\angle a$?
a. The measure of $\angle a$ is 32°.
b. The supplement is 148°.

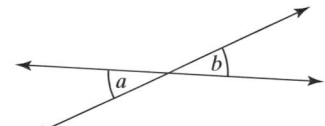

Figure for Exercise 54

55. Find the measures of the vertical angles labeled in the figure by first solving for x.
$x = 20$; the vertical angles measure 37°.

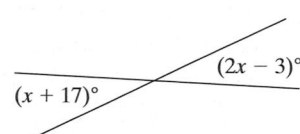

56. Find the measures of the vertical angles labeled in the figure by first solving for y.
$y = 40$; the vertical angles measure 146°.

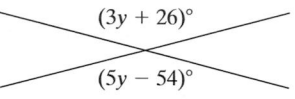

57. The largest angle in a triangle is three times the smallest angle. The middle angle is two times the smallest angle. Given that the sum of the angles in a triangle is 180°, find the measure of each angle. **(See Example 5.)**
The measures of the angles are 30°, 60°, and 90°.

58. The smallest angle in a triangle measures 90° less than the largest angle. The middle angle measures 60° less than the largest angle. Find the measure of each angle.
The measures of the angles are 20°, 50°, and 110°.

59. The smallest angle in a triangle is half the largest angle. The middle angle measures 30° less than the largest angle. Find the measure of each angle.
The measures of the angles are 42°, 54°, and 84°.

60. The largest angle of a triangle is three times the middle angle. The smallest angle measures 10° less than the middle angle. Find the measure of each angle.
The measures of the angles are 38°, 28°, and 114°.

 Writing Translating Expression Geometry Scientific Calculator Video NS&E

61. Find the value of x and the measure of each angle labeled in the figure.

$x = 17$; the measures of the angles are 34° and 56°.

$(3x + 5)°$

$(2x)°$

62. Find the value of y and the measure of each angle labeled in the figure.

$y = 26.5$; the measures of the angles are 28.5° and 61.5°.

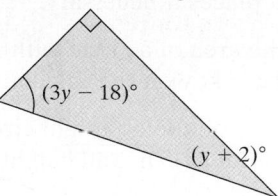

$(3y - 18)°$

$(y + 2)°$

63. a. A rectangle has length l and width w. Write a formula for the area.

$A = lw$

b. Solve the formula for the width, w. $w = \dfrac{A}{l}$

c. The area of a rectangular volleyball court is 1740.5 ft^2 and the length is 59 ft. Find the width.

The width is 29.5 ft.

Area = 1740.5 ft^2

59 ft

64. a. A parallelogram has height h and base b. Write a formula for the area.

$A = bh$

b. Solve the formula for the base, b. $b = \dfrac{A}{h}$

c. Find the base of the parallelogram pictured if the area is 40 m^2.

The base is 8 m.

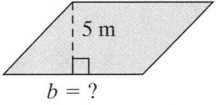

5 m

$b = ?$

65. a. A rectangle has length l and width w. Write a formula for the perimeter.

$P = 2l + 2w$

b. Solve the formula for the length, l. $l = \dfrac{P - 2w}{2}$

c. The perimeter of the soccer field at Giants Stadium is 338 m. If the width is 66 m, find the length.   The length is 103 m.

Perimeter = 338 m

66 m

66. a. A triangle has height h and base b. Write a formula for the area. $A = \dfrac{1}{2}bh$

b. Solve the formula for the height, h. $h = \dfrac{2A}{b}$

c. Find the height of the triangle pictured if the area is 12 km^2.

The height is 4 km.

$h = ?$

$b = 6$ km

67. a. A circle has a radius of r. Write a formula for the circumference. **(See Example 6.)**

$C = 2\pi r$

b. Solve the formula for the radius, r. $r = \dfrac{C}{2\pi}$

c. The circumference of the circular Buckingham Fountain in Chicago is approximately 880 ft. Find the radius. Round to the nearest foot.

The radius is approximately 140 ft.

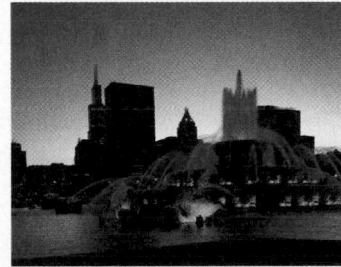

68. a. The length of each side of a square is s. Write a formula for the perimeter of the square. $P = 4s$

b. Solve the formula for the length of a side, s. $s = \dfrac{P}{4}$

c. The Pyramid of Khufu (known as the Great Pyramid) at Giza has a square base. If the distance around the bottom is 921.6 m, find the length of the sides at the bottom of the pyramid.

The length of each side at the bottom of the pyramid is 230.4 m.

s

s

s

s

 Writing   Translating Expression   Geometry   Scientific Calculator   Video   NS&E

Expanding Your Skills

For Exercises 69–70, find the indicated area or volume. Be sure to include the proper units and round each answer to two decimal places if necessary.

 69. a. Find the area of a circle with radius 11.5 m. Use the π key on the calculator. 415.48 m²

b. Find the volume of a right circular cylinder with radius 11.5 m and height 25 m. 10,386.89 m³

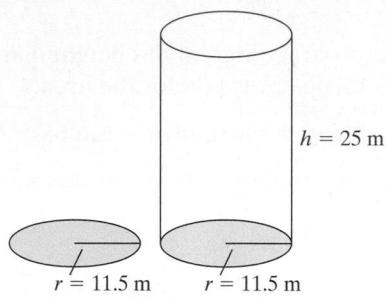

$h = 25$ m

$r = 11.5$ m $r = 11.5$ m

 70. a. Find the area of a parallelogram with base 30 in. and height 12 in.
360 in.²

b. Find the area of a triangle with base 30 in. and height 12 in.
180 in.²

c. Compare the areas found in parts (a) and (b).
The area of the triangle is one-half the area of the parallelogram.

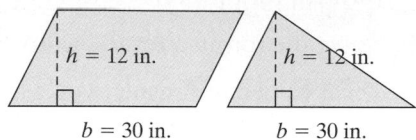

$h = 12$ in. $h = 12$ in.

$b = 30$ in. $b = 30$ in.

Section 2.7 Mixture Applications and Uniform Motion

Concepts

1. Applications Involving Cost
2. Applications Involving Mixtures
3. Applications Involving Uniform Motion

1. Applications Involving Cost

In Examples 1 and 2, we will look at different kinds of mixture problems. The first example "mixes" two types of movie tickets, adult tickets that sell for $8 and children's tickets that sell for $6. Furthermore, there were 300 tickets sold for a total revenue of $2040. Before attempting the problem, we should try to gain some familiarity. Let's try a few combinations to see how many of each type of ticket might have been sold.

Suppose 100 adult tickets were sold and 200 children's tickets were sold (a total of 300 tickets).

- 100 adult tickets at $8 each gives   100($8) = $800
- 200 children's tickets at $6 each gives   200($6) = $1200

                                      Total revenue: $2000 (not enough)

Suppose 150 adult tickets were sold and 150 children's tickets were sold (a total of 300 tickets).

- 150 adult tickets at $8 each gives   150($8) = $1200
- 150 children's tickets at $6 each gives   150($6) = $900

                                        Total revenue: $2100 (too much)

As you can see, the trial-and-error process can be tedious and time-consuming. Therefore we will use algebra to determine the correct combination of each type of ticket.

Suppose we let x represent the number of adult tickets, then the number of children's tickets is the *total minus* x. That is,

$$\left(\begin{array}{c} \text{Number of} \\ \text{children's tickets} \end{array} \right) = \left(\begin{array}{c} \text{total number} \\ \text{of tickets} \end{array} \right) - \left(\begin{array}{c} \text{number of} \\ \text{adult tickets, } x \end{array} \right)$$

Number of children's tickets $= 300 - x$.

Notice that the number of tickets sold times the price per ticket gives the revenue.

- x adult tickets at $8 each gives a revenue of: $x(\$8)$ or simply $8x$.
- $300 - x$ children's tickets at $6 each gives: $(300 - x)(\$6)$ or $6(300 - x)$

This will help us set up an equation in Example 1.

Example 1   Solving a Mixture Problem Involving Ticket Sales

Classroom Example: p. 158, Exercise 14

At one showing of *WALL-E*, 300 tickets were sold. Adult tickets cost $8 and tickets for children cost $6. If the total revenue from ticket sales was $2040, determine the number of each type of ticket sold.

Solution:

Let x represent the number of adult tickets sold.

Step 1: Read the problem.

$300 - x$ is the number of children's tickets.

Step 2: Label the variables.

	$8 Tickets	$6 Tickets	Total
Number of tickets	x	$300 - x$	300
Revenue	$8x$	$6(300 - x)$	2040

$$\left(\begin{array}{c}\text{Revenue from}\\\text{adult tickets}\end{array}\right) + \left(\begin{array}{c}\text{revenue from}\\\text{children's tickets}\end{array}\right) = \left(\begin{array}{c}\text{total}\\\text{revenue}\end{array}\right)$$

Step 3: Write an equation in words.

$$8x \qquad + \qquad 6(300 - x) \qquad = \qquad 2040$$

Step 4: Write a mathematical equation.

$$8x + 6(300 - x) = 2040$$

Step 5: Solve the equation.

$$8x + 1800 - 6x = 2040$$

$$2x + 1800 = 2040$$

$$2x = 240$$

$$x = 120$$

Step 6: Interpret the results.

There were 120 adult tickets sold.
The number of children's tickets is $300 - x$ which is 180.

Avoiding Mistakes

Check that the answer is reasonable. 120 adult tickets and 180 children's tickets makes 300 total tickets.

Furthermore, 120 adult tickets at $8 each amounts to $960, and 180 children's tickets at $6 amounts to $1080. The total revenue is $2040 as expected.

Skill Practice

1. At a Performing Arts Center, seats in the orchestra section cost $18 and seats in the balcony cost $12. If there were 120 seats sold for one performance, for a total revenue of $1920, how many of each type of seat were sold?

Answer

1. There were 80 seats in the orchestra section, and there were 40 in the balcony.

Classroom Example: p. 159, Exercise 24

2. Applications Involving Mixtures

Example 2 Solving a Mixture Application

How many liters (L) of a 60% antifreeze solution must be added to 8 L of a 10% antifreeze solution to produce a 20% antifreeze solution?

Solution:

The information can be organized in a table. Notice that an algebraic equation is derived from the second row of the table. This relates the number of liters of pure antifreeze in each container.

Step 1: Read the problem.

	60% Antifreeze	10% Antifreeze	Final Mixture: 20% Antifreeze
Number of liters of solution	x	8	$(8 + x)$
Number of liters of pure antifreeze	$0.60x$	$0.10(8)$	$0.20(8 + x)$

Step 2: Label the variables.

The amount of pure antifreeze in the final solution equals the sum of the amounts of antifreeze in the first two solutions.

$$\left(\begin{array}{c}\text{Pure antifreeze} \\ \text{from solution 1}\end{array}\right) + \left(\begin{array}{c}\text{pure antifreeze} \\ \text{from solution 2}\end{array}\right) = \left(\begin{array}{c}\text{pure antifreeze} \\ \text{in the final solution}\end{array}\right)$$

Step 3: Write an equation in words.

$$0.60x \quad + \quad 0.10(8) \quad = \quad 0.20(8 + x)$$

$$0.60x + 0.10(8) = 0.20(8 + x)$$

Step 4: Write a mathematical equation.

$$0.6x + 0.8 = 1.6 + 0.2x$$

Step 5: Solve the equation.

$$0.6x - 0.2x + 0.8 = 1.6 + 0.2x - 0.2x$$ Subtract $0.2x$.

$$0.4x + 0.8 = 1.6$$

$$0.4x + 0.8 - 0.8 = 1.6 - 0.8$$ Subtract 0.8.

$$0.4x = 0.8$$

$$\frac{0.4x}{0.4} = \frac{0.8}{0.4}$$ Divide by 0.4.

$$x = 2$$

Step 6: Interpret the result.

Therefore, 2 L of 60% antifreeze solution is necessary to make a final solution that is 20% antifreeze.

Skill Practice

2. How many gallons of a 5% bleach solution must be added to 10 gallons (gal) of a 20% bleach solution to produce a solution that is 15% bleach?

Answer

2. 5 gal is needed.

3. Applications Involving Uniform Motion

The formula (distance) = (rate)(time) or simply, $d = rt$, relates the distance traveled to the rate of travel and the time of travel.

For example, if a car travels at 60 mph for 3 hours, then

$$d = (60 \text{ mph})(3 \text{ hours})$$
$$= 180 \text{ miles}$$

If a car travels at 60 mph for x hours, then

$$d = (60 \text{ mph})(x \text{ hours})$$
$$= 60x \text{ miles}$$

Example 3 **Solving an Application Involving Distance, Rate, and Time**

Classroom Example: p. 159, Exercise 32

One bicyclist rides 4 mph faster than another bicyclist. The faster rider takes 3 hr to complete a race, while the slower rider takes 4 hr. Find the speed for each rider.

Solution:

Step 1: Read the problem.

The problem is asking us to find the speed of each rider.

Let x represent the speed of the slower rider. Then $(x + 4)$ is the speed of the faster rider.

Step 2: Label the variables and organize the information given in the problem. A distance-rate-time chart may be helpful.

	Distance	Rate	Time
Faster rider	$3(x + 4)$	$x + 4$	3
Slower rider	$4(x)$	x	4

To complete the first column, we can use the relationship, $d = rt$.

Because the riders are riding in the same race, their distances are equal.

$$\left(\begin{array}{c} \text{Distance} \\ \text{by faster rider} \end{array} \right) = \left(\begin{array}{c} \text{distance} \\ \text{by slower rider} \end{array} \right)$$

Step 3: Set up a verbal model.

$$3(x + 4) = 4(x)$$

Step 4: Write a mathematical equation.

$$3x + 12 = 4x$$

Step 5: Solve the equation.

$$12 = x$$

Subtract $3x$ from both sides.

The variable x represents the slower rider's rate. The quantity $x + 4$ is the faster rider's rate. Thus, if $x = 12$, then $x + 4 = 16$.

The slower rider travels 12 mph and the faster rider travels 16 mph.

Avoiding Mistakes

Check that the answer is reasonable. If the slower rider rides at 12 mph for 4 hr, he travels 48 mi. If the faster rider rides at 16 mph for 3 hr, he also travels 48 mi as expected.

Skill Practice

3. An express train travels 25 mph faster than a cargo train. It takes the express train 6 hr to travel a route, and it takes 9 hr for the cargo train to travel the same route. Find the speed of each train.

Answer

3. The express train travels 75 mph, and the cargo train travels 50 mph.

Classroom Example: p. 160,
Exercise 38

Example 4 Solving an Application Involving Distance, Rate, and Time

Two families that live 270 mi apart plan to meet for an afternoon picnic at a park that is located between their two homes. Both families leave at 9.00 A.M., but one family averages 12 mph faster than the other family. If the families meet at the designated spot $2\frac{1}{2}$ hr later, determine

  a. The average rate of speed for each family.

  b. The distance each family traveled to the picnic.

Solution:

For simplicity, we will call the two families, Family A and Family B. Let Family A be the family that travels at the slower rate (Figure 2-10).

Step 1:   Read the problem and draw a sketch.

270 miles

Family A ———————→ ←——————— Family B

Figure 2-10

Let x represent the rate of Family A.

Then $(x + 12)$ is the rate of Family B.

Step 2:   Label the variables.

	Distance	Rate	Time
Family A	2.5x	x	2.5
Family B	2.5(x + 12)	x + 12	2.5

To complete the first column, we can use the relationship $d = rt$.

    To set up an equation, recall that the total distance between the two families is given as 270 mi.

$$\begin{pmatrix} \text{Distance} \\ \text{traveled by} \\ \text{Family A} \end{pmatrix} + \begin{pmatrix} \text{distance} \\ \text{traveled by} \\ \text{Family B} \end{pmatrix} = \begin{pmatrix} \text{total} \\ \text{distance} \end{pmatrix}$$

Step 3:   Create a verbal equation.

$$2.5x \quad + \quad 2.5(x + 12) \quad = \quad 270$$

Step 4:   Write a mathematical equation.

$$2.5x + 2.5(x + 12) = 270$$

Step 5:   Solve for x.

$$2.5x + 2.5x + 30 = 270$$

$$5.0x + 30 = 270$$

$$5x = 240$$

$$x = 48$$

  a. Family A traveled 48 mph.

Family B traveled $x + 12 = 48 + 12 = 60$ mph.

Step 6:   Interpret the results and write the answer in words.

b. To compute the distance each family traveled, use $d = rt$.

Family A traveled (48 mph)(2.5 hr) = 120 mi.

Family B traveled (60 mph)(2.5 hr) = 150 mi.

Skill Practice

4. A Piper Cub airplane has an average air speed that is 10 mph faster than a Cessna 150 airplane. If the combined distance traveled by these two small planes is 690 mi after 3 hr, what is the average speed of each plane?

Answer

4. The Cessna's speed is 110 mph, and the Piper Cub's speed is 120 mph.

Section 2.7 Practice Exercises

Study Skills Exercise

1. The following is a list of steps to help you solve word problems. Check those that you follow on a regular basis when solving a word problem. Place an asterisk next to the steps that you need to improve.

_____ Read through the entire problem before writing anything down.

_____ Write down exactly what you are being asked to find.

_____ Write down what is known and assign variables to what is unknown.

_____ Draw a figure or diagram if it will help you understand the problem.

_____ Highlight key words like total, sum, difference, etc.

_____ Translate the word problem to a mathematical problem.

_____ After solving, check that your answer makes sense.

Review Exercises

For Exercises 2–3, solve for the indicated variable.

2. $ax - by = c$ for x $x = \dfrac{c + by}{a}$

3. $cd = r$ for c $c = \dfrac{r}{d}$

For Exercises 4–6, solve each equation.

4. $-2d + 11 = 4 - d$ {7}

5. $3(2y + 5) - 8(y - 1) = 3y + 3$ {4}

6. $0.02x + 0.04(10 - x) = 1.26$ {-43}

Concept 1: Applications Involving Cost

For Exercises 7–12, write an algebraic expression as indicated.

7. Two numbers total 200. Let t represent one of the numbers. Write an algebraic expression for the other number. $200 - t$

8. The total of two numbers is 43. Let s represent one of the numbers. Write an algebraic expression for the other number. $43 - s$

9. Olivia needs to bring 100 cookies to her friend's party. She has already baked x cookies. Write an algebraic expression for the number of cookies Olivia still needs to bake. $100 - x$

10. Rachel needs a mixture of 55 pounds (lb) of nuts consisting of peanuts and cashews. Let p represent the number of pounds of peanuts in the mixture. Write an algebraic expression for the number of pounds of cashews that she needs to add. $55 - p$

11. Max has a total of $3000 in two bank accounts. Let y represent the amount in one account. Write an algebraic expression for the amount in the other account. $3000 - y$

12. Roberto has a total of $7500 in two savings accounts. Let z represent the amount in one account. Write an algebraic expression for the amount in the other account. $7500 - z$

13. A church had an ice cream social and sold tickets for $3 and $2. When the social was over, 81 tickets had been sold totaling $215. How many of each type of ticket did the church sell? **(See Example 1.)**

53 tickets were sold at $3 and 28 tickets were sold at $2.

	$3 Tickets	$2 Tickets	Total
Number of tickets			
Cost of tickets			

14. Anna is a teacher at an elementary school. She purchased 72 tickets to take the first-grade children and some parents on a field trip to the zoo. She purchased children's tickets for $10 each and adult tickets for $18 each. She spent a total of $856. How many of each type of ticket did she buy?   Anna purchased 17 adult tickets and 55 children's tickets.

	Adults	Children	Total
Number of tickets			
Cost of tickets			

15. Josh downloaded 25 tunes from an online site for his MP3 player. Some songs cost $0.90 each, while others were $1.50 each. He spent a total of $27.30. How many of each type of song did he download?

Josh downloaded 17 songs for $0.90 and 8 songs for $1.50.

16. During the past year, Kris purchased 32 books at a wholesale club store. She purchased softcover books for $4.50 each and hardcover books for $13.50 each. The total cost of the books was $243. How many of each type of book did she purchase?

Kris purchased 21 softcover books and 11 hardcover books.

17. Christopher has three times the number of Nintendo® DS games as Nintendo® Wii games. Each Nintendo® DS game costs $30 while each Nintendo® Wii game costs $50. How many games of each type does Christopher have if he spent a total of $700 on all the games?

Christopher has 5 Wii games and 15 DS games.

18. Steven wants to buy some candy with his birthday money. He can choose from Jelly Belly jelly beans that sell for $6.99 per pound and Brach's variety that sells for $3.99. He likes to have twice the amount of jelly beans as Brach's variety. If he spent a total of $53.91, how many pounds of each type of candy did he buy?

Steven bought 6 lb of jelly beans and 3 lb of Brach's variety.

Concept 2: Applications Involving Mixtures

For Exercises 19–22, write an algebraic expression as indicated.

19. A container holds 7 ounces (oz) of liquid. Let x represent the number of ounces of liquid in another container. Write an expression for the total amount of liquid. $x + 7$

20. A bucket contains 2.5 L of a bleach solution. Let n represent the number of liters of bleach solution in a second bucket. Write an expression for the total amount of bleach solution. $n + 2.5$

21. If Miguel invests $2000 in a certificate of deposit and *d* dollars in a stock, write an expression for the total amount he invested. *d + 2000*

22. James has $5000 in one savings account. Let *y* represent the amount he has in another savings account. Write an expression for the total amount of money in both accounts. *y + 5000*

23. How many ounces of a 50% antifreeze solution must be mixed with 10 oz of an 80% antifreeze solution to produce a 60% antifreeze solution? **(See Example 2.)** Mix 20 oz of 50% antifreeze solution.

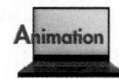
Animation

	50% Antifreeze	80% Antifreeze	Final Mixture: 60% Antifreeze
Number of ounces of solution			
Number of ounces of pure antifreeze			

24. How many liters of a 10% alcohol solution must be mixed with 12 L of a 5% alcohol solution to produce an 8% alcohol solution? Mix 18 L of 10% alcohol solution.

	10% Alcohol	5% Alcohol	Final Mixture: 8% Alcohol
Number of liters of solution			
Number of liters of pure alcohol			

25. A pharmacist needs to mix a 1% saline (salt) solution with 24 milliliters (mL) of a 16% saline solution to obtain a 9% saline solution. How many milliliters of the 1% solution must she use? The pharmacist needs to use 21 mL of the 1% saline solution.

26. A landscaper needs to mix a 75% pesticide solution with 30 gal of a 25% pesticide solution to obtain a 60% pesticide solution. How many gallons of the 75% solution must he use? The landscaper needs to use 70 gal of the 75% pesticide solution.

27. To clean a concrete driveway, a contractor needs a solution that is 30% acid. How many ounces of a 50% acid solution must be mixed with 15 oz of a 21% solution to obtain a 30% acid solution? The contractor needs to mix 6.75 oz of 50% acid solution.

28. A veterinarian needs a mixture that contains 12% of a certain medication to treat an injured bird. How many milliliters of a 16% solution should be mixed with 6 mL of a 7% solution to obtain a solution that is 12% medication? The veterinarian needs to use 7.5 mL of the 16% solution.

Concept 3: Applications Involving Uniform Motion

29. a. If a car travels 60 mph for 5 hr, find the distance traveled. 300 mi

b. If a car travels at *x* miles per hour for 5 hr, write an expression that represents the distance traveled. *5x*

c. If a car travels at *x* + 12 mph for 5 hr, write an expression that represents the distance traveled. *5(x + 12)* or *5x + 60*

30. a. If a plane travels 550 mph for 2.5 hr, find the distance traveled. 1375 mi

b. If a plane travels at *x* miles per hour for 2.5 hr, write an expression that represents the distance traveled. *2.5x*

c. If a plane travels at *x* − 100 mph for 2.5 hr, write an expression that represents the distance traveled. *2.5(x − 100)* or *2.5x − 250*

31. A woman can walk 2 mph faster down a trail to Cochita Lake than she can on the return trip uphill. It takes her 2 hr to get to the lake and 4 hr to return. What is her speed walking down to the lake? **(See Example 3.)** She walks 4 mph to the lake.

	Distance	Rate	Time
Downhill to the lake			
Uphill from the lake			

32. A car travels 20 mph slower in a bad rain storm than in sunny weather. The car travels the same distance in 2 hr in sunny weather as it does in 3 hr in rainy weather. Find the speed of the car in sunny weather. The car travels 60 mph in sunny weather.

	Distance	Rate	Time
Rain storm			
Sunny weather			

33. Bryan hiked up to the top of City Creek in 3 hr and then returned down the canyon to the trailhead in another 2 hr. His speed downhill was 1 mph faster than his speed uphill. How far up the canyon did he hike?   Bryan hiked 6 mi up the canyon.

34. Kevin hiked up Lamb's Canyon in 2 hr and then ran back down in 1 hr. His speed running downhill was 2.5 mph greater than his speed hiking uphill. How far up the canyon did he hike?   Kevin hiked 5 mi up the canyon.

35. Hazel and Emilie fly from Atlanta to San Diego. The flight from Atlanta to San Diego is against the wind and takes 4 hr. The return flight with the wind takes 3.5 hr. If the wind speed is 40 mph, find the speed of the plane in still air.   The plane travels 600 mph in still air.

36. A boat on the Potomac River travels the same distance downstream in $\frac{2}{3}$ hr as it does going upstream in 1 hr. If the speed of the current is 3 mph, find the speed of the boat in still water.   The speed of the boat is 15 mph in still water.

37. Two cars are 200 mi apart and traveling toward each other on the same road. They meet in 2 hr. One car is traveling 4 mph faster than the other. What is the speed of each car? **(See Example 4.)**   The slower car travels 48 mph and the faster car travels 52 mph.

38. Two cars are 238 mi apart and traveling toward each other along the same road. They meet in 2 hr. One car is traveling 5 mph slower than the other. What is the speed of each car?   The cars are traveling 62 mph and 57 mph.

39. After Hurricane Katrina, a rescue vehicle leaves a station at noon and heads for New Orleans. An hour later a second vehicle traveling 10 mph faster leaves the same station. By 4:00 P.M., the first vehicle reaches its destination, and the second is still 10 mi away. How fast is each vehicle?   The speeds of the vehicles are 40 mph and 50 mph.

40. A truck leaves a truck stop at 9:00 A.M. and travels toward Sturgis, Wyoming. At 10:00 A.M., a motorcycle leaves the same truck stop and travels the same route. The motorcycle travels 15 mph faster than the truck. By noon, the truck has traveled 20 mi further than the motorcycle. How fast is each vehicle?   The speed of the motorcycle is 65 mph and the speed of the truck is 50 mph.

41. Two boats traveling in the same direction leave a harbor at noon. After 2 hr, they are 40 mi apart. If one boat travels twice as fast as the other, find the rate of each boat.   The rates of the boats are 20 mph and 40 mph.

42. Two canoes travel down a river, starting at 9:00 A.M. One canoe travels twice as fast as the other. After 3.5 hr, the canoes are 5.25 mi apart. Find the speed of each canoe.   The canoes travel 1.5 mph and 3 mph.

Mixed Exercises

43. A certain granola mixture is 10% peanuts.

    a. If a container has 20 lb of granola, how many pounds of peanuts are there?   2 lb

    b. If a container has x pounds of granola, write an expression that represents the number of pounds of peanuts in the granola. $0.10x$

    c. If a container has $x + 3$ lb of granola, write an expression that represents the number of pounds of peanuts. $0.10(x + 3) = 0.10x + 0.30$

44. A certain blend of coffee sells for $9.00 per pound.

    a. If a container has 20 lb of coffee, how much will it cost. $180

    b. If a container has x pounds of coffee, write an expression that represents the cost. $9.00x$

    c. If a container has $40 - x$ pounds of this coffee, write an expression that represents the cost. $9(40 - x) = 360 - 9x$

45. The Coffee Company mixes coffee worth $12 per pound with coffee worth $8 per pound to produce 50 lb of coffee worth $8.80 per pound. How many pounds of the $12 coffee and how many pounds of the $8 coffee must be used?   Mix 10 lb of coffee sold at $12 per pound and 40 lb of coffee sold at $8 per pound.

	$12 Coffee	$8 Coffee	Total
Number of pounds			
Value of coffee			

46. The Nut House sells pecans worth $4 per pound and cashews worth $6 per pound. How many pounds of pecans and how many pounds of cashews must be mixed to form 16 lb of a nut mixture worth $4.50 per pound?   Mix 12 lb of pecans and 4 lb of cashews.

	$4 Pecans	$6 Cashews	Total
Number of pounds			
Value of nuts			

47. A boat in distress, 21 nautical miles from a marina, travels toward the marina at 3 knots (nautical miles per hour). A coast guard cruiser leaves the marina and travels toward the boat at 25 knots. How long will it take for the boats to reach each other?   The boats will meet in $\frac{3}{4}$ hr (45 min).

48. An air traffic controller observes a plane heading from New York to San Francisco traveling at 450 mph. At the same time, another plane leaves San Francisco and travels 500 mph to New York. If the distance between the airports is 2850 mi, how long will it take for the planes to pass each other?   The planes will pass in 3 hr.

49. Surfer Sam purchased a total of 21 items at the surf shop. He bought wax for $3.00 per package and sunscreen for $8.00 per bottle. He spent a total amount of $88.00. How many of each item did he purchase?   Sam purchased 16 packages of wax and 5 bottles of sunscreen.

50. Tonya Toast loves jam. She purchased 30 jars of gourmet jam for $178.50. She bought raspberry jam for $6.25 per jar and strawberry jam for $5.50 per jar. How many jars of each did she purchase?   Tonya purchased 18 jars of raspberry and 12 jars of strawberry.

51. How many quarts of 85% chlorine solution must be mixed with 5 quarts of 25% chlorine solution to obtain a 45% chlorine solution?   2.5 quarts of 85% chlorine solution

52. How many liters of a 58% sugar solution must be added to 14 L of a 40% sugar solution to obtain a 50% sugar solution?   17.5 L of 58% sugar solution.

Expanding Your Skills

53. How much pure water must be mixed with 12 L of a 40% alcohol solution to obtain a 15% alcohol solution? (*Hint:* Pure water is 0% alcohol.)
20 L of water must be added.

54. How much pure water must be mixed with 10 oz of a 60% alcohol solution to obtain a 25% alcohol solution?   14 oz of water must be added.

55. Amtrak Acela Express is a high-speed train that runs in the United States between Washington, D.C. and Boston. In Japan, a bullet train along the Sanyo line operates at an average speed of 60 km/hr faster than the Amtrak Acela Express. It takes the Japanese bullet train 2.7 hr to travel the same distance as the Acela Express can travel in 3.375 hr. Find the speed of each train.   The Japanese bullet train travels 300 km/hr and the Acela Express travels 240 km/hr.

56. Amtrak Acela Express is a high-speed train along the northeast corridor between Washington, D.C. and Boston. Since its debut, it cuts the travel time from 4 hr 10 min to 3 hr 20 min. On average, if the Acela Express is 30 mph faster than the old train, find the speed of the Acela Express. (*Hint:* 4 hr 10 min = $4\frac{1}{6}$ hr.)   The speed of the Acela Express in 150 mph.

Linear Inequalities   Section 2.8

1. Graphing Linear Inequalities

Consider the following two statements.

$$2x + 7 = 11 \quad \text{and} \quad 2x + 7 < 11$$

The first statement is an equation (it has an = sign). The second statement is an inequality (it has an inequality symbol, <). In this section, we will learn how to solve linear *inequalities*, such as $2x + 7 < 11$.

> **DEFINITION**   **A Linear Inequality in One Variable**
>
> A **linear inequality in one variable**, x, is defined as any relationship of the form:
>
> $ax + b < 0,\ ax + b \leq 0,\ ax + b > 0,$ or $ax + b \geq 0$, where $a \neq 0$.

Concepts

1. Graphing Linear Inequalities
2. Set-Builder Notation and Interval Notation
3. Addition and Subtraction Properties of Inequality
4. Multiplication and Division Properties of Inequality
5. Inequalities of the Form $a < x < b$
6. Applications of Linear Inequalities

 Writing   Translating Expression   Geometry   Scientific Calculator   Video   NS&E

The following inequalities are linear equalities in one variable.

$$2x - 3 < 0 \qquad -4z - 3 > 0 \qquad a \le 4 \qquad 5.2y \ge 10.4$$

The number line is a useful tool to visualize the solution set of an equation or inequality. For example, the solution set to the equation $x = 2$ is $\{2\}$ and may be graphed as a single point on the number line.

$x = 2$

The solution set to an inequality is the set of real numbers that make the inequality a true statement. For example, the solution set to the inequality $x \ge 2$ is all real numbers 2 or greater. Because the solution set has an infinite number of values, we cannot list all of the individual solutions. However, we can graph the solution set on the number line.

$x \ge 2$

The square bracket symbol, [, is used on the graph to indicate that the point $x = 2$ is included in the solution set. By convention, square brackets, either [or], are used to *include* a point on a number line. Parentheses, (or), are used to *exclude* a point on a number line.

The solution set of the inequality $x > 2$ includes the real numbers greater than 2 but not including 2. Therefore, a (symbol is used on the graph to indicate that $x = 2$ is not included.

$x > 2$

In Example 1, we demonstrate how to graph linear inequalities. To graph an inequality means that we graph its solution set. That is, we graph all of the values on the number line that make the inequality true.

Classroom Examples: p. 172, Exercises 6 and 10

Example 1 **Graphing Linear Inequalities**

Graph the solution sets.

a. $x > -1$ **b.** $c \le \dfrac{7}{3}$ **c.** $3 > y$

Solution:

a. $x > -1$

The solution set is the set of all real numbers strictly greater than -1. Therefore, we graph the region on the number line to the right of -1. Because $x = -1$ is not included in the solution set, we use the (symbol at $x = -1$.

Instructor Note: Students sometimes confuse the meaning of $x > 1$ to think it means the set $\{2, 3, 4 \ldots\}$. They don't think about the real number line. They don't see that 1.00000001 is a solution.

b. $c \le \frac{7}{3}$ is equivalent to $c \le 2\frac{1}{3}$.

The solution set is the set of all real numbers less than or equal to $2\frac{1}{3}$. Therefore, graph the region on the number line to the left of and including $2\frac{1}{3}$. Use the symbol] to indicate that $c = 2\frac{1}{3}$ is included in the solution set.

c. $3 > y$ This inequality reads "3 is greater than y." This is equivalent to saying, "y is less than 3." The inequality $3 > y$ can also be written as $y < 3$.

$y < 3$

The solution set is the set of real numbers less than 3. Therefore, graph the region on the number line to the left of 3. Use the symbol) to denote that the endpoint, 3, is not included in the solution.

Skill Practice Graph the solution sets.

1. $y < 0$ **2.** $x \geq -\dfrac{5}{4}$ **3.** $5 \geq a$

TIP: Some textbooks use a closed circle or an open circle (● or ○) rather than a bracket or parenthesis to denote inclusion or exclusion of a value on the real number line. For example, the solution sets for the inequalities $x > -1$ and $c \leq \frac{7}{3}$ are graphed here.

$x > -1$

$c \leq \frac{7}{3}$

A statement that involves more than one inequality is called a **compound inequality**. One type of compound inequality is used to indicate that one number is between two others. For example, the inequality $-2 < x < 5$ means that $-2 < x$ and $x < 5$. In words, this is easiest to understand if we read the variable first: x is greater than -2 and x is less than 5. The numbers satisfied by these two conditions are those between -2 and 5.

Example 2   Graphing a Compound Inequality

Graph the solution set of the inequality: $-4.1 < y \leq -1.7$

Classroom Example: p. 172, Exercise 12

Solution:

$-4.1 < y \leq -1.7$ means that

$-4.1 < y$ and $y \leq -1.7$

Shade the region of the number line greater than -4.1 and less than or equal to -1.7.

Skill Practice Graph the solution set.

4. $0 \leq y \leq 8.5$

Answers

1.

2.

3.

4.

2. Set-Builder Notation and Interval Notation

Graphing the solution set to an inequality is one way to define the set. Two other methods are to use **set-builder notation** or **interval notation**.

Set-Builder Notation

The solution to the inequality $x \geq 2$ can be expressed in set-builder notation as follows:

the set of all x such that x is greater than or equal to 2

Interval Notation

To understand interval notation, first think of a number line extending infinitely far to the right and infinitely far to the left. Sometimes we use the infinity symbol, ∞, or negative infinity symbol, $-\infty$, to label the far right and far left ends of the number line (Figure 2-11).

Figure 2-11

To express the solution set of an inequality in interval notation, sketch the graph first. Then use the endpoints to define the interval.

Inequality	Graph	Interval Notation
$x \geq 2$		$[2, \infty)$

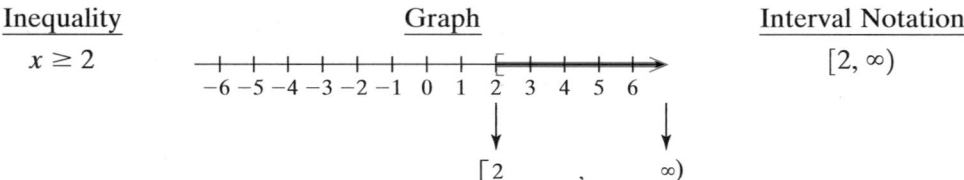

The graph of the solution set $x \geq 2$ begins at 2 and extends infinitely far to the right. The corresponding interval notation begins at 2 and extends to ∞. Notice that a square bracket [is used at 2 for both the graph and the interval notation. A parenthesis is always used at ∞ and for $-\infty$, because there is no endpoint.

PROCEDURE Using Interval Notation

- The endpoints used in interval notation are always written from left to right. That is, the smaller number is written first, followed by a comma, followed by the larger number.
- A parenthesis, (or), indicates that an endpoint is excluded from the set.
- A square bracket, [or], indicates that an endpoint is included in the set.
- Parentheses, (and), are always used with $-\infty$ and ∞, respectively.

In Table 2-1, we present examples of eight different scenarios for interval notation and the corresponding graph.

Table 2-1

Interval Notation	Graph	Interval Notation	Graph
(a, ∞)		$[a, \infty)$	
$(-\infty, a)$		$(-\infty, a]$	
(a, b)		$[a, b]$	
$(a, b]$		$[a, b)$	

Example 3 Using Set-Builder Notation and Interval Notation

Complete the chart.

Classroom Examples: pp. 172–173, Exercises 20, 24, and 30

Set-Builder Notation	Graph	Interval Notation
	$\leftarrow\!+\!+\!+\!+\!\rightarrow\!+\!+\!+\!+\!+\!+\!+\!+\!\rightarrow$ $-6\ -5\ -4\ -3\ -2\ -1\ \ 0\ \ 1\ \ 2\ \ 3\ \ 4\ \ 5\ \ 6$	
		$[-\frac{1}{2}, \infty)$
$\{y \mid -2 \leq y < 4\}$		

Solution:

Set-Builder Notation	Graph	Interval Notation
$\{x \mid x < -3\}$	$-6\ -5\ -4\ -3\ -2\ -1\ \ 0\ \ 1\ \ 2\ \ 3\ \ 4\ \ 5\ \ 6$	$(-\infty, -3)$
$\{x \mid x \geq -\frac{1}{2}\}$	$-6\ -5\ -4\ -3\ -2\ -1\ \ 0\ \ 1\ \ 2\ \ 3\ \ 4\ \ 5\ \ 6$ $-\frac{1}{2}$	$[-\frac{1}{2}, \infty)$
$\{y \mid -2 \leq y < 4\}$	$-6\ -5\ -4\ -3\ -2\ -1\ \ 0\ \ 1\ \ 2\ \ 3\ \ 4\ \ 5\ \ 6$	$[-2, 4)$

Skill Practice Express each of the following in set-builder notation and interval notation.

5. [graph with bracket at -2]

6. $x < \dfrac{3}{2}$

7. [graph from -3 to 1]

3. Addition and Subtraction Properties of Inequality

The process to solve a linear inequality is very similar to the method used to solve linear equations. Recall that adding or subtracting the same quantity to both sides of an equation results in an equivalent equation. The addition and subtraction properties of inequality state that the same is true for an inequality.

Answers

5. $\{x \mid x \geq -2\}$; $[-2, \infty)$

6. $\left\{x \mid x < \dfrac{3}{2}\right\}$; $\left(-\infty, \dfrac{3}{2}\right)$

7. $\{x \mid -3 < x \leq 1\}$; $(-3, 1]$

PROPERTY Addition and Subtraction Properties of Inequality

Let a, b, and c represent real numbers.

1. *Addition Property of Inequality: If $a < b$,
   then $a + c < b + c$

2. *Subtraction Property of Inequality: If $a < b$,
   then $a - c < b - c$

*These properties may also be stated for $a \leq b$, $a > b$, and $a \geq b$.

To illustrate the addition and subtraction properties of inequality, consider the inequality $5 > 3$. If we add or subtract a real number such as 4 to both sides, the left-hand side will still be greater than the right-hand side. (See Figure 2-12.)

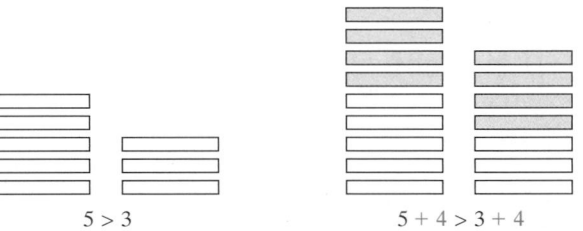

$5 > 3$ $5 + 4 > 3 + 4$

Figure 2-12

Classroom Example: p. 174, Exercise 52

Example 4   Solving a Linear Inequality

Solve the inequality and graph the solution set. Express the solution set in set-builder notation and in interval notation.

$$-2p + 5 < -3p + 6$$

Solution:

$$-2p + 5 < -3p + 6$$

$$-2p + 3p + 5 < -3p + 3p + 6 \qquad \text{Addition property of inequality (add } 3p \text{ to both sides).}$$

$$p + 5 < 6 \qquad \text{Simplify.}$$

$$p + 5 - 5 < 6 - 5 \qquad \text{Subtraction property of inequality.}$$

$$p < 1$$

Instructor Note: Ask students whether 1 is a solution to the inequality.

Graph:

$$\overset{\xleftarrow{\qquad\qquad\qquad\quad\ \ }}{\underset{-6\ -5\ -4\ -3\ -2\ -1\ \ 0\ \ 1\ \ 2\ \ 3\ \ 4\ \ 5\ \ 6}{\!\mid\ \mid\ \mid\ \mid\ \mid\ \mid\ \mid\ \mid\ \mid\ \mid\ \mid\ \mid\ \mid}}$$

Set-builder notation: $\{p \,|\, p < 1\}$

Interval notation: $(-\infty, 1)$

Skill Practice Solve the inequality and graph the solution set. Express the solution set in set-builder notation and interval notation.

8. $2y - 5 < y - 11$

Answer

8. $\overset{\xleftarrow{\qquad\qquad\qquad\qquad}}{\underset{-6}{\qquad\quad}}$

$\{x \,|\, x < -6\}$; $(-\infty, -6)$

TIP: The solution to an inequality gives a set of values that make the original inequality true. Therefore, you can test your final answer by using *test points*. That is, pick a value in the proposed solution set and verify that it makes the original inequality true. Furthermore, any test point picked outside the solution set should make the original inequality false. Here we test the solutions from Example 4.

Pick $p = -4$ as an arbitrary test point within the proposed solution set.

$$-2p + 5 < -3p + 6$$
$$-2(-4) + 5 \overset{?}{<} -3(-4) + 6$$
$$8 + 5 \overset{?}{<} 12 + 6$$
$$13 < 18 \; ✔ \quad \text{True}$$

Pick $p = 3$ as an arbitrary test point outside the proposed solution set.

$$-2p + 5 < -3p + 6$$
$$-2(3) + 5 \overset{?}{<} -3(3) + 6$$
$$-6 + 5 \overset{?}{<} -9 + 6$$
$$-1 \overset{?}{<} -3 \quad \text{False}$$

4. Multiplication and Division Properties of Inequality

Multiplying both sides of an equation by the same quantity results in an equivalent equation. However, the same is not always true for an inequality. If you multiply or divide an inequality by a negative quantity, the direction of the inequality symbol must be reversed.

For example, consider multiplying or dividing the inequality, $4 < 5$ by -1.

Multiply/Divide by -1
$$4 < 5$$
$$-4 > -5$$

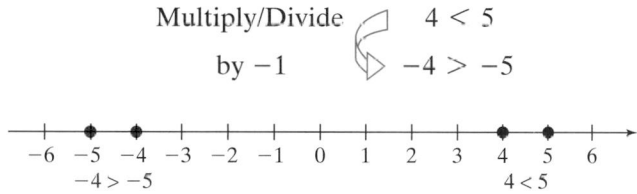

Figure 2-13

The number 4 lies to the left of 5 on the number line. However, -4 lies to the right of -5 (Figure 2-13). Changing the sign of two numbers changes their relative position on the number line. This is stated formally in the multiplication and division properties of inequality.

Instructor Note: Show that this works for other situations. Start with two negative numbers or one positive and one negative. Show that multiplying or dividing by -1 changes the direction of the inequality sign.

PROPERTY Multiplication and Division Properties of Inequality

Let a, b, and c represent real numbers.

*If c is positive and $a < b$, then $ac < bc$ and $\dfrac{a}{c} < \dfrac{b}{c}$

*If c is negative and $a < b$, then $ac > bc$ and $\dfrac{a}{c} > \dfrac{b}{c}$

The second statement indicates that if both sides of an inequality are multiplied or divided by a negative quantity, the inequality sign must be reversed.

*These properties may also be stated for $a \le b$, $a > b$, and $a \ge b$.

Classroom Example: p. 174, Exercise 78

Example 5 Solving a Linear Inequality

Solve the inequality $-5x - 3 \leq 12$. Graph the solution set and write the answer in interval notation.

Solution:

$$-5x - 3 \leq 12$$

$$-5x - 3 + 3 \leq 12 + 3 \qquad \text{Add 3 to both sides.}$$

$$-5x \leq 15$$

$$\frac{-5x}{-5} \geq \frac{15}{-5} \qquad \text{Divide by } -5. \text{ Reverse the direction of the inequality sign.}$$

$$x \geq -3$$

Interval notation: $[-3, \infty)$

TIP: The inequality $-5x - 3 \leq 12$, could have been solved by isolating x on the right-hand side of the inequality. This would create a positive coefficient on the variable term and eliminate the need to divide by a negative number.

$$-5x - 3 \leq 12$$

$$-3 \leq 5x + 12$$

$$-15 \leq 5x \qquad \text{Notice that the coefficient of } x \text{ is positive.}$$

$$\frac{-15}{5} \leq \frac{5x}{5} \qquad \text{Do not reverse the inequality sign because we are dividing by a positive number.}$$

$$-3 \leq x, \text{ or equivalently, } x \geq -3$$

Skill Practice Solve. Graph the solution set and express the solution in interval notation.

9. $-5p + 2 > 22$

Classroom Example: p. 175, Exercise 94

Example 6 Solving a Linear Inequality

Solve the inequality. Graph the solution set and write the answer in interval notation.

$$1.4x + 4.5 < 0.2x - 0.3$$

Solution:

$$1.4x + 4.5 < 0.2x - 0.3$$

$$1.4x - 0.2x + 4.5 < 0.2x - 0.2x - 0.3 \qquad \text{Subtract } 0.2x \text{ from both sides.}$$

$$1.2x + 4.5 < -0.3 \qquad \text{Simplify.}$$

$$1.2x + 4.5 - 4.5 < -0.3 - 4.5 \qquad \text{Subtract 4.5 from both sides.}$$

$$1.2x < -4.8 \qquad \text{Simplify.}$$

$$\frac{1.2x}{1.2} < \frac{-4.8}{1.2} \qquad \text{Divide by 1.2. The direction of the inequality sign is } not \text{ reversed because we divided by a positive number.}$$

$$x < -4$$

Answer

9.

$(-\infty, -4)$

Interval notation: $(-\infty, -4)$

Skill Practice Solve. Graph the solution set and express the solution in interval notation.

10. $1.1x - 0.8 > 0.1x + 4.2$

Example 7 **Solving a Linear Inequality**

Classroom Example: p. 174, Exercise 90

Solve the inequality $-\frac{1}{4}k + \frac{1}{6} \leq 2 + \frac{2}{3}k$. Graph the solution set and write the answer in interval notation.

Solution:

$$-\frac{1}{4}k + \frac{1}{6} \leq 2 + \frac{2}{3}k$$

$$12\left(-\frac{1}{4}k + \frac{1}{6}\right) \leq 12\left(2 + \frac{2}{3}k\right)$$
Multiply both sides by 12 to clear fractions. (Because we multiplied by a positive number, the inequality sign is not reversed.)

$$\frac{12}{1}\left(-\frac{1}{4}k\right) + \frac{12}{1}\left(\frac{1}{6}\right) \leq 12(2) + \frac{12}{1}\left(\frac{2}{3}k\right)$$
Apply the distributive property.

$$-3k + 2 \leq 24 + 8k$$
Simplify.

$$-3k - 8k + 2 \leq 24 + 8k - 8k$$
Subtract $8k$ from both sides.

$$-11k + 2 \leq 24$$

$$-11k + 2 - 2 \leq 24 - 2$$
Subtract 2 from both sides.

$$-11k \leq 22$$

$$\frac{-11k}{-11} \geq \frac{22}{-11}$$
Divide both sides by -11. Reverse the inequality sign.

$$k \geq -2$$

Graph:

Interval notation: $[-2, \infty)$

Skill Practice Solve. Graph the solution set and express the solution in interval notation.

11. $\frac{1}{5}t + 7 \leq \frac{1}{2}t - 2$

---

5. Inequalities of the Form $a < x < b$

To solve a compound inequality of the form $a < x < b$ we can work with the inequality as a three-part inequality and isolate the variable, x, as demonstrated in Example 8.

Answers

10.
$(5, \infty)$

11.
$[30, \infty)$

Classroom Example: p. 174,
Exercise 72

Example 8 Solving a Compound Inequality of the Form $a < x < b$

Solve the inequality: $-3 \leq 2x + 1 < 7$. Graph the solution and write the answer in interval notation.

Solution:

To solve the compound inequality $-3 \leq 2x + 1 < 7$ isolate the variable x in the middle. The operations performed on the middle portion of the inequality must also be performed on the left-hand side and right-hand side.

$$-3 \leq 2x + 1 < 7$$

$$-3 - 1 \leq 2x + 1 - 1 < 7 - 1 \qquad \text{Subtract 1 from all three parts of the inequality.}$$

$$-4 \leq 2x < 6 \qquad \text{Simplify.}$$

$$\frac{-4}{2} \leq \frac{2x}{2} < \frac{6}{2} \qquad \text{Divide by 2 in all three parts of the inequality.}$$

$$-2 \leq x < 3$$

Graph:

```
  +--+--+--+--[==+==+==+==)--+--+--+-->
 -6 -5 -4 -3 -2 -1  0  1  2  3  4  5  6
```

Interval notation: $[-2, 3)$

Skill Practice Solve. Graph the solution set and express the solution in interval notation.

12. $-3 \leq -5 + 2y < 11$

6. Applications of Linear Inequalities

Table 2-2 provides several commonly used translations to express inequalities.

Table 2-2

English Phrase	Mathematical Inequality
a is less than b	$a < b$
a is greater than b a exceeds b	$a > b$
a is less than or equal to b a is at most b a is no more than b	$a \leq b$
a is greater than or equal to b a is at least b a is no less than b	$a \geq b$

Classroom Examples: p. 175,
Exercises 106 and 108

Example 9 Translating Expressions Involving Inequalities

Write the English phrases as mathematical inequalities.

a. Claude's annual salary, s, is no more than $40,000.

b. A citizen must be at least 18 years old to vote. (Let a represent a citizen's age.)

c. An amusement park ride has a height requirement between 48 in. and 70 in. (Let h represent height in inches.)

Answer

12.

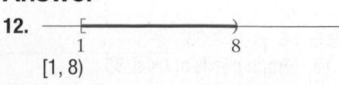

$[1, 8)$

Solution:

a. $s \le 40{,}000$ Claude's annual salary, s, is no more than \$40,000.

b. $a \ge 18$ A citizen must be at least 18 years old to vote.

c. $48 < h < 70$ An amusement park ride has a height requirement between 48 in. and 70 in.

Skill Practice   Write the English phrase as a mathematical inequality.

13. Bill needs a score of at least 92 on the final exam. Let x represent Bill's score.

14. Fewer than 19 cars are in the parking lot. Let c represent the number of cars.

15. The heights, h, of women who wear petite size clothing are typically between 58 in. and 63 in., inclusive.

Linear inequalities are found in a variety of applications. Example 10 can help you determine the minimum grade you need on an exam to get an A in your math course.

Example 10   **Solving an Application with Linear Inequalities**

Classroom Example: p. 175, Exercise 112

To earn an A in a math class, Alsha must average at least 90 on all of her tests. Suppose Alsha has scored 79, 86, 93, 90, and 95 on her first five math tests. Determine the minimum score she needs on her sixth test to get an A in the class.

Solution:

Let x represent the score on the sixth exam.   Label the variable.

$$\left(\begin{array}{c} \text{Average of} \\ \text{all tests} \end{array} \right) \ge 90$$ Create a verbal model.

$$\frac{79 + 86 + 93 + 90 + 95 + x}{6} \ge 90$$ The average score is found by taking the sum of the test scores and dividing by the number of scores.

$$\frac{443 + x}{6} \ge 90$$ Simplify.

$$6\left(\frac{443 + x}{6} \right) \ge (90)6$$ Multiply both sides by 6 to clear fractions.

$$443 + x \ge 540$$ Solve the inequality.

$$x \ge 540 - 443$$ Subtract 443 from both sides.

$$x \ge 97$$ Interpret the results.

Alsha must score at least 97 on her sixth exam to receive an A in the course.

Skill Practice

16. To get at least a B in math, Simon must average 80 on all tests. Suppose Simon has scored 60, 72, 98, and 85 on the first four tests. What score does he need on the fifth test to receive a B?

Answers

13. $x \ge 92$
14. $c < 19$
15. $58 \le h \le 63$
16. Simon needs at least 85.

Section 2.8   Practice Exercises

Study Skills Exercises

1. Find the page numbers for the Chapter Review Exercises, the Chapter Test, and the Cumulative Review Exercises for this chapter.

   Chapter Review Exercises _____   Chapter Test _____

   Cumulative Review Exercises _____

   Compare these features and state the advantages of each.

2. Define the key terms.

   a. linear inequality in one variable   **b. compound inequality**

   c. set-builder notation   **d. interval notation**

Review Problems

3. Solve the equation. $3(x + 2) - (2x - 7) = -(5x - 1) - 2(x + 6)$ $\{-3\}$

4. Solve the equation. $6 - 8(x + 3) + 5x = 5x - (2x - 5) + 13$ $\{-6\}$

Concept 1: Graphing Linear Inequalities

For Exercises 5–16, graph the solution set of each inequality. **(See Examples 1–2.)**

5. $x > 5$

6. $x \geq -7.2$

7. $x \leq \dfrac{5}{2}$

8. $x < -1$

9. $13 > p$

10. $-12 \geq t$

11. $2 \leq y \leq 6.5$

12. $-3 \leq m \leq \dfrac{8}{9}$

13. $0 < x < 4$

14. $-4 < y < 1$

15. $1 < p \leq 8$

16. $-3 \leq t < 3$

Concept 2: Set-Builder Notation and Interval Notation

For Exercises 17–22, graph each inequality and write the solution set in interval notation. **(See Example 3.)**

Set-Builder Notation	Graph	Interval Notation
17. $\{x \mid x \geq 6\}$		$[6, \infty)$
18. $\left\{x \mid \dfrac{1}{2} < x \leq 4\right\}$		$\left(\dfrac{1}{2}, 4\right]$
19. $\{x \mid x \leq 2.1\}$		$(-\infty, 2.1]$
20. $\left\{x \mid x > \dfrac{7}{3}\right\}$		$\left(\dfrac{7}{3}, \infty\right)$
21. $\{x \mid -2 < x \leq 7\}$		$(-2, 7]$
22. $\{x \mid x < -5\}$		$(-\infty, -5)$

Animation

For Exercises 23–28, write each set in set-builder notation and in interval notation. **(See Example 3.)**

Set-Builder Notation	Graph	Interval Notation
23. $\left\{x \mid x > \dfrac{3}{4}\right\}$	$\xleftarrow{\qquad}\underset{\frac{3}{4}}{(}\xrightarrow{\qquad}$	$\left(\dfrac{3}{4}, \infty\right)$
24. $\{x \mid x \le -0.3\}$	$\xleftarrow{\qquad}\underset{-0.3}{]}\xrightarrow{\quad}$	$(-\infty, -0.3]$
25. $\{x \mid -1 < x < 8\}$	$\xleftarrow{}\underset{-1}{(}\xrightarrow{\quad}\underset{8}{)}\xrightarrow{}$	$(-1, 8)$
26. $\{x \mid x \ge 0\}$	$\xleftarrow{\quad}\underset{0}{[}\xrightarrow{\qquad}$	$[0, \infty)$
27. $\{x \mid x \le -14\}$	$\xleftarrow{}\underset{-14}{]}\xrightarrow{\qquad}$	$(-\infty, -14]$
28. $\{x \mid 0 < x \le 9\}$	$\xleftarrow{\quad}\underset{0}{(}\xrightarrow{}\underset{9}{]}\xrightarrow{}$	$(0, 9]$

For Exercises 29–34, graph each set and write the set in set-builder notation. **(See Example 3.)**

Set-Builder Notation	Graph	Interval Notation
29. $\{x \mid x \ge 18\}$	$\underset{18}{[}\xrightarrow{\qquad}$	$[18, \infty)$
30. $\{x \mid -10 \le x \le -2\}$	$\underset{-10}{[}\xrightarrow{}\underset{-2}{]}\xrightarrow{}$	$[-10, -2]$
31. $\{x \mid x < -0.6\}$	$\xleftarrow{}\underset{-0.6}{)}\xrightarrow{\qquad}$	$(-\infty, -0.6)$
32. $\left\{x \mid x < \dfrac{5}{3}\right\}$	$\xleftarrow{}\underset{\frac{5}{3}}{)}\xrightarrow{\qquad}$	$\left(-\infty, \dfrac{5}{3}\right)$
33. $\{x \mid -3.5 \le x < 7.1\}$	$\underset{-3.5}{[}\xrightarrow{}\underset{7.1}{)}\xrightarrow{}$	$[-3.5, 7.1)$
34. $\{x \mid x \ge -10\}$	$\underset{-10}{[}\xrightarrow{\qquad}$	$[-10, \infty)$

Concepts 3–4: Properties of Inequality

For Exercises 35–42, solve the equation in part (a). For part (b), solve the inequality and graph the solution set. Write the answer in set-builder notation and interval notation. **(See Examples 4–7.)**

35. a. $x + 3 = 6$ {3}

b. $x + 3 > 6$

$\xleftarrow{\quad}\underset{3}{(}\xrightarrow{\qquad}$

$\{r \mid r > 3\}; (3, \infty)$

36. a. $y - 6 = 12$ {18}

b. $y - 6 \ge 12$

$\xleftarrow{\quad}\underset{18}{[}\xrightarrow{\qquad}$

$\{y \mid y \ge 18\}; [18, \infty)$

37. a. $p - 4 = 9$ {13}

b. $p - 4 \le 9$

$\xleftarrow{\qquad}\underset{13}{]}\xrightarrow{}$

$\{p \mid p \le 13\}; (-\infty, 13]$

38. a. $k + 8 = 10$ {2}

b. $k + 8 < 10$

$\xleftarrow{\qquad}\underset{2}{)}\xrightarrow{}$

$\{k \mid k < 2\}; (-\infty, 2)$

39. a. $4c = -12$ {−3}

b. $4c < -12$

$\xleftarrow{}\underset{-3}{)}\xrightarrow{\qquad}$

$\{c \mid c < -3\}; (-\infty, -3)$

40. a. $5d = -35$ {−7}

b. $5d > -35$

$\xleftarrow{}\underset{-7}{(}\xrightarrow{\qquad}$

$\{d \mid d > -7\}; (-7, \infty)$

41. a. $-10z = 15$ $\left\{-\dfrac{3}{2}\right\}$

b. $-10z \le 15$

$\xleftarrow{}\underset{-\frac{3}{2}}{[}\xrightarrow{\qquad}$

$\left\{z \mid z \ge -\dfrac{3}{2}\right\}; \left[-\dfrac{3}{2}, \infty\right)$

42. a. $-2w = 14$ {−7}

b. $-2w < 14$

$\xleftarrow{}\underset{-7}{(}\xrightarrow{\qquad}$

$\{w \mid w > -7\}; (-7, \infty)$

Concept 5: Inequalities of the Form $a < x < b$

For Exercises 43–48, graph the solution and write the set in interval notation. **(See Example 8.)**

43. $-1 < y \le 4$ $(-1, 4]$

$\xleftarrow{}\underset{-1}{(}\xrightarrow{}\underset{4}{]}\xrightarrow{}$

44. $2.5 \le t < 5.7$ $[2.5, 5.7)$

$\xleftarrow{}\underset{2.5}{[}\xrightarrow{}\underset{5.7}{)}\xrightarrow{}$

45. $0 < x + 3 < 8$ $(-3, 5)$

$\xleftarrow{}\underset{-3}{(}\xrightarrow{}\underset{5}{)}\xrightarrow{}$

46. $-2 \le x - 4 \le 3$ $[2, 7]$

$\xleftarrow{}\underset{2}{[}\xrightarrow{}\underset{7}{]}\xrightarrow{}$

47. $8 \le 4x \le 24$ $[2, 6]$

$\xleftarrow{}\underset{2}{[}\xrightarrow{}\underset{6}{]}\xrightarrow{}$

48. $-9 < 3x < 12$ $(-3, 4)$

$\xleftarrow{}\underset{-3}{(}\xrightarrow{}\underset{4}{)}\xrightarrow{}$

 Writing   Translating Expression   Geometry   Scientific Calculator   Video   NS&E

Mixed Exercises

For Exercises 49–96, solve each inequality. Graph the solution set and write the set in interval notation. (See Exercises 4–8.)

49. $x + 5 \le 6$ $(-\infty, 1]$

50. $y - 7 < 6$ $(-\infty, 13)$

51. $3q - 7 > 2q + 3$ $(10, \infty)$

52. $5r + 4 \ge 4r - 1$ $[-5, \infty)$

53. $4 < 1 + x$ $(3, \infty)$

54. $3 > z - 6$ $(-\infty, 9)$

55. $2 \ge a - 6$ $(-\infty, 8]$

56. $7 \le b + 12$ $[-5, \infty)$

57. $3c > 6$ $(2, \infty)$

58. $4d \le 12$ $(-\infty, 3]$

59. $-3c > 6$ $(-\infty, -2)$

60. $-4d \le 12$ $[-3, \infty)$

61. $-h \le -14$ $[14, \infty)$

62. $-q > -7$ $(-\infty, 7)$

63. $12 \ge -\dfrac{x}{2}$ $[-24, \infty)$

64. $6 < -\dfrac{m}{3}$ $(-\infty, -18)$

65. $-2 \le p + 1 < 4$ $[-3, 3)$

66. $0 < k + 7 < 6$ $(-7, -1)$

67. $-3 < 6h - 3 < 12$ $\left(0, \dfrac{5}{2}\right)$

68. $-6 \le 4a - 2 \le 12$ $\left[-1, \dfrac{7}{2}\right]$

69. $5 < \dfrac{1}{2}x < 6$ $(10, 12)$

70. $-6 \le 3x \le 12$ $[-2, 4]$

71. $-5 \le 4x - 1 < 15$ $[-1, 4)$

72. $-2 < \dfrac{1}{3}x - 2 \le 2$ $(0, 12]$

73. $54 \le 0.6z$ $[90, \infty)$

74. $28 < -0.7w$ $(-\infty, -40)$

75. $-\dfrac{2}{3}y < 6$ $(-9, \infty)$

76. $\dfrac{3}{4}x \le -12$ $(-\infty, -16]$

77. $-2x - 4 \le 11$ $\left[-\dfrac{15}{2}, \infty\right)$

78. $-3x + 1 > 0$ $\left(-\infty, \dfrac{1}{3}\right)$

79. $-12 > 7x + 9$ $(-\infty, -3)$

80. $8 < 2x - 10$ $(9, \infty)$

81. $-7b - 3 \le 2b$ $\left[-\dfrac{1}{3}, \infty\right)$

82. $3t \ge 7t - 35$ $\left(-\infty, \dfrac{35}{4}\right]$

83. $4n + 2 < 6n + 8$ $(-3, \infty)$

84. $2w - 1 \le 5w + 8$ $[-3, \infty)$

85. $8 - 6(x - 3) > -4x + 12$ $(-\infty, 7)$

86. $3 - 4(h - 2) > -5h + 6$ $(-5, \infty)$

87. $3(x + 1) - 2 \le \dfrac{1}{2}(4x - 8)$ $(-\infty, -5]$

88. $8 - (2x - 5) \ge \dfrac{1}{3}(9x - 6)$ $(-\infty, 3]$

89. $\dfrac{7}{6}p + \dfrac{4}{3} \ge \dfrac{11}{6}p - \dfrac{7}{6}$ $\left(-\infty, \dfrac{15}{4}\right]$

90. $\dfrac{1}{3}w - \dfrac{1}{2} \le \dfrac{5}{6}w + \dfrac{1}{2}$ $[-2, \infty)$

91. $\dfrac{y - 6}{3} > y + 4$ $(-\infty, -9)$

92. $\dfrac{5t + 7}{2} < t - 4$ $(-\infty, -5)$

93. $-1.2a - 0.4 < -0.4a + 2$ $(-3, \infty)$

 Writing   Translating Expression   Geometry   Scientific Calculator   Video   NS&E

94. $-0.4c + 1.2 > -2c - 0.4$ $(-1, \infty)$ **95.** $-2x + 5 \geq -x + 5$ $(-\infty, 0]$ **96.** $4x - 6 < 5x - 6$ $(0, \infty)$

For Exercises 97–100, determine whether the given number is a solution to the inequality.

97. $-2x + 5 < 4;$ $x = -2$ No

98. $-3y - 7 > 5;$ $y = 6$ No

99. $4(p + 7) - 1 > 2 + p;$ $p = 1$ Yes

100. $3 - k < 2(-1 + k);$ $k = 4$ Yes

Concept 6: Applications of Linear Inequalities

↔ For Exercises 101–110, write each English phrase as a mathematical inequality. **(See Example 9.)**

101. The length of a fish, L, was at least 10 in.
$L \geq 10$

102. Tasha's average test score, t, exceeded 90.
$t > 90$

103. The wind speed, w, exceeded 75 mph. $w > 75$

104. The height of a cave, h, was no more than 2 ft.
$h \leq 2$

105. The temperature of the water in Blue Spring, t, is no more than 72°F. $t \leq 72$

106. The temperature on the tennis court, t, was no less than 100°F. $t \geq 100$

107. The length of the hike, L, was no less than 8 km. $L \geq 8$

108. The depth, d, of a certain pool was at most 10 ft. $d \leq 10$

109. The snowfall, h, in Monroe County is between 2 inches and 5 inches. $2 < h < 5$

110. The cost, c, of carpeting a room is between $300 and $400. $300 < c < 400$

111. The average summer rainfall for Miami, Florida, for June, July, and August is 7.4 in. per month. If Miami receives 5.9 in. of rain in June and 6.1 in. in July, how much rain is required in August to exceed the 3-month summer average? **(See Example 10.)**   More than 10.2 in. of rain is needed.

112. The average winter snowfall for Burlington, Vermont, for December, January, and February is 18.7 in. per month. If Burlington receives 22 in. of snow in December and 24 in. in January, how much snow is required in February to exceed the 3-month winter average?
More than 10.1 in. of snow is needed.

113. An artist paints wooden birdhouses. She buys the birdhouses for $9 each. However, for large orders, the price per birdhouse is discounted by a percentage off the original price. Let x represent the number of birdhouses ordered. The corresponding discount is given in the table.

Size of Order	Discount
$x \leq 49$	0%
$50 \leq x \leq 99$	5%
$100 \leq x \leq 199$	10%
$x \geq 200$	20%

a. If the artist places an order for 190 birdhouses, compute the total cost.
$1539

b. Which costs more: 190 birdhouses or 200 birdhouses? Explain your answer.
200 birdhouses cost $1440. It is cheaper to purchase 200 birdhouses because the discount is greater.

114. A wholesaler sells T-shirts to a surf shop at $8 per shirt. However, for large orders, the price per shirt is discounted by a percentage off the original price. Let x represent the number of shirts ordered. The corresponding discount is given in the table.

Number of Shirts Ordered	Discount
$x \leq 24$	0%
$25 \leq x \leq 49$	2%
$50 \leq x \leq 99$	4%
$100 \leq x \leq 149$	6%
$x > 150$	8%

a. If the surf shop orders 50 shirts, compute the total cost. $384

b. Which costs more: 148 shirts or 150 shirts? Explain your answer.
It costs $1112.96 for 148 shirts and $1104.00 for 150 shirts. 150 shirts cost less than 148 shirts because the discount is greater.

115. A cell phone provider offers one plan that charges $4.95 for the text messaging feature plus $0.09 for each individual incoming or outgoing text. Alternatively, the provider offers a second plan with a flat rate of $18.00 for unlimited text messaging. How many text messages would result in the unlimited option being the better deal?
If there were more than 145 text messages, the unlimited option would be a better deal.

116. Melissa runs a landscaping business. She has equipment and fuel expenses of $313 per month. If she charges $45 for each lawn, how many lawns must she service to make a profit of at least $600 a month?
Melissa must service more than 20 lawns.

117. Madison is planning a 5-night trip to Cancun, Mexico, with her friends. The airfare is $475, her share of the hotel room is $54 per night, and her budget for food and entertainment is $350. She has $700 in savings and has a job earning $10 per hour babysitting. What is the minimum number of hours of babysitting that Madison needs so that she will earn enough money to take the trip?   Madison needs to babysit a minimum of 39.5 hr.

118. Luke and Landon are both tutors. Luke charges $50 for an initial assessment and $25 per hour for each hour he tutors. Landon charges $100 for an initial assessment and $20 per hour for tutoring. After how many hours of tutoring will Luke surpass Landon in earnings?   After 10 hr of tutoring, Luke's earnings will surpass Landon's earnings.

Expanding Your Skills

For Exercises 119–124, solve the inequality. Graph the solution set and write the set in interval notation.

119. $3(x + 2) - (2x - 7) \le (5x - 1) - 2(x + 6)$
$[13, \infty)$

120. $6 - 8(y + 3) + 5y > 5y - (2y - 5) + 13$ $(-\infty, -6)$

121. $-2 - \dfrac{w}{4} \le \dfrac{1 + w}{3}$ $[-4, \infty)$

122. $\dfrac{z - 3}{4} - 1 > \dfrac{z}{2}$ $(-\infty, -7)$

123. $-0.703 < 0.122p - 2.472$ $(14.5, \infty)$

124. $3.88 - 1.335t \ge 5.66$ $(-\infty, -1.\overline{3}]$

Group Activity

Computing Body Mass Index (BMI)

Materials: Calculator

Estimated Time: 10 minutes

Group Size: 2

Body mass index is a statistical measure of an individual's weight in relation to the person's height. It is computed by

$$\text{BMI} = \frac{703W}{h^2} \qquad \text{where } W \text{ is a person's weight in } pounds.$$
$$h \text{ is the person's height in } inches.$$

The NIH categorizes body mass indices as follows:

1. Compute the body mass index for a person 5'4" tall weighing 160 lb. Is this person's weight considered ideal?

27.5; No, the person is considered overweight.

Body Mass Index (BMI)	Weight Status
$18.5 \le \text{BMI} \le 24.9$	considered ideal
$25.0 \le \text{BMI} \le 29.9$	considered overweight
$\text{BMI} \ge 30.0$	considered obese

2. At the time that basketball legend Michael Jordan played for the Chicago Bulls, he was 210 lb and stood 6'6" tall. What was Michael Jordan's body mass index?   24.3

3. For a fixed height, body mass index is a function of a person's weight only. For example, for a person 72 in. tall (6 ft), solve the following inequality to determine the person's ideal weight range.

136.4 lb $\le W \le$ 183.6 lb

$$18.5 \le \frac{703W}{(72)^2} \le 24.9$$

 Writing   Translating Expression   Geometry   Scientific Calculator   Video   NS&E

4. At the time that professional bodybuilder, Jay Cutler, won the Mr. Olympia contest he was 260 lb and stood 5′10″ tall.

    a. What was Jay Cutler's body mass index?   37.3

    b. As a bodybuilder, Jay Cutler has an extraordinarily small percentage of body fat. Yet, according to the chart, would he be considered overweight or obese? Why do you think that the formula is not an accurate measurement of Mr. Cutler's weight status?   Jay Cutler's BMI was 37.3 which placed him in the "obese" category. However, BMI is meant to be used as a simple means of classifying physically inactive individuals with an average body composition. The BMI formula does not account for other factors affecting a person's weight such as fitness level, muscle mass, bone structure, and gender.

Chapter 2   Summary

Section 2.1   Addition, Subtraction, Multiplication, and Division Properties of Equality

Key Concepts

An equation is an algebraic statement that indicates two expressions are equal. A **solution to an equation** is a value of the variable that makes the equation a true statement. The set of all solutions to an equation is the solution set of the equation.

    A **linear equation in one variable** can be written in the form $ax + b = 0$, where $a \neq 0$.

Addition Property of Equality:

If $a = b$, then $a + c = b + c$

Subtraction Property of Equality:

If $a = b$, then $a - c = b - c$

Multiplication Property of Equality:

If $a = b$, then $ac = bc$

Division Property of Equality:

If $a = b$, then $\dfrac{a}{c} = \dfrac{b}{c}$ $(c \neq 0)$

Examples

Example 1

$2x + 1 = 9$ is an equation with solution set $\{4\}$.

Check: $2(4) + 1 \overset{?}{=} 9$

$$8 + 1 \overset{?}{=} 9$$

$$9 \overset{?}{=} 9 \; ✔ \quad \text{True}$$

Example 2

$$x - 5 = 12$$
$$x - 5 + 5 = 12 + 5$$
$$x = 17 \qquad \text{The solution set is } \{17\}.$$

Example 3

$$z + 1.44 = 2.33$$
$$z + 1.44 - 1.44 = 2.33 - 1.44$$
$$z = 0.89 \qquad \text{The solution set is } \{0.89\}.$$

Example 4

$$\frac{3}{4}x = 12$$

$$\frac{4}{3} \cdot \frac{3}{4}x = 12 \cdot \frac{4}{3}$$

$$x = 16 \qquad \text{The solution set is } \{16\}.$$

Example 5

$$16 = 8y$$
$$\frac{16}{8} = \frac{8y}{8}$$
$$2 = y \qquad \text{The solution set is } \{2\}.$$

Section 2.2   Solving Linear Equations

Key Concepts

Steps for Solving a Linear Equation in One Variable:

1. Simplify both sides of the equation.
   - Clear parentheses
   - Combine *like* terms
2. Use the addition or subtraction property of equality to collect the variable terms on one side of the equation.
3. Use the addition or subtraction property of equality to collect the constant terms on the other side of the equation.
4. Use the multiplication or division property of equality to make the coefficient of the variable term equal to 1.
5. Check your answer.

A **conditional equation** is true for some values of the variable but is false for other values.

An equation that has all real numbers as its solution set is an **identity**.

An equation that has no solution is a **contradiction**.

Examples

Example 1

$$5y + 7 = 3(y - 1) + 2$$

$5y + 7 = 3y - 3 + 2$	Clear parentheses.
$5y + 7 = 3y - 1$	Combine *like* terms.
$2y + 7 = -1$	Collect the variable terms.
$2y = -8$	Collect the constant terms.
$y = -4$	Divide both sides by 2.

Check:

$$5(-4) + 7 \stackrel{?}{=} 3[(-4) - 1] + 2$$
$$-20 + 7 \stackrel{?}{=} 3(-5) + 2$$
$$-13 \stackrel{?}{=} -15 + 2$$

The solution set is $\{-4\}$. $-13 \stackrel{?}{=} -13$ ✔ True

Example 2

$x + 5 = 7$ is a conditional equation because it is true only on the condition that $x = 2$.

Example 3

$$x + 4 = 2(x + 2) - x$$
$$x + 4 = 2x + 4 - x$$
$$x + 4 = x + 4$$
$$4 = 4 \quad \text{is an identity}$$

Solution set: The set of real numbers.

Example 4

$$y - 5 = 2(y + 3) - y$$
$$y - 5 = 2y + 6 - y$$
$$y - 5 = y + 6$$
$$-5 = 6 \quad \text{is a contradiction}$$

Solution set: $\{\ \}$

Section 2.3 Linear Equations: Clearing Fractions and Decimals

Key Concepts

Steps for Solving a Linear Equation in One Variable:

1. Simplify both sides of the equation.
   - Clear parentheses
   - Consider clearing fractions or decimals (if any are present) by multiplying both sides of the equation by a common denominator of all terms
   - Combine *like* terms
2. Use the addition or subtraction property of equality to collect the variable terms on one side of the equation.
3. Use the addition or subtraction property of equality to collect the constant terms on the other side of the equation.
4. Use the multiplication or division property of equality to make the coefficient of the variable term equal to 1.
5. Check your answer.

Examples

Example 1

$$\frac{1}{2}x - 2 - \frac{3}{4}x = \frac{7}{4}$$

$$\frac{4}{1}\left(\frac{1}{2}x - 2 - \frac{3}{4}x\right) = \frac{4}{1}\left(\frac{7}{4}\right) \qquad \text{Multiply by the LCD.}$$

$$2x - 8 - 3x = 7 \qquad \text{Apply distributive property.}$$

$$-x - 8 = 7 \qquad \text{Combine \emph{like} terms.}$$

$$-x = 15 \qquad \text{Add 8 to both sides.}$$

$$x = -15 \qquad \text{Divide by } -1.$$

The solution set is $\{-15\}$.

Example 2

$$-1.2x - 5.1 = 16.5$$

$$10(-1.2x - 5.1) = 10(16.5) \qquad \text{Multiply both sides by 10.}$$

$$-12x - 51 = 165$$

$$-12x = 216$$

$$\frac{-12x}{-12} = \frac{216}{-12}$$

$$x = -18$$

The solution set is $\{-18\}$.

Section 2.4   Applications of Linear Equations: Introduction to Problem Solving

Key Concepts

Problem-Solving Steps for Word Problems:

1. Read the problem carefully.
2. Assign labels to unknown quantities.
3. Develop a verbal model.
4. Write a mathematical equation.
5. Solve the equation.
6. Interpret the results and write the answer in words.

Example

Example 1

The perimeter of a triangle is 54 m. The lengths of the sides are represented by three consecutive even integers. Find the lengths of the three sides.

1. Read the problem.

2. Let x represent one side, $x + 2$ represent the second side, and $x + 4$ represent the third side.

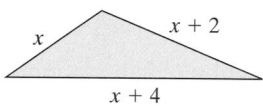

3. (First side) + (second side) + (third side) = perimeter

4. $x + (x + 2) + (x + 4) = 54$

5. $3x + 6 = 54$
   $3x = 48$
   $x = 16$

6. $x = 16$ represents the length of the shortest side. The lengths of the other sides are given by $x + 2 = 18$ and $x + 4 = 20$.

   The lengths of the three sides are 16 m, 18 m, and 20 m.

Section 2.5   Applications Involving Percents

Key Concepts

The following formula will help you solve basic percent problems.

$$\text{Amount} = (\text{percent})(\text{base})$$

One common use of percents is in computing **sales tax**.

Another use of percent is in computing **simple interest** using the formula:

$$\left(\begin{array}{c}\text{Simple}\\\text{interest}\end{array}\right) = (\text{principal})\left(\begin{array}{c}\text{annual}\\\text{interest}\\\text{rate}\end{array}\right)\left(\begin{array}{c}\text{time in}\\\text{years}\end{array}\right)$$

or $I = Prt$.

Examples

Example 1

A dinette set costs \$1260.00 after a 5% sales tax is included. What was the price before tax?

$$\left(\begin{array}{c}\text{Price}\\\text{before tax}\end{array}\right) + (\text{tax}) = \left(\begin{array}{c}\text{total}\\\text{price}\end{array}\right)$$

$$x \quad + 0.05x = 1260$$
$$1.05x = 1260$$
$$x = 1200$$

The dinette set cost \$1200 before tax.

Example 2

John Li invests \$5400 at 2.5% simple interest. How much interest does he earn after 5 years?

$$I = Prt$$
$$I = (\$5400)(0.025)(5)$$
$$I = \$675$$

Section 2.6   Formulas and Applications of Geometry

Key Concepts

A **literal equation** is an equation that has more than one variable. Often such an equation can be manipulated to solve for different variables.

Formulas from Section A.2 can be used in applications involving geometry.

Examples

Example 1

$$P = 2a + b, \text{ solve for } a.$$

$$P - b = 2a + b - b$$
$$P - b = 2a$$
$$\frac{P - b}{2} = \frac{2a}{2}$$
$$\frac{P - b}{2} = a \quad \text{or} \quad a = \frac{P - b}{2}$$

Example 2

Find the length of a side of a square whose perimeter is 28 ft.

Use the formula $P = 4s$. Substitute 28 for P and solve:

$$P = 4s$$
$$28 = 4s$$
$$7 = s$$

The length of a side of the square is 7 ft.

Section 2.7   Mixture Applications and Uniform Motion

Examples

Example 1 illustrates a mixture problem.

Example 1

How much 80% disinfectant solution should be mixed with 8 L of a 30% disinfectant solution to make a 40% solution?

	80% Solution	30% Solution	40% Solution
Amount of Solution	x	8	$x + 8$
Amount of Pure Disinfectant	$0.80x$	$0.30(8)$	$0.40(x + 8)$

$0.80x + 0.30(8) = 0.40(x + 8)$

$\quad 0.80x + 2.4 = 0.40x + 3.2$

$\quad 0.40x + 2.4 = 3.2 \qquad$ Subtract $0.40x$.

$\qquad 0.40x = 0.80 \qquad$ Subtract 2.4.

$\qquad\quad x = 2 \qquad$ Divide by 0.40.

2 L of 80% solution is needed.

Examples

Example 2 illustrates a uniform motion problem.

Example 2

Jack and Diane participate in a bicycle race. Jack rides the first half of the race in 1.5 hr. Diane rides the second half at a rate 5 mph slower than Jack and completes her portion in 2 hr. How fast does each person ride?

	Distance	Rate	Time
Jack	$1.5x$	x	1.5
Diane	$2(x - 5)$	$x - 5$	2

$$\begin{pmatrix} \text{Distance} \\ \text{Jack rides} \end{pmatrix} = \begin{pmatrix} \text{distance} \\ \text{Diane rides} \end{pmatrix}$$

$\quad 1.5x \quad = \quad 2(x - 5)$

$\qquad 1.5x = 2x - 10$

$\quad -0.5x = -10 \qquad$ Subtract $2x$.

$\qquad\quad x = 20 \qquad$ Divide by -0.5.

Jack's speed is x. Jack rides 20 mph. Diane's speed is $x - 5$, which is 15 mph.

Section 2.8   Linear Inequalities

Key Concepts

A **linear inequality in one variable**, x, is any relationship in the form: $ax + b < 0$, $ax + b > 0$, $ax + b \leq 0$, or $ax + b \geq 0$, where $a \neq 0$.

The solution set to an inequality can be expressed as a graph or in **set-builder notation** or in **interval notation**.

When graphing an inequality or when writing interval notation, a parenthesis, (or), is used to denote that an endpoint is *not included* in a solution set. A square bracket, [or], is used to show that an endpoint *is included* in a solution set. Parenthesis (or) are always used with $-\infty$ and ∞, respectively.

The inequality $a < x < b$ is used to show that x is greater than a and less than b. That is, x is *between a and b*.

Multiplying or dividing an inequality by a negative quantity requires the direction of the inequality sign to be reversed.

Example

Example 1

$\qquad -2x + 6 \geq 14$

$-2x + 6 - 6 \geq 14 - 6 \qquad$ Subtract 6.

$\qquad\quad -2x \geq 8 \qquad$ Simplify.

$\qquad\quad \dfrac{-2x}{-2} \leq \dfrac{8}{-2} \qquad$ Divide by -2. Reverse the inequality sign.

$\qquad\qquad x \leq -4$

Graph:

Set-builder notation: $\{x \mid x \leq -4\}$

Interval notation: $(-\infty, -4]$

Chapter 2   Review Exercises

Section 2.1

1. Label the following as either an expression or an equation:

   a. $3x + y = 10$
   Equation
   b. $9x + 10y - 2xy$
   Expression
   c. $4(x + 3) = 12$
   Equation
   d. $-5x = 7$
   Equation

 2. Explain how to determine whether an equation is linear in one variable.   A linear equation can be written in the form $ax + b = 0, a \neq 0$.

3. Determine if the given equation is a linear equation in one variable. Answer yes or no.

   a. $4x^2 + 8 = -10$
   No
   b. $x + 18 = 72$
   Yes
   c. $-3 + 2y^2 = 0$
   No
   d. $-4p - 5 = 6p$
   Yes

4. For the equation, $4y + 9 = -3$, determine if the given numbers are solutions.

   a. $y = 3$ No
   b. $y = -3$ Yes

For Exercises 5–12, solve each equation using the addition property, subtraction property, multiplication property, or division property of equality.

5. $a + 6 = -2$ $\{-8\}$
6. $6 = z - 9$ $\{15\}$

7. $-\dfrac{3}{4} + k = \dfrac{9}{2}$ $\left\{\dfrac{21}{4}\right\}$
8. $0.1r = 7$ $\{70\}$

9. $-5x = 21$ $\left\{-\dfrac{21}{5}\right\}$
10. $\dfrac{t}{3} = -20$ $\{-60\}$

11. $-\dfrac{2}{5}k = \dfrac{4}{7}$ $\left\{-\dfrac{10}{7}\right\}$
12. $-m = -27$ $\{27\}$

13. The quotient of a number and negative six is equal to negative ten. Find the number.
    The number is 60.

14. The difference of a number and $-\frac{1}{8}$ is $\frac{5}{12}$. Find the number.   The number is $\dfrac{7}{24}$.

15. Four subtracted from a number is negative twelve. Find the number.
    The number is -8.

16. The product of a number and $\frac{1}{4}$ is $-\frac{1}{2}$. Find the number.   The number is -2.

Section 2.2

For Exercises 17–28, solve each equation.

17. $4d + 2 = 6$ $\{1\}$
18. $5c - 6 = -9$ $\left\{-\dfrac{3}{5}\right\}$

19. $-7c = -3c - 8$ $\{2\}$
20. $-28 = 5w + 2$ $\{-6\}$

21. $\dfrac{b}{3} + 1 = 0$ $\{-3\}$
22. $\dfrac{2}{3}h - 5 = 7$ $\{18\}$

23. $-3p + 7 = 5p + 1$ $\left\{\dfrac{3}{4}\right\}$
24. $4t - 6 = 12t + 18$ $\{-3\}$

25. $4a - 9 = 3(a - 3)$ $\{0\}$
26. $3(2c + 5) = -2(c - 8)$ $\left\{\dfrac{1}{8}\right\}$

27. $7b + 3(b - 1) + 3 = 2(b + 8)$ $\{2\}$

28. $2 + (18 - x) + 2(x - 1) = 4(x + 2) - 8$ $\{6\}$

 29. Explain the difference between an equation that is a contradiction and an equation that is an identity.   A contradiction has no solution and an identity is true for all real numbers.

For Exercises 30–35, label each equation as a conditional equation, a contradiction, or an identity.

30. $x + 3 = 3 + x$
    Identity
31. $3x - 19 = 2x + 1$
    Conditional equation

32. $5x + 6 = 5x - 28$
    Contradiction
33. $2x - 8 = 2(x - 4)$
    Identity

34. $-8x - 9 = -8(x - 9)$
    Contradiction
35. $4x - 4 = 3x - 2$
    Conditional equation

Section 2.3

For Exercises 36–53, solve each equation.

36. $\dfrac{x}{8} - \dfrac{1}{4} - \dfrac{1}{2}$ $\{6\}$
37. $\dfrac{y}{15} - \dfrac{2}{3} = \dfrac{4}{5}$ $\{22\}$

38. $\dfrac{x + 5}{2} - \dfrac{2x + 10}{9} = 5$ $\{13\}$

39. $\dfrac{x - 6}{3} - \dfrac{2x + 8}{2} = 12$ $\{-27\}$

40. $\dfrac{1}{10}p - 3 = \dfrac{2}{5}p$ $\{-10\}$
41. $\dfrac{1}{4}y - \dfrac{3}{4} = \dfrac{1}{2}y + 1$ $\{-7\}$

42. $-\dfrac{1}{4}(2 - 3t) = \dfrac{3}{4}$ $\left\{\dfrac{5}{3}\right\}$
43. $\dfrac{2}{7}(w + 4) = \dfrac{1}{2}$ $\left\{-\dfrac{9}{4}\right\}$

44. $17.3 - 2.7q = 10.55$ $\{2.5\}$

45. $4.9z + 4.6 = 3.2z - 2.2$ $\{-4\}$

46. $5.74a + 9.28 = 2.24a - 5.42$ $\{-4.2\}$

47. $62.84t - 123.66 = 4(2.36 + 2.4t)$ $\{2.5\}$

 Writing   Translating Expression   Geometry   Scientific Calculator   Video   NS&E

48. $0.05x + 0.10(24 - x) = 0.75(24)$ {−312}

49. $0.20(x + 4) + 0.65x = 0.20(854)$ {200}

50. $100 - (t - 6) = -(t - 1)$ { }

51. $3 - (x + 4) + 5 = 3x + 10 - 4x$ { }

52. $5t - (2t + 14) = 3t - 14$ The set of real numbers

53. $9 - 6(2z + 1) = -3(4z - 1)$
The set of real numbers

Section 2.4

54. Twelve added to the sum of a number and two is forty-four. Find the number.   The number is 30.

55. Twenty added to the sum of a number and six is thirty-seven. Find the number.   The number is 11.

56. Three times a number is the same as the difference of twice the number and seven. Find the number.   The number is −7.

57. Eight less than five times a number is forty-eight less than the number. Find the number.
The number is −10.

58. Three times the largest of three consecutive even integers is 76 more than the sum of the other two integers. Find the integers.
The integers are 66, 68, and 70.

59. Ten times the smallest of three consecutive integers is 213 more than the sum of the other two integers. Find the integers.
The integers are 27, 28, and 29.

60. The perimeter of a triangle is 78 in. The lengths of the sides are represented by three consecutive integers. Find the lengths of the sides of the triangle.   The sides are 25 in., 26 in., and 27 in.

61. The perimeter of a pentagon (a five-sided polygon) is 190 cm. The five sides are represented by consecutive integers. Find the lengths of the sides.   The sides are 36 cm, 37 cm, 38 cm, 39 cm, and 40 cm.

62. The average salary for a major league baseball player in 2005 was $2.675 million. This was 2.5 times the average salary in 2000. What was the average salary in 2000?
The average salary was $1.07 million in 2000.

63. The state of Indiana has approximately 2.1 million more people than Kentucky. Together their population totals 10.3 million. Approximately how many people are in each state?   Indiana has
6.2 million people and Kentucky has 4.1 million.

Section 2.5

For Exercises 64–69, solve each problem involving percents.

64. What is 35% of 68?
23.8

65. What is 4% of 720?
28.8

66. 53.5 is what percent of 428?   12.5%

67. 68.4 is what percent of 72?   95%

68. 24 is 15% of what number?   160

69. 8.75 is 0.5% of what number?   1750

70. A couple spent a total of $50.40 for dinner. This included a 20% tip and 6% sales tax on the price of the meal. What was the price of the dinner before tax and tip?   The dinner was $40
before tax and tip.

71. Anna Tsao invested $3000 in an account paying 8% simple interest.

   a. How much interest will she earn in $3\frac{1}{2}$ years?
   $840

   b. What will her balance be at that time?
   $3840

72. Eduardo invested money in an account earning 4% simple interest. At the end of 5 years, he had a total of $14,400. How much money did he originally invest?   He invested $12,000.

73. A novel is discounted 30%. The sale price is $20.65. What was the original price?   The novel
originally cost $29.50.

Section 2.6

For Exercises 74–81, solve for the indicated variable.

74. $C = K - 273$ for K $K = C + 273$

75. $K = C + 273$ for C $C = K - 273$

76. $P = 4s$ for s $s = \dfrac{P}{4}$

77. $P = 3s$ for s $s = \dfrac{P}{3}$

78. $y = mx + b$ for x $x = \dfrac{y - b}{m}$

79. $a + bx = c$ for x $x = \dfrac{c - a}{b}$

80. $2x + 5y = -2$ for y $y = \dfrac{-2x - 2}{5}$

81. $4(a + b) = Q$ for b $b = \dfrac{Q - 4a}{4}$ or $b = \dfrac{Q}{4} - a$

 Writing   Translating Expression   Geometry   Scientific Calculator   Video   NS&E

For Exercises 82–88, use the appropriate geometry formula to solve the problem.

82. Find the height of a parallelogram whose area is 42 m² and whose base is 6 m.   The height is 7 m.

83. The volume of a cone is given by the formula $V = \frac{1}{3}\pi r^2 h$.

  a. Solve the formula for h. $h = \frac{3V}{\pi r^2}$

  b. Find the height of a right circular cone whose volume is 47.8 in.³ and whose radius is 3 in. Round to the nearest tenth of an inch.
  The height is 5.1 in.

84. The smallest angle of a triangle is 2° more than $\frac{1}{4}$ of the largest angle. The middle angle is 2° less than the largest angle. Find the measure of each angle.   The angles are 22°, 78°, and 80°.

85. A carpenter uses a special saw to cut an angle on a piece of framing. If the angles are complementary and one angle is 10° more than the other, find the measure of each angle.   The angles are 50° and 40°.

86. A rectangular window has width 1 ft less than its length. The perimeter is 18 ft. Find the length and the width of the window.
The length is 5 ft, and the width is 4 ft.

87. Find the measure of the vertical angles by first solving for x. $x = 20$. The angle measure is 65°.

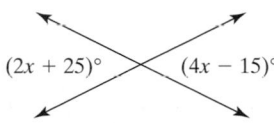

$(2x + 25)°$ $(4x - 15)°$

88. Find the measure of angle y.

The measure of angle y is 53°.

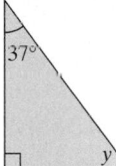

37°

y

Section 2.7

89. In stormy conditions, a delivery truck can travel a route in 14 hr. In good weather, the same trip can be made in 10.5 hr because the truck travels 15 km/hr faster. Find the speed of the truck in stormy weather and the speed in good weather.
The truck travels 45 km/hr in bad weather and 60 km/hr in good weather.

90. Winston and Gus ride their bicycles in a relay. Each person rides the same distance. Winston rides 3 mph faster than Gus and finishes the course in 2.5 hr. Gus finishes in 3 hr. How fast does each person ride?   Gus rides 15 mph and Winston rides 18 mph.

91. Two cars leave a rest stop on Interstate I-10 at the same time. One heads east and the other heads west. One car travels 55 mph and the other 62 mph. How long will it take for them to be 327.6 mi apart?   The cars will be 327.6 mi apart after 2.8 hr (2 hr and 48 min).

92. Two hikers begin at the same time at opposite ends of a 9-mi trail and walk toward each other. One hiker walks 2.5 mph and the other walks 1.5 mph. How long will it be before they meet?
They meet in 2.25 hr (2 hr and 15 min).

93. How much ground beef with 24% fat should be mixed with 8 lb of ground sirloin that is 6% fat to make a mixture that is 9.6% fat?   2 lb of 24% fat content beef is needed.

94. A soldering compound with 40% lead (the rest is tin) must be combined with 80 lb of solder that is 75% lead to make a compound that is 68% lead? How much solder with 40% lead should be used?   20 lb of the 40% solder should be used.

Section 2.8

For Exercises 95–97, graph each inequality and write the set in interval notation.

95. $\{x \mid x > -2\}$ $(-2, \infty)$

96. $\left\{x \mid x \le \frac{1}{2}\right\}$ $\left(-\infty, \frac{1}{2}\right]$

97. $\{x \mid -1 < x \le 4\}$
$(-1, 4]$

 98. A landscaper buys potted geraniums from a nursery at a price of $5 per plant. However, for large orders, the price per plant is discounted by a percentage off the original price. Let x represent the number of potted plants ordered. The corresponding discount is given in the following table.

Number of Plants	Discount
$x \le 99$	0%
$100 \le x \le 199$	2%
$200 \le x \le 299$	4%
$x \ge 300$	6%

  a. Find the cost to purchase 130 plants. $637

  b. Which costs more, 300 plants or 295 plants? Explain your answer.   300 plants cost $1410, and 295 plants cost $1416. 300 plants cost less.

For Exercises 99–108, solve the inequality. Graph the solution set and express the answer in set-builder notation and interval notation.

99. $c + 6 < 23$

$\{c \mid c < 17\};\ (-\infty, 17)$ 17

100. $3w - 4 > -5$

$\left\{w \mid w > -\dfrac{1}{3}\right\};\ \left(-\dfrac{1}{3}, \infty\right)$ $-\dfrac{1}{3}$

101. $-2x - 7 \geq 5$

$\{x \mid x \leq -6\};\ (-\infty, -6]$ -6

102. $5(y + 2) \leq -4$

$\left\{y \mid y \leq -\dfrac{14}{5}\right\};\ \left(-\infty, -\dfrac{14}{5}\right]$ $-\dfrac{14}{5}$

103. $-\dfrac{3}{7}a \leq -21$

$\{a \mid a \geq 49\};\ [49, \infty)$ 49

104. $1.3 > 0.4t - 12.5$

$\{t \mid t < 34.5\};\ (-\infty, 34.5)$ 34.5

105. $4k + 23 < 7k - 31$

$\{k \mid k > 18\};\ (18, \infty)$ 18

106. $\dfrac{6}{5}h - \dfrac{1}{5} \leq \dfrac{3}{10} + h$

$\left\{h \mid h \leq \dfrac{5}{2}\right\};\ \left(-\infty, \dfrac{5}{2}\right]$ $\dfrac{5}{2}$

107. $-6 < 2b \leq 14$

$\{b \mid -3 < b \leq 7\};\ (-3, 7]$ -3 7

108. $-2 \leq z + 4 \leq 9$

$\{z \mid -6 \leq z \leq 5\};\ [-6, 5]$ -6 5

109. The summer average rainfall for Bermuda for June, July, and August is 5.3 in. per month. If Bermuda receives 6.3 in. of rain in June and 7.1 in. in July, how much rain is required in August to exceed the 3-month summer average?
More than 2.5 in. is required.

110. Matthew has $15.00 to spend on dinner. Of this, 25% will cover the tax and tip, resulting in $11.25 for him to spend on food. If Matthew wants veggies and blue cheese, fries, and a drink, what is the maximum number of chicken wings he can get? Matthew can have at most 18 wings.

Wing Special

25¢
5:00–7:00 P.M.

*Add veggies and blue cheese for $2.50
*Add fries for $2.50
*Add a drink for $1.75

Chapter 2 Test

1. Which of the equations have -3 as a solution set?

a. $4x + 1 = 10$
b. $6(x - 1) = x - 21$
c. $5x - 2 = 2x + 1$
d. $\dfrac{1}{3}x + 1 = 0$ b, d

2. a. Simplify: $3x - 1 + 2x + 8$ $5x + 7$
b. Solve: $3x - 1 = 2x + 8$ $\{9\}$

For Exercises 3–13, solve each equation.

3. $t + 3 = -13$ $\{-16\}$
4. $8 = p - 4$ $\{12\}$

5. $\dfrac{t}{8} = -\dfrac{2}{9}$ $\left\{-\dfrac{16}{9}\right\}$
6. $-3x + 5 = -2$ $\left\{\dfrac{7}{3}\right\}$

7. $2(p - 4) = p + 7$ $\{15\}$

8. $2 + d = 2 - 3(d - 5) - 2$ $\left\{\dfrac{13}{4}\right\}$

9. $\dfrac{3}{7} + \dfrac{2}{5}x = -\dfrac{1}{5}x + 1$ $\left\{\dfrac{20}{21}\right\}$
10. $3h + 1 = 3(h + 1)$ $\{\ \}$

11. $\dfrac{3x + 1}{2} - \dfrac{4x - 3}{3} = 1$ $\{-3\}$

12. $0.5c - 1.9 = 2.8 + 0.6c$ $\{-47\}$

13. $-5(x + 2) + 8x = -2 + 3x - 8$
The set of real numbers

14. Solve the equation for y: $3x + y = -4$
$y = -3x - 4$

15. Solve $C = 2\pi r$ for r. $r = \dfrac{C}{2\pi}$

16. 13% of what is 11.7? 90

17. One number is four plus one-half of another. The sum of the numbers is 31. Find the numbers.
The numbers are 18 and 13.

18. The perimeter of a pentagon (a five-sided polygon) is 315 in. The five sides are represented by consecutive integers. Find the measures of the sides.
The sides are 61 in., 62 in., 63 in., 64 in., and 65 in.

 19. The total bill for a pair of basketball shoes (including sales tax) is $87.74. If the tax rate is 7%, find the cost of the shoes before tax.
The cost was $82.00.

20. A couple purchased two hockey tickets and two basketball tickets for $153.92. A hockey ticket cost $4.32 more than a basketball ticket. What were the prices of the individual tickets? Each basketball ticket was $36.32, and each hockey ticket was $40.64.

21. Clarita borrowed money at a 6% simple interest rate. If she paid back a total of $8000 at the end of 10 yr, how much did she originally borrow?
Clarita originally borrowed $5000.

22. The length of a soccer field for international matches is 40 m less than twice its width. If the perimeter is 370 m, what are the dimensions of the field? The field is 110 m long and 75 m wide.

23. Given the triangle, find the measures of each angle by first solving for y. $y = 30$; The measures of the angles are 30°, 39°, and 111°.

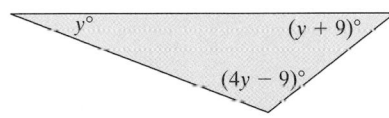

24. Paula mixes macadamia nuts that cost $9.00 per pound with 50 lb of peanuts that cost $5.00 per pound. How many pounds of macadamia nuts should she mix to make a nut mixture that costs $6.50 per pound?
Paula needs 30 lb of macadamia nuts.

25. Two families leave their homes at the same time to meet for lunch. The families live 210 mi apart, and one family drives 5 mph slower than the other. If it takes them 2 hr to meet at a point between their homes, how fast does each family travel?
One family travels 55 mph and the other travels 50 mph.

 26. Two angles are complementary. One angle is 26° more than the other angle. What are the measures of the angles? The measures of the angles are 32° and 58°.

27. Graph the inequalities and write the sets in interval notation.

a. $\{x \mid x < 0\}$ $(-\infty, 0)$

b. $\{x \mid -2 \le x < 5\}$ $[-2, 5)$

For Exercises 28–31, solve the inequality. Graph the solution and write the solution set in set-builder notation and interval notation.

28. $5x + 14 > -2x$
$\{x \mid x > -2\}$; $(-2, \infty)$

29. $2(3 - x) \ge 14$
$\{x \mid x \le -4\}$; $(-\infty, -4]$

30. $3(2y - 4) + 1 > 2(2y - 3) - 8$
$\left\{y \mid y > -\frac{3}{2}\right\}$; $\left(-\frac{3}{2}, \infty\right)$

31. $-13 \le 3p + 2 \le 5$
$\{p \mid -5 \le p \le 1\}$; $[-5, 1]$

32. The average winter snowfall for Syracuse, New York, for December, January, and February is 27.5 in. per month. If Syracuse receives 24 in. of snow in December and 32 in. in January, how much snow is required in February to exceed the 3-month average? More than 26.5 in. is required.

Chapters 1–2 Cumulative Review Exercises

For Exercises 1–5, perform the indicated operations.

1. $\left| -\frac{1}{5} + \frac{7}{10} \right|$ $\frac{1}{2}$

2. $5 - 2[3 - (4 - 7)]$ -7

3. $-\frac{2}{3} + \left(\frac{1}{2}\right)^2$ $-\frac{5}{12}$

4. $-3^2 + (-5)^2$ 16

5. $\sqrt{5 - (-20) - 3^2}$ 4

For Exercises 6–7, translate the mathematical expressions and simplify the results.

6. The square root of the difference of five squared and nine $\sqrt{5^2 - 9}$; 4

7. The sum of -14 and 12 $-14 + 12$; -2

8. List the terms of the expression: $-7x^2y + 4xy - 6$ $-7x^2y, 4xy, -6$

9. Simplify: $-4[2x - 3(x + 4)] + 5(x - 7)$ $9x + 13$

For Exercises 10–15, solve each equation.

10. $8t - 8 = 24$ $\{4\}$

11. $-2.5x - 5.2 = 12.8$ $\{-7.2\}$

 Writing Translating Expression Geometry Scientific Calculator Video NS&E

12. $-5(p - 3) + 2p = 3(5 - p)$ The set of real numbers

13. $\dfrac{x + 3}{5} - \dfrac{x + 2}{2} = 2$ $\{-8\}$

14. $\dfrac{2}{9}x - \dfrac{1}{3} = x + \dfrac{1}{9}$ $\left\{-\dfrac{4}{7}\right\}$

15. $-0.6w = 48$ $\{-80\}$

16. The sum of two consecutive odd integers is 156. Find the integers.   The numbers are 77 and 79.

17. The total bill for a man's three-piece suit (including sales tax) is \$374.50. If the tax rate is 7%, find the cost of the suit before tax.
The cost before tax was \$350.00.

 18. The area of a triangle is 41 cm². Find the height of the triangle if the base is 12 cm.

The height is $\frac{41}{6}$ cm or $6\frac{5}{6}$ cm.

12 cm

For Exercises 19–20, solve the inequality. Graph the solution set on a number line and express the solution in set-builder notation and interval notation.

19. $-3x - 3(x + 1) < 9$
$\{x \,|\, x > -2\}; (-2, \infty)$

20. $-6 \le 2x - 4 \le 14$
$\{x \,|\, -1 \le x \le 9\}; [-1, 9]$

Graphing Linear Equations in Two Variables

3

Chapter 3

In this chapter, we will need the skill of solving an equation for a particular variable.

Are You Prepared?

This puzzle will practice that skill. For each equation, solve for the variable *y*. Then match the equation with an answer below. Write the word associated with the answer in the blanks below to form a sentence.

1. $3x + 2y = 6$ **2.** $-4x - y = 7$ **3.** $x - 2y = -3$ **4.** $2x + y = 9$

5. $2x - 4y = 10$ **6.** $2x + 3y = 9$ **7.** $6x + 3y = -5$ **8.** $x - 3y = 1$

$y = \frac{1}{2}x + \frac{3}{2}$	IS	$y = -\frac{3}{2}x + 3$	THE
$y = -2x + 9$	WRITTEN	$y = 4x - 7$	POINT
$y = -2x - \frac{5}{3}$	INTERCEPT	$y = -\frac{2}{3}x + 3$	SLOPE
$y = -\frac{2}{3}x - 3$	TO	$y = -4x - 7$	EQUATION
$y = \frac{1}{2}x - \frac{5}{2}$	IN	$y = \frac{1}{3}x - \frac{1}{3}$	FORM

$$\underset{1}{\text{THE}} \quad \underset{2}{\text{EQUATION}} \quad y = mx + b \quad \underset{3}{\text{IS}} \quad \underset{4}{\text{WRITTEN}}$$

$$\underset{5}{\text{IN}} \quad \underset{6}{\text{SLOPE-}}\underset{7}{\text{INTERCEPT}} \quad \underset{8}{\text{FORM}}$$

Rectangular Coordinate System

1. Interpreting Graphs

Mathematics is a powerful tool used by scientists and has directly contributed to the highly technical world in which we live. Applications of mathematics have led to advances in the sciences, business, computer technology, and medicine.

One fundamental application of mathematics is the graphical representation of numerical information (or **data**). For example, Table 3-1 represents the number of clients admitted to a drug and alcohol rehabilitation program over a 12-month period.

Table 3-1

	Month	Number of Clients
Jan.	1	55
Feb.	2	62
March	3	64
April	4	60
May	5	70
June	6	73
July	7	77
Aug.	8	80
Sept.	9	80
Oct.	10	74
Nov.	11	85
Dec.	12	90

In table form, the information is difficult to picture and interpret. It appears that on a monthly basis, the number of clients fluctuates. However, when the data are represented in a graph, an upward trend is clear (Figure 3-1).

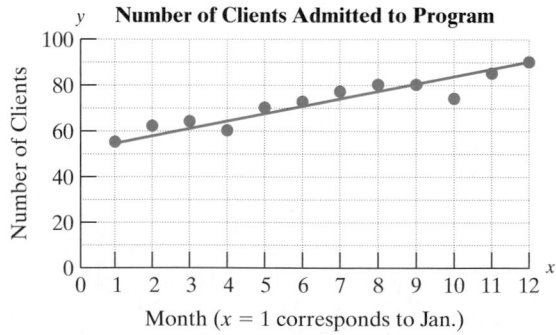

Month ($x = 1$ corresponds to Jan.)

Figure 3-1

From the increase in clients shown in this graph, management for the rehabilitation center might make plans for the future. If the trend continues, management might consider expanding its facilities and increasing its staff to accommodate the expected increase in clients.

Example 1 Interpreting a Graph

Classroom Example: p. 195, Exercise 4

Refer to Figure 3-1 and Table 3-1.

a. For which month was the number of clients the greatest?

b. How many clients were served in the first month (January)?

c. Which month corresponds to 60 clients served?

d. Between which two months did the number of clients decrease?

e. Between which two months did the number of clients remain the same?

Solution:

a. Month 12 (December) corresponds to the highest point on the graph, which represents the most clients.

b. In month 1 (January), there were 55 clients served.

c. Month 4 (April).

d. The number of clients decreased between months 3 and 4 and between months 9 and 10.

e. The number of clients remained the same between months 8 and 9.

Skill Practice Refer to Figure 3-1 and Table 3-1.

1. How many clients were served in October?

2. Which month corresponds to 70 clients?

3. What is the difference between the number of clients in month 12 and month 1?

4. For which month was the number of clients the least?

2. Plotting Points in a Rectangular Coordinate System

In Example 1, two variables are represented, time and the number of clients. To picture two variables, we use a graph with two real number lines drawn at right angles to each other (Figure 3-2). This forms a **rectangular coordinate system**. The horizontal line is called the **x-axis**, and the vertical line is called the **y-axis**. The point where the lines intersect is called the **origin**. On the x-axis, the numbers to the right of the origin are positive and the numbers to the left are negative. On the y-axis, the numbers above the origin are positive and the numbers below are negative. The x- and y-axes divide the graphing area into four regions called **quadrants**.

Animation

Figure 3-2

Answers

1. 74 clients
2. Month 5 (May)
3. 35 clients
4. Month 1 (January)

Points graphed in a rectangular coordinate system are defined by two numbers as an **ordered pair**, (x, y). The first number (called the **x-coordinate**, or the abscissa) is the horizontal position from the origin. The second number (called the **y-coordinate**, or the ordinate) is the vertical position from the origin. Example 2 shows how points are plotted in a rectangular coordinate system.

Classroom Example: p. 196, Exercise 10

Example 2   **Plotting Points in a Rectangular Coordinate System**

Plot the points.

a. $(4, 5)$ **b.** $(-4, -5)$ **c.** $(-1, 3)$ **d.** $(3, -1)$

e. $\left(\dfrac{1}{2}, -\dfrac{7}{3}\right)$ **f.** $(-2, 0)$ **g.** $(0, 0)$ **h.** $(\pi, 1.1)$

Solution:

See Figure 3-3.

a. The ordered pair $(4, 5)$ indicates that $x = 4$ and $y = 5$. Beginning at the origin, move 4 units in the positive x-direction (4 units to the right), and from there move 5 units in the positive y-direction (5 units up). Then plot the point. The point is in Quadrant I.

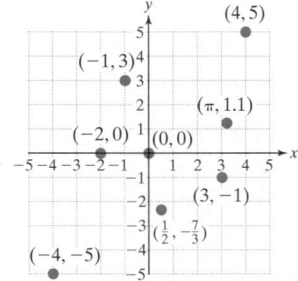

Figure 3-3

b. The ordered pair $(-4, -5)$ indicates that $x = -4$ and $y = -5$. Move 4 units in the negative x-direction (4 units to the left), and from there move 5 units in the negative y-direction (5 units down). Then plot the point. The point is in Quadrant III.

> **TIP:** Notice that changing the order of the x- and y-coordinates changes the location of the point. For example, the point $(-1, 3)$ is in Quadrant II, whereas $(3, -1)$ is in Quadrant IV (Figure 3-3). This is why points are represented by *ordered* pairs. The order of the coordinates is important.

c. The ordered pair $(-1, 3)$ indicates that $x = -1$ and $y = 3$. Move 1 unit to the left and 3 units up. The point is in Quadrant II.

d. The ordered pair $(3, -1)$ indicates that $x = 3$ and $y = -1$. Move 3 units to the right and 1 unit down. The point is in Quadrant IV.

e. The improper fraction $-\dfrac{7}{3}$ can be written as the mixed number $-2\dfrac{1}{3}$. Therefore, to plot the point $\left(\dfrac{1}{2}, -\dfrac{7}{3}\right)$ move to the right $\dfrac{1}{2}$ unit, and down $2\dfrac{1}{3}$ units. The point is in Quadrant IV.

f. The point $(-2, 0)$ indicates $y = 0$. Therefore, the point is on the x-axis.

Avoiding Mistakes

Points that lie on either of the axes do not lie in any quadrant.

g. The point $(0, 0)$ is at the origin.

h. The irrational number, π, can be approximated as 3.14. Thus, the point $(\pi, 1.1)$ is located approximately 3.14 units to the right and 1.1 units up. The point is in Quadrant I.

Answer

5.

Skill Practice

5. Plot the points.

$A(3, 4)$ $B(-2, 2)$ $C(4, 0)$ $D\left(\dfrac{5}{2}, -\dfrac{1}{2}\right)$ $E(-5, -2)$

3. Applications of Plotting and Identifying Points

The effective use of graphs for mathematical models requires skill in identifying points and interpreting graphs.

Example 3 Determining Points from a Graph

A map of a national park is drawn so that the origin is placed at the ranger station (Figure 3-4). Four fire observation towers are located at points A, B, C, and D. Estimate the coordinates of the fire towers relative to the ranger station (all distances are in miles).

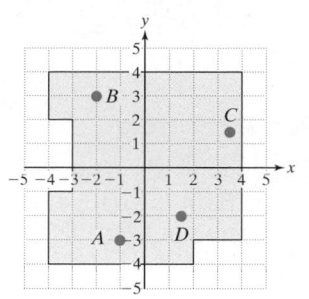

Figure 3-4

Classroom Example: p. 197, Exercise 26

Solution:

Point A: $(-1, -3)$

Point B: $(-2, 3)$

Point C: $(3\frac{1}{2}, 1\frac{1}{2})$ or $(\frac{7}{2}, \frac{3}{2})$ or $(3.5, 1.5)$

Point D: $(1\frac{1}{2}, -2)$ or $(\frac{3}{2}, -2)$ or $(1.5, -2)$

Skill Practice

6. Towers are located at points A, B, C, and D. Estimate the coordinates of the towers.

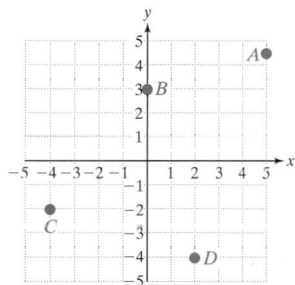

Example 4 Plotting Points in an Application

Classroom Example: p. 197, Exercise 28

The daily low temperatures (in degrees Fahrenheit) for one week in January for Sudbury, Ontario, Canada, are given in Table 3-2.

a. Write an ordered pair for each row in the table using the day number as the x-coordinate and the temperature as the y-coordinate.

b. Plot the ordered pairs from part (a) on a rectangular coordinate system.

Table 3-2

Day Number, x	Temperature (°F), y
1	-3
2	-5
3	1
4	6
5	5
6	0
7	-4

Solution:

a. Each ordered pair represents the day number and the corresponding low temperature for that day.

$(1, -3)$ $(2, -5)$ $(3, 1)$ $(4, 6)$ $(5, 5)$ $(6, 0)$ $(7, -4)$

Answer

6. $A(5, 4\frac{1}{2})$
   $B(0, 3)$
   $C(-4, -2)$
   $D(2, -4)$

b.

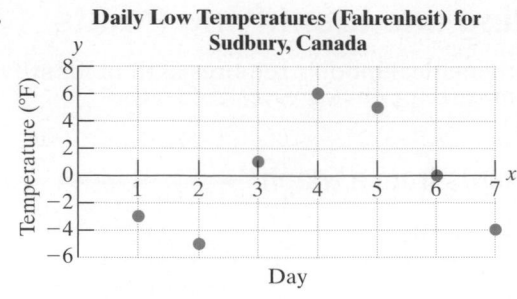

Daily Low Temperatures (Fahrenheit) for Sudbury, Canada

TIP: The graph in Example 4(b) shows only Quadrants I and IV because all *x*-coordinates are positive.

Answer

7.

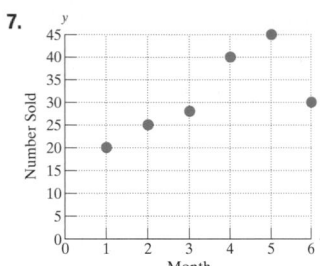

Skill Practice

7. The table shows the number of homes sold in a certain town for a 6-month period. Plot the ordered pairs.

Month, x	Number Sold, y
1	20
2	25
3	28
4	40
5	45
6	30

Section 3.1 Practice Exercises

Boost *your* GRADE at ALEKS.com!

- Practice Problems
- Self-Tests
- NetTutor
- e-Professors
- Videos

For additional exercises, see Classroom Activities 3.1A–3.1B in the *Instructor's Resource Manual* at www.mhhe.com/moh.

Study Skills Exercises

1. Before you proceed further in Chapter 3, make your test corrections for the Chapter 2 test. See Exercise 1 of Section 2.1 for instructions.

2. Define the key terms.

   a. data   **b. ordered pair**   **c. origin**   **d. quadrant**   **e. rectangular coordinate system**

   f. *x*-axis   **g. *y*-axis**   **h. *x*-coordinate**   **i. *y*-coordinate**

Concept 1: Interpreting Graphs

For Exercises 3–6, refer to the graphs to answer the questions. **(See Example 1.)**

3. The number of patients served by a certain hospice care center for the first 12 months after it opened is shown in the graph.

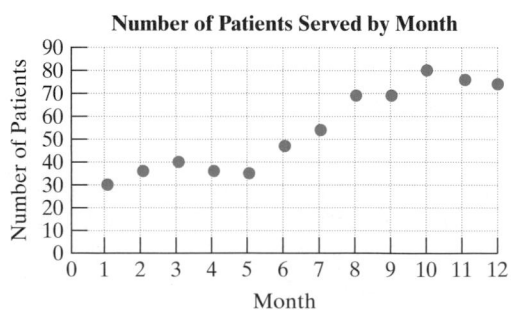

Number of Patients Served by Month

   a. For which month was the number of patients greatest?
   Month 10

   b. How many patients did the center serve in the first month?
   30

   c. Between which months did the number of patients decrease?
   Between months 3 and 5 and between months 10 and 12

   d. Between which two months did the number of patients remain the same?   Months 8 and 9

   e. Which month corresponds to 40 patients served?   Month 3

   f. Approximately how many patients were served during the 10th month?   80

 Writing   Translating Expression   Geometry   Scientific Calculator   Video   NS&E

4. The number of housing permits (in thousands) issued by a county in Texas between 2003 and 2009 is shown in the graph.

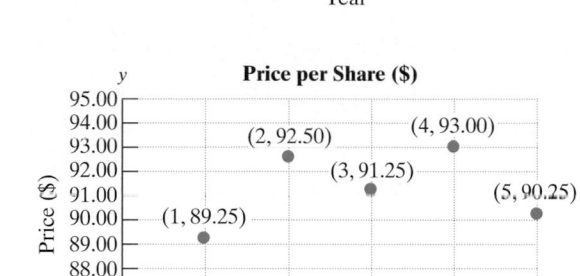

a. For which year was the number of permits greatest?   2009

b. How many permits did the county issue in 2003?
   6 thousand or 6000

c. Between which years did the number of permits decrease?
   Between 2003 and 2004

d. Between which two years did the number of permits remain the same?   Between 2007 and 2008

e. Which year corresponds to 7000 permits issued?   2006

5. The price per share of a stock (in dollars) over a period of 5 days is shown in the graph.

a. Interpret the meaning of the ordered pair $(1, 89.25)$.
   On day 1 the price per share was $89.25.

b. What was the increase in price between day 3 and day 4?
   $1.75

c. What was the change in price between day 4 and day 5?
   $-$2.75

6. The price per share of a stock (in dollars) over a period of 5 days is shown in the graph.

a. Interpret the meaning of the ordered pair $(1, 10.125)$.
   On day 1 the price per share was $10.125.

b. What was the change between day 4 and day 5?
   $-$0.875

c. What is the change between day 1 and day 5? $-$1.50

Concept 2: Plotting Points in a Rectangular Coordinate System

7. Plot the points on a rectangular coordinate system.
(See Example 2.)

a. $(2, 6)$	**b.** $(6, 2)$	**c.** $(-7, 3)$
d. $(-7, -3)$	**e.** $(0, -3)$	**f.** $(-3, 0)$
g. $(6, -4)$	**h.** $(0, 5)$	

8. Plot the points on a rectangular coordinate system.

a. $(4, 5)$	**b.** $(-4, 5)$	**c.** $(-6, 0)$
d. $(6, 0)$	**e.** $(4, -5)$	**f.** $(-4, -5)$
g. $(0, -2)$	**h.** $(0, 0)$	

9. Plot the points on a rectangular coordinate system.

a. $(-1, 5)$ b. $(0, 4)$ c. $\left(-2, -\dfrac{3}{2}\right)$

d. $(2, -1.75)$ e. $(4, 2)$ f. $(-6, 0)$

10. Plot the points on a rectangular coordinate system.

a. $(7, 0)$ b. $(-3, -2)$ c. $(6\frac{3}{5}, 1)$

d. $(0, 1.5)$ e. $\left(\dfrac{7}{2}, -4\right)$ f. $\left(-\dfrac{7}{2}, 4\right)$

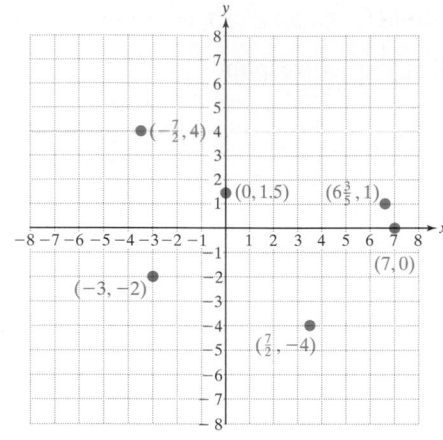

For Exercises 11–18, identify the quadrant in which the given point is located.

11. $(13, -2)$ IV

12. $(25, 16)$ I

13. $(-8, 14)$ II

14. $(-82, -71)$ III

15. $(-5, -19)$ III

16. $(-31, 6)$ II

17. $\left(\dfrac{5}{2}, \dfrac{7}{4}\right)$ I

18. $(9, -40)$ IV

19. Explain why the point $(0, -5)$ is *not* located in Quadrant IV.
$(0, -5)$ lies on the *y*-axis.

20. Explain why the point $(-1, 0)$ is *not* located in Quadrant II.
$(-1, 0)$ lies on the *x*-axis.

21. Where is the point $\left(\frac{7}{8}, 0\right)$ located?
$\left(\frac{7}{8}, 0\right)$ is located on the *x*-axis.

22. Where is the point $\left(0, \frac{6}{5}\right)$ located?
$\left(0, \frac{6}{5}\right)$ is located on the *y*-axis.

Concept 3: Applications of Plotting and Identifying Points

For Exercises 23–24, refer to the graph. **(See Example 3.)**

23. Estimate the coordinates of the points $A, B, C, D, E,$ and F.
$A(-4, 2), B(\frac{1}{2}, 4), C(3, -4), D(-3, -4), E(0, -3), F(5, 0)$

24. Estimate the coordinates of the points $G, H, I, J, K,$ and L.
$G(-5, -2), H(1, -5), I(3\frac{1}{2}, 2), J(-1\frac{1}{2}, 3), K(-2, 0), L(0, 2)$

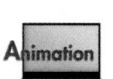

25. A map of a park is laid out with the visitor center located at the origin. Five visitors are in the park located at points $A, B, C, D,$ and E. All distances are in meters.

a. Estimate the coordinates of each visitor. **(See Example 3.)**
$A(400, 200), B(200, -150), C(-300, -200), D(-300, 250), E(0, 450)$

b. How far apart are visitors C and D?   450 m

26. A townhouse has a sprinkler system in the backyard. With the water source at the origin, the sprinkler heads are located at points $A, B, C, D,$ and E. All distances are in feet.

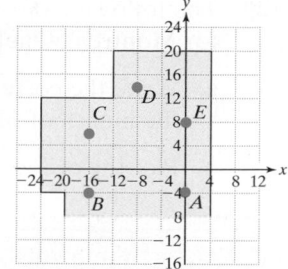

   a. Estimate the coordinates of each sprinkler head.
     $A(0, -4), B(-16, -4), C(-16, 6), D(-8, 14), E(0, 8)$
   b. How far is the distance from sprinkler head B to C?   10 ft

27. A movie theater has kept records of popcorn sales versus movie attendance.

   a. Use the table to write the corresponding ordered pairs using the movie attendance as the x-variable and sales of popcorn as the y-variable. Interpret the meaning of the first ordered pair. **(See Example 4.)**

     $(250, 225), (175, 193), (315, 330), (220, 209), (450, 570), (400, 480), (190, 185)$; the ordered pair $(250, 225)$ means that 250 people produce \$225 in popcorn sales.

   b. Plot the data points on a rectangular coordinate system.

Movie Attendance (Number of People)	Sales of Popcorn ($)
250	225
175	193
315	330
220	209
450	570
400	480
190	185

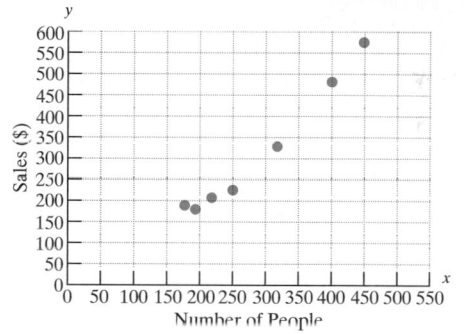

28. The age and systolic blood pressure (in millimeters of mercury, mm Hg) for eight different women are given in the table.

   a. Write the corresponding ordered pairs using the woman's age as the x-variable and the systolic blood pressure as the y-variable. Interpret the meaning of the first ordered pair. $(57, 149), (41, 120), (71, 158), (36, 115),$
  $(64, 151), (25, 110), (40, 118), (77, 165)$; the ordered pair $(57, 149)$ means that a 57-year-old woman has a systolic blood pressure of 149 mm Hg.
   b. Plot the data points on a rectangular coordinate system.

Age (Years)	Systolic Blood Pressure (mm Hg)
57	149
41	120
71	158
36	115
64	151
25	110
40	118
77	165

 Writing   Translating Expression   Geometry   Scientific Calculator   Video   NS&E

29. The following table shows the average temperature in degrees Celsius for Montreal, Quebec, Canada, by month.

Month, x		Temperature (°C), y
Jan.	1	−10.2
Feb.	2	−9.0
March	3	−2.5
April	4	5.7
May	5	13.0
June	6	18.3
July	7	20.9
Aug.	8	19.6
Sept.	9	14.8
Oct.	10	8.7
Nov.	11	2.0
Dec.	12	−6.9

   a. Write the corresponding ordered pairs, letting $x = 1$ correspond to the month of January. (1, −10.2), (2, −9.0), (3, −2.5), (4, 5.7), (5, 13.0), (6, 18.3), (7, 20.9), (8, 19.6), (9, 14.8), (10, 8.7), (11, 2.0), (12, −6.9).

   b. Plot the ordered pairs on a rectangular coordinate system.

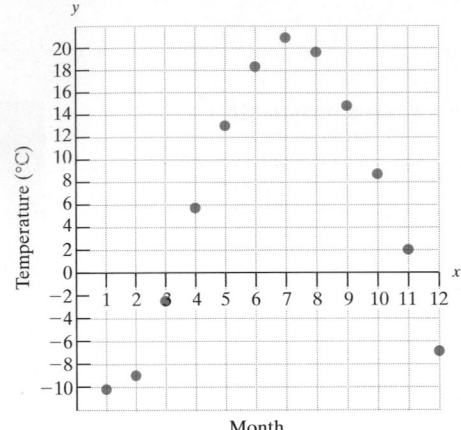

30. The table shows the average temperature in degrees Fahrenheit for Fairbanks, Alaska, by month.

Month, x		Temperature (°F), y
Jan.	1	−12.8
Feb.	2	−4.0
March	3	8.4
April	4	30.2
May	5	48.2
June	6	59.4
July	7	61.5
Aug.	8	56.7
Sept.	9	45.0
Oct.	10	25.0
Nov.	11	6.1
Dec.	12	−10.1

   a. Write the corresponding ordered pairs, letting $x = 1$ correspond to the month of January. (1, −12.8), (2, −4.0), (3, 8.4), (4, 30.2), (5, 48.2), (6, 59.4), (7, 61.5), (8, 56.7), (9, 45.0), (10, 25.0), (11, 6.1), (12, −10.1).

   b. Plot the ordered pairs on a rectangular coordinate system.

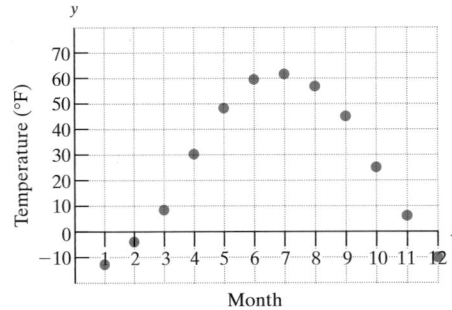

Expanding Your Skills

31. The data in the table give the percent of males and females who have completed 4 or more years of college education for selected years. Let x represent the number of years since 1960. Let y represent the percent of men and the percent of women that completed 4 or more years of college.

Year	x	Percent, y Men	Percent, y Women
1960	0	9.7	5.8
1970	10	13.5	8.1
1980	20	20.1	12.8
1990	30	24.4	18.4
2000	40	27.8	23.6
2005	45	28.9	26.5

 Writing   Translating Expression   Geometry   Scientific Calculator   Video   NS&E

a. Plot the data points for men and for women on the same graph.

b. Is the percentage of men with 4 or more years of college increasing or decreasing?   Increasing

c. Is the percentage of women with 4 or more years of college increasing or decreasing?   Increasing

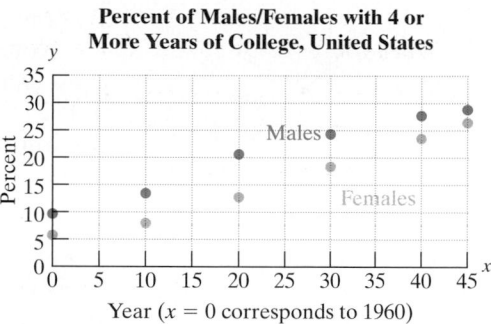

Percent of Males/Females with 4 or More Years of College, United States

32. Use the data and graph from Exercise 31 to answer the questions.

a. In which year was the difference in percentages between men and women with 4 or more years of college the greatest?   1980

b. In which year was the difference in percentages between men and women the least?   2005

c. If the trend continues beyond the data in the graph, does it seem possible that in the future, the percentage of women with 4 or more years of college will be greater than or equal to the percentage of men?   Yes

Linear Equations in Two Variables

1. Definition of a Linear Equation in Two Variables

Recall that an equation in the form $ax + b = 0$, where $a \neq 0$, is called a linear equation in one variable. A solution to such an equation is a value of x that makes the equation a true statement. For example, $3x + 6 = 0$ has a solution of -2.

In this section, we will look at linear equations in *two* variables.

Concepts

1. Definition of a Linear Equation in Two Variables
2. Graphing Linear Equations in Two Variables by Plotting Points
3. x- and y-Intercepts
4. Horizontal and Vertical Lines

DEFINITION   Linear Equation in Two Variables

Let A, B, and C be real numbers such that A and B are not both zero. Then, an equation that can be written in the form:

$$Ax + By = C$$

is called a **linear equation in two variables**.

The equation $x + y = 4$ is a linear equation in two variables. A solution to such an equation is an ordered pair (x, y) that makes the equation a true statement. Several solutions to the equation $x + y = 4$ are listed here:

Solution:	Check:
(x, y)	$x + y = 4$
$(2, 2)$	$(2) + (2) = 4$ ✔
$(1, 3)$	$(1) + (3) = 4$ ✔
$(4, 0)$	$(4) + (0) = 4$ ✔
$(-1, 5)$	$(-1) + (5) = 4$ ✔

Animation

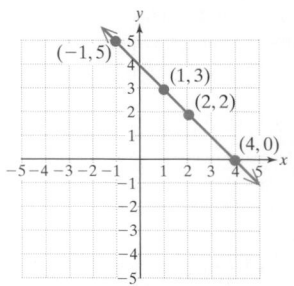

Figure 3-5

Classroom Examples: p. 209, Exercises 10 and 12

By graphing these ordered pairs, we see that the solution points line up (Figure 3-5).

Notice that there are infinitely many solutions to the equation $x + y = 4$ so they cannot all be listed. Therefore, to visualize all solutions to the equation $x + y = 4$, we draw the line through the points in the graph. Every point on the line represents an ordered pair solution to the equation $x + y = 4$, and the line represents the set of *all* solutions to the equation.

Example 1 **Determining Solutions to a Linear Equation**

For the linear equation, $4x - 5y = 8$, determine whether the given ordered pair is a solution.

a. $(2, 0)$ **b.** $(3, 1)$ **c.** $\left(1, -\dfrac{4}{5}\right)$

Solution:

a.
$$4x - 5y = 8$$
$$4(2) - 5(0) \overset{?}{=} 8 \qquad\qquad \text{Substitute } x = 2 \text{ and } y = 0.$$
$$8 - 0 \overset{?}{=} 8 \ \checkmark \ \text{True} \qquad \text{The ordered pair } (2, 0) \text{ is a solution.}$$

b.
$$4x - 5y = 8$$
$$4(3) - 5(1) \overset{?}{=} 8 \qquad\qquad \text{Substitute } x = 3 \text{ and } y = 1.$$
$$12 - 5 \neq 8 \qquad\qquad \text{The ordered pair } (3, 1) \text{ is } not \text{ a solution.}$$

c.
$$4x - 5y = 8$$
$$4(1) - 5\left(-\dfrac{4}{5}\right) \overset{?}{=} 8 \qquad \text{Substitute } x = 1 \text{ and } y = -\dfrac{4}{5}.$$
$$4 + 4 \overset{?}{=} 8 \ \checkmark \ \text{True} \qquad \text{The ordered pair } \left(1, -\dfrac{4}{5}\right) \text{ is a solution.}$$

Skill Practice Given the equation $3x - 2y = -12$, determine whether the given ordered pair is a solution.

1. $(4, 0)$ **2.** $(-2, 3)$ **3.** $\left(1, \dfrac{15}{2}\right)$

2. Graphing Linear Equations in Two Variables by Plotting Points

In this section, we will graph linear equations in two variables.

DEFINITION **The Graph of an Equation in Two Variables**

The graph of an equation in two variables is the graph of all ordered pair solutions to the equation.

The word *linear* means "relating to or resembling a line." It is not surprising then that the solution set for any linear equation in two variables forms a line in a rectangular coordinate system. Because two points determine a line, to graph a linear

Answers

1. No   **2.** Yes   **3.** Yes

equation it is sufficient to find two solution points and draw the line between them. We will find three solution points and use the third point as a check point. This process is demonstrated in Example 2.

Example 2   Graphing a Linear Equation

Graph the equation $x - 2y = 8$.

Classroom Example: p. 209, Exercise 18

Solution:

We will find three ordered pairs that are solutions to $x - 2y = 8$. To find the ordered pairs, choose arbitrary values of x or y, such as those shown in the table. Then complete the table to find the corresponding ordered pairs.

x	y
2	
	−1
0	

$(2, \quad)$

$(\quad , -1)$

$(0, \quad)$

TIP: Usually we try to choose arbitrary values that will be convenient to graph.

From the first row, substitute $x = 2$:

$x - 2y = 8$

$(2) - 2y = 8$

$-2y = 6$

$y = -3$

From the second row, substitute $y = -1$:

$x - 2y = 8$

$x - 2(-1) = 8$

$x + 2 = 8$

$x = 6$

From the third row, substitute $x = 0$:

$x - 2y = 8$

$(0) - 2y = 8$

$-2y = 8$

$y = -4$

The completed table is shown below with the corresponding ordered pairs.

x	y
2	−3
6	−1
0	−4

$(2, -3)$

$(6, -1)$

$(0, -4)$

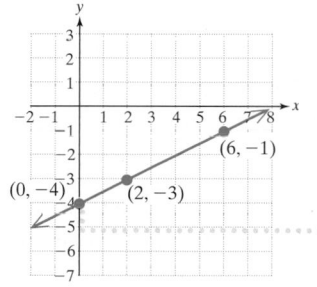

Figure 3-6

Avoiding Mistakes

Only two points are needed to graph a line. However, in Example 2, we found a third ordered pair, $(0, -4)$. Notice that this point "lines up" with the other two points. If the three points do not line up, then we know that a mistake was made in solving for at least one of the ordered pairs.

To graph the equation, plot the three solutions and draw the line through the points (Figure 3-6).

Skill Practice

4. Graph the equation $2x + y = 6$.

In Example 2, the original values for x and y given in the table were picked arbitrarily by the authors. It is important to note, however, that once you pick an arbitrary value for x, the corresponding y-value is determined by the equation. Similarly, once you pick an arbitrary value for y, the x-value is determined by the equation.

Answer

4.

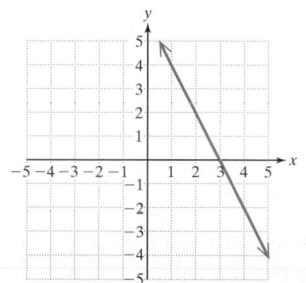

Classroom Example: p. 209, Exercise 22

Example 3 Graphing a Linear Equation

Graph the equation $4x + 3y = 15$.

Solution:

We will find three ordered pairs that are solutions to the equation $4x + 3y = 15$. In the table, we have selected arbitrary values for x and y and must complete the ordered pairs. Notice that in this case, we are choosing zero for x and zero for y to illustrate that the resulting equation is often easy to solve.

x	y	
0		→ (0,)
	0	→ (, 0)
3		→ (3,)

From the first row, substitute $x = 0$:	From the second row, substitute $y = 0$:	From the third row, substitute $x = 3$:
$4x + 3y = 15$	$4x + 3y = 15$	$4x + 3y = 15$
$4(0) + 3y = 15$	$4x + 3(0) = 15$	$4(3) + 3y = 15$
$3y = 15$	$4x = 15$	$12 + 3y = 15$
$y = 5$	$x = \dfrac{15}{4}$ or $3\dfrac{3}{4}$	$3y = 3$
		$y = 1$

The completed table is shown with the corresponding ordered pairs.

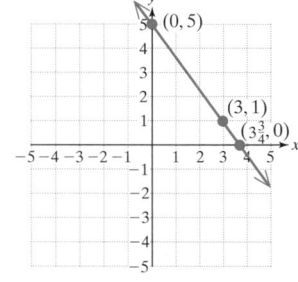

x	y	
0	5	→ (0, 5)
$3\frac{3}{4}$	0	→ ($3\frac{3}{4}$, 0)
3	1	→ (3, 1)

To graph the equation, plot the three solutions and draw the line through the points (Figure 3-7).

Figure 3-7

TIP: A line is drawn with arrows to indicate the line extends infinitely in both directions. Without the arrows we would have a line segment.

Skill Practice

5. Graph the equation $2x + 3y = 12$.

Answer

5.
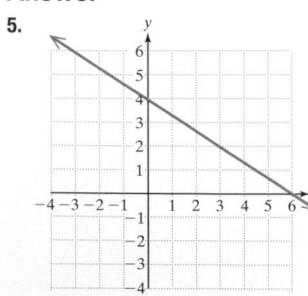

Example 4 Graphing a Linear Equation

Graph the equation $y = -\dfrac{1}{3}x + 1$.

Solution:

Because the y-variable is isolated in the equation, it is easy to substitute a value for x and simplify the right-hand side to find y. Since any number for x can be picked, choose numbers that are multiples of 3. These will simplify easily when multiplied by $-\frac{1}{3}$.

Classroom Example: p. 211, Exercise 38

x	*y*
3	
0	
−3	

$$y = -\frac{1}{3}x + 1$$

Let *x* = 3:   Let *x* = 0:   Let *x* = −3:

$$y = -\frac{1}{3}(3) + 1 \qquad y = -\frac{1}{3}(0) + 1 \qquad y = -\frac{1}{3}(-3) + 1$$

$$y - -1 + 1 \qquad\qquad y = 0 + 1 \qquad\qquad y = 1 + 1$$

$$y = 0 \qquad\qquad\quad y = 1 \qquad\qquad\quad y = 2$$

x	*y*
3	0
0	1
−3	2

The line through the three ordered pairs $(3, 0)$, $(0, 1)$, and $(-3, 2)$ is shown in Figure 3-8. The line represents the set of all solutions to the equation $y = -\frac{1}{3}x + 1$.

Figure 3-8

Skill Practice

6. Graph the equation $y = \frac{1}{2}x + 3$.

3. *x*- and *y*-Intercepts

The *x*- and *y*-intercepts are the points where the graph intersects the *x*- and *y*-axes, respectively. From Example 4, we see that the *x*-intercept is at the point $(3, 0)$ and the *y*-intercept is at the point $(0, 1)$. See Figure 3-8. Notice that a *y*-intercept is a point on the *y*-axis and must have an *x*-coordinate of 0. Likewise, an *x*-intercept is a point on the *x*-axis and must have a *y*-coordinate of 0.

DEFINITION   *x*- and *y*-Intercepts

An ***x*-intercept** of a graph is a point $(a, 0)$ where the graph intersects the *x*-axis.

A ***y*-intercept** of a graph is a point $(0, b)$ where the graph intersects the *y*-axis.

In some applications, an *x*-intercept is defined as the *x*-coordinate of a point of intersection that a graph makes with the *x*-axis. For example, if an *x*-intercept is at the point $(3, 0)$, it is sometimes stated simply as 3 (the *y*-coordinate is assumed to be 0). Similarly, a *y*-intercept is sometimes defined as the *y*-coordinate of a point of intersection that a graph makes with the *y*-axis. For example, if a *y*-intercept is at the point $(0, 7)$, it may be stated simply as 7 (the *x*-coordinate is assumed to be 0).

Although any two points may be used to graph a line, in some cases it is convenient to use the *x*- and *y*-intercepts of the line. To find the *x*- and *y*-intercepts of any two-variable equation in *x* and *y*, follow these steps:

PROCEDURE   Finding *x*- and *y*-Intercepts

- Find the *x*-intercept(s) by substituting $y = 0$ into the equation and solving for *x*.
- Find the *y*-intercept(s) by substituting $x = 0$ into the equation and solving for *y*.

Answer

6.

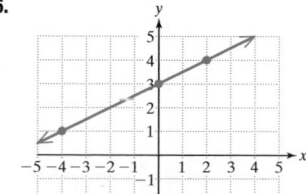

Classroom Example: p. 212,
Exercise 54

Example 5   Finding the *x*- and *y*-Intercepts of a Line

Given the equation $-3x + 2y = 8$,

a. Find the *x*-intercept.

b. Find the *y*-intercept.

c. Graph the equation.

Solution:

a. To find the *x*-intercept,
substitute $y = 0$.

$$-3x + 2y = 8$$
$$-3x + 2(0) = 8$$
$$-3x \quad\;\; = 8$$
$$\frac{-3x}{-3} = \frac{8}{-3}$$
$$x = -\frac{8}{3}$$

The *x*-intercept is $\left(-\frac{8}{3}, 0\right)$.

b. To find the *y*-intercept,
substitute $x = 0$.

$$-3x + 2y = 8$$
$$-3(0) + 2y = 8$$
$$2y = 8$$
$$y = 4$$

The *y*-intercept is $(0, 4)$.

> **Avoiding Mistakes**
>
> Be sure to write the *x*- and
> *y*-intercepts as two separate
> ordered pairs: $\left(-\frac{8}{3}, 0\right)$ and $(0, 4)$.

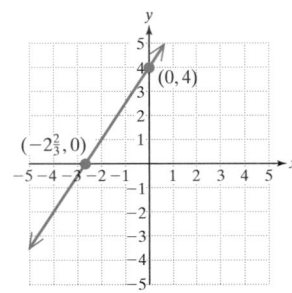

Figure 3-9

c. The line through the ordered pairs $\left(-\frac{8}{3}, 0\right)$ and $(0, 4)$ is shown in Figure 3-9.
Note that the point $\left(-\frac{8}{3}, 0\right)$ can be written as $\left(-2\frac{2}{3}, 0\right)$.
   The line represents the set of all solutions to the equation
$-3x + 2y = 8$.

Skill Practice   Given the equation $x - 3y = -4$,

7. Find the *x*-intercept.   **8.** Find the *y*-intercept.   **9.** Graph the equation.

Classroom Example: p. 212,
Exercise 60

Example 6   Finding the *x*- and *y*-Intercepts of a Line

Given the equation $4x + 5y = 0$,

a. Find the *x*-intercept.

b. Find the *y*-intercept.

c. Graph the equation.

Solution:

Answers

7. $(-4, 0)$ **8.** $\left(0, \dfrac{4}{3}\right)$

9.

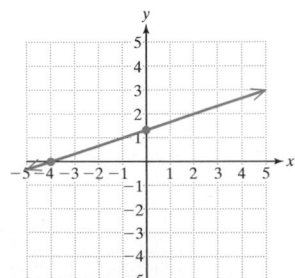

a. To find the *x*-intercept,
substitute $y = 0$.

$$4x + 5y = 0$$
$$4x + 5(0) = 0$$
$$4x \quad\;\; = 0$$
$$x = 0$$

The *x*-intercept is $(0, 0)$.

b. To find the *y*-intercept,
substitute $x = 0$.

$$4x + 5y = 0$$
$$4(0) + 5y = 0$$
$$5y = 0$$
$$y = 0$$

The *y*-intercept is $(0, 0)$.

c. Because the x-intercept and the y-intercept are the same point (the origin), one or more additional points are needed to graph the line. In the table, we have arbitrarily selected additional values for x and y to find two more points on the line.

x	y
-5	
	2

Let $x = -5$: $4x + 5y = 0$

$\qquad\quad 4(-5) + 5y = 0$

$\qquad\quad -20 + 5y = 0$

$\qquad\qquad\quad 5y = 20$

$\qquad\qquad\quad\ y = 4$

$(-5, 4)$ is a solution.

Let $y = 2$: $4x + 5y = 0$

$\qquad\quad 4x + 5(2) = 0$

$\qquad\quad 4x + 10 = 0$

$\qquad\qquad\ 4x = -10$

$\qquad\qquad\ \ x = -\dfrac{10}{4}$

$\qquad\qquad\ \ x = -\dfrac{5}{2}$

$\left(-\frac{5}{2}, 2\right)$ is a solution.

The line through the ordered pairs $(0, 0)$, $(-5, 4)$, and $\left(-\frac{5}{2}, 2\right)$ is shown in Figure 3-10. Note that the point $\left(-\frac{5}{2}, 2\right)$ can be written as $\left(-2\frac{1}{2}, 2\right)$.

The line represents the set of all solutions to the equation $4x + 5y = 0$.

x	y
-5	4
$-\frac{5}{2}$	2
0	0

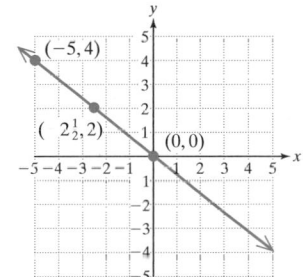

Figure 3-10

Skill Practice Given the equation $2x - 3y = 0$,

10. Find the x-intercept.   **11.** Find the y-intercept.

12. Graph the equation. (*Hint:* You may need to find an additional point.)

4. Horizontal and Vertical Lines

Recall that a linear equation can be written in the form of $Ax + By = C$, where A and B are not both zero. However, if A or B is 0, then the line is either parallel to the x-axis (horizontal) or parallel to the y-axis (vertical), respectively.

DEFINITION Equations of Vertical and Horizontal Lines

1. A **vertical line** can be represented by an equation of the form $x = k$, where k is a constant.
2. A **horizontal line** can be represented by an equation of the form $y = k$, where k is a constant.

Instructor Note: Have students go back to the definition of a linear equation in two variables at the beginning of Section 3.2. Ask how equations like $x = 3$ and $y = -2$ fit the requirements of a linear equation in 2 variables.

Answers

10. $(0, 0)$ **11.** $(0, 0)$

12.

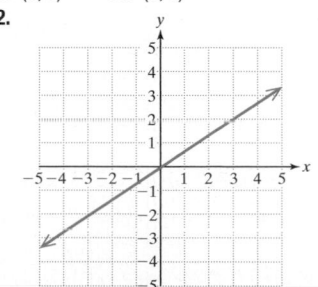

Classroom Example: p. 213,
Exercise 72

Example 7 **Graphing a Horizontal Line**

Graph the equation $y = 3$.

Solution:

Because this equation is in the form $y = k$, the line is horizontal and must cross the y-axis at $y = 3$ (Figure 3-11).

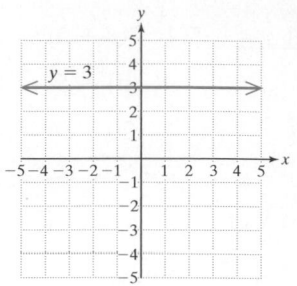

Figure 3-11

Alternative Solution:

Create a table of values for the equation $y = 3$. The choice for the y-coordinate must be 3, but x can be any real number.

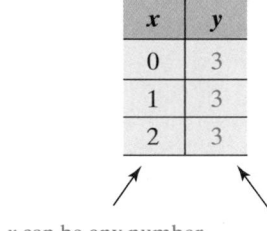

x	y
0	3
1	3
2	3

x can be any number. y must be 3.

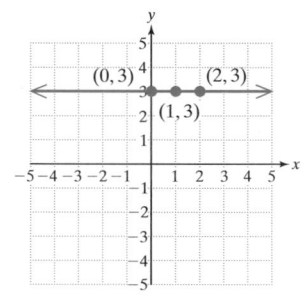

TIP: Notice that a horizontal line has a y-intercept, but does not have an x-intercept (unless the horizontal line is the x-axis itself).

Skill Practice

13. Graph the equation. $y = -2$

Classroom Example: p. 213,
Exercise 74

Example 8 **Graphing a Vertical Line**

Graph the equation $4x = -8$.

Solution:

Because the equation does not have a y-variable, we can solve the equation for x.

$$4x = -8 \quad \text{is equivalent to} \quad x = -2$$

This equation is in the form $x = k$, indicating that the line is vertical and must cross the x-axis at $x = -2$ (Figure 3-12).

Figure 3-12

Answer

13.

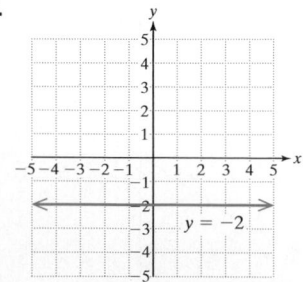

Alternative Solution:

Create a table of values for the equation $x = -2$. The choice for the x-coordinate must be -2, but y can be any real number.

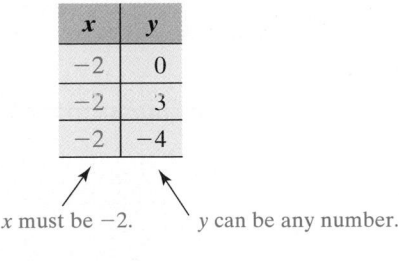

x	y
-2	0
-2	3
-2	-4

x must be -2. y can be any number.

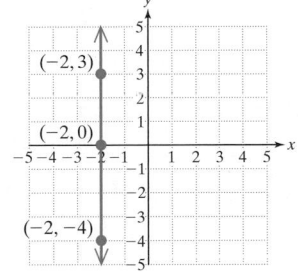

TIP: Notice that a vertical line has an x-intercept but does not have a y-intercept (unless the vertical line is the y-axis itself).

Answer

14.

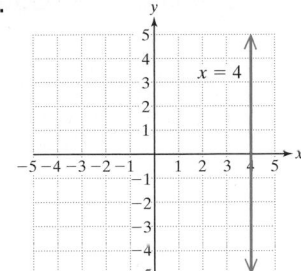

Skill Practice

14. Graph the equation. $3x = 12$

Calculator Connections

Topic: Graphing Linear Equations on an Appropriate Viewing Window

A viewing window of a graphing calculator shows a portion of a rectangular coordinate system. The standard viewing window for many calculators shows the x-axis between -10 and 10 and the y-axis between -10 and 10 (Figure 3-13). Furthermore, the scale defined by the "tick" marks on both the x- and y-axes is usually set to 1.

The "Standard Viewing Window"

Figure 3-13

To graph an equation in x and y on a graphing calculator, the equation must be written with the y-variable isolated. For example, to graph the equation $x + 3y = 3$, we solve for y by applying the steps for solving a literal equation. The result, $y = -\frac{1}{3}x + 1$, can now be entered into a graphing calculator. To enter the equation $y = -\frac{1}{3}x + 1$, use parentheses around the fraction $\frac{1}{3}$. The *Graph* option displays the graph of the line.

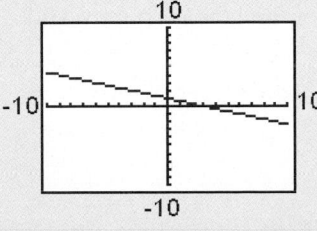

Sometimes the standard viewing window does not provide an adequate display for the graph of an equation. For example, the graph of $y = -x + 15$ is visible only in a small portion of the upper right corner of the standard viewing window.

To see where this line crosses the x- and y-axes, we can change the viewing window to accommodate larger values of x and y. Most calculators have a *Range* feature or *Window* feature that allows the user to change the minimum and maximum x- and y-values.

To get a better picture of the equation $y = -x + 15$, change the minimum x-value to -10 and the maximum x-value to 20. Similarly, use a minimum y-value of -10 and a maximum y-value of 20.

Calculator Exercises

For Exercises 1–8, graph the equations on the standard viewing window.

1. $y = -2x + 5$ **2.** $y = 3x - 1$

3. $y = \dfrac{1}{2}x - \dfrac{7}{2}$ **4.** $y = -\dfrac{3}{4}x + \dfrac{5}{3}$

5. $4x - 7y = 21$ **6.** $2x + 3y = 12$

7. $-3x - 4y = 6$ **8.** $-5x + 4y = 10$

For Exercises 9–12, graph the equations on the given viewing window.

9. $y = 3x + 15$

Window: $-10 \le x \le 10$
$-5 \le y \le 20$

10. $y = -2x - 25$

Window: $-30 \le x \le 30$
$-30 \le y \le 30$

Xscl = 3 (sets the x-axis tick marks to increments of 3)

Yscl = 3 (sets the y-axis tick marks to increments of 3)

11. $y = -0.2x + 0.04$

Window: $-0.1 \le x \le 0.3$
$-0.1 \le y \le 0.1$

Xscl = 0.01 (sets the x-axis tick marks to increments of 0.01)

Yscl = 0.01 (sets the y-axis tick marks to increments of 0.01)

12. $y = 0.3x - 0.5$

Window: $-1 \le x \le 3$
$-1 \le y \le 1$

Xscl = 0.1 (sets the x-axis tick marks to increments of 0.1)

Yscl = 0.1 (sets the y-axis tick marks to increments of 0.1)

Section 3.2   Practice Exercises

Boost *your* GRADE at
ALEKS.com!

- Practice Problems
- Self-Tests
- NetTutor

- e-Professors
- Videos

For additional exercises, see Classroom Activities 3.2A–3.2C in the *Instructor's Resource Manual* at www.mhhe.com/moh.

Study Skills Exercises

1. Check your progress by answering these questions.

Yes _____ No _____   Did you have sufficient time to study for the test on Chapter 2? If not, what could you have done to create more time for studying?

Yes _____ No _____   Did you work all of the assigned homework problems in Chapter 2?

Yes _____ No _____   If you encountered difficulty, did you see your instructor or tutor for help?

Yes _____ No _____   Have you taken advantage of the textbook supplements such as the *Student Solutions Manual*?

2. Define the key terms.

a. horizontal line   **b. linear equation in two variables**   **c. vertical line**

d. x-intercept   **e. y-intercept**

Review Exercises

For Exercises 3–8, refer to the figure to give the coordinates of the labeled points, and state the quadrant or axis where the point is located.

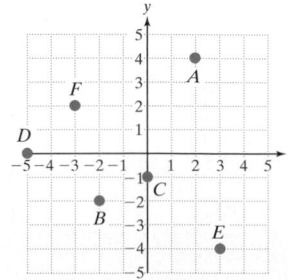

3. A (2, 4); quadrant I   **4.** B (−2, −2); quadrant III

5. C (0, −1); y-axis   **6.** D (−5, 0); x-axis

7. E (3, −4); quadrant IV   **8.** F (−3, 2); quadrant II

Concept 1: Definition of a Linear Equation in Two Variables

For Exercises 9–17, determine if the given ordered pair is a solution to the equation. **(See Example 1.)**

9. $x - y = 6$; $(8, 2)$ Yes

10. $y = 3x - 2$; $(1, 1)$ Yes

 11. $y = -\frac{1}{3}x + 3$; $(-3, 4)$ Yes

12. $y = -\frac{5}{2}x + 5$; $\left(\frac{4}{5}, -3\right)$ No

13. $4x + 5y = 1$; $\left(\frac{1}{4}, -\frac{2}{5}\right)$ No

14. $y = 7$; $(0, 7)$ Yes

15. $y = -2$; $(-2, 6)$ No

16. $x = 1$; $(0, 1)$ No

17. $x = -5$; $(-5, 6)$ Yes

Concept 2: Graphing Linear Equations in Two Variables by Plotting Points

For Exercises 18–31, complete each table, and graph the corresponding ordered pairs. Draw the line defined by the points to represent all solutions to the equation. **(See Examples 2–4.)**

18. $x + y = 3$

x	y
2	1
0	3
-1	4
3	0

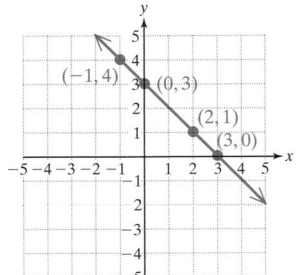

19. $x + y = -2$

x	y
1	-3
-2	0
-3	1
-4	2

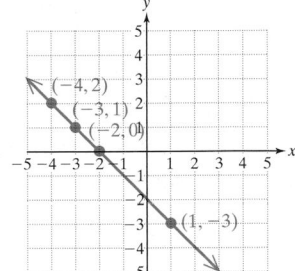

20. $y = 5x + 1$

x	y
1	6
0	1
-1	-4

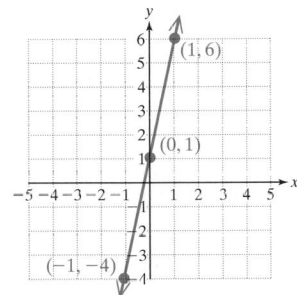

21. $y = -3x - 3$

x	y
-2	3
-1	0
-4	9

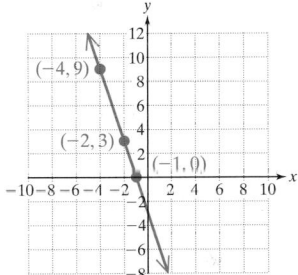

22. $2x - 3y = 6$

x	y
0	-2
3	0
2	-2/3

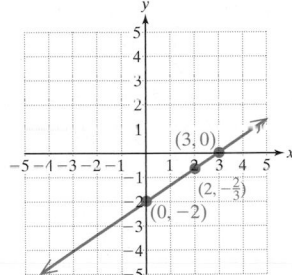

23. $4x + 2y = 8$

x	y
0	4
2	0
3	-2

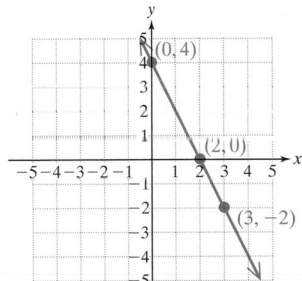

24. $y = \frac{2}{7}x - 5$

x	y
7	-3
-7	-7
0	-5

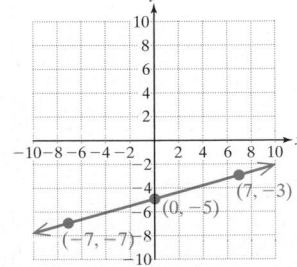

25. $y = -\frac{3}{5}x - 2$

x	y
0	2
5	-5
10	-8

 Writing   Translating Expression   Geometry   Scientific Calculator   Video   NS&E

26. $y = 3$

x	y
2	3
0	3
−1	3

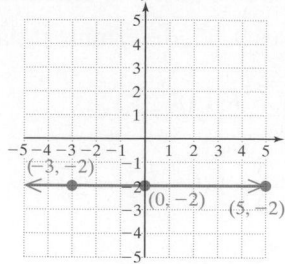

27. $y = -2$

x	y
0	−2
−3	−2
5	−2

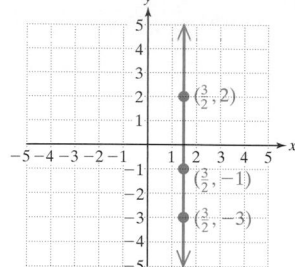

28. $x = -4$

x	y
−4	1
−4	−2
−4	4

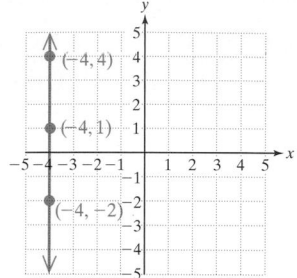

29. $x = \frac{3}{2}$

x	y
3/2	−1
3/2	2
3/2	−3

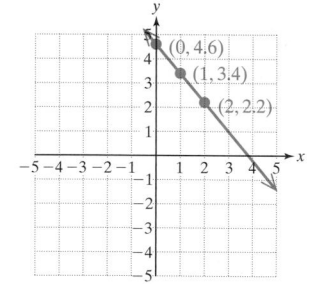

30. $y = -3.4x + 5.8$

x	y
0	5.8
1	2.4
2	−1

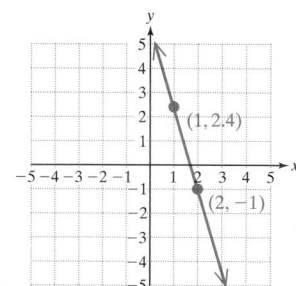

31. $y = -1.2x + 4.6$

x	y
0	4.6
1	3.4
2	2.2

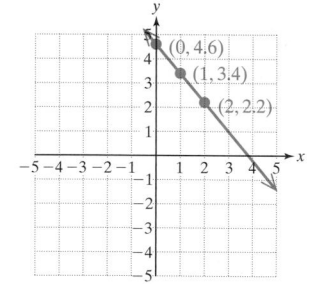

For Exercises 32–43, graph each line by making a table of at least three ordered pairs and plotting the points.

32. $x - y = 2$

33. $x - y = 4$

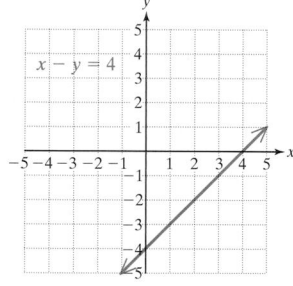

34. $-3x + y = -6$

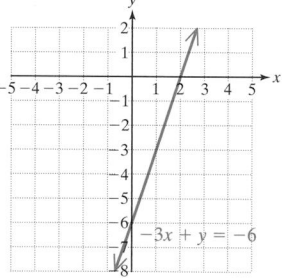

35. $2x - 5y = 10$

36. $y = 4x$

37. $y = -2x$

38. $y = -\dfrac{1}{2}x + 3$

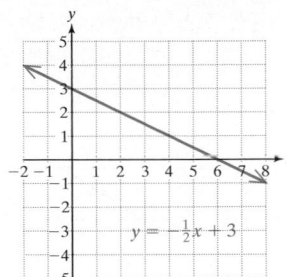

39. $y = \dfrac{1}{4}x - 2$

40. $x + y = 0$

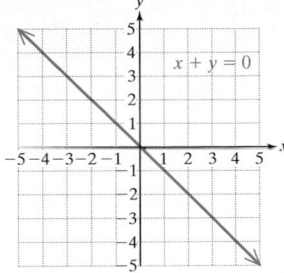

41. $-x + y = 0$

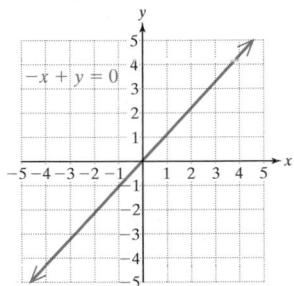

42. $50x - 40y = 200$

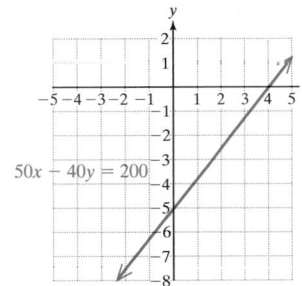

43. $-30x - 20y = 60$

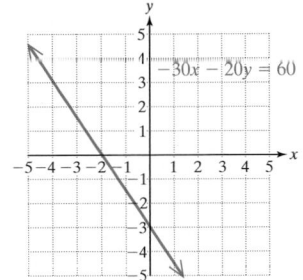

Concept 3: *x*- and *y*-Intercepts

44. The *x*-intercept is on which axis?   *x*-axis

45. The *y*-intercept is on which axis?   *y*-axis

For Exercises 46–49, estimate the coordinates of the *x*- and *y*-intercepts.

46.

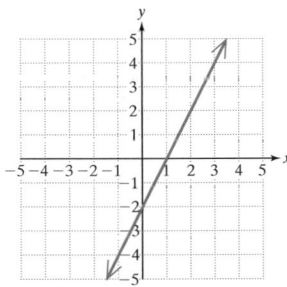

x-intercept: $(1, 0)$;
y-intercept: $(0, -2)$

47.

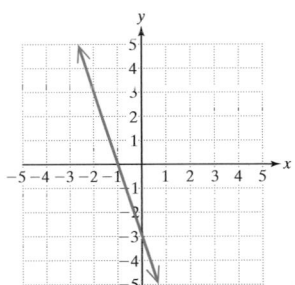

x-intercept: $(-1, 0)$;
y-intercept: $(0, -3)$

48.

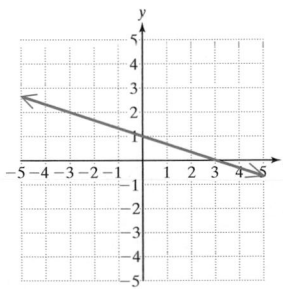

x-intercept: $(3, 0)$;
y-intercept: $(0, 1)$

49.

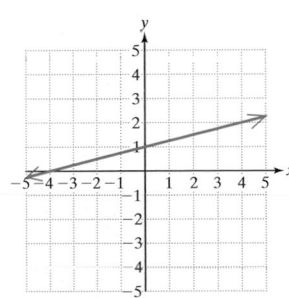

x-intercept: $(-4, 0)$;
y-intercept: $(0, 1)$

For Exercises 50–53, determine the *x*- and *y*-intercepts from the values in each table.

50.

x	*y*
−1	3
0	6
2	0
1	9

x-intercept: $(2, 0)$;
y-intercept: $(0, 6)$

51.

x	*y*
1	15
0	10
−5	5
−2	0

x-intercept: $(-2, 0)$;
y-intercept: $(0, 10)$

52.

x	*y*
7	0
1	12
2	10
0	14

x-intercept: $(7, 0)$;
y-intercept: $(0, 14)$

53.

x	*y*
0	4
−2	3
−8	0
6	7

x-intercept: $(-8, 0)$;
y-intercept: $(0, 4)$

 Writing   Translating Expression   Geometry   Scientific Calculator   Video   NS&E

For Exercises 54–65, find the *x*- and *y*-intercepts (if they exist), and graph the line. **(See Examples 5–6.)**

54. $5x + 2y = 5$ x-intercept: $(1, 0)$;
y-intercept: $\left(0, \frac{5}{2}\right)$

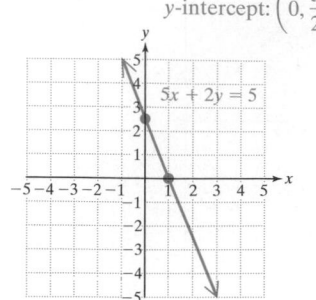

55. $4x - 3y = -9$ x-intercept: $\left(-\frac{9}{4}, 0\right)$;
y-intercept: $(0, 3)$

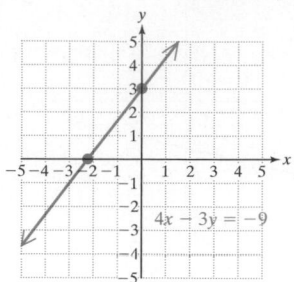

56. $y = \frac{2}{3}x - 1$ x-intercept: $\left(\frac{3}{2}, 0\right)$;
y-intercept: $(0, -1)$

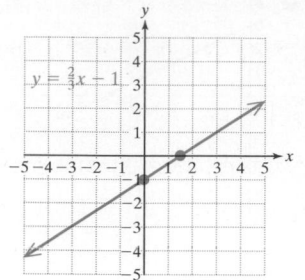

57. $y = -\frac{3}{4}x + 2$ x-intercept: $\left(\frac{8}{3}, 0\right)$;
y-intercept: $(0, 2)$

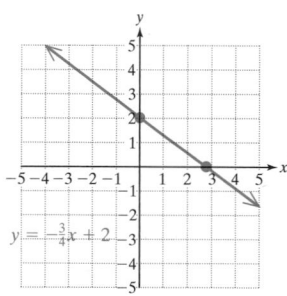

58. $x - 3 = y$ x-intercept: $(3, 0)$;
y-intercept: $(0, -3)$

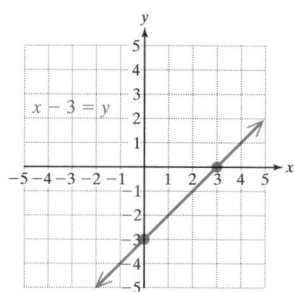

59. $2x + 8 = y$ x-intercept: $(-4, 0)$;
y-intercept: $(0, 8)$

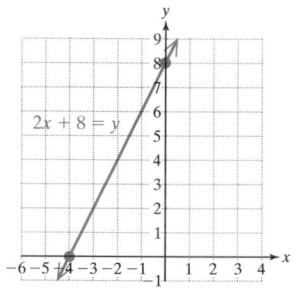

60. $-3x + y = 0$ x-intercept: $(0, 0)$;
y-intercept: $(0, 0)$

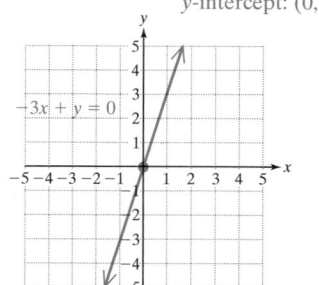

61. $2x - 2y = 0$ x-intercept: $(0, 0)$;
y-intercept: $(0, 0)$

 62. $25y = 10x + 100$ x-intercept: $(-10, 0)$;
y-intercept: $(0, 4)$

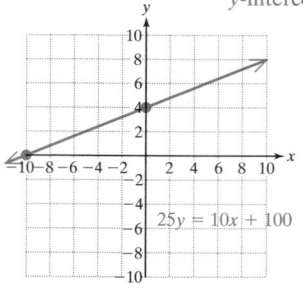

63. $20x = -40y + 200$
x-intercept: $(10, 0)$; y-intercept: $(0, 5)$

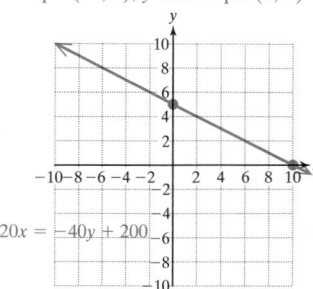

64. $x = 2y$
x-intercept: $(0, 0)$; y-intercept: $(0, 0)$

65. $x = -5y$
x-intercept: $(0, 0)$; y-intercept: $(0, 0)$

Concept 4: Horizontal and Vertical Lines

For Exercises 66–69, answer true or false. If the statement is false, rewrite it to be true.

66. The line defined by $x = 3$ is horizontal.
False, $x = 3$ is vertical.

67. The line defined by $y = -4$ is horizontal. True

68. A line parallel to the y-axis is vertical. True

69. A line perpendicular to the x-axis is vertical. True

For Exercises 70–78,

a. Identify the equation as representing a horizontal or vertical line.

b. Graph the line.

c. Identify the x- and y-intercepts if they exist. **(See Examples 7–8.)**

70. $x = 3$ a. Vertical line c. x-intercept:
(3, 0); no y-intercept

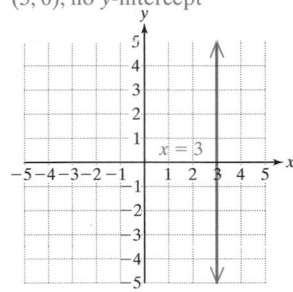

71. $y = -1$ a. Horizontal line
c. no x-intercept; y-intercept: $(0, -1)$

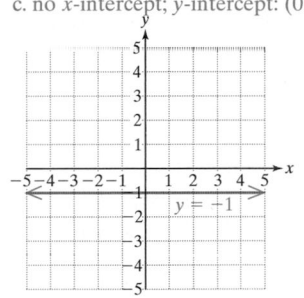

72. $-2y = 8$ a. Horizontal line
c. no x-intercept; y-intercept: $(0, -4)$

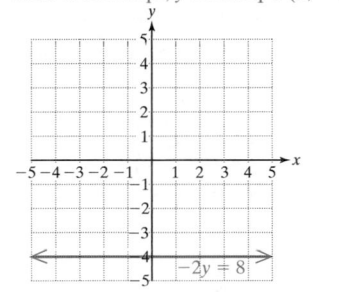

73. $5x = 20$ a. Vertical line
c. x-intercept: (4, 0); no y-intercept

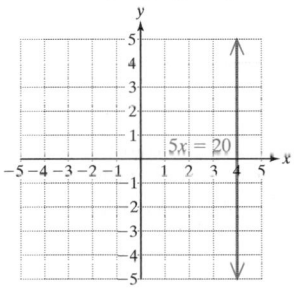

74. $x - 3 = -7$ a. Vertical line
c. x-intercept: $(-4, 0)$; no y-intercept

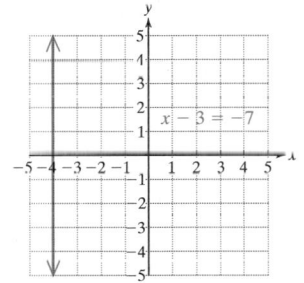

75. $y + 8 = 11$ a. Horizontal line
c. no x-intercept; y-intercept (0, 3)

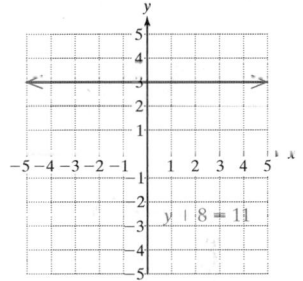

76. $3y = 0$ a. Horizontal line
c. All points on the x-axis are
x-intercepts; y-intercept: (0, 0)

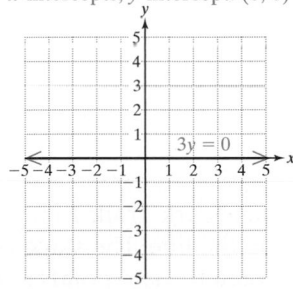

77. $5x = 0$ a. Vertical line
c. All points on the y-axis are
y-intercepts; x-intercept: (0, 0)

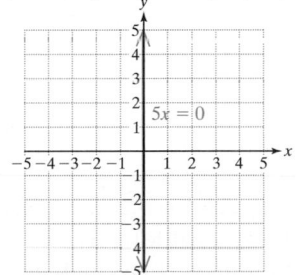

78. $2x + 7 = 10$ a. Vertical line
c. x-intercept: $(\frac{3}{2}, 0)$; no y-intercept

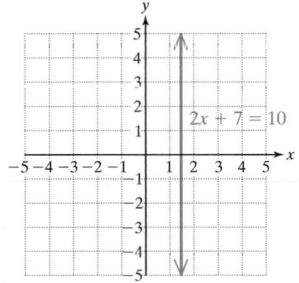

79. Explain why not every line has both an x- and a y-intercept.   A horizontal line may not have an x-intercept.
A vertical line may not have a y-intercept.

80. Which of the lines has an x-intercept?

  a. $2x - 3y = 6$ **b.** $x = 5$ **c.** $2y = 8$ **d.** $-x + y = 0$ a, b, d

81. Which of the lines has a y-intercept?

  a. $y = 2$ **b.** $x + y = 0$ **c.** $2x - 10 = 2$ **d.** $x + 4y = 8$ a, b, d

 Writing   Translating Expression   Geometry   Scientific Calculator   Video   NS&E

Expanding Your Skills

82. The store "CDs R US" sells all compact disks for $13.99. The following equation represents the revenue, y, (in dollars) generated by selling x CDs.

$$y = 13.99x \quad (x \geq 0)$$

a. Find y when $x = 13$.　$y = 181.87$

b. Find x when $y = 279.80$.　$x = 20$

c. Write the ordered pairs from parts (a) and (b), and interpret their meaning in the context of the problem.　(13, 181.87) Selling 13 compact disks yields $181.87 in revenue. (20, 279.80) Selling 20 compact disks yields $279.80 in revenue.

d. Graph the ordered pairs and the line defined by the points.

83. The value of a car depreciates once it is driven off of the dealer's lot. For a Hyundai Accent, the value of the car is given by the equation $y = -1025x + 12{,}215 \, (x \geq 0)$ where y is the value of the car in dollars x years after its purchase. (*Source: Kelly Blue Book*)

a. Find y when $x = 1$.　$y = 11{,}190$

b. Find x when $y = 9140$.　$x = 3$

c. Write the ordered pairs from parts (a) and (b), and interpret their meaning in the context of the problem.　(1, 11,190) One year after purchase the value of the car is $11,190. (3, 9140) Three years after purchase the value of the car is $9140.

Section 3.3 **Slope of a Line and Rate of Change**

Concepts

1. **Introduction to Slope**
2. **Slope Formula**
3. **Parallel and Perpendicular Lines**
4. **Applications of Slope: Rate of Change**

1. Introduction to Slope

The x- and y-intercepts represent the points where a line crosses the x- and y-axes. Another important feature of a line is its slope. Geometrically, the slope of a line measures the "steepness" of the line. For example, two hiking trails are depicted by the lines in Figure 3-14.

Park Trail　　　Mt. Dora Trail

Figure 3-14

By visual inspection, Mt. Dora Trail is "steeper" than Park Trail. To measure the slope of a line quantitatively, consider two points on the line. The **slope** of the line is the ratio of the vertical change (change in y) between the two points and the horizontal change (change in x). As a memory device, we might think of the slope of a line as "rise over run." See Figure 3-15.

$$\text{Slope} = \frac{\text{change in } y}{\text{change in } x} = \frac{\text{rise}}{\text{run}}$$

Figure 3-15

To move from point A to point B on Park Trail, rise 2 ft and move to the right 6 ft (Figure 3-16).

To move from point A to point B on Mt. Dora Trail, rise 5 ft and move to the right 4 ft (Figure 3-17).

Mt. Dora Trail
(Change in x)
4 ft

(Change in y)
5 ft

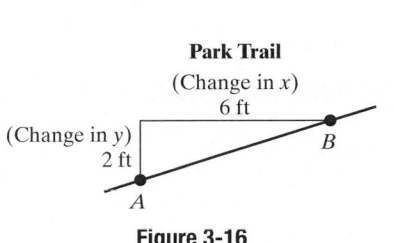

Park Trail
(Change in x)
6 ft
(Change in y)
2 ft

Figure 3-16

Figure 3-17

> **TIP:** To find the slope, you can use any two points on the line. The ratio of rise to run will be the same.

$$\text{Slope} = \frac{\text{change in } y}{\text{change in } x} = \frac{2 \text{ ft}}{6 \text{ ft}} = \frac{1}{3}$$

$$\text{Slope} = \frac{\text{change in } y}{\text{change in } x} = \frac{5 \text{ ft}}{4 \text{ ft}} = \frac{5}{4}$$

The slope of Mt. Dora Trail is greater than the slope of Park Trail, confirming the observation that Mt. Dora Trail is steeper. On Mt. Dora Trail there is a 5-ft change in elevation for every 4 ft of horizontal distance (a 5:4 ratio). On Park Trail there is only a 2-ft change in elevation for every 6 ft of horizontal distance (a 1:3 ratio).

Example 1 **Finding Slope in an Application**

Determine the slope of the ramp up the stairs.

Classroom Example: p. 222, Exercise 12

Solution:

$$\text{Slope} = \frac{\text{change in } y}{\text{change in } x} = \frac{8 \text{ ft}}{16 \text{ ft}}$$

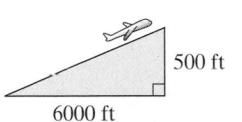

8 ft

16 ft

$$\frac{8}{16} = \frac{1}{2} \qquad \text{Write the ratio for the slope and simplify.}$$

The slope is $\frac{1}{2}$.

Skill Practice

1. Determine the slope of the aircraft's takeoff path.

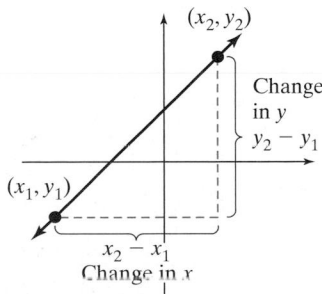

500 ft

6000 ft

2. Slope Formula

The slope of a line may be found using any two points on the line—call these points (x_1, y_1) and (x_2, y_2). The numbers to the right and below the variables are called *subscripts*. In this instance, the subscript 1 indicates the coordinates of the first point, and the subscript 2 indicates the coordinates of the second point. The change in y between the points can be found by taking the difference of the y values: $y_2 - y_1$. The change in x can be found by taking the difference of the x values in the same order: $x_2 - x_1$ (Figure 3-18).

The slope of a line is often symbolized by the letter m and is given by the following formula.

(x_2, y_2)

Change in y

$y_2 - y_1$

(x_1, y_1)

$x_2 - x_1$
Change in x

Figure 3-18

Answer

1. $\dfrac{500}{6000} = \dfrac{1}{12}$

Classroom Example: p. 224,
Exercise 38

> **FORMULA   Slope Formula**
>
> The slope of a line passing through the distinct points (x_1, y_1) and (x_2, y_2) is
>
> $$m = \frac{y_2 - y_1}{x_2 - x_1} \quad \text{provided } x_2 - x_1 \neq 0.$$

Example 2   **Finding the Slope of a Line Given Two Points**

Find the slope of the line through the points $(-1, 3)$ and $(-4, -2)$.

Solution:

To use the slope formula, first label the coordinates of each point and then substitute the coordinates into the slope formula.

$$\underset{(x_1, y_1)}{(-1, 3)} \quad \text{and} \quad \underset{(x_2, y_2)}{(-4, -2)} \qquad \text{Label the points.}$$

Avoiding Mistakes

When calculating slope, always write the change in y in the numerator.

$$m = \frac{y_2 - y_1}{x_2 - x_1} = \frac{(-2) - (3)}{(-4) - (-1)} \qquad \text{Apply the slope formula.}$$

$$= \frac{-5}{-3}$$

$$= \frac{5}{3} \qquad \qquad \text{Simplify to lowest terms.}$$

The slope of the line can be verified from the graph (Figure 3-19).

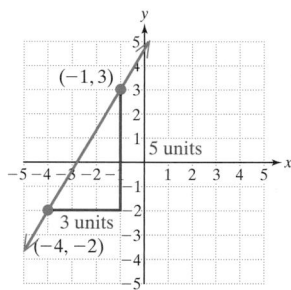

Figure 3-19

Skill Practice   Find the slope of the line through the given points.

2. $(-5, 2)$ and $(1, 3)$

> **TIP:**   The slope formula is not dependent on which point is labeled (x_1, y_1) and which point is labeled (x_2, y_2). In Example 2, reversing the order in which the points are labeled results in the same slope.
>
> $$\underset{(x_2, y_2)}{(-1, 3)} \quad \text{and} \quad \underset{(x_1, y_1)}{(-4, -2)} \qquad \text{Label the points.}$$
>
> $$m = \frac{(3) - (-2)}{(-1) - (-4)} = \frac{5}{3} \qquad \text{Apply the slope formula.}$$

Answer

2. $\dfrac{1}{6}$

When you apply the slope formula, you will see that the slope of a line may be positive, negative, zero, or undefined.

- Lines that increase, or rise, from left to right have a positive slope.
- Lines that decrease, or fall, from left to right have a negative slope.
- Horizontal lines have a slope of zero.
- Vertical lines have an undefined slope.

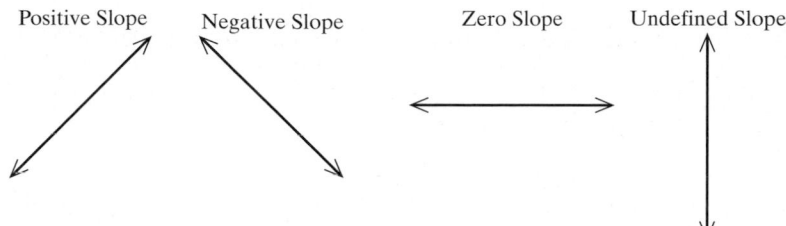

Positive Slope   Negative Slope   Zero Slope   Undefined Slope

---

Example 3 **Finding the Slope of a Line Given Two Points**

Classroom Example: p. 224, Exercise 46

Find the slope of the line passing through the points $(-5, \frac{1}{2})$ and $(2, -\frac{3}{2})$.

Solution:

$$\underset{(x_1, y_1)}{\left(-5, \frac{1}{2}\right)} \quad \text{and} \quad \underset{(x_2, y_2)}{\left(2, -\frac{3}{2}\right)} \qquad \text{Label the points.}$$

$$m = \frac{y_2 - y_1}{x_2 - x_1} = \frac{\left(-\frac{3}{2}\right) - \left(\frac{1}{2}\right)}{(2) - (-5)} \qquad \text{Apply the slope formula.}$$

$$= \frac{-\frac{4}{2}}{2 + 5} \qquad \begin{array}{l}\text{Simplify the numerator and} \\ \text{denominator separately.}\end{array}$$

$$= \frac{-2}{7} \quad \text{or} \quad -\frac{2}{7}$$

By graphing the points $(-5, \frac{1}{2})$ and $(2, -\frac{3}{2})$, we can verify that the slope is $-\frac{2}{7}$ (Figure 3-20). Notice that the line slopes downward from left to right.

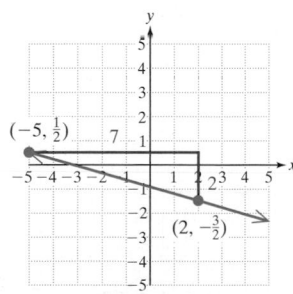

Figure 3-20

Skill Practice Find the slope of the line through the given points.

3. $\left(\frac{2}{3}, 0\right)$ and $\left(-\frac{1}{6}, 5\right)$

Answer

3. -6

Classroom Example: p. 224,
Exercise 44

Example 4   Determining the Slope of a Vertical Line

Find the slope of the line passing through the points $(2, -1)$ and $(2, 4)$.

Solution:

$$\underset{(x_1, y_1)}{(2, -1)} \quad \text{and} \quad \underset{(x_2, y_2)}{(2, 4)} \qquad \text{Label the points.}$$

$$m = \frac{y_2 - y_1}{x_2 - x_1} = \frac{(4) - (-1)}{(2) - (2)} \qquad \begin{array}{l}\text{Apply the slope} \\ \text{formula.}\end{array}$$

$$m = \frac{5}{0} \quad \text{Undefined}$$

Because the slope, m, is undefined, we expect the points to form a vertical line as shown in Figure 3-21.

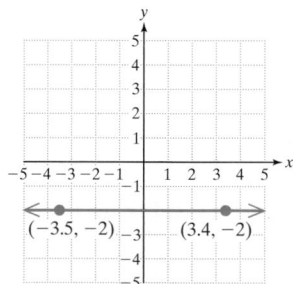

Figure 3-21

Skill Practice   Find the slope of the line through the given points.

4. $(5, 6)$ and $(5, -2)$

Classroom Example: p. 224,
Exercise 42

Example 5   Determine the Slope of a Horizontal Line

Find the slope of the line passing through the points $(3.4, -2)$ and $(-3.5, -2)$.

Solution:

$$\underset{(x_1, y_1)}{(3.4, -2)} \quad \text{and} \quad \underset{(x_2, y_2)}{(-3.5, -2)} \qquad \text{Label the points.}$$

$$m = \frac{y_2 - y_1}{x_2 - x_1} = \frac{(-2) - (-2)}{(-3.5) - (3.4)} \qquad \text{Apply the slope formula.}$$

$$= \frac{-2 + 2}{-3.5 - 3.4} = \frac{0}{-6.9} = 0 \qquad \text{Simplify.}$$

Because the slope is 0, we expect the points to form a horizontal line, as shown in Figure 3-22.

Figure 3-22

Skill Practice   Find the slope of the line through the given points.

5. $(3, 8)$ and $(-5, 8)$

Answers

4. Undefined   **5.** 0

3. Parallel and Perpendicular Lines

Lines in the same plane that do not intersect are called **parallel lines**. Parallel lines have the same slope and different *y*-intercepts (Figure 3-23).

Lines that intersect at a right angle are **perpendicular lines**. If two lines are perpendicular then the slope of one line is the opposite of the reciprocal of the slope of the other line (provided neither line is vertical) (Figure 3-24).

Instructor Note: If you use calculators for graphing lines, try putting two lines with slopes that are similar ($y = x$ and $y = \frac{19}{20}x + 1$). They will appear parallel, but clearly we can show they are not by inspecting the equations. Sometimes students don't value what we do by hand until they see it does not always appear correctly on the calculator.

Figure 3-23

Figure 3-24

PROPERTY   Slopes of Parallel Lines

If m_1 and m_2 represent the slopes of two parallel (nonvertical) lines, then

$$m_1 = m_2.$$

See Figure 3-23.

PROPERTY   Slopes of Perpendicular Lines

If $m_1 \neq 0$ and $m_2 \neq 0$ represent the slopes of two perpendicular lines, then

$$m_1 = -\frac{1}{m_2} \text{ or equivalently, } m_1 m_2 = -1. \text{ See Figure 3-24.}$$

Instructor Note: Ask students how we know that all vertical lines are parallel and all horizontal lines are parallel.

Example 6   **Determining the Slope of Parallel and Perpendicular Lines**

Classroom Example: p. 224, Exercise 54

Suppose a given line has a slope of -6.

a. Find the slope of a line parallel to the line with the given slope.

b. Find the slope of a line perpendicular to the line with the given slope.

Solution:

a. Parallel lines must have the same slope. The slope of a line parallel to the given line is $m = -6$.

b. For perpendicular lines, the slope of one line must be the opposite of the reciprocal of the other. The slope of a line perpendicular to the given line is $m = +\frac{1}{6}$.

Skill Practice A given line has a slope of $\frac{5}{3}$.

6. Find the slope of a line parallel to the given line.

7. Find the slope of a line perpendicular to the given line.

Answers

6. $\dfrac{5}{3}$ **7.** $-\dfrac{3}{5}$

If the slopes of two lines are known, then we can compare the slopes to determine if the lines are parallel, perpendicular, or neither.

Classroom Example: p. 224,
Exercise 68

Example 7   **Determining If Lines Are Parallel, Perpendicular, or Neither**

Lines l_1 and l_2 pass through the given points. Determine if l_1 and l_2 are parallel, perpendicular, or neither.

$$l_1: \quad (2, -7) \text{ and } (4, 1) \qquad\qquad l_2: \quad (-3, 1) \text{ and } (1, 0)$$

Solution:

Find the slope of each line.

$$l_1: \quad \underset{(x_1, y_1)}{(2, -7)} \ \text{ and } \ \underset{(x_2, y_2)}{(4, 1)} \qquad\qquad l_2: \quad \underset{(x_1, y_1)}{(-3, 1)} \ \text{ and } \ \underset{(x_2, y_2)}{(1, 0)}$$

> **TIP:** You can check that two lines are perpendicular by checking that the product of their slopes is −1.
>
> $$4\left(-\frac{1}{4}\right) = -1$$

$$m_1 = \frac{1 - (-7)}{4 - 2} \qquad\qquad m_2 = \frac{0 - 1}{1 - (-3)}$$

$$m_1 = \frac{8}{2} \qquad\qquad m_2 = \frac{-1}{4}$$

$$m_1 = 4 \qquad\qquad m_2 = -\frac{1}{4}$$

One slope is the opposite of the reciprocal of the other slope. Therefore, the lines are perpendicular.

Skill Practice Determine if lines l_1 and l_2 are parallel, perpendicular, or neither.

8. $l_1: \quad (-2, -3) \text{ and } (4, -1)$
   $l_2: \quad (0, 2) \text{ and } (-3, 1)$

4. Applications of Slope: Rate of Change

In many applications, the interpretation of slope refers to the *rate of change* of the *y*-variable to the *x*-variable.

Classroom Example: p. 225,
Exercise 76

Example 8   **Interpreting Slope in an Application**

The annual median income for males in the United States for selected years is shown in Figure 3-25. The trend is approximately linear. Find the slope of the line and interpret the meaning of the slope in the context of the problem.

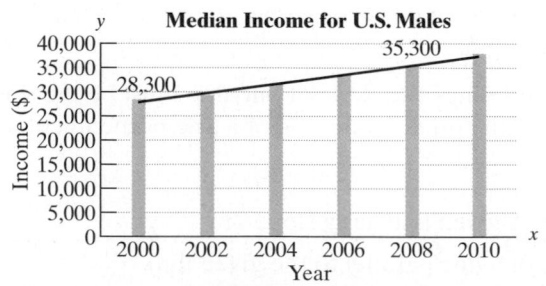

Figure 3-25

Source: U.S. Department of the Census

Answer

8. Parallel

Solution:

To determine the slope we need to know two points on the line. From the graph, the median income for males in the year 2000 was approximately $28,300. This gives us the ordered pair (2000, 28,300). In the year 2008, the income was $35,300. This gives the ordered pair (2008, 35,300).

$$\underset{(x_1, y_1)}{(2000, 28{,}300)} \quad \text{and} \quad \underset{(x_2, y_2)}{(2008, 35{,}300)} \qquad \text{Label the points.}$$

$$m = \frac{y_2 - y_1}{x_2 - x_1} = \frac{35{,}300 - 28{,}300}{2008 - 2000} \qquad \text{Apply the slope formula.}$$

$$= \frac{7000}{8}$$

$$= 875 \qquad \text{Simplify.}$$

The slope is 875. This tells us the rate of change of the *y*-variable (income) to the *x*-variable (years). This means that men's median income in the United States increased at a rate of $875 per year during this time period.

Skill Practice

9. In the year 2000, the population of Alaska was approximately 630,000. By 2005, it had grown to 670,000. Use the ordered pairs (2000, 630,000) and (2005, 670,000) to determine the slope of the line through the points. Then interpret the meaning in the context of this problem.

Answer

9. $m = 8000$; The population of Alaska increased at a rate of 8000 people per year.

Section 3.3 Practice Exercises

Study Skills Exercises

1. Each night after finishing your homework, choose two or three odd-numbered problems or examples from that section. Write the problem with the directions on one side of a 3 × 5 card. On the back write the section, page, and problem number along with the answer. Each week, shuffle your cards and pull out a few at random, to give yourself a review of $\frac{1}{2}$-hr or more.

2. Define the key terms.   **a. parallel lines**   **b. perpendicular lines**   **c. slope**

Review Exercises

For Exercises 3–8, find the *x*- and *y*-intercepts (if they exist). Then graph the line.

3. $x - 3y = 6$ *x*-intercept: (6, 0); *y*-intercept: (0, −2)

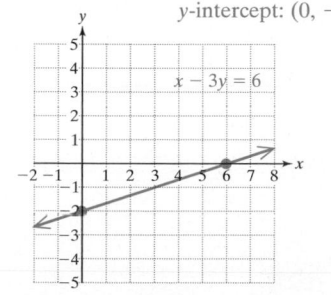

4. $x - 5 = 2$ *x*-intercept: (7, 0); *y*-intercept: none

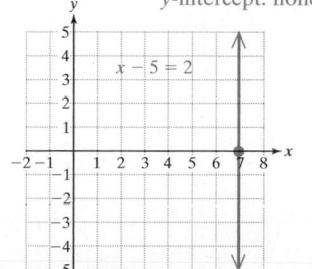

5. $y = \frac{2}{3}x$ *x*-intercept: (0, 0); *y*-intercept: (0, 0)

 Writing   Translating Expression   Geometry   Scientific Calculator   Video   NS&E

6. $2y - 3 = 0$ *x*-intercept: none;
    y-intercept: $(0, \frac{3}{2})$

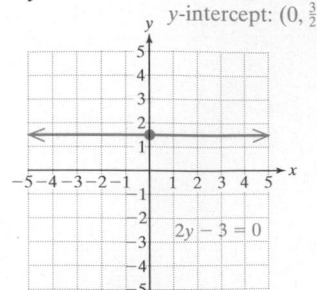

7. $4x + y = 8$ *x*-intercept: $(2, 0)$;
    y-intercept: $(0, 8)$

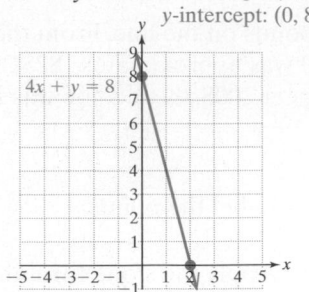

8. $2x = 4y$ *x*-intercept: $(0, 0)$;
    y-intercept: $(0, 0)$

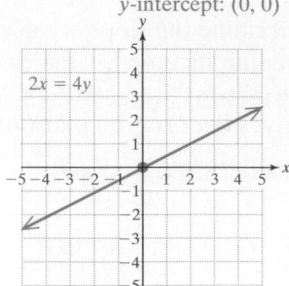

Concept 1: Introduction to Slope

9. Determine the slope of the roof.
(See Example 1.)

$m = \dfrac{1}{3}$

10. Determine the slope of the stairs.

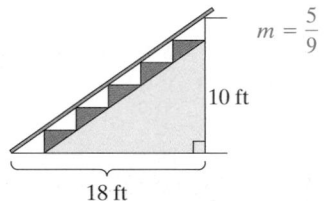

$m = \dfrac{5}{9}$

11. Calculate the slope of the handrail.

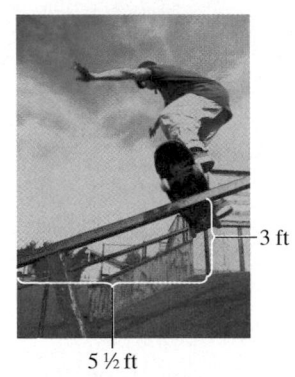

$m = \dfrac{6}{11}$

12. Determine the slope of the treadmill.

$m = \dfrac{1}{8}$

Concept 2: Slope Formula

For Exercises 13–16, fill in the blank with the appropriate term: zero, negative, positive, or undefined.

13. The slope of a line parallel to the *y*-axis is <u>Undefined</u>.

14. The slope of a horizontal line is <u>Zero</u>.

15. The slope of a line that rises from left to right is <u>Positive</u>.

16. The slope of a line that falls from left to right is <u>Negative</u>.

For Exercises 17–25, determine if the slope is positive, negative, zero, or undefined.

17. Negative

18. Undefined

19. Zero

20. Negative

21. Undefined

22. Zero

23. Positive

24. Positive

25. Negative

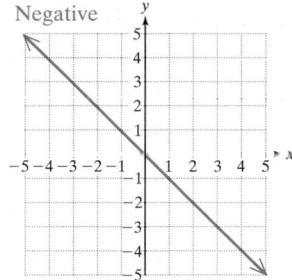

For Exercises 26–34, determine the slope by using the slope formula and any two points on the line. Check your answer by drawing a right triangle and labeling the "rise" and "run."

26. $m = 2$

27. $m = \dfrac{1}{2}$

28. $m = -\dfrac{1}{3}$

29. $m = -3$

30. $m = 0$

31. $m = 0$

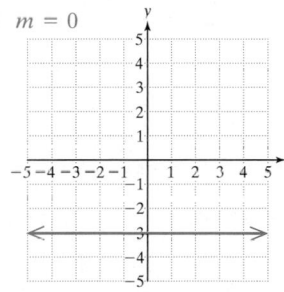

32. The slope is undefined.

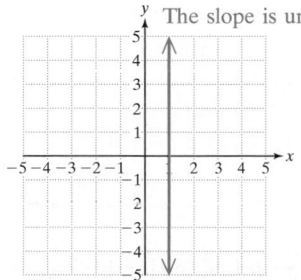

33. The slope is undefined.

34. $m = -1$

 Writing   Translating Expression   Geometry Scientific Calculator   Video NS&E

For Exercises 35–52, find the slope of the line that passes through the two points. **(See Examples 2–5.)**

35. $(2, 4)$ and $(-4, 2)$ $\dfrac{1}{3}$

36. $(-5, 4)$ and $(-11, 12)$ $-\dfrac{4}{3}$

37. $(-2, 3)$ and $(1, -6)$ -3

38. $(-3, -4)$ and $(5, -6)$ $-\dfrac{1}{4}$

39. $(1, 5)$ and $(-4, 2)$ $\dfrac{3}{5}$

40. $(-6, -1)$ and $(-2, -3)$ $-\dfrac{1}{2}$

41. $(5, 3)$ and $(-2, 3)$ Zero

42. $(0, -1)$ and $(-4, -1)$ Zero

43. $(2, -7)$ and $(2, 5)$ Undefined

44. $(-4, 3)$ and $(-4, -4)$ Undefined

45. $\left(\dfrac{1}{2}, \dfrac{3}{5}\right)$ and $\left(\dfrac{1}{4}, -\dfrac{4}{5}\right)$ $\dfrac{28}{5}$

46. $\left(-\dfrac{2}{7}, \dfrac{1}{3}\right)$ and $\left(\dfrac{8}{7}, -\dfrac{5}{6}\right)$ $-\dfrac{49}{60}$

47. $(3, -1)$ and $(-5, 6)$ $-\dfrac{7}{8}$

48. $(-6, 5)$ and $(-10, 4)$ $\dfrac{1}{4}$

49. $(6.8, -3.4)$ and $(-3.2, 1.1)$ -0.45 or $-\dfrac{9}{20}$

50. $(-3.15, 8.25)$ and $(6.85, -4.25)$ -1.25 or $-\dfrac{5}{4}$

51. $(1994, 3.5)$ and $(2000, 2.6)$ -0.15 or $-\dfrac{3}{20}$

52. $(1988, 4.65)$ and $(1998, 9.25)$ 0.46 or $\dfrac{23}{50}$

Concept 3: Parallel and Perpendicular Lines

For Exercises 53–60, the slope of a line is given. **(See Example 6.)**

a. Determine the slope of a line parallel to the line with the given slope.

b. Determine the slope of a line perpendicular to the line with the given slope.

53. $m = -2$ a. -2 b. $\dfrac{1}{2}$

54. $m = \dfrac{2}{3}$ a. $\dfrac{2}{3}$ b. $-\dfrac{3}{2}$

55. $m = 0$ a. 0   b. undefined

56. The slope is undefined.   a. undefined   b. 0

57. $m = \dfrac{4}{5}$ a. $\dfrac{4}{5}$ b. $-\dfrac{5}{4}$

58. $m = -4$ a. -4 b. $\dfrac{1}{4}$

59. The slope is undefined.   a. undefined   b. 0

60. $m = 0$ a. 0   b. undefined

For Exercises 61–66, let m_1 and m_2 represent the slopes of two lines. Determine if the lines are parallel, perpendicular, or neither. **(See Example 6.)**

61. $m_1 = -2, m_2 = \dfrac{1}{2}$ Perpendicular

62. $m_1 = \dfrac{2}{3}, m_2 = \dfrac{3}{2}$ Neither

63. $m_1 = 1, m_2 = \dfrac{4}{4}$ Parallel

64. $m_1 = \dfrac{3}{4}, m_2 = -\dfrac{8}{6}$ Perpendicular

65. $m_1 = \dfrac{2}{7}, m_2 = -\dfrac{2}{7}$ Neither

66. $m_1 = 5, m_2 = 5$ Parallel

For Exercises 67–72, find the slopes of the lines l_1 and l_2 defined by the two given points. Then determine whether l_1 and l_2 are parallel, perpendicular, or neither. **(See Example 7.)**

67. l_1: $(2, 4)$ and $(-1, -2)$
l_2: $(1, 7)$ and $(0, 5)$
l_1: $m = 2$, l_2: $m = 2$; parallel

68. l_1: $(0, 0)$ and $(-2, 4)$
l_2: $(1, -5)$ and $(-1, -1)$
l_1: $m = -2$, l_2: $m = -2$; parallel

69. l_1: $(1, 9)$ and $(0, 4)$
l_2: $(5, 2)$ and $(10, 1)$
l_1: $m = 5$, l_2: $m = -\dfrac{1}{5}$; perpendicular

70. l_1: $(3, -4)$ and $(-1, -8)$
l_2: $(5, -5)$ and $(-2, 2)$
l_1: $m = 1$, l_2: $m = -1$; perpendicular

71. l_1: $(4, 4)$ and $(0, 3)$
l_2: $(1, 7)$ and $(-1, -1)$
l_1: $m = \dfrac{1}{4}$, l_2: $m = 4$; neither

72. l_1: $(3, 5)$ and $(-2, -5)$
l_2: $(2, 0)$ and $(-4, -3)$
l_1: $m = 2$, l_2: $m = \dfrac{1}{2}$; neither

Concept 4: Applications of Slope: Rate of Change

73. For a recent year, the average earnings for male workers between the ages of 25 and 34 with a high school diploma was $32,000. Comparing this value in constant dollars to the average earnings 15 years later showed that the average earnings have decreased to $29,600. Find the average rate of change in dollars per year. [*Hint:* Use the ordered pairs $(0, 32{,}000)$ and $(15, 29{,}600)$.]   The average rate of change is $-\$160$ per year.

 Writing   Translating Expression   Geometry   Scientific Calculator   Video   NS&E

74. In 1992, approximately 10.4 million Americans earned an Associate Degree. By 2007, the number increased to 18.2 million. Let x represent the year, and let y represent the number of Americans (in millions) who earned an Associate Degree for a given year. Find the average rate of change in the number of Americans earning Associate Degrees per year. (*Source:* U.S. Census Bureau) The slope of 0.52 means that the number of Americans earning Associate Degrees increased at a rate of 0.52 million (520,000) per year during this time period.

75. In 1980, there were 304 thousand male inmates in federal and state prisons. By 2009, the number increased to 1609 thousand. Let x represent the year, and let y represent the number of prisoners (in thousands). **(See Example 8.)**

   a. Using the ordered pairs (1980, 304) and (2009, 1609), find the slope of the line. $m = 45$

   b. Interpret the slope in the context of this problem.
The number of male prisoners increased at a rate of 45 thousand per year during this time period.

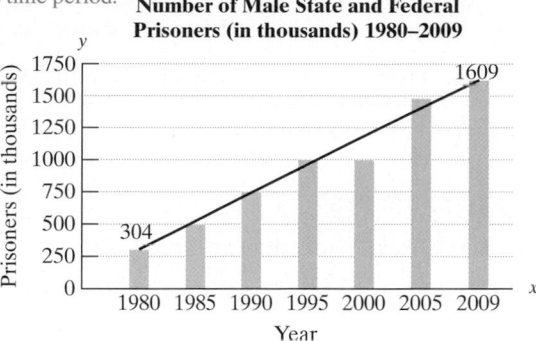

Number of Male State and Federal Prisoners (in thousands) 1980–2009

(*Source:* U.S. Bureau of Justice Statistics)

76. In the year 1980, there were 12 thousand female inmates in federal and state prisons. By 2009, the number increased to 128 thousand. Let x represent the year, and let y represent the number of prisoners (in thousands).

   a. Using the ordered pairs (1980, 12) and (2009, 128), find the slope of the line. $m = 4$

   b. Interpret the slope in the context of this problem.
The number of female prisoners increased at a rate of 4 thousand per year during this time period.

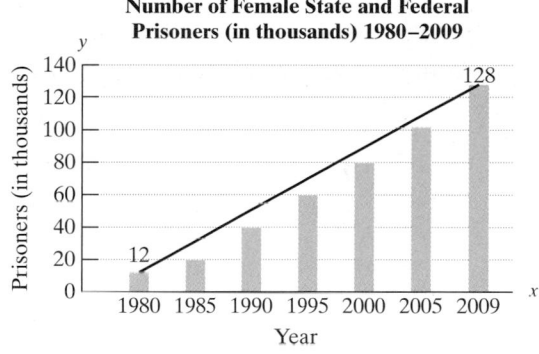

Number of Female State and Federal Prisoners (in thousands) 1980–2009

(*Source:* U.S. Bureau of Justice Statistics)

77. The distance, d (in miles), between a lightning strike and an observer is given by the equation $d = 0.2t$, where t is the time (in seconds) between seeing lightning and hearing thunder.

Distance Between Lightning Strike and an Observer

$d = 0.2t$

   a. If an observer counts 5 sec between seeing lightning and hearing thunder, how far away was the lightning strike?   1 mi

   b. If an observer counts 10 sec between seeing lightning and hearing thunder, how far away was the lightning strike?   2 mi

   c. If an observer counts 15 sec between seeing lightning and hearing thunder, how far away was the lightning strike?   3 mi

   d. What is the slope of the line? Interpret the meaning of the slope in the context of this problem. $m = 0.2$; The distance between a lightning strike and an observer increases by 0.2 mi for every additional second between seeing lightning and hearing thunder.

 Writing   Translating Expression   Geometry   Scientific Calculator   Video   NS&E

78. Michael wants to buy an efficient Smart car that according to the latest EPA standards gets 33 mpg in the city and 40 mpg on the highway. The car that Michael picked out costs $12,600. His dad agreed to purchase the car if Michael would pay it off in equal monthly payments for the next 60 months. The equation $y = -210x + 12{,}600$ represents the amount, y (in dollars), that Michael owes his father after x months.

    a. How much does Michael owe his dad after 5 months?
    Michael owes $11,550 after 5 months.
    b. Determine the slope of the line and interpret its meaning in the context of this problem.
    $m = -210$; The amount Michael owes his father decreases by $210 per month.

Mixed Exercises

For Exercises 79–82, determine the slope of the line passing through points A and B.

79. Point A is located 3 units up and 4 units to the right of point B. $m = \dfrac{3}{4}$

80. Point A is located 2 units up and 5 units to the left of point B. $m = -\dfrac{2}{5}$

81. Point A is located 5 units to the right of point B. $m = 0$

82. Point A is located 3 units down from point B.   The slope is undefined.

83. Graph the line through the point $(1, -2)$ having slope $\frac{2}{3}$. Then give two other points on the line.

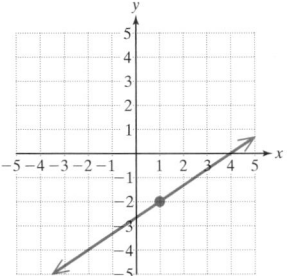

For example: $(4, 0)$ and $(-2, -4)$

84. Graph the line through the point $(-2, -3)$ having slope $\frac{3}{4}$. Then give two other points on the line.

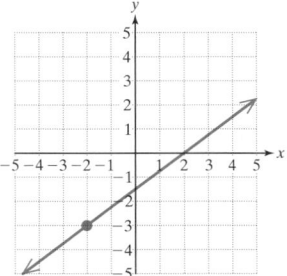

For example: $(2, 0)$ and $(-6, -6)$

85. Graph the line through the point $(2, 2)$ having slope -3. Then give two other points on the line.

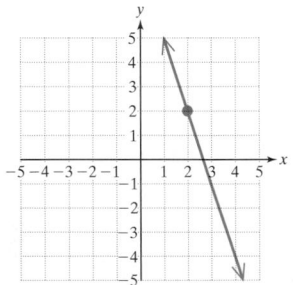

For example: $(3, -1)$ and $(1, 5)$

86. Graph the line through the point $(-1, 3)$ having slope -2. Then give two other points on the line.

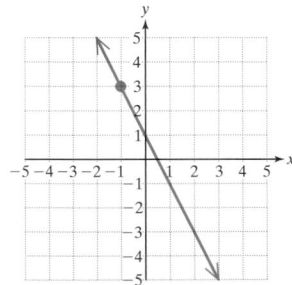

For example: $(0, 1)$ and $(-2, 5)$

For Exercises 87–92, draw a line as indicated. Answers may vary.

87. Draw a line with a positive slope and a positive *y*-intercept.

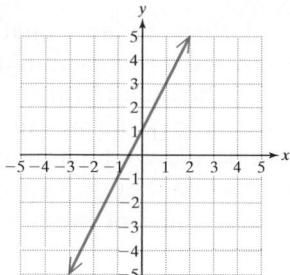

88. Draw a line with a positive slope and a negative *y*-intercept.

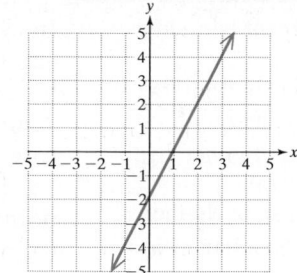

89. Draw a line with a negative slope and a negative *y*-intercept.

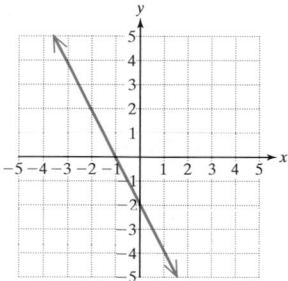

90. Draw a line with a negative slope and positive *y*-intercept.

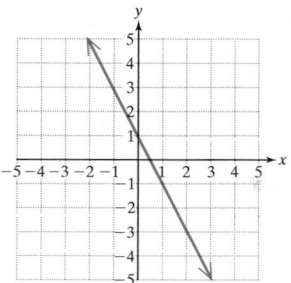

91. Draw a line with a zero slope and a positive *y*-intercept.

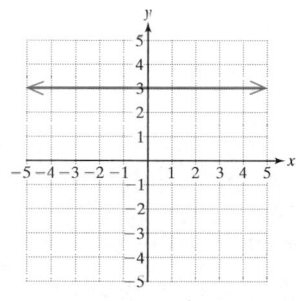

92. Draw a line with undefined slope and a negative *x*-intercept.

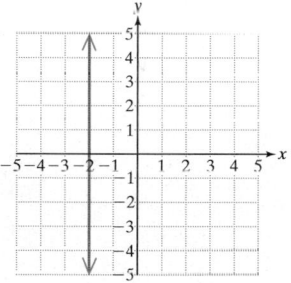

Expanding Your Skills

93. Determine the slope between the points $(a + b, 4m - n)$ and $(a - b, m + 2n)$. $\dfrac{3m - 3n}{2b}$ or $\dfrac{-3m + 3n}{-2b}$

94. Determine the slope between the points $(3c - d, s + t)$ and $(c - 2d, s - t)$. $\dfrac{2t}{2c + d}$ or $\dfrac{-2t}{-2c - d}$

95. Determine the *x*-intercept of the line $ax + by = c$. $\left(\dfrac{c}{a}, 0\right)$

96. Determine the *y*-intercept of the line $ax + by = c$. $\left(0, \dfrac{c}{b}\right)$

97. Find another point on the line that contains the point $(2, -1)$ and has a slope of $\frac{2}{5}$.   For example: $(7, 1)$

98. Find another point on the line that contains the point $(-3, 4)$ and has a slope of $\frac{1}{4}$.   For example: $(1, 5)$

Section 3.4 **Slope-Intercept Form of a Line**

Concepts

1. Slope-Intercept Form of a Line
2. Graphing a Line from Its Slope and y-Intercept
3. Determining Whether Two Lines Are Parallel, Perpendicular, or Neither
4. Writing an Equation of a Line Using Slope-Intercept Form

Section 3.4 | Slope-Intercept Form of a Line

1. Slope-Intercept Form of a Line

In Section 3.2, we learned that the solutions to an equation of the form $Ax + By = C$ (where A and B are not both zero) represent a line in a rectangular coordinate system. An equation of a line written in this way is said to be in **standard form**. In this section, we will learn a new form, called **slope-intercept form**, which is useful in determining the slope and y-intercept of a line.

Let $(0, b)$ represent the y-intercept of a line. Let (x, y) represent any other point on the line. See Figure 3-26. Then the slope of the line can be found as follows:

Let $(0, b)$ represent (x_1, y_1), and let (x, y) represent (x_2, y_2). Apply the slope formula.

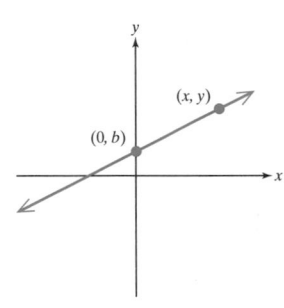

Figure 3-26

$$m = \frac{(y_2 - y_1)}{(x_2 - x_1)} \rightarrow m = \frac{y - b}{x - 0}$$ Apply the slope formula.

$$m = \frac{y - b}{x}$$ Simplify.

$$mx = \left(\frac{y - b}{x}\right)x$$ Multiply by x to clear fractions.

$$mx = y - b$$

$$mx + b = y - b + b$$ To isolate y, add b to both sides.

$$mx + b = y \quad \text{or} \quad y = mx + b$$ The equation is in slope-intercept form.

DEFINITION **Slope-Intercept Form of a Line**

$y = mx + b$ is the slope-intercept form of a line.

m is the slope and the point $(0, b)$ is the y-intercept.

Classroom Examples: p. 234, Exercises 12 and 16

Example 1 **Identifying the Slope and y-Intercept of a Line**

For each equation, identify the slope and y-intercept.

a. $y = 3x - 1$ **b.** $y = -2.7x + 5$ **c.** $y = 4x$

Solution:

Each equation is written in slope-intercept form, $y = mx + b$. The slope is the coefficient of x, and the y-intercept is determined by the constant term.

a. $y = 3x - 1$ The slope is 3. The y-intercept is $(0, -1)$.

b. $y = -2.7x + 5$ The slope is -2.7. The y-intercept is $(0, 5)$.

c. $y = 4x$ can be written as $y = 4x + 0$. The slope is 4. The y-intercept is $(0, 0)$.

Skill Practice Identify the slope and the y-intercept.

1. $y = 4x + 6$ **2.** $y = 3.5x - 4.2$ **3.** $y = -7$

Answers

1. slope: 4; y-intercept: $(0, 6)$
2. slope: 3.5; y-intercept: $(0, -4.2)$
3. slope: 0; y-intercept: $(0, -7)$

Given the equation of a line, we can write the equation in slope-intercept form by solving the equation for the y-variable. This is demonstrated in Example 2.

Example 2   Identifying the Slope and y-Intercept of a Line

Classroom Example: p. 234, Exercise 22

Given the equation of the line $-5x - 2y = 6$,

a. Write the equation in slope-intercept form.

b. Identify the slope and y-intercept.

Solution:

a. Write the equation in slope-intercept form, $y = mx + b$, by solving for y.

$$-5x - 2y = 6$$

$$-2y = 5x + 6 \qquad \text{Add } 5x \text{ to both sides.}$$

$$\frac{-2y}{-2} = \frac{5x + 6}{-2} \qquad \text{Divide both sides by } -2.$$

$$y = \frac{5x}{-2} + \frac{6}{-2} \qquad \text{Divide each term by } -2 \text{ and simplify.}$$

$$y = -\frac{5}{2}x - 3 \qquad \text{Slope-intercept form}$$

b. The slope is $-\frac{5}{2}$, and the y-intercept is $(0, -3)$.

Skill Practice Given the equation of the line $2x - 6y = -3$.

4. Write the equation in slope-intercept form.

5. Identify the slope and the y-intercept.

2. Graphing a Line from Its Slope and y-Intercept

Slope-intercept form is a useful tool to graph a line. The y-intercept is a known point on the line. The slope indicates the direction of the line and can be used to find a second point. Using slope-intercept form to graph a line is demonstrated in the next example.

Example 3   Graphing a Line Using the Slope and y-Intercept

Classroom Example: p. 236, Exercise 42

Graph the equation of the line $y = -\frac{5}{2}x - 3$ by using the slope and y-intercept.

Solution:

First plot the y-intercept, $(0, -3)$.

The slope $m = -\frac{5}{2}$ can be written as

$$m = \frac{-5}{2} \quad \begin{array}{l} \longleftarrow \text{The change in } y \text{ is } -5. \\ \longleftarrow \text{The change in } x \text{ is } 2. \end{array}$$

To find a second point on the line, start at the y-intercept and move down 5 units and to the right 2 units. Then draw the line through the two points (Figure 3-27).

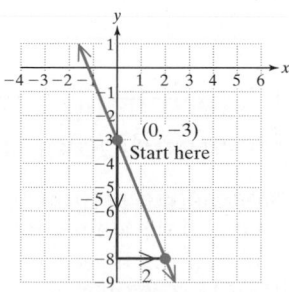

Figure 3-27

Answers

4. $y = \frac{1}{3}x + \frac{1}{2}$

5. slope is $\frac{1}{3}$; y-intercept is $\left(0, \frac{1}{2}\right)$

Similarly, the slope can be written as

$$m = \frac{5}{-2}$$ ⟵ The change in y is 5.
⟵ The change in x is -2.

To find a second point, start at the y-intercept and move up 5 units and to the left 2 units. Then draw the line through the two points (Figure 3-28).

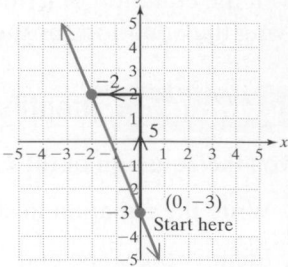

Figure 3-28

Skill Practice

6. Graph the equation by using the slope and the y-intercept. $\quad y = 2x - 3$

Classroom Example: p. 236, Exercise 50

Example 4 **Graphing a Line Using the Slope and y-Intercept**

Graph the equation of the line $y = 4x$ by using the slope and y-intercept.

Solution:

The line can be written as $y = 4x + 0$. Therefore, we can plot the y-intercept at $(0, 0)$. The slope $m = 4$ can be written as

$$m = \frac{4}{1}$$ ⟵ The change in y is 4.
⟵ The change in x is 1.

To find a second point on the line, start at the y-intercept and move up 4 units and to the right 1 unit. Then draw the line through the two points (Figure 3-29).

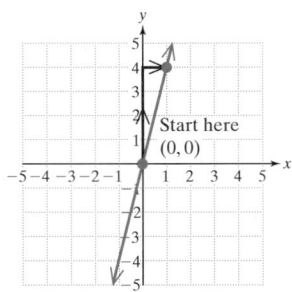

Figure 3-29

Skill Practice

7. Graph the equation by using the slope and the y-intercept. $\quad y = -\dfrac{1}{4}x$

Answers

6–7.

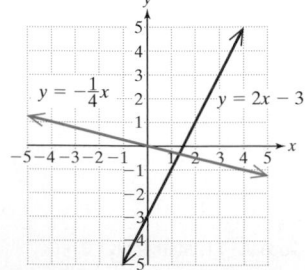

3. Determining Whether Two Lines Are Parallel, Perpendicular, or Neither

The slope-intercept form provides a means to find the slope of a line by inspection. Recall that if the slopes of two lines are known, then we can compare the slopes to determine if the lines are parallel, perpendicular, or neither parallel nor perpendicular. (Two distinct nonvertical lines are parallel if their slopes are equal. Two lines are perpendicular if the slope of one line is the opposite of the reciprocal of the slope of the other line.)

Example 5 Determining If Two Lines Are Parallel, Perpendicular, or Neither

Classroom Examples: p. 236, Exercises 54 and 56

For each pair of lines, determine if they are parallel, perpendicular, or neither.

a. l_1: $y = 3x - 5$ **b.** l_1: $y = \frac{3}{2}x + 2$

l_2: $y = 3x + 1$ l_2: $y = \frac{2}{3}x + 1$

Solution:

a. l_1: $y = 3x - 5$ The slope of l_1 is 3.

l_2: $y = 3x + 1$ The slope of l_2 is 3.

Because the slopes are the same, the lines are parallel.

b. l_1: $y = \frac{3}{2}x + 2$ The slope of l_1 is $\frac{3}{2}$.

l_2: $y = \frac{2}{3}x + 1$ The slope of l_2 is $\frac{2}{3}$.

The slopes are not the same. Therefore, the lines are not parallel. The values of the slopes are reciprocals, but they are not opposite in sign. Therefore, the lines are not perpendicular. The lines are neither parallel nor perpendicular.

Skill Practice For each pair of lines determine if they are parallel, perpendicular, or neither.

8. $y = 3x - 5$ **9.** $y = \dfrac{5}{6}x - \dfrac{1}{2}$

    $y = -3x - 15$ $y = \dfrac{5}{6}x + \dfrac{1}{2}$

Example 6 Determining if Two Lines Are Parallel, Perpendicular, or Neither

Classroom Examples: p. 236, Exercises 62 and 64

For each pair of lines, determine if they are parallel, perpendicular, or neither.

a. l_1: $x - 3y = -9$ **b.** l_1: $x = 2$

l_2: $3x = -y + 4$ l_2: $2y = 8$

Solution:

a. First write the equation of each line in slope-intercept form.

l_1: $x - 3y = -9$ l_2: $3x = -y + 4$

     $-3y = -x - 9$ $3x + y = 4$

     $\dfrac{-3y}{-3} = \dfrac{-x}{-3} - \dfrac{9}{-3}$ $y = -3x + 4$

         $y = \dfrac{1}{3}x + 3$

l_1: $y = \frac{1}{3}x + 3$ The slope of l_1 is $\frac{1}{3}$.

l_2: $y = -3x + 4$ The slope of l_2 is -3.

The slope of $\frac{1}{3}$ is the opposite of the reciprocal of -3. Therefore, the lines are perpendicular.

Answers

8. Neither   **9.** Parallel

b. The equation $x = 2$ represents a vertical line because the equation is in the form $x = k$.

The equation $2y = 8$ can be simplified to $y = 4$, which represents a horizontal line.

In this example, we do not need to analyze the slopes because vertical lines and horizontal lines are perpendicular.

Skill Practice For each pair of lines, determine if they are parallel, perpendicular, or neither.

10. $x - 5y = 10$ **11.** $y = -5$
     $5x - 1 = -y$ $x = 6$

4. Writing an Equation of a Line Using Slope-Intercept Form

The slope-intercept form of a line can be used to write an equation of a line when the slope is known and the y-intercept is known.

Classroom Example: p. 237, Exercise 70

Example 7 **Writing an Equation of a Line Using Slope-Intercept Form**

Write an equation of the line whose slope is $\frac{2}{3}$ and whose y-intercept is $(0, 8)$.

Solution:

The slope is given as $m = \frac{2}{3}$, and the y-intercept $(0, b)$ is given as $(0, 8)$. Substitute the values $m = \frac{2}{3}$ and $b = 8$ into the slope-intercept form of a line.

$$y = mx + b$$
$$y = \frac{2}{3}x + 8$$

Skill Practice

12. Write an equation of the line whose slope is -4 and y-intercept is $(0, -10)$.

Classroom Example: p. 237, Exercise 74

Example 8 **Writing an Equation of a Line Using Slope-Intercept Form**

Write an equation of the line having a slope of 2 and passing through the point $(-3, 1)$.

Solution:

To find an equation of a line using slope-intercept form, it is necessary to find the values of m and b. The slope is given in the problem as $m = 2$. Therefore, the slope-intercept form becomes

$$y = mx + b$$
$$y = 2x + b$$

Answers

10. Perpendicular   **11.** Perpendicular
12. $y = -4x - 10$

Because the point $(-3, 1)$ is on the line, it is a solution to the equation. Therefore, to find b, substitute the values of x and y from the ordered pair $(-3, 1)$ and solve the resulting equation.

$$y = 2x + b$$

$$1 = 2(-3) + b \qquad \text{Substitute } y = 1 \text{ and } x = -3.$$

$$1 = -6 + b \qquad \text{Simplify and solve for } b.$$

$$7 = b$$

Now with m and b known, the slope-intercept form is $y = 2x + 7$.

TIP: The equation from Example 8 can be checked by graphing the line $y = 2x + 7$. The slope $m = 2$ can be written as $m = \frac{2}{1}$. Therefore, to graph the line, start at the y-intercept $(0, 7)$ and move up 2 units and to the right 1 unit.

The graph verifies that the line passes through the point $(-3, 1)$ as it should.

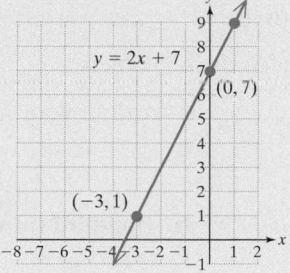

Skill Practice

13. Write an equation of the line having a slope of -3 and passing through the point $(-2, -5)$.

Answer

13. $y = -3x - 11$

Calculator Connections

Topic: Using the *ZSquare* Option in Zoom

In Example 6(a) we found that the equations $y = \frac{1}{3}x + 3$ and $y = -3x + 4$ represent perpendicular lines. We can verify our results by graphing the lines on a graphing calculator.

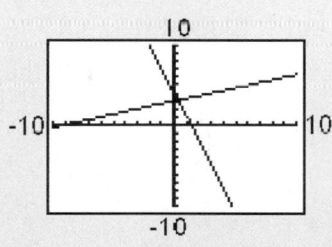

Notice that the lines do not appear perpendicular in the calculator display. That is, they do not appear to form a right angle at the point of intersection. Because many calculators have a rectangular screen, the standard viewing window is elongated in the horizontal direction. To eliminate this distortion, try using a *ZSquare* option, which is located under the Zoom menu. This feature will set the viewing window so that equal distances on the display denote an equal number of units on the graph.

Calculator Exercises

For each pair of lines, determine if the lines are parallel, perpendicular, or neither. Then use a square viewing window to graph the lines on a graphing calculator to verify your results.

1. $x + y = 1$
$x - y = -3$ Perpendicular

2. $3x + y = -2$
$6x + 2y = 6$ Parallel

3. $2x - y = 4$
$3x + 2y = 4$ Neither

4. Graph the lines defined by $y = x + 1$ and $y = 0.99x + 3$. Are these lines parallel? Explain.
The lines may appear parallel; however, they are not parallel because the slopes are different.

5. Graph the lines defined by $y = -2x - 1$ and $y = -2x - 0.99$. Are these lines the same? Explain.
The lines may appear to coincide on a graph; however, they are not the same line because the y-intercepts are different.

6. Graph the line defined by $y = 0.001x + 3$. Is this line horizontal? Explain.
The line may appear to be horizontal, but it is not. The slope is 0.001 rather than 0.

Section 3.4 Practice Exercises

Boost *your* GRADE at ALEKS.com!

 ALEKS version 3.0

- Practice Problems
- Self-Tests
- NetTutor
- e-Professors
- Videos

For additional exercises, see Classroom Activities 3.4A–3.4C in the *Instructor's Resource Manual* at www.mhhe.com/moh.

Study Skills Exercises

1. When taking a test, go through the test and do all the problems that you know first. Then go back and work on the problems that were more difficult. Give yourself a time limit for how much time you spend on each problem (maybe 3 to 5 min the first time through). Circle the importance of each statement.

	not important	somewhat important	very important
a. Read through the entire test first.	1	2	3
b. If time allows, go back and check each problem.	1	2	3
c. Write out all steps instead of doing the work in your head.	1	2	3

2. Define the key terms.

   a. **slope-intercept form of a line**   b. **standard form of a line**

Review Exercises

For Exercises 3–10, determine the *x*- and *y*-intercepts, if they exist.

3. $x - 5y = 10$
   x-intercept: $(10, 0)$;
   y-intercept: $(0, -2)$

4. $3x + y = -12$
   x-intercept: $(-4, 0)$;
   y-intercept: $(0, -12)$

5. $3y = -9$
   x-intercept: none;
   y-intercept: $(0, -3)$

6. $2 + y = 5$
   x-intercept: none;
   y-intercept: $(0, 3)$

7. $-4x = 6y$
   x-intercept: $(0, 0)$;
   y-intercept: $(0, 0)$

8. $-x + 3 = 8$
   x-intercept: $(-5, 0)$;
   y-intercept: none

9. $5x = 20$
   x-intercept: $(4, 0)$;
   y-intercept: none

10. $y = \frac{1}{2}x$
    x-intercept: $(0, 0)$;
    y-intercept: $(0, 0)$

Concept 1: Slope-Intercept Form of a Line

For Exercises 11–30, identify the slope and *y*-intercept, if they exist. **(See Examples 1–2.)**

11. $y = -2x + 3$
    $m = -2$; *y*-intercept: $(0, 3)$

12. $y = \frac{2}{3}x + 5$
    $m = \frac{2}{3}$; *y*-intercept: $(0, 5)$

13. $y = x - 2$
    $m = 1$; *y*-intercept: $(0, -2)$

14. $y = -x + 6$
    $m = -1$; *y*-intercept: $(0, 6)$

15. $y = -x$
    $m = -1$; *y*-intercept: $(0, 0)$

16. $y = -5x$
    $m = -5$; *y*-intercept: $(0, 0)$

17. $y = \frac{3}{4}x - 1$
    $m = \frac{3}{4}$; *y*-intercept: $(0, -1)$

18. $y = x - \frac{5}{3}$
    $m = 1$; *y*-intercept: $\left(0, -\frac{5}{3}\right)$

19. $2x - 5y = 4$
    $m = \frac{2}{5}$; *y*-intercept: $\left(0, -\frac{4}{5}\right)$

20. $3x + 2y = 9$
    $m = -\frac{3}{2}$; *y*-intercept: $\left(0, \frac{9}{2}\right)$

21. $3x - y = 5$
    $m = 3$; *y*-intercept: $(0, -5)$

22. $7x - 3y = -6$
    $m = \frac{7}{3}$; *y*-intercept: $(0, 2)$

23. $x + y = 6$
    $m = -1$; *y*-intercept: $(0, 6)$

24. $x - y = 1$
    $m = 1$; *y*-intercept: $(0, -1)$

25. $x + 6 = 8$
    Undefined slope; no *y*-intercept

26. $-4 + x = 1$
    Undefined slope; no *y*-intercept

27. $-8y = 2$
    $m = 0$; *y*-intercept: $\left(0, -\frac{1}{4}\right)$

28. $1 - y = 9$
    $m = 0$; *y*-intercept: $(0, -8)$

29. $3y - 2x = 0$
    $m = \frac{2}{3}$; *y*-intercept: $(0, 0)$

30. $5x = 6y$
    $m = \frac{5}{6}$; *y*-intercept: $(0, 0)$

Concept 2: Graphing a Line from Its Slope and *y*-Intercept

For Exercises 31–34, graph the line using the slope and *y*-intercept. **(See Examples 3–4.)**

31. Graph the line through the point $(0, 2)$, having a slope of -4.

32. Graph the line through the point $(0, -1)$, having a slope of -3.

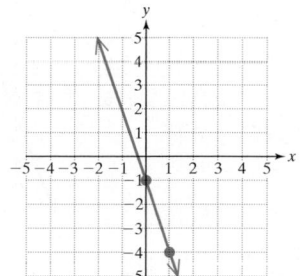

33. Graph the line through the point $(0, -5)$, having a slope of $\frac{3}{2}$.

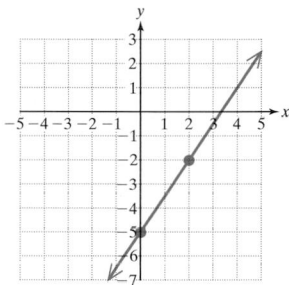

34. Graph the line through the point $(0, 3)$, having a slope of $-\frac{1}{4}$.

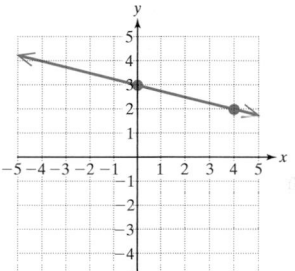

For Exercises 35–40, match the equation with the graph (a–f) by identifying if the slope is positive or negative and if the *y*-intercept is positive, negative, or zero.

35. $y = 2x + 3$ b

36. $y = -3x - 2$ d

37. $y = -\frac{1}{3}x + 3$ e

38. $y = \frac{1}{2}x - 2$ a

39. $y = x$ c

40. $y = -2x$ f

a.

b.

c.

d.

e.

f.

 Writing   Translating Expression   Geometry   Scientific Calculator   Video   NS&E

For Exercises 41–52, write each equation in slope-intercept form (if possible) and graph the line. **(See Examples 3–4.)**

41. $x - 2y = 6$
$y = \frac{1}{2}x - 3$

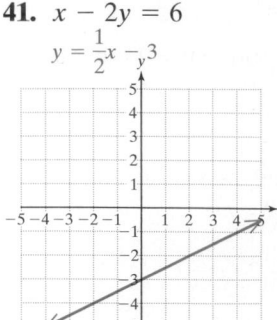

42. $5x - 2y = 2$
$y = \frac{5}{2}x - 1$

43. $2x + y = 9$
$y = -2x + 9$

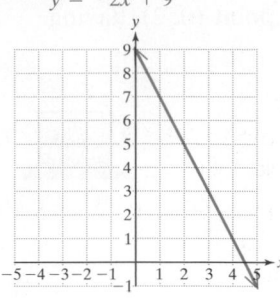

44. $-6x + y = 8$
$y = 6x + 8$

45. $2x = -4y + 6$
$y = -\frac{1}{2}x + \frac{3}{2}$

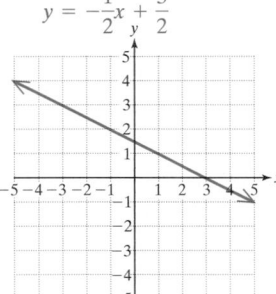

46. $3x = y - 7$
$y = 3x + 7$

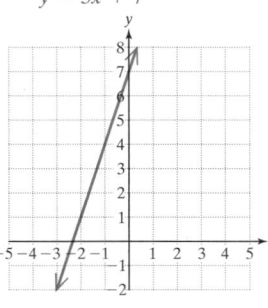

47. $x + y = 0$
$y = -x$

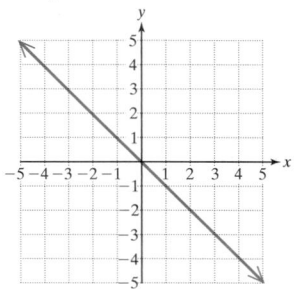

48. $x - y = 0$
$y = x$

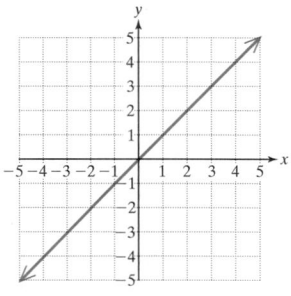

49. $5y = 4x$
$y = \frac{4}{5}x$

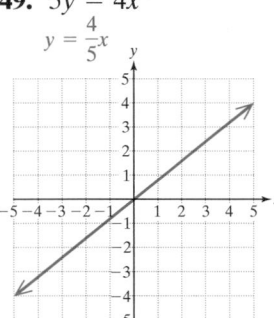

50. $-2x = 5y$
$y = -\frac{2}{5}x$

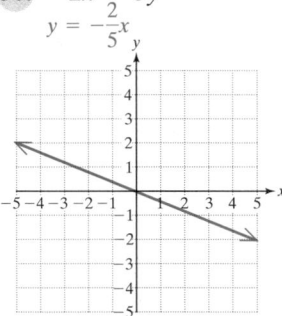

51. $3y + 2 = 0$
$y = -\frac{2}{3}$

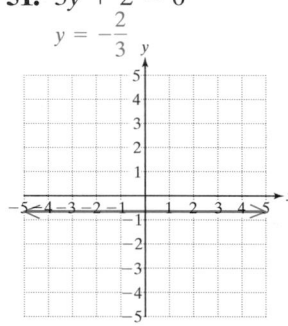

52. $1 + 5y = 6$
$y = 1$

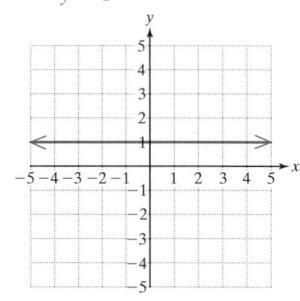

Concept 3: Determining Whether Two Lines Are Parallel, Perpendicular, or Neither

For Exercises 53–68, determine if the equations represent parallel lines, perpendicular lines, or neither.
(See Examples 5–6.)

53. l_1: $y = -2x - 3$

  l_2: $y = \frac{1}{2}x + 4$
  Perpendicular

54. l_1: $y = \frac{4}{3}x - 2$

  l_2: $y = -\frac{3}{4}x + 6$
  Perpendicular

55. l_1: $y = \frac{4}{5}x - \frac{1}{2}$

  l_2: $y = \frac{5}{4}x - \frac{2}{3}$
  Neither

56. l_1: $y = \frac{1}{5}x + 1$

  l_2: $y = 5x - 3$
  Neither

57. l_1: $y = -9x + 6$

  l_2: $y = -9x - 1$
  Parallel

58. l_1: $y = 4x - 1$

  l_2: $y = 4x + \frac{1}{2}$
  Parallel

59. l_1: $x = 3$

  l_2: $y = \frac{7}{4}$
  Perpendicular

60. l_1: $y = \frac{2}{3}$

  l_2: $x = 6$
  Perpendicular

61. l_1: $2x = 4$

  l_2: $6 = x$
  Parallel

62. l_1: $2y = 7$

  l_2: $y = 4$
  Parallel

63. l_1: $2x + 3y = 6$

  l_2: $3x - 2y = 12$
  Perpendicular

64. l_1: $4x + 5y = 20$

  l_2: $5x - 4y = 60$
  Perpendicular

 Writing   Translating Expression   Geometry   Scientific Calculator   Video   NS&E

65. l_1: $4x + 2y = 6$ **66.** l_1: $3x + y = 5$ **67.** l_1: $y = \dfrac{1}{5}x - 3$ **68.** l_1: $y = \dfrac{1}{3}x + 2$

l_2: $4x + 8y = 16$ l_2: $x + 3y = 18$ l_2: $2x - 10y = 20$ l_2: $-x + 3y = 12$
Neither   Neither   Parallel   Parallel

Concept 4: Writing an Equation of a Line Using Slope-Intercept Form

For Exercises 69–80, write an equation of the line given the following information. Write the answer in slope-intercept form if possible. **(See Examples 7–8.)**

69. The slope is $-\frac{1}{3}$, and the y-intercept is $(0, 2)$.
$y = -\dfrac{1}{3}x + 2$

70. The slope is $\frac{2}{3}$, and the y-intercept is $(0, -1)$.
$y = \dfrac{2}{3}x - 1$

71. The slope is 10, and the y-intercept is $(0, -19)$.
$y = 10x - 19$

72. The slope is -14, and the y-intercept is $(0, 2)$.
$y = -14x + 2$

73. The slope is 6, and the line passes through the point $(1, -2)$. $y = 6x - 8$

74. The slope is -4, and the line passes through the point $(4, -3)$. $y = -4x + 13$

75. The slope is $\frac{1}{2}$, and the line passes through the point $(-4, -5)$. $y = \dfrac{1}{2}x - 3$

76. The slope is $-\frac{2}{3}$, and the line passes through the point $(3, -1)$. $y = -\dfrac{2}{3}x + 1$

77. The slope is 0, and the y-intercept is -11.
$y = -11$

78. The slope is 0, and the y-intercept is $\dfrac{6}{7}$. $y = \dfrac{6}{7}$

79. The slope is 5, and the line passes through the origin. $y = 5x$

80. The slope is -3, and the line passes through the origin. $y = -3x$

Expanding Your Skills

81. The number of reported cases of Lyme disease in the United States can be modeled by the equation $y = 1203x + 10{,}006$. In this equation, x represents the number of years since 1993, and y represents the number of cases of Lyme disease.

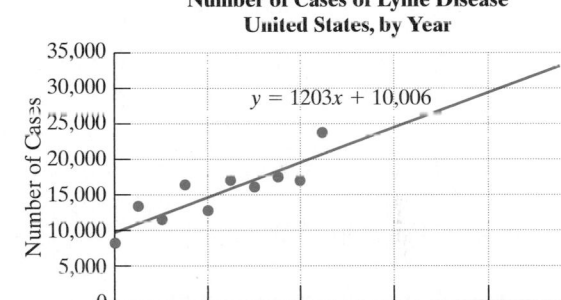

Number of Cases of Lyme Disease United States, by Year

a. What is the slope of this line and what does it mean in the context of this problem? $m = 1203$; The slope represents the rate of increase in cases of Lyme disease per year.

b. What is the y-intercept, and what does it mean in the context of this problem?
$(0, 10{,}006)$; In the year 1993 there were 10,006 cases reported.

c. Use the model to estimate the number of cases of Lyme disease in the year 2010. $1203(17) + 10{,}006 = 30{,}457$ cases

d. During what year would the predicted number of cases be 28,051? $x = 15$; the year 2008

82. A phone bill is determined each month by a $16.95 flat fee plus $0.10/min of long distance. The equation $C = 0.10x + 16.95$ represents the total monthly cost, C, for x minutes of long distance.

Phone Bill Cost Versus Number of Minutes of Long Distance

a. Identify the slope. Interpret the meaning of the slope in the context of this problem.
$m = 0.10$. The cost increases by $0.10/min of long distance.

b. Identify the C-intercept. Interpret the meaning of the C-intercept in the context of this problem.
$(0, 16.95)$. The monthly bill for 0 min is $16.95.

c. Use the equation to determine the total cost of 234 min of long distance.   The cost is $40.35

 Writing   Translating Expression   Geometry   Scientific Calculator   Video   NS&E

83. A linear equation is written in standard form if it can be written as $Ax + By = C$, where A and B are not both zero. Write the equation $Ax + By = C$ in slope-intercept form to show that the slope is given by the ratio, $-\frac{A}{B}$. ($B \neq 0$.) $y = -\frac{A}{B}x + \frac{C}{B}$; the slope is $-\frac{A}{B}$.

For Exercises 84–87, use the result of Exercise 83 to find the slope of the line.

84. $2x + 5y = 8$ $m = -\frac{2}{5}$ **85.** $6x + 7y = -9$ $m = -\frac{6}{7}$ **86.** $4x - 3y = -5$ $m = \frac{4}{3}$ **87.** $11x - 8y = 4$ $m = \frac{11}{8}$

Problem Recognition Exercises

Linear Equations in Two Variables

For Exercises 1–20, choose the equation(s) from the column on the right whose graph satisfies the condition described. Give all possible answers.

1. Line whose slope is positive.   a, c, d

2. Line whose slope is negative.   b, f, h

3. Line that passes through the origin.   a

4. Line that contains the point $(3, -2)$.   f

5. Line whose y-intercept is $(0, 4)$.   b, f

6. Line whose y-intercept is $(0, -5)$.   c

7. Line whose slope is $\frac{1}{2}$.   c, d

8. Line whose slope is -2.   f

9. Line whose slope is 0.   e

10. Line whose slope is undefined.   g

11. Line that is parallel to the line with equation $y = -\frac{2}{3}x + 4$.   b

12. Line perpendicular to the line with equation $y = 2x + 9$.   h

13. Line that is vertical.   g

14. Line that is horizontal.   e

15. Line whose x-intercept is $(10, 0)$.   c

16. Line whose x-intercept is $(6, 0)$.   b, h

17. Line that is parallel to the x-axis.   e

18. Line that is perpendicular to the y-axis.   e

19. Line with a negative slope and positive y-intercept.   b, f, h

20. Line with a positive slope and negative y-intercept.   c, d

a. $y = 5x$

b. $2x + 3y = 12$

c. $y = \frac{1}{2}x - 5$

d. $3x - 6y = 10$

e. $2y = -8$

f. $y = -2x + 4$

g. $3x = 1$

h. $x + 2y = 6$

 Writing   Translating Expression   Geometry   Scientific Calculator   Video   NS&E

Point-Slope Formula

1. Writing an Equation of a Line Using the Point-Slope Formula

In Section 3.4, the slope-intercept form of a line was used as a tool to construct an equation of a line. Another useful tool to determine an equation of a line is the point-slope formula. The point-slope formula can be derived from the slope formula as follows:

Suppose a line passes through a given point (x_1, y_1) and has slope m. If (x, y) is any other point on the line, then:

$$m = \frac{y - y_1}{x - x_1}$$ Slope formula

$$m(x - x_1) = \frac{y - y_1}{x - x_1}(x - x_1)$$ Clear fractions.

$$m(x - x_1) = y - y_1$$

$$y - y_1 = m(x - x_1)$$ Point-slope formula

Concepts

1. Writing an Equation of a Line Using the Point-Slope Formula
2. Writing an Equation of a Line Given Two Points
3. Writing an Equation of a Line Parallel or Perpendicular to Another Line
4. Different Forms of Linear Equations: A Summary

FORMULA Point-Slope Formula

The **point-slope formula** is given by

$$y - y_1 = m(x - x_1)$$

where m is the slope of the line and (x_1, y_1) is a known point on the line.

Example 1 demonstrates how to use the point-slope formula to find an equation of a line when a point on the line and slope are given.

Example 1 Writing an Equation of a Line Using the Point-Slope Formula

Use the point-slope formula to write an equation of the line having a slope of 3 and passing through the point $(-2, -4)$. Write the answer in slope-intercept form.

Solution:

The slope of the line is given: $m = 3$

A point on the line is given: $(x_1, y_1) = (-2, -4)$

The point-slope formula:

$y - y_1 = m(x - x_1)$

$y - (-4) = 3[x - (-2)]$ Substitute $m = 3$, $x_1 = -2$, and $y_1 = -4$.

$y + 4 = 3(x + 2)$ Simplify. Because the final answer is required in slope-intercept form, simplify the equation and solve for y.

$y + 4 = 3x + 6$ Apply the distributive property.

$y = 3x + 2$ Slope-intercept form

Classroom Example: p. 244, Exercise 12

Instructor Note: Show students an alternative method.
$y = mx + b$ replace m, x, y
$-4 = 3(-2) + b$
$-4 = -6 + b$
$2 = b$

$y = mx + b$ replace m, b
$y = 3x + 2$

Skill Practice

1. Use the point-slope formula to write an equation of the line having a slope of -4 and passing through $(-1, 5)$. Write the answer in slope-intercept form.

Answer

1. $y = -4x + 1$

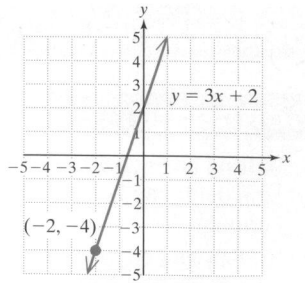

Figure 3-30

Classroom Example: p. 244, Exercise 20

The equation $y = 3x + 2$ from Example 1 is graphed in Figure 3-30. Notice that the line does indeed pass through the point $(-2, -4)$.

2. Writing an Equation of a Line Given Two Points

Example 2 is similar to Example 1; however, the slope must first be determined from two given points.

Example 2   Writing an Equation of a Line Given Two Points

Use the point-slope formula to find an equation of the line passing through the points $(-2, 5)$ and $(4, -1)$. Write the final answer in slope-intercept form.

Solution:

Given two points on a line, the slope can be determined by using the slope formula.

$$\begin{array}{ccc} (-2, 5) & \text{and} & (4, -1) \\ (x_1, y_1) & & (x_2, y_2) \end{array} \qquad \text{Label the points.}$$

$$m = \frac{y_2 - y_1}{x_2 - x_1} = \frac{(-1) - (5)}{(4) - (-2)} = \frac{-6}{6} = -1$$

To apply the point-slope formula, use the slope, $m = -1$ and either given point. We will choose the point $(-2, 5)$ as (x_1, y_1).

$$y - y_1 = m(x - x_1)$$

$$y - 5 = -1[x - (-2)] \qquad \text{Substitute } m = -1, x_1 = -2, \text{ and } y_1 = 5.$$

$$y - 5 - -1(x + 2) \qquad \text{Simplify.}$$

$$y - 5 = -x - 2$$

$$y = -x + 3$$

TIP: The point-slope formula can be applied using either given point for (x_1, y_1). In Example 2, using the point $(4, -1)$ for (x_1, y_1) produces the same result.

$$y - y_1 = m(x - x_1)$$

$$y - (-1) = -1(x - 4)$$

$$y + 1 = -x + 4$$

$$y = -x + 3$$

Skill Practice

2. Use the point-slope formula to write an equation of the line passing through the points $(1, -1)$ and $(-1, -5)$.

The solution to Example 2 can be checked by graphing the line $y = -x + 3$ using the slope and y-intercept. Notice that the line passes through the points $(-2, 5)$ and $(4, -1)$ as expected. See Figure 3-31.

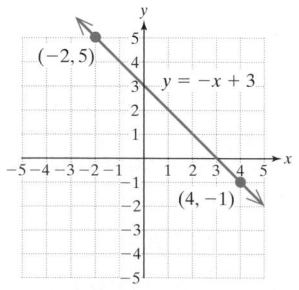

Figure 3-31

Answer

2. $y = 2x - 3$

3. Writing an Equation of a Line Parallel or Perpendicular to Another Line

Example 3 Writing an Equation of a Line Parallel to Another Line

Classroom Example: p. 245, Exercise 30

Use the point-slope formula to find an equation of the line passing through the point $(-1, 0)$ and parallel to the line $y = -4x + 3$. Write the final answer in slope-intercept form.

Solution:

Figure 3-32 shows the line $y = -4x + 3$ (pictured in black) and a line parallel to it (pictured in blue) that passes through the point $(-1, 0)$. The equation of the given line, $y = -4x + 3$, is written in slope-intercept form, and its slope is easily identified as -4. The line parallel to the given line must also have a slope of -4.

Apply the point-slope formula using $m = -4$ and the point $(x_1, y_1) = (-1, 0)$.

$$y - y_1 = m(x - x_1)$$
$$y - 0 = -4[x - (-1)]$$
$$y = -4(x + 1)$$
$$y = -4x - 4$$

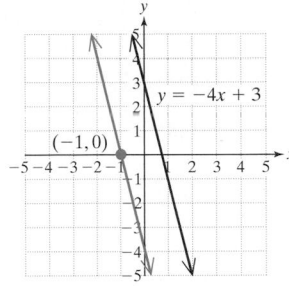

Figure 3-32

> **TIP:** When writing an equation of a line, slope-intercept form or standard form is usually preferred. For instance, the solution to Example 3 can be written as follows.
>
> Slope-intercept form:
> $y = -4x - 4$
>
> Standard form:
> $4x + y = -4$

Skill Practice

3. Use the point-slope formula to write an equation of the line passing through $(8, 2)$ and parallel to the line $y = \frac{3}{4}x - \frac{1}{2}$.

Example 4 Writing an Equation of a Line Perpendicular to Another Line

Classroom Example: p. 245, Exercise 34

Use the point-slope formula to find an equation of the line passing through the point $(-3, 1)$ and perpendicular to the line $3x + y = -2$. Write the final answer in slope-intercept form.

Solution:

The given line can be written in slope-intercept form as $y = -3x - 2$. The slope of this line is -3. Therefore, the slope of a line perpendicular to the given line is $\frac{1}{3}$.

Apply the point-slope formula with $m = \frac{1}{3}$, and $(x_1, y_1) = (-3, 1)$.

$y - y_1 = m(x - x_1)$	Point-slope formula
$y - (1) = \frac{1}{3}[x - (-3)]$	Substitute $m = \frac{1}{3}$, $x_1 = -3$, and $y_1 = 1$.
$y - 1 = \frac{1}{3}(x + 3)$	To write the final answer in slope-intercept form, simplify the equation and solve for y.
$y - 1 = \frac{1}{3}x + 1$	Apply the distributive property.
$y = \frac{1}{3}x + 2$	Add 1 to both sides.

Answer

3. $y = \dfrac{3}{4}x - 4$

A sketch of the perpendicular lines $y = \frac{1}{3}x + 2$ and $y = -3x - 2$ is shown in Figure 3-33. Notice that the line $y = \frac{1}{3}x + 2$ passes through the point $(-3, 1)$.

Figure 3-33

Skill Practice

4. Write an equation of the line passing through the point $(10, 4)$ and perpendicular to the line $x + 2y = 1$.

4. Different Forms of Linear Equations: A Summary

A linear equation can be written in several different forms, as summarized in Table 3-3.

Table 3-3

Form	Example	Comments
Standard Form $Ax + By = C$	$4x + 2y = 8$	A and B must not both be zero.
Horizontal Line $y = k$ (k is constant)	$y = 4$	The slope is zero, and the y-intercept is $(0, k)$.
Vertical Line $x = k$ (k is constant)	$x = -1$	The slope is undefined, and the x-intercept is $(k, 0)$.
Slope-Intercept Form $y = mx + b$ the slope is m y-intercept is $(0, b)$	$y = -3x + 7$ Slope $= -3$ y-intercept is $(0, 7)$	Solving a linear equation for y results in slope-intercept form. The coefficient of the x-term is the slope, and the constant defines the location of the y-intercept.
Point-Slope Formula $y - y_1 = m(x - x_1)$	$m = -3$ $(x_1, y_1) = (4, 2)$ $y - 2 = -3(x - 4)$	This formula is typically used to build an equation of a line when a point on the line is known and the slope of the line is known.

Although standard form and slope-intercept form can be used to express an equation of a line, often the slope-intercept form is used to give a *unique* representation of the line. For example, the following linear equations are all written in standard form, yet they each define the same line.

$$2x + 5y = 10$$

$$-4x - 10y = -20$$

$$6x + 15y = 30$$

$$\frac{2}{5}x + y = 2$$

The line can be written uniquely in slope-intercept form as: $y = -\frac{2}{5}x + 2$.

Although it is important to understand and apply slope-intercept form and the point-slope formula, they are not necessarily applicable to all problems, particularly when dealing with a horizontal or vertical line.

Answer

4. $y = 2x - 16$

Example 5 Writing an Equation of a Line

Classroom Example: p. 246, Exercise 48

Find an equation of the line passing through the point $(2, -4)$ and parallel to the x-axis.

Solution:

Because the line is parallel to the x-axis, the line must be horizontal. Recall that all horizontal lines can be written in the form $y = k$, where k is a constant. A quick sketch can help find the value of the constant. See Figure 3-34.

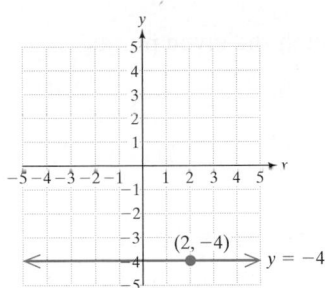

Figure 3-34

Because the line must pass through a point whose y-coordinate is -4, then the equation of the line must be $y = -4$.

Skill Practice

5. Write an equation for the vertical line that passes through the point $(-7, 2)$.

Answer

5. $x = -7$

Section 3.5 Practice Exercises

Study Skills Exercises

1. Prepare a one-page summary sheet with the most important information that you need for the test. On the day of the test, look at this sheet several times to refresh your memory instead of trying to memorize new information.

2. Define the key term **point-slope formula**.

Review Exercises

For Exercises 3–6, graph each equation.

3. $2x - 3y = -3$

4. $y = -2x$

 Writing   Translating Expression   Geometry   Scientific Calculator   Video   NS&E

5. $3 - y = 9$

6. $y = \dfrac{4}{5}x$

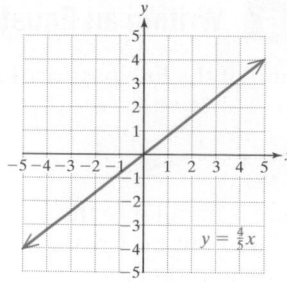

For Exercises 7–10, find the slope of the line that passes through the given points.

7. $(1, -3)$ and $(2, 6)$ 9

8. $(2, -4)$ and $(-2, 4)$ −2

9. $(-2, 5)$ and $(5, 5)$ 0

10. $(6.1, 2.5)$ and $(6.1, -1.5)$ Undefined

Concept 1: Writing an Equation of a Line Using the Point-Slope Formula

For Exercises 11–16, use the point-slope formula (if possible) to write an equation of the line given the following information. **(See Example 1.)**

11. The slope is 3, and the line passes through the point $(-2, 1)$.
$y = 3x + 7$ or $3x - y = -7$

12. The slope is -2, and the line passes through the point $(1, -5)$.
$y = -2x - 3$ or $2x + y = -3$

13. The slope is -4, and the line passes through the point $(-3, -2)$.
$y = -4x - 14$ or $4x + y = -14$

14. The slope is 5, and the line passes through the point $(-1, -3)$.
$y = 5x + 2$ or $5x - y = -2$

15. The slope is $-\frac{1}{2}$, and the line passes through $(-1, 0)$.
$y = -\dfrac{1}{2}x - \dfrac{1}{2}$ or $x + 2y = -1$

16. The slope is $-\frac{3}{4}$, and the line passes through $(2, 0)$.
$y = -\dfrac{3}{4}x + \dfrac{3}{2}$ or $3x + 4y = 6$

Concept 2: Writing an Equation of a Line Given Two Points

For Exercises 17–22, use the point-slope formula to write an equation of the line given the following information. **(See Example 2.)**

17. The line passes through the points $(-2, -6)$ and $(1, 0)$. $y = 2x - 2$ or $2x - y = 2$

18. The line passes through the points $(-2, 5)$ and $(0, 1)$. $y = -2x + 1$ or $2x + y = 1$

19. The line passes through the points $(0, -4)$ and $(-1, -3)$. $y = -x - 4$ or $x + y = -4$

20. The line passes through the points $(1, -3)$ and $(-7, 2)$. $y = -\dfrac{5}{8}x - \dfrac{19}{8}$ or $5x + 8y = -19$

21. The line passes through the points $(2.2, -3.3)$ and $(12.2, -5.3)$.
$y = -0.2x - 2.86$ or $20x + 100y = -286$

22. The line passes through the points $(4.7, -2.2)$ and $(-0.3, 6.8)$.
$y = -1.8x + 6.26$ or $180x + 100y = 626$

For Exercises 23–28, find an equation of the line through the given points. Write the final answer in slope-intercept form.

23.

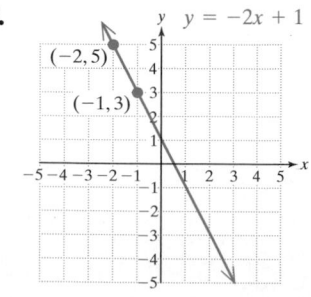

$y = -2x + 1$

24.

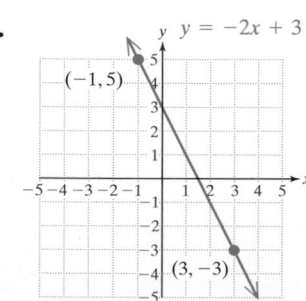

$y = -2x + 3$

25.

$y = 2x + 4$

26.

27.

28.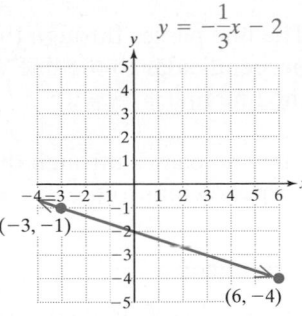

Concept 3: Writing an Equation of a Line Parallel or Perpendicular to Another Line

For Exercises 29–36, use the point-slope formula to write an equation of the line given the following information. **(See Examples 3–4.)**

29. The line passes through the point $(-3, 1)$ and is parallel to the line $y = 4x + 3$.
$y = 4x + 13$ or $4x - y = -13$

30. The line passes through the point $(1, -1)$ and is parallel to the line $y = 3x + 1$.
$y = 3x - 13$ or $3x - y = 13$

31. The line passes through the point $(4, 0)$ and is parallel to the line $3x + 2y = 8$. $y = -\dfrac{3}{2}x + 6$ or $3x + 2y = 12$

32. The line passes through the point $(2, 0)$ and is parallel to the line $5x + 3y = 6$. $y = -\dfrac{5}{3}x + \dfrac{10}{3}$ or $5x + 3y = 10$

33. The line passes through the point $(-5, 2)$ and is perpendicular to the line $y = \frac{1}{2}x + 3$.
$y = -2x - 8$ or $2x + y = -8$

34. The line passes through the point $(-2, -2)$ and is perpendicular to the line $y = \frac{1}{3}x - 5$.
$y = -3x - 8$ or $3x + y = -8$

35. The line passes through the point $(0, -6)$ and is perpendicular to the line $-5x + y = 4$.
$y = -\dfrac{1}{5}x - 6$ or $x + 5y = -30$

36. The line passes through the point $(0, -8)$ and is perpendicular to the line $2x - y = 5$.
$y = -\dfrac{1}{2}x - 8$ or $x + 2y = -16$

Concept 4: Different Forms of Linear Equations: A Summary

For Exercises 37–42, match the form or formula on the left with its name on the right.

37. $x = k$ iv

38. $y = mx + b$ v

39. $m = \dfrac{y_2 - y_1}{x_2 - x_1}$ vi

40. $y - y_1 = m(x - x_1)$ ii

41. $y = k$ iii

42. $Ax + By = C$ i

i.   Standard form

ii.   Point-slope formula

iii.   Horizontal line

iv.   Vertical line

v.   Slope-intercept form

vi.   Slope formula

For Exercises 43–48, find an equation for the line given the following information. **(See Example 5.)**

43. The line passes through the point $(3, 1)$ and is parallel to the line $y = -4$.
See the figure.
$y = 1$

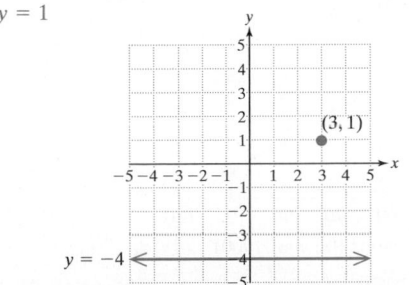

44. The line passes through the point $(-1, 1)$ and is parallel to the line $y = 2$.
See the figure.
$y = 1$

 Writing   Translating Expression   Geometry   Scientific Calculator   Video   NS&E

45. The line passes through the point $(2, 6)$ and is perpendicular to the line $y = 1$. (*Hint:* Sketch the line first.) $x = 2$

46. The line passes through the point $(0, 3)$ and is perpendicular to the line $y = -5$. (*Hint:* Sketch the line first.) $x = 0$

47. The line passes through the point $(2, 2)$ and is perpendicular to the line $x = 0$. $y = 2$

48. The line passes through the point $(5, -2)$ and is perpendicular to the line $x = 0$. $y = -2$

Mixed Exercises

For Exercises 49–60, write an equation of the line given the following information.

49. The slope is $\frac{1}{4}$, and the line passes through the point $(-8, 6)$. $y = \frac{1}{4}x + 8$ or $x - 4y = -32$

50. The slope is $\frac{2}{5}$, and the line passes through the point $(-5, 4)$. $y = \frac{2}{5}x + 6$ or $2x - 5y = -30$

51. The line passes through the point $(4, 4)$ and is parallel to the line $3x - y = 6$.
$y = 3x - 8$ or $3x - y = 8$

52. The line passes through the point $(-1, -7)$ and is parallel to the line $5x + y = -5$.
$y = -5x - 12$ or $5x + y = -12$

53. The slope is 4.5, and the line passes through the point $(5.2, -2.2)$. $y = 4.5x - 25.6$ or $45x - 10y = 256$

54. The slope is -3.6, and the line passes through the point $(10.0, 8.2)$. $y = -3.6x + 44.2$ or $36x + 10y = 442$

55. The slope is undefined, and the line passes through the point $(-6, -3)$. $x = -6$

56. The slope is undefined, and the line passes through the point $(2, -1)$. $x = 2$

57. The slope is 0, and the line passes through the point $(3, -2)$. $y = -2$

58. The slope is 0, and the line passes through the point $(0, 5)$. $y = 5$

59. The line passes through the points $(-4, 0)$ and $(-4, 3)$. $x = -4$

60. The line passes through the points $(1, 3)$ and $(1, -4)$. $x = 1$

| Section 3.6 | Applications of Linear Equations and Modeling |

Concepts

1. Interpreting a Linear Equation in Two Variables
2. Writing a Linear Model Using Observed Data Points
3. Writing a Linear Model Given a Fixed Value and a Rate of Change

Classroom Example: p. 251, Exercise 10

1. Interpreting a Linear Equation in Two Variables

Linear equations can often be used to describe (or model) the relationship between two variables in a real-world event.

Example 1   Interpreting a Linear Equation

From 1900 to 2005, the number of tigers in India decreased. This decrease can be approximated by the equation $y = -350x + 42,000$. The variable y represents the number of tigers left in India, and x represents the number of years since 1900.

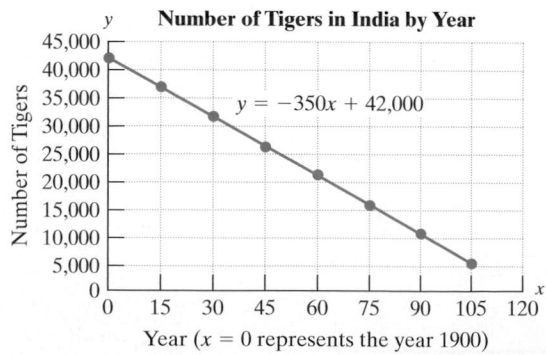

Number of Tigers in India by Year

Year ($x = 0$ represents the year 1900)

a. Use the equation to predict the number of tigers in 1960.

b. Use the equation to predict the number of tigers in 2010.

c. Determine the slope of the line. Interpret the meaning of the slope in terms of the number of tigers and the year.

d. Determine the x-intercept. Interpret the meaning of the x-intercept in terms of the number of tigers.

Solution:

a. The year 1960 is 60 yr since 1900. Substitute $x = 60$ into the equation.

$$y = -350x + 42{,}000$$

$$y = -350(60) + 42{,}000$$

$$-21{,}000 \qquad \text{There were approximately 21,000 tigers in India in 1960.}$$

b. The year 2010 is 110 yr since 1900. Substitute $x = 110$.

$$y = -350(110) + 42{,}000$$

$$= 3500 \qquad \text{There will be approximately 3500 tigers in India in 2010.}$$

c. The slope is -350. $\qquad$ The slope means that the tiger population is decreasing by 350 tigers per year.

d. To find the x-intercept, substitute $y = 0$.

$$y = -350x + 42{,}000$$

$$0 = -350x + 42{,}000 \qquad \text{Substitute 0 for } y.$$

$$-42{,}000 = -350x$$

$$120 = x$$

The x-intercept is $(120, 0)$. This means that 120 yr after the year 1900, the tiger population would be expected to reach zero. That is, in the year 2020, there will be no tigers left in India if this linear trend continues.

Skill Practice

1. The cost y (in dollars) for a local move by a small moving company is given by $y = 60x + 100$, where x is the number of hours required for the move.

a. How much would be charged for a move that required 3 hr?

b. How much would be charged for a move that required 8 hr?

c. What is the slope of the line and what does it mean in the context of this problem?

d. Determine the y-intercept and interpret its meaning in the context of this problem.

Answers

1. a. $280 **b.** $580

c. 60; This means that for each additional hour of service, the cost of the move goes up by $60.

d. (0, 100); The $100 charge is a fixed fee in addition to the hourly rate.

2. Writing a Linear Model Using Observed Data Points

Example 2 Writing a Linear Model from Observed Data Points

The monthly sales of hybrid cars sold in the United States are given for a recent year. The sales for the first 8 months of the year are shown in Figure 3-35. The value $x = 0$ represents January, $x = 1$ represents February, and so on.

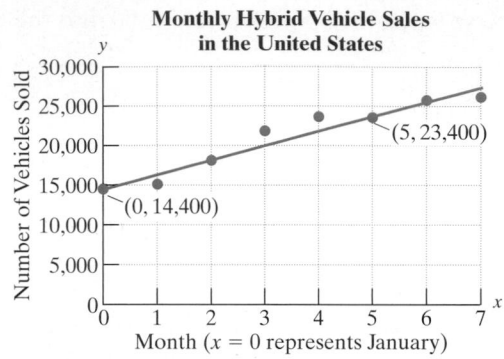

Figure 3-35

a. Use the data points from Figure 3-35 to find a linear equation that represents the monthly sales of hybrid cars in the United States. Let x represent the month number and let y represent the number of vehicles sold.

b. Use the linear equation in part (a) to estimate the number of hybrid vehicles sold in month 7 (August).

Solution:

a. The ordered pairs $(0, 14{,}400)$ and $(5, 23{,}400)$ are given in the graph. Use these points to find the slope.

$$\underset{(x_1, y_1)}{(0, 14{,}400)} \quad \text{and} \quad \underset{(x_2, y_2)}{(5, 23{,}400)} \qquad \text{Label the points.}$$

$$m = \frac{y_2 - y_1}{x_2 - x_1} = \frac{23{,}400 - 14{,}400}{5 - 0}$$

$$= \frac{9000}{5}$$

$$= 1800 \qquad \qquad \text{The slope is 1800. This indicates that sales increased by approximately 1800 per month during this time period.}$$

With $m = 1800$, and the y-intercept given as $(0, 14{,}400)$, we have the following linear equation in slope-intercept form.

$$y = 1800x + 14{,}400$$

b. To approximate the sales in month number 7, substitute $x = 7$ into the equation from part (a).

$$y = 1800(7) + 14{,}400 \qquad \qquad \text{Substitute } x = 7.$$

$$= 27{,}000$$

The monthly sales for August (month 7) would be 27,000 vehicles.

Skill Practice

2. Soft drink sales at a concession stand at a softball stadium have increased linearly over the course of the summer softball season.

   a. Use the given data points to find a linear equation that relates the sales, y, to week number, x.

   b. Use the equation to predict the number of soft drinks sold in week 10.

3. Writing a Linear Model Given a Fixed Value and a Rate of Change

Another way to look at the equation $y = mx + b$ is to identify the term mx as the variable term and the term b as the constant term. The value of the term mx will change with the value of x (this is why the slope, m, is called a *rate of change*). However, the term b will remain constant regardless of the value of x. With these ideas in mind, we can write a linear equation if the rate of change and the constant are known.

Example 3 **Writing a Linear Model** ————

Classroom Example: p. 253, Exercise 20

A stack of posters to advertise a production by the theater department costs $19.95 plus $1.50 per poster at the printer.

a. Write a linear equation to compute the cost, c, of buying x posters.

b. Use the equation to compute the cost of 125 posters.

Solution:

a. The constant cost is $19.95. The variable cost is $1.50 per poster. If m is replaced with 1.50 and b is replaced with 19.95, the equation is

   $$c = 1.50x + 19.95 \qquad \text{where } c \text{ is the cost (in dollars) of buying } x \text{ posters.}$$

b. Because x represents the number of posters, substitute $x = 125$.

   $$c = 1.50(125) + 19.95$$
   $$= 187.5 + 19.95$$
   $$= 207.45$$

The total cost of buying 125 posters is $207.45.

Skill Practice

3. The monthly cost for a "minimum use" cellular phone is $19.95 plus $0.10 per minute for all calls.

   a. Write a linear equation to compute the cost, c, of using t minutes.

   b. Use the equation to determine the cost of using 150 minutes.

Calculator Connections

Topic: Using the Evaluate Feature on a Graphing Calculator

In Example 3, the equation $c = 1.50x + 19.95$ was used to represent the cost, c, to buy x posters. To graph this equation on a graphing calculator, first replace the variable c by y.

$$y = 1.50x + 19.95$$

We enter the equation into the calculator and set the viewing window.

To evaluate the equation for a user-defined value of x, use the *Value* feature in the CALC menu. In this case, we entered $x = 125$, and the calculator returned $y = 207.45$.

Calculator Exercises

Use a graphing calculator to graph the lines on an appropriate viewing window. Evaluate the equation at the given values of x.

1. $y = -4.6x + 27.1$ at $x = 3$ 13.3

2. $y = -3.6x - 42.3$ at $x = 0$ −42.3

3. $y = 40x + 105$ at $x = 6$ 345

4. $y = 20x - 65$ at $x = 8$ 95

Section 3.6   Practice Exercises

Boost *your* GRADE at ALEKS.com!

ALEKS version 3.0

- Practice Problems
- Self-Tests
- NetTutor
- e-Professors
- Videos

For additional exercises, see Classroom Activities 3.6A–3.6C in the *Instructor's Resource Manual* at www.mhhe.com/moh.

Study Skills Exercise

1. On test day, take a look at any formulas or important points that you had to memorize before you enter the classroom. Then when you sit down to take your test, write these formulas on the test or on scrap paper. This is called a memory dump. Write down the formulas from Chapter 3.

Review Exercises

2. Determine the slope of the line defined by $2x - 8y = 15$. $m = \dfrac{1}{4}$

For Exercises 3–8, find the x- and y-intercepts of the lines, if possible.

3. $5x + 6y = 30$ x-intercept: $(6, 0)$;
   y-intercept: $(0, 5)$

4. $3x + 4y = 1$ x-intercept: $(\frac{1}{3}, 0)$;
   y-intercept: $(0, \frac{1}{4})$

5. $y = -2x - 4$ x-intercept: $(-2, 0)$;
   y-intercept: $(0, -4)$

6. $y = 5x$ x-intercept: $(0, 0)$;
   y-intercept: $(0, 0)$

7. $y = -9$ x-intercept: none;
   y-intercept: $(0, -9)$

8. $x = 2$ x-intercept: $(2, 0)$;
   y-intercept: none

 Writing   Translating Expression   Geometry   Scientific Calculator   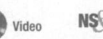 Video   NS E

Concept 1: Interpreting a Linear Equation in Two Variables

9. The minimum hourly wage, y (in dollars per hour), in the United States can be approximated by the equation $y = 0.14x + 1.60$. In this equation, x represents the number of years since 1970 ($x = 0$ represents 1970, $x = 5$ represents 1975, and so on). **(See Example 1.)**

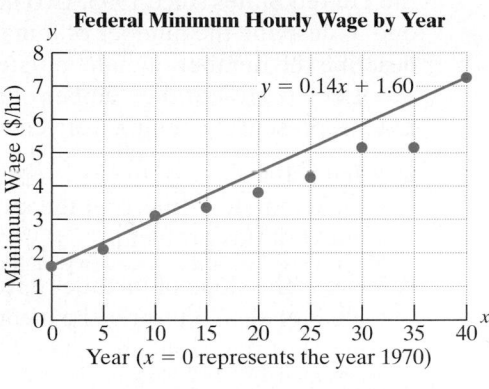

Federal Minimum Hourly Wage by Year

 a. Use the equation to approximate the minimum wage in the year 1980. $3.00

 b. Use the equation to predict the minimum wage in 2010. $7.20

 c. Determine the y-intercept. Interpret the meaning of the y-intercept in the context of this problem. The y-intercept is $(0, 1.6)$. This indicates that the minimum wage was $1.60 per hour in the year 1970.

 d. Determine the slope. Interpret the meaning of the slope in the context of this problem. The slope is 0.14. This indicates that the minimum wage has risen approximately $0.14 per year during this period.

10. The average daily temperature in January for cities along the eastern seaboard of the United States and Canada generally decreases for cities farther north. A city's latitude in the northern hemisphere is a measure of how far north it is on the globe.

The average temperature, y (measured in degrees Fahrenheit), can be described by the equation

$$y = -2.333x + 124.0 \quad \text{where } x \text{ is the latitude of the city.}$$

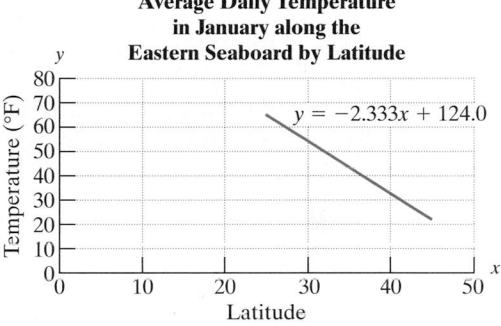

Average Daily Temperature in January along the Eastern Seaboard by Latitude

(*Source:* U.S. National Oceanic and Atmospheric Administration)

 a. Use the equation to predict the average daily temperature in January for Philadelphia, Pennsylvania, whose latitude is 40.0°N. Round to one decimal place. 30.7°

 b. Use the equation to predict the average daily temperature in January for Edmundston, New Brunswick, Canada, whose latitude is 47.4°N. Round to one decimal place. 13.4°

 c. What is the slope of the line? Interpret the meaning of the slope in terms of latitude and temperature. $m = -2.333$. The average temperature in January decreases at a rate of 2.333° per 1° of latitude.

 d. From the equation, determine the value of the x-intercept. Round to one decimal place. Interpret the meaning of the x-intercept in terms of latitude and temperature. $(53.2, 0)$. At 53.2° latitude, the average temperature in January is 0°.

11. Veterinarians keep records of the weights of animals that are brought in for examination. Grindel, the cat, weighed 42 oz when she was 70 days old. She weighed 46 oz when she was 84 days old. Her sister, Frisco weighed 40 oz when she was 70 days old and 48 oz at 84 days old.

Weight vs Age

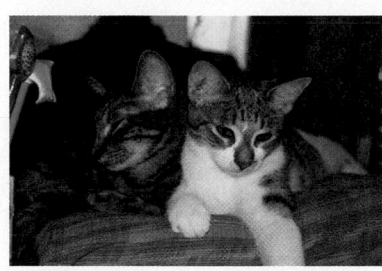

 a. Compute the slope of the line representing Grindel's weight. $m = \frac{2}{7}$

 b. Compute the slope of the line representing Frisco's weight. $m = \frac{4}{7}$

 c. Interpret the meaning of each slope in the context of this problem. $m = \frac{2}{7}$ means that Grindel's weight increased at a rate of 2 oz in 7 days. $m = \frac{4}{7}$ means that Frisco's weight increased at a rate of 4 oz in 7 days.

 d. Which cat gained weight more rapidly during this time period? Frisco gained weight more rapidly.

 Writing   Translating Expression   Geometry   Scientific Calculator   Video   NS&E

12. The graph depicts the rise in the number of jail inmates in the United States since 1995. Two linear equations are given: one to describe the number of female inmates and one to describe the number of male inmates by year.

Let y represent the number of inmates (in thousands). Let x represent the number of years since 1995.

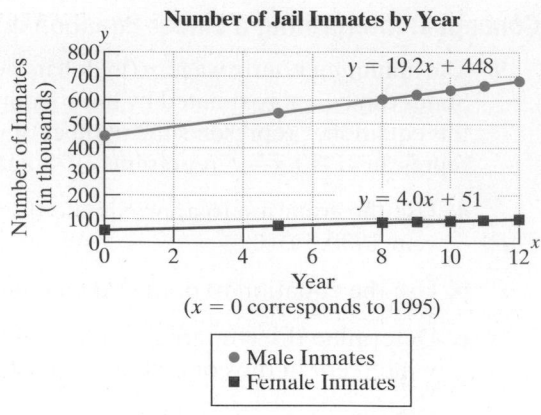

Number of Jail Inmates by Year

$y = 19.2x + 448$

$y = 4.0x + 51$

Year
($x = 0$ corresponds to 1995)

● Male Inmates
■ Female Inmates

(*Source:* U.S. Bureau of Justice Statistics)

a. What is the slope of the line representing the number of female inmates? Interpret the meaning of the slope in the context of this problem. $m = 4$. The number of female inmates has increased by 4 thousand per year since 1995.

b. What is the slope of the line representing the number of male inmates? Interpret the meaning of the slope in the context of this problem. $m = 19.2$. The number of male inmates has increased by 19.2 thousand per year since 1995.

c. Which group, males or females, has the larger slope? What does this imply about the rise in the number of male and female prisoners?   Males. The number of male inmates is increasing at a faster rate than the number of female inmates.

d. Assuming this trend continues, use the equation to predict the number of female inmates in 2015.
131 thousand or 131,000

13. The electric bill charge for a certain utility company is $0.095 per kilowatt-hour plus a fixed monthly tax of $11.95. The total cost, y, depends on the number of kilowatt-hours, x, according to the equation $y = 0.095x + 11.95$, $x \geq 0$.

a. Determine the cost of using 1000 kilowatt-hours. $106.95

b. Determine the cost of using 2000 kilowatt-hours. $201.95

c. Determine the y-intercept. Interpret the meaning of the y-intercept in the context of this problem.
(0, 11.95). For 0 kilowatt-hours used, the cost consists of only the fixed monthly tax of $11.95.

d. Determine the slope. Interpret the meaning of the slope in the context of this problem.
$m = 0.095$. The cost increases at a rate of $0.095 for each kilowatt-hour used.

14. For a recent year, children's admission to the Minnesota State Fair was $8. Ride tickets were $0.75 each. The equation $y = 0.75x + 8$ represented the cost, y, in dollars to be admitted to the fair and to purchase x ride tickets.

a. Determine the slope of the line represented by $y = 0.75x + 8$. Interpret the meaning of the slope in the context of this problem.
$m = 0.75$; The slope means that the cost increases at a rate of 75¢ per ride.

b. Determine the y-intercept. Interpret its meaning in the context of this problem.
(0, 8); The cost was $8 if 0 rides were purchased.

c. Use the equation to determine how much money a child needed for admission and to ride 10 rides.
$15.50

Concept 2: Writing a Linear Model Using Observed Data Points

15. Meteorologists often measure the intensity of a tropical storm or hurricane by the maximum sustained wind speed and the minimum pressure. The relationship between these two quantities is approximately linear. Hurricane Katrina had a maximum sustained wind speed of 150 knots and a minimum pressure of 902 mb (millibars). Hurricane Ophelia had maximum sustained winds of 75 knots and a pressure of 976 mb. **(See Example 2.)**

Pressure vs. Wind Speed

(75, 976)

(150, 902)

Wind Speed (knots)

a. Find the slope of the line between these two points. Round to one decimal place. $m = -1.0$

b. Using the slope found in part (a) and the point (75, 976), find a linear model that represents the minimum pressure of a hurricane, y, versus its maximum sustained wind speed, x. $y = -x + 1051$

c. Hurricane Dennis had a maximum wind speed of 130 knots. Using the equation you found in part (b), predict the minimum pressure.   The minimum pressure was approximately 921 mb.

 Writing   Translating Expression   Geometry   Scientific Calculator   ● Video   NS&E

16. The figure depicts a relationship between a person's height, y (in inches), and the length of the person's arm, x (measured in inches from shoulder to wrist).

a. Use the points $(17, 57.75)$ and $(24, 82.25)$ to find a linear equation relating height to arm length.
$y = 3.5x - 1.75$

b. What is the slope of the line? Interpret the slope in the context of this problem. $m = 3.5$. For each additional inch in length of a person's arm, the person's height increases by 3.5 in.

c. Use the equation from part (a) to estimate the height of a person whose arm length is 21.5 in.
73.5 in. or 6 ft $1\frac{1}{2}$ in.

Height Versus Arm Length

Height (inches) vs Arm Length (inches); points $(24, 82.25)$ and $(17, 57.75)$

17. Wind energy is one type of renewable energy that does not produce dangerous greenhouse gases as a by-product. The graph shows the consumption of wind energy in the United States for selected years. The variable y represents the amount of wind energy in trillions of Btu, and the variable x represents the number of years since 2000.

a. Use the points $(0, 57)$ and $(4, 143)$ to determine the slope of the line. $m = 21.5$
The slope means that the consumption of wind energy in the
b. Interpret the slope in the context of this problem?
United States increased by 21.5 trillion Btu per year.
c. Use the points $(0, 57)$ and $(4, 143)$ to find a linear equation relating the consumption of wind energy, y, to the number of years, x, since 2000. $y = 21.5x + 57$

d. If this linear trend continues beyond the observed data values, use the equation in part (c) to predict the consumption of wind energy in the year 2010. 272 trillion Btu

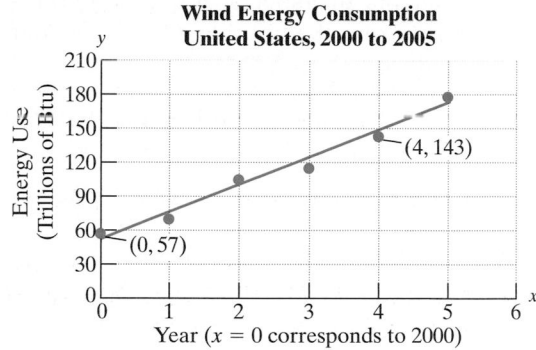

Wind Energy Consumption United States, 2000 to 2005

Energy Use (Trillions of Btu) vs Year ($x = 0$ corresponds to 2000); points $(0, 57)$ and $(4, 143)$

(*Source:* United States Department of Energy)

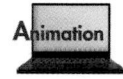

18. The graph shows the average height for boys based on age. Let x represent a boy's age, and let y represent his height (in inches).

a. Find a linear equation that represents the height of a boy versus his age. $y = 2.5x + 31$

b. Use the linear equation found in part (a) to predict the average height of a 5-year-old boy. 43.5 in.

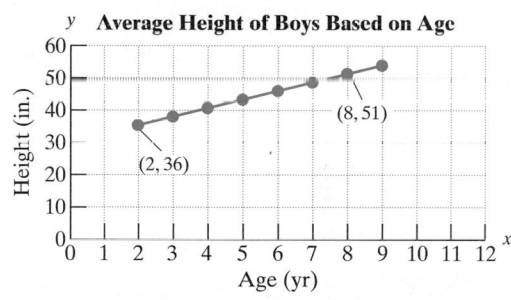

Average Height of Boys Based on Age

Height (in.) vs Age (yr); points $(2, 36)$ and $(8, 51)$

(*Source:* National Parenting Council)

Concept 3: Writing a Linear Model Given a Fixed Value and a Rate of Change

19. Andrés has a cell phone plan with AT&T Wireless. His bill is determined each month by a $39.99 flat fee plus $0.20 for each text message sent or received. **(See Example 3.)**

a. Write a linear model to compute the monthly cost, y, of Andrés' cell phone bill if x text messages are sent or received. $y = 0.20x + 39.99$

b. Use the equation to compute Andrés' cell phone bill for a month in which he sent or received a total of 40 text messages. $47.99

20. Anabel lives in New York and likes to keep in touch with her family in Texas. She uses 10-10-987 to call them. The cost of a long distance call is $0.53 plus $0.06 per minute.

a. Write an equation that represents the cost, C, of a long distance call that is x minutes long. $C = 0.06x + 0.53$

b. Use the equation to compute the cost of a long distance phone call that lasted 32 minutes. $2.45

 Writing   Translating Expression   Geometry   Scientific Calculator   Video   NS&E

21. The cost to rent a 10 ft by 10 ft storage space is $90 per month plus a nonrefundable deposit of $105.

   a. Write a linear equation to compute the cost, y, of renting a 10 ft by 10 ft space for x months. $y = 90x + 105$

   b. What is the cost of renting such a storage space for 1 year (12 months)? $1185.00

22. An air-conditioning and heating company has a fixed monthly cost of $5000. Furthermore, each service call costs the company $25.

   a. Write a linear equation to compute the total cost, y, for 1 month if x service calls are made. $y = 25x + 5000$

   b. Use the equation to compute the cost for 1 month if 150 service calls are made. $8750.00

23. A bakery that specializes in bread rents a booth at a flea market. The daily cost to rent the booth is $100. Each loaf of bread costs the bakery $0.80 to produce.

   a. Write a linear equation to compute the total cost, y, for 1 day if x loaves of bread are produced. $y = 0.8x + 100$

   b. Use the equation to compute the cost for 1 day if 200 loaves of bread are produced. $260.00

24. A beverage company rents a booth at an art show to sell lemonade. The daily cost to rent a booth is $35. Each lemonade costs $0.50 to produce.

   a. Write a linear equation to compute the total cost, y, for 1 day if x lemonades are produced. $y = 0.5x + 35$

   b. Use the equation to compute the cost for 1 day if 350 lemonades are produced. $210.00

Group Activity

Modeling a Linear Equation

Materials: Yardstick or other device for making linear measurements

Estimated Time: 15–20 minutes

Group Size: 3

1. The members of each group should measure the length of their arms (in inches) from elbow to wrist. Record this measurement as x and the person's height (in inches) as y. Write these values as ordered pairs for each member of the group. Then write the ordered pairs on the board.

2. Next, copy the ordered pairs collected from all groups in the class and plot the ordered pairs. (This is called a "scatter diagram".)   Answers will vary throughout this exercise.

 Writing   Translating Expression   Geometry   Scientific Calculator   Video   NS&E

3. Select two ordered pairs that seem to follow the upward trend of the data. Using these data points, determine the slope of the line.

Slope: —————————————————

4. Using the data points and slope from question 3, find an equation of the line through the two points. Write the equation in slope-intercept form, $y = mx + b$.

Equation: —————————————————

5. Using the equation from question 4, estimate the height of a person whose arm length from elbow to wrist is 8.5 in.

6. Suppose a crime scene investigator uncovers a partial skeleton and identifies a bone as a human ulna (the ulna is one of two bones in the forearm and extends from elbow to wrist). If the length of the bone is 12 in., estimate the height of the person before death. Would you expect this person to be male or female?

Chapter 3   Summary

Section 3.1   Rectangular Coordinate System

Key Concepts

Graphical representation of numerical **data** is often helpful to study problems in real-world applications.

    A **rectangular coordinate system** is made up of a horizontal line called the **x-axis** and a vertical line called the **y-axis**. The point where the lines meet is the **origin**. The four regions of the plane are called **quadrants**.

    The point (x, y) is an **ordered pair**. The first element in the ordered pair is the point's horizontal position from the origin. The second element in the ordered pair is the point's vertical position from the origin.

Example

Example 1

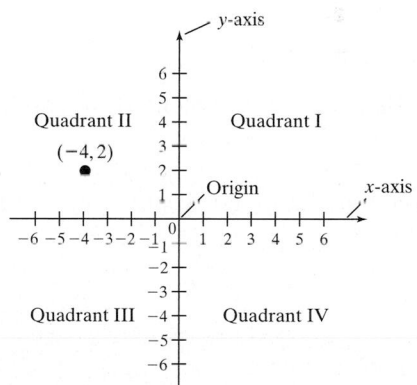

Section 3.2 Linear Equations in Two Variables

Key Concepts

An equation written in the form $Ax + By = C$ (where A and B are not both zero) is a **linear equation in two variables**.

    A solution to a linear equation in x and y is an ordered pair (x, y) that makes the equation a true statement. The graph of the set of all solutions of a linear equation in two variables is a line in a rectangular coordinate system.

    A linear equation can be graphed by finding at least two solutions and graphing the line through the points.

Examples

Example 1

Graph the equation $2x + y = 2$.

Select arbitrary values of x or y such as those shown in the table. Then complete the table to find the corresponding ordered pairs.

x	y	
0	2	$\longrightarrow (0, 2)$
-1	4	$\longrightarrow (-1, 4)$
1	0	$\longrightarrow (1, 0)$

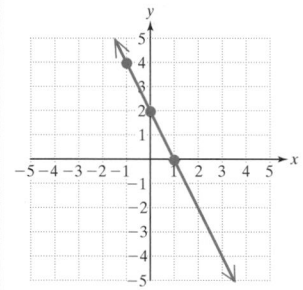

Example 2

For the line $2x + y = 2$, find the x- and y-intercepts.

An **x-intercept** of a graph is a point $(a, 0)$ where the graph intersects the x-axis.
To find the x-intercept, let $y = 0$ and solve for x.

A **y-intercept** of a graph is a point $(0, b)$ where the graph intersects the y-axis.
To find the y-intercept, let $x = 0$ and solve for y.

x-intercept	y-intercept
$2x + (0) = 2$	$2(0) + y = 2$
$2x = 2$	$0 + y = 2$
$x = 1$	$y = 2$
$(1, 0)$	$(0, 2)$

Example 3

A **vertical line** can be represented by an equation of the form $x = k$.

A **horizontal line** can be represented by an equation of the form $y = k$.

$x = 3$ represents a vertical line $y = 3$ represents a horizontal line

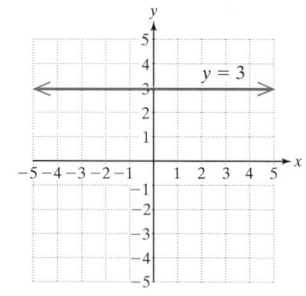

Section 3.3   Slope of a Line and Rate of Change

Key Concepts

The **slope**, m, of a line between two points (x_1, y_1) and (x_2, y_2) is given by

$$m = \frac{y_2 - y_1}{x_2 - x_1} \quad \text{or} \quad \frac{\text{change in } y}{\text{change in } x}$$

The slope of a line may be positive, negative, zero, or undefined.

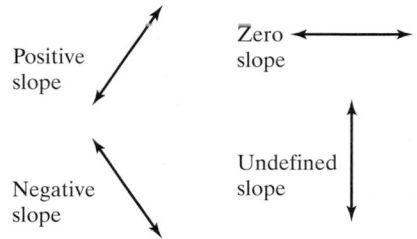

If m_1 and m_2 represent the slopes of two **parallel lines** (nonvertical), then $m_1 = m_2$.

If $m_1 \neq 0$ and $m_2 \neq 0$ represent the slopes of two nonvertical **perpendicular lines**, then

$$m_1 = -\frac{1}{m_2} \text{ or equivalently, } m_1 m_2 = -1.$$

Examples

Example 1

Find the slope of the line between $(1, -5)$ and $(-3, 7)$.

$$m = \frac{7 - (-5)}{-3 - 1} = \frac{12}{-4} = -3$$

Example 2

The slope of the line $y = -2$ is 0 because the line is horizontal.

Example 3

The slope of the line $x = 4$ is undefined because the line is vertical.

Example 4

The slopes of two distinct lines are given. Determine whether the lines are parallel, perpendicular, or neither.

a. $m_1 = -7$ and $m_2 = -7$ Parallel

b. $m_1 = -\dfrac{1}{5}$ and $m_2 = 5$ Perpendicular

c. $m_1 = -\dfrac{3}{2}$ and $m_2 = -\dfrac{2}{3}$ Neither

| Section 3.4 | **Slope-Intercept Form of a Line** |

Key Concepts

The **slope-intercept form** of a line is

$$y = mx + b$$

where m is the slope of the line and $(0, b)$ is the y-intercept.

Slope-intercept form is used to identify the slope and y-intercept of a line when the equation is given.

Slope-intercept form can also be used to graph a line.

Examples

Example 1

Find the slope and y-intercept.

$7x - 2y = 4$

$$-2y = -7x + 4 \qquad \text{Solve for } y.$$

$$\frac{-2y}{-2} = \frac{-7x}{-2} + \frac{4}{-2}$$

$$y = \frac{7}{2}x - 2$$

The slope is $\frac{7}{2}$. The y-intercept is $(0, -2)$.

Example 2

Graph the line.

$$y = \frac{7}{2}x - 2$$

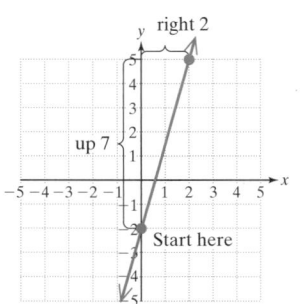

| Section 3.5 | **Point-Slope Formula** |

Key Concepts

The **point-slope formula** is used primarily to construct an equation of a line given a point and the slope.

Equations of Lines—A Summary:

Standard form: $Ax + By = C$
Horizontal line: $y = k$
Vertical line: $x = k$
Slope-intercept form: $y = mx + b$
Point-slope formula: $y - y_1 = m(x - x_1)$

Example

Example 1

Find an equation of the line passing through the point $(6, -4)$ and having a slope of $-\frac{1}{2}$.

Label the given information:
$m = -\frac{1}{2}$ and $(x_1, y_1) = (6, -4)$

$$y - y_1 = m(x - x_1)$$

$$y - (-4) = -\frac{1}{2}(x - 6)$$

$$y + 4 = -\frac{1}{2}x + 3$$

$$y = -\frac{1}{2}x - 1$$

Section 3.6 Applications of Linear Equations and Modeling

Key Concepts

Linear equations can often be used to describe or model the relationship between variables in a real-world event. In such applications, the slope may be interpreted as a rate of change.

Example

Example 1

The number of drug-related arrests for a small city has been growing approximately linearly since 1980.

Let y represent the number of drug arrests, and let x represent the number of years after 1980.

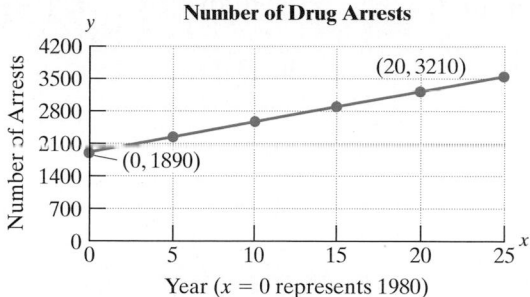

Number of Drug Arrests

Year ($x = 0$ represents 1980)

a. Use the ordered pairs $(0, 1890)$ and $(20, 3210)$ to find an equation of the line shown in the graph.

$$m = \frac{y_2 - y_1}{x_2 - x_1} = \frac{3210 - 1890}{20 - 0}$$

$$= \frac{1320}{20} = 66$$

The slope is 66, indicating that the number of drug arrests is increasing at a rate of 66 per year. $m = 66$, and the y-intercept is $(0, 1890)$. Hence:

$$y = mx + b \implies y = 66x + 1890$$

b. Use the equation in part (a) to predict the number of drug-related arrests in the year 2010. (The year 2010 is 30 years after 1980. Hence, $x = 30$.)

$$y = 66(30) + 1890$$

$$y = 3870$$

The number of drug arrests is predicted to be 3870 by the year 2010.

Chapter 3   Review Exercises

Section 3.1

1. Graph the points on a rectangular coordinate system.

   a. $\left(\dfrac{1}{2}, 5\right)$ **b.** $(-1, 4)$ **c.** $(2, -1)$

   d. $(0, 3)$ **e.** $(0, 0)$ **f.** $\left(-\dfrac{8}{5}, 0\right)$

   g. $(-2, -5)$ **h.** $(3, 1)$

   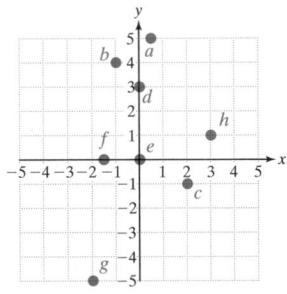

2. Estimate the coordinates of the points $A, B, C,$ $D, E,$ and $F.$

   $A(4, -3);\ B(-3, -2);\ C(\tfrac{5}{2}, 5);\ D(-4, 1);\ E(-\tfrac{1}{2}, 0);\ F(0, -5)$

   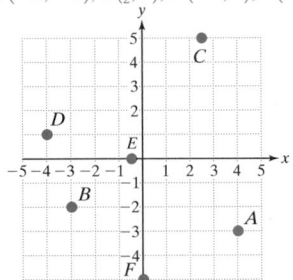

For Exercises 3–8, determine the quadrant in which the given point is located.

   3. $(-2, -10)$ III   **4.** $(-4, 6)$ II

   5. $(3, -5)$ IV   **6.** $\left(\dfrac{1}{2}, \dfrac{7}{5}\right)$ I

   7. $(\pi, -2.7)$ IV   **8.** $(-1.2, -6.8)$ III

   9. On which axis is the point $(2, 0)$ located?   x-axis

   10. On which axis is the point $(0, -3)$ located?   y-axis

11. The price per share of a stock (in dollars) over a period of 5 days is shown in the graph.

   a. Interpret the meaning of the ordered pair $(1, 26.25)$.   On day 1, the price was $26.25.

   b. On which day was the price the highest?
   Day 2

   c. What was the increase in price between day 1 and day 2? $2.25

12. The number of space shuttle launches for selected years is given by the ordered pairs. Let x represent the number of years since 1995. Let y represent the number of launches.

   $(1, 7)$ $(2, 8)$ $(3, 5)$ $(4, 3)$

   $(5, 5)$ $(6, 6)$ $(7, 5)$ $(8, 1)$

   a. Interpret the meaning of the ordered pair $(8, 1)$.   In 2003 (8 years after 1995), there was only one space shuttle launch (this was the year that the Columbia and its crew were lost).

   b. Plot the points on a rectangular coordinate system.

   Number of Shuttles Launched

Section 3.2

For Exercises 13–16, determine if the given ordered pair is a solution to the equation.

13. $5x - 3y = 12$; $(0, 4)$ No

14. $2x - 4y = -6$; $(3, 0)$ No

15. $y = \frac{1}{3}x - 2$; $(9, 1)$ Yes

16. $y = -\frac{2}{5}x + 1$; $(-10, 5)$ Yes

For Exercises 17–20, complete the table and graph the corresponding ordered pairs. Graph the line through the points to represent all solutions to the equation.

17. $3x - y = 5$

x	y
2	1
3	4
1	-2

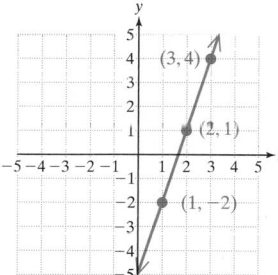

18. $\frac{1}{2}x + 3y = 6$

x	y
0	2
-2	7/3
-6	3

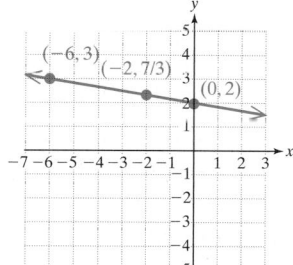

19. $y = \frac{2}{3}x - 1$

x	y
0	-1
3	1
-6	-5

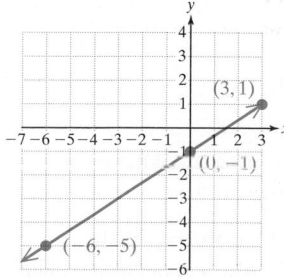

20. $y = -2x - 3$

x	y
0	-3
-3	3
1	-5

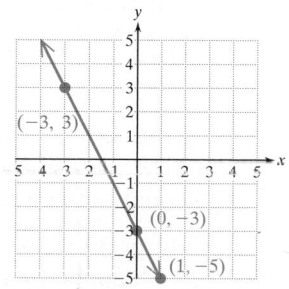

For Exercises 21–24, graph the equation.

21. $x + 2y = 4$

22. $x - y = 5$

23. $y = 3x$

24. $y = \frac{1}{4}x$

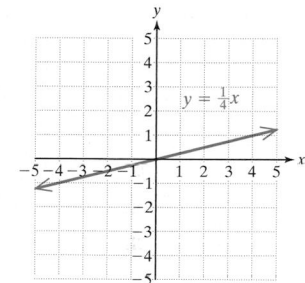

For Exercises 25–28, identify the line as horizontal or vertical. Then graph the equation.

25. $3x - 2 = 10$ Vertical

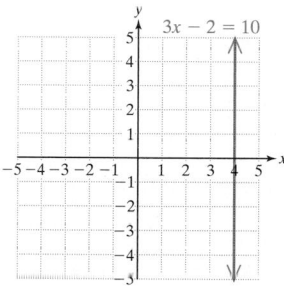

26. $2x + 1 = -2$ Vertical

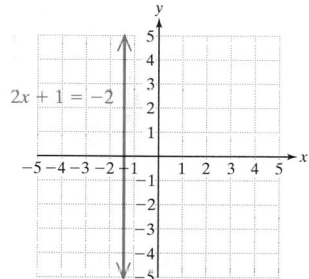

27. $6y + 1 = 13$
Horizontal

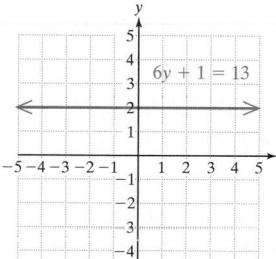

28. $5y - 1 = 14$
Horizontal

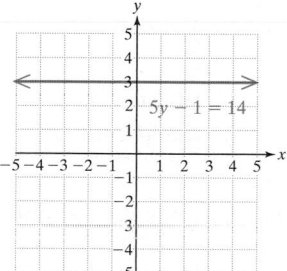

For Exercises 29–36, find the x- and y-intercepts if they exist.

29. $-4x + 8y = 12$ x-intercept: $(-3, 0)$; y-intercept: $\left(0, \frac{3}{2}\right)$

30. $2x + y = 6$ x-intercept: $(3, 0)$; y-intercept: $(0, 6)$

31. $y = 8x$ x-intercept: $(0, 0)$; y-intercept: $(0, 0)$

32. $5x - y = 0$ x-intercept: $(0, 0)$; y-intercept: $(0, 0)$

33. $6y = -24$ x-intercept: none; y-intercept: $(0, -4)$

34. $2y - 3 = 1$ x-intercept: none; y-intercept: $(0, 2)$

35. $2x + 5 = 0$ x-intercept: $\left(-\frac{5}{2}, 0\right)$; y-intercept: none

36. $-3x + 1 = 0$ x-intercept: $\left(\frac{1}{3}, 0\right)$; y-intercept: none

Section 3.3

37. What is the slope of the ladder leaning up against the wall? $m = \dfrac{12}{5}$

12 ft

5 ft

38. Point A is located 4 units down and 2 units to the right of point B. What is the slope of the line through points A and B? -2

39. Determine the slope of the line that passes through the points $(7, -9)$ and $(-5, -1)$. $-\dfrac{2}{3}$

40. Determine the slope of the line that has x- and y-intercepts of $(-1, 0)$ and $(0, 8)$. 8

41. Determine the slope of the line that passes through the points $(3, 0)$ and $(3, -7)$.   Undefined

42. Determine the slope of the horizontal line given by $y = -1$. 0

43. A given line has a slope of -5.

  a. What is the slope of a line parallel to the given line? -5

  b. What is the slope of a line perpendicular to the given line? $\dfrac{1}{5}$

44. A given line has a slope of 0.

  a. What is the slope of a line parallel to the given line? 0

  b. What is the slope of a line perpendicular to the given line?   Undefined

For Exercises 45–48, find the slopes of the lines l_1 and l_2 from the two given points. Then determine whether l_1 and l_2 are parallel, perpendicular, or neither.

45. l_1: $(3, 7)$ and $(0, 5)$ $m_1 = \dfrac{2}{3}$

  l_2: $(6, 3)$ and $(-3, -3)$ $m_2 = \dfrac{2}{3}$; parallel

46. l_1: $(-2, 1)$ and $(-1, 9)$ $m_1 = 8$

  l_2: $(0, -6)$ and $(2, 10)$ $m_2 = 8$; parallel

47. l_1: $\left(0, \frac{5}{6}\right)$ and $(2, 0)$ $m_1 = -\dfrac{5}{12}$

  l_2: $\left(0, \frac{6}{5}\right)$ and $\left(-\frac{1}{2}, 0\right)$ $m_2 = \dfrac{12}{5}$; perpendicular

48. l_1: $(1, 1)$ and $(1, -8)$ $m_1 = $ undefined

  l_2: $(4, -5)$ and $(7, -5)$ $m_2 = 0$; perpendicular

49. Carol's electric bill had an initial reading of 35,955 kilowatt-hours at the beginning of the month. At the end of the month the reading was 37,005 kilowatt-hours. Let x represent the day of the month and y represent the reading on the meter in kilowatt-hours.

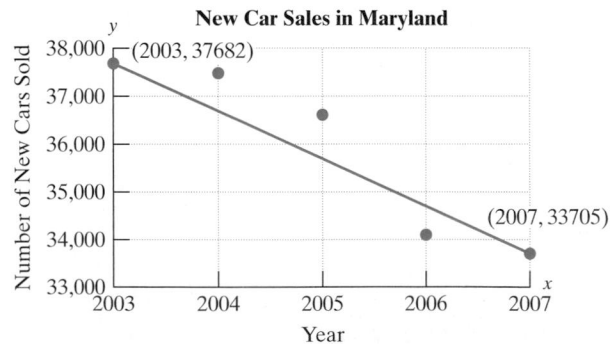

  a. Using the ordered pairs $(1, 35955)$ and $(31, 37005)$, find the slope of the line. $m = 35$

  b. Interpret the slope in the context of this problem.   The number of kilowatt-hours increased at a rate of 35 kilowatt-hours per day.

50. New car sales were recorded for selected years in Maryland. Let x represent the year and y represent the number of new cars sold.

New Car Sales in Maryland

  a. Using the ordered pairs $(2003, 37682)$ and $(2007, 33705)$, find the slope of the line. Round to the nearest whole unit. $m = -994$

  b. Interpret the slope in the context of this problem.   The number of new cars sold in Maryland decreased at a rate of 994 cars per year.

 Writing   Translating Expression   Geometry   Scientific Calculator   Video   NS E

Section 3.4

For Exercises 51–56, write each equation in slope-intercept form. Identify the slope and the y-intercept.

51. $5x - 2y = 10$ $\quad y = \frac{5}{2}x - 5;$
$m = \frac{5}{2};$ y-intercept: $(0, -5)$

52. $3x + 4y = 12$ $y = -\frac{3}{4}x + 3;$
$m = -\frac{3}{4};$ y-intercept: $(0, 3)$

53. $x - 3y = 0$ $\quad y = \frac{1}{3}x;$
$m = \frac{1}{3};$ y-intercept: $(0, 0)$

54. $5y - 8 = 4$ $\quad y = \frac{12}{5};$
$m = 0;$ y-intercept: $\left(0, \frac{12}{5}\right)$

55. $2y = -5$
$y = -\frac{5}{2}; m = 0;$ y-intercept: $\left(0, -\frac{5}{2}\right)$

56. $y - x = 0$
$y = x; m = 1;$ y-intercept: $(0, 0)$

For Exercises 57–62, determine whether the equations represent parallel lines, perpendicular lines, or neither.

57. l_1: $y = \frac{3}{5}x + 3$

l_2: $y = \frac{5}{3}x + 1$

Neither

58. l_1: $2x - 5y = 10$

l_2: $5x + 2y = 20$

Perpendicular

59. l_1: $3x + 2y = 6$

l_2: $-6x - 4y = 4$

Parallel

60. l_1: $y = \frac{1}{4}x - 3$

l_2: $-x + 4y = 8$

Parallel

61. l_1: $2x = 4$

l_2: $y = 6$ Perpendicular

62. l_1: $y = \frac{2}{9}x + 4$

l_2: $y = \frac{9}{2}x - 3$

Neither

63. Write an equation of the line whose slope is $-\frac{4}{3}$ and whose y-intercept is $(0, -1)$.
$y = -\frac{4}{3}x - 1$ or $4x + 3y = -3$

64. Write an equation of the line that passes through the origin and has a slope of 5.
$y = 5x$ or $5x - y = 0$

65. Write an equation of the line with slope $-\frac{4}{3}$ that passes through the point $(-6, 2)$.
$y = -\frac{4}{3}x - 6$ or $4x + 3y = -18$

66. Write an equation of the line with slope 5 that passes through the point $(-1, -8)$.
$y = 5x - 3$ or $5x - y = 3$

Section 3.5

67. Write a linear equation in two variables in slope-intercept form. (Answers may vary.)
For example: $y = 3x + 2$

68. Write a linear equation in two variables in standard form. (Answers may vary.)
For example: $5x + 2y = -4$

69. Write the slope formula to find the slope of the line between the points (x_1, y_1) and (x_2, y_2).
$m = \dfrac{y_2 - y_1}{x_2 - x_1}$

70. Write the point-slope formula. $\quad y - y_1 = m(x - x_1)$

71. Write an equation of a vertical line (answers may vary). For example: $x = 6$

72. Write an equation of a horizontal line (answers may vary). For example: $y = -5$

For Exercises 73–78, write an equation of a line given the following information.

73. The slope is -6, and the line passes through the point $(-1, 8)$. $\quad y = -6x + 2$ or $6x + y = 2$

74. The slope is $\frac{2}{3}$, and the line passes through the point $(5, 5)$. $\quad y = \frac{2}{3}x + \frac{5}{3}$ or $2x - 3y = -5$

75. The line passes through the points $(0, -4)$ and $(8, -2)$. $\quad y = \frac{1}{4}x - 4$ or $x - 4y = 16$

76. The line passes through the points $(2, -5)$ and $(8, -5)$. $\quad y = -5$

77. The line passes through the point $(5, 12)$ and is perpendicular to the line $y = -\frac{5}{6}x - 3$.
$y = \frac{6}{5}x + 6$ or $6x - 5y = -30$

78. The line passes through the point $(-6, 7)$ and is parallel to the line $4x - y = 0$. $\quad y = 4x + 31$ or $4x - y = -31$

Section 3.6

79. The graph shows the average height for girls based on age (*Source:* National Parenting Council). Let x represent a girl's age, and let y represent her height (in inches).

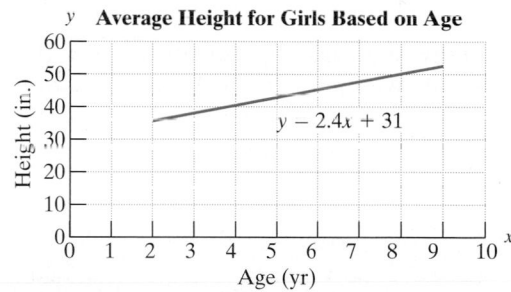

Average Height for Girls Based on Age

$y = 2.4x + 31$

a. Use the equation to estimate the average height of a 7-year-old girl. 47.8 in.

b. What is the slope of the line? Interpret the meaning of the slope in the context of the problem. The slope is 2.4 and indicates that the average height for girls increases at a rate of 2.4 in. per year.

80. Sally wants to teach at the local community college. She learns that the starting salary in 2002 was $33,000. In 2008, the starting salary was $38,400. Let x represent the number of years since 2002, and let y represent the starting salary.

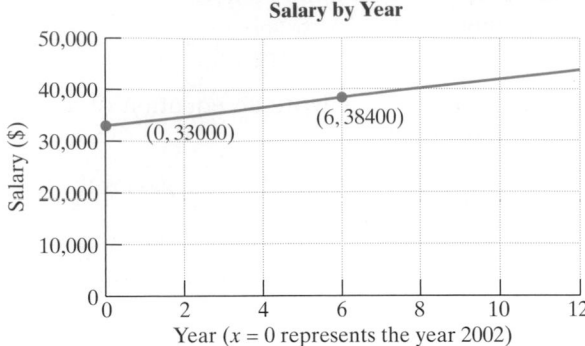

Salary by Year

a. Use the points $(0, 33000)$ and $(6, 38400)$ to find a linear equation to represent the salary, y, according to the year, x. $y = 900x + 33,000$

b. Interpret the meaning of the slope in the context of this problem.
$m = 900$; The rate of change in starting salary per year is $900.

81. A water purification company charges $20 per month and a $55 installation fee.

a. Write a linear equation to compute the total cost, y, of renting this system for x months.
$y = 20x + 55$
b. Use the equation from part (a) to determine the total cost to rent the system for 9 months.
$235

82. A small cleaning company has a fixed monthly cost of $700 and a variable cost of $8 per service call.

a. Write a linear equation to compute the total cost, y, of making x service calls in one month. $y = 8x + 700$

b. Use the equation from part (a) to determine the total cost of making 80 service calls. $1340

Chapter 3   Test

1. In which quadrant is the given point located?

a. $\left(-\dfrac{7}{2}, 4\right)$ **b.** $(4.6, -2)$ **c.** $(-37, -45)$
   II   IV   III

2. What is the y-coordinate for a point on the x-axis?
0

3. What is the x-coordinate for a point on the y-axis?
0

4. Holiday retail sales for several years in the U.S. are given in the table. Let $x = 1$ represent the year 2001, $x = 2$ represent 2002, and so on. Let y represent the holiday retail sales in billions of dollars.

Year	Let x Represent the Year 2001	Total Retail Sales, y (in billions)
2001	1	$368
2003	3	$389
2005	5	$436
2007	7	$460
2008	8	$470

Source: National Retail Federation

a. Write the data as ordered pairs and interpret the meaning of the first ordered pair.
$(1, 368)$ In the year 2001, the total amount spent on holiday sales was $368 billion.
$(3, 389)$ $(5, 436)$, $(7, 460)$ $(8, 470)$

b. Graph the ordered pairs on a rectangular coordinate system.

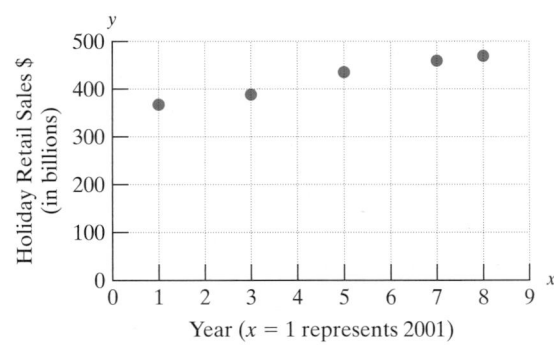

c. From the graph, estimate the holiday retail sales in the year 2006.   Approximately $450 billion

5. Determine whether the ordered pair is a solution to the equation $2x - y = 6$.

a. $(0, 6)$ No   **b.** $(4, 2)$ Yes

c. $(3, 0)$ Yes   **d.** $\left(\dfrac{9}{2}, 3\right)$ Yes

6. Given the equation $y = \frac{1}{4}x - 2$, complete the table. Plot the ordered pairs and graph the line through the points to represent the set of all solutions to the equation.

x	y
0	-2
4	-1
6	$-\frac{1}{2}$

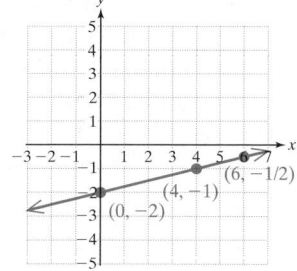

For Exercises 7–9, graph the equations.

7. $y = 3x + 2$

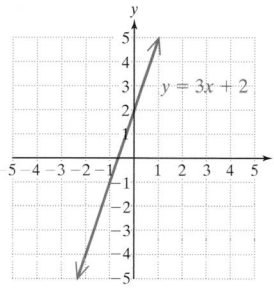

8. $2x + 5y = 0$

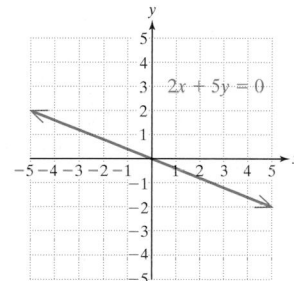

9. $3x + 2y = 8$

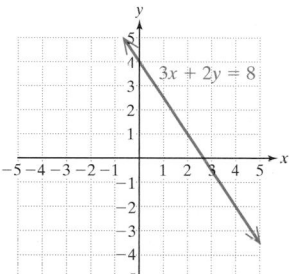

For Exercises 10–11, determine whether the equation represents a horizontal or vertical line. Then graph the line.

10. $-6y = 18$ Horizontal

11. $5x + 1 = 8$ Vertical

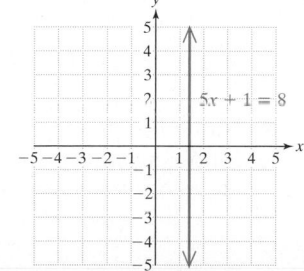

For Exercises 12–15, determine the x- and y-intercepts if they exist.

12. $-4x + 3y = 6$
x-intercept: $\left(-\frac{3}{2}, 0\right)$; y-intercept: $(0, 2)$

13. $2y = 6x$
x-intercept: $(0, 0)$; y-intercept: $(0, 0)$

14. $x = 4$ x-intercept: $(4, 0)$; y-intercept: none

15. $y - 3 = 0$
x-intercept: none; y-intercept: $(0, 3)$

16. What is the slope of the hill? $\frac{2}{5}$

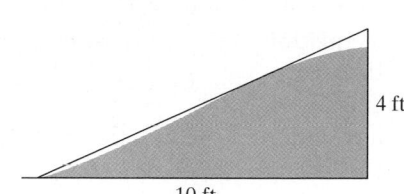

4 ft

10 ft

17. a. Find the slope of the line that passes through the points $(-2, 0)$ and $(-5, -1)$. $\frac{1}{3}$

b. Find the slope of the line $4x - 3y = 9$. $\frac{4}{3}$

18. a. What is the slope of a line parallel to the line $x + 4y = -16$? $-\frac{1}{4}$

b. What is the slope of a line perpendicular to the line $x + 4y = -16$?   4

19. a. What is the slope of the line $x = 5$?   Undefined

b. What is the slope of the line $y = -3$?   0

20. Carlos called a local truck rental company and got quotes for renting a truck. He was told that it would cost $41.95 to rent a truck for one day to travel 20 miles. It costs $89.95 to rent the truck for one day to travel 100 miles. Let x represent the number of miles driven and y represent the cost of the rental.

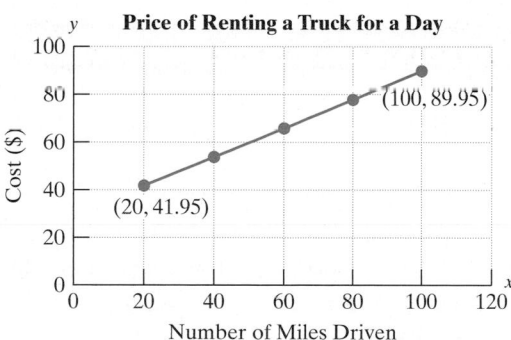

Price of Renting a Truck for a Day

$(100, 89.95)$

$(20, 41.95)$

Cost ($)

Number of Miles Driven

a. Using the ordered pairs $(20, 41.95)$ and $(100, 89.95)$, find the slope of the line. $m = 0.6$

b. Interpret the slope in the context of this problem.   The cost of renting a truck increases at a rate of $0.60 per mile.

Writing   Translating Expression   Geometry   Scientific Calculator   Video   NS&E

21. Determine whether the lines through the given points are parallel, perpendicular, or neither.

l_1: $(1, 4), (-1, -2)$ l_2: $(0, -5), (-2, -11)$
Parallel

22. Determine whether the equations represent parallel lines, perpendicular lines, or neither.

l_1: $2y = 3x - 3$ l_2: $4x = -6y + 1$
Perpendicular

23. Write an equation of the line that has y-intercept $(0, \frac{1}{2})$ and slope $\frac{1}{4}$. $y = \frac{1}{4}x + \frac{1}{2}$ or $x - 4y = -2$

24. Write an equation of the line that has slope -1 and passes through the point $(-5, 2)$.
$y = -x - 3$ or $x + y = -3$

25. Write an equation of the line that passes through the points $(2, 8)$ and $(4, 1)$.
$y = -\frac{7}{2}x + 15$ or $7x + 2y = 30$

26. Write an equation of the line that passes through the point $(2, -6)$ and is parallel to the x-axis. $y = -6$

27. Write an equation of the line that passes through the point $(3, 0)$ and is parallel to the line $2x + 6y = -5$. $y = -\frac{1}{3}x + 1$ or $x + 3y = 3$

28. Write an equation of the line that passes through the point $(-3, -1)$ and is perpendicular to the line $x + 3y = 9$. $y = 3x + 8$ or $3x - y = -8$

29. To attend a state fair, the cost is $10 per person to cover exhibits and musical entertainment. There is an additional cost of $1.50 per ride.

   a. Write an equation that gives the total cost, y, of visiting the state fair and going on x rides.
$y = 1.5x + 10$

   b. Use the equation from part (a) to determine the cost of going to the state fair and going on 10 rides. $25

30. The number of medical doctors for selected years is shown in the graph. Let x represent the number of years since 1980, and let y represent the number of medical doctors (in thousands) in the United States.

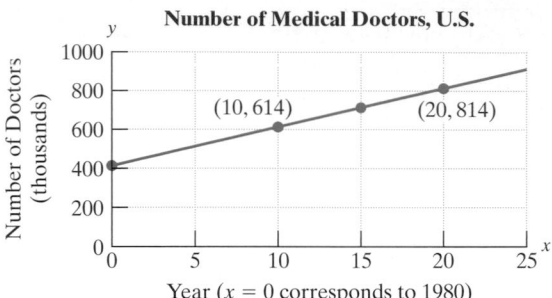

Number of Medical Doctors, U.S.

   a. Find the slope of the line shown in the graph. Interpret the meaning of the slope in the context of this problem. $m = 20$; The slope indicates that there is an increase of 20 thousand medical doctors per year.

   b. Find an equation of the line.
$y = 20x + 414$

   c. Use the equation from part (b) to predict the number of medical doctors in the United States for the year 2010.
1014 thousand or, equivalently, 1,014,000

Chapters 1–3   Cumulative Review Exercises

1. Identify the number as rational or irrational.

   a. -3 **b.** $\frac{5}{4}$ **c.** $\sqrt{10}$ **d.** 0
     Rational   Rational   Irrational   Rational

2. Write the opposite and the absolute value for each number.

   a. $-\frac{2}{3}$ $\frac{2}{3}; \frac{2}{3}$ **b.** 5.3 $-5.3; 5.3$

3. Simplify the expression using the order of operations. $32 \div 2 \cdot 4 + 5$ 69

4. Add. $3 + (-8) + 2 + (-10)$ -13

5. Subtract. $16 - 5 - (-7)$ 18

For Exercises 6–7, translate the English phrase into an algebraic expression. Then evaluate the expression.

6. The quotient of $\frac{3}{4}$ and $-\frac{7}{8}$ $\frac{3}{4} \div \left(-\frac{7}{8}\right); -\frac{6}{7}$

7. The product of -2.1 and -6 $(-2.1)(-6); 12.6$

8. Name the property that is illustrated by the following statement. $6 + (8 + 2) = (6 + 8) + 2$
The associative property of addition

 Writing   Translating Expression   Geometry   Scientific Calculator   Video   NS&E

For Exercises 9–12, solve each equation.

9. $6x - 10 = 14$ **10.** $3(m + 2) - 3 = 2m + 8$
{4}   {5}

11. $\dfrac{2}{3}y - \dfrac{1}{6} = y + \dfrac{4}{3}$ **12.** $1.7z + 2 = -2(0.3z + 1.3)$
$\left\{-\dfrac{9}{2}\right\}$ {−2}

13. The area of Texas is 267,277 mi². If this is 712 mi² less than 29 times the area of Maine, find the area of Maine.   9241 mi²

14. For the formula $3a + b = c$, solve for a. $a = \dfrac{c - b}{3}$

15. Graph the equation $-6x + 2y = 0$.

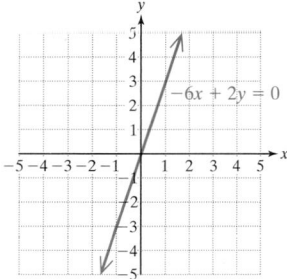

16. Find the x- and y-intercepts of $-2x + 4y = 4$.
x-intercept: $(-2, 0)$; y-intercept: $(0, 1)$

17. Write the equation in slope-intercept form. Then identify the slope and the y-intercept.
$3x + 2y = -12$
$y = -\dfrac{3}{2}x - 6$;   slope: $-\dfrac{3}{2}$; y-intercept: $(0, -6)$

18. Explain why the line $2x + 3 = 5$ has only one intercept. $2x + 3 - 5$ can be written as $x - 1$, which represents a vertical line. A vertical line of the form $x = k \ (k \neq 0)$ has an x-intercept of $(k, 0)$ and no y-intercept.

19. Find an equation of a line passing through $(2, -5)$ with slope -3. $y = -3x + 1$ or $3x + y = 1$

20. Find an equation of the line passing through $(0, 6)$ and $(-3, 4)$. $y = \frac{2}{3}x + 6$ or $2x - 3y = -18$

Systems of Linear Equations

4

CHAPTER OUTLINE

Chapter 4

This chapter is devoted to solving systems of linear equations. Applications of systems of equations involve two or more variables subject to two or more constraints.

Are You Prepared?

To prepare yourself, consider this example. At a movie theater, one group of students bought three drinks and two small popcorns for a total of $13.00 (excluding tax). Another group bought five drinks and three popcorns for $20.50. There are two unknown quantities in this scenario: the cost per drink and the cost per popcorn.

   Fill in the blanks below using trial and error to determine the cost per drink and the cost per popcorn. You have the correct answer if both equations are true.

In this column, fill in the cost per drink.

In this column, fill in the cost per popcorn.

$$3(\qquad) + 2(\qquad) \overset{?}{=} \$13.00$$
$$5(\qquad) + 3(\qquad) \overset{?}{=} \$20.50$$

Are these both true?

If you have trouble with this puzzle, don't fret. Later in the chapter, we'll use the power of algebra to set up and solve a system of equations that will take the guess work away!   One drink costs $2.00 and one small popcorn costs $3.50.

Solving Systems of Equations by the Graphing Method

Concepts

1. Solutions to a System of Linear Equations
2. Dependent and Inconsistent Systems of Linear Equations
3. Solving Systems of Linear Equations by Graphing

1. Solutions to a System of Linear Equations

Recall from Section 3.2 that a linear equation in two variables has an infinite number of solutions. The set of all solutions to a linear equation forms a line in a rectangular coordinate system. Two or more linear equations form a **system of linear equations**. For example, here are three systems of equations:

$$x - 3y = -5 \qquad\qquad y = \tfrac{1}{4}x - \tfrac{3}{4} \qquad\qquad 5a + \ b = 4$$
$$2x + 4y = 10 \qquad\qquad -2x + 8y = -6 \qquad\qquad -10a - 2b = 8$$

A **solution to a system of linear equations** is an ordered pair that is a solution to *each* individual linear equation.

Classroom Examples: p. 276, Exercises 4 and 6

Example 1 Determining Solutions to a System of Linear Equations

Determine whether the ordered pairs are solutions to the system.

$$x + y = 4$$
$$-2x + y = -5$$

a. $(3, 1)$ **b.** $(0, 4)$

Solution:

a. Substitute the ordered pair $(3, 1)$ into both equations:

$$x + y = 4 \longrightarrow (3) + (1) \overset{?}{=} 4 \ \checkmark \qquad \text{True}$$
$$-2x + y = -5 \longrightarrow -2(3) + (1) \overset{?}{=} -5 \checkmark \qquad \text{True}$$

Avoiding Mistakes

It is important to test an ordered pair in *both* equations to determine if the ordered pair is a solution.

Because the ordered pair $(3, 1)$ is a solution to each equation, it is a solution to the *system* of equations.

b. Substitute the ordered pair $(0, 4)$ into both equations.

$$x + y = 4 \longrightarrow (0) + (4) \overset{?}{=} 4 \ \checkmark \qquad \text{True}$$
$$-2x + y = -5 \longrightarrow -2(0) + (4) \overset{?}{=} -5 \qquad \text{False}$$

Because the ordered pair $(0, 4)$ is not a solution to the second equation, it is *not* a solution to the system of equations.

Skill Practice Determine whether the ordered pair is a solution to the system. $5x - 2y = 24$
$$2x + \ y = 6$$

1. $(6, 3)$ **2.** $(4, -2)$

A solution to a system of two linear equations may be interpreted graphically as a point of intersection between the two lines. Using slope-intercept form to graph the lines from Example 1, we have

$$l_1: \quad x + y = 4 \longrightarrow y = -x + 4$$
$$l_2: \quad -2x + y = -5 \longrightarrow y = \ 2x - 5$$

Answers

1. No
2. Yes

All points on l_1 are solutions to the equation $y = -x + 4$.

All points on l_2 are solutions to the equation $y = 2x - 5$.

The point of intersection $(3, 1)$ is the only point that is a solution to both equations. (See Figure 4-1).

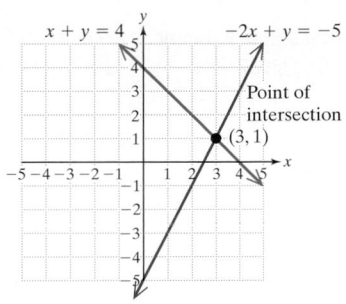

Figure 4-1

2. Dependent and Inconsistent Systems of Linear Equations

When two lines are drawn in a rectangular coordinate system, three geometric relationships are possible:

1. Two lines may intersect at *exactly one point.*

2. Two lines may intersect at *no point.* This occurs if the lines are parallel.

3. Two lines may intersect at *infinitely many points* along the line. This occurs if the equations represent the same line (the lines coincide).

If a system of linear equations has one or more solutions, the system is said to be **consistent**. If a linear equation has no solution, it is said to be **inconsistent**.

If two equations represent the same line, then all points along the line are solutions to the system of equations. In such a case, the system is characterized as a **dependent system**. An **independent system** is one in which the two equations represent different lines.

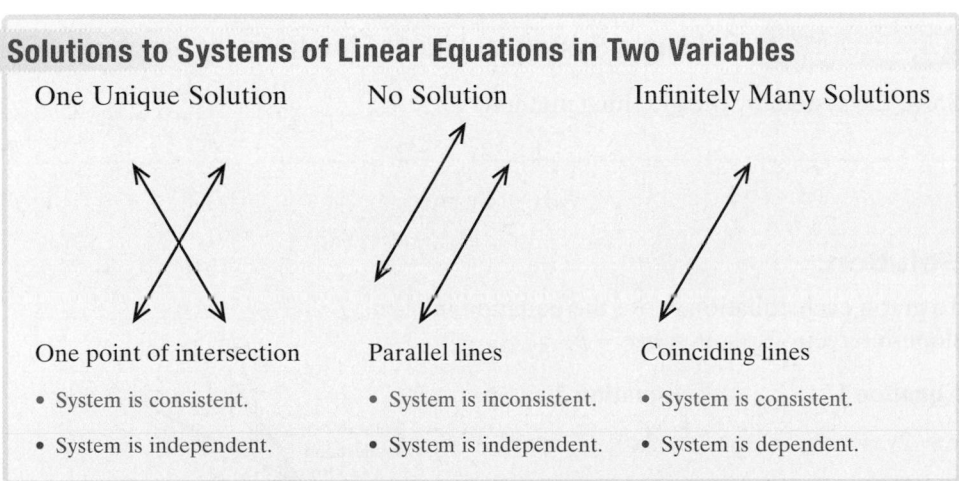

Solutions to Systems of Linear Equations in Two Variables

One Unique Solution	No Solution	Infinitely Many Solutions
One point of intersection	Parallel lines	Coinciding lines
• System is consistent.	• System is inconsistent.	• System is consistent.
• System is independent.	• System is independent.	• System is dependent.

3. Solving Systems of Linear Equations by Graphing

One way to find a solution to a system of equations is to graph the equations and find the point (or points) of intersection. This is called the *graphing method* to solve a system of equations.

Classroom Example: p. 278, Exercise 32

Example 2 Solving a System of Linear Equations by Graphing

Solve the system by the graphing method.

$$y = 2x$$
$$y = 2$$

Solution:

The equation $y = 2x$ is written in slope-intercept form as $y = 2x + 0$. The line passes through the origin, with a slope of 2.

The line $y = 2$ is a horizontal line and has a slope of 0.

Because the lines have different slopes, the lines must be different and nonparallel. From this, we know that the lines must intersect at exactly one point. Graph the lines to find the point of intersection (Figure 4-2).

The point $(1, 2)$ appears to be the point of intersection. This can be confirmed by substituting $x = 1$ and $y = 2$ into both original equations.

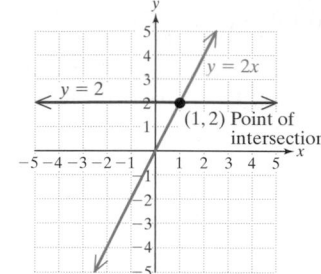

Figure 4-2

$$y = 2x \qquad (2) \overset{?}{=} 2(1) \checkmark \quad \text{True}$$
$$y = 2 \qquad (2) \overset{?}{=} 2 \checkmark \qquad \text{True}$$

The solution set is $\{(1, 2)\}$.

Skill Practice Solve the system by the graphing method.

3. $y = -3x$
   $x = -1$

Classroom Example: p. 278, Exercise 30

Example 3 Solving a System of Linear Equations by Graphing

Solve the system by the graphing method.

$$x - 2y = -2$$
$$-3x + 2y = 6$$

Solution:

To graph each equation, write the equation in slope-intercept form, $y = mx + b$.

Equation 1

$$x - 2y = -2$$
$$-2y = -x - 2$$
$$\frac{-2y}{-2} = \frac{-x}{-2} - \frac{2}{-2}$$
$$y = \frac{1}{2}x + 1$$

Equation 2

$$-3x + 2y = 6$$
$$2y = 3x + 6$$
$$\frac{2y}{2} = \frac{3x}{2} + \frac{6}{2}$$
$$y = \frac{3}{2}x + 3$$

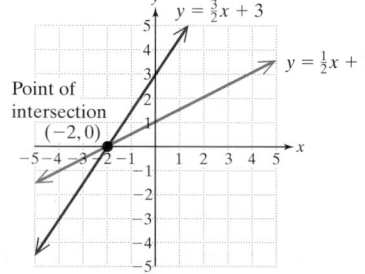

Figure 4-3

Answer

3. $\{(-1, 3)\}$

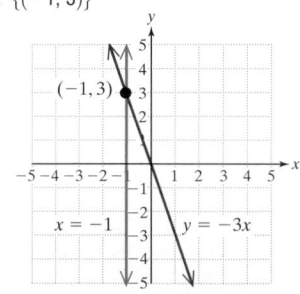

From their slope-intercept forms, we see that the lines have different slopes, indicating that the lines are different and nonparallel. Therefore, the lines must intersect at exactly one point. Graph the lines to find that point (Figure 4-3).

The point $(-2, 0)$ appears to be the point of intersection. This can be confirmed by substituting $x = -2$ and $y = 0$ into both equations.

$$x - 2y = -2 \longrightarrow (-2) - 2(0) \stackrel{?}{=} -2 \ ✔ \quad \text{True}$$

$$-3x + 2y = 6 \longrightarrow -3(-2) + 2(0) \stackrel{?}{=} 6 \ ✔ \quad \text{True}$$

The solution set is $\{(-2, 0)\}$.

Skill Practice Solve the system by the graphing method.

4. $y = 2x - 3$
   $6x + 2y = 4$

TIP: In Examples 2 and 3, the lines could also have been graphed by using the *x*- and *y*-intercepts or by using a table of points. However, the advantage of writing the equations in slope-intercept form is that we can compare the slopes and *y*-intercepts of each line.

1. If the slopes differ, the lines are different and nonparallel and must cross in exactly one point.
2. If the slopes are the same and the *y*-intercepts are different, the lines are parallel and will not intersect.
3. If the slopes are the same and the *y*-intercepts are the same, the two equations represent the same line.

Example 4 **Graphing an Inconsistent System**

Classroom Example: p. 278, Exercise 34

Solve the system by graphing.

$$-x + 3y = -6$$

$$6y = 2x + 6$$

Solution:

To graph the lines, write each equation in slope-intercept form.

Answers

4. $\{(1, -1)\}$

Equation 1	**Equation 2**
$-x + 3y = -6$	$6y = 2x + 6$
$3y = x - 6$	
$\dfrac{3y}{3} = \dfrac{x}{3} - \dfrac{6}{3}$	$\dfrac{6y}{6} = \dfrac{2x}{6} + \dfrac{6}{6}$
$y = \dfrac{1}{3}x - 2$	$y = \dfrac{1}{3}x + 1$

Figure 4-4

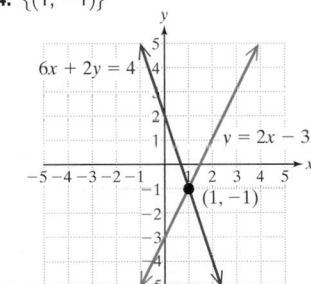

Because the lines have the same slope but different *y*-intercepts, they are parallel (Figure 4-4). Two parallel lines do not intersect, which implies that the system has no solution, $\{\ \}$. The system is inconsistent.

Skill Practice Solve the system by graphing.

5. $4x + y = 8$
   $y = -4x + 3$

5.

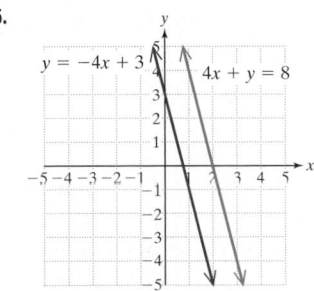

The lines are parallel. The system is inconsistent, $\{\ \}$.

Classroom Example: p. 278, Exercise 36

Example 5 Graphing a Dependent System

Solve the system by graphing. $x + 4y = 8$

$$y = -\frac{1}{4}x + 2$$

Solution:

Write the first equation in slope-intercept form. The second equation is already in slope-intercept form.

Equation 1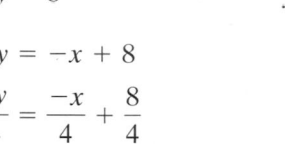

$x + 4y = 8$

$4y = -x + 8$

$\dfrac{4y}{4} = \dfrac{-x}{4} + \dfrac{8}{4}$

$y = -\dfrac{1}{4}x + 2$

Equation 2

$y = -\dfrac{1}{4}x + 2$

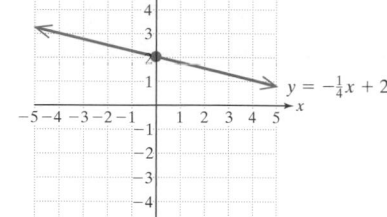

Figure 4-5

Notice that the slope-intercept forms of the two lines are identical. Therefore, the equations represent the same line (Figure 4-5). The system is dependent, and the solution to the system of equations is the set of all points on the line.

Because the ordered pairs in the solution set cannot all be listed, we can write the solution in set-builder notation: $\{(x, y) \mid y = -\frac{1}{4}x + 2\}$. This can be read as "the set of all ordered pairs (x, y) such that the ordered pairs satisfy the equation $y = -\frac{1}{4}x + 2$."

In summary:

- There are infinitely many solutions to the system of equations.
- The solution set is $\{(x, y) \mid y = -\frac{1}{4}x + 2\}$.
- The system is dependent.

Skill Practice Solve the system by graphing.

6. $x - 3y = 6$

    $y = \dfrac{1}{3}x - 2$

Answer

6.

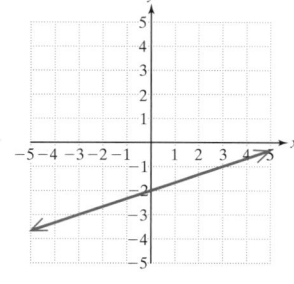

$\left\{ (x, y) \mid y = \dfrac{1}{3}x - 2 \right\}$

The system is dependent.

Calculator Connections

Topic: Graphing Systems of Linear Equations in Two Variables

The solution to a system of equations can be found by using either a *Trace* feature or an *Intersect* feature on a graphing calculator to find the point of intersection between two graphs.

For example, consider the system:

$$-2x + y = 6$$
$$5x + y = -1$$

First graph the equations together on the same viewing window. Recall that to enter the equations into the calculator, the equations must be written with the y variable isolated.

$$-2x + y = 6 \xrightarrow{\text{Isolate } y.} y = 2x + 6$$
$$5x + y = -1 \longrightarrow y = -5x - 1$$

By inspection of the graph, it appears that the solution is $(-1, 4)$. The *Trace* option on the calculator may come close to $(-1, 4)$ but may not show the exact solution (Figure 4-6). However, an *Intersect* feature on a graphing calculator may provide the exact solution (Figure 4-7). See your user's manual for further details.

Using *Trace*   Using *Intersect*

Figure 4-6   **Figure 4-7**

Calculator Exercises

Use a graphing calculator to graph each linear equation on the same viewing window. Use a *Trace* or *Intersect* feature to find the point(s) of intersection.

1. $y = 2x - 3$ $\{(2, 1)\}$

$y = -4x + 9$

2. $y = -\dfrac{1}{2}x + 2$ $\{(6, -1)\}$

$y = \dfrac{1}{3}x - 3$

3. $x + y = 4$ (Example 1)

$-2x + y = -5$ $\{(3, 1)\}$

4. $x - 2y = -2$ (Example 3)

$-3x + 2y = 6$

$\{(-2, 0)\}$

5. $-x + 3y = -6$ (Example 4)

$6y = 2x + 6$

$\{ \ \}$

6. $x + 4y = 8$ (Example 5)

$y = -\dfrac{1}{4}x + 2$ $\left\{(x, y) \,|\, y = -\dfrac{1}{4}x + 2\right\}$

Section 4.1   Practice Exercises

Study Skills Exercises

1. Figure out your grade at this point. Are you earning the grade that you want? If not, maybe organizing a study group would help.

In a study group, check the activities that you might try to help you learn and understand the material.

_____ Quiz each other by asking each other questions.

_____ Practice teaching each other.

_____ Share and compare class notes.

_____ Support and encourage each other.

_____ Work together on exercises and sample problems.

 Writing   Translating Expression   Geometry   Scientific Calculator   Video   NS&E

2. Define the key terms.

   a. system of linear equations   **b.** solution to a system of linear equations   **c.** consistent system

   d. inconsistent system   **e.** dependent system   **f.** independent system

Concept 1: Solutions to a System of Linear Equations

For Exercises 3–10, determine if the given point is a solution to the system. **(See Example 1.)**

3. $3x - y = 7$ $(2, -1)$

   $x - 2y = 4$ Yes

4. $x - y = 3$ $(4, 1)$

   $x + y = 5$ Yes

5. $4y = -3x + 12$ $(0, 4)$

   $y = \dfrac{2}{3}x - 4$ No

6. $y = -\dfrac{1}{3}x + 2$ $(9, -1)$

   $x = 2y + 6$ No

7. $3x - 6y = 9$ $\left(4, \dfrac{1}{2}\right)$

   $x - 2y = 3$ Yes

8. $x - y = 4$ $(6, 2)$

   $3x - 3y = 12$ Yes

9. $\dfrac{1}{3}x = \dfrac{2}{5}y - \dfrac{4}{5}$ $(0, 2)$

   $\dfrac{3}{4}x + \dfrac{1}{2}y = 2$ No

10. $\dfrac{1}{4}x + \dfrac{1}{2}y = \dfrac{3}{2}$ $(4, 1)$

   $y = \dfrac{3}{2}x - 6$ No

Concept 2: Dependent and Inconsistent Systems of Linear Equations

For Exercises 11–14, match the graph of the system of equations with the appropriate description of the solution.

11.   b

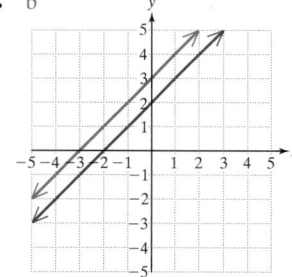

a. The solution set is $\{(1, 3)\}$.

b. $\{\ \}$

c. There are infinitely many solutions.

d. The solution set is $\{(0, 0)\}$.

12. c

13. d

14. a

 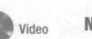

15. Graph each system of equations.

a. $y = 2x - 3$

$y = 2x + 5$

b. $y = 2x + 1$

$y = 4x - 1$

c. $y = 3x - 5$

$y = 3x - 5$

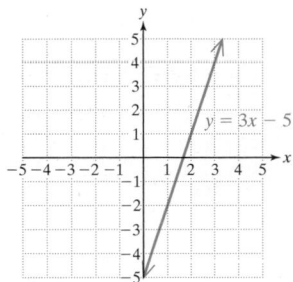

For Exercises 16–26, determine which system of equations (a, b, or c) makes the statement true. (*Hint:* Refer to the graphs from Exercise 15.)

a. $y = 2x - 3$ **b.** $y = 2x + 1$ **c.** $y = 3x - 5$

$y = 2x + 5$ $y = 4x - 1$ $y = 3x - 5$

16. The lines are parallel.   a

17. The lines coincide.   c

18. The lines intersect at exactly one point.   b

19. The system is inconsistent.   a

20. The system is dependent.   c

21. The lines have the same slope but different y-intercepts.   a

22. The lines have the same slope and same y-intercept.   c

23. The lines have different slopes.   b

24. The system has exactly one solution.   b

25. The system has infinitely many solutions.   c

26. The system has no solution.   a

Concept 3: Solving Systems of Linear Equations by Graphing

For Exercises 27–50, solve the systems by graphing. If a system does not have a unique solution, identify the system as inconsistent or dependent. **(See Examples 2–5.)**

27. $y = -x + 4$

$y = \ x - 2$ $\{(3, 1)\}$

28. $y = 3x + 2$

$y = 2x$ $\{(-2, -4)\}$

29. $2x + y = 0$

$3x + y = 1$ $\{(1, -2)\}$

30. $x + y = -1$
$2x - y = -5$ $\{(-2, 1)\}$

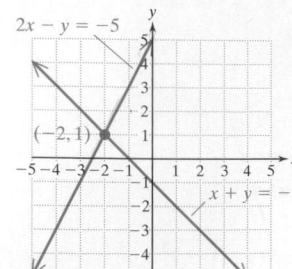

31. $2x + y = 6$
$x = 1$ $\{(1, 4)\}$

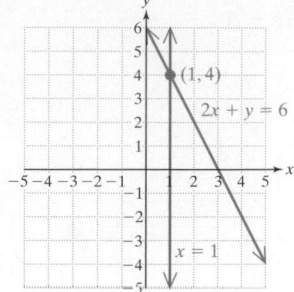

32. $4x + 3y = 9$
$x = 3$ $\{(3, -1)\}$

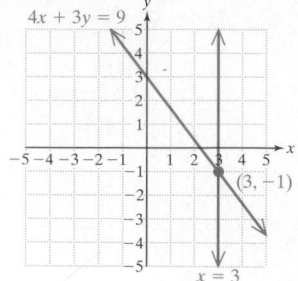

33. $-6x - 3y = 0$ { };
$4x + 2y = 4$ inconsistent system

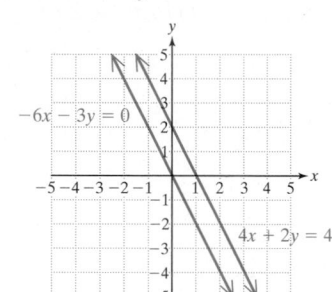

34. $2x - 6y = 12$ { };
$-3x + 9y = 12$ inconsistent system

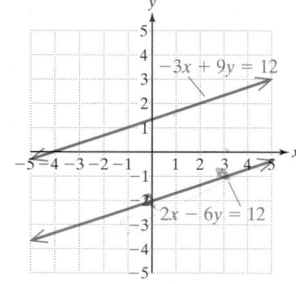

35. $-2x + y = 3$ Infinitely many solutions;
$6x - 3y = -9$ $\{(x, y) | -2x + y = 3\}$; dependent system

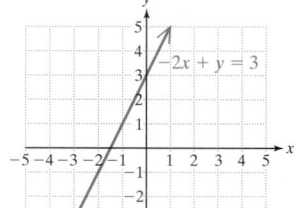

36. $x + 3y = 0$ Infinitely many solutions;
$-2x - 6y = 0$ $\{(x, y) | x + 3y = 0\}$; dependent system

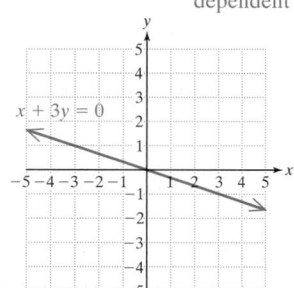

37. $y = 6$
$2x + 3y = 12$ $\{(-3, 6)\}$

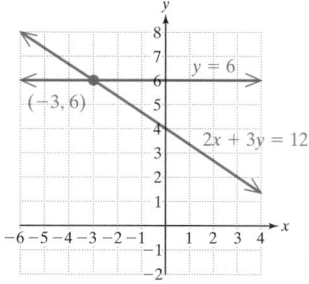

38. $y = -2$
$x - 2y = 10$ $\{(6, -2)\}$

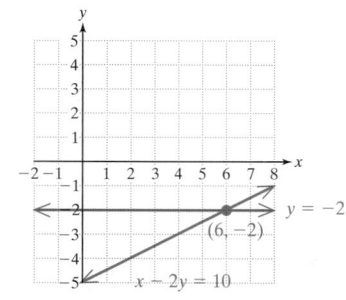

39. $x = 4 + y$
$3y = -3x$ $\{(2, -2)\}$

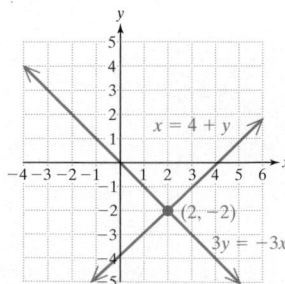

40. $3y = 4x$
$x - y = -1$ $\{(3, 4)\}$

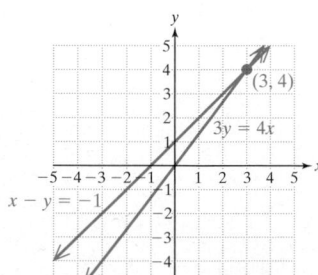

41. $-x + y = 3$ { };
$4y = 4x + 6$ inconsistent system

42. $x - y = 4$ { };
   inconsistent system
   $3y = 3x + 6$

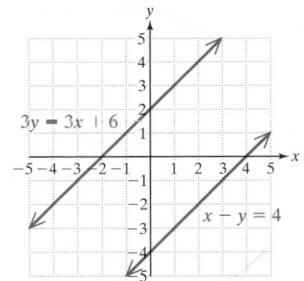

43. $x = 4$
   $2y = 4$ {(4, 2)}

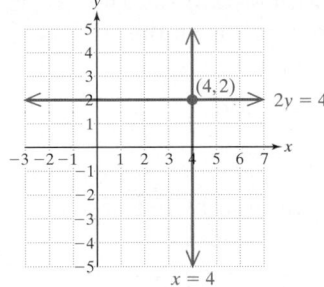

44. $-3x = 6$
   $y = 2$ {(-2, 2)}

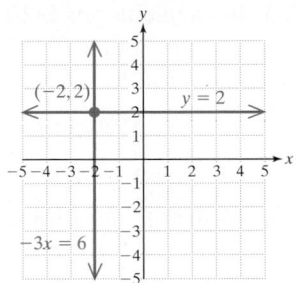

45. $2x + y = 4$
   $4x - 2y = 0$ {(1, 2)}

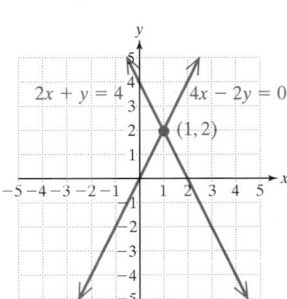

46. $3x + 3y = 3$
   $2x - y = 5$ {(2, -1)}

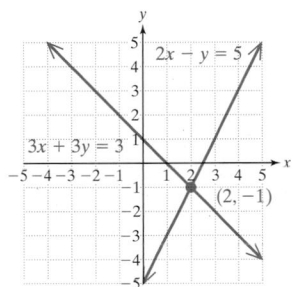

47. $y = 0.5x + 2$ Infinitely many
   solutions;
   $-x + 2y = 4$ {(x, y)|y = 0.5x + 2};
   dependent system

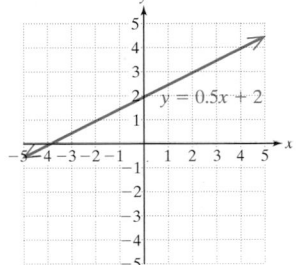

48. $3x - 4y = 6$ Infinitely many
   solutions;
   $-6x + 8y = -12$ {(x, y)|3x - 4y = 6};
   dependent system

49. $x - 3y = 0$
   $y = -x - 4$ {(-3, -1)}

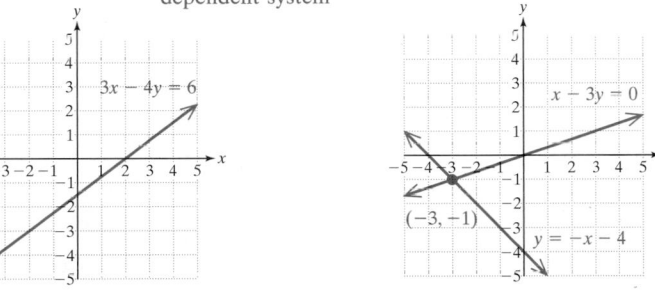

50. $-6x + 3y = -6$
   $4x + y = -2$ {(0, -2)}

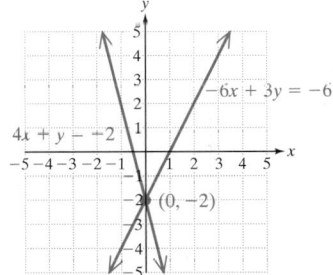

51. Costco Wholesale offers two types of memberships. The Executive Membership is $100 a year, including an annual 2% reward. The Business Membership is $50 a year without a reward. The total cost for membership, y, depends on the amount of money spent on merchandise, x, and can be represented by the following equations:

   Executive membership: $y = 100 - 0.02x$

   Business membership: $y = 50$

   According to the graph, how much money spent on merchandise would result in the same cost for each membership?
   The same cost occurs when $2500 of merchandise is purchased.

 Writing   Translating Expression   Geometry   Scientific Calculator   Video   NS&E

52. The cost to rent a 10 ft by 10 ft storage space is different for two different storage companies. The Storage Bin charges $90 per month plus a nonrefundable deposit of $120. AAA Storage charges $110 per month with no deposit. The total cost, y, to rent a 10 ft by 10 ft space depends on the number of months, x, according to the equations

The Storage Bin: $y = 90x + 120$

AAA Storage: $y = 110x$

From the graph, determine the number of months required for which the cost to rent space is equal for both companies.   For 6 months, the cost is $660 for each company.

For the systems graphed in Exercises 53–54, explain why the ordered pair cannot be a solution to the system of equations.

53. $(-3, 1)$ The point of intersection is below the x-axis and cannot have a positive y-coordinate.

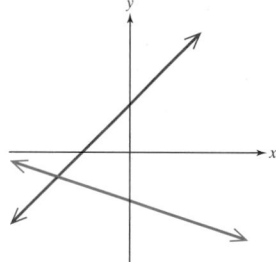

54. $(-1, -4)$ The point of intersection is above the x-axis and cannot have a negative y-coordinate.

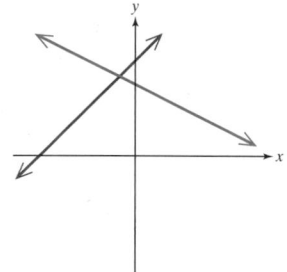

Expanding Your Skills

55. Write a system of linear equations whose solution set is $\{(2, 1)\}$.   For example: $4x + y = 9$
$-2x - y = -5$

56. Write a system of linear equations whose solution set is $\{(1, 4)\}$.   For example: $x - 3y = -11$
$3x + y = 7$

57. One equation in a system of linear equations is $x + y = 4$. Write a second equation such that the system will have no solution. (Answers may vary.)   For example: $2x + 2y = 1$

58. One equation in a system of linear equations is $x - y = 3$. Write a second equation such that the system will have infinitely many solutions. (Answers may vary.)   For example: $3x - 3y = 9$

Section 4.2 Solving Systems of Equations by the Substitution Method

Concepts

1. Solving Systems of Linear Equations by the Substitution Method
2. Applications of the Substitution Method

1. Solving Systems of Linear Equations by the Substitution Method

In Section 4.1, we used the graphing method to find the solution set to a system of equations. However, sometimes it is difficult to determine the solution using this method because of limitations in the accuracy of the graph. This is particularly true when the coordinates of a solution are not integer values or when the solution is a point not sufficiently close to the origin. Identifying the coordinates of the point $\left(\frac{3}{17}, -\frac{23}{9}\right)$ or $(-251, 8349)$, for example, might be difficult from a graph.

 Writing   Translating Expression   Geometry   Scientific Calculator   Video   NS&E

In this section and the next, we will cover two algebraic methods to solve a system of equations that do not require graphing. The first method, called the *substitution method*, is demonstrated in Examples 1–5.

Example 1 **Solving a System of Linear Equations by Using the Substitution Method**

Classroom Example: p. 288, Exercise 14

Solve the system by using the substitution method.

$$x = 2y - 3$$
$$-4x + 3y = 2$$

Solution:

The variable x has been isolated in the first equation. The quantity $2y - 3$ is equal to x and therefore can be substituted for x in the second equation. This leaves the second equation in terms of y only.

First equation: $\quad\quad x = \underbrace{2y - 3}$

Second equation: $\quad -4x + 3y = 2$

$\quad\quad -4(2y - 3) + 3y = 2 \quad\quad$ This equation now contains only one variable.

$\quad\quad -8y + 12 + 3y = 2 \quad\quad$ Solve the resulting equation.

$\quad\quad\quad\quad -5y + 12 = 2$

$\quad\quad\quad\quad\quad\quad -5y = -10$

$\quad\quad\quad\quad\quad\quad\quad y = 2$

To find x, substitute $y = 2$ back into the first equation.

$$x = 2y - 3$$
$$x = 2(2) - 3$$
$$x = 1$$

Check the ordered pair $(1, 2)$ in both original equations.

$x = 2y - 3 \longrightarrow 1 \overset{?}{=} 2(2) - 3 \checkmark \quad\quad$ True

$-4x + 3y = 2 \longrightarrow -4(1) + 3(2) \overset{?}{=} 2 \checkmark \quad$ True

The solution set is $\{(1, 2)\}$.

Avoiding Mistakes

Remember to solve for *both* variables in the system.

Skill Practice Solve the system by using the substitution method.

1. $2x + 3y = -2$
$\quad y = x + 1$

Instructor Note: Remind students that they can also graph a system of equations to determine if an answer is reasonable.

In Example 1, we eliminated the x variable from the second equation by substituting an equivalent expression for x. The resulting equation was relatively simple to solve because it had only one variable. This is the premise of the substitution method.

Answer
1. $\{(-1, 0)\}$

The substitution method can be summarized as follows.

> **PROCEDURE** Solving a System of Equations by the Substitution Method
>
> **Step 1** Isolate one of the variables from one equation.
> **Step 2** Substitute the quantity found in step 1 into the other equation.
> **Step 3** Solve the resulting equation.
> **Step 4** Substitute the value found in step 3 back into the equation in step 1 to find the value of the remaining variable.
> **Step 5** Check the ordered pair in both original equations.

Classroom Example: p. 288, Exercise 22

Example 2 Solving a System of Linear Equations by Using the Substitution Method

Solve the system by using the substitution method.

$$x + y = 4$$
$$-5x + 3y = -12$$

Solution:

The x or y variable in the first equation is easy to isolate because the coefficients are both 1. While either variable can be isolated, we arbitrarily choose to solve for the x variable.

$x + y = 4 \longrightarrow x = 4 - y$ **Step 1:** Solve the first equation for x.

$-5(4 - y) + 3y = -12$ **Step 2:** Substitute $4 - y$ for x in the other equation.

$-20 + 5y + 3y = -12$ **Step 3:** Solve for y.

$-20 + 8y = -12$

$8y = 8$

$y = 1$

$x = 4 - y$ **Step 4:** Substitute $y = 1$ into the equation $x = 4 - y$.

$x = 4 - 1$

$x = 3$

Step 5: Check the ordered pair $(3, 1)$ in both original equations.

$$x + y = 4 \qquad (3) + (1) \overset{?}{=} 4 \checkmark \qquad \text{True}$$
$$-5x + 3y = -12 \qquad -5(3) + 3(1) \overset{?}{=} -12 \checkmark \qquad \text{True}$$

The solution set is $\{(3, 1)\}$.

Avoiding Mistakes

Although we solved for y first, be sure to write the x-coordinate first in the ordered pair. Remember that $(1, 3)$ is not the same as $(3, 1)$.

TIP: The solution to a system of linear equations can be confirmed by graphing. The system from Example 2 is graphed here.

Skill Practice Solve the system by using the substitution method.

2. $\quad x + y = 3$
$\quad -2x + 3y = 9$

Answer

2. $\{(0, 3)\}$

Example 3 **Solving a System of Linear Equations by Using the Substitution Method**

Classroom Example: p. 288, Exercise 24

Solve the system by using the substitution method.

$$3x + 5y = 17$$
$$2x - y = -6$$

Solution:

The y variable in the second equation is the easiest variable to isolate because its coefficient is -1.

$3x + 5y = 17$

$2x - y = -6 \longrightarrow -y = -2x - 6$

$\qquad\qquad\qquad y = \underbrace{2x + 6}$ **Step 1:** Solve the second equation for y.

$3x + 5(2x + 6) = 17$ **Step 2:** Substitute the quantity $2x + 6$ for y in the other equation.

$3x + 10x + 30 = 17$ **Step 3:** Solve for x.

$\qquad 13x + 30 = 17$

$\qquad\qquad 13x = 17 - 30$

$\qquad\qquad 13x = -13$

$\qquad\qquad\quad x = -1$

$y = 2x + 6$ **Step 4:** Substitute $x = -1$ into the equation $y = 2x + 6$.

$y = 2(-1) + 6$

$y = -2 + 6$

$y = 4$

Step 5: The ordered pair $(-1, 4)$ can be checked in the original equations to verify the answer.

$3x + 5y = 17 \longrightarrow 3(-1) + 5(4) \overset{?}{=} 17 \longrightarrow -3 + 20 \overset{?}{=} 17$ ✔ True

$2x - y = -6 \longrightarrow 2(-1) - (4) \overset{?}{=} -6 \longrightarrow -2 - 4 \overset{?}{=} -6$ ✔ True

The solution set is $\{(-1, 4)\}$.

Skill Practice Solve the system by using the substitution method.

3. $x + 4y = 11$
$\quad 2x - 5y = -4$

Avoiding Mistakes

Do not substitute $y = 2x + 6$ into the same equation from which it came. This mistake will result in an identity:

$$2x - y = -6$$
$$2x - (2x + 6) = -6$$
$$2x - 2x - 6 = -6$$
$$-6 = -6$$

Answer

3. $\{(3, 2)\}$

Recall from Section 4.1, that a system of linear equations may represent two parallel lines. In such a case, there is no solution to the system.

Classroom Example: p. 288, Exercise 26

Example 4 Solving an Inconsistent System Using Substitution

Solve the system by using the substitution method.

$$2x + 3y = 6$$
$$y = -\tfrac{2}{3}x + 4$$

Solution:

$$2x + 3y = 6$$

$$y = \underbrace{-\tfrac{2}{3}x + 4}$$

Step 1: The variable y is already isolated in the second equation.

$$2x + 3(-\tfrac{2}{3}x + 4) = 6$$

Step 2: Substitute $y = -\tfrac{2}{3}x + 4$ from the second equation into the first equation.

$$2x - 2x + 12 = 6$$

Step 3: Solve the resulting equation.

$$12 = 6 \quad \text{(contradiction)}$$

The equation results in a contradiction. There are no values of x and y that will make 12 equal to 6. Therefore, the solution set is { }, and the system is inconsistent.

Skill Practice Solve the system by using the substitution method.

4. $y = -\dfrac{1}{2}x + 3$
$2x + 4y = 5$

Instructor Note: Remind students that in Chapter 2 when we solved equations in one variable, a contradiction had no solution. For example, the equation $x + 3 = x + 2$ has no solution.

TIP: The answer to Example 4 can be verified by writing each equation in slope-intercept form and graphing the lines.

Equation 1

$$2x + 3y = 6$$

$$3y = -2x + 6$$

$$\dfrac{3y}{3} = \dfrac{-2x}{3} + \dfrac{6}{3}$$

$$y = -\dfrac{2}{3}x + 2$$

Equation 2

$$y = -\dfrac{2}{3}x + 4$$

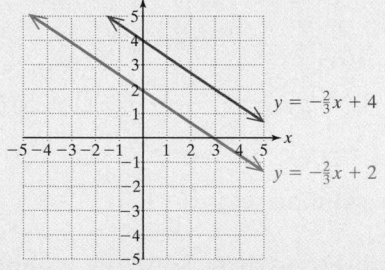

The equations indicate that the lines have the same slope but different y-intercepts. Therefore, the lines must be parallel. There is no point of intersection, indicating that the system has no solution, { }.

Answer

4. { }

Recall that a system of two linear equations may represent the same line. In such a case, the solution is the set of all points on the line.

Classroom Example: p. 289, Exercise 40

Example 5	**Solving a Dependent System Using Substitution**

Solve the system by using the substitution method.

$$\frac{1}{2}x - \frac{1}{4}y = 1$$

$$6x - 3y = 12$$

Solution:

$\frac{1}{2}x - \frac{1}{4}y = 1$

$6x - 3y = 12$

To make the first equation easier to work with, we have the option of clearing fractions.

$\frac{1}{2}x - \frac{1}{4}y = 1$ $\xrightarrow{\text{Multiply by 4.}}$ $4\left(\frac{1}{2}x\right) - 4\left(\frac{1}{4}y\right) = 4(1) \longrightarrow 2x - y = 4$

Now the system becomes:

$2x - y = 4$

$6x - 3y = 12$

The y variable in the first equation is the easiest to isolate because its coefficient is -1.

$2x - y = 4 \xrightarrow{\text{Solve for } y.} -y = -2x + 4 \rightarrow y = \underline{2x - 4}$ **Step 1:** Isolate one of the variables.

$6x - 3y = 12$

$6x - 3(2x - 4) = 12$ **Step 2:** Substitute $y = 2x - 4$ from the first equation into the second equation.

$6x - 6x + 12 = 12$ **Step 3:** Solve the resulting equation.

$12 = 12$ (identity)

Because the equation produces an identity, all values of x make this equation true. Thus, x can be any real number. Substituting any real number, x, into the equation $y = 2x - 4$ produces an ordered pair on the line $y = 2x - 4$. Hence, the solution set to the system of equations is the set of all ordered pairs on the line $y = 2x - 4$. This can be written as $\{(x, y) \mid y = 2x - 4\}$. The system is dependent.

Skill Practice Solve the system by using the substitution method.

5. $2x + \frac{1}{3}y = -\frac{1}{3}$

$12x + 2y = -2$

Answer

5. Infinitely many solutions; $\{(x, y) \mid 12x + 2y = -2\}$; dependent system

TIP: The solution to Example 5 can be verified by writing each equation in slope-intercept form and graphing the lines.

Equation 1	**Equation 2**

Clear fractions $\dfrac{1}{2}x - \dfrac{1}{4}y = 1$ $6x - 3y = 12$

$2x - y = 4$ $-3y = -6x + 12$

$-y = -2x + 4$ $\dfrac{-3y}{-3} = \dfrac{-6x}{-3} + \dfrac{12}{-3}$

$y = 2x - 4$ $y = 2x - 4$

$y = 2x - 4$

Notice that the slope-intercept forms for both equations are identical. The equations represent the same line, indicating that the system is dependent. Each point on the line is a solution to the system of equations.

The following summary reviews the three different geometric relationships between two lines and the solutions to the corresponding systems of equations.

SUMMARY   **Interpreting Solutions to a System of Two Linear Equations**

- The lines may intersect at one point (yielding one unique solution).
- The lines may be parallel and have no point of intersection (yielding no solution). This is detected algebraically when a contradiction (false statement) is obtained (for example, $0 = -3$ or $12 = 6$).
- The lines may be the same and intersect at all points on the line (yielding an infinite number of solutions). This is detected algebraically when an identity is obtained (for example, $0 = 0$ or $12 = 12$).

2. Applications of the Substitution Method

In Chapter 2, we solved word problems using one linear equation and one variable. In this chapter, we investigate application problems with two unknowns. In such a case, we can use two variables to represent the unknown quantities. However, if two variables are used, we must write a system of *two* distinct equations.

Classroom Example: p. 289, Exercise 52

Example 6   **Applying the Substitution Method**

One number is 3 more than 4 times another. Their sum is 133. Find the numbers.

Solution:

We can use two variables to represent the two unknown numbers.

Let x represent one number.
Let y represent the other number.   Label the variables.

We must now write two equations. Each of the first two sentences gives a relationship between x and y:

One number is 3 more than 4 times another. $\longrightarrow$ $x = 4y + 3$ (first equation)

Their sum is 133. $\longrightarrow$ $x + y = 133$ (second equation)

$(4y + 3) + y = 133$	Substitute $x = 4y + 3$ into the second equation, $x + y = 133$.
$5y + 3 = 133$	Solve the resulting equation.
$5y = 130$	
$y = 26$	
$x = 4y + 3$	
$x = 4(26) + 3$	To solve for x, substitute $y = 26$ into the equation $x = 4y + 3$.
$x = 104 + 3$	
$x = 107$	

One number is 26, and the other is 107.

Skill Practice

6. One number is 16 more than another. Their sum is 92. Use a system of equations to find the numbers.

> **TIP:** Check that the numbers 26 and 107 meet the conditions of Example 6.
> - 4 times 26 is 104. Three more than 104 is 107. ✔
> - The sum of the numbers should be 133: $26 + 107 = 133$ ✔

Example 7 **Using the Substitution Method in a Geometry Application**

Classroom Example: p. 289, Exercise 56

Two angles are supplementary. The measure of one angle is 15° more than twice the measure of the other angle. Find the measures of the two angles.

Solution:

Let x represent the measure of one angle.
Let y represent the measure of the other angle.

The sum of the measures of supplementary angles is 180° ⟶ $x + y = 180$

The measure of one angle is 15° more than
twice the other angle ⟶ $x = 2y + 15$

$x + y = 180$	
$x = 2y + 15$	The x variable in the second equation is already isolated.
$(2y + 15) + y = 180$	Substitute $2y + 15$ into the first equation for x.
$2y + 15 + y = 180$	Solve the resulting equation.
$3y + 15 = 180$	
$3y = 165$	
$y = 55$	
$x = 2y + 15$	Substitute $y = 55$ into the equation $x = 2y + 15$.
$x = 2(55) + 15$	
$x = 110 + 15$	
$x = 125$	

One angle is 55°, and the other is 125°.

> **TIP:** Check that the angles 55° and 125° meet the conditions of Example 7.
> - Because $55° + 125° = 180°$, the angles are supplementary. ✔
> - The angle 125° is 15° more than twice 55°: $125° = 2(55°) + 15°$ ✔

Answer
6. One number is 38, and the other number is 54.

Answer

7. The measures of the angles are 23° and 67°.

Skill Practice

7. The measure of one angle is 2° less than 3 times the measure of another angle. The angles are complementary. Use a system of equations to find the measures of the two angles.

Section 4.2 Practice Exercises

Review Exercises

For Exercises 1–6, write each pair of lines in slope-intercept form. Then identify whether the lines intersect in exactly one point or if the lines are parallel or coinciding.

1. $2x - y = 4$ $y = 2x - 4$

   $-2y = -4x + 8$
   $y = 2x - 4$; coinciding lines

2. $x - 2y = 5$ $y = \frac{1}{2}x - \frac{5}{2}$

   $3x = 6y + 15$
   $y = \frac{1}{2}x - \frac{5}{2}$; coinciding lines

3. $2x + 3y = 6$ $y = -\frac{2}{3}x + 2$

   $x - y = 5$
   $y = x - 5$; intersecting lines

4. $x - y = -1$ $y = x + 1$

   $x + 2y = 4$ $y = -\frac{1}{2}x + 2$;
   intersecting lines

5. $2x = \frac{1}{2}y + 2$ $y = 4x - 4$

   $4x - y = 13$ $y = 4x - 13$; parallel lines

6. $4y = 3x$ $y = \frac{3}{4}x$

   $3x - 4y = 15$ $y = \frac{3}{4}x - \frac{15}{4}$; parallel lines

Concept 1: Solving Systems of Linear Equations by the Substitution Method

For Exercises 7–10, solve each system using the substitution method. **(See Example 1.)**

7. $3x + 2y = -3$

   $y = 2x - 12$
   $\{(3, -6)\}$

8. $4x - 3y = -19$

   $y = -2x + 13$
   $\{(2, 9)\}$

9. $x = -4y + 16$

   $3x + 5y = 20$
   $\{(0, 4)\}$

10. $x = -y + 3$

    $-2x + y = 6$
    $\{(-1, 4)\}$

11. Given the system: $4x - 2y = -6$

    $3x + y = 8$

    a. Which variable from which equation is easiest to isolate and why? *y* in the second equation is easiest to isolate because its coefficient is 1.
    b. Solve the system using the substitution method.
    $\{(1, 5)\}$

12. Given the system: $x - 5y = 2$

    $11x + 13y = 22$

    a. Which variable from which equation is easiest to isolate and why? *x* in the first equation is easiest to isolate because its coefficient is 1.
    b. Solve the system using the substitution method.
    $\{(2, 0)\}$

For Exercises 13–48, solve each system using the substitution method. **(See Examples 1–5.)**

13. $x = 3y - 1$ $\{(5, 2)\}$

    $2x - 4y = 2$

14. $2y = x + 9$ $\{(-1, 4)\}$

    $y = -3x + 1$

15. $-2x + 5y = 5$ $\{(10, 5)\}$

    $x = 4y - 10$

16. $y = -2x + 27$ $\{(11, 5)\}$

    $3x - 7y = -2$

17. $4x - y = -1$ $\left\{\left(\frac{1}{2}, 3\right)\right\}$

    $2x + 4y = 13$

18. $5x - 3y = -2$ $\left\{\left(\frac{1}{5}, 1\right)\right\}$

    $10x - y = 1$

19. $4x - 3y = 11$ $\{(5, 3)\}$

    $x = 5$

20. $y = -3x - 9$ $\{(-7, 12)\}$

    $y = 12$

21. $4x = 8y + 4$ $\{(1, 0)\}$

    $5x - 3y = 5$

22. $3y = 6x - 6$ $\{(2, 2)\}$

    $-3x + y = -4$

23. $x - 3y = -11$ $\{(1, 4)\}$

    $6x - y = 2$

24. $-2x - y = 9$ $\{(-6, 3)\}$

    $x + 7y = 15$

25. $3x + 2y = -1$

    $\frac{3}{2}x + y = 4$
    { };
    inconsistent system

26. $5x - 2y = 6$

    $-\frac{5}{2}x + y = 5$
    { };
    inconsistent system

27. $10x - 30y = -10$
    Infinitely many solutions;
    $2x - 6y = -2$
    $\{(x, y) | 2x - 6y = -2\}$;
    dependent system

28. $3x + 6y = 6$
    Infinitely many solutions;
    $-6x - 12y = -12$
    $\{(x, y) | 3x + 6y = 6\}$;
    dependent system

29. $2x + y = 3$
$y = -7$
$\{(5, -7)\}$

30. $-3x = 2y + 23$
$x = -1$
$\{(-1, -10)\}$

31. $x + 2y = -2$ $\left\{\left(-5, \frac{3}{2}\right)\right\}$
$4x = -2y - 17$

32. $x + y = 1$ $\left\{\left(-\frac{1}{3}, \frac{4}{3}\right)\right\}$
$2x - y = -2$

33. $y = -\frac{1}{2}x - 4$ $\{(2, -5)\}$
$y = \quad 4x - 13$

34. $y = \frac{2}{3}x - 3$ $\{(3, -1)\}$
$y = 6x - 19$

35. $y = 6$ $\{(-4, 6)\}$
$y - 4 = -2x - 6$

36. $x = 9$ $\{(9, -1)\}$
$x - 3 = 6y + 12$

37. $3x + 2y = 4$
$2x - 3y = -6$
$\{(0, 2)\}$

38. $4x + 3y = 4$
$-2x + 5y = -2$
$\{(1, 0)\}$

39. $y = 0.25x + 1$
Infinitely many solutions;
$-x + 4y = 4$
$\{(x, y) | y = 0.25x + 1\}$;
dependent system

40. $y = 0.75x - 3$
Infinitely many solutions;
$-3x + 4y = -12$
$\{(x, y) | y = 0.75x - 3\}$;
dependent system

41. $11x + 6y = 17$
$5x - 4y = 1$
$\{(1, 1)\}$

42. $3x - 8y = 7$
$10x - 5y = 45$
$\{(5, 1)\}$

43. $x + 2y = 4$
$4y = -2x - 8$
$\{\ \}$; inconsistent system

44. $-y = x - 6$
$2x + 2y = 4$
$\{\ \}$; inconsistent system

45. $2x = 3 - y$
$x + y = 4$ $\{(-1, 5)\}$

46. $2x = 4 + 2y$
$3x + y = 10$ $\{(3, 1)\}$

47. $\frac{x}{3} + \frac{y}{2} = -4$
$x - 3y = 6$ $\{(-6, -4)\}$

48. $x - 2y = -5$
$\frac{2x}{3} + \frac{y}{3} = 0$ $\{(-1, 2)\}$

Concept 2: Applications of the Substitution Method

For Exercises 49–58, set up a system of linear equations and solve for the indicated quantities. **(See Examples 6–7.)**

49. Two numbers have a sum of 106. One number is 10 less than the other. Find the numbers.
The numbers are 48 and 58.

50. Two positive numbers have a difference of 8. The larger number is 2 less than 3 times the smaller number. Find the numbers.
The numbers are 13 and 5.

51. The difference between two positive numbers is 26. The larger number is 3 times the smaller. Find the numbers.
The numbers are 13 and 39.

52. The sum of two numbers is 956. One number is 94 less than 6 times the other. Find the numbers.
The numbers are 150 and 806.

53. Two angles are supplementary. One angle is 15° more than 10 times the other angle. Find the measure of each angle.
The angles are 165° and 15°.

54. Two angles are complementary. One angle is 1° less than 6 times the other angle. Find the measure of each angle. The angles are 13° and 77°.

55. Two angles are complementary. One angle is 10° more than 3 times the other angle. Find the measure of each angle. The angles are 70° and 20°.

56. Two angles are supplementary. One angle is 5° less than twice the other angle. Find the measure of each angle. The angles are $118\frac{1}{3}°$ and $61\frac{2}{3}°$.

57. In a right triangle, one of the acute angles is 6° less than the other acute angle. Find the measure of each acute angle. The angles are 42° and 48°.

58. In a right triangle, one of the acute angles is 9° less than twice the other acute angle. Find the measure of each acute angle. The angles are 57° and 33°.

 Writing   Translating Expression   Geometry   Scientific Calculator   Video   NS&E

Expanding Your Skills

59. The following system of equations is dependent and has infinitely many solutions. Find three ordered pairs that are solutions to the system of equations.

$$y = 2x + 3$$
$$-4x + 2y = 6$$

For example: $(0, 3), (1, 5), (-1, 1)$

60. The following system of equations is dependent and has infinitely many solutions. Find three ordered pairs that are solutions to the system of equations.

$$y = -x + 1$$
$$2x + 2y = 2$$

For example: $(0, 1), (1, 0), (-1, 2)$

Section 4.3	Solving Systems of Equations by the Addition Method

Concepts

1. Solving Systems of Linear Equations by Using the Addition Method
2. Summary of Methods for Solving Systems of Linear Equations in Two Variables

Classroom Example: p. 297, Exercise 10

1. Solving Systems of Linear Equations by Using the Addition Method

Thus far in Chapter 4 we have used the graphing method and the substitution method to solve a system of linear equations in two variables. In this section, we present another algebraic method to solve a system of linear equations, called the *addition method* (sometimes called the *elimination method*). The purpose of the addition method is to eliminate one variable.

Example 1 Solving a System of Linear Equations by Using the Addition Method

Solve the system by using the addition method.

$$x + y = -2$$
$$x - y = -6$$

Solution:

To eliminate one of the variables, we use the addition property of equality. This states that adding the same quantity on each side of an equation results in an equivalent equation. That is, if A = B and C = D, then A + C = B + D. We will add the two equations vertically.

Notice that the coefficients of the *y* variables are opposites:

Coefficient is 1.

$$x + 1y = -2$$
$$x - 1y = -6$$

Coefficient is -1.

Because the coefficients of the *y* variables are opposites, we can add the two equations to eliminate the *y* variable.

$$x + y = -2$$
$$\underline{x - y = -6}$$
$$2x \quad\;\; = -8 \quad\leftarrow\text{ After adding the equations, we have one equation and one variable.}$$

$$2x = -8 \qquad \text{Solve the resulting equation.}$$
$$x = -4$$

To find the value of y, substitute $x = -4$ into *either* of the original equations.

$$x + y = -2 \qquad \text{First equation}$$
$$(-4) + y = -2$$
$$y = -2 + 4$$
$$y = 2 \qquad \text{The ordered pair is } (-4, 2).$$

<u>Check:</u>

$$x + y = -2 \longrightarrow (-4) + (2) \overset{?}{=} -2 \longrightarrow -2 \overset{?}{=} -2 \ ✔ \ \text{True}$$
$$x - y = -6 \longrightarrow (-4) - (2) \overset{?}{=} -6 \longrightarrow -6 \overset{?}{=} -6 \ ✔ \ \text{True}$$

The solution set is $\{(-4, 2)\}$.

Skill Practice Solve the system by using the addition method.

1. $x + y = 13$
   $2x - y = 2$

TIP: Notice that the value $x = -4$ could have been substituted into the second equation, to obtain the same value for y.

$$x - y = -6$$
$$(-4) - y = -6$$
$$-y = -6 + 4$$
$$-y = -2$$
$$y = 2$$

It is important to note that the addition method works on the premise that the two equations have *opposite* values for the coefficients of one of the variables. Sometimes it is necessary to manipulate the original equations to create two coefficients that are opposites. This is accomplished by multiplying one or both equations by an appropriate constant. The process is outlined as follows.

PROCEDURE Solving a System of Equations by the Addition Method

Step 1 Write both equations in standard form: $Ax + By = C$.

Step 2 Clear fractions or decimals (optional).

Step 3 Multiply one or both equations by nonzero constants to create opposite coefficients for one of the variables.

Step 4 Add the equations from step 3 to eliminate one variable.

Step 5 Solve for the remaining variable.

Step 6 Substitute the known value from step 5 into one of the original equations to solve for the other variable.

Step 7 Check the ordered pair in both equations.

Instructor Note: Point out that in step 3 it does not matter whether we create opposites for the x variables or the y variables.

Answer

1. $\{(5, 8)\}$

Classroom Example: p. 297,
Exercise 14

Example 2   Solving a System of Linear Equations
by Using the Addition Method

Solve the system by using the addition method.

$$3x + 5y = 17$$

$$2x - y = -6$$

Solution:

$3x + 5y = 17$ **Step 1:**   Both equations are already written in standard form.

$2x - y = -6$ **Step 2:**   There are no fractions or decimals.

Notice that neither the coefficients of x nor the coefficients of y are opposites. However, multiplying the second equation by 5 creates the term $-5y$ in the second equation. This is the opposite of the term $+5y$ in the first equation.

Avoiding Mistakes

Remember to multiply the chosen constant on *both* sides of the equation.

$$
\begin{array}{l}
3x + 5y = 17 \\
2x - y = -6 \xrightarrow[\text{Multiply by 5.}]{}
\end{array}
\qquad
\begin{array}{l}
3x + 5y = 17 \\
\underline{10x - 5y = -30} \\
13x = -13
\end{array}
$$

Step 3:   Multiply the second equation by 5.

Step 4:   Add the equations.

$$13x = -13$$ **Step 5:**   Solve the equation.

$$x = -1$$

TIP: In Example 2, we could have eliminated the x variable by multiplying the first equation by 2 and the second equation by -3.

$$
\begin{array}{l}
3x + 5y = 17 \\
3(-1) + 5y = 17 \\
-3 + 5y = 17 \\
5y = 20 \\
y = 4
\end{array}
$$

First equation

Step 6:   Substitute $x = -1$ into one of the original equations.

Step 7:   Check $(-1, 4)$ in both original equations.

Check:

$$3x + 5y = 17 \longrightarrow 3(-1) + 5(4) \overset{?}{=} 17 \longrightarrow -3 + 20 \overset{?}{=} 17 \checkmark \quad \text{True}$$

$$2x - y = -6 \longrightarrow 2(-1) - (4) \overset{?}{=} -6 \longrightarrow -2 - 4 \overset{?}{=} -6 \checkmark \quad \text{True}$$

The solution set is $\{(-1, 4)\}$.

Skill Practice   Solve the system by using the addition method.

2. $4x + 3y = 3$
  $x - 2y = 9$

In Example 3, the system of equations uses the variables a and b instead of x and y. In such a case, we will write the solution as an ordered pair with the variables written in alphabetical order, such as (a, b).

Answer

2. $\{(3, -3)\}$

Example 3 **Solving a System of Linear Equations by Using the Addition Method**

Classroom Example: p. 298, Exercise 18

Solve the system by using the addition method.

$$5b = 7a + 8$$
$$-4a - 2b = -10$$

Solution:

Step 1: Write the equations in standard form.

The first equation becomes: $\quad 5b = 7a + 8 \longrightarrow -7a + 5b = 8$

The system becomes: $\quad -7a + 5b = 8$
$$-4a - 2b = -10$$

Step 2: There are no fractions or decimals.

Step 3: We need to obtain opposite coefficients on either the a or b term.

Notice that neither the coefficients of a nor the coefficients of b are opposites. However, it is possible to change the coefficients of b to 10 and -10 (this is because the LCM of 5 and 2 is 10). This is accomplished by multiplying the first equation by 2 and the second equation by 5.

$$-7a + 5b = 8 \quad \xrightarrow{\text{Multiply by 2.}} \quad -14a + 10b = 16$$
$$-4a - 2b = -10 \quad \xrightarrow{\text{Multiply by 5.}} \quad \underline{-20a - 10b = -50}$$
$$-34a \qquad\quad = -34 \qquad$$

Step 4: Add the equations.

$$-34a = -34$$

Step 5: Solve the resulting equation.

$$\frac{-34a}{-34} = \frac{-34}{-34}$$

$$a = 1$$

$5b = 7a + 8$ First equation

Step 6: Substitute $a = 1$ into one of the original equations.

$$5b = 7(1) + 8$$

$$5b = 15$$

$$b = 3$$

Step 7: Check $(1, 3)$ in the original equations.

Check:

$$5b = 7a + 8 \longrightarrow 5(3) \overset{?}{=} 7(1) + 8 \longrightarrow 15 \overset{?}{=} 7 + 8 \checkmark \quad \text{True}$$

$$-4a - 2b = -10 \longrightarrow -4(1) - 2(3) \overset{?}{=} -10 \longrightarrow -4 - 6 \overset{?}{=} -10 \checkmark \quad \text{True}$$

The solution set is $\{(1, 3)\}$.

Skill Practice Solve the system by using the addition method.

3. $8n = 4 - 5m$
$7m + 6n = -10$

Answer

3. $\{(-4, 3)\}$

Classroom Example: p. 298, Exercise 22

Example 4 Solving a System of Linear Equations by Using the Addition Method

Solve the system by using the addition method.

$$34x - 22y = 4$$
$$17x - 88y = -19$$

Solution:

The equations are already in standard form. There are no fractions or decimals to clear.

$$34x - 22y = 4 \longrightarrow 34x - 22y = 4$$
$$17x - 88y = -19 \xrightarrow{\text{Multiply by } -2.} \underline{-34x + 176y = 38}$$
$$154y = 42$$

Solve for y. $\quad 154y = 42$

$$\frac{154y}{154} = \frac{42}{154}$$

Simplify. $\qquad y = \dfrac{3}{11}$

To find the value of x, we normally substitute y into one of the original equations and solve for x. In this example, we will show an alternative method for finding x. By repeating the addition method, this time eliminating y, we can solve for x. This approach enables us to avoid substitution of the fractional value for y.

$$34x - 22y = 4 \xrightarrow{\text{Multiply by } -4.} -136x + 88y = -16$$
$$17x - 88y = -19 \longrightarrow \underline{17x - 88y = -19}$$
$$-119x \qquad = -35$$

Solve for x. $\quad -119x = -35$

$$\frac{-119x}{-119} = \frac{-35}{-119}$$

Simplify. $\qquad x = \dfrac{5}{17}$

The ordered pair $\left(\frac{5}{17}, \frac{3}{11}\right)$ can be checked in the original equations.

$$34x - 22y = 4 \qquad\qquad\qquad 17x - 88y = -19$$

$$34\left(\frac{5}{17}\right) - 22\left(\frac{3}{11}\right) \overset{?}{=} 4 \qquad\qquad 17\left(\frac{5}{17}\right) - 88\left(\frac{3}{11}\right) \overset{?}{=} -19$$

$$10 - 6 \overset{?}{=} 4 ✔ \text{ True} \qquad\qquad 5 - 24 \overset{?}{=} -19 ✔ \text{ True}$$

The solution set is $\left\{\left(\dfrac{5}{17}, \dfrac{3}{11}\right)\right\}$.

Skill Practice Solve the system by using the addition method.

4. $15x - 16y = 1$
$\quad 45x + 4y = 16$

Answer

4. $\left\{\left(\dfrac{1}{3}, \dfrac{1}{4}\right)\right\}$

Example 5 **Solving an Inconsistent System by the Addition Method**

Classroom Example: p. 298, Exercise 32

Solve the system by using the addition method.

$$2x - 5y = 10$$

$$\frac{1}{2}x - \frac{5}{4}y = 1$$

Solution:

$$2x - 5y = 10$$

$$\frac{1}{2}x - \frac{5}{4}y = 1$$ **Step 1:** The equations are in standard form.

Step 2: Multiply both sides of the second equation by 4 to clear fractions.

$$\frac{1}{2}x - \frac{5}{4}y = 1 \longrightarrow 4\left(\frac{1}{2}x - \frac{5}{4}y\right) = 4(1) \longrightarrow 2x - 5y = 4$$

Now the system becomes

$$2x - 5y = 10$$

$$2x - 5y = 4$$

To make either the x coefficients or y coefficients opposites, multiply either equation by -1.

$$2x - 5y = 10 \xrightarrow{\text{Multiply by } -1.} -2x + 5y = -10$$ **Step 3:** Create opposite coefficients.

$$2x - 5y = 4 \longrightarrow \underline{2x - 5y = 4}$$

$$0 = 6$$ **Step 4:** Add the equations.

Because the result is a contradiction, the solution set is { }, and the system of equations is inconsistent. Writing each equation in slope-intercept form verifies that the lines are parallel (Figure 4-8).

$$2x - 5y - 10 \xrightarrow{\text{slope-intercept form}} y = \frac{2}{5}x - 2$$

$$\frac{1}{2}x - \frac{5}{4}y = 1 \xrightarrow{\text{slope-intercept form}} y = \frac{2}{5}x - \frac{4}{5}$$

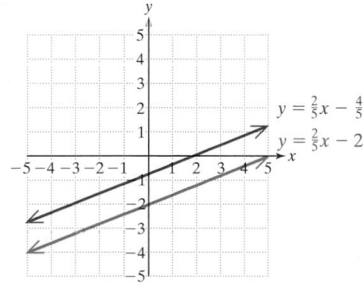

Figure 4-8

Skill Practice Solve the system by using the addition method.

5. $\dfrac{2}{3}x - \dfrac{3}{4}y = 2$

$8x - 9y = 6$

Answer

5. { }.

Classroom Example: p. 298, Exercise 34

| Example 6 | Solving a Dependent System by the Addition Method |

Solve the system by using the addition method. $3x - y = 4$

$$2y = 6x - 8$$

Solution:

$3x - y = 4 \longrightarrow 3x - y = 4$ **Step 1:** Write the equations in standard form.

$2y = 6x - 8 \longrightarrow -6x + 2y = -8$ **Step 2:** There are no fractions or decimals.

Notice that the equations differ exactly by a factor of -2, which indicates that these two equations represent the same line. Multiply the first equation by 2 to create opposite coefficients for the variables.

$$
\begin{array}{ll}
& \text{Multiply by 2.} \\
3x - y = 4 \xrightarrow{\hspace{2cm}} & 6x - 2y = 8 \quad \textbf{Step 3:} \quad \text{Create opposite} \\
-6x + 2y = -8 & \underline{-6x + 2y = -8} \qquad\qquad\quad \text{coefficients.} \\
& \qquad\quad\ 0 = 0 \quad\ \ \textbf{Step 4:} \quad \text{Add the equations.}
\end{array}
$$

Because the resulting equation is an identity, the original equations represent the same line. This can be confirmed by writing each equation in slope-intercept form.

$$3x - y = 4 \longrightarrow -y = -3x + 4 \longrightarrow y = 3x - 4$$

$$-6x + 2y = -8 \longrightarrow 2y = 6x - 8 \longrightarrow y = 3x - 4$$

The solution is the set of all points on the line, or equivalently, $\{(x, y) \mid y = 3x - 4\}$.

Skill Practice Solve the system by using the addition method.

  6. $3x = 3y + 15$
      $2x - 2y = 10$

2. Summary of Methods for Solving Systems of Linear Equations in Two Variables

If no method of solving a system of linear equations is specified, you may use the method of your choice. However, we recommend the following guidelines:

  1. If one of the equations is written with a variable isolated, the substitution method is a good choice. For example:

$$
\begin{array}{ccc}
2x + 5y = 2 & \text{or} & y = \dfrac{1}{3}x - 2 \\
x = y - 6 & & x - 6y = 9
\end{array}
$$

  2. If both equations are written in standard form, $Ax + By = C$, where none of the variables has coefficients of 1 or -1, then the addition method is a good choice.

$$4x + 5y = 12$$

$$5x + 3y = 15$$

  3. If both equations are written in standard form, $Ax + By = C$, and at least one variable has a coefficient of 1 or -1, then either the substitution method or the addition method is a good choice.

Answer
6. $\{(x, y) \mid 2x - 2y = 10\}$

Section 4.3 Practice Exercises

Study Skills Exercise

1. Now that you have learned three methods of solving a system of linear equations with two variables, choose a system and solve it all three ways. There are two advantages to this. One is to check your answer (you should get the same answer using all three methods). The second advantage is to show you which method is the easiest for you to use.

   Solve the system by using the graphing method, the substitution method, and the addition method.

   $$2x + y = -7$$
   $$x - 10 = 4y$$

Review Exercises

For Exercises 2–5, check whether the given ordered pair is a solution to the system.

2. $x + y = 8$ $(5, 3)$ Yes
   $y = x - 2$

3. $x = y + 1$ $(3, 2)$ No
   $-x + 2y = 0$

4. $3x + 2y = 14$ $(5, -2)$ No
   $5x - 2y = 29$

5. $x = 2y - 11$ $(-3, 4)$ Yes
   $-x + 5y = 23$

Concept 1: Solving a System of Linear Equations by Using the Addition Method

For Exercises 6–7, answer as true or false.

6. Given the system $5x - 4y = 1$
                    $7x - 2y = 5$

   a. To eliminate the y variable using the addition method, multiply the second equation by 2.
   False, multiply by -2.

   b. To eliminate the x variable, multiply the first equation by 7 and the second equation by -5.   True

7. Given the system $3x + 5y = -1$
                     $9x - 8y = -26$

   a. To eliminate the x variable using the addition method, multiply the first equation by -3.
   True

   b. To eliminate the y variable, multiply the first equation by 8 and the second equation by -5.   False, multiply the second equation by 5.

8. Given the system $3x - 4y = 2$
                     $17x + y = 35$

   a. Which variable, x or y, is easier to eliminate using the addition method? y would be easier.

   b. Solve the system using the addition method.
   $\{(2, 1)\}$

9. Given the system $-2x + 5y = -15$
                     $6x - 7y = 21$

   a. Which variable, x or y, is easier to eliminate using the addition method? x would be easier.

   b. Solve the system using the addition method.
   $\{(0, -3)\}$

For Exercises 10–24, solve each system using the addition method. **(See Examples 1–4.)**

10. $x + 2y = 8$ $\{(2, 3)\}$
    $5x - 2y = 4$

11. $2x - 3y = 11$ $\{(4, -1)\}$
    $-4x + 3y = -19$

12. $a + b = 3$ $\{(5, -2)\}$
    $3a + b = 13$

13. $-2u + 6v = 10$ $\{(4, 3)\}$
    $-2u + v = -5$

14. $-3x + y = 1$ $\{(0, 1)\}$
    $-6x - 2y = -2$

15. $5m - 2n = 4$ $\{(2, 3)\}$
    $3m + n = 9$

16. $3x - 5y = 13$ $\{(1, -2)\}$
$x - 2y = 5$

17. $7a + 2b = -1$ $\{(1, -4)\}$
$3a - 4b = 19$

18. $6c - 2d = -2$ $\{(1, 4)\}$
$5c = -3d + 17$

19. $2s + 3t = -1$ $\{(1, -1)\}$
$5s = 2t + 7$

20. $6y - 4z = -2$ $\{(3, 5)\}$
$4y + 6z = 42$

21. $4k - 2r = -4$ $\{(-4, -6)\}$
$3k - 5r = 18$

22. $2x + 3y = 6$ $\left\{\left(\frac{21}{5}, -\frac{4}{5}\right)\right\}$
$x - y = 5$

23. $6x + 6y = 8$ $\left\{\left(\frac{7}{9}, \frac{5}{9}\right)\right\}$
$9x - 18y = -3$

24. $2x - 5y = 4$ $\left\{\left(\frac{8}{9}, -\frac{4}{9}\right)\right\}$
$3x - 3y = 4$

25. In solving a system of equations, suppose you get the statement $0 = 5$. How many solutions will the system have? What can you say about the graphs of these equations?
The system will have no solution. The lines are parallel.

26. In solving a system of equations, suppose you get the statement $0 = 0$. How many solutions will the system have? What can you say about the graphs of these equations?
There are infinitely many solutions. The lines coincide.

27. In solving a system of equations, suppose you get the statement $3 = 3$. How many solutions will the system have? What can you say about the graphs of these equations?
There are infinitely many solutions. The lines coincide.

28. In solving a system of equations, suppose you get the statement $2 = -5$. How many solutions will the system have? What can you say about the graphs of these equations?
The system will have no solution. The lines are parallel.

29. Suppose in solving a system of linear equations, you get the statement $x = 0$. How many solutions will the system have? What can you say about the graphs of these equations?
The system will have one solution. The lines intersect at a point whose x-coordinate is 0.

30. Suppose in solving a system of linear equations, you get the statement $y = 0$. How many solutions will the system have? What can you say about the graphs of these equations?
The system will have one solution. The lines intersect at a point whose y-coordinate is 0.

For Exercises 31–42, solve each system using the addition method. **(See Examples 5–6.)**

31. $-2x + y = -5$ $\{ \}$; inconsistent system
$8x - 4y = 12$

32. $x - 3y = 2$ $\{ \}$; inconsistent system
$-5x + 15y = 10$

33. $x + 2y = 2$ Infinitely many solutions;
$-3x - 6y = -6$ $\{(x, y) | x + 2y = 2\}$; dependent system

34. $4x - 3y = 6$ Infinitely many solutions;
$-12x + 9y = -18$ $\{(x, y) | 4x - 3y = 6\}$; dependent system

35. $3a + 2b = 11$ $\{(1, 4)\}$
$7a - 3b = -5$

36. $4y + 5z = -2$
$5y - 3z = 16$
$\{(2, -2)\}$

37. $3x - 5y = 7$
$5x - 2y = -1$
$\{(-1, -2)\}$

38. $4s + 3t = 9$ $\{(0, 3)\}$
$3s + 4t = 12$

39. $2x + 2 = -3y + 9$
$3x - 10 = -4y$
$\{(2, 1)\}$

40. $-3x + 6 + 7y = 5$ $\{(5, 2)\}$
$5y = 2x$

41. $4x - 5y = 0$
$8(x - 1) = 10y$
$\{ \}$; inconsistent system

42. $y = 2x + 1$
$-3(2x - y) = 0$
$\{ \}$; inconsistent system

Concept 2: Summary of Methods for Solving Systems of Linear Equations in Two Variables

For Exercises 43–63, solve each system of equations by either the addition method or the substitution method.

43. $5x - 2y = 4$ $\{(2, 3)\}$
$y = -3x + 9$

44. $-x = 8y + 5$ $\{(-5, 0)\}$
$4x - 3y = -20$

45. $0.1x + 0.1y = 0.6$ $\{(3.5, 2.5)\}$
$0.1x - 0.1y = 0.1$

46. $0.1x + 0.1y = 0.2$ $\{(2.5, -0.5)\}$
$0.1x - 0.1y = 0.3$

47. $3x = 5y - 9$ $\left\{\left(\frac{1}{3}, 2\right)\right\}$
$2y = 3x + 3$

48. $10x - 5 = 3y$ $\left\{\left(\frac{1}{2}, 0\right)\right\}$
$4x + 5y = 2$

 Writing Translating Expression 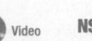 Geometry Scientific Calculator Video NS·E

49. $y = -5x - 5$ $\{(-2, 5)\}$
$6x - 3 = -3y$

50. $4x + 5y = -2$ $\{(-3, 2)\}$
$3x = -2y - 5$

51. $x = -\dfrac{1}{2}$ $\left\{\left(-\dfrac{1}{2}, 1\right)\right\}$
$6x - 5y = -8$

52. $4x - 2y = 1$ $\left\{\left(\dfrac{7}{4}, 3\right)\right\}$
$y = 3$

53. $0.02x + 0.04y = 0.12$ $\{(0, 3)\}$
$0.03x - 0.05y = -0.15$

54. $-0.04x + 0.03y = 0.03$ $\{(0, 1)\}$
$-0.06x - 0.02y = -0.02$

55. $8x - 16y = 24$
$2x - 4y = 0$
{ }; inconsistent system

56. $y = -\dfrac{1}{2}x - 5$
$2x + 4y = -8$
{ }; inconsistent system

57. $\dfrac{m}{2} + \dfrac{n}{5} = \dfrac{13}{10}$
$3m - 3n = m - 10$
$\{(1, 4)\}$

58. $\dfrac{a}{4} - \dfrac{3b}{2} = \dfrac{15}{2}$ $\{(0, -5)\}$
$a + 2b = -10$

59. $2m - 6n = m + 4$ $\{(4, 0)\}$
$3m + 8 = 5m - n$

60. $m - 3n = 10$ $\{(4, -2)\}$
$3m + 12n = -12$

61. $9a - 2b = 8$
$18a + 6 = 4b + 22$
Infinitely many solutions;
$\{(a, b)|9a - 2b = 8\}$; dependent system

62. $a = 5 + 2b$ Infinitely many solutions;
$3a - 6b = 15$ $\{(a, b)|a = 5 + 2b\}$; dependent system

63. $6x - 5y = 7$ $\left\{\left(\dfrac{7}{16}, -\dfrac{7}{8}\right)\right\}$
$4x - 6y = 7$

For Exercises 64–69, set up a system of linear equations, and solve for the indicated quantities.

64. The sum of two positive numbers is 26. Their difference is 14. Find the numbers.
The numbers are 20 and 6.

65. The difference of two positive numbers is 2. The sum of the numbers is 36. Find the numbers.
The numbers are 17 and 19.

66. Eight times the smaller of two numbers plus 2 times the larger number is 44. Three times the smaller number minus 2 times the larger number is zero. Find the numbers.
The numbers are 4 and 6.

67. Six times the smaller of two numbers minus the larger number is -9. Ten times the smaller number plus five times the larger number is 5. Find the numbers.
The numbers are -1 and 3.

68. Twice the difference of two angles is 64°. If the angles are complementary, find the measures of the angles. The angles are 61° and 29°.

69. The difference of an angle and twice another angle is 42°. If the angles are supplementary, find the measures of the angles.
The angles are 46° and 134°.

For Exercises 70–72, solve the system by using each of the three methods: (a) the graphing method, (b) the substitution method, and (c) the addition method.

70. $2x + y = 1$
$-4x - 2y = -2$
Infinitely many solutions;
$\{(x, y)|2x + y = 1\}$

71. $3x + y = 6$
$-2x + 2y = 4$
$\{(1, 3)\}$

72. $2x - 2y = 6$
$5y = 5x + 5$
{ }

Expanding Your Skills

73. Explain why a system of linear equations cannot have exactly two solutions. One line within the system of equations would have to "bend" for the system to have exactly two points of intersection. This is not possible.

74. The solution set to the system of linear equations is $\{(1, 2)\}$. Find A and B.

$Ax + 3y = 8$ $A = 2, B = -4$
$x + By = -7$

75. The solution set to the system of linear equations is $\{(-3, 4)\}$. Find A and B.

$4x + Ay = -32$ $A = -5, B = 2$
$Bx + 6y = 18$

Problem Recognition Exercises

Systems of Equations

For Exercises 1–6 determine the number of solutions to the system without solving the system. Explain your answers.

1. $y = -4x + 2$
$y = -4x + 2$
Infinitely many solutions. The equations represent the same line.

2. $y = -4x + 6$
$y = -4x + 1$
No solution. The equations represent parallel lines.

3. $y = 4x - 3$
$y = -4x + 5$
One solution. The equations represent intersecting lines.

4. $y = 7$
$2x + 3y = 1$
One solution. The equations represent intersecting lines.

5. $2x + 3y = 1$
$2x + 3y = 8$
No solution. The equations represent parallel lines.

6. $8x - 2y = 6$
$12x - 3y = 9$
Infinitely many solutions. The equations represent the same line.

For Exercises 7–26, solve each system using the method of your choice.

7. $x = -2y + 5$ $\{(5, 0)\}$
$2x - 4y = 10$

8. $y = -3x - 4$ $\{(1, -7)\}$
$2x - y = 9$

9. $3x - 2y = 22$ $\{(4, -5)\}$
$5x + 2y = 10$

10. $-4x + 2y = -2$ $\{(2, 3)\}$
$4x - 5y = -7$

11. $\dfrac{1}{3}x + \dfrac{1}{2}y = \dfrac{2}{3}$ $\{(2, 0)\}$
$-\dfrac{2}{3}x + y = -\dfrac{4}{3}$

12. $\dfrac{1}{4}x + \dfrac{2}{5}y = 6$ $\{(8, 10)\}$
$\dfrac{1}{2}x - \dfrac{1}{10}y = 3$

13. $2c + 7d = -1$ $\left\{\left(2, -\dfrac{5}{7}\right)\right\}$
$c = 2$

14. $-3w + 5z = -6$ $\left\{\left(-\dfrac{14}{3}, -4\right)\right\}$
$z = -4$

15. $y = 0.4x - 0.3$
$-4x + 10y = 20$
$\{\ \}$; inconsistent system

16. $x = -0.5y + 0.1$
$-10x - 5y = 2$
$\{\ \}$; inconsistent system

17. $3a + 7b = -3$ $\{(-1, 0)\}$
$-11a + 3b = 11$

18. $2v - 5w = 10$ $\{(5, 0)\}$
$9v + 7w = 45$

19. $y = 2x - 14$
$4x - 2y = 28$
Infinitely many solutions; $\{(x, y)|y = 2x - 14\}$; dependent system

20. $x = 5y - 9$
$-2x + 10y = 18$
Infinitely many solutions; $\{(x, y)|x = 5y - 9\}$; dependent system

21. $x + y = 3200$ $\{(2200, 1000)\}$
$0.06x + 0.04y = 172$

22. $x + y = 4500$
$0.07x + 0.05y = 291$
$\{(3300, 1200)\}$

23. $3x + y - 7 = x - 4$ $\{(5, -7)\}$
$3x - 4y + 4 = -6y + 5$

24. $7y - 8y - 3 = -3x + 4$
$10x - 5y - 12 = 13$ $\{(2, -1)\}$

25. $3x - 6y = -1$ $\left\{\left(\dfrac{2}{3}, \dfrac{1}{2}\right)\right\}$
$9x + 4y = 8$

26. $8x - 2y = 5$ $\left\{\left(\dfrac{1}{4}, -\dfrac{3}{2}\right)\right\}$
$12x + 4y = -3$

✏️ Writing   ↔ Translating Expression   📐 Geometry   🖩 Scientific Calculator   Video

Applications of Linear Equations in Two Variables

1. Applications Involving Cost

In Sections 2.4–2.7, we solved several applied problems by setting up a linear equation in one variable. When solving an application that involves two unknowns, sometimes it is convenient to use a system of linear equations in two variables.

Classroom Example: p. 307, Exercise 10

Example 1 Using a System of Linear Equations Involving Cost

At a movie theater a couple buys one large popcorn and two drinks for $9.00. A group of teenagers buys two large popcorns and five drinks for $20.50. Find the cost of one large popcorn and the cost of one drink.

Solution:

In this application we have two unknowns, which we can represent by x and y.

Let x represent the cost of one large popcorn.
Let y represent the cost of one drink.

We must now write two equations. Each of the first two sentences in the problem gives a relationship between x and y:

$$\begin{pmatrix} \text{Cost of 1} \\ \text{large popcorn} \end{pmatrix} + \begin{pmatrix} \text{cost of 2} \\ \text{drinks} \end{pmatrix} = \begin{pmatrix} \text{total} \\ \text{cost} \end{pmatrix} \longrightarrow x + 2y = 9.00$$

$$\begin{pmatrix} \text{Cost of 2} \\ \text{large popcorns} \end{pmatrix} + \begin{pmatrix} \text{cost of 5} \\ \text{drinks} \end{pmatrix} = \begin{pmatrix} \text{total} \\ \text{cost} \end{pmatrix} \longrightarrow 2x + 5y = 20.50$$

To solve this system, we may either use the substitution method or the addition method. We will use the substitution method by solving for x in the first equation.

$$x + 2y = 9.00 \longrightarrow x = -2y + 9.00 \qquad \text{Isolate } x \text{ in the first equation.}$$

$$2x + 5y = 20.50$$

$$2(-2y + 9.00) + 5y = 20.50 \qquad \text{Substitute } x = -2y + 9.00 \text{ into the other equation.}$$

$$-4y + 18.00 + 5y = 20.50 \qquad \text{Solve for } y$$

$$y + 18.00 = 20.50$$

$$y = 2.50$$

$$x = -2y + 9.00$$

$$x = -2(2.50) + 9.00 \qquad \text{Substitute } y = 2.50 \text{ into the equation } x = -2y + 9.00.$$

$$x = -5.00 + 9.00$$

$$x = 4.00$$

The cost of one large popcorn is $4.00 and the cost of one drink is $2.50.

Check by verifying that the solutions meet the specified conditions.

$$1 \text{ popcorn} + 2 \text{ drinks} = 1(\$4.00) + 2(\$2.50) = \$9.00 \ ✔ \quad \text{True}$$

$$2 \text{ popcorns} + 5 \text{ drinks} = 2(\$4.00) + 5(\$2.50) = \$20.50 \ ✔ \quad \text{True}$$

Classroom Example: p. 308,
Exercise 18

Skill Practice

1. Lynn went to a fast-food restaurant and spent $20.00. She purchased 4 hamburgers and 5 orders of fries. The next day, Ricardo went to the same restaurant and purchased 10 hamburgers and 7 orders of fries. He spent $41.20. Use a system of equations to determine the cost of a burger and the cost of an order of fries.

2. Applications Involving Principal and Interest

In Section 2.5, we learned that simple interest is interest computed on the principal amount of money invested (or borrowed). Simple interest, I, is found by using the formula

$$I = Prt \qquad \text{where } P \text{ is the principal,}$$
$$r \text{ is the annual interest rate, and}$$
$$t \text{ is the time in years.}$$

In Example 2, we apply the concept of simple interest to two accounts to produce a desired amount of interest after 1 year.

Example 2 — Using a System of Linear Equations Involving Investments

Joanne has a total of $6000 to deposit in two accounts. One account earns 3.5% simple interest and the other earns 2.5% simple interest. If the total amount of interest at the end of 1 year is $195, find the amount she deposited in each account.

Solution:

Let x represent the principal deposited in the 2.5% account.
Let y represent the principal deposited in the 3.5% account.

	2.5% Account	3.5% Account	Total
Principal	x	y	6000
Interest $(I = Prt)$	$0.025x(1)$	$0.035y(1)$	195

Each row of the table yields an equation in x and y:

$$\begin{pmatrix} \text{Principal} \\ \text{invested} \\ \text{at } 2.5\% \end{pmatrix} + \begin{pmatrix} \text{principal} \\ \text{invested} \\ \text{at } 3.5\% \end{pmatrix} = \begin{pmatrix} \text{total} \\ \text{principal} \end{pmatrix} \longrightarrow x + y = 6000$$

$$\begin{pmatrix} \text{Interest} \\ \text{earned} \\ \text{at } 2.5\% \end{pmatrix} + \begin{pmatrix} \text{interest} \\ \text{earned} \\ \text{at } 3.5\% \end{pmatrix} = \begin{pmatrix} \text{total} \\ \text{interest} \end{pmatrix} \longrightarrow 0.025x + 0.035y = 195$$

We will choose the addition method to solve the system of equations. First multiply the second equation by 1000 to clear decimals.

Answer

1. The cost of a burger is $3.00, and the cost of an order of fries is $1.60.

Multiply by −25.

$$x + y = 6000 \longrightarrow \quad x + y = 6000 \quad \longrightarrow -25x - 25y = -150,000$$
$$0.025x + 0.035y = 195 \longrightarrow 25x + 35y = 195,000 \longrightarrow \underline{\quad 25x + 35y = \quad 195,000}$$

Multiply by 1000.

$$10y = \quad 45,000$$

$10y = 45,000$ After eliminating the x variable, solve for y.

$$\frac{10y}{10} = \frac{45,000}{10}$$

$y = 4500$ The amount invested in the 3.5% account is $4500.

$x + y = 6000$ Substitute $y = 4500$ into the equation $x + y = 6000$.

$x + 4500 = 6000$

$x = 1500$ The amount invested in the 2.5% account is $1500.

Joanne deposited $1500 in the 2.5% account and $4500 in the 3.5% account.

To check, verify that the conditions of the problem have been met.

1. The sum of $1500 and $4500 is $6000 as desired. ✔ True

2. The interest earned on $1500 at 2.5% is: 0.025($1500) = $37.50
   The interest earned on $4500 at 3.5% is: 0.035($4500) = $157.50

   Total interest: $195.00 ✔ True

Skill Practice

2. Addie has a total of $8000 in two accounts. One pays 5% interest, and the other pays 6.5% interest. At the end of one year, she earned $475 interest. Use a system of equations to determine the amount invested in each account.

3. Applications Involving Mixtures

Example 3 **Using a System of Linear Equations in a Mixture Application**

Classroom Example: p. 308, Exercise 22

According to new hospital standards, a certain disinfectant solution needs to be 20% alcohol instead of 10% alcohol. There is a 40% alcohol disinfectant available to adjust the mixture. Determine the amount of 10% solution and the amount of 40% solution to produce 30 L of a 20% solution.

Solution:

Each solution contains a percentage of alcohol plus some other mixing agent such as water. Before we set up a system of equations to model this situation, it is helpful to have background understanding of the problem. In Figure 4-9, the liquid depicted in blue is pure alcohol and the liquid shown in gray is the mixing agent (such as water). Together these liquids form a solution. (Realistically the mixture may not separate as shown, but this image may be helpful for your understanding.)

Let x represent the number of liters of 10% solution.
Let y represent the number of liters of 40% solution.

Answer

2. $3000 is invested at 5%, and $5000 is invested at 6.5%.

Figure 4-9

The information given in the statement of the problem can be organized in a chart.

	10% Alcohol	40% Alcohol	20% Alcohol
Number of liters of solution	x	y	30
Number of liters of pure alcohol	$0.10x$	$0.40y$	$0.20(30) = 6$

From the first row, we have

$$\begin{pmatrix} \text{Amount of} \\ 10\% \text{ solution} \end{pmatrix} + \begin{pmatrix} \text{amount of} \\ 40\% \text{ solution} \end{pmatrix} = \begin{pmatrix} \text{total amount} \\ \text{of } 20\% \text{ solution} \end{pmatrix} \longrightarrow x + y = 30$$

From the second row, we have

$$\begin{pmatrix} \text{Amount of} \\ \text{alcohol in} \\ 10\% \text{ solution} \end{pmatrix} + \begin{pmatrix} \text{amount of} \\ \text{alcohol in} \\ 40\% \text{ solution} \end{pmatrix} = \begin{pmatrix} \text{total amount of} \\ \text{alcohol in} \\ 20\% \text{ solution} \end{pmatrix} \longrightarrow 0.10x + 0.40y = 6$$

We will solve the system with the addition method by first clearing decimals.

$$
\begin{array}{lll}
x + y = 30 & \xrightarrow{} \quad x + y = 30 & \xrightarrow{\text{Multiply by } -1.} \quad -x - y = -30 \\
0.10x + 0.40y = 6 & \xrightarrow{} \quad x + 4y = 60 & \xrightarrow{} \quad \underline{x + 4y = 60} \\
& \phantom{\xrightarrow{}} \text{Multiply by 10.} & 3y = 30
\end{array}
$$

$3y = 30$ After eliminating the x variable, solve for y.

$y = 10$ 10 L of 40% solution is needed.

$x + y = 30$ Substitute $y = 10$ into either of the original equations.

$x + (10) = 30$

$x = 20$ 20 L of 10% solution is needed.

10 L of 40% solution must be mixed with 20 L of 10% solution.

Skill Practice

3. How many ounces of 20% and 35% acid solution should be mixed together to obtain 15 oz of 30% acid solution?

Answer

3. 10 oz of the 35% solution, and 5 oz of the 20% solution.

4. Applications Involving Distance, Rate, and Time

The following formula relates the distance traveled to the rate and time of travel.

$$d = rt \qquad \text{distance} = \text{rate} \cdot \text{time}$$

For example, if a car travels at 60 mph for 3 hr, then

$$d = (60 \text{ mph})(3 \text{ hr})$$
$$= 180 \text{ mi}$$

If a car travels at 60 mph for x hr, then

$$d = (60 \text{ mph})(x \text{ hr})$$
$$= 60x \text{ mi}$$

The relationship $d = rt$ is used in Example 4.

Example 4 **Using a System of Linear Equations in a Distance, Rate, and Time Application**

Classroom Example: p. 308, Exercise 28

A plane travels with the wind from Kansas City, Missouri, to Denver, Colorado, a distance of 600 mi in 2 hr. The return trip against the same wind takes 3 hr. Find the speed of the plane in still air, and find the speed of the wind.

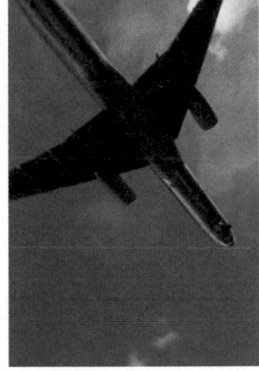

Solution:

Let p represent the speed of the plane in still air.
Let w represent the speed of the wind.

Notice that when the plane travels with the wind, the net speed is $p + w$. When the plane travels against the wind, the net speed is $p - w$.

The information given in the problem can be organized in a chart.

	Distance	Rate	Time
With the wind	600	$p + w$	2
Against the wind	600	$p - w$	3

To set up two equations in p and w, recall that $d = rt$.

From the first row, we have

$$\begin{pmatrix} \text{Distance} \\ \text{with the wind} \end{pmatrix} = \begin{pmatrix} \text{rate with} \\ \text{the wind} \end{pmatrix}\begin{pmatrix} \text{time traveled} \\ \text{with the wind} \end{pmatrix} \longrightarrow 600 = (p + w) \cdot 2$$

From the second row, we have

$$\begin{pmatrix} \text{Distance} \\ \text{against the wind} \end{pmatrix} = \begin{pmatrix} \text{rate against} \\ \text{the wind} \end{pmatrix}\begin{pmatrix} \text{time traveled} \\ \text{against the wind} \end{pmatrix} \longrightarrow 600 = (p - w) \cdot 3$$

Using the distributive property to clear parentheses produces the following system:

$$2p + 2w = 600$$
$$3p - 3w = 600$$

The coefficients of the w variable can be changed to 6 and -6 by multiplying the first equation by 3 and the second equation by 2.

$$2p + 2w = 600 \xrightarrow{\text{Multiply by 3.}} 6p + 6w = 1800$$
$$3p - 3w = 600 \xrightarrow[\text{Multiply by 2.}]{} \underline{6p - 6w = 1200}$$
$$12p \quad\;\; = 3000$$

$$12p = 3000$$

$$\frac{12p}{12} = \frac{3000}{12}$$

$$p = 250 \qquad \text{The speed of the plane in still air is 250 mph.}$$

> **TIP:** To create opposite coefficients on the w variables, we could have divided the first equation by 2 and divided the second equation by 3:
>
> $$2p + 2w = 600 \xrightarrow{\text{Divide by 2.}} p + w = 300$$
> $$3p - 3w = 600 \xrightarrow[\text{Divide by 3.}]{} \underline{p - w = 200}$$
> $$2p \quad\;\; = 500$$
> $$p = 250$$

$$2p + 2w = 600 \qquad \text{Substitute } p = 250 \text{ into the first equation.}$$
$$2(250) + 2w = 600$$
$$500 + 2w = 600$$
$$2w = 100$$
$$w = 50 \qquad \text{The speed of the wind is 50 mph.}$$

The speed of the plane in still air is 250 mph. The speed of the wind is 50 mph.

Skill Practice

4. Dan and Cheryl paddled their canoe 40 mi in 5 hr with the current and 16 mi in 8 hr against the current. Find the speed of the current and the speed of the canoe in still water.

Answer

4. The speed of the canoe in still water is 5 mph. The speed of the current is 3 mph.

Section 4.4 Practice Exercises

Review Exercises

For Exercises 1–4, solve each system of equations by three different methods:

a. Graphing method   **b.** Substitution method   **c.** Addition method

1. $-2x + y = 6$

$\quad 2x + y = 2 \quad \{(-1, 4)\}$

2. $x - y = 2$

$\quad x + y = 6 \quad \{(4, 2)\}$

 Writing   Translating Expression   Geometry   Scientific Calculator   Video   NS&E

3. $y = -2x + 6$

$4x - 2y = 8$ $\left\{ \left(\dfrac{5}{2}, 1 \right) \right\}$

4. $2x = y + 4$

$4x = 2y + 8$ Infinitely many solutions;
$\{(x, y) | 2x = y + 4\}$; dependent system

For Exercises 5–8, set up a system of linear equations in two variables and solve for the unknown quantities.

5. One number is eight more than twice another. Their sum is 20. Find the numbers.

The numbers are 4 and 16.

6. The difference of two positive numbers is 264. The larger number is three times the smaller number. Find the numbers.

The numbers are 132 and 396.

7. Two angles are complementary. The measure of one angle is 10° less than nine times the measure of the other. Find the measure of each angle.

The angles are 80° and 10°.

8. Two angles are supplementary. The measure of one angle is 9° more than twice the measure of the other angle. Find the measure of each angle.

The angles are 123° and 57°.

Concept 1: Applications Involving Cost

9. Two video games and three DVDs can be rented for $34.10. One video game and two DVDs can be rented for $19.80. Find the cost to rent one video game and the cost to rent one DVD.

(See Example 1.)

It costs $8.80 to rent a video game and $5.50 to rent a DVD.

10. Tanya bought three adult tickets and one children's ticket to a movie for $32.00. Li bought two adult tickets and five children's tickets for $49.50. Find the cost of one adult ticket and the cost of one children's ticket.   Adult tickets cost $8.50 each, and children's tickets cost $6.50 each.

11. Marcela bought 100 shares of a technology stock and 200 shares of a mutual fund for $3800. Her sister, Erin, bought 300 shares of technology stock and 50 shares of a mutual fund for $5350. Find the cost per share of the technology stock, and the cost per share of the mutual fund.

Technology stock costs $16 per share, and the mutual fund costs $11 per share.

12. Eight students in Ms. Reese's class are Lil Wayne fans. They all decided to purchase Lil Wayne's latest CD, *Tha Carter III*. Some of the students purchased the CD from a local record store for $14.50. The rest of the students purchased the CD from an online discount store for $12.00 per CD. If the total amount spent by eight students is $103.50, how many of the students purchased the CD for $12.00?   Five students purchased Lil Wayne's CD for $12.00.

13. Mylee buys a combination of 44¢ stamps and 61¢ stamps at the Post Office. If she spends exactly $23.70 on 50 stamps, how many of each type did she buy?

Mylee bought forty 44¢ stamps and ten 61¢ stamps.

14. Zoey purchased some beef and some chicken for a family barbeque. The beef cost $6.00 per pound and the chicken cost $4.50 per pound. She bought a total of 18 lb of meat and spent $96. How much of each type of meat did she purchase?

She bought 10 lb of beef and 8 lb of chicken.

Concept 2: Applications Involving Principal and Interest

15. Shanelle invested $10,000, and at the end of 1 year, she received $805 in interest. She invested part of the money in an account earning 10% simple interest and the remaining money in an account earning 7% simple interest. How much did she invest in each account? **(See Example 2.)**

Shanelle invested $3500 in the 10% account and $6500 in the 7% account.

	10% Account	7% Account	Total
Principal invested			
Interest earned			

16. $12,000 was borrowed from two sources, one that charges 12% simple interest and the other that charges 8% simple interest. If the total interest at the end of 1 year was $1240, how much money was borrowed from each source?

$7000 was borrowed from the 12% account and $5000 was borrowed from the 8% account.

	12% Account	8% Account	Total
Principal borrowed			
Interest earned			

17. Troy borrowed a total of $12,000 in two different loans to help pay for his new Chevy Silverado. One loan charges 9% simple interest, and the other charges 6% simple interest. If he is charged $810 in interest after 1 year, find the amount borrowed at each rate.
$9000 was borrowed at 6%, and $3000 was borrowed at 9%.

18. Kamal has a total of $4000 to invest in two accounts. One account earns 2% simple interest, and the other earns 5% simple interest. How much should be invested in each account to earn exactly $155 at the end of 1 year?
$1500 must be invested in the 2% account and $2500 invested in the 5% account.

19. Suppose a rich uncle dies and leaves you an inheritance of $30,000. You decide to invest part of the money in a relatively safe bond fund that returns 8%. You invest the rest of the money in a riskier stock fund that you hope will return 12% at the end of 1 year. If you need $3120 at the end of 1 year to make a down payment on a car, how much should you invest at each rate?
Invest $12,000 in the bond fund and $18,000 in the stock fund.

20. As part of his retirement strategy, John plans to invest $200,000 in two different funds. He projects that the moderately high risk investments should return, over time, about 9% per year, while the low risk investments should return about 4% per year. If he wants a supplemental income of $12,000 a year, how should he divide his investments?
He should invest $80,000 at 9% and $120,000 at 4%.

Concept 3: Applications Involving Mixtures

 21. How much 50% disinfectant solution must be mixed with a 40% disinfectant solution to produce 25 gal of a 46% disinfectant solution?
(See Example 3.)   15 gal of the 50% mixture should be mixed with 10 gal of the 40% mixture.

	50% Mixture	40% Mixture	46% Mixture
Amount of solution			
Amount of disinfectant			

22. How many gallons of 20% antifreeze solution and a 10% antifreeze solution must be mixed to obtain 40 gal of a 16% antifreeze solution?
24 gal of the 20% mixture should be mixed with 16 gal of the 10% mixture.

	20% Mixture	10% Mixture	16% Mixture
Amount of solution			
Amount of antifreeze			

23. How much 45% disinfectant solution must be mixed with a 30% disinfectant solution to produce 20 gal of a 39% disinfectant solution?
12 gal of the 45% disinfectant solution should be mixed with 8 gal of the 30% disinfectant solution.

24. How many gallons of a 25% antifreeze solution and a 15% antifreeze solution must be mixed to obtain 15 gal of a 23% antifreeze solution?
12 gal of the 25% antifreeze solution should be mixed with 3 gal of the 15% antifreeze solution.

25. A nurse needs 50 mL of a 16% salt solution for a patient. She can only find a 13% salt solution and an 18% salt solution in the supply room. How many milliliters of the 13% solution should be mixed with the 18% solution to produce the desired amount of the 16% solution?   She should mix 20 mL of the 13% solution with 30 mL of the 18% solution.

26. Meadowsilver Dairy keeps two kinds of milk on hand, skim milk that has 0.3% butterfat and whole milk that contains 3.3% butterfat. How many gallons of each type of milk does the company need to produce 300 gallons of 1% milk for the P&A grocery store?
It needs 230 gal of skim milk and 70 gal of whole milk.

Concept 4: Applications Involving Distance, Rate, and Time

27. It takes a boat 2 hr to go 16 mi downstream with the current and 4 hr to return against the current. Find the speed of the boat in still water and the speed of the current. **(See Example 4.)**   The speed of the boat in still water is 6 mph, and the speed of the current is 2 mph.

	Distance	Rate	Time
Downstream			
Upstream			

28. A boat takes 1.5 hr to go 12 mi upstream against the current. It can go 24 mi downstream with the current in the same amount of time. Find the speed of the current and the speed of the boat in still water.   The speed of the boat is 12 mph, and the speed of the current is 4 mph.

	Distance	Rate	Time
Upstream			
Downstream			

29. A plane can fly 960 mi with the wind in 3 hr. It takes the same amount of time to fly 840 mi against the wind. What is the speed of the plane in still air and the speed of the wind? The speed of the plane in still air is 300 mph, and the wind is 20 mph.

30. A plane flies 720 mi with the wind in 3 hr. The return trip takes 4 hr. What is the speed of the wind and the speed of the plane in still air? The speed of the plane in still air is 210 mph, and the wind is 30 mph.

31. Tony Markins flew from JFK Airport to London. It took him 6 hr to fly with the wind, and 8 hr on the return flight against the wind. If the distance is approximately 3600 mi, determine the speed of the plane in still air and the speed of the wind. The speed of the plane in still air is 525 mph and the speed of the wind is 75 mph.

32. A riverboat cruise upstream on the Mississippi River from New Orleans, Louisiana, to Natchez, Mississippi, takes 10 hr and covers 140 mi. The return trip downstream with the current takes only 7 hr. Find the speed of the riverboat in still water and the speed of the current. The speed of the boat in still water is 17 mph and the speed of the current is 3 mph.

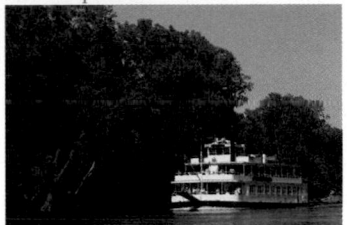

Mixed Exercises

33. Debi has $2.80 in a collection of dimes and nickels. The number of nickels is five more than the number of dimes. Find the number of each type of coin. There are 17 dimes and 22 nickels.

34. A child is collecting state quarters and new $1 coins. If she has a total of 25 coins, and the number of quarters is nine more than the number of dollar coins, how many of each type of coin does she have? She has eight $1 coins and 17 quarters.

35. In the 1961–1962 NBA basketball season, Wilt Chamberlain of the Philadelphia Warriors made 2432 baskets. Some of the baskets were free throws (worth 1 point each) and some were field goals (worth 2 points each). The number of field goals was 762 more than the number of free throws.

  a. How many field goals did he make and how many free throws did he make? 835 free throws and 1597 field goals

  b. What was the total number of points scored? 4029 points

  c. If Wilt Chamberlain played 80 games during this season, what was the average number of points per game? Approximately 50 points per game

36. In the 1971–1972 NBA basketball season, Kareem Abdul-Jabbar of the Milwaukee Bucks made 1663 baskets. Some of the baskets were free throws (worth 1 point each) and some were field goals (worth 2 points each). The number of field goals he scored was 151 more than twice the number of free throws.

  a. How many field goals did he make and how many free throws did he make? 504 free throws and 1159 field goals

  b. What was the total number of points scored? 2822 points

  c. If Kareem Abdul-Jabbar played 81 games during this season, what was the average number of points per game? Approximately 35 points per game

37. A small plane can fly 350 mi with a tailwind in $1\frac{3}{4}$ hr. In the same amount of time, the same plane can travel only 210 mi with a headwind. What is the speed of the plane in still air and the speed of the wind? The speed of the plane in still air is 160 mph, and the wind is 40 mph.

38. A plane takes 2 hr to travel 1000 mi with the wind. It can travel only 880 mi against the wind in the same amount of time. Find the speed of the wind and the speed of the plane in still air. The speed of the plane in still air is 470 mph, and the wind is 30 mph.

39. A total of $60,000 is invested in two accounts, one that earns 5.5% simple interest, and one that earns 6.5% simple interest. If the total interest at the end of 1 year is $3750, find the amount invested in each account. $15,000 was invested in the 5.5% account, and $45,000 was invested in the 6.5% account.

40. Jacques borrows a total of $15,000. Part of the money is borrowed from a bank that charges 12% simple interest per year. Jacques borrows the remaining part of the money from his sister and promises to pay her 7% simple interest per year. If Jacques' total interest for the year is $1475, find the amount he borrowed from each source. Jacques borrowed $8500 at 12%, and $6500 at 7%.

 Writing   Translating Expression   Geometry   Scientific Calculator   Video   NS&E

41. At the holidays, Erica likes to sell a candy/nut mixture to her neighbors. She wants to combine candy that costs $1.80 per pound with nuts that cost $1.20 per pound. If Erica needs 20 lb of mixture that will sell for $1.56 per pound, how many pounds of candy and how many pounds of nuts should she use?   12 lb of candy should be mixed with 8 lb of nuts.

42. Mary Lee's natural food store sells a combination of teas. The most popular is a mixture of a tea that sells for $3.00 per pound with one that sells for $4.00 per pound. If she needs 40 lb of tea that will sell for $3.65 per pound, how many pounds of each tea should she use?   14 lb of $3 per pound tea should be mixed with 26 lb of $4 per pound tea.

43. In the 1994 Super Bowl, the Dallas Cowboys scored four more points than twice the number of points scored by the Buffalo Bills. If the total number of points scored by both teams was 43, find the number of points scored by each team.   Dallas scored 30 points, and Buffalo scored 13 points.

44. In the 1973 Super Bowl, the Miami Dolphins scored twice as many points as the Washington Redskins. If the total number of points scored by both teams was 21, find the number of points scored by each team.   Miami scored 14 points, and Washington scored 7 points.

Expanding Your Skills

45. In a survey conducted among 500 college students, 340 said that the campus lacked adequate lighting. If $\frac{4}{5}$ of the women and $\frac{1}{2}$ of the men said that they thought the campus lacked adequate lighting, how many men and how many women were in the survey?   There were 300 women and 200 men in the survey.

46. During a 1-hr television program, there were 22 commercials. Some commercials were 15 sec and some were 30 sec long. Find the number of 15-sec commercials and the number of 30-sec commercials if the total playing time for commercials was 9.5 min.   There are six 15-sec commercials and sixteen 30-sec commercials.

Section 4.5   Systems of Linear Equations in Three Variables

Concepts

1. **Solutions to Systems of Linear Equations in Three Variables**
2. **Solving Systems of Linear Equations in Three Variables**

1. Solutions to Systems of Linear Equations in Three Variables

In Sections 4.1–4.3, we solved systems of linear equations in two variables. In this section, we will expand the discussion to solving systems involving three variables.

A **linear equation in three variables** can be written in the form $Ax + By + Cz = D$, where A, B, and C are not all zero. For example, the equation $2x + 3y + z = 6$ is a linear equation in three variables. Solutions to this equation are **ordered triples** of the form (x, y, z) that satisfy the equation. Some solutions to the equation $2x + 3y + z = 6$ are

Solution: Check:

$(1, 1, 1) \longrightarrow 2(1) + 3(1) + (1) = 6$ ✔ True

$(2, 0, 2) \longrightarrow 2(2) + 3(0) + (2) = 6$ ✔ True

$(0, 1, 3) \longrightarrow 2(0) + 3(1) + (3) = 6$ ✔ True

Infinitely many ordered triples serve as solutions to the equation $2x + 3y + z = 6$.

The set of all ordered triples that are solutions to a linear equation in three variables may be represented graphically by a plane in space. Figure 4-10 shows a portion of the plane $2x + 3y + z = 6$ in a 3-dimensional coordinate system.

A solution to a system of linear equations in three variables is an ordered triple that satisfies *each* equation. Geometrically, a solution is a point of intersection of the planes represented by the equations in the system.

A system of linear equations in three variables may have *one unique solution, infinitely many solutions,* or *no solution.*

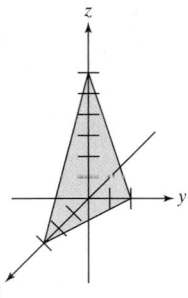

Figure 4-10

Instructor Note: 3D physical models work well here. It is hard to visualize on a flat page.

One unique solution (planes intersect at one point)
- The system is consistent.
- The system is independent.

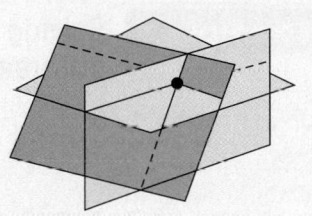

No solution (the three planes do not all intersect)
- The system is inconsistent.
- The system is independent.

Infinitely many solutions (planes intersect at infinitely many points)
- The system is consistent.
- The system is dependent.

2. Solving Systems of Linear Equations in Three Variables

To solve a system involving three variables, the goal is to eliminate one variable. This reduces the system to two equations in two variables. One strategy for eliminating a variable is to pair up the original equations two at a time.

> **PROCEDURE** **Solving a System of Three Linear Equations in Three Variables**
>
> **Step 1** Write each equation in standard form $Ax + By + Cz = D$.
>
> **Step 2** Choose a pair of equations, and eliminate one of the variables by using the addition method.
>
> **Step 3** Choose a different pair of equations and eliminate the *same* variable.
>
> **Step 4** Once steps 2 and 3 are complete, you should have two equations in two variables. Solve this system by using the methods from Sections 4.2 and 4.3.
>
> **Step 5** Substitute the values of the variables found in step 4 into any of the three original equations that contain the third variable. Solve for the third variable.
>
> **Step 6** Check the ordered triple in each of the original equations.

Classroom Example: p. 317, Exercise 12

Example 1 **Solving a System of Linear Equations in Three Variables**

Solve the system.

$$2x + y - 3z = -7$$
$$3x - 2y + z = 11$$
$$-2x - 3y - 2z = 3$$

Solution:

A $\quad 2x + y - 3z = -7$

B $\quad 3x - 2y + z = 11$

C $\quad -2x - 3y - 2z = 3$

Step 1: The equations are already in standard form.

- It is often helpful to label the equations.
- The y-variable can be easily eliminated from equations A and B and from equations A and C. This is accomplished by creating opposite coefficients for the y-terms and then adding the equations.

Step 2: Eliminate the y-variable from equations A and B.

A $2x + y - 3z = -7 \xrightarrow{\text{Multiply by 2.}} 4x + 2y - 6z = -14$

B $3x - 2y + z = 11 \longrightarrow \underline{3x - 2y + z = 11}$

$$7x \qquad - 5z = -3 \quad \boxed{D}$$

Step 3: Eliminate the y-variable again, this time from equations $\boxed{A}$ and $\boxed{C}$.

$\boxed{A}$ $2x + y - 3z = -7$ $\xrightarrow{\text{Multiply by 3.}}$ $6x + 3y - 9z = -21$

$\boxed{C}$ $-2x - 3y - 2z = 3$ $\longrightarrow$ $\underline{-2x - 3y - 2z = 3}$

$\hspace{5cm} 4x \hspace{1.5cm} - 11z = -18 \boxed{E}$

Step 4: Now equations $\boxed{D}$ and $\boxed{E}$ can be paired up to form a linear system in two variables. Solve this system.

$\boxed{D}$ $7x - 5z = -3$ $\xrightarrow{\text{Multiply by } -4.}$ $-28x + 20z = 12$

$\boxed{E}$ $4x - 11z = -18$ $\xrightarrow[\text{Multiply by 7.}]{}$ $\underline{28x - 77z = -126}$

$\hspace{5cm} -57z = -114$

$\hspace{5cm} z = 2$

Once one variable has been found, substitute this value into either equation in the two-variable system, that is, either equation $\boxed{D}$ or $\boxed{E}$.

$\boxed{D}$ $7x - 5z = -3$

$\hspace{0.5cm} 7x - 5(2) = -3$ $\hspace{1cm}$ Substitute $z = 2$ into equation $\boxed{D}$.

$\hspace{0.5cm} 7x - 10 = -3$

$\hspace{1.3cm} 7x = 7$

$\hspace{1.7cm} x = 1$

$\boxed{A}$ $2x + y - 3z = -7$

$\hspace{0.5cm} 2(1) + y - 3(2) = -7$

$\hspace{1.3cm} 2 + y - 6 = -7$

$\hspace{2cm} y - 4 = -7$

$\hspace{2.5cm} y = -3$

Step 5: Now that two variables are known, substitute these values for x and z into any of the original three equations to find the remaining variable y. Substitute $x = 1$ and $z = 2$ into equation $\boxed{A}$.

Step 6: Check the ordered triple, $(1, -3, 2)$, in the three original equations.

Check: $\hspace{0.5cm} 2x + y - 3z = -7 \rightarrow 2(1) + (-3) - 3(2) = -7$ ✔ True

$\hspace{1.8cm} 3x - 2y + z = 11 \rightarrow 3(1) - 2(-3) + (2) = 11$ ✔ True

$\hspace{1.8cm} -2x - 3y - 2z = 3 \rightarrow -2(1) - 3(-3) - 2(2) = 3$ ✔ True

The solution set is $\{(1, -3, 2)\}$.

Skill Practice X Y Z

1. Solve the system.

$$x + 2y + z = 1$$
$$3x - y + 2z = 13$$
$$2x + 3y - z = -8$$

Answer

1. $\{(1, -2, 4)\}$

Classroom Example: p. 317, Exercise 22

Example 2 Solving a System of Linear Equations in Three Variables

Solve the system:
$$3x + y - 5 = 0$$
$$z = 7 + 2y$$
$$x + 3z = 17$$

Solution:

A $3x + y \quad\quad = 5$ **Step 1:** Write equations in standard form,
B $\quad\quad -2y + z = 7$ $\quad\quad\quad Ax + By + Cz = D.$
C $x \quad\quad + 3z = 17$

Steps 2 and 3: Note equation C is missing a y-variable. Therefore, we can eliminate the y-variable by pairing up equations A and B.

A $3x + y \quad = 5$ $\xrightarrow{\text{Multiply by 2.}}$ $6x + 2y \quad = 10$
B $\quad -2y + z = 7$ $\longrightarrow$ $\quad\quad \underline{-2y + z = 7}$
$\quad\quad\quad\quad\quad\quad\quad\quad\quad\quad\quad 6x \quad\quad + z = 17$ D

Step 4: Now we pair up equations C and D to eliminate the z-variable.

C $x + 3z = 17$ $\longrightarrow$ $\quad\quad x + 3z = 17$
D $6x + z = 17$ $\xrightarrow[\text{Multiply by } -3.]{}$ $\underline{-18x - 3z = -51}$
$\quad\quad\quad\quad\quad\quad\quad\quad\quad\quad -17x \quad\quad\quad = -34$
$\quad\quad\quad\quad\quad\quad\quad\quad\quad\quad\quad\quad\quad x = \quad 2$

Step 5: Now substitute $x = 2$ into equations A and C to find the remaining variables.

A $\quad 3x + y = \quad 5$ $\quad\quad\quad\quad$ C $\quad x + 3z = 17$
$\quad\quad 3(2) + y = \quad 5$ $\quad\quad\quad\quad\quad\quad (2) + 3z = 17$
$\quad\quad\quad 6 + y = \quad 5$ $\quad\quad\quad\quad\quad\quad\quad\quad 3z = 15$
$\quad\quad\quad\quad\quad y = -1$ $\quad\quad\quad\quad\quad\quad\quad\quad z = \quad 5$

Step 6: Check $(2, -1, 5)$ in the three original equations.

$\underline{\text{Check:}}$ $3x + y - 5 = 0 \longrightarrow 3(2) + (-1) - 5 = 0$ ✔ True
$\quad\quad\quad\quad z = 7 + 2y \quad\longrightarrow 5 = 7 + 2(-1)$ ✔ True
$\quad\quad\quad\quad x + 3z = 17 \quad\longrightarrow (2) + 3(5) = 17$ ✔ True

The solution set is $\{(2, -1, 5)\}$.

Skill Practice

2. Solve the system.

$$4y = x + 4$$
$$2x + z = 5$$
$$y - 14 = 4z$$

Example 3 Solving a Dependent System of Linear Equations

Classroom Example: p
Exercise 44

Solve the system. If there is not a unique solution, label the system as either dependent or inconsistent.

$$\boxed{A} \quad 3x + y - z = 8$$
$$\boxed{B} \quad 2x - y + 2z = 3$$
$$\boxed{C} \quad x + 2y - 3z = 5$$

Solution:

First, make a decision regarding the variable to eliminate. The y-variable is particularly easy to eliminate because the coefficients of y in equations $\boxed{A}$ and $\boxed{B}$ are already opposites. The y-variable can be eliminated from equations $\boxed{B}$ and $\boxed{C}$ by multiplying equation $\boxed{B}$ by 2.

$$\boxed{A} \quad 3x + y - z = 8$$
$$\boxed{B} \quad 2x - y + 2z = 3$$

$$\overline{\quad 5x \quad + \quad z = 11 \quad} \boxed{D}$$

Pair up equations $\boxed{A}$ and $\boxed{B}$ to eliminate y.

$$\boxed{B} \quad 2x - y + 2z = 3 \xrightarrow{\text{Multiply by 2.}} 4x - 2y + 4z = 6$$
$$\boxed{C} \quad x + 2y - 3z = 5 \longrightarrow \quad x + 2y - 3z = 5$$

$$\overline{\quad 5x \quad + \quad z = 11 \quad} \boxed{E}$$

Pair up equations $\boxed{B}$ and $\boxed{C}$ to eliminate y.

Because equations $\boxed{D}$ and $\boxed{E}$ are equivalent equations, it appears that this is a dependent system. By eliminating variables we obtain the identity $0 = 0$.

$$\boxed{D} \quad 5x + z = 11 \xrightarrow{\text{Multiply by } -1.} -5x - z = -11$$
$$\boxed{E} \quad 5x + z = 11 \longrightarrow \quad 5x + z = \quad 11$$

$$\overline{\qquad\qquad 0 = \quad 0}$$

The result $0 = 0$ indicates that there are infinitely many solutions and that the system is dependent.

Skill Practice

3. Solve the system. If the system does not have a unique solution, identify the system as dependent or inconsistent.

$$x + y + z = 8$$
$$2x - y + z = 6$$
$$-5x - 2y - 4z = -30$$

Answer

3. Dependent system

Classroom Example: p. 318,
Exercise 38

| Example 4 | Solving an Inconsistent System of Linear Equations |

Solve the system. If there is not a unique solution, identify the system as either dependent or inconsistent.

$$2x + 3y - 7z = 4$$
$$-4x - 6y + 14z = 1$$
$$5x + y - 3z = 6$$

Solution:

We will eliminate the x-variable.

$\boxed{A}$ $\quad 2x + 3y - 7z = 4 \xrightarrow{\text{Multiply by 2.}} 4x + 6y - 14z = 8$

$\boxed{B}$ $\quad -4x - 6y + 14z = 1 \longrightarrow \underline{-4x - 6y + 14z = 1}$

$\boxed{C}$ $\quad 5x + y - 3z = 6 \hspace{4cm} 0 = 9 \quad$ (contradiction)

The result $0 = 9$ is a contradiction, indicating that the system has no solution, { }. The system is inconsistent.

Skill Practice

4. Solve the system. If the system does not have a unique solution, identify the system as dependent or inconsistent.

$$x - 2y + z = 5$$
$$x - 3y + 2z = -7$$
$$-2x + 4y - 2z = 6$$

Answer

4. The system is inconsistent, { }.

Section 4.5 Practice Exercises

Study Skills Exercise

1. Define the key term.

   a. linear equation in three variables   **b. ordered triple**

Review Exercises

For Exercises 2–4, solve the systems by using two methods: (**a**) the substitution method and (**b**) the addition method.

2. $3x + y = 4$
   $4x + y = 5$ $\quad \{(1, 1)\}$

3. $\quad 2x - 5y = 3$ $\quad$ { }; inconsistent system
   $-4x + 10y = 3$

4. $4x - 6y = 5$
   $x = \dfrac{3}{2}y + \dfrac{5}{4}$ $\quad$ Infinitely many solutions; $\{(x, y) \mid 4x - 6y = 5\}$

 Writing   Translating Expression   Geometry   Scientific Calculator   Video   NS&E

5. Two cars leave Kansas City at the same time. One travels east and one travels west. After 3 hr the cars are 369 mi apart. If one car travels 7 mph slower than the other, find the speed of each car.
The speeds are 65 mph and 58 mph.

Concept 1: Solutions to Systems of Linear Equations in Three Variables

6. How many solutions are possible when solving a system of three equations with three variables?
One solution, no solution, or infinitely many solutions

7. Which of the following points are solutions to the system? $(4, 0, 2)$ is a solution.

$$(2, 1, 7), (3, -10, -6), (4, 0, 2)$$

$$2x - y + z = 10$$
$$4x + 2y - 3z = 10$$
$$x - 3y + 2z = 8$$

8. Which of the following points are solutions to the system? $(4, 2, 1)$ is a solution.

$$(1, 1, 3), (0, 0, 4), (4, 2, 1)$$

$$-3x - 3y - 6z = -24$$
$$-9x - 6y + 3z = -45$$
$$9x + 3y - 9z = 33$$

9. Which of the following points are solutions to the system? $(1, 1, 1)$ is a solution.

$$(12, 2, -2), (4, 2, 1), (1, 1, 1)$$

$$-x - y - 4z = -6$$
$$x - 3y + z = -1$$
$$4x + y - z = 4$$

10. Which of the following points are solutions to the system?   None

$$(0, 4, 3), (3, 6, 10), (3, 3, 1)$$

$$x + 2y - z = 5$$
$$x - 3y + z = -5$$
$$-2x + y - z = -4$$

Concept 2: Solving Systems of Linear Equations in Three Variables

For Exercises 11–34, solve the system of equations. **(See Examples 1–2.)**

11. $\quad 2x + y - 3z = -12 \quad \{(1, -2, 4)\}$
$\quad\ \ 3x - 2y - z - \quad 3$
$\quad -x + 5y + 2z = -3$

12. $-3x - 2y + 4z = -15$
$\quad\ \ 2x + 5y - 3z = \quad 3$
$\quad\ \ 4x - y + 7z = \quad 15$
$\quad \{(5, -2, -1)\}$

13. $\quad x - 3y - 4z = -7 \quad \{(-1, 2, 0)\}$
$\quad 5x + 2y + 2z = -1$
$\quad 4x - y - 5z = -6$

14. $\quad 6x - 5y + z - \quad 7 \quad \{(2, 0, -5)\}$
$\quad\ \ 5x + 3y + 2z = \quad 0$
$\quad -2x + y - 3z = 11$

15. $-3x + y - z = \quad 8$
$\quad -4x + 2y + 3z = -3$
$\quad\ \ 2x + 3y - 2z = -1$
$\quad \{(-2, -1, -3)\}$

16. $\quad 2x + 3y + 3z = \quad 15 \quad \left\{\left(1, 1, \frac{10}{3}\right)\right\}$
$\quad\ \ 3x - 6y - 6z = -23$
$\quad -9x - 3y + 6z = \quad 8$

17. $4x + 2z = 12 + 3y$
$\quad 2y = 3x + 3z - 5$
$\quad\ y = 2x + 7z + 8$
$\quad \{(1, -4, -2)\}$

18. $\quad y = 2x + z + 1$
$\quad -3x - 1 = -2y + 2z$
$\quad\ \ 5x + 3z - 16 - 3y$
$\quad \{(-1, 3, 4)\}$

19. $\quad x + y + z = \quad 6 \quad \{(1, 2, 3)\}$
$\quad -x + y - z = -2$
$\quad\ \ 2x + 3y + z = \quad 11$

20. $\quad x - y - z = -11 \quad \{(2, 13, 0)\}$
$\quad x + y - z = \quad 15$
$\quad 2x - y + z = -9$

21. $2x - 3y + 2z = -1 \quad \{(-6, 1, 7)\}$
$\quad x + 2y = -4$
$\quad x + z = 1$

22. $\quad x + y + z = 2 \quad \{(2, 1, -1)\}$
$\quad 2x - z = 5$
$\quad\ \ 3y + z = 2$

23. $4x + 9y = 8 \quad \left\{\left(\frac{1}{2}, \frac{2}{3}, -\frac{5}{6}\right)\right\}$
$\quad 8x + 6z = -1$
$\quad\ \ 6y + 6z = -1$

24. $3x + 2z = 11 \quad \left\{\left(4, \frac{1}{2}, -\frac{1}{2}\right)\right\}$
$\quad\ \ y - 7z = 4$
$\quad x - 6y = 1$

25. $\quad 2x + 3y - 2z = 8$
$\quad\ \ x - 4y + z = -8 \quad \left\{\left(\frac{1}{2}, 2, -\frac{1}{2}\right)\right\}$
$\quad -4x + 3y + 2z = 3$

26. $5x - 3y + z = 4$
$\quad -x + 6y + 4z = 1 \quad \left\{\left(1, \frac{1}{3}, 0\right)\right\}$
$\quad\ \ 2x + 3y - z = 3$

27. $\quad 5y = -7 + 4z$
$\quad x + 3y + 3 = 0 \quad \{(6, -3, -2)\}$
$\quad 2x = 14 + z$

28. $4(x - z) = -1$
$\quad 3y + z = 1 \quad \left\{\left(\frac{3}{4}, 0, 1\right)\right\}$
$\quad 4x = 3 + y$

 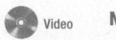

29.
$$x + z = -16 + 3y$$
$$2(x + z) = 12 - 5y$$
$$3x + 8 = y - z$$
$$\{(0, 4, -4)\}$$

30.
$$4(x - 2y) = 8 - 3z$$
$$4y + 13 = 3x + z$$
$$x - 3y = -2(z + 2)$$
$$\{(7, 1, -4)\}$$

31.
$$\tfrac{1}{3}x + \tfrac{1}{2}y + \tfrac{1}{6}z = \tfrac{1}{6}$$
$$\tfrac{1}{5}x + y - \tfrac{3}{5}z = \tfrac{4}{5}$$
$$x - \tfrac{4}{9}y + \tfrac{2}{3}z = \tfrac{1}{3}$$
$$\{(1, 0, -1)\}$$

32.
$$\tfrac{1}{2}x + \tfrac{5}{2}z = -1$$
$$\tfrac{1}{4}x - \tfrac{1}{6}y - \tfrac{2}{3}z = 3$$
$$-\tfrac{1}{2}x + \tfrac{5}{8}y + \tfrac{1}{8}z = -3$$
$$\{(8, 2, -2)\}$$

33.
$$0.1x - 0.6y + z = -6.8$$
$$0.7x - 0.3z = -14$$
$$y + 0.5z = 8$$
$$\{(-20, 8, 0)\}$$

34.
$$0.5x + y = 10$$
$$-0.2y + 0.5z = 0.5$$
$$-0.3x - z = -6$$
$$\{(10, 5, 3)\}$$

Mixed Exercises

For Exercises 35–46, solve the system. If there is not a unique solution, label the system as either dependent or inconsistent. **(See Examples 1–4.)**

35.
$$2x + y + 3z = 2$$
$$x - y + 2z = -4$$
$$x + 3y - z = 1$$
$$\{(-9, 5, 5)\}$$

36.
$$x + y = z$$
$$3(x - y) + 6z = 1 - y$$
$$7x + 3(y + 1) = 7 - z$$
$$\{(-3, 7, 4)\}$$

37.
$$6x - 2y + 2z = 2$$
$$4x + 8y - 2z = 5$$
$$-2x - 4y + z = -2$$
Inconsistent system

38.
$$3x + 2y + z = 3$$
$$x - 3y + z = 4$$
$$-6x - 4y - 2z = 1$$
Inconsistent system

39.
$$\tfrac{1}{2}x + \tfrac{2}{3}y = \tfrac{5}{2}$$
$$\tfrac{1}{5}x - \tfrac{1}{2}z = -\tfrac{3}{10} \quad \{(1, 3, 1)\}$$
$$\tfrac{1}{3}y - \tfrac{1}{4}z = \tfrac{3}{4}$$

40.
$$\tfrac{1}{2}x + \tfrac{1}{4}y + z = 3$$
$$\tfrac{1}{8}x + \tfrac{1}{4}y + \tfrac{1}{4}z = \tfrac{9}{8}$$
$$x - y - \tfrac{2}{3}z = \tfrac{1}{3}$$
$$\{(3, 2, 1)\}$$

41.
$$3(2x + y) = 4(3z - 1)$$
$$y + 4z = 2(3 + 5x)$$
$$2(x + z) = y - 1 \quad \left\{\left(-\tfrac{1}{2}, \tfrac{1}{3}, \tfrac{1}{6}\right)\right\}$$

42.
$$5(y - 2z) = 9x - 11$$
$$2(3x + z) = 5 + y$$
$$3x = z + 2(y + 1) \quad \left\{\left(\tfrac{2}{3}, -\tfrac{1}{5}, \tfrac{2}{5}\right)\right\}$$

43.
$$2x + y = 3(z - 1)$$
$$3x - 2(y - 2z) = 1$$
$$2(2x - 3z) = -6 - 2y$$
Dependent system

44.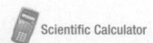
$$2x + y = -3$$
$$2y + 16z = -10$$
$$-7x - 3y + 4z = 8$$
Dependent system

45.
$$-0.1y + 0.2z = 0.2$$
$$0.1x + 0.1y + 0.1z = 0.2$$
$$-0.1x + 0.3z = 0.2$$
$$\{(1, 0, 1)\}$$

46.
$$0.1x - 0.2y = 0$$
$$0.3y + 0.1z = -0.1$$
$$0.4x - 0.1z = 1.2$$
$$\{(2, 1, -4)\}$$

Expanding Your Skills

The systems in Exercises 47–50 are called homogeneous systems because each system has $(0, 0, 0)$ as a solution. However, if a system is dependent, it will have infinitely many more solutions. For each system determine whether $(0, 0, 0)$ is the only solution or if the system is dependent.

47.
$$2x - 4y + 8z = 0$$
$$-x - 3y + z = 0$$
$$x - 2y + 5z = 0$$
$$\{(0, 0, 0)\}$$

48.
$$2x - 4y + z = 0$$
$$x - 3y - z = 0$$
$$3x - y + 2z = 0$$
$$\{(0, 0, 0)\}$$

49.
$$4x - 2y - 3z = 0$$
$$-8x - y + z = 0$$
$$2x - y - \tfrac{3}{2}z = 0$$
Dependent system

50.
$$5x + y = 0$$
$$4y - z = 0$$
$$5x + 5y - z = 0$$
Dependent system

Applications of Systems of Linear Equations in Three Variables

1. Applications Involving Geometry

In this section we solve several applications of linear equations in three variables.

Objectives

1. **Applications Involving Geometry**
2. **Applications Involving Mixtures**

Classroom Example: p. 321, Exercise 6

> **Example 1** **Applying Systems of Linear Equations in Three Variables**

In a triangle, the smallest angle measures 10° more than one-half of the largest angle. The middle angle measures 12° more than the smallest angle. Find the measure of each angle.

Solution:

Let x represent the measure of the smallest angle.

Let y represent the measure of the middle angle.

Let z represent the measure of the largest angle.

To solve for three variables, we need to establish three independent relationships among x, y, and z.

A	$x = \dfrac{z}{2} + 10$	The smallest angle measures 10° more than one-half the measure of the largest angle.
B	$y = x + 12$	The middle angle measures 12° more than the measure of the smallest angle.
C	$x + y + z = 180$	The sum of the interior angles of a triangle measures 180°.

Clear fractions and write each equation in standard form.

Standard Form

$$\boxed{A}\quad x = \frac{z}{2} + 10 \xrightarrow{\text{Multiply by 2.}} 2x = z + 20 \longrightarrow 2x - z = 20$$

$$\boxed{B}\quad y = x + 12 \longrightarrow -x + y = 12$$

$$\boxed{C}\quad x + y + z = 180 \longrightarrow x + y + z = 180$$

Notice equation $\boxed{B}$ is missing the z-variable. Therefore, we can eliminate z again by pairing up equations $\boxed{A}$ and $\boxed{C}$.

$$\boxed{A}\quad 2x - z = 20$$
$$\boxed{C}\quad \underline{x + y + z = 180}$$
$$\quad 3x + y = 200 \quad \boxed{D}$$

$$\boxed{B} \; -x + y = 12 \xrightarrow{\text{Multiply by } -1.} x - y = -12$$

Pair up equations $\boxed{B}$ and

$$\boxed{D} \; 3x + y = 200 \longrightarrow \quad 3x + y = 200$$

$\boxed{D}$ to form a system of two variables.

$$\underline{4x \quad\;\; = 188}$$

$$x = 47 \qquad \text{Solve for } x.$$

From equation $\boxed{B}$ we have $-x + y = 12 \longrightarrow \quad -47 + y = 12 \rightarrow y = 59$

From equation $\boxed{C}$ we have $x + y + z = 180 \rightarrow 47 + 59 + z = 180 \rightarrow z = 74$

The smallest angle measures 47°, the middle angle measures 59°, and the largest angle measures 74°.

Skill Practice

1. The perimeter of a triangle is 30 in. The shortest side is 4 in. shorter than the longest side. The longest side is 6 in. less than the sum of the other two sides. Find the length of each side.

2. Applications Involving Mixtures

Classroom Example: p. 322, Exercise 14

| Example 2 | **Applying Systems of Linear Equations to Nutrition** |

Doctors have become increasingly concerned about the sodium intake in the U.S. diet. Recommendations by the American Medical Association indicate that most individuals should not exceed 2400 mg of sodium per day.

Liz ate 1 slice of pizza, 1 serving of ice cream, and 1 glass of soda for a total of 1030 mg of sodium. David ate 3 slices of pizza, no ice cream, and 2 glasses of soda for a total of 2420 mg of sodium. Melinda ate 2 slices of pizza, 1 serving of ice cream, and 2 glasses of soda for a total of 1910 mg of sodium. How much sodium is in one serving of each item?

Solution:

Let x represent the sodium content of 1 slice of pizza.

Let y represent the sodium content of 1 serving of ice cream.

Let z represent the sodium content of 1 glass of soda.

From Liz's meal we have: $\qquad \boxed{A} \;\; x + y + \;\; z = 1030$

From David's meal we have: $\qquad \boxed{B} \; 3x \qquad + 2z = 2420$

From Melinda's meal we have: $\qquad \boxed{C} \; 2x + y + 2z = 1910$

Equation $\boxed{B}$ is missing the y-variable. Eliminating y from equations $\boxed{A}$ and $\boxed{C}$, we have

$$\boxed{A} \;\; x + y + \;\; z = 1030 \xrightarrow{\text{Multiply by } -1.} -x - y - \;\; z = -1030$$

$$\boxed{C} \; 2x + y + 2z = 1910 \longrightarrow \quad \underline{2x + y + 2z = \;\;\; 1910}$$

$$\boxed{D} \; x \qquad + z = \quad 880$$

Solve the system formed by equations $\boxed{B}$ and $\boxed{D}$.

$$\boxed{B} \; 3x + 2z = 2420 \longrightarrow \qquad 3x + 2z = \;\; 2420$$

$$\boxed{D} \;\; x + \;\; z = \;\; 880 \xrightarrow[\text{Multiply by } -2.]{} \quad \underline{-2x - 2z = -1760}$$

$$x \qquad\;\; = \quad 660$$

Answer

1. The sides are 8 in., 10 in., and 12 in.

From equation $\boxed{D}$ we have $x + z = 880 \longrightarrow 660 + z = 880 \longrightarrow z = 220$

From equation $\boxed{A}$ we have $x + y + z = 1030 \rightarrow 660 + y + 220 = 1030 \rightarrow y = 150$

Therefore, 1 slice of pizza has 660 mg of sodium, 1 serving of ice cream has 150 mg of sodium, and 1 glass of soda has 220 mg of sodium.

Skill Practice

2. Annette, Barb, and Carlita work in a clothing shop. One day the three had combined sales of $1480. Annette sold $120 more than Barb. Barb and Carlita combined sold $280 more than Annette. How much did each person sell?

Answer

2. Annette sold $600, Barb sold $480, and Carlita sold $400.

Section 4.6 Practice Exercises

Review Exercises

For Exercises 1–4, solve the system. If there is not a unique solution label the system as either dependent or inconsistent.

1.
$$\begin{aligned} -5y - z &= -8 \\ x + 10y + 2z &= 9 \\ -3x + y &= 21 \end{aligned}$$
$\{(-7, 0, 8)\}$

2.
$$\begin{aligned} 8x - y + 2z &= 18 \\ x + y - 5z &= -21 \\ 4x - 0.5y + z &= 9 \end{aligned}$$
Dependent system

3.
$$\begin{aligned} \frac{1}{2}x - y + \frac{5}{6}z &= 1 \\ \frac{3}{2}x - 3y + \frac{5}{2}z &= 6 \\ -\frac{1}{4}x + y - \frac{1}{3}z &= -2 \end{aligned}$$
Inconsistent system

4.
$$\begin{aligned} 12x - y + z &= -6 \\ -6x + 2y - 3z &= 5 \\ 6x + y - z &= 3 \end{aligned}$$
$\left\{\left(-\frac{1}{6}, 8, 4\right)\right\}$

Concept 1: Applications Involving Geometry

5. A triangle has one angle that measures 5° more than twice the smallest angle, and the largest angle measures 11° less than 3 times the measure of the smallest angle. Find the measures of the three angles. (See Example 1.)
   $67°, 82°, 31°$

6. The largest angle of a triangle measures 4° less than 5 times the measure of the smallest angle. The middle angle measures twice that of the smallest angle. Find the measures of the three angles. $111°, 46°, 23°$

7. One angle of a triangle measures 6° more than twice the measure of the smallest angle. The third angle measures 1° less than four times the smallest. Find the measures of the three angles. $25°, 56°, 99°$

8. In a triangle the smallest angle measures 12° less than the middle angle. The measure of the largest angle is equal to the sum of the other two. Find the measures of the three angles. $39°, 51°, 90°$

 Writing   Translating Expression   Geometry   Scientific Calculator   Video   NS&E

9. The perimeter of a triangle is 55 cm. The measure of the shortest side is 8 cm less than the middle side. The measure of the longest side is 1 cm less than the sum of the other two sides. Find the lengths of the sides.
10 cm, 18 cm, 27 cm

10. The perimeter of a triangle is 5 ft. The longest side of the triangle measures 20 in. more than the shortest side. The middle side is 3 times the measure of the shortest side. Find the lengths of the three sides in *inches*.
8 in., 24 in., 28 in.

11. The perimeter of a triangle is 4.5 ft. The shortest side measures 2 in. less than half the longest side. The longest side measures 2 in. less than the sum of the other two sides. Find the lengths of the sides in *inches*.
11 in., 17 in., 26 in.

12. The perimeter of a triangle is 7 m. The longest side measures twice the shortest side and the sum of the measures of the smallest side and the middle side is 1 m more than the measure of the longest side. Find the lengths of the sides. $1\frac{1}{2}$ m, $2\frac{1}{2}$ m, 3m

Concept 2: Applications Involving Mixtures

13. Sean kept track of his fiber intake from three sources for 3 weeks. The first week he had 3 servings of a fiber supplement, 1 serving of oatmeal, and 4 servings of cereal, which totaled 19 g of fiber. The second week he had 2 servings of the fiber supplement, 4 servings of oatmeal, and 2 servings of cereal totaling 25 g. The third week he had 5 servings of the fiber supplement, 3 servings of oatmeal, and 2 servings of cereal for a total of 30 g. Find the amount of fiber in one serving of each of the following: the fiber supplement, the oatmeal, and the cereal. **(See Example 2.)** The fiber supplement has 3 g; the oatmeal has 4 g; and the cereal has 1.5 g.

14. Natalie kept track of her calcium intake from three sources for 3 days. The first day she had 1 glass of milk, 1 serving of ice cream, and 1 calcium supplement in pill form which totaled 1180 mg of calcium. The second day she had 2 glasses of milk, 1 serving of ice cream, and 1 calcium supplement totaling 1680 mg. The third day she had 1 glass of milk, 2 servings of ice cream, and 1 calcium supplement for a total of 1260 mg. Find the amount of calcium in one glass of milk, in one serving of ice cream, and in one calcium supplement. The milk has 500 mg; the ice cream has 80 mg; and the calcium supplement has 600 mg.

15. Kyoki invested a total of $10,000 into bonds, mutual funds, and a money market account. He put the same amount of money in the money market account as he did in bonds. For 1 year, the bonds paid 5% interest, the mutual funds paid 8%, and the money market paid 4%. At the end of the year, Kyoki earned $660 in interest. How much did he invest in each account? Kyoki invested $2000 in bonds, $6000 in mutual funds, and $2000 in the money market account.

16. Walter had $25,000 to invest. He spit the money into three types of investment: small caps earning 6%, global market investments earning 10%, and a balanced fund earning 9%. He put twice as much money in the global account as he did in the balanced fund. If his earnings for the first year totaled $2160, how much did he invest in each account? Walter invested $7000 in small caps, $6000 in the balanced fund, and $12,000 in global markets.

17. Winston deposited $4500 into three certificates of deposit: a 24-month CD paying 5% interest, a 30-month CD paying 5.5% interest, and an 18-month CD paying 4% interest. He put $1000 more in the CD with the 5.5% rate than he put in the 4% rate. After the first year, he earned a total of $225 interest. How much did he deposit into each CD? $1500 at 5%, $2000 at 5.5%, $1000 at 4%

18. Raeann deposited $8000 into three accounts at her credit union: a checking account that pays 1.2% interest, a savings account that pays 2.5% interest, and a money market account that pays 3% interest. If she put three times more money in the 3% account than she did in the 1.2% account, and her total interest for 1 year was $202, how much did she deposit into each account? $1000 at 1.2%, $4000 at 2.5%, $3000 at 3%

19. A movie theater charges $7 for adults, $5 for children under age 17, and $4 for seniors over age 60. For one showing of *Batman* the theater sold 222 tickets and took in $1383. If twice as many adult tickets were sold as the total of children and senior tickets, how many tickets of each kind were sold?
148 adult tickets, 51 children's tickets, 23 senior tickets

20. Goofie Golf has 18 holes that are par 3, par 4, or par 5. Most of the holes are par 4. In fact, there are 3 times as many par 4s as par 3s. There are 3 more par 5s than par 3s. How many of each type are there?
Three par 3s, nine par 4s, six par 5s

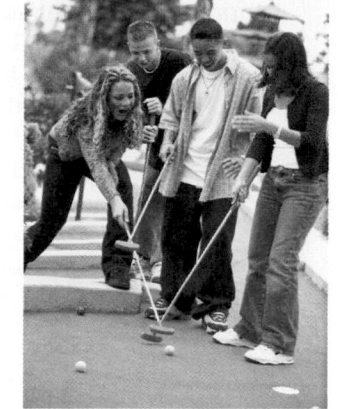

21. Combining peanuts, pecans, and cashews makes a party mixture of nuts. If the amount of peanuts equals the amount of pecans and cashews combined, and if there are twice as many cashews as pecans, how many ounces of each nut is used to make 48 oz of party mixture?
24 oz peanuts, 8 oz pecans, 16 oz cashews

22. Souvenir hats, T-shirts, and jackets are sold at a rock concert. Three hats, two T-shirts, and one jacket cost $140. Two hats, two T-shirts, and two jackets cost $170. One hat, three T-shirts, and two jackets cost $180. Find the prices of the individual items.   Hat $15, T-shirt $25, jacket $45

23. In 2002, Baylor University in Waco, Texas, had twice as many students as Vanderbilt University in Nashville, Tennessee. Pace University in New York City had 2800 more students than Vanderbilt University. If the enrollment for all three schools totaled 27,200, find the enrollment for each school.   Vanderbilt 6100, Baylor 12,200, Pace 8900

24. Annie and Maria traveled overseas for seven days and stayed in three different hotels in three different cities: Stockholm, Sweden; Oslo, Norway; and Paris, France.

The total bill for all seven nights (not including tax) was $1040. The total tax was $106. The nightly cost (excluding tax) to stay at the hotel in Paris was $80 more than the nightly cost (excluding tax) to stay in Oslo. Find the cost per night for each hotel excluding tax.   Paris hotel $200/night; Stockholm hotel $150/night; Oslo hotel $120/night

City	Number of Nights	Cost/Night ($)	Tax Rate
Paris, France	1	x	8%
Stockholm, Sweden	4	y	11%
Oslo, Norway	2	z	10%

Group Activity

Creating Linear Models from Data

Materials: Two pieces of rope for each group. The ropes should be of different thicknesses. The piece of thicker rope should be between 4 and 5 ft long. The thinner piece of rope should be 8 to 12 in. shorter than the thicker rope. You will also need a yardstick or other device for making linear measurements.

Estimated Time: 30–35 minutes

Group Size: 4 (2 pairs)

 Writing   Translating Expression   Geometry   Scientific Calculator   Video   NS&E

1. Each group of 4 should divide into two pairs, and each pair will be given a piece of rope. Each pair will measure the initial length of rope. Then students will tie a series of knots in the rope and measure the new length after each knot is tied. (*Hint:* Try to tie the knots with an equal amount of force each time. Also, as the ropes are straightened for measurement, try to use the same amount of tension in the rope.) The results should be recorded in the table.

Thick Rope			Thin Rope	
Number of Knots, x	Length (in.), y		Number of Knots, x	Length (in.), y
0			0	
1			1	
2			2	
3			3	
4			4	

Answers will vary throughout this exercise.

2. Graph each set of data points. Use a different color pen or pencil for each set of points. Does it appear that each set of data follows a linear trend? Draw a line through each set of points.

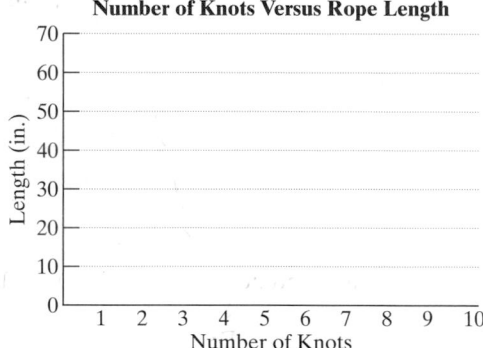

3. Each time a knot is tied, the rope decreases in length. Using the results from question 1, compute the average amount of length lost per knot tied.

For the thick rope, the length decreases by _____ inches per knot tied.

For the thin rope, the length decreases by _____ inches per knot tied.

4. For each set of data points, find an equation of the line through the points. Write the equation in slope-intercept form, $y = mx + b$.

[*Hint:* The slope of the line will be negative and will be represented by the amount of length lost per knot (see question 3). The value of b will be the original length of the rope.]

Equation for the thick rope: _____

Equation for the thin rope: _____

5. Next, you will try to predict the number of knots that you need to tie in each rope so that the ropes will be equal in length. To do this, solve the system of equations in question 4.

Solution to the system of equations: (_____, _____)

number of knots, x length, y

Interpret the meaning of the ordered pair in terms of the number of knots tied and the length of the ropes.

6. Check your answer from question 5 by actually tying the required number of knots in each rope. After doing this, are the ropes the same length? What is the length of each rope? Does this match the length predicted from question 5?

 Writing   Translating Expression   Geometry   Scientific Calculator   Video   NS&E

Chapter 4 Summary

Section 4.1 Solving Systems of Equations by the Graphing Method

Key Concepts

A **system of two linear equations** can be solved by graphing.

A **solution to a system of linear equations** is an ordered pair that satisfies each equation in the system. Graphically, this represents a point of intersection of the lines.

There may be one solution, infinitely many solutions, or no solution.

One solution	Infinitely many solutions	No solution
Consistent	Consistent	Inconsistent
Independent	Dependent	Independent

A system of equations is **consistent** if there is at least one solution. A system is **inconsistent** if there is no solution.

A linear system in x and y is **dependent** if two equations represent the same line. The solution set is the set of all points on the line. If two linear equations represent different lines, then the system of equations is **independent**.

Examples

Example 1

Solve by using the graphing method.

$x + y = 3$

$2x - y = 0$

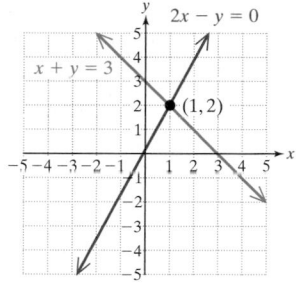

The solution set is $\{(1, 2)\}$.

Example 2

Solve by using the graphing method.

$3x - 2y = 2$

$-6x + 4y = 4$

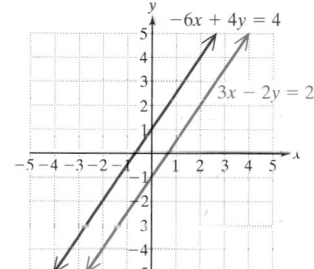

There is no solution, $\{\ \}$. The system is inconsistent.

Example 3

Solve by using the graphing method.

$x + 2y = 2$

$-3x - 6y = -6$

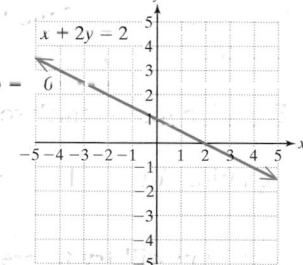

The system is dependent, and the solution set consists of all points on the line, given by $\{(x, y) \mid x + 2y = 2\}$.

Section 4.2 Solving Systems of Equations by the Substitution Method

Key Concepts

Solving a System of Equations by Using the Substitution Method:

1. Isolate one of the variables from one equation.
2. Substitute the quantity found in step 1 into the other equation.
3. Solve the resulting equation.
4. Substitute the value found in step 3 back into the equation in step 1 to find the remaining variable.
5. Check the ordered pair in both original equations.

An inconsistent system has no solution and is detected algebraically by a contradiction (such as $0 = 3$).

If two linear equations represent the same line, the system is dependent. This is detected algebraically by an identity (such as $0 = 0$).

Examples

Example 1

Solve by using the substitution method.

$$x + 4y = -11$$
$$3x - 2y = -5$$

Isolate x in the first equation: $x = -4y - 11$
Substitute into the second equation.

$$3(-4y - 11) - 2y = -5 \qquad \text{Solve the equation.}$$
$$-12y - 33 - 2y = -5$$
$$-14y = 28$$
$$y = -2$$

$$x = -4y - 11 \qquad \text{Substitute } y = -2.$$
$$x = -4(-2) - 11 \qquad \text{Solve for } x.$$
$$x = -3$$

The ordered pair $(-3, -2)$ checks in both the original equations. The solution set is $\{(-3, -2)\}$.

Example 2

Solve by using the substitution method.

$$3x + y = 4$$
$$-6x - 2y = 2$$

Isolate y in the first equation: $y = -3x + 4$.
Substitute into the second equation.

$$-6x - 2(-3x + 4) = 2$$
$$-6x + 6x - 8 = 2$$
$$-8 = 2 \qquad \text{Contradiction}$$

The system is inconsistent and has no solution, $\{\ \}$.

Example 3

Solve by using the substitution method.

$$y = x + 2 \qquad y \text{ is already isolated.}$$
$$x - y = -2$$

$$x - (x + 2) = -2 \qquad \text{Substitute } y = x + 2 \text{ into the}$$
$$x - x - 2 = -2 \qquad \text{second equation.}$$
$$-2 = -2 \qquad \text{Identity}$$

The system is dependent. The solution set is all points on the line $y = x + 2$ or $\{(x, y) | y = x + 2\}$.

Section 4.3   Solving Systems of Equations by the Addition Method

Key Concepts

Solving a System of Linear Equations

by Using the Addition Method:

1. Write both equations in standard form: $Ax + By = C$.
2. Clear fractions or decimals (optional).
3. Multiply one or both equations by a nonzero constant to create opposite coefficients for one of the variables.
4. Add the equations to eliminate one variable.
5. Solve for the remaining variable.
6. Substitute the known value into one of the original equations to solve for the other variable.
7. Check the ordered pair in both equations.

Example

Example 1

Solve by using the addition method.

$$5x = -4y - 7 \qquad \text{Write the first equation in}$$
$$6x - 3y = 15 \qquad \text{standard form.}$$

$$
\begin{aligned}
5x + 4y &= -7 \xrightarrow{\text{Multiply by 3.}} 15x + 12y = -21 \\
6x - 3y &= 15 \xrightarrow{\text{Multiply by 4.}} \underline{24x - 12y = 60} \\
& \hspace{4.6cm} 39x = 39 \\
& \hspace{5.6cm} x = 1
\end{aligned}
$$

$$5x = -4y - 7$$
$$5(1) = -4y - 7$$
$$5 = -4y - 7$$
$$12 = -4y$$
$$-3 = y \qquad \text{The ordered pair } (1, -3) \text{ checks in both original equations. The solution set is } \{(1, -3)\}.$$

Section 4.4   Applications of Linear Equations in Two Variables

Examples

Example 1

A riverboat travels 36 mi with the current in 2 hr. The return trip takes 3 hr against the current. Find the speed of the current and the speed of the boat in still water.

Let x represent the speed of the boat in still water.
Let y represent the speed of the current.

	Distance	Rate	Time
Against current	36	$x - y$	3
With current	36	$x + y$	2

Distance = (rate)(time)

$$36 = (x - y) \cdot 3 \longrightarrow 36 = 3x - 3y$$
$$36 = (x + y) \cdot 2 \longrightarrow 36 = 2x + 2y$$

$$36 = 3x - 3y \xrightarrow{\text{Multiply by 2.}} 72 = 6x - 6y$$
$$36 = 2x + 2y \xrightarrow[\text{Multiply by 3.}]{} 108 = 6x + 6y$$
$$180 = 12x$$
$$15 = x$$

$$36 = 2(15) + 2y$$
$$36 = 30 + 2y$$
$$6 = 2y$$
$$3 = y$$

The speed of the boat in still water is 15 mph, and the speed of the current is 3 mph.

Example 2

Diane borrows a total of $15,000. Part of the money is borrowed from a lender that charges 8% simple interest. She borrows the rest of the money from her mother and will pay back the money at 5% interest. If the total interest after 1 year is $900, how much did she borrow from each source?

	8%	5%	Total
Principal	x	y	15,000
Interest	$0.08x$	$0.05y$	900

$$x + y = 15,000$$
$$0.08x + 0.05y = 900$$

Substitute $x = 15,000 - y$ into the second equation.

$$0.08(15,000 - y) + 0.05y = 900$$
$$1200 - 0.08y + 0.05y = 900$$
$$1200 - 0.03y = 900$$
$$-0.03y = -300$$
$$y = 10,000$$

$$x = 15,000 - 10,000$$
$$= 5000$$

The amount borrowed at 8% is $5000.
The amount borrowed from her mother is $10,000.

Section 4.5   Systems of Linear Equations in Three Variables

Key Concepts

A **linear equation in three variables** can be written in the form $Ax + By + Cz = D$, where A, B, and C are not all zero. The graph of a linear equation in three variables is a plane in space.

A solution to a system of linear equations in three variables is an **ordered triple** that satisfies each equation. Graphically, a solution is a point of intersection among three planes.

A system of linear equations in three variables may have one unique solution, infinitely many solutions (dependent system), or no solution (inconsistent system).

Example

Example 1

$\boxed{A}\quad x + 2y - z = 4$

$\boxed{B}\quad 3x - y + z = 5$

$\boxed{C}\quad 2x + 3y + 2z = 7$

$\boxed{A}$ and $\boxed{B}$

$$x + 2y - z = 4$$
$$\underline{3x - y + z = 5}$$
$$4x + y \quad\ = 9 \ \boxed{D}$$

$2 \cdot \boxed{A}$ and $\boxed{C}$

$$2x + 4y - 2z = 8$$
$$\underline{2x + 3y + 2z = 7}$$
$$4x + 7y \quad\ = 15 \ \boxed{E}$$

$\boxed{D}\quad 4x + y = 9 \ \rightarrow\ -4x - y = -9$

$\boxed{E}\quad 4x + 7y = 15 \ \rightarrow\ \underline{\ 4x + 7y = 15}$

$$6y = 6$$
$$y = 1$$

Substitute $y = 1$ into either equation $\boxed{D}$ or $\boxed{E}$.

$\boxed{D}\quad 4x + (1) = 9$

$$4x = 8$$
$$x = 2$$

Substitute $x = 2$ and $y = 1$ into equation $\boxed{A}$, $\boxed{B}$, or $\boxed{C}$.

$\boxed{A}\quad (2) + 2(1) - z = 4$

$$z = 0$$

The solution set is $\{(2, 1, 0)\}$.

> ## Section 4.6   Applications of Systems of Linear Equations in Three Variables

Key Concepts

In application problems where there are three unknowns, it is often useful to set up a system of linear equations in three variables.

With three variables, three independent relationships among $x, y,$ and z are required.

Example

Example 1

In a triangle, the middle angle measures 55° more than the smallest angle. The largest angle measures 10° more than the sum of the other two angles. Find the measures of the angles.

Let x = measure of the smallest angle

Let y = measure of the middle angle

Let z = measure of the largest angle

First recall that the sum of the angles in a triangle is 180°.

$$\begin{array}{lcl} & & \text{standard form} \\ x + y + z = 180 & \longrightarrow & x + y + z = 180 \\ y = x + 55 & \longrightarrow & -x + y \quad\;\; = 55 \\ z = x + y + 10 & \longrightarrow & -x - y + z = 10 \end{array}$$

Solving the system yields $x = 15, y = 70,$ and $z = 95$.

The measures of the three angles are 15°, 70°, and 95°.

Chapter 4   Review Exercises

Section 4.1

For Exercises 1–4, determine if the ordered pair is a solution to the system.

1. $x - 4y = -4$ $(4, 2)$

$x + 2y = 8$ Yes

2. $x - 6y = 6$ $(12, 1)$

$-x + y = 4$ No

3. $3x + y = 9$ $(1, 3)$

$y = 3$ No

4. $2x - y = 8$ $(2, -4)$

$x = 2$ Yes

For Exercises 5–10, identify whether the system represents intersecting lines, parallel lines, or coinciding lines by comparing their slopes and y-intercepts.

5. $y = -\frac{1}{2}x + 4$

$y = x - 1$
Intersecting lines (the lines have different slopes)

6. $y = -3x + 4$

$y = 3x + 4$
Intersecting lines (the lines have different slopes)

7. $y = -\frac{4}{7}x + 3$

$y = -\frac{4}{7}x - 5$
Parallel lines (the lines have the same slope but different y-intercepts)

8. $y = 5x - 3$

$y = \frac{1}{5}x - 3$
Intersecting lines (the lines have different slopes)

9. $y = 9x - 2$

$9x - y = 2$
Coinciding lines (the lines have the same slope and same y-intercept)

10. $x = -5$

$y = 2$
Intersecting lines (the lines have different slopes)

For Exercises 11–18, solve each system by graphing. If a system does not have a unique solution, identify the system as inconsistent or dependent.

11. $y = -\frac{2}{3}x - 2$
$\{(0, -2)\}$
$-x + 3y = -6$

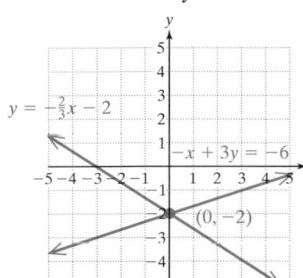

12. $y = -2x - 1$ $\{(-2, 3)\}$

$x + 2y = 4$

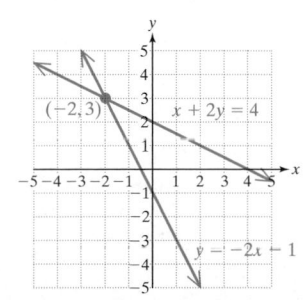

13. $4x = -2y + 10$

$2x + y = 5$

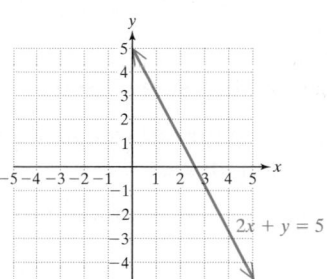

Infinitely many solutions; $\{(x, y) \mid 2x + y = 5\}$; dependent system

14. $10y = 2x - 10$

$-x + 5y = -5$

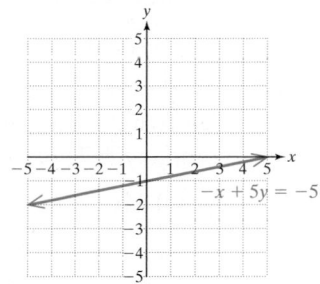

Infinitely many solutions; $\{(x, y) \mid -x + 5y = -5\}$; dependent system

15. $6x - 3y = 9$

$y = -1$ $\{(1, -1)\}$

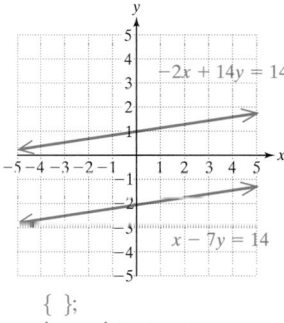

16. $5x + y = -3$

$x = -1$ $\{(-1, 2)\}$

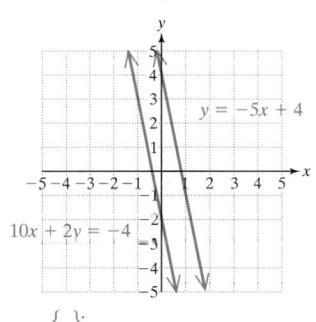

17. $x - 7y = 14$

$-2x + 14y = 14$

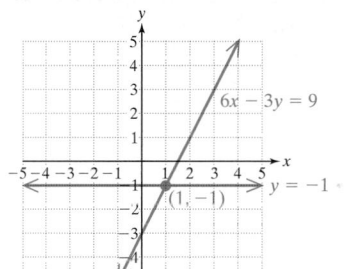

{ };
inconsistent system

18. $y = -5x + 4$

$10x + 2y = -4$

{ };
inconsistent system

 Writing   Translating Expression   Geometry   Scientific Calculator   Video   NS E

19. One phone company charges $0.15 a minute for calls but adds a $3.90 charge each month. Another company does not have a monthly fee but charges $0.25 per minute. The cost per month (in $), y_1, for the first company is given by the equation:

$$y_1 = 0.15x + 3.90 \quad \text{where } x \text{ represents the number of minutes used}$$

The cost per month (in $), y_2, for the second company is given by the equation:

$$y_2 = 0.25x \quad \text{where } x \text{ represents the number of minutes used.}$$

Find the number of minutes at which the cost per month for each company is the same. Using 39 minutes per month, the cost per month for each company is $9.75.

Section 4.2

For Exercises 20–23, solve each system using the substitution method.

20. $6x + y = 2$ $\left\{\left(\frac{2}{3}, -2\right)\right\}$
$y = 3x - 4$

21. $2x + 3y = -5$ $\{(-4, 1)\}$
$x = y - 5$

22. $2x + 6y = 10$
$x = -3y + 6$
{ }; inconsistent system

23. $4x + 2y = 4$
$y = -2x + 2$
Infinitely many solutions; $\{(x, y)\,|\,y = -2x + 2\}$; dependent system

24. Given the system:

$$x + 2y = 11$$
$$5x + 4y = 40$$

a. Which variable from which equation is easiest to isolate and why? x in the first equation is easiest to isolate because its coefficient is 1.
b. Solve the system using the substitution method. $\left\{\left(6, \frac{5}{2}\right)\right\}$

25. Given the system:

$$4x - 3y = 9$$
$$2x + y = 12$$

a. Which variable from which equation is easiest to isolate and why? y in the second equation is easiest to isolate because its coefficient is 1.
b. Solve the system using the substitution method. $\left\{\left(\frac{9}{2}, 3\right)\right\}$

For Exercises 26–29, solve each system using the substitution method.

26. $3x - 2y = 23$ $\{(5, -4)\}$
$x + 5y = -15$

27. $x + 5y = 20$ $\{(0, 4)\}$
$3x + 2y = 8$

28. $x - 3y = 9$
$5x - 15y = 45$
Infinitely many solutions; $\{(x, y)\,|\,x - 3y = 9\}$; dependent system

29. $-3x + y = 15$
$6x - 2y = 12$
{ }; inconsistent system

30. The difference of two positive numbers is 42. The larger number is 2 more than 6 times the smaller number. Find the numbers. The numbers are 50 and 8.

31. In a right triangle, one of the acute angles is 6° less than the other acute angle. Find the measure of each acute angle. The angles are 42° and 48°.

32. Two angles are supplementary. One angle measures 14° less than two times the other angle. Find the measure of each angle. The angles are $115\frac{1}{3}°$ and $64\frac{2}{3}°$.

Section 4.3

33. Explain the process for solving a system of two equations using the addition method. See page 291

34. Given the system:

$$3x - 5y = 1$$
$$2x - y = -4$$

a. Which variable, x or y, is easier to eliminate using the addition method? (Answers may vary.)
b. Solve the system using the addition method. $\{(-3, -2)\}$

35. Given the system:

$$9x - 2y = 14$$
$$4x + 3y = 14$$

a. Which variable, x or y, is easier to eliminate using the addition method? (Answers may vary.)
b. Solve the system using the addition method. $\{(2, 2)\}$

For Exercises 36–43, solve each system using the addition method.

36. $2x + 3y = 1$ $\{(2, -1)\}$
$x - 2y = 4$

37. $x + 3y = 0$ $\{(-6, 2)\}$
$-3x - 10y = -2$

38. $8x + 8 = -6y + 6$
$10x = 9y - 8$ $\left\{\left(-\frac{1}{2}, \frac{1}{3}\right)\right\}$

39. $12x = 5y + 5$
$5y = -1 - 4x$ $\left\{\left(\frac{1}{4}, -\frac{2}{5}\right)\right\}$

40. $-4x - 6y = -2$
$6x + 9y = 3$
Infinitely many solutions; $\{(x, y)\,|\,-4x - 6y = -2\}$; dependent system

41. $-8x - 4y = 16$
$10x + 5y = 5$
{ }; inconsistent system

 Writing   Translating Expression   Geometry   Scientific Calculator   Video   NS&E

42. $\dfrac{1}{2}x - \dfrac{3}{4}y = -\dfrac{1}{2}$

$\dfrac{1}{3}x + y = -\dfrac{10}{3}$

$\{(-4, -2)\}$

43. $0.5x - 0.2y = 0.5$

$0.4x + 0.7y = 0.4$

$\{(1, 0)\}$

44. Given the system:

$$4x + 9y = -7$$
$$y = 2x - 13$$

a. Which method would you choose to solve the system, the substitution method or the addition method? Explain your choice. (Answers may vary.)

b. Solve the system. $\{(5, -3)\}$

45. Given the system:

$$5x - 8y = -2$$
$$3x - 7y = 1$$

a. Which method would you choose to solve the system, the substitution method or the addition method? Explain your choice. (Answers may vary.)

b. Solve the system. $\{(-2, -1)\}$

Section 4.4

46. Miami Metrozoo charges $11.50 for adult admission and $6.75 for children under 12. The total bill before tax for a school group of 60 people is $443. How many adults and how many children were admitted?
There were 8 adult tickets and 52 children's tickets sold.

47. As part of his retirement strategy Winston plans to invest $600,000 in two different funds. He projects that the high-risk investments should return, over time, about 12% per year, while the low-risk investments should return about 4% per year. If he wants a supplemental income of $30,000 a year, how should he divide his investments?
He should invest $75,000 at 12% and $525,000 at 4%.

48. Suppose that whole milk with 4% fat is mixed with 1% low fat milk to make a 2% reduced fat milk. How much of the whole milk should be mixed with the low fat milk to make 60 gal of 2% reduced fat milk?   20 gal of whole milk should be mixed with 40 gal of low fat milk.

49. A boat travels 80 mi downstream with the current in 4 hr and 80 mi upstream against the current in 5 hr. Find the speed of the current and the speed of the boat in still water.
The speed of the boat is 18 mph, and that of the current is 2 mph.

50. A plane travels 870 mi against a headwind in 3 hr. Traveling with a tailwind, the plane travels 700 mi in 2 hr. Find the speed of the plane in still air and the speed of the wind.
The plane's speed in still air is 320 mph. The wind speed is 30 mph.

51. At Conseco Fieldhouse, home of the Indiana Pacers, the total cost of a soft drink and a hot dog is $8.00. The price of the hot dog is $1.00 more than the cost of the soft drink. Find the cost of a soft drink and the cost of a hot dog.
A hot dog costs $4.50 and a drink costs $3.50.

52. In a recent election, 5700 votes were cast and 3675 voters voted for the winning candidate. If $\frac{5}{8}$ of the women and $\frac{2}{3}$ of the men voted for the winning candidate, how many men and how many women voted?
3000 women and 2700 men voted.

53. Ray played two rounds of golf at Pebble Beach for a total score of 154. If his score in the second round is 10 more than his score in the first round, find the scores for each round.
The score was 72 on the first round and 82 on the second round.

Section 4.5

For Exercises 54–59, solve the systems of equations. If a system does not have a unique solution, label the system as either dependent or inconsistent.

54. $5x + 5y + 5z = 30$
$-x + y + z = 2$
$10x + 6y - 2z = 4$
$\{(2, -1, 5)\}$

55. $5x + 3y - z = 5$
$x + 2y + z = 6$
$-x - 2y - z = 8$
Inconsistent system

56. $x + y + z = 4$
$-x - 2y - 3z = -6$
$2x + 4y + 6z = 12$
Dependent system

57. $3x + 4z = 5$
$2y + 3z = 2$
$2x - 5y = 8$
$\{(-1, -2, 2)\}$

58. $3(x - y) = -1 - 5z - y$

$3y + 6 = 2z + x$ $\{(1, -3, -2)\}$

$5x + 1 = 3(z - y) - y$

59. $2a = -3c - 2$

$2b - 8 = 5c$ $\{(-1, 4, 0)\}$

$7a + 3b = 5$

Section 4.6

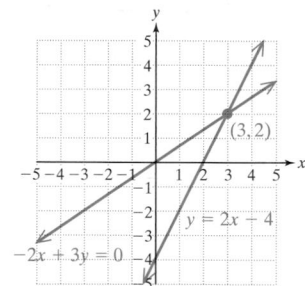 **60.** The perimeter of a right triangle is 30 ft. One leg is 2 ft longer than twice the shortest leg. The hypotenuse is 2 ft less than 3 times the shortest leg. Find the lengths of the sides of this triangle. 5, 12, and 13 ft

61. Three pumps are working to drain a construction site. Working together, the pumps can drain 950 gal/hr of water. The slowest pump drains 150 gal/hr less than the fastest pump. The fastest pump drains 150 gal/hr less than the sum of the other two pumps. How many gallons can each pump drain per hour? The pumps can drain 250, 300, and 400 gal/hr.

62. Theresa had $12,000 to invest among three mutual funds. Fund A had a 9% yield for the year. Fund B had a 14% yield, and Fund C lost 4% for the year. She invested three times as much in Fund A as in Fund C. If she gained $1020, in 1 year, how much was invested in each fund? She invested $6000 in Fund A, $4000 in Fund B, and $2000 in Fund C.

63. In a triangle, the largest angle measures 76° more than the sum of the other two angles. The middle angle measures 3 times the smallest angle. Find the measure of each angle. The angles are 13°, 39°, and 128°.

Chapter 4   Test

1. Write each line in slope-intercept form. Then determine if the lines represent intersecting lines, parallel lines, or coinciding lines.

$5x + 2y = -6$ $y = -\frac{5}{2}x - 3$

$-\frac{5}{2}x - y = -3$ $y = -\frac{5}{2}x + 3$

Parallel lines

For Exercises 2–3, solve each system by graphing.

2. $y = 2x - 4$

$-2x + 3y = 0$

$\{(3, 2)\}$

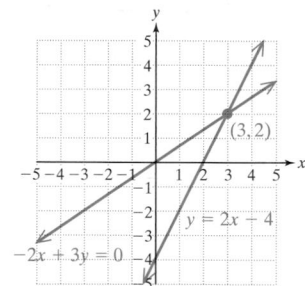

3. $2x + 4y = 12$

$2y - 6 = -x$

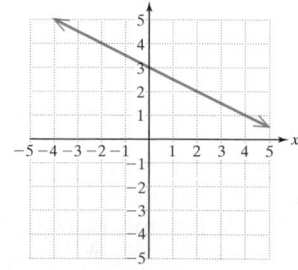

Infinitely many solutions;
$\{(x, y) | 2x + 4y = 12\}$; dependent system

4. Solve the system using the substitution method.

$x = 5y - 2$

$2x + y = -4$ $\{(-2, 0)\}$

5. In the 2005 WNBA (basketball) season, the league's leading scorer was Sheryl Swoopes from the Houston Comets. Swoopes scored 17 points more than the second leading scorer, Lauren Jackson from the Seattle Storm. Together they scored a total of 1211 points. How many points did each player score?
Swoopes scored 614 points and Jackson scored 597.

6. Solve the system using the addition method.

$3x - 6y = 8$

$2x + 3y = 3$ $\left\{\left(2, -\frac{1}{3}\right)\right\}$

7. How many milliliters of a 50% acid solution and how many milliliters of a 20% acid solution must be mixed to produce 36 mL of a 30% acid solution? 12 mL of the 50% acid solution should be mixed with 24 mL of the 20% solution.

8. a. How many solutions does a system of two linear equations have if the equations represent parallel lines? No solution

 Writing   Translating Expression   Geometry   Scientific Calculator   Video NS&E

b. How many solutions does a system of two linear equations have if the equations represent coinciding lines?
Infinitely many solutions

c. How many solutions does a system of two linear equations have if the equations represent intersecting lines? One solution

For Exercises 9–14, solve each system using any method.

9. $\frac{1}{3}x + y = \frac{7}{3}$

$x = \frac{3}{2}y - 11$

$\{(-5, 4)\}$

10. $2x - 12 = y$

$2x - \frac{1}{2}y = x + 5$

$\{\ \}$

11. $3x - 4y = 29$ $\{(3, -5)\}$

$2x + 5y = -19$

12. $2x = 6y - 14$ $\{(-1, 2)\}$

$2y = 3 - x$

13. $-0.25x - 0.05y = 0.2$ Infinitely many solutions;

$10x + 2y = -8$ $\{(x, y) \mid 10x + 2y = -8\}$

14. $3x + 3y = -2y - 7$ $\{(1, -2)\}$

$-3y = 10 - 4x$

15. At Best Buy, Latrell buys four CDs and two DVDs for $54 from the sale rack. Kendra buys two CDs and three DVDs from the same rack for $49. What is the price per CD and the price per DVD?
CDs cost $8 each and DVDs cost $11 each.

16. The cost to ride the trolley one way in San Diego is $2.25. Kelly and Hazel had to buy eight tickets for their group.

a. What was the total amount of money required? $18 was required.

b. Kelly and Hazel had only quarters and $1 bills. They also determined that they used twice as many quarters as $1 bills. How many quarters and how many $1 bills did they use?
They used 24 quarters and 12 $1 bills.

17. Suppose a total of $5000 is borrowed from two different loans. One loan charges 10% simple interest, and the other charges 8% simple interest. How much was borrowed at each rate if $424 in interest is charged at the end of 1 year?
$1200 was borrowed at 10%, and $3800 was borrowed at 8%.

18. Mark needs to move to a new apartment and is trying to find the most affordable moving truck. He will only need the truck for one day. After checking the U-Haul website, he finds that he can rent a 10-ft truck for $20.95 a day plus $1.89 per mile. He then checks the Public Storage

website and finds the charge to be $37.95 a day plus $1.19 per mile for the same size truck. Determine the number of miles for which the cost to rent from either company would be the same. Round the answer to the nearest mile.
They would be the same cost for a distance of approximately 24 mi.

19. A plane travels 910 mi in 2 hr against the wind and 1090 mi in 2 hr with the same wind. Find the speed of the plane in still air and the speed of the wind. The plane travels 500 mph in still air, and the wind speed is 45 mph.

20. The number of calories in a piece of cake is 20 less than 3 times the number of calories in a scoop of ice cream. Together, the cake and ice cream have 460 calories. How many calories are in each? The cake has 340 calories, and the ice cream has 120 calories.

21. How much 10% acid solution should be mixed with a 25% acid solution to create 100 mL of a 16% acid solution?
60 mL of 10% solution and 40 mL of 25% solution.

For Exercises 22–24, solve the system of equations.

22. $2x + 2y + 4z = -6$

$3x + y + 2z = 29$

$x - y - z = 44$ $\{(16, -37, 9)\}$

23. $2(x + z) = 6 + x - 3y$

$2x = 11 + y - z$

$x + 2(y + z) = 8$ $\{(2, -2, 5)\}$

24. $3x - 4y = 6 - 2z$

$x - 3y + 2z = 9$

$2x = y - 1$ $\{\ \}$

25. The perimeter of a triangle is 43 ft. The shortest side is one-third the length of the middle side. The longest side is 3 feet more than four times the shortest side. Find the lengths of the three sides.
The sides are 5 ft, 15 ft, and 23 ft.

26. Bennet invested a total of $11,500 among three mutual funds. At the end of one year, Fund A had a 6% yield, Fund B had an 8% yield, and Fund C lost 5%. Twice as much money was invested in Fund B as in Fund C. At the end of one year, the total gain was $550. How much was invested in each fund? $5500 was invested in Fund A. $4000 was invested in Fund B, and $2000 was invested in Fund C.

27. Working together, Joanne, Kent, and Geoff can process 504 orders per day for their business. Kent can process 20 more orders per day than Joanne can process. Geoff can process 104 fewer orders per day than Kent and Joanne combined. Find the number of orders that each person can process per day. Joanne 142 orders; Kent 162 orders; Geoff 200 orders

Chapters 1–4 Cumulative Review Exercises

1. Simplify.

$$\frac{|2 - 5| + 10 \div 2 + 3}{\sqrt{10^2 - 8^2}} \quad \frac{11}{6}$$

2. Solve for x. $\frac{1}{3}x - \frac{3}{4} = \frac{1}{2}(x + 2)$ $\left\{-\frac{21}{2}\right\}$

3. Solve for a. $-4(a + 3) + 2 = -5(a + 1) + a$ $\{\ \}$

4. Solve for y. $3x - 2y = 6$ $y = \frac{3}{2}x - 3$

5. Solve for x. $z = \frac{x - m}{5}$ $x = 5z + m$

6. Solve for z. Graph the solution set on a number line and write the solution in interval notation:

$$-2(3z + 1) \le 5(z - 3) + 10$$

$\left[\frac{3}{11}, \infty\right)$

7. The largest angle in a triangle is 110°. Of the remaining two angles, one is 4° less than the other angle. Find the measure of the three angles.
The angles are 37°, 33°, and 110°.

8. Two hikers start at opposite ends of an 18-mi trail and walk toward each other. One hiker walks predominately down hill and averages 2 mph faster than the other hiker. Find the average rate of each hiker if they meet in 3 hr.
The rates of the hikers are 2 mph and 4 mph.

9. Jesse Ventura became the 38th governor of Minnesota by receiving 37% of the votes. If approximately 2,060,000 votes were cast, how many did Mr. Ventura get?
Jesse Ventura received approximately 762,200 votes.

10. The YMCA wants to raise $2500 for its summer program for disadvantaged children. If the YMCA has already raised $900, what percent of its goal has been achieved?
36% of the goal has been achieved.

11. Two angles are complementary. One angle measures 17° more than the other angle. Find the measure of each angle. The angles are 36.5° and 53.5°.

12. Find the slope and y-intercept of the line $5x + 3y = -6$. Slope: $-\frac{5}{3}$; y-intercept: $(0, -2)$

13. The slope of a given line is $-\frac{2}{3}$.

   a. What is the slope of a line parallel to the given line? $-\frac{2}{3}$

   b. What is the slope of a line perpendicular to the given line? $\frac{3}{2}$

14. Find an equation of the line passing through the point $(2, -3)$ and having a slope of -3. Write the final answer in slope-intercept form. $y = -3x + 3$

15. Sketch the following equations on the same graph.

   a. $2x + 5y = 10$

   b. $2y = 4$

   c. Find the point of intersection and check the solution in each equation.

   $\{(0, 2)\}$

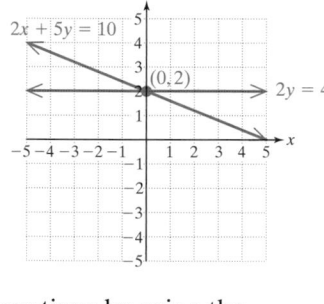

16. Solve the system of equations by using the substitution method.

$$2x + 5y = 10$$
$$2y = 4$$

$\{(0, 2)\}$

17. How many gallons of a 15% antifreeze solution should be mixed with a 60% antifreeze solution to produce 60 gal of a 45% antifreeze solution? 20 gal of the 15% solution should be mixed with 40 gal of the 60% solution.

18. Use a system of linear equations to solve for x and y. x is 27°; y is 63°

 19. In 1920, the average speed for the winner of the Indianapolis 500 car race was 88.6 mph. In 1990, a track record was reached with the speed of 186.0 mph.

    a. Find the slope of the line shown in the figure. Round to one decimal place.   1.4

b. Interpret the meaning of the slope in the context of this problem.   Between 1920 and 1990, the winning speed in the Indianapolis 500 increased on average by 1.4 mph per year.

20. Solve the system.

$$x + 3y + z = 5$$
$$2x + 4y - z = -2$$
$$6x + 2y + 5z = 26 \quad \{(1, 0, 4)\}$$

Polynomials and Properties of Exponents

5

CHAPTER OUTLINE

Chapter 5

In this chapter we will learn about polynomials and how to add, subtract, multiply, and divide them.

Are You Prepared?

The skills we need to practice include clearing parentheses and combining like terms.

Simplify each expression. Find the answer in the table and cross out the letter above it. When you have finished, the answer to the statement will remain.

1. $6x - (4x + 2) - 7$
2. $2x + 3(x - 5) + x$
3. $5 + 2(4x - 1) + 2x$

4. $5(x - 6) - 3(2x + 1)$
5. $3(8 - x) + 5x$
6. $7(2 + 3x) - 8$

A polynomial that has two terms is called a <u>BINOMIAL</u> .

P	B	E	I	N	D	O	K	M	Y	T	I	A	L
$-x - 33$	$8x - 24$	$2x + 24$	$5x - 14$	$2x - 5$	$6x - 15$	$-x - 27$	$10x + 3$	$8x + 5$	$2x - 9$	$21x + 6$	$35x - 8$	$-8x - 30$	$x - 21$

Section 5.1 Exponents: Multiplying and Dividing Common Bases

1. Review of Exponential Notation

Recall that an **exponent** is used to show repeated multiplication of the **base**.

DEFINITION b^n

Let b represent any real number and n represent a positive integer. Then,

$$b^n = \underbrace{b \cdot b \cdot b \cdot b \cdot \ldots b}_{n \text{ factors of } b}$$

Classroom Example: p. 347, Exercise 2

Example 1 Identifying Parts of an Exponential Expression

For each expression, identify the exponent and base. Then evaluate the expression.

a. 6^2 **b.** $\left(-\dfrac{1}{2}\right)^3$ **c.** 0.8^4

Solution:

Expression	Base	Exponent	Result
a. 6^2	6	2	$(6)(6) = 36$
b. $\left(-\dfrac{1}{2}\right)^3$	$-\dfrac{1}{2}$	3	$\left(-\dfrac{1}{2}\right)\left(-\dfrac{1}{2}\right)\left(-\dfrac{1}{2}\right) = -\dfrac{1}{8}$
c. 0.8^4	0.8	4	$(0.8)(0.8)(0.8)(0.8) = 0.4096$

Skill Practice For each expression, identify the base and exponent.

1. 8^3 **2.** $\left(-\dfrac{1}{4}\right)^2$ **3.** 0.2^4

Note that if no exponent is explicitly written for an expression, then the expression has an implied exponent of 1. For example, $x = x^1$.

Consider an expression such as $3y^6$. The factor 3 has an exponent of 1, and the factor y has an exponent of 6. That is, the expression $3y^6$ is interpreted as 3^1y^6.

2. Evaluating Expressions with Exponents

Recall from Section 1.6 that particular care must be taken when evaluating exponential expressions involving negative numbers. An exponential expression with a negative base is written with parentheses around the base, such as $(-3)^2$.

To evaluate $(-3)^2$, we have: $(-3)^2 = (-3)(-3) = 9$

If no parentheses are present, the expression -3^2, is the *opposite* of 3^2, or equivalently, $-1 \cdot 3^2$.

$$-3^2 = -1(3^2) = -1(3)(3) = -9$$

Answers

1. Base 8; exponent 3
2. Base $-\dfrac{1}{4}$; exponent 2
3. Base 0.2; exponent 4

Example 2 Evaluating Expressions with Exponents

Classroom Examples: p. 347, Exercises 24 and 26

Evaluate each expression.

a. -5^4 **b.** $(-5)^4$ **c.** $(-0.2)^3$ **d.** -0.2^3

Solution:

a. -5^4

$= -1 \cdot 5^4$ 5 is the base with exponent 4.

$= -1 \cdot 5 \cdot 5 \cdot 5 \cdot 5$ Multiply -1 times four factors of 5.

$= -625$

b. $(-5)^4$

$= (-5)(-5)(-5)(-5)$ Parentheses indicate that -5 is the base with exponent 4.

$= 625$ Multiply four factors of -5.

c. $(-0.2)^3$ Parentheses indicate that -0.2 is the base with exponent 3.

$= (-0.2)(-0.2)(-0.2)$ Multiply three factors of -0.2.

$= -0.008$

d. -0.2^3

$= -1 \cdot 0.2^3$ 0.2 is the base with exponent 3.

$= -1 \cdot 0.2 \cdot 0.2 \cdot 0.2$ Multiply -1 times three factors of 0.2.

$= -0.008$

Skill Practice Evaluate each expression.

4. -2^4 **5.** $(-2)^4$ **6.** $(-0.1)^3$ **7.** -0.1^3

Example 3 Evaluating Expressions with Exponents

Classroom Examples: p. 348, Exercises 48 and 52

Evaluate each expression for $a = 2$ and $b = -3$.

a. $5a^2$ **b.** $(5a)^2$ **c.** $5ab^2$ **d.** $(b + a)^2$

Solution:

a. $5a^2$

$= 5(\ )^2$ Use parentheses to substitute a number for a variable.

$= 5(2)^2$ Substitute $a = 2$.

$= 5(4)$ Simplify exponents before multiplying.

$= 20$

b. $(5a)^2$

$= [5(\ )]^2$ Use parentheses to substitute a number for a variable. The original parentheses are replaced with brackets.

$= [5(2)]^2$ Substitute $a = 2$.

$= (10)^2$ Simplify inside the parentheses first.

$= 100$

Answers

4. -16 **5.** 16

6. -0.001 **7.** -0.001

c. $5ab^2$

$= 5(2)(-3)^2$ Substitute $a = 2$, $b = -3$.

$= 5(2)(9)$ Simplify exponents before multiplying.

$= 90$ Multiply.

d. $(b + a)^2$

$= [(-3) + (2)]^2$ Substitute $b = -3$ and $a = 2$.

$= (-1)^2$ Simplify within the parentheses first.

$= 1$

Skill Practice Evaluate each expression for $x = 2$ and $y = -5$.

8. $6x^2$ **9.** $(6x)^2$ **10.** $2xy^2$ **11.** $(y - x)^2$

3. Multiplying and Dividing Common Bases

In this section, we investigate the effect of multiplying or dividing two quantities with the same base. For example, consider the expressions: x^5x^2 and $\frac{x^5}{x^2}$. Simplifying each expression, we have:

$$x^5x^2 = (x \cdot x \cdot x \cdot x \cdot x)(x \cdot x) = \overbrace{x \cdot x \cdot x \cdot x \cdot x \cdot x \cdot x}^{7 \text{ factors of } x} = x^7$$

$$\frac{x^5}{x^2} = \frac{x \cdot x \cdot x \cdot \overset{1}{\cancel{x}} \cdot \overset{1}{\cancel{x}}}{\cancel{x} \cdot \cancel{x}} = \frac{x \cdot x \cdot x}{1} = x^3$$

These examples suggest that to multiply two quantities with the same base, we add the exponents. To divide two quantities with the same base, we subtract the exponent in the denominator from the exponent in the numerator. These rules are stated formally in the following two properties.

PROPERTY Multiplication of Like Bases

Assume that b is a real number and that m and n represent positive integers. Then,

$$b^m b^n = b^{m+n}$$

PROPERTY Division of Like Bases

Assume that $b \neq 0$ is a real number and that m and n represent positive integers. Then,

$$\frac{b^m}{b^n} = b^{m-n}$$

Answers

8. 24   **9.** 144   **10.** 100

11. 49

Example 4 Simplifying Expressions with Exponents

Classroom Examples: p. 348, Exercises 64 and 66

Simplify the expressions.

a. $w^3 w^4$ **b.** $2^3 \cdot 2^4$

Solution:

a. $w^3 w^4$ $(w \cdot w \cdot w)(w \cdot w \cdot w \cdot w)$

$= w^{3+4}$ To multiply like bases, add the exponents.

$= w^7$

b. $2^3 \cdot 2^4$ $(2 \cdot 2 \cdot 2)(2 \cdot 2 \cdot 2 \cdot 2)$

$= 2^{3+4}$ To multiply like bases, add the exponents (the base is unchanged).

$= 2^7$ or 128

Avoiding Mistakes

When we multiply like bases, we add the exponents. The base does not change. In Example 4(b), we have $2^3 \cdot 2^4 = 2^7$.

Skill Practice Simplify the expressions.

12. $q^4 q^8$ **13.** $8^4 \cdot 8^8$

Example 5 Simplifying Expressions with Exponents

Classroom Examples: p. 348, Exercises 76 and 80

Simplify the expressions.

a. $\dfrac{t^6}{t^4}$ **b.** $\dfrac{5^6}{5^4}$

Solution:

a. $\dfrac{t^6}{t^4}$ $\dfrac{t \cdot t \cdot t \cdot t \cdot t \cdot t}{t \cdot t \cdot t \cdot t}$

$= t^{6-4}$ To divide like bases, subtract the exponents.

$= t^2$

b. $\dfrac{5^6}{5^4}$ $\dfrac{5 \cdot 5 \cdot 5 \cdot 5 \cdot 5 \cdot 5}{5 \cdot 5 \cdot 5 \cdot 5}$

$= 5^{6-4}$ To divide like bases, subtract the exponents (the base is unchanged).

$= 5^2$ or 25

Skill Practice Simplify the expressions.

14. $\dfrac{y^{15}}{y^8}$ **15.** $\dfrac{3^{15}}{3^8}$

Answers

12. q^{12} **13.** 8^{12}
14. y^7 **15.** 3^7

Classroom Example: p. 348,
Exercise 86

Example 6 **Simplifying Expressions with Exponents**

Simplify the expressions. **a.** $\dfrac{z^4 z^5}{z^3}$ **b.** $\dfrac{10^7}{10^2 \cdot 10}$

Solution:

a. $\dfrac{z^4 z^5}{z^3}$

$= \dfrac{z^{4+5}}{z^3}$ Add the exponents in the numerator (the base is unchanged).

$= \dfrac{z^9}{z^3}$

$= z^{9-3}$ Subtract the exponents.

$= z^6$

b. $\dfrac{10^7}{10^2 \cdot 10}$

$= \dfrac{10^7}{10^2 \cdot 10^1}$ Note that 10 is equivalent to 10^1.

$= \dfrac{10^7}{10^{2+1}}$ Add the exponents in the denominator (the base is unchanged).

$= \dfrac{10^7}{10^3}$

$= 10^{7-3}$ Subtract the exponents.

$= 10^4$ or 10,000   Simplify.

Skill Practice Simplify the expressions.

16. $\dfrac{a^3 a^8}{a^7}$ **17.** $\dfrac{5^9}{5^2 \cdot 5^5}$

4. Simplifying Expressions with Exponents

Classroom Examples: pp. 348–349,
Exercises 94 and 104

Example 7 **Simplifying Expressions with Exponents**

Use the commutative and associative properties of real numbers and the properties of exponents to simplify the expressions.

a. $(-3p^2 q^4)(2pq^5)$ **b.** $\dfrac{16w^9 z^3}{4w^8 z}$

Solution:

Instructor Note: Remind students to multiply coefficients but add exponents.

a. $(-3p^2 q^4)(2pq^5)$

$= (-3 \cdot 2)(p^2 p)(q^4 q^5)$ Apply the associative and commutative properties of multiplication to group coefficients and like bases.

$= (-3 \cdot 2)p^{2+1} q^{4+5}$ Add the exponents when multiplying like bases.

$= -6p^3 q^9$ Simplify.

Answers

16. a^4 **17.** 5^2 or 25

Instructor Note: Remind students to divide coefficients but subtract exponents.

Amount invested
159,308 - 309 336

Annual Rate of
return 707

709
1018
334
345 - 346 349 885

Compound interest
345 - 34

Simple Interest

$I = Prt$
$= 1000(0.08)(3)$
$= 240$

... bases.

... dividing like bases.

... the formula $I = Prt$,
... ate, and t is the time in
... However, in most day-
... d or borrowed is com-
... ginal principal and on

... s. Compare the total
... versus if the interest is

40

ual interest may be

annual interest
number of years.
nnually for 3 years,

Classroom Example: p. 349, Exercise 114

Example 8 Using Exponents in an Application

Find the amount in an account after 8 years if the initial investment is $7000, invested at 2.25% interest compounded annually.

Solution:

Identify the values for each variable.

$P = 7000$

$r = 0.0225$

$t = 8$

Note that the decimal form of a percent is used for calculations.

$$A = P(1 + r)^t$$

$$= 7000(1 + 0.0225)^8 \qquad \text{Substitute.}$$

$$= 7000(1.0225)^8 \qquad \text{Simplify inside the parentheses.}$$

$$\approx 7000(1.194831142) \qquad \text{Approximate } (1.0225)^8.$$

$$\approx 8363.82 \qquad \text{Multiply (round to the nearest cent).}$$

The amount in the account after 8 years is $8363.82.

Skill Practice

20. Find the amount in an account after 3 years if the initial investment is $4000 invested at 5% interest compounded annually.

Answer

20. $4630.50

Calculator Connections

Topic: Review of Evaluating Exponential Expressions on a Calculator

In Example 8, it was necessary to evaluate the expression $(1.0225)^8$. Recall that the ⌃ or y^x key may be used to enter expressions with exponents.

Scientific Calculator

Enter: 1.0225 $\boxed{y^x}$ 8 $\boxed{=}$ **Result:** $\boxed{1.194831142}$

Graphing Calculator

```
1.0225^8
        1.194831142
```

Calculator Exercises

Use a calculator to evaluate the expressions.

1. $(1.06)^5$

2. $(1.02)^{40}$

3. $5000(1.06)^5$

4. $2000(1.02)^{40}$

5. $3000(1 + 0.06)^2$

6. $1000(1 + 0.05)^3$

Section 5.1   Practice Exercises

For this exercise set, assume all variables represent nonzero real numbers.

Study Skills Exercise

1. Define the key terms.

   a. exponent   **b. base**   **c. simple interest**   **d. compound interest**

Concept 1: Review of Exponential Notation

For Exercises 2–9, identify the base and the exponent. **(See Example 1.)**

2. c^3 Base: c; exponent: 3

3. x^4 Base: x; exponent: 4

4. 5^2 Base: 5; exponent: 2

5. 3^5 Base: 3; exponent: 5

6. $(-4)^8$ Base: -4; exponent: 8

7. $(-1)^4$ Base: -1; exponent: 4

8. x Base: x; exponent: 1

9. 13 Base: 13; exponent: 1

10. What base corresponds to the exponent 5 in the expression $x^3y^5z^2$? y

11. What base corresponds to the exponent 2 in the expression w^3v^2? v

12. What is the exponent for the factor of 2 in the expression $2x^3$? 1

13. What is the exponent for the factor of p in the expression pq^7? 1

For Exercises 14–22, write the expression using exponents.

14. $(4n)(4n)(4n)$ $(4n)^3$

15. $(-6b)(-6b)$ $(-6b)^2$

16. $4 \cdot n \cdot n \cdot n$ $4n^3$

17. $-6 \cdot b \cdot b$ $-6b^2$

18. $(x-5)(x-5)(x-5)$ $(x-5)^3$

19. $(y+2)(y+2)(y+2)(y+2)$ $(y+2)^4$

20. $\dfrac{4}{x \cdot x \cdot x \cdot x \cdot x}$ $\dfrac{4}{x^5}$

21. $\dfrac{-2}{t \cdot t \cdot t}$ $\dfrac{-2}{t^3}$

22. $\dfrac{5 \cdot x \cdot x \cdot x}{(y-7)(y-7)}$ $\dfrac{5x^3}{(y-7)^2}$

Concept 2: Evaluating Expressions with Exponents

For Exercises 23–30, evaluate the two expressions and compare the answers. Do the expressions have the same value? **(See Example 2.)**

23. -5^2 and $(-5)^2$
No; $-5^2 = -25$ and $(-5)^2 = 25$

24. -3^4 and $(-3)^4$
No; $-3^4 = -81$ and $(-3)^4 = 81$

25. -2^5 and $(-2)^5$
Yes; $-2^5 = -32$ and $(-2)^5 = -32$

26. -5^3 and $(-5)^3$
Yes; $-5^3 = -125$ and $(-5)^3 = -125$

27. $\left(\dfrac{1}{2}\right)^3$ and $\dfrac{1}{2^3}$
Yes; $\left(\dfrac{1}{2}\right)^3 = \dfrac{1}{8}$ and $\dfrac{1}{2^3} = \dfrac{1}{8}$

28. $\left(\dfrac{1}{5}\right)^2$ and $\dfrac{1}{5^2}$
Yes; $\left(\dfrac{1}{5}\right)^2 = \dfrac{1}{25}$ and $\dfrac{1}{5^2} = \dfrac{1}{25}$

29. $\left(\dfrac{3}{10}\right)^2$ and $(0.3)^2$
Yes; $\left(\dfrac{3}{10}\right)^2 = \dfrac{9}{100}$ and $(0.3)^2 = 0.09$

30. $\left(\dfrac{7}{10}\right)^3$ and $(0.7)^3$
Yes; $\left(\dfrac{7}{10}\right)^3 = \dfrac{343}{1000}$ and $(0.7)^3 = 0.343$

For Exercises 31–38, evaluate each expression. **(See Example 2.)**

31. 16^1 16

32. 20^1 20

33. $(-1)^{21}$ -1

34. $(-1)^{30}$ 1

35. $\left(-\dfrac{1}{3}\right)^2$ $\dfrac{1}{9}$

36. $\left(-\dfrac{1}{4}\right)^3$ $-\dfrac{1}{64}$

37. $-\left(\dfrac{2}{5}\right)^2$ $-\dfrac{4}{25}$

38. $-\left(\dfrac{3}{5}\right)^2$ $-\dfrac{9}{25}$

 Writing   Translating Expression   Geometry   Scientific Calculator   Video   NS&E

For Exercises 39–46, simplify using the order of operations.

39. $3 \cdot 2^4$ 48

40. $2 \cdot 0^5$ 0

41. $-4(-1)^7$ 4

42. $-3(-1)^4$ −3

43. $6^2 - 3^3$ 9

44. $4^3 + 2^3$ 72

45. $2 \cdot 3^2 + 4 \cdot 2^3$ 50

46. $6^2 - 3 \cdot 1^3$ 33

For Exercises 47–58, evaluate each expression for $a = -4$ and $b = 5$. **(See Example 3.)**

47. $-4b^2$ −100

48. $3a^2$ 48

49. $(-4b)^2$ 400

50. $(3a)^2$ 144

51. $(a + b)^2$ 1

52. $(a - b)^2$ 81

53. $a^2 + 2ab + b^2$ 1

54. $a^2 - 2ab + b^2$ 81

55. $-10ab^2$ 1000

56. $-6a^3b$ 1920

57. $-10a^2b$ −800

58. $-a^2b$ −80

Concept 3: Multiplying and Dividing Common Bases

59. Expand the following expressions first. Then simplify using exponents.

a. $x^4 \cdot x^3$
$(x \cdot x \cdot x \cdot x)(x \cdot x \cdot x) = x^7$

b. $5^4 \cdot 5^3$
$(5 \cdot 5 \cdot 5 \cdot 5)(5 \cdot 5 \cdot 5) = 5^7$

60. Expand the following expressions first. Then simplify using exponents.

a. $y^2 \cdot y^4$
$(y \cdot y)(y \cdot y \cdot y \cdot y) = y^6$

b. $3^2 \cdot 3^4$
$(3 \cdot 3)(3 \cdot 3 \cdot 3 \cdot 3) = 3^6$

For Exercises 61–72, simplify each expression. Write the answers in exponent form. **(See Example 4.)**

61. $z^5 z^3$ z^8

62. $w^4 w^7$ w^{11}

63. $a \cdot a^8$ a^9

64. $p^4 p$ p^5

65. $4^5 \cdot 4^9$ 4^{14}

66. $6^7 \cdot 6^5$ 6^{12}

67. $\left(\frac{2}{3}\right)^3\left(\frac{2}{3}\right)$ $\left(\frac{2}{3}\right)^4$

68. $\left(\frac{1}{x}\right)\left(\frac{1}{x}\right)^2$ $\left(\frac{1}{x}\right)^3$

69. $c^5 c^2 c^7$ c^{14}

70. $b^7 b^2 b^8$ b^{17}

71. $x \cdot x^4 \cdot x^{10} \cdot x^3$ x^{18}

72. $z^7 \cdot z^{11} \cdot z^{60} \cdot z$ z^{79}

73. Expand the expressions. Then simplify.

a. $\dfrac{p^8}{p^3}$

b. $\dfrac{8^8}{8^3}$

$\dfrac{p \cdot p \cdot p \cdot p \cdot p \cdot p \cdot p \cdot p}{p \cdot p \cdot p} = p^5$

$\dfrac{8 \cdot 8 \cdot 8 \cdot 8 \cdot 8 \cdot 8 \cdot 8 \cdot 8}{8 \cdot 8 \cdot 8} = 8^5$

74. Expand the expressions. Then simplify.

a. $\dfrac{w^5}{w^2}$

b. $\dfrac{4^5}{4^2}$

$\dfrac{w \cdot w \cdot w \cdot w \cdot w}{w \cdot w} = w^3$

$\dfrac{4 \cdot 4 \cdot 4 \cdot 4 \cdot 4}{4 \cdot 4} = 4^3$

For Exercises 75–90, simplify each expression. Write the answers in exponent form. **(See Examples 5–6.)**

75. $\dfrac{x^8}{x^6}$ x^2

76. $\dfrac{z^5}{z^4}$ z

77. $\dfrac{a^{10}}{a}$ a^9

78. $\dfrac{b^{12}}{b}$ b^{11}

79. $\dfrac{7^{13}}{7^6}$ 7^7

80. $\dfrac{2^6}{2^4}$ 2^2

81. $\dfrac{5^8}{5}$ 5^7

82. $\dfrac{3^5}{3}$ 3^4

83. $\dfrac{y^{13}}{y^{12}}$ y

84. $\dfrac{w^7}{w^6}$ w

85. $\dfrac{h^3 h^8}{h^7}$ h^4

86. $\dfrac{n^5 n^4}{n^2}$ n^7

87. $\dfrac{7^2 \cdot 7^6}{7}$ 7^7

88. $\dfrac{5^3 \cdot 5^8}{5}$ 5^{10}

89. $\dfrac{10^{20}}{10^3 \cdot 10^8}$ 10^9

90. $\dfrac{3^{15}}{3^2 \cdot 3^{10}}$ 3^3

Concept 4: Simplifying Expressions with Exponents (Mixed Exercises)

For Exercises 91–112, use the commutative and associative properties of real numbers and the properties of exponents to simplify. **(See Example 7.)**

91. $(2x^3)(3x^4)$ $6x^7$

92. $(10y)(2y^3)$ $20y^4$

93. $(5a^2b)(8a^3b^4)$ $40a^5b^5$

94. $(10xy^3)(3x^4y)$ $30x^5y^4$

95. $(r^6 s^4)(13r^2 s)$
$13r^8 s^5$

96. $(6p^2 q^8)(7p^5 q^3)$
$42p^7 q^{11}$

97. $s^3 \cdot t^5 \cdot t \cdot t^{10} \cdot s^6$
$s^9 t^{16}$

98. $c \cdot c^4 \cdot d^2 \cdot c^3 \cdot d^3$
$c^8 d^5$

 Writing Translating Expression Geometry Scientific Calculator ⬤ Video NS&E

99. $(-2v^2)(3v)(5v^5)$
$-30v^8$

100. $(10q^5)(-3q^8)(q)$
$-30q^{14}$

 101. $\left(\frac{2}{3}m^{13}n^8\right)(24m^7n^2)$
$16m^{20}n^{10}$

102. $\left(\frac{1}{4}c^6d^6\right)(28c^2d^7)$
$7c^8d^{13}$

103. $\dfrac{14c^4d^5}{7c^3d}$ $2cd^4$

104. $\dfrac{36h^5k^2}{9h^3k}$ $4h^2k$

105. $\dfrac{z^3z^{11}}{z^4z^6}$ z^4

106. $\dfrac{w^{12}w^2}{w^4w^5}$ w^5

107. $\dfrac{25h^3jk^5}{12h^2k}$ $\dfrac{25hjk^4}{12}$

108. $\dfrac{15m^5np^{12}}{4mp^9}$ $\dfrac{15m^4np^3}{4}$

109. $(-4p^6q^8r^4)(2pqr^2)$
$-8p^7q^9r^6$

110. $(-5a^4bc)(-10a^2b)$
$50a^6b^2c$

111. $\dfrac{-12s^2tu^3}{4su^2}$ $-3stu$

112. $\dfrac{15w^5x^{10}y^3}{-15w^4x}$ $-wx^9y^3$

Concept 5: Applications of Exponents

 Use the formula $A = P(1 + r)^t$ for Exercises 113–116. **(See Example 8.)**

113. Find the amount in an account after 2 years if the initial investment is $5000, invested at 7% interest compounded annually. $5724.50

114. Find the amount in an account after 5 years if the initial investment is $2000, invested at 4% interest compounded annually. $2433.31

115. Find the amount in an account after 3 years if the initial investment is $4000, invested at 6% interest compounded annually. $4764.06

116. Find the amount in an account after 4 years if the initial investment is $10,000, invested at 5% interest compounded annually. $12,155.06

For Exercises 117–120, use the geometry formulas found on the inside back cover.

117. Find the area of the pizza shown in the figure. Round to the nearest square inch.   201 in.^{2}

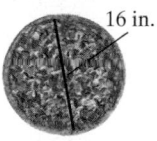

16 in.

118. Find the volume of the sphere shown in the figure. Round to the nearest cubic centimeter.
113 cm^3

$r = 3$ cm

119. Find the volume of a spherical balloon that is 8 in. in diameter. Round to the nearest cubic inch.
268 in.^{3}

120. Find the area of a circular pool 50 ft in diameter. Round to the nearest square foot.
1963 ft^2

Expanding Your Skills

For Exercises 121–128, simplify each expression using the addition or subtraction rules of exponents. Assume that $a, b, m,$ and n represent positive integers.

121. x^nx^{n+1} x^{2n+1}

122. y^ay^{2a} y^{3a}

123. $p^{3m+5}p^{-m-2}$ p^{2m+3}

124. $q^{4b-3}q^{-4b+4}$ q

125. $\dfrac{z^{b+1}}{z^b}$ z

126. $\dfrac{w^{5n+3}}{w^{2n}}$ w^{3n+3}

127. $\dfrac{r^{3a+3}}{r^{3a}}$ r^3

128. $\dfrac{t^{3+2m}}{t^{2m}}$ t^3

 Writing   Translating Expression   Geometry   Scientific Calculator   Video   NS&E

Section 5.2   More Properties of Exponents

1. Power Rule for Exponents

The expression $(x^2)^3$ indicates that the quantity x^2 is cubed.

$$(x^2)^3 = (x^2)(x^2)(x^2) = (x \cdot x)(x \cdot x)(x \cdot x) = x^6$$

From this example, it appears that to raise a base to successive powers, we multiply the exponents and leave the base unchanged. This is stated formally as the power rule for exponents.

PROPERTY Power Rule for Exponents

Assume that b is a real number and that m and n represent positive integers. Then,

$$(b^m)^n = b^{m \cdot n}$$

Classroom Examples: p. 353,
Exercises 12 and 22

Example 1 Simplifying Expressions with Exponents

Simplify the expressions.

  a. $(s^4)^2$ **b.** $(3^4)^2$ **c.** $(x^2 x^5)^4$

Solution:

a. $(s^4)^2$

     $= s^{4 \cdot 2}$ Multiply exponents (the base is unchanged).

     $= s^8$

b. $(3^4)^2$

     $= 3^{4 \cdot 2}$ Multiply exponents (the base is unchanged).

     $= 3^8$ or 6561

c. $(x^2 x^5)^4$

     $= (x^7)^4$ Simplify inside the parentheses by adding exponents.

     $= x^{7 \cdot 4}$ Multiply exponents (the base is unchanged).

     $= x^{28}$

Skill Practice Simplify the expressions.

  1. $(y^3)^5$ **2.** $(2^8)^{10}$ **3.** $(q^5 q^4)^3$

2. The Properties $(ab)^m = a^m b^m$ and $\left(\frac{a}{b}\right)^m = \frac{a^m}{b^m}$

Consider the following expressions and their simplified forms:

$$(xy)^3 = (xy)(xy)(xy) = (x \cdot x \cdot x)(y \cdot y \cdot y) = x^3 y^3$$

$$\left(\frac{x}{y}\right)^3 = \left(\frac{x}{y}\right)\left(\frac{x}{y}\right)\left(\frac{x}{y}\right) = \left(\frac{x \cdot x \cdot x}{y \cdot y \cdot y}\right) = \frac{x^3}{y^3}$$

The expressions were simplified using the commutative and associative properties of multiplication. The simplified forms for each expression could have been reached in one step by applying the exponent to each factor inside the parentheses.

Answers
1. y^{15} **2.** 2^{80} **3.** q^{27}

PROPERTY   Power of a Product and Power of a Quotient

Assume that a and b are real numbers. Let m represent a positive integer. Then,

$$(ab)^m = a^m b^m$$

$$\left(\frac{a}{b}\right)^m = \frac{a^m}{b^m}, \quad b \neq 0$$

Avoiding Mistakes

The power rule of exponents can be applied to a product of bases but in general cannot be applied to a sum or difference of bases.

$$(ab)^n = a^n b^n$$

but $(a + b)^n \neq a^n + b^n$

Applying these properties of exponents, we have

$$(xy)^3 = x^3 y^3 \quad \text{and} \quad \left(\frac{x}{y}\right)^3 = \frac{x^3}{y^3}$$

Example 2   Simplifying Expressions with Exponents

Simplify the expressions.

a. $(-2xyz)^4$ **b.** $(5x^2y^7)^3$ **c.** $\left(\dfrac{2}{5}\right)^3$ **d.** $\left(\dfrac{1}{3xy^4}\right)^2$

Classroom Examples: p. 354, Exercises 28 and 32

Solution:

a. $(-2xyz)^4$

$= (-2)^4 x^4 y^4 z^4$ Raise each factor within parentheses to the fourth power.

$= 16x^4 y^4 z^4$

b. $(5x^2y^7)^3$

$= 5^3(x^2)^3(y^7)^3$ Raise each factor within parentheses to the third power.

$= 125x^6 y^{21}$ Multiply exponents and simplify.

Instructor Note: Remind students that they can write exponents of 1 where appropriate to avoid confusion. For example, $(5x^2y^7)^3 = (5^1x^2y^7)^3$.

c. $\left(\dfrac{2}{5}\right)^3$

$= \dfrac{(2)^3}{(5)^3}$ Raise each factor within parentheses to the third power.

$= \dfrac{8}{125}$ Simplify.

d. $\left(\dfrac{1}{3xy^4}\right)^2$

$= \dfrac{1^2}{3^2 x^2 (y^4)^2}$ Square each factor within parentheses.

$= \dfrac{1}{9x^2 y^8}$ Multiply exponents and simplify.

Skill Practice Simplify the expressions.

4. $(3abc)^5$ **5.** $(-2t^2w^4)^3$ **6.** $\left(\dfrac{3}{4}\right)^3$ **7.** $\left(\dfrac{2x^3}{y^5}\right)^2$

Answers

4. $3^5a^5b^5c^5$ or $243a^5b^5c^5$

5. $-8t^6w^{12}$ **6.** $\dfrac{27}{64}$ **7.** $\dfrac{4x^6}{y^{10}}$

The properties of exponents can be used along with the properties of real numbers to simplify complicated expressions.

Classroom Example: p. 354, Exercise 56

Example 3 Simplifying Expressions with Exponents

Simplify the expression. $\dfrac{(x^2)^6(x^3)}{(x^7)^2}$

Solution:

$$\dfrac{(x^2)^6(x^3)}{(x^7)^2}$$ Clear parentheses by applying the power rule.

$$= \dfrac{x^{2\cdot6}x^3}{x^{7\cdot2}}$$ Multiply exponents.

$$= \dfrac{x^{12}x^3}{x^{14}}$$

$$= \dfrac{x^{12+3}}{x^{14}}$$ Add exponents in the numerator.

$$= \dfrac{x^{15}}{x^{14}}$$

$$= x^{15-14}$$ Subtract exponents.

$$= x$$ Simplify.

Skill Practice Simplify the expression.

8. $\dfrac{(k^5)^2k^8}{(k^2)^4}$

Classroom Example: p. 354, Exercise 60

Example 4 Simplifying Expressions with Exponents

Simplify the expression. $(3cd^2)(-2cd^3)^3$

Solution:

$(3cd^2)(-2cd^3)^3$ Clear parentheses by applying the power rule.

$= 3cd^2 \cdot (-2)^3c^3d^9$ Raise each factor in the second parentheses to the third power.

$= 3 \cdot (-2)^3cc^3d^2d^9$ Group like factors.

$= 3 \cdot (-8)c^{1+3}d^{2+9}$ Add exponents on like bases.

$= -24c^4d^{11}$ Simplify.

Skill Practice Simplify the expression.

9. $(4x^4y)(2x^3y^4)^4$

Answers

8. k^{10} **9.** $64x^{16}y^{17}$

Example 5   **Simplifying Expressions with Exponents**

Simplify the expression. $\left(\dfrac{x^7yz^4}{8xz^3}\right)^2$

Classroom Example: p. 354, Exercise 68

Solution:

$$\left(\dfrac{x^7yz^4}{8xz^3}\right)^2$$

$$=\left(\dfrac{x^{7-1}yz^{4-3}}{8}\right)^2$$ First simplify inside the parentheses by subtracting exponents on like bases.

$$=\left(\dfrac{x^6yz}{8}\right)^2$$

$$=\dfrac{(x^6)^2y^2z^2}{8^2}$$ Apply the power rule of exponents.

$$=\dfrac{x^{12}y^2z^2}{64}$$

Skill Practice   Simplify the expression.

10. $\left(\dfrac{w^2y^4}{6y^3}\right)^2$

Answer

10. $\dfrac{w^4y^2}{36}$

Section 5.2   Practice Exercises

Boost *your* GRADE at ALEKS.com!

ALEKS®
version 3.0

• Practice Problems
• Self-Tests
• NetTutor

• e-Professors
• Videos

For additional exercises, see Classroom Activity 5.2A in the *Instructor's Resource Manual* at www.mhhe.com/moh.

For this exercise set assume all variables represent nonzero real numbers.

Review Exercises

For Exercises 1–8, simplify.

1. $4^2 \cdot 4^7$ 4^9

2. $5^8 \cdot 5^3 \cdot 5$ 5^{12}

3. $a^{13} \cdot a \cdot a^6$ a^{20}

4. $y^{14}y^3$ y^{17}

5. $\dfrac{d^{13}d}{d^5}$ d^9

6. $\dfrac{3^8 \cdot 3}{3^2}$ 3^7

7. $\dfrac{7^{11}}{7^5}$ 7^6

8. $\dfrac{z^4}{z^3}$ z

9. Explain when to add exponents versus when to multiply exponents.   When multiplying expressions with the same base, add the exponents. When raising an expression with an exponent to a power, multiply the exponents.

10. Explain when to add exponents versus when to subtract exponents.   When multiplying expressions with the same base, add the exponents. When dividing expressions with the same base, subtract the exponents.

Concept 1: Power Rule for Exponents

For Exercises 11–22, simplify and write answers in exponent form. **(See Example 1.)**

11. $(5^3)^4$ 5^{12}

12. $(2^8)^7$ 2^{56}

13. $(12^3)^2$ 12^6

14. $(6^4)^4$ 6^{16}

15. $(y^7)^2$ y^{14}

16. $(z^6)^4$ z^{24}

17. $(w^5)^5$ w^{25}

18. $(t^3)^6$ t^{18}

19. $(a^2a^4)^6$ a^{36}

20. $(z \cdot z^3)^2$ z^8

21. $(y^3y^4)^2$ y^{14}

22. $(w^5w)^4$ w^{24}

Writing   ⟷ Translating Expression   Geometry   Scientific Calculator   Video   NS&E

23. Evaluate the two expressions and compare the answers: $(2^2)^3$ and $(2^3)^2$. They are both equal to 2^6.

24. Evaluate the two expressions and compare the answers: $(4^4)^2$ and $(4^2)^4$. They are both equal to 4^8.

 25. Evaluate the two expressions and compare the answers. Which expression is greater? Why?

$$4^{3^2} \quad \text{and} \quad (4^3)^2$$

$4^{3^2} = 4^9$; $(4^3)^2 = 4^6$; the expression 4^{3^2} is greater than $(4^3)^2$.

26. Evaluate the two expressions and compare the answers. Which expression is greater? Why?

$$3^{5^2} \quad \text{and} \quad (3^5)^2$$

$3^{5^2} = 3^{25}$; $(3^5)^2 = 3^{10}$; the expression 3^{5^2} is greater than $(3^5)^2$.

Concept 2: The Properties $(ab)^m = a^m b^m$ and $\left(\frac{a}{b}\right)^m = \frac{a^m}{b^m}$

For Exercises 27–42, use the appropriate property to clear the parentheses. **(See Example 2.)**

27. $(5w)^2$ $25w^2$

28. $(4y)^3$ $64y^3$

29. $(srt)^4$ $s^4 r^4 t^4$

30. $(wxy)^6$ $w^6 x^6 y^6$

31. $\left(\frac{2}{r}\right)^4$ $\frac{16}{r^4}$

32. $\left(\frac{1}{t}\right)^8$ $\frac{1}{t^8}$

33. $\left(\frac{x}{y}\right)^5$ $\frac{x^5}{y^5}$

34. $\left(\frac{w}{z}\right)^7$ $\frac{w^7}{z^7}$

35. $(-3a)^4$ $81a^4$

36. $(2x)^5$ $32x^5$

37. $(-3abc)^3$ $-27a^3 b^3 c^3$

38. $(-5xyz)^2$ $25x^2 y^2 z^2$

39. $\left(-\frac{4}{x}\right)^3$ $-\frac{64}{x^3}$

40. $\left(-\frac{1}{w}\right)^4$ $\frac{1}{w^4}$

41. $\left(-\frac{a}{b}\right)^2$ $\frac{a^2}{b^2}$

42. $\left(-\frac{r}{s}\right)^3$ $-\frac{r^3}{s^3}$

Mixed Exercises

For Exercises 43–74, simplify. **(See Examples 3–5.)**

43. $(6u^2 v^4)^3$ $6^3 u^6 v^{12}$ or $216\, u^6 v^{12}$

44. $(3a^5 b^2)^6$ $3^6 a^{30} b^{12}$ or $729 a^{30} b^{12}$

45. $5(x^2 y)^4$ $5x^8 y^4$

46. $18(u^3 v^4)^2$ $18u^6 v^8$

47. $(-h^4)^7$ $-h^{28}$

48. $(-k^6)^3$ $-k^{18}$

49. $(-m^2)^6$ m^{12}

50. $(-n^3)^8$ n^{24}

51. $\left(\frac{4}{rs^4}\right)^5$ $\frac{4^5}{r^5 s^{20}}$ or $\frac{1024}{r^5 s^{20}}$

52. $\left(\frac{2}{h^7 k}\right)^3$ $\frac{8}{h^{21} k^3}$

53. $\left(\frac{3p}{q^3}\right)^5$ $\frac{3^5 p^5}{q^{15}}$ or $\frac{243 p^5}{q^{15}}$

54. $\left(\frac{5x^2}{y^3}\right)^4$ $\frac{5^4 x^8}{y^{12}}$ or $\frac{625 x^8}{y^{12}}$

55. $\frac{y^8 (y^3)^4}{(y^2)^3}$ y^{14}

56. $\frac{(w^3)^2 (w^4)^5}{(w^4)^2}$ w^{18}

57. $(x^2)^5 (x^3)^7$ x^{31}

58. $(y^3)^4 (y^2)^5$ y^{22}

59. $(2a^2 b)^3 (5a^4 b^3)^2$ $200 a^{14} b^9$

60. $(4c^3 d^5)^2 (3cd^3)^2$ $144 c^8 d^{16}$

61. $(-2p^2 q^4)^4$ $16 p^8 q^{16}$

62. $(-7x^4 y^5)^2$ $49 x^8 y^{10}$

63. $(-m^7 n^3)^5$ $-m^{35} n^{15}$

64. $(-a^3 b^6)^7$ $-a^{21} b^{42}$

65. $\frac{(5a^3 b)^4 (a^2 b)^4}{(5ab)^2}$ $25 a^{18} b^6$

66. $\frac{(6s^3)^2 (s^4 t^5)^2}{(3s^4 t^2)^2}$ $4 s^6 t^6$

67. $\left(\frac{2c^3 d^4}{3c^2 d}\right)^2$ $\frac{4c^2 d^6}{9}$

68. $\left(\frac{x^3 y^5 z}{5xy^2}\right)^2$ $\frac{x^4 y^6 z^2}{25}$

69. $(2c^3 d^2)^5 \left(\frac{c^6 d^8}{4c^2 d}\right)^3$ $\frac{c^{27} d^{31}}{2}$

70. $\left(\frac{s^5 t^6}{2s^2 t}\right)^2 (10s^3 t^3)^2$ $25 s^{12} t^{16}$

71. $\left(\frac{-3a^3 b}{c^2}\right)^3$ $-\frac{27 a^9 b^3}{c^6}$

72. $\left(\frac{-4x^2}{y^4 z}\right)^3$ $-\frac{64 x^6}{y^{12} z^3}$

73. $\frac{(-8b^6)^2 (b^3)^5}{4b}$ $16 b^{26}$

74. $\frac{(-6a^2)^2 (a^3)^4}{9a}$ $4 a^{15}$

Expanding Your Skills

For Exercises 75–82, simplify each expression using the addition or subtraction properties of exponents. Assume that a, b, m, and n represent positive integers.

75. $(x^m)^2$ x^{2m}

76. $(y^3)^n$ y^{3n}

77. $(5a^{2n})^3$ $125 a^{6n}$

78. $(3b^4)^m$ $3^m b^{4m}$

79. $\left(\frac{m^2}{n^3}\right)^b$ $\frac{m^{2b}}{n^{3b}}$

80. $\left(\frac{x^5}{y^3}\right)^m$ $\frac{x^{5m}}{y^{3m}}$

81. $\left(\frac{3a^3}{5b^4}\right)^n$ $\frac{3^n a^{3n}}{5^n b^{4n}}$

82. $\left(\frac{4m^6}{3n^2}\right)^b$ $\frac{4^b m^{6b}}{3^b n^{2b}}$

 Writing   Translating Expression   Geometry   Scientific Calculator   Video   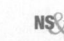 NS&E

Definitions of b^0 and b^{-n}

In Sections 5.1 and 5.2, we learned several rules that enable us to manipulate expressions containing *positive* integer exponents. In this section, we present definitions that can be used to simplify expressions with negative exponents or with an exponent of zero.

Concepts

1. **Definition of b^0**
2. **Definition of b^{-n}**
3. **Properties of Integer Exponents: A Summary**

1. Definition of b^0

To begin, consider the following pattern.

$$3^3 = 27$$
$$3^2 = 9$$
$$3^1 = 3$$
$$3^0 = 1$$

Divide by 3.

Divide by 3.

Divide by 3.

As the exponents decrease by 1, the resulting expressions are divided by 3.

For the pattern to continue, we define $3^0 = 1$.

This pattern suggests that we should define an expression with a zero exponent as follows.

DEFINITION   Definition of b^0

Let b be a nonzero real number. Then, $b^0 = 1$.

Avoiding Mistakes

$b^0 = 1$ provided that b is not zero. Therefore, the expression 0^0 cannot be simplified by this rule.

Example 1   **Simplifying Expressions with a Zero Exponent**

Simplify. Assume that $z \neq 0$.

a. 4^0 b. $(-4)^0$ c. -4^0

d. z^0 e. $-4z^0$ f. $(4z)^0$

Classroom Examples: p. 362, Exercises 14, 18, and 24

Solution:

a. $4^0 = 1$ By definition

b. $(-4)^0 = 1$ By definition

c. $-4^0 = -1 \cdot 4^0 = -1 \cdot 1 = -1$ The exponent 0 applies only to 4.

d. $z^0 = 1$ By definition

e. $-4z^0 = -4 \cdot z^0 = -4 \cdot 1 = -4$ The exponent 0 applies only to z.

f. $(4z)^0 = 1$ The parentheses indicate that the exponent, 0, applies to both factors 4 and z.

Skill Practice Evaluate the expressions. Assume that $x \neq 0$ and $y \neq 0$.

1. 7^0 2. $(-7)^0$ 3. -5^0

4. y^0 5. $-2x^0$ 6. $(2x)^0$

The definition of b^0 is consistent with the other properties of exponents learned thus far. For example, we know that $1 = \frac{5^3}{5^3}$. If we subtract exponents, the result is 5^0.

Subtract exponents.

$$1 = \frac{5^3}{5^3} = 5^{3-3} = 5^0. \qquad \text{Therefore, } 5^0 \text{ must be defined as 1.}$$

2. Definition of b^{-n}

To understand the concept of a *negative* exponent, consider the following pattern.

$3^3 = 27$

> Divide by 3.

$3^2 = 9$

> Divide by 3.   As the exponents decrease by

$3^1 = 3$

> Divide by 3.   1, the resulting expressions are divided by 3.

$3^0 = 1$

> Divide by 3.

$3^{-1} = \dfrac{1}{3}$ ⟵——————— For the pattern to continue, we define $3^{-1} = \dfrac{1}{3^1} = \dfrac{1}{3}$.

$3^{-2} = \dfrac{1}{9}$ ⟵——————— For the pattern to continue, we define $3^{-2} = \dfrac{1}{3^2} = \dfrac{1}{9}$.

$3^{-3} = \dfrac{1}{27}$ ⟵——————— For the pattern to continue, we define $3^{-3} = \dfrac{1}{3^3} = \dfrac{1}{27}$.

This pattern suggests that $3^{-n} = \frac{1}{3^n}$ for all integers, n. In general, we have the following definition involving negative exponents.

DEFINITION Definition of b^{-n}

Let n be an integer and b be a nonzero real number. Then,

$$b^{-n} = \left(\frac{1}{b}\right)^n \quad \text{or} \quad \frac{1}{b^n}$$

The definition of b^{-n} implies that to evaluate b^{-n}, take the reciprocal of the base and change the sign of the exponent.

Change the sign of the exponent.

Change the sign of the exponent.

$$4^{-2} = \left(\frac{1}{4}\right)^2 \quad \text{or} \quad \frac{1}{4^2} \qquad\qquad \left(\frac{a}{b}\right)^{-n} = \left(\frac{b}{a}\right)^n$$

Reciprocal of the base

Reciprocal of the base

Example 2 Simplifying Expressions with Negative Exponents

Classroom Examples: pp. 362–363, Exercises 34 and 44

Simplify. Assume that $c \neq 0$.

a. c^{-3} **b.** 5^{-1} **c.** $(-3)^{-4}$

Solution:

a. $c^{-3} = \dfrac{1}{c^3}$ By definition

b. $5^{-1} = \dfrac{1}{5^1}$ By definition

$= \dfrac{1}{5}$ Simplify.

c. $(-3)^{-4} = \dfrac{1}{(-3)^4}$ The base is -3 and must be enclosed in parentheses.

$= \dfrac{1}{81}$ Simplify. Note that $(-3)^4 = (-3)(-3)(-3)(-3) = 81$.

Avoiding Mistakes

A negative exponent does *not* affect the sign of the base.

Skill Practice Simplify. Assume that $p \neq 0$.

7. p^{-4} **8.** 3^{-3} **9.** $(-5)^{-2}$

Example 3 Simplifying Expressions with Negative Exponents

Classroom Examples: pp. 362–363, Exercises 30 and 46

Simplify. Assume that $y \neq 0$.

a. $\left(\dfrac{1}{6}\right)^{-2}$ **b.** $\left(-\dfrac{3}{5}\right)^{-3}$ **c.** $\dfrac{1}{y^{-5}}$

Solution:

a. $\left(\dfrac{1}{6}\right)^{-2} = 6^2$ Take the reciprocal of the base, and change the sign of the exponent.

$= 36$ Simplify.

b. $\left(-\dfrac{3}{5}\right)^{-3} = \left(-\dfrac{5}{3}\right)^3$ Take the reciprocal of the base, and change the sign of the exponent.

$= -\dfrac{125}{27}$ Simplify.

c. $\dfrac{1}{y^{-5}} = \left(\dfrac{1}{y}\right)^{-5}$ Apply the power of a quotient rule from Section 5.2.

$= (y)^5$ Take the reciprocal of the base, and change the sign of the exponent.

$= y^5$

TIP: Example 3(c) implies $\dfrac{1}{b^{-n}} = b^n$, for $b \neq 0$.

Skill Practice Simplify. Assume that $w \neq 0$.

10. $\left(\dfrac{1}{3}\right)^{-1}$ **11.** $\left(-\dfrac{2}{5}\right)^{-2}$ **12.** $\dfrac{1}{w^{-7}}$

Answers

7. $\dfrac{1}{p^4}$ **8.** $\dfrac{1}{3^3}$ or $\dfrac{1}{27}$

9. $\dfrac{1}{(-5)^2}$ or $\dfrac{1}{25}$ **10.** 3

11. $\dfrac{25}{4}$ **12.** w^7

Classroom Examples: pp. 362–363, Exercises 36, 38, and 42

Example 4 Simplifying Expressions with Negative Exponents

Simplify. Assume that $x \neq 0$.

a. $(5x)^{-3}$ **b.** $5x^{-3}$ **c.** $-5x^{-3}$

Solution:

a. $(5x)^{-3} = \left(\dfrac{1}{5x}\right)^3$ Take the reciprocal of the base, and change the sign of the exponent.

      $= \dfrac{(1)^3}{(5x)^3}$ Apply the exponent of 3 to each factor within parentheses.

      $= \dfrac{1}{125x^3}$ Simplify.

b. $5x^{-3} = 5 \cdot x^{-3}$ Note that the exponent, -3, applies only to x.

      $= 5 \cdot \dfrac{1}{x^3}$ Rewrite x^{-3} as $\dfrac{1}{x^3}$.

      $= \dfrac{5}{x^3}$ Multiply.

c. $-5x^{-3} = -5 \cdot x^{-3}$ Note that the exponent, -3, applies only to x, and that -5 is a coefficient.

      $= -5 \cdot \dfrac{1}{x^3}$ Rewrite x^{-3} as $\dfrac{1}{x^3}$.

      $= -\dfrac{5}{x^3}$ Multiply.

Skill Practice Simplify. Assume that $w \neq 0$.

13. $(2w)^{-4}$ **14.** $2w^{-4}$ **15.** $-2w^{-4}$

It is important to note that the definition of b^{-n} is consistent with the other properties of exponents learned thus far. For example, consider the expression

$$\frac{x^4}{x^7} = \frac{\cancel{x} \cdot \cancel{x} \cdot \cancel{x} \cdot \cancel{x}}{\cancel{x} \cdot \cancel{x} \cdot \cancel{x} \cdot \cancel{x} \cdot x \cdot x \cdot x} = \frac{1}{x^3}$$

Subtract exponents.   Hence, $x^{-3} = \dfrac{1}{x^3}$

By subtracting exponents, we have $\dfrac{x^4}{x^7} = x^{4-7} = x^{-3}$

3. Properties of Integer Exponents: A Summary

The definitions of b^0 and b^{-n} allow us to extend the properties of exponents learned in Sections 5.1 and 5.2 to include integer exponents. These are summarized in Table 5-1.

Answers

13. $\dfrac{1}{16w^4}$ **14.** $\dfrac{2}{w^4}$

15. $-\dfrac{2}{w^4}$

Table 5-1

<table>
<tr><td colspan="3" align="center">**Properties of Integer Exponents**
Assume that a and b are real numbers ($b \neq 0$) and that m and n represent integers.</td></tr>
<tr><th align="center">Property</th><th align="center">Example</th><th align="center">Details/Notes</th></tr>
<tr>
<td>Multiplication of Like Bases

$b^m b^n = b^{m+n}$</td>
<td>$b^2 b^4 = b^{2+4} = b^6$</td>
<td>$b^2 b^4 = (b \cdot b)(b \cdot b \cdot b \cdot b) = b^6$</td>
</tr>
<tr>
<td>Division of Like Bases

$\dfrac{b^m}{b^n} = b^{m-n}$</td>
<td>$\dfrac{b^5}{b^2} = b^{5-2} = b^3$</td>
<td>$\dfrac{b^5}{b^2} = \dfrac{\not b \cdot \not b \cdot b \cdot b \cdot b}{\not b \cdot \not b} = b^3$</td>
</tr>
<tr>
<td>The Power Rule

$(b^m)^n = b^{m \cdot n}$</td>
<td>$(b^4)^2 = b^{4 \cdot 2} = b^8$</td>
<td>$(b^4)^2 = (b \cdot b \cdot b \cdot b)(b \cdot b \cdot b \cdot b) = b^8$</td>
</tr>
<tr>
<td>Power of a Product

$(ab)^m = a^m b^m$</td>
<td>$(ab)^3 = a^3 b^3$</td>
<td>$(ab)^3 = (ab)(ab)(ab)$
$= (a \cdot a \cdot a)(b \cdot b \cdot b) = a^3 b^3$</td>
</tr>
<tr>
<td>Power of a Quotient

$\left(\dfrac{a}{b}\right)^m = \dfrac{a^m}{b^m}$</td>
<td>$\left(\dfrac{a}{b}\right)^3 = \dfrac{a^3}{b^3}$</td>
<td>$\left(\dfrac{a}{b}\right)^3 = \left(\dfrac{a}{b}\right)\left(\dfrac{a}{b}\right)\left(\dfrac{a}{b}\right) = \dfrac{a \cdot a \cdot a}{b \cdot b \cdot b} = \dfrac{a^3}{b^3}$</td>
</tr>
<tr><td colspan="3" align="center">**Definitions**
Assume that b is a real number ($b \neq 0$) and that n represents an integer.</td></tr>
<tr><th align="center">Definition</th><th align="center">Example</th><th align="center">Details/Notes</th></tr>
<tr>
<td>$b^0 = 1$</td>
<td>$(4)^0 = 1$</td>
<td>Any nonzero quantity raised to the zero power equals 1.</td>
</tr>
<tr>
<td>$b^{-n} = \left(\dfrac{1}{b}\right)^n = \dfrac{1}{b^n}$</td>
<td>$b^{-5} = \left(\dfrac{1}{b}\right)^5 = \dfrac{1}{b^5}$</td>
<td>To simplify a negative exponent, take the reciprocal of the base and make the exponent positive.</td>
</tr>
</table>

Example 5 **Simplifying Expressions with Exponents**

Classroom Example: p. 363, Exercise 74

Simplify the expressions. Write the answers with positive exponents only. Assume all variables are nonzero.

   a. $\dfrac{a^3 b^{-2}}{c^{-5}}$ **b.** $\dfrac{x^2 x^{-7}}{x^3}$ **c.** $\dfrac{z^2}{w^{-4} w^4 z^{-8}}$

Solution:

a. $\dfrac{a^3 b^{-2}}{c^{-5}}$

$= \dfrac{a^3}{1} \cdot \dfrac{b^{-2}}{1} \cdot \dfrac{1}{c^{-5}}$

$= \dfrac{a^3}{1} \cdot \dfrac{1}{b^2} \cdot \dfrac{c^5}{1}$ Simplify negative exponents.

$= \dfrac{a^3 c^5}{b^2}$ Multiply.

b. $\dfrac{x^2 x^{-7}}{x^3}$

$$= \dfrac{x^{2+(-7)}}{x^3} \qquad \text{Add the exponents in the numerator.}$$

$$= \dfrac{x^{-5}}{x^3} \qquad \text{Simplify.}$$

$$= x^{-5-3} \qquad \text{Subtract the exponents.}$$

$$= x^{-8}$$

$$= \dfrac{1}{x^8} \qquad \text{Simplify the negative exponent.}$$

c. $\dfrac{z^2}{w^{-4} w^4 z^{-8}}$

$$= \dfrac{z^2}{w^{-4+4} z^{-8}} \qquad \text{Add the exponents in the denominator.}$$

$$= \dfrac{z^2}{w^0 z^{-8}}$$

$$= \dfrac{z^2}{(1) z^{-8}} \qquad \text{Recall that } w^0 = 1.$$

$$= z^{2-(-8)} \qquad \text{Subtract the exponents.}$$

$$= z^{10} \qquad \text{Simplify.}$$

Skill Practice Simplify the expressions. Assume all variables are nonzero.

16. $\dfrac{x^{-6}}{y^4 z^{-8}}$ **17.** $\dfrac{x^3 x^{-8}}{x^4}$ **18.** $\dfrac{p^3}{w^7 w^{-7} z^{-2}}$

Classroom Examples: p. 363, Exercises 82 and 92

Example 6   Simplifying Expressions with Exponents

Simplify the expressions. Write the answers with positive exponents only. Assume that all variables are nonzero.

a. $(-4ab^{-2})^{-3}$ **b.** $\left(\dfrac{2p^{-4} q^3}{5p^2 q}\right)^{-2}$

Solution:

a. $(-4ab^{-2})^{-3}$

$$= (-4)^{-3} a^{-3} (b^{-2})^{-3} \qquad \text{Apply the power rule of exponents.}$$

$$= (-4)^{-3} a^{-3} b^6$$

$$= \dfrac{1}{(-4)^3} \cdot \dfrac{1}{a^3} \cdot b^6 \qquad \text{Simplify the negative exponents.}$$

$$= \dfrac{1}{-64} \cdot \dfrac{1}{a^3} \cdot b^6 \qquad \text{Simplify.}$$

$$= -\dfrac{b^6}{64a^3} \qquad \text{Multiply fractions.}$$

Answers

16. $\dfrac{z^8}{y^4 x^6}$ **17.** $\dfrac{1}{x^9}$ **18.** $p^3 z^2$

b. $\left(\dfrac{2p^{-4}q^3}{5p^2q} \right)^{-2}$ First simplify within the parentheses.

$= \left(\dfrac{2p^{-4-2}q^{3-1}}{5} \right)^{-2}$ Divide like bases by subtracting exponents.

$= \left(\dfrac{2p^{-6}q^2}{5} \right)^{-2}$ Simplify.

$= \dfrac{(2p^{-6}q^2)^{-2}}{(5)^{-2}}$ Apply the power rule of a quotient.

$= \dfrac{2^{-2}(p^{-6})^{-2}(q^2)^{-2}}{5^{-2}}$ Apply the power rule of a product.

$= \dfrac{2^{-2}p^{12}q^{-4}}{5^{-2}}$ Simplify

$= \dfrac{5^2 p^{12}}{2^2 q^4}$ Simplify the negative exponents.

$= \dfrac{25p^{12}}{4q^4}$ Simplify.

Skill Practice Simplify the expressions. Assume all variables are nonzero.

19. $(-5x^{-2}y^3)^{-2}$ **20.** $\left(\dfrac{3x^{-3}y^{-2}}{4xy^{-3}} \right)^{-2}$

Example 7 **Simplifying an Expression with Exponents**

Classroom Example: p. 363, Exercise 96

Simplify the expression $2^{-1} + 3^{-1} + 5^0$. Write the answer with positive exponents only.

Solution:

$2^{-1} + 3^{-1} + 5^0$

$= \dfrac{1}{2} + \dfrac{1}{3} + 1$ Simplify negative exponents. Simplify $5^0 = 1$.

$= \dfrac{3}{6} + \dfrac{2}{6} + \dfrac{6}{6}$ The least common denominator is 6.

$= \dfrac{11}{6}$ Simplify.

Skill Practice Simplify the expressions.

21. $2^{-1} + 4^{-2} + 3^0$

Answers

19. $\dfrac{x^4}{25y^6}$ **20.** $\dfrac{16x^8}{9y^2}$ **21.** $\dfrac{25}{16}$

Section 5.3 Practice Exercises

For this exercise set, assume all variables represent nonzero real numbers.

Study Skills Exercise

1. To help you remember the properties of exponents, write them on 3×5 cards. On each card, write a property on one side and an example using that property on the other side. Keep these cards with you, and when you have a spare moment (such as waiting at the doctor's office), pull out these cards and go over the properties.

Review Exercises

For Exercises 2–9, simplify.

2. $b^3 b^8$ b^{11}

3. $c^7 c^2$ c^9

4. $\dfrac{x^6}{x^2}$ x^4

5. $\dfrac{y^9}{y^8}$ y

6. $\dfrac{9^4 \cdot 9^8}{9}$ 9^{11}

7. $\dfrac{3^{14}}{3^3 \cdot 3^5}$ 3^6 or 729

8. $(6ab^3c^2)^5$ $6^5 a^5 b^{15} c^{10}$ or $7776 a^5 b^{15} c^{10}$

9. $(7w^7 z^2)^4$ $7^4 w^{28} z^8$ or $2401 w^{28} z^8$

Concept 1: Definition of b^0

10. Simplify.

   a. 8^0 1   **b.** $\dfrac{8^4}{8^4}$ 1

11. Simplify.

   a. d^0 1   **b.** $\dfrac{d^3}{d^3}$ 1

12. Simplify.

   a. m^0 1   **b.** $\dfrac{m^5}{m^5}$ 1

For Exercises 13–24, simplify. **(See Example 1.)**

13. p^0 1

14. k^0 1

15. 5^0 1

16. 2^0 1

17. -4^0 -1

18. -1^0 -1

19. $(-6)^0$ 1

20. $(-2)^0$ 1

21. $(8x)^0$ 1

22. $(-3y^3)^0$ 1

23. $-7x^0$ -7

24. $6y^0$ 6

Concept 2: Definition of b^{-n}

25. Simplify and write the answers with positive exponents.

   a. t^{-5} $\dfrac{1}{t^5}$ **b.** $\dfrac{t^3}{t^8}$ $\dfrac{1}{t^5}$

26. Simplify and write the answers with positive exponents.

   a. 4^{-3} $\dfrac{1}{4^3}$ **b.** $\dfrac{4^2}{4^5}$ $\dfrac{1}{4^3}$

For Exercises 27–46, simplify. **(See Examples 2–4.)**

27. $\left(\dfrac{2}{7}\right)^{-3}$ $\dfrac{343}{8}$

28. $\left(\dfrac{5}{4}\right)^{-1}$ $\dfrac{4}{5}$

29. $\left(-\dfrac{1}{5}\right)^{-2}$ 25

30. $\left(-\dfrac{1}{3}\right)^{-3}$ -27

31. a^{-3} $\dfrac{1}{a^3}$

32. c^{-5} $\dfrac{1}{c^5}$

33. 12^{-1} $\dfrac{1}{12}$

34. 4^{-2} $\dfrac{1}{16}$

35. $(4b)^{-2}$ $\dfrac{1}{16b^2}$

36. $(3z)^{-1}$ $\dfrac{1}{3z}$

37. $6x^{-2}$ $\dfrac{6}{x^2}$

38. $7y^{-1}$ $\dfrac{7}{y}$

39. $(-8)^{-2}$ $\dfrac{1}{64}$ **40.** -8^{-2} $-\dfrac{1}{64}$ **41.** $-3y^{-4}$ $-\dfrac{3}{y^4}$ **42.** $-6a^{-2}$ $-\dfrac{6}{a^2}$

43. $(-t)^{-3}$ $-\dfrac{1}{t^3}$ **44.** $(-r)^{-5}$ $-\dfrac{1}{r^5}$ **45.** $\dfrac{1}{a^{-5}}$ a^5 **46.** $\dfrac{1}{b^{-6}}$ b^6

Concept 3: Properties of Integer Exponents: A Summary

47. Correct the following statement.

$$\dfrac{x^4}{x^{-6}} = x^{4-6} = x^{-2} \qquad \dfrac{x^4}{x^{-6}} = x^{4-(-6)} = x^{10}$$

48. Correct the following statement.

$$\dfrac{y^5}{y^{-3}} = y^{5-3} = y^2 \qquad \dfrac{y^5}{y^{-3}} = y^{5-(-3)} = y^8$$

49. Correct the following statement.

$$2a^{-3} = \dfrac{1}{2a^3} \qquad 2a^{-3} = 2 \cdot \dfrac{1}{a^3} = \dfrac{2}{a^3}$$

50. Correct the following statement.

$$5b^{-2} = \dfrac{1}{5b^2} \qquad 5b^{-2} = 5 \cdot \dfrac{1}{b^2} = \dfrac{5}{b^2}$$

Mixed Exercises

For Exercises 51–94, simplify each expression. Write the answer with positive exponents only. **(See Examples 5–6.)**

51. $x^{-8}x^4$ $\dfrac{1}{x^4}$ **52.** s^5s^{-6} $\dfrac{1}{s}$ **53.** $a^{-8}a^8$ 1 **54.** q^3q^{-3} 1

55. $y^{17}y^{-13}$ y^4 **56.** $b^{20}b^{-14}$ b^6 **57.** $(m^{-6}n^9)^3$ $\dfrac{n^{27}}{m^{18}}$ **58.** $(c^4d^{-5})^{-2}$ $\dfrac{d^{10}}{c^8}$

59. $(-3j^{-5}k^6)^4$ $\dfrac{81k^{24}}{j^{20}}$ **60.** $(6xy^{-11})^{-3}$ $\dfrac{y^{33}}{6^3x^3}$ or $\dfrac{y^{33}}{216x^3}$ **61.** $\dfrac{p^3}{p^9}$ $\dfrac{1}{p^6}$ **62.** $\dfrac{q^2}{q^{10}}$ $\dfrac{1}{q^8}$

63. $\dfrac{r^{-5}}{r^{-2}}$ $\dfrac{1}{r^3}$ **64.** $\dfrac{u^{-2}}{u^{-6}}$ u^4 **65.** $\dfrac{a^2}{a^{-6}}$ a^8 **66.** $\dfrac{p^3}{p^{-5}}$ p^8

67. $\dfrac{y^{-2}}{y^6}$ $\dfrac{1}{y^8}$ **68.** $\dfrac{s^{-4}}{s^3}$ $\dfrac{1}{s^7}$ **69.** $\dfrac{7^3}{7^2 \cdot 7^8}$ $\dfrac{1}{7^7}$ **70.** $\dfrac{3^4 \cdot 3}{3^7}$ $\dfrac{1}{9}$

71. $\dfrac{a^2a}{a^3}$ 1 **72.** $\dfrac{t^5}{t^2t^3}$ 1 **73.** $\dfrac{a^{-1}b^2}{a^3b^8}$ $\dfrac{1}{a^4b^6}$ **74.** $\dfrac{k^{-4}h^{-1}}{k^6h}$ $\dfrac{1}{k^{10}h^2}$

75. $\dfrac{w^{-8}(w^2)^{-5}}{w^3}$ $\dfrac{1}{w^{21}}$ **76.** $\dfrac{p^2p^{-7}}{(p^2)^3}$ $\dfrac{1}{p^{11}}$ **77.** $\dfrac{3^{-2}}{3}$ $\dfrac{1}{27}$ **78.** $\dfrac{5^{-1}}{5}$ $\dfrac{1}{25}$

79. $\left(\dfrac{p^{-1}q^5}{p^{-6}}\right)^0$ 1 **80.** $\left(\dfrac{ab^{-4}}{a^{-5}}\right)^0$ 1 **81.** $(8x^3y^0)^{-2}$ $\dfrac{1}{64x^6}$ **82.** $(3u^2v^0)^{-3}$ $\dfrac{1}{27u^6}$

83. $(-8y^{-12})(2y^{16}z^{-2})$ $\dfrac{16y^4}{z^2}$ **84.** $(5p^{-2}q^5)(-2p^{-4}q^{-1})$ $-\dfrac{10q^4}{p^6}$ **85.** $\dfrac{-18a^{10}b^6}{108a^{-2}b^6}$ $-\dfrac{a^{12}}{6}$ **86.** $\dfrac{-35x^{-4}y^{-3}}{-21x^2y^{-3}}$ $\dfrac{5}{3x^6}$

87. $\dfrac{(-4c^{12}d^7)^2}{(5c^{-3}d^{10})^{-1}}$ $80c^{21}d^{24}$ **88.** $\dfrac{(s^5t^{-2})^4}{(3s^{-4}t^6)^{-2}}$ $9s^4t^4$ **89.** $\dfrac{(2x^3y^2)^{-3}}{(3x^2y^4)^{-2}}$ $\dfrac{9y^2}{8x^5}$ **90.** $\dfrac{(5p^4q)^{-3}}{(p^3q^5)^{-4}}$ $\dfrac{q^{17}}{125}$

91. $\left(\dfrac{5cd^{-3}}{10d^5}\right)^{-2}$ $\dfrac{4d^{16}}{c^2}$ **92.** $\left(\dfrac{4m^{10}n^4}{2m^{12}n^{-2}}\right)^{-1}$ $\dfrac{m^2}{2n^6}$ **93.** $(2xy^3)\left(\dfrac{9xy}{4x^3y^2}\right)$ $\dfrac{9y^2}{2x}$ **94.** $(-3a^3)\left(\dfrac{ab}{27a^4b^2}\right)$ $-\dfrac{1}{9b}$

For Exercises 95–102, simplify. **(See Example 7.)**

95. $5^{-1} + 2^{-2}$ $\dfrac{9}{20}$ **96.** $4^{-2} + 8^{-1}$ $\dfrac{3}{16}$ **97.** $10^0 - 10^{-1}$ $\dfrac{9}{10}$ **98.** $3^0 - 3^{-2}$ $\dfrac{8}{9}$

99. $2^{-2} + 1^{-2}$ $\dfrac{5}{4}$ **100.** $4^{-1} + 8^{-1}$ $\dfrac{3}{8}$ **101.** $4 \cdot 5^0 - 2 \cdot 3^{-1}$ $\dfrac{10}{3}$ **102.** $2 \cdot 4^0 - 3 \cdot 4^{-1}$ $\dfrac{5}{4}$

 Writing   Translating Expression   Geometry   Scientific Calculator   Video   NS&E

Section 5.4 ## Scientific Notation

Concepts

1. Writing Numbers in Scientific Notation
2. Writing Numbers in Standard Form
3. Multiplying and Dividing Numbers in Scientific Notation

1. Writing Numbers in Scientific Notation

In many applications in mathematics, it is necessary to work with very large or very small numbers. For example, the number of movie tickets sold in the United States recently is estimated to be 1,500,000,000. The weight of a flea is approximately 0.00066 lb. To avoid writing numerous zeros in very large or small numbers, scientific notation was devised as a shortcut.

The principle behind scientific notation is to use a power of 10 to express the magnitude of the number. For example, the numbers 4000 and 0.07 can be written as:

$$4000 = 4 \times 1000 = 4 \times 10^3$$

$$0.07 = 7.0 \times 0.01 = 7.0 \times 10^{-2} \qquad \text{Note that } 10^{-2} = \frac{1}{100} = 0.01$$

> **DEFINITION** Scientific Notation
>
> A positive number expressed in the form: $a \times 10^n$, where $1 \leq a < 10$ and n is an integer is said to be written in **scientific notation**.

To write a positive number in scientific notation, we apply the following guidelines:

1. Move the decimal point so that its new location is to the right of the first nonzero digit. The number should now be greater than or equal to 1 but less than 10. Count the number of places that the decimal point is moved.

2. If the original number is *large* (greater than or equal to 10), use the number of places the decimal point was moved as a *positive* power of 10.

$$450,000 = 4.5 \times 100,000 = 4.5 \times 10^5$$

5 places

Animation

3. If the original number is *small* (between 0 and 1), use the number of places the decimal point was moved as a *negative* power of 10.

$$0.0002 = 2.0 \times 0.0001 = 2.0 \times 10^{-4}$$

4 places

4. If the original number is greater than or equal to 1 but less than 10, use 0 as the power of 10.

$$7.592 = 7.592 \times 10^0 \qquad \textit{Note: } \text{A number between 1 and 10 is seldom written in scientific notation.}$$

5. If the original number is negative, then $-10 < a \leq -1$.

$$-450,000 = -4.5 \times 100,000 = -4.5 \times 10^5$$

5 places

Classroom Examples: p. 368,
Exercises 22 and 26

Example 1 **Writing Numbers in Scientific Notation**

Write the numbers in scientific notation.

a. 53,000   **b.** 0.00053

Solution:

a. $53{,}000. = 5.3 \times 10^4$ To write 53,000 in scientific notation, the decimal point must be moved four places to the left. Because 53,000 is larger than 10, a *positive* power of 10 is used.

b. $0.00053 = 5.3 \times 10^{-4}$ To write 0.00053 in scientific notation, the decimal point must be moved four places to the right. Because 0.00053 is less than 1, a *negative* power of 10 is used.

Skill Practice Write the numbers in scientific notation.

1. 175,000,000   **2.** 0.000005

Example 2 **Writing Numbers in Scientific Notation**

Classroom Examples: p. 368, Exercises 30 and 32

Write the numbers in scientific notation.

a. The number of movie tickets sold in the United States for a recent year is estimated to be 1,500,000,000.

b. The weight of a flea is approximately 0.00066 lb.

c. The temperature on a January day in Fargo dropped to $-43°$F.

d. A bench is 8.2 ft long.

Solution:

a. $1{,}500{,}000{,}000 = 1.5 \times 10^9$ **b.** $0.00066 \text{ lb} = 6.6 \times 10^{-4} \text{ lb}$

c. $-43°\text{F} = -4.3 \times 10^1 \text{ °F}$ **d.** $8.2 \text{ ft} = 8.2 \times 10^0 \text{ ft}$

Skill Practice Write the numbers in scientific notation.

3. The population of the Earth is approximately 6,360,000,000.
4. The weight of a grain of salt is approximately 0.000002 ounces.

---

2. Writing Numbers in Standard Form

Example 3 **Writing Numbers in Standard Form**

Classroom Examples: p. 369, Exercises 40 and 50

Write the numbers in standard form.

a. The mass of a proton is approximately 1.67×10^{-24} g.

b. The "nearby" star Vega is approximately 1.552×10^{14} miles from Earth.

Solution:

a. $1.67 \times 10^{-24} \text{ g} = 0.000\,000\,000\,000\,000\,000\,000\,001\,67 \text{ g}$

Because the power of 10 is negative, the value of 1.67×10^{-24} is a decimal number between 0 and 1. Move the decimal point 24 places to the *left*.

b. $1.552 \times 10^{14} \text{ miles} = 155{,}200{,}000{,}000{,}000 \text{ miles}$

Because the power of 10 is a positive integer, the value of 1.552×10^{14} is a large number greater than 10. Move the decimal point 14 places to the *right*.

Answers

1. 1.75×10^8 **2.** 5.0×10^{-6}
3. 6.36×10^9 **4.** 2.0×10^{-6} oz

3. Multiplying and Dividing Numbers in Scientific Notation

To multiply or divide two numbers in scientific notation, use the commutative and associative properties of multiplication to group the powers of 10. For example:

$$400 \times 2000 = (4 \times 10^2)(2 \times 10^3) = (4 \cdot 2) \times (10^2 \cdot 10^3) = 8 \times 10^5$$

$$\frac{0.00054}{150} = \frac{5.4 \times 10^{-4}}{1.5 \times 10^2} = \left(\frac{5.4}{1.5}\right) \times \left(\frac{10^{-4}}{10^2}\right) = 3.6 \times 10^{-6}$$

Classroom Examples: p. 369,
Exercises 54 and 68

Example 4 **Multiplying and Dividing Numbers in Scientific Notation**

Multiply or divide as indicated.

a. $(8.7 \times 10^4)(2.5 \times 10^{-12})$ **b.** $\dfrac{4.25 \times 10^{13}}{8.5 \times 10^{-2}}$

Solution:

a. $(8.7 \times 10^4)(2.5 \times 10^{-12})$

$= (8.7 \cdot 2.5) \times (10^4 \cdot 10^{-12})$	Commutative and associative properties of multiplication
$= 21.75 \times 10^{-8}$	The number 21.75 is not in proper scientific notation because 21.75 is not between 1 and 10.
$= (2.175 \times 10^1) \times 10^{-8}$	Rewrite 21.75 as 2.175×10^1.
$= 2.175 \times (10^1 \times 10^{-8})$	Associative property of multiplication
$= 2.175 \times 10^{-7}$	Simplify.

b. $\dfrac{4.25 \times 10^{13}}{8.5 \times 10^{-2}}$

$= \left(\dfrac{4.25}{8.5}\right) \times \left(\dfrac{10^{13}}{10^{-2}}\right)$	Commutative and associative properties
$= 0.5 \times 10^{15}$	The number 0.5×10^{15} is not in proper scientific notation because 0.5 is not between 1 and 10.
$= (5.0 \times 10^{-1}) \times 10^{15}$	Rewrite 0.5 as 5.0×10^{-1}.
$= 5.0 \times (10^{-1} \times 10^{15})$	Associative property of multiplication
$= 5.0 \times 10^{14}$	Simplify.

> **Skill Practice** Multiply or divide as indicated.
>
> **7.** $(7 \times 10^5)(5 \times 10^3)$ **8.** $\dfrac{1 \times 10^{-2}}{4 \times 10^{-7}}$

Answers
5. 0.000 000 055
6. 2,000,000,000,000,000,000,000,000,000,000
7. 3.5×10^9
8. 2.5×10^4

Calculator Connections

Topic: Using Scientific Notation

Both scientific and graphing calculators can perform calculations involving numbers written in scientific notation. Most calculators use an EE key or an EXP key to enter the power of 10.

Scientific Calculator

Enter: 2.7 EE 5 =   or   2.7 EXP 5 =   **Result:** | 270000 |

Enter: 7.1 EE 3 +○-   =   or   7.1 EXP 3 +○-   =   **Result:** | 0.0071 |

Graphing Calculator

```
2.7E5
            270000
7.1E-3
              .0071
```

We recommend that you use parentheses to enclose each number written in scientific notation when performing calculations. Try using your calculator to perform the calculations from Example 4.

a. $(8.7 \times 10^4)(2.5 \times 10^{-12})$ **b.** $\dfrac{4.25 \times 10^{13}}{8.5 \times 10^{-2}}$

Scientific Calculator

Enter: (8.7 EE 4) × (2.5 EE 12 +○-) =   **Result:** | 0.000000218 |

Enter: (4.25 EE 13) ÷ (8.5 EE 2 +○-) =   **Result:** | 5E14 |

Notice that the answer to part (b) is shown on the calculator in scientific notation. The calculator does not have enough room to display 14 zeros. Also notice that the calculator rounds the answer to part (a). The exact answer is 2.175×10^{-7} or 0.0000002175.

Graphing Calculator

```
(8.7E4)*(2.5E-12
)
         2.175E-7
(4.25E13)/(8.5E-
2)
             5E14
```

Avoiding Mistakes

A display of 5E14 on a calculator does not mean 5^{14}. It is scientific notation and means 5×10^{14}.

Calculator Exercises

Use a calculator to perform the indicated operations:

1. $(5.2 \times 10^6)(4.6 \times 10^{-3})$

2. $(2.19 \times 10^{-8})(7.84 \times 10^{-4})$

3. $\dfrac{4.76 \times 10^{-5}}{2.38 \times 10^9}$

4. $\dfrac{8.5 \times 10^4}{4.0 \times 10^{-1}}$

5. $\dfrac{(9.6 \times 10^7)(4.0 \times 10^{-3})}{2.0 \times 10^{-2}}$

6. $\dfrac{(5.0 \times 10^{-12})(6.4 \times 10^{-5})}{(1.6 \times 10^{-8})(4.0 \times 10^2)}$

Section 5.4 Practice Exercises

Boost *your* GRADE at
ALEKS.com!

ALEKS
version 3.0

- Practice Problems
- Self-Tests
- NetTutor

- e-Professors
- Videos

For additional exercises, see Classroom Activities
5.4A–5.4B in the *Instructor's Resource Manual*
at www.mhhe.com/moh.

Study Skills Exercise

1. Define the key term **scientific notation**.

Review Exercises

For Exercises 2–13, simplify each expression. Assume all variables represent nonzero real numbers.

2. $a^3 a^{-4}$ $\dfrac{1}{a}$

3. $b^5 b^8$ b^{13}

4. $10^3 \cdot 10^{-4}$ $\dfrac{1}{10}$

5. $10^5 \cdot 10^8$ 10^{13}

6. $\dfrac{x^3}{x^6}$ $\dfrac{1}{x^3}$

7. $\dfrac{y^2}{y^7}$ $\dfrac{1}{y^5}$

8. $(c^4 d^2)^3$ $c^{12} d^6$

9. $(x^5 y^{-3})^4$ $\dfrac{x^{20}}{y^{12}}$

10. $\dfrac{z^9 z^4}{z^3}$ z^{10}

11. $\dfrac{w^{-2} w^5}{w^{-1}}$ w^4

12. $\dfrac{10^9 \cdot 10^4}{10^3}$ 10^{10}

13. $\dfrac{10^{-2} \cdot 10^5}{10^{-1}}$ 10^4

Concept 1: Writing Numbers in Scientific Notation

 14. Explain how scientific notation might be valuable in studying astronomy. Answers may vary.
For example: Scientific notation would be helpful in writing the distance between Earth and the stars or planets.

15. Explain how you would write the number 0.000 000 000 23 in scientific notation.   Move the decimal point
between the 2 and 3 and multiply by 10^{-10}; 2.3×10^{-10}.

16. Explain how you would write the number 23,000,000,000,000 in scientific notation.   Move the decimal point
between the 2 and 3 and multiply by 10^{13}; 2.3×10^{13}.

Animation

For Exercises 17–28, write the number in scientific notation. **(See Example 1.)**

17. 50,000 5×10^4

18. 900,000 9×10^5

19. 208,000 2.08×10^5

20. 420,000,000 4.2×10^8

21. 6,010,000 6.01×10^6

22. 75,000 7.5×10^4

23. 0.000008 8×10^{-6}

24. 0.003 3×10^{-3}

25. 0.000125 1.25×10^{-4}

26. 0.00000025 2.5×10^{-7}

27. 0.006708 6.708×10^{-3}

28. 0.02004 2.004×10^{-2}

For Exercises 29–34, write each number in scientific notation. **(See Example 2.)**

29. The mass of a proton is approximately
0.000 000 000 000 000 000 000 000 0017 g. 1.7×10^{-24} g

30. The total combined salaries of the president,
vice president, senators, and representatives of
the United States federal government is
approximately \$85,000,000. $\$8.5 \times 10^7$

31. The Bill Gates Foundation has over
\$27,000,000,000 from which it makes
contributions to global charities. $\$2.7 \times 10^{10}$

32. One gram is equivalent to 0.0035 oz.
3.5×10^{-3} oz

33. In the world's largest tanker disaster, *Amoco
Cadiz* spilled 68,000,000 gal of oil off Portsall,
France, causing widespread environmental
damage over 100 miles of Brittany coast.
6.8×10^7 gal; 1.0×10^2 miles

34. The human heart pumps about 1400 L of blood
per day. That means that it pumps approximately
10,000,000 L per year. 1.4×10^3 L; 1.0×10^7 L

 Writing   Translating Expression   Geometry   Scientific Calculator   Video   NS&E

Concept 2: Writing Numbers in Standard Form

35. Explain how you would write the number 3.1×10^{-9} in standard form. Move the decimal point nine places to the left; 0.000 000 0031.

36. Explain how you would write the number 3.1×10^9 in standard form. Move the decimal point nine places to the right; 3,100,000,000.

For Exercises 37–52, write each number in standard form. **(See Example 3.)**

37. 5×10^{-5} 0.00005

38. 2×10^{-7} 0.0000002

39. 2.8×10^3 2800

40. 9.1×10^6 9,100,000

41. 6.03×10^{-4} 0.000603

42. 7.01×10^{-3} 0.00701

43. 2.4×10^6 2,400,000

44. 3.1×10^4 31,000

45. 1.9×10^{-2} 0.019

46. 2.8×10^{-6} 0.0000028

47. 7.032×10^3 7032

48. 8.205×10^2 820.5

49. One picogram (pg) is equal to 1×10^{-12} g.   0.000 000 000 001 g

50. A nanometer (nm) is approximately 3.94×10^{-8} in.
0.000 000 0394 in.

51. A normal diet contains between 1.6×10^3 Cal and 2.8×10^3 Cal per day.
1600 calories and 2800 calories

52. The total land area of Texas is approximately 2.62×10^5 square miles.
262,000 square miles

Concept 3: Multiplying and Dividing Numbers in Scientific Notation

For Exercises 53–72, multiply or divide as indicated. Write the answers in scientific notation. **(See Example 4.)**

53. $(2.5 \times 10^6)(2.0 \times 10^{-2})$ 5.0×10^4

54. $(2.0 \times 10^{-7})(3.0 \times 10^{13})$ 6.0×10^6

55. $(1.2 \times 10^4)(3 \times 10^7)$ 3.6×10^{11}

56. $(3.2 \times 10^{-3})(2.5 \times 10^8)$ 8×10^5

57. $\dfrac{7.7 \times 10^6}{3.5 \times 10^2}$ 2.2×10^4

58. $\dfrac{9.5 \times 10^{11}}{1.9 \times 10^3}$ 5×10^8

59. $\dfrac{9.0 \times 10^{-6}}{4.0 \times 10^7}$ 2.25×10^{-13}

60. $\dfrac{7.0 \times 10^{-2}}{5.0 \times 10^9}$ 1.4×10^{-11}

61. $80,000,000,000 \times 4000$ 3.2×10^{14}

62. 0.0006×0.03 1.8×10^{-5}

63. $(3.2 \times 10^{-4})(7.6 \times 10^{-7})$
2.432×10^{-10}

64. $(5.9 \times 10^{12})(3.6 \times 10^9)$
2.124×10^{22}

65. $\dfrac{210,000,000,000}{0.007}$ 3.0×10^{13}

66. $\dfrac{160,000,000,000,000}{0.00008}$ 2.0×10^{18}

67. $\dfrac{5.7 \times 10^{-2}}{9.5 \times 10^{-8}}$ 6.0×10^5

68. $\dfrac{2.72 \times 10^{-6}}{6.8 \times 10^{-4}}$ 4.0×10^{-3}

69. $6,000,000,000 \times 0.0000000023$
1.38×10^1

70. $0.000055 \times 40,000$ 2.2×10^0

71. $\dfrac{0.0000000003}{6000}$ 5.0×10^{-14}

72. $\dfrac{420,000}{0.0000021}$ 2.0×10^{11}

Mixed Exercises

73. If a piece of paper is 3.0×10^{-3} in. thick, how thick is a stack of 1.25×10^3 pieces of paper?
3.75 in.

74. A box of staples contains 5.0×10^3 staples and weighs 15 oz. How much does one staple weigh? Write your answer in scientific notation.
3.0×10^{-3} oz

75. Bill Gates owned approximately 1,100,000,000 shares of Microsoft stock. If the stock price was $27 per share, how much was Bill Gates' stock worth? 2.97×10^{10}

76. A state lottery had a jackpot of 5.2×10^7. This week the winner was a group of office employees that included 13 people. How much would each person receive? 4.0×10^6 or $4,000,000

 Writing   Translating Expression   Geometry   Scientific Calculator   Video   NS&E

For Exercises 77–78, use the formula $v = f\lambda$. In this formula, v represents velocity of light (in meters per second), f represents the frequency (in cycles per second, Hz), λ represents wavelength of light (in meters).

77. Light travels at approximately 3.0×10^8 m/s. If green light has a frequency of 5.6×10^{14} Hz, find the wavelength of green light. $\approx 5.4 \times 10^{-7}$ m

78. Light travels at approximately 3.0×10^8 m/s. If red light has a wavelength of 7.0×10^{-7} m, find the frequency of red light. $\approx 4.3 \times 10^{14}$ Hz

79. Dinosaurs became extinct about 65 million years ago.

   a. Write the number 65 million in scientific notation. 6.5×10^7

   b. How many days is 65 million years? 2.3725×10^{10} days

   c. How many hours is 65 million years? 5.694×10^{11} hr

   d. How many seconds is 65 million years? 2.04984×10^{15} sec

80. The Earth is 111,600,000 km from the Sun.

   a. Write the number 111,600,000 in scientific notation. 1.116×10^8

   b. If there are 1000 m in a kilometer, how many meters is the Earth from the Sun? 1.116×10^{11} m

   c. If there are 100 cm in a meter, how many centimeters is the Earth from the Sun? 1.116×10^{13} cm

Problem Recognition Exercises

Properties of Exponents

Simplify completely. Assume that all variables represent nonzero real numbers.

1. $t^3 t^5$ $\quad t^8$

2. $2^3 2^5$ $\quad 2^8$ or 256

3. $\dfrac{y^7}{y^2}$ $\quad y^5$

4. $\dfrac{p^9}{p^3}$ $\quad p^6$

5. $(r^2 s^4)^2$ $\quad r^4 s^8$

6. $(ab^3 c^2)^3$ $\quad a^3 b^9 c^6$

7. $\dfrac{w^4}{w^{-2}}$ $\quad w^6$

8. $\dfrac{m^{-14}}{m^2}$ $\quad \dfrac{1}{m^{16}}$

9. $\dfrac{y^{-7} x^4}{z^{-3}}$ $\quad \dfrac{x^4 z^3}{y^7}$

10. $\dfrac{a^3 b^{-6}}{c^{-8}}$ $\quad \dfrac{a^3 c^8}{b^6}$

11. $(2.5 \times 10^{-3})(5.0 \times 10^5)$ $\quad 1.25 \times 10^3$

12. $(3.1 \times 10^6)(4.0 \times 10^{-2})$ $\quad 1.24 \times 10^5$

13. $\dfrac{4.8 \times 10^7}{6.0 \times 10^{-2}}$ $\quad 8.0 \times 10^8$

14. $\dfrac{5.4 \times 10^{-2}}{9.0 \times 10^6}$ $\quad 6.0 \times 10^{-9}$

15. $\dfrac{1}{p^{-6} p^{-8} p^{-1}}$ $\quad p^{15}$

16. $p^6 p^8 p$ $\quad p^{15}$

17. $\dfrac{v^9}{v^{11}}$ $\quad \dfrac{1}{v^2}$

18. $(c^5 d^4)^{10}$ $\quad c^{50} d^{40}$

19. $\left(\dfrac{1}{2}\right)^{-1} + \left(\dfrac{1}{3}\right)^0$ $\quad 3$

20. $\left(\dfrac{1}{4}\right)^0 - \left(\dfrac{1}{5}\right)^{-1}$ $\quad -4$

21. $(2^5 b^{-3})^{-3}$ $\quad \dfrac{b^9}{2^{15}}$

22. $(3^{-2} y^3)^{-2}$ $\quad \dfrac{81}{y^6}$

23. $\left(\dfrac{3x}{2y}\right)^{-4}$ $\quad \dfrac{16y^4}{81x^4}$

24. $\left(\dfrac{6c}{5d^3}\right)^{-2}$ $\quad \dfrac{25d^6}{36c^2}$

25. $(3ab^2)(a^2 b)^3$ $\quad 3a^7 b^5$

26. $(4x^2 y^3)^3 (xy^2)$ $\quad 64x^7 y^{11}$

27. $\left(\dfrac{xy^2}{x^3 y}\right)^4$ $\quad \dfrac{y^4}{x^8}$

28. $\left(\dfrac{a^3 b}{a^5 b^3}\right)^5$ $\quad \dfrac{1}{a^{10} b^{10}}$

29. $\dfrac{(t^{-2})^3}{t^{-4}}$ $\quad \dfrac{1}{t^2}$

30. $\dfrac{(p^3)^{-4}}{p^{-5}}$ $\quad \dfrac{1}{p^7}$

31. $\left(\dfrac{2w^2 x^3}{3y^0}\right)^3$ $\quad \dfrac{8w^6 x^9}{27}$

32. $\left(\dfrac{5a^0 b^4}{4c^3}\right)^2$ $\quad \dfrac{25b^8}{16c^6}$

33. $\dfrac{q^3 r^{-2}}{s^{-1} t^5}$ $\quad \dfrac{q^3 s}{r^2 t^5}$

34. $\dfrac{n^{-3} m^2}{p^{-3} q^{-1}}$ $\quad \dfrac{m^2 p^3 q}{n^3}$

35. $\dfrac{(y^{-3})^2 (y^5)}{(y^{-3})^{-4}}$ $\quad \dfrac{1}{y^{13}}$

36. $\dfrac{(w^2)^{-4}(w^{-2})}{(w^5)^{-4}}$ $\quad w^{10}$

37. $\left(\dfrac{-2a^2 b^{-3}}{a^{-4} b^{-5}}\right)^{-3}$ $\quad -\dfrac{1}{8a^{18} b^6}$

38. $\left(\dfrac{-3x^{-4} y^3}{2x^5 y^{-2}}\right)^{-2}$ $\quad \dfrac{4x^{18}}{9y^{10}}$

39. $(5h^{-2} k^0)^3 (5k^{-2})^{-4}$ $\quad \dfrac{k^8}{5h^6}$

40. $(6m^3 n^{-5})^{-4}(6m^0 n^{-2})^5$ $\quad \dfrac{6n^{10}}{m^{12}}$

 Writing Translating Expression Geometry Scientific Calculator   Video   NS&E

Addition and Subtraction of Polynomials

1. Introduction to Polynomials

One commonly used algebraic expression is called a polynomial. A **polynomial** in one variable, x, is defined as a single term or a sum of terms of the form ax^n, where a is a real number and the exponent, n, is a nonnegative integer. For each term, a is called the **coefficient**, and n is called the **degree of the term**. For example:

Concepts

1. Introduction to Polynomials
2. Addition of Polynomials
3. Subtraction of Polynomials
4. Polynomials and Applications to Geometry

Term (Expressed in the Form ax^n)	Coefficient	Degree
$-12z^7$	-12	7
$x^3 \longrightarrow$ rewrite as $1x^3$	1	3
$10w \longrightarrow$ rewrite as $10w^1$	10	1
$7 \longrightarrow$ rewrite as $7x^0$	7	0

Instructor Note: Ask students why a constant has degree 0.

If a polynomial has exactly one term, it is categorized as a **monomial**. A two-term polynomial is called a **binomial**, and a three-term polynomial is called a **trinomial**. Usually the terms of a polynomial are written in descending order according to degree. The term with highest degree is called the **leading term**, and its coefficient is called the **leading coefficient**. The **degree of a polynomial** is the greatest degree of all of its terms. Thus, when written in descending order, the leading term determines the degree of the polynomial.

	Expression	Descending Order	Leading Coefficient	Degree of Polynomial
Monomials	$-3x^4$	$-3x^4$	-3	4
	17	17	17	0
Binomials	$4y^3 - 6y^5$	$-6y^5 + 4y^3$	-6	5
	$\dfrac{1}{2} - \dfrac{1}{4}c$	$-\dfrac{1}{4}c + \dfrac{1}{2}$	$-\dfrac{1}{4}$	1
Trinomials	$4p - 3p^3 + 8p^6$	$8p^6 - 3p^3 + 4p$	8	6
	$7a^4 - 1.2a^8 + 3a^3$	$-1.2a^8 + 7a^4 + 3a^3$	-1.2	8

Example 1 Identifying the Parts of a Polynomial

Given the polynomial: $4.5a - 2.7a^{10} + 1.6 - 3.7a^5$

a. List the terms of the polynomial, and state the coefficient and degree of each term.

b. Write the polynomial in descending order.

c. State the degree of the polynomial and the leading coefficient.

Classroom Example: p. 377, Exercise 16

Instructor Note: Give students some examples of expressions that are not polynomials, such as $\dfrac{1}{x}$ or $2\sqrt{x}$.

Solution:

a. term: $4.5a$ coefficient: 4.5 degree: 1

   term: $-2.7a^{10}$ coefficient: -2.7 degree: 10

   term: 1.6 coefficient: 1.6 degree: 0

   term: $-3.7a^5$ coefficient: -3.7 degree: 5

b. $-2.7a^{10} - 3.7a^5 + 4.5a + 1.6$

c. The degree of the polynomial is 10 and the leading coefficient is -2.7.

Skill Practice

1. Given the polynomial: $5x^3 - x + 8x^4 + 3x^2$
   a. Write the polynomial in descending order.
   b. State the degree of the polynomial.
   c. State the coefficient of the leading term.

Polynomials may have more than one variable. In such a case, the degree of a term is the sum of the exponents of the variables contained in the term. For example, the term, $32x^2y^5z$, has degree 8 because the exponents applied to x, y, and z are 2, 5, and 1, respectively. The following polynomial has a degree of 11 because the highest degree of its terms is 11.

$$32x^2y^5z \quad - \quad 2x^3y \quad + \quad 2x^2yz^8 \quad + \quad 7$$

$$\begin{array}{cccc}
\uparrow & \uparrow & \uparrow & \uparrow \\
\text{degree} & \text{degree} & \text{degree} & \text{degree} \\
8 & 4 & 11 & 0
\end{array}$$

2. Addition of Polynomials

Recall that two terms are *like* terms if they each have the same variables, and the corresponding variables are raised to the same powers.

Same exponents   Same exponents

Like Terms: $3x^2, -7x^2$ $-5yz^3, yz^3$

Same variables   Same variables

Different exponents

Unlike Terms: $9z^2, 12z^6$ $\frac{1}{3}w^6, \frac{2}{5}p^6$ $4y, 7$

Different variables   Different variables

Recall that the distributive property is used to add or subtract *like* terms. For example,

$$3x^2 + 9x^2 - 2x^2$$

$$= (3 + 9 - 2)x^2 \qquad \text{Apply the distributive property.}$$

$$= (10)x^2 \qquad \text{Simplify.}$$

$$= 10x^2$$

Avoiding Mistakes

Note that when adding terms, the exponents do *not* change.

$$2x^3 + 3x^3 \neq 5x^6$$

Answers

1. a. $8x^4 + 5x^3 + 3x^2 - x$
   b. 4   c. 8

Example 2   **Adding Polynomials**

Classroom Example: p. 377, Exercise 28

Add the polynomials. $3x^2y + 5x^2y$

Solution:

$3x^2y + 5x^2y$

$\quad = (3 + 5)x^2y$ Apply the distributive property.

$\quad = (8)x^2y$

$\quad = 8x^2y$ Simplify.

Skill Practice Add the polynomials.

2. $13a^2b^3 + 2a^2b^3$

It is the distributive property that enables us to add *like* terms. We shorten the process by adding the coefficients of *like* terms.

Example 3   **Adding Polynomials**

Classroom Example: p. 377, Exercise 30

Add the polynomials. $(-3c^3 + 5c^2 - 7c) + (11c^3 + 6c^2 + 3)$

Solution:

$(-3c^3 + 5c^2 - 7c) + (11c^3 + 6c^2 + 3)$

$\quad = -3c^3 + 11c^3 + 5c^2 + 6c^2 - 7c + 3$ Clear parentheses, and group *like* terms.

$\quad = 8c^3 + 11c^2 - 7c + 3$ Combine *like* terms.

> **TIP:** Polynomials can also be added by combining *like* terms in columns. The sum of the polynomials from Example 3 is shown here.
>
> $\begin{array}{r} -3c^3 + 5c^2 - 7c + 0 \\ + 11c^3 + 6c^2 + 0c + 3 \\ \hline 8c^3 + 11c^2 - 7c + 3 \end{array}$ Place holders such as 0 and 0c may be used to help line up *like* terms.

Skill Practice Add the polynomials.

3. $(7q^2 - 2q + 4) + (5q^2 + 6q - 9)$

Example 4   **Adding Polynomials**

Classroom Example: p. 377, Exercise 32

Add the polynomials. $(4w^2 - 2x) + (3w^2 - 4x^2 + 6x)$

Solution:

$(4w^2 - 2x) + (3w^2 - 4x^2 + 6x)$

$\quad = 4w^2 + 3w^2 - 4x^2 - 2x + 6x$ Clear parentheses and group *like* terms.

$\quad = 7w^2 - 4x^2 + 4x$

Skill Practice Add the polynomials.

4. $(5x^2 - 4xy + y^2) + (-3x^2 - 5y^2)$

Answers

2. $15a^2b^3$
3. $12q^2 + 4q - 5$
4. $2x^2 - 4xy - 4y^2$

3. Subtraction of Polynomials

Subtraction of two polynomials requires us to find the opposite of the polynomial being subtracted. To find the opposite of a polynomial, take the opposite of each term. This is equivalent to multiplying the polynomial by -1.

Classroom Example: p. 378, Exercise 46

Example 5   Finding the Opposite of a Polynomial

Find the opposite of the polynomials.

  a. $5x$ **b.** $3a - 4b - c$ **c.** $5.5y^4 - 2.4y^3 + 1.1y$

Solution:

Expression	Opposite	Simplified Form
a. $5x$	$-(5x)$	$-5x$
b. $3a - 4b - c$	$-(3a - 4b - c)$	$-3a + 4b + c$
c. $5.5y^4 - 2.4y^3 + 1.1y$	$-(5.5y^4 - 2.4y^3 + 1.1y)$	$-5.5y^4 + 2.4y^3 - 1.1y$

TIP: Notice that the sign of each term is changed when finding the opposite of a polynomial.

Skill Practice Find the opposite of the polynomials.

  5. $x - 3$ **6.** $3y^2 - 2xy + 6x + 2$ **7.** $-2.1w^3 + 4.9w^2 - 1.9w$

Subtraction of two polynomials is similar to subtracting real numbers. Add the opposite of the second polynomial to the first polynomial.

DEFINITION   Subtraction of Polynomials

  If A and B are polynomials, then $A - B = A + (-B)$.

Classroom Example: p. 378, Exercise 58

Example 6   Subtracting Polynomials

Subtract the polynomials. $(-4p^4 + 5p^2 - 3) - (11p^2 + 4p - 6)$

Solution:

$$(-4p^4 + 5p^2 - 3) - (11p^2 + 4p - 6)$$

$$= (-4p^4 + 5p^2 - 3) + (-11p^2 - 4p + 6) \qquad \text{Add the opposite of the second polynomial.}$$

$$= -4p^4 + 5p^2 - 11p^2 - 4p - 3 + 6 \qquad \text{Group \textit{like} terms.}$$

$$= -4p^4 - 6p^2 - 4p + 3 \qquad \text{Combine \textit{like} terms.}$$

TIP: Two polynomials can also be subtracted in columns by adding the opposite of the second polynomial to the first polynomial. Place holders (shown in red) may be used to help line up *like* terms.

$$
\begin{array}{l}
-4p^4 + 0p^3 + 5p^2 + 0p - 3 \\
-(0p^4 + 0p^3 + 11p^2 + 4p - 6)
\end{array}
\xrightarrow{\text{Add the opposite}}
\begin{array}{l}
-4p^4 + 0p^3 + 5p^2 + 0p - 3 \\
+\ \underline{-0p^4 - 0p^3 - 11p^2 - 4p + 6} \\
-4p^4 - 6p^2 - 4p + 3
\end{array}
$$

The difference of the polynomials is $-4p^4 - 6p^2 - 4p + 3$.

Answers

5. $-x + 3$
6. $-3y^2 + 2xy - 6x - 2$
7. $2.1w^3 - 4.9w^2 + 1.9w$

Skill Practice Subtract the polynomials.

8. $(x^2 + 3x - 2) - (4x^2 + 6x + 1)$

Example 7 Subtracting Polynomials

Subtract the polynomials. $(a^2 - 2ab + 7b^2) - (-8a^2 - 6ab + 2b^2)$

Classroom Example: p. 378, Exercise 60

Solution:

$(a^2 - 2ab + 7b^2) - (-8a^2 - 6ab + 2b^2)$

$= (a^2 - 2ab + 7b^2) + (8a^2 + 6ab - 2b^2)$ Add the opposite of the second polynomial.

$= a^2 + 8a^2 - 2ab + 6ab + 7b^2 - 2b^2$ Group *like* terms.

$= 9a^2 + 4ab + 5b^2$ Combine *like* terms.

Skill Practice Subtract the polynomials.

9. $(-3y^2 + xy + 2x^2) - (-2y^2 - 3xy - 8x^2)$

Subtracting polynomials can also be accomplished by clearing parentheses and combining *like* terms.

$(a^2 - 2ab + 7b^2) - (-8a^2 - 6ab + 2b^2)$

$= a^2 - 2ab + 7b^2 + 8a^2 + 6ab - 2b^2$ Clear parentheses

$= 9a^2 + 4ab + 5b^2$ Combine *like* terms

Example 8 Subtracting Polynomials

Subtract $\frac{1}{3}t^4 + \frac{1}{2}t^2$ from $t^2 - 4$, and simplify the result.

Classroom Example: p. 378, Exercise 72

Solution:

To subtract a from b, we write $b - a$. Thus, to subtract $\overbrace{\frac{1}{3}t^4 + \frac{1}{2}t^2}^{a}$ from $\overbrace{t^2 - 4}^{b}$, we have

$$(t^2 - 4) - \left(\frac{1}{3}t^4 + \frac{1}{2}t^2\right)$$

where b labels (t^2-4) and a labels $\left(\frac{1}{3}t^4 + \frac{1}{2}t^2\right)$.

Avoiding Mistakes

Example 8 involves subtracting two *expressions*. This is not an equation. Therefore, we cannot clear fractions.

$= t^2 - 4 - \frac{1}{3}t^4 - \frac{1}{2}t^2$ Apply the distributive property.

$= -\frac{1}{3}t^4 + t^2 - \frac{1}{2}t^2 - 4$ Group *like* terms in descending order.

$= -\frac{1}{3}t^4 + \frac{2}{2}t^2 - \frac{1}{2}t^2 - 4$ The t^2-terms are the only *like* terms.

    Get a common denominator for the t^2-terms.

$= -\frac{1}{3}t^4 + \frac{1}{2}t^2 - 4$ Add *like* terms.

Skill Practice

10. Subtract $\frac{3}{4}x^2 + \frac{2}{5}$ from $x^2 + 3x$.

Answers

8. $-3x^2 - 3x - 3$
9. $-y^2 + 4xy + 10x^2$
10. $\frac{1}{4}x^2 + 3x - \frac{2}{5}$

4. Polynomials and Applications to Geometry

| Example 9 | Subtracting Polynomials in Geometry |

If the perimeter of the triangle in Figure 5-1 can be represented by the polynomial $2x^2 + 5x + 6$, find a polynomial that represents the length of the missing side.

Figure 5-1

Solution:

The missing side of the triangle can be found by subtracting the sum of the two known sides from the perimeter.

$$\begin{pmatrix} \text{Length} \\ \text{of missing} \\ \text{side} \end{pmatrix} = (\text{perimeter}) - \begin{bmatrix} \text{sum of the} \\ \text{two known sides} \end{bmatrix}$$

$$\begin{pmatrix} \text{Length} \\ \text{of missing} \\ \text{side} \end{pmatrix} = (2x^2 + 5x + 6) - [(2x - 3) + (x^2 + 1)]$$

$$= 2x^2 + 5x + 6 - [2x - 3 + x^2 + 1] \quad \text{Clear inner parentheses.}$$

$$= 2x^2 + 5x + 6 - (x^2 + 2x - 2) \quad \text{Combine } like \text{ terms within } [\ \ ].$$

$$= 2x^2 + 5x + 6 - x^2 - 2x + 2 \quad \text{Apply the distributive property.}$$

$$= 2x^2 - x^2 + 5x - 2x + 6 + 2 \quad \text{Group } like \text{ terms.}$$

$$= x^2 + 3x + 8 \quad \text{Combine } like \text{ terms.}$$

The polynomial $x^2 + 3x + 8$ represents the length of the missing side.

Skill Practice

11. If the perimeter of the triangle is represented by the polynomial $6x - 9$, find the polynomial that represents the missing side.

Section 5.5 Practice Exercises

Boost *your* **GRADE at ALEKS.com!**

ALEKS version 3.0

- Practice Problems
- Self-Tests
- NetTutor
- e-Professors
- Videos

For additional exercises, see Classroom Activities 5.5A–5.5C in the *Instructor's Resource Manual* at www.mhhe.com/moh.

Study Skills Exercise

1. Define the key terms.

    a. polynomial   **b. coefficient**   **c. degree of term**

    d. monomial   **e. binomial**   **f. trinomial**

    g. leading term   **h. leading coefficient**   **i. degree of polynomial**

 Writing   Translating Expression   Geometry   Scientific Calculator   Video   NS&E

Review Exercises

For Exercises 2–7, simplify each expression.

2. $\dfrac{p^3 \cdot 4p}{p^2}$ $4p^2$

3. $(3x)^2(5x^{-4})$ $\dfrac{45}{x^2}$

4. $(6y^{-3})(2y^9)$ $12y^6$

5. $\dfrac{8t^{-6}}{4t^{-2}}$ $\dfrac{2}{t^4}$

6. $\dfrac{8^3 \cdot 8^{-4}}{8^{-2} \cdot 8^6}$ $\dfrac{1}{8^5}$

7. $\dfrac{3^4 \cdot 3^{-8}}{3^{12} \cdot 3}$ $\dfrac{1}{3^{12}}$

8. Explain the difference between 3.0×10^7 and 3^7. 3.0×10^7 is in scientific notation in which 10 is raised to the seventh power. 3^7 is not in scientific notation and 3 is being raised to the seventh power.

9. Explain the difference between 4.0×10^{-2} and 4^{-2}. 4.0×10^{-2} is in scientific notation in which 10 is raised to the -2 power. 4^{-2} is not in scientific notation and 4 is being raised to the -2 power.

Concept 1: Introduction to Polynomials

10. Write the polynomial in descending order. $10 - 8a - a^3 + 2a^2 + a^5$ $a^5 - a^3 + 2a^2 - 8a + 10$

11. Write the polynomial in descending order. $6 + 7x^2 - 7x^4 + 9x$ $-7x^4 + 7x^2 + 9x + 6$

12. Write the polynomial in descending order. $\dfrac{1}{2}y + y^2 - 12y^4 + y^3 - 6$ $-12y^4 + y^3 + y^2 + \frac{1}{2}y - 6$

For Exercises 13–24, categorize the expression as a monomial, a binomial, or a trinomial. Then identify the coefficient and degree of the leading term. **(See Example 1.)**

13. $10a^2 + 5a$
Binomial; 10; 2

14. $7z + 13z^2 - 15$
Trinomial; 13; 2

15. $7.4 + 2.1x^3 - 1.8x$
Trinomial; 2.1; 3

16. $8.2w + 0.9w^4 - 1.2w^2$
Trinomial; 0.9; 4

17. $2t - t^4$
Binomial; -1; 4

18. $7x + 2$
Binomial; 7; 1

19. $12y^4 - 3y + 1$
Trinomial; 12; 4

20. $5bc^2$
Monomial; 5; 3

21. 23
Monomial; 23; 0

22. $4 - 2c$
Binomial; -2; 1

23. $-32xyz$
Monomial; -32; 3

24. $w^4 - w^2$
Binomial; 1; 4

Concept 2: Addition of Polynomials

25. Explain why the terms $3x$ and $3x^2$ are not *like* terms. The exponents on the x-factors are different.

26. Explain why the terms $4w^3$ and $4z^3$ are not *like* terms. The variables are different.

For Exercises 27–42, add the polynomials. **(See Examples 2–4.)**

27. $23x^2y + 12x^2y$ $35x^2y$

28. $-5ab^3 + 17ab^3$ $12ab^3$

29. $3b^5d^2 + (5b^5d^2 - 9d)$ $8b^5d^2 - 9d$

30. $4c^2d^3 + (3cd - 10c^2d^3)$ $-6c^2d^3 + 3cd$

31. $(7y^2 + 2y - 9) + (-3y^2 - y)$ $4y^2 + y - 9$

32. $(-3w^2 + 4w - 6) + (5w^2 + 2)$ $2w^2 + 4w - 4$

33. $(6.1y + 3.2x) + (4.8y - 3.2x)$ $10.9y$

34. $(2.7m - 0.5h) + (-3.2m + 0.2h)$ $-0.5m - 0.3h$

35. $\ \ 6a + 2b - 5c$ $4a - 8c$
$+\ \underline{-2a - 2b - 3c}$

36. $\ -13x + 5y + 10z$ $-16x + 2y + 12z$
$+\ \underline{-3x - 3y +\ \ 2z}$

37. $\left(\dfrac{2}{5}a + \dfrac{1}{4}b - \dfrac{5}{6}\right) + \left(\dfrac{3}{5}a - \dfrac{3}{4}b - \dfrac{7}{6}\right)$ $a - \frac{1}{2}b - 2$

38. $\left(\dfrac{5}{9}x + \dfrac{1}{10}y\right) + \left(-\dfrac{4}{9}x + \dfrac{3}{10}y\right)$ $\frac{1}{9}x + \frac{2}{5}y$

39. $\left(z - \dfrac{8}{3}\right) + \left(\dfrac{4}{3}z^2 - z + 1\right)$ $\frac{4}{3}z^2 - \frac{5}{3}$

40. $\left(-\dfrac{7}{5}r + 1\right) + \left(-\dfrac{3}{5}r^2 + \dfrac{7}{5}r + 1\right)$ $-\frac{3}{5}r^2 + 2$

41. $\ \ 7.9t^3 + 2.6t - 1.1$
$+\ \underline{-3.4t^2 + 3.4t - 3.1}$ $7.9t^3 - 3.4t^2 + 6t - 4.2$

42. $\ \ 0.34y^2 + 1.23$
$+\ \underline{3.42y - 7.56}$ $0.34y^2 + 3.42y - 6.33$

 Writing   Translating Expression   Geometry   Scientific Calculator   Video   NS&E

Concept 3: Subtraction of Polynomials

For Exercises 43–48, find the opposite of each polynomial. **(See Example 5.)**

43. $4h - 5$
$-4h + 5$

44. $5k - 12$
$-5k + 12$

45. $-2.3m^2 + 3.1m - 1.5$
$2.3m^2 - 3.1m + 1.5$

46. $-11.8n^2 - 6.7n + 9.3$
$11.8n^2 + 6.7n - 9.3$

47. $3v^3 + 5v^2 + 10v + 22$
$-3v^3 - 5v^2 - 10v - 22$

48. $7u^4 + 3v^2 + 17$
$-7u^4 - 3v^2 - 17$

For Exercises 49–68, subtract the polynomials. **(See Examples 6–7.)**

49. $4a^3b^2 - 12a^3b^2$ $-8a^3b^2$

50. $5yz^4 - 14yz^4$ $-9yz^4$

51. $-32x^3 - 21x^3$ $-53x^3$

52. $-23c^5 - 12c^5$ $-35c^5$

53. $(7a - 7) - (12a - 4)$ $-5a - 3$

54. $(4x + 3v) - (-3x + v)$ $7x + 2v$

55.
$$\begin{array}{r} 4k + 3 \\ - (-12k - 6) \\ \hline 16k + 9 \end{array}$$

56.
$$\begin{array}{r} 3h - 15 \\ - (8h + 13) \\ \hline -5h - 28 \end{array}$$

57. $25m^4 - (23m^4 + 14m)$ $2m^4 - 14m$

58. $3x^2 - (-x^2 - 12)$ $4x^2 + 12$

59. $(5s^2 - 3st - 2t^2) - (2s^2 + st + t^2)$
$3s^2 - 4st - 3t^2$

60. $(6k^2 + 2kp + p^2) - (3k^2 - 6kp + 2p^2)$
$3k^2 + 8kp - p^2$

61.
$$\begin{array}{r} 10r - 6s + 2t \\ - (12r - 3s - t) \\ \hline -2r - 3s + 3t \end{array}$$

62.
$$\begin{array}{r} a - 14b + 7c \\ - (-3a - 8b + 2c) \\ \hline 4a - 6b + 5c \end{array}$$

63. $\left(\frac{7}{8}x + \frac{2}{3}y - \frac{3}{10}\right) - \left(\frac{1}{8}x + \frac{1}{3}y\right)$ $\frac{3}{4}x + \frac{1}{3}y - \frac{3}{10}$

64. $\left(r - \frac{1}{12}s\right) - \left(\frac{1}{2}r - \frac{5}{12}s - \frac{4}{11}\right)$ $\frac{1}{2}r + \frac{1}{3}s + \frac{4}{11}$

65. $\left(\frac{2}{3}h^2 - \frac{1}{5}h - \frac{3}{4}\right) - \left(\frac{4}{3}h^2 - \frac{4}{5}h + \frac{7}{4}\right)$ $-\frac{2}{3}h^2 + \frac{3}{5}h - \frac{5}{2}$

66. $\left(\frac{3}{8}p^3 - \frac{5}{7}p^2 - \frac{2}{5}\right) - \left(\frac{5}{8}p^3 - \frac{2}{7}p^2 + \frac{7}{5}\right)$
$-\frac{1}{4}p^3 - \frac{3}{7}p^2 - \frac{9}{5}$

67.
$$\begin{array}{r} 4.5x^4 - 3.1x^2 \quad\quad - 6.7 \\ - (2.1x^4 \quad\quad + 4.4x + 1.2) \\ \hline 2.4x^4 - 3.1x^2 - 4.4x - 7.9 \end{array}$$

68.
$$\begin{array}{r} 1.3c^2 \quad\quad + 4.8 \\ - (4.3c^2 - 2c - 2.2) \\ \hline -3c^2 + 2c + 7 \end{array}$$

69. Find the difference of $(4b^3 + 6b - 7)$ and $(-12b^2 + 11b + 5)$. $4b^3 + 12b^2 - 5b - 12$

70. Find the difference of $(-5y^2 + 3y - 21)$ and $(-4y^2 - 5y + 23)$. $-y^2 + 8y - 44$

71. Subtract $\left(\frac{3}{2}x^2 - 5x\right)$ from $(-2x^2 - 11)$.
(See Example 8.) $-\frac{7}{2}x^2 + 5x - 11$

72. Subtract $\left(a^5 - \frac{1}{3}a^3 + 5a\right)$ from $\left(\frac{3}{4}a^5 + \frac{1}{2}a^4 + 6a\right)$. $-\frac{1}{4}a^5 + \frac{1}{2}a^4 + \frac{1}{3}a^3 + a$

Concept 4: Polynomials and Applications to Geometry

73. Find a polynomial that represents the perimeter of the figure. $4y^3 + 2y^2 + 2$

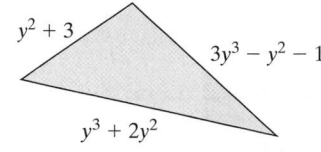

$y^2 + 3$
$3y^3 - y^2 - 1$
$y^3 + 2y^2$

74. Find a polynomial that represents the perimeter of the figure. $9t^3 + t^2$

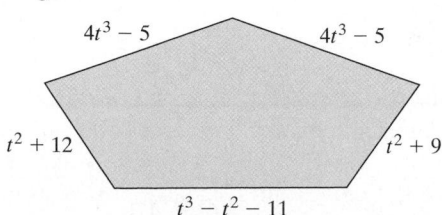

$4t^3 - 5$ $4t^3 - 5$
$t^2 + 12$ $t^2 + 9$
$t^3 - t^2 - 11$

75. If the perimeter of the figure can be represented by the polynomial $5a^2 - 2a + 1$, find a polynomial that represents the length of the missing side. **(See Example 9.)** $3a^2 - 3a + 5$

$a - 3$

$2a^2 - 1$

 76. If the perimeter of the figure can be represented by the polynomial $6w^3 - 2w - 3$, find a polynomial that represents the length of the missing side. $4w^3 - 6w^2 - 2w$

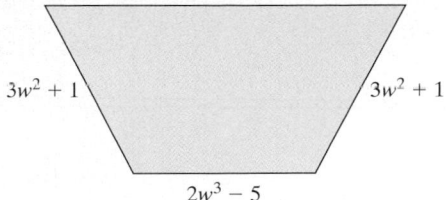

$3w^2 + 1$ $3w^2 + 1$

$2w^3 - 5$

Mixed Exercises

For Exercises 77–92, perform the indicated operation.

77. $(2ab^2 + 9a^2b) + (7ab^2 - 3ab + 7a^2b)$ $9ab^2 - 3ab + 16a^2b$

78. $(8x^2y - 3xy - 6xy^2) + (3x^2y - 12xy)$
$11x^2y$ $15xy$ $6xy^2$

79. $4z^5 \quad + \ z^3 - 3z + 13$
$-(\quad - z^4 - 8z^3 \quad + 15)$
$\overline{4z^5 + z^4 + 9z^3 - 3z - 2}$

80. $-15t^4 \quad - 23t^2 + 16t$
$-(\quad 21t^3 + 18t^2 + \ t)$
$\overline{-15t^4 - 21t^3 - 41t^2 + 15t}$

81. $(9x^4 + 2x^3 - x + 5) + (9x^3 - 3x^2 + 8x + 3) - (7x^4 - x + 12)$ $2x^4 + 11x^3 - 3x^2 + 8x - 4$

82. $(-6y^3 - 9y^2 + 23) - (7y^2 + 2y - 11) + (3y^3 - 25)$
$-3y^3 - 16y^2 - 2y + 9$

83. $(0.2w^2 + 3w + 1.3) - (w^3 - 0.7w + 2)$
$-w^3 + 0.2w^2 + 3.7w - 0.7$

84. $(8.1u^3 - 5.2u^2 + 4) + (2.8u^3 + 6.3u - 7)$
$10.9u^3 - 5.2u^2 + 6.3u - 3$

85. $(7p^2q - 3pq^2) - (8p^2q + pq) + (4pq - pq^2)$
$-p^2q - 4pq^2 + 3pq$

86. $(12c^2d - 2cd + 8cd^2) - (-c^2d + 4cd) - (5cd - 2cd^2)$ $13c^2d - 11cd + 10cd^2$

87. $(5x - 2x^3) + (2x^3 - 5x)$ 0

88. $(p^2 - 4p + 2) - (2 + p^2 - 4p)$ 0

89. $2a^2b - 4ab + \ ab^2$
$-(2a^2b + \ ab - 5ab^2)$
$\overline{-5ab + 6ab^2}$

90. $-3xy + \ 7xy^2 + 5x^2y$
$+(\ 8xy \quad 11xy^2 \ 3x^2y)$
$\overline{-11xy - 4xy^2 + 8x^2y}$

91. $[(3y^2 - 5y) - (2y^2 + y - 1)] + (10y^2 - 4y - 5)$
$11y^2 - 10y - 4$

92. $(12c^3 - 5c^2 - 2c) + [(7c^3 - 2c^2 + c) - (4c^3 + 4c)]$
$15c^3 - 7c^2 \quad 5c$

Expanding Your Skills

93. Write a binomial of degree 3. (Answers may vary.)
For example: $x^3 + 6$

94. Write a trinomial of degree 6. (Answers may vary.)
For example: $5x^6 + x - 4$

95. Write a monomial of degree 5. (Answers may vary.)
For example: $8x^5$

96. Write a monomial of degree 1. (Answers may vary.)
For example: $3x$

97. Write a trinomial with the leading coefficient -6. (Answers may vary.)
For example: $-6x^2 + 2x + 5$

98. Write a binomial with the leading coefficient 13. (Answers may vary.)   For example: $13x + 7$

Multiplication of Polynomials and Special Products   Section 5.6

1. Multiplication of Polynomials

The properties of exponents covered in Sections 5.1–5.3 can be used to simplify many algebraic expressions including the multiplication of monomials. To multiply monomials, first use the associative and commutative properties of multiplication to group coefficients and like bases. Then simplify the result by using the properties of exponents.

Concepts

1. **Multiplication of Polynomials**
2. **Special Case Products: Difference of Squares and Perfect Square Trinomials**
3. **Applications to Geometry**

 Writing   Translating Expression   Geometry   Scientific Calculator   Video   NS&E

Classroom Example: p. 386,
Exercise 18

Example 1   **Multiplying Monomials**

Multiply the monomials.

    a. $(3x^4)(4x^2)$ **b.** $(-4c^5d)(2c^2d^3e)$ **c.** $\left(\dfrac{1}{3}a^4b^3\right)\left(\dfrac{3}{4}b^7\right)$

Solution:

    a. $(3x^4)(4x^2)$

         $= (3 \cdot 4)(x^4 x^2)$ Group coefficients and like bases.

         $= 12x^6$ Multiply the coefficients and add the exponents on x.

    b. $(-4c^5d)(2c^2d^3e)$

         $= (-4 \cdot 2)(c^5 c^2)(dd^3)(e)$ Group coefficients and like bases.

         $= -8c^7 d^4 e$ Simplify.

    c. $\left(\dfrac{1}{3}a^4b^3\right)\left(\dfrac{3}{4}b^7\right)$

         $= \left(\dfrac{1}{3} \cdot \dfrac{3}{4}\right)(a^4)(b^3 b^7)$ Group coefficients and like bases.

         $= \dfrac{1}{4}a^4 b^{10}$ Simplify.

Skill Practice   Multiply the monomials.

    1. $(-5y)(6y^3)$ **2.** $(7x^2y)(-2x^3y^4)$ **3.** $\left(\dfrac{2}{5}w^5z^3\right)\left(\dfrac{15}{4}w^4\right)$

The distributive property is used to multiply polynomials: $a(b + c) = ab + ac$.

Classroom Example: p. 386,
Exercise 24

Example 2   **Multiplying a Polynomial by a Monomial**

Multiply the polynomials.

    a. $2t(4t - 3)$ **b.** $-3a^2\left(-4a^2 + 2a - \dfrac{1}{3}\right)$

Solution:

    a. $2t(4t - 3)$

         $= (2t)(4t) + (2t)(-3)$ Apply the distributive property by multiplying each term by $2t$.

         $= 8t^2 - 6t$ Simplify each term.

    b. $-3a^2\left(-4a^2 + 2a - \dfrac{1}{3}\right)$

         $= (-3a^2)(-4a^2) + (-3a^2)(2a) + (-3a^2)\left(-\dfrac{1}{3}\right)$ Apply the distributive property by multiplying each term by $-3a^2$.

         $= 12a^4 - 6a^3 + a^2$ Simplify each term.

Answers

1. $-30y^4$
2. $-14x^5y^5$
3. $\dfrac{3}{2}w^9z^3$

Skill Practice Multiply the polynomials.

4. $-4a(5a - 3)$ **5.** $-4p\left(2p^2 - 6p + \dfrac{1}{4}\right)$

Thus far, we have illustrated polynomial multiplication involving monomials. Next, the distributive property will be used to multiply polynomials with more than one term.

$$(x + 3)(x + 5) = x(x + 5) + 3(x + 5) \qquad \text{Apply the distributive property.}$$
$$= x(x + 5) + 3(x + 5) \qquad \text{Apply the distributive property again.}$$
$$= (x)(x) + (x)(5) + (3)(x) + (3)(5)$$
$$= x^2 + 5x + 3x + 15$$
$$= x^2 + 8x + 15 \qquad \text{Combine } like \text{ terms.}$$

Note: Using the distributive property results in multiplying each term of the first polynomial by each term of the second polynomial.

$$(x + 3)(x + 5) = (x)(x) + (x)(5) + (3)(x) + (3)(5)$$
$$= x^2 + 5x + 3x + 15$$
$$= x^2 + 8x + 15$$

Example 3   **Multiplying a Polynomial by a Polynomial**

Classroom Example: p. 386, Exercise 30

Multiply the polynomials. $(c - 7)(c + 2)$

Solution:

 $(c - 7)(c + 2)$ Multiply each term in the first polynomial by each term in the second. That is, apply the distributive property.

$$= (c)(c) + (c)(2) + (-7)(c) + (-7)(2)$$
$$= c^2 + 2c - 7c - 14 \qquad \text{Simplify.}$$
$$= c^2 - 5c - 14 \qquad \text{Combine } like \text{ terms.}$$

Instructor Note: Mention to students that the product $(c - 7)(c + 2)$ requires multiple applications of the distributive property. First distribute c, then distribute -7.

TIP: Notice that the product of two *binomials* equals the sum of the products of the **F**irst terms, the **O**uter terms, the **I**nner terms, and the **L**ast terms. The acronym **FOIL** (First Outer Inner Last) can be used as a memory device to multiply two binomials.

Skill Practice Multiply the polynomials.

6. $(x + 2)(x + 8)$

Answers
4. $20a^2 + 12a$
5. $-8p^3 + 24p^2 - p$
6. $x^2 + 10x + 16$

Classroom Example: p. 386,
Exercise 42

Example 4   **Multiplying a Polynomial by a Polynomial**

Multiply the polynomials. $(10x + 3y)(2x - 4y)$

Solution:

$(10x + 3y)(2x - 4y)$ Multiply each term in the first polynomial by each term in the second. That is, apply the distributive property.

$$= (10x)(2x) + (10x)(-4y) + (3y)(2x) + (3y)(-4y)$$

$$= 20x^2 - 40xy + 6xy - 12y^2 \qquad \text{Simplify each term.}$$

$$= 20x^2 - 34xy - 12y^2 \qquad \text{Combine } like \text{ terms.}$$

Skill Practice   Multiply the polynomials.

7. $(4a - 3c)(5a - 2c)$

Classroom Example: p. 386,
Exercise 44

Avoiding Mistakes

It is important to note that the acronym FOIL does not apply to Example 5 because the product does not involve two binomials.

Example 5   **Multiplying a Polynomial by a Polynomial**

Multiply the polynomials. $(y - 2)(3y^2 + y - 5)$

Solution:

$(y - 2)(3y^2 + y - 5)$ Multiply each term in the first polynomial by each term in the second.

$$= (y)(3y^2) + (y)(y) + (y)(-5) + (-2)(3y^2) + (-2)(y) + (-2)(-5)$$

$$= 3y^3 + y^2 - 5y - 6y^2 - 2y + 10 \qquad \text{Simplify each term.}$$

$$= 3y^3 - 5y^2 - 7y + 10 \qquad \text{Combine } like \text{ terms.}$$

TIP: Multiplication of polynomials can be performed vertically by a process similar to column multiplication of real numbers. For example,

$$
\begin{array}{r}
235 \\
\times\ \ 21 \\
\hline
235 \\
4700 \\
\hline
4935
\end{array}
\qquad
\begin{array}{r}
3y^2 + y - 5 \\
\times \qquad y - 2 \\
\hline
-6y^2 - 2y + 10 \\
3y^3 + y^2 - 5y + \ \ 0 \\
\hline
3y^3 - 5y^2 - 7y + 10
\end{array}
$$

Note: When multiplying by the column method, it is important to *align like* terms vertically before adding terms.

Skill Practice   Multiply the polynomials.

8. $(2y + 4)(3y^2 - 5y + 2)$

Answers

7. $20a^2 - 23ac + 6c^2$
8. $6y^3 + 2y^2 - 16y + 8$

2. Special Case Products: Difference of Squares and Perfect Square Trinomials

In some cases the product of two binomials takes on a special pattern.

I. The first special case occurs when multiplying the sum and difference of the same two terms. For example:

$(2x + 3)(2x - 3)$

$= 4x^2 - 6x + 6x - 9$

$= 4x^2 - 9$

Notice that the middle terms are opposites. This leaves only the difference between the square of the first term and the square of the second term. For this reason, the product is called a *difference of squares*.

Note: The binomials $2x + 3$ and $2x - 3$ are called **conjugates**. In one expression, $2x$ and 3 are added, and in the other, $2x$ and 3 are subtracted.

II. The second special case involves the square of a binomial. For example:

$(3x + 7)^2$

$= (3x + 7)(3x + 7)$

$= 9x^2 + 21x + 21x + 49$

$= 9x^2 + 42x + 49$

$= (3x)^2 + 2(3x)(7) + (7)^2$

When squaring a binomial, the product will be a trinomial called a *perfect square trinomial*. The first and third terms are formed by squaring each term of the binomial. The middle term equals twice the product of the terms in the binomial.

Note: The expression $(3x - 7)^2$ also expands to a perfect square trinomial, but the middle term will be negative:

$$(3x - 7)(3x - 7) = 9x^2 - 21x - 21x + 49 = 9x^2 - 42x + 49$$

FORMULA   Special Case Product Formulas

1. $(a + b)(a - b) = a^2 - b^2$ The product is called a **difference of squares**.

2. $(a + b)^2 = a^2 + 2ab + b^2$ ⎫
$(a - b)^2 = a^2 - 2ab + b^2$ ⎬   The product is called a **perfect square trinomial**.

You should become familiar with these special case products because they will be used again in the next chapter to factor polynomials.

Instructor Note: Have students substitute some numbers to confirm that $(a + b)^2 \neq a^2 + b^2$.

Example 6   **Multiplying Conjugates**

Multiply the conjugates.

a. $(x - 9)(x + 9)$ **b.** $\left(\frac{1}{2}p - 6\right)\left(\frac{1}{2}p + 6\right)$

Classroom Examples: p. 387, Exercises 56 and 62

Solution:

a. $(x - 9)(x + 9)$ Apply the formula: $(a + b)(a - b) = a^2 - b^2$.

$= (x)^2 - (9)^2$ Substitute $a = x$ and $b = 9$.

$= x^2 - 81$

TIP: The product of two conjugates can be checked by applying the distributive property:

$(x - 9)(x + 9)$

$= x^2 + 9x - 9x - 81$

$= x^2 - 81$

b. $\left(\frac{1}{2}p - 6\right)\left(\frac{1}{2}p + 6\right)$ Apply the formula: $(a + b)(a - b) = a^2 - b^2$.

$$= \overset{\overset{a^2 - b^2}{\downarrow \qquad \downarrow}}{\left(\frac{1}{2}p\right)^2 - (6)^2}$$ Substitute $a = \frac{1}{2}p$ and $b = 6$.

$$= \frac{1}{4}p^2 - 36$$ Simplify each term.

Skill Practice Multiply the conjugates.

9. $(a + 7)(a - 7)$ **10.** $\left(\frac{4}{5}x - 10\right)\left(\frac{4}{5}x + 10\right)$

Classroom Examples: p. 387, Exercises 72 and 74

Example 7 **Squaring Binomials**

Square the binomials.

a. $(3w - 4)^2$ **b.** $(5x^2 + 2)^2$

Solution:

a. $(3w - 4)^2$ Apply the formula:
$(a - b)^2 = a^2 - 2ab + b^2$.

$$= \overset{a^2 - 2ab + b^2}{(3w)^2 - 2(3w)(4) + (4)^2}$$ Substitute $a = 3w, b = 4$.

$$= 9w^2 - 24w + 16$$ Simplify each term.

TIP: The square of a binomial can be checked by explicitly writing the product of the two binomials and applying the distributive property:

$$(3w - 4)^2 = (3w - 4)(3w - 4) = 9w^2 - 12w - 12w + 16$$
$$= 9w^2 - 24w + 16$$

Avoiding Mistakes

The property for squaring two factors is different than the property for squaring two terms:
$(ab)^2 = a^2b^2$ but
$(a + b)^2 = a^2 + 2ab + b^2$

b. $(5x^2 + 2)^2$ Apply the formula:
$(a + b)^2 = a^2 + 2ab + b^2$.

$$= \overset{a^2 + 2ab + b^2}{(5x^2)^2 + 2(5x^2)(2) + (2)^2}$$ Substitute $a = 5x^2, b = 2$.

$$= 25x^4 + 20x^2 + 4$$ Simplify each term.

Skill Practice Square the binomials.

11. $(2x + 3)^2$ **12.** $(5c^2 - 6)^2$

Answers

9. $a^2 - 49$
10. $\frac{16}{25}x^2 - 100$
11. $4x^2 + 12x + 9$
12. $25c^4 - 60c^2 + 36$

3. Applications to Geometry

Example 8 Using Special Case Products in an Application of Geometry

Classroom Example: p. 388, Exercise 86

Find a polynomial that represents the volume of the cube (Figure 5-2).

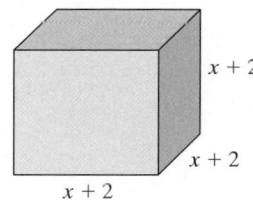

$x + 2$

$x + 2$

$x + 2$

Figure 5-2

Solution:

$$\text{Volume} = (\text{length})(\text{width})(\text{height})$$

$$V = (x + 2)(x + 2)(x + 2) \qquad \text{or} \qquad V = (x + 2)^3$$

To expand $(x + 2)(x + 2)(x + 2)$, multiply the first two factors. Then multiply the result by the last factor.

$$V = \underbrace{(x + 2)(x + 2)}(x + 2)$$

$$= (x^2 + 4x + 4)(x + 2)$$

> **TIP:** $(x + 2)(x + 2) = (x + 2)^2$ and results in a perfect square trinomial.
>
> $$(x + 2)^2 = (x)^2 + 2(x)(2) + (2)^2$$
> $$= x^2 + 4x + 4$$

$$= (x^2)(x) + (x^2)(2) + (4x)(x) + (4x)(2) + (4)(x) + (4)(2) \qquad \text{Apply the distributive property.}$$

$$= x^3 + 2x^2 + 4x^2 + 8x + 4x + 8 \qquad \text{Group } like \text{ terms.}$$

$$= x^3 + 6x^2 + 12x + 8 \qquad \text{Combine } like \text{ terms.}$$

The volume of the cube can be represented by

$$V = (x + 2)^3 = x^3 + 6x^2 + 12x + 8.$$

Skill Practice

13. Find the polynomial that represents the volume of the cube.

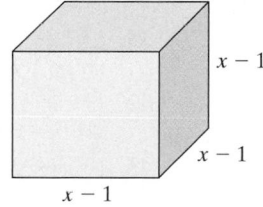

$x - 1$

$x - 1$

$x - 1$

Answer

13. The volume of the cube can be represented by $x^3 - 3x^2 + 3x - 1$.

Section 5.6 Practice Exercises

Study Skills Exercise

1. Define the key terms.

   a. conjugates   **b. difference of squares**   **c. perfect square trinomial**

Review Exercises

For Exercises 2–9, simplify each expression (if possible).

2. $4x + 5x$ $9x$ **3.** $2y^2 - 4y^2$ $-2y^2$ **4.** $(4x)(5x)$ $20x^2$ **5.** $(2y^2)(-4y^2)$ $-8y^4$

6. $-5a^3b - 2a^3b$ $-7a^3b$ **7.** $7uvw^2 + uvw^2$ $8uvw^2$ **8.** $(-5a^3b)(-2a^3b)$ $10a^6b^2$ **9.** $(7uvw^2)(uvw^2)$ $7u^2v^2w^4$

Concept 1: Multiplication of Polynomials

For Exercises 10–18, multiply the expressions. **(See Example 1.)**

10. $8(4x)$ $32x$ **11.** $-2(6y)$ $-12y$ **12.** $-10(5z)$ $-50z$

13. $7(3p)$ $21p$ **14.** $(x^{10})(4x^3)$ $4x^{13}$ **15.** $(a^{13}b^4)(12ab^4)$ $12a^{14}b^8$

16. $(4m^3n^7)(-3m^6n)$ $-12m^9n^8$ **17.** $(2c^7d)(-c^3d^{11})$ $-2c^{10}d^{12}$ **18.** $(-5u^2v)(-8u^3v^2)$ $40u^5v^3$

For Exercises 19–54, multiply the polynomials. **(See Examples 2–5.)**

19. $8pq(2pq - 3p + 5q)$
$16p^2q^2 - 24p^2q + 40pq^2$

20. $5ab(2ab + 6a - 3b)$
$10a^2b^2 + 30a^2b - 15ab^2$

21. $(k^2 - 13k - 6)(-4k)$
$-4k^3 + 52k^2 + 24k$

22. $(h^2 + 5h - 12)(-2h)$
$-2h^3 - 10h^2 + 24h$

23. $-15pq(3p^2 + p^3q^2 - 2q)$
$-45p^3q - 15p^4q^3 + 30pq^2$

24. $-4u^2v(2u - 5uv^3 + v)$
$-8u^3v + 20u^3v^4 - 4u^2v^2$

25. $(y + 10)(y + 9)$
$y^2 + 19y + 90$

26. $(x + 5)(x + 6)$
$x^2 + 11x + 30$

27. $(m - 12)(m - 2)$
$m^2 - 14m + 24$

28. $(n - 7)(n - 2)$
$n^2 - 9n + 14$

29. $(3p - 2)(4p + 1)$
$12p^2 - 5p - 2$

30. $(7q + 11)(q - 5)$
$7q^2 - 24q - 55$

31. $(-4w + 8)(-3w + 2)$
$12w^2 - 32w + 16$

32. $(-6z + 10)(-2z + 4)$
$12z^2 - 44z + 40$

33. $(p - 3w)(p - 11w)$
$p^2 - 14pw + 33w^2$

34. $(y - 7x)(y - 10x)$
$y^2 - 17xy + 70x^2$

35. $(6x - 1)(2x + 5)$
$12x^2 + 28x - 5$

36. $(3x + 7)(x - 8)$
$3x^2 - 17x - 56$

37. $(4a - 9)(1.5a - 2)$
$6a^2 - 21.5a + 18$

38. $(2.1y - 0.5)(y + 3)$
$2.1y^2 + 5.8y - 1.5$

39. $(3t - 7)(3t + 1)$
$9t^2 - 18t - 7$

40. $(5w - 2)(2w - 5)$
$10w^2 - 29w + 10$

41. $(3m + 4n)(m + 8n)$
$3m^2 + 28mn + 32n^2$

42. $(7y + z)(3y + 5z)$
$21y^2 + 38yz + 5z^2$

43. $(5s + 3)(s^2 + s - 2)$
$5s^3 + 8s^2 - 7s - 6$

44. $(t - 4)(2t^2 - t + 6)$
$2t^3 - 9t^2 + 10t - 24$

45. $(3w - 2)(9w^2 + 6w + 4)$
$27w^3 - 8$

46. $(z + 5)(z^2 - 5z + 25)$
$z^3 + 125$

47. $(p^2 + p - 5)(p^2 + 4p - 1)$
$p^4 + 5p^3 - 2p^2 - 21p + 5$

48. $(-x^2 - 2x + 4)(x^2 + 2x - 6)$
$-x^4 - 4x^3 + 6x^2 + 20x - 24$

49. $3a^2 - 4a + 9$
$\underline{\times \qquad 2a - 5}$
$6a^3 - 23a^2 + 38a - 45$

50. $7x^2 - 3x - 4$
$\underline{\times \qquad 5x + 1}$
$35x^3 - 8x^2 - 23x - 4$

51. $4x^2 - 12xy + 9y^2$
$\underline{\times \qquad 2x - 3y}$
$8x^3 - 36x^2y + 54xy^2 - 27y^3$

52. $25a^2 + 10ab + b^2$
$\underline{\times \qquad 5a + b}$
$125a^3 + 75a^2b + 15ab^2 + b^3$

53. $6x + 2y$
$\underline{\times\ 0.2x + 1.2y}$
$1.2x^2 + 7.6xy + 2.4y^2$

54. $4.5a + 2b$
$\underline{\times\ 2a - 1.8b}$
$9a^2 - 4.1ab - 3.6b^2$

Concept 2: Special Case Products: Difference of Squares and Perfect Square Trinomials

For Exercises 55–66, multiply the conjugates. **(See Example 6.)**

55. $(y - 6)(y + 6)$
$y^2 - 36$

56. $(x + 3)(x - 3)$
$x^2 - 9$

57. $(3a - 4b)(3a + 4b)$
$9a^2 - 16b^2$

58. $(5y + 7x)(5y - 7x)$
$25y^2 - 49x^2$

59. $(9k + 6)(9k - 6)$
$81k^2 - 36$

60. $(2h - 5)(2h + 5)$
$4h^2 - 25$

61. $\left(\dfrac{2}{3}t - 3\right)\left(\dfrac{2}{3}t + 3\right)$
$\dfrac{4}{9}t^2 - 9$

62. $\left(\dfrac{1}{4}r - 1\right)\left(\dfrac{1}{4}r + 1\right)$
$\dfrac{1}{16}r^2 - 1$

63. $(u^3 + 5v)(u^3 - 5v)$
$u^6 - 25v^2$

64. $(8w^2 - x)(8w^2 + x)$
$64w^4 - x^2$

65. $\left(\dfrac{2}{3} - p\right)\left(\dfrac{2}{3} + p\right)$
$\dfrac{4}{9} - p^2$

66. $\left(\dfrac{1}{8} - q\right)\left(\dfrac{1}{8} + q\right)$
$\dfrac{1}{64} - q^2$

For Exercises 67–78, square the binomials. **(See Example 7.)**

67. $(a + 5)^2$
$a^2 + 10a + 25$

68. $(a - 3)^2$
$a^2 - 6a + 9$

69. $(x - y)^2$
$x^2 - 2xy + y^2$

70. $(x + y)^2$
$x^2 + 2xy + y^2$

71. $(2c + 5)^2$
$4c^2 + 20c + 25$

72. $(5d - 9)^2$
$25d^2 - 90d + 81$

73. $(3t^2 - 4s)^2$
$9t^4 - 24st^2 + 16s^2$

74. $(u^2 + 4v)^2$
$u^4 + 8u^2v + 16v^2$

75. $(7 - t)^2$
$t^2 - 14t + 49$

76. $(4 + w)^2$
$w^2 + 8w + 16$

77. $(3 + 4q)^2$
$16q^2 + 24q + 9$

78. $(2 - 3b)^2$
$9b^2 - 12b + 4$

79. a. Evaluate $(2 + 4)^2$ by working within the parentheses first.   36

   b. Evaluate $2^2 + 4^2$.   20

   c. Compare the answers to parts (a) and (b) and make a conjecture about $(a + b)^2$ and $a^2 + b^2$.
   $(a + b)^2 \neq a^2 + b^2$ in general.

80. a. Evaluate $(6 - 5)^2$ by working within the parentheses first.   1

   b. Evaluate $6^2 - 5^2$.   11

   c. Compare the answers to parts (a) and (b) and make a conjecture about $(a - b)^2$ and $a^2 - b^2$.
   $(a - b)^2 \neq a^2 - b^2$ in general.

Concept 3: Applications to Geometry

81. Find a polynomial expression that represents the area of the rectangle shown in the figure.
$4x^2 - 25$

82. Find a polynomial expression that represents the area of the rectangle shown in the figure.
$36 - y^2$

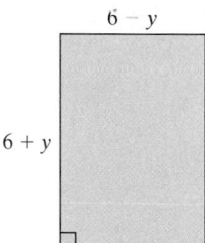

83. Find a polynomial expression that represents the area of the square shown in the figure.
$16p^2 + 40p + 25$

84. Find a polynomial expression that represents the area of the square shown in the figure.
$49q^2 - 42q + 9$

85. Find a polynomial that represents the volume of the cube shown in the figure. **(See Example 8.)**
(Recall: $V = s^3$) $27p^3 - 135p^2 + 225p - 125$

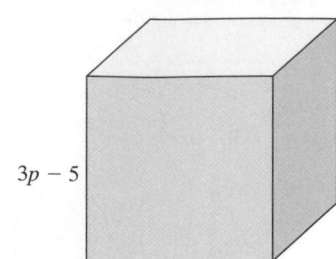

$3p - 5$

86. Find a polynomial that represents the volume of the rectangular solid shown in the figure.
(Recall: $V = lwh$) $r^3 - 15r^2 + 63r - 49$

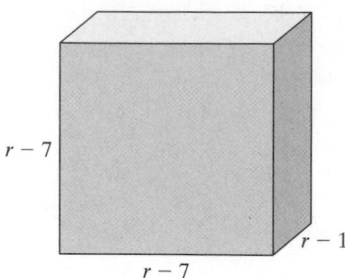

$r - 7$
$r - 1$
$r - 7$

87. Find a polynomial that represents the area of the triangle shown in the figure.
(Recall: $A = \frac{1}{2}bh$) $15a^5 - 6a^2$

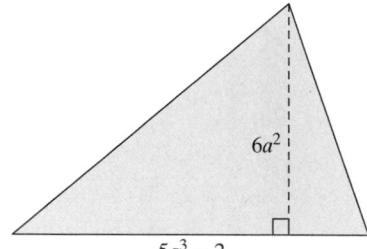

$6a^2$
$5a^3 - 2$

88. Find a polynomial that represents the area of the triangle shown in the figure. $3t^3 - 12t$

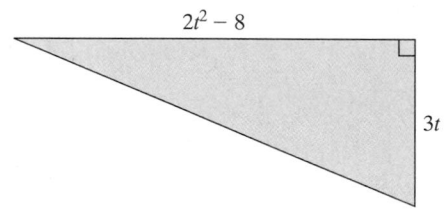

$2t^2 - 8$
$3t$

Mixed Exercises

For Exercises 89–118, multiply the expressions.

89. $(7x + y)(7x - y)$ $49x^2 - y^2$

90. $(9w - 4z)(9w + 4z)$ $81w^2 - 16z^2$

91. $(5s + 3t)^2$ $25s^2 + 30st + 9t^2$

92. $(5s - 3t)^2$ $25s^2 - 30st + 9t^2$

93. $(7x - 3y)(3x - 8y)$
$21x^2 - 65xy + 24y^2$

94. $(5a - 4b)(2a - b)$
$10a^2 - 13ab + 4b^2$

95. $\left(\frac{2}{3}t + 2\right)(3t + 4)$ $2t^2 + \frac{26}{3}t + 8$

96. $\left(\frac{1}{5}s + 6\right)(5s - 3)$ $s^2 + \frac{147}{5}s - 18$

97. $(5z + 3)(z^2 + 4z - 1)$
$5z^3 + 23z^2 + 7z - 3$

98. $(2k - 5)(2k^2 + 3k + 5)$
$4k^3 - 4k^2 - 5k - 25$

99. $(3a - 2)(5a + 1 + 2a^2)$
$6a^3 + 11a^2 - 7a - 2$

100. $(u + 4)(2 - 3u + u^2)$
$u^3 + u^2 - 10u + 8$

101. $(y^2 + 2y + 4)(y - 5)$
$y^3 - 3y^2 - 6y - 20$

102. $(w^2 - w + 6)(w + 2)$
$w^3 + w^2 + 4w + 12$

103. $\left(\frac{1}{3}m - n\right)^2$ $\frac{1}{9}m^2 - \frac{2}{3}mn + n^2$

104. $\left(\frac{2}{5}p - q\right)^2$ $\frac{4}{25}p^2 - \frac{4}{5}pq + q^2$

105. $6w^2(7w - 14)$ $42w^3 - 84w^2$

106. $4v^3(v + 12)$ $4v^4 + 48v^3$

107. $(4y - 8.1)(4y + 8.1)$
$16y^2 - 65.61$

108. $(2h + 2.7)(2h - 2.7)$
$4h^2 - 7.29$

109. $(3c^2 + 4)(7c^2 - 8)$
$21c^4 + 4c^2 - 32$

110. $(5k^3 - 9)(k^3 - 2)$
$5k^6 - 19k^3 + 18$

111. $(3.1x + 4.5)^2$
$9.61x^2 + 27.9x + 20.25$

112. $(2.5y + 1.1)^2$
$6.25y^2 + 5.5y + 1.21$

113. $(k - 4)^3$
$k^3 - 12k^2 + 48k - 64$

114. $(h + 3)^3$
$h^3 + 9h^2 + 27h + 27$

115. $(5x + 3)^3$
$125x^3 + 225x^2 + 135x + 27$

116. $(2a - 4)^3$
$8a^3 - 48a^2 + 96a - 64$

117. $(y^2 + 2y + 1)(2y^2 - y + 3)$
$2y^4 + 3y^3 + 3y^2 + 5y + 3$

118. $(2w^2 - w - 5)(3w^2 + 2w + 1)$
$6w^4 + w^3 - 15w^2 - 11w - 5$

 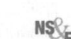

Expanding Your Skills

For Exercises 119–122, multiply the expressions containing more than two factors.

119. $2a(3a - 4)(a + 5)$ $6a^3 + 22a^2 - 40a$

120. $5x(x + 2)(6x - 1)$ $30x^3 + 55x^2 - 10x$

121. $(x - 3)(2x + 1)(x - 4)$ $2x^3 - 13x^2 + 17x + 12$

122. $(y - 2)(2y - 3)(y + 3)$ $2y^3 - y^2 - 15y + 18$

123. What binomial when multiplied by $(3x + 5)$ will produce a product of $6x^2 - 11x - 35$?
   [*Hint:* Let the quantity $(a + b)$ represent the unknown binomial.] Then find a and b such that
   $(3x + 5)(a + b) = 6x^2 - 11x - 35$. $2x - 7$

124. What binomial when multiplied by $(2x - 4)$ will produce a product of $2x^2 + 8x - 24$? $x + 6$

For Exercises 125–127, determine what values of k would create a perfect square trinomial.

125. $x^2 + kx + 25$ $k = 10$ or -10

126. $w^2 + kw + 9$ $k = 6$ or -6

127. $a^2 + ka + 16$ $k = 8$ or -8

Division of Polynomials   Section 5.7

1. Division by a Monomial

Concepts

1. **Division by a Monomial**
2. **Long Division**
3. **Synthetic Division**

Division of polynomials is presented in this section as two separate cases. The first case illustrates division by a monomial divisor. The second case illustrates division by a polynomial with two or more terms.

   To divide a polynomial by a monomial, divide each individual term in the polynomial by the divisor and simplify the result.

PROCEDURE Dividing a Polynomial by a Monomial

If a, b, and c are polynomials such that $c \neq 0$, then

$$\frac{a + b}{c} = \frac{a}{c} + \frac{b}{c} \qquad \text{Similarly,} \qquad \frac{a - b}{c} = \frac{a}{c} - \frac{b}{c}$$

Example 1 Dividing a Polynomial by a Monomial

Classroom Example: p. 397, Exercise 22

Divide the polynomials.

a. $\dfrac{3x^4 - 6x^3 + 9x}{3x}$

b. $(10c^3d - 15c^2d^2 + 2cd^3) \div (-5c^2d^2)$

Solution:

a. $\dfrac{3x^4 - 6x^3 + 9x}{3x}$

$= \dfrac{3x^4}{3x} - \dfrac{6x^3}{3x} + \dfrac{9x}{3x}$ Divide each term in the numerator by $3x$.

$= x^3 - 2x^2 + 3$ Simplify each term, using the properties of exponents.

Instructor Note: A short example can demonstrate that we cannot cancel terms.

$\dfrac{33}{3} = 11$, but $\dfrac{30 + \cancel{3}}{\cancel{3}} \neq 30$

b. $(10c^3d - 15c^2d^2 + 2cd^3) \div (-5c^2d^2)$

$$= \frac{10c^3d - 15c^2d^2 + 2cd^3}{-5c^2d^2}$$

$$= \frac{10c^3d}{-5c^2d^2} - \frac{15c^2d^2}{-5c^2d^2} + \frac{2cd^3}{-5c^2d^2} \qquad \text{Divide each term in the numerator by } -5c^2d^2.$$

$$= -\frac{2c}{d} + 3 - \frac{2d}{5c} \qquad \text{Simplify each term.}$$

Skill Practice   Divide.

1. $\dfrac{18y^3 - 6y^2 - 12y}{6y}$ **2.** $(-24a^3b^2 - 16a^2b^3 + 8ab) \div (-8ab)$

2. Long Division

If the divisor has two or more terms, a long division process similar to the division of whole numbers is used.

Classroom Example: p. 397, Exercise 28

Example 2   **Using Long Division to Divide Polynomials**

Divide the polynomials by using long division.

$$(3x^2 - 14x - 10) \div (x - 2)$$

Solution:

$x - 2 \overline{)3x^2 - 14x - 10}$ Divide the leading term in the dividend by the leading term in the divisor.

$\dfrac{3x^2}{x} = 3x$. This is the first term in the quotient.

$$\begin{array}{r} 3x \\ x - 2 \overline{)3x^2 - 14x - 10} \\ \underline{3x^2 - 6x} \end{array}$$

Multiply $3x$ by the divisor and record the result: $3x(x - 2) = 3x^2 - 6x$.

TIP: Take a minute to compare the long division process with numbers to the process of dividing polynomials.

$$\begin{array}{r} 148 \\ 31\overline{)4602} \\ \underline{-31} \\ 150 \\ \underline{-124} \\ 262 \\ \underline{-248} \\ 14 \end{array}$$

$$\begin{array}{r} 3x \\ x - 2 \overline{)3x^2 - 14x - 10} \\ \underline{-3x^2 + 6x} \\ -8x \end{array}$$

Next, subtract the quantity $3x^2 - 6x$. To do this, add its opposite.

$$\begin{array}{r} 3x - 8 \\ x - 2 \overline{)3x^2 - 14x - 10} \\ \underline{-3x^2 + 6x} \downarrow \\ -8x - 10 \\ \underline{-8x + 16} \end{array}$$

Bring down next column and repeat the process.

Divide the leading term by x: $\dfrac{-8x}{x} = -8$

Multiply the divisor by -8 and record the result: $-8(x - 2) = -8x + 16$.

Answers

1. $3y^2 - y - 2$

2. $3a^2b + 2ab^2 - 1$

$$\begin{array}{r} 3x - 8 \\ x - 2\overline{)3x^2 - 14x - 10} \\ \underline{-3x^2 + 6x} \\ -8x - 10 \\ \underline{+8x - 16} \\ -26 \end{array}$$

Subtract the quantity $-8x + 16$ by adding its opposite.

The remainder is -26. We do not continue because the degree of the remainder is less than the degree of the divisor.

Summary:

The quotient is	$3x - 8$
The remainder is	-26
The divisor is	$x - 2$
The dividend is	$3x^2 - 14x - 10$

The solution to a long division problem is often written in the form:

$$\text{Quotient} + \frac{\text{remainder}}{\text{divisor}}.$$

This answer is $3x - 8 + \dfrac{-26}{x - 2}$.

Skill Practice Divide.

3. $(4x^2 + 6x - 8) \div (x + 3)$

TIP: The division of polynomials can be checked in the same fashion as the division of real numbers. To check, we know that

$$\text{Dividend} = (\text{divisor})(\text{quotient}) + \text{remainder}$$

$$3x^2 - 14x - 10 \overset{?}{=} (x - 2)(3x - 8) + (-26)$$
$$\overset{?}{=} 3x^2 - 8x - 6x + 16 + (-26)$$
$$\overset{?}{=} 3x^2 - 14x - 10 \ \checkmark \ \text{True}$$

Example 3 Using Long Division to Divide Polynomials

Divide the polynomials by using long division: $(-2x^3 - 10x^2 + 56) \div (2x - 4)$

Classroom Example: p. 397, Exercise 36

Solution:

First note that the dividend has a missing power of x and can be written as $-2x^3 - 10x^2 + 0x + 56$. The term $0x$ is a placeholder for the missing term. It is helpful to use the placeholder to keep the powers of x lined up.

$$\begin{array}{r} -x^2 \\ 2x - 4\overline{)-2x^3 - 10x^2 + 0x + 56} \\ \underline{-2x^3 + 4x^2} \end{array}$$

Leave space for the missing power of x.

Divide $\dfrac{-2x^3}{2x} = -x^2$ to get the first term of the quotient.

TIP: To get the first term in the quotient, you can also ask, "What can be multiplied by $2x$ to get $-2x^3$?"

Answer

3. $4x - 6 + \dfrac{10}{x + 3}$

$$\begin{array}{r} -x^2 - 7x \\ 2x - 4 \overline{\smash{\big)}-2x^3 - 10x^2 + 0x + 56} \\ \underline{2x^3 - 4x^2} \\ -14x^2 + 0x \\ \underline{-14x^2 + 28x} \end{array}$$

— Subtract by adding the opposite.

Bring down the next column.

Divide $\dfrac{-14x^2}{2x} = -7x$ to get the next term in the quotient.

$$\begin{array}{r} -x^2 - 7x - 14 \\ 2x - 4 \overline{\smash{\big)}-2x^3 - 10x^2 + 0x + 56} \\ \underline{2x^3 - 4x^2} \\ -14x^2 + 0x \\ \underline{14x^2 - 28x} \\ -28x + 56 \\ \underline{-28x + 56} \end{array}$$

— Subtract by adding the opposite.

Bring down the next column.

Divide $\dfrac{-28x}{2x} = -14$ to get the next term in the quotient.

$$\begin{array}{r} -x^2 - 7x - 14 \\ 2x - 4 \overline{\smash{\big)}-2x^3 - 10x^2 + 0x + 56} \\ \underline{2x^3 - 4x^2} \\ -14x^2 + 0x \\ \underline{14x^2 - 28x} \\ -28x + 56 \\ \underline{28x - 56} \\ 0 \end{array}$$

Subtract by adding the opposite.

← The remainder is 0.

The answer is $-x^2 - 7x - 14$.

Skill Practice Divide.

4. $\dfrac{4y^3 - 2y + 2}{2y + 2}$

In Example 3, the quotient is $-x^2 - 7x - 14$ and the remainder is 0. Because the remainder is zero, $2x - 4$ divides *evenly* into $-2x^3 - 10x^2 + 56$. For this reason, the divisor and quotient are *factors* of $-2x^3 - 10x^2 + 56$. To check, we have

$$\text{Dividend} = (\text{divisor})\,(\text{quotient}) + \text{remainder}$$

$$-2x^3 - 10x^2 + 56 \overset{?}{=} (2x - 4)(-x^2 - 7x - 14) + 0$$

$$\overset{?}{=} -2x^3 - 14x^2 - 28x + 4x^2 + 28x + 56$$

$$\overset{?}{=} -2x^3 - 10x^2 + 56 \ \checkmark \ \text{True}$$

Answer

4. $2y^2 - 2y + 1$

Example 4 Using Long Division to Divide Polynomials

Classroom Example: p. 397, Exercise 44

Divide. $(15x^3 - 4x + 9x^4 - 5) \div (3x^2 - 4)$

Solution:

Write the dividend in descending powers of x. $9x^4 + 15x^3 - 4x - 5$
The dividend has a missing power of x^2. $9x^4 + 15x^3 + 0x^2 - 4x - 5$

The divisor has a missing power of x and can be written as $3x^2 + 0x - 4$.

$$
\begin{array}{r}
3x^2 + 5x + 4 \\
3x^2 + 0x - 4 \overline{)9x^4 + 15x^3 + 0x^2 - 4x - 5} \\
-(9x^4 + 0x^3 - 12x^2) \\
\hline
15x^3 + 12x^2 - 4x \\
-(15x^3 + 0x^2 - 20x) \\
\hline
12x^2 + 16x - 5 \\
-(12x^2 + 0x - 16) \\
\hline
16x + 11
\end{array}
$$

The remainder is $16x + 11$. The degree of the remainder is less than the degree of the divisor.

TIP: Both the divisor and dividend must be written in descending order before performing polynomial division.

The answer is $3x^2 + 5x + 4 + \dfrac{16x + 11}{3x^2 - 4}$.

Skill Practice Divide.

5. $(x^3 + 1 + 2x^2) \div (x^2 + 1)$

3. Synthetic Division

In this section, we introduced the process of long division to divide two polynomials. Next, we will learn another technique, called **synthetic division**, to divide two polynomials. Synthetic division can be used when dividing a polynomial by a first-degree divisor of the form $x - r$, where r is a constant. Synthetic division is considered a "shortcut" because it uses the coefficients of the divisor and dividend without writing the variables.

Consider dividing the polynomials $(3x^2 - 14x - 10) \div (x - 2)$.

$$
\begin{array}{r}
3x - 8 \\
x - 2 \overline{)3x^2 - 14x - 10} \\
-(3x^2 - 6x) \\
\hline
-8x - 10 \\
-(-8x + 16) \\
\hline
-26
\end{array}
$$

Answer

5. $x + 2 + \dfrac{-x - 1}{x^2 + 1}$

First note that the divisor $x - 2$ is in the form $x - r$, where $r = 2$. Therefore, synthetic division can be used to find the quotient and remainder.

Step 1: Write the value ⟶ $2\rfloor$ 3 -14 -10 ⟵ **Step 2:** Write the
of r in a box. coefficients of the
$\overline{\hphantom{xxxxxxx}}$ dividend to the
3 ⟵ right of the box.

Step 3: Skip a line and **Step 4:** Bring down the
draw a horizontal leading coefficient
line below the from the dividend
list of coefficients. and write it below
the line.

$2\rfloor$ 3 -14 -10 **Step 6:** Add the numbers
in the column
Step 5: Multiply the value ⟶ 6 above the line
of r by the number $\overline{\hphantom{xxxxxxx}}$ $(-14 + 6)$, and
below the line 3 -8 ⟵ write the result
$(2 \times 3 = 6)$. We the below the line.
result in the next
column above the line.

Repeat steps 5 and 6 until all columns have been completed.

Step 7: To get the final $2\rfloor$ 3 -14 -10 A box is usually
result, we use the 6 -16 drawn around
numbers below $\overline{\hphantom{xxxxxxx}}$ the remainder.
the line. The 3 -8 $\lfloor -26$
number in the last
column is the
remainder. The Quotient: $3x - 8$,   remainder: -26
other numbers are
the coefficients of
the quotient.

The degree of the quotient will always be 1 less than that of the dividend. Because the dividend is a second-degree polynomial, the quotient will be a first-degree polynomial. In this case, the quotient is $3x - 8$ and the remainder is -26.

Classroom Example: p. 398,
Exercise 60

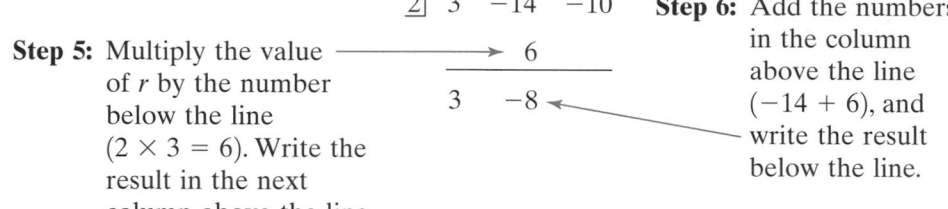

Example 5 Using Synthetic Division to Divide Polynomials

Divide the polynomials $(5x + 4x^3 - 6 + x^4) \div (x + 3)$ by using synthetic division.

Solution:

As with long division, the terms of the dividend and divisor should be written in descending order. Furthermore, missing powers must be accounted for by using placeholders (shown here in red).

$$5x + 4x^3 - 6 + x^4$$

$$= x^4 + 4x^3 + 0x^2 + 5x - 6$$

To use synthetic division, the divisor must be in the form $(x - r)$. The divisor $x + 3$ can be written as $x - (-3)$. Hence, $r = -3$.

Step 1: Write the value of r in a box. 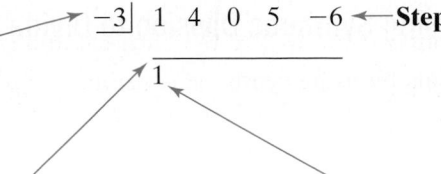 ←**Step 2:** Write the coefficients of the dividend to the right of the box.

$$\begin{array}{r|rrrrr} -3 & 1 & 4 & 0 & 5 & -6 \\ \hline & 1 & & & & \end{array}$$

Step 3: Skip a line and draw a horizontal line below the list of coefficients.

Step 4: Bring down the leading coefficient from the dividend and write it below the line.

Step 5: Multiply the value of r by the number below the line ($-3 \times 1 = -3$). Write the result in the next column above the line.

$$\begin{array}{r|rrrrr} -3 & 1 & 4 & 0 & 5 & -6 \\ & & -3 & & & \\ \hline & 1 & 1 & & & \end{array}$$

Step 6: Add the numbers in the column above the line: $4 + (-3) = 1.$

Repeat steps 5 and 6:

$$\begin{array}{r|rrrrr} -3 & 1 & 4 & 0 & 5 & -6 \\ & & -3 & -3 & 9 & -42 \\ \hline & 1 & 1 & -3 & 14 & \boxed{-48} \end{array}$$

remainder
constant
x-term coefficient
x^2-term coefficient
x^3-term coefficient

The quotient is
$x^3 + x^2 - 3x + 14.$

The remainder is $-48.$

The answer is $x^3 + x^2 - 3x + 14 + \dfrac{-48}{x + 3}.$

Skill Practice Divide the polynomials by using synthetic division.

6. $(5y^2 - 4y + 2y^3 - 5) \div (y + 3)$

Instructor Note: Emphasize to the student that the divisor must be in the form $x - r$.

TIP: It is interesting to compare the long division process to the synthetic division process. For Example 5, long division is shown on the left, and synthetic division is shown on the right. Notice that the same pattern of coefficients used in long division appears in the synthetic division process.

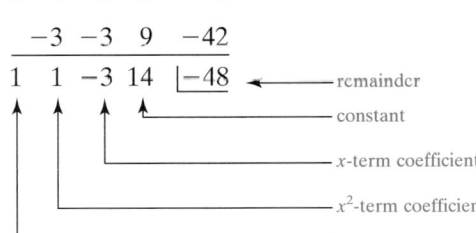

$$\begin{array}{r}
x^3 + x^2 - 3x + 14 \\
x + 3 \overline{\smash{)}\; x^4 + 4x^3 + 0x^2 + 5x - 6} \\
\underline{-(x^4 + 3x^3)} \\
x^3 + 0x^2 \\
\underline{-(x^3 + 3x^2)} \\
-3x^2 + 5x \\
\underline{-(-3x^2 - 9x)} \\
14x - 6 \\
\underline{-(14x + 42)} \\
-48
\end{array}$$

$$\begin{array}{r|rrrrr} -3 & 1 & 4 & 0 & 5 & -6 \\ & & -3 & -3 & 9 & -42 \\ \hline & 1 & 1 & -3 & 14 & \boxed{-48} \end{array}$$

$x^3 \quad x^2 \quad x \quad$ constant remainder

Quotient: $x^3 + x^2 - 3x + 14$
Remainder: -48

Answer

6. $2y^2 - y - 1 + \dfrac{-2}{y + 3}$

Classroom Example: p. 398, Exercise 64

Example 6 Using Synthetic Division to Divide Polynomials

Divide the polynomials by using synthetic division. $(p^4 - 81) \div (p - 3)$

Solution:

$(p^4 - 81) \div (p - 3)$

$(p^4 + 0p^3 + 0p^2 + 0p - 81) \div (p - 3)$ Insert placeholders (red) for missing powers of p.

$$
\begin{array}{r|rrrrr}
3 & 1 & 0 & 0 & 0 & -81 \\
  &   & 3 & 9 & 27 & 81 \\
\hline
  & 1 & 3 & 9 & 27 & \underline{|0}
\end{array}
$$

Quotient: $p^3 + 3p^2 + 9p + 27$

Remainder: 0

The answer is $p^3 + 3p^2 + 9p + 27$.

Skill Practice Divide the polynomials by using synthetic division.

7. $(x^3 + 1) \div (x + 1)$

Answer

7. $x^2 - x + 1$

Section 5.7 Practice Exercises

Study Skills Exercise

1. Define the key term **synthetic division**.

Review Exercises

2. a. Add $(3x + 1) + (2x - 5)$. $5x - 4$

  b. Multiply $(3x + 1)(2x - 5)$. $6x^2 - 13x - 5$

3. a. Subtract $(a - 10b) - (5a + b)$. $-4a - 11b$

  b. Multiply $(a - 10b)(5a + b)$. $5a^2 - 49ab - 10b^2$

4. a. Subtract $(2y^2 + 1) - (y^2 - 5y + 1)$. $y^2 + 5y$

  b. Multiply $(2y^2 + 1)(y^2 - 5y + 1)$.
$2y^4 - 10y^3 + 3y^2 - 5y + 1$

5. a. Add $(x^2 - x) + (6x^2 + x + 2)$. $7x^2 + 2$

  b. Multiply $(x^2 - x)(6x^2 + x + 2)$.
$6x^4 - 5x^3 + x^2 - 2x$

For Exercises 6–8, answers may vary.

6. Write an example of a product of two binomials and simplify.   For example: $(2y + 3)(y - 5) = 2y^2 - 7y - 15$

7. Write an example of the square of a binomial and simplify.   For example: $(5y + 1)^2 = 25y^2 + 10y + 1$

8. Write an example of the product of conjugates and simplify.   For example: $(6p - 1)(6p + 1) = 36p^2 - 1$

Concept 1: Division by a Monomial

For Exercises 9–24, divide the polynomials. Check your answer by multiplication. **(See Example 1.)**

9. $\dfrac{16t^4 - 4t^2 + 20t}{-4t}$ $-4t^3 + t - 5$

10. $\dfrac{2x^3 + 8x^2 - 2x}{-2x}$ $-x^2 - 4x + 1$

11. $(36y + 24y^2 + 6y^3) \div (3y)$ $12 + 8y + 2y^2$

12. $(6p^2 - 18p^4 + 30p^5) \div (6p)$ $p - 3p^3 + 5p^4$

 Writing   Translating Expression   Geometry   Scientific Calculator   Video   NS&E

13. $(4x^3y + 12x^2y^2 - 4xy^3) \div (4xy)$ $x^2 + 3xy - y^2$

14. $(25m^5n - 10m^4n + m^3n) \div (5m^3n)$ $5m^2 - 2m + \frac{1}{5}$

15. $(-8y^4 - 12y^3 + 32y^2) \div (-4y^2)$
$2y^2 + 3y - 8$

16. $(12y^5 - 8y^6 + 16y^4 - 10y^3) \div (2y^3)$
$6y^2 - 4y^3 + 8y - 5$

17. $(3p^4 - 6p^3 + 2p^2 - p) \div (-6p)$ $-\frac{1}{2}p^3 + p^2 - \frac{1}{3}p + \frac{1}{6}$

18. $(-4q^3 + 8q^2 - q) \div (-12q)$ $\frac{1}{3}q^2 - \frac{2}{3}q + \frac{1}{12}$

19. $(a^3 + 5a^2 + a - 5) \div (a)$ $a^2 + 5a + 1 - \frac{5}{a}$

20. $(2m^5 - 3m^4 + m^3 - m^2 + 9m) \div (m^2)$
$2m^3 \quad 3m^2 \mid m - 1 + \frac{9}{m}$

21. $\dfrac{6s^3t^5 - 8s^2t^4 + 10st^2}{-2st^4}$ $-3s^2t + 4s - \frac{5}{t^2}$

22. $\dfrac{-8r^4w^2 - 4r^3w + 2w^3}{-4r^3w}$ $2rw + 1 - \frac{w^2}{2r^3}$

23. $(8p^4q^7 - 9p^5q^6 - 11p^3q - 4) \div (p^2q)$
$8p^2q^6 - 9p^3q^5 - 11p - \frac{4}{p^2q}$

24. $(20a^5b^5 - 20a^3b^2 + 5a^2b + 6) \div (a^2b)$
$20a^3b^4 - 20ab + 5 + \frac{6}{a^2b}$

Concept 2: Long Division

25. a. Divide $(2x^3 - 7x^2 + 5x - 1) \div (x - 2)$, and identify the divisor, quotient, and remainder.
Divisor $(x - 2)$; quotient $(2x^2 - 3x - 1)$; remainder (-3)
b. Explain how to check by using multiplication.
Multiply the quotient and the divisor, then add the remainder. The result should equal the dividend.

26. a. Divide $(x^3 + 4x^2 + 7x - 3) \div (x + 3)$, and identify the divisor, quotient, and remainder.
Divisor $(x + 3)$; quotient $(x^2 + x + 4)$; remainder (-15)
b. Explain how to check by using multiplication.
Multiply the quotient and the divisor, then add the remainder. The result should equal the dividend.

For Exercises 27–46, divide the polynomials by using long division. Check your answer by multiplication.
(See Examples 2–4.)

27. $(x^2 + 11x + 19) \div (x + 4)$ $x + 7 + \frac{-9}{x + 4}$

28. $(x^3 - 7x^2 - 13x + 3) \div (x + 2)$ $x^2 - 9x + 5 + \frac{-7}{x + 2}$

29. $(3y^3 - 7y^2 - 4y + 3) \div (y - 3)$ $3y^2 + 2y + 2 + \frac{9}{y - 3}$

30. $(z^3 - 2z^2 + 2z - 5) \div (z - 4)$ $z^2 + 2z + 10 + \frac{35}{z - 4}$

31. $(-12a^2 + 77a - 121) \div (3a - 11)$ $-4a + 11$

32. $(28x^2 - 29x + 6) \div (4x - 3)$ $7x - 2$

33. $(9y + 18y^2 - 20) \div (3y + 4)$ $6y - 5$

34. $(-2y + 3y^2 - 1) \div (y - 1)$ $3y + 1$

35. $(18x^3 + 7x + 12) \div (3x - 2)$ $6x^2 + 4x + 5 + \frac{22}{3x - 2}$

36. $(8x^3 - 6x + 22) \div (2x - 1)$ $4x^2 + 2x - 2 + \frac{20}{2x - 1}$

37. $(8a^3 + 1) \div (2a + 1)$ $4a^2 - 2a + 1$

38. $(81x^4 - 1) \div (3x + 1)$ $27x^3 - 9x^2 + 3x - 1$

39. $(x^4 - x^3 - x^2 \mid 4x - 2) \div (x^2 + x - 1)$
$x^2 - 2x + 2$

40. $(2a^5 - 7a^4 + 11a^3 - 22a^2 + 29a - 10) \div (2a^2 - 5a + 2)$
$a^3 - a^2 + 2a - 5$

41. $(2x^3 - 10x + x^4 - 25) \div (x^2 - 5)$ $x^2 + 2x + 5$

42. $(-5x^3 + x^4 - 4 - 10x) \div (x^2 + 2)$ $x^2 - 5x - 2$

43. $(x^4 - 3x^2 + 10) \div (x^2 - 2)$ $x^2 - 1 + \frac{8}{x^2 - 2}$

44. $(3y^4 - 25y^2 - 18) \div (y^2 - 3)$ $3y^2 - 16 + \frac{-66}{y^2 - 3}$

45. $(n^4 - 16) \div (n - 2)$ $n^3 + 2n^2 + 4n + 8$

46. $(m^3 + 27) \div (m + 3)$ $m^2 - 3m + 9$

Concept 3: Synthetic Division

47. Explain the conditions under which you may use synthetic division to divide polynomials. The divisor must be of the form $x - r$.

48. Can synthetic division be used directly to divide $(4x^4 + 3x^3 - 7x + 9)$ by $(2x + 5)$? Explain why or why not.
No. The divisor is not of the form $x - r$.

49. Can synthetic division be used to divide $(6x^5 - 3x^2 + 2x - 14)$ by $(x^2 - 3)$? Explain why or why not.
No. The divisor is not of the form $x - r$.

50. Can synthetic division be used to divide $(3x^4 - x + 1)$ by $(x - 5)$? Explain why or why not. Yes, the divisor is of the form $x - r$.

51. The following table represents the result of a synthetic division.

$$\begin{array}{r|rrrr} 5\!\!| & 1 & -2 & -4 & 3 \\ & & 5 & 15 & 55 \\ \hline & 1 & 3 & 11 & \underline{|58} \end{array}$$

Use x as the variable.

a. Identify the divisor. $x - 5$

b. Identify the quotient. $x^2 + 3x + 11$

c. Identify the remainder. 58

52. The following table represents the result of a synthetic division.

$$\begin{array}{r|rrrrr} -2\!\!| & 2 & 3 & 0 & -1 & 6 \\ & & -4 & 2 & -4 & 10 \\ \hline & 2 & -1 & 2 & -5 & \underline{|16} \end{array}$$

Use x as the variable.

a. Identify the divisor. $x + 2$

b. Identify the quotient. $2x^3 - x^2 + 2x - 5$

c. Identify the remainder. 16

For Exercises 53–68, divide by using synthetic division. Check your answer by multiplication. **(See Examples 5–6.)**

53. $(x^2 - 2x - 48) \div (x - 8)$
$x + 6$

54. $(x^2 - 4x - 12) \div (x - 6)$
$x + 2$

55. $(t^2 - 3t - 4) \div (t + 1)$
$t - 4$

56. $(h^2 + 7h + 12) \div (h + 3)$
$h + 4$

57. $(5y^2 + 5y + 1) \div (y - 1)$
$5y + 10 + \dfrac{11}{y - 1}$

58. $(3w^2 + w - 5) \div (w + 2)$
$3w - 5 + \dfrac{5}{w + 2}$

59. $(3 + 7y^2 - 4y + 3y^3) \div (y + 3)$
$3y^2 - 2y + 2 + \dfrac{-3}{y + 3}$

60. $(2z - 2z^2 + z^3 - 5) \div (z + 3)$
$z^2 - 5z + 17 + \dfrac{-56}{z + 3}$

61. $(x^3 - 3x^2 + 4) \div (x - 2)$
$x^2 - x - 2$

62. $(3y^4 - 25y^2 - 18) \div (y - 3)$
$3y^3 + 9y^2 + 2y + 6$

63. $(a^5 - 32) \div (a - 2)$
$a^4 + 2a^3 + 4a^2 + 8a + 16$

64. $(b^3 + 27) \div (b + 3)$ $b^2 - 3b + 9$

65. $(x^3 - 216) \div (x - 6)$
$x^2 + 6x + 36$

66. $(y^4 - 16) \div (y + 2)$ $y^3 - 2y^2 + 4y - 8$

67. $(4w^4 - w^2 + 6w - 3) \div \left(w - \dfrac{1}{2}\right)$
$4w^3 + 2w^2 + 6$

68. $(-12y^4 - 5y^3 - y^2 + y + 3) \div \left(y + \dfrac{3}{4}\right)$ $-12y^3 + 4y^2 - 4y + 4$

Mixed Exercises

For Exercises 69–80, divide the polynomials by using an appropriate method.

69. $(-x^3 - 8x^2 - 3x - 2) \div (x + 4)$
$-x^2 - 4x + 13 + \dfrac{-54}{x + 4}$

70. $(8xy^2 - 9x^2y + 6x^2y^2) \div (x^2y^2)$ $\dfrac{8}{x} - \dfrac{9}{y} + 6$

71. $(22x^2 - 11x + 33) \div (11x)$ $2x - 1 + \dfrac{3}{x}$

72. $(2m^3 - 4m^2 + 5m - 33) \div (m - 3)$ $2m^2 + 2m + 11$

73. $(12y^3 - 17y^2 + 30y - 10) \div (3y^2 - 2y + 5)$
$4y - 3 + \dfrac{4y + 5}{3y^2 - 2y + 5}$

74. $(90h^{12} - 63h^9 + 45h^8 - 36h^7) \div (9h^9)$ $10h^3 - 7 + \dfrac{5}{h} - \dfrac{4}{h^2}$

75. $(4x^4 + 6x^3 + 3x - 1) \div (2x^2 + 1)$
$2x^2 + 3x - 1$

76. $(y^4 - 3y^3 - 5y^2 - 2y + 5) \div (y + 2)$
$y^3 - 5y^2 + 5y - 12 + \dfrac{29}{y + 2}$

77. $(16k^{11} - 32k^{10} + 8k^8 - 40k^4) \div (8k^8)$
$2k^3 - 4k^2 + 1 - \dfrac{5}{k^4}$

78. $(4m^3 - 18m^2 + 22m - 10) \div (2m^2 - 4m + 3)$
$2m - 5 + \dfrac{-4m + 5}{2m^2 - 4m + 3}$

79. $(5x^3 + 9x^2 + 10x) \div (5x^2)$ $x + \dfrac{9}{5} + \dfrac{2}{x}$

80. $(15k^4 + 3k^3 + 4k^2 + 4) \div (3k^2 - 1)$
$5k^2 + k + 3 + \dfrac{k + 7}{3k^2 - 1}$

Expanding Your Skills

81. Given $P(x) = 4x^3 + 10x^2 - 8x - 20$,

a. Evaluate $P(-4)$. -84

b. Divide. $(4x^3 + 10x^2 - 8x - 20) \div (x + 4)$ $4x^2 - 6x + 16 + \dfrac{-84}{x + 4}$

c. Compare the value found in part (a) to the remainder found in part (b). The values are the same.

82. Given $P(x) = -3x^3 - 12x^2 + 5x - 8$,

a. Evaluate $P(-6)$. 178

b. Divide. $(-3x^3 - 12x^2 + 5x - 8) \div (x + 6)$ $-3x^2 + 6x - 31 + \dfrac{178}{x + 6}$

c. Compare the value found in part (a) to the remainder found in part (b). The values are the same.

 Writing   ⟷ Translating Expression   ◁ Geometry   Scientific Calculator   Video   NS‑E

83. Based on your solutions to Exercises 81–82, make a conjecture about the relationship between the value of a polynomial function $P(x)$ at $x = r$, and the value of the remainder of $P(x) \div (x - r)$. $P(r)$ equals the remainder of $P(x) \div (x - r)$.

84. a. Use synthetic division to divide. $(7x^2 - 16x + 9) \div (x - 1)$ $7x - 9$

    b. Based on your solution to part (a), is $x - 1$ a *factor* of $7x^2 - 16x + 9$?   Yes

85. a. Use synthetic division to divide. $(8x^2 + 13x + 5) : (x + 1)$ $8x + 5$

    b. Based on your solution to part (a), is $x + 1$ a *factor* of $8x^2 + 13x + 5$?   Yes

Problem Recognition Exercises

Operations on Polynomials

Perform the indicated operations.

1. a. $(3x + 1)^2$

    b. $(3x + 1)(3x - 1)$ **a.** $9x^2 + 6x + 1$
                                    b. $9x^2 - 1$

    c. $(3x + 1) - (3x - 1)$ **c.** 2

2. a. $(9m - 5) - (9m + 5)$

    b. $(9m - 5)(9m + 5)$ **a.** -10
                                   b. $81m^2 - 25$

    c. $(9m - 5)^2$ **c.** $81m^2 - 90m + 25$

3. a. $\dfrac{4x^2 + 8x - 10}{2x}$ **a.** $2x + 4 - \dfrac{5}{x}$

    b. $\dfrac{4x^2 + 8x - 10}{2x - 1}$ **b.** $2x + 5 + \dfrac{-5}{2x - 1}$

    c. $(4x^2 + 8x - 10) \div (x - 1)$ **c.** $4x + 12 + \dfrac{2}{x - 1}$

4. a. $\dfrac{3y^2 - 15y + 4}{3y}$ **a.** $y - 5 + \dfrac{4}{3y}$

    b. $\dfrac{3y^2 - 15y + 4}{3y + 6}$ **b.** $y - 7 + \dfrac{46}{3y + 6}$

    c. $(3y^2 - 15y + 4) \div (y + 6)$ **c.** $3y - 33 + \dfrac{202}{y + 6}$

5. a. $(p - 5)(p + 5) - (p^2 + 5)$

    b. $(p - 5)(p + 5) - (p + 5)^2$ **a.** -30
                                   b. $-10p - 50$

    c. $(p - 5)(p + 5) - (p^2 - 25)$ **c.** 0

6. a. $(x + 4)(x - 4) - (x + 4)^2$

    b. $(x + 4)(x - 4) - (x^2 + 4)$ **a.** $-8x - 32$
                                   b. -20

    c. $(x + 4)(x - 4) - (x^2 - 16)$ **c.** 0

7. $(5t^2 - 6t + 2) - (3t^2 - 7t + 3)$ $2t^2 + t - 1$

8. $-5x^2(3x^2 + x - 2)$ $-15x^4 - 5x^3 + 10x^2$

9. $(6z + 5)(6z - 5)$ $36z^2 - 25$

10. $(6y^3 + 2y^2 + y - 2) + (3y^3 - 4y + 3)$ $9y^3 + 2y^2 - 3y + 1$

11. $(3b - 4)(2b - 1)$ $6b^2 - 11b + 4$

12. $(5a + 2)(2a^2 + 3a + 1)$ $10a^3 + 19a^2 + 11a + 2$

13. $(t^3 - 4t^2 + t - 9) + (t + 12) - (2t^2 - 6t)$ $t^3 - 6t^2 + 8t + 3$

14. $(2b^3 - 3b - 10) \div (b - 2)$ $2b^2 + 4b + 5$

15. $(k + 4)^2 + (-4k + 9)$ $k^2 + 4k + 25$

16. $(3x^4 - 11x^3 - 4x^2 - 5x + 20) \div (x - 4)$ $3x^3 + x^2 - 5$

17. $-2t(t^2 + 6t - 3) + t(3t + 2)(3t - 2)$ $7t^3 - 12t^2 + 2t$

18. $\dfrac{7x^2y^3 - 14xy^2 - x^2}{-7xy}$ $-xy^2 + 2y + \dfrac{x}{7y}$

19. $\left(\dfrac{1}{4}p^3 - \dfrac{1}{6}p^2 + 5\right) - \left(-\dfrac{2}{3}p^3 + \dfrac{1}{3}p^2 - \dfrac{1}{5}p\right)$ $\dfrac{11}{12}p^3 - \dfrac{1}{2}p^2 + \dfrac{1}{5}p + 5$

20. $-6w^3(1.2w - 2.6w^2 + 5.1w^3)$ $-30.6w^6 + 15.6w^5 - 7.2w^4$

21. $(6a^2 - 4b)^2$ $36a^4 - 48a^2b + 16b^2$

22. $\left(\dfrac{1}{2}z^2 - \dfrac{1}{3}\right)\left(\dfrac{1}{2}z^2 + \dfrac{1}{3}\right)$ $\dfrac{1}{4}z^4 - \dfrac{1}{9}$

23. $(m - 3)^2 - 2(m + 8)$ $m^2 - 8m - 7$

24. $(2x - 5)(x + 1) - (x - 3)^2$ $x^2 + 3x - 14$

25. $(m^2 - 6m + 7)(2m^2 + 4m - 3)$ $2m^4 - 8m^3 - 13m^2 + 46m - 21$

26. $(x^3 - 64) \div (x - 4)$ $x^2 + 4x + 16$

27. $[5 - (a + b)]^2$ $25 - 10a - 10b + a^2 + 2ab + b^2$

28. $[a - (x - y)][a + (x - y)]$ $a^2 - x^2 + 2xy - y^2$

29. $(x + y)^2 - (x - y)^2$ $4xy$

30. $(a - 4)^3$ $a^3 - 12a^2 + 48a - 64$

31. $\left(-\dfrac{1}{2}x + \dfrac{1}{3}\right)\left(\dfrac{1}{4}x - \dfrac{1}{2}\right)$ $-\dfrac{1}{8}x^2 + \dfrac{1}{3}x - \dfrac{1}{6}$

32. $-3x^2y^3z^4\left(\dfrac{1}{6}x^4yzw^3\right)$ $-\dfrac{1}{2}x^6y^4z^5w^3$

 Writing   Translating Expression   Geometry   Scientific Calculator   Video   NS&E

Group Activity

The Pythagorean Theorem and a Geometric "Proof"

Estimated Time: 10–15 minutes

Group Size: 2

Right triangles occur in many applications of mathematics. By definition, a right triangle is a triangle that contains a 90° angle. The two shorter sides in a right triangle are referred to as the "legs," and the longest side is called the "hypotenuse." In the triangle, the legs are labeled as a and b, and the hypotenuse is labeled as c.

Right triangles have an important property that the sum of the squares of the two legs of a right triangle equals the square of the hypotenuse. This fact is referred to as the Pythagorean theorem. In symbols, the Pythagorean theorem is stated as:

$$a^2 + b^2 = c^2$$

1. The following triangles are right triangles. Verify that $a^2 + b^2 = c^2$. (The units may be left off when performing these calculations.)

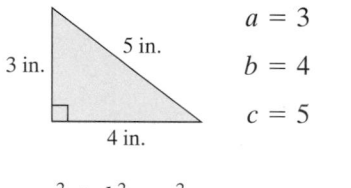

$a = 3$
$b = 4$
$c = 5$

$a^2 + b^2 = c^2$
$(3)^2 + (4)^2 \overset{?}{=} (5)^2$
$9 + 16 = 25$ ✔

$a =$ _____
$b =$ _____
$c =$ _____

$a^2 + b^2 = c^2$
$(\rule{1cm}{0.4pt})^2 + (\rule{1cm}{0.4pt})^2 \overset{?}{=} (\rule{1cm}{0.4pt})^2$
$\rule{1cm}{0.4pt} + \rule{1cm}{0.4pt} = \rule{1cm}{0.4pt}$ ✔

2. The following geometric "proof" of the Pythagorean theorem uses addition, subtraction, and multiplication of polynomials. Consider the square figure. The length of each side of the large outer square is $(a + b)$. Therefore, the area of the large outer square is $(a + b)^2$.

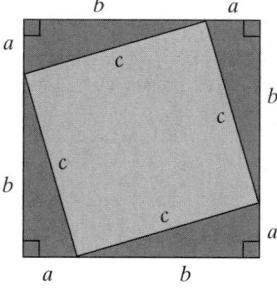

The area of the large outer square can also be found by adding the area of the inner square (pictured in light gray) plus the area of the four right triangles (pictured in dark gray).

Area of inner square: c^2 Area of the four right triangles: $4 \cdot (\frac{1}{2} \, a \, b)$

½ Base · Height

3. Now equate the two expressions representing the area of the large outer square:

$$\left(\begin{array}{c} \text{Area of outer} \\ \text{square} \end{array} \right) = \left(\begin{array}{c} \text{area of inner} \\ \text{square} \end{array} \right) + \left(\begin{array}{c} \text{4 times the area} \\ \text{of the right triangles} \end{array} \right)$$

$(a + b)^2 = c^2 + 4 \cdot (\frac{1}{2}ab)$;

$a^2 + 2ab + b^2 = c^2 + 2ab$;

$a^2 + b^2 = c^2$

$$(a + b)^2 \qquad = \qquad c^2 \qquad + \qquad 4 \cdot (\tfrac{1}{2}ab)$$

$$\rule{2cm}{0.4pt} = \rule{2cm}{0.4pt} + \rule{2cm}{0.4pt}$$ ←——Clear parentheses on both sides of the equation.

$$\rule{2cm}{0.4pt} = \rule{2cm}{0.4pt}$$ ←——Subtract $2ab$ from both sides.

Chapter 5   Summary

Key Concepts

Definition

$$b^n = \underbrace{b \cdot b \cdot b \cdot b \cdot \ldots b}_{n \text{ factors of } b} \qquad b \text{ is the base,} \\ n \text{ is the exponent}$$

Examples

Example 1

$$3^4 = 3 \cdot 3 \cdot 3 \cdot 3 = 81 \qquad 3 \text{ is the base} \\ 4 \text{ is the exponent}$$

Example 2

Compare: $(-5)^2$ versus -5^2

versus $\begin{cases} (-5)^2 = (-5)(-5) = 25 \\ \\ -5^2 = -1(5^2) = -1(5)(5) = -25 \end{cases}$

Multiplying Like Bases

$b^m b^n = b^{m+n}$ (m, n positive integers)

Example 3

Simplify: $x^3 \cdot x^4 \cdot x^2 \cdot x = x^{10}$

Dividing Like Bases

$\dfrac{b^m}{b^n} = b^{m-n}$ ($b \neq 0, m, n,$ positive integers)

Example 4

Simplify: $\dfrac{c^4 d^{10}}{c d^5} = c^{4-1} d^{10-5} = c^3 d^5$

Key Concepts

Power Rule for Exponents

$(b^m)^n = b^{mn}$ ($b \neq 0, m, n$ positive integers)

Power of a Product and Power of a Quotient

Assume m and n are positive integers and a and b are real numbers where $b \neq 0$.
Then,

$(ab)^m = a^m b^m$ and $\left(\dfrac{a}{b}\right)^m = \dfrac{a^m}{b^m}$

Examples

Example 1

Simplify: $(x^4)^5 = x^{20}$

Example 2

Simplify: $(4uv^2)^3 = 4^3 u^3 (v^2)^3 = 64 u^3 v^6$

Example 3

Simplify: $\left(\dfrac{p^5 q^3}{5pq^2}\right)^2 = \left(\dfrac{p^{5-1} q^{3-2}}{5}\right)^2 = \left(\dfrac{p^4 q}{5}\right)^2$

$$= \dfrac{p^8 q^2}{25}$$

Section 5.3 Definitions of b^0 and b^{-n}

Key Concepts

Definitions

If b is a nonzero real number and n is an integer, then:

1. $b^0 = 1$

2. $b^{-n} = \left(\dfrac{1}{b}\right)^n = \dfrac{1}{b^n}$

Examples

Example 1

Simplify: $4^0 = 1$

Example 2

Simplify: $y^{-7} = \dfrac{1}{y^7}$

Example 3

Simplify: $\dfrac{8a^0b^{-2}}{c^{-5}d}$

$$= \dfrac{8(1)c^5}{b^2d} = \dfrac{8c^5}{b^2d}$$

Section 5.4 Scientific Notation

Key Concepts

A positive number written in **scientific notation** is expressed in the form:

$a \times 10^n$ where $1 \leq a < 10$ and n is an integer.

$35{,}000 = 3.5 \times 10^4$

$0.000\,000\,548 = 5.48 \times 10^{-7}$

Examples

Example 1

Multiply: $(3.5 \times 10^4)(2.0 \times 10^{-6})$

$$= 7.0 \times 10^{-2}$$

Example 2

Divide: $\dfrac{2.1 \times 10^{-9}}{8.4 \times 10^3} = 0.25 \times 10^{-9-3}$

$$= 0.25 \times 10^{-12}$$

$$= (2.5 \times 10^{-1}) \times 10^{-12}$$

$$= 2.5 \times 10^{-13}$$

Section 5.5 Addition and Subtraction of Polynomials

Key Concepts

A **polynomial** in one variable is a sum of terms of the form ax^n, where a is a real number and the exponent, n, is a nonnegative integer. For each term, a is called the **coefficient** of the term and n is the **degree of the term**. The term with highest degree is the **leading term**, and its coefficient is called the **leading coefficient**. The **degree of the polynomial** is the largest degree of all its terms.

To add or subtract polynomials, add or subtract *like* terms.

Examples

Example 1

Given: $4x^5 - 8x^3 + 9x - 5$

Coefficients of each term: $4, -8, 9, -5$

Degree of each term: $5, 3, 1, 0$

Leading term: $4x^5$

Leading coefficient: 4

Degree of polynomial: 5

Example 2

Perform the indicated operations:

$$(2x^4 - 5x^3 + 1) - (x^4 + 3) + (x^3 - 4x - 7)$$
$$= 2x^4 - 5x^3 + 1 - x^4 - 3 + x^3 - 4x - 7$$
$$= 2x^4 - x^4 - 5x^3 + x^3 - 4x + 1 - 3 - 7$$
$$= x^4 - 4x^3 - 4x - 9$$

Section 5.6 Multiplication of Polynomials and Special Products

Key Concepts

Multiplying Monomials

Use the commutative and associative properties of multiplication to group coefficients and like bases.

Multiplying Polynomials

Multiply each term in the first polynomial by each term in the second polynomial.

Product of Conjugates

Results in a **difference of squares**

$$(a + b)(a - b) = a^2 - b^2$$

Square of a Binomial

Results in a **perfect square trinomial**

$$(a + b)^2 = a^2 + 2ab + b^2$$
$$(a - b)^2 = a^2 - 2ab + b^2$$

Examples

Example 1

Multiply: $(5a^2b)(-2ab^3)$
$$= (5 \cdot -2)(a^2a)(bb^3)$$
$$= -10a^3b^4$$

Example 2

Multiply: $(x - 2)(3x^2 - 4x + 11)$
$$= 3x^3 - 4x^2 + 11x - 6x^2 + 8x - 22$$
$$= 3x^3 - 10x^2 + 19x - 22$$

Example 3

Multiply: $(3w - 4v)(3w + 4v)$
$$= (3w)^2 - (4v)^2$$
$$= 9w^2 - 16v^2$$

Example 4

Multiply: $(5c - 8d)^2$
$$= (5c)^2 - 2(5c)(8d) + (8d)^2$$
$$= 25c^2 - 80cd + 64d^2$$

Section 5.7   Division of Polynomials

Key Concepts

Division of Polynomials

1. Division by a monomial, use the properties:

$$\frac{a+b}{c} = \frac{a}{c} + \frac{b}{c} \quad \text{and} \quad \frac{a-b}{c} = \frac{a}{c} - \frac{b}{c}$$

2. If the divisor has more than one term, use long division.

3. If the divisor is of the form $x - r$, then synthetic division may be used.

Examples

Example 1

Divide: $\dfrac{-3x^2 - 6x + 9}{-3x}$

$$= \frac{-3x^2}{-3x} - \frac{6x}{-3x} + \frac{9}{-3x}$$

$$= x + 2 - \frac{3}{x}$$

Example 2

Divide: $(3x^2 - 5x + 1) \div (x + 2)$

$$
\begin{array}{r}
3x - 11 \\
x+2\overline{)3x^2 - 5x + 1} \\
\underline{-(3x^2 + 6x)} \\
-11x + 1 \\
\underline{-(-11x - 22)} \\
23
\end{array}
$$

$$3x - 11 + \frac{23}{x+2}$$

Example 3

Divide: $(4x^3 - 2x - 5) \div (x - 1)$

$$
\begin{array}{r}
\underline{1|}\quad 4 \quad\ 0 \quad -2 \quad -5 \\
\quad\quad\quad 4 \quad\ \ 4 \quad\ \ 2 \\
\hline
4 \quad\ 4 \quad\ \ 2 \ \underline{|-3}
\end{array}
$$

$$4x^2 + 4x + 2 + \frac{-3}{x-1}$$

Chapter 5   Review Exercises

Section 5.1

For Exercises 1–4, identify the base and the exponent.

1. 5^3
Base: 5;
exponent: 3

2. x^4
Base: x;
exponent: 4

3. $(-2)^0$
Base: -2;
exponent: 0

4. y
Base: y;
exponent: 1

5. Evaluate the expressions.

   a. 6^2 36   **b.** $(-6)^2$ 36   **c.** -6^2 -36

6. Evaluate the expressions.

   a. 4^3 64   **b.** $(-4)^3$ -64 **c.** -4^3 -64

For Exercises 7–18, simplify and write the answers in exponent form. Assume that all variables represent nonzero real numbers.

7. $5^3 \cdot 5^{10}$ 5^{13}

8. $a^7 a^4$ a^{11}

9. $x \cdot x^6 \cdot x^2$ x^9

10. $6^3 \cdot 6 \cdot 6^5$ 6^9

11. $\dfrac{10^7}{10^4}$ 10^3

12. $\dfrac{y^{14}}{y^8}$ y^6

13. $\dfrac{b^9}{b}$ b^8

14. $\dfrac{7^8}{7}$ 7^7

15. $\dfrac{k^2k^3}{k^4}$ k

16. $\dfrac{8^4 \cdot 8^7}{8^{11}}$ 1

17. $\dfrac{2^8 \cdot 2^{10}}{2^3 \cdot 2^7}$ 2^8

18. $\dfrac{q^3q^{12}}{qq^8}$ q^6

19. Explain why $2^2 \cdot 4^4$ does *not* equal 8^6.
Exponents are added only when multiplying factors with the same base. In such a case, the base does not change.

20. Explain why $\frac{10^5}{5^2}$ does *not* equal 2^3.
Exponents are subtracted only when dividing factors with the same base. In such a case, the base does not change.

For Exercises 21–22, use the formula

$$A = P(1 + r)^t$$

21. Find the amount in an account after 3 years if the initial investment is $6000, invested at 6% interest compounded annually. $7146.10

22. Find the amount in an account after 2 years if the initial investment is $20,000, invested at 5% interest compounded annually. $22,050

Section 5.2

For Exercises 23–40, simplify each expression. Write the answer in exponent form. Assume all variables represent nonzero real numbers.

23. $(7^3)^4$ 7^{12}

24. $(c^2)^6$ c^{12}

25. $(p^4p^2)^3$ p^{18}

26. $(9^5 \cdot 9^2)^4$ 9^{20}

27. $\left(\dfrac{a}{b}\right)^2$ $\dfrac{a^2}{b^2}$

28. $\left(\dfrac{1}{3}\right)^4$ $\dfrac{1}{3^4}$

29. $\left(\dfrac{5}{c^2d^5}\right)^2$ $\dfrac{5^2}{c^4d^{10}}$

30. $\left(-\dfrac{m^2}{4n^6}\right)^5$ $-\dfrac{m^{10}}{4^5n^{30}}$

31. $(2ab^2)^4$ $2^4a^4b^8$

32. $(-x^7y)^2$ $x^{14}y^2$

33. $\left(\dfrac{-3x^3}{5y^2z}\right)^3$ $-\dfrac{3^3x^9}{5^3y^6z^3}$

34. $\left(\dfrac{r^3}{s^2t^6}\right)^5$ $\dfrac{r^{15}}{s^{10}t^{30}}$

35. $\dfrac{a^4(a^2)^8}{(a^3)^3}$ a^{11}

36. $\dfrac{(8^3)^4 \cdot 8^{10}}{(8^4)^5}$ 8^2

37. $\dfrac{(4h^2k)^2(h^3k)^4}{(2hk^3)^2}$ $4h^{14}$

38. $\dfrac{(p^3q)^3(2p^2q^4)^4}{(8p)(pq^3)^2}$ $2p^{14}q^{13}$

39. $\left(\dfrac{2x^4y^3}{4xy^2}\right)^2$ $\dfrac{x^6y^2}{4}$

40. $\left(\dfrac{a^4b^6}{ab^4}\right)^3$ a^9b^6

Section 5.3

For Exercises 41–62, simplify each expression. Assume all variables represent nonzero real numbers.

41. 8^0 1

42. $(-b)^0$ 1

43. $-x^0$ -1

44. 1^0 1

45. $2y^0$ 2

46. $(2y)^0$ 1

47. z^{-5} $\dfrac{1}{z^5}$

48. 10^{-4} $\dfrac{1}{10^4}$

49. $(6a)^{-2}$ $\dfrac{1}{36a^2}$

50. $6a^{-2}$ $\dfrac{6}{a^2}$

51. $4^0 + 4^{-2}$ $\dfrac{17}{16}$

52. $9^{-1} + 9^0$ $\dfrac{10}{9}$

53. $t^{-6}t^{-2}$ $\dfrac{1}{t^8}$

54. r^8r^{-9} $\dfrac{1}{r}$

55. $\dfrac{12x^{-2}y^3}{6x^4y^{-4}}$ $\dfrac{2y^7}{x^6}$

56. $\dfrac{8ab^{-3}c^0}{10a^{-5}b^{-4}c^{-1}}$ $\dfrac{4a^6bc}{5}$

57. $(-2m^2n^{-4})^{-4}$ $\dfrac{n^{16}}{16m^8}$

58. $(3u^{-5}v^2)^{-3}$ $\dfrac{u^{15}}{27v^6}$

59. $\dfrac{(k^{-6})^{-2}(k^3)}{5k^{-6}k^0}$ $\dfrac{k^{21}}{5}$

60. $\dfrac{(3h)^{-2}(h^{-5})^{-3}}{h^{-4}h^8}$ $\dfrac{h^9}{9}$

61. $2 \cdot 3^{-1} - 6^{-1}$ $\dfrac{1}{2}$

62. $2^{-1} - 2^{-2} + 2^0$ $\dfrac{5}{4}$

Section 5.4

63. Write the numbers in scientific notation.

a. In a recent year there were 97,400,000 packages of M&Ms sold in the United States.
9.74×10^7

b. The thickness of a piece of paper is 0.0042 in.
4.2×10^{-3} in.

64. Write the numbers in standard form.

a. A pH of 10 means the hydrogen ion concentration is 1×10^{-10} units.   0.000 000 0001

b. A fundraising event for neurospinal research raised 2.56×10^5. $256,000

For Exercises 65–68, perform the indicated operations. Write the answers in scientific notation.

65. $(4.1 \times 10^{-6})(2.3 \times 10^{11})$
9.43×10^5

66. $\dfrac{9.3 \times 10^3}{6.0 \times 10^{-7}}$ 1.55×10^{10}

67. $\dfrac{2000}{0.000008}$ 2.5×10^8

68. $(0.000078)(21,000,000)$ 1.638×10^3

69. Use your calculator to evaluate 5^{20}. Why is scientific notation necessary on your calculator to express the answer? ≈ 9.5367 × 10¹³. This number has too many digits to fit on most calculator displays.

70. Use your calculator to evaluate $(0.4)^{30}$. Why is scientific notation necessary on your calculator to express the answer? ≈ 1.1529 × 10⁻¹². This number has too many digits to fit on most calculator displays.

71. The average distance between the Earth and Sun is 9.3×10^7 mi.

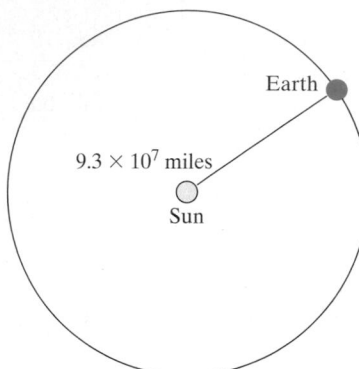

Earth

9.3 × 10⁷ miles

Sun

a. If the Earth's orbit is approximated by a circle, find the total distance the Earth travels around the Sun in one orbit. (*Hint:* The circumference of a circle is given by $C = 2\pi r$.) Express the answer in scientific notation.
≈ 5.84 × 10⁸ mi

b. If the Earth makes one complete trip around the Sun in 1 year (365 days = 8.76×10^3 hr), find the average speed that the Earth travels around the Sun in miles per hour. Express the answer in scientific notation.
≈ 6.67 × 10⁴ mph

72. The average distance between the planet Mercury and the Sun is 3.6×10^7 mi.

a. If Mercury's orbit is approximated by a circle, find the total distance Mercury travels around the Sun in one orbit. (*Hint:* The circumference of a circle is given by $C = 2\pi r$.) Express the answer in scientific notation. ≈ 2.26 × 10⁸ mi

b. If Mercury makes one complete trip around the Sun in 88 days (2.112×10^3 hr), find the average speed that Mercury travels around the Sun in miles per hour. Express the answer in scientific notation.
≈ 1.07 × 10⁵ mph

Section 5.5

73. For the polynomial $7x^4 - x + 6$

a. Classify as a monomial, a binomial, or a trinomial. Trinomial

b. Identify the degree of the polynomial. 4

c. Identify the leading coefficient. 7

74. For the polynomial $2y^3 - 5y^7$

a. Classify as a monomial, a binomial, or a trinomial. Binomial

b. Identify the degree of the polynomial. 7

c. Identify the leading coefficient. −5

For Exercises 75–80, add or subtract as indicated.

75. $(4x + 2) + (3x - 5)$ 7x − 3

76. $(7y^2 - 11y - 6) - (8y^2 + 3y - 4)$ −y² − 14y − 2

77. $(9a^2 - 6) - (-5a^2 + 2a)$ 14a² − 2a − 6

78. $\left(5x^3 - \dfrac{1}{4}x^2 + \dfrac{5}{8}x + 2\right) + \left(\dfrac{5}{2}x^3 + \dfrac{1}{2}x^2 - \dfrac{1}{8}x\right)$
$\frac{15}{2}x^3 + \frac{1}{4}x^2 + \frac{1}{2}x + 2$

79. $8w^4 \qquad - 6w + 3$ 10w⁴ + 2w³ − 7w + 4
$+ 2w^4 + 2w^3 - w + 1$

80. $-0.02b^5 + b^4 \qquad - 0.7b + 0.3$
$+ \quad 0.03b^5 \qquad - 0.1b^3 + \quad b + 0.03$
0.01b⁵ + b⁴ − 0.1b³ + 0.3b + 0.33

81. Subtract $(9x^2 + 4x + 6)$ from $(7x^2 - 5x)$.
−2x² − 9x − 6

82. Find the difference of $(x^2 - 5x - 3)$ and $(6x^2 + 4x + 9)$. −5x² − 9x − 12

83. Write a trinomial of degree 2 with a leading coefficient of −5. (Answers may vary.)
For example, −5x² + 2x − 4

84. Write a binomial of degree 5 with leading coefficient 6. (Answers may vary.)
For example, 6x⁵ + 8

85. Find a polynomial that represents the perimeter of the given rectangle. 6w + 6

2w + 3

w

Section 5.6

For Exercises 86–103, multiply the expressions.

86. $(25x^4y^3)(-3x^2y)$
−75x⁶y⁴

87. $(9a^6)(2a^2b^4)$
18a⁸b⁴

88. $5c(3c^3 - 7c + 5)$
15c⁴ − 35c² + 25c

89. $(x^2 + 5x - 3)(-2x)$
−2x³ − 10x² + 6x

90. $(5k - 4)(k + 1)$
5k² + k − 4

91. $(4t - 1)(5t + 2)$
20t² + 3t − 2

92. $(q + 8)(6q - 1)$
6q² + 47q − 8

93. $(2a - 6)(a + 5)$
2a² + 4a − 30

94. $\left(7a + \dfrac{1}{2}\right)^2$
49a² + 7a + $\frac{1}{4}$

95. $(b - 4)^2$
b² − 8b + 16

96. $(4p^2 + 6p + 9)(2p - 3)$ $8p^3 - 27$

97. $(2w - 1)(-w^2 - 3w - 4)$ $-2w^3 - 5w^2 - 5w + 4$

98. $\begin{array}{r} 2x^2 - 3x + 4 \\ \times\ \underline{\quad 2x - 1} \\ 4x^3 - 8x^2 + 11x - 4 \end{array}$ **99.** $\begin{array}{r} 4a^2 + \ a - 5 \\ \times\ \underline{\quad 3a + 2} \\ 12a^3 + 11a^2 - 13a - 10 \end{array}$

100. $(b - 4)(b + 4)$ $b^2 - 16$

101. $\left(\dfrac{1}{3}r^4 - s^2\right)\left(\dfrac{1}{3}r^4 + s^2\right)$ $\dfrac{1}{9}r^8 - s^4$

102. $(-7z^2 + 6)^2$ $49z^4 - 84z^2 + 36$

103. $(2h + 3)(h^4 - h^3 + h^2 - h + 1)$ $2h^5 + h^4 - h^3 + h^2 - h + 3$

 104. Find a polynomial that represents the area of the given rectangle. $2x^2 + 3x - 20$

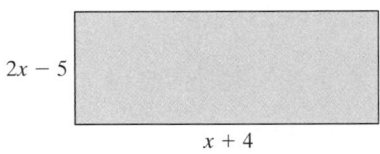

$2x - 5$

$x + 4$

Section 5.7

For Exercises 105–117, divide the polynomials.

105. $\dfrac{20y^3 - 10y^2}{5y}$ $4y^2 - 2y$

106. $(18a^3b^2 - 9a^2b - 21ab^2) \div 9ab$ $2a^2b - a - 3b$

107. $(12x^4 - 8x^3 + 4x^2) \div (-4x^2)$ $-3x^2 + 2x - 1$

108. $\dfrac{10z^7w^4 - 15z^3w^2 - 20zw}{-20z^2w}$ $-\dfrac{z^5w^3}{2} + \dfrac{3zw}{4} + \dfrac{1}{z}$

109. $\dfrac{x^2 + 7x + 10}{x + 5}$ $x + 2$

110. $(2t^2 + t - 10) \div (t - 2)$ $2t + 5$

111. $(2p^2 + p - 16) \div (2p + 7)$ $p - 3 + \dfrac{5}{2p + 7}$

112. $\dfrac{5a^2 + 27a - 22}{5a - 3}$ $a + 6 + \dfrac{-4}{5a - 3}$

113. $\dfrac{b^3 - 125}{b - 5}$ $b^2 + 5b + 25$

114. $(z^3 + 4z^2 + 5z + 20) \div (5 + z^2)$ $z + 4$

115. $(y^4 - 4y^3 + 5y^2 - 3y + 2) \div (y^2 + 3)$ $y^2 - 4y + 2 + \dfrac{9y - 4}{y^2 + 3}$

116. $(3t^4 - 8t^3 + t^2 - 4t - 5) \div (3t^2 + t + 1)$ $t^2 - 3t + 1 + \dfrac{-2t - 6}{3t^2 + t + 1}$

117. $\dfrac{2w^4 + w^3 + 4w - 3}{2w^2 - w + 3}$ $w^2 + w - 1$

Chapter 5   Test

Assume all variables represent nonzero real numbers.

1. Expand the expression using the definition of exponents, then simplify: $\dfrac{3^4 \cdot 3^3}{3^6}$

$\dfrac{(3 \cdot 3 \cdot 3 \cdot 3) \cdot (3 \cdot 3 \cdot 3)}{3 \cdot 3 \cdot 3 \cdot 3 \cdot 3 \cdot 3} = 3$

For Exercises 2–13, simplify each expression. Write the answer with positive exponents only.

2. $9^5 \cdot 9$ 9^6

3. $\dfrac{q^{10}}{q^2}$ q^8

4. $(3a^2b)^3$ $27a^6b^3$

5. $\left(\dfrac{2x}{y^3}\right)^4$ $\dfrac{16x^4}{y^{12}}$

6. $(-7)^0$ 1

7. c^{-3} $\dfrac{1}{c^3}$

8. $\dfrac{14^3 \cdot 14^9}{14^{10} \cdot 14}$ 14

9. $\dfrac{(s^2t)^3(7s^4t)^4}{(7s^2t^3)^2}$ $49s^{18}t$

10. $(2a^0b^{-6})^2$ $\dfrac{4}{b^{12}}$

11. $\left(\dfrac{6a^{-5}b}{8ab^{-2}}\right)^{-2}$ $\dfrac{16a^{12}}{9b^6}$

12. $3^0 + 2^{-1} - 4^{-1}$ $\dfrac{5}{4}$

13. $4 \cdot 8^{-1} + 16^0$ $\dfrac{3}{2}$

14. a. Write the number in scientific notation: $43{,}000{,}000{,}000$ 4.3×10^{10}

 b. Write the number in standard form: 5.6×10^{-6} $0.000\ 0056$

15. Multiply: $(1.2 \times 10^6)(7.0 \times 10^{-15})$ 8.4×10^{-9}

16. Divide: $\dfrac{60{,}000}{0.008}$ 7.5×10^6

17. The average amount of water flowing over Niagara Falls is 1.68×10^5 m³/min.

    a. How many cubic meters of water flow over the falls in one day? $2.4192 \times 10^8\,\text{m}^3$

    b. How many cubic meters of water flow over the falls in one year? $8.83008 \times 10^{10}\,\text{m}^3$

18. Write the polynomial in descending order:
$4x + 5x^3 - 7x^2 + 11$ $5x^3 - 7x^2 + 4x + 11$

    a. Identify the degree of the polynomial.   3

    b. Identify the leading coefficient of the polynomial.   5

19. Add the polynomials.
$(5t^4 - 2t^2 - 17) + (12t^3 + 2t^2 + 7t - 2)$
$5t^4 + 12t^3 + 7t - 19$

20. Perform the indicated operations.

$(7w^2 - 11w - 6) + (8w^2 + 3w + 4) - (-9w^2 - 5w + 2)$ $24w^2 - 3w - 4$

21. Subtract $(3x^2 - 5x^3 + 2x)$ from $(10x^3 - 4x^2 + 1)$.
$15x^3 - 7x^2 - 2x + 1$

For Exercises 22–28, multiply the polynomials.

22. $-2x^3(5x^2 + x - 15)$
$-10x^5 - 2x^4 + 30x^3$

23. $(4a - 3)(2a - 1)$
$8a^2 - 10a + 3$

24. $(4y - 5)(y^2 - 5y + 3)$
$4y^3 - 25y^2 + 37y - 15$

25. $(2 + 3b)(2 - 3b)$
$4 - 9b^2$

26. $(5z - 6)^2$
$25z^2 - 60z + 36$

27. $(5x + 3)(3x - 2)$
$15x^2 - x - 6$

28. $(y^2 - 5y + 2)(y - 6)$ $y^3 - 11y^2 + 32y - 12$

29. Find the perimeter and the area of the rectangle shown in the figure.   Perimeter: $12x - 2$; area: $5x^2 - 13x - 6$

For Exercises 30–35, divide:

30. $(-12x^8 + x^6 - 8x^3) \div (4x^2)$ $-3x^6 + \dfrac{x^4}{4} - 2x$

31. $\dfrac{16a^3b - 2a^2b^2 + 8ab}{-4ab}$ $-4a^2 + \dfrac{ab}{2} - 2$

32. $\dfrac{2y^2 - 13y + 21}{y - 3}$ $2y - 7$

33. $(x^4 - 2x - 25) \div (x + 2)$ $x^3 - 2x^2 + 4x - 10 + \dfrac{-5}{x + 2}$

34. $(-5w^2 + 2w^3 - 2w + 5) \div (2w + 3)$
$w^2 - 4w + 5 + \dfrac{-10}{2w + 3}$

35. $\dfrac{3x^4 + x^3 + 4x - 33}{x^2 + 4}$ $3x^2 + x - 12 + \dfrac{15}{x^2 + 4}$

Chapters 1–5   Cumulative Review Exercises

For Exercises 1–2, simplify completely.

1. $-5 - \dfrac{1}{2}[4 - 3(-7)]$ $-\dfrac{35}{2}$ **2.** $|-3^2 + 5|$ 4

3. Translate the phrase into a mathematical expression and simplify:

The difference of the square of five and the square root of four. $5^2 - \sqrt{4}$; 23

4. Solve for x: $\dfrac{1}{2}(x - 6) + \dfrac{2}{3} = \dfrac{1}{4}x$ $\left\{\dfrac{28}{3}\right\}$

5. Solve for y: $-2y - 3 = -5(y - 1) + 3y$ $\{\ \}$

6. For a point in a rectangular coordinate system, in which quadrant are both the x- and y-coordinates negative?   Quadrant III

7. For a point in a rectangular coordinate system, on which axis is the x-coordinate zero and the y-coordinate nonzero? y-axis

8. In a triangle, one angle measures $23°$ more than the smallest angle. The third angle measures $10°$ more than the sum of the other two angles. Find the measure of each angle.
The measures are $31°$, $54°$, $95°$.

 Writing   Translating Expression   Geometry   Scientific Calculator   Video   NS E

9. A snow storm lasts for 9 hr and dumps snow at a rate of $1\frac{1}{2}$ in./hr. If there was already 6 in. of snow on the ground before the storm, the snow depth is given by the equation:

$y = \dfrac{3}{2}x + 6$ where y is the snow depth in inches and $x \geq 0$ is the time in hours.

a. Find the snow depth after 4 hr.   12 in.

b. Find the snow depth at the end of the storm.
19.5 in.

c. How long had it snowed when the total depth of snow was $14\frac{1}{4}$ in.?   5.5 hr

10. Solve the system of equations. $\{(-3, 4)\}$

$$5x + 3y = -3$$
$$3x + 2y = -1$$

11. Solve the inequality. Graph the solution set on the real number line and express the solution in interval notation. $2 - 3(2x + 4) \leq -2x - (x - 5)$
$[-5, \infty)$

For Exercises 12–15, perform the indicated operations.

12. $(2x^2 + 3x - 7) - (-3x^2 + 12x + 8)$ $5x^2 - 9x - 15$

13. $(2y + 3z)(-y - 5z)$ $-2y^2 - 13yz - 15z^2$

14. $(4t - 3)^2$ $16t^2 - 24t + 9$ 15. $\left(\dfrac{2}{5}a + \dfrac{1}{3}\right)\left(\dfrac{2}{5}a - \dfrac{1}{3}\right)$ $\dfrac{4}{25}a^2 - \dfrac{1}{9}$

For Exercises 16–17, divide the polynomials.

16. $(12a^4b^3 - 6a^2b^2 + 3ab) \div (-3ab)$
$-4a^3b^2 + 2ab - 1$

17. $\dfrac{4m^3 - 5m + 2}{m - 2}$ $4m^2 + 8m + 11 + \dfrac{24}{m - 2}$

For Exercises 18–19, use the properties of exponents to simplify the expressions. Write the answers with positive exponents only. Assume all variables represent nonzero real numbers.

18. $\left(\dfrac{2c^2d^4}{8cd^6}\right)^2$ $\dfrac{c^2}{16d^4}$ 19. $\dfrac{10a^{-2}b^{-3}}{5a^0b^{-6}}$ $\dfrac{2b^3}{a^2}$

20. The given formula is used by scientists to approximate error tolerance when predicting future results from observed data.

$$\dfrac{M}{3 \cdot (2^3)} = Tolerance$$

Find M for a tolerance value of $\dfrac{25}{3} \times 10^{-5}$.
$M = 2.0 \times 10^{-3}$ or 0.002

Factoring Polynomials

6

CHAPTER OUTLINE

Chapter 6

This chapter is devoted to factoring polynomials for the purpose of solving equations.

Are You Prepared?

Along the way, we will need the skill of recognizing perfect squares and perfect cubes. A perfect square is a number that is a square of a rational number. For example, 49 is a perfect square because $49 = 7^2$. We also will need to recognize perfect cubes. A perfect cube is a number that is a cube of a rational number. For example, 125 is a perfect cube because $125 = 5^3$.

   To complete the puzzle, first answer the questions and fill in the appropriate box. Then fill the grid so that every row, every column, and every 2×3 box contains the digits 1 through 6.

A. What number squared is 1?
B. What number squared is 16?
C. What number cubed is 1?
D. What number squared is 36?
E. What number squared is 25?
F. What number cubed is 64?
G. What number cubed is 8?
H. What number cubed is 27?
I. What number squared is 4?
J. What number squared is 9?

5	2	6	A 1	3	B 4
3	C 1	4	2	D 6	E 5
F 4	6	1	5	G 2	H 3
I 2	3	5	4	1	6
1	4	3	6	5	2
6	5	2	J 3	4	1

| Section 6.1 | Greatest Common Factor and Factoring by Grouping |

Concepts

1. Identifying the Greatest Common Factor

2. Factoring out the Greatest Common Factor

3. Factoring out a Negative Factor

4. Factoring out a Binomial Factor

5. Factoring by Grouping

1. Identifying the Greatest Common Factor

Chapter 6 is devoted to a mathematical operation called **factoring**. To factor an integer means to write the integer as a product of two or more integers. To factor a polynomial means to express the polynomial as a product of two or more polynomials.

In the product $2 \cdot 5 = 10$, for example, 2 and 5 are factors of 10.

In the product $(3x + 4)(2x - 1) = 6x^2 + 5x - 4$, the quantities $(3x + 4)$ and $(2x - 1)$ are factors of $6x^2 + 5x - 4$.

We begin our study of factoring by factoring integers. The number 20, for example, can be factored as $1 \cdot 20$ or $2 \cdot 10$ or $4 \cdot 5$ or $2 \cdot 2 \cdot 5$. The product $2 \cdot 2 \cdot 5$ (or equivalently $2^2 \cdot 5$) consists only of prime numbers and is called the **prime factorization**.

The **greatest common factor** (denoted **GCF**) of two or more integers is the greatest factor common to each integer. To find the greatest common factor of two or more integers, it is often helpful to express the numbers as a product of prime factors as shown in the next example.

Classroom Example: p. 419, Exercise 6

| **Example 1** Identifying the Greatest Common Factor |

Find the greatest common factor.

a. 24 and 36   **b.** 105, 40, and 60

Solution:

First find the prime factorization of each number. Then find the product of common factors.

a.
$$2\lfloor 24 \qquad 2\lfloor 36$$
$$2\lfloor 12 \qquad 2\lfloor 18$$
$$2\lfloor 6 \qquad 3\lfloor 9$$
$$\quad 3 \qquad \quad 3$$

Factors of 24 = $2 \cdot 2 \cdot 2 \cdot 3$ ← Common factors are circled.
Factors of 36 = $2 \cdot 2 \cdot 3 \cdot 3$

The numbers 24 and 36 share two factors of 2 and one factor of 3. Therefore, the greatest common factor is $2 \cdot 2 \cdot 3 = 12$.

b.
$$5\lfloor 105 \qquad 5\lfloor 40 \qquad 5\lfloor 60$$
$$3\lfloor 21 \qquad 2\lfloor 8 \qquad 3\lfloor 12$$
$$\quad 7 \qquad 2\lfloor 4 \qquad 2\lfloor 4$$
$$\qquad \qquad \quad 2 \qquad \quad 2$$

Factors of 105 = $3 \cdot 7 \cdot 5$

Factors of 40 = $2 \cdot 2 \cdot 2 \cdot 5$

Factors of 60 = $2 \cdot 2 \cdot 3 \cdot 5$

The greatest common factor is 5.

Skill Practice Find the GCF.

1. 12 and 20   **2.** 45, 75, and 30

In Example 2, we find the greatest common factor of two or more variable terms.

Example 2 **Identifying the Greatest Common Factor**

Find the GCF among each group of terms.

a. $7x^3, 14x^2, 21x^4$ **b.** $15a^4b, 25a^3b^2$ **c.** $8c^2d^7e, 6c^3d^4$

Solution:

List the factors of each term.

a. $7x^3 = 7 \cdot x \cdot x \cdot x$

$14x^2 = 2 \cdot 7 \cdot x \cdot x$ The GCF is $7x^2$.

$21x^4 = 3 \cdot 7 \cdot x \cdot x \cdot x \cdot x$

b. $15a^4b = 3 \cdot 5 \cdot a \cdot a \cdot a \cdot a \cdot b$

$25a^3b^2 = 5 \cdot 5 \cdot a \cdot a \cdot a \cdot b \cdot b$ The GCF is $5a^3b$.

TIP: Notice that the expressions $15a^4b$ and $25a^3b^2$ share factors of 5, a, and b. The GCF is the product of the common factors, where each factor is raised to the lowest power to which it occurs in all the original expressions.

$15a^4b = 3 \cdot 5a^4b$ Lowest power of 5 is 1: 5^1

$25a^3b^2 = 5^2a^3b^2$ Lowest power of a is 3: a^3 The GCF is $5a^3b$.

Lowest power of b is 1: b^1

c. $8c^2d^7e = 2^3c^2d^7e$

$6c^3d^4 = 2 \cdot 3c^3d^4$ The common factors are 2, c, and d.

The lowest power of 2 is 1: 2^1

The lowest power of c is 2: c^2 The GCF is $2c^2d^4$.

The lowest power of d is 4: d^4

Skill Practice Find the GCF.

3. $10z^3, 15z^5, 40z$ **4.** $6w^3y^5, 21w^4y^2$ **5.** $9m^2np^8, 15n^4p^5$

Sometimes polynomials share a common binomial factor, as shown in Example 3.

Example 3 **Identifying the Greatest Common Binomial Factor**

Find the greatest common factor of the terms: $3x(a + b)$ and $2y(a + b)$

Solution:

$3x(a + b)$ The only common factor is the binomial $(a + b)$.

$2y(a + b)$ The GCF is $(a + b)$.

Skill Practice Find the GCF.

6. $a(x + 2)$ and $b(x + 2)$

Classroom Example: p. 420, Exercise 10

Classroom Example: p. 420, Exercise 14

Answers

3. $5z$ **4.** $3w^3y^2$
5. $3np^5$ **6.** $(x + 2)$

2. Factoring out the Greatest Common Factor

The process of factoring a polynomial is the reverse process of multiplying polynomials. Both operations use the distributive property: $ab + ac = a(b + c)$.

Multiply

$$5y(y^2 + 3y + 1) = 5y(y^2) + 5y(3y) + 5y(1)$$
$$= 5y^3 + 15y^2 + 5y$$

Factor

$$5y^3 + 15y^2 + 5y = 5y(y^2) + 5y(3y) + 5y(1)$$
$$= 5y(y^2 + 3y + 1)$$

> **PROCEDURE   Factoring out the Greatest Common Factor**
>
> **Step 1**   Identify the GCF of all terms of the polynomial.
> **Step 2**   Write each term as the product of the GCF and another factor.
> **Step 3**   Use the distributive property to remove the GCF.
>
> *Note:* To check the factorization, multiply the polynomials to remove parentheses.

Classroom Examples: p. 420, Exercises 18 and 22

> **Example 4**   Factoring out the Greatest Common Factor

Factor out the GCF.

a. $4x - 20$ **b.** $6w^2 + 3w$

Instructor Note: Tell students that a problem is factored only if the GCF has been removed. The expression $2(2x - 10)$ is not factored completely.

Solution:

a. $4x - 20$ The GCF is 4.

$\quad = 4(x) - 4(5)$ Write each term as the product of the GCF and another factor.

$\quad = 4(x - 5)$ Use the distributive property to factor out the GCF.

> **TIP:** Any factoring problem can be checked by multiplying the factors:
>
> $$\text{Check: } 4(x - 5) = 4x - 20 \checkmark$$

Avoiding Mistakes

In Example 4(b), the GCF, $3w$, is equal to one of the terms of the polynomial. In such a case, you must leave a 1 in place of that term after the GCF is factored out.

b. $6w^2 + 3w$ The GCF is $3w$.

$\quad = 3w(2w) + 3w(1)$ Write each term as the product of $3w$ and another factor.

$\quad = 3w(2w + 1)$ Use the distributive property to factor out the GCF.

$$\text{Check: } 3w(2w + 1) = 6w^2 + 3w \checkmark$$

Skill Practice Factor out the GCF.

7. $6w + 18$ **8.** $21m^3 - 7m$

Answers

7. $6(w + 3)$ **8.** $7m(3m^2 - 1)$

Example 5	**Factoring out the Greatest Common Factor**

Classroom Examples: p. 420, Exercises 24 and 34

Factor out the GCF.

a. $15y^3 + 12y^4$ **b.** $9a^4b - 18a^5b + 27a^6b$

Solution:

a. $15y^3 + 12y^4$ The GCF is $3y^3$.

$= 3y^3(5) + 3y^3(4y)$ Write each term as the product of $3y^3$ and another factor.

$= 3y^3(5 + 4y)$ Use the distributive property to factor out the GCF.

Check: $3y^3(5 + 4y) = 15y^3 + 12y^4$ ✔

TIP: When factoring out the GCF from a polynomial, the terms within parentheses are found by dividing the original terms by the GCF. For example:

$15y^3 + 12y^4$ The GCF is $3y^3$.

$$\frac{15y^3}{3y^3} = 5 \quad \text{and} \quad \frac{12y^4}{3y^3} = 4y$$

Thus, $15y^3 + 12y^4 = 3y^3(5 + 4y)$

---

b. $9a^4b - 18a^5b + 27a^6b$ The GCF is $9a^4b$.

$= 9a^4b(1) - 9a^4b(2a) + 9a^4b(3a^2)$ Write each term as the product of $9a^4b$ and another factor.

$= 9a^4b(1 - 2a + 3a^2)$ Use the distributive property to factor out the GCF.

Check: $9a^4b(1 - 2a + 3a^2)$
$= 9a^4b - 18a^5b + 27a^6b$ ✔

Skill Practice Factor out the GCF.

9. $9y^2 - 6y^5$ **10.** $50s^3t - 40st^2 + 10st$

The greatest common factor of the polynomial $2x + 5y$ is 1. If we factor out the GCF, we have $1(2x + 5y)$. A polynomial whose only factors are itself and 1 is called a **prime polynomial**.

3. Factoring out a Negative Factor

Usually it is advantageous to factor out the *opposite* of the GCF when the leading coefficient of the polynomial is negative. This is demonstrated in the next example. Notice that this *changes the signs* of the remaining terms inside the parentheses.

Instructor Note: Remind students that first we put the polynomial in descending order, then determine if the leading coefficient is negative.

Answers

9. $3y^2(3 - 2y^3)$
10. $10st(5s^2 - 4t + 1)$

Classroom Example: p. 420,
Exercise 42

Example 6 Factoring out a Negative Factor

Factor out -3 from the polynomial $-3x^2 + 6x - 33$.

Solution:

$$-3x^2 + 6x - 33 \qquad \text{The GCF is 3. However, in this case, we will factor out the } \textit{opposite} \text{ of the GCF, } -3.$$

$$= -3(x^2) + (-3)(-2x) + (-3)(11) \qquad \text{Write each term as the product of } -3 \text{ and another factor.}$$

$$= -3[x^2 + (-2x) + 11] \qquad \text{Factor out } -3.$$

$$= -3(x^2 - 2x + 11) \qquad \text{Simplify. Notice that each sign within the trinomial has changed.}$$

Check: $-3(x^2 - 2x + 11) = -3x^2 + 6x - 33$ ✔

Skill Practice Factor out -2 from the polynomial.

11. $-2x^2 - 10x + 16$

Classroom Example: p. 420,
Exercise 44

Example 7 Factoring out a Negative Factor

Factor out the quantity $-4pq$ from the polynomial $-12p^3q - 8p^2q^2 + 4pq^3$.

Solution:

$$-12p^3q - 8p^2q^2 + 4pq^3 \qquad \text{The GCF is } 4pq. \text{ However, in this case, we will factor out the } \textit{opposite} \text{ of the GCF, } -4pq.$$

$$= -4pq(3p^2) + (-4pq)(2pq) + (-4pq)(-q^2) \qquad \text{Write each term as the product of } -4pq \text{ and another factor.}$$

$$= -4pq[3p^2 + 2pq + (-q^2)] \qquad \text{Factor out } -4pq. \text{ Notice that each sign within the trinomial has changed.}$$

$$= -4pq(3p^2 + 2pq - q^2) \qquad \text{To verify that this is the correct factorization and that the signs are correct, multiply the factors.}$$

Check: $-4pq(3p^2 + 2pq - q^2) = -12p^3q - 8p^2q^2 + 4pq^3$ ✔

Skill Practice Factor out $-5xy$ from the polynomial.

12. $-10x^2y + 5xy - 15xy^2$

4. Factoring out a Binomial Factor

The distributive property can also be used to factor out a common factor that consists of more than one term, as shown in Example 8.

Answers

11. $-2(x^2 + 5x - 8)$
12. $-5xy(2x - 1 + 3y)$

Example 8 Factoring out a Binomial Factor

Factor out the GCF. $2w(x + 3) - 5(x + 3)$

Classroom Example: p. 420, Exercise 48

Solution:

$2w(x + 3) - 5(x + 3)$ The greatest common factor is the quantity $(x + 3)$.

$= (x + 3)(2w - 5)$ Use the distributive property to factor out the GCF.

Skill Practice Factor out the GCF.

13. $8y(a + b) + 9(a + b)$

5. Factoring by Grouping

When two binomials are multiplied, the product before simplifying contains four terms. For example:

$$(x + 4)(3a + 2b) = (x + 4)(3a) + (x + 4)(2b)$$
$$= (x + 4)(3a) + (x + 4)(2b)$$
$$= 3ax + 12a + 2bx + 8b$$

In Example 9, we learn how to reverse this process. That is, given a four-term polynomial, we will factor it as a product of two binomials. The process is called *factoring by grouping.*

PROCEDURE Factoring by Grouping

To factor a four-term polynomial by grouping:

Step 1 Identify and factor out the GCF from all four terms.

Step 2 Factor out the GCF from the first pair of terms. Factor out the GCF from the second pair of terms. (Sometimes it is necessary to factor out the opposite of the GCF.)

Step 3 If the two terms share a common binomial factor, factor out the binomial factor.

Example 9 Factoring by Grouping

Factor by grouping. $3ax + 12a + 2bx + 8b$

Classroom Example: p. 421, Exercise 58

Solution:

$3ax + 12a + 2bx + 8b$ **Step 1:** Identify and factor out the GCF from all four terms. In this case, the GCF is 1.

$= 3ax + 12a \vdots + 2bx + 8b$ Group the first pair of terms and the second pair of terms.

Answer

13. $(a + b)(8y + 9)$

$$= 3a(x + 4) + 2b(x + 4)$$

Step 2: Factor out the GCF from each pair of terms. *Note:* The two terms now share a common binomial factor of $(x + 4)$.

$$= (x + 4)(3a + 2b)$$

Step 3: Factor out the common binomial factor.

<u>Check:</u> $(x + 4)(3a + 2b) = 3ax + 2bx + 12a + 8b$ ✔

Note: Step 2 results in two terms with a common binomial factor. If the two binomials are different, step 3 cannot be performed. In such a case, the original polynomial may not be factorable by grouping, or different pairs of terms may need to be grouped and inspected.

Skill Practice Factor by grouping.

14. $5x + 10y + ax + 2ay$

TIP: One frequently asked question when factoring is whether the order can be switched between the factors. The answer is yes. Because multiplication is commutative, the order in which the factors are written does not matter.

$$(x + 4)(3a + 2b) = (3a + 2b)(x + 4)$$

Classroom Example: p. 421, Exercise 60

Example 10 Factoring by Grouping

Factor by grouping. $ax + ay - x - y$

Solution:

$$ax + ay - x - y$$

Step 1: Identify and factor out the GCF from all four terms. In this case, the GCF is 1.

$$= ax + ay \mathbin{\vdots} - x - y$$

Group the first pair of terms and the second pair of terms.

$$= a(x + y) - 1(x + y)$$

Step 2: Factor out a from the first pair of terms.

Factor out -1 from the second pair of terms. (This causes sign changes within the second parentheses.) The terms in parentheses now match.

$$= (x + y)(a - 1)$$

Step 3: Factor out the common binomial factor.

<u>Check:</u> $(x + y)(a - 1) = x(a) + x(-1) + y(a) + y(-1)$

$$= ax - x + ay - y ✔$$

Skill Practice Factor by grouping.

15. $tu - tv - u + v$

Avoiding Mistakes

In step 2, the expression $a(x + y) - (x + y)$ is not yet factored completely because it is a *difference*, not a product. To factor the expression, you must carry it one step further.

$$a(x + y) - 1(x + y)$$
$$= (x + y)(a - 1)$$

The factored form must be represented as a product.

Answers

14. $(x + 2y)(5 + a)$
15. $(u - v)(t - 1)$

Example 11 Factoring by Grouping

Classroom Example: p. 421, Exercise 74

Factor by grouping. $16w^4 - 40w^3 - 12w^2 + 30w$

Solution:

$16w^4 - 40w^3 - 12w^2 + 30w$

Step 1: Identify and factor out the GCF from all four terms. In this case, the GCF is $2w$.

$= 2w[8w^3 - 20w^2 - 6w + 15]$

$= 2w[8w^3 - 20w^2 \mid - 6w + 15]$

Group the first pair of terms and the second pair of terms.

$= 2w[4w^2(2w - 5) - 3(2w - 5)]$

Step 2: Factor out $4w^2$ from the first pair of terms.

Factor out -3 from the second pair of terms. (This causes sign changes within the second parentheses.) The terms in parentheses now match.

$= 2w[(2w - 5)(4w^2 - 3)]$

Step 3: Factor out the common binomial factor.

$= 2w(2w - 5)(4w^2 - 3)$

Skill Practice Factor by grouping.

16. $3ab^2 + 6b^2 - 12ab - 24b$

Answer

16. $3b(a + 2)(b - 4)$

Section 6.1 Practice Exercises

Study Skills Exercises

1. The final exam is just around the corner. Your old tests and quizzes provide good material to study for the final exam. Use your old tests to make a list of the chapters on which you need to concentrate. Ask your professor for help if there are still concepts that you do not understand.

2. Define the key terms.

    a. factoring   **b. greatest common factor (GCF)**

    c. prime factorization   **d. prime polynomial**

Concept 1: Identifying the Greatest Common Factor

For Exercises 3–14, identify the greatest common factor. **(See Examples 1–3.)**

3. $28, 63$ 7   **4.** $24, 40$ 8   **5.** $42, 30, 60$ 6

6. $20, 52, 32$ 4   **7.** $3xy, 7y$ y **8.** $10mn, 11n$ n

9. $12w^3z$, $16w^2z$ $4w^2z$

10. $20cd$, $15c^3d$ $5cd$

11. $8x^3y^4z^2$, $12xy^5z^4$, $6x^2y^8z^3$ $2xy^4z^2$

12. $15r^2s^2t^5$, $5r^3s^4t^3$, $30r^4s^3t^2$ $5r^2s^2t^2$

13. $7(x - y)$, $9(x - y)$ $(x - y)$

14. $(2a - b)$, $3(2a - b)$ $(2a - b)$

Concept 2: Factoring out the Greatest Common Factor

15. **a.** Use the distributive property to multiply $3(x - 2y)$. $3x - 6y$

   b. Use the distributive property to factor $3x - 6y$. $3(x - 2y)$

16. **a.** Use the distributive property to multiply $a^2(5a + b)$. $5a^3 + a^2b$

   b. Use the distributive property to factor $5a^3 + a^2b$. $a^2(5a + b)$

For Exercises 17–36, factor out the GCF. **(See Examples 4–5.)**

17. $4p + 12$ $4(p + 3)$

18. $3q - 15$ $3(q - 5)$

19. $5c^2 - 10c + 15$
   $5(c^2 - 2c + 3)$

20. $16d^3 + 24d^2 + 32d$
   $8d(2d^2 + 3d + 4)$

21. $x^5 + x^3$ $x^3(x^2 + 1)$

22. $y^2 - y^3$ $y^2(1 - y)$

23. $t^4 - 4t + 8t^2$
   $t(t^3 - 4 + 8t)$

24. $7r^3 - r^5 + r^4$
   $r^3(7 - r^2 + r)$

25. $2ab + 4a^3b$
   $2ab(1 + 2a^2)$

26. $5u^3v^2 - 5uv$
   $5uv(u^2v - 1)$

27. $38x^2y - 19x^2y^4$
   $19x^2y(2 - y^3)$

28. $100a^5b^3 + 16a^2b$
   $4a^2b(25a^3b^2 + 4)$

29. $6x^3y^5 - 18xy^9z$
   $6xy^5(x^2 - 3y^4z)$

30. $15mp^7q^4 + 12m^4q^3$
   $3mq^3(5p^7q + 4m^3)$

31. $5 + 7y^3$ The expression is prime because it is not factorable.

32. $w^3 - 5u^3v^2$ The expression is prime because it is not factorable.

 33. $42p^3q^2 + 14pq^2 - 7p^4q^4$ $7pq^2(6p^2 + 2 - p^3q^2)$

34. $8m^2n^3 - 24m^2n^2 + 4m^3n$ $4m^2n(2n^2 - 6n + m)$

35. $t^5 + 2rt^3 - 3t^4 + 4r^2t^2$ $t^2(t^3 + 2rt - 3t^2 + 4r^2)$

36. $u^2v + 5u^3v^2 - 2u^2 + 8uv$ $u(uv + 5u^2v^2 - 2u + 8v)$

Concept 3: Factoring out a Negative Factor

37. For the polynomial $-2x^3 - 4x^2 + 8x$

   a. Factor out $-2x$.
      $-2x(x^2 + 2x - 4)$

   b. Factor out $2x$.
      $2x(-x^2 - 2x + 4)$

38. For the polynomial $-9y^5 + 3y^3 - 12y$

   a. Factor out $-3y$.
      $-3y(3y^4 - y^2 + 4)$

   b. Factor out $3y$.
      $3y(-3y^4 + y^2 - 4)$

39. Factor out -1 from the polynomial $-8t^2 - 9t - 2$. $-1(8t^2 + 9t + 2)$

40. Factor out -1 from the polynomial $-6x^3 - 2x - 5$. $-1(6x^3 + 2x + 5)$

For Exercises 41–46, factor out the opposite of the greatest common factor. **(See Examples 6–7.)**

41. $-15p^3 - 30p^2$ $-15p^2(p + 2)$

42. $-24m^3 - 12m^4$ $-12m^3(2 + m)$

43. $-3m^4n^2 + 6m^2n - 9mn^2$
   $-3mn(m^3n - 2m + 3n)$

44. $-12p^3t + 2p^2t^3 + 6pt^2$
   $-2pt(6p^2 - pt^2 - 3t)$

45. $-7x - 6y - 2z$ $-1(7x + 6y + 2z)$

46. $-4a + 5b - c$ $-1(4a - 5b + c)$

Concept 4: Factoring out a Binomial Factor

For Exercises 47–52, factor out the GCF. **(See Example 8.)**

47. $13(a + 6) - 4b(a + 6)$
   $(a + 6)(13 - 4b)$

48. $7(x^2 + 1) - y(x^2 + 1)$
   $(x^2 + 1)(7 - y)$

49. $8v(w^2 - 2) + (w^2 - 2)$
   $(w^2 - 2)(8v + 1)$

50. $t(r + 2) + (r + 2)$
   $(r + 2)(t + 1)$

51. $21x(x + 3) + 7x^2(x + 3)$
   $7x(x + 3)^2$

52. $5y^3(y - 2) - 15y(y - 2)$
   $5y(y - 2)(y^2 - 3)$

Concept 5: Factoring by Grouping

For Exercises 53–72, factor by grouping. **(See Examples 9–10.)**

53. $8a^2 - 4ab + 6ac - 3bc$
$(2a - b)(4a + 3c)$

54. $4x^3 + 3x^2y + 4xy^2 + 3y^3$
$(4x + 3y)(x^2 + y^2)$

55. $3q + 3p + qr + pr$
$(q + p)(3 + r)$

56. $xy - xz + 7y - 7z$
$(y - z)(x + 7)$

57. $6x^2 + 3x + 4x + 2$
$(2x + 1)(3x + 2)$

58. $4y^2 + 8y + 7y + 14$
$(y + 2)(4y + 7)$

59. $2t^2 + 6t - t - 3$
$(t + 3)(2t - 1)$

60. $2p^2 - p - 2p + 1$
$(2p - 1)(p - 1)$

61. $6y^2 - 2y - 9y + 3$
$(3y - 1)(2y - 3)$

62. $5a^2 + 30a - 2a - 12$
$(a + 6)(5a - 2)$

63. $b^4 + b^3 - 4b - 4$
$(b + 1)(b^3 - 4)$

64. $8w^5 + 12w^2 - 10w^3 - 15$
$(2w^3 + 3)(4w^2 - 5)$

65. $3j^2k + 15k + j^2 + 5$
$(j^2 + 5)(3k + 1)$

66. $2ab^2 - 6ac + b^2 - 3c$
$(b^2 - 3c)(2a + 1)$

67. $14w^6x^6 + 7w^6 - 2x^6 - 1$
$(2x^6 + 1)(7w^6 - 1)$

68. $18p^4q - 9p^5 - 2q + p$
$(2q - p)(9p^4 - 1)$

69. $ay + bx + by + ax$
(*Hint:* Rearrange the terms.)
$(y + x)(a + b)$

70. $2c + 3ay + ac + 6y$
$(c + 3y)(2 + a)$

71. $vw^2 - 3 + w - 3wv$
$(vw + 1)(w - 3)$

72. $2x^2 + 6m + 12 + x^2m$
$(m + 2)(6 + x^2)$

Mixed Exercises

For Exercises 73–78, factor out the GCF first. Then factor by grouping. **(See Example 11.)**

73. $15x^4 + 15x^2y^2 + 10x^3y + 10xy^3$
$5x(x^2 + y^2)(3x + 2y)$

74. $2a^3b - 4a^2b + 32ab - 64b$
$2b(a - 2)(a^2 + 16)$

75. $4abx - 4b^2x - 4ab + 4b^2$
$4b(a - b)(x - 1)$

76. $p^2q - pq^2 - rp^2q + rpq^2$
$pq(p - q)(1 - r)$

77. $6st^2 - 18st - 6t^4 + 18t^3$
$6t(t - 3)(s - t^2)$

78. $15j^3 - 10j^2k - 15j^2k^2 + 10jk^3$
$5j(3j - 2k)(j - k^2)$

79. The formula $P = 2l + 2w$ represents the perimeter, P, of a rectangle given the length, l, and the width, w. Factor out the GCF and write an equivalent formula in factored form.
$P = 2(l + w)$

80. The formula $P = 2a + 2b$ represents the perimeter, P, of a parallelogram given the base, b, and an adjacent side, a. Factor out the GCF and write an equivalent formula in factored form.
$P = 2(a + b)$

81. The formula $S = 2\pi r^2 + 2\pi rh$ represents the surface area, S, of a cylinder with radius, r, and height, h. Factor out the GCF and write an equivalent formula in factored form.
$S = 2\pi r(r + h)$

82. The formula $A = P + Prt$ represents the total amount of money, A, in an account that earns simple interest at a rate, r, for t years. Factor out the GCF and write an equivalent formula in factored form. $A = P(1 + rt)$

Expanding Your Skills

83. Factor out $\frac{1}{7}$ from $\frac{1}{7}x^2 + \frac{3}{7}x - \frac{5}{7}$. $\frac{1}{7}(x^2 + 3x - 5)$

84. Factor out $\frac{1}{5}$ from $\frac{6}{5}y^2 - \frac{4}{5}y + \frac{1}{5}$. $\frac{1}{5}(6y^2 - 4y + 1)$

85. Factor out $\frac{1}{4}$ from $\frac{5}{4}w^2 + \frac{3}{4}w + \frac{9}{4}$. $\frac{1}{4}(5w^2 + 3w + 9)$

86. Factor out $\frac{1}{6}$ from $\frac{1}{6}p^2 - \frac{3}{6}p + \frac{5}{6}$. $\frac{1}{6}(p^2 - 3p + 5)$

87. Write a polynomial that has a GCF of $3x$. (Answers may vary.) For example: $6x^2 + 9x$

88. Write a polynomial that has a GCF of $7y$. (Answers may vary.) For example: $14y - 21y^3 + 7y^2$

89. Write a polynomial that has a GCF of $4p^2q$. (Answers may vary.)
For example: $16p^4q^2 + 8p^3q - 4p^2q$

90. Write a polynomial that has a GCF of $2ab^2$. (Answers may vary.) For example: $18a^2b^3 - 2ab^2$

 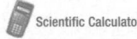

Section 6.2 **Factoring Trinomials of the Form $x^2 + bx + c$**

1. Factoring Trinomials with a Leading Coefficient of 1

In Section 5.6, we learned how to multiply two binomials. We also saw that such a product often results in a trinomial. For example:

$$(x + 3)(x + 7) = x^2 + \underbrace{7x + 3x}_{} + 21 = x^2 + 10x + 21$$

Product of first terms

Product of last terms

Sum of products of inner terms and outer terms

In this section, we want to reverse the process. That is, given a trinomial, we want to *factor* it as a product of two binomials. In particular, we begin our study with the case in which a trinomial has a leading coefficient of 1.

Consider the quadratic trinomial $x^2 + bx + c$. To produce a leading term of x^2, we can construct binomials of the form $(x + \ \ )(x + \ \ )$. The remaining terms can be obtained from two integers, p and q, whose product is c and whose sum is b.

$$x^2 + bx + c = (x + p)(x + q) = x^2 + qx + px + pq$$

Factors of c

$$= x^2 + \underbrace{(q + p)}_{\text{Sum} = b}x + \underbrace{pq}_{\text{Product} = c}$$

This process is demonstrated in Example 1.

Classroom Example: p. 426, Exercise 8

Example 1 **Factoring a Trinomial of the Form $x^2 + bx + c$**

Factor. $x^2 + 4x - 45$

Solution:

$x^2 + 4x - 45 = (x + \square)(x + \square)$ The product of the first terms in the binomials must equal the leading term of the trinomial $x \cdot x = x^2$.

We must fill in the blanks with two integers whose product is -45 and whose sum is 4. The factors must have opposite signs to produce a negative product. The possible factorizations of -45 are:

Product $= -45$	Sum
$-1 \cdot 45$	44
$-3 \cdot 15$	12
$-5 \cdot 9$	4
$-9 \cdot 5$	-4
$-15 \cdot 3$	-12
$-45 \cdot 1$	-44

$$x^2 + 4x - 45 = (x + \square)(x + \square)$$

$$= [x + (-5)](x + 9) \qquad \text{Fill in the blanks with } -5 \text{ and } 9.$$

$$= (x - 5)(x + 9) \qquad \text{Factored form}$$

$$\underline{\text{Check:}}$$

$$(x - 5)(x + 9) = x^2 + 9x - 5x - 45$$

$$= x^2 + 4x - 45 \checkmark$$

Skill Practice Factor.

1. $x^2 - 5x - 14$

Multiplication of polynomials is a commutative operation. Therefore, in Example 1, we can express the factorization as $(x - 5)(x + 9)$ or as $(x + 9)(x - 5)$.

Example 2 Factoring a Trinomial of the Form $x^2 + bx + c$

Classroom Example: p. 426, Exercise 14

Factor. $w^2 - 15w + 50$

Solution:

$$w^2 - 15w + 50 = (w + \square)(w + \square) \qquad \text{The product } w \cdot w = w^2.$$

Find two integers whose product is 50 and whose sum is -15. To form a positive product, the factors must be either both positive or both negative. The sum must be negative, so we will choose negative factors of 50.

Product = 50	**Sum**
$(-1)(-50)$	-51
$(-2)(-25)$	-27
$(-5)(-10)$	-15

$$w^2 - 15w + 50 = (w + \square)(w + \square)$$

$$= [w + (-5)][w + (-10)]$$

$$= (w - 5)(w - 10) \qquad \text{Factored form}$$

$$\underline{\text{Check:}}$$

$$(w - 5)(w - 10) = w^2 - 10w - 5w + 50$$

$$= w^2 - 15w + 50 \checkmark$$

Skill Practice Factor.

2. $z^2 - 16z + 48$

Practice will help you become proficient in factoring polynomials. As you do your homework, keep these important guidelines in mind:

- To factor a trinomial, write the trinomial in descending order such as $x^2 + bx + c$.
- For all factoring problems, always factor out the GCF from all terms first.

Answers

1. $(x - 7)(x + 2)$
2. $(z - 4)(z - 12)$

Furthermore, we offer the following rules for determining the signs within the binomial factors.

PROCEDURE **Sign Rules for Factoring Trinomials**

Given the trinomial $x^2 + bx + c$, the signs within the binomial factors are determined as follows:

Case 1 If c is *positive*, then the signs in the binomials must be the same (either both positive or both negative). The correct choice is determined by the middle term. If the middle term is positive, then both signs must be positive. If the middle term is negative, then both signs must be negative.

$$c \text{ is positive.} \qquad\qquad c \text{ is positive.}$$
$$x^2 + 6x + 8 \qquad\qquad x^2 - 6x + 8$$
$$(x + 2)(x + 4) \qquad\qquad (x - 2)(x - 4)$$
$$\text{Same signs} \qquad\qquad \text{Same signs}$$

Case 2 If c is *negative*, then the signs in the binomials must be different.

$$c \text{ is negative.} \qquad\qquad c \text{ is negative.}$$
$$x^2 + 2x - 35 \qquad\qquad x^2 - 2x - 35$$
$$(x + 7)(x - 5) \qquad\qquad (x - 7)(x + 5)$$
$$\text{Different signs} \qquad\qquad \text{Different signs}$$

Classroom Examples: p. 427, Exercises 32 and 40

Example 3 **Factoring Trinomials**

Factor. **a.** $-8p - 48 + p^2$ **b.** $-40t - 30t^2 + 10t^3$

Solution:

a. $-8p - 48 + p^2$

$= p^2 - 8p - 48$ Write in descending order.

$= (p \quad \square)(p \quad \square)$ Find two integers whose product is -48 and whose sum is -8. The numbers are -12 and 4.

$= (p - 12)(p + 4)$ Factored form

b. $-40t - 30t^2 + 10t^3$

$= 10t^3 - 30t^2 - 40t$ Write in descending order.

$= 10t(t^2 - 3t - 4)$ Factor out the GCF.

$= 10t(t \quad \square)(t \quad \square)$ Find two integers whose product is -4 and whose sum is -3. The numbers are -4 and 1.

$= 10t(t - 4)(t + 1)$ Factored form

Skill Practice Factor.

3. $-5w + w^2 - 6$ **4.** $30y^3 + 2y^4 + 112y^2$

Answers

3. $(w - 6)(w + 1)$
4. $2y^2(y + 8)(y + 7)$

Example 4   Factoring Trinomials

Factor.   **a.** $-a^2 + 6a - 8$ **b.** $-2c^2 - 22cd - 60d^2$

Solution:

a. $-a^2 + 6a - 8$

$= -1(a^2 - 6a + 8)$

$= -1(a \quad \square)(a \quad \square)$

$= -1(a - 4)(a - 2)$

It is generally easier to factor a trinomial with a *positive* leading coefficient. Therefore, we will factor out -1 from all terms.

Find two integers whose product is 8 and whose sum is -6. The numbers are -4 and -2.

b. $-2c^2 - 22cd - 60d^2$

$= -2(c^2 + 11cd + 30d^2)$ Factor out -2.

$= -2(c \quad \square d)(c \quad \square d)$ Notice that the second pair of terms has a factor of d. This will produce a product of d^2.

$= -2(c + 5d)(c + 6d)$ Find two integers whose product is 30 and whose sum is 11. The numbers are 5 and 6.

Skill Practice Factor.

   5. $-x^2 + x + 12$ **6.** $-3a^2 + 15ab - 12b^2$

To factor a trinomial of the form $x^2 + bx + c$, we must find two integers whose product is c and whose sum is b. If no such integers exist, then the trinomial is prime.

Example 5   Factoring Trinomials

Factor. $x^2 - 13x + 14$

Solution:

$x^2 - 13x + 14$ The trinomial is in descending order. The GCF is 1.

$= (x \quad \square)(x \quad \square)$ Find two integers whose product is 14 and whose sum is -13. No such integers exist.

The trinomial $x^2 - 13x + 14$ is prime.

Skill Practice Factor.

   7. $x^2 - 7x + 28$

Classroom Examples: p. 427, Exercises 44 and 46

Avoiding Mistakes

Recall that factoring out -1 from a polynomial changes the signs of all terms within parentheses.

Instructor Note: Show students how a sign difference between two expressions can affect the factors used.
1. $x^2 - 10x + 24, x^2 - 10x - 24$
2. $x^2 - 5x + 6, x^2 - 5x - 6$
3. $x^2 - 13x + 30, x^2 - 13x - 30$

Classroom Example: p. 426, Exercise 18

Answers
5. $-(x - 4)(x + 3)$
6. $-3(a - b)(a - 4b)$
7. Prime

Section 6.2 Practice Exercises

Boost *your* GRADE at
ALEKS.com!

 ALEKS
version 3.0

• Practice Problems
• Self-Tests
• NetTutor

• e-Professors
• Videos

For additional exercises, see Classroom Activity
6.2A in the *Instructor's Resource Manual*
at www.mhhe.com/moh.

Review Exercises

For Exercises 1–6, factor completely.

1. $4x^3y^7 - 12x^4y^5 + 8xy^8$ $4xy^5(x^2y^2 - 3x^3 + 2y^3)$

2. $9a^6b^3 - 27a^3b^6 - 3a^2b^2$ $3a^2b^2(3a^4b - 9ab^4 - 1)$

3. $3t(t - 5) - 6(t - 5)$ $3(t - 5)(t - 2)$

4. $4(3x - 2) + 8x(3x - 2)$ $4(3x - 2)(1 + 2x)$

5. $ax + 2bx - 5a - 10b$ $(a + 2b)(x - 5)$

6. $m^2 - mx - 3pm + 3px$ $(m - x)(m - 3p)$

Concept 1: Factoring Trinomials with a Leading Coefficient of 1   Animation

For Exercises 7–20, factor completely. **(See Examples 1, 2, and 5.)**

7. $x^2 + 10x + 16$ $(x + 8)(x + 2)$

8. $y^2 + 18y + 80$ $(y + 10)(y + 8)$

9. $z^2 - 11z + 18$ $(z - 9)(z - 2)$

10. $w^2 - 7w + 12$ $(w - 3)(w - 4)$

11. $z^2 - 3z - 18$ $(z - 6)(z + 3)$

12. $w^2 + 4w - 12$ $(w + 6)(w - 2)$

13. $p^2 - 3p - 40$ $(p - 8)(p + 5)$

14. $a^2 - 10a + 9$ $(a - 9)(a - 1)$

15. $t^2 + 6t - 40$ $(t + 10)(t - 4)$

16. $m^2 - 12m + 11$ $(m - 11)(m - 1)$

17. $x^2 - 3x + 20$ Prime

18. $y^2 + 6y + 18$ Prime

19. $n^2 + 8n + 16$ $(n + 4)^2$

20. $v^2 + 10v + 25$ $(v + 5)^2$

For Exercises 21–24, assume that b and c represent positive integers.

21. When factoring a polynomial of the form $x^2 + bx + c$, pick an appropriate combination of signs. a

    a. (+)(+)   **b.** (−)(−)   **c.** (+)(−)

22. When factoring a polynomial of the form $x^2 + bx - c$, pick an appropriate combination of signs. c

    a. (+)(+)   **b.** (−)(−)   **c.** (+)(−)

23. When factoring a polynomial of the form $x^2 - bx - c$, pick an appropriate combination of signs. c

    a. (+)(+)   **b.** (−)(−)   **c.** (+)(−)

24. When factoring a polynomial of the form $x^2 - bx + c$, pick an appropriate combination of signs. b

    a. (+)(+)   **b.** (−)(−)   **c.** (+)(−)

25. Which is the correct factorization of $y^2 - y - 12$? Explain. $(y - 4)(y + 3)$ or $(y + 3)(y - 4)$
They are both correct because multiplication of polynomials is a commutative operation.

26. Which is the correct factorization of $x^2 + 14x + 13$? Explain. $(x + 13)(x + 1)$ or $(x + 1)(x + 13)$
They are both correct because multiplication of polynomials is a commutative operation.

27. Which is the correct factorization of $w^2 + 2w + 1$? Explain. $(w + 1)(w + 1)$ or $(w + 1)^2$
The expressions are equal and both are correct.

28. Which is the correct factorization of $z^2 - 4z + 4$? Explain. $(z - 2)(z - 2)$ or $(z - 2)^2$
The expressions are equal and both are correct.

29. In what order should a trinomial be written before attempting to factor it?   Descending order

30. Referring to page 423, write two important guidelines to follow when factoring trinomials.
To factor a trinomial, write the trinomial in descending order such as $x^2 + bx + c$. For all factoring problems, always factor out the GCF from all terms.

For Exercises 31–66, factor completely. Be sure to factor out the GCF when necessary.   **(See Examples 3–4.)**

31. $-13x + x^2 - 30$
$(x - 15)(x + 2)$

32. $12y - 160 + y^2$
$(y + 20)(y - 8)$

33. $-18w + 65 + w^2$
$(w - 13)(w - 5)$

34. $17t + t^2 + 72$
$(t + 8)(t + 9)$

35. $22t + t^2 + 72$
$(t + 18)(t + 4)$

36. $10q - 1200 + q^2$
$(q - 30)(q + 40)$

37. $3x^2 - 30x - 72$
$3(x - 12)(x + 2)$

38. $2z^2 + 4z - 198$
$2(z + 11)(z - 9)$

39. $8p^3 - 40p^2 + 32p$
$8p(p - 1)(p - 4)$

40. $5w^4 - 35w^3 + 50w^2$
$5w^2(w - 2)(w - 5)$

41. $y^4z^2 - 12y^3z^2 + 36y^2z^2$
$y^2z^2(y - 6)(y - 6)$ or $y^2z^2(y - 6)^2$

42. $t^4u^2 + 6t^3u^2 + 9t^2u^2$
$t^2u^2(t + 3)(t + 3)$ or $t^2u^2(t + 3)^2$

43. $-x^2 + 10x - 24$
$-(x - 4)(x - 6)$

44. $-y^2 - 12y - 35$
$-(y + 5)(y + 7)$

45. $-5a^2 + 5ax + 30x^2$
$-5(a - 3x)(a + 2x)$

46. $-2m^2 + 10mn + 12n^2$
$-2(m + n)(m - 6n)$

47. $-4 - 2c^2 - 6c$
$-2(c + 2)(c + 1)$

48. $-40d - 30 - 10d^2$
$-10(d + 3)(d + 1)$

49. $x^3y^3 - 19x^2y^3 + 60xy^3$
$xy^3(x - 4)(x - 15)$

50. $y^2z^5 + 17yz^5 + 60z^5$
$z^5(y + 5)(y + 12)$

51. $12p^2 - 96p + 84$
$12(p - 7)(p - 1)$

52. $5w^2 - 40w - 45$
$5(w - 9)(w + 1)$

53. $-2m^2 + 22m - 20$
$-2(m - 10)(m - 1)$

54. $-3x^2 - 36x - 81$
$-3(x + 9)(x + 3)$

55. $c^2 + 6cd + 5d^2$ $(c + 5d)(c + d)$

56. $x^2 + 8xy + 12y^2$ $(x + 6y)(x + 2y)$

57. $a^2 - 9ab + 14b^2$ $(a - 2b)(a - 7b)$

58. $m^2 - 15mn + 44n^2$
$(m - 4n)(m - 11n)$

59. $a^2 + 4a + 18$ Prime

60. $b^2 - 6a + 15$ Prime

61. $2q + q^2 - 63$ $(q - 7)(q + 9)$

62. $-32 - 4t + t^2$ $(t - 8)(t + 4)$

63. $x^2 + 20x + 100$ $(x + 10)^2$

64. $z^2 - 24z + 144$ $(z - 12)^2$

65. $t^2 + 18t - 40$ $(t + 20)(t - 2)$

66. $d^2 + 2d - 99$ $(d + 11)(d - 9)$

67. A student factored a trinomial as $(2x - 4)(x - 3)$. The instructor did not give full credit. Why?   The student forgot
to factor out the GCF before factoring the trinomial further. The polynomial is not factored completely, because $(2x - 4)$ has a common factor of 2.

68. A student factored a trinomial as $(y + 2)(5y - 15)$. The instructor did not give full credit. Why?   The student forgot
to factor out the GCF before factoring the trinomial further. The polynomial is not factored completely, because $(5y - 15)$ has a common factor of 5.

69. What polynomial factors as $(x - 4)(x + 13)$? $x^2 + 9x - 52$

70. What polynomial factors as $(q - 7)(q + 10)$? $q^2 + 3q - 70$

Expanding Your Skills

For Exercises 71–74, factor completely.

71. $x^4 + 10x^2 + 9$
$(x^2 + 1)(x^2 + 9)$

72. $y^4 + 4y^2 - 21$
$(y^2 - 3)(y^2 + 7)$

73. $w^4 + 2w^2 - 15$
$(w^2 + 5)(w^2 - 3)$

74. $p^4 - 13p^2 + 40$
$(p^2 - 8)(p^2 - 5)$

75. Find all integers, b, that make the trinomial $x^2 + bx + 6$ factorable. $7, 5, -7, -5$

76. Find all integers, b, that make the trinomial $x^2 + bx + 10$ factorable. $11, 7, -11, -7$

77. Find a value of c that makes the trinomial $x^2 + 6x + c$ factorable.   For example: $c = -16$

78. Find a value of c that makes the trinomial $x^2 + 8x + c$ factorable.   For example: $c = 7$

Writing   ←→ Translating Expression   Geometry   Scientific Calculator   Video

Section 6.3   Factoring Trinomials: Trial-and-Error Method

Concept

1. Factoring Trinomials by the Trial-and-Error Method

In Section 6.2, we learned how to factor trinomials of the form $x^2 + bx + c$. These trinomials have a leading coefficient of 1. In this section and Section 6.4, we will consider the more general case in which the leading coefficient may be *any* nonzero integer. That is, we will factor quadratic trinomials of the form $ax^2 + bx + c$ (where $a \neq 0$). The method presented in this section is called the trial-and-error method.

1. Factoring Trinomials by the Trial-and-Error Method

To understand the basis of factoring trinomials of the form $ax^2 + bx + c$, first consider the multiplication of two binomials:

$$\overset{\text{Product of } 2 \cdot 1}{\downarrow} \qquad \overset{\text{Product of } 3 \cdot 2}{\downarrow}$$

$$(2x + 3)(1x + 2) = 2x^2 + \underbrace{\mathbf{4x + 3x}}_{\substack{\text{Sum of products of inner} \\ \text{terms and outer terms}}} + 6 = 2x^2 + 7x + 6$$

To factor the trinomial, $2x^2 + 7x + 6$, this operation is reversed.

$$\overset{\text{Factors of 2}}{\overbrace{\qquad\qquad}}$$

$$2x^2 + 7x + 6 = (\square x \quad \square)(\square x \quad \square)$$

$$\underbrace{\qquad\qquad}_{\text{Factors of 6}}$$

We need to fill in the blanks so that the product of the first terms in the binomials is $2x^2$ and the product of the last terms in the binomials is 6. Furthermore, the factors of $2x^2$ and 6 must be chosen so that the sum of the products of the inner terms and outer terms equals $7x$.

To produce the product $2x^2$, we might try the factors $2x$ and x within the binomials:

$$(2x \quad \square)(x \quad \square)$$

To produce a product of 6, the remaining terms in the binomials must either both be positive or both be negative. To produce a positive middle term, we will try positive factors of 6 in the remaining blanks until the correct product is found. The possibilities are $1 \cdot 6, 2 \cdot 3, 6 \cdot 1$, and $3 \cdot 2$.

$(2x + 1)(x + 6) = 2x^2 + 12x + 1x + 6 = 2x^2 + 13x + 6$ Wrong middle term

$(2x + 2)(x + 3) = 2x^2 + 6x + 2x + 6 = 2x^2 + 8x + 6$ Wrong middle term

$(2x + 6)(x + 1) = 2x^2 + 2x + 6x + 6 = 2x^2 + 8x + 6$ Wrong middle term

$(2x + 3)(x + 2) = 2x^2 + 4x + 3x + 6 = 2x^2 + 7x + 6$ Correct!

The correct factorization of $2x^2 + 7x + 6$ is $(2x + 3)(x + 2)$. ✔

As this example shows, we factor a trinomial of the form $ax^2 + bx + c$ by shuffling the factors of a and c within the binomials until the correct product is obtained. However, sometimes it is not necessary to test all the possible combinations of factors. In the previous example, the GCF of the original trinomial is 1. Therefore, any binomial factor whose terms share a common factor *greater than 1* does not need to be considered. In this case, the possibilities $(2x + 2)(x + 3)$ and $(2x + 6)(x + 1)$ cannot work.

$$\underbrace{(2x + 2)}(x + 3) \qquad \underbrace{(2x + 6)}(x + 1)$$

Common   Common
factor of 2   factor of 2

PROCEDURE   Trial-and-Error Method to Factor $ax^2 + bx + c$

Step 1   Factor out the GCF.

Step 2   List all pairs of positive factors of a and pairs of positive factors of c. Consider the reverse order for one of the lists of factors.

Step 3   Construct two binomials of the form:

Factors of a
$$(\Box x \quad \Box)(\Box x \quad \Box)$$
Factors of c

Step 4   Test each combination of factors and signs until the correct product is found.

Step 5   If no combination of factors produces the correct product, the trinomial cannot be factored further.

Before we begin Example 1, keep these two important guidelines in mind:

- For any factoring problem you encounter, always factor out the GCF from all terms first.

- To factor a trinomial, write the trinomial in the form $ax^2 + bx + c$.

Example 1   Factoring a Trinomial by the Trial-and-Error Method

Classroom Example: p. 435, Exercise 14

Factor the trinomial by the trial-and-error method. $10x^2 - 9x - 1$

Solution:

$10x^2 - 9x - 1$ **Step 1:**   Factor out the GCF from all terms. In this case, the GCF is 1.

The trinomial is written in the form $ax^2 + bx + c$.

To factor $10x^2 - 9x - 1$, two binomials must be constructed in the form:

Factors of 10

$(\Box x \quad \Box)(\Box x \quad \Box)$

Factors of -1

Step 2:   To produce the product $10x^2$, we might try $5x$ and $2x$, or $10x$ and $1x$. To produce a product of -1, we will try the factors $(1)(-1)$ and $(-1)(1)$.

Step 3:   Construct all possible binomial factors using different combinations of the factors of $10x^2$ and -1.

$$(5x + 1)(2x - 1) = 10x^2 - 5x + 2x - 1 = 10x^2 - 3x - 1 \qquad \text{Wrong middle term}$$

$$(5x - 1)(2x + 1) = 10x^2 + 5x - 2x - 1 = 10x^2 + 3x - 1 \qquad \text{Wrong middle term}$$

Because the numbers 1 and -1 did not produce the correct trinomial when coupled with $5x$ and $2x$, try using $10x$ and $1x$.

$$(10x - 1)(1x + 1) = 10x^2 + 10x - 1x - 1 = 10x^2 + 9x - 1 \qquad \text{Wrong middle term}$$

$$(10x + 1)(1x - 1) = 10x^2 - 10x + 1x - 1 = 10x^2 - 9x - 1 \qquad \text{Correct!}$$

Therefore, $10x^2 - 9x - 1 = (10x + 1)(x - 1)$.

Skill Practice Factor using the trial-and-error method.

1. $3b^2 + 8b + 4$

In Example 1, the factors of -1 must have opposite signs to produce a negative product. Therefore, one binomial factor is a sum and one is a difference. Determining the correct signs is an important aspect of factoring trinomials. We suggest the following guidelines:

PROCEDURE **Sign Rules for the Trial-and-Error Method**

Given the trinomial $ax^2 + bx + c$, $(a > 0)$, the signs can be determined as follows:

- If *c is positive*, then the signs in the binomials must be the same (either both positive or both negative). The correct choice is determined by the middle term. If the middle term is positive, then both signs must be positive. If the middle term is negative, then both signs must be negative.

$$\begin{array}{cc}
c \text{ is positive} & c \text{ is positive} \\
\downarrow & \downarrow \\
20x^2 + 43x + 21 & 20x^2 - 43x + 21 \\
(4x + 3)(5x + 7) & (4x - 3)(5x - 7) \\
\underbrace{\qquad\qquad}_{\text{Same signs}} & \underbrace{\qquad\qquad}_{\text{Same signs}}
\end{array}$$

- If *c is negative*, then the signs in the binomial must be different. The middle term in the trinomial determines which factor gets the positive sign and which gets the negative sign.

$$\begin{array}{cc}
c \text{ is negative} & c \text{ is negative} \\
\downarrow & \downarrow \\
x^2 + 3x - 28 & x^2 - 3x - 28 \\
(x + 7)(x - 4) & (x - 7)(x + 4) \\
\underbrace{\qquad\qquad}_{\text{Different signs}} & \underbrace{\qquad\qquad}_{\text{Different signs}}
\end{array}$$

TIP: Look at the sign on the third term. If it is a sum, the signs will be the same in the two binomials. If it is a difference, the signs in the two binomials will be different: sum–same sign; difference–different signs.

Answer

1. $(3b + 2)(b + 2)$

Example 2 **Factoring a Trinomial by the Trial-and-Error Method**

Classroom Example: p. 435, Exercise 20

Factor the trinomial. $13y - 6 + 8y^2$

Solution:

$13y - 6 + 8y^2$

$= 8y^2 + 13y - 6$ Write the polynomial in descending order.

$(\square y \ \square)(\square y \ \square)$ **Step 1:** The GCF is 1.

Factors of 8	**Factors of 6**
$1 \cdot 8$	$1 \cdot 6$
$2 \cdot 4$	$2 \cdot 3$
	$\left.\begin{array}{l}3 \cdot 2 \\ 6 \cdot 1\end{array}\right\}$ (reverse order)

Step 2: List the positive factors of 8 and positive factors of 6. Consider the reverse order in one list of factors.

Step 3: Construct all possible binomial factors using different combinations of the factors of 8 and 6.

$$\left.\begin{array}{l}(2y \ \ 1)(4y \ \ 6) \\ (2y \ \ 2)(4y \ \ 3) \\ (2y \ \ 3)(4y \ \ 2) \\ (2y \ \ 6)(4y \ \ 1) \\ (1y \ \ 1)(8y \ \ 6) \\ (1y \ \ 3)(8y \ \ 2)\end{array}\right\}$$

Without regard to signs, these factorizations cannot work because the terms in the binomials share a common factor greater than 1.

Test the remaining factorizations. Keep in mind that to produce a product of -6, the signs within the parentheses must be opposite (one positive and one negative). Also, the sum of the products of the inner terms and outer terms must be combined to form $13y$.

 $(1y \ \ 6)(8y \ \ 1)$ *Incorrect.* Wrong middle term.
Regardless of the signs, the product of inner terms, $48y$, and the product of outer terms, $1y$, cannot be combined to form the middle term $13y$.

 $(1y \ \ 2)(8y \ \ 3)$ *Correct.* The terms $16y$ and $3y$ can be combined to form the middle term $13y$, provided the signs are applied correctly. We require $+16y$ and $-3y$.

The correct factorization of $8y^2 + 13y - 6$ is $(y + 2)(8y - 3)$.

Skill Practice Factor.

2. $-25w + 6w^2 + 4$

Remember that the first step in any factoring problem is to remove the GCF. By removing the GCF, the remaining terms of the trinomial will be simpler and may have smaller coefficients.

Answer

2. $(6w - 1)(w - 4)$

Classroom Example: p. 436, Exercise 32

Example 3 **Factoring a Trinomial by the Trial-and-Error Method**

Factor the trinomial by the trial-and-error method. $40x^3 - 104x^2 + 10x$

Solution:

$40x^3 - 104x^2 + 10x$

$= 2x(20x^2 - 52x + 5)$ **Step 1:** The GCF is $2x$.

$= 2x(\Box x \quad \Box)(\Box x \quad \Box)$ **Step 2:** List the factors of 20 and factors of 5. Consider the reverse order in one list of factors.

Factors of 20	Factors of 5
$1 \cdot 20$	$1 \cdot 5$
$2 \cdot 10$	$5 \cdot 1$
$4 \cdot 5$	

Step 3: Construct all possible binomial factors using different combinations of the factors of 20 and factors of 5. The signs in the parentheses must both be negative.

> **TIP:** Notice that when the GCF, $2x$, is removed from the original trinomial, the new trinomial has smaller coefficients. This makes the factoring process simpler. It is easier to list the factors of 20 and 5 than the factors of 40 and 10.

$\left. \begin{array}{l} = 2x(1x - 1)(20x - 5) \\ = 2x(2x - 1)(10x - 5) \\ = 2x(4x - 1)(5x - 5) \end{array} \right\}$ *Incorrect.* Once the GCF has been removed from the original polynomial, the binomial factors cannot contain a GCF greater than 1.

$= 2x(1x - 5)(20x - 1)$ *Incorrect.*   Wrong middle term.

$\quad 2x(x - 5)(20x - 1)$
$\quad = 2x(20x^2 - 1x - 100x + 5)$
$\quad = 2x(20x^2 - 101x + 5)$

$= 2x(4x - 5)(5x - 1)$ *Incorrect.*   Wrong middle term.

$\quad 2x(4x - 5)(5x - 1)$
$\quad = 2x(20x^2 - 4x - 25x + 5)$
$\quad = 2x(20x^2 - 29x + 5)$

$= 2x(2x - 5)(10x - 1)$ *Correct.* $2x(2x - 5)(10x - 1)$
$\quad = 2x(20x^2 - 2x - 50x + 5)$
$\quad = 2x(20x^2 - 52x + 5)$
$\quad = 40x^3 - 104x^2 + 10x$

The correct factorization is $2x(2x - 5)(10x - 1)$.

Skill Practice Factor.

3. $8t^3 + 38t^2 + 24t$

Often it is easier to factor a trinomial when the leading coefficient is positive. If the leading coefficient is negative, consider factoring out the opposite of the GCF.

Answer

3. $2t(4t + 3)(t + 4)$

Example 4 **Factoring a Trinomial by the Trial-and-Error Method**

Classroom Example: p. 436, Exercise 36

Factor. $-45x^2 - 3xy + 18y^2$

Solution:

$-45x^2 - 3xy + 18y^2$

$= -3(15x^2 + xy - 6y^2)$ **Step 1:** Factor out -3 to make the leading coefficient positive.

$= -3(\Box x \quad \Box y)(\Box x \quad \Box y)$ **Step 2:** List the factors of 15 and 6.

Factors of 15	**Factors of 6**
$1 \cdot 15$	$1 \cdot 6$
$3 \cdot 5$	$2 \cdot 3$
	$3 \cdot 2$
	$6 \cdot 1$

Step 3: We will construct all binomial combinations, without regard to signs first.

$\left.\begin{array}{l} -3(x \quad y)(15x \quad 6y) \\ -3(x \quad 2y)(15x \quad 3y) \\ -3(3x \quad 3y)(5x \quad 2y) \\ -3(3x \quad 6y)(5x \quad y) \end{array}\right\}$ *Incorrect.*   The binomials contain a common factor.

Test the remaining factorizations. The signs within parentheses must be opposite to produce a product of $-6y^2$. Also, the sum of the products of the inner terms and outer terms must be combined to form $1xy$.

$-3(x \quad 3y)(15x \quad 2y)$ *Incorrect.*   Regardless of signs, $45xy$ and $2xy$ cannot be combined to equal xy.

$-3(x \quad 6y)(15x \quad y)$ *Incorrect.*   Regardless of signs, $90xy$ and xy cannot be combined to equal xy.

$-3(3x \quad y)(5x \quad 6y)$ *Incorrect.*   Regardless of signs, $5xy$ and $18xy$ cannot be combined to equal xy.

$-3(3x \quad 2y)(5x \quad 3y)$ *Correct.*   The terms $10xy$ and $9xy$ can be combined to form xy provided that the signs are applied correctly. We require $10xy$ and $-9xy$.

$-3(3x + 2y)(5x - 3y)$ Factored form

Avoiding Mistakes

Do not forget to write the GCF in the final answer.

Skill Practice Factor.

4. $-4x^2 + 26xy - 40y^2$

Recall that a prime polynomial is a polynomial whose only factors are itself and 1. Not every trinomial is factorable by the methods presented in this text.

Answer

4. $-2(2x - 5y)(x - 4y)$

Classroom Example: p. 436, Exercise 52

Example 5   **Factoring a Trinomial by the Trial-and-Error Method**

Factor the trinomial by the trial-and-error method. $2p^2 - 8p + 3$

Solution:

$2p^2 - 8p + 3$

$= (1p \;\square\;)(2p \;\square\;)$

Factors of 2	**Factors of 3**
$1 \cdot 2$	$1 \cdot 3$
	$3 \cdot 1$

Step 1:   The GCF is 1.

Step 2:   List the factors of 2 and the factors of 3.

Step 3:   Construct all possible binomial factors using different combinations of the factors of 2 and 3. Because the third term in the trinomial is positive, both signs in the binomial must be the same. Because the middle term coefficient is negative, both signs will be negative.

$(p - 1)(2p - 3) = 2p^2 - 3p - 2p + 3$

$\qquad\qquad\qquad = 2p^2 - 5p + 3 \qquad\qquad$ *Incorrect.*   Wrong middle term.

$(p - 3)(2p - 1) = 2p^2 - p - 6p + 3$

$\qquad\qquad\qquad = 2p^2 - 7p + 3 \qquad\qquad$ *Incorrect.*   Wrong middle term.

None of the combinations of factors results in the correct product. Therefore, the polynomial $2p^2 - 8p + 3$ is prime and cannot be factored further.

Skill Practice Factor.

5. $3a^2 + a + 4$

In Example 6, we use the trial-and-error method to factor a higher degree trinomial into two binomial factors.

Classroom Example: p. 436, Exercise 38

Example 6   **Factoring a Higher Degree Trinomial**

Factor the trinomial. $3x^4 + 8x^2 + 5$

Solution:

$3x^4 + 8x^2 + 5$

$= (\square x^2 + \square)(\square x^2 + \square)$

Step 1:   The GCF is 1.

Step 2:   To produce the product $3x^4$, we must use $3x^2$ and $1x^2$. To produce a product of 5, we will try the factors $(1)(5)$ and $(5)(1)$.

Step 3:   Construct all possible binomial factors using the combinations of factors of $3x^4$ and 5.

$(3x^2 + 1)(x^2 + 5) = 3x^4 + 15x^2 + 1x^2 + 5 = 3x^4 + 16x^2 + 5 \qquad$ Wrong middle term.

$(3x^2 + 5)(x^2 + 1) = 3x^4 + 3x^2 + 5x^2 + 5 = 3x^4 + 8x^2 + 5 \qquad$ Correct!

Therefore, $3x^4 + 8x^2 + 5 = (3x^2 + 5)(x^2 + 1)$

Skill Practice Factor.

6. $2y^4 - y^2 - 15$

Answers

5. Prime   **6.** $(y^2 - 3)(2y^2 + 5)$

Section 6.3 Practice Exercises

Review Exercises

For Exercises 1–6, factor completely.

1. $21a^2b^2 + 12ab^2 - 15a^2b$
$3ab(7ab + 4b - 5a)$

2. $5uv^2 - 10u^2v + 25u^2v^2$
$5uv(v - 2u + 5uv)$

3. $mn - m - 2n + 2$
$(n - 1)(m - 2)$

4. $5x - 10 - xy + 2y$
$(x - 2)(5 - y)$

5. $6a^2 - 30a - 84$
$6(a - 7)(a + 2)$

6. $10b^2 + 20b - 240$
$10(b + 6)(b - 4)$

Concept 1: Factoring Trinomials by the Trial-and-Error Method

For Exercises 7–10, assume a, b, and c represent positive integers

7. When factoring a polynomial of the form $ax^2 + bx + c$, pick an appropriate combination of signs.   a

   a. (+)(+)

   b. (−)(−)

   c. (+)(−)

8. When factoring a polynomial of the form $ax^2 - bx - c$, pick an appropriate combination of signs.   c

   a. (+)(+)

   b. (−)(−)

   c. (+)(−)

9. When factoring a polynomial of the form $ax^2 - bx + c$, pick an appropriate combination of signs.   b

   a. (+)(+)

   b. (−)(−)

   c. (+)(−)

10. When factoring a polynomial of the form $ax^2 + bx - c$, pick an appropriate combination of signs.   c

   a. (+)(+)

   b. (−)(−)

   c. (+)(−)

For Exercises 11–28, factor completely by using the trial-and-error method. **(See Examples 1, 2, and 5.)**

11. $2y^2 - 3y - 2$
$(2y + 1)(y - 2)$

12. $2w^2 + 5w - 3$
$(2w - 1)(w + 3)$

13. $3n^2 + 13n + 4$
$(3n + 1)(n + 4)$

14. $2a^2 + 7a + 6$
$(2u + 3)(u + 2)$

15. $5x^2 - 14x - 3$
$(5x + 1)(x - 3)$

16. $7y^2 + 9y - 10$
$(7y - 5)(y + 2)$

17. $12c^2 - 5c - 2$
$(4c + 1)(3c - 2)$

18. $6z^2 + z - 12$
$(3z - 4)(2z + 3)$

19. $-12 + 10w^2 + 37w$
$(10w - 3)(w + 4)$

20. $-10 + 10p^2 + 21p$
$(2p + 5)(5p - 2)$

21. $-5q - 6 + 6q^2$
$(3q + 2)(2q - 3)$

22. $17a - 2 + 3a^2$
Prime

23. $6b - 23 + 4b^2$
Prime

24. $8 + 7x^2 - 18x$
$(7x - 4)(x - 2)$

25. $-8 + 25m^2 - 10m$
$(5m + 2)(5m - 4)$

26. $8q^2 + 31q - 4$
$(8q - 1)(q + 4)$

27. $6y^2 + 19xy - 20x^2$
$(6y - 5x)(y + 4x)$

28. $12y^2 - 73yz + 6z^2$
$(12y - z)(y - 6z)$

For Exercises 29–36, factor completely. Be sure to factor out the GCF first. **(See Examples 3–4.)**

29. $2m^2 - 12m - 80$
$2(m + 4)(m - 10)$

30. $3c^2 - 33c + 72$
$3(c - 8)(c - 3)$

31. $2y^5 + 13y^4 + 6y^3$
$y^3(2y + 1)(y + 6)$

32. $3u^8 - 13u^7 + 4u^6$
$u^6(3u - 1)(u - 4)$

33. $-a^2 - 15a + 34$
$-(a + 17)(a - 2)$

34. $-x^2 - 7x - 10$
$-(x + 2)(x + 5)$

35. $-80m^2 + 100mp + 30p^2$
$-10(4m + p)(2m - 3p)$

36. $-60w^2 - 550wz + 500z^2$
$-10(w + 10z)(6w - 5z)$

For Exercises 37–42, factor the higher degree polynomial. **(See Example 6.)**

37. $x^4 + 10x^2 + 9$
$(x^2 + 1)(x^2 + 9)$

38. $y^4 + 4y^2 - 21$
$(y^2 - 3)(y^2 + 7)$

39. $w^4 + 2w^2 - 15$
$(w^2 + 5)(w^2 - 3)$

40. $p^4 - 13p^2 + 40$
$(p^2 - 8)(p^2 - 5)$

41. $2x^4 - 7x^2 - 15$
$(2x^2 + 3)(x^2 - 5)$

42. $5y^4 + 11y^2 + 2$
$(5y^2 + 1)(y^2 + 2)$

Mixed Exercises

For Exercises 43–84, factor each trinomial completely.

43. $20z - 18 - 2z^2$
$-2(z - 9)(z - 1)$

44. $25t - 5t^2 - 30$
$-5(t - 2)(t - 3)$

45. $42 - 13q + q^2$
$(q - 7)(q - 6)$

46. $-5w - 24 + w^2$
$(w - 8)(w + 3)$

47. $6t^2 + 7t - 3$
$(2t + 3)(3t - 1)$

48. $4p^2 - 9p + 2$
$(4p - 1)(p - 2)$

49. $4m^2 - 20m + 25$
$(2m - 5)^2$

50. $16r^2 + 24r + 9$
$(4r + 3)^2$

51. $5c^2 - c + 2$
Prime

52. $7s^2 + 2s + 9$
Prime

53. $6x^2 - 19xy + 10y^2$
$(2x - 5y)(3x - 2y)$

54. $15p^2 + pq - 2q^2$
$(3p - q)(5p + 2q)$

55. $12m^2 + 11mn - 5n^2$
$(4m + 5n)(3m - n)$

56. $4a^2 + 5ab - 6b^2$
$(4a - 3b)(a + 2b)$

57. $30r^2 + 5r - 10$
$5(3r + 2)(2r - 1)$

58. $36x^2 - 18x - 4$
$2(6x + 1)(3x - 2)$

59. $4s^2 - 8st + t^2$
Prime

60. $6u^2 - 10uv + 5v^2$
Prime

61. $10t^2 - 23t - 5$
$(2t - 5)(5t + 1)$

62. $16n^2 + 14n + 3$
$(8n + 3)(2n + 1)$

63. $14w^2 + 13w - 12$
$(7w - 4)(2w + 3)$

64. $12x^2 - 16x + 5$
$(6x - 5)(2x - 1)$

65. $a^2 - 10a - 24$
$(a - 12)(a + 2)$

66. $b^2 + 6b - 7$
$(b + 7)(b - 1)$

67. $x^2 + 9xy + 20y^2$
$(x + 5y)(x + 4y)$

68. $p^2 - 13pq + 36q^2$
$(p - 9q)(p - 4q)$

69. $a^2 + 21ab + 20b^2$
$(a + 20b)(a + b)$

70. $x^2 - 17xy - 18y^2$
$(x - 18y)(x + y)$

71. $t^2 - 10t + 21$
$(t - 7)(t - 3)$

72. $z^2 - 15z + 36$
$(z - 12)(z - 3)$

73. $5d^3 + 3d^2 - 10d$
$d(5d^2 + 3d - 10)$

74. $3y^3 - y^2 + 12y$
$y(3y^2 - y + 12)$

75. $4b^3 - 4b^2 - 80b$
$4b(b - 5)(b + 4)$

76. $2w^2 + 20w + 42$
$2(w + 7)(w + 3)$

77. $x^2y^2 - 13xy^2 + 30y^2$
$y^2(x - 3)(x - 10)$

78. $p^2q^2 - 14pq^2 + 33q^2$
$q^2(p - 3)(p - 11)$

79. $-12u^3 - 22u^2 + 20u$
$-2u(2u + 5)(3u - 2)$

80. $-18z^4 + 15z^3 + 12z^2$
$-3z^2(3z - 4)(2z + 1)$

81. $8x^4 + 14x^2 + 3$
$(2x^2 + 3)(4x^2 + 1)$

82. $6y^4 - 5y^2 - 4$
$(3y^2 - 4)(2y^2 + 1)$

83. $10z^4 + 9z^2 - 9$
$(5z^2 - 3)(2z^2 + 3)$

84. $6p^4 + 17p^2 + 10$
$(6p^2 + 5)(p^2 + 2)$

Expanding Your Skills

For Exercises 85–88, each pair of trinomials looks similar but differs by one sign. Factor each trinomial and see how their factored forms differ.

85. a. $x^2 - 10x - 24$ $(x - 12)(x + 2)$

    b. $x^2 - 10x + 24$ $(x - 6)(x - 4)$

86. a. $x^2 - 13x - 30$ $(x - 15)(x + 2)$

    b. $x^2 - 13x + 30$ $(x - 10)(x - 3)$

87. a. $x^2 - 5x - 6$ $(x - 6)(x + 1)$

    b. $x^2 - 5x + 6$ $(x - 2)(x - 3)$

88. a. $x^2 - 10x + 9$ $(x - 9)(x - 1)$

    b. $x^2 + 10x + 9$ $(x + 9)(x + 1)$

Factoring Trinomials: AC-Method

In Section 6.2, we factored trinomials with a leading coefficient of 1. In Section 6.3, we learned the trial-and-error method to factor the more general case in which the leading coefficient is any integer. In this section, we provide an alternative method to factor trinomials, called the ac method.

1. Factoring Trinomials by the AC-Method

The product of two binomials results in a four-term expression that can sometimes be simplified to a trinomial. To factor the trinomial, we want to reverse the process.

Multiply:

Multiply the binomials.   Add the middle terms.

$$(2x + 3)(x + 2) = \longrightarrow 2x^2 + 4x + 3x + 6 = \longrightarrow 2x^2 + 7x + 6$$

Factor:

$$2x^2 + 7x + 6 = \longrightarrow 2x^2 + 4x + 3x + 6 = \longrightarrow (2x + 3)(x + 2)$$

Rewrite the middle term as   Factor by grouping.
a sum or difference of terms.

To factor a quadratic trinomial, $ax^2 + bx + c$, by the ac-method, we rewrite the middle term, bx, as a sum or difference of terms. The goal is to produce a four-term polynomial that can be factored by grouping. The process is outlined as follows.

PROCEDURE AC-Method: Factoring $ax^2 + bx + c$ ($a \neq 0$)

Step 1 Factor out the GCF from all terms.

Step 2 Multiply the coefficients of the first and last terms (ac).

Step 3 Find two integers whose product is ac and whose sum is b. (If no pair of integers can be found, then the trinomial cannot be factored further.)

Step 4 Rewrite the middle term, bx, as the sum of two terms whose coefficients are the integers found in step 3.

Step 5 Factor the polynomial by grouping.

Instructor Note: We use the phrase *prime polynomial* to mean that a polynomial is not factorable over the *integers*.

The ac-method for factoring trinomials is illustrated in Example 1. However, before we begin, keep these two important guidelines in mind:

- For any factoring problem you encounter, always factor out the GCF from all terms first.
- To factor a trinomial, write the trinomial in the form $ax^2 + bx + c$.

Classroom Example: p. 442,
Exercise 14

Example 1 Factoring a Trinomial by the AC-Method

Factor the trinomial by the ac-method. $2x^2 + 7x + 6$

Solution:

$2x^2 + 7x + 6$

Step 1: Factor out the GCF from all terms. In this case, the GCF is 1. The trinomial is written in the form $ax^2 + bx + c$.

$a = 2, b = 7, c = 6$

Step 2: Find the product $ac = (2)(6) = 12$.

12	12
$1 \cdot 12$	$(-1)(-12)$
$2 \cdot 6$	$(-2)(-6)$
$3 \cdot 4$	$(-3)(-4)$

Step 3: List all factors of ac and search for the pair whose sum equals the value of b. That is, list the factors of 12 and find the pair whose sum equals 7.

The numbers 3 and 4 satisfy both conditions: $3 \cdot 4 = 12$ and $3 + 4 = 7$.

$2x^2 + 7x + 6$

$= 2x^2 + 3x + 4x + 6$

Step 4: Write the middle term of the trinomial as the sum of two terms whose coefficients are the selected pair of numbers: 3 and 4.

$= 2x^2 + 3x \mid + 4x + 6$

Step 5: Factor by grouping.

$= x(2x + 3) + 2(2x + 3)$

$= (2x + 3)(x + 2)$

Check: $(2x + 3)(x + 2) = 2x^2 + 4x + 3x + 6$

$= 2x^2 + 7x + 6$ ✔

Skill Practice Factor by the ac-method.

   1. $2x^2 + 5x + 3$

TIP: One frequently asked question is whether the order matters when we rewrite the middle term of the trinomial as two terms (step 3). The answer is no. From the previous example, the two middle terms in step 3 could have been reversed to obtain the same result:

$$2x^2 + 7x + 6$$
$$= 2x^2 + 4x + 3x + 6$$
$$= 2x(x + 2) + 3(x + 2)$$
$$= (x + 2)(2x + 3)$$

This example also points out that the order in which two factors are written does not matter. The expression $(x + 2)(2x + 3)$ is equivalent to $(2x + 3)(x + 2)$ because multiplication is a commutative operation.

Answer

1. $(x + 1)(2x + 3)$

Example 2 Factoring a Trinomial by the AC-Method

Factor the trinomial by the ac-method. $-2x + 8x^2 - 3$

Classroom Example: p. 442, Exercise 28

Solution:

$-2x + 8x^2 - 3$ First rewrite the polynomial in the form $ax^2 + bx + c$.

$= 8x^2 - 2x - 3$ **Step 1:** The GCF is 1.

$a = 8, b = -2, c = -3$ **Step 2:** Find the product $ac = (8)(-3) = -24$.

-24	-24
$-1 \cdot 24$	$-24 \cdot 1$
$-2 \cdot 12$	$-12 \cdot 2$
$-3 \cdot 8$	$-8 \cdot 3$
$-4 \cdot 6$	$-6 \cdot 4$

Step 3: List all the factors of -24 and find the pair of factors whose sum equals -2.

The numbers -6 and 4 satisfy both conditions: $(-6)(4) = -24$ and $-6 + 4 = -2$.

> **Avoiding Mistakes**
>
> Before factoring a trinomial, be sure to write the trinomial in descending order. That is, write it in the form $ax^2 + bx + c$.

$= 8x^2 \quad 2x \quad 3$ **Step 4:** Write the middle term of the trinomial as two terms whose coefficients are the selected pair of numbers, -6 and 4.

$= 8x^2 - 6x + 4x - 3$

$= 8x^2 - 6x \mid + 4x - 3$ **Step 5:** Factor by grouping.

$= 2x(4x - 3) + 1(4x - 3)$

$= (4x - 3)(2x + 1)$

Check: $(4x - 3)(2x + 1) = 8x^2 + 4x - 6x - 3$

$= 8x^2 - 2x - 3$ ✔

Skill Practice Factor by the ac-method.

2. $13w + 6w^2 + 6$

Example 3 Factoring a Trinomial by the AC-Method

Factor the trinomial by the ac-method. $10x^3 - 85x^2 + 105x$

Classroom Example: p. 442, Exercise 38

Solution:

$10x^3 - 85x^2 + 105x$ **Step 1:** Factor out the GCF of $5x$.

$= 5x(2x^2 - 17x + 21)$ The trinomial is in the form $ax^2 + bx + c$.

$a = 2, b = -17, c = 21$ **Step 2:** Find the product $ac = (2)(21) = 42$.

42	42
$1 \cdot 42$	$(-1)(-42)$
$2 \cdot 21$	$(-2)(-21)$
$3 \cdot 14$	$(-3)(-14)$
$6 \cdot 7$	$(-6)(-7)$

Step 3: List all the factors of 42 and find the pair whose sum equals -17.

The numbers -3 and -14 satisfy both conditions: $(-3)(-14) = 42$ and $-3 + (-14) = -17$.

Answer

2. $(2w + 3)(3w + 2)$

$$= 5x(2x^2 - 17x + 21)$$

Step 4: Write the middle term of the trinomial as two terms whose coefficients are the selected pair of numbers, -3 and -14.

$$= 5x(2x^2 - 3x - 14x + 21)$$

$$= 5x(2x^2 - 3x \mid - 14x + 21)$$ **Step 5:** Factor by grouping.

$$= 5x[x(2x - 3) - 7(2x - 3)]$$

$$= 5x(2x - 3)(x - 7)$$

Avoiding Mistakes

Be sure to bring down the GCF in each successive step as you factor.

TIP: Notice when the GCF is removed from the original trinomial, the new trinomial has smaller coefficients. This makes the factoring process simpler because the product ac is smaller. It is much easier to list the factors of 42 than the factors of 1050.

Original trinomial	**With the GCF factored out**
$10x^3 - 85x^2 + 105x$	$5x(2x^2 - 17x + 21)$
$ac = (10)(105) = 1050$	$ac = (2)(21) = 42$

Skill Practice Factor by the ac-method.

3. $9y^3 - 30y^2 + 24y$

In most cases, it is easier to factor a trinomial with a positive leading coefficient.

Classroom Example: p. 442, Exercise 36

Example 4   Factoring a Trinomial by the AC-Method

Factor the trinomial by the ac-method. $-18x^2 + 21xy + 15y^2$

Solution:

$-18x^2 + 21xy + 15y^2$

$= -3(6x^2 - 7xy - 5y^2)$

Step 1: Factor out the GCF.

Factor out -3 to make the leading term positive.

Step 2: The product $ac = (6)(-5) = -30$.

Step 3: The numbers -10 and 3 have a product of -30 and a sum of -7.

$= -3[6x^2 - 10xy + 3xy - 5y^2]$ **Step 4:** Rewrite the middle term, $-7xy$ as $-10xy + 3xy$.

$= -3[6x^2 - 10xy \mid + 3xy - 5y^2]$ **Step 5:** Factor by grouping.

$= -3[2x(3x - 5y) + y(3x - 5y)]$

$= -3(3x - 5y)(2x + y)$ Factored form

Skill Practice Factor.

4. $-8x^2 - 8xy + 30y^2$

Answers

3. $3y(3y - 4)(y - 2)$
4. $-2(2x - 3y)(2x + 5y)$

Recall that a prime polynomial is a polynomial whose only factors are itself and 1. It also should be noted that not every trinomial is factorable by the methods presented in this text.

Example 5 Factoring a Trinomial by the AC-Method

Classroom Example: p. 442, Exercise 26

Factor the trinomial by the ac-method. $2p^2 - 8p + 3$

Solution:

$2p^2 - 8p + 3$ **Step 1:** The GCF is 1.

Step 2: The product $ac = 6$.

$\dfrac{6}{1 \cdot 6}$	$\dfrac{6}{(-1)(-6)}$
$2 \cdot 3$	$(-2)(-3)$

Step 3: List the factors of 6. Notice that no pair of factors has a sum of -8. Therefore, the trinomial cannot be factored.

The trinomial $2p^2 - 8p + 3$ is a prime polynomial.

Skill Practice Factor.

5. $4x^2 + 5x + 2$

In Example 6, we use the ac-method to factor a higher degree trinomial.

Example 6 Factoring a Higher Degree Trinomial

Classroom Example: p. 442, Exercise 42

Factor the trinomial by the ac-method. $2x^4 + 5x^2 + 2$

Solution:

$2x^4 + 5x^2 + 2$ **Step 1:** The GCF is 1.

$a = 2, b = 5, c = 2$ **Step 2:** Find the product $ac = (2)(2) = 4$.

Step 3: The numbers 1 and 4 have a product of 4 and a sum of 5.

$2x^4 + x^2 + 4x^2 + 2$ **Step 4:** Rewrite the middle term, $5x^2$, as $x^2 + 4x^2$.

$2x^4 + x^2 \mid + 4x^2 + 2$ **Step 5:** Factor by grouping.

$x^2(2x^2 + 1) + 2(2x^2 + 1)$

$(2x^2 + 1)(x^2 + 2)$ Factored form

Skill Practice Factor.

6. $3y^4 + 2y^2 - 8$

Answers

5. Prime
6. $(3y^2 - 4)(y^2 + 2)$

Section 6.4 Practice Exercises

Review Exercises

For Exercises 1–4, factor completely.

1. $2pr + 12p - 6r - 36$ $2(p - 3)(r + 6)$

2. $5x(x - 2) - 2(x - 2)$ $(x - 2)(5x - 2)$

3. $8(y + 5) + 9y(y + 5)$ $(y + 5)(8 + 9y)$

4. $6ab + 24b - 12a - 48$ $6(a + 4)(b - 2)$

Concept 1: Factoring Trinomials by the AC-Method

For Exercises 5–12, find the pair of integers whose product and sum are given.

5. Product: 12   Sum: 13   12, 1

6. Product: 12   Sum: 7   3, 4

7. Product: 8   Sum: −9   −8, −1

8. Product: −4   Sum: −3   −4, 1

9. Product: −20   Sum: 1   5, −4

10. Product: −6   Sum: −1   −3, 2

11. Product: −18   Sum: 7   9, −2

12. Product: −72   Sum: −6   −12, 6

For Exercises 13–30, factor the trinomials using the ac-method.   **(See Examples 1, 2, and 5.)**

13. $3x^2 + 13x + 4$ $(x + 4)(3x + 1)$

14. $2y^2 + 7y + 6$ $(2y + 3)(y + 2)$

15. $4w^2 - 9w + 2$ $(w - 2)(4w - 1)$

16. $2p^2 - 3p - 2$ $(p - 2)(2p + 1)$

17. $x^2 + 7x - 18$ $(x + 9)(x - 2)$

18. $y^2 - 6y - 40$ $(y - 10)(y + 4)$

19. $2m^2 + 5m - 3$ $(m + 3)(2m - 1)$

20. $6n^2 + 7n - 3$ $(2n + 3)(3n - 1)$

21. $8k^2 - 6k - 9$ $(4k + 3)(2k - 3)$

22. $9h^2 - 3h - 2$ $(3h - 2)(3h + 1)$

23. $4k^2 - 20k + 25$ $(2k - 5)^2$

24. $16h^2 + 24h + 9$ $(4h + 3)^2$

25. $5x^2 + x + 7$ Prime

26. $4y^2 - y + 2$ Prime

27. $10 + 9z^2 - 21z$ $(3z - 5)(3z - 2)$

28. $13x + 4x^2 - 12$
$(4x - 3)(x + 4)$

29. $12y^2 + 8yz - 15z^2$
$(6y - 5z)(2y + 3z)$

30. $20a^2 + 3ab - 9b^2$
$(5a - 3b)(4a + 3b)$

For Exercises 31–38, factor completely. Be sure to factor out the GCF first.   **(See Examples 3–4.)**

31. $50y + 24 + 14y^2$
$2(7y + 4)(y + 3)$

32. $-24 + 10w + 4w^2$
$2(2w - 3)(w + 4)$

33. $-15w^2 + 22w + 5$
$-(3w - 5)(5w + 1)$

34. $-16z^2 + 34z + 15$
$-(8z + 3)(2z - 5)$

35. $-12x^2 + 20xy - 8y^2$
$-4(x - y)(3x - 2y)$

36. $-6p^2 - 21pq - 9q^2$
$-3(2p + q)(p + 3q)$

37. $18y^3 + 60y^2 + 42y$
$6y(y + 1)(3y + 7)$

38. $8t^3 - 4t^2 - 40t$
$4t(2t - 5)(t + 2)$

For Exercises 39–44, factor the higher degree polynomial.   **(See Example 6.)**

39. $a^4 + 5a^2 + 6$
$(a^2 + 2)(a^2 + 3)$

40. $y^4 - 2y^2 - 35$
$(y^2 + 5)(y^2 - 7)$

41. $6x^4 - x^2 - 15$
$(3x^2 - 5)(2x^2 + 3)$

42. $8t^4 + 2t^2 - 3$
$(4t^2 + 3)(2t^2 - 1)$

43. $8p^4 + 37p^2 - 15$
$(8p^2 - 3)(p^2 + 5)$

44. $2a^4 + 11a^2 + 14$
$(2a^2 + 7)(a^2 + 2)$

Mixed Exercises

For Exercises 45–80, factor completely.

45. $20p^2 - 19p + 3$
$(5p - 1)(4p - 3)$

46. $4p^2 + 5pq - 6q^2$
$(p + 2q)(4p - 3q)$

47. $6u^2 - 19uv + 10v^2$
$(3u - 2v)(2u - 5v)$

48. $15m^2 + mn - 2n^2$
$(5m + 2n)(3m - n)$

49. $12a^2 + 11ab - 5b^2$
$(4a + 5b)(3a - b)$

50. $3r^2 - rs - 14s^2$
$(r + 2s)(3r - 7s)$

 51. $3h^2 + 19hk - 14k^2$
$(h + 7k)(3h - 2k)$

52. $2u^2 + uv - 15v^2$
$(2u - 5v)(u + 3v)$

53. $2x^2 - 13xy + y^2$ Prime

54. $3p^2 + 20pq - q^2$ Prime

55. $3 - 14z + 16z^2$
$(2z - 1)(8z - 3)$

56. $10w + 1 + 16w^2$
$(8w + 1)(2w + 1)$

57. $b^2 + 16 - 8b$
$(b - 4)^2$

58. $1 + q^2 - 2q$
$(q - 1)^2$

 59. $25x - 5x^2 - 30$
$-5(x - 2)(x - 3)$

60. $20a - 18 - 2a^2$
$-2(a - 1)(a - 9)$

61. $-6 - t + t^2$
$(t - 3)(t + 2)$

62. $-6 + m + m^2$
$(m + 3)(m - 2)$

63. $v^2 + 2v + 15$ Prime

64. $x^2 - x - 1$ Prime

65. $72x^2 + 18x - 2$
$2(12x - 1)(3x + 1)$

66. $20y^2 - 78y - 8$
$2(10y + 1)(y - 4)$

67. $p^3 - 6p^2 - 27p$
$p(p + 3)(p - 9)$

68. $w^5 - 11w^4 + 28w^3$
$w^3(w - 4)(w - 7)$

69. $3x^3 + 10x^2 + 7x$
$x(3x + 7)(x + 1)$

 70. $4r^3 + 3r^2 - 10r$
$r(4r - 5)(r + 2)$

71. $2p^3 + 120p - 38p^2$
$2p(p - 15)(p - 4)$

72. $-4q^2 + 4q^3 - 80q$
$4q(q - 5)(q + 4)$

73. $x^2y^2 + 14x^2y + 33x^2$
$x^2(y + 3)(y + 11)$

74. $a^2b^2 + 13ab^2 + 30b^2$
$b^2(a + 10)(a + 3)$

75. $-k^2 - 7k - 10$
$-1(k + 2)(k + 5)$

76. $-m^2 - 15m + 34$
$-1(m - 2)(m + 17)$

77. $-3n^2 - 3n + 90$
$-3(n + 6)(n - 5)$

78. $-2h^2 + 28h - 90$
$-2(h - 9)(h - 5)$

79. $x^4 - 7x^2 + 10$
$(x^2 - 2)(x^2 - 5)$

80. $m^4 + 10m^2 + 21$
$(m^2 + 3)(m^2 + 7)$

81. Is the expression $(2x + 4)(x - 7)$ factored completely? Explain why or why not.

No. $(2x + 4)$ contains a common factor of 2.

82. Is the expression $(3x + 1)(5x - 10)$ factored completely? Explain why or why not.

No. $(5x - 10)$ contains a common factor of 5.

Difference of Squares and Perfect Square Trinomials

Section 6.5

1. Factoring a Difference of Squares

Up to this point, we have learned several methods of factoring, including:

- Factoring out the greatest common factor from a polynomial
- Factoring a four-term polynomial by grouping
- Factoring trinomials by the ac-method or by the trial-and-error method

Concepts

1. Factoring a Difference of Squares
2. Factoring Perfect Square Trinomials

In this section, we begin by factoring a special binomial called a difference of squares. Recall from Section 5.6 that the product of two conjugates results in a **difference of squares**:

$$(a + b)(a - b) = a^2 - b^2$$

Therefore, to factor a difference of squares, the process is reversed. Identify a and b and construct the conjugate factors.

> **FORMULA** **Factored Form of a Difference of Squares**
>
> $$a^2 - b^2 = (a + b)(a - b)$$

 Writing Translating Expression Geometry Scientific Calculator Video NS&E

To help recognize a difference of squares, we recommend that you become familiar with the first several perfect squares.

Perfect Squares	**Perfect Squares**	**Perfect Squares**
$1 = (1)^2$	$36 = (6)^2$	$121 = (11)^2$
$4 = (2)^2$	$49 = (7)^2$	$144 = (12)^2$
$9 = (3)^2$	$64 = (8)^2$	$169 = (13)^2$
$16 = (4)^2$	$81 = (9)^2$	$196 = (14)^2$
$25 = (5)^2$	$100 = (10)^2$	$225 = (15)^2$

It is also important to recognize that a variable expression is a perfect square if its exponent is a multiple of 2. For example:

Perfect Squares

$$x^2 = (x)^2$$
$$x^4 = (x^2)^2$$
$$x^6 = (x^3)^2$$
$$x^8 = (x^4)^2$$
$$x^{10} = (x^5)^2$$

Classroom Examples: p. 449, Exercises 16 and 18

Example 1 Factoring Differences of Squares

Factor the binomials.

a. $y^2 - 25$ **b.** $49s^2 - 4t^4$ **c.** $18w^2z - 2z$

Solution:

a. $y^2 - 25$ The binomial is a difference of squares.

   $= (y)^2 - (5)^2$ Write in the form: $a^2 - b^2$, where $a = y$, $b = 5$.

   $= (y + 5)(y - 5)$ Factor as $(a + b)(a - b)$.

b. $49s^2 - 4t^4$ The binomial is a difference of squares.

   $= (7s)^2 - (2t^2)^2$ Write in the form $a^2 - b^2$, where $a = 7s$ and $b = 2t^2$.

   $= (7s + 2t^2)(7s - 2t^2)$ Factor as $(a + b)(a - b)$.

c. $18w^2z - 2z$ The GCF is $2z$.

   $= 2z(9w^2 - 1)$ $(9w^2 - 1)$ is a difference of squares.

   $= 2z[(3w)^2 - (1)^2]$ Write in the form: $a^2 - b^2$, where $a = 3w$, $b = 1$.

   $= 2z(3w + 1)(3w - 1)$ Factor as $(a + b)(a - b)$.

Skill Practice Factor the binomials.

  1. $a^2 - 64$ **2.** $25q^2 - 49w^2$ **3.** $98m^3n - 50mn$

Answers

1. $(a + 8)(a - 8)$
2. $(5q + 7w)(5q - 7w)$
3. $2mn(7m + 5)(7m - 5)$

The difference of squares $a^2 - b^2$ factors as $(a - b)(a + b)$. However, the *sum* of squares is not factorable.

PROPERTY **Sum of Squares**

Suppose a and b have no common factors. Then the **sum of squares** $a^2 + b^2$ is *not* factorable over the real numbers.

That is, $a^2 + b^2$ is prime over the real numbers.

To see why $a^2 + b^2$ is not factorable, consider the product of binomials:

$$(a + b)(a - b) = a^2 - b^2 \qquad \text{Wrong sign}$$

$$(a + b)(a + b) = a^2 + 2ab + b^2 \qquad \text{Wrong middle term}$$

$$(a - b)(a - b) = a^2 - 2ab + b^2 \qquad \text{Wrong middle term}$$

After exhausting all possibilities, we see that if a and b share no common factors, then the sum of squares $a^2 + b^2$ is a prime polynomial.

Example 2 **Factoring Binomials**

Factor the binomials, if possible.   **a.** $p^2 - 9$ **b.** $p^2 + 9$

Solution:

a. $p^2 - 9$ Difference of squares

    $= (p - 3)(p + 3)$ Factor as $a^2 - b^2 = (a - b)(a + b)$.

b. $p^2 + 9$ Sum of squares

    Prime (cannot be factored)

Skill Practice Factor the binomials, if possible.

4. $t^2 - 144$ **5.** $t^2 + 144$

Classroom Example: p. 449, Exercise 24

Some factoring problems require several steps. Always be sure to factor completely.

Example 3 **Factoring a Difference of Squares**

Factor completely. $w^4 - 81$

Solution:

$w^4 - 81$ The GCF is 1. $w^4 - 81$ is a difference of squares.

$= (w^2)^2 - (9)^2$ Write in the form: $a^2 - b^2$, where $a = w^2, b = 9$.

$= (w^2 + 9)(w^2 - 9)$ Factor as $(a + b)(a - b)$.

$= (w^2 + 9)(w + 3)(w - 3)$ Note that $w^2 - 9$ can be factored further as a difference of squares. (The binomial $w^2 + 9$ is a sum of squares and cannot be factored further.)

Skill Practice Factor completely.

6. $y^4 - 1$

Classroom Example: p. 450, Exercise 36

Answers
4. $(t - 12)(t + 12)$
5. Prime
6. $(y + 1)(y - 1)(y^2 + 1)$

Classroom Example: p. 450,
Exercise 44

Example 4   Factoring a Polynomial

Factor completely. $y^3 - 5y^2 - 4y + 20$

Solution:

$y^3 - 5y^2 - 4y + 20$ The GCF is 1. The polynomial has four terms.
                                 Factor by grouping.

$= y^3 - 5y^2 \mid - 4y + 20$

$= y^2(y - 5) - 4(y - 5)$

$= (y - 5)(y^2 - 4)$ The expression $y^2 - 4$ is a difference of squares

$= (y - 5)(y - 2)(y + 2)$ and can be factored further as $(y - 2)(y + 2)$.

Check: $(y - 5)(y - 2)(y + 2) = (y - 5)(y^2 - 2y + 2y - 4)$

$= (y - 5)(y^2 - 4)$

$= (y^3 - 4y - 5y^2 + 20)$

$= y^3 - 5y^2 - 4y + 20$ ✔

Skill Practice Factor completely.

7. $p^3 + 7p^2 - 9p - 63$

2. Factoring Perfect Square Trinomials

Recall from Section 5.6 that the square of a binomial always results in a **perfect square trinomial**.

$(a + b)^2 = (a + b)(a + b) \xrightarrow{\text{Multiply.}} = a^2 + 2ab + b^2$

$(a - b)^2 = (a - b)(a - b) \xrightarrow{\text{Multiply.}} = a^2 - 2ab + b^2$

For example, $(3x + 5)^2 = (3x)^2 + 2(3x)(5) + (5)^2$

$= 9x^2 + 30x + 25$ (perfect square trinomial)

We now want to reverse this process by factoring a perfect square trinomial. The trial-and-error method or the ac-method can always be used; however, if we recognize the pattern for a perfect square trinomial, we can use one of the following formulas to reach a quick solution.

> **FORMULA   Factored Form of a Perfect Square Trinomial**
>
> $$a^2 + 2ab + b^2 = (a + b)^2$$
>
> $$a^2 - 2ab + b^2 = (a - b)^2$$

For example, $4x^2 + 36x + 81$ is a perfect square trinomial with $a = 2x$ and $b = 9$. Therefore, it factors as

$$4x^2 + 36x + 81 = (2x)^2 + 2(2x)(9) + (9)^2 = (2x + 9)^2$$

$$a^2 \ + 2 \ (a)(b) + (b)^2 = (a + b)^2$$

Answer

7. $(p - 3)(p + 3)(p + 7)$

To apply the formula to factor a perfect square trinomial, we must first be sure that the trinomial is indeed a perfect square trinomial.

PROCEDURE Checking for a Perfect Square Trinomial

Step 1 Determine whether the first and third terms are both perfect squares and have positive coefficients.

Step 2 If this is the case, identify a and b and determine if the middle term equals $2ab$ or $-2ab$.

Example 5 Factoring Perfect Square Trinomials

Classroom Examples: p. 450, Exercises 56 and 58

Factor the trinomials completely.

a. $x^2 + 14x + 49$　　　**b.** $25y^2 - 20y + 4$

Solution:

a. $x^2 + 14x + 49$　　　The GCF is 1.

- The first and third terms are positive.
- The first term is a perfect square: $x^2 = (x)^2$.
- The third term is a perfect square: $49 = (7)^2$.

Perfect squares

$x^2 + 14x + 49$

- The middle term is twice the product of x and 7: $14x = 2(x)(7)$

$= (x)^2 + 2(x)(7) + (7)^2$　　　The trinomial is in the form $a^2 + 2ab + b^2$, where $a = x$ and $b = 7$.

$= (x + 7)^2$　　　Factor as $(a + b)^2$.

> **TIP:** The sign of the middle term in a perfect square trinomial determines the sign within the binomial of the factored form.
>
> $a^2 + 2ab + b^2 = (a + b)^2$
>
> $a^2 - 2ab + b^2 = (a - b)^2$

b. $25y^2 - 20y + 4$　　　The GCF is 1.

Perfect squares

$25y^2 - 20y + 4$

- The first and third terms are positive.
- The first term is a perfect square: $25y^2 = (5y)^2$.
- The third term is a perfect square: $4 = (2)^2$.

$= (5y)^2 - 2(5y)(2) + (2)^2$　•　In the middle: $20y = 2(5y)(2)$

$= (5y - 2)^2$　　　Factor as $(a - b)^2$.

Skill Practice Factor completely.

8. $x^2 - 6x + 9$　　　**9.** $81w^2 + 72w + 16$

Answers
8. $(x - 3)^2$
9. $(9w + 4)^2$

Classroom Examples: p. 450,
Exercises 64 and 66

Example 6 **Factoring Perfect Square Trinomials**

Factor the trinomials completely.

a. $18c^3 - 48c^2d + 32cd^2$ **b.** $5w^2 + 50w + 45$

Solution:

a. $18c^3 - 48c^2d + 32cd^2$

$= 2c(9c^2 - 24cd + 16d^2)$ The GCF is $2c$.

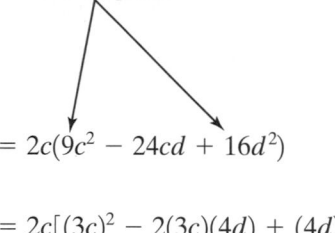

$= 2c(9c^2 - 24cd + 16d^2)$

- The first and third terms are positive.

- The first term is a perfect square: $9c^2 = (3c)^2$.

- The third term is a perfect square: $16d^2 = (4d)^2$.

$= 2c[(3c)^2 - 2(3c)(4d) + (4d)^2]$ • In the middle: $24cd = 2(3c)(4d)$

$= 2c(3c - 4d)^2$ Factor as $(a - b)^2$.

b. $5w^2 + 50w + 45$

$= 5(w^2 + 10w + 9)$ The GCF is 5.

Perfect squares

The first and third terms are perfect squares.

$= 5(w^2 + 10w + 9)$

$$w^2 = (w)^2 \quad \text{and} \quad 9 = (3)^2$$

However, the middle term is not 2 times the product of w and 3. Therefore, this is not a perfect square trinomial.

$$10w \neq 2(w)(3)$$

$= 5(w + 9)(w + 1)$ To factor, use the trial-and-error method.

> **TIP:** If you do not recognize that a trinomial is a perfect square trinomial, you can still use the trial-and-error method or ac-method to factor it.

Skill Practice Factor completely.

10. $5z^3 + 20z^2w + 20z\,w^2$ **11.** $40x^2 + 130x + 90$

Classroom Example: p. 450,
Exercise 88

Example 7 **Factoring a Four-Term Polynomial by Grouping Three Terms**

Factor completely. $x^2 - y^2 - 6y - 9$

Solution:

Grouping "2 by 2" will not work to factor this polynomial. However, if we factor out -1 from the last three terms, the resulting trinomial will be a perfect square trinomial.

Answers
10. $5z(z + 2w)^2$
11. $10(4x + 9)(x + 1)$

$x^2 - y^2 - 6y - 9$ Group the last three terms.

$= x^2 - 1(y^2 + 6y + 9)$ Factor out -1 from the last three terms.

$= x^2 - (y + 3)^2$ Factor the perfect square trinomial $y^2 + 6y + 9$ as $(y + 3)^2$.

     The quantity $x^2 - (y + 3)^2$ is a difference of squares, $a^2 - b^2$, where $a = x$ and $b = (y + 3)$.

$= [x - (y + 3)][x + (y + 3)]$ Factor as $a^2 - b^2 = (a + b)(a - b)$.

$= (x - y - 3)(x + y + 3)$ Apply the distributive property to clear the inner parentheses.

Skill Practice Factor completely.

12. $x^2 + 10x + 25 - y^2$

> **Avoiding Mistakes**
>
> When factoring the expression $x^2 - (y + 3)^2$ as a difference of squares, be sure to use parentheses around the quantity $(y + 3)$. This will help you remember to "distribute the negative" in the expression $[x - (y + 3)]$.
>
> $$[x - (y + 3)] = (x - y - 3)$$

Answer

12. $(x + 5 - y)(x + 5 + y)$

Section 6.5   Practice Exercises

Study Skills Exercise

1. Define the key terms.

     a. difference of squares   **b.** sum of squares   **c.** perfect square trinomial

Review Exercises

For Exercises 2–10, factor completely.

2. $3x^2 + x - 10$
$(3x - 5)(x + 2)$

3. $6x^2 - 17x + 5$
$(3x - 1)(2x - 5)$

4. $6a^2b + 3a^3b$
$3a^2b(2 + a)$

5. $15x^2y^5 - 10xy^6$
$5xy^5(3x - 2y)$

6. $5p^2q + 20p^2 - 3pq - 12p$
$p(5p - 3)(q + 4)$

7. $ax + ab - 6x - 6b$
$(x + b)(a - 6)$

8. $-6x + 5 + x^2$
$(x - 1)(x - 5)$

9. $6y - 40 + y^2$
$(y + 10)(y - 4)$

10. $a^2 + 7a + 1$
Prime

Concept 1: Factoring a Difference of Squares

11. What binomial factors as $(x - 5)(x + 5)$? $x^2 - 25$

12. What binomial factors as $(n - 3)(n + 3)$? $n^2 - 9$

13. What binomial factors as $(2p - 3q)(2p + 3q)$?
$4p^2 - 9q^2$

14. What binomial factors as $(7x - 4y)(7x + 4y)$?
$49x^2 - 16y^2$

For Exercises 15–42, factor each binomial completely. **(See Examples 1–3.)**

15. $x^2 - 36$ $(x - 6)(x + 6)$

16. $r^2 - 81$ $(r - 9)(r + 9)$

17. $3w^2 - 300$
$3(w + 10)(w - 10)$

18. $t^3 - 49t$
$t(t + 7)(t - 7)$

19. $4a^2 - 121b^2$
$(2a - 11b)(2a + 11b)$

20. $9x^2 - y^2$
$(3x - y)(3x + y)$

21. $49m^2 - 16n^2$
$(7m - 4n)(7m + 4n)$

22. $100a^2 - 49b^2$
$(10a - 7b)(10a + 7b)$

23. $9q^2 + 16$ Prime

24. $36 + s^2$ Prime

25. $y^2 - 4z^2$
$(y + 2z)(y - 2z)$

26. $b^2 - 144c^2$
$(b + 12c)(b - 12c)$

27. $a^2 - b^4$
$(a - b^2)(a + b^2)$

28. $y^4 - x^2$
$(y^2 - x)(y^2 + x)$

29. $25p^2q^2 - 1$
$(5pq - 1)(5pq + 1)$

30. $81s^2t^2 - 1$
$(9st - 1)(9st + 1)$

31. $c^2 - \dfrac{1}{25}$ $\left(c - \dfrac{1}{5}\right)\left(c + \dfrac{1}{5}\right)$ **32.** $z^2 - \dfrac{1}{4}$ $\left(z - \dfrac{1}{2}\right)\left(z + \dfrac{1}{2}\right)$ **33.** $50 - 32t^2$
$2(5 - 4t)(5 + 4t)$ **34.** $63 - 7h^2$
$7(3 - h)(3 + h)$

35. $x^4 - 256$
$(x + 4)(x - 4)(x^2 + 16)$ **36.** $y^4 - 625$
$(y + 5)(y - 5)(y^2 + 25)$ **37.** $16 - z^4$
$(2 - z)(2 + z)(4 + z^2)$ **38.** $81 - a^4$
$(3 - a)(3 + a)(9 + a^2)$

39. $2x^2 + 128$
$2(x^2 + 64)$ **40.** $3y^2 + 48$
$3(y^2 + 16)$ **41.** $100x^2y^4 - w^2$
$(10xy^2 - w)(10xy^2 + w)$ **42.** $s^2t^2 - 81r^4$
$(st - 9r^2)(st + 9r^2)$

For Exercises 43–50, factor each polynomial completely. **(See Example 4.)**

43. $x^3 + 5x^2 - 9x - 45$
$(x + 3)(x - 3)(x + 5)$ **44.** $b^3 + 6b^2 - 4b - 24$
$(b + 2)(b - 2)(b + 6)$ **45.** $c^3 - c^2 - 25c + 25$
$(c + 5)(c - 5)(c - 1)$ **46.** $t^3 + 2t^2 - 16t - 32$
$(t + 4)(t - 4)(t + 2)$

47. $2x^2 - 18 + x^2y - 9y$
$(2 + y)(x + 3)(x - 3)$ **48.** $5a^2 - 5 + a^2b - b$
$(5 + b)(a + 1)(a - 1)$ **49.** $x^2y^2 - 9x^2 - 4y^2 + 36$
$(x + 2)(x - 2)(y + 3)(y - 3)$ **50.** $w^2z^2 - w^2 - 25z^2 + 25$
$(w + 5)(w - 5)(z + 1)(z - 1)$

Concept 2: Factoring Perfect Square Trinomials

51. Multiply. $(3x + 5)^2$ $9x^2 + 30x + 25$ **52.** Multiply. $(2y - 7)^2$ $4y^2 - 28y + 49$

53. a. Which trinomial is a perfect square trinomial? $x^2 + 4x + 4$ or $x^2 + 5x + 4$
a. $x^2 + 4x + 4$ is a perfect square trinomial.
b. Factor the trinomials from part (a).
b. $x^2 + 4x + 4 = (x + 2)^2$;
$x^2 + 5x + 4 = (x + 1)(x + 4)$

54. a. Which trinomial is a perfect square trinomial? $x^2 + 13x + 36$ or $x^2 + 12x + 36$
a. $x^2 + 12x + 36$ is a perfect square trinomial.
b. Factor the trinomials from part (a).
b. $x^2 + 13x + 36 = (x + 9)(x + 4)$;
$x^2 + 12x + 36 = (x + 6)^2$

For Exercises 55–72, factor completely. (*Hint:* Look for the pattern of a perfect square trinomial.) **(See Examples 5–6.)**

55. $x^2 + 18x + 81$
$(x + 9)^2$ **56.** $y^2 - 8y + 16$
$(y - 4)^2$ **57.** $25z^2 - 20z + 4$
$(5z - 2)^2$

58. $36p^2 + 60p + 25$
$(6p + 5)^2$ **59.** $49a^2 + 42ab + 9b^2$
$(7a + 3b)^2$ **60.** $25m^2 - 30mn + 9n^2$
$(5m - 3n)^2$

61. $-2y + y^2 + 1$
$(y - 1)^2$ **62.** $4 + w^2 - 4w$
$(w - 2)^2$ **63.** $80z^2 + 120zw + 45w^2$
$5(4z + 3w)^2$

64. $36p^2 - 24pq + 4q^2$
$4(3p - q)^2$ **65.** $9y^2 + 78y + 25$
$(3y + 25)(3y + 1)$ **66.** $4y^2 + 20y + 9$
$(2y + 9)(2y + 1)$

67. $2a^2 - 20a + 50$
$2(a - 5)^2$ **68.** $3t^2 + 18t + 27$
$3(t + 3)^2$ **69.** $4x^2 + x + 9$
Prime

70. $c^2 - 4c + 16$
Prime **71.** $4x^2 + 4xy + y^2$
$(2x + y)^2$ **72.** $100y^2 + 20yz + z^2$
$(10y + z)^2$

For Exercises 73–80, factor the difference of squares.

73. $(y - 3)^2 - 9$
$y(y - 6)$ **74.** $(x - 2)^2 - 4$
$x(x - 4)$ **75.** $(2p + 1)^2 - 36$
$(2p - 5)(2p + 7)$

76. $(4q + 3)^2 - 25$
$8(2q - 1)(q + 2)$ **77.** $16 - (t + 2)^2$
$(-t + 2)(t + 6)$ or $-(t - 2)(t + 6)$ **78.** $81 - (a + 5)^2$
$(-a + 4)(a + 14)$ or $-(a - 4)(a + 14)$

79. $100 - (2b - 5)^2$
$(-2b + 15)(2b + 5)$ or $-(2b - 15)(2b + 5)$ **80.** $49 - (3k - 7)^2$ $3k(-3k + 14)$ or $-3k(3k - 14)$

For Exercises 81–90, factor each polynomial by grouping. **(See Example 7.)**

81. $x^2 + 12x + 36 - a^2$
$(x + 6 - a)(x + 6 + a)$ **82.** $a^2 + 10a + 25 - b^2$
$(a + 5 + b)(a + 5 - b)$ **83.** $p^2 + 2pq + q^2 - 81$
$(p + q - 9)(p + q + 9)$

84. $m^2 - 2mn + n^2 - 9$
$(m - n - 3)(m - n + 3)$ **85.** $b^2 - (x^2 + 4x + 4)$
$(b - x - 2)(b + x + 2)$ **86.** $p^2 - (y^2 - 6y + 9)$
$(p - y + 3)(p + y - 3)$

87. $4 - u^2 + 2uv - v^2$
$(2 + u - v)(2 - u + v)$ **88.** $25 - a^2 - 2ab - b^2$
$(5 - a - b)(5 + a + b)$ **89.** $6ax - by + 2bx - 3ay$
$(3a + b)(2x - y)$

90. $5pq - 12 - 4q + 15p$
$(q + 3)(5p - 4)$

Expanding Your Skills

 91. a. Write a polynomial that represents the area of the shaded region in the figure.
$a^2 - b^2$

b. Factor the expression from part (a).
$(a - b)(a + b)$

 92. a. Write a polynomial that represents the area of the shaded region in the figure.
$g^2 - h^2$

b. Factor the expression from part (a).
$(g - h)(g + h)$

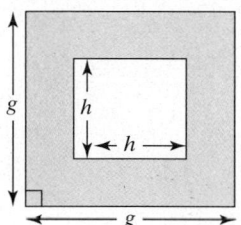

Sum and Difference of Cubes

Section 6.6

1. Factoring a Sum or Difference of Cubes

Concepts

1. **Factoring a Sum or Difference of Cubes**
2. **Factoring Binomials: A Summary**

A binomial $a^2 - b^2$ is a difference of squares and can be factored as $(a - b)(a + b)$. Furthermore, if a and b share no common factors, then a sum of squares $a^2 + b^2$ is not factorable over the real numbers. In this section, we will learn that both a difference of cubes, $a^3 - b^3$, and a sum of cubes, $a^3 + b^3$, are factorable.

FORMULA **Factored Form of a Sum or Difference of Cubes**

Sum of Cubes: $a^3 + b^3 = (a + b)(a^2 - ab + b^2)$

Difference of Cubes: $a^3 - b^3 = (a - b)(a^2 + ab + b^2)$

Multiplication can be used to confirm the formulas for factoring a sum or difference of cubes:

$$(a + b)(a^2 - ab + b^2) = a^3 - a^2b + ab^2 + a^2b - ab^2 + b^3 = a^3 + b^3 \checkmark$$

$$(a - b)(a^2 + ab + b^2) = a^3 + a^2b + ab^2 - a^2b - ab^2 - b^3 = a^3 - b^3 \checkmark$$

To help you remember the formulas for factoring a sum or difference of cubes, keep the following guidelines in mind:

- The factored form is the product of a binomial and a trinomial.
- The first and third terms in the trinomial are the squares of the terms within the binomial factor.
- Without regard to signs, the middle term in the trinomial is the product of terms in the binomial factor.

Square the first term of the binomial.   Product of terms in the binomial.

$$x^3 + 8 = (x)^3 + (2)^3 = (x + 2)[(x)^2 - (x)(2) + (2)^2]$$

Square the last term of the binomial.

TIP: To help remember the placement of the signs in factoring the sum or difference of cubes, remember SOAP: **S**ame sign, **O**pposite signs, **A**lways **P**ositive.

- The sign within the binomial factor is the same as the sign of the original binomial.
- The first and third terms in the trinomial are always positive.
- The sign of the middle term in the trinomial is opposite the sign within the binomial.

$$x^3 + 8 = (x)^3 + (2)^3 = (x \overset{\text{Same sign}}{+} 2)[(x)^2 \underset{\text{Opposite signs}}{-} (x)(2) + (2)^2]$$

To help you recognize a sum or difference of cubes, we recommend that you familiarize yourself with the first several perfect cubes:

Perfect Cubes	**Perfect Cubes**
$1 = (1)^3$	$216 = (6)^3$
$8 = (2)^3$	$343 = (7)^3$
$27 = (3)^3$	$512 = (8)^3$
$64 = (4)^3$	$729 = (9)^3$
$125 = (5)^3$	$1000 = (10)^3$

It is also helpful to recognize that a variable expression is a perfect cube if its exponent is a multiple of 3. For example:

Perfect Cubes

$$x^3 = (x)^3$$
$$x^6 = (x^2)^3$$
$$x^9 = (x^3)^3$$
$$x^{12} = (x^4)^3$$

Classroom Example: p. 456, Exercise 16

Example 1   Factoring a Sum of Cubes

Factor. $w^3 + 64$

Solution:

$w^3 + 64$ w^3 and 64 are perfect cubes.

$= (w)^3 + (4)^3$ Write as $a^3 + b^3$, where $a = w$, $b = 4$.

$a^3 + b^3 = (a + b)(a^2 - ab + b^2)$ Apply the formula for a sum of cubes.

$(w)^3 + (4)^3 = (w + 4)[(w)^2 - (w)(4) + (4)^2]$

$= (w + 4)(w^2 - 4w + 16)$ Simplify.

Skill Practice Factor.

1. $p^3 + 125$

Answer

1. $(p + 5)(p^2 - 5p + 25)$

Example 2 **Factoring a Difference of Cubes**

Factor. $27p^3 - 1000q^3$

Classroom Example: p. 456, Exercise 26

Solution:

$27p^3 - 1000q^3$ $27p^3$ and $1000q^3$ are perfect cubes.

$= (3p)^3 - (10q)^3$ Write as $a^3 - b^3$, where $a = 3p, b = 10q$.

$\quad a^3 - b^3 = (a - b)(a^2 + ab + b^2)$ Apply the formula for a difference of cubes.

$(3p)^3 - (10q)^3 = (3p - 10q)[(3p)^2 + (3p)(10q) + (10q)^2]$

$\qquad\qquad = (3p - 10q)(9p^2 + 30pq + 100q^2)$ Simplify.

Skill Practice Factor.

2. $8y^3 - 27z^3$

2. Factoring Binomials: A Summary

After removing the GCF, the next step in any factoring problem is to recognize what type of pattern it follows. Exponents that are divisible by 2 are perfect squares and those divisible by 3 are perfect cubes. The formulas for factoring binomials are summarized in the following box:

> **SUMMARY Factored Forms of Binomials**
>
> Difference of Squares: $a^2 - b^2 = (a + b)(a - b)$
> Difference of Cubes: $a^3 - b^3 = (a - b)(a^2 + ab + b^2)$
> Sum of Cubes: $a^3 + b^3 = (a + b)(a^2 - ab + b^2)$

Example 3 **Factoring Binomials**

Factor completely.

Classroom Examples: p. 457, Exercises 50 and 52

a. $27y^3 + 1$ **b.** $\dfrac{1}{25}m^2 - \dfrac{1}{4}$ **c.** $z^6 - 8w^3$

Solution:

a. $27y^3 + 1$ Sum of cubes: $27y^3 = (3y)^3$ and $1 = (1)^3$.

$= (3y)^3 + (1)^3$ Write as $a^3 + b^3$, where $a = 3y$ and $b = 1$.

$= (3y + 1)((3y)^2 - (3y)(1) + (1)^2)$ Apply the formula $a^3 + b^3 = (a + b)(a^2 - ab + b^2)$.

$= (3y + 1)(9y^2 - 3y + 1)$ Simplify.

Answer

2. $(2y - 3z)(4y^2 + 6yz + 9z^2)$

b. $\dfrac{1}{25}m^2 - \dfrac{1}{4}$ Difference of squares

$= \left(\dfrac{1}{5}m\right)^2 - \left(\dfrac{1}{2}\right)^2$ Write as $a^2 - b^2$, where $a = \frac{1}{5}m$ and $b = \frac{1}{2}$.

$= \left(\dfrac{1}{5}m + \dfrac{1}{2}\right)\left(\dfrac{1}{5}m - \dfrac{1}{2}\right)$ Apply the formula $a^2 - b^2 = (a + b)(a - b)$.

c. $z^6 - 8w^3$ Difference of cubes: $z^6 = (z^2)^3$ and $8w^3 = (2w)^3$

$= (z^2)^3 - (2w)^3$ Write as $a^3 - b^3$, where $a = z^2$ and $b = 2w$.

$= (z^2 - 2w)[(z^2)^2 + (z^2)(2w) + (2w)^2]$ Apply the formula $a^3 - b^3 = (a - b)(a^2 + ab + b^2)$.

$= (z^2 - 2w)(z^4 + 2z^2w + 4w^2)$ Simplify.

Each factorization in this example can be checked by multiplying.

Skill Practice Factor completely.

3. $1000x^3 + 1$ **4.** $25p^2 - \dfrac{1}{9}$ **5.** $27a^6 - b^3$

Some factoring problems require more than one method of factoring. In general, when factoring a polynomial, be sure to factor completely.

Classroom Example: p. 457,
Exercise 58

Example 4   **Factoring a Polynomial**

Factor completely. $3y^4 - 48$

Solution:

$3y^4 - 48$

$= 3(y^4 - 16)$ Factor out the GCF. The binomial is a difference of squares.

$= 3[(y^2)^2 - (4)^2]$ Write as $a^2 - b^2$, where $a = y^2$ and $b = 4$.

$= 3(y^2 + 4)(y^2 - 4)$ Apply the formula $a^2 - b^2 = (a + b)(a - b)$.

$y^2 + 4$ is a sum of squares and cannot be factored.

$= 3(y^2 + 4)(y + 2)(y - 2)$ $y^2 - 4$ is a difference of squares and can be factored further.

Skill Practice Factor completely.

6. $2x^4 - 2$

Answers

3. $(10x + 1)(100x^2 - 10x + 1)$

4. $\left(5p - \dfrac{1}{3}\right)\left(5p + \dfrac{1}{3}\right)$

5. $(3a^2 - b)(9a^4 + 3a^2b + b^2)$

6. $2(x^2 + 1)(x - 1)(x + 1)$

Example 5   **Factoring a Polynomial**

Factor completely. $4x^3 + 4x^2 - 25x - 25$

Classroom Example: p. 457, Exercise 64

Solution:

$4x^3 + 4x^2 - 25x - 25$ The GCF is 1.

$= 4x^3 + 4x^2 \mid - 25x - 25$ The polynomial has four terms. Factor by grouping.

$= 4x^2(x + 1) - 25(x + 1)$

$= (x + 1)(4x^2 - 25)$ $4x^2 - 25$ is a difference of squares.

$= (x + 1)(2x + 5)(2x - 5)$

Skill Practice Factor completely.

7. $x^3 + 6x^2 - 4x - 24$

Example 6   **Factoring a Binomial**

Factor the binomial $x^6 - y^6$ as

a. A difference of cubes   **b.** A difference of squares

Classroom Example: p. 457, Exercise 48

Solution:

a. $x^6 - y^6$

Difference of cubes

$= (x^2)^3 - (y^2)^3$ Write as $a^3 - b^3$, where $a = x^2$ and $b = y^2$.

$= (x^2 - y^2)[(x^2)^2 + (x^2)(y^2) + (y^2)^2]$ Apply the formula $a^3 - b^3 = (a - b)(a^2 + ab + b^2)$.

$= (x^2 - y^2)(x^4 + x^2y^2 + y^4)$ Factor $x^2 - y^2$ as a difference of squares.

$= (x + y)(x - y)(x^4 + x^2y^2 + y^4)$

b. $x^6 - y^6$

Difference of squares

$= (x^3)^2 - (y^3)^2$ Write as $a^2 - b^2$, where $a = x^3$ and $b = y^3$.

$= (x^3 + y^3)(x^3 - y^3)$ Apply the formula $a^2 - b^2 = (a + b)(a - b)$.

Sum of cubes   Difference of cubes

Factor $x^3 + y^3$ as a sum of cubes.

Factor $x^3 - y^3$ as a difference of cubes.

$= (x + y)(x^2 - xy + y^2)(x - y)(x^2 + xy + y^2)$

Answer

7. $(x + 6)(x + 2)(x - 2)$

Notice that the expressions x^6 and y^6 are both perfect squares and perfect cubes because both exponents are multiples of 2 and of 3. Consequently, $x^6 - y^6$ can be factored initially as either the difference of squares or as the difference of cubes. In such a case, it is recommended that you factor the expression as a difference of squares first because it factors more completely into polynomials of lower degree.

$$x^6 - y^6 = (x + y)(x^2 - xy + y^2)(x - y)(x^2 + xy + y^2)$$

Answer

8. $(z + 2)(z - 2)(z^2 + 2z + 4)$
$(z^2 - 2z + 4)$

Skill Practice Factor completely.

8. $z^6 - 64$

Section 6.6 Practice Exercises

Study Skills Exercise

1. Define the key terms.

   a. sum of cubes   **b. difference of cubes**

Review Exercises

For Exercises 2–10, factor completely.

2. $600 - 6x^2$
$6(10 - x)(10 + x)$

3. $20 - 5t^2$
$5(2 - t)(2 + t)$

4. $ax + bx + 5a + 5b$
$(a + b)(x + 5)$

5. $2t + 2u + st + su$
$(t + u)(2 + s)$

6. $5y^2 + 13y - 6$
$(5y - 2)(y + 3)$

7. $3v^2 + 5v - 12$
$(3v - 4)(v + 3)$

8. $40a^3b^3 - 16a^2b^2 + 24a^3b$
$8a^2b(5ab^2 - 2b + 3a)$

9. $-c^2 - 10c - 25$
$-(c + 5)^2$

10. $-z^2 + 6z - 9$
$-(z - 3)^2$

Concept 1: Factoring a Sum or Difference of Cubes

11. Identify the expressions that are perfect cubes:
    $x^3, 8, 9, y^6, a^4, b^2, 3p^3, 27q^3, w^{12}, r^3s^6$
    $x^3, 8, y^6, 27q^3, w^{12}, r^3s^6$

12. Identify the expressions that are perfect cubes:
    $z^9, -81, 30, 8, 6x^3, y^{15}, 27a^3, b^2, p^3q^2, -1$
    $z^9, 8, y^{15}, 27a^3, -1$

13. From memory, write the formula to factor a sum of cubes:

    $a^3 + b^3 = \underline{(a + b)(a^2 - ab + b^2)}$

14. From memory, write the formula to factor a difference of cubes:

    $a^3 - b^3 = \underline{(a - b)(a^2 + ab + b^2)}$

For Exercises 15–30, factor the sums or differences of cubes. **(See Examples 1–2.)**

15. $y^3 - 8$
$(y - 2)(y^2 + 2y + 4)$

16. $x^3 + 27$
$(x + 3)(x^2 - 3x + 9)$

17. $1 - p^3$
$(1 - p)(1 + p + p^2)$

18. $q^3 + 1$
$(q + 1)(q^2 - q + 1)$

19. $w^3 + 64$
$(w + 4)(w^2 - 4w + 16)$

20. $8 - t^3$
$(2 - t)(4 + 2t + t^2)$

21. $x^3 - 1000$
$(x - 10)(x^2 + 10x + 100)$

22. $8y^3 - 27$
$(2y - 3)(4y^2 + 6y + 9)$

23. $64t^3 + 1$
$(4t + 1)(16t^2 - 4t + 1)$

24. $125r^3 + 1$
$(5r + 1)(25r^2 - 5r + 1)$

25. $1000a^3 + 27$
$(10a + 3)(100a^2 - 30a + 9)$

26. $216b^3 - 125$
$(6b - 5)(36b^2 + 30b + 25)$

27. $n^3 - \dfrac{1}{8}$
$\left(n - \dfrac{1}{2}\right)\left(n^2 + \dfrac{1}{2}n + \dfrac{1}{4}\right)$

28. $\dfrac{8}{27} + m^3$
$\left(\dfrac{2}{3} + m\right)\left(\dfrac{4}{9} - \dfrac{2}{3}m + m^2\right)$

29. $125m^3 + 8$
$(5m + 2)(25m^2 - 10m + 4)$

30. $27p^3 - 64$
$(3p - 4)(9p^2 + 12p + 16)$

 Writing   Translating Expression   Geometry   Scientific Calculator   Video   NS&E

Concept 2: Factoring Binomials: A Summary

For Exercises 31–66, factor completely. **(See Examples 3–6.)**

31. $x^4 - 4$
$(x^2 - 2)(x^2 + 2)$

32. $b^4 - 25$
$(b^2 - 5)(b^2 + 5)$

33. $a^2 + 9$
Prime

34. $w^2 + 36$
Prime

35. $t^3 + 64$
$(t + 4)(t^2 - 4t + 16)$

36. $u^3 + 27$
$(u + 3)(u^2 - 3u + 9)$

37. $g^3 - 4$
Prime

38. $h^3 - 25$
Prime

39. $4b^3 + 108$
$4(b + 3)(b^2 - 3b + 9)$

40. $3c^3 - 24$
$3(c - 2)(c^2 + 2c + 4)$

41. $5p^2 - 125$
$5(p - 5)(p + 5)$

42. $2q^4 - 8$
$2(q^2 - 2)(q^2 + 2)$

43. $\dfrac{1}{64} - 8h^3$
$(\frac{1}{4} - 2h)(\frac{1}{16} + \frac{1}{2}h + 4h^2)$

44. $\dfrac{1}{125} + k^6$
$(\frac{1}{5} + k^2)(\frac{1}{25} - \frac{1}{5}k^2 + k^4)$

45. $x^4 - 16$
$(x - 2)(x + 2)(x^2 + 4)$

46. $p^4 - 81$
$(p - 3)(p + 3)(p^2 + 9)$

47. $q^6 - 64$
$(q - 2)(q^2 + 2q + 4)$
$(q + 2)(q^2 - 2q + 4)$

48. $a^6 - 1$
$(a - 1)(a^2 + a + 1)$
$(a + 1)(a^2 - a + 1)$

49. $\dfrac{4}{9}x^2 - w^2$
$(\frac{2}{3}x - w)(\frac{2}{3}x + w)$

50. $\dfrac{16}{25}y^2 - x^2$
$(\frac{4}{5}y - x)(\frac{4}{5}y + x)$

51. $x^9 + 64y^3$
$(x^3 + 4y)(x^6 - 4x^3y + 16y^2)$

52. $125w^3 - z^9$
$(5w - z^3)(25w^2 + 5wz^3 + z^6)$

53. $2x^3 + 3x^2 - 2x - 3$
$(2x + 3)(x - 1)(x + 1)$

54. $3x^3 + x^2 - 12x - 4$
$(3x + 1)(x - 2)(x + 2)$

55. $16x^4 - y^4$
$(2x - y)(2x + y)(4x^2 + y^2)$

56. $1 - t^4$
$(1 - t)(1 + t)(1 + t^2)$

57. $81y^4 - 16$
$(3y - 2)(3y + 2)(9y^2 + 4)$

58. $u^5 - 256u$
$u(u - 4)(u + 4)(u^2 + 16)$

59. $a^3 + b^6$
$(a + b^2)(a^2 - ab^2 + b^4)$

60. $u^6 - v^3$
$(u^2 - v)(u^4 + u^2v + v^2)$

61. $16x^4 - 625y^4$
$(2x - 5y)(2x + 5y)(4x^2 + 25y^2)$

62. $a^4 - 81b^4$
$(a - 3b)(a + 3b)(a^2 + 9b^2)$

63. $k^3 + 4k^2 - 9k - 36$
$(k + 4)(k - 3)(k + 3)$

64. $w^3 - 2w^2 - 4w + 8$
$(w - 2)^2(w + 2)$

65. $2t^3 - 10t^2 - 2t + 10$
$2(t - 5)(t - 1)(t + 1)$

66. $9a^3 + 27a^2 - 4a - 12$
$(a + 3)(3a - 2)(3a + 2)$

Expanding Your Skills

For Exercises 67–70, factor completely.

67. $\dfrac{64}{125}p^3 - \dfrac{1}{8}q^3$
$(\frac{4}{5}p - \frac{1}{2}q)(\frac{16}{25}p^2 + \frac{2}{5}pq + \frac{1}{4}q^2)$

68. $\dfrac{1}{1000}r^3 + \dfrac{8}{27}s^3$
$(\frac{1}{10}r + \frac{2}{3}s)(\frac{1}{100}r^2 - \frac{1}{15}rs + \frac{4}{9}s^2)$

69. $a^{12} + b^{12}$
$(a^4 + b^4)(a^8 - a^4b^4 + b^8)$

70. $a^9 - b^9$
$(a - b)(a^2 + ab + b^2)(a^6 + a^3b^3 + b^6)$

Use Exercises 71–72 to investigate the relationship between division and factoring.

71. a. Use long division to divide $x^3 - 8$ by $(x - 2)$.   The quotient is $x^2 + 2x + 4$.

b. Factor $x^3 - 8$. $(x - 2)(x^2 + 2x + 4)$

72. a. Use long division to divide $y^3 + 27$ by $(y + 3)$.   The quotient is $y^2 - 3y + 9$.

b. Factor $y^3 + 27$. $(y + 3)(y^2 - 3y + 9)$

73. What trinomial multiplied by $(x - 4)$ gives a difference of cubes? $x^2 + 4x + 16$

74. What trinomial multiplied by $(p + 5)$ gives a sum of cubes? $p^2 - 5p + 25$

75. Write a binomial that when multiplied by $(4x^2 - 2x + 1)$ produces a sum of cubes. $2x + 1$

76. Write a binomial that when multiplied by $(9y^2 + 15y + 25)$ produces a difference of cubes. $3y - 5$

Problem Recognition Exercises

Factoring Strategy

> **PROCEDURE** Factoring Strategy
>
> **Step 1** Factor out the GCF (Section 6.1).
>
> **Step 2** Identify whether the polynomial has two terms, three terms, or more than three terms.
>
> **Step 3** If the polynomial has more than three terms, try factoring by grouping (Section 6.1).
>
> **Step 4** If the polynomial has three terms, check first for a perfect square trinomial (Section 6.5). Otherwise, factor the trinomial with the trial-and-error method or the ac-method (Sections 6.3 or 6.4).
>
> **Step 5** If the polynomial has two terms, determine if it fits the pattern for
> - A difference of squares: $a^2 - b^2 = (a - b)(a + b)$ (Section 6.5)
> - A sum of squares: $a^2 + b^2$ prime
> - A difference of cubes: $a^3 - b^3 = (a - b)(a^2 + ab + b^2)$ (Section 6.6)
> - A sum of cubes: $a^3 + b^3 = (a + b)(a^2 - ab + b^2)$ (Section 6.6)
>
> **Step 6** Be sure to factor the polynomial completely.
>
> **Step 7** Check by multiplying.

1. What is meant by a prime polynomial?   A prime polynomial cannot be factored further.

2. What is the first step in factoring any polynomial?   Factor out the GCF.

3. When factoring a binomial, what patterns can you look for?   Look for a difference of squares: $a^2 - b^2$, a difference of cubes: $a^3 - b^3$, or a sum of cubes: $a^3 + b^3$.

4. What technique should be considered when factoring a four-term polynomial?   Grouping

For Exercises 5–73,

a. Factor out the GCF from each polynomial. Then identify the category in which the polynomial best fits. Choose from
- difference of squares
- sum of squares
- difference of cubes
- sum of cubes
- trinomial (perfect square trinomial)
- trinomial (nonperfect square trinomial)
- four terms-grouping
- none of these

Instructor Note: The following exercises involve a sum or difference of cubes: 10, 12, 13, 18, 23, 28, 29.

b. Factor the polynomial completely.

5. $2a^2 - 162$ a. Difference of squares   b. $2(a - 9)(a + 9)$

6. $y^2 + 4y + 3$ a. Nonperfect square trinomial   b. $(y + 3)(y + 1)$

7. $6w^2 - 6w$ a. None of these   b. $6w(w - 1)$

8. $16z^4 - 81$ a. Difference of squares   b. $(2z + 3)(2z - 3)(4z^2 + 9)$

9. $3t^2 + 13t + 4$ a. Nonperfect square trinomial   b. $(3t + 1)(t + 4)$

10. $5r^3 + 5$ a. Sum of cubes   b. $5(r + 1)(r^2 - r + 1)$

11. $3ac + ad - 3bc - bd$ a. Four terms-grouping   b. $(3c + d)(a - b)$

12. $x^3 - 125$ a. Difference of cubes   b. $(x - 5)(x^2 + 5x + 25)$

13. $y^3 + 8$ a. Sum of cubes   b. $(y + 2)(y^2 - 2y + 4)$

14. $7p^2 - 29p + 4$ a. Nonperfect square trinomial   b. $(7p - 1)(p - 4)$

15. $3q^2 - 9q - 12$ a. Nonperfect square trinomial   b. $3(q - 4)(q + 1)$

16. $-2x^2 + 8x - 8$ a. Perfect square trinomial   b. $-2(x - 2)^2$

17. $18a^2 + 12a$ a. None of these
b. $6a(3a + 2)$

18. $54 - 2y^3$
a. Difference of cubes
b. $2(3 - y)(9 + 3y + y^2)$

19. $4t^2 - 100$ a. Difference of squares
b. $4(t - 5)(t + 5)$

20. $4t^2 - 31t - 8$
a. Nonperfect square trinomial
b. $(4t + 1)(t - 8)$

21. $10c^2 + 10c + 10$
a. Nonperfect square trinomial
b. $10(c^2 + c + 1)$

22. $2xw - 10x + 3yw - 15y$
a. Four terms-grouping
b. $(w - 5)(2x + 3y)$

23. $x^3 + 0.001$
a. Sum of cubes
b. $(x + 0.1)(x^2 - 0.1x + 0.01)$

24. $4q^2 - 9$
a. Difference of squares
b. $(2q - 3)(2q + 3)$

25. $64 + 16k + k^2$
a. Perfect square trinomial
b. $(8 + k)^2$

26. $s^2t + 5t + 6s^2 + 30$
a. Four terms-grouping
b. $(t + 6)(s^2 + 5)$

27. $x^2 + 2x + 1 - y^2$
a. Four terms-grouping
b. $(x + 1 - y)(x + 1 + y)$

28. $w^3 + y^3$ a. Sum of cubes
b. $(w + y)(w^2 - wy + y^2)$

29. $a^3 - c^3$
a. Difference of cubes
b. $(a - c)(a^2 + ac + c^2)$

30. $3y^2 + y + 1$
a. Nonperfect square trinomial
b. Prime

31. $c^2 + 8c + 9$
a. Nonperfect square trinomial
b. Prime

32. $a^2 + 2a + 1$
a. Perfect square trinomial
b. $(a + 1)^2$

33. $b^2 + 10b + 25$
a. Perfect square trinomial
b. $(b + 5)^2$

34. $-t^2 - 4t + 32$
a. Nonperfect square trinomial
b. $-1(t + 8)(t - 4)$

35. $-p^3 - 5p^2 - 4p$
a. Nonperfect square trinomial
b. $-p(p + 4)(p + 1)$

36. $x^2y^2 - 49$ a. Difference of squares
b. $(xy - 7)(xy + 7)$

37. $6x^2 - 21x - 45$
a. Nonperfect square trinomial
b. $3(2x + 3)(x - 5)$

38. $20y^2 - 14y + 2$
a. Nonperfect square trinomial
b. $2(5y - 1)(2y - 1)$

39. $5a^2bc^3 - 7abc^2$ a. None of these
b. $abc^2(5ac - 7)$

40. $8a^2 - 50$ a. Difference of squares
b. $2(2a - 5)(2a + 5)$

41. $t^2 + 2t - 63$
a. Nonperfect square trinomial
b. $(t + 9)(t - 7)$

42. $b^2 + 2b - 80$
a. Nonperfect square trinomial
b. $(b + 10)(b - 8)$

43. $ab + ay - b^2 - by$
a. Four terms-grouping
b. $(b + y)(a - b)$

44. $6x^3y^4 + 3x^2y^5$ a. None of these
b. $3x^2y^4(2x + y)$

45. $14u^2 - 11uv + 2v^2$
a. Nonperfect square trinomial
b. $(7u - 2v)(2u - v)$

46. $y^2 - 6y + 9 - t^2$
a. Four term-grouping
b. $(y - 3 - t)(y - 3 + t)$

47. $4q^2 - 8q - 6$
a. Nonperfect square trinomial
b. $2(2q^2 - 4q - 3)$

48. $9w^2 + 3w - 15$
a. Nonperfect square trinomial
b. $3(3w^2 + w - 5)$

49. $9m^2 + 16n^2$ a. Sum of squares
b. Prime

50. $5b^2 - 30b + 45$
a. Perfect square trinomial
b. $5(b - 3)^2$

51. $6r^2 + 11r + 3$
a. Nonperfect square trinomial
b. $(3r + 1)(2r + 3)$

52. $4s^2 + 4s - 15$
a. Nonperfect square trinomial
b. $(2s - 3)(2s + 5)$

53. $16a^4 - 1$
a. Difference of squares
b. $(2a - 1)(2a + 1)(4a^2 + 1)$

54. $p^3 + p^2c - 9p - 9c$
a. Four terms-grouping
b. $(p + c)(p - 3)(p + 3)$

55. $81u^2 - 90uv + 25v^2$
a. Perfect square trinomial
b. $(9u - 5v)^2$

56. $4x^2 + 16$ a. Sum of squares
b. $4(x^2 + 4)$

57. $x^2 - 5x - 6$
a. Nonperfect square trinomial
b. $(x - 6)(x + 1)$

58. $q^2 + q - 7$
a. Nonperfect square trinomial
b. Prime

59. $2ax - 6ay + 4bx - 12by$
a. Four terms-grouping
b. $2(x - 3y)(a + 2b)$

60. $8m^3 - 10m^2 - 3m$
a. Nonperfect square trinomial
b. $m(4m + 1)(2m - 3)$

61. $21x^4y + 41x^3y + 10x^2y$
a. Nonperfect square trinomial
b. $x^2y(3x + 5)(7x + 2)$

62. $2m^4 - 128$
a. Difference of squares
b. $2(m^2 - 8)(m^2 + 8)$

63. $8uv - 6u + 12v - 9$
a. Four terms-grouping
b. $(4v - 3)(2u + 3)$

64. $4t^2 - 20t + st - 5s$
a. Four terms-grouping
b. $(t - 5)(4t + s)$

65. $12x^2 - 12x + 3$
a. Perfect square trinomial
b. $3(2x - 1)^2$

66. $p^2 + 2pq + q^2$
a. Perfect square trinomial
b. $(p + q)^2$

67. $6n^3 + 5n^2 - 4n$
a. Nonperfect square trinomial
b. $n(2n - 1)(3n + 4)$

68. $4k^3 + 4k^2 - 3k$
a. Nonperfect square trinomial
b. $k(2k - 1)(2k + 3)$

69. $64 - y^2$
a. Difference of squares
b. $(8 - y)(8 + y)$

70. $36b - b^3$ a. Difference of squares
b. $b(6 - b)(6 + b)$

71. $b^2 - 4b + 10$
a. Nonperfect square trinomial
b. Prime

72. $y^2 + 6y + 8$
a. Nonperfect square trinomial
b. $(y + 4)(y + 2)$

73. $c^4 - 12c^2 + 20$
a. Nonperfect square trinomial
b. $(c^2 - 10)(c^2 - 2)$

Solving Equations Using the Zero Product Rule

Section 6.7

1. Definition of a Quadratic Equation

In Section 2.1, we solved linear equations in one variable. These are equations of the form $ax + b = 0$ $(a \neq 0)$. A linear equation in one variable is sometimes called a first-degree polynomial equation because the highest degree of all its terms is 1. A second-degree polynomial equation in one variable is called a quadratic equation.

Concepts

1. **Definition of a Quadratic Equation**
2. **Zero Product Rule**
3. **Solving Equations by Factoring**

 Writing   Translating Expression   Geometry   Scientific Calculator   Video   NS&E

> **DEFINITION** A Quadratic Equation in One Variable
>
> If a, b, and c are real numbers such that $a \neq 0$, then a **quadratic equation** is an equation that can be written in the form
>
> $$ax^2 + bx + c = 0.$$

The following equations are quadratic because they can each be written in the form $ax^2 + bx + c = 0$, $(a \neq 0)$.

$$-4x^2 + 4x = 1 \qquad x(x - 2) = 3 \qquad (x - 4)(x + 4) = 9$$

$$-4x^2 + 4x - 1 = 0 \qquad x^2 - 2x = 3 \qquad x^2 - 16 = 9$$

$$x^2 - 2x - 3 = 0 \qquad x^2 - 25 = 0$$

$$x^2 + 0x - 25 = 0$$

2. Zero Product Rule

One method for solving a quadratic equation is to factor and apply the zero product rule. The **zero product rule** states that if the product of two factors is zero, then one or both of its factors is zero.

> **PROPERTY** Zero Product Rule
>
> If $ab = 0$, then $a = 0$ or $b = 0$.

Classroom Example: p. 465, Exercise 14

Example 1 Applying the Zero Product Rule

Solve the equation by using the zero product rule. $(x - 4)(x + 3) = 0$

Solution:

$(x - 4)(x + 3) = 0$	Apply the zero product rule.
$x - 4 = 0$ or $x + 3 = 0$	Set each factor equal to zero.
$x = 4$ or $x = -3$	Solve each equation for x.

Check: $x = 4$ Check: $x = -3$

$(4 - 4)(4 + 3) \overset{?}{=} 0$ $(-3 - 4)(-3 + 3) \overset{?}{=} 0$

$(0)(7) \overset{?}{=} 0 \checkmark$ $(-7)(0) \overset{?}{=} 0 \checkmark$

The solution set is $\{4, -3\}$.

Skill Practice Solve.

1. $(x + 1)(x - 8) = 0$

Answer

1. $\{-1, 8\}$

Example 2 Applying the Zero Product Rule

Solve the equation by using the zero product rule.　$(x + 8)(4x + 1) = 0$

Classroom Example: p. 465, Exercise 20

Solution:

$(x + 8)(4x + 1) = 0$	Apply the zero product rule.
$x + 8 = 0$　or　$4x + 1 = 0$	Set each factor equal to zero.
$x = -8$　or　$4x = -1$	Solve each equation for x.
$x = -8$　or　$x = -\dfrac{1}{4}$	The solutions check in the original equation.

The solution set is $\left\{ -8, -\dfrac{1}{4} \right\}$.

Skill Practice Solve.

2. $(4x - 5)(x + 6) = 0$

Example 3 Applying the Zero Product Rule

Solve the equation using the zero product rule.　$x(3x - 7) = 0$

Classroom Example: p. 465, Exercise 22

Solution:

$x(3x - 7) = 0$	Apply the zero product rule.
$x = 0$　or　$3x - 7 = 0$	Set each factor equal to zero.
$x = 0$　or　$3x = 7$	Solve each equation for x.
$x = 0$　or　$x = \dfrac{7}{3}$	The solutions check in the original equation.

The solution set is $\left\{ 0, \dfrac{7}{3} \right\}$.

Skill Practice Solve.

3. $x(4x + 9) = 0$

3. Solving Equations by Factoring

Quadratic equations, like linear equations, arise in many applications in mathematics, science, and business. The following steps summarize the factoring method for solving a quadratic equation.

PROCEDURE Solving a Quadratic Equation by Factoring

Step 1 Write the equation in the form: $ax^2 + bx + c = 0$.

Step 2 Factor the quadratic expression completely.

Step 3 Apply the zero product rule. That is, set each factor equal to zero and solve the resulting equations.

Note: The solution(s) found in step 3 may be checked by substitution in the original equation.

Answers

2. $\left\{ \dfrac{5}{4}, -6 \right\}$　　3. $\left\{ 0, -\dfrac{9}{4} \right\}$

Classroom Example: p. 465, Exercise 30

Instructor Note: Show students why $2x^2 - 9x = 5$ cannot be solved as:

$$2x^2 - 9x = 5$$
$$x(2x - 9) = 5$$
$$x = 5 \quad \text{or} \quad 2x - 9 = 5$$

Example 4 Solving a Quadratic Equation

Solve the quadratic equation. $2x^2 - 9x = 5$

Solution:

$$2x^2 - 9x = 5$$

$$2x^2 - 9x - 5 = 0 \qquad \text{Write the equation in the form } ax^2 + bx + c = 0.$$

$$(2x + 1)(x - 5) = 0 \qquad \text{Factor the polynomial completely.}$$

$$2x + 1 = 0 \quad \text{or} \quad x - 5 = 0 \qquad \text{Set each factor equal to zero.}$$

$$2x = -1 \quad \text{or} \quad x = 5 \qquad \text{Solve each equation.}$$

$$x = -\frac{1}{2} \quad \text{or} \quad x = 5$$

Check: $x = -\dfrac{1}{2}$ Check: $x = 5$

$$2x^2 - 9x = 5 \qquad\qquad 2x^2 - 9x = 5$$

$$2\left(-\frac{1}{2}\right)^2 - 9\left(-\frac{1}{2}\right) \overset{?}{=} 5 \qquad 2(5)^2 - 9(5) \overset{?}{=} 5$$

$$2\left(\frac{1}{4}\right) + \frac{9}{2} \overset{?}{=} 5 \qquad 2(25) - 45 \overset{?}{=} 5$$

$$\frac{1}{2} + \frac{9}{2} \overset{?}{=} 5 \qquad\qquad 50 - 45 \overset{?}{=} 5 \ ✔$$

$$\frac{10}{2} \overset{?}{=} 5 \ ✔$$

The solution set is $\left\{-\dfrac{1}{2}, 5\right\}$.

Skill Practice Solve the quadratic equation.

4. $2y^2 + 19y = -24$

Classroom Example: p. 465, Exercise 46

Example 5 Solving a Quadratic Equation

Solve the quadratic equation. $4x^2 + 24x = 0$

Solution:

$$4x^2 + 24x = 0 \qquad \text{The equation is already in the form } ax^2 + bx + c = 0. \text{ (Note that } c = 0.)$$

$$4x(x + 6) = 0 \qquad \text{Factor completely.}$$

$$4x = 0 \quad \text{or} \quad x + 6 = 0 \qquad \text{Set each factor equal to zero.}$$

$$x = 0 \quad \text{or} \quad x = -6 \qquad \text{The solutions check in the original equation.}$$

The solution set is $\{0, -6\}$.

Skill Practice Solve the quadratic equation.

5. $5s^2 = 45$

Answers

4. $\left\{-8, -\dfrac{3}{2}\right\}$ **5.** $\{3, -3\}$

Example 6 Solving a Quadratic Equation

Classroom Example: p. 465, Exercise 54

Solve the quadratic equation. $5x(5x + 2) = 10x + 9$

Solution:

$5x(5x + 2) = 10x + 9$	
$25x^2 + 10x = 10x + 9$	Clear parentheses.
$25x^2 + 10x - 10x - 9 = 0$	Set the equation equal to zero.
$25x^2 - 9 = 0$	The equation is in the form $ax^2 + bx + c = 0$. (Note that $b = 0$.)
$(5x - 3)(5x + 3) = 0$	Factor completely.
$5x - 3 = 0$ or $5x + 3 = 0$	Set each factor equal to zero.
$5x = 3$ or $5x = -3$	Solve each equation.
$\dfrac{5x}{5} = \dfrac{3}{5}$ or $\dfrac{5x}{5} = \dfrac{-3}{5}$	
$x = \dfrac{3}{5}$ or $x = -\dfrac{3}{5}$	The solutions check in the original equation.

The solution set is $\left\{ \dfrac{3}{5}, -\dfrac{3}{5} \right\}$.

Skill Practice Solve the quadratic equation.

6. $4z(z + 3) = 4z + 5$

The zero product rule can be used to solve higher degree polynomial equations provided the equations can be set to zero and written in factored form.

Example 7 Solving a Higher Degree Polynomial Equation

Classroom Example: p. 465, Exercise 38

Solve the equation. $-6(y + 3)(y - 5)(2y + 7) = 0$

Solution:

$-6(y + 3)(y - 5)(2y + 7) = 0$	The equation is already in factored form and equal to zero.
	Set each factor equal to zero.
	Solve each equation for y.

$-6 \neq 0$ or $y + 3 = 0$ or $y - 5 = 0$ or $2y + 7 = 0$

No solution, $\qquad y = -3$ or $\quad y = 5$ or $\quad y = -\dfrac{7}{2}$

Answer

6. $\left\{ -\dfrac{5}{2}, \dfrac{1}{2} \right\}$

Notice that when the constant factor is set equal to zero, the result is a contradiction, $-6 = 0$. The constant factor does not produce a solution to the equation. Therefore, the solution set is $\{-3, 5, -\frac{7}{2}\}$. Each solution can be checked in the original equation.

Skill Practice Solve the equation.

7. $5(p - 4)(p + 7)(2p - 9) = 0$

Classroom Example: p. 466, Exercise 68

Example 8 **Solving a Higher Degree Polynomial Equation**

Solve the equation. $w^3 + 5w^2 - 9w - 45 = 0$

Solution:

$w^3 + 5w^2 - 9w - 45 = 0$	This is a higher degree polynomial equation.
$w^3 + 5w^2 \vdots - 9w - 45 = 0$	The equation is already set equal to zero. Now factor.
$w^2(w + 5) - 9(w + 5) = 0$ $(w + 5)(w^2 - 9) = 0$	Because there are four terms, try factoring by grouping.
$(w + 5)(w - 3)(w + 3) = 0$	$w^2 - 9$ is a difference of squares and can be factored further.
$w + 5 = 0$ or $w - 3 = 0$ or $w + 3 = 0$	Set each factor equal to zero.
$w = -5$ or $w = 3$ or $w = -3$	Solve each equation.

The solution set is $\{-5, 3, -3\}$. Each solution checks in the original equation.

Skill Practice Solve the equation.

8. $x^3 + 3x^2 - 4x - 12 = 0$

Answers

7. $\left\{4, -7, \frac{9}{2}\right\}$ **8.** $\{-2, -3, 2\}$

Section 6.7 Practice Exercises

Study Skills Exercise

1. Define the key terms.

   a. quadratic equation   **b. zero product rule**

Review Exercises

For Exercises 2–7, factor completely.

2. $6a - 8 - 3ab + 4b$
    $(3a - 4)(2 - b)$

3. $4b^2 - 44b + 120$
    $4(b - 5)(b - 6)$

4. $8u^2v^2 - 4uv$
    $4uv(2uv - 1)$

5. $3x^2 + 10x - 8$
    $(3x - 2)(x + 4)$

6. $3h^2 - 75$
    $3(h - 5)(h + 5)$

7. $4x^2 + 16y^2$
    $4(x^2 + 4y^2)$

 Writing   Translating Expression   Geometry   Scientific Calculator   Video   NS&E

Concept 1: Definition of a Quadratic Equation

For Exercises 8–13, identify the equations as linear, quadratic, or neither.

8. $4 - 5x = 0$
Linear

9. $5x^3 + 2 = 0$
Neither

10. $3x - 6x^2 = 0$
Quadratic

11. $1 - x + 2x^2 = 0$
Quadratic

12. $7x^4 + 8 = 0$
Neither

13. $3x + 2 = 0$
Linear

Concept 2: Zero Product Rule

For Exercises 14–22, solve each equation using the zero product rule. **(See Examples 1–3.)**

14. $(x - 5)(x + 1) = 0$ $\quad \{5, -1\}$

15. $(x + 3)(x - 1) = 0$ $\quad \{-3, 1\}$

16. $(3x - 2)(3x + 2) = 0$ $\quad \left\{\frac{2}{3}, -\frac{2}{3}\right\}$

17. $(2x - 7)(2x + 7) = 0$ $\quad \left\{\frac{7}{2}, -\frac{7}{2}\right\}$

18. $2(x - 7)(x - 7) = 0$ $\quad \{7\}$

19. $3(x + 5)(x + 5) = 0$ $\quad \{-5\}$

20. $(3x - 2)(2x - 3) = 0$ $\quad \left\{\frac{2}{3}, \frac{3}{2}\right\}$

21. $x(5x - 1) = 0$ $\quad \left\{0, \frac{1}{5}\right\}$

22. $x(3x + 8) = 0$ $\quad \left\{0, -\frac{8}{3}\right\}$

23. For a quadratic equation of the form $ax^2 + bx + c = 0$, what must be done before applying the zero product rule? _The polynomial must be factored completely._

24. What are the requirements needed to use the zero product rule to solve a quadratic equation or higher degree polynomial equation? _The equation must have one side equal to zero and the other side factored completely._

Concept 3: Solving Equations by Factoring

For Exercises 25–72, solve each equation. **(See Examples 4–8.)**

25. $p^2 - 2p - 15 = 0$ $\quad \{5, -3\}$

26. $y^2 - 7y - 8 = 0$ $\quad \{8, -1\}$

27. $z^2 + 10z - 24 = 0$ $\quad \{-12, 2\}$

28. $w^2 - 10w + 16 = 0$ $\quad \{8, 2\}$

29. $2q^2 - 7q = 4$ $\quad \left\{4, -\frac{1}{2}\right\}$

30. $4x^2 - 11x = 3$ $\quad \left\{-\frac{1}{4}, 3\right\}$

31. $0 = 9x^2 - 4$ $\quad \left\{\frac{2}{3}, -\frac{2}{3}\right\}$

32. $4a^2 - 49 = 0$ $\quad \left\{\frac{7}{2}, -\frac{7}{2}\right\}$

33. $2k^2 - 28k + 96 = 0$ $\quad \{6, 8\}$

34. $0 = 2t^2 + 20t + 50$ $\quad \{-5\}$

35. $0 = 2m^3 - 5m^2 - 12m$ $\quad \left\{0, -\frac{3}{2}, 4\right\}$

36. $3n^3 + 4n^2 + n = 0$ $\quad \left\{0, -\frac{1}{3}, -1\right\}$

37. $5(3p + 1)(p - 3)(p + 6) = 0$ $\quad \left\{-\frac{1}{3}, 3, -6\right\}$

38. $4(2x - 1)(x - 10)(x + 7) = 0$ $\quad \left\{\frac{1}{2}, 10, -7\right\}$

39. $x(x - 4)(2x + 3) = 0$ $\quad \left\{0, 4, -\frac{3}{2}\right\}$

40. $x(3x + 1)(x + 1) = 0$ $\quad \left\{0, -\frac{1}{3}, -1\right\}$

41. $-5x(2x + 9)(x - 11) = 0$ $\quad \left\{0, -\frac{9}{2}, 11\right\}$

42. $-3x(x + 7)(3x - 5) = 0$ $\quad \left\{0, -7, \frac{5}{3}\right\}$

43. $x^3 - 16x = 0$ $\quad \{0, 4, -4\}$

44. $t^3 - 36t = 0$ $\quad \{0, 6, -6\}$

45. $3x^2 + 18x = 0$ $\quad \{-6, 0\}$

46. $2y^2 - 20y = 0$ $\quad \{0, 10\}$

47. $16m^2 = 9$ $\quad \left\{\frac{3}{4}, -\frac{3}{4}\right\}$

48. $9n^2 = 1$ $\quad \left\{\frac{1}{3}, -\frac{1}{3}\right\}$

49. $2y^3 + 14y^2 = -20y$ $\quad \{0, -5, -2\}$

50. $3d^3 - 6d^2 = 24d$ $\quad \{0, -2, 4\}$

51. $5t - 2(t - 7) = 0$ $\quad \left\{-\frac{14}{3}\right\}$

52. $8h = 5(h - 9) + 6$ $\quad \{-13\}$

53. $2c(c - 8) = -30$ $\quad \{5, 3\}$

54. $3q(q - 3) = 12$ $\quad \{-1, 4\}$

55. $b^3 = -4b^2 - 4b$ $\quad \{0, -2\}$

56. $x^3 + 36x = 12x^2$ $\quad \{0, 6\}$

57. $3(a^2 + 2a) = 2a^2 - 9$ $\quad \{-3\}$

58. $9(k - 1) = -4k^2$ $\quad \left\{\frac{3}{4}, -3\right\}$

59. $2n(n + 2) = 6$ $\quad \{-3, 1\}$

60. $3p(p - 1) = 18$ $\quad \{3, -2\}$

61. $x(2x + 5) - 1 = 2x^2 + 3x + 2$ $\quad \left\{\frac{3}{2}\right\}$

62. $3z(z - 2) - z = 3z^2 + 4$ $\quad \left\{-\frac{4}{7}\right\}$

63. $27q^2 = 9q$ $\quad \left\{0, \frac{1}{3}\right\}$

64. $21w^2 = 14w$ $\quad \left\{0, \frac{2}{3}\right\}$

65. $3(c^2 - 2c) = 0$ $\quad \{0, 2\}$

66. $2(4d^2 + d) = 0$ $\quad \left\{0, -\frac{1}{4}\right\}$

 Writing Translating Expression Geometry Scientific Calculator Video NS&E

67. $y^3 - 3y^2 - 4y + 12 = 0$ $\{3, -2, 2\}$ **68.** $t^3 + 2t^2 - 16t - 32 = 0$ $\{-2, 4, -4\}$ **69.** $(x - 1)(x + 2) = 18$ $\{-5, 4\}$

70. $(w + 5)(w - 3) = 20$ $\{-7, 5\}$ **71.** $(p + 2)(p + 3) = 1 - p$ $\{-5, -1\}$ **72.** $(k - 6)(k - 1) = -k - 2$ $\{4, 2\}$

Problem Recognition Exercises

Polynomial Expressions Versus Polynomial Equations

For Exercises 1–36, factor each expression or solve each equation.

1. a. $x^2 + 6x - 7$ $(x + 7)(x - 1)$
  b. $x^2 + 6x - 7 = 0$ $\{-7, 1\}$

2. a. $c^2 + 8c + 12$ $(c + 6)(c + 2)$
  b. $c^2 + 8c + 12 = 0$ $\{-6, -2\}$

3. a. $2y^2 + 7y + 3$ $(2y + 1)(y + 3)$
  b. $2y^2 + 7y + 3 = 0$ $\left\{-\dfrac{1}{2}, -3\right\}$

4. a. $3x^2 - 8x + 5$ $(3x - 5)(x - 1)$
  b. $3x^2 - 8x + 5 = 0$ $\left\{\dfrac{5}{3}, 1\right\}$

5. a. $5q^2 + q - 4 = 0$ $\left\{\dfrac{4}{5}, -1\right\}$
  b. $5q^2 + q - 4$ $(5q - 4)(q + 1)$

6. a. $6a^2 - 7a - 3 = 0$ $\left\{-\dfrac{1}{3}, \dfrac{3}{2}\right\}$
  b. $6a^2 - 7a - 3$ $(3a + 1)(2a - 3)$

7. a. $a^2 - 64 = 0$ $\{-8, 8\}$
  b. $a^2 - 64$ $(a + 8)(a - 8)$

8. a. $v^2 - 100 = 0$ $\{-10, 10\}$
  b. $v^2 - 100$ $(v + 10)(v - 10)$

9. a. $4b^2 - 81$ $(2b + 9)(2b - 9)$
  b. $4b^2 - 81 = 0$ $\left\{-\dfrac{9}{2}, \dfrac{9}{2}\right\}$

10. a. $36t^2 - 49$ $(6t + 7)(6t - 7)$
  b. $36t^2 - 49 = 0$ $\left\{-\dfrac{7}{6}, \dfrac{7}{6}\right\}$

11. a. $8x^2 + 16x + 6 = 0$ $\left\{-\dfrac{3}{2}, -\dfrac{1}{2}\right\}$
  b. $8x^2 + 16x + 6$ $2(2x + 3)(2x + 1)$

12. a. $12y^2 + 40y + 32 = 0$ $\left\{-\dfrac{4}{3}, -2\right\}$
  b. $12y^2 + 40y + 32$ $4(3y + 4)(y + 2)$

13. a. $x^3 - 8x^2 - 20x$ $x(x - 10)(x + 2)$
  b. $x^3 - 8x^2 - 20x = 0$ $\{0, 10, -2\}$

14. a. $k^3 + 5k^2 - 14k$ $k(k + 7)(k - 2)$
  b. $k^3 + 5k^2 - 14k = 0$ $\{0, -7, 2\}$

15. a. $b^3 + b^2 - 9b - 9 = 0$
    $\{-1, 3, -3\}$
  b. $b^3 + b^2 - 9b - 9$
    $(b + 1)(b - 3)(b + 3)$

16. a. $x^3 - 8x^2 - 4x + 32 = 0$
    $\{8, -2, 2\}$
  b. $x^3 - 8x^2 - 4x + 32$
    $(x - 8)(x + 2)(x - 2)$

17. $2s^2 - 6s + rs - 3r$ $(s - 3)(2s + r)$

18. $6t^2 + 3t + 10tu + 5u$
  $(2t + 1)(3t + 5u)$

19. $8x^3 - 2x = 0$ $\left\{-\dfrac{1}{2}, 0, \dfrac{1}{2}\right\}$

20. $2b^3 - 50b = 0$ $\{-5, 0, 5\}$

21. $2x^3 - 4x^2 + 2x = 0$ $\{0, 1\}$

22. $3t^3 + 18t^2 + 27t = 0$ $\{-3, 0\}$

23. $7c^2 - 2c + 3 = 7(c^2 + c)$ $\left\{\dfrac{1}{3}\right\}$

24. $3z(2z + 4) = -7 + 6z^2$ $\left\{-\dfrac{7}{12}\right\}$

25. $8w^3 + 27$ $(2w + 3)(4w^2 - 6w + 9)$

26. $1000q^3 - 1$
  $(10q - 1)(100q^2 + 10q + 1)$

27. $5z^2 + 2z = 7$ $\left\{-\dfrac{7}{5}, 1\right\}$

28. $4h^2 + 25h = -6$ $\left\{-6, -\dfrac{1}{4}\right\}$

29. $3b(b + 6) = b - 10$ $\left\{-\dfrac{2}{3}, -5\right\}$

30. $3y^2 + 1 = y(y - 3)$ $\left\{-1, -\dfrac{1}{2}\right\}$

31. $5(2x - 3) - 2(3x + 1) = 4 - 3x$
  $\{3\}$

32. $11 - 6a = -4(2a - 3) - 1$ $\{0\}$

33. $4s^2 = 64$ $\{-4, 4\}$

34. $81v^2 = 36$ $\left\{-\dfrac{2}{3}, \dfrac{2}{3}\right\}$

35. $(x - 3)(x - 4) = 6$ $\{1, 6\}$

36. $(x + 5)(x + 9) = 21$ $\{-2, -12\}$

Applications of Quadratic Equations

1. Applications of Quadratic Equations

In this section we solve applications using the Problem-Solving Strategies outlined in Section 2.4.

Concepts

1. Applications of Quadratic Equations
2. Pythagorean Theorem

Example 1 Translating to a Quadratic Equation

Classroom Example: p. 471, Exercise 16

The product of two consecutive integers is 14 more than 6 times the smaller integer.

Solution:

Let x represent the first (smaller) integer.

Then $x + 1$ represents the second (larger) integer.   Label the variables.

(Smaller integer)(larger integer) $= 6 \cdot$ (smaller integer) $+ 14$ Verbal model

$\quad\quad x(x + 1) = 6(x) + 14$ Algebraic equation

$\quad\quad x^2 + x = 6x + 14$ Simplify.

$x^2 + x - 6x - 14 = 0$ Set one side of the equation equal to zero.

$\quad\quad x^2 - 5x - 14 = 0$

$\quad\quad (x - 7)(x + 2) = 0$ Factor.

$x - 7 = 0 \quad$ or $\quad x + 2 = 0$ Set each factor equal to zero.

$\quad x = 7 \quad$ or $\quad\quad x = -2$ Solve for x.

Recall that x represents the smaller integer. Therefore, there are two possibilities for the pairs of consecutive integers.

If $x = 7$, then the larger integer is $x + 1$ or $7 + 1 = 8$.

If $x = -2$, then the larger integer is $x + 1$ or $-2 + 1 = -1$.

The integers are 7 and 8, or -2 and -1.

Skill Practice

1. The product of two consecutive odd integers is 9 more than 10 times the smaller integer. Find the pair of integers.

Example 2 Using a Quadratic Equation in a Geometry Application

Classroom Example: p. 471, Exercise 18

A rectangular sign has an area of 40 ft². If the width is 3 feet shorter than the length, what are the dimensions of the sign?

Label the variables.

Solution:

Let x represent the length of the sign. Then $x - 3$ represents the width (Figure 6–1).

The problem gives information about the length of the sides and about the area. Therefore, we can form a relationship by using the formula for the area of a rectangle.

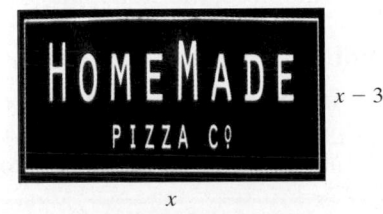

$x - 3$

x

Figure 6-1

Answer

1. The integers are 9 and 11 or -1 and 1.

$$A = l \cdot w \qquad\qquad \text{Area equals length times width.}$$

$$40 = x(x - 3) \qquad\qquad \text{Set up an algebraic equation.}$$

$$40 = x^2 - 3x \qquad\qquad \text{Clear parentheses.}$$

$$0 = x^2 - 3x - 40 \qquad\qquad \text{Write the equation in the form,}$$
$$ax^2 + bx + c = 0.$$

$$0 = (x - 8)(x + 5) \qquad\qquad \text{Factor.}$$

$$0 = x - 8 \quad \text{or} \quad 0 = x + 5 \qquad \text{Set each factor equal to zero.}$$

$$8 = x \quad\quad \text{or} \quad -5 \cancel{=} x \qquad \text{Because } x \text{ represents the length of a}$$
rectangle, reject the negative solution.

The variable x represents the length of the sign. The length is 8 ft.

The expression $x - 3$ represents the width. The width is $(8 - 3)$ ft, or 5 ft.

Skill Practice

2. The length of a rectangle is 5 ft more than the width. The area is 36 ft². Find the length and width.

Classroom Example: p. 472, Exercise 28

| **Example 3** | **Using a Quadratic Equation in an Application** |

A stone is dropped off a 64-ft cliff and falls into the ocean below. The height of the stone above sea level is given by the equation

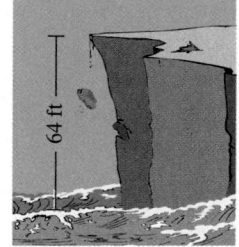

$$h = -16t^2 + 64 \qquad \text{where } h \text{ is the stone's height}$$
in feet, and t is the time
in seconds.

Find the time required for the stone to hit the water.

Solution:

When the stone hits the water, its height is zero. Therefore, substitute $h = 0$ into the equation.

$$h = -16t^2 + 64 \qquad\qquad \text{The equation is quadratic.}$$

$$0 = -16t^2 + 64 \qquad\qquad \text{Substitute } h = 0.$$

$$0 = -16(t^2 - 4) \qquad\qquad \text{Factor out the GCF.}$$

$$0 = -16(t - 2)(t + 2) \qquad \text{Factor as a difference of squares.}$$

$$-16 \cancel{=} 0 \quad \text{or} \quad t - 2 = 0 \quad \text{or} \quad t + 2 = 0 \qquad \text{Set each factor to}$$
zero.

$$\text{No solution,} \qquad\qquad t = 2 \quad \text{or} \quad t \cancel{=} -2 \quad \text{Solve for } t.$$

The negative value of t is rejected because the stone cannot fall for a negative time. Therefore, the stone hits the water after 2 sec.

Skill Practice

3. An object is launched into the air from the ground and its height is given by $h = -16t^2 + 144t$, where h is the height in feet after t seconds. Find the time required for the object to hit the ground.

Answers

2. The width is 4 ft, and the length is 9 ft.
3. The object hits the ground in 9 sec.

2. Pythagorean Theorem

Recall that a right triangle is a triangle that contains a 90° angle. Furthermore, the sum of the squares of the two legs (the shorter sides) of a right triangle equals the square of the hypotenuse (the longest side). This important fact is known as the Pythagorean theorem. The Pythagorean theorem is an enduring landmark of mathematical history from which many mathematical ideas have been built. Although the theorem is named after Pythagoras (sixth century B.C.E.), a Greek mathematician and philosopher, it is thought that the ancient Babylonians were familiar with the principle more than a thousand years earlier.

For the right triangle shown in Figure 6-2, the **Pythagorean theorem** is stated as:

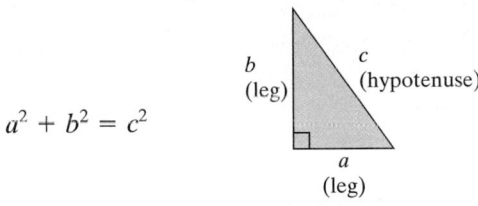

$$a^2 + b^2 = c^2$$

Figure 6-2

In this formula, a and b are the legs of the right triangle and c is the hypotenuse. Notice that the hypotenuse is the longest side of the right triangle and is opposite the 90° angle.

The triangle shown below is a right triangle. Notice that the lengths of the sides satisfy the Pythagorean theorem.

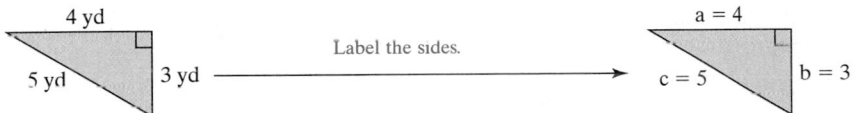

The shorter sides are labeled as a and b.

Label the sides.

The longest side is the hypotenuse. It is always labeled as c.

$a^2 + b^2 = c^2$	Apply the Pythagorean theorem.
$(4)^2 + (3)^2 = (5)^2$	Substitute $a = 4$, $b = 3$, and $c = 5$.
$16 + 9 = 25$	
$25 = 25$ ✔	

Example 4 **Applying the Pythagorean Theorem**

Find the length of the missing side of the right triangle.

Classroom Example: p. 473, Exercise 32

Solution:

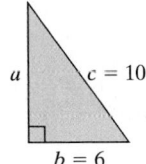

	Label the triangle.
$a^2 + b^2 = c^2$	Apply the Pythagorean theorem.
$a^2 + 6^2 = 10^2$	Substitute $b = 6$ and $c = 10$.
$a^2 + 36 = 100$	Simplify.
	The equation is quadratic. Set the equation equal to zero.

$$a^2 + 36 - 100 = 100 - 100 \qquad \text{Subtract 100 from both sides.}$$

$$a^2 - 64 = 0$$

$$(a + 8)(a - 8) = 0 \qquad \text{Factor.}$$

$$a + 8 = 0 \quad \text{or} \quad a - 8 = 0 \qquad \text{Set each factor equal to zero.}$$

$$a \neq -8 \quad \text{or} \quad a = 8 \qquad \text{Because } x \text{ represents the length of a side of a triangle, reject the negative solution.}$$

The third side is 8 ft.

Skill Practice

4. Find the length of the missing side.

15 m   9 m

Classroom Example: p. 473, Exercise 40

Example 5   **Using a Quadratic Equation in an Application**

A 13-ft board is used as a ramp to unload furniture off a loading platform. If the distance between the top of the board and the ground is 7 ft less than the distance between the bottom of the board and the base of the platform, find both distances.

Solution:

Let x represent the distance between the bottom of the board and the base of the platform. Then $x - 7$ represents the distance between the top of the board and the ground (Figure 6-3).

13 ft

$x - 7$

x

Figure 6-3

Avoiding Mistakes

Recall that the square of a binomial results in a perfect square trinomial.

$(a - b)^2 = a^2 - 2ab + b^2$

$(x - 7)^2 = x^2 - 2(x)(7) + 7^2$

$\qquad = x^2 - 14x + 49$

Don't forget the middle term.

$$a^2 + b^2 = c^2 \qquad \text{Pythagorean theorem}$$

$$x^2 + (x - 7)^2 = (13)^2$$

$$x^2 + (x)^2 - 2(x)(7) + (7)^2 = 169$$

$$x^2 + x^2 - 14x + 49 = 169$$

$$2x^2 - 14x + 49 = 169 \qquad \text{Combine } like \text{ terms.}$$

$$2x^2 - 14x + 49 - 169 = 169 - 169 \qquad \text{Set the equation equal to zero.}$$

$$2x^2 - 14x - 120 = 0 \qquad \text{Write the equation in the form } ax^2 + bx + c = 0.$$

$$2(x^2 - 7x - 60) = 0 \qquad \text{Factor.}$$

$$2(x - 12)(x + 5) = 0$$

$$2 \neq 0 \quad \text{or} \quad x - 12 = 0 \quad \text{or} \quad x + 5 = 0 \qquad \text{Set each factor equal to zero.}$$

$$x = 12 \quad \text{or} \quad x \neq -5 \qquad \text{Solve both equations for } x.$$

Answer

4. The length of the third side is 12 m.

Recall that x represents the distance between the bottom of the board and the base of the platform. We reject the negative value of x because a distance cannot be negative. Therefore, the distance between the bottom of the board and the base of the platform is 12 ft. The distance between the top of the board and the ground is $x - 7 = 5$ ft.

Skill Practice

5. A 5-yd ladder leans against a wall. The distance from the bottom of the wall to the top of the ladder is 1 yd more than the distance from the bottom of the wall to the bottom of the ladder. Find both distances.

5 yd
$x + 1$
x

Answer

5. The distance along the wall to the top of the ladder is 4 yd. The distance on the ground from the ladder to the wall is 3 yd.

Section 6.8   Practice Exercises

Study Skills Exercise

1. Define the key term **Pythagorean theorem**.

Review Exercises

For Exercises 2–7, solve the quadratic equations.

2. $(6x + 1)(x + 4) = 0$ $\left\{-\frac{1}{6}, -4\right\}$ 3. $9x(3x + 2) = 0$ $\left\{0, -\frac{2}{3}\right\}$ 4. $4x^2 - 1 = 0$ $\left\{-\frac{1}{2}, \frac{1}{2}\right\}$

5. $x^2 - 5x = 6$ $\{6, -1\}$ 6. $x(x - 20) = -100$ $\{10\}$ 7. $6x^2 - 7x - 10 = 0$ $\left\{-\frac{5}{6}, 2\right\}$

8. Explain what is wrong with the following problem: $(x - 3)(x + 2) = 5$
   $$x - 3 = 5 \quad \text{or} \quad x + 2 = 5.$$
   A factored expression must be set equal to zero to use the zero product rule.

Concept 1: Applications of Quadratic Equations

9. If eleven is added to the square of a number, the result is sixty. Find all such numbers.
   The numbers are 7 and −7.

10. If a number is added to two times its square, the result is thirty-six. Find all such numbers.
    The numbers are $-\frac{9}{2}$ and 4.

11. If twelve is added to six times a number, the result is twenty-eight less than the square of the number. Find all such numbers.
    The numbers are 10 and −4.

12. The square of a number is equal to twenty more than the number. Find all such numbers.
    The numbers are 5 and −4.

13. The product of two consecutive odd integers is sixty-three. Find all such integers. **(See Example 1.)**
    The numbers are −9 and −7, or 7 and 9.

14. The product of two consecutive even integers is forty-eight. Find all such integers.
    The numbers are 6 and 8, or −8 and −6.

15. The sum of the squares of two consecutive integers is sixty-one. Find all such integers.
    The numbers are 5 and 6, or −6 and −5.

16. The sum of the squares of two consecutive even integers is fifty-two. Find all such integers. The numbers are 4 and 6 or −6 and −4.

17. *Las Meninas* (Spanish for *The Maids of Honor*) is a famous painting by Spanish painter Diego Velazquez. This work is regarded as one of the most important paintings in western art history. The height of the painting is approximately 2 ft more than its width. If the total area is 99 ft², determine the dimensions of the painting.
    (See Example 2.)   The height of the painting is 11 ft and the width is 9 ft.

18. The width of a rectangular painting is 2 in. less than the length. The area is 120 in.² Find the length and width.   The painting has length 12 in. and width 10 in.

x

$x - 2$

 Writing   Translating Expression   Geometry   Scientific Calculator   Video   NS&E

19. The width of a rectangular slab of concrete is 3 m less than the length. The area is 28 m².

 a. What are the dimensions of the rectangle?
  The slab is 7 m by 4 m.
 b. What is the perimeter of the rectangle?
  The perimeter is 22 m.

20. The width of a rectangular picture is 7 in. less than the length. The area of the picture is 78 in.²

 a. What are the dimensions of the picture?
  The picture is 13 in. by 6 in.
 b. What is the perimeter of the picture?
  The perimeter is 38 in.

21. The base of a triangle is 3 ft more than the height. If the area is 14 ft², find the base and the height.   The base is 7 ft and the height is 4 ft.

22. The height of a triangle is 15 cm more than the base. If the area is 125 cm², find the base and the height.   The base is 10 cm and the height is 25 cm.

23. Find the bases and height for the trapezoid, given that the area is 60 cm². Recall that the area of a trapezoid is $A = \dfrac{1}{2}(b_1 + b_2)h$.

The bases measure 10 cm and 5 cm. The height is 8 cm.

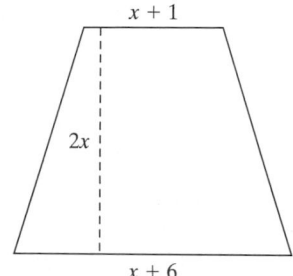

24. Find the bases and height for the trapezoid, given that the area is 8 ft².

The bases measure 5 ft and 3 ft. The height is 2 ft.

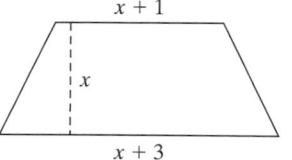

25. In a physics experiment, a ball is dropped off a 144-ft platform. The height of the ball above the ground is given by the equation

$$h = -16t^2 + 144$$ where h is the ball's height in feet, and t is the time in seconds after the ball is dropped ($t \geq 0$).

Find the time required for the ball to hit the ground. (*Hint:* Let $h = 0$.) **(See Example 3.)**
The ball hits the ground in 3 sec.

26. A stone is dropped off a 256-ft cliff. The height of the stone above the ground is given by the equation

$$h = -16t^2 + 256$$ where h is the stone's height in feet, and t is the time in seconds after the stone is dropped ($t \geq 0$).

Find the time required for the stone to hit the ground.   The stone hits the ground in 4 sec.

27. An object is shot straight up into the air from ground level with an initial speed of 24 ft/sec. The height of the object (in feet) is given by the equation

$$h = -16t^2 + 24t$$ where t is the time in seconds after launch ($t \geq 0$).

Find the time(s) when the object is at ground level.   The object is at ground level at 0 sec and 1.5 sec.

28. A rocket is launched straight up into the air from the ground with initial speed of 64 ft/sec. The height of the rocket (in feet) is given by the equation

$$h = -16t^2 + 64t$$ where t is the time in seconds after launch ($t \geq 0$).

Find the time(s) when the rocket is at ground level.   The rocket is at ground level at 0 sec and 4 sec.

Concept 2: Pythagorean Theorem

29. Sketch a right triangle and label the sides with the words *leg* and *hypotenuse*.

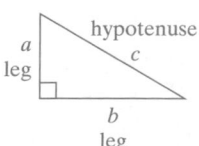

30. State the Pythagorean theorem.
 Given a right triangle with legs a and b and hypotenuse c, then $a^2 + b^2 = c^2$.

For Exercises 31–34, find the length of the missing side of the right triangle. **(See Example 4.)**

31.

24 cm

c

7 cm

c = 25 cm

32.

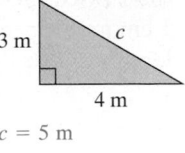

3 m

c

4 m

c = 5 m

33.

a

17 in.

8 in.

a = 15 in.

34.

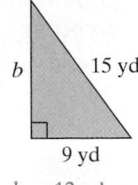

b

15 yd

9 yd

b = 12 yd

35. Find the length of the supporting brace.
The brace is 20 in. long.

16 in.

12 in.

?

36. Find the height of the airplane above the ground.
The height is 9 km.

?

15 km

12 km

37. Darcy holds the end of a kite string 3 ft (1 yd) off the ground and wants to estimate the height of the kite. Her friend Jenna is 24 yd away from her, standing directly under the kite as shown in the figure. If Darcy has 30 yd of string out, find the height of the kite (ignore the sag in the string). The kite is 19 yd high.

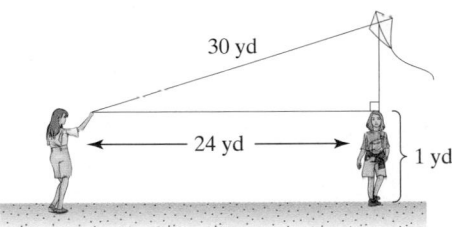

30 yd

24 yd

1 yd

38. Two cars leave the same point at the same time, one traveling north and the other traveling east. After an hour, one car has traveled 48 mi and the other has traveled 64 mi. How many miles apart were they at that time? They were 80 mi apart.

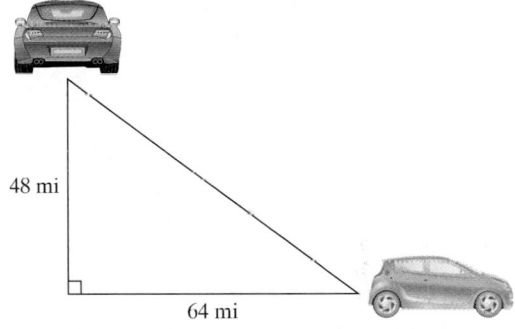

48 mi

64 mi

39. A 17-ft ladder rests against the side of a house. The distance between the top of the ladder and the ground is 7 ft more than the distance between the base of the ladder and the bottom of the house. Find both distances. **(See Example 5.)**
The bottom of the ladder is 8 ft from the house. The distance from the top of the ladder to the ground is 15 ft.

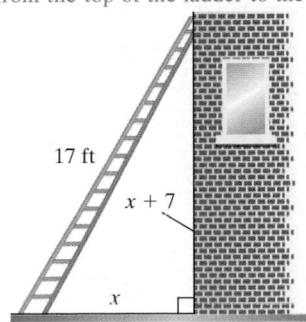

17 ft

x + 7

x

40. Two boats leave a marina. One travels east, and the other travels south. After 30 min, the second boat has traveled 1 mi farther than the first boat and the distance between the boats is 5 mi. Find the distance each boat traveled.
The first boat traveled 3 mi; the second boat traveled 4 mi.

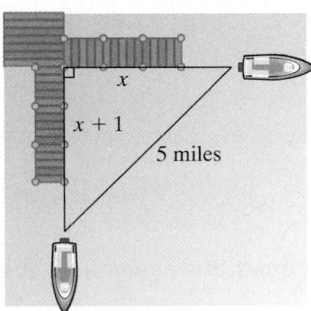

x

x + 1

5 miles

 Writing   Translating Expression   Geometry   Scientific Calculator   Video   NS&E

41. One leg of a right triangle is 4 m less than the hypotenuse. The other leg is 2 m less than the hypotenuse. Find the length of the hypotenuse.
The hypotenuse is 10 m.

 42. The longer leg of a right triangle is 1 cm less than twice the shorter leg. The hypotenuse is 1 cm greater than twice the shorter leg. Find the length of the shorter leg. The shorter leg is 8 cm.

Group Activity

Building a Factoring Test

Estimated Time: 15–20 minutes

Group Size: 3

Answers will vary throughout this exercise.

In this activity, each group will make a test for this chapter. Then the groups will trade papers and take the test.

For questions 1–8, write a polynomial that has the given conditions.

1. A trinomial with a GCF not equal to 1. The GCF should include a constant and at least one variable.

1. _____

2. A four-term polynomial that is factorable by grouping.

2. _____

3. A factorable trinomial with a leading coefficient of 1. (The trinomial should factor as a product of two binomials.)

3. _____

4. A factorable trinomial with a leading coefficient not equal to 1. (The trinomial should factor as a product of two binomials.)

4. _____

5. A trinomial that requires the GCF to be removed. The resulting trinomial should factor as a product of two binomials.

5. _____

6. A difference of squares.

6. _____

7. A difference of cubes.

7. _____

8. A sum of cubes.

8. _____

9. Write a quadratic *equation* that has solution set $\{4, -7\}$.

9. _____

10. Write a quadratic *equation* that has solution set $\left\{0, -\dfrac{2}{3}\right\}$.

10. _____

 Writing   Translating Expression   Geometry   Scientific Calculator   Video   NS&E

Chapter 6   Summary

Section 6.1 — Greatest Common Factor and Factoring by Grouping

Key Concepts

The **greatest common factor** (GCF) is the greatest factor common to all terms of a polynomial. To factor out the GCF from a polynomial, use the distributive property.

A four-term polynomial may be factorable by grouping.

Steps to Factoring by Grouping

1. Identify and factor out the GCF from all four terms.
2. Factor out the GCF from the first pair of terms. Factor out the GCF or its opposite from the second pair of terms.
3. If the two terms share a common binomial factor, factor out the binomial factor.

Examples

Example 1

$3x(a + b) - 5(a + b)$ Greatest common factor is $(a + b)$.

$= (a + b)(3x - 5)$

Example 2

$60xa - 30xb - 80ya + 40yb$

$= 10[6xa - 3xb - 8ya + 4yb]$ Factor out GCF.

$= 10[3x(2a - b) - 4y(2a - b)]$ Factor by grouping.

$= 10(2a - b)(3x - 4y)$

Section 6.2 — Factoring Trinomials of the Form $x^2 + bx + c$

Key Concepts

Factoring a Trinomial with a Leading Coefficient of 1

A trinomial of the form $x^2 + bx + c$ factors as

$$x^2 + bx + c = (x \;\; \square)(x \;\; \square)$$

where the remaining terms are given by two integers whose product is c and whose sum is b.

Example

Example 1

$x^2 - 14x + 45$ The integers -5 and -9 have a product of 45

$= (x \;\; \square)(x \;\; \square)$ and a sum of -14.

$= (x - 5)(x - 9)$

Section 6.3 — Factoring Trinomials: Trial-and-Error Method

Key Concepts

Trial-and-Error Method for Factoring Trinomials in the Form $ax^2 + bx + c$ (where $a \neq 0$)

1. Factor out the GCF from all terms.
2. List the pairs of factors of a and the pairs of factors of c. Consider the reverse order in one of the lists.
3. Construct two binomials of the form

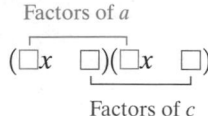

4. Test each combination of factors and signs until the product forms the correct trinomial.
5. If no combination of factors produces the correct product, the trinomial cannot be factored further.

Example

Example 1

$10y^2 + 35y - 20$

$= 5(2y^2 + 7y - 4)$

The pairs of factors of 2 are: $2 \cdot 1$
The pairs of factors of -4 are:

$$-1(4) \qquad 1(-4)$$
$$-2(2) \qquad 2(-2)$$
$$-4(1) \qquad 4(-1)$$

$(2y - 2)(y + 2) = 2y^2 + 2y - 4$	No
$(2y - 4)(y + 1) = 2y^2 - 2y - 4$	No
$(2y + 1)(y - 4) = 2y^2 - 7y - 4$	No
$(2y + 2)(y - 2) = 2y^2 - 2y - 4$	No
$(2y + 4)(y - 1) = 2y^2 + 2y - 4$	No
$(2y - 1)(y + 4) = 2y^2 + 7y - 4$	Yes

$10y^2 + 35y - 20 = 5(2y - 1)(y + 4)$

Section 6.4 — Factoring Trinomials: AC-Method

Key Concepts

AC-Method for Factoring Trinomials of the Form $ax^2 + bx + c$ (where $a \neq 0$)

1. Factor out the GCF from all terms.
2. Find the product ac.
3. Find two integers whose product is ac and whose sum is b. (If no pair of integers can be found, then the trinomial cannot be factored further.)
4. Rewrite the middle term (bx) as the sum of two terms whose coefficients are the integers found in step 3.
5. Factor the polynomial by grouping.

Example

Example 1

$10y^2 + 35y - 20$

$= 5(2y^2 + 7y - 4)$ First factor out GCF.

Identify the product $ac = (2)(-4) = -8$.

Find two integers whose product is -8 and whose sum is 7. The numbers are 8 and -1.

$5[2y^2 + 8y - 1y - 4]$

$= 5[2y(y + 4) - 1(y + 4)]$

$= 5(y + 4)(2y - 1)$

Section 6.5 — Difference of Squares and Perfect Square Trinomials

Key Concepts

Factoring a Difference of Squares

$$a^2 - b^2 = (a - b)(a + b)$$

Factoring a Perfect Square Trinomial

The factored form of a **perfect square trinomial** is the square of a binomial:

$$a^2 + 2ab + b^2 = (a + b)^2$$
$$a^2 - 2ab + b^2 = (a - b)^2$$

Examples

Example 1

$$25z^2 - 4y^2$$
$$= (5z - 2y)(5z + 2y)$$

Example 2

Factor: $25y^2 + 10y + 1$

$$= (5y)^2 + 2(5y)(1) + (1)^2$$

$$= (5y + 1)^2$$

Section 6.6 — Sum and Difference of Cubes

Key Concepts

Factoring a Sum or Difference of Cubes

$$a^3 - b^3 = (a - b)(a^2 + ab + b^2)$$

$$a^3 + b^3 = (a + b)(a^2 - ab + b^2)$$

Examples

Example 1

$$m^3 - 64$$
$$= (m)^3 - (4)^3$$
$$= (m - 4)(m^2 + 4m + 16)$$

Example 2

$$x^6 + 8y^3$$
$$= (x^2)^3 + (2y)^3$$
$$= (x^2 + 2y)(x^4 - 2x^2y + 4y^2)$$

Section 6.7   Solving Equations Using the Zero Product Rule

Key Concepts

An equation of the form $ax^2 + bx + c = 0$, where $a \neq 0$, is a **quadratic equation**.

The zero product rule states that if $ab = 0$, then $a = 0$ or $b = 0$. The zero product rule can be used to solve a quadratic equation or a higher degree polynomial equation that is factored and set to zero.

Examples

Example 1

The equation $2x^2 - 17x + 30 = 0$ is a quadratic equation.

Example 2

$3w(w - 4)(2w + 1) = 0$

$3w = 0$ or $w - 4 = 0$ or $2w + 1 = 0$

$w = 0$ or $w = 4$ or $w = -\dfrac{1}{2}$

The solution set is $\left\{0, 4, -\dfrac{1}{2}\right\}$.

Example 3

$4x^2 = 34x - 60$

$4x^2 - 34x + 60 = 0$

$2(2x^2 - 17x + 30) = 0$

$2(2x - 5)(x - 6) = 0$

$2 \neq 0$ or $2x - 5 = 0$ or $x - 6 = 0$

$$x = \frac{5}{2} \quad \text{or} \quad x = 6$$

The solution set is $\left\{\dfrac{5}{2}, 6\right\}$.

Section 6.8 Applications of Quadratic Equations

Key Concepts

Use the zero product rule to solve applications.

Examples

Example 1

Find two consecutive integers such that the sum of their squares is 61.

Let x represent one integer.
Let $x + 1$ represent the next consecutive integer.

$$x^2 + (x + 1)^2 = 61$$
$$x^2 + x^2 + 2x + 1 = 61$$
$$2x^2 + 2x - 60 = 0$$
$$2(x^2 + x - 30) = 0$$
$$2(x - 5)(x + 6) = 0$$
$$x = 5 \quad \text{or} \quad x = -6$$

If $x = 5$, then the next consecutive integer is 6.
If $x = -6$, then the next consecutive integer is -5.
The integers are 5 and 6, or -6 and -5.

Some applications involve the Pythagorean theorem.

$$a^2 + b^2 = c^2$$

Example 2

Find the length of the missing side.

$$x^2 + (7)^2 = (25)^2$$
$$x^2 + 49 = 625$$
$$x^2 - 576 = 0$$
$$(x - 24)(x + 24) = 0$$
$$x = 24 \quad \text{or} \quad x = -24$$

The length of the side is 24 ft.

Chapter 6   Review Exercises

Section 6.1

For Exercises 1–4, identify the greatest common factor for each group of terms.

1. $15a^2b^4, 30a^3b, 9a^5b^3$
$3a^2b$

2. $3(x + 5), x(x + 5)$
$x + 5$

3. $2c^3(3c - 5), 4c(3c - 5)$
$2c(3c - 5)$

4. $-2wyz, -4xyz$
$-2yz$ or $2yz$

For Exercises 5–10, factor out the greatest common factor.

5. $6x^2 + 2x^4 - 8x$
$2x(3x + x^3 - 4)$

6. $11w^3y^3 - 44w^2y^5$
$11w^2y^3(w - 4y^2)$

7. $-t^2 + 5t$
$t(-t + 5)$ or $-t(t - 5)$

8. $-6u^2 - u$
$u(-6u - 1)$ or $-u(6u + 1)$

9. $3b(b + 2) - 7(b + 2)$ $(b + 2)(3b - 7)$

10. $2(5x + 9) + 8x(5x + 9)$ $2(5x + 9)(1 + 4x)$

For Exercises 11–14, factor by grouping.

11. $7w^2 + 14w + wb + 2b$ $(w + 2)(7w + b)$

12. $b^2 - 2b + yb - 2y$ $(b - 2)(b + y)$

13. $60y^2 - 45y - 12y + 9$ $3(4y - 3)(5y - 1)$

14. $6a - 3a^2 - 2ab + a^2b$ $a(2 - a)(3 - b)$

Section 6.2

For Exercises 15–24, factor completely.

15. $x^2 - 10x + 21$
$(x - 3)(x - 7)$

16. $y^2 - 19y + 88$
$(y - 8)(y - 11)$

17. $-6z + z^2 - 72$
$(z - 12)(z + 6)$

18. $-39 + q^2 - 10q$
$(q - 13)(q + 3)$

19. $3p^2w + 36pw + 60w$
$3w(p + 10)(p + 2)$

20. $2m^4 + 26m^3 + 80m^2$
$2m^2(m + 8)(m + 5)$

21. $-t^2 + 10t - 16$
$-(t - 8)(t - 2)$

22. $-w^2 - w + 20$
$-(w - 4)(w + 5)$

23. $a^2 + 12ab + 11b^2$
$(a + b)(a + 11b)$

24. $c^2 - 3cd - 18d^2$
$(c - 6d)(c + 3d)$

Section 6.3

For Exercises 25–28, let a, b, and c represent positive integers.

25. When factoring a polynomial of the form $ax^2 - bx - c$, should the signs of the binomials be both positive, both negative, or different?
Different

26. When factoring a polynomial of the form $ax^2 - bx + c$, should the signs of the binomials be both positive, both negative, or different?
Both negative

27. When factoring a polynomial of the form $ax^2 + bx + c$, should the signs of the binomials be both positive, both negative, or different?
Both positive

28. When factoring a polynomial of the form $ax^2 + bx - c$, should the signs of the binomials be both positive, both negative, or different?
Different

For Exercises 29–42, factor each trinomial using the trial-and-error method.

29. $2y^2 - 5y - 12$
$(2y + 3)(y - 4)$

30. $4w^2 - 5w - 6$
$(4w + 3)(w - 2)$

31. $10z^2 + 29z + 10$
$(2z + 5)(5z + 2)$

32. $8z^2 + 6z - 9$
$(4z - 3)(2z + 3)$

33. $2p^2 - 5p + 1$
Prime

34. $5r^2 - 3r + 7$
Prime

35. $10w^2 - 60w - 270$
$10(w - 9)(w + 3)$

36. $-3y^2 + 18y + 48$
$-3(y - 8)(y + 2)$

37. $9c^2 - 30cd + 25d^2$
$(3c - 5d)^2$

38. $x^2 + 12x + 36$
$(x + 6)^2$

39. $6g^2 + 7gh + 2h^2$
$(3g + 2h)(2g + h)$

40. $12m^2 - 32mn + 5n^2$
$(6m - n)(2m - 5n)$

41. $v^4 - 2v^2 - 3$
$(v^2 + 1)(v^2 - 3)$

42. $x^4 + 7x^2 + 10$
$(x^2 + 5)(x^2 + 2)$

Section 6.4

For Exercises 43–44, find a pair of integers whose product and sum are given.

43. Product: -5 sum: 4 $5, -1$

44. Product: 15 sum: -8 $-3, -5$

For Exercises 45–58, factor each trinomial using the ac-method.

45. $3c^2 - 5c - 2$
$(c - 2)(3c + 1)$

46. $4y^2 + 13y + 3$
$(y + 3)(4y + 1)$

47. $t^2 + 13tw + 12w^2$
$(t + 12w)(t + w)$

48. $4x^4 + 17x^2 - 15$
$(4x^2 - 3)(x^2 + 5)$

49. $w^4 + 7w^2 + 10$
$(w^2 + 5)(w^2 + 2)$

50. $p^2 - 8pq + 15q^2$
$(p - 3q)(p - 5q)$

51. $-40v^2 - 22v + 6$
$-2(4v + 3)(5v - 1)$

52. $40s^2 + 30s - 100$
$10(4s - 5)(s + 2)$

53. $a^3b - 10a^2b^2 + 24ab^3$
$ab(a - 6b)(a - 4b)$

54. $2z^6 + 8z^5 - 42z^4$
$2z^4(z + 7)(z - 3)$

 Writing   Translating Expression   Geometry   Scientific Calculator   Video   NS&E

55. $m + 9m^2 - 2$
Prime

56. $2 + 6p^2 + 19p$
Prime

57. $49x^2 + 140x + 100$
$(7x + 10)^2$

58. $9w^2 - 6wz + z^2$
$(3w - z)^2$

Section 6.5

For Exercises 59–60, write the formula to factor each binomial, if possible.

59. $a^2 - b^2$
$(a - b)(a + b)$

60. $a^2 + b^2$
Prime

For Exercises 61–76, factor completely.

61. $a^2 - 49$
$(a - 7)(a + 7)$

62. $d^2 - 64$
$(d - 8)(d + 8)$

63. $100 - 81t^2$
$(10 - 9t)(10 + 9t)$

64. $4 - 25k^2$
$(2 - 5k)(2 + 5k)$

65. $x^2 + 16$
Prime

66. $y^2 + 121$
Prime

67. $y^2 + 12y + 36$
$(y + 6)^2$

68. $t^2 + 16t + 64$
$(t + 8)^2$

69. $9a^2 - 12a + 4$
$(3a - 2)^2$

70. $25x^2 - 40x + 16$
$(5x - 4)^2$

71. $-3v^2 - 12v - 12$
$-3(v + 2)^2$

72. $-2x^2 + 20x - 50$
$-2(x - 5)^2$

73. $2c^4 - 18$
$2(c^2 - 3)(c^2 + 3)$

74. $72x^2 - 2y^2$
$2(6x - y)(6x + y)$

75. $p^3 + 3p^2 - 16p - 48$
$(p + 3)(p - 4)(p + 4)$

76. $4k - 8 - k^3 + 2k^2$
$(k - 2)(2 - k)(2 + k)$
or $-1(k - 2)^2(2 + k)$

Section 6.6

For Exercises 77–78, write the formula to factor each binomial, if possible.

77. $a^3 + b^3$
$(a + b)(a^2 - ab + b^2)$

78. $a^3 - b^3$
$(a - b)(a^2 + ab + b^2)$

For Exercises 79–92, factor completely using the factoring summary found on page 453.

79. $64 + u^3$
$(4 + a)(16 - 4a + a^2)$

80. $125 - b^3$
$(5 - b)(25 + 5b + b^2)$

81. $p^6 + 8$
$(p^2 + 2)(p^4 - 2p^2 + 4)$

82. $q^6 - \dfrac{1}{27}$
$\left(q^2 - \dfrac{1}{3}\right)\left(q^4 + \dfrac{1}{3}q^2 + \dfrac{1}{9}\right)$

83. $6x^3 - 48$
$6(x - 2)(x^2 + 2x + 4)$

84. $7y^3 + 7$
$7(y + 1)(y^2 - y + 1)$

85. $x^3 - 36x$
$x(x - 6)(x + 6)$

86. $q^4 - 64q$
$q(q - 4)(q^2 + 4q + 16)$

87. $8h^2 + 20$
$4(2h^2 + 5)$

88. $m^2 - 8m$
$m(m - 8)$

89. $x^3 + 4x^2 - x - 4$
$(x + 4)(x + 1)(x - 1)$

90. $5p^4q - 20q^3$
$5q(p^2 - 2q)(p^2 + 2q)$

91. $8n + n^4$
$n(2 + n)(4 - 2n + n^2)$

92. $14m^3 - 14$
$14(m - 1)(m^2 + m + 1)$

Section 6.7

93. For which of the following equations can the zero product rule be applied directly? Explain.

$(x - 3)(2x + 1) = 0$ or $(x - 3)(2x + 1) = 6$

$(x - 3)(2x + 1) = 0$ can be solved directly by the zero product rule because it is a product of factors set equal to zero.

For Exercises 94–109, solve each equation using the zero product rule.

94. $(4x - 1)(3x + 2) = 0$ $\left\{\dfrac{1}{4}, -\dfrac{2}{3}\right\}$

95. $(a - 9)(2a - 1) = 0$ $\left\{9, \dfrac{1}{2}\right\}$

96. $3w(w + 3)(5w + 2) = 0$ $\left\{0, -3, -\dfrac{2}{5}\right\}$

97. $6u(u - 7)(4u - 9) = 0$ $\left\{0, 7, \dfrac{9}{4}\right\}$

98. $7k^2 - 9k - 10 = 0$ $\left\{-\dfrac{5}{7}, 2\right\}$

99. $4h^2 - 23h - 6 = 0$ $\left\{-\dfrac{1}{4}, 6\right\}$

100. $q^2 - 144 = 0$
$\{12, -12\}$

101. $r^2 = 25$
$\{5, -5\}$

102. $5v^2 - v = 0$ $\left\{0, \dfrac{1}{5}\right\}$

103. $x(x - 6) = -8$
$\{4, 2\}$

104. $36t^2 + 60t = -25$ $\left\{-\dfrac{5}{6}\right\}$

105. $9s^2 + 12s = -4$
$\left\{-\dfrac{2}{3}\right\}$

106. $3(y^2 + 4) = 20y$
$\left\{\dfrac{2}{3}, 6\right\}$

107. $2(p^2 + 66) = -13p$
$\left\{-\dfrac{11}{2}, 12\right\}$

108. $2y^3 - 18y^2 = -28y$
$\{0, 7, 2\}$

109. $x^3 - 4x = 0$
$\{0, 2, -2\}$

Section 6.8

110. The base of a parallelogram is 1 ft longer than twice the height. If the area is 78 ft^2, what are the base and height of the parallelogram?
The height is 6 ft, and the base is 13 ft.

111. A ball is tossed into the air from ground level with initial speed of 16 ft/sec. The height of the ball is given by the equation.

$h = -16t^2 + 16t$ $(t \geq 0)$ where h is the ball's height in feet, and t is the time in seconds

Find the time(s) when the ball is at ground level.
The ball is at ground level at 0 and 1 sec.

112. Find the length of the ramp.
The ramp is 13 ft long.

113. A right triangle has one leg that is 2 ft longer than the other leg. The hypotenuse is 2 ft less than twice the shorter leg. Find the lengths of all sides of the triangle.
The legs are 6 ft and 8 ft; the hypotenuse is 10 ft.

114. If the square of a number is subtracted from 60, the result is −4. Find all such numbers.
The numbers are −8 and 8.

115. The product of two consecutive integers is 44 more than 14 times their sum.
The numbers are 29 and 30, or −2 and −1.

 116. The base of a triangle is 1 m longer than twice the height. If the area of the triangle is 18 m², find the base and height.
The height is 4 m, and the base is 9 m.

Chapter 6   Test

1. Factor out the GCF. $15x^4 - 3x + 6x^3$
$3x(5x^3 - 1 + 2x^2)$

2. Factor by grouping. $7a - 35 - a^2 + 5a$
$(a - 5)(7 - a)$

3. Factor the trinomial. $6w^2 - 43w + 7$
$(6w - 1)(w - 7)$

4. Factor the difference of squares. $169 - p^2$
$(13 - p)(13 + p)$

5. Factor the perfect square trinomial.
$q^2 - 16q + 64$ $(q - 8)^2$

6. Factor the sum of cubes. $8 + t^3$
$(2 + t)(4 - 2t + t^2)$

For Exercises 7–26, factor completely.

7. $a^2 + 12a + 32$
$(a + 4)(a + 8)$

8. $x^2 + x - 42$
$(x + 7)(x - 6)$

9. $2y^2 - 17y + 8$
$(2y - 1)(y - 8)$

10. $6z^2 + 19z + 8$
$(2z + 1)(3z + 8)$

11. $9t^2 - 100$
$(3t - 10)(3t + 10)$

12. $v^2 - 81$
$(v + 9)(v - 9)$

13. $3a^2 + 27ab + 54b^2$
$3(a + 6b)(a + 3b)$

14. $c^4 - 1$
$(c - 1)(c + 1)(c^2 + 1)$

15. $xy - 7x + 3y - 21$
$(y - 7)(x + 3)$

16. $49 + p^2$ Prime

17. $-10u^2 + 30u - 20$
$-10(u - 2)(u - 1)$

18. $12t^2 - 75$
$3(2t - 5)(2t + 5)$

19. $5y^2 - 50y + 125$
$5(y - 5)^2$

20. $21q^2 + 14q$
$7q(3q + 2)$

21. $2x^3 + x^2 - 8x - 4$
$(2x + 1)(x - 2)(x + 2)$

22. $y^3 - 125$
$(y - 5)(y^2 + 5y + 25)$

23. $m^2n^2 - 81$
$(mn - 9)(mn + 9)$

24. $16a^2 - 64b^2$
$16(a - 2b)(a + 2b)$

25. $64x^3 - 27y^6$
$(4x - 3y^2)(16x^2 + 12xy^2 + 9y^4)$

26. $3x^2y - 6xy - 24y$
$3y(x - 4)(x + 2)$

For Exercises 27–31, solve the equation.

27. $(2x - 3)(x + 5) = 0$
$\left\{\frac{3}{2}, -5\right\}$

28. $x^2 - 7x = 0$ $\{0, 7\}$

29. $x^2 - 6x = 16$ $\{8, -2\}$

30. $x(5x + 4) = 1$
$\left\{\frac{1}{5}, -1\right\}$

31. $y^3 + 10y^2 - 9y - 90 = 0$
$\{3, -3, -10\}$

 32. A tennis court has an area of 312 yd². If the length is 2 yd more than twice the width, find the dimensions of the court.
The tennis court is 12 yd by 26 yd.

33. The product of two consecutive odd integers is 35. Find the integers.
The two integers are 5 and 7, or −5 and −7.

34. The height of a triangle is 5 in. less than the length of the base. The area is 42 in². Find the length of the base and the height of the triangle.
The base is 12 in., and the height is 7 in.

 35. The hypotenuse of a right triangle is 2 ft less than three times the shorter leg. The longer leg is 3 ft less than three times the shorter leg. Find the length of the shorter leg.

The shorter leg is 5 ft.

 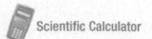

Chapters 1–6   Cumulative Review Exercises

1. Simplify. $\dfrac{|4 - 25 \div (-5) \cdot 2|}{\sqrt{8^2 + 6^2}}$ $\dfrac{7}{5}$

2. Solve. $5 - 2(t + 4) = 3t + 12$ $\{-3\}$

3. Solve for y. $3x - 2y = 8$ $y = \dfrac{3}{2}x - 4$

4. A child's piggy bank has 29 coins in quarters, dimes, and nickels. The number of nickels is two more than the number of quarters. The number of dimes is three less than the number of quarters. How many of each type of coin is in the piggy bank?
  There are 10 quarters, 12 nickels, and 7 dimes.

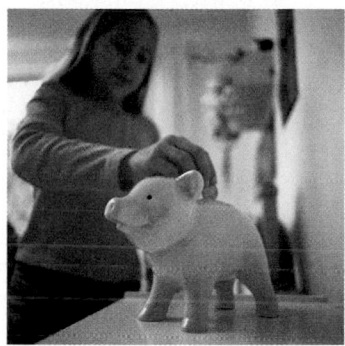

5. Solve the inequality. Graph the solution on a number line and write the solution set in interval notation. $[-4, \infty)$

$$-\dfrac{5}{12}x \le \dfrac{5}{3}$$

6. Given the equation $y = x + 4$,

  a. Is the equation linear?   Yes

  b. Identify the slope.   1

  c. Identify the y-intercept. $(0, 4)$

  d. Identify the x-intercept. $(-4, 0)$

  e. Graph the line.

7. Consider the equation $x = 5$,

  a. Does the equation represent a horizontal or vertical line?   Vertical line

  b. Determine the slope of the line, if it exists.
  Undefined

  c. Identify the x-intercept, if it exists. $(5, 0)$

  d. Identify the y-intercept, if it exists.
  Does not exist

8. Find an equation of the line passing through the point $(-3, 5)$ and having a slope of 3. Write the final answer in slope-intercept form. $y = 3x + 14$

For Exercises 9–10, solve the system.

9. $2x - 3y = 4$ $\{(5, 2)\}$
  $5x - 6y = 13$

10. $\;\; x + y - 3z = 10$ $\{(7, 0, -1)\}$
  $\;\; 2x - y + 2z = 12$
  $\;\; x - 2y - z = 8$

For Exercises 11–14, perform the indicated operations.

11. $2\left(\dfrac{1}{3}y^3 - \dfrac{3}{2}y^2 - 7\right) - \left(\dfrac{2}{3}y^3 + \dfrac{1}{2}y^2 + 5y\right)$
  $-\dfrac{7}{2}y^2 - 5y - 14$

12. $(4p^2 - 5p - 1)(2p - 3)$ $8p^3 - 22p^2 + 13p + 3$

13. $(2w - 7)^2$ $4w^2 - 28w + 49$

14. $(r^4 + 2r^3 - 5r + 1) \div (r - 3)$
  $r^3 + 5r^2 + 15r + 40 + \dfrac{121}{r - 3}$

15. Simplify. $\dfrac{c^{12}c^{-5}}{c^3}$ c^4

16. Simplify. $\left(\dfrac{6a^2b^{-4}}{2a^4b^{-5}}\right)^{-2}$ $\dfrac{u^4}{9b^2}$

17. Divide. Write the final answer in scientific notation. $\dfrac{8.0 \times 10^{-3}}{5.0 \times 10^{-6}}$ 1.6×10^3

For Exercises 18–19, factor completely.

18. $w^4 - 16$ $(w - 2)(w + 2)(w^2 + 4)$

19. $2ax + 10bx - 3ya - 15yb$ $(a + 5b)(2x - 3y)$

20. Solve. $4x(2x - 1)(x + 5) = 0$ $\left\{0, \dfrac{1}{2}, -5\right\}$

 Writing   Translating Expression   Geometry   Scientific Calculator   Video   NS&E

Rational Expressions

7

CHAPTER OUTLINE

Chapter 7

In this chapter, we define a rational expression as a ratio of two polynomials. Then we perform operations on rational expressions and solve rational equations.

Are You Prepared?

It will be helpful to review operations with fractions before you begin this chapter. Try the matching puzzle, then record the letter in the spaces below to complete the sentence.

1. Add. $\dfrac{7}{4} + \dfrac{5}{3} + \dfrac{1}{2}$ **2.** Multiply. $\dfrac{5}{3} \cdot \dfrac{11}{4}$

3. Fraction that is not in lowest terms.

4. In this expression, a common denominator is not required.

5. Fractions can be eliminated from this equation by multiplying by the LCD.

a. $\dfrac{7}{8}x + \dfrac{2}{3} = \dfrac{1}{2}$ **t.** $\dfrac{45}{12}$

r. $\dfrac{47}{12}$ **p.** $\dfrac{34}{3} \cdot \dfrac{1}{4}$

n. $\dfrac{7}{8} + \dfrac{1}{3} - \dfrac{1}{2}$ **o.** $\dfrac{55}{12}$

e. $\dfrac{7}{8}$ **f.** $\dfrac{1}{8} + \dfrac{7}{9}$

The enemy of a good student is $\underset{4}{\text{p}}\,\underset{1}{\text{r}}\,\underset{2}{\text{o}}\,\text{c}\,\underset{1}{\text{r}}\,\underset{5}{\text{a}}\,\underset{3}{\text{s}}\,\text{t}\,\text{i}\,\underset{5}{\text{n}}\,\underset{3}{\text{a}}\,\text{t}\,\underset{2}{\text{i}}\,\text{o}\,\text{n}$.

Introduction to Rational Expressions

Concepts

1. Definition of a Rational Expression
2. Evaluating Rational Expressions
3. Restricted Values of a Rational Expression
4. Simplifying Rational Expressions
5. Simplifying a Ratio of −1

1. Definition of a Rational Expression

In Section 1.2, we defined a rational number as the ratio of two integers, $\frac{p}{q}$, where $q \neq 0$.

$$\text{Examples of rational numbers:} \quad \frac{2}{3}, \; -\frac{1}{5}, \; 9$$

In a similar way, we define a **rational expression** as the ratio of two polynomials, $\frac{p}{q}$, where $q \neq 0$.

$$\text{Examples of rational expressions:} \quad \frac{3x-6}{x^2-4}, \quad \frac{3}{4}, \quad \frac{6r^5+2r}{7}$$

2. Evaluating Rational Expressions

Classroom Examples: p. 493, Exercises 6 and 10

Example 1 **Evaluating a Rational Expression**

Evaluate the rational expression (if possible) for the given values of x: $\dfrac{12}{x-3}$

a. $x = 0$ **b.** $x = 1$ **c.** $x = -3$ **d.** $x = 3$

Solution:

Substitute the given value for the variable. Then use the order of operations to simplify.

a. $\dfrac{12}{x-3}$

$\dfrac{12}{(0)-3}$ Substitute $x = 0$.

$= \dfrac{12}{-3}$

$= -4$

b. $\dfrac{12}{x-3}$

$\dfrac{12}{(1)-3}$ Substitute $x = 1$.

$= \dfrac{12}{-2}$

$= -6$

Instructor Note: Memory Device: Zero **un**der the line is **un**defined.

c. $\dfrac{12}{x-3}$

$\dfrac{12}{(-3)-3}$ Substitute $x = -3$.

$= \dfrac{12}{-6}$

$= -2$

d. $\dfrac{12}{x-3}$

$\dfrac{12}{(3)-3}$ Substitute $x = 3$.

$= \dfrac{12}{0}$ Undefined.

Recall that division by zero is undefined.

Skill Practice Evaluate the expression for the given values of x. $\dfrac{x-3}{x+5}$

1. $x = 2$ **2.** $x = 0$ **3.** $x = 3$ **4.** $x = -5$

Answers

1. $-\dfrac{1}{7}$ **2.** $-\dfrac{3}{5}$

3. 0 **4.** Undefined

3. Restricted Values of a Rational Expression

From Example 1 we see that not all values of x can be substituted into a rational expression. The values that make the denominator zero must be restricted. The expression $\dfrac{12}{x - 3}$ is undefined for $x = 3$, so we call $x = 3$ a restricted value.

Restricted values of a rational expression are all values that make the expression undefined, that is, make the denominator equal to zero.

Example 2 **Finding the Restricted Values of Rational Expressions**

Classroom Examples: p. 494, Exercises 14 and 24

Identify the restricted values for each expression.

a. $\dfrac{y - 3}{2y + 7}$ b. $\dfrac{-5}{x}$

Solution:

a. $\dfrac{y - 3}{2y + 7}$

$2y + 7 = 0$ Set the denominator equal to zero.

$2y - -7$ Solve the equation.

$\dfrac{2y}{2} = \dfrac{-7}{2}$

$y = -\dfrac{7}{2}$ The restricted value is $y = -\dfrac{7}{2}$.

Instructor Note: Ask the students to find the restricted values of a rational expression that has no variable in the denominator.

For example: $\dfrac{3x + 7}{8}$

b. $\dfrac{-5}{x}$

$x = 0$ Set the denominator equal to zero.

The restricted value is $x = 0$.

Skill Practice Identify the restricted values.

5. $\dfrac{a + 2}{2a - 8}$ 6. $\dfrac{2}{t}$

Answers

5. $a = 4$ **6.** $t = 0$

Classroom Examples: p. 494, Exercises 18 and 20

Example 3 Finding the Restricted Values of Rational Expressions

Identify the restricted values for each expression.

a. $\dfrac{a + 10}{a^2 - 25}$ b. $\dfrac{2x^3 + 5}{x^2 + 9}$

Solution:

a. $\dfrac{a + 10}{a^2 - 25}$

$a^2 - 25 = 0$ Set the denominator equal to zero. The equation is quadratic.

$(a - 5)(a + 5) = 0$ Factor.

$a - 5 = 0$ or $a + 5 = 0$ Set each factor equal to zero.

$a = 5$ or $a = -5$

The restricted values are $a = 5$ and $a = -5$.

b. $\dfrac{2x^3 + 5}{x^2 + 9}$

$x^2 + 9 = 0$

$x^2 = -9$

The quantity x^2 cannot be negative for any real number, x, so the denominator $x^2 + 9$ cannot equal zero. Therefore, there are no restricted values.

Skill Practice Identify the restricted values.

7. $\dfrac{w - 4}{w^2 - 9}$ 8. $\dfrac{8}{z^4 + 1}$

4. Simplifying Rational Expressions

Instructor Note: Remind students that we can reduce common factors, but not terms. We know that $\frac{33}{3} = 11$. If we rewrite as $\frac{30 + 3}{3}$ it is incorrect to say $\frac{30 + \cancel{3}}{\cancel{3}} = 30$.

In many cases, it is advantageous to simplify or reduce a fraction to lowest terms. The same is true for rational expressions.

The method for simplifying rational expressions mirrors the process for simplifying fractions. In each case, factor the numerator and denominator. Common factors in the numerator and denominator form a ratio of 1 and can be reduced.

Simplifying a fraction: $\dfrac{21}{35} \xrightarrow{\text{Factor}} \dfrac{3 \cdot \overset{1}{\cancel{7}}}{5 \cdot \cancel{7}} = \dfrac{3}{5} \cdot (1) = \dfrac{3}{5}$

Simplifying a rational expression: $\dfrac{2x - 6}{x^2 - 9} \xrightarrow{\text{Factor}} \dfrac{2(\overset{1}{\cancel{x - 3}})}{(x + 3)(\cancel{x - 3})} = \dfrac{2}{(x + 3)}(1) = \dfrac{2}{x + 3}$

Informally, to simplify a rational expression, we simplify the ratio of common factors to 1. Formally, this is accomplished by applying the fundamental principle of rational expressions.

Answers

7. $w = 3, w = -3$
8. There are no restricted values.

PROPERTY   **Fundamental Principle of Rational Expressions**

Let p, q, and r represent polynomials where $q \neq 0$ and $r \neq 0$. Then

$$\frac{pr}{qr} = \frac{p}{q} \cdot \frac{r}{r} = \frac{p}{q} \cdot 1 = \frac{p}{q}$$

Example 4   **Simplifying a Rational Expression**

Classroom Example: p. 495, Exercise 40

Given the expression $\dfrac{2p - 14}{p^2 - 49}$

  a. Factor the numerator and denominator.

  b. Identify the restricted values.

  c. Simplify the rational expression.

Solution:

  a. $\dfrac{2p - 14}{p^2 - 49}$ Factor out the GCF in the numerator.

      $= \dfrac{2(p - 7)}{(p + 7)(p - 7)}$ Factor the denominator as a difference of squares.

  b. $(p + 7)(p - 7) = 0$ To find the restricted values, set the denominator equal to zero. The equation is quadratic.

      $p + 7 = 0$ or $p - 7 = 0$ Set each factor equal to 0.

      $p = -7$ or $p = 7$ The restricted values are -7 and 7.

Avoiding Mistakes

The restricted values of a rational expression are always determined *before* simplifying the expression.

  c. $\dfrac{2(\overset{1}{\cancel{p - 7}})}{(p + 7)(\cancel{p - 7})}$ Simplify the ratio of common factors to 1.

      $= \dfrac{2}{p + 7}$ (provided $p \neq 7$ and $p \neq -7$)

Skill Practice   Given $\dfrac{5z + 25}{z^2 + 3z - 10}$

  9. Factor the numerator and the denominator.

  10. Identify the restricted values.   **11.** Simplify the rational expression.

In Example 4, it is important to note that the expressions

$$\frac{2p - 14}{p^2 - 49} \quad \text{and} \quad \frac{2}{p + 7}$$

are equal for all values of p that make each expression a real number. Therefore,

$$\frac{2p - 14}{p^2 - 49} = \frac{2}{p + 7}$$

for all values of p except $p = 7$ and $p = -7$. (At $p = 7$ and $p = -7$, the original expression is undefined.) This is why the restricted values are determined before the expression is simplified.

Instructor Note: Show students a simpler example of restricted values such as:

$$\frac{x - 4}{x - 4} = 1 \quad \text{except when } x = 4.$$

Answers

  9. $\dfrac{5(z + 5)}{(z + 5)(z - 2)}$

  10. $z = -5, z = 2$

  11. $\dfrac{5}{z - 2} \ (z \neq 2, z \neq -5)$

From this point forward, we will write statements of equality between two rational expressions with the assumption that they are equal for all values of the variable for which each expression is defined.

Classroom Example: p. 495,
Exercise 44

Example 5 Simplifying a Rational Expression

Simplify the rational expression. $\dfrac{18a^4}{9a^5}$

Solution:

$\dfrac{18a^4}{9a^5}$

TIP: The expression $\dfrac{18a^4}{9a^5}$ can also be simplified using the properties of exponents.

$\dfrac{18a^4}{9a^5} = 2a^{4-5} = 2a^{-1} = \dfrac{2}{a}$

$= \dfrac{2 \cdot 3 \cdot 3 \cdot a \cdot a \cdot a \cdot a}{3 \cdot 3 \cdot a \cdot a \cdot a \cdot a \cdot a}$ Factor the numerator and denominator.

$= \dfrac{2 \cdot (3 \cdot 3 \cdot \overset{1}{\cancel{a \cdot a \cdot a \cdot a}})}{(3 \cdot 3 \cdot \cancel{a \cdot a \cdot a \cdot a}) \cdot a}$ Simplify common factors.

$= \dfrac{2}{a}$

Skill Practice Simplify the rational expression.

12. $\dfrac{15q^3}{9q^2}$

Classroom Example: p. 495,
Exercise 64

Example 6 Simplifying a Rational Expression

Simplify the rational expression. $\dfrac{2c - 8}{10c^2 - 80c + 160}$

Solution:

$\dfrac{2c - 8}{10c^2 - 80c + 160}$

Avoiding Mistakes

Given the expression

$\dfrac{2c - 8}{10c^2 - 80c + 160}$

do not be tempted to reduce before factoring. The terms $2c$ and $10c^2$ cannot be "canceled" because they are *terms* not factors.

The numerator and denominator must be in factored form before simplifying.

$= \dfrac{2(c - 4)}{10(c^2 - 8c + 16)}$ Factor out the GCF.

$= \dfrac{2(c - 4)}{10(c - 4)^2}$ Factor the denominator.

$= \dfrac{\overset{1}{2}(\overset{1}{\cancel{c - 4}})}{2 \cdot 5(\cancel{c - 4})(c - 4)}$ Simplify the ratio of common factors to 1.

$= \dfrac{1}{5(c - 4)}$

Skill Practice Simplify the rational expression.

13. $\dfrac{x^2 - 1}{2x^2 - x - 3}$

Answers

12. $\dfrac{5q}{3}$ **13.** $\dfrac{x - 1}{2x - 3}$

The process to simplify a rational expression is based on the identity property of multiplication. Therefore, this process applies only to factors (remember that factors are multiplied). For example:

$$\frac{3x}{3y} = \frac{3 \cdot x}{3 \cdot y} = \frac{\overset{1}{\cancel{3}}}{\cancel{3}} \cdot \frac{x}{y} = 1 \cdot \frac{x}{y} = \frac{x}{y}$$

$\uparrow$
Simplify

Terms that are added or subtracted cannot be reduced to lowest terms. For example:

$$\frac{x + 3}{y + 3}$$

$\uparrow$
Cannot be simplified

The objective of simplifying a rational expression is to create an equivalent expression that is simpler to use. Consider the rational expression from Example 6 in its original form and in its reduced form. If we substitute a value c into each expression, we see that the reduced form is easier to evaluate. For example, substitute $c = 3$:

Original Expression	**Simplified Expression**
$\dfrac{2c - 8}{10c^2 - 80c + 160}$	$\dfrac{1}{5(c - 4)}$

Substitute $c = 3$

$$= \frac{2(3) - 8}{10(3)^2 - 80(3) + 160} \qquad = \frac{1}{5(3 - 4)}$$

$$= \frac{6 - 8}{10(9) - 240 + 160} \qquad = \frac{1}{5(-1)}$$

$$= \frac{-2}{90 - 240 + 160} \qquad = -\frac{1}{5}$$

$$= \frac{-2}{10} \quad \text{or} \quad -\frac{1}{5}$$

5. Simplifying a Ratio of −1

When two factors are identical in the numerator and denominator, they form a ratio of 1 and can be reduced. Sometimes we encounter two factors that are opposites and form a ratio of −1. For example:

Simplified Form	**Details/Notes**
$\dfrac{-5}{5} = -1$	The ratio of a number and its opposite is −1.
$\dfrac{100}{-100} = -1$	The ratio of a number and its opposite is −1.

$$\frac{x + 7}{-x - 7} = -1 \qquad \frac{x + 7}{-x - 7} = \frac{x + 7}{-1(x + 7)} = \frac{\overset{1}{\cancel{x + 7}}}{-1\cancel{(x + 7)}} = \frac{1}{-1} = -1$$

factor out −1

$$\frac{2 - x}{x - 2} = -1 \qquad \frac{2 - x}{x - 2} = \frac{-1(-2 + x)}{x - 2} = \frac{-1\overset{1}{\cancel{(x - 2)}}}{\cancel{x - 2}} = \frac{-1}{1} = -1$$

Recognizing factors that are opposites is useful when simplifying rational expressions.

TIP: We recommend that you recognize the following two patterns:

$$\frac{a + b}{b + a} = 1 \quad \text{and} \quad \frac{a - b}{b - a} = -1$$

Avoiding Mistakes

While the expression $2 - x$ and $x - 2$ are opposites, the expressions $2 - x$ and $2 + x$ are *not*.

Therefore $\dfrac{2 - x}{2 + x}$ does not simplify to −1.

Classroom Example: p. 496,
Exercise 92

Example 7   **Simplifying a Rational Expression**

Simplify the rational expression. $\dfrac{3c - 3d}{d - c}$

Solution:

$$\dfrac{3c - 3d}{d - c}$$

$$= \dfrac{3(c - d)}{d - c} \qquad \text{Factor the numerator and denominator.}$$

Notice that $(c - d)$ and $(d - c)$ are opposites and form a ratio of -1.

$$= \dfrac{3(\overset{-1}{\cancel{c - d}})}{\cancel{d - c}} \qquad \underline{\text{Details:}} \quad \dfrac{3(c - d)}{d - c} = \dfrac{3(c - d)}{-1(-d + c)} = \dfrac{3(c - d)}{-1(c - d)}$$

$$= 3(-1) \qquad\qquad\qquad\qquad\qquad\qquad\qquad\qquad = \dfrac{3}{-1} = -3$$

$$= -3$$

Skill Practice   Simplify the rational expression.

14. $\dfrac{2t - 12}{6 - t}$

TIP: It is important to recognize that a rational expression can be written in several equivalent forms. In particular, two numbers with opposite signs form a negative quotient. Therefore, a number such as $-\frac{3}{4}$ can be written as:

$$-\dfrac{3}{4} \quad \text{or} \quad \dfrac{-3}{4} \quad \text{or} \quad \dfrac{3}{-4}$$

The negative sign can be written in the numerator, in the denominator, or out in front of the fraction. We demonstrate this concept in Example 8.

Classroom Example: p. 496,
Exercise 98

Example 8   **Simplifying a Rational Expression**

Simplify the rational expression. $\dfrac{5 - y}{y^2 - 25}$

Solution:

$$\dfrac{5 - y}{y^2 - 25}$$

$$= \dfrac{5 - y}{(y - 5)(y + 5)} \qquad \text{Factor the numerator and denominator.}$$

Notice that $5 - y$ and $y - 5$ are opposites and form a ratio of -1.

Answer

14. -2

$$= \frac{5 \overset{-1}{-y}}{(y-5)(y+5)} \qquad \underline{\text{Details:}} \quad \frac{5-y}{(y-5)(y+5)} = \frac{-1(-5+y)}{(y-5)(y+5)}$$

$$= \frac{-1(y-5)}{(y-5)(y+5)} = \frac{-1}{y+5}$$

$$= \frac{-1}{y+5} \qquad \text{or} \qquad \frac{1}{-(y+5)} \qquad \text{or} \qquad -\frac{1}{y+5}$$

Skill Practice Simplify the rational expression.

15. $\dfrac{b-a}{a^2-b^2}$

Answer

15. $\dfrac{-1}{a+b}$

Section 7.1 Practice Exercises

Study Skills Exercises

1. Review Section 1.1 in this text. Write an example of how to simplify (reduce) a fraction, multiply two fractions, divide two fractions, add two fractions, and subtract two fractions. Then as you learn about rational expressions, compare the operations on rational expressions with those on fractions. This is a great place to use 3×5 cards again. Write an example of an operation with fractions on one side and the same operation with rational expressions on the other side.

2. Define the key terms.

   a. rational expression   **b. restricted values of a rational expression**

Concept 1: Definition of a Rational Expression

3. **a.** What is a rational number?   A number $\dfrac{p}{q}$, where p and q are integers and $q \neq 0$

   b. What is a rational expression?   An expression $\dfrac{p}{q}$, where p and q are polynomials and $q \neq 0$

4. **a.** Write an example of a rational number. (Answers will vary.)   For example: $\dfrac{2}{3}$

   b. Write an example of a rational expression. (Answers will vary.)   For example: $\dfrac{3x^2+1}{2x+5}$

Concept 2: Evaluating Rational Expressions

For Exercises 5–10, substitute the given number into the expression and simplify (if possible). **(See Example 1.)**

5. $\dfrac{1}{x-6}$; $x=-2$ $-\dfrac{1}{8}$

6. $\dfrac{w-10}{w+6}$; $w=0$ $-\dfrac{5}{3}$

7. $\dfrac{w-4}{2w+8}$; $w=0$ $-\dfrac{1}{2}$

8. $\dfrac{y-8}{2y^2+y-1}$; $y=8$ 0

9. $\dfrac{(a-7)(a+1)}{(a-2)(a+5)}$; $a=2$ Undefined

10. $\dfrac{(a+4)(a+1)}{(a-4)(a-1)}$; $a=1$ Undefined

 Writing   Translating Expression   Geometry   Scientific Calculator   Video   NS·E

11. A bicyclist rides 24 mi against a wind and returns 24 mi with the same wind. His average speed for the return trip traveling with the wind is 8 mph faster than his speed going out against the wind. If x represents the bicyclist's speed going out against the wind, then the total time, t, required for the round trip is given by

$$t = \frac{24}{x} + \frac{24}{x+8}$$ where t is measured in hours.

a. Find the time required for the round trip if the cyclist rides 12 mph against the wind. $3\frac{1}{5}$ hr or 3.2 hr

b. Find the time required for the round trip if the cyclist rides 24 mph against the wind. $1\frac{3}{4}$ hr or 1.75 hr

12. The manufacturer of mountain bikes has a fixed cost of $56,000, plus a variable cost of $140 per bike. The average cost per bike, y (in dollars), is given by the equation:

$$y = \frac{56{,}000 + 140x}{x}$$ where x represents the number of bikes produced.

a. Find the average cost per bike if the manufacturer produces 1000 bikes.
$196
b. Find the average cost per bike if the manufacturer produces 2000 bikes.
$168
c. Find the average cost per bike if the manufacturer produces 10,000 bikes.
$145.60

Concept 3: Restricted Values of a Rational Expression

For Exercises 13–24, identify the restricted values. **(See Examples 2–3.)**

13. $\dfrac{5}{k+2}$ $k = -2$

14. $\dfrac{-3}{h-4}$ $h = 4$

15. $\dfrac{x+5}{(2x-5)(x+8)}$ $x = \frac{5}{2}, x = -8$

16. $\dfrac{4y+1}{(3y+7)(y+3)}$ $y = -\frac{7}{3}, y = -3$

17. $\dfrac{m+12}{m^2+5m+6}$ $m = -2, m = -3$

18. $\dfrac{c-11}{c^2-5c-6}$ $c = 6, c = -1$

19. $\dfrac{x-4}{x^2+9}$
There are no restricted values.

20. $\dfrac{x+1}{x^2+4}$
There are no restricted values.

21. $\dfrac{y^2-y-12}{12}$
There are no restricted values.

22. $\dfrac{z^2+10z+9}{9}$
There are no restricted values.

23. $\dfrac{t-5}{t}$ $t = 0$

24. $\dfrac{2w+7}{w}$ $w = 0$

25. Construct a rational expression that is undefined for $x = 2$. (Answers will vary.)   For example: $\dfrac{1}{x-2}$

26. Construct a rational expression that is undefined for $x = 5$. (Answers will vary.)   For example: $\dfrac{1}{x-5}$

27. Construct a rational expression that is undefined for $x = -3$ and $x = 7$. (Answers will vary.)
For example: $\dfrac{1}{(x+3)(x-7)}$

28. Construct a rational expression that is undefined for $x = -1$ and $x = 4$. (Answers will vary.)
For example: $\dfrac{1}{(x+1)(x-4)}$

29. Evaluate the expressions for $x = -1$.

a. $\dfrac{3x^2-2x-1}{6x^2-7x-3}$ $\frac{2}{5}$ b. $\dfrac{x-1}{2x-3}$ $\frac{2}{5}$

30. Evaluate the expressions for $x = 4$.

a. $\dfrac{(x+5)^2}{x^2+6x+5}$ $\frac{9}{5}$ b. $\dfrac{x+5}{x+1}$ $\frac{9}{5}$

31. Evaluate the expressions for $x = 1$.

a. $\dfrac{5x+5}{x^2-1}$ b. $\dfrac{5}{x-1}$
Undefined   Undefined

32. Evaluate the expressions for $x = 3$.

a. $\dfrac{2x^2-4x-6}{2x^2-18}$ b. $\dfrac{x+1}{x+3}$
Undefined $\dfrac{2}{3}$

Concept 4: Simplifying Rational Expressions

For Exercises 33–42,

   a. Identify the restricted values.

   b. Simplify the rational expression. **(See Example 4.)**

33. $\dfrac{3y + 6}{6y + 12}$ a. $y = -2$ b. $\dfrac{1}{2}$

34. $\dfrac{8x - 8}{4x - 4}$ a. $x = 1$ b. 2

35. $\dfrac{t^2 - 1}{t + 1}$ a. $t = -1$ b. $t - 1$

36. $\dfrac{r^2 - 4}{r - 2}$ a. $r = 2$ b. $r + 2$

37. $\dfrac{7w}{21w^2 - 35w}$ a. $w = 0$, $w = \dfrac{5}{3}$ b. $\dfrac{1}{3w - 5}$

38. $\dfrac{12a^2}{24a^2 - 18a}$ a. $a = 0$, $a = \dfrac{3}{4}$ b. $\dfrac{2a}{4a - 3}$

39. $\dfrac{9x^2 - 4}{6x + 4}$ a. $x = -\dfrac{2}{3}$ b. $\dfrac{3x - 2}{2}$

40. $\dfrac{8n - 20}{4n^2 - 25}$ a. $n = \dfrac{5}{2}$, $n = -\dfrac{5}{2}$ b. $\dfrac{4}{2n + 5}$

41. $\dfrac{a^2 + 3a - 10}{a^2 + a - 6}$ a. $a = -3$, $a = 2$ b. $\dfrac{a + 5}{a + 3}$

42. $\dfrac{t^2 + 3t - 10}{t^2 + t - 20}$ a. $t = -5$, $t = 4$ b. $\dfrac{t - 2}{t - 4}$

For Exercises 43–84, simplify the rational expression. **(See Examples 5–6.)**

43. $\dfrac{7b^2}{21b}$ $\dfrac{b}{3}$

44. $\dfrac{15c^3}{3c^5}$ $\dfrac{5}{c^2}$

45. $\dfrac{18st^5}{12st^3}$ $\dfrac{3t^2}{2}$

46. $\dfrac{20a^4b^2}{25ab^2}$ $\dfrac{4a^3}{5}$

47. $\dfrac{-24x^2y^5z}{8xy^4z^3}$ $-\dfrac{3xy}{z^2}$

48. $\dfrac{60rs^4t^2}{-12r^4s^2t^3}$ $-\dfrac{5s^2}{r^3t}$

49. $\dfrac{3(y + 2)}{6(y + 2)}$ $\dfrac{1}{2}$

50. $\dfrac{8(x - 1)}{4(x - 1)}$ 2

51. $\dfrac{(p - 3)(p + 5)}{(p + 5)(p + 4)}$ $\dfrac{p - 3}{p + 4}$

52. $\dfrac{(c + 4)(c - 1)}{(c + 4)(c + 2)}$ $\dfrac{c - 1}{c + 2}$

53. $\dfrac{(m + 11)}{4(m + 11)(m - 11)}$ $\dfrac{1}{4(m - 11)}$

54. $\dfrac{(n - 7)}{9(n + 2)(n - 7)}$ $\dfrac{1}{9(n + 2)}$

55. $\dfrac{x(2x + 1)^2}{4x^3(2x + 1)}$ $\dfrac{2x + 1}{4x^2}$

56. $\dfrac{(p + 2)(p - 3)^4}{(p + 2)^2(p - 3)^2}$ $\dfrac{(p - 3)^2}{p + 2}$

57. $\dfrac{5}{20a - 25}$ $\dfrac{1}{4a - 5}$

58. $\dfrac{7}{14c - 21}$ $\dfrac{1}{2c - 3}$

59. $\dfrac{4w - 8}{w^2 - 4}$ $\dfrac{4}{w + 2}$

60. $\dfrac{3x + 15}{x^2 - 25}$ $\dfrac{3}{x - 5}$

61. $\dfrac{3x^2 - 6x}{9xy + 18x}$ $\dfrac{x - 2}{3(y + 2)}$

62. $\dfrac{6p^2 + 12p}{2pq - 4p}$ $\dfrac{3(p + 2)}{q - 2}$

63. $\dfrac{2x + 4}{x^2 - 3x - 10}$ $\dfrac{2}{x - 5}$

64. $\dfrac{5z + 15}{z^2 - 4z - 21}$ $\dfrac{5}{z - 7}$

65. $\dfrac{a^2 - 49}{a - 7}$ $a + 7$

66. $\dfrac{b^2 - 64}{b - 8}$ $b + 8$

67. $\dfrac{q^2 + 25}{q + 5}$ Cannot simplify

68. $\dfrac{r^2 + 36}{r + 6}$ Cannot simplify

69. $\dfrac{y^2 + 6y + 9}{2y^2 + y - 15}$ $\dfrac{y + 3}{2y - 5}$

70. $\dfrac{h^2 + h - 6}{h^2 + 2h - 8}$ $\dfrac{h + 3}{h + 4}$

71. $\dfrac{3x^2 + 7x - 6}{x^2 + 7x + 12}$ $\dfrac{3x - 2}{x + 4}$

72. $\dfrac{x^2 - 5x - 14}{2x^2 - x - 10}$ $\dfrac{x - 7}{2x - 5}$

73. $\dfrac{5q^2 + 5}{q^4 - 1}$ $\dfrac{5}{(q + 1)(q - 1)}$

74. $\dfrac{4t^2 + 16}{t^4 - 16}$ $\dfrac{4}{(t - 2)(t + 2)}$

75. $\dfrac{ac - ad + 2bc - 2bd}{2ac + ad + 4bc + 2bd}$ (*Hint:* Factor by grouping.) $\dfrac{c - d}{2c + d}$

76. $\dfrac{3pr - ps - 3qr + qs}{3pr - ps + 3qr - qs}$ (*Hint:* Factor by grouping.) $\dfrac{p - q}{p + q}$

77. $\dfrac{2t^2 - 3t}{2t^4 - 13t^3 + 15t^2}$ $\dfrac{1}{t(t - 5)}$

78. $\dfrac{4m^3 + 3m^2}{4m^3 + 7m^2 + 3m}$ $\dfrac{m}{m + 1}$

79. $\dfrac{49p^2 - 28pq + 4q^2}{14p - 4q}$ $\dfrac{7p - 2q}{2}$

80. $\dfrac{3x - 3y}{2x^2 - 4xy + 2y^2}$ $\dfrac{3}{2(x - y)}$

81. $\dfrac{5x^3 + 4x^2 - 45x - 36}{x^2 - 9}$ $5x + 4$

82. $\dfrac{x^2 - 1}{ax^3 - bx^2 - ax + b}$ $\dfrac{1}{ax - b}$

83. $\dfrac{2x^2 - xy - 3y^2}{2x^2 - 11xy + 12y^2}$ $\dfrac{x + y}{x - 4y}$

84. $\dfrac{2c^2 + cd - d^2}{5c^2 + 3cd - 2d^2}$ $\dfrac{2c - d}{5c - 2d}$

✏️ Writing   ↔ Translating Expression   ◁ Geometry   🖩 Scientific Calculator   💿 Video   NS&E

Concept 5: Simplifying a Ratio of −1

85. What is the relationship between $x - 2$ and $2 - x$?   They are opposites.

86. What is the relationship between $w + p$ and $-w - p$?   They are opposites.

For Exercises 87–98, simplify the rational expressions. **(See Examples 7–8.)**

87. $\dfrac{x - 5}{5 - x}$ -1

88. $\dfrac{8 - p}{p - 8}$ -1

89. $\dfrac{-4 - y}{4 + y}$ -1

90. $\dfrac{z + 10}{-z - 10}$ -1

91. $\dfrac{3y - 6}{12 - 6y}$ $-\dfrac{1}{2}$

92. $\dfrac{4q - 4}{12 - 12q}$ $-\dfrac{1}{3}$

93. $\dfrac{k + 5}{5 - k}$ Cannot simplify

94. $\dfrac{2 + n}{2 - n}$ Cannot simplify

95. $\dfrac{10x - 12}{10x + 12}$ $\dfrac{5x - 6}{5x + 6}$

96. $\dfrac{4t - 16}{16 + 4t}$ $\dfrac{t - 4}{4 + t}$

97. $\dfrac{x^2 - x - 12}{16 - x^2}$ $-\dfrac{x + 3}{4 + x}$

98. $\dfrac{49 - b^2}{b^2 - 10b + 21}$ $-\dfrac{7 + b}{b - 3}$

Expanding Your Skills

For Exercises 99–102, factor and simplify.

99. $\dfrac{w^3 - 8}{w^2 + 2w + 4}$ $w - 2$

100. $\dfrac{y^3 + 27}{y^2 - 3y + 9}$ $y + 3$

101. $\dfrac{z^2 - 16}{z^3 - 64}$ $\dfrac{z + 4}{z^2 + 4z + 16}$

102. $\dfrac{x^2 - 25}{x^3 + 125}$ $\dfrac{x - 5}{x^2 - 5x + 25}$

Section 7.2   Multiplication and Division of Rational Expressions

Concepts

1. Multiplication of Rational Expressions
2. Division of Rational Expressions

1. Multiplication of Rational Expressions

Recall from Section 1.1 that to multiply fractions, we multiply the numerators and multiply the denominators. The same is true for multiplying rational expressions.

> **PROPERTY   Multiplication of Rational Expressions**
>
> Let $p, q, r,$ and s represent polynomials, such that $q \neq 0, s \neq 0$. Then,
>
> $$\frac{p}{q} \cdot \frac{r}{s} = \frac{pr}{qs}$$

For example:

Multiply the Fractions

$$\frac{2}{3} \cdot \frac{5}{7} = \frac{10}{21}$$

Multiply the Rational Expressions

$$\frac{2x}{3y} \cdot \frac{5z}{7} = \frac{10xz}{21y}$$

To simplify, factor the numerator and denominator and reduce ratios of common factors to 1.

$$\frac{15}{14} \cdot \frac{21}{10} = \frac{3 \cdot 5}{2 \cdot 7} \cdot \frac{3 \cdot 7}{2 \cdot 5} = \frac{3 \cdot \overset{1}{\cancel{5}} \cdot 3 \cdot \overset{1}{\cancel{7}}}{2 \cdot \cancel{7} \cdot 2 \cdot \cancel{5}} = \frac{9}{4}$$

The same process is also used to multiply rational expressions.

> **TIP:** We can also reduce ratios of common factors to 1 before multiplying:
>
> $$\frac{15}{14} \cdot \frac{21}{10} = \frac{3 \cdot \overset{1}{\cancel{5}}}{2 \cdot \cancel{7}} \cdot \frac{3 \cdot \cancel{7}}{2 \cdot \cancel{5}} = \frac{9}{4}$$

> **PROCEDURE Multiplying Rational Expressions**
> **Step 1** Factor the numerator and denominator of each fraction.
> **Step 2** Multiply the numerators, and multiply the denominators.
> **Step 3** Reduce the ratios of common factors to 1 or -1 and simplify.

Example 1 Multiplying Rational Expressions

Multiply. $\dfrac{5a^2b}{2} \cdot \dfrac{6a}{10b}$

Solution:

$\dfrac{5a^2b}{2} \cdot \dfrac{6a}{10b}$

$= \dfrac{5 \cdot a \cdot a \cdot b}{2} \cdot \dfrac{2 \cdot 3 \cdot a}{2 \cdot 5 \cdot b}$ Factor into prime factors.

$= \dfrac{\overset{1}{\cancel{5}} \cdot a \cdot a \cdot \overset{1}{\cancel{b}} \cdot \overset{1}{\cancel{2}} \cdot 3 \cdot a}{2 \cdot \cancel{2} \cdot \cancel{5} \cdot \cancel{b}}$ Multiply and reduce common factors to 1.

$= \dfrac{3a^3}{2}$ Simplify.

Skill Practice Multiply.

1. $\dfrac{7a}{3b} \cdot \dfrac{15b}{14a^2}$

Classroom Example: p. 501, Exercise 10

Example 2 Multiplying Rational Expressions

Multiply. $\dfrac{3c - 3d}{6c} \cdot \dfrac{2}{c^2 - d^2}$

Solution:

$\dfrac{3c - 3d}{6c} \cdot \dfrac{2}{c^2 - d^2}$

$= \dfrac{3(c - d)}{2 \cdot 3 \cdot c} \cdot \dfrac{2}{(c - d)(c + d)}$ Factor.

$= \dfrac{\overset{1}{\cancel{3}}(\overset{1}{\cancel{c - d}}) \cdot \overset{1}{\cancel{2}}}{\cancel{2} \cdot \cancel{3} \cdot c \cdot (\cancel{c - d})(c + d)}$ Multiply and reduce common factors to 1.

$= \dfrac{1}{c(c + d)}$ Simplify.

Skill Practice Multiply.

2. $\dfrac{4x - 8}{x + 6} \cdot \dfrac{x^2 + 6x}{2x}$

Classroom Example: p. 501, Exercise 16

Avoiding Mistakes

If all the factors in the numerator reduce to a ratio of 1, a factor of 1 is left in the numerator.

Answers

1. $\dfrac{5}{2a}$ 2. $2(x - 2)$

Classroom Example: p. 501,
Exercise 20

Example 3 Multiplying Rational Expressions

Multiply. $\dfrac{35 - 5x}{5x + 5} \cdot \dfrac{x^2 + 5x + 4}{x^2 - 49}$

Solution:

$\dfrac{35 - 5x}{5x + 5} \cdot \dfrac{x^2 + 5x + 4}{x^2 - 49}$

$= \dfrac{5(7 - x)}{5(x + 1)} \cdot \dfrac{(x + 4)(x + 1)}{(x - 7)(x + 7)}$ Factor the numerators and denominators completely.

$= \dfrac{\overset{1}{\cancel{5}}(\overset{-1}{\cancel{7 - x}})(x + 4)\overset{1}{\cancel{(x + 1)}}}{\cancel{5}\cancel{(x + 1)}\cancel{(x - 7)}(x + 7)}$ Multiply and reduce common factors to 1 and −1.

$= \dfrac{-1(x + 4)}{x + 7}$ Simplify.

$= \dfrac{-(x + 4)}{x + 7}$ or $\dfrac{x + 4}{-(x + 7)}$ or $-\dfrac{x + 4}{x + 7}$

TIP: The ratio $\frac{7 - x}{x - 7} = -1$ because $7 - x$ and $x - 7$ are opposites.

Skill Practice Multiply.

3. $\dfrac{p^2 + 4p + 3}{5p + 10} \cdot \dfrac{p^2 - p - 6}{9 - p^2}$

2. Division of Rational Expressions

Recall that to divide two fractions, multiply the first fraction by the reciprocal of the second.

$$\dfrac{21}{10} \div \dfrac{49}{15} \xrightarrow[\text{of the second fraction}]{\text{multiply by the reciprocal}} \dfrac{21}{10} \cdot \dfrac{15}{49} \xrightarrow{\text{factor}} \dfrac{3 \cdot \overset{1}{\cancel{7}} \cdot 3 \cdot \overset{1}{\cancel{5}}}{2 \cdot \cancel{5} \cdot \cancel{7} \cdot 7} = \dfrac{9}{14}$$

The same process is used to divide rational expressions.

> **PROPERTY** Division of Rational Expressions
>
> Let $p, q, r,$ and s represent polynomials, such that $q \neq 0, r \neq 0, s \neq 0$. Then,
>
> $$\dfrac{p}{q} \div \dfrac{r}{s} = \dfrac{p}{q} \cdot \dfrac{s}{r} = \dfrac{ps}{qr}$$

Classroom Example: p. 502,
Exercise 32

Example 4 Dividing Rational Expressions

Divide. $\dfrac{5t - 15}{2} \div \dfrac{t^2 - 9}{10}$

Solution:

$\dfrac{5t - 15}{2} \div \dfrac{t^2 - 9}{10}$

$= \dfrac{5t - 15}{2} \cdot \dfrac{10}{t^2 - 9}$

Avoiding Mistakes

When dividing rational expressions, take the reciprocal of the second fraction and change to multiplication *before* reducing like factors.

Multiply the first fraction by the reciprocal of the second.

Answer

3. $\dfrac{-(p + 1)}{5}$ or $\dfrac{p + 1}{-5}$ or $-\dfrac{p + 1}{5}$

$$= \frac{5(t-3)}{2} \cdot \frac{2 \cdot 5}{(t-3)(t+3)}$$ Factor each polynomial.

$$= \frac{5\overset{1}{\cancel{(t-3)}} \cdot \overset{1}{\cancel{2}} \cdot 5}{\cancel{2}\cancel{(t-3)}(t+3)}$$ Multiply and reduce common factors to 1.

$$= \frac{25}{t+3}$$ Simplify.

Skill Practice Divide.

4. $\dfrac{7y-14}{y+1} \div \dfrac{y^2+2y-8}{2y+2}$

Example 5   **Dividing Rational Expressions**

Classroom Example: p. 502, Exercise 38

Divide. $\dfrac{p^2-11p+30}{10p^2-250} \div \dfrac{30p-5p^2}{2p+4}$

Solution:

$$\frac{p^2-11p+30}{10p^2-250} \div \frac{30p-5p^2}{2p+4}$$

$$= \frac{p^2-11p+30}{10p^2-250} \cdot \frac{2p+4}{30p-5p^2}$$ Multiply the first fraction by the reciprocal of the second.

Factor the trinomial.
$p^2 - 11p + 30 = (p-5)(p-6)$

$$= \frac{(p-5)(p-6)}{2 \cdot 5(p-5)(p+5)} \cdot \frac{2(p+2)}{5p(6-p)}$$ Factor out the GCF.
$2p + 4 = 2(p+2)$

Factor out the GCF. Then factor the difference of squares.
$10p^2 - 250 = 10(p^2 - 25)$
$\qquad\qquad\quad = 2 \cdot 5(p-5)(p+5)$

Factor out the GCF.
$30p - 5p^2 = 5p(6-p)$

$$= \frac{\overset{1}{\cancel{(p-5)}}\overset{-1}{\cancel{(p-6)}} \cdot \overset{1}{\cancel{2}}(p+2)}{\cancel{2} \cdot 5\cancel{(p-5)}(p+5) \cdot 5p\cancel{(6-p)}}$$ Multiply and reduce common factors to 1 and -1.

$$= -\frac{p+2}{25p(p+5)}$$ Simplify.

Skill Practice Divide.

5. $\dfrac{4x^2-9}{2x^2-x-3} \div \dfrac{20x+30}{x^2+7x+6}$

TIP: In Example 5, leave the answer in factored form.

Answers

4. $\dfrac{14}{y+4}$ **5.** $\dfrac{x+6}{10}$

Classroom Example: p. 502, Exercise 28

Example 6 Dividing Rational Expressions

Divide. $\dfrac{\dfrac{3x}{4y}}{\dfrac{5x}{6y}}$

Solution:

$\dfrac{\dfrac{3x}{4y}}{\dfrac{5x}{6y}}$ ← This fraction bar denotes division ($\div$). This expression is called a complex fraction because it has one or more rational expressions in its numerator or denominator.

$= \dfrac{3x}{4y} \div \dfrac{5x}{6y}$

$= \dfrac{3x}{4y} \cdot \dfrac{6y}{5x}$ Multiply by the reciprocal of the second fraction.

$= \dfrac{3 \cdot \overset{1}{x} \cdot \overset{1}{2} \cdot 3 \cdot \overset{1}{y}}{\overset{}{2} \cdot 2 \cdot \overset{}{y} \cdot 5 \cdot \overset{}{x}}$ Reduce common factors to 1.

$= \dfrac{9}{10}$ Simplify.

Skill Practice Divide.

6. $\dfrac{\dfrac{a^3b}{9c}}{\dfrac{4ab}{3c^3}}$

Sometimes multiplication and division of rational expressions appear in the same problem. In such a case, apply the order of operations by multiplying or dividing in order from left to right.

Classroom Example: p. 503, Exercise 66

Example 7 Multiplying and Dividing Rational Expressions

Perform the indicated operations. $\dfrac{4}{c^2 - 9} \div \dfrac{6}{c - 3} \cdot \dfrac{3c}{8}$

Solution:

In this example, division occurs first, before multiplication. Parentheses may be inserted to reinforce the proper order.

$\left(\dfrac{4}{c^2 - 9} \div \dfrac{6}{c - 3} \right) \cdot \dfrac{3c}{8}$

$= \left(\dfrac{4}{c^2 - 9} \cdot \dfrac{c - 3}{6} \right) \cdot \dfrac{3c}{8}$ Multiply the first fraction by the reciprocal of the second.

Answer

6. $\dfrac{a^2c^2}{12}$

$$= \left(\frac{2 \cdot 2}{(c-3)(c+3)} \cdot \frac{c-3}{2 \cdot 3} \right) \cdot \frac{3 \cdot c}{2 \cdot 2 \cdot 2}$$

Now that each operation is written as multiplication, factor the polynomials and reduce the common factors.

$$= \frac{\overset{1}{2} \cdot \overset{1}{2} \cdot \overset{1}{(c-3)} \cdot \overset{1}{3} \cdot c}{\overset{}{(c-3)}(c+3) \cdot 2 \cdot 3 \cdot 2 \cdot 2 \cdot 2}$$

$$= \frac{c}{4(c+3)}$$

Simplify.

Skill Practice Perform the indicated operations.

7. $\dfrac{v}{v+2} \div \dfrac{5v^2}{v^2-4} \cdot \dfrac{v}{10}$

Answer

7. $\dfrac{v-2}{50}$

Section 7.2 Practice Exercises

Boost *your* GRADE at ALEKS.com!

ALEKS version 3.0

- Practice Problems
- Self-Tests
- NetTutor
- e-Professors
- Videos

For additional exercises, see Classroom Activities 7.2A–7.2B in the *Instructor's Resource Manual* at www.mhhe.com/moh.

Review Exercises

For Exercises 1–8, multiply or divide the fractions.

1. $\dfrac{3}{5} \cdot \dfrac{1}{2}$ $\dfrac{3}{10}$

2. $\dfrac{6}{7} \cdot \dfrac{5}{12}$ $\dfrac{5}{14}$

3. $\dfrac{3}{4} \div \dfrac{3}{8}$ 2

4. $\dfrac{18}{5} \div \dfrac{2}{5}$ 9

5. $6 \cdot \dfrac{5}{12}$ $\dfrac{5}{2}$

6. $\dfrac{7}{25} \cdot 5$ $\dfrac{7}{5}$

7. $\dfrac{\frac{21}{4}}{\frac{7}{5}}$ $\dfrac{15}{4}$

8. $\dfrac{\frac{9}{2}}{\frac{3}{4}}$ 6

Concept 1: Multiplication of Rational Expressions

For Exercises 9–24, multiply. **(See Examples 1–3.)**

9. $\dfrac{2xy}{5x^2} \cdot \dfrac{15}{4y}$ $\dfrac{3}{2x}$

10. $\dfrac{7s}{t^2} \cdot \dfrac{t^2}{14s^2}$ $\dfrac{1}{2s}$

11. $\dfrac{6x^3}{9x^6y^2} \cdot \dfrac{18x^4y^7}{4y}$ $3xy^4$

12. $\dfrac{10a^2b}{15b^2} \cdot \dfrac{30b}{2a^3}$ $\dfrac{10}{a}$

13. $\dfrac{4x-24}{20x} \cdot \dfrac{5x}{8}$ $\dfrac{x-6}{8}$

14. $\dfrac{5a+20}{a} \cdot \dfrac{3a}{10}$ $\dfrac{3(a+4)}{2}$

 15. $\dfrac{3y+18}{y^2} \cdot \dfrac{4y}{6y+36}$ $\dfrac{2}{y}$

16. $\dfrac{2p-4}{6p} \cdot \dfrac{4p^2}{8p-16}$ $\dfrac{p}{6}$

17. $\dfrac{10}{2-a} \cdot \dfrac{a-2}{16}$ $-\dfrac{5}{8}$

18. $\dfrac{w-3}{6} \cdot \dfrac{20}{3-w}$ $-\dfrac{10}{3}$

19. $\dfrac{b^2-a^2}{a-b} \cdot \dfrac{a}{a^2-ab}$ $-\dfrac{b+a}{b}$

20. $\dfrac{(x-y)^2}{x^2+xy} \cdot \dfrac{x}{y-x}$ $\dfrac{x-y}{x+y}$

21. $\dfrac{y^2+2y+1}{5y-10} \cdot \dfrac{y^2-3y+2}{y^2-1}$ $\dfrac{y+1}{5}$

22. $\dfrac{6a^2-6}{a^2+6a+5} \cdot \dfrac{a^2+5a}{12a}$ $\dfrac{a-1}{2}$

23. $\dfrac{10x}{2x^2+3x+1} \cdot \dfrac{x^2+7x+6}{5x}$ $\dfrac{2(x+6)}{2x+1}$

24. $\dfrac{p-3}{p^2+p-12} \cdot \dfrac{4p+16}{p+1}$ $\dfrac{4}{p+1}$

 Writing   Translating Expression   Geometry   Scientific Calculator   Video   NS&E

Concept 2: Division of Rational Expressions

For Exercises 25–38, divide. **(See Examples 4–6.)**

25. $\dfrac{4x}{7y} \div \dfrac{2x^2}{21xy}$ 6

26. $\dfrac{6cd}{5d^2} \div \dfrac{8c^3}{10d}$ $\dfrac{3}{2c^2}$

27. $\dfrac{\dfrac{8m^4n^5}{5n^6}}{\dfrac{24mn}{15m^3}}$ $\dfrac{m^6}{n^2}$

28. $\dfrac{\dfrac{10a^3b}{3a}}{\dfrac{5b}{9ab}}$ $6a^3b$

29. $\dfrac{4a + 12}{6a - 18} \div \dfrac{3a + 9}{5a - 15}$ $\dfrac{10}{9}$

30. $\dfrac{8m - 16}{3m + 3} \div \dfrac{5m - 10}{2m + 2}$ $\dfrac{16}{15}$

31. $\dfrac{3x - 21}{6x^2 - 42x} \div \dfrac{7}{12x}$ $\dfrac{6}{7}$

32. $\dfrac{4a^2 - 4a}{9a - 9} \div \dfrac{5}{12a}$ $\dfrac{16a^2}{15}$

33. $\dfrac{m^2 - n^2}{9} \div \dfrac{3n - 3m}{27m}$ $-m(m + n)$

34. $\dfrac{9 - t^2}{15t + 15} \div \dfrac{t - 3}{5t}$ $-\dfrac{t(3 + t)}{3(t + 1)}$

35. $\dfrac{3p + 4q}{p^2 + 4pq + 4q^2} \div \dfrac{4}{p + 2q}$ $\dfrac{3p + 4q}{4(p + 2q)}$

36. $\dfrac{x^2 + 2xy + y^2}{2x - y} \div \dfrac{x + y}{5}$ $\dfrac{5(x + y)}{2x - y}$

37. $\dfrac{p^2 - 2p - 3}{p^2 - p - 6} \div \dfrac{p^2 - 1}{p^2 + 2p}$ $\dfrac{p}{p - 1}$

38. $\dfrac{4t^2 - 1}{t^2 - 5t} \div \dfrac{2t^2 + 5t + 2}{t^2 - 3t - 10}$ $\dfrac{2t - 1}{t}$

Mixed Exercises

For Exercises 39–64, multiply or divide as indicated.

39. $(w + 3) \cdot \dfrac{w}{2w^2 + 5w - 3}$ $\dfrac{w}{2w - 1}$

40. $\dfrac{5t + 1}{5t^2 - 31t + 6} \cdot (t - 6)$ $\dfrac{5t + 1}{5t - 1}$

41. $(r - 5) \cdot \dfrac{4r}{2r^2 - 7r - 15}$ $\dfrac{4r}{2r + 3}$

42. $\dfrac{q + 1}{5q^2 - 28q - 12} \cdot (5q + 2)$ $\dfrac{q + 1}{q - 6}$

43. $\dfrac{\dfrac{5t - 10}{12}}{\dfrac{4t - 8}{8}}$ $\dfrac{5}{6}$

44. $\dfrac{\dfrac{6m + 6}{5}}{\dfrac{3m + 3}{10}}$ 4

45. $\dfrac{2a^2 + 13a - 24}{8a - 12} \div (a + 8)$ $\dfrac{1}{4}$

46. $\dfrac{3y^2 + 20y - 7}{5y + 35} \div (3y - 1)$ $\dfrac{1}{5}$

47. $\dfrac{y^2 + 5y - 36}{y^2 - 2y - 8} \cdot \dfrac{y + 2}{y - 6}$ $\dfrac{y + 9}{y - 6}$

48. $\dfrac{z^2 - 11z + 28}{z - 1} \cdot \dfrac{z + 1}{z^2 - 6z - 7}$ $\dfrac{z - 4}{z - 1}$

49. $\dfrac{2t^2 + t - 1}{t^2 + 3t + 2} \cdot \dfrac{t + 4}{2t - 1}$ $\dfrac{t + 4}{t + 2}$

50. $\dfrac{3p^2 - 2p - 8}{3p^2 - 5p - 12} \cdot \dfrac{p + 1}{p - 2}$ $\dfrac{p + 1}{p - 3}$

51. $(5t - 1) \div \dfrac{5t^2 + 9t - 2}{3t + 8}$ $\dfrac{3t + 8}{t + 2}$

52. $(2q - 3) \div \dfrac{2q^2 + 5q - 12}{q - 7}$ $\dfrac{q - 7}{q + 4}$

53. $\dfrac{x^2 + 2x - 3}{x^2 - 3x + 2} \cdot \dfrac{x^2 + 2x - 8}{x^2 + 4x + 3}$ $\dfrac{x + 4}{x + 1}$

54. $\dfrac{y^2 + y - 12}{y^2 - y - 20} \cdot \dfrac{y^2 + y - 30}{y^2 - 2y - 3}$ $\dfrac{y + 6}{y + 1}$

55. $\dfrac{\dfrac{w^2 - 6w + 9}{8}}{\dfrac{9 - w^2}{4w + 12}}$ $-\dfrac{w - 3}{2}$

56. $\dfrac{\dfrac{p^2 - 6p + 8}{24}}{\dfrac{16 - p^2}{6p + 6}}$ $-\dfrac{(p - 2)(p + 1)}{4(4 + p)}$

57. $\dfrac{5k^2 + 7k + 2}{k^2 + 5k + 4} \div \dfrac{5k^2 + 17k + 6}{k^2 + 10k + 24}$ $\dfrac{k + 6}{k + 3}$

58. $\dfrac{4h^2 - 5h + 1}{h^2 + h - 2} \div \dfrac{6h^2 - 7h + 2}{2h^2 + 3h - 2}$ $\dfrac{4h - 1}{3h - 2}$

59. $\dfrac{ax + a + bx + b}{2x^2 + 4x + 2} \cdot \dfrac{4x + 4}{a^2 + ab}$ $\dfrac{2}{a}$

60. $\dfrac{3my + 9m + ny + 3n}{9m^2 + 6mn + n^2} \cdot \dfrac{30m + 10n}{5y^2 + 15y}$ $\dfrac{2}{y}$

61. $\dfrac{y^4 - 1}{2y^2 - 3y + 1} \div \dfrac{2y^2 + 2}{8y^2 - 4y}$ $2y(y + 1)$

62. $\dfrac{x^4 - 16}{6x^2 + 24} \div \dfrac{x^2 - 2x}{3x}$ $\dfrac{x + 2}{2}$

63. $\dfrac{x^2 - xy - 2y^2}{x + 2y} \div \dfrac{x^2 - 4xy + 4y^2}{x^2 - 4y^2}$ $x + y$

64. $\dfrac{4m^2 - 4mn - 3n^2}{8m^2 - 18n^2} \div \dfrac{3m + 3n}{6m^2 + 15mn + 9n^2}$ $\dfrac{2m + n}{2}$

For Exercises 65–70, multiply or divide as indicated. **(See Example 7.)**

65. $\dfrac{y^3 - 3y^2 + 4y - 12}{y^4 - 16} \cdot \dfrac{3y^2 + 5y - 2}{3y^2 - 10y + 3} \div \dfrac{3}{6y - 12}$ 2

66. $\dfrac{x^2 - 25}{3x^2 + 3xy} \cdot \dfrac{x^2 + 4x + xy + 4y}{x^2 + 9x + 20} \div \dfrac{x - 5}{x}$ $\dfrac{1}{3}$

67. $\dfrac{a^2 - 5a}{a^2 + 7a + 12} \div \dfrac{a^3 - 7a^2 + 10a}{a^2 + 9a + 18} \div \dfrac{a + 6}{a + 4}$ $\dfrac{1}{a - 2}$

68. $\dfrac{t^2 + t - 2}{t^2 + 5t + 6} \div \dfrac{t - 1}{t} \div \dfrac{5t - 5}{t + 3}$ $\dfrac{t}{5(t - 1)}$

69. $\dfrac{p^3 - q^3}{p - q} \cdot \dfrac{p + q}{2p^2 + 2pq + 2q^2}$ $\dfrac{p + q}{2}$

70. $\dfrac{r^3 + s^3}{r - s} \div \dfrac{r^2 + 2rs + s^2}{r^2 - s^2}$ $r^2 - rs + s^2$

Least Common Denominator

1. Least Common Denominator

In Sections 7.1 and 7.2, we learned how to simplify, multiply, and divide rational expressions. Our next goal is to add and subtract rational expressions. As with fractions, rational expressions may be added or subtracted only if they have the same denominator.

The **least common denominator (LCD)** of two or more rational expressions is defined as the least common multiple of the denominators. For example, consider the fractions $\frac{1}{20}$ and $\frac{1}{8}$. By inspection, you can probably see that the least common denominator is 40. To understand why, find the prime factorization of both denominators:

$$20 = 2^2 \cdot 5 \qquad \text{and} \qquad 8 = 2^3$$

A common multiple of 20 and 8 must be a multiple of 5, a multiple of 2^2, and a multiple of 2^3. However, any number that is a multiple of $2^3 = 8$ is automatically a multiple of $2^2 = 4$. Therefore, it is sufficient to construct the least common denominator as the product of unique prime factors, in which each factor is raised to its highest power.

$$\text{The LCD of } \frac{1}{20} \text{ and } \frac{1}{8} \text{ is } 2^3 \cdot 5 = 40.$$

Concepts

1. **Least Common Denominator**
2. **Writing Rational Expressions with the Least Common Denominator**

> **PROCEDURE**   **Finding the Least Common Denominator of Two or More Rational Expressions**
>
> **Step 1**   Factor all denominators completely.
> **Step 2**   The LCD is the product of unique prime factors from the denominators, in which each factor is raised to the highest power to which it appears in any denominator.

Classroom Example: p. 508, Exercise 20

Example 1 Finding the Least Common Denominator

Find the LCD of the rational expressions.

a. $\dfrac{5}{14}; \dfrac{3}{49}; \dfrac{1}{8}$ **b.** $\dfrac{5}{3x^2z}; \dfrac{7}{x^5y^3}$

Solution:

a. Factor the denominators, 14, 49, and 8.

	2's	7's
14 =	2	7
49 =		$\boxed{7^2}$
8 =	$\boxed{2^3}$	

We circle the factor of 2 raised to its greatest power. We circle the factor of 7 raised to its greatest power. The LCD is their product.

The least common denominator (LCD) is $2^3 \cdot 7^2 = 392$.

b. The denominators are already factored.

	3's	x's	y's	z's
$3x^2z =$	$\boxed{3}$	x^2		$\boxed{z}$
$x^5y^3 =$		$\boxed{x^5}$	$\boxed{y^3}$	

We circle the factors of $3, x, y,$ and z, each raised to its corresponding highest power.

The least common denominator (LCD) is $3^1x^5y^3z^1$ or simply $3x^5y^3z$.

Skill Practice Find the LCD for each set of expressions.

1. $\dfrac{3}{8}; \dfrac{7}{10}; \dfrac{1}{15}$ **2.** $\dfrac{1}{5a^3b^2}; \dfrac{1}{10a^4b}$

Classroom Examples: p. 508, Exercises 26 and 28

Example 2 Finding the Least Common Denominator

Find the LCD for each pair of rational expressions.

a. $\dfrac{a+b}{a^2-25}; \dfrac{1}{2a-10}$ **b.** $\dfrac{x-5}{x^2-2x}; \dfrac{1}{x^2-4x+4}$

Solution:

a. $\dfrac{a+b}{a^2-25}; \dfrac{1}{2a-10}$

$= \dfrac{a+b}{(a-5)(a+5)}; \dfrac{1}{2(a-5)}$ Factor the denominators.

The LCD is $2(a-5)(a+5)$.   The LCD is the product of unique factors, each raised to its highest power.

Answers

1. 120   **2.** $10a^4b^2$

b. $\dfrac{x-5}{x^2-2x}; \dfrac{1}{x^2-4x+4}$

$= \dfrac{x-5}{x(x-2)}; \dfrac{1}{(x-2)^2}$ Factor the denominators.

The LCD is $x(x-2)^2$.   The LCD is the product of unique factors, each raised to its highest power.

Skill Practice Find the LCD.

3. $\dfrac{x}{x^2-16}; \dfrac{2}{3x+12}$ **4.** $\dfrac{6}{t^2+5t-14}; \dfrac{8}{t^2-3t+2}$

2. Writing Rational Expressions with the Least Common Denominator

To add or subtract two rational expressions, the expressions must have the same denominator. Therefore, we must first practice the skill of converting each rational expression into an equivalent expression with the LCD as its denominator.

> **PROCEDURE**   **Writing Equivalent Fractions with Common Denominators**
>
> **Step 1**   Identify the LCD for the expressions.
> **Step 2**   Multiply the numerator and denominator of each fraction by the factors from the LCD that are missing from the original denominators.

Example 3   **Converting to the Least Common Denominator**

Classroom Examples: p. 509, Exercises 34 and 40

Find the LCD of each pair of rational expressions. Then convert each expression to an equivalent fraction with the denominator equal to the LCD.

a. $\dfrac{3}{2ab}; \dfrac{6}{5a^2}$ **b.** $\dfrac{4}{x+1}; \dfrac{7}{x-4}$

Solution:

a. $\dfrac{3}{2ab}; \dfrac{6}{5a^2}$ The LCD is $10a^2b$.

$\dfrac{3}{2ab} = \dfrac{3 \cdot 5a}{2ab \cdot 5a} = \dfrac{15a}{10a^2b}$ The first expression is missing the factor $5a$ from the denominator.

$\dfrac{6}{5a^2} = \dfrac{6 \cdot 2b}{5a^2 \cdot 2b} = \dfrac{12b}{10a^2b}$ The second expression is missing the factor $2b$ from the denominator.

Answers
3. $3(x-4)(x+4)$
4. $(t+7)(t-2)(t-1)$

b. $\dfrac{4}{x+1}$; $\dfrac{7}{x-4}$ The LCD is $(x+1)(x-4)$.

$$\frac{4}{x+1} = \frac{4(x-4)}{(x+1)(x-4)} = \frac{4x-16}{(x+1)(x-4)}$$

The first expression is missing the factor $(x-4)$ from the denominator.

$$\frac{7}{x-4} = \frac{7(x+1)}{(x-4)(x+1)} = \frac{7x+7}{(x-4)(x+1)}$$

The second expression is missing the factor $(x+1)$ from the denominator.

Skill Practice For each pair of expressions, find the LCD, and then convert each expression to an equivalent fraction with the denominator equal to the LCD.

5. $\dfrac{2}{rs^2}$; $\dfrac{-1}{r^3s}$ **6.** $\dfrac{5}{x-3}$; $\dfrac{x}{x+1}$

Classroom Example: p. 509, Exercise 46

Example 4   **Converting to the Least Common Denominator**

Find the LCD of the pair of rational expressions. Then convert each expression to an equivalent fraction with the denominator equal to the LCD.

$$\frac{w+2}{w^2-w-12}; \frac{1}{w^2-9}$$

Solution:

$$\frac{w+2}{w^2-w-12}; \frac{1}{w^2-9}$$

To find the LCD, factor each denominator.

$$\frac{w+2}{(w-4)(w+3)}; \frac{1}{(w-3)(w+3)}$$

The LCD is $(w-4)(w+3)(w-3)$.

$$\frac{w+2}{(w-4)(w+3)} = \frac{(w+2)(w-3)}{(w-4)(w+3)(w-3)}$$

The first expression is missing the factor $(w-3)$ from the denominator.

$$= \frac{w^2-w-6}{(w-4)(w+3)(w-3)}$$

$$\frac{1}{(w-3)(w+3)} = \frac{1(w-4)}{(w-3)(w+3)(w-4)}$$

The second expression is missing the factor $(w-4)$ from the denominator.

$$= \frac{w-4}{(w-3)(w+3)(w-4)}$$

Skill Practice Find the LCD. Then convert each expression to an equivalent expression with the denominator equal to the LCD.

7. $\dfrac{z}{z^2-4}$; $\dfrac{-3}{z^2-z-2}$

Answers

5. $\dfrac{2}{rs^2} = \dfrac{2r^2}{r^3s^2}$; $\dfrac{-1}{r^3s} = \dfrac{-s}{r^3s^2}$

6. $\dfrac{5}{x-3} = \dfrac{5x+5}{(x-3)(x+1)}$

$\dfrac{x}{x+1} = \dfrac{x^2-3x}{(x+1)(x-3)}$

7. $\dfrac{z^2+z}{(z-2)(z+2)(z+1)}$;

$\dfrac{-3z-6}{(z-2)(z+2)(z+1)}$

Example 5   Converting to the Least Common Denominator

Classroom Example: p. 509, Exercise 48

Convert each expression to an equivalent expression with the denominator equal to the LCD.

$$\frac{3}{x-7} \quad \text{and} \quad \frac{1}{7-x}$$

Solution:

Notice that the expressions $x - 7$ and $7 - x$ are opposites and differ by a factor of -1. Therefore, we may use either $x - 7$ or $7 - x$ as a common denominator. Each case is shown below.

TIP: In Example 5, the expressions

$$\frac{3}{x-7} \quad \text{and} \quad \frac{1}{7-x}$$

have opposite factors in the denominators. In such a case, you do not need to include *both* factors in the LCD.

Converting to the Denominator $x - 7$

$\dfrac{3}{x-7}; \dfrac{1}{7-x}$ Leave the first fraction unchanged because it has the desired LCD.

$\dfrac{1}{7-x} = \dfrac{(-1)1}{(-1)(7-x)}$ Multiply the *second* rational expression by the ratio $\frac{-1}{-1}$ to change its denominator to $x - 7$.

$\quad = \dfrac{-1}{-7+x}$ Apply the distributive property.

$\quad = \dfrac{-1}{x-7}$

Converting to the Denominator $7 - x$

$\dfrac{3}{x-7}; \dfrac{1}{7-x}$ Leave the second fraction unchanged because it has the desired LCD.

$\dfrac{3}{x-7} = \dfrac{(-1)3}{(-1)(x-7)};$ Multiply the *first* rational expression by the ratio $\frac{-1}{-1}$ to change its denominator to $7 - x$.

$\quad = \dfrac{-3}{-x+7}$ Apply the distributive property.

$\quad = \dfrac{-3}{7-x}$

Skill Practice

8. a. Find the LCD of the expressions. $\dfrac{9}{w-2}; \dfrac{11}{2-w}$

   b. Convert each expression to an equivalent fraction with denominator equal to the LCD.

Answer

8. a. The LCD is $(w - 2)$ or $(2 - w)$.

  b. $\dfrac{9}{w-2} = \dfrac{9}{w-2};$

$\dfrac{11}{2-w} = \dfrac{-11}{w-2}$

or

$\dfrac{9}{w-2} = \dfrac{-9}{2-w};$

$\dfrac{11}{2-w} = \dfrac{11}{2-w}$

Section 7.3   Practice Exercises

Boost *your* GRADE at ALEKS.com!

ALEKS version 3.0

- Practice Problems
- Self-Tests
- NetTutor

- e-Professors
- Videos

For additional exercises, see Classroom Activities 7.3A–7.3C in the *Instructor's Resource Manual* at www.mhhe.com/moh.

Study Skills Exercise

1. Define the key term **least common denominator (LCD)**.

  Writing   Translating Expression   Geometry   Scientific Calculator   Video   NS&E

Review Exercises

2. Evaluate the expression for the given values of *x*. $\dfrac{2x}{x+5}$

    a. $x = 1$ $\dfrac{1}{3}$ **b.** $x = 5$ 1   **c.** $x = -5$ Undefined

For Exercises 3–4, identify the restricted values. Then simplify the expression.

3. $\dfrac{3x+3}{5x^2-5}$ $x = 1, x = -1;$ $\dfrac{3}{5(x-1)}$

4. $\dfrac{x+2}{x^2-3x-10}$ $x = -2, x = 5;$ $\dfrac{1}{x-5}$

For Exercises 5–8, multiply or divide as indicated.

5. $\dfrac{a+3}{a+7} \cdot \dfrac{a^2+3a-10}{a^2+a-6}$ $\dfrac{a+5}{a+7}$

6. $\dfrac{6(a+2b)}{2(a-3b)} \cdot \dfrac{4(a+3b)(a-3b)}{9(a+2b)(a-2b)}$ $\dfrac{4(a+3b)}{3(a-2b)}$

7. $\dfrac{16y^2}{9y+36} \div \dfrac{8y^3}{3y+12}$ $\dfrac{2}{3y}$

8. $\dfrac{5w^2+6w+1}{w^2+5w+6} \div (5w+1)$ $\dfrac{w+1}{(w+2)(w+3)}$

9. Which of the expressions are equivalent to $-\dfrac{5}{x-3}$? Circle all that apply.

    a. $\dfrac{-5}{x-3}$ **b.** $\dfrac{5}{-x+3}$ **c.** $\dfrac{5}{3-x}$ **d.** $\dfrac{5}{-(x-3)}$ a, b, c, d

10. Which of the expressions are equivalent to $\dfrac{4-a}{6}$? Circle all that apply.

    a. $\dfrac{a-4}{-6}$ **b.** $\dfrac{a-4}{6}$ **c.** $\dfrac{-(4-a)}{-6}$ **d.** $-\dfrac{a-4}{6}$ a, c, d

Concept 1: Least Common Denominator

11. Explain why the least common denominator of $\frac{1}{x^3}, \frac{1}{x^5}$, and $\frac{1}{x^4}$ is x^5.
    x^5 is the greatest power of x that appears in any denominator.

12. Explain why the least common denominator of $\frac{2}{y^3}, \frac{9}{y^6}$, and $\frac{4}{y^5}$ is y^6.
    y^6 is the greatest power of y that appears in any denominator.

For Exercises 13–30, identify the LCD. **(See Examples 1–2.)**

13. $\dfrac{4}{15}; \dfrac{5}{9}$ 45

14. $\dfrac{7}{12}; \dfrac{1}{18}$ 36

15. $\dfrac{1}{16}; \dfrac{1}{4}; \dfrac{1}{6}$ 48

16. $\dfrac{1}{2}; \dfrac{11}{12}; \dfrac{3}{8}$ 24

17. $\dfrac{1}{7}; \dfrac{2}{9}$ 63

18. $\dfrac{2}{3}; \dfrac{5}{8}$ 24

19. $\dfrac{1}{3x^2y}; \dfrac{8}{9xy^3}$ $9x^2y^3$

20. $\dfrac{5}{2a^4b^2}; \dfrac{1}{8ab^3}$ $8a^4b^3$

21. $\dfrac{6}{w^2}; \dfrac{7}{y}$ w^2y

22. $\dfrac{2}{r}; \dfrac{3}{s^2}$ rs^2

23. $\dfrac{p}{(p+3)(p-1)}; \dfrac{2}{(p+3)(p+2)}$
    $(p+3)(p-1)(p+2)$

24. $\dfrac{6}{(q+4)(q-4)}; \dfrac{q^2}{(q+1)(q+4)}$
    $(q+4)(q-4)(q+1)$

25. $\dfrac{7}{3t(t+1)}; \dfrac{10t}{9(t+1)^2}$
    $9t(t+1)^2$

26. $\dfrac{13x}{15(x-1)^2}; \dfrac{5}{3x(x-1)}$
    $15x(x-1)^2$

27. $\dfrac{y}{y^2-4}; \dfrac{3y}{y^2+5y+6}$
    $(y-2)(y+2)(y+3)$

28. $\dfrac{4}{w^2-3w+2}; \dfrac{w}{w^2-4}$
    $(w-1)(w-2)(w+2)$

29. $\dfrac{5}{3-x}; \dfrac{7}{x-3}$ $3-x$ or $x-3$

30. $\dfrac{4}{x-6}; \dfrac{9}{6-x}$ $x-6$ or $6-x$

 Writing   ⟷ Translating Expression   Geometry   Scientific Calculator   Video   NS&E

31. Explain why a common denominator of

$$\frac{b + 1}{b - 1} \quad \text{and} \quad \frac{b}{1 - b}$$

could be either $(b - 1)$ or $(1 - b)$.

Because $(b - 1)$ and $(1 - b)$ are opposites, they differ by a factor of -1.

32. Explain why a common denominator of

$$\frac{1}{6 - t} \quad \text{and} \quad \frac{t}{t - 6}$$

could be either $(6 - t)$ or $(t - 6)$.

Because $(6 - t)$ and $(t - 6)$ are opposites, they differ by a factor of -1.

Concept 2: Writing Rational Expressions with the Least Common Denominator

For Exercises 33–56, find the LCD. Then convert each expression to an equivalent expression with the denominator equal to the LCD. **(See Examples 3–5.)**

33. $\dfrac{6}{5x^2}; \dfrac{1}{x}$ $\quad \dfrac{6}{5x^2}; \dfrac{5x}{5x^2}$

34. $\dfrac{3}{y}; \dfrac{7}{9y^2}$ $\quad \dfrac{27y}{9y^2}; \dfrac{7}{9y^2}$

35. $\dfrac{4}{5x^2}; \dfrac{y}{6x^3}$ $\quad \dfrac{24x}{30x^3}; \dfrac{5y}{30x^3}$

36. $\dfrac{3}{15b^2}; \dfrac{c}{3b^2}$ $\quad \dfrac{3}{15b^2}; \dfrac{5c}{15b^2}$

37. $\dfrac{5}{6a^2b}; \dfrac{a}{12b}$ $\quad \dfrac{10}{12a^2b}; \dfrac{a^3}{12a^2b}$

38. $\dfrac{x}{15y^2}; \dfrac{y}{5xy}$ $\quad \dfrac{x^2}{15xy^2}; \dfrac{3y^2}{15xy^2}$

39. $\dfrac{6}{m + 4}; \dfrac{3}{m - 1}$ $\quad \dfrac{6m - 6}{(m + 4)(m - 1)}; \dfrac{3m + 12}{(m + 4)(m - 1)}$

40. $\dfrac{3}{n - 5}; \dfrac{7}{n + 2}$ $\quad \dfrac{3n + 6}{(n - 5)(n + 2)}; \dfrac{7n - 35}{(n - 5)(n + 2)}$

41. $\dfrac{6}{2x - 5}; \dfrac{1}{x + 3}$ $\quad \dfrac{6x + 18}{(2x - 5)(x + 3)}; \dfrac{2x - 5}{(2x - 5)(x + 3)}$

42. $\dfrac{4}{m + 3}; \dfrac{-3}{5m + 1}$ $\quad \dfrac{20m + 4}{(m + 3)(5m + 1)}; \dfrac{-3m - 9}{(m + 3)(5m + 1)}$

43. $\dfrac{6}{(w + 3)(w - 8)}; \dfrac{w}{(w - 8)(w + 1)}$ $\quad \dfrac{6w + 6}{(w + 3)(w - 8)(w + 1)}; \dfrac{w^2 + 3w}{(w + 3)(w - 8)(w + 1)}$

44. $\dfrac{t}{(t + 2)(t + 12)}; \dfrac{18}{(t - 2)(t + 2)}$ $\quad \dfrac{t^2 - 2t}{(t + 2)(t - 2)(t + 12)}; \dfrac{18t + 216}{(t + 2)(t - 2)(t + 12)}$

45. $\dfrac{6p}{p^2 - 4}; \dfrac{3}{p^2 + 4p + 4}$ $\quad \dfrac{6p^2 + 12p}{(p - 2)(p + 2)^2}; \dfrac{3p - 6}{(p - 2)(p + 2)^2}$

46. $\dfrac{5}{t^2 - 6t + 9}; \dfrac{t}{t^2 - 9}$ $\quad \dfrac{5t + 15}{(t - 3)^2(t + 3)}; \dfrac{t^2 - 3t}{(t - 3)^2(t + 3)}$

47. $\dfrac{1}{a - 4}; \dfrac{a}{4 - a}$ $\quad \dfrac{1}{a - 4}; \dfrac{-a}{a - 4}$ or $\dfrac{-1}{4 - a}; \dfrac{a}{4 - a}$

48. $\dfrac{3b}{2b - 5}; \dfrac{2b}{5 - 2b}$ $\quad \dfrac{3b}{2b - 5}; \dfrac{-2b}{2b - 5}$ or $\dfrac{-3b}{5 - 2b}; \dfrac{2b}{5 - 2b}$

49. $\dfrac{4}{x - 7}; \dfrac{y}{14 - 2x}$ $\quad \dfrac{8}{2(x - 7)}; \dfrac{-y}{2(x - 7)}$ or $\dfrac{-8}{2(7 - x)}; \dfrac{y}{2(7 - x)}$

50. $\dfrac{4}{3x - 15}; \dfrac{z}{5 - x}$ $\quad \dfrac{4}{3(x - 5)}; \dfrac{-3z}{3(x - 5)}$ or $\dfrac{-4}{3(5 - x)}; \dfrac{3z}{3(5 - x)}$

51. $\dfrac{1}{a + b}; \dfrac{6}{-a - b}$ $\quad \dfrac{1}{a + b}; \dfrac{-6}{a + b}$ or $\dfrac{-1}{-a - b}; \dfrac{6}{-a - b}$

52. $\dfrac{p}{-q - 8}; \dfrac{1}{q + 8}$ $\quad \dfrac{p}{-q - 8}; \dfrac{-1}{-q - 8}$ or $\dfrac{-p}{q + 8}; \dfrac{1}{q + 8}$

53. $\dfrac{-3}{24y + 8}; \dfrac{5}{18y + 6}$ $\quad \dfrac{-9}{24(3y + 1)}; \dfrac{20}{24(3y + 1)}$

54. $\dfrac{r}{10r + 5}; \dfrac{2}{16r + 8}$ $\quad \dfrac{8r}{40(2r + 1)}; \dfrac{10}{40(2r + 1)}$

55. $\dfrac{3}{5z}; \dfrac{1}{z + 4}$ $\quad \dfrac{3z + 12}{5z(z + 4)}; \dfrac{5z}{5z(z + 4)}$

56. $\dfrac{-1}{4a - 8}; \dfrac{5}{4a}$ $\quad \dfrac{-a}{4a(a - 2)}; \dfrac{5a - 10}{4a(a - 2)}$

Expanding Your Skills

For Exercises 57–60, find the LCD. Then convert each expression to an equivalent expression with the denominator equal to the LCD.

57. $\dfrac{z}{z^2 + 9z + 14}; \dfrac{-3z}{z^2 + 10z + 21}; \dfrac{5}{z^2 + 5z + 6}$ $\quad \dfrac{z^2 + 3z}{(z + 2)(z + 7)(z + 3)}; \dfrac{-3z^2 - 6z}{(z + 2)(z + 7)(z + 3)}; \dfrac{5z + 35}{(z + 2)(z + 7)(z + 3)}$

58. $\dfrac{6}{w^2 - 3w - 4}; \dfrac{1}{w^2 + 6w + 5}; \dfrac{-9w}{w^2 + w - 20}$ $\quad \dfrac{6w + 30}{(w - 4)(w + 1)(w + 5)}; \dfrac{w - 4}{(w - 4)(w + 1)(w + 5)}; \dfrac{-9w^2 - 9w}{(w - 4)(w + 1)(w + 5)}$

59. $\dfrac{3}{p^3 - 8}; \dfrac{p}{p^2 - 4}; \dfrac{5p}{p^2 + 2p + 4}$ $\quad \dfrac{3p + 6}{(p - 2)(p^2 + 2p + 4)(p + 2)}; \dfrac{p^3 + 2p^2 + 4p}{(p - 2)(p^2 + 2p + 4)(p + 2)}; \dfrac{5p^3 - 20p}{(p - 2)(p^2 + 2p + 4)(p + 2)}$

60. $\dfrac{7}{n^3 + 125}; \dfrac{n}{n^2 - 25}; \dfrac{12}{n^2 - 5n + 25}$ $\quad \dfrac{7n - 35}{(n + 5)(n^2 - 5n + 25)(n - 5)}; \dfrac{n^3 - 5n^2 + 25n}{(n + 5)(n^2 - 5n + 25)(n - 5)}; \dfrac{12n^2 - 300}{(n + 5)(n^2 - 5n + 25)(n - 5)}$

 Writing Translating Expression Geometry Scientific Calculator ● Video NS&E

Section 7.4   Addition and Subtraction of Rational Expressions

1. Addition and Subtraction of Rational Expressions with the Same Denominator

To add or subtract rational expressions, the expressions must have the same denominator. As with fractions, add or subtract rational expressions with the same denominator by combining the terms in the numerator and then writing the result over the common denominator. Then, if possible, simplify the expression.

> **PROPERTY   Addition and Subtraction of Rational Expressions**
>
> Let p, q, and r represent polynomials where $q \neq 0$. Then,
>
> **1.** $\dfrac{p}{q} + \dfrac{r}{q} = \dfrac{p+r}{q}$ **2.** $\dfrac{p}{q} - \dfrac{r}{q} = \dfrac{p-r}{q}$

Classroom Examples: p. 516, Exercises 8 and 12

Example 1   **Adding and Subtracting Rational Expressions with the Same Denominator**

Add or subtract as indicated.   **a.** $\dfrac{1}{12} + \dfrac{7}{12}$ **b.** $\dfrac{2}{5p} - \dfrac{7}{5p}$

Solution:

a. $\dfrac{1}{12} + \dfrac{7}{12}$ The fractions have the same denominator.

$= \dfrac{1+7}{12}$ Add the terms in the numerators, and write the result over the common denominator.

$= \dfrac{\overset{2}{\cancel{8}}}{\underset{3}{\cancel{12}}}$

$= \dfrac{2}{3}$ Simplify.

b. $\dfrac{2}{5p} - \dfrac{7}{5p}$ The rational expressions have the same denominator.

$= \dfrac{2-7}{5p}$ Subtract the terms in the numerators, and write the result over the common denominator.

$= \dfrac{-5}{5p}$

$= \dfrac{-\overset{-1}{\cancel{5}}}{\cancel{5}p}$ Simplify.

$= -\dfrac{1}{p}$

Skill Practice   Add or subtract as indicated.

Answers

1. $\dfrac{1}{2}$ **2.** $-\dfrac{1}{d}$

1. $\dfrac{3}{14} + \dfrac{4}{14}$ **2.** $\dfrac{2}{7d} - \dfrac{9}{7d}$

Example 2 **Adding and Subtracting Rational Expressions with the Same Denominator**

Classroom Example: p. 516, Exercise 18

Add or subtract as indicated.

a. $\dfrac{2}{3d + 5} + \dfrac{7d}{3d + 5}$ **b.** $\dfrac{x^2}{x - 3} - \dfrac{-5x + 24}{x - 3}$

Solution:

a. $\dfrac{2}{3d + 5} + \dfrac{7d}{3d + 5}$ The rational expressions have the same denominator.

$= \dfrac{2 + 7d}{3d + 5}$ Add the terms in the numerators, and write the result over the common denominator.

$= \dfrac{7d + 2}{3d + 5}$ Because the numerator and denominator share no common factors, the expression is in lowest terms.

b. $\dfrac{x^2}{x - 3} - \dfrac{-5x + 24}{x - 3}$ The rational expressions have the same denominator.

$= \dfrac{x^2 - (-5x + 24)}{x - 3}$ Subtract the terms in the numerators, and write the result over the common denominator.

$= \dfrac{x^2 + 5x - 24}{x - 3}$ Simplify the numerator.

$= \dfrac{(x + 8)(x - 3)}{(x - 3)}$ Factor the numerator and denominator to determine if the rational expression can be simplified.

$= \dfrac{(x + 8)\overset{1}{\cancel{(x - 3)}}}{\cancel{(x - 3)}}$ Simplify.

$= x + 8$

Avoiding Mistakes

When subtracting rational expressions, use parentheses to group the terms in the numerator that follow the subtraction sign. This will help you remember to apply the distributive property.

Instructor Note: Have students consider the alternative method for subtraction. Rewrite as addition and change the signs of the numerator in the second fraction.

$\dfrac{x^2}{x - 3} - \dfrac{-5x + 24}{x - 3}$ becomes

$\dfrac{x^2}{x - 3} + \dfrac{5x - 24}{x - 3}$

Skill Practice Add or subtract as indicated.

3. $\dfrac{x^2 + 2}{x + 3} + \dfrac{4x + 1}{x + 3}$ **4.** $\dfrac{4t - 9}{2t + 1} - \dfrac{t - 5}{2t + 1}$

2. Addition and Subtraction of Rational Expressions with Different Denominators

To add or subtract two rational expressions with unlike denominators, we must convert the expressions to equivalent expressions with the same denominator. For example, consider adding

$$\frac{1}{10} + \frac{12}{5y}$$

The LCD is $10y$. For each expression, identify the factors from the LCD that are missing from the denominator. Then multiply the numerator and denominator of the expression by the missing factor(s).

$$\underset{\underset{y}{\text{Missing}}}{\frac{1}{10}} + \underset{\underset{2}{\text{Missing}}}{\frac{12}{5y}}$$

Answers

3. $x + 1$ **4.** $\dfrac{3t - 4}{2t + 1}$

$$= \frac{1 \cdot y}{10 \cdot y} + \frac{12 \cdot 2}{5y \cdot 2}$$

$$= \frac{y}{10y} + \frac{24}{10y}$$ The rational expressions now have the same denominators.

$$= \frac{y + 24}{10y}$$ Add the numerators.

After successfully adding or subtracting two rational expressions, always check to see if the final answer is simplified. If necessary, factor the numerator and denominator, and reduce common factors. The expression

$$\frac{y + 24}{10y}$$

is in lowest terms because the numerator and denominator do not share any common factors.

PROCEDURE Adding or Subtracting Rational Expressions

Step 1 Factor the denominators of each rational expression.

Step 2 Identify the LCD.

Step 3 Rewrite each rational expression as an equivalent expression with the LCD as its denominator.

Step 4 Add or subtract the numerators, and write the result over the common denominator.

Step 5 Simplify.

Classroom Example: p. 517, Exercise 32

Example 3 Subtracting Rational Expressions with Different Denominators

Subtract. $\dfrac{4}{7k} - \dfrac{3}{k^2}$

Solution:

$$\frac{4}{7k} - \frac{3}{k^2}$$

Step 1: The denominators are already factored.

Step 2: The LCD is $7k^2$.

$$= \frac{4 \cdot k}{7k \cdot k} - \frac{3 \cdot 7}{k^2 \cdot 7}$$ **Step 3:** Write each expression with the LCD.

$$= \frac{4k}{7k^2} - \frac{21}{7k^2}$$

$$= \frac{4k - 21}{7k^2}$$ **Step 4:** Subtract the numerators, and write the result over the LCD.

Step 5: The expression is in lowest terms because the numerator and denominator share no common factors.

Skill Practice Subtract.

5. $\dfrac{4}{3x} - \dfrac{1}{2x^2}$

Answer

5. $\dfrac{8x - 3}{6x^2}$

Example 4 Subtracting Rational Expressions with Different Denominators

Classroom Example: p. 517, Exercise 42

Subtract. $\dfrac{2q - 4}{3} - \dfrac{q + 1}{2}$

Solution:

$\dfrac{2q - 4}{3} - \dfrac{q + 1}{2}$ **Step 1:** The denominators are already factored.

    Step 2: The LCD is 6.

$= \dfrac{2(2q - 4)}{2 \cdot 3} - \dfrac{3(q + 1)}{3 \cdot 2}$ **Step 3:** Write each expression with the LCD.

$= \dfrac{2(2q - 4) - 3(q + 1)}{6}$ **Step 4:** Subtract the numerators, and write the result over the LCD.

$= \dfrac{4q - 8 - 3q - 3}{6}$

$= \dfrac{q - 11}{6}$ **Step 5:** The expression is in lowest terms because the numerator and denominator share no common factors.

Skill Practice Subtract.

6. $\dfrac{t}{12} - \dfrac{t - 2}{4}$

Example 5 Adding Rational Expressions with Different Denominators

Classroom Example: p. 517, Exercise 40

Add. $\dfrac{1}{x - 5} + \dfrac{-10}{x^2 - 25}$

Solution:

$\dfrac{1}{x - 5} + \dfrac{-10}{x^2 - 25}$

$= \dfrac{1}{x - 5} + \dfrac{-10}{(x - 5)(x + 5)}$ **Step 1:** Factor the denominators.

    Step 2: The LCD is $(x - 5)(x + 5)$.

$= \dfrac{1(x + 5)}{(x - 5)(x + 5)} + \dfrac{-10}{(x - 5)(x + 5)}$ **Step 3:** Write each expression with the LCD.

$= \dfrac{1(x + 5) + (-10)}{(x - 5)(x + 5)}$ **Step 4:** Add the numerators, and write the result over the LCD.

$= \dfrac{x + 5 - 10}{(x - 5)(x + 5)}$

$= \dfrac{\overset{1}{\cancel{x - 5}}}{\cancel{(x - 5)}(x + 5)}$ **Step 5:** Simplify.

$= \dfrac{1}{x + 5}$

Answer

6. $\dfrac{-t + 3}{6}$

Classroom Example: p. 518,
Exercise 68

Skill Practice Add.

7. $\dfrac{1}{x-4} + \dfrac{-8}{x^2-16}$

Example 6 **Adding and Subtracting Rational Expressions with Different Denominators**

Subtract. $\dfrac{p+2}{p-1} - \dfrac{2}{p+6} - \dfrac{14}{p^2+5p-6}$

Solution:

$\dfrac{p+2}{p-1} - \dfrac{2}{p+6} - \dfrac{14}{p^2+5p-6}$

$= \dfrac{p+2}{p-1} - \dfrac{2}{p+6} - \dfrac{14}{(p-1)(p+6)}$ **Step 1:** Factor the denominators.

Step 2: The LCD is $(p-1)(p+6)$.

Step 3: Write each expression with the LCD.

$= \dfrac{(p+2)(p+6)}{(p-1)(p+6)} - \dfrac{2(p-1)}{(p+6)(p-1)} - \dfrac{14}{(p-1)(p+6)}$

$= \dfrac{(p+2)(p+6) - 2(p-1) - 14}{(p-1)(p+6)}$ **Step 4:** Combine the numerators, and write the result over the LCD.

$= \dfrac{p^2 + 6p + 2p + 12 - 2p + 2 - 14}{(p-1)(p+6)}$ **Step 5:** Clear parentheses in the numerator.

$= \dfrac{p^2 + 6p}{(p-1)(p+6)}$ Combine *like* terms.

$= \dfrac{p(p+6)}{(p-1)(p+6)}$ Factor the numerator to determine if the expression is in lowest terms.

$= \dfrac{p(\overset{1}{\cancel{p+6}})}{(p-1)(\cancel{p+6})}$ Simplify.

$= \dfrac{p}{p-1}$

Skill Practice Subtract.

8. $\dfrac{2y}{y-1} - \dfrac{1}{y} - \dfrac{2y+1}{y^2-y}$

When the denominators of two rational expressions are opposites, we can produce identical denominators by multiplying one of the expressions by the ratio $\frac{-1}{-1}$. This is demonstrated in Example 7.

Answers

7. $\dfrac{1}{x+4}$ **8.** $\dfrac{2y-3}{y-1}$

Classroom Example: p. 517, Exercise 50

Example 7 **Adding Rational Expressions with Different Denominators**

Add the rational expressions. $\dfrac{1}{d-7} + \dfrac{5}{7-d}$

Solution:

$\dfrac{1}{d-7} + \dfrac{5}{7-d}$

The expressions $d - 7$ and $7 - d$ are opposites and differ by a factor of -1. Therefore, multiply the numerator and denominator of *either* expression by -1 to obtain a common denominator.

$= \dfrac{1}{d-7} + \dfrac{(-1)5}{(-1)(7-d)}$

Note that $-1(7-d) = -7 + d$ or $d - 7$.

$= \dfrac{1}{d-7} + \dfrac{-5}{d-7}$

Simplify.

$= \dfrac{1+(-5)}{d-7}$

Add the terms in the numerators, and write the result over the common denominator.

$- \dfrac{-4}{d-7}$

Skill Practice Add.

9. $\dfrac{3}{p-8} + \dfrac{1}{8-p}$

3. Using Rational Expressions in Translations

Example 8 **Using Rational Expressions in Translations**

Classroom Example: p. 518, Exercise 80

Write the English phrase as a mathematical expression. Then simplify by combining the rational expressions.

The difference of the reciprocal of n and the quotient of n and 3

Solution:

The difference of the reciprocal of n and the quotient of n and 3

The difference of

$$\left(\dfrac{1}{n}\right) - \left(\dfrac{n}{3}\right)$$

The reciprocal of n The quotient of n and 3

$\dfrac{1}{n} - \dfrac{n}{3}$

The LCD is $3n$.

$= \dfrac{3 \cdot 1}{3 \cdot n} - \dfrac{n \cdot n}{3 \cdot n}$

Write each expression with the LCD.

$= \dfrac{3 - n^2}{3n}$

Subtract the numerators.

Answer

9. $\dfrac{2}{p-8}$ or $\dfrac{-2}{8-p}$

Answer

10. $1 + \dfrac{2}{a}; \dfrac{a+2}{a}$

> **Skill Practice** Write the English phrase as a mathematical expression. Then simplify by combining the rational expressions.
>
> **10.** The sum of 1 and the quotient of 2 and a.

Section 7.4 Practice Exercises

Review Exercises

1. For the rational expression $\dfrac{x^2 - 4x - 5}{x^2 - 7x + 10}$

   a. Find the value of the expression (if possible) when $x = 0, 1, -1, 2,$ and 5. $-\dfrac{1}{2}, -2, 0,$ undefined, undefined

   b. Factor the denominator and identify the restricted values. $(x-5)(x-2); x=5, x=2$

   c. Simplify the expression. $\dfrac{x+1}{x-2}$

2. For the rational expression $\dfrac{a^2 + a - 2}{a^2 - 4a - 12}$

   a. Find the value of the expression (if possible) when $a = 0, 1, -2, 2,$ and 6. $\dfrac{1}{6}, 0,$ undefined, $-\dfrac{1}{4},$ undefined

   b. Factor the denominator, and identify the restricted values. $(a-6)(a+2); a=6, a=-2$

   c. Simplify the expression. $\dfrac{a-1}{a-6}$

For Exercises 3–4, multiply or divide as indicated.

3. $\dfrac{2x^2 - x - 3}{2x^2 - 3x - 9} \div \dfrac{x^2 - 1}{4x + 6}$ $\dfrac{2(2x-3)}{(x-3)(x-1)}$

4. $\dfrac{6t - 1}{5t - 30} \cdot \dfrac{10t - 25}{2t^2 - 3t - 5}$ $\dfrac{6t-1}{(t+1)(t-6)}$

Concept 1: Addition and Subtraction of Rational Expressions with the Same Denominator

For Exercises 5–26, add or subtract the expressions with like denominators as indicated. **(See Examples 1–2.)**

5. $\dfrac{7}{8} + \dfrac{3}{8}$ $\dfrac{5}{4}$

6. $\dfrac{1}{3} + \dfrac{7}{3}$ $\dfrac{8}{3}$

7. $\dfrac{9}{16} - \dfrac{3}{16}$ $\dfrac{3}{8}$

8. $\dfrac{14}{15} - \dfrac{4}{15}$ $\dfrac{2}{3}$

9. $\dfrac{5a}{a+2} - \dfrac{3a-4}{a+2}$ 2

10. $\dfrac{2b}{b-3} - \dfrac{b-9}{b-3}$ $\dfrac{b+9}{b-3}$

11. $\dfrac{5c}{c+6} + \dfrac{30}{c+6}$ 5

12. $\dfrac{12}{2+d} + \dfrac{6d}{2+d}$ 6

13. $\dfrac{5}{t-8} - \dfrac{2t+1}{t-8}$ $\dfrac{-2(t-2)}{t-8}$

14. $\dfrac{7p+1}{2p+1} - \dfrac{p-4}{2p+1}$ $\dfrac{6p+5}{2p+1}$

15. $\dfrac{9x^2}{3x-7} - \dfrac{49}{3x-7}$ $3x+7$

16. $\dfrac{4w^2}{2w-1} - \dfrac{1}{2w-1}$ $2w+1$

17. $\dfrac{m^2}{m+5} + \dfrac{10m+25}{m+5}$ $m+5$

18. $\dfrac{k^2}{k-3} - \dfrac{6k-9}{k-3}$ $k-3$

19. $\dfrac{2a}{a+2} + \dfrac{4}{a+2}$ 2

20. $\dfrac{5b}{b+4} + \dfrac{20}{b+4}$ 5

21. $\dfrac{x^2}{x+5} - \dfrac{25}{x+5}$ $x-5$

22. $\dfrac{y^2}{y-7} - \dfrac{49}{y-7}$ $y+7$

23. $\dfrac{r}{r^2 + 3r + 2} + \dfrac{2}{r^2 + 3r + 2}$ $\dfrac{1}{r + 1}$

24. $\dfrac{x}{x^2 - x - 12} - \dfrac{4}{x^2 - x - 12}$ $\dfrac{1}{x + 3}$

25. $\dfrac{1}{3y^2 + 22y + 7} - \dfrac{-3y}{3y^2 + 22y + 7}$ $\dfrac{1}{y + 7}$

26. $\dfrac{5}{2x^2 + 13x + 20} + \dfrac{2x}{2x^2 + 13x + 20}$ $\dfrac{1}{x + 4}$

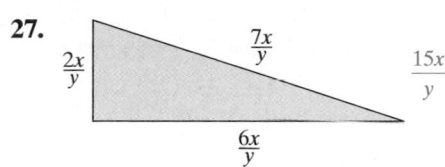 For Exercises 27–28, find an expression that represents the perimeter of the figure (assume that $x > 0$, $y > 0$, and $t > 0$).

27.

28.

Concept 2: Addition and Subtraction of Rational Expressions with Different Denominators

For Exercises 29–70, add or subtract the expressions with unlike denominators as indicated. **(See Examples 3–7.)**

29. $\dfrac{5}{4} + \dfrac{3}{2a}$ $\dfrac{5a + 6}{4a}$

30. $\dfrac{11}{6p} + \dfrac{-7}{4p}$ $\dfrac{1}{12p}$

31. $\dfrac{4}{5xy^3} + \dfrac{2x}{15y^2}$ $\dfrac{2(6 + x^2y)}{15xy^3}$

32. $\dfrac{5}{3a^2b} - \dfrac{7}{6b^2}$ $\dfrac{10b - 7a^2}{6a^2b^2}$

33. $\dfrac{2}{s^3t^3} - \dfrac{3}{s^4t}$ $\dfrac{2s - 3t^2}{s^4t^3}$

34. $\dfrac{1}{p^2q} - \dfrac{2}{pq^3}$ $\dfrac{q^2 - 2p}{p^2q^3}$

35. $\dfrac{z}{3z - 9} - \dfrac{z - 2}{z - 3}$ $-\dfrac{2}{3}$

36. $\dfrac{3w - 8}{2w - 4} - \dfrac{w - 3}{w - 2}$ $\dfrac{1}{2}$

37. $\dfrac{5}{a + 1} + \dfrac{4}{3a + 3}$ $\dfrac{19}{3(a + 1)}$

38. $-\dfrac{2}{c - 4} + \dfrac{1}{5c - 20}$ $\dfrac{11}{5(c - 4)}$

39. $\dfrac{k}{k^2 - 9} - \dfrac{4}{k - 3}$ $\dfrac{-3(k + 4)}{(k - 3)(k + 3)}$

40. $\dfrac{7}{h + 2} + \dfrac{2h - 3}{h^2 - 4}$ $\dfrac{9h - 17}{(h - 2)(h + 2)}$

41. $\dfrac{3a - 7}{6a + 10} - \dfrac{10}{3a^2 + 5a}$ $\dfrac{a - 4}{2a}$

42. $\dfrac{k + 2}{8k} - \dfrac{3 - k}{12k}$ $\dfrac{5}{24}$

43. $\dfrac{x}{x - 4} + \dfrac{3}{x + 1}$ $\dfrac{(x + 6)(x - 2)}{(x - 4)(x + 1)}$

44. $\dfrac{4}{y - 3} + \dfrac{y}{y - 5}$ $\dfrac{(y + 5)(y - 4)}{(y - 5)(y - 3)}$

45. $\dfrac{6a}{a^2 - b^2} + \dfrac{2a}{a^2 + ab}$ $\dfrac{2(4a - b)}{(a + b)(a - b)}$

46. $\dfrac{7x}{x^2 + 2xy + y^2} + \dfrac{3x}{x^2 + xy}$ $\dfrac{10x + 3y}{(x + y)^2}$

47. $\dfrac{p}{3} - \dfrac{4p - 1}{-3}$ $\dfrac{5p - 1}{3}$ or $\dfrac{-5p + 1}{-3}$

48. $\dfrac{r}{7} - \dfrac{r - 5}{-7}$ $\dfrac{2r - 5}{7}$ or $\dfrac{-2r + 5}{-7}$

49. $\dfrac{4n}{n - 8} - \dfrac{2n - 1}{8 - n}$ $\dfrac{6n - 1}{n - 8}$ or $\dfrac{-6n + 1}{8 - n}$

50. $\dfrac{m}{m - 2} - \dfrac{3m + 1}{2 - m}$ $\dfrac{4m + 1}{m - 2}$ or $\dfrac{-4m - 1}{2 - m}$

51. $\dfrac{5}{x} + \dfrac{3}{x + 2}$ $\dfrac{2(4x + 5)}{x(x + 2)}$

52. $\dfrac{6}{y - 1} + \dfrac{9}{y}$ $\dfrac{3(5y - 3)}{y(y - 1)}$

53. $\dfrac{5}{p - 3} - \dfrac{2}{p - 1}$ $\dfrac{3p + 1}{(p - 3)(p - 1)}$

54. $\dfrac{1}{7x} + \dfrac{5}{2y^2}$ $\dfrac{2y^2 + 35x}{14xy^2}$

55. $\dfrac{y}{4y + 2} + \dfrac{3y}{6y + 3}$ $\dfrac{3y}{2(2y + 1)}$

56. $\dfrac{4}{q^2 - 2q} - \dfrac{5}{3q - 6}$ $\dfrac{12 - 5q}{3q(q - 2)}$

57. $\dfrac{4w}{w^2 + 2w - 3} + \dfrac{2}{1 - w}$ $\dfrac{2(w - 3)}{(w + 3)(w - 1)}$

58. $\dfrac{z - 23}{z^2 - z - 20} - \dfrac{2}{5 - z}$ $\dfrac{3}{z + 4}$

59. $\dfrac{3a - 8}{a^2 - 5a + 6} + \dfrac{a + 2}{a^2 - 6a + 8}$ $\dfrac{4a - 13}{(a - 3)(a - 4)}$

60. $\dfrac{3b + 5}{b^2 + 4b + 3} + \dfrac{-b + 5}{b^2 + 2b - 3}$ $\dfrac{2b}{(b + 1)(b - 1)}$

61. $\dfrac{3x}{x^2 + x - 6} + \dfrac{x}{x^2 + 5x + 6}$ $\dfrac{4x(x + 1)}{(x + 3)(x - 2)(x + 2)}$

62. $\dfrac{x}{x^2 + 5x + 4} - \dfrac{2x}{x^2 - 2x - 3}$ $\dfrac{-x(x + 11)}{(x + 1)(x + 4)(x - 3)}$

63. $\dfrac{y}{2y^2 - y - 1} - \dfrac{3y}{2y^2 - 7y - 4}$ $\dfrac{-y}{(y - 4)(y - 1)}$

64. $\dfrac{2}{5y^2 + 4y - 1} + \dfrac{3}{5y^2 - 11y + 2}$ $\dfrac{1}{(y + 1)(y - 2)}$

65. $\dfrac{3}{2p - 1} - \dfrac{4p + 4}{4p^2 - 1}$ $\dfrac{1}{2p + 1}$

66. $\dfrac{1}{3q - 2} - \dfrac{6q + 4}{9q^2 - 4}$ $\dfrac{-1}{3q - 2}$

67. $\dfrac{1}{m + n} + \dfrac{1}{m - n} + \dfrac{2n}{m^2 - n^2}$ $\dfrac{2}{m - n}$

68. $\dfrac{x}{x + y} - \dfrac{2xy}{x^2 - y^2} + \dfrac{y}{x - y}$ $\dfrac{x - y}{x + y}$

69. $\dfrac{2}{a + b} + \dfrac{2}{a - b} - \dfrac{4a}{a^2 - b^2}$ 0

70. $\dfrac{-2x}{x^2 - y^2} + \dfrac{1}{x + y} - \dfrac{1}{x - y}$ $\dfrac{-2}{x - y}$

For Exercises 71–72, find an expression that represents the perimeter of the figure (assume that $x > 0$ and $t > 0$).

71.

$\dfrac{2}{x + 3}$ $\dfrac{2(3x + 7)}{(x + 3)(x + 2)}$

$\dfrac{1}{x + 2}$

72.

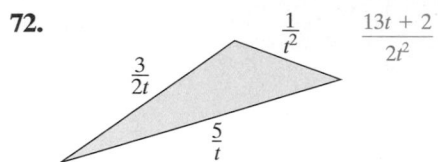

$\dfrac{1}{t^2}$ $\dfrac{13t + 2}{2t^2}$

$\dfrac{3}{2t}$ $\dfrac{5}{t}$

Concept 3: Using Rational Expressions in Translations

73. Let a number be represented by n. Write the reciprocal of n. $\dfrac{1}{n}$

74. Write the reciprocal of the sum of a number and 6. $\dfrac{1}{n + 6}$

75. Write the quotient of 5 and the sum of a number and 2. $\dfrac{5}{n + 2}$

76. Write the quotient of 12 and p. $\dfrac{12}{p}$

For Exercises 77–80, translate the English phrases into algebraic expressions. Then simplify by combining the rational expressions. **(See Example 8.)**

77. The sum of a number and the quantity seven times the reciprocal of the number. $n + \left(7 \cdot \dfrac{1}{n}\right); \dfrac{n^2 + 7}{n}$

78. The sum of a number and the quantity five times the reciprocal of the number. $n + \left(5 \cdot \dfrac{1}{n}\right); \dfrac{n^2 + 5}{n}$

79. The difference of the reciprocal of n and the quotient of 2 and n. $\dfrac{1}{n} - \dfrac{2}{n}; -\dfrac{1}{n}$

80. The difference of the reciprocal of m and the quotient of $3m$ and 7. $\dfrac{1}{m} - \dfrac{3m}{7}; \dfrac{7 - 3m^2}{7m}$

Expanding Your Skills

For Exercises 81–86, perform the indicated operations.

81. $\dfrac{-3}{w^3 + 27} - \dfrac{1}{w^2 - 9}$ $\dfrac{-w^2}{(w + 3)(w - 3)(w^2 - 3w + 9)}$

82. $\dfrac{m}{m^3 - 1} + \dfrac{1}{(m - 1)^2}$ $\dfrac{2m^2 + 1}{(m - 1)^2(m^2 + m + 1)}$

83. $\dfrac{2p}{p^2 + 5p + 6} - \dfrac{p + 1}{p^2 + 2p - 3} + \dfrac{3}{p^2 + p - 2}$ $\dfrac{p^2 - 2p + 7}{(p + 2)(p + 3)(p - 1)}$

84. $\dfrac{3t}{8t^2 + 2t - 1} - \dfrac{5t}{2t^2 - 9t - 5} + \dfrac{2}{4t^2 - 21t + 5}$ $\dfrac{-17t^2 - 6t + 2}{(2t + 1)(4t - 1)(t - 5)}$

85. $\dfrac{3m}{m^2 + 3m - 10} + \dfrac{5}{4 - 2m} - \dfrac{1}{m + 5}$ $\dfrac{-m - 21}{2(m + 5)(m - 2)}$ or $\dfrac{m + 21}{2(m + 5)(2 - m)}$

86. $\dfrac{2n}{3n^2 - 8n - 3} + \dfrac{1}{6 - 2n} - \dfrac{3}{3n + 1}$ $\dfrac{-5n + 17}{2(3n + 1)(n - 3)}$ or $\dfrac{5n - 17}{2(3n + 1)(3 - n)}$

For Exercises 87–90, simplify by applying the order of operations.

87. $\left(\dfrac{2}{k + 1} + 3\right)\left(\dfrac{k + 1}{4k + 7}\right)$ $\dfrac{3k + 5}{4k + 7}$

88. $\left(\dfrac{p + 1}{3p + 4}\right)\left(\dfrac{1}{p + 1} + 2\right)$ $\dfrac{2p + 3}{3p + 4}$

89. $\left(\dfrac{1}{10a} - \dfrac{b}{10a^2}\right) \div \left(\dfrac{1}{10} - \dfrac{b}{10a}\right)$ $\dfrac{1}{a}$

90. $\left(\dfrac{1}{2m} + \dfrac{n}{2m^2}\right) \div \left(\dfrac{1}{4} + \dfrac{n}{4m}\right)$ $\dfrac{2}{m}$

 Writing   Translating Expression   Geometry   Scientific Calculator   Video   NS&E

Problem Recognition Exercises

Operations on Rational Expressions

In Sections 7.1–7.4, we learned how to simplify, add, subtract, multiply, and divide rational expressions. The procedure for each operation is different, and it takes considerable practice to determine the correct method to apply for a given problem. The following review exercises give you the opportunity to practice the specific techniques for simplifying rational expressions.

For Exercises 1–20, perform any indicated operations, and simplify the expression.

1. $\dfrac{5}{3x+1} - \dfrac{2x-4}{3x+1}$ $\dfrac{-2x+9}{3x+1}$

2. $\dfrac{\dfrac{w+1}{w^2-16}}{\dfrac{w+1}{w+4}}$ $\dfrac{1}{w-4}$

3. $\dfrac{3}{y} \cdot \dfrac{y^2-5y}{6y-9}$ $\dfrac{y-5}{2y-3}$

4. $\dfrac{-1}{x+3} + \dfrac{2}{2x-1}$ $\dfrac{7}{(x+3)(2x-1)}$

5. $\dfrac{x-9}{9x-x^2}$ $-\dfrac{1}{x}$

6. $\dfrac{1}{p} - \dfrac{3}{p^2+3p} + \dfrac{p}{3p+9}$ $\dfrac{1}{3}$

7. $\dfrac{c^2+5c+6}{c^2+c-2} \div \dfrac{c}{c-1}$ $\dfrac{c+3}{c}$

8. $\dfrac{2x^2-5x-3}{x^2-9} \cdot \dfrac{x^2+6x+9}{10x+5}$ $\dfrac{x+3}{5}$

9. $\dfrac{6a^2b^3}{72ab^7c}$ $\dfrac{a}{12b^4c}$

10. $\dfrac{2a}{a+b} - \dfrac{b}{a-b} - \dfrac{-4ab}{a^2-b^2}$ $\dfrac{2a-b}{a-b}$

11. $\dfrac{p^2+10pq+25q^2}{p^2+6pq+5q^2} \div \dfrac{10p+50q}{2p^2-2q^2}$ $\dfrac{p-q}{5}$

12. $\dfrac{3k-8}{k-5} + \dfrac{k-12}{k-5}$ 4

13. $\dfrac{20x^2+10x}{4x^3+4x^2+x}$ $\dfrac{10}{2x+1}$

14. $\dfrac{w^2-81}{w^2+10w+9} \cdot \dfrac{w^2+w+2zw+2z}{w^2-9w+zw-9z}$ $\dfrac{w+2z}{w+z}$

15. $\dfrac{8x^2-18x-5}{4x^2-25} \div \dfrac{4x^2-11x-3}{3x-9}$ $\dfrac{3}{2x+5}$

16. $\dfrac{xy+7x+5y+35}{x^2+ax+5x+5a}$ $\dfrac{y+7}{x+a}$

17. $\dfrac{a}{a^2-9} - \dfrac{3}{6a-18}$ $\dfrac{1}{2(a+3)}$

18. $\dfrac{4}{y^2-36} + \dfrac{2}{y^2-4y-12}$ $\dfrac{2(3y+10)}{(y-6)(y+6)(y+2)}$

19. $(t^2+5t-24)\left(\dfrac{t+8}{t-3}\right)$ $(t+8)^2$

20. $\dfrac{6b^2-7b-10}{b-2}$ $6b+5$

Section 7.5	Complex Fractions

1. Simplifying Complex Fractions (Method I)

A **complex fraction** is a fraction whose numerator or denominator contains one or more rational expressions. For example,

$$\dfrac{\dfrac{1}{ab}}{\dfrac{2}{b}} \qquad \text{and} \qquad \dfrac{1 + \dfrac{3}{4} - \dfrac{1}{6}}{\dfrac{1}{2} + \dfrac{1}{3}}$$

are complex fractions.

Two methods will be presented to simplify complex fractions. The first method (Method I) follows the order of operations to simplify the numerator and denominator separately before dividing. The process is summarized as follows.

> **PROCEDURE** Simplifying a Complex Fraction (Method I)
>
> **Step 1** Add or subtract expressions in the numerator to form a single fraction. Add or subtract expressions in the denominator to form a single fraction.
> **Step 2** Divide the rational expressions from step 1 by multiplying the numerator of the complex fraction by the reciprocal of the denominator of the complex fraction.
> **Step 3** Simplify to lowest terms if possible.

Classroom Example: p. 526, Exercise 12

Example 1	Simplifying a Complex Fraction (Method I)

Simplify the expression. $\dfrac{\dfrac{1}{ab}}{\dfrac{2}{b}}$

Solution:

Step 1: The numerator and denominator of the complex fraction are already single fractions.

$$\dfrac{\dfrac{1}{ab}}{\dfrac{2}{b}} \longleftarrow \text{This fraction bar denotes division } (\div).$$

$$= \dfrac{1}{ab} \div \dfrac{2}{b}$$

$$= \dfrac{1}{ab} \cdot \dfrac{b}{2} \qquad \textbf{Step 2:} \text{ Multiply the numerator of the complex fraction by the reciprocal of } \tfrac{2}{b}, \text{ which is } \tfrac{b}{2}.$$

$$= \dfrac{1}{a\cancel{b}} \cdot \dfrac{\overset{1}{\cancel{b}}}{2} \qquad \textbf{Step 3:} \text{ Reduce common factors and simplify.}$$

$$= \dfrac{1}{2a}$$

Skill Practice Simplify the expression.

1. $\dfrac{\dfrac{6x}{y}}{\dfrac{9}{2y}}$

Sometimes it is necessary to simplify the numerator and denominator of a complex fraction before the division can be performed. This is illustrated in Example 2.

Example 2 Simplifying a Complex Fraction (Method I)

Classroom Example: p. 526, Exercise 16

Simplify the expression. $\dfrac{1 + \dfrac{3}{4} - \dfrac{1}{6}}{\dfrac{1}{2} + \dfrac{1}{3}}$

Solution:

$\dfrac{1 + \dfrac{3}{4} - \dfrac{1}{6}}{\dfrac{1}{2} + \dfrac{1}{3}}$

Step 1: Combine fractions in the numerator and denominator separately.

$= \dfrac{1 \cdot \dfrac{12}{12} + \dfrac{3}{4} \cdot \dfrac{3}{3} - \dfrac{1}{6} \cdot \dfrac{2}{2}}{\dfrac{1}{2} \cdot \dfrac{3}{3} + \dfrac{1}{3} \cdot \dfrac{2}{2}}$

The LCD in the numerator is 12.
The LCD in the denominator is 6.

$= \dfrac{\dfrac{12}{12} + \dfrac{9}{12} - \dfrac{2}{12}}{\dfrac{3}{6} + \dfrac{2}{6}}$

$= \dfrac{\dfrac{19}{12}}{\dfrac{5}{6}}$

Form a single fraction in the numerator and in the denominator.

$= \dfrac{19}{12} \cdot \dfrac{6}{5}$

Step 2: Multiply by the reciprocal of $\frac{5}{6}$, which is $\frac{6}{5}$.

$= \dfrac{19 \cdot \overset{1}{6}}{\underset{2}{12} \cdot 5}$

Step 3: Reduce and simplify.

$= \dfrac{19}{10}$

Skill Practice Simplify the expression.

2. $\dfrac{\dfrac{3}{4} - \dfrac{1}{6} + 2}{\dfrac{1}{3} + \dfrac{1}{2}}$

Answers
1. $\dfrac{4x}{3}$ 2. $\dfrac{31}{10}$

Classroom Example: p. 526,
Exercise 24

Example 3 Simplifying a Complex Fraction (Method I)

Simplify the expression. $\dfrac{\dfrac{1}{x} + \dfrac{1}{y}}{x - \dfrac{y^2}{x}}$

Solution:

$\dfrac{\dfrac{1}{x} + \dfrac{1}{y}}{x - \dfrac{y^2}{x}}$

The LCD in the numerator is xy. The LCD in the denominator is x.

$= \dfrac{\dfrac{1 \cdot y}{x \cdot y} + \dfrac{1 \cdot x}{y \cdot x}}{\dfrac{x \cdot x}{1 \cdot x} - \dfrac{y^2}{x}}$

Rewrite the expressions using common denominators.

$= \dfrac{\dfrac{y}{xy} + \dfrac{x}{xy}}{\dfrac{x^2}{x} - \dfrac{y^2}{x}}$

$= \dfrac{\dfrac{y + x}{xy}}{\dfrac{x^2 - y^2}{x}}$

Form single fractions in the numerator and denominator.

$= \dfrac{y + x}{xy} \cdot \dfrac{x}{x^2 - y^2}$

Multiply by the reciprocal of the denominator.

$= \dfrac{\overset{1}{\cancel{(y + x)}} \cdot \overset{1}{x}}{xy\cancel{(x + y)}(x - y)}$

Factor and reduce. Note that $(y + x) = (x + y)$.

$= \dfrac{1}{y(x - y)}$

Simplify.

Skill Practice Simplify the expression.

3. $\dfrac{1 - \dfrac{1}{p}}{\dfrac{p}{w} + \dfrac{w}{p}}$

2. Simplifying Complex Fractions (Method II)

We will now simplify the expressions from Examples 2 and 3 again using a second method to simplify complex fractions (Method II). Recall that multiplying the numerator and denominator of a rational expression by the same quantity does not change the value of the expression because we are multiplying by a number equivalent to 1. This is the basis for Method II.

Answer

3. $\dfrac{w(p - 1)}{p^2 + w^2}$

PROCEDURE Simplifying a Complex Fraction (Method II)

Step 1 Multiply the numerator and denominator of the complex fraction by the LCD of *all* individual fractions within the expression.

Step 2 Apply the distributive property, and simplify the numerator and denominator.

Step 3 Simplify to lowest terms if possible.

Example 4 Simplifying a Complex Fraction (Method II)

Classroom Example: p. 526, Exercise 16

Simplify the expression.

$$\dfrac{1 + \dfrac{3}{4} - \dfrac{1}{6}}{\dfrac{1}{2} + \dfrac{1}{3}}$$

Solution:

$$\dfrac{1 + \dfrac{3}{4} - \dfrac{1}{6}}{\dfrac{1}{2} + \dfrac{1}{3}}$$

The LCD of the expressions $1, \frac{3}{4}, \frac{1}{6}, \frac{1}{2},$ and $\frac{1}{3}$ is 12.

TIP: In step 1, we are multiplying the original expression by $\frac{12}{12}$, which equals 1.

$$= \dfrac{12\left(1 + \dfrac{3}{4} - \dfrac{1}{6}\right)}{12\left(\dfrac{1}{2} + \dfrac{1}{3}\right)}$$

Step 1: Multiply the numerator and denominator of the complex fraction by 12.

$$= \dfrac{12 \cdot 1 + 12 \cdot \dfrac{3}{4} - 12 \cdot \dfrac{1}{6}}{12 \cdot \dfrac{1}{2} + 12 \cdot \dfrac{1}{3}}$$

Step 2: Apply the distributive property.

$$= \dfrac{12 \cdot 1 + \overset{3}{\cancel{12}} \cdot \dfrac{3}{\cancel{4}} - \overset{2}{\cancel{12}} \cdot \dfrac{1}{\cancel{6}}}{\underset{6}{\cancel{12}} \cdot \dfrac{1}{\cancel{2}} + \underset{4}{\cancel{12}} \cdot \dfrac{1}{\cancel{3}}}$$

Simplify each term.

$$= \dfrac{12 + 9 - 2}{6 + 4}$$

$$= \dfrac{19}{10}$$

Step 3: Simplify.

Skill Practice Simplify the expression.

4. $\dfrac{1 - \dfrac{3}{5}}{\dfrac{1}{4} - \dfrac{7}{10} + 1}$

Answer

4. $\dfrac{8}{11}$

Classroom Example: p. 526, Exercise 26

Example 5 Simplifying a Complex Fraction (Method II)

Simplify the expression. $\dfrac{\dfrac{1}{x} + \dfrac{1}{y}}{x - \dfrac{y^2}{x}}$

Solution:

$\dfrac{\dfrac{1}{x} + \dfrac{1}{y}}{x - \dfrac{y^2}{x}}$　　　The LCD of the expressions $\frac{1}{x}, \frac{1}{y}, x$, and $\frac{y^2}{x}$ is xy.

$= \dfrac{xy\left(\dfrac{1}{x} + \dfrac{1}{y}\right)}{xy\left(x - \dfrac{y^2}{x}\right)}$　　　**Step 1:** Multiply numerator and denominator of the complex fraction by xy.

$= \dfrac{xy \cdot \dfrac{1}{x} + xy \cdot \dfrac{1}{y}}{xy \cdot x - xy \cdot \dfrac{y^2}{x}}$　　　**Step 2:** Apply the distributive property, and simplify each term.

$= \dfrac{y + x}{x^2 y - y^3}$

$= \dfrac{y + x}{y(x^2 - y^2)}$　　　**Step 3:** Factor completely, and reduce common factors.

$= \dfrac{\overset{1}{\cancel{y + x}}}{y\cancel{(x + y)}(x - y)}$　　　Note that $(y + x) = (x + y)$.

$= \dfrac{1}{y(x - y)}$

Skill Practice Simplify the expression.

5. $\dfrac{\dfrac{z}{3} - \dfrac{3}{z}}{1 + \dfrac{3}{z}}$

Answer

5. $\dfrac{z - 3}{3}$

Example 6 **Simplifying a Complex Fraction (Method II)**

Simplify the expression.
$$\frac{\dfrac{1}{k+1} - 1}{\dfrac{1}{k+1} + 1}$$

Classroom Example: p. 526, Exercise 28

Solution:

$$\frac{\dfrac{1}{k+1} - 1}{\dfrac{1}{k+1} + 1}$$

The LCD of $\dfrac{1}{k+1}$ and 1 is $(k+1)$.

$$= \frac{(k+1)\left(\dfrac{1}{k+1} - 1\right)}{(k+1)\left(\dfrac{1}{k+1} + 1\right)}$$

Step 1: Multiply numerator and denominator of the complex fraction by $(k+1)$.

$$= \frac{(k+1) \cdot \dfrac{1}{(k+1)} - (k+1) \cdot 1}{(k+1) \cdot \dfrac{1}{(k+1)} + (k+1) \cdot 1}$$

Step 2: Apply the distributive property.

$$= \frac{1 - (k+1)}{1 + (k+1)}$$

Simplify.

$$= \frac{1 - k - 1}{1 + k + 1}$$

$$= \frac{-k}{k+2}$$

Step 3: The expression is already in lowest terms.

Skill Practice Simplify the expression.

6. $\dfrac{\dfrac{4}{p-3} + 1}{1 + \dfrac{2}{p-3}}$

Answer

6. $\dfrac{p+1}{p-1}$

Section 7.5 Practice Exercises

Study Skills Exercise

1. Define the key term **complex fraction**.

Review Exercises

For Exercises 2–3, simplify the expression.

2. $\dfrac{y(2y+9)}{y^2(2y+9)}$ $\dfrac{1}{y}$

3. $\dfrac{a+5}{2a^2 + 7a - 15}$ $\dfrac{1}{2a-3}$

 Writing   Translating Expression   Geometry   Scientific Calculator   Video   NS&E

For Exercises 4–6, perform the indicated operations.

4. $\dfrac{2}{w-2} + \dfrac{3}{w}$ $\quad \dfrac{5w-6}{w(w-2)}$

5. $\dfrac{6}{5} - \dfrac{3}{5k-10}$ $\quad \dfrac{3(2k-5)}{5(k-2)}$

6. $\dfrac{x^2-2xy+y^2}{x^4-y^4} \div \dfrac{3x^2y-3xy^2}{x^2+y^2}$

$\dfrac{1}{3xy(x+y)}$

Concepts 1–2: Simplifying Complex Fractions (Methods I and II)

For Exercises 7–34, simplify the complex fractions using either method. **(See Examples 1–6.)**

7. $\dfrac{\frac{7}{18y}}{\frac{2}{9}}$ $\quad \dfrac{7}{4y}$

8. $\dfrac{\frac{a^2}{2a-3}}{\frac{5a}{8a-12}}$ $\quad \dfrac{4a}{5}$

9. $\dfrac{\frac{3x+2y}{2y}}{\frac{6x+4y}{2}}$ $\quad \dfrac{1}{2y}$

10. $\dfrac{\frac{2x-10}{4}}{\frac{x^2-5x}{3x}}$ $\quad \dfrac{3}{2}$

11. $\dfrac{\frac{8a^4b^3}{3c}}{\frac{a^7b^2}{9c}}$ $\quad \dfrac{24b}{a^3}$

12. $\dfrac{\frac{12x^2}{5y}}{\frac{8x^6}{9y^2}}$ $\quad \dfrac{27y}{10x^4}$

13. $\dfrac{\frac{4r^3s}{t^5}}{\frac{2s^7}{r^2t^9}}$ $\quad \dfrac{2r^5t^4}{s^6}$

14. $\dfrac{\frac{5p^4q}{w^4}}{\frac{10p^2}{qw^2}}$ $\quad \dfrac{p^2q^2}{2w^2}$

15. $\dfrac{\frac{1}{8}+\frac{4}{3}}{\frac{1}{2}-\frac{5}{12}}$ $\quad \dfrac{35}{2}$

16. $\dfrac{\frac{8}{9}-\frac{1}{3}}{\frac{7}{6}+\frac{1}{9}}$ $\quad \dfrac{10}{23}$

 17. $\dfrac{\frac{1}{h}+\frac{1}{k}}{\frac{1}{hk}}$ $\quad k+h$

18. $\dfrac{\frac{1}{b}+1}{\frac{1}{b}}$ $\quad 1+b$

19. $\dfrac{\frac{n+1}{n^2-9}}{\frac{2}{n+3}}$ $\quad \dfrac{n+1}{2(n-3)}$

20. $\dfrac{\frac{5}{k-5}}{\frac{k+1}{k^2-25}}$ $\quad \dfrac{5(k+5)}{k+1}$

 21. $\dfrac{2+\frac{1}{x}}{4+\frac{1}{x}}$ $\quad \dfrac{2x+1}{4x+1}$

22. $\dfrac{6+\frac{6}{k}}{1+\frac{1}{k}}$ $\quad 6$

23. $\dfrac{\frac{m}{7}-\frac{7}{m}}{\frac{1}{7}+\frac{1}{m}}$ $\quad m-7$

24. $\dfrac{\frac{2}{p}+\frac{p}{2}}{\frac{p}{3}-\frac{3}{p}}$ $\quad \dfrac{3(4+p^2)}{2(p-3)(p+3)}$

25. $\dfrac{\frac{1}{5}-\frac{1}{y}}{\frac{7}{10}+\frac{1}{y^2}}$ $\quad \dfrac{2y(y-5)}{7y^2+10}$

26. $\dfrac{\frac{1}{m^2}+\frac{2}{3}}{\frac{1}{m}-\frac{5}{6}}$ $\quad \dfrac{2(3+2m^2)}{m(6-5m)}$

 27. $\dfrac{\frac{8}{a+4}+2}{\frac{12}{a+4}-2}$ $\quad \dfrac{a+8}{a-2}$ or $\dfrac{a+8}{2-a}$

28. $\dfrac{\frac{2}{w+1}+3}{\frac{3}{w+1}+4}$ $\quad \dfrac{3w+5}{4w+7}$

29. $\dfrac{1-\frac{4}{t^2}}{1-\frac{2}{t}-\frac{8}{t^2}}$ $\quad \dfrac{t-2}{t-4}$

30. $\dfrac{1-\frac{9}{p^2}}{1-\frac{1}{p}-\frac{6}{p^2}}$ $\quad \dfrac{p+3}{p+2}$

31. $\dfrac{t+4+\frac{3}{t}}{t-4-\frac{5}{t}}$ $\quad \dfrac{t+3}{t-5}$

32. $\dfrac{\frac{9}{4m}+\frac{9}{2m^2}}{\frac{3}{2}+\frac{3}{m}}$ $\quad \dfrac{3}{2m}$

33. $\dfrac{\frac{1}{k-6}-1}{\frac{2}{k-6}-2}$ $\quad \dfrac{1}{2}$

34. $\dfrac{\frac{3}{y-3}+4}{8+\frac{6}{y-3}}$ $\quad \dfrac{1}{2}$

 For Exercises 35–38, write the English phrases as algebraic expressions. Then simplify the expressions.

35. The sum of one-half and two-thirds, divided by five. $\dfrac{\frac{1}{2}+\frac{2}{3}}{5}; \dfrac{7}{30}$

36. The quotient of ten and the difference of two-fifths and one-fourth. $\dfrac{10}{\frac{2}{5}-\frac{1}{4}}; \dfrac{200}{3}$

37. The quotient of three and the sum of two-thirds and three-fourths. $\dfrac{3}{\frac{2}{3}+\frac{3}{4}}; \dfrac{36}{17}$

38. The difference of three-fifths and one-half, divided by four. $\dfrac{\frac{3}{5}-\frac{1}{2}}{4}; \dfrac{1}{40}$

39. In electronics, resistors oppose the flow of current. For two resistors in parallel, the total resistance is given by

$$R = \frac{1}{\dfrac{1}{R_1} + \dfrac{1}{R_2}}$$

a. Find the total resistance if $R_1 = 2 \ \Omega$ (ohms) and $R_2 = 3 \ \Omega$. $\frac{6}{5}\Omega$

b. Find the total resistance if $R_1 = 10 \ \Omega$ and $R_2 = 15 \ \Omega$. $6 \ \Omega$

40. Suppose that Joëlle makes a round trip to a location that is d miles away. If the average rate going to the location is r_1 and the average rate on the return trip is given by r_2, the average rate of the entire trip, R, is given by

$$R = \frac{2d}{\dfrac{d}{r_1} + \dfrac{d}{r_2}}$$

a. Find the average rate of a trip to a destination 30 mi away when the average rate going there was 60 mph and the average rate returning home was 45 mph. (Round to the nearest tenth of a mile per hour.)
51.4 mph average

b. Find the average rate of a trip to a destination that is 50 mi away if the driver travels at the same rates as in part (a). (Round to the nearest tenth of a mile per hour.)
51.4 mph

c. Compare your answers from parts (a) and (b) and explain the results in the context of the problem.
Because the rates going to and leaving from the destination are the same, the average rate is unchanged. The average rate is not affected by the distance traveled.

Expanding Your Skills

For Exercises 41–48, simplify the complex fractions using either method.

41. $\dfrac{2x^{-1} + 8y^{-1}}{4x^{-1}}$ $\frac{y + 4x}{2y}$ **42.** $\dfrac{6a^{-1} + 4b^{-1}}{8b^{-1}}$ $\frac{3b + 2a}{4a}$ **43.** $\dfrac{(mn)^{-2}}{m^{-2} + n^{-2}}$ $\frac{1}{n^2 + m^2}$ **44.** $\dfrac{(xy)^{-1}}{2x^{-1} + 3y^{-1}}$ $\frac{1}{2y + 3x}$

$\left(Hint: 2x^{-1} = \dfrac{2}{x} \right)$

45. $\dfrac{\dfrac{1}{z^2 - 9} + \dfrac{2}{z + 3}}{\dfrac{3}{z - 3}}$ $\frac{2z - 5}{3(z + 3)}$ **46.** $\dfrac{\dfrac{5}{w^2 - 25} - \dfrac{3}{w + 5}}{\dfrac{4}{w - 5}}$ $\frac{-3w + 20}{4(w + 5)}$ **47.** $\dfrac{\dfrac{2}{x - 1} + 2}{\dfrac{2}{x + 1} - 2}$ $-\frac{x + 1}{x - 1}$ or $\frac{x + 1}{1 - x}$ **48.** $\dfrac{\dfrac{1}{y - 3} + 1}{\dfrac{2}{y + 3} - 1}$ $-\frac{(y + 3)(y - 2)}{(y + 1)(y - 3)}$

For Exercises 49–50, simplify the complex fractions. (*Hint:* Use the order of operations and begin with the fraction on the lower right.)

49. $1 + \dfrac{1}{1 + 1}$ $\frac{3}{2}$

50. $1 + \dfrac{1}{1 + \dfrac{1}{1 + 1}}$ $\frac{5}{3}$

Rational Equations

Section 7.6

1. Introduction to Rational Equations

Thus far we have studied two specific types of equations in one variable: linear equations and quadratic equations. Recall,

$ax + b = 0$, where $a \neq 0$, is a **linear equation**

$ax^2 + bx + c = 0$, where $a \neq 0$, is a **quadratic equation**.

Concepts

1. **Introduction to Rational Equations**
2. **Solving Rational Equations**
3. **Solving Formulas Involving Rational Expressions**

We will now study another type of equation called a rational equation.

> **DEFINITION** Rational Equation
>
> An equation with one or more rational expressions is called a **rational equation**.

The following equations are rational equations:

$$\frac{y}{2} + \frac{y}{4} = 6 \qquad \frac{1}{x} + \frac{1}{3} = \frac{5}{6} \qquad \frac{6}{t^2 - 7t + 12} + \frac{2t}{t - 3} = \frac{3t}{t - 4}$$

To understand the process of solving a rational equation, first review the process of clearing fractions from Section 2.3. We can clear the fractions in an equation by multiplying both sides of the equation by the LCD of all terms.

Classroom Example: p. 536, Exercise 12

Example 1 Solving a Rational Equation

Solve. $\dfrac{y}{2} + \dfrac{y}{4} = 6$

Solution:

$\dfrac{y}{2} + \dfrac{y}{4} = 6$ The LCD of all terms in the equation is 4.

$4\left(\dfrac{y}{2} + \dfrac{y}{4}\right) = 4(6)$ Multiply both sides of the equation by 4 to clear fractions.

$\overset{2}{\cancel{4}} \cdot \dfrac{y}{2} + \overset{1}{\cancel{4}} \cdot \dfrac{y}{4} = 4(6)$ Apply the distributive property.

$2y + y = 24$ Clear fractions.

$3y = 24$ Solve the resulting equation (linear).

$y = 8$

Check: $\dfrac{y}{2} + \dfrac{y}{4} = 6$

$\dfrac{(8)}{2} + \dfrac{(8)}{4} \overset{?}{=} 6$

$4 + 2 \overset{?}{=} 6$

The solution set is $\{8\}$. $6 \overset{?}{=} 6$ ✔ (True)

Skill Practice Solve the equation.

1. $\dfrac{t}{5} - \dfrac{t}{4} = 2$

Answer
1. $\{-40\}$

2. Solving Rational Equations

The same process of clearing fractions is used to solve rational equations when variables are present in the denominator. Variables in the denominator make it necessary to take note of the restricted values.

Example 2 Solving a Rational Equation

Classroom Example: p. 536, Exercise 26

Solve the equation. $\dfrac{x+1}{x} + \dfrac{1}{3} = \dfrac{5}{6}$

Solution:

$$\frac{x+1}{x} + \frac{1}{3} = \frac{5}{6}$$

The LCD of all the expressions is $6x$. The restricted value is $x = 0$.

$$6x \cdot \left(\frac{x+1}{x} + \frac{1}{3}\right) = 6x \cdot \left(\frac{5}{6}\right)$$

Multiply by the LCD.

$$\overset{1}{6x} \cdot \left(\frac{x+1}{\not x}\right) + \overset{2}{\not 6x} \cdot \left(\frac{1}{\not 3}\right) = \overset{1}{\not 6x} \cdot \left(\frac{5}{\not 6}\right)$$

Apply the distributive property.

$$6(x+1) + 2x = 5x$$

Clear fractions.

$$6x + 6 + 2x = 5x$$

Solve the resulting equation.

$$8x + 6 = 5x$$

$$3x = -6$$

$$x = -2$$

-2 is not a restricted value.

Check: $\dfrac{x+1}{x} + \dfrac{1}{3} = \dfrac{5}{6}$

$$\frac{(-2)+1}{(-2)} + \frac{1}{3} \overset{?}{=} \frac{5}{6}$$

$$\frac{-1}{-2} + \frac{1}{3} \overset{?}{=} \frac{5}{6}$$

$$\frac{1}{2} + \frac{1}{3} \overset{?}{=} \frac{5}{6}$$

$$\frac{3}{6} + \frac{2}{6} \overset{?}{=} \frac{5}{6}$$

$$\frac{5}{6} \overset{?}{=} \frac{5}{6} \quad ✔ \text{ (True)}$$

The solution set is $\{-2\}$.

Skill Practice Solve the equation.

2. $\dfrac{3}{4} + \dfrac{5+a}{a} = \dfrac{1}{2}$

Answer

2. $\{-4\}$

Classroom Example: p. 537,
Exercise 32

Example 3 Solving a Rational Equation

Solve the equation. $\quad 1 + \dfrac{3a}{a-2} = \dfrac{6}{a-2}$

Solution:

$$1 + \dfrac{3a}{a-2} = \dfrac{6}{a-2}$$

The LCD of all the expressions is $a - 2$. The restricted value is $a = 2$.

$$(a-2)\left(1 + \dfrac{3a}{a-2}\right) = (a-2)\left(\dfrac{6}{a-2}\right)$$

Multiply by the LCD.

$$(a-2)1 + (a\overset{1}{-}2)\left(\dfrac{3a}{a-2}\right) = (a\overset{1}{-}2)\left(\dfrac{6}{a-2}\right)$$

Apply the distributive property.

$$a - 2 + 3a = 6$$

Solve the resulting equation (linear).

$$4a - 2 = 6$$

$$4a = 8$$

$$a = 2$$

2 is a restricted value.

Check: $\quad 1 + \dfrac{3a}{a-2} = \dfrac{6}{a-2}$

$$1 + \dfrac{3(2)}{(2)-2} \overset{?}{=} \dfrac{6}{(2)-2}$$

$$1 + \dfrac{6}{0} \overset{?}{=} \dfrac{6}{0}$$

The denominator is 0 when $a = 2$.

Instructor Note: Have students explain the difference between

$$\dfrac{2}{x+3} + \dfrac{5}{x+2}$$

and

$$\dfrac{2}{x+3} = \dfrac{5}{x+2}$$

Because the value $a = 2$ makes the denominator zero in one (or more) of the rational expressions within the equation, the equation is undefined for $a = 2$. No other potential solutions exist for the equation, therefore, the solution set is { }.

Skill Practice Solve the equation.

3. $\dfrac{x}{x+1} - 2 = \dfrac{-1}{x+1}$

Examples 1–3 show that the steps to solve a rational equation mirror the process of clearing fractions from Section 2.3. However, there is one significant difference. The solutions of a rational equation must not make the denominator equal to zero for any expression within the equation.

Answer

3. { } (The value −1 does not check.)

The steps to solve a rational equation are summarized as follows.

> **PROCEDURE** Solving a Rational Equation
>
> **Step 1** Factor the denominators of all rational expressions. Identify the restricted values.
> **Step 2** Identify the LCD of all expressions in the equation.
> **Step 3** Multiply both sides of the equation by the LCD.
> **Step 4** Solve the resulting equation.
> **Step 5** Check potential solutions in the original equation.

After multiplying by the LCD and then simplifying, the rational equation will be either a linear equation or higher degree equation.

Example 4 Solving a Rational Equation

Classroom Example: p. 536, Exercise 24

Solve the equation. $1 - \dfrac{4}{p} = -\dfrac{3}{p^2}$

Solution:

$$1 - \frac{4}{p} = -\frac{3}{p^2}$$

Step 1: The denominators are already factored. The restricted value is $p = 0$.

Step 2: The LCD of all expressions is p^2.

$$p^2\left(1 - \frac{4}{p}\right) = p^2\left(-\frac{3}{p^2}\right)$$

Step 3: Multiply by the LCD.

$$p^2(1) - \overset{p}{\cancel{p^2}}\left(\frac{4}{\cancel{p}}\right) = \overset{1}{\cancel{p^2}}\left(-\frac{3}{\cancel{p^2}}\right)$$

Apply the distributive property.

$$p^2 - 4p = -3$$

Step 4: Solve the resulting quadratic equation.

$$p^2 - 4p + 3 = 0$$

$$(p - 3)(p - 1) = 0$$

Set the equation equal to zero and factor.

$$p - 3 = 0 \quad \text{or} \quad p - 1 = 0$$

Set each factor equal to zero.

$$p = 3 \quad \text{or} \quad p = 1$$

Step 5: $\underline{\text{Check: } p = 3} \qquad \underline{\text{Check: } p = 1}$

3 and 1 are not restricted values.

$$1 - \frac{4}{p} = -\frac{3}{p^2} \qquad 1 - \frac{4}{p} = -\frac{3}{p^2}$$

$$1 - \frac{4}{(3)} \overset{?}{=} -\frac{3}{(3)^2} \qquad 1 - \frac{4}{(1)} \overset{?}{=} -\frac{3}{(1)^2}$$

$$\frac{3}{3} - \frac{4}{3} \overset{?}{=} -\frac{3}{9} \qquad 1 - 4 \overset{?}{=} -3$$

The solution set is $\{3, 1\}$.

$$-\frac{1}{3} \overset{?}{=} -\frac{1}{3} \;✔ \qquad -3 \overset{?}{=} -3 \;✔$$

Skill Practice Solve the equation.

4. $\dfrac{z}{2} - \dfrac{1}{2z} = \dfrac{12}{z}$

Answer

1. $\{5, -5\}$

Classroom Example: p. 537, Exercise 42

Example 5 Solving a Rational Equation

Solve the equation. $\dfrac{6}{t^2 - 7t + 12} + \dfrac{2t}{t - 3} = \dfrac{3t}{t - 4}$

Solution:

$$\frac{6}{t^2 - 7t + 12} + \frac{2t}{t - 3} = \frac{3t}{t - 4}$$

$$\frac{6}{(t - 3)(t - 4)} + \frac{2t}{t - 3} = \frac{3t}{t - 4}$$

Step 1: Factor the denominators. The restricted values are $t = 3$ and $t = 4$.

Step 2: The LCD is $(t - 3)(t - 4)$.

Step 3: Multiply by the LCD on both sides.

$$(t - 3)(t - 4)\left(\frac{6}{(t - 3)(t - 4)} + \frac{2t}{t - 3}\right) = (t - 3)(t - 4)\left(\frac{3t}{t - 4}\right)$$

$$(t - 3)(t - 4)\left(\frac{6}{(t - 3)(t - 4)}\right) + (t - 3)(t - 4)\left(\frac{2t}{t - 3}\right) = (t - 3)(t - 4)\left(\frac{3t}{t - 4}\right)$$

$$6 + 2t(t - 4) = 3t(t - 3)$$

$$6 + 2t^2 - 8t = 3t^2 - 9t$$

Step 4: Solve the resulting equation.

$$0 = 3t^2 - 2t^2 - 9t + 8t - 6$$

Because the resulting equation is quadratic, set the equation equal to zero and factor.

$$0 = t^2 - t - 6$$

$$0 = (t - 3)(t + 2)$$

$$t - 3 = 0 \quad \text{or} \quad t + 2 = 0$$

Set each factor equal to zero.

$$t = 3 \quad \text{or} \quad t = -2$$

3 is a restricted value, but -2 is not restricted.

Step 5: Check the potential solutions in the original equation.

Check: $t = 3$

3 cannot be a solution to the equation because it will make the denominator zero in the original equation.

$$\frac{6}{t^2 - 7t + 12} + \frac{2t}{t - 3} = \frac{3t}{t - 4}$$

$$\frac{6}{(3)^2 - 7(3) + 12} + \frac{2(3)}{(3) - 3} \stackrel{?}{=} \frac{3(3)}{(3) - 4}$$

$$\frac{6}{0} + \frac{6}{0} \stackrel{?}{=} \frac{9}{-1}$$

Zero in the denominator

The solution set is $\{-2\}$.

Check: $t = -2$

$$\frac{6}{t^2 - 7t + 12} + \frac{2t}{t - 3} = \frac{3t}{t - 4}$$

$$\frac{6}{(-2)^2 - 7(-2) + 12} + \frac{2(-2)}{(-2) - 3} \stackrel{?}{=} \frac{3(-2)}{(-2) - 4}$$

$$\frac{6}{4 + 14 + 12} + \frac{-4}{-5} \stackrel{?}{=} \frac{-6}{-6}$$

$$\frac{6}{30} + \frac{4}{5} \stackrel{?}{=} 1$$

$$\frac{1}{5} + \frac{4}{5} \stackrel{?}{=} 1 \quad \checkmark \text{ (True)}$$

$t = -2$ is a solution.

Skill Practice Solve the equation.

5. $\dfrac{-8}{x^2 + 6x + 8} + \dfrac{x}{x + 4} = \dfrac{2}{x + 2}$

Answer

5. $\{4\}$ (The value -4 does not check.)

| Example 6 | **Translating to a Rational Equation** |

Classroom Example: p. 537, Exercise 48

Ten times the reciprocal of a number is added to four. The result is equal to the quotient of twenty-two and the number. Find the number.

Solution:

Let x represent the number.

$$
\underset{\substack{\uparrow \\ \text{is added} \\ \text{to four}}}{4} \; + \; \overset{\substack{10 \quad \text{the reciprocal} \\ \text{times} \quad \text{of a number}}}{10\left(\dfrac{1}{x}\right)} \; \underset{\substack{\uparrow \\ \text{the result} \\ \text{is equal to}}}{=} \; \overset{\substack{\text{the quotient of} \\ \text{22 and the number}}}{\dfrac{22}{x}}
$$

$$4 + \frac{10}{x} = \frac{22}{x}$$

Step 1: The denominators are already factored. The restricted value is $x = 0$.

Step 2: The LCD is x.

$$x\left(4 + \frac{10}{x}\right) = x\left(\frac{22}{x}\right)$$

Step 3: Multiply both sides by the LCD.

$$4x + 10 = 22$$

Apply the distributive property.

$$4x = 12$$

Step 4: Solve the resulting linear equation.

$x = 3$ is a potential solution.

Step 5: 3 is not a restricted value. Substituting $x = 3$ into the original equation verifies that it is a solution.

The number is 3.

Skill Practice

6. The quotient of ten and a number is two less than four times the reciprocal of the number. Find the number.

3. Solving Formulas Involving Rational Expressions

A rational equation may have more than one variable. To solve for a specific variable within a rational equation, we can still apply the principle of clearing fractions.

Classroom Example: p. 537, Exercise 54

Example 7 Solving Formulas Involving Rational Equations

Solve for k. $\quad F = \dfrac{ma}{k}$

Solution:

To solve for k, we must clear fractions so that k appears in the numerator.

$$F = \frac{ma}{k} \qquad \text{The LCD is } k.$$

$$k \cdot (F) = k \cdot \left(\frac{ma}{k}\right) \qquad \text{Multiply both sides of the equation by the LCD.}$$

$$kF = ma \qquad \text{Clear fractions.}$$

$$\frac{kF}{F} = \frac{ma}{F} \qquad \text{Divide both sides by } F.$$

$$k = \frac{ma}{F}$$

Skill Practice

7. Solve for t. $\quad C = \dfrac{rt}{d}$

Classroom Example: p. 537, Exercise 56

Example 8 Solving Formulas Involving Rational Equations

Solve for b. $\quad h = \dfrac{2A}{B + b}$

Solution:

To solve for b, we must clear fractions so that b appears in the numerator.

$$h = \frac{2A}{B + b} \qquad \text{The LCD is } (B + b).$$

Avoiding Mistakes

Algebra is case-sensitive. The variables B and b represent different values.

$$h(B + b) = \left(\frac{2A}{B + b}\right) \cdot (B + b) \qquad \text{Multiply both sides of the equation by the LCD.}$$

$$hB + hb = 2A \qquad \text{Apply the distributive property.}$$

$$hb = 2A - hB \qquad \text{Subtract } hB \text{ from both sides to isolate the } b \text{ term.}$$

$$\frac{hb}{h} = \frac{2A - hB}{h} \qquad \text{Divide by } h.$$

$$b = \frac{2A - hB}{h}$$

Skill Practice

8. Solve the formula for x. $\quad y = \dfrac{3}{x - 2}$

Answers

7. $t = \dfrac{Cd}{r}$

8. $x = \dfrac{3 + 2y}{y}$ or $x = \dfrac{3}{y} + 2$

TIP: The solution to Example 8 can be written in several forms. The quantity

$$\frac{2A - hB}{h}$$

can be left as a single rational expression or can be split into two fractions and simplified.

$$b = \frac{2A - hB}{h} = \frac{2A}{h} - \frac{hB}{h} = \frac{2A}{h} - B$$

Example 9 Solving Formulas Involving Rational Equations

Classroom Example: p. 537, Exercise 64

Solve for z. $y = \dfrac{x - z}{x + z}$

Solution:

To solve for z, we must clear fractions so that z appears in the numerator.

$y = \dfrac{x - z}{x + z}$ \qquad LCD is $(x + z)$.

$y(x + z) = \left(\dfrac{x - z}{x + z}\right)(x + z)$ \qquad Multiply both sides of the equation by the LCD.

$yx + yz = x - z$ \qquad Apply the distributive property.

$yz + z = x - yx$ \qquad Collect z terms on one side of the equation and collect terms not containing z on the other side.

$z(y + 1) = x - yx$ \qquad Factor out z.

$z = \dfrac{x - yx}{y + 1}$ \qquad Divide by $y + 1$ to solve for z.

Skill Practice

9. Solve for h. $\quad \dfrac{b}{x} = \dfrac{a}{h} + 1$

Answer

9. $h = \dfrac{ax}{b - x}$ or $\dfrac{-ax}{x - b}$

Section 7.6 Practice Exercises

Study Skills Exercise

1. Define the key terms.

   a. linear equation \qquad b. quadratic equation \qquad c. rational equation

 Writing   Translating Expression   Geometry   Scientific Calculator   Video   NS&E

Review Exercises

For Exercises 2–7, perform the indicated operations.

2. $\dfrac{2}{x-3} - \dfrac{3}{x^2-x-6}$
$\dfrac{2x+1}{(x-3)(x+2)}$

3. $\dfrac{2x-6}{4x^2+7x-2} \div \dfrac{x^2-5x+6}{x^2-4}$
$\dfrac{2}{4x-1}$

4. $\dfrac{2y}{y-3} + \dfrac{4}{y^2-9}$ $\dfrac{2(y+2)(y+1)}{(y-3)(y+3)}$

5. $\dfrac{h-\dfrac{1}{h}}{\dfrac{1}{5}-\dfrac{1}{5h}}$ $5(h+1)$

6. $\dfrac{w-4}{w^2-9} \cdot \dfrac{w-3}{w^2-8w+16}$ $\dfrac{1}{(w+3)(w-4)}$

7. $1 + \dfrac{1}{x} - \dfrac{12}{x^2}$ $\dfrac{(x+4)(x-3)}{x^2}$

Concept 1: Introduction to Rational Equations

For Exercises 8–13, solve the equations by first clearing the fractions. **(See Example 1.)**

8. $\dfrac{1}{3}z + \dfrac{2}{3} = -2z + 10$ {4}

9. $\dfrac{5}{2} + \dfrac{1}{2}b = 5 - \dfrac{1}{3}b$ {3}

10. $\dfrac{3}{2}p + \dfrac{1}{3} = \dfrac{2p-3}{4}$ $\left\{-\dfrac{13}{12}\right\}$

11. $\dfrac{5}{3} - \dfrac{1}{6}k = \dfrac{3k+5}{4}$ $\left\{\dfrac{5}{11}\right\}$

12. $\dfrac{2x-3}{4} + \dfrac{9}{10} = \dfrac{x}{5}$ $\left\{-\dfrac{1}{2}\right\}$

13. $\dfrac{4y+2}{3} - \dfrac{7}{6} = -\dfrac{y}{6}$ $\left\{\dfrac{1}{3}\right\}$

Concept 2: Solving Rational Equations

14. For the equation

$$\dfrac{1}{w} - \dfrac{1}{2} = -\dfrac{1}{4}$$

   a. Identify the restricted values. $w = 0$

   b. Identify the LCD of the fractions in the equation. $4w$

   c. Solve the equation.   {4}

15. For the equation

$$\dfrac{3}{z} - \dfrac{4}{5} = -\dfrac{1}{5}$$

   a. Identify the restricted values. $z = 0$

   b. Identify the LCD of the fractions in the equation. $5z$

   c. Solve the equation.   {5}

16. Identify the LCD of all the denominators in the equation.

$$\dfrac{x+1}{x^2+2x-3} = \dfrac{1}{x+3} - \dfrac{1}{x-1}$$ $(x+3)(x-1)$

For Exercises 17–46, solve the equations. **(See Examples 2–5.)**

17. $\dfrac{1}{8} = \dfrac{3}{5} + \dfrac{5}{y}$ $\left\{-\dfrac{200}{19}\right\}$

18. $\dfrac{2}{7} - \dfrac{1}{x} = \dfrac{2}{3}$ $\left\{-\dfrac{21}{8}\right\}$

19. $\dfrac{4}{t} = \dfrac{3}{t} + \dfrac{1}{8}$ {8}

20. $\dfrac{9}{b} - \dfrac{8}{b} = \dfrac{1}{4}$ {4}

21. $\dfrac{5}{6x} + \dfrac{7}{x} = 1$ $\left\{\dfrac{47}{6}\right\}$

22. $\dfrac{14}{3x} - \dfrac{5}{x} = 2$ $\left\{-\dfrac{1}{6}\right\}$

23. $1 - \dfrac{2}{y} = \dfrac{3}{y^2}$ {3, −1}

24. $1 - \dfrac{2}{m} = \dfrac{8}{m^2}$ {4, −2}

25. $\dfrac{a+1}{a} = 1 + \dfrac{a-2}{2a}$ {4}

26. $\dfrac{7b-4}{5b} = \dfrac{9}{5} - \dfrac{4}{b}$ {8}

27. $\dfrac{w}{5} - \dfrac{w+3}{w} = -\dfrac{3}{w}$
{5} (The value 0 does not check.)

28. $\dfrac{t}{12} + \dfrac{t+3}{3t} = \dfrac{1}{t}$
{−4} (The value 0 does not check.)

 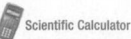

29. $\dfrac{2}{m+3} = \dfrac{5}{4m+12} - \dfrac{3}{8}$
$\{-5\}$

30. $\dfrac{2}{4n-4} - \dfrac{7}{4} = \dfrac{-3}{n-1}$ $\{3\}$

31. $\dfrac{p}{p-4} - 5 = \dfrac{4}{p-4}$
$\{\ \}$ (The value 4 does not check.)

32. $\dfrac{-5}{q+5} = \dfrac{q}{q+5} + 2$
$\{\ \}$ (The value -5 does not check.)

33. $\dfrac{2t}{t+2} - 2 = \dfrac{t-8}{t+2}$ $\{4\}$

34. $\dfrac{4w}{w-3} - 3 = \dfrac{3w-1}{w-3}$ $\{5\}$

35. $\dfrac{x^2-x}{x-2} = \dfrac{12}{x-2}$ $\{4, -3\}$

36. $\dfrac{x^2+9}{x+4} = \dfrac{-10x}{x+4}$ $\{-9, -1\}$

37. $\dfrac{x^2+3x}{x-1} = \dfrac{4}{x-1}$
$\{-4\}$ (The value 1 does not check.)

38. $\dfrac{2x^2-21}{2x-3} = \dfrac{-11x}{2x-3}$
$\{-7\}$ (The value $\frac{3}{2}$ does not check.)

39. $\dfrac{2x}{x+4} - \dfrac{8}{x-4} = \dfrac{2x^2+32}{x^2-16}$
$\{\ \}$ (The value -4 does not check.)

40. $\dfrac{4x}{x+3} - \dfrac{12}{x-3} = \dfrac{4x^2+36}{x^2-9}$
$\{\ \}$ (The value -3 does not check.)

41. $\dfrac{x}{x+6} = \dfrac{72}{x^2-36} + 4$ $\{4\}$ (The value -6 does not check.)

42. $\dfrac{y}{y+4} = \dfrac{32}{y^2-16} + 3$ $\{2\}$ (The value -4 does not check.)

43. $\dfrac{5}{3x-3} - \dfrac{2}{x-2} = \dfrac{7}{x^2-3x+2}$ $\{-25\}$

44. $\dfrac{6}{5a+10} - \dfrac{1}{a-5} = \dfrac{4}{a^2-3a-10}$ $\{60\}$

45. $\dfrac{y-2}{y-3} = \dfrac{11}{y^2-7y+12} + \dfrac{y}{y-4}$ $\{-1\}$

46. $\dfrac{6}{w+1} - \dfrac{3}{w+5} = \dfrac{18}{w^2+6w+5}$ $\{-3\}$

For Exercises 47–50, translate to a rational equation and solve. **(See Example 6.)**

47. The reciprocal of a number is added to three. The result is the quotient of 25 and the number. Find the number.   The number is 8.

48. The difference of three and the reciprocal of a number is equal to the quotient of 20 and the number. Find the number.   The number is 7.

49. If a number added to five is divided by the difference of the number and two, the result is three-fourths. Find the number.   The number is -26.

50. If twice a number added to three is divided by the number plus one, the result is three-halves. Find the number.   The number is -3.

Concept 3: Solving Formulas Involving Rational Expressions

For Exercises 51–68, solve for the indicated variable. **(See Examples 7–9.)**

51. $K = \dfrac{ma}{F}$ for m $m = \dfrac{FK}{a}$

52. $K = \dfrac{ma}{F}$ for a $a = \dfrac{FK}{m}$

53. $K = \dfrac{IR}{E}$ for E $E = \dfrac{IR}{K}$

54. $K = \dfrac{IR}{E}$ for R $R = \dfrac{KE}{I}$

55. $I = \dfrac{E}{R+r}$ for R
$R = \dfrac{E-Ir}{I}$ or $R = \dfrac{E}{I} - r$

56. $I = \dfrac{E}{R+r}$ for r
$r = \dfrac{E-IR}{I}$ or $r = \dfrac{E}{I} - R$

57. $h = \dfrac{2A}{B+b}$ for B
$B = \dfrac{2A-hb}{h}$ or $B = \dfrac{2A}{h} - b$

58. $\dfrac{C}{\pi r} = 2$ for r
$r = \dfrac{C}{2\pi}$

59. $\dfrac{V}{\pi h} = r^2$ for h
$h = \dfrac{V}{r^2\pi}$

60. $\dfrac{V}{lw} = h$ for w
$w = \dfrac{V}{lh}$

61. $x = \dfrac{at+b}{t}$ for t
$t = \dfrac{b}{x-a}$ or $t = \dfrac{-b}{a-x}$

62. $\dfrac{T+mf}{m} = g$ for m
$m = \dfrac{T}{g-f}$ or $m = \dfrac{-T}{f-g}$

63. $\dfrac{x-y}{xy} = z$ for x
$x = \dfrac{y}{1-yz}$ or $x = \dfrac{-y}{yz-1}$

64. $\dfrac{w-n}{wn} = P$ for w
$w = \dfrac{n}{1-Pn}$ or $w = \dfrac{-n}{Pn-1}$

65. $a + b = \dfrac{2A}{h}$ for h $h = \dfrac{2A}{a+b}$

66. $1 + rt = \dfrac{A}{P}$ for P
$P = \dfrac{A}{1+rt}$

67. $\dfrac{1}{R} = \dfrac{1}{R_1} + \dfrac{1}{R_2}$ for R
$R = \dfrac{R_1R_2}{R_2+R_1}$

68. $\dfrac{b+a}{ab} = \dfrac{1}{f}$ for b
$b = \dfrac{fa}{a-f}$ or $b = \dfrac{-fa}{f-a}$

 Writing   Translating Expression   Geometry   Scientific Calculator   Video   NS E

Problem Recognition Exercises

Comparing Rational Equations and Rational Expressions

Often adding or subtracting rational expressions is confused with solving rational equations. When adding rational expressions, we combine the terms to simplify the expression. When solving an equation, we clear the fractions and find numerical solutions, if possible. Both processes begin with finding the LCD, but the LCD is used differently in each process. Compare these two examples.

Example 1:

Add. $\dfrac{4}{x} + \dfrac{x}{3}$ (The LCD is $3x$.)

$$= \frac{3}{3} \cdot \left(\frac{4}{x}\right) + \left(\frac{x}{3}\right) \cdot \frac{x}{x}$$

$$= \frac{12}{3x} + \frac{x^2}{3x}$$

$$= \frac{12 + x^2}{3x} \quad \text{The answer is a rational expression.}$$

Example 2:

Solve. $\dfrac{4}{x} + \dfrac{x}{3} = -\dfrac{8}{3}$ (The LCD is $3x$.)

$$\frac{3x}{1}\left(\frac{4}{x} + \frac{x}{3}\right) = \frac{3x}{1}\left(-\frac{8}{3}\right)$$

$$12 + x^2 = -8x$$

$$x^2 + 8x + 12 = 0$$

$$(x + 2)(x + 6) = 0$$

$$x + 2 = 0 \text{ or } x + 6 = 0$$

$$x = -2 \text{ or } x = -6 \quad \text{The answer is the set } \{-2, -6\}.$$

For Exercises 1–20, solve the equation or simplify the expression by combining the terms.

1. $\dfrac{y}{2y + 4} - \dfrac{2}{y^2 + 2y}$ $\dfrac{y - 2}{2y}$

2. $\dfrac{1}{x + 2} + 2 = \dfrac{x + 11}{x + 2}$ $\{6\}$

3. $\dfrac{5t}{2} - \dfrac{t - 2}{3} = 5$ $\{2\}$

4. $3 - \dfrac{2}{a - 5}$ $\dfrac{3a - 17}{a - 5}$

5. $\dfrac{7}{6p^2} + \dfrac{2}{9p} + \dfrac{1}{3p^2}$ $\dfrac{4p + 27}{18p^2}$

6. $\dfrac{3b}{b + 1} - \dfrac{2b}{b - 1}$ $\dfrac{b(b - 5)}{(b - 1)(b + 1)}$

7. $4 + \dfrac{2}{h - 3} = 5$ $\{5\}$

8. $\dfrac{2}{w + 1} + \dfrac{3}{(w + 1)^2}$ $\dfrac{2w + 5}{(w + 1)^2}$

9. $\dfrac{1}{x - 6} - \dfrac{3}{x^2 - 6x} = \dfrac{4}{x}$ $\{7\}$

10. $\dfrac{3}{m} - \dfrac{6}{5} = -\dfrac{3}{m}$ $\{5\}$

11. $\dfrac{7}{2x + 2} + \dfrac{3x}{4x + 4}$ $\dfrac{3x + 14}{4(x + 1)}$

12. $\dfrac{10}{2t - 1} - 1 = \dfrac{t}{2t - 1}$ $\left\{\dfrac{11}{3}\right\}$

13. $\dfrac{3}{5x} + \dfrac{7}{2x} = 1$ $\left\{\dfrac{41}{10}\right\}$

14. $\dfrac{7}{t^2 - 5t} - \dfrac{3}{t - 5}$ $\dfrac{7 - 3t}{t(t - 5)}$

15. $\dfrac{5}{2a - 1} + 4$ $\dfrac{8a + 1}{2a - 1}$

16. $p - \dfrac{5p}{p - 2} = -\dfrac{10}{p - 2}$ $\{5\}$ (The value of 2 does not check.)

17. $\dfrac{3}{u} + \dfrac{12}{u^2 - 3u} = \dfrac{u + 1}{u - 3}$ $\{-1\}$ (The value 3 does not check.)

18. $\dfrac{5}{4k} - \dfrac{2}{6k}$ $\dfrac{11}{12k}$

19. $\dfrac{-2h}{h^2 - 9} + \dfrac{3}{h - 3}$ $\dfrac{h + 9}{(h - 3)(h + 3)}$

20. $\dfrac{3y}{y^2 - 5y + 4} = \dfrac{2}{y - 4} + \dfrac{3}{y - 1}$ $\{7\}$

Applications of Rational Equations and Proportions

1. Solving Proportions

In this section, we look at how rational equations can be used to solve a variety of applications. The first type of rational equation that will be applied is called a proportion.

Concepts

1. **Solving Proportions**
2. **Applications of Proportions and Similar Triangles**
3. **Distance, Rate, and Time Applications**
4. **Work Applications**

> **DEFINITION** Proportion
>
> An equation that equates two ratios or rates is called a **proportion**. Thus, for $b \neq 0$ and $d \neq 0$, $\frac{a}{b} = \frac{c}{d}$ is a proportion.

A proportion can be solved by multiplying both sides of the equation by the LCD and clearing fractions.

Example 1 Solving a Proportion

Solve the proportion. $\quad \dfrac{3}{11} = \dfrac{123}{w}$

Classroom Example: p. 547, Exercise 10

Solution:

$$\frac{3}{11} = \frac{123}{w} \qquad \text{The LCD is } 11w.$$

$$11w\left(\frac{3}{11}\right) = 11w\left(\frac{123}{w}\right) \qquad \text{Multiply by the LCD and clear fractions.}$$

$$3w = 11 \cdot 123 \qquad \text{Solve the resulting equation (linear).}$$

$$3w = 1353$$

$$\frac{3w}{3} = \frac{1353}{3}$$

$$w = 451$$

Check: $w = 451$

$$\frac{3}{11} = \frac{123}{w}$$

$$\frac{3}{11} \overset{?}{=} \frac{123}{(451)}$$

The solution set is $\{451\}$.

$$\frac{3}{11} \overset{?}{=} \frac{3}{11} \ \checkmark \ \text{(True)} \qquad \text{Simplify to lowest terms.}$$

Skill Practice Solve the proportion.

1. $\dfrac{10}{b} = \dfrac{2}{33}$

Answer

1. $\{165\}$

2. Applications of Proportions and Similar Triangles

Classroom Example: p. 547, Exercise 28

Example 2   Using a Proportion in an Application

For a recent year, the population of Alabama was approximately 4.2 million. At that time, Alabama had seven representatives in the U.S. House of Representatives. In the same year, North Carolina had a population of approximately 7.2 million. If representation in the House is based on population in equal proportions for each state, how many representatives did North Carolina have?

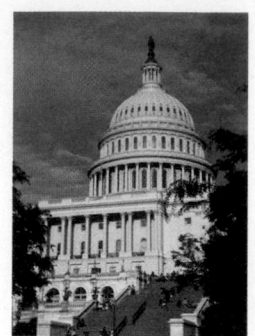

TIP: The equation from Example 2 could have been solved by first equating the cross products:

$$\frac{4.2}{7} \diagup\hspace{-0.9em}\diagdown \frac{7.2}{x}$$

$$4.2x = (7.2)(7)$$

$$4.2x = 50.4$$

$$x = 12$$

Solution:

Let x represent the number of representatives for North Carolina.

Set up a proportion by writing two equivalent ratios.

$$\boxed{\begin{array}{c}\text{Population of Alabama} \\ \hline \text{number of representatives}\end{array}} \rightarrow \frac{4.2}{7} = \frac{7.2}{x} \leftarrow \boxed{\begin{array}{c}\text{Population of North Carolina} \\ \hline \text{number of representatives}\end{array}}$$

$$\frac{4.2}{7} = \frac{7.2}{x}$$

$$7x \cdot \frac{4.2}{7} = 7x \cdot \frac{7.2}{x} \qquad \text{Multiply by the LCD, } 7x.$$

$$4.2x = (7.2)(7) \qquad \text{Solve the resulting linear equation.}$$

$$4.2x = 50.4$$

$$\frac{4.2x}{4.2} = \frac{50.4}{4.2}$$

$$x = 12 \qquad \text{North Carolina had 12 representatives.}$$

Skill Practice

2. A university has a ratio of students to faculty of 105 to 2. If the student population at the university is 15,750, how many faculty members are needed?

Proportions are used in geometry with **similar triangles**. Two triangles are similar if their angles have equal measure. In such a case, the lengths of the corresponding sides are proportional. The triangles in Figure 7-1 are similar. Therefore, the following ratios are equivalent.

$$\frac{a}{x} = \frac{b}{y} = \frac{c}{z}$$

Figure 7-1

Answer

2. 300 faculty members are needed.

Example 3 **Using Similar Triangles to Find an Unknown Side in a Triangle**

Classroom Example: p. 548, Exercise 34

The triangles in Figure 7-2 are similar.

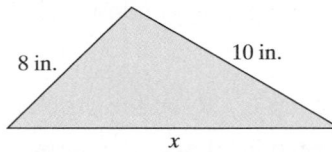

Figure 7-2

a. Solve for x.   **b.** Solve for y.

Solution:

a. The lengths of the upper right sides of the triangles are given. These form a known ratio of $\frac{10}{6}$. Because the triangles are similar, the ratio of the other corresponding sides must be equal to $\frac{10}{6}$. To solve for x, we have

Bottom side from large triangle	$\rightarrow$	$\dfrac{x}{9 \text{ in.}} = \dfrac{10 \text{ in.}}{6 \text{ in.}}$	$\leftarrow$	Right side from large triangle
bottom side from small triangle	$\rightarrow$		$\leftarrow$	right side from small triangle

$$\frac{x}{9} = \frac{10}{6} \qquad \text{The LCD is 18.}$$

$$\overset{2}{\cancel{18}} \cdot \left(\frac{x}{9}\right) = \overset{3}{\cancel{18}} \cdot \left(\frac{10}{\cancel{6}}\right) \qquad \text{Multiply by the LCD.}$$

$$2x = 30 \qquad \text{Clear fractions.}$$

$$x = 15 \qquad \text{Divide by 2.}$$

The length of side x is 15 in.

b. To solve for y, the ratio of the upper left sides of the triangles must equal $\frac{10}{6}$.

Left side from large triangle	$\rightarrow$	$\dfrac{8 \text{ in.}}{y} = \dfrac{10 \text{ in.}}{6 \text{ in.}}$	$\leftarrow$	Right side from large triangle
left side from small triangle	$\rightarrow$		$\leftarrow$	right side from small triangle

$$\frac{8}{y} = \frac{10}{6} \qquad \text{The LCD is } 6y.$$

$$6y \cdot \left(\frac{8}{\cancel{y}}\right) = \cancel{6}y \cdot \left(\frac{10}{\cancel{6}}\right) \qquad \text{Multiply by the LCD.}$$

$$48 = 10y \qquad \text{Clear fractions.}$$

$$\frac{48}{10} = \frac{10y}{10}$$

$$4.8 = y$$

The length of side y is 4.8 in.

Skill Practice

3. The two triangles shown are similar triangles. Solve for the lengths of the missing sides.

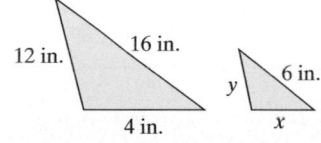

Answer

3. $x = 1.5$ in., and $y = 4.5$ in.

Classroom Example: p. 548, Exercise 38

Example 4 Using Similar Triangles in an Application

A tree that is 20 ft from a house is to be cut down. Use the following information and similar triangles to find the height of the tree to ensure that it will not hit the house.

The shadow cast by a yardstick is 2 ft long. The shadow cast by the tree is 11 ft long.

Solution:	**Step 1:** Read the problem.
Let x represent the height of the tree.	**Step 2:** Label the variables.

We will assume that the measurements were taken at the same time of day. Therefore, the angle of the Sun is the same on both objects, and we can set up similar triangles (Figure 7-3).

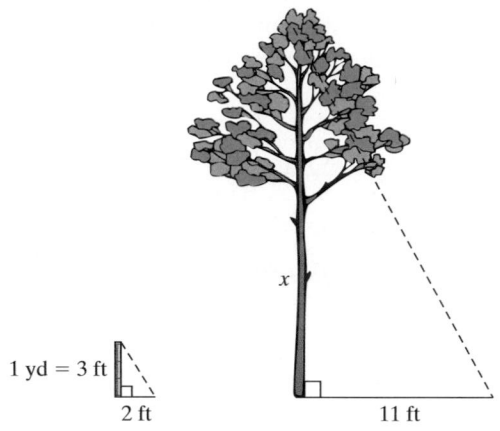

1 yd = 3 ft

2 ft   11 ft

Figure 7-3

Step 3: Create a verbal model.

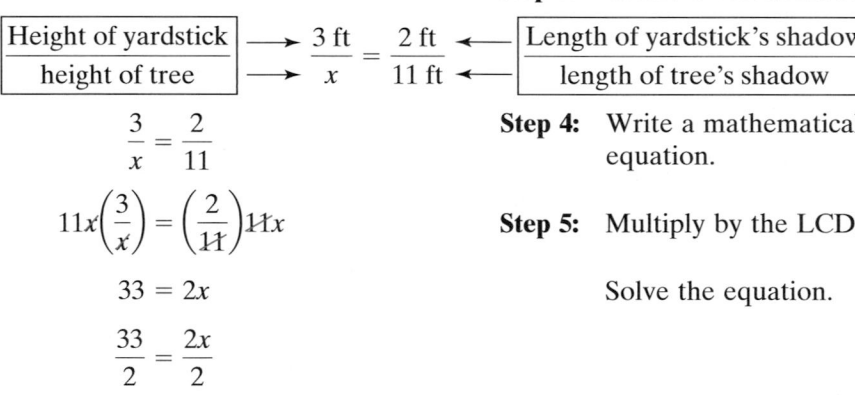

| Height of yardstick / height of tree | $\dfrac{3\text{ ft}}{x} = \dfrac{2\text{ ft}}{11\text{ ft}}$ | Length of yardstick's shadow / length of tree's shadow |

$$\frac{3}{x} = \frac{2}{11}$$

Step 4: Write a mathematical equation.

$$11x\left(\frac{3}{x}\right) = \left(\frac{2}{11}\right)11x$$

Step 5: Multiply by the LCD.

$$33 = 2x$$

Solve the equation.

$$\frac{33}{2} = \frac{2x}{2}$$

$$16.5 = x$$

Step 6: Interpret the results, and write the answer in words.

The tree is 16.5 ft high.

The tree is less than 20 ft high so it will not hit the house.

Skill Practice

4. The Sun casts a 3.2-ft shadow of a 6 ft man. At the same time, the Sun casts a 80-ft shadow of a building. How tall is the building?

Answer

4. The building is 150 ft tall.

3. Distance, Rate, and Time Applications

In Sections 2.7 and 4.4 we presented applications involving the relationship among the variables distance, rate, and time. Recall that $d = rt$.

Example 5 **Using a Rational Equation in a Distance, Rate, and Time Application**

Classroom Example: p. 549, Exercise 42

A small plane flies 440 mi with the wind from Memphis, TN, to Oklahoma City, OK. In the same amount of time, the plane flies 340 miles against the wind from Oklahoma City to Little Rock, AR (see Figure 7-4). If the wind speed is 30 mph, find the speed of the plane in still air.

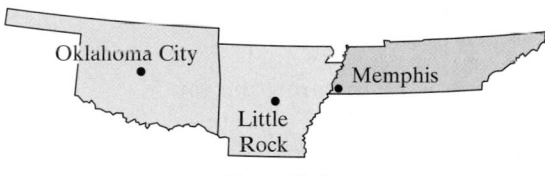

Figure 7-4

Solution:

Let x represent the speed of the plane in still air.

Then $x + 30$ is the speed of the plane with the wind.

$x - 30$ is the speed of the plane against the wind.

Organize the given information in a chart.

	Distance	Rate	Time
With the wind	440	$x + 30$	$\dfrac{440}{x + 30}$
Against the wind	340	$x - 30$	$\dfrac{340}{x - 30}$

Because $d = rt$, then $t = \dfrac{d}{r}$

The plane travels with the wind for the same amount of time as it travels against the wind, so we can equate the two expressions for time.

$$\left(\begin{array}{c}\text{Time with}\\ \text{the wind}\end{array}\right) = \left(\begin{array}{c}\text{time against}\\ \text{the wind}\end{array}\right)$$

$$\frac{440}{x + 30} = \frac{340}{x - 30} \qquad \text{The LCD is } (x + 30)(x - 30).$$

$$(x + 30)(x - 30) \cdot \frac{440}{x + 30} = (x + 30)(x - 30) \cdot \frac{340}{x - 30}$$

$$440(x - 30) = 340(x + 30)$$

$$440x - 13{,}200 = 340x + 10{,}200 \qquad \text{Solve the resulting linear equation.}$$

$$100x = 23{,}400$$

$$x = 234$$

The plane's speed in still air is 234 mph.

TIP: The equation

$$\frac{440}{x + 30} = \frac{340}{x - 30}$$

is a proportion. The fractions can also be cleared by equating the cross products.

$$\frac{440}{x + 30} \times \frac{340}{x - 30}$$

$$440(x - 30) = 340(x + 30)$$

Skill Practice

5. Alison paddles her kayak in a river where the current of the water is 2 mph. She can paddle 20 mi with the current in the same time that she can paddle 10 mi against the current. Find the speed of the kayak in still water.

Classroom Example: p. 549, Exercise 48

Example 6 Using a Rational Equation in a Distance, Rate, and Time Application

A motorist drives 100 mi between two cities in a bad rainstorm. For the return trip in sunny weather, she averages 10 mph faster and takes $\frac{1}{2}$ hr less time. Find the average speed of the motorist in the rainstorm and in sunny weather.

Solution:

Let x represent the motorist's speed during the rain.

Then $x + 10$ represents the speed in sunny weather.

	Distance	Rate	Time
Trip during rainstorm	100	x	$\dfrac{100}{x}$
Trip during sunny weather	100	$x + 10$	$\dfrac{100}{x + 10}$

Because $d = rt$, then $t = \dfrac{d}{r}$

Because the same distance is traveled in $\frac{1}{2}$ hr less time, the difference between the time of the trip during the rainstorm and the time during sunny weather is $\frac{1}{2}$ hr.

Avoiding Mistakes

The equation

$$\frac{100}{x} - \frac{100}{x + 10} = \frac{1}{2}$$

is not a proportion because the left-hand side has more than one fraction. Do not try to multiply the cross products. Instead, multiply by the LCD to clear fractions.

$$\left(\begin{array}{c}\text{Time during} \\ \text{the rainstorm}\end{array}\right) - \left(\begin{array}{c}\text{time during} \\ \text{sunny weather}\end{array}\right) = \left(\frac{1}{2} \text{ hr}\right) \qquad \text{Verbal model}$$

$$\frac{100}{x} - \frac{100}{x + 10} = \frac{1}{2} \qquad \begin{array}{l}\text{Mathematical} \\ \text{equation}\end{array}$$

$$2x(x + 10)\left(\frac{100}{x} - \frac{100}{x + 10}\right) = 2x(x + 10)\left(\frac{1}{2}\right) \qquad \begin{array}{l}\text{Multiply by} \\ \text{the LCD.}\end{array}$$

$$2x(x + 10)\left(\frac{100}{x}\right) - 2x(x + 10)\left(\frac{100}{x + 10}\right) = 2x(x + 10)\left(\frac{1}{2}\right) \qquad \begin{array}{l}\text{Apply the} \\ \text{distributive} \\ \text{property.}\end{array}$$

$$200(x + 10) - 200x = x(x + 10) \qquad \text{Clear fractions.}$$

$$200x + 2000 - 200x = x^2 + 10x \qquad \begin{array}{l}\text{Solve the} \\ \text{resulting} \\ \text{equation} \\ \text{(quadratic).}\end{array}$$

$$2000 = x^2 + 10x$$

$$0 = x^2 + 10x - 2000 \qquad \begin{array}{l}\text{Set the} \\ \text{equation equal} \\ \text{to zero.}\end{array}$$

$$0 = (x - 40)(x + 50) \qquad \text{Factor.}$$

$$x = 40 \qquad \text{or} \qquad x \neq -50$$

Answer

5. The speed of the kayak is 6 mph.

Because a rate of speed cannot be negative, reject $x = -50$. Therefore, the speed of the motorist in the rainstorm is 40 mph. Because $x + 10 = 40 + 10 = 50$, the average speed for the return trip in sunny weather is 50 mph.

Skill Practice

6. Harley rode his mountain bike 12 mi to the top of the mountain and the same distance back down. His speed going up was 8 mph slower than coming down. The ride up took 2 hr longer than the ride coming down. Find his speeds.

4. Work Applications

Example 7 demonstrates how work rates are related to a portion of a job that can be completed in one unit of time.

Example 7 Using a Rational Equation in a Work Problem

Classroom Example: p. 549, Exercise 52

A new printing press can print the morning edition in 2 hr, whereas the old printer required 4 hr. How long would it take to print the morning edition if both printers were working together?

Solution:

One method to solve this problem is to add rates.

Let x represent the time required for both printers working together to complete the job.

$$\left(\begin{matrix} \text{Rate} \\ \text{of old printer} \end{matrix} \right) + \left(\begin{matrix} \text{rate} \\ \text{of new printer} \end{matrix} \right) = \left(\begin{matrix} \text{rate of} \\ \text{both working together} \end{matrix} \right)$$

$$\frac{1 \text{ job}}{4 \text{ hr}} \quad + \quad \frac{1 \text{ job}}{2 \text{ hr}} \quad = \quad \frac{1 \text{ job}}{x \text{ hr}}$$

$$\frac{1}{4} + \frac{1}{2} = \frac{1}{x}$$

$$4x\left(\frac{1}{4} + \frac{1}{2} \right) = 4x\left(\frac{1}{x} \right) \qquad \text{The LCD is } 4x.$$

$$\overset{1}{\cancel{4x}} \cdot \frac{1}{\cancel{4}} + \overset{2}{\cancel{4x}} \cdot \frac{1}{\cancel{2}} = \overset{1}{\cancel{4x}} \cdot \frac{1}{\cancel{x}} \qquad \text{Apply the distributive property.}$$

$$x + 2x = 4 \qquad \text{Solve the resulting linear equation.}$$

$$3x = 4$$

$$x = \frac{4}{3} \qquad \text{The time required to print the morning edition using both printers is } 1\tfrac{1}{3} \text{ hr or equivalently, 1 hr 20 min.}$$

Skill Practice

7. The computer at a bank can process and prepare the bank statements in 30 hr. A new faster computer can do the job in 20 hr. If the bank uses both computers together, how long will it take to process the statements?

Answers

6. Uphill speed was 4 mph; downhill speed was 12 mph.
7. 12 hr

An alternative approach to Example 7 is to determine the portion of the job that each printer can complete in 1 hr and extend that rate to the portion of the job completed in x hours.

- The old printer can perform the job in 4 hr. Therefore, it completes $\frac{1}{4}$ of the job in 1 hr and $\frac{1}{4}x$ jobs in x hours.
- The new printer can perform the job in 2 hr. Therefore, it completes $\frac{1}{2}$ of the job in 1 hr and $\frac{1}{2}x$ jobs in x hours.

The sum of the portions of the job completed by each printer must equal one whole job.

$$\begin{pmatrix} \text{Portion of job} \\ \text{completed by} \\ \text{old printer} \end{pmatrix} + \begin{pmatrix} \text{portion of job} \\ \text{completed by} \\ \text{new printer} \end{pmatrix} = \begin{pmatrix} 1 \\ \text{whole} \\ \text{job} \end{pmatrix}$$

$$\frac{1}{4}x + \frac{1}{2}x = 1 \qquad \text{The LCD is 4.}$$

$$4\left(\frac{1}{4}x + \frac{1}{2}x\right) = 4(1) \qquad \text{Multiply by the LCD.}$$

$$x + 2x = 4 \qquad \text{Solve the resulting linear equation.}$$

$$3x = 4$$

$$x = \frac{4}{3} \qquad \text{The time required using both printers is } 1\frac{1}{3} \text{ hr.}$$

Section 7.7 Practice Exercises

Study Skills Exercise

1. Define the key terms.

   a. proportion   **b. similar triangles**

Review Exercises

For Exercises 2–7, determine whether each of the following is an equation or an expression. If it is an equation, solve it. If it is an expression, perform the indicated operation.

2. $\dfrac{b}{5} + 3 = 9$ Equation; {30}

3. $\dfrac{m}{m-1} - \dfrac{2}{m+3}$ Expression; $\dfrac{m^2 + m + 2}{(m-1)(m+3)}$

4. $\dfrac{2}{a+5} + \dfrac{5}{a^2-25}$ Expression; $\dfrac{2a-5}{(a+5)(a-5)}$

5. $\dfrac{3y+6}{20} \div \dfrac{4y+8}{8}$ Expression; $\dfrac{3}{10}$

6. $\dfrac{z^2+z}{24} \cdot \dfrac{8}{z+1}$ Expression; $\dfrac{z}{3}$

7. $\dfrac{3}{p+3} = \dfrac{12p+19}{p^2+7p+12} - \dfrac{5}{p+4}$ Equation; {2}

8. Determine whether 1 is a solution to the equation. $\dfrac{1}{x-1} + \dfrac{1}{2} = \dfrac{2}{x^2-1}$ No

 Writing   Translating Expression   Geometry   Scientific Calculator   Video NS&E

Concept 1: Solving Proportions

For Exercises 9–22, solve the proportions. **(See Example 1.)**

9. $\dfrac{8}{5} = \dfrac{152}{p}$ {95}

10. $\dfrac{6}{7} = \dfrac{96}{y}$ {112}

11. $\dfrac{19}{76} = \dfrac{z}{4}$ {1}

12. $\dfrac{15}{135} = \dfrac{w}{9}$ {1}

13. $\dfrac{5}{3} = \dfrac{a}{8}$ $\left\{\dfrac{40}{3}\right\}$

14. $\dfrac{b}{14} = \dfrac{3}{8}$ $\left\{\dfrac{21}{4}\right\}$

15. $\dfrac{2}{1.9} = \dfrac{x}{38}$ {40}

16. $\dfrac{16}{1.3} = \dfrac{30}{p}$ {2.4375}

17. $\dfrac{y+1}{2y} = \dfrac{2}{3}$ {3}

18. $\dfrac{w-2}{4w} = \dfrac{1}{6}$ {6}

19. $\dfrac{9}{2z-1} = \dfrac{3}{z}$ {−1}

20. $\dfrac{1}{t} = \dfrac{1}{4-t}$ {2}

21. $\dfrac{8}{9a-1} = \dfrac{5}{3a+2}$ {1}

22. $\dfrac{4p+1}{3} = \dfrac{2p-5}{6}$ $\left\{-\dfrac{7}{6}\right\}$

23. Charles' law describes the relationship between the initial and final temperature and volume of a gas held at a constant pressure.

$$\frac{V_i}{V_f} = \frac{T_i}{T_f}$$

  a. Solve the equation for V_f. $V_f = \dfrac{V_i T_f}{T_i}$

  b. Solve the equation for T_f. $T_f = \dfrac{T_i V_f}{V_i}$

24. The relationship between the area, height, and base of a triangle is given by the proportion

$$\frac{A}{b} = \frac{h}{2}$$

  a. Solve the equation for A. $A = \dfrac{hb}{2}$

  b. Solve the equation for b. $b = \dfrac{2A}{h}$

Concept 2: Applications of Proportions and Similar Triangles

For Exercises 25–32, solve using proportions.

25. Toni drives her Honda Civic 132 mi on the highway on 4 gal of gas. At this rate how many miles can she drive on 9 gal of gas? **(See Example 2.)** Toni can drive 297 mi on 9 gal of gas.

26. Tim takes his pulse for 10 sec and counts 12 beats. How many beats per minute is this? This is 72 beats/min.

27. Suppose a household of 4 people produces 128 lb of garbage in one week. At this rate, how many pounds will 48 people produce in 1 week? They would produce 1536 lb.

28. According to the website for the state of Virginia, 0.8 million tons of clothing is reused or recycled out of 7 million tons of clothing discarded. If 17.5 million tons of clothing is discarded, how many tons will be reused or recycled?
2 million tons of clothing will be reused or recycled.

29. Andrew is on a low-carbohydrate diet. If his diet book tells him that an 8-oz serving of pineapple contains 19.2 g of carbohydrate, how many grams of carbohydrate does a 5-oz serving contain?
5 oz contains 12 g of carbohydrate.

30. Cooking oatmeal requires 1 cup of water for every $\frac{1}{2}$ cup of oats. How many cups of water will be required for $\frac{3}{4}$ cup of oats? 1.5 cups of water would be necessary.

31. According to a building code, a wheelchair ramp must be at least 12 ft long for each foot of height. If the height of a newly constructed ramp is to be $1\frac{2}{3}$ ft, find the minimum acceptable length. The minimum length is 20 ft.

32. A map has a scale of 50 mi/in. If two cities measure 6.5 in. apart, how many miles does this represent?
This represents 325 mi.

 Writing   Translating Expression   Geometry   Scientific Calculator   Video   NS&E

For Exercises 33–36, the figures are similar. Solve for x and y. **(See Example 3.)**

33.

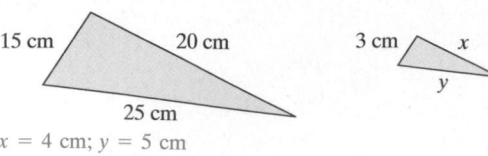

$x = 4$ cm; $y = 5$ cm

34.

$x = 10$ in.; $y = 9$ in.

35. $x = 3.75$ cm; $y = 4.5$ cm

36.

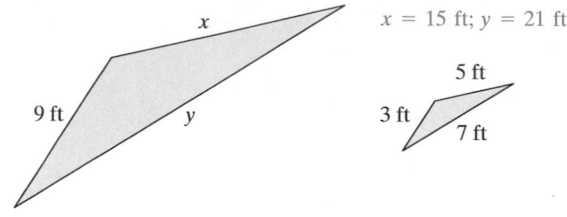

$x = 15$ ft; $y = 21$ ft

37. To estimate the height of a light pole, a mathematics student measures the length of a shadow cast by a meterstick and the length of the shadow cast by the light pole. Find the height of the light pole. **(See Example 4.)** The height of the pole is 7 m.

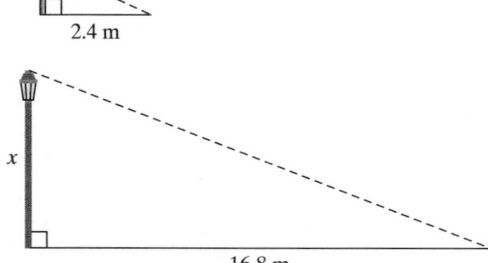

38. To estimate the height of a building, a student measures the length of a shadow cast by a yardstick and the length of the shadow cast by the building. Find the height of the building. The height is 36 ft.

39. A 6-ft-tall man standing 54 ft from a light post casts an 18-ft shadow. What is the height of the light post? The light post is 24 ft high.

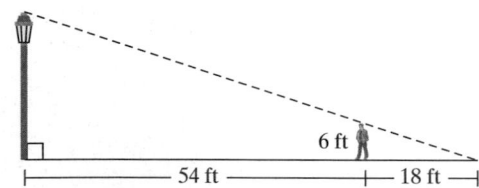

40. For a science project at school, a student must measure the height of a tree. The student measures the length of the shadow of the tree and then measures the length of the shadow cast by a yardstick. Use similar triangles to find the height of the tree. The tree is 36 ft high.

Concept 3: Distance, Rate, and Time Applications

41. A boat travels 54 mi upstream against the current in the same amount of time it takes to travel 66 mi downstream with the current. If the current is 2 mph, what is the speed of the boat in still water? (Use $t = \frac{d}{r}$ to complete the table.) **(See Example 5.)** The speed of the boat is 20 mph.

	Distance	Rate	Time
With the current (downstream)			
Against the current (upstream)			

42. A plane flies 630 mi with the wind in the same time that it takes to fly 455 mi against the wind. If this plane flies at the rate of 217 mph in still air, what is the speed of the wind? (Use $t = \frac{d}{r}$ to complete the table.) The wind speed is 35 mph.

	Distance	Rate	Time
With the wind			
Against the wind			

43. The jet stream is a fast flowing air current found in the atmosphere at around 36,000 ft above the surface of the Earth. During one summer day, the speed of the jet stream is 35 mph. A plane flying with the jet stream can fly 700 mi in the same amount of time that it would take to fly 500 mi against the jet stream. What is the speed of the plane in still air? The plane flies 210 mph in still air.

44. A fisherman travels 9 mi downstream with the current in the same time that he travels 3 mi upstream against the current. If the speed of the current is 6 mph, what is the speed at which the fisherman travels in still water? The speed of the boat in still water is 12 mph.

45. An athlete in training rides his bike 20 mi and then immediately follows with a 10-mi run. The total workout takes him 2.5 hr. He also knows that he bikes about twice as fast as he runs. Determine his biking speed and his running speed. He runs 8 mph and bikes 16 mph.

46. Devon can cross-country ski 5 km/hr faster than his sister Shanelle. Devon skis 45 km in the same time Shanelle skis 30 km. Find their speeds. Shanelle skis 10 km/hr and Devon skis 15 km/hr.

47. Floyd can walk 2 mph faster then his wife, Rachel. It takes Rachel 3 hr longer than Floyd to hike a 12-mi trail through the park. Find their speeds. **(See Example 6.)** Floyd walks 4 mph and Rachel walks 2 mph.

48. Janine bikes 3 mph faster than her sister, Jessica. Janine can ride 36 mi in 1 hr less time than Jessica can ride the same distance. Find each of their speeds. Janine's speed is 12 mph and Jessica's is 9 mph.

49. Sergio rode his bike 4 mi. Then he got a flat tire and had to walk back 4 mi. It took him 1 hr longer to walk than it did to ride. If his rate walking was 9 mph less than his rate riding, find the two rates. Sergio rode 12 mph and walked 3 mph.

50. Amber jogs 10 km in $\frac{3}{4}$ hr less than she can walk the same distance. If her walking rate is 3 km/hr less than her jogging rate, find her rates jogging and walking (in km/hr). Amber jogs 8 km/hr and walks 5 km/hr.

Concept 4: Work Applications

51. If the cold-water faucet is left on, the sink will fill in 10 min. If the hot-water faucet is left on, the sink will fill in 12 min. How long would it take to fill the sink if both faucets are left on? **(See Example 7.)** $5\frac{5}{11}$ $(5.\overline{45})$ min

52. The CUT-IT-OUT lawn mowing company consists of two people: Tina and Bill. If Tina cuts a lawn by herself, she can do it in 4 hr. If Bill cuts the same lawn himself, it takes him an hour longer than Tina. How long would it take them if they worked together? $2\frac{2}{9}$ $(2.\overline{2})$ hr

53. A manuscript needs to be printed. One printer can do the job in 50 min, and another printer can do the job in 40 min. How long would it take if both printers were used? $22\frac{2}{9}$ $(22.\overline{2})$ min

54. A pump can empty a small pond in 4 hr. Another more efficient pump can do the job in 3 hr. How long would it take to empty the pond if both pumps were used? $1\frac{5}{7}$ (approximately 1.7) hr

 Writing Translating Expression Geometry Scientific Calculator Video

55. A pipe can fill a reservoir in 16 hr. A drainage pipe can drain the reservoir in 24 hr. How long would it take to fill the reservoir if the drainage pipe was left open by mistake? (*Hint:* The rate at which water drains should be negative.)   48 hr

56. A hole in the bottom of a child's plastic swimming pool can drain the pool in 60 min. If the pool had no hole, a hose could fill the pool in 40 min. How long would it take the hose to fill the pool with the hole?   120 min

57. Tim and Al are bricklayers. Tim can construct an outdoor grill in 5 days. If Al helps Tim, they can build it in only 2 days. How long would it take Al to build the grill alone? $3\frac{1}{3}$ ($3.\overline{3}$) days

58. Norma is a new and inexperienced secretary. It takes her 3 hr to prepare a mailing. If her boss helps her, the mailing can be completed in 1 hr. How long would it take the boss to do the job by herself? $1\frac{1}{2}$ (1.5) hr

Expanding Your Skills

For Exercises 59–62, solve using proportions.

59. The ratio of smokers to nonsmokers in a restaurant is 2 to 7. There are 100 more nonsmokers than smokers. How many smokers and nonsmokers are in the restaurant?

There are 40 smokers and 140 nonsmokers.

60. The ratio of fiction to nonfiction books sold in a bookstore is 5 to 3. One week there were 180 more fiction books sold than nonfiction. Find the number of fiction and nonfiction books sold during that week.   There are 450 fiction and 270 nonfiction books sold.

61. There are 440 students attending a biology lecture. The ratio of male to female students at the lecture is 6 to 5. How many men and women are attending the lecture?   There are 240 men and 200 women.

62. The ratio of dogs to cats at the humane society is 5 to 8. The total number of dogs and cats is 650. How many dogs and how many cats are at the humane society?   There are 250 dogs and 400 cats.

Group Activity

Computing Monthly Mortgage Payments

Materials: A calculator

Estimated Time: 15–20 minutes

Group Size: 3

When a person borrows money to buy a house, the bank usually requires a down payment of between 0% and 20% of the cost of the house. The bank then issues a loan for the remaining balance on the house. The loan to buy a house is called a *mortgage*. Monthly payments are made to pay off the mortgage over a period of years.

A formula to calculate the monthly payment, P, for a loan is given by the complex fraction:

$$P = \frac{\dfrac{Ar}{12}}{1 - \dfrac{1}{\left(1 + \dfrac{r}{12}\right)^{12t}}}$$

where
P is the monthly payment
A is the original amount of the mortgage
r is the annual interest rate written as a decimal
t is the term of the loan in years

Suppose a person wants to buy a $200,000 house. The bank requires a down payment of 20%, and the loan is issued for 30 years at 7.5% interest.

1. Find the amount of the down payment. _____$40,000_____

2. Find the amount of the mortgage. _____$160,000_____

3. Find the monthly payment (to the nearest cent). _____$1118.74_____

 Writing   Translating Expression   Geometry   Scientific Calculator   Video   NS&E

4. Multiply the monthly payment found in question 3 by the total number of months in a 30-year period. Interpret what this value means in the context of the problem.

$402,746.40; This is the total amount owed to the bank.

5. How much total interest was paid on the loan for the house? ___$242,746.40___

6. What was the total amount paid to the bank (include the down payment). ___$442,746.40___

Chapter 7 Summary

Section 7.1 Introduction to Rational Expressions

Key Concepts

A **rational expression** is a ratio of the form $\frac{p}{q}$ where p and q are polynomials and $q \neq 0$.

Restricted values of a rational expression are those values that, when substituted for the variable, make the expression undefined. To find restricted values, set the denominator equal to 0 and solve the equation.

Simplifying a Rational Expression

Factor the numerator and denominator completely, and reduce factors whose ratio is equal to 1 or to -1. A rational expression written in lowest terms will still have the same restricted values as the original expression.

Examples

Example 1

$$\frac{x + 2}{x^2 - 5x - 14} \quad \text{is a rational expression.}$$

Example 2

To find the restricted values of $\dfrac{x + 2}{x^2 - 5x - 14}$ factor the

denominator: $\dfrac{x + 2}{(x + 2)(x - 7)}$

The restricted values are $x = -2$ and $x = 7$.

Example 3

Simplify the rational expression. $\dfrac{x + 2}{x^2 - 5x - 14}$

$$\frac{\overset{1}{\cancel{x + 2}}}{\cancel{(x + 2)}(x - 7)} \quad \text{Simplify.}$$

$$= \frac{1}{x - 7} \quad \text{(provided } x \neq 7, x \neq -2\text{).}$$

Section 7.2 Multiplication and Division of Rational Expressions

Key Concepts

Multiplying Rational Expressions

Multiply the numerators and multiply the denominators. That is, if $q \neq 0$ and $s \neq 0$, then

$$\frac{p}{q} \cdot \frac{r}{s} = \frac{pr}{qs}$$

Factor the numerator and denominator completely. Then reduce factors whose ratio is 1 or -1.

Examples

Example 1

Multiply. $\dfrac{b^2 - a^2}{a^2 - 2ab + b^2} \cdot \dfrac{a^2 - 3ab + 2b^2}{2a + 2b}$

$$= \frac{(b - a)(b + a)}{(a - b)(a - b)} \cdot \frac{(a - 2b)(a - b)}{2(a + b)}$$

$$= \frac{\overset{-1}{\cancel{(b - a)}}\overset{1}{\cancel{(b + a)}}(a - 2b)\overset{1}{\cancel{(a - b)}}}{\cancel{(a - b)}\cancel{(a - b)} \cdot 2\cancel{(a + b)}}$$

$$= -\frac{a - 2b}{2} \quad \text{or} \quad \frac{2b - a}{2}$$

Dividing Rational Expressions

Multiply the first expression by the reciprocal of the second expression. That is, for $q \neq 0$, $r \neq 0$, and $s \neq 0$,

$$\frac{p}{q} \div \frac{r}{s} = \frac{p}{q} \cdot \frac{s}{r} = \frac{ps}{qr}$$

Example 2

Divide. $\quad \dfrac{x-2}{15} \div \dfrac{x^2+2x-8}{20x}$

$$= \frac{x-2}{15} \cdot \frac{20x}{x^2+2x-8}$$

$$= \frac{(x-2)}{3 \cdot 5} \cdot \frac{2 \cdot 2 \cdot 5 \cdot x}{(x-2)(x+4)}$$

$$= \frac{\overset{1}{\cancel{(x-2)}} \cdot 2 \cdot 2 \cdot \overset{1}{\cancel{5}} \cdot x}{3 \cdot \cancel{5}\,\cancel{(x-2)}(x+4)}$$

$$= \frac{4x}{3(x+4)}$$

Section 7.3   Least Common Denominator

Key Concepts

Converting a Rational Expression to an Equivalent Expression with a Different Denominator

Multiply numerator and denominator of the rational expression by the missing factors necessary to create the desired denominator.

Finding the Least Common Denominator (LCD) of Two or More Rational Expressions

1. Factor all denominators completely.
2. The LCD is the product of unique factors from the denominators, where each factor is raised to its highest power.

Examples

Example 1

Convert $\dfrac{-3}{x-2}$ to an equivalent expression with the indicated denominator:

$$\frac{-3}{x-2} = \frac{}{5(x-2)(x+2)}$$

Multiply numerator and denominator by the missing factors from the denominator.

$$\frac{-3 \cdot 5(x+2)}{(x-2) \cdot 5(x+2)} = \frac{-15x-30}{5(x-2)(x+2)}$$

Example 2

Identify the LCD. $\quad \dfrac{1}{8x^3y^2z}; \ \dfrac{5}{6xy^4}$

1. Write the denominators as a product of prime factors:

$$\frac{1}{2^3x^3y^2z}; \ \frac{5}{2 \cdot 3xy^4}$$

2. The LCD is $2^3 \cdot 3x^3y^4z$ or $24x^3y^4z$

Section 7.4 — Addition and Subtraction of Rational Expressions

Key Concepts

To add or subtract rational expressions, the expressions must have the same denominator.

Steps to Add or Subtract Rational Expressions

1. Factor the denominators of each rational expression.
2. Identify the LCD.
3. Rewrite each rational expression as an equivalent expression with the LCD as its denominator.
4. Add or subtract the numerators, and write the result over the common denominator.
5. Simplify.

Example

Example 1

Add. $\dfrac{c-2}{c+1} + \dfrac{12c-3}{2c^2-c-3}$

$= \dfrac{c-2}{c+1} + \dfrac{12c-3}{(2c-3)(c+1)}$

The LCD is $(2c-3)(c+1)$.

$= \dfrac{(2c-3)(c-2)}{(2c-3)(c+1)} + \dfrac{12c-3}{(2c-3)(c+1)}$

$= \dfrac{2c^2-4c-3c+6+12c-3}{(2c-3)(c+1)}$

$= \dfrac{2c^2+5c+3}{(2c-3)(c+1)}$

$= \dfrac{(2c+3)\cancel{(c+1)}}{(2c-3)\cancel{(c+1)}} = \dfrac{2c+3}{2c-3}$

Section 7.5 — Complex Fractions

Key Concepts

Complex fractions can be simplified by using Method I or Method II.

Method I

1. Add or subtract expressions in the numerator to form a single fraction. Add or subtract expressions in the denominator to form a single fraction.
2. Divide the rational expressions from step 1 by multiplying the numerator of the complex fraction by the reciprocal of the denominator of the complex fraction.
3. Simplify to lowest terms, if possible.

Examples

Example 1

Simplify. $\dfrac{1 - \dfrac{4}{w^2}}{1 - \dfrac{1}{w} - \dfrac{6}{w^2}} = \dfrac{\dfrac{w^2}{w^2} - \dfrac{4}{w^2}}{\dfrac{w^2}{w^2} - \dfrac{w}{w^2} - \dfrac{6}{w^2}}$

$= \dfrac{\dfrac{w^2-4}{w^2}}{\dfrac{w^2-w-6}{w^2}} = \dfrac{w^2-4}{w^2} \cdot \dfrac{w^2}{w^2-w-6}$

$= \dfrac{(w-2)(w+2)}{w^2} \cdot \dfrac{w^2}{(w-3)(w+2)}$

$= \dfrac{(w-2)\cancel{(w+2)} \cdot \overset{1}{\cancel{w^2}}}{\cancel{w^2}(w-3)\cancel{(w+2)}}$

$= \dfrac{w-2}{w-3}$

Method II

1. Multiply the numerator and denominator of the complex fraction by the LCD of all individual fractions within the expression.
2. Apply the distributive property, and simplify the result.
3. Simplify to lowest terms, if possible.

Example 2

Simplify.
$$\frac{1 - \dfrac{4}{w^2}}{1 - \dfrac{1}{w} - \dfrac{6}{w^2}} = \frac{w^2\left(1 - \dfrac{4}{w^2}\right)}{w^2\left(1 - \dfrac{1}{w} - \dfrac{6}{w^2}\right)}$$

$$= \frac{w^2 - 4}{w^2 - w - 6} = \frac{(w - 2)\cancel{(w + 2)}^{\,1}}{(w - 3)\cancel{(w + 2)}}$$

$$= \frac{w - 2}{w - 3}$$

Section 7.6 Rational Equations

Key Concepts

An equation with one or more rational expressions is called a **rational equation**.

Steps to Solve a Rational Equation

1. Factor the denominators of all rational expressions. Identify the restricted values.
2. Identify the LCD of all expressions in the equation.
3. Multiply both sides of the equation by the LCD.
4. Solve the resulting equation.
5. Check each potential solution in the original equation.

Examples

Example 1

Solve. $\dfrac{1}{w} - \dfrac{1}{2w - 1} = \dfrac{-2w}{2w - 1}$ The restricted values are $w = 0$ and $w = \frac{1}{2}$.

The LCD is $w(2w - 1)$.

$$\cancel{w}(2w - 1)\frac{1}{\cancel{w}} - w\cancel{(2w - 1)}\frac{1}{\cancel{2w - 1}}$$

$$= w\cancel{(2w - 1)}\frac{-2w}{\cancel{2w - 1}}$$

$$(2w - 1)(1) - w(1) = w(-2w)$$

$$2w - 1 - w = -2w^2 \qquad \text{Quadratic equation}$$

$$2w^2 + w - 1 = 0$$

$$(2w - 1)(w + 1) = 0$$

$$w \cancel{=} \tfrac{1}{2} \quad \text{or} \quad w = -1$$
$$\text{Does not check.} \qquad \text{Checks.}$$

The solution set is $\{-1\}$.

Example 2

Solve for I. $q = \dfrac{VQ}{I}$

$$I \cdot q = \frac{VQ}{\cancel{I}} \cdot \cancel{I}$$

$$Iq = VQ$$

$$I = \frac{VQ}{q}$$

Section 7.7   Applications of Rational Equations and Proportions

Key Concepts

Solving Proportions

An equation that equates two rates or ratios is called a **proportion**:

$$\frac{a}{b} = \frac{c}{d} \quad (b \neq 0, d \neq 0)$$

To solve a proportion, multiply both sides of the equation by the LCD.

Examples 2 and 3 give applications of rational equations.

Example 2

Two cars travel from Los Angeles to Las Vegas. One car travels an average of 8 mph faster than the other car. If the faster car travels 189 mi in the same time as the slower car travels 165 mi, what is the average speed of each car?

Let r represent the speed of the slower car.
Let $r + 8$ represent the speed of the faster car.

	Distance	Rate	Time
Slower car	165	r	$\dfrac{165}{r}$
Faster car	189	$r + 8$	$\dfrac{189}{r + 8}$

$$\frac{165}{r} = \frac{189}{r + 8}$$

$$165(r + 8) = 189r$$

$$165r + 1320 = 189r$$

$$1320 = 24r$$

$$55 = r$$

The slower car travels 55 mph, and the faster car travels $55 + 8 = 63$ mph.

Examples

Example 1

A 90-g serving of a particular ice cream contains 10 g of fat. How much fat does 400 g of the same ice cream contain?

$$\frac{10 \text{ g fat}}{90 \text{ g ice cream}} = \frac{x \text{ grams fat}}{400 \text{ g ice cream}}$$

$$\frac{10}{90} = \frac{x}{400}$$

$$\overset{40}{\cancel{3600}} \cdot \left(\frac{10}{\cancel{90}}\right) = \left(\frac{x}{\cancel{400}}\right) \cdot \overset{9}{\cancel{3600}}$$

$$400 = 9x$$

$$x = \frac{400}{9} \approx 44.4 \text{ g}$$

Example 3

Beth and Cecelia have a house cleaning business. Beth can clean a particular house in 5 hr by herself. Cecelia can clean the same house in 4 hr. How long would it take if they cleaned the house together?

Let x be the number of hours it takes for both Beth and Cecelia to clean the house.

Beth's rate is $\dfrac{1 \text{ job}}{5 \text{ hr}}$. Cecelia's rate is $\dfrac{1 \text{ job}}{4 \text{ hr}}$.

The rate together is $\dfrac{1 \text{ job}}{x \text{ hr}}$.

$$\frac{1}{5} + \frac{1}{4} = \frac{1}{x} \qquad \text{Add the rates.}$$

$$20x\left(\frac{1}{5} + \frac{1}{4}\right) = 20x\left(\frac{1}{x}\right)$$

$$4x + 5x = 20$$

$$9x = 20$$

$$x = \frac{20}{9}$$

It takes $\dfrac{20}{9}$ hr or $2\dfrac{2}{9}$ hr working together.

Chapter 7 Review Exercises

Section 7.1

1. For the rational expression $\dfrac{t-2}{t+9}$

  a. Evaluate the expression (if possible) for
$t = 0, 1, 2, -3, -9$ $-\dfrac{2}{9}, -\dfrac{1}{10}, 0, -\dfrac{5}{6},$ undefined

  b. Identify the restricted values. $t = -9$

2. For the rational expression $\dfrac{k+1}{k-5}$

  a. Evaluate the expression for $k = 0, 1, 5,$
$-1, -2$ $-\dfrac{1}{5}, -\dfrac{1}{2},$ undefined, $0, \dfrac{1}{7}$

  b. Identify the restricted values. $k = 5$

3. Which of the rational expressions are equal to -1?   a, c, d

  a. $\dfrac{2-x}{x-2}$ **b.** $\dfrac{x-5}{x+5}$

  c. $\dfrac{-x-7}{x+7}$ **d.** $\dfrac{x^2-4}{4-x^2}$

For Exercises 4–13, identify the restricted values. Then simplify the expressions.

4. $\dfrac{x-3}{(2x-5)(x-3)}$ $x = \dfrac{5}{2}, x = 3; \dfrac{1}{2x-5}$

5. $\dfrac{h+7}{(3h+1)(h+7)}$ $h = -\dfrac{1}{3}, h = -7; \dfrac{1}{3h+1}$

6. $\dfrac{4a^2+7a-2}{a^2-4}$ $a = 2, a = -2; \dfrac{4a-1}{a-2}$

7. $\dfrac{2w^2+11w+12}{w^2-16}$ $w = 4, w = -4; \dfrac{2w+3}{w-4}$

8. $\dfrac{z^2-4z}{8-2z}$ $z = 4; -\dfrac{z}{2}$

9. $\dfrac{15-3k}{2k^2-10k}$ $k = 0, k = 5; -\dfrac{3}{2k}$

10. $\dfrac{2b^2+4b-6}{4b+12}$ $b = -3; \dfrac{b-1}{2}$

11. $\dfrac{3m^2-12m-15}{9m+9}$ $m = -1; \dfrac{m-5}{3}$

12. $\dfrac{n+3}{n^2+6n+9}$ $n = -3; \dfrac{1}{n+3}$

13. $\dfrac{p+7}{p^2+14p+49}$ $p = -7; \dfrac{1}{p+7}$

Section 7.2

For Exercises 14–27, multiply or divide as indicated.

14. $\dfrac{3y^3}{3y-6} \cdot \dfrac{y-2}{y}$ y^2

15. $\dfrac{2u+10}{u} \cdot \dfrac{u^3}{4u+20}$ $\dfrac{u^2}{2}$

16. $\dfrac{11}{v-2} \cdot \dfrac{2v^2-8}{22}$ $v+2$

17. $\dfrac{8}{x^2-25} \cdot \dfrac{3x+15}{16}$ $\dfrac{3}{2(x-5)}$

18. $\dfrac{4c^2+4c}{c^2-25} \div \dfrac{8c}{c^2-5c}$ $\dfrac{c(c+1)}{2(c+5)}$

19. $\dfrac{q^2-5q+6}{2q+4} \div \dfrac{2q-6}{q+2}$ $\dfrac{q-2}{4}$

20. $\left(\dfrac{-2t}{t+1}\right)(t^2-4t-5)$ $-2t(t-5)$

21. $(s^2-6s+8)\left(\dfrac{4s}{s-2}\right)$ $4s(s-4)$

22. $\dfrac{\dfrac{a^2+5a+1}{7a-7}}{\dfrac{a^2+5a+1}{a-1}}$ $\dfrac{1}{7}$

23. $\dfrac{\dfrac{n^2+n+1}{n^2-4}}{\dfrac{n^2+n+1}{n+2}}$ $\dfrac{1}{n-2}$

24. $\dfrac{5h^2-6h+1}{h^2-1} \div \dfrac{16h^2-9}{4h^2+7h+3} \cdot \dfrac{3-4h}{30h-6}$ $-\dfrac{1}{6}$

25. $\dfrac{3m-3}{6m^2+18m+12} \cdot \dfrac{2m^2-8}{m^2-3m+2} \div \dfrac{m+3}{m+1}$ $\dfrac{1}{m+3}$

26. $\dfrac{x-2}{x^2-3x-18} \cdot \dfrac{6-x}{x^2-4}$ $\dfrac{-1}{(x+3)(x+2)}$

27. $\dfrac{4y^2-1}{1+2y} \div \dfrac{y^2-4y-5}{5-y}$ $-\dfrac{2y-1}{y+1}$

Section 7.3

For Exercises 28–33, identify the LCD. Then write each fraction as an equivalent fraction with the LCD as its denominator.

28. $\dfrac{2}{5a}; \dfrac{3}{10b}$ LCD $= 10ab$; $\dfrac{4b}{10ab}; \dfrac{3a}{10ab}$

29. $\dfrac{7}{4x}; \dfrac{11}{6y}$ LCD $= 12xy$; $\dfrac{21y}{12xy}; \dfrac{22x}{12xy}$

30. $\dfrac{1}{x^2y^4}; \dfrac{3}{xy^5}$ LCD $= x^2y^5$; $\dfrac{y}{x^2y^5}; \dfrac{3x}{x^2y^5}$

31. $\dfrac{5}{ab^3}; \dfrac{3}{ac^2}$ LCD $= ab^3c^2$; $\dfrac{5c^2}{ab^3c^2}; \dfrac{3b^3}{ab^3c^2}$

32. $\dfrac{5}{p+2}; \dfrac{p}{p-4}$ LCD $= (p+2)(p-4)$; $\dfrac{5p-20}{(p+2)(p-4)}; \dfrac{p^2+2p}{(p+2)(p-4)}$

33. $\dfrac{6}{q}; \dfrac{1}{q+8}$ LCD $= q(q+8)$; $\dfrac{6q+48}{q(q+8)}; \dfrac{q}{q(q+8)}$

34. Determine the LCD.

$$\dfrac{6}{n^2-9}; \dfrac{5}{n^2-n-6}$$
  LCD $= (n+3)(n-3)(n+2)$

35. Determine the LCD.

$$\dfrac{8}{m^2-16}; \dfrac{7}{m^2-m-12}$$
  LCD $= (m+4)(m-4)(m+3)$

 Writing   Translating Expression   Geometry   Scientific Calculator   Video   NS&E

36. State two possible LCDs that could be used to add the fractions. $c - 2$ or $2 - c$

$$\frac{7}{c - 2} + \frac{4}{2 - c}$$

37. State two possible LCDs that could be used to subtract the fractions. $3 - x$ or $x - 3$

$$\frac{10}{3 - x} - \frac{5}{x - 3}$$

Section 7.4

For Exercises 38–49, add or subtract as indicated.

38. $\dfrac{h + 3}{h + 1} + \dfrac{h - 1}{h + 1}$ 2

39. $\dfrac{b - 6}{b - 2} + \dfrac{b + 2}{b - 2}$ 2

40. $\dfrac{a^2}{a - 5} - \dfrac{25}{a - 5}$ $a + 5$

41. $\dfrac{x^2}{x + 7} - \dfrac{49}{x + 7}$ $x - 7$

42. $\dfrac{y}{y^2 - 81} + \dfrac{2}{9 - y}$
$\dfrac{-y - 18}{(y - 9)(y + 9)}$ or $\dfrac{y + 18}{(9 - y)(y + 9)}$

43. $\dfrac{3}{4 - t^2} + \dfrac{t}{2 - t}$
$\dfrac{t^2 + 2t + 3}{(2 - t)(2 + t)}$

44. $\dfrac{4}{3m} - \dfrac{1}{m + 2}$ $\dfrac{m + 8}{3m(m + 2)}$

45. $\dfrac{5}{2r + 12} - \dfrac{1}{r}$ $\dfrac{3(r - 4)}{2r(r + 6)}$

46. $\dfrac{4p}{p^2 + 6p + 5} - \dfrac{3p}{p^2 + 5p + 4}$ $\dfrac{p}{(p + 4)(p + 5)}$

47. $\dfrac{3q}{q^2 + 7q + 10} - \dfrac{2q}{q^2 + 6q + 8}$ $\dfrac{q}{(q + 5)(q + 4)}$

48. $\dfrac{1}{h} + \dfrac{h}{2h + 4} - \dfrac{2}{h^2 + 2h}$ $\dfrac{1}{2}$

49. $\dfrac{x}{3x + 9} - \dfrac{3}{x^2 + 3x} + \dfrac{1}{x}$ $\dfrac{1}{3}$

Section 7.5

For Exercises 50–57, simplify the complex fractions.

50. $\dfrac{\dfrac{a - 4}{3}}{\dfrac{a - 2}{3}}$ $\dfrac{a - 4}{a - 2}$

51. $\dfrac{\dfrac{z + 5}{z}}{\dfrac{z - 5}{3}}$ $\dfrac{3(z + 5)}{z(z - 5)}$

52. $\dfrac{\dfrac{2 - 3w}{2}}{\dfrac{2}{w} - 3}$ $\dfrac{w}{2}$

53. $\dfrac{\dfrac{2}{y} + 6}{\dfrac{3y + 1}{4}}$ $\dfrac{8}{y}$

54. $\dfrac{\dfrac{y}{x} - \dfrac{x}{y}}{\dfrac{1}{x} + \dfrac{1}{y}}$ $y - x$

55. $\dfrac{\dfrac{b}{a} - \dfrac{a}{b}}{\dfrac{1}{b} - \dfrac{1}{a}}$ $-(b + a)$

56. $\dfrac{\dfrac{6}{p + 2} + 4}{\dfrac{8}{p + 2} - 4}$ $-\dfrac{2p + 7}{2p}$

57. $\dfrac{\dfrac{25}{k + 5} + 5}{\dfrac{5}{k + 5} - 5}$ $-\dfrac{k + 10}{k + 4}$

Section 7.6

For Exercises 58–65, solve the equations.

58. $\dfrac{2}{x} + \dfrac{1}{2} = \dfrac{1}{4}$ $\{-8\}$

59. $\dfrac{1}{y} + \dfrac{3}{4} = \dfrac{1}{4}$ $\{-2\}$

60. $\dfrac{2}{h - 2} + 1 = \dfrac{h}{h + 2}$ $\{0\}$

61. $\dfrac{w}{w - 1} = \dfrac{3}{w + 1} + 1$ $\{2\}$

62. $\dfrac{t + 1}{3} - \dfrac{t - 1}{6} = \dfrac{1}{6}$ $\{-2\}$

63. $\dfrac{w + 1}{w - 3} - \dfrac{3}{w} = \dfrac{12}{w^2 - 3w}$ $\{-1\}$ (The value 3 does not check.)

64. $\dfrac{1}{z + 2} = \dfrac{4}{z^2 - 4} - \dfrac{1}{z - 2}$ $\{\ \}$ (The value 2 does not check.)

65. $\dfrac{y + 1}{y + 3} = \dfrac{y^2 - 11y}{y^2 + y - 6} - \dfrac{y - 3}{y - 2}$ $\{-11, 1\}$

66. Four times a number is added to 5. The sum is then divided by 6. The result is $\frac{7}{2}$. Find the number. The number is 4.

67. Solve the formula $\dfrac{V}{h} = \dfrac{\pi r^2}{3}$ for h. $h = \dfrac{3V}{\pi r^2}$

68. Solve the formula $\dfrac{A}{b} = \dfrac{h}{2}$ for b. $b = \dfrac{2A}{h}$

Section 7.7

For Exercises 69–70, solve the proportions.

69. $\dfrac{m + 2}{8} = \dfrac{m}{3}$ $\left\{\dfrac{6}{5}\right\}$

70. $\dfrac{12}{a} = \dfrac{5}{8}$ $\left\{\dfrac{96}{5}\right\}$

71. A bag of popcorn states that it contains 4 g of fat per serving. If a serving is 2 oz, how many grams of fat are in a 5-oz bag? It contains 10 g of fat.

 Writing   Translating Expression Geometry Scientific Calculator   Video NS&E

72. Bud goes 10 mph faster on his Harley Davidson motorcycle than Ed goes on his Honda motorcycle. If Bud travels 105 mi in the same time that Ed travels 90 mi, what are the rates of the two bikers?
Ed travels at 60 mph, and Bud travels at 70 mph.

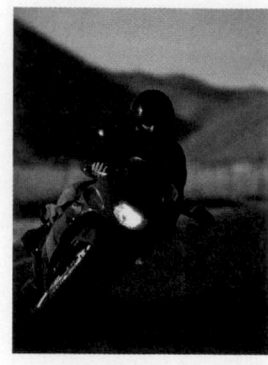

73. There are two pumps set up to fill a small swimming pool. One pump takes 24 min by itself to fill the pool, but the other takes 56 min by itself. How long would it take if both pumps work together?
Together the pumps would fill the pool in 16.8 min.

74. Consider the similar triangles shown here. Find the values of x and y. $x = 11; y = 26$

Chapter 7   Test

For Exercises 1–2,

  a. Identify the restricted values.

  b. Simplify the rational expression.

1. $\dfrac{5(x - 2)(x + 1)}{30(2 - x)}$
  a. $x = 2$ b. $-\dfrac{x + 1}{6}$

2. $\dfrac{7a^2 - 42a}{a^3 - 4a^2 - 12a}$
  a. $a = 6, a = -2, a = 0$ b. $\dfrac{7}{a + 2}$

3. Identify the rational expressions that are equal to -1.   b, c, d

  a. $\dfrac{x + 4}{x - 4}$ **b.** $\dfrac{7 - 2x}{2x - 7}$ **c.** $\dfrac{9x^2 + 16}{-9x^2 - 16}$ **d.** $-\dfrac{x + 5}{x + 5}$

4. Find the LCD of the following pairs of rational expressions.

  a. $\dfrac{x}{3(x + 3)}; \dfrac{7}{5(x + 3)}$ **b.** $\dfrac{-2}{3x^2y}; \dfrac{4}{xy^2}$
    $15(x + 3)$ $3x^2y^2$

For Exercises 5–13, perform the indicated operation.

5. $\dfrac{2}{y^2 + 4y + 3} + \dfrac{1}{3y + 9}$ $\dfrac{y + 7}{3(y + 3)(y + 1)}$

6. $\dfrac{9 - b^2}{5b + 15} \div \dfrac{b - 3}{b + 3}$ $-\dfrac{b + 3}{5}$

7. $\dfrac{y^2}{y - 6} - \dfrac{12y - 36}{y - 6}$ $y - 6$

8. $\dfrac{x + 5}{4x - 8} \div \dfrac{x^2 - 25}{x^2 - x - 2} \cdot \dfrac{3x + 21}{6x + 6}$ $\dfrac{x + 7}{8(x - 5)}$

9. $\dfrac{\dfrac{2}{w + 1} + 1}{\dfrac{8}{w + 1} + 4}$ $\dfrac{1}{4}$

10. $\dfrac{w^2 - 4w}{w^2 - 8w + 16} \cdot \dfrac{w - 4}{w^2 + w}$ $\dfrac{1}{w + 1}$

11. $\dfrac{t}{t - 2} - \dfrac{8}{t^2 - 4}$ $\dfrac{t + 4}{t + 2}$

12. $\dfrac{1}{x + 4} + \dfrac{2}{x^2 + 2x - 8} + \dfrac{x}{x - 2}$ $\dfrac{x(x + 5)}{(x + 4)(x - 2)}$

13. $\dfrac{1 - \dfrac{4}{m}}{m - \dfrac{16}{m}}$ $\dfrac{1}{m + 4}$

For Exercises 14–18, solve the equation.

14. $\dfrac{3}{a} + \dfrac{5}{2} = \dfrac{7}{a}$ $\left\{\dfrac{8}{5}\right\}$

15. $\dfrac{p}{p - 1} + \dfrac{1}{p} = \dfrac{p^2 + 1}{p^2 - p}$ $\{2\}$

16. $\dfrac{3}{c - 2} - \dfrac{1}{c + 1} = \dfrac{7}{c^2 - c - 2}$ $\{1\}$

17. $\dfrac{4x}{x - 4} = 3 + \dfrac{16}{x - 4}$
  $\{ \ \}$ (The value 4 does not check.)

18. $\dfrac{y^2 + 7y}{y - 2} - \dfrac{36}{2y - 4} = 4$
  $\{-5\}$ (The value 2 does not check.)

19. Solve the formula $\dfrac{C}{2} = \dfrac{A}{r}$ for r. $r = \dfrac{2A}{C}$

20. Solve the proportion.

$$\dfrac{y + 7}{-4} = \dfrac{1}{4}\quad \{-8\}$$

21. A recipe for vegetable soup calls for $\frac{1}{2}$ cup of carrots for six servings. How many cups of carrots are needed to prepare 15 servings?
$1\frac{1}{4}$ (1.25) cups of carrots

22. A motorboat can travel 28 mi downstream in the same amount of time as it can travel 18 mi upstream. Find the speed of the current if the boat can travel 23 mph in still water.
The speed of the current is 5 mph.

23. Two printers working together can complete a job in 2 hr. If one printer requires 6 hr to do the job alone, how many hours would the second printer need to complete the job alone?
It would take the second printer 3 hr to do the job working alone.

24. Consider the similar triangles shown here. Find the values of a and b. $a = 5.6; b = 12$

 Writing   Translating Expression   Geometry   Scientific Calculator Video NSE

Chapters 1–7   Cumulative Review Exercises

For Exercises 1–2, simplify completely.

1. $\left(\dfrac{1}{2}\right)^{-4} + 2^4$ 32

2. $|3 - 5| + |-2 + 7|$
   7

3. Solve. $\dfrac{1}{2} - \dfrac{3}{4}(y - 1) = \dfrac{5}{12}$ $\left\{\dfrac{10}{9}\right\}$

4. Complete the table.

Set-Builder Notation	Graph	Interval Notation
$\{x \mid x \geq -1\}$	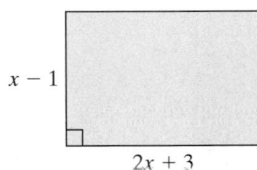	$[-1, \infty)$
$\{x \mid x < 5\}$		$(-\infty, 5)$

5. The perimeter of a rectangular swimming pool is 104 m. The length is 1 m more than twice the width. Find the length and width.
The width is 17 m and the length is 35 m.

6. The height of a triangle is 2 in. less than the base. The area is 40 in.^{2} Find the base and height of the triangle.   The base is 10 in. and the height is 8 in.

7. Simplify. $\left(\dfrac{4x^{-1}y^{-2}}{z^4}\right)^{-2}(2y^{-1}z^3)^3$ $\dfrac{x^2yz^{17}}{2}$

8. The length and width of a rectangle are given in terms of x.

$x - 1$

$2x + 3$

a. Write a polynomial that represents the perimeter of the rectangle. $6x + 4$

b. Write a polynomial that represents the area of the rectangle. $2x^2 + x - 3$

9. Factor completely. $25x^2 - 30x + 9$ $(5x - 3)^2$

10. Factor. $10cd + 5d - 6c - 3$ $(2c + 1)(5d - 3)$

11. Identify the restricted values of the expression.

$$\dfrac{x + 3}{(x - 5)(2x + 1)}$$ $x = 5, x = -\dfrac{1}{2}$

12. Solve the system.

$\begin{aligned} x + 2y &= -7 \\ 6x + 3y &= -6 \end{aligned}$ $\{(1, -4)\}$

13. Divide. $\dfrac{2x - 6}{x^2 - 16} \div \dfrac{10x^2 - 90}{x^2 - x - 12}$ $\dfrac{1}{5(x + 4)}$

14. Simplify.

$$\dfrac{\dfrac{3}{4} - \dfrac{1}{x}}{\dfrac{1}{3x} - \dfrac{1}{4}}$$ -3

15. Solve. $\dfrac{7}{y^2 - 4} = \dfrac{3}{y - 2} + \dfrac{2}{y + 2}$ $\{1\}$

16. Solve the proportion.

$$\dfrac{2b - 5}{6} = \dfrac{4b}{7}$$ $\left\{-\dfrac{7}{2}\right\}$

17. Determine the x- and y-intercepts.

a. $-2x + 4y = 8$ x-intercept: $(-4, 0)$; y-intercept: $(0, 2)$

b. $y = 5x$ x-intercept: $(0, 0)$; y-intercept: $(0, 0)$

18. Determine the slope

a. of the line containing the points $(0, -6)$ and $(-5, 1)$. $m = -\dfrac{7}{5}$

b. of the line $y = -\dfrac{2}{3}x - 6$. $m = -\dfrac{2}{3}$

c. of a line parallel to a line having a slope of 4. $m = 4$

d. of a line perpendicular to a line having a slope of 4. $m = -\dfrac{1}{4}$

19. Find an equation of a line passing through the point $(1, 2)$ and having a slope of 5. Write the answer in slope-intercept form. $y = 5x - 3$

20. A group of teenagers buys 2 large popcorns and 6 drinks at the movie theater for $16. A couple buys 1 large popcorn and 2 drinks for $6.50. Find the price for 1 large popcorn and the price for 1 drink.   One large popcorn costs $3.50, and one drink costs $1.50.

 Writing   Translating Expression   Geometry   Scientific Calculator   Video   NS&E

Relations and Functions

CHAPTER OUTLINE

Chapter 8

In this chapter we will introduce relations, functions, and function notation. To prepare yourself for function notation, practice evaluating expressions.

Are You Prepared?

Substitute the value of x into each expression and evaluate. Then find the answer in the box and write the corresponding letter in the appropriate blank below.

Expression: $x^2 - 5$

1. $x = 6$

2. $x = a^2$

3. $x = a + 1$

Expression: $4x - 3$

4. $x = 12$

5. $x = a^2$

6. $x = a + 1$

Expression: $-x^2 + 1$

7. $x = -3$

8. $x = a^2$

Expression: $x^2 - 2x$

9. $x = 3$

10. $x = a^2$

11. $x = a + 1$

Expression: $|x + 5|$

12. $x = -7$

13. $x = a^2$

14. $x = a + 1$

M	L
2	$a^2 + 2a - 4$
O	I
$4a^2 - 3$	-8
R	I
$a^4 - 2a^2$	$|a + 6|$
N	A
3	$a^2 + 5$
A	N
$a^2 - 1$	31
T	O
$a^4 - 5$	$-a^4 + 1$
E	D
45	$4a + 1$

The set of first components of a $\underset{10}{\text{R}}\ \underset{4}{\text{E}}\ \underset{3}{\text{L}}\ \underset{13}{\text{A}}\ \underset{2}{\text{T}}\ \underset{14}{\text{I}}\ \underset{8}{\text{O}}\ \underset{1}{\text{N}}$

is called the $\underset{6}{\text{D}}\ \underset{5}{\text{O}}\ \underset{12}{\text{M}}\ \underset{11}{\text{A}}\ \underset{7}{\text{I}}\ \underset{9}{\text{N}}$.

Section 8.1 | Introduction to Relations

1. Definition of a Relation

In many naturally occurring phenomena, two variables may be linked by some other type of relationship. Table 8-1 shows a correspondence between the length of a woman's femur and her height. (The femur is the large bone in the thigh attached to the knee and hip.)

Table 8-1

Length of Femur (cm) x	Height (in.) y		Ordered Pair
45.5	65.5	⟶	(45.5, 65.5)
48.2	68.0	⟶	(48.2, 68.0)
41.8	62.2	⟶	(41.8, 62.2)
46.0	66.0	⟶	(46.0, 66.0)
50.4	70.0	⟶	(50.4, 70.0)

Each data point from Table 8-1 may be represented as an ordered pair. In this case, the first value represents the length of a woman's femur and the second, the woman's height. The set of ordered pairs {(45.5, 65.5), (48.2, 68.0), (41.8, 62.2), (46.0, 66.0), (50.4, 70.0)} defines a relation between femur length and height.

2. Domain and Range of a Relation

Instructor Note: To help students remember domain and range, "D" is earlier in the alphabet than "R," just as x is earlier in the alphabet than y.

> **DEFINITION** Relation in x and y
>
> A set of ordered pairs (x, y) is called a **relation in x and y**. Furthermore,
> - The set of first components in the ordered pairs is called the **domain of the relation**.
> - The set of second components in the ordered pairs is called the **range of the relation**.

Classroom Example: p. 567, Exercise 4

Example 1 Finding the Domain and Range of a Relation

Find the domain and range of the relation linking the length of a woman's femur to her height {(45.5, 65.5), (48.2, 68.0), (41.8, 62.2), (46.0, 66.0), (50.4, 70.0)}.

Solution:

Domain: {45.5, 48.2, 41.8, 46.0, 50.4}   Set of first components

Range: {65.5, 68.0, 62.2, 66.0, 70.0}   Set of second components

Skill Practice Find the domain and range of the relation.

1. $\left\{ (0, 0), (-8, 4), \left(\frac{1}{2}, 1\right), (-3, 4), (-8, 0) \right\}$

Answer

1. Domain: $\left\{ 0, -8, \frac{1}{2}, -3 \right\}$;
   range: {0, 4, 1}

The x and y components that constitute the ordered pairs in a relation do not need to be numerical. This is demonstrated in Example 2.

Classroom Example: p. 567, Exercise 6

Example 2	**Writing a Relation and Finding Its Domain and Range**

Table 8-2 gives five states in the United States and the corresponding number of representatives in the House of Representatives for a recent year.

a. The data in the table define a relation. Write a list of ordered pairs for this relation.

b. Write the domain and range.

Table 8-2

State x	Number of Representatives y
Alabama	7
California	53
Colorado	7
Florida	25
Kansas	4

Solution:

a. {(Alabama, 7), (California, 53), (Colorado, 7), (Florida, 25), (Kansas, 4)}

b. Domain: {Alabama, California, Colorado, Florida, Kansas}

   Range: {7, 53, 25, 4}   (*Note:* The element 7 is not listed twice.)

Skill Practice The table depicts six types of animals and their average longevity.

2. Write the ordered pairs indicated by the relation in the table.

3. Find the domain and range of the relation.

Animal x	Longevity (Years) y
Bear	22.5
Cat	11
Cow	20.5
Deer	12.5
Dog	11
Elephant	35

A relation may consist of a finite number of ordered pairs or an infinite number of ordered pairs. Furthermore, a relation may be defined by several different methods.

- A relation may be defined as a set of ordered pairs.

$$\{(1, 2), (-3, 4), (1, -4), (3, 4)\}$$

- A relation may be defined by a correspondence (Figure 8-1). The corresponding ordered pairs are {(1, 2), (1, −4), (−3, 4), (3, 4)}.

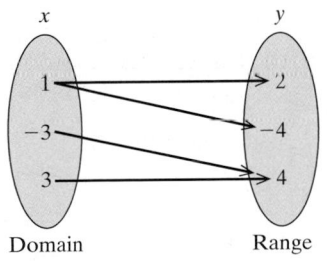

Figure 8-1

- A relation may be defined by a graph (Figure 8-2). The corresponding ordered pairs are {(1, 2), (−3, 4), (1, −4), (3, 4)}.

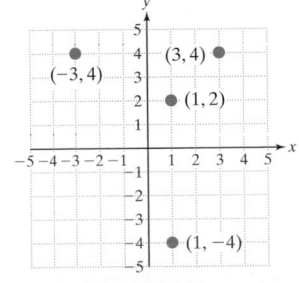

Figure 8-2

Answers

2. {(Bear, 22.5), (Cat, 11), (Cow, 20.5), (Deer, 12.5), (Dog, 11), (Elephant, 35)}

3. Domain: {Bear, Cat, Cow, Deer, Dog, Elephant}; range: {22.5, 11, 20.5, 12.5, 35}

- A relation may be expressed by an equation such as $x = y^2$. The solutions to this equation define an infinite set of ordered pairs of the form $\{(x, y) \mid x = y^2\}$. The solutions can also be represented by a graph in a rectangular coordinate system (Figure 8-3).

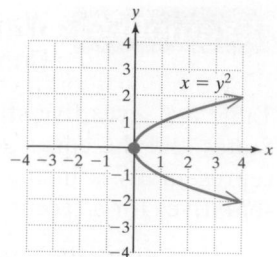

Figure 8-3

Classroom Examples: pp. 567–568,
Exercises 8 and 14

Example 3   **Finding the Domain and Range of a Relation**

Write the relation as a set of ordered pairs. Then find the domain and range.

a.

b.

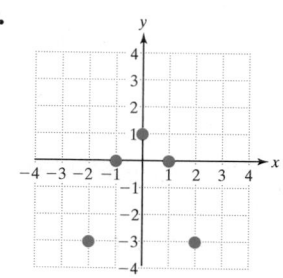

Solution:

a. From the figure, the relation defines the set of ordered pairs:
$\{(3, -9), (2, -9), (-7, -9)\}$

Domain: $\{3, 2, -7\}$

Range: $\{-9\}$

b. The points in the graph make up the set of ordered pairs:
$\{(-2, -3), (-1, 0), (0, 1), (1, 0), (2, -3)\}$

Domain: $\{-2, -1, 0, 1, 2\}$

Range: $\{-3, 0, 1\}$

Skill Practice   Find the domain and range of the relations.

4.

5.

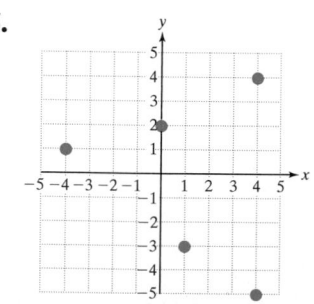

Example 4 **Finding the Domain and Range of a Relation**

Use interval notation to express the domain and range of the relation.

Classroom Examples: pp. 568–569, Exercises 16 and 26

a.

b.

Solution:

a.

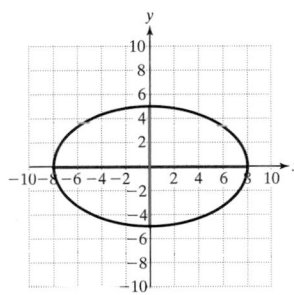

The domain consists of an infinite number of x-values extending from -8 to 8 (shown in red). The range consists of all y-values from -5 to 5 (shown in blue). Thus, the domain and range must be expressed in set-builder notation or in interval notation.

Domain: $[-8, 8]$

Range: $[-5, 5]$

b.

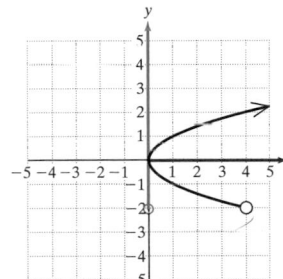

The arrow on the curve indicates that the graph extends infinitely far up and to the right. The open circle means that the graph will end at the point $(4, -2)$, but not include that point.

Domain: $[0, \infty)$

Range: $(-2, \infty)$

Skill Practice Use interval notation to express the domain and range of the relations.

6.

7.

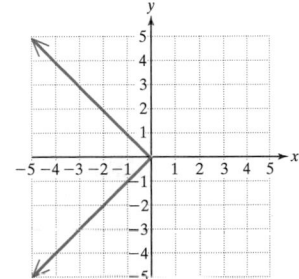

Answers
6. Domain: $[-4, 0]$
  Range: $[-2, 2]$
7. Domain: $(-\infty, 0]$
  Range: $(-\infty, \infty)$

3. Applications Involving Relations

Classroom Example: p. 570, Exercise 34

Table 8-3

Length of Femur (cm) x	Height (in.) y
45.5	65.5
48.2	68.0
41.8	62.2
46.0	66.0
50.4	70.0

Example 5   Analyzing a Relation

The data in Table 8-3 depict the length of a woman's femur and her corresponding height. Based on these data, a forensics specialist can find a linear relationship between height y (in inches) and femur length x (in centimeters):

$$y = 0.91x + 24 \qquad 40 \le x \le 55$$

From this type of relationship, the height of a woman can be inferred based on skeletal remains.

a. Find the height of a woman whose femur is 46.0 cm.

b. Find the height of a woman whose femur is 51.0 cm.

c. Why is the domain restricted to $40 \le x \le 55$?

Solution:

a. $y = 0.91x + 24$

$\quad = 0.91(46.0) + 24 \qquad$ Substitute $x = 46.0$ cm.

$\quad = 65.86 \qquad\qquad\quad$ The woman is approximately 65.9 in. tall.

b. $y = 0.91x + 24$

$\quad = 0.91(51.0) + 24 \qquad$ Substitute $x = 51.0$ cm.

$\quad = 70.41 \qquad\qquad\quad$ The woman is approximately 70.4 in. tall.

c. The domain restricts femur length to values between 40 cm and 55 cm inclusive. These values are within the normal lengths for an adult female and are in the proximity of the observed data (Figure 8-4).

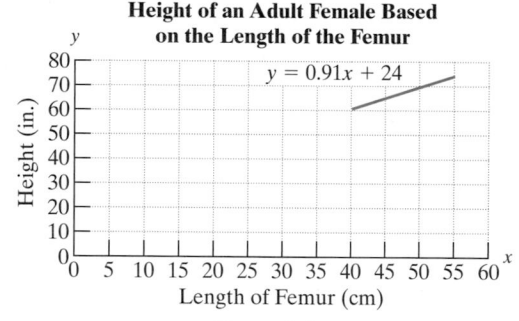

Height of an Adult Female Based on the Length of the Femur

$y = 0.91x + 24$

Figure 8-4

Skill Practice The linear equation, $y = -0.014x + 64.5$, for $1500 \le x \le 4000$, relates the weight of a car, x (in pounds), to its gas mileage, y (in mpg).

8. Find the gas mileage in miles per gallon for a car weighing 2550 lb.

9. Find the gas mileage for a car weighing 2850 lb.

10. Why is the domain restricted to $1500 \le x \le 4000$?

Answers

8. 28.8 mpg   **9.** 24.6 mpg
10. The relation is valid only for cars weighing between 1500 lb and 4000 lb, inclusive.

| Section 8.1 | **Practice Exercises** |

Study Skills Exercises

1. Define the key terms.

   a. relation in *x* and *y*   **b. domain of a relation**   **c. range of a relation**

Concept 2: Domain and Range of a Relation

2. Explain how to determine the domain and range of a relation represented by a set of ordered pairs.
   The domain is the set consisting of the first coordinates of the ordered pairs. The range is the set consisting of the second coordinates
   of the ordered pairs.

For Exercises 3–14,

   a. Write the relation as a set of ordered pairs.

   b. Determine the domain and range. **(See Examples 1–3.)**

3.

State	% of Population Uninsured
Alabama	15.3
Florida	20.2
Massachusetts	13.4
California	18.8
Minnesota	7.9

a. {(Alabama, 15.3), (Florida, 20.2), (Massachusetts, 13.4), (California, 18.8), (Minnesota, 7.9)}
b. Domain: {Alabama, Florida, Massachusetts, California, Minnesota}; range: {15.3, 20.2, 13.4, 18.8, 7.9}

4.

x	y
0	3
−2	$\frac{1}{2}$
−7	1
−2	8
5	1

a. {(0, 3), $(-2, \frac{1}{2})$, (−7, 1), (−2, 8), (5, 1)}
b. Domain: {0, −2, −7, 5}; range: {3, $\frac{1}{2}$, 1, 8}

5.

Country	Year of First Man or Woman in Space
USSR	1961
USA	1962
Poland	1978
Vietnam	1980
Cuba	1980

a. {(USSR, 1961), (USA, 1962), (Poland, 1978), (Vietnam, 1980), (Cuba, 1980)}
b. Domain: {USSR, USA, Poland, Vietnam, Cuba}; range: {1961, 1962, 1978, 1980}

6.

State, x	Year of Statehood, y
Maine	1820
Nebraska	1823
Utah	1847
Hawaii	1959
Alaska	1959

a. {(Maine, 1820), (Nebraska, 1823), (Utah, 1847), (Hawaii, 1959), (Alaska, 1959)}
b. Domain: {Maine, Nebraska, Utah, Hawaii, Alaska}; range: {1820, 1823, 1847, 1959}

7.

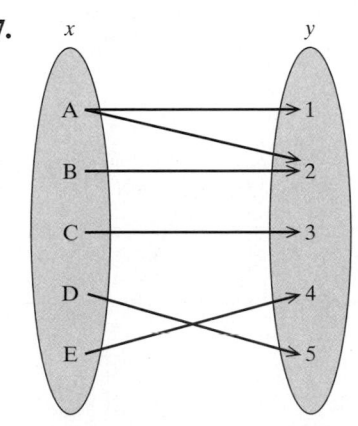

a. {(A, 1), (A, 2), (B, 2), (C, 3), (D, 5), (E, 4)}
b. Domain: {A, B, C, D, E}; range: {1, 2, 3, 4, 5}

8.

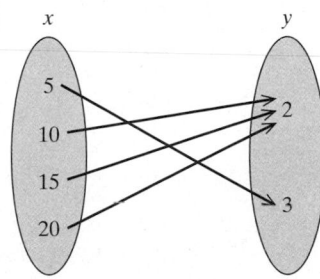

a. {(5, 3), (10, 2), (15, 2), (20, 2)}
b. Domain: {5, 10, 15, 20}; range: {2, 3}

9.

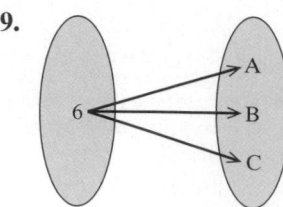

a. {(6, A), (6, B), (6, C)}
b. Domain: {6};
range: {A, B, C}

10.

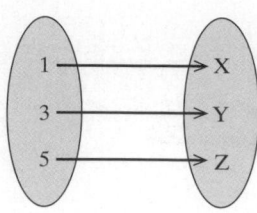

a. {(1, X), (3, Y), (5, Z)}
b. Domain: {1, 3, 5};
range: {X, Y, Z}

11.

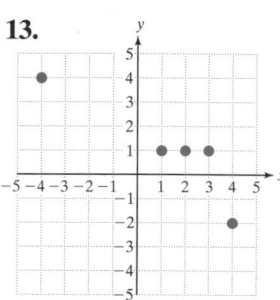

a. {(−4, 1), (0, 3), (1, −1), (3, 0)}
b. Domain: {−4, 0, 1, 3};
range: {−1, 0, 1, 3}

12.

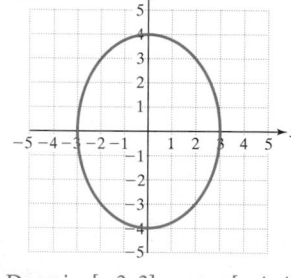

a. {(−2, 0), (−2, 4), (2, −1), (3, 4), (4, −4)}
b. Domain: {−2, 2, 3, 4};
range: {−4, −1, 0, 4}

13.

a. {(−4, 4), (1, 1), (2, 1), (3, 1), (4, −2)}
b. Domain: {−4, 1, 2, 3, 4};
range: {−2, 1, 4}

14.

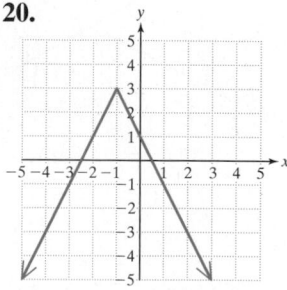

a. {(−3, 3), (−3, −2), (0, 0), (2, 0), (2, 3)}
b. Domain: {−3, 0, 2};
range: {−2, 0, 3}

For Exercises 15–30, find the domain and range of the relations. Use interval notation where appropriate.
(See Example 4.)

15.

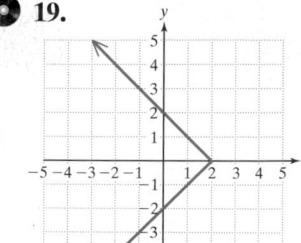

Domain: [0, 4]; range: [−2, 2]

16.

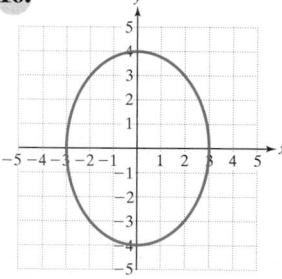

Domain: [−3, 3]; range: [−4, 4]

17.

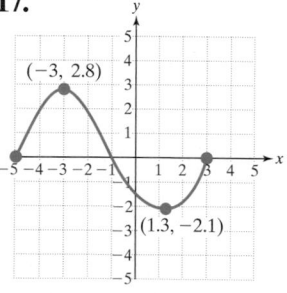

(−3, 2.8)
(1.3, −2.1)

Domain: [−5, 3]; range: [−2.1, 2.8]

18.

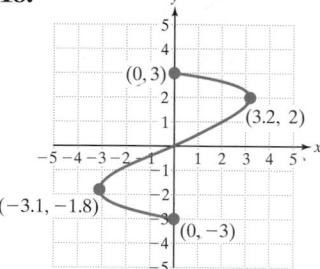

(0, 3)
(3.2, 2)
(−3.1, −1.8)
(0, −3)

Domain: [−3.1, 3.2]; range: [−3, 3]

19.

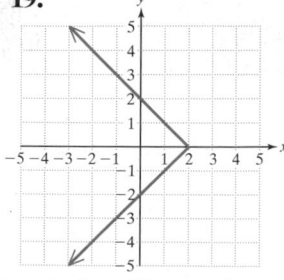

Domain: (−∞, 2]; range: (−∞, ∞)

20.

Domain: (−∞, ∞); range: (−∞, 3]

21.

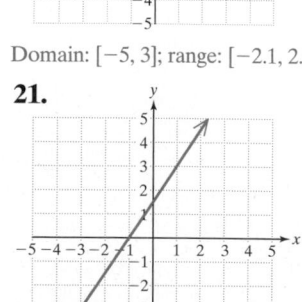

Domain: (−∞, ∞); range: (−∞, ∞)

22.

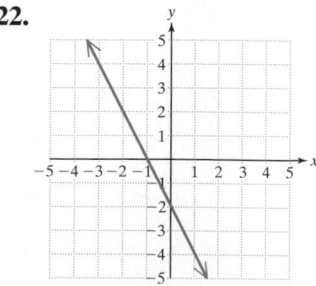

Domain: (−∞, ∞); range: (−∞, ∞)

 Writing   Translating Expression   Geometry   Scientific Calculator   Video   NS⁰E

23.

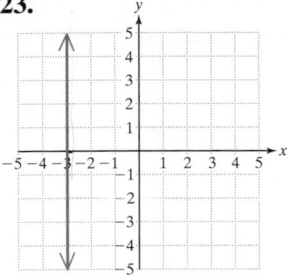

Domain: $\{-3\}$; range: $(-\infty, \infty)$

24.

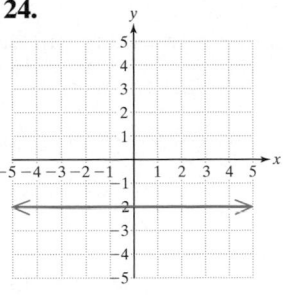

Domain: $(-\infty, \infty)$; range: $\{-2\}$

25.

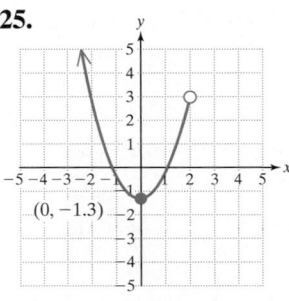

(0, −1.3)

Domain: $(-\infty, 2)$; range: $[-1.3, \infty)$

26.

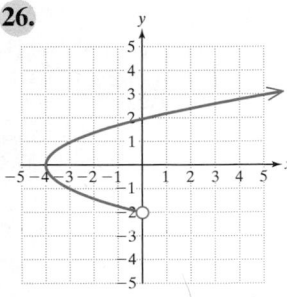

Domain: $[-4, \infty)$; range: $(-2, \infty)$

27.

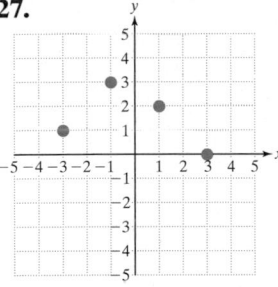

Domain: $\{-3, -1, 1, 3\}$;
range: $\{0, 1, 2, 3\}$

28.

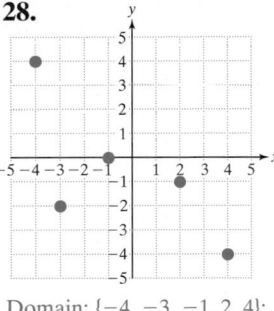

Domain: $\{-4, -3, -1, 2, 4\}$;
range: $\{-4, -2, -1, 0, 4\}$

29.

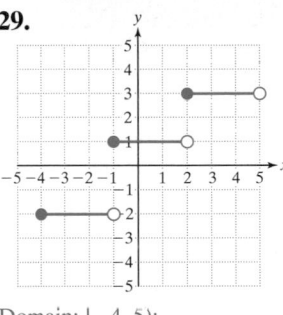

Domain: $[-4, 5)$;
range: $\{-2, 1, 3\}$

30.

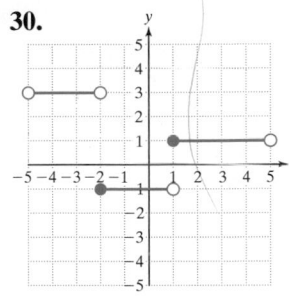

Domain: $(-5, 5)$;
range: $\{-1, 1, 3\}$

Concept 3: Applications Involving Relations

31. The table gives a relation between the month of the year and the average precipitation for that month for Miami, Florida. **(See Example 5.)**

   a. What is the range element corresponding to April?
     2.85

   b. What is the range element corresponding to June?
     9.33

   c. Which element in the domain corresponds to the least value in the range?   Dec.

   d. Complete the ordered pair: (, 2.66)   Nov.

   e. Complete the ordered pair: (Sept.,)   7.63

   f. What is the domain of this relation?   {Jan., Feb., Mar., Apr., May, June, July, Aug., Sept., Oct., Nov., Dec.}

Month x	Precipitation (in.) y	Month x	Precipitation (in.) y
Jan.	2.01	July	5.70
Feb.	2.08	Aug.	7.58
Mar.	2.39	Sept.	7.63
Apr.	2.85	Oct.	5.64
May	6.21	Nov.	2.66
June	9.33	Dec.	1.83

Source: U.S. National Oceanic and Atmospheric Administration

32. The table gives a relation between a person's age and the person's maximum recommended heart rate.

   a. What is the domain?   {20, 30, 40, 50, 60}

   b. What is the range?   {200, 190, 180, 170, 160}

   c. The range element 200 corresponds to what element in the domain?   20

   d. Complete the ordered pair: (50,)   170

   e. Complete the ordered pair: (, 190)   30

Age (years) x	Maximum Recommended Heart Rate (Beats per Minute) y
20	200
30	190
40	180
50	170
60	160

33. The population of Canada, y (in millions), can be approximated by the relation $y = 0.146x + 31$, where x represents the number of years since 2000.

   a. Approximate the population of Canada in the year 2006.   31.876 million or 31,876,000

   b. In what year will the population of Canada reach approximately 32,752,000?   The year 2012

 Writing   Translating Expression   Geometry   Scientific Calculator   Video   NS&E

34. As of April 2006, the world record times for selected women's track and field events are shown in the table. The women's world record time y (in seconds) required to run x meters can be approximated by the relation $y = 0.159x - 10.79$.

Distance (m)	Time (sec)	Winner's Name and Country
100	10.49	Florence Griffith Joyner (United States)
200	21.34	Florence Griffith Joyner (United States)
400	47.60	Marita Koch (East Germany)
800	113.28	Jarmila Kratochvilova (Czechoslovakia)
1000	148.98	Svetlana Masterkova (Russia)
1500	230.46	Qu Yunxia (China)

a. Predict the time required for a 500-m race.   68.71 sec

b. Use this model to predict the time for a 1000-m race. Is this value exactly the same as the data value given in the table? Explain.   148.21 sec. The time is not exactly the same because the equation represents approximate times.

Expanding Your Skills

35. a. Define a relation with four ordered pairs such that the first element of the ordered pair is the name of a friend and the second element is your friend's place of birth.
For example: {(Julie, New York), (Peggy, Florida), (Stephen, Kansas), (Pat, New York)}
b. State the domain and range of this relation.
Domain: {Julie, Peggy, Stephen, Pat}; range: {New York, Florida, Kansas}

36. a. Define a relation with four ordered pairs such that the first element is a state and the second element is its capital.   For example: {(Michigan, Lansing), (Florida, Tallahassee), (Texas, Austin), (New York, Albany)}

b. State the domain and range of this relation.   Domain: {Michigan, Florida, Texas, New York}; range: {Lansing, Tallahassee, Austin, Albany}

37. Use a mathematical equation to define a relation whose second component y is 1 less than 2 times the first component x. $y = 2x - 1$

38. Use a mathematical equation to define a relation whose second component y is 3 more than the first component x. $y = x + 3$

39. Use a mathematical equation to define a relation whose second component is the square of the first component. $y = x^2$

40. Use a mathematical equation to define a relation whose second component is one-fourth the first component. $y = \frac{1}{4}x$

Introduction to Functions

1. Definition of a Function

In this section, we introduce a special type of relation called a function.

1. **Definition of a Function**
2. **Vertical Line Test**
3. **Function Notation**
4. **Finding Function Values from a Graph**
5. **Domain of a Function**

> **DEFINITION Function**
>
> Given a relation in x and y, we say "y is a **function** of x" if, for each element x in the domain, there is exactly one value of y in the range.
>
> *Note:* This means that no two ordered pairs may have the same first coordinate and different second coordinates.

To understand the difference between a relation that is a function and a relation that is not a function, consider Example 1.

Example 1 Determining Whether a Relation Is a Function

Determine which of the relations define y as a function of x.

a.

b.

c.

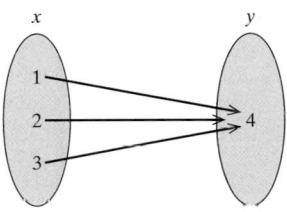

Classroom Examples: p. 578, Exercises 6 and 10

Solution:

a. This relation is defined by the set of ordered pairs

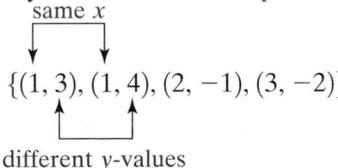

When $x = 1$, there are *two* possible range elements: $y = 3$ and $y = 4$. Therefore, this relation is *not* a function.

b. This relation is defined by the set of ordered pairs $\{(1, 4), (2, -1), (3, 2)\}$.

Notice that no two ordered pairs have the same value of x but different values of y. Therefore, this relation *is* a function.

c. This relation is defined by the set of ordered pairs $\{(1, 4), (2, 4), (3, 4)\}$.

Notice that no two ordered pairs have the same value of x but different values of y. Therefore, this relation *is* a function.

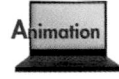

Skill Practice Determine if the relations define *y* as a function of *x*.

1.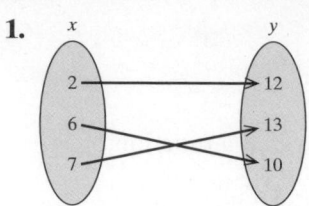

2. $\{(4, 2), (-5, 4), (0, 0), (8, 4)\}$

3. $\{(-1, 6), (8, 9), (-1, 4), (-3, 10)\}$

2. Vertical Line Test

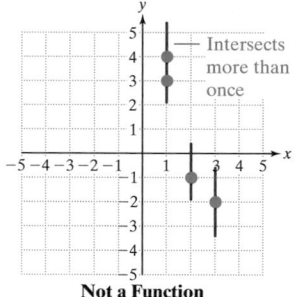

Figure 8-5

A relation that is not a function has at least one domain element *x* paired with more than one range value *y*. For example, the set $\{(4, 2), (4, -2)\}$ does not define a function because two different *y*-values correspond to the same *x*. These two points are aligned vertically in the *xy*-plane, and a vertical line drawn through one point also intersects the other point (see Figure 8-5). If a vertical line drawn through a graph of a relation intersects the graph in more than one point, the relation cannot be a function. This idea is stated formally as the **vertical line test**.

> **PROCEDURE** The Vertical Line Test
>
> Consider a relation defined by a set of points (x, y) in a rectangular coordinate system. The graph defines *y* as a function of *x* if no vertical line intersects the graph in more than one point.

The vertical line test can be demonstrated by graphing the ordered pairs from the relations in Example 1.

a. $\{(1, 3), (1, 4), (2, -1), (3, -2)\}$　　**b.** $\{(1, 4), (2, -1), (3, 2)\}$

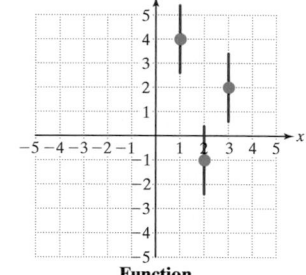

Not a Function
A vertical line intersects in more than one point.

Function
No vertical line intersects more than once.

Example 2　**Using the Vertical Line Test**

Use the vertical line test to determine whether the relations define *y* as a function of *x*.

a. 　　**b.**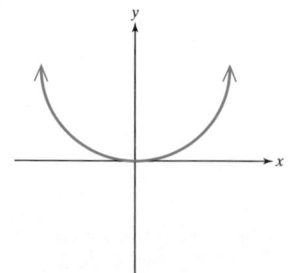

Answers

1. Yes　**2.** Yes　**3.** No

Solution:

a.

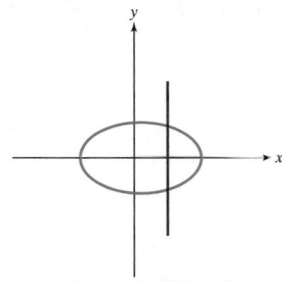

Not a Function
A vertical line intersects
in more than one point.

b.

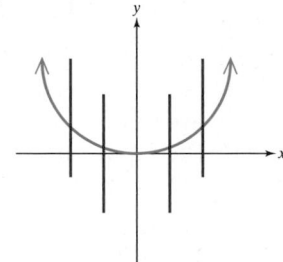

Function
No vertical line intersects
in more than one point.

Skill Practice Use the vertical line test to determine whether the relations
define y as a function of x.

4.

5.

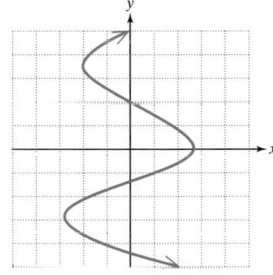

3. Function Notation

A function is defined as a relation with the added restriction that each value in the
domain must have only one corresponding y value in the range. In mathematics,
functions are often given by rules or equations to define the relationship between
two or more variables. For example, the equation $y = 2x$ defines the set of ordered
pairs such that the y value is twice the x value.

When a function is defined by an equation, we often use **function notation**. For
example, the equation $y = 2x$ may be written in function notation as

$f(x) = 2x$ • f is the name of the function.

          • x is an input value from the domain of the function.

          • $f(x)$ is the function value (y value) corresponding to x.

The notation $f(x)$ is read as "f of x" or "the value of the function f at x." ··············

A function may be evaluated at different values of x by substituting x-values
from the domain into the function. For example, to evaluate the function defined
by $f(x) = 2x$ at $x = 5$, substitute $x = 5$ into the function.

$$f(x) = 2x$$

$$f(5) = 2(5)$$

$$f(5) = 10$$

> **Avoiding Mistakes**
>
> Be sure to note that $f(x)$ is *not f · x*.

TIP: $f(5) = 10$ can be
written as the ordered pair
(5, 10).

Answers

4. Yes   **5.** No

Thus, when $x = 5$, the corresponding function value is 10. We say:

- f of 5 is 10.
- f at 5 is 10.
- f evaluated at 5 is 10.

The names of functions are often given by either lowercase or uppercase letters, such as f, g, h, p, K, and M. The input variable may also be a letter other than x. For example, the function $y = P(t)$ might represent population as a function of time.

Classroom Examples: p. 579,
Exercises 18 and 22

Example 3 Evaluating a Function

Given the function defined by $g(x) = \frac{1}{2}x - 1$, find the function values.

a. $g(0)$ **b.** $g(2)$ **c.** $g(4)$ **d.** $g(-2)$

Solution:

a. $g(x) = \dfrac{1}{2}x - 1$

$g(0) = \dfrac{1}{2}(0) - 1$

$= 0 - 1$

$= -1$

We say that "g of 0 is -1."
This is equivalent to the ordered
pair $(0, -1)$.

b. $g(x) = \dfrac{1}{2}x - 1$

$g(2) = \dfrac{1}{2}(2) - 1$

$= 1 - 1$

$= 0$

We say that "g of 2 is 0."
This is equivalent to the ordered
pair $(2, 0)$.

c. $g(x) = \dfrac{1}{2}x - 1$

$g(4) = \dfrac{1}{2}(4) - 1$

$= 2 - 1$

$= 1$

We say that "g of 4 is 1."
This is equivalent to the ordered
pair $(4, 1)$.

d. $g(x) = \dfrac{1}{2}x - 1$

$g(-2) = \dfrac{1}{2}(-2) - 1$

$= -1 - 1$

$= -2$

We say that "g of -2 is -2."
This is equivalent to the ordered
pair $(-2, -2)$.

Skill Practice Given the function defined by $f(x) = -2x - 3$, find the function values.

6. $f(1)$ **7.** $f(0)$ **8.** $f(-3)$ **9.** $f\left(\dfrac{1}{2}\right)$

Figure 8-6

In Example 3, notice that $g(0)$, $g(2)$, $g(4)$, and $g(-2)$ correspond to the ordered pairs $(0, -1)$, $(2, 0)$, $(4, 1)$, and $(-2, -2)$. In the graph, these points "line up." The graph of *all* ordered pairs defined by this function is a line with a slope of $\frac{1}{2}$ and y-intercept of $(0, -1)$ (Figure 8-6). This should not be surprising because the function defined by $g(x) = \frac{1}{2}x - 1$ is equivalent to $y = \frac{1}{2}x - 1$.

Answers

6. -5 **7.** -3 **8.** 3   **9.** -4

Calculator Connections

The values of $g(x)$ in Example 3 can be found using a *Table* feature.

$$Y_1 = \tfrac{1}{2}x - 1$$

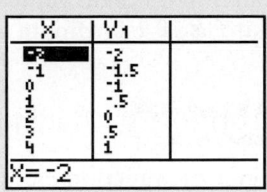

Function values can also be evaluated by using a *Value* (or *Eval*) feature. The value of $g(4)$ is shown here.

A function may be evaluated at numerical values or at algebraic expressions, as shown in Example 4.

Classroom Examples: p. 579, Exercises 24 and 38

Example 4 Evaluating Functions

Given the functions defined by $f(x) = x^2 - 2x$ and $g(x) = 3x + 5$, find the function values.

a. $f(t)$ **b.** $g(w + 4)$ **c.** $f(-t)$

Solution:

a. $f(x) = x^2 - 2x$

$f(t) = (t)^2 - 2(t)$ Substitute $x = t$ for all values of x in the function.

$\quad\;\; = t^2 - 2t$ Simplify.

b. $\quad g(x) = 3x + 5$

$g(w + 4) = 3(w + 4) + 5$ Substitute $x = w + 4$ for all values of x in the function.

$\quad\quad\quad = 3w + 12 + 5$

$\quad\quad\quad = 3w + 17$ Simplify.

c. $\quad f(x) = x^2 - 2x$ Substitute $-t$ for x.

$f(-t) = (-t)^2 \quad 2(-t)$

$\quad\;\; = t^2 + 2t$ Simplify.

Skill Practice Given the function defined by $g(x) = 4x - 3$, find the function values.

10. $g(a)$ **11.** $g(x + h)$ **12.** $g(-x)$

Answers

10. $4a - 3$ **11.** $4x + 4h - 3$

12. $-4x - 3$

4. Finding Function Values from a Graph

We can find function values by looking at a graph of the function. The value of $f(a)$ refers to the y-coordinate of a point with x-coordinate a.

Example 5   Finding Function Values from a Graph

Consider the function pictured in Figure 8-7.

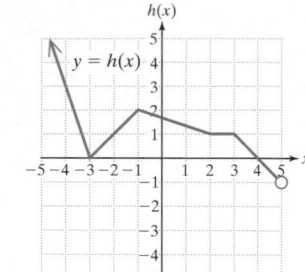

a. Find $h(-1)$.

b. Find $h(2)$.

c. Find $h(5)$.

d. For what value of x is $h(x) = 3$?

e. For what values of x is $h(x) = 0$?

Figure 8-7

Solution:

a. $h(-1) = 2$ This corresponds to the ordered pair $(-1, 2)$.

b. $h(2) = 1$ This corresponds to the ordered pair $(2, 1)$.

c. $h(5)$ is not defined.   The value 5 is not in the domain.

d. $h(x) = 3$ for $x = -4$ This corresponds to the ordered pair $(-4, 3)$.

e. $h(x) = 0$ for $x = -3$ and $x = 4$ These are the ordered pairs $(-3, 0)$ and $(4, 0)$.

Skill Practice Refer to the function graphed here.

13. Find $f(0)$.

14. Find $f(-2)$.

15. Find $f(5)$.

16. For what value(s) of x is $f(x) = 0$?

17. For what value(s) of x is $f(x) = -4$?

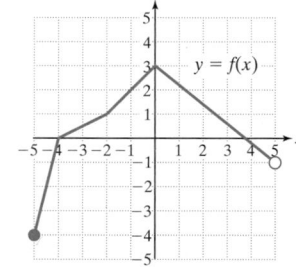

5. Domain of a Function

A function is a relation, and it is often necessary to determine its domain and range. Consider a function defined by the equation $y = f(x)$. The **domain** of f is the set of all x-values that when substituted into the function produce a real number. The **range** of f is the set of all y-values corresponding to the values of x in the domain.

To find the domain of a function defined by $y = f(x)$, keep these guidelines in mind.

- Exclude values of x that make the denominator of a fraction zero.

- Exclude values of x that make the expression within a square root negative.

Answers

13. 3   14. 1

15. not defined

16. $x = -4$ and $x = 4$

17. $x = -5$

| Example 6 | Finding the Domain of a Function

Classroom Examples: p. 581, Exercises 74, 80, and 88

Write the domain in interval notation.

a. $f(x) = \dfrac{x + 7}{2x - 1}$ 　　**b.** $h(x) = \dfrac{x - 4}{x^2 + 9}$

c. $k(t) = \sqrt{t + 4}$ 　　**d.** $g(t) = t^2 - 3t$

Instructor Note: Example 6 shows students that they can find the domain of a function without needing its graph. If you want to emphasize the graphical relationship, show the students the graphs of these functions in class. Or have the students graph the functions on a graphing calculator.

Solution:

a. $f(x) = \frac{x+7}{2x-1}$ will not be a real number when the denominator is zero, that is, when

$$2x - 1 = 0$$

$$2x = 1$$

$$x = \frac{1}{2}$$ 　　The value $x = \frac{1}{2}$ must be *excluded* from the domain.

The number line indicates that the domain consists of two intervals, $(-\infty, \frac{1}{2})$ and $(\frac{1}{2}, \infty)$. We use the notation $\cup$ to combine the two intervals. The symbol $\cup$ stands for union. The union of two intervals consists of all the numbers in the first interval, along with all the numbers in the second. This will be discussed further in Section 9.1.

Interval notation: $\left(-\infty, \dfrac{1}{2}\right) \cup \left(\dfrac{1}{2}, \infty\right)$

b. For $h(x) = \frac{x-4}{x^2+9}$ the quantity x^2 is greater than or equal to 0 for all real numbers x, and the number 9 is positive. The sum $x^2 + 9$ must be *positive* for all real numbers x. The denominator will never be zero; therefore, the domain is the set of all real numbers.

Interval notation: $(-\infty, \infty)$

c. The function defined by $k(t) = \sqrt{t + 4}$ will not be a real number when the radicand is negative. The domain is the set of all t values that make the radicand *greater than or equal to zero:*

$$t + 4 \geq 0$$

$$t \geq -4$$

Interval notation: $[-4, \infty)$

d. The function defined by $g(t) = t^2 - 3t$ has no restrictions on its domain because any real number substituted for t will produce a real number. The domain is the set of all real numbers.

Interval notation: $(-\infty, \infty)$

Skill Practice Write the domain in interval notation.

18. $f(x) = \dfrac{2x + 1}{x - 9}$ 　　**19.** $k(x) = \dfrac{-5}{4x^2 + 1}$

20. $g(x) = \sqrt{x - 2}$ 　　**21.** $h(x) = x + 6$

Answers

18. $(-\infty, 9) \cup (9, \infty)$ 　**19.** $(-\infty, \infty)$
20. $[2, \infty)$ 　**21.** $(-\infty, \infty)$

Section 8.2 Practice Exercises

Study Skills Exercise

1. Define the key terms.

   a. function   **b. function notation**   **c. domain**   **d. range**   **e. vertical line test**

Review Exercises

For Exercises 2–4, **a.** write the relation as a set of ordered pairs, **b.** identify the domain, and **c.** identify the range.

2.

Parent, x	Child, y
Kevin	Kayla
Kevin	Kira
Kathleen	Katie
Kathleen	Kira

a. {(Kevin, Kayla), (Kevin, Kira),
(Kathleen, Katie), (Kathleen, Kira)}
b. {Kevin, Kathleen}
c. {Kayla, Katie, Kira}

3.

a. {(−2,−4), (−1, −1), (0, 0), (1, −1), (2, −4)}
b. {−2, −1, 0, 1, 2} c. {−4, −1, 0}

4.

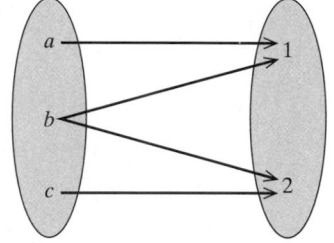

a. {(a, 1), (b, 1), (b, 2), (c, 2)}
b. {a, b, c} c. {1, 2}

Concept 1: Definition of a Function

For Exercises 5–10, determine if the relation defines y as a function of x. **(See Example 1.)**

5.

Function

6.

Not a function

7.

Not a function

8.

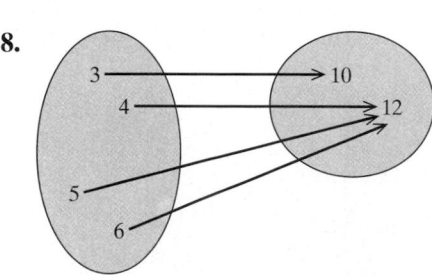

Function

9. {(1, 2), (3, 4), (5, 4), (−9, 3)}

Function

10. $\left\{(0, -1.1), \left(\frac{1}{2}, 8\right), (1.1, 8), \left(4, \frac{1}{2}\right)\right\}$

Function

Concept 2: Vertical Line Test

For Exercises 11–16, use the vertical line test to determine whether the relation defines y as a function of x.
(See Example 2.)

11.

Not a function

12.

Function

13.

Function

14.

Not a function

15.

Not a function

16.

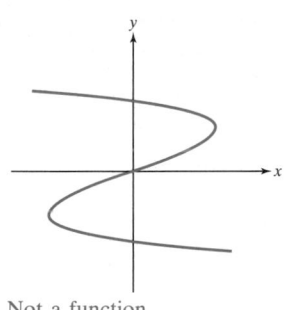

Not a function

Concept 3: Function Notation

Consider the functions defined by $f(x) = 6x - 2$, $g(x) = -x^2 - 4x + 1$, $h(x) = 7$, and $k(x) = |x - 2|$. For Exercises 17–48, find the following. **(See Examples 3–4.)**

17. $g(2)$ -11

18. $k(2)$ 0

19. $g(0)$ 1

20. $h(0)$ 7

21. $k(0)$ 2

22. $f(0)$ -2

23. $f(t)$ $6t - 2$

24. $g(a)$ $-a^2 - 4a + 1$

25. $h(u)$ 7

26. $k(v)$ $|v - 2|$

27. $g(-3)$ 4

28. $h(-5)$ 7

29. $k(-2)$ 4

30. $f(-6)$ -38

31. $f(x + 1)$ $6x + 4$

32. $h(x + 1)$ 7

33. $g(2x)$ $-4x^2 - 8x + 1$

34. $k(x - 3)$ $|x - 5|$

35. $g(-\pi)$ $-\pi^2 + 4\pi + 1$

36. $g(a^2)$ $-a^4 - 4a^2 + 1$

37. $h(a + b)$ 7

38. $f(x + h)$ $6x + 6h - 2$

39. $f(-a)$ $-6a - 2$

40. $g(-b)$ $-b^2 + 4b + 1$

41. $k(-c)$ $|-c - 2|$

42. $h(-x)$ 7

43. $f\left(\dfrac{1}{2}\right)$ 1

44. $g\left(\dfrac{1}{4}\right)$ $-\dfrac{1}{16}$

45. $h\left(\dfrac{1}{7}\right)$ 7

46. $k\left(\dfrac{3}{2}\right)$ $\dfrac{1}{2}$

47. $f(-2.8)$ -18.8

48. $k(-5.4)$ 7.4

Consider the functions $p = \{(\frac{1}{2}, 6), (2, -7), (1, 0), (3, 2\pi)\}$ and $q = \{(6, 4), (2, -5), (\frac{3}{4}, \frac{1}{5}), (0, 9)\}$. For Exercises 49–56, find the function values.

49. $p(2)$ -7

50. $p(1)$ 0

51. $p(3)$ 2π

52. $p\left(\dfrac{1}{2}\right)$ 6

53. $q(2)$ -5

54. $q\left(\dfrac{3}{4}\right)$ $\dfrac{1}{5}$

55. $q(6)$ 4

56. $q(0)$ 9

Concept 4: Finding Function Values from a Graph

57. The graph of $y = f(x)$ is given. **(See Example 5.)**

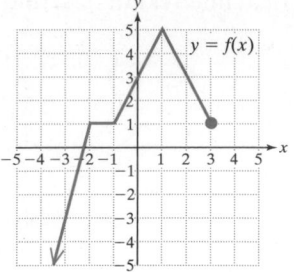

a. Find $f(0)$.   3

b. Find $f(3)$.   1

c. Find $f(-2)$.   1

d. For what value(s) of x is $f(x) = -3$? $x = -3$

e. For what value(s) of x is $f(x) = 3$? $x = 0, x = 2$

f. Write the domain of f. $(-\infty, 3]$

g. Write the range of f. $(-\infty, 5]$

58. The graph of $y = g(x)$ is given.

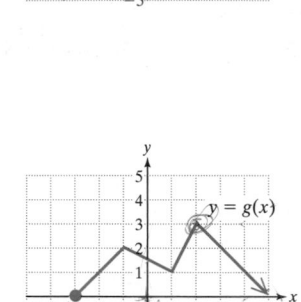

a. Find $g(-1)$.   2

b. Find $g(1)$.   1

c. Find $g(4)$.   1

d. For what value(s) of x is $g(x) = 3$? $x = 2$

e. For what value(s) of x is $g(x) = 0$? $x = -3, x = 5$

f. Write the domain of g. $[-3, \infty)$

g. Write the range of g. $(-\infty, 3]$

59. The graph of $y = H(x)$ is given.

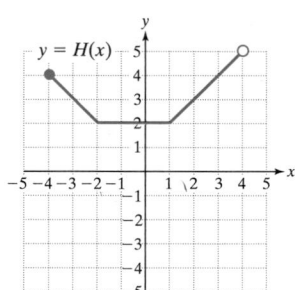

a. Find $H(-3)$.   3

b. Find $H(4)$.
$H(4)$ is not defined because 4 is not in the domain of H.

c. Find $H(3)$.   4

d. For what value(s) of x is $H(x) = 3$?
$x = -3$ and $x = 2$

e. For what value(s) of x is $H(x) = 2$?
All x on the interval $[-2, 1]$

f. Write the domain of H. $[-4, 4)$

g. Write the range of H. $[2, 5)$

60. The graph of $y = K(x)$ is given.

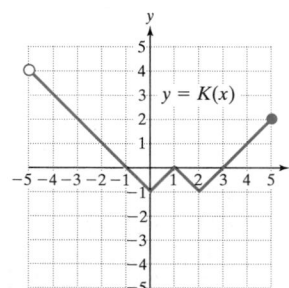

a. Find $K(0)$. -1

b. Find $K(-5)$.
$K(-5)$ is not defined because -5 is not in the domain of K.

c. Find $K(1)$.   0

d. For what value(s) of x is $K(x) = 0$?
$x = -1, x = 1$, and $x = 3$

e. For what value(s) of x is $K(x) = 3$? $x = -4$

f. Write the domain of K. $(-5, 5]$

g. Write the range of K. $[-1, 4)$

 Writing   Translating Expression   Geometry   Scientific Calculator   Video   NS&E

For Exercises 61–70, refer to the functions $y = f(x)$ and $y = g(x)$, defined as follows:

$$f = \{(-3, 5), (-7, -3), (-\tfrac{3}{2}, 4), (1.2, 5)\}$$

$$g = \{(0, 6), (2, 6), (6, 0), (1, 0)\}$$

61. Identify the domain of f. $\{-3, -7, -\tfrac{3}{2}, 1.2\}$

62. Identify the range of f. $\{5, -3, 4\}$

63. Identify the range of g. $\{6, 0\}$

64. Identify the domain of g. $\{0, 2, 6, 1\}$

65. For what value(s) of x is $f(x) = 5$? $x = -3$ and $x = 1.2$

66. For what value(s) of x is $f(x) = -3$? $x = -7$

67. For what value(s) of x is $g(x) = 0$? $x = 6$ and $x = 1$

68. For what value(s) of x is $g(x) = 6$? $x = 0$ and $x = 2$

69. Find $f(-7)$. -3

70. Find $g(0)$. 6

Concept 5: Domain of a Function

71. Explain how to determine the domain of the function defined by $f(x) = \dfrac{x + 6}{x - 2}$. The domain is the set of all real numbers for which the denominator is not zero. Set the denominator equal to zero, and solve the resulting equation. The solution(s) to the equation must be excluded from the domain. In this case, setting $x - 2 = 0$ indicates that $x = 2$ must be excluded from the domain. The domain is $(-\infty, 2) \cup (2, \infty)$.

72. Explain how to determine the domain of the function defined by $g(x) = \sqrt{x - 3}$.   The domain is the set of all real numbers for which $x - 3$ is nonnegative. Set the quantity $x - 3 \geq 0$ and solve the inequality. The solution set for the inequality is the domain of the function. Thus, the domain is $[3, \infty)$.

For Exercises 73–88, find the domain. Write the answers in interval notation. **(See Example 6.)**

73. $k(x) = \dfrac{x - 3}{x + 6}$
$(-\infty, \ 6) \cup (-6, \infty)$

74. $m(x) = \dfrac{x - 1}{x - 4}$
$(-\infty, 4) \cup (4, \infty)$

75. $f(t) = \dfrac{5}{t}$
$(-\infty, 0) \cup (0, \infty)$

76. $g(t) = \dfrac{t - 7}{t}$
$(-\infty, 0) \cup (0, \infty)$

77. $h(p) = \dfrac{p - 4}{p^2 + 1}$
$(-\infty, \infty)$

78. $n(p) = \dfrac{p + 8}{p^2 + 2}$
$(-\infty, \infty)$

79. $h(t) = \sqrt{t + 7}$
$[-7, \infty)$

80. $k(t) = \sqrt{t - 5}$
$[5, \infty)$

81. $f(a) = \sqrt{a - 3}$
$[3, \infty)$

82. $g(a) = \sqrt{a + 2}$
$[-2, \infty)$

83. $m(x) = \sqrt{1 - 2x}$
$(-\infty, \tfrac{1}{2}]$

84. $n(x) = \sqrt{12 - 6x}$
$(-\infty, 2]$

85. $p(t) = 2t^2 + t - 1$
$(-\infty, \infty)$

86. $q(t) = t^3 + t - 1$
$(-\infty, \infty)$

87. $f(x) = x + 6$
$(-\infty, \infty)$

88. $g(x) = 8x - \pi$
$(-\infty, \infty)$

Mixed Exercises

89. The height (in feet) of a ball that is dropped from an 80-ft building is given by $h(t) = -16t^2 + 80$, where t is the time in seconds after the ball is dropped.

   a. Find $h(1)$ and $h(1.5)$. $h(1) = 64$ and $h(1.5) = 44$

   b. Interpret the meaning of the function values found in part (a). $h(1) = 64$ means that after 1 sec, the height of the ball is 64 ft. $h(1.5) = 44$ means that after 1.5 sec, the height of the ball is 44 ft.

90. A ball is dropped from a 50-m building. The height (in meters) after t sec is given by $h(t) = -4.9t^2 + 50$.

   a. Find $h(1)$ and $h(1.5)$. $h(1) = 45.1$ and $h(1.5) = 38.975$

   b. Interpret the meaning of the function values found in part (a). $h(1) = 45.1$ means that after 1 sec, the height of the ball is 45.1 m. $h(1.5) = 38.975$ means that after 1.5 sec, the height of the ball is 38.975 m.

91. If Alicia rides a bike at an average speed of 11.5 mph, the distance that she rides can be represented by $d(t) = 11.5t$, where t is the time in hours.

   a. Find $d(1)$ and $d(1.5)$. $d(1) = 11.5$ and $d(1.5) = 17.25$

   b. Interpret the meaning of the function values found in part (a). $d(1) = 11.5$ means that after 1 hr, the distance traveled is 11.5 mi. $d(1.5) = 17.25$ means that after 1.5 hr, the distance traveled is 17.25 mi.

 Writing   Translating Expression   Geometry   Scientific Calculator   Video   NS E

92. If Miguel walks at an average of 5.9 km/hr, the distance that he walks can be represented by $d(t) = 5.9t$, where t is the time in hours.

    a. Find $d(1)$ and $d(2)$. $d(1) = 5.9$ and $d(2) = 11.8$

    b. Interpret the meaning of the function values found in part (a). $d(1) = 5.9$ means that after 1 hr, Miguel had walked 5.9 km. $d(2) = 11.8$ means that after 2 hr, Miguel had walked 11.8 km.

93. The graph shows the number of violent crimes (in millions) committed in the United States from 2000 to 2005. The variable x represents the number of years since 2000 ($x = 0$ represents the year 2000) and $f(x)$ is the number of violent crimes (in millions).

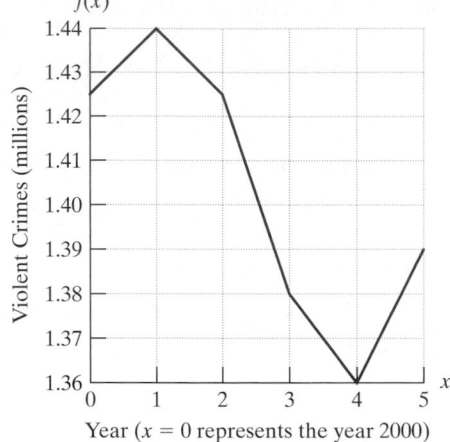

    a. Approximate $f(1)$ and interpret the meaning in the context of this problem.
    a. $f(1) \approx 1.44$ means in 2001 there were approximately 1.44 million violent crimes.

    b. Approximate $f(5)$ and interpret the meaning in the context of this problem.
    b. $f(5) \approx 1.39$ means in 2005 there were approximately 1.39 million violent crimes.

    c. Approximate the year(s) in which the number of violent crimes was equal to 1.425 million.
    c. In 2000 and 2002 ($x = 0$ and $x = 2$) there were approximately 1.425 million violent crimes.

94. Brian's score on an exam is a function of the number of hours he spends studying. The function defined by

$$P(x) = \frac{100x^2}{50 + x^2} \quad (x \geq 0)$$ indicates that he will achieve a score of $P\%$ if he studies for x hours.

Evaluate $P(0)$, $P(5)$, $P(10)$, $P(15)$, $P(20)$, and $P(25)$ and confirm the values on the graph. (Round to one decimal place.) Interpret $P(25)$ in the context of this problem.

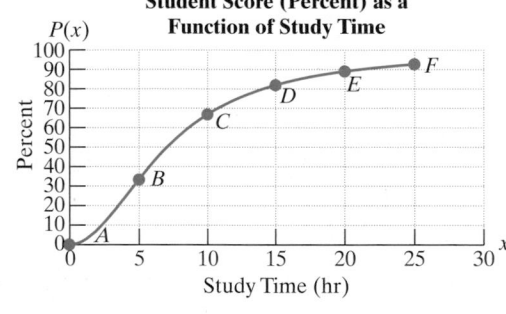

    $P(0) = 0\%$
    $P(5) \approx 33.3\%$
    $P(10) \approx 66.7\%$
    $P(15) \approx 81.8\%$
    $P(20) \approx 88.9\%$
    $P(25) \approx 92.6\%$. If Brian studies 25 hr he will get a score of 92.6%.

For Exercises 95–98, write a function defined by $y = f(x)$ subject to the conditions given.

95. The value of $f(x)$ is three more than two times x.
$f(x) = 2x + 3$

96. The value of $f(x)$ is four less than the square of x.
$f(x) = x^2 - 4$

97. The value of $f(x)$ is ten less than the absolute value of x. $f(x) = |x| - 10$

98. The value of $f(x)$ is sixteen times the square root of x. $f(x) = 16\sqrt{x}$

Expanding Your Skills

For Exercises 99–100, write the domain in interval notation.

99. $q(x) = \dfrac{2}{\sqrt{x + 2}}$

$(-2, \infty)$

100. $p(x) = \dfrac{8}{\sqrt{x - 4}}$

$(4, \infty)$

Graphing Calculator Exercises

101. Graph $k(t) = \sqrt{t - 5}$. Use the graph to support your answer to Exercise 80.

102. Graph $h(t) = \sqrt{t + 7}$. Use the graph to support your answer to Exercise 79.

 Writing   Translating Expression   Geometry   Scientific Calculator Video NS&E

Graphs of Functions

1. Linear and Constant Functions

A function may be expressed as a mathematical equation that relates two or more variables. In this section, we will look at several elementary functions.

Recall from Section 3.2 that an equation in the form $y = k$, where k is a constant, is a horizontal line. In function notation, this can be written as $f(x) = k$. For example, the graph of the function defined by $f(x) = 3$ is a horizontal line, as shown in Figure 8-8.

We say that a function defined by $f(x) = k$ is a constant function because for any value of x, the function value is constant.

An equation of the form $y = mx + b$ is represented graphically by a line with slope m and y-intercept $(0, b)$. In function notation, this may be written as $f(x) = mx + b$. A function in this form is called a linear function. For example, the function defined by $f(x) = 2x - 3$ is a linear function with slope $m = 2$ and y-intercept $(0, -3)$ (Figure 8-9).

Figure 8-8

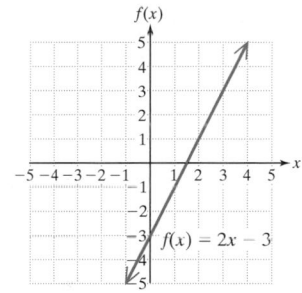

Figure 8-9

1. Linear and Constant Functions
2. Graphs of Basic Functions
3. Definition of a Quadratic Function
4. Finding the x- and y-Intercepts of a Graph Defined by $y = f(x)$

DEFINITION Linear Function and Constant Function

Let m and b represent real numbers such that $m \neq 0$. Then:

A function that can be written in the form $f(x) = mx + b$ is a **linear function**.
A function that can be written in the form $f(x) = b$ is a **constant function**.

Note: The graphs of linear and constant functions are lines.

---

2. Graphs of Basic Functions

At this point, we are able to recognize the equations and graphs of linear and constant functions. In addition to linear and constant functions, the following equations define six basic functions that will be encountered in the study of algebra:

Equation	Function Notation	Type of Function
$y = x$	$f(x) = x$	Identity function
$y = x^2$	$f(x) = x^2$	Quadratic function
$y = x^3$	$f(x) = x^3$	Cubic function
$y = |x|$	$f(x) = |x|$	Absolute value function
$y = \sqrt{x}$	$f(x) = \sqrt{x}$	Square root function
$y = \dfrac{1}{x}$	$f(x) = \dfrac{1}{x}$	Reciprocal function

equivalent function notation

The graph of the function defined by $f(x) = x$ is linear, with slope $m = 1$ and y-intercept $(0, 0)$ (Figure 8-10).

To determine the shapes of the other basic functions, we can plot several points to establish the pattern of the graph. Analyzing the equation itself may also provide insight to the domain, range, and shape of the graph. To demonstrate this, we will graph $f(x) = x^2$ and $g(x) = \frac{1}{x}$.

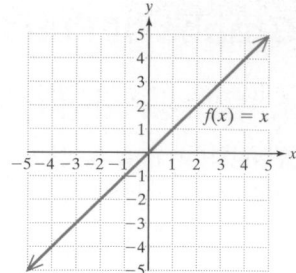

Figure 8-10

Classroom Example: p. 591, Exercise 12

Example 1 **Graphing Basic Functions**

Graph the function defined by $f(x) = x^2$.

Solution:

The domain of the function given by $f(x) = x^2$ (or equivalently $y = x^2$) is all real numbers.

To graph the function, choose arbitrary values of x within the domain of the function. Be sure to choose values of x that are positive and values that are negative to determine the behavior of the function to the right and left of the origin (Table 8-4). The graph of $f(x) = x^2$ is shown in Figure 8-11.

The function values are equated to the square of x, so $f(x)$ will always be greater than or equal to zero. Hence, the y-coordinates on the graph will never be negative. The range of the function is $[0, \infty)$. The arrows on each branch of the graph imply that the pattern continues indefinitely.

Table 8-4

x	$f(x) = x^2$
0	0
1	1
2	4
3	9
−1	1
−2	4
−3	9

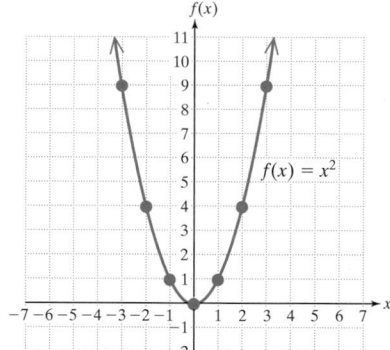

Figure 8-11

Skill Practice

1. Graph $f(x) = -x^2$ by first making a table of points.

Answer

1.

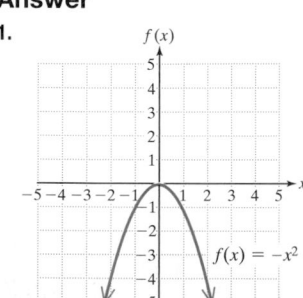

Example 2 **Graphing Basic Functions**

Classroom Example: p. 591, Exercise 16

Graph the function defined by $g(x) = \dfrac{1}{x}$.

Solution:

$g(x) = \dfrac{1}{x}$ Notice that $x = 0$ is not in the domain of the function. From the equation $y = \frac{1}{x}$, the y values will be the reciprocal of the x-values. The graph defined by $g(x) = \frac{1}{x}$ is shown in Figure 8-12.

x	$g(x) = \dfrac{1}{x}$
1	1
2	$\frac{1}{2}$
3	$\frac{1}{3}$
-1	-1
-2	$-\frac{1}{2}$
-3	$-\frac{1}{3}$

x	$g(x) = \dfrac{1}{x}$
$\frac{1}{2}$	2
$\frac{1}{3}$	3
$\frac{1}{4}$	4
$-\frac{1}{2}$	-2
$-\frac{1}{3}$	3
$-\frac{1}{4}$	-4

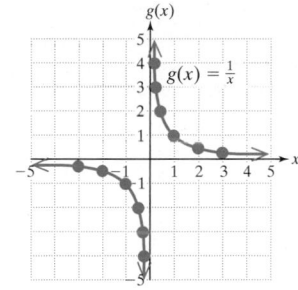

Figure 8-12

Notice that as x approaches ∞ and $-\infty$, the y values approach zero, and the graph approaches the x-axis. In this case, the x-axis is called a *horizontal asymptote*. Similarly, the graph of the function approaches the y-axis as x gets close to zero. In this case, the y-axis is called a *vertical asymptote*. In general terms, an asymptote is a line that a curve approaches more and more closely but never reaches.

Skill Practice

2. Graph $h(x) = |x| - 1$ by first making a table of points.

Calculator Connections

Topic: Graphing Nonlinear Functions

To enter a function, let $f(x) = y$. That is, to graph $f(x) = x^2$, enter Y1 $= x^2$.

To graph $g(x) = \dfrac{1}{x}$, enter Y1 $= 1/x$.

Answer

2.

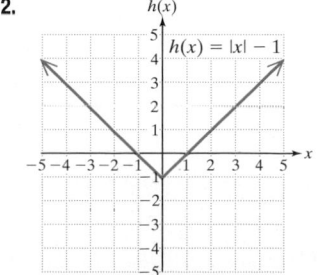

Summary of Six Basic Functions and Their Graphs

Function	Graph	Domain and Range
1. $f(x) = x$ Identity function		Domain $(-\infty, \infty)$ Range $(-\infty, \infty)$
2. $f(x) = x^2$ Quadratic function		Domain $(-\infty, \infty)$ Range $[0, \infty)$
3. $f(x) = x^3$ Cubic function		Domain $(-\infty, \infty)$ Range $(-\infty, \infty)$
4. $f(x) = |x|$ Absolute value function		Domain $(-\infty, \infty)$ Range $[0, \infty)$
5. $f(x) = \sqrt{x}$ Square root function		Domain $[0, \infty)$ Range $[0, \infty)$
6. $f(x) = \dfrac{1}{x}$ Reciprocal function		Domain $(-\infty, 0) \cup (0, \infty)$ Range $(-\infty, 0) \cup (0, \infty)$

TIP: Recall that the symbol $\cup$ means the combination (or union) of the two intervals.

The shapes of these six graphs will be developed in the homework exercises. These functions are used often in the study of algebra. Therefore, we recommend that you associate an equation with its graph and commit each to memory.

3. Definition of a Quadratic Function

In Example 1 we graphed the function defined by $f(x) = x^2$ by plotting points. This function belongs to a special category called quadratic functions.

> **DEFINITION Quadratic Function**
>
> A **quadratic function** is a function defined by
>
> $$f(x) = ax^2 + bx + c \qquad \text{where } a, b, \text{ and } c \text{ are real numbers and } a \neq 0.$$

The graph of a quadratic function is in the shape of a **parabola**. The leading coefficient, a, determines the direction of the parabola.

- If $a > 0$, then the parabola opens upward, and the vertex is the minimum point on the parabola. For example, the graph of $f(x) = x^2$ is shown in Figure 8-13.
- If $a < 0$, then the parabola opens downward, and the vertex is the maximum point on the parabola. For example, the graph of $f(x) = -x^2$ is shown in Figure 8-14.

Figure 8-13

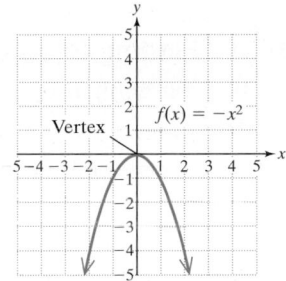

Figure 8-14

Example 3 Identifying Functions

Classroom Examples: p. 592, Exercises 18, 20, 22, and 28

Identify each function as linear, constant, quadratic, or none of these.

a. $f(x) = -4$ **b.** $f(x) = x^2 + 3x + 2$ **c.** $f(x) = 7 - 2x$

d. $f(x) = \dfrac{4x + 8}{8}$ **e.** $f(x) = \dfrac{6}{x} + 2$

Solution:

a. $f(x) = -4$ is a constant function. It is in the form $f(x) = b$, where $b = -4$.

b. $f(x) = x^2 + 3x + 2$ is a quadratic function. It is in the form $f(x) = ax^2 + bx + c$, where $a \ne 0$.

c. $f(x) = 7 - 2x$ is linear. Writing it in the form $f(x) = mx + b$, we get $f(x) = -2x + 7$, where $m = -2$ and $b = 7$.

d. $f(x) = \dfrac{4x + 8}{8}$ is linear. Writing it in the form $f(x) = mx + b$, we get

$$f(x) = \frac{4x}{8} + \frac{8}{8}$$

$$= \frac{1}{2}x + 1, \text{ where } m = \frac{1}{2} \text{ and } b = 1.$$

e. $f(x) = \dfrac{6}{x} + 2$ fits none of these categories.

Skill Practice Identify each function as constant, linear, quadratic, or none of these.

3. $m(x) = -2x^2 - 3x + 7$ **4.** $n(x) = -6$

5. $W(x) = \dfrac{4}{3}x - \dfrac{1}{2}$ **6.** $R(x) = \dfrac{4}{3x} - \dfrac{1}{2}$

Answers

3. Quadratic
4. Constant
5. Linear
6. None of these

4. Finding the *x*- and *y*-Intercepts of a Graph Defined by $y = f(x)$

In Section 3.2, we learned that to find the *x*-intercept, we substitute $y = 0$ and solve the equation for *x*. Using function notation, this is equivalent to finding the real solutions of the equation $f(x) = 0$. To find the *y*-intercept, substitute $x = 0$ and solve the equation for *y*. In function notation, this is equivalent to finding $f(0)$.

PROCEDURE Finding Intercepts Using Function Notation

Given a function defined by $y = f(x)$,

Step 1 The *x*-intercepts are the real solutions to the equation $f(x) = 0$.

Step 2 The *y*-intercept is given by $f(0)$.

Classroom Example: p. 592, Exercise 32

Example 4 Finding *x*- and *y*-Intercepts

Given the function defined by $f(x) = 2x - 4$:

a. Find the *x*-intercept(s).

b. Find the *y*-intercept.

c. Graph the function.

Solution:

a. To find the *x*-intercept(s), find the real solutions to the equation $f(x) = 0$.

$$f(x) = 2x - 4$$

$$0 = 2x - 4 \qquad \text{Substitute } f(x) = 0.$$

$$4 = 2x$$

$$2 = x \qquad \text{The } x\text{-intercept is } (2, 0).$$

b. To find the *y*-intercept, evaluate $f(0)$.

$$f(0) = 2(0) - 4 \qquad \text{Substitute } x = 0.$$

$$f(0) = -4 \qquad \text{The } y\text{-intercept is } (0, -4).$$

c. This function is linear, with a *y*-intercept of $(0, -4)$, an *x*-intercept of $(2, 0)$, and a slope of 2 (Figure 8-15).

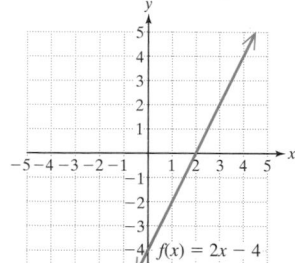

Figure 8-15

Skill Practice Consider $f(x) = -5x + 1$.

7. Find the *x*-intercept.

8. Find the *y*-intercept.

9. Graph the function.

Answers

7. $\left(\frac{1}{5}, 0\right)$ **8.** $(0, 1)$

9.

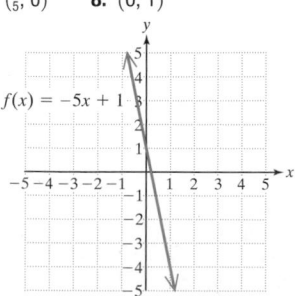

Calculator Connections

Topic: Finding *x*- and *y*-Intercepts

Refer to Example 4 with $f(x) = 2x - 4$. To find the *y*-intercept, let $x = 0$. We can do this using the *Value* key.

To find the *x*-intercept, use the *Zero* feature. To use this feature you must give bounds for the *x*-intercept. To find a left bound, place the curser to the left of the *x*-intercept and press Enter. For the right bound, place the curser to the right of the *x*-intercept and press Enter.

Then make a guess by placing the curser near the *x*-intercept. Press Enter and the *x*-intercept will be displayed.

Example 5   Finding *x*- and *y*-Intercepts

For the function pictured in Figure 8-16, estimate

a. The real values of *x* for which $f(x) = 0$.

b. The value of $f(0)$.

Classroom Example: p. 593, Exercise 42

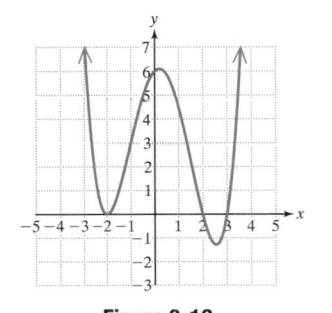

Figure 8-16

Solution:

a. The real values of x for which $f(x) = 0$ are the x-intercepts of the function. For this graph, the x-intercepts are located at $x = -2$, $x = 2$, and $x = 3$.

b. The value of $f(0)$ is the value of y at $x = 0$. That is, $f(0)$ is the y-intercept, $f(0) = 6$.

Skill Practice Use the function pictured.

10. a. Estimate the real value(s) of x for which $f(x) = 0$

   b. Estimate the value of $f(0)$.

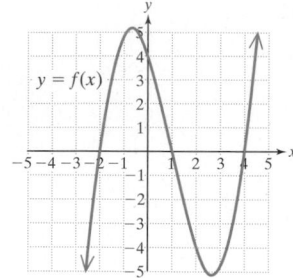

Answer

10. a. $x = -2$, $x = 1$, and $x = 4$
   b. $f(0) = 4$

Section 8.3 Practice Exercises

Study Skills Exercise

1. Define the key terms.

   a. linear function   **b. constant function**   **c. quadratic function**   **d. parabola**

Review Exercises

2. Given: $g = \{(6, 1), (5, 2), (4, 3), (3, 4)\}$

   a. Is this relation a function?   Yes

   b. List the elements in the domain. $\{6, 5, 4, 3\}$

   c. List the elements in the range. $\{1, 2, 3, 4\}$

3. Given: $f = \{(7, 3), (2, 3), (-5, 3)\}$

   a. Is this relation a function?   Yes

   b. List the elements in the domain. $\{7, 2, -5\}$

   c. List the elements in the range. $\{3\}$

4. Given: $f(x) = \sqrt{x + 4}$

   a. Evaluate $f(0), f(-3), f(-4),$ and $f(-5),$ if possible. $f(0) = 2, f(-3) = 1, f(-4) = 0,$ and $f(-5)$ cannot be evaluated
   because $x = -5$ is not in the domain of $f.$
   b. Write the domain of this function in interval notation. $[-4, \infty)$

5. The force (measured in pounds) to stretch a certain spring x inches is given by $f(x) = 3x$. Evaluate $f(3)$ and $f(10)$, and interpret the results in the context of this problem. $f(3) = 9$ means that 9 lb of force is required to stretch the
   spring 3 in. $f(10) = 30$ means that 30 lb of force is required to stretch the spring 10 in.

6. The velocity (in feet per second) of falling object is given by $V(t) = -32t$, where t is the time in seconds after the object was released. Evaluate $V(2)$ and interpret the results in the context of this problem.
   $V(2) = -64$ means that 2 sec after release, the object is falling at 64 ft/sec.

Concept 1: Linear and Constant Functions

7. Fill in the blank with the word *vertical* or *horizontal*. The graph of a constant function is a _____ line.

horizontal

8. For the linear function defined by $f(x) = mx + b$, identify the slope and y-intercept.

m is the slope, and $(0, b)$ is the y-intercept.

9. Graph the constant function $f(x) = 2$. Then use the graph to identify the domain and range of f. Domain $(-\infty, \infty)$; range $\{2\}$

10. Graph the linear function $g(x) = -2x + 1$. Then use the graph to identify the domain and range of g. Domain $(-\infty, \infty)$; range $(-\infty, \infty)$

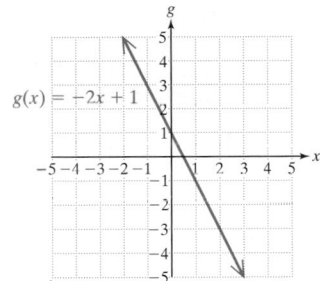

Concept 2: Graphs of Basic Functions

For Exercises 11–16, sketch a graph by completing the table and plotting the points. **(See Examples 1–2.)**

11. $f(x) = \dfrac{1}{x}$

x	$f(x)$
-2	$-\frac{1}{2}$
-1	-1
$-\frac{1}{2}$	-2
$-\frac{1}{4}$	-4

x	$f(x)$
$\frac{1}{4}$	4
$\frac{1}{2}$	2
1	1
2	$\frac{1}{2}$

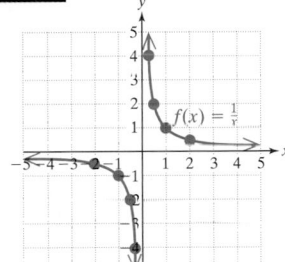

12. $g(x) = |x|$

x	$g(x)$
-2	2
-1	1
0	0
1	1
2	2

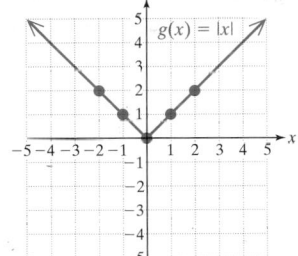

13. $h(x) = x^3$

x	$h(x)$
-2	-8
-1	-1
0	0
1	1
2	8

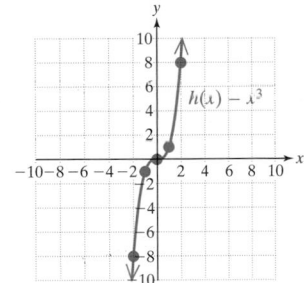

14. $k(x) = x$

x	$k(x)$
2	2
-1	-1
0	0
1	1
2	2

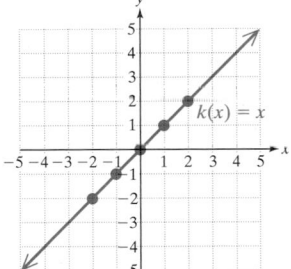

15. $q(x) = x^2$

x	$q(x)$
-2	4
-1	1
0	0
1	1
2	4

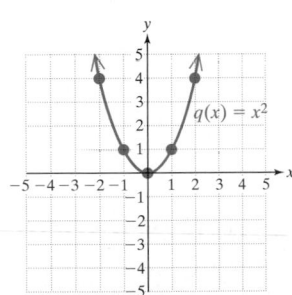

16. $p(x) = \sqrt{x}$

x	$p(x)$
0	0
1	1
4	2
9	3
16	4

 Writing   Translating Expression   Geometry   Scientific Calculator   Video   NS&E

Concept 3: Definition of a Quadratic Function

For Exercises 17–28, determine if the function is constant, linear, quadratic, or none of these. **(See Example 3.)**

17. $f(x) = 2x^2 + 3x + 1$ ● **18.** $g(x) = -x^2 + 4x + 12$ **19.** $k(x) = -3x - 7$ **20.** $h(x) = -x - 3$
    Quadratic   Quadratic   Linear   Linear

21. $m(x) = \dfrac{4}{3}$ **22.** $n(x) = 0.8$ **23.** $p(x) = \dfrac{2}{3x} + \dfrac{1}{4}$ **24.** $Q(x) = \dfrac{1}{5x} - 3$
    Constant   Constant   None of these   None of these

25. $t(x) = \dfrac{2}{3}x + \dfrac{1}{4}$ **26.** $r(x) = \dfrac{1}{5}x - 3$ **27.** $w(x) = \sqrt{4 - x}$ **28.** $T(x) = -|x + 10|$
    Linear   Linear   None of these   None of these

Concept 4: Finding the *x*- and *y*-Intercepts of a Graph Defined by $y = f(x)$

For Exercises 29–36, find the *x*- and *y*-intercepts, and graph the function. **(See Example 4.)**

29. $f(x) = 5x - 10$ **30.** $f(x) = -3x + 12$ ● **31.** $g(x) = -6x + 5$

       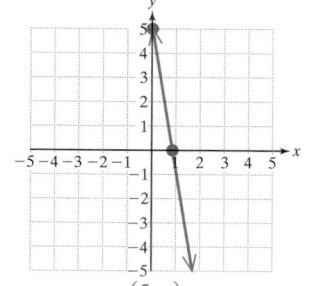

x-intercept: $(2, 0)$; *y*-intercept: $(0, -10)$ *x*-intercept: $(4, 0)$; *y*-intercept: $(0, 12)$ *x*-intercept: $\left(\dfrac{5}{6}, 0\right)$; *y*-intercept: $(0, 5)$

32. $h(x) = 2x + 9$ **33.** $f(x) = 18$ **34.** $g(x) = -7$

       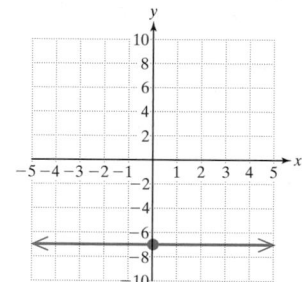

x-intercept: $\left(-\dfrac{9}{2}, 0\right)$; *y*-intercept: $(0, 9)$ *x*-intercept: none; *y*-intercept: $(0, 18)$ *x*-intercept: none; *y*-intercept: $(0, -7)$

35. $g(x) = \dfrac{2}{3}x + 2$ **36.** $h(x) = -\dfrac{3}{5}x - 3$

   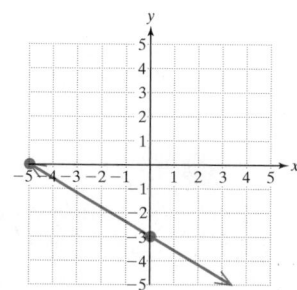

x-intercept: $(-3, 0)$; *y*-intercept: $(0, 2)$ *x*-intercept: $(-5, 0)$; *y*-intercept: $(0, -3)$

For Exercises 37–42, use the graph to estimate

    a. The real values of x for which $f(x) = 0$.   **b.** The value of $f(0)$. **(See Example 5.)**

37.
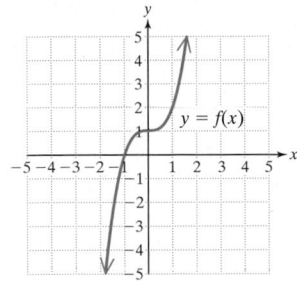

a. $x = -1$
b. $f(0) = 1$

38.
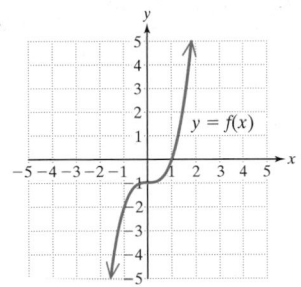

a. $x = 1$
b. $f(0) = -1$

39.
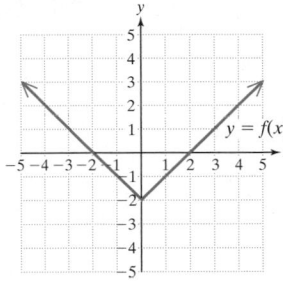

a. $x = -2$ and $x = 2$ b. $f(0) = -2$

40.
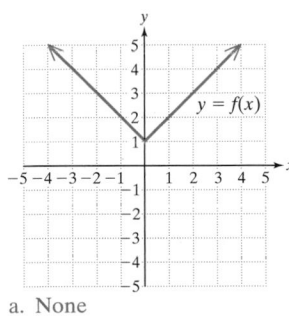

a. None
b. $f(0) = 1$

41.
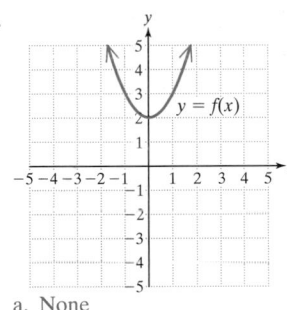

a. None
b. $f(0) = 2$

42.
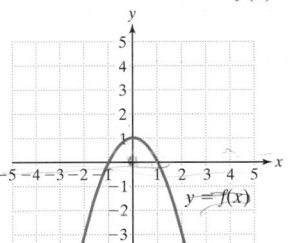

a. $x = 1$ and $x = -1$
b. $f(0) = 1$

Mixed Exercises

For Exercises 43–52,

    a. Identify the domain of the function.

    b. Identify the y-intercept.

    c. Match the function with its graph by recognizing the basic shape of the graph and using the results from parts (a) and (b). Plot additional points if necessary.

43. $q(x) = 2x^2$
a. $(-\infty, \infty)$ b. $(0, 0)$ c. vi

44. $p(x) = -2x^2 + 1$
a. $(-\infty, \infty)$ b. $(0, 1)$ c. iii

45. $h(x) = x^3 + 1$
a. $(-\infty, \infty)$ b. $(0, 1)$ c. viii

46. $k(x) = x^3 - 2$
a. $(-\infty, \infty)$ b. $(0, -2)$ c. v

47. $r(x) = \sqrt{x + 1}$
a. $[-1, \infty)$ b. $(0, 1)$ c. vii

48. $s(x) = \sqrt{x + 4}$
a. $[-4, \infty)$ b. $(0, 2)$ c. i

49. $f(x) = \dfrac{1}{x - 3}$
a. $(-\infty, 3) \cup (3, \infty)$ b. $\left(0, -\dfrac{1}{3}\right)$ c. ii

50. $g(x) = \dfrac{1}{x + 1}$
a. $(-\infty, -1) \cup (-1, \infty)$ b. $(0, 1)$ c. x

51. $k(x) = |x + 2|$
a. $(-\infty, \infty)$ b. $(0, 2)$ c. iv

52. $h(x) = |x - 1| + 2$
a. $(-\infty, \infty)$ b. $(0, 3)$ c. ix

i.

ii.

iii.

iv.

v.

vi.

vii.

viii.

ix.

x.
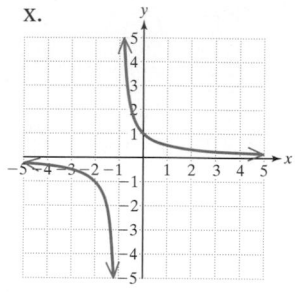

53. Suppose that a student has an 80% average on all of her chapter tests in her Intermediate Algebra class. This counts as $\frac{3}{4}$ of the student's overall grade. The final exam grade counts as the remaining $\frac{1}{4}$ of the student's overall grade. The student's overall course grade, $G(x)$, can be computed by

$$G(x) = \frac{3}{4}(80) + \frac{1}{4}x, \text{ where } x \text{ is the student's grade on the final exam.}$$

a. Is this function linear, quadratic, or neither?   Linear

b. Evaluate $G(90)$ and interpret its meaning in the context of the problem. $G(90) = 82.5$. This means that if the student gets a 90% score on her final exam, then her overall course average is 82.5%.

c. Evaluate $G(50)$ and interpret its meaning in the context of the problem. $G(50) = 72.5$. This means that if the student gets a 50% score on her final exam, then her overall course average is 72.5%.

54. The median weekly earnings, $E(x)$ in dollars, for women 16 yr and older working full time can be approximated by $E(x) = 0.14x^2 + 7.8x + 540$. For this function, x represents the number of years since 2000. (*Source:* U.S. Department of Labor)

a. Is this function linear, quadratic, or neither?   Quadratic

b. Evaluate $E(5)$ and interpret its meaning in the context of this problem. $E(5) = 582.5$; This means that for $x = 5$ (the year 2005), the median weekly earnings for women was $582.50.

c. Evaluate $E(10)$ and interpret its meaning in the context of this problem. $E(10) = 632$; This means that for $x = 10$ (the year 2010), the median weekly earnings for women would be $632.

Graphing Calculator Exercises

For Exercises 55–60, use a graphing calculator to graph the basic functions. Verify your answers from the table on page 586.

55. $f(x) = x$

56. $f(x) = x^2$

57. $f(x) = x^3$

58. $f(x) = |x|$

59. $f(x) = \sqrt{x}$

60. $f(x) = \dfrac{1}{x}$

For Exercises 61–64, find the x- and y-intercepts using a graphing calculator and the *Value* and *Zero* features.

61. $y = -\dfrac{1}{8}x + 1$
x-intercept: $(8, 0)$
y-intercept: $(0, 1)$

62. $y = -\dfrac{1}{2}x - 3$
x-intercept: $(-6, 0)$
y-intercept: $(0, -3)$

63. $y = \dfrac{4}{5}x + 4$
x-intercept: $(-5, 0)$
y-intercept: $(0, 4)$

64. $y = \dfrac{7}{2}x - 7$
x-intercept: $(2, 0)$
y-intercept: $(0, -7)$

 Writing   Translating Expression   Geometry   Scientific Calculator   Video   NS&E

Problem Recognition Exercises

Characteristics of Relations

Exercises 1–15 refer to the sets of points (x, y) described in a–h.

a. $\{(0, 8), (1, 4), (\frac{1}{2}, 4), (-3, 5), (2, 1)\}$

b. $\{(-6, 4), (2, 3), (-9, 6), (2, 1), (0, 10)\}$

c. $c(x) = 3x^2 - 2x - 1$

d. $d(x) = 5x - 9$

e.

f.

g.

h.

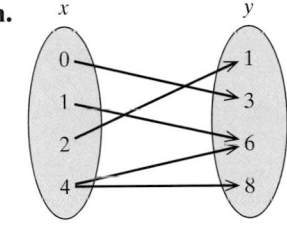

1. Which relations define y as a function of x?
   a, c, d, f, g

2. Which relations contain the point $(2, 1)$?
   a, b, d, f, h

3. Use relation (c) to find $c(-1)$.
   4

4. Use relation (f) to find $f(-4)$.
   2

5. Find the domain of relation (a).
   $\{0, 1, \frac{1}{2}, -3, 2\}$

6. Find the range of relation (b).
   $\{4, 3, 6, 1, 10\}$

7. Find the domain of relation (g).
   $[-2, 4]$

8. Find the range of relation (f).
   $[0, \infty)$

9. Use relation (h) to complete the ordered pair $(\_\_, 3)$.
   0

10. Find the x-intercept(s) of the graph of relation (d). $\left(\frac{9}{5}, 0\right)$

11. Find the y-intercept(s) of the graph shown in relation (e).
   $(0, -1), (0, 1)$

12. Use relation (g) to determine the value of x such that $g(x) = 2$.
   1

13. Which relation describes a quadratic function?
   c

14. Which relation describes a linear function?
   d

15. Use relation (d) to find the value of x such that $d(x) = 6$.
   3

Objectives

1. Algebra of Functions
2. Composition of Functions
3. Multiple Operations on Functions

1. Algebra of Functions

Addition, subtraction, multiplication, and division can be used to create a new function from two or more functions. The domain of the new function will be the intersection of the domains of the original functions.

> **DEFINITION   Sum, Difference, Product, and Quotient of Functions**
>
> Given two functions f and g, the functions $f + g$, $f - g$, $f \cdot g$, and $\frac{f}{g}$ are defined as
>
> $$(f + g)(x) = f(x) + g(x)$$
> $$(f - g)(x) = f(x) - g(x)$$
> $$(f \cdot g)(x) = f(x) \cdot g(x)$$
> $$\left(\frac{f}{g}\right)(x) = \frac{f(x)}{g(x)} \quad \text{provided } g(x) \neq 0$$

Instructor Note: Ask students why we make the restriction that $g(x) \neq 0$.

For example, suppose $f(x) = |x|$ and $g(x) = 3$. Taking the sum of the functions produces a new function denoted by $f + g$. In this case, $(f + g)(x) = |x| + 3$. Graphically, the y-values of the function $f + g$ are given by the sum of the corresponding y-values of f and g. This is depicted in Figure 8-17. The function $f + g$ appears in red. In particular, notice that $(f + g)(2) = f(2) + g(2) = 2 + 3 = 5$.

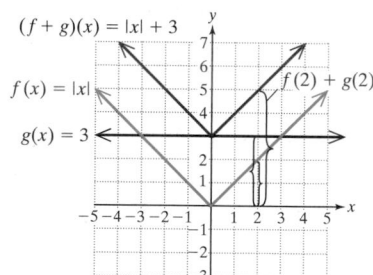

Figure 8-17

Classroom Examples: p. 600, Exercises 4, 6, 10, and 12

> **Example 1   Adding, Subtracting, Multiplying and Dividing Functions**
>
> Given: $g(x) = 4x \qquad h(x) = x^2 - 3x \qquad k(x) = x - 2$
>
> **a.** Find $(g + h)(x)$.   **b.** Find $(h - g)(x)$.
>
> **c.** Find $(g \cdot k)(x)$.   **d.** Find $\left(\dfrac{k}{h}\right)(x)$.

Solution:

a. $(g + h)(x) = g(x) + h(x)$

$\qquad\qquad = (4x) + (x^2 - 3x)$

$\qquad\qquad = 4x + x^2 - 3x$

$\qquad\qquad = x^2 + x \qquad\qquad$ Simplify.

b. $(h - g)(x) = h(x) - g(x)$

$\qquad\qquad = (x^2 - 3x) - (4x)$

$\qquad\qquad = x^2 - 3x - 4x$

$\qquad\qquad = x^2 - 7x \qquad\qquad$ Simplify.

c. $(g \cdot k)(x) = g(x) \cdot k(x)$

$\qquad = (4x)(x - 2)$

$\qquad = 4x^2 - 8x$ Simplify.

d. $\left(\dfrac{k}{h}\right)(x) = \dfrac{k(x)}{h(x)}$

$\qquad = \dfrac{x - 2}{x^2 - 3x}$ From the denominator we have $x^2 - 3x \neq 0$ or, equivalently, $x(x - 3) \neq 0$. Hence, $x \neq 3$ and $x \neq 0$.

Skill Practice Given $f(x) = x - 1$, $g(x) = 5x^2 + x$, and $h(x) = x^2$, find

1. $(f + g)(x)$ **2.** $(g - f)(x)$ **3.** $(g \cdot h)(x)$ **4.** $\left(\dfrac{f}{h}\right)(x)$

2. Composition of Functions

> **DEFINITION**   **Composition of Functions**
>
> The **composition** of f and g, denoted $f \circ g$, is defined by the rule
>
> $\qquad (f \circ g)(x) = f(g(x))$ provided that $g(x)$ is in the domain of f
>
> The composition of g and f, denoted $g \circ f$, is defined by the rule
>
> $\qquad (g \circ f)(x) = g(f(x))$ provided that $f(x)$ is in the domain of g
>
> Note: $f \circ g$ is also read as "f compose g," and $g \circ f$ is also read as "g compose f."

For example, given $f(x) = 2x - 3$ and $g(x) = x + 5$, we have

$(f \circ g)(x) = f(g(x))$

$\qquad = f(x + 5)$ Substitute $g(x) = x + 5$ into the function f.

$\qquad = 2(x + 5) - 3$

$\qquad = 2x + 10 - 3$

$\qquad = 2x + 7$

In this composition, the function g is the innermost operation and acts on x first. Then the output value of function g becomes the domain element of the function f, as shown in the figure.

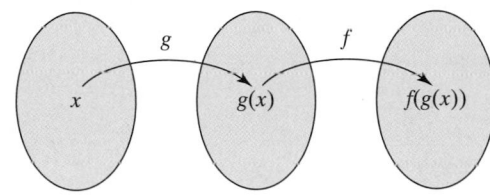

Answers

1. $5x^2 + 2x - 1$ **2.** $5x^2 + 1$

3. $5x^4 + x^3$ **4.** $\dfrac{x - 1}{x^2}, x \neq 0$

Classroom Example: p. 600,
Exercise 20

Example 2 **Composing Functions**

Given: $f(x) = x - 5$, $g(x) = x^2$, and $n(x) = \sqrt{x + 2}$, find

a. $(f \circ g)(x)$

b. $(g \circ f)(x)$

c. $(n \circ f)(x)$

Solution:

a. $(f \circ g)(x) = f(g(x))$

$\qquad\qquad = f(x^2)$ Evaluate the function f at x^2.

$\qquad\qquad = (x^2) - 5$ Replace x by x^2 in the function f.

$\qquad\qquad = x^2 - 5$

> **TIP:** Examples 2(a) and 2(b) illustrate that the order in which two functions are composed may result in different functions. That is, $f \circ g$ does not necessarily equal $g \circ f$.

b. $(g \circ f)(x) = g(f(x))$

$\qquad\qquad = g(x - 5)$ Evaluate the function g at $(x - 5)$.

$\qquad\qquad = (x - 5)^2$ Replace x by $(x - 5)$ in function g.

$\qquad\qquad = x^2 - 10x + 25$ Simplify.

c. $(n \circ f)(x) = n(f(x))$

$\qquad\qquad = n(x - 5)$ Evaluate the function n at $x - 5$.

$\qquad\qquad = \sqrt{(x - 5) + 2}$ Replace x by the quantity $(x - 5)$ in function n.

$\qquad\qquad = \sqrt{x - 3}$

Skill Practice Given $f(x) = 2x^2$, $g(x) = x + 3$, and $h(x) = \sqrt{x - 1}$, find

5. $(f \circ g)(x)$ **6.** $(g \circ f)(x)$ **7.** $(h \circ g)(x)$

3. Multiple Operations on Functions

Classroom Examples: p. 601,
Exercises 36 and 42

Example 3 **Combining Functions**

Given the functions defined by $f(x) = x - 7$ and $h(x) = 2x^3$, find the function values, if possible.

a. $(f \cdot h)(3)$ **b.** $\left(\dfrac{h}{f}\right)(7)$ **c.** $(h \circ f)(2)$

Solution:

a. $(f \cdot h)(3) = f(3) \cdot h(3)$ $(f \cdot h)(3)$ is a product (not a composition).

$\qquad\qquad = (3 - 7) \cdot 2(3)^3$

$\qquad\qquad = (-4) \cdot 2(27)$

$\qquad\qquad = -216$

b. $\left(\dfrac{h}{f}\right)(7) = \dfrac{h(7)}{f(7)} = \dfrac{2(7)^3}{7 - 7}$

The value $x = 7$ will make the denominator equal to 0. Therefore, $\left(\dfrac{h}{f}\right)(7)$ is undefined.

Answers

5. $2x^2 + 12x + 18$ **6.** $2x^2 + 3$

7. $\sqrt{x + 2}$

c. $(h \circ f)(2) = h(f(2))$ Evaluate $f(2)$ first. $f(2) = 2 - 7 = -5$.

       $= h(-5)$ Substitute the result into function h.

       $= 2(-5)^3$

       $= 2(-125)$

       $= -250$

Skill Practice Given $h(x) = x + 4$ and $k(x) = x^2 - 3$, find

8. $(h \cdot k)(-2)$ **9.** $\left(\dfrac{k}{h}\right)(-4)$ **10.** $(k \circ h)(1)$

Instructor Note: For a class that has some advanced students, it can be useful to have them consider the question: What two functions could be composed to form a third? For example, how could we define $g(x)$ and $h(x)$ so that $(g \circ h)(x) = f(x)$ when $f(x) = \sqrt{x + 2}$? If students can see that $h(x) = x + 2$ and $g(x) = \sqrt{x}$, then the chain rule in calculus will be easier to grasp.

Classroom Examples: p. 601, Exercises 50, 58, and 60

Example 4 **Finding Function Values from a Graph**

For the functions f and g pictured, find the function values if possible.

a. $g(2)$

b. $(f - g)(-3)$

c. $\left(\dfrac{g}{f}\right)(5)$

d. $(f \circ g)(4)$

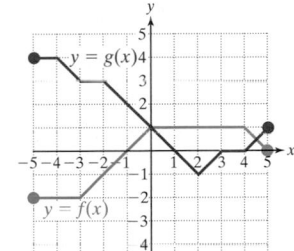

Solution:

a. $g(2) = -1$ The value $g(2)$ represents the y-value of $y = g(x)$ (the red graph) when $x = 2$. Because the point $(2, -1)$ lies on the graph, $g(2) = -1$.

b. $(f - g)(-3) = f(-3) - g(-3)$ Evaluate the difference of $f(-3)$ and $g(-3)$.

       $= -2 - (3)$ Estimate function values from the graph.

       $= -5$

c. $\left(\dfrac{g}{f}\right)(5) = \dfrac{g(5)}{f(5)}$ Evaluate the quotient of $g(5)$ and $f(5)$.

       $= \dfrac{1}{0}$ (undefined)

The function $\dfrac{g}{f}$ is undefined at 5 because the denominator is zero.

d. $(f \circ g)(4) = f(g(4))$ From the red graph, find the value of $g(4)$ first. We see that $g(4) = 0$.

       $= f(0)$ From the blue graph, find the value of f at $x = 0$.

       $= 1$

Answers

8. 2   **9.** undefined   **10.** 22

Skill Practice Find the values from the graph.

11. $g(3)$

12. $(f + g)(-4)$

13. $\left(\dfrac{f}{g}\right)(2)$

14. $(g \circ f)(-2)$

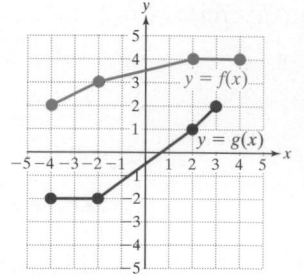

Answers

11. 2   **12.** 0

13. 4   **14.** 2

Section 8.4   Practice Exercises

Boost _your_ GRADE at ALEKS.com!

ALEKS
version 3.0

- Practice Problems
- Self-Tests
- NetTutor

- e-Professors
- Videos

For additional exercises, see Classroom Activities 8.4A–8.4C in the _Instructor's Resource Manual_ at www.mhhe.com/moh.

Study Skills Exercise

1. Define the key term **composition of functions**.

Concept 1: Algebra of Functions

2. Given $f(x) = x^2$ and $g(x) = 2x - 3$, find

   a. $f(-2)$ 4   **b.** $g(-2)$ −7   **c.** $(f + g)(-2)$ −3

For Exercises 3–14, refer to the functions defined below.

$$f(x) = x + 4 \qquad g(x) = 2x^2 + 4x \qquad h(x) = x^2 + 1 \qquad k(x) = \frac{1}{x}$$

Find the indicated functions. **(See Example 1.)**

3. $(f + g)(x)$
$(f + g)(x) = 2x^2 + 5x + 4$

4. $(f - g)(x)$
$(f - g)(x) = -2x^2 - 3x + 4$

5. $(g - f)(x)$
$(g - f)(x) = 2x^2 + 3x - 4$

6. $(f + h)(x)$
$(f + h)(x) = x^2 + x + 5$

7. $(f \cdot h)(x)$
$(f \cdot h)(x) = x^3 + 4x^2 + x + 4$

8. $(h \cdot k)(x)$
$(h \cdot k)(x) = \dfrac{x^2 + 1}{x}, x \neq 0$

9. $(g \cdot f)(x)$
$(g \cdot f)(x) = 2x^3 + 12x^2 + 16x$

10. $(f \cdot k)(x)$
$(f \cdot k)(x) = \dfrac{x + 4}{x}, x \neq 0$

11. $\left(\dfrac{h}{f}\right)(x)$ $\left(\dfrac{h}{f}\right)(x) = \dfrac{x^2 + 1}{x + 4}, x \neq -4$

12. $\left(\dfrac{g}{f}\right)(x)$
$\left(\dfrac{g}{f}\right)(x) = \dfrac{2x^2 + 4x}{x + 4}, x \neq -4$

13. $\left(\dfrac{f}{g}\right)(x)$
$\left(\dfrac{f}{g}\right)(x) = \dfrac{x + 4}{2x^2 + 4x}, x \neq 0, x \neq -2$

14. $\left(\dfrac{f}{h}\right)(x)$
$\left(\dfrac{f}{h}\right)(x) = \dfrac{x + 4}{x^2 + 1}$

Concept 2: Composition of Functions

For Exercises 15–22, find the indicated functions. Use f, g, h, and k as defined in Exercises 3–14. **(See Example 2.)**

15. $(f \circ g)(x)$
$(f \circ g)(x) = 2x^2 + 4x + 4$

16. $(f \circ k)(x)$ $(f \circ k)(x) = \dfrac{1}{x} + 4, x \neq 0$

17. $(g \circ f)(x)$
$(g \circ f)(x) = 2x^2 + 20x + 48$

18. $(k \circ f)(x)$ $(k \circ f)(x) = \dfrac{1}{x + 4}, x \neq -4$

19. $(k \circ h)(x)$ $(k \circ h)(x) = \dfrac{1}{x^2 + 1}$

20. $(h \circ k)(x)$
$(h \circ k)(x) = \dfrac{1}{x^2} + 1, x \neq 0$

21. $(k \circ g)(x)$
$(k \circ g)(x) = \dfrac{1}{2x^2 + 4x}, x \neq 0, x \neq -2$

22. $(g \circ k)(x)$ $(g \circ k)(x) = \dfrac{2}{x^2} + \dfrac{4}{x}, x \neq 0$

23. Based on your answers to Exercises 15 and 17, is it true in general that $(f \circ g)(x) = (g \circ f)(x)$?   No

24. Based on your answers to Exercises 16 and 18, is it true in general that $(f \circ k)(x) = (k \circ f)(x)$?   No

 Writing   Translating Expression   Geometry   Scientific Calculator   Video NS&E

For Exercises 25–28, find $(f \circ g)(x)$ and $(g \circ f)(x)$.

25. $f(x) = x^2 - 3x + 1, g(x) = 5x$
$(f \circ g)(x) = 25x^2 - 15x + 1;$
$(g \circ f)(x) = 5x^2 - 15x + 5$

26. $f(x) = 3x^2 + 8, g(x) = 2x - 4$
$(f \circ g)(x) = 12x^2 - 48x + 56;$
$(g \circ f)(x) = 6x^2 + 12$

27. $f(x) = |x|, g(x) = x^3 - 1$
$(f \circ g)(x) = |x^3 - 1|;$
$(g \circ f)(x) = |x|^3 - 1$

28. $f(x) = \dfrac{1}{x + 2}, g(x) = |x + 2|$
$(f \circ g)(x) = \dfrac{1}{|x + 2| + 2};$
$(g \circ f)(x) = \left| \dfrac{1}{x + 2} + 2 \right|$ or $\left| \dfrac{2x + 5}{x + 2} \right|, x \neq -2$

29. For $h(x) = 5x - 4$,
find $(h \circ h)(x)$.
$(h \circ h)(x) = 25x - 24$

30. For $k(x) = -x^2 + 1$,
find $(k \circ k)(x)$.
$(k \circ k)(x) = -x^4 + 2x^2$

Concept 3: Multiple Operations on Functions

For Exercises 31–46, refer to the functions defined below.

$$m(x) = x^3 \qquad n(x) = x - 3 \qquad r(x) = \sqrt{x + 4} \qquad p(x) = \frac{1}{x + 2}$$

Find each function value if possible. **(See Example 3.)**

31. $(m \cdot r)(0)$ 0

32. $(n \cdot p)(0)$ $-\dfrac{3}{2}$

33. $(m + r)(-4)$ -64

34. $(n - m)(4)$ -63

 35. $(r \circ n)(3)$ 2

36. $(n \circ r)(5)$ 0

37. $(p \circ m)(-1)$ 1

38. $(m \circ n)(5)$ 8

39. $(m \circ p)(2)$ $\dfrac{1}{64}$

40. $(r \circ m)(2)$ $\sqrt{12}$ or $2\sqrt{3}$

41. $(r + p)(-3)$ 0

42. $(n + p)(-2)$ Undefined

43. $(m \circ p)(-2)$
Not a real number

44. $(r \circ m)(-2)$
Not a real number

45. $\left(\dfrac{r}{n}\right)(12)$ $\dfrac{4}{9}$

46. $\left(\dfrac{n}{m}\right)(2)$ $-\dfrac{1}{8}$

For Exercises 47–64, approximate each function value from the graph, if possible. **(See Example 4.)**

47. $f(-4)$ -2

48. $f(1)$ 2

49. $g(-2)$ 2

50. $g(3)$ -3

 51. $(f + g)(2)$ 0

52. $(g - f)(3)$ -6

53. $(f \cdot g)(-1)$ 1

54. $(g \cdot f)(-4)$ -4

55. $\left(\dfrac{g}{f}\right)(0)$ 0

56. $\left(\dfrac{f}{g}\right)(-2)$ 0

57. $\left(\dfrac{f}{g}\right)(0)$ Undefined

58. $\left(\dfrac{g}{f}\right)(-2)$ Undefined

59. $(g \circ f)(-1)$ -1

60. $(f \circ g)(0)$ 2

61. $(f \circ g)(-4)$ 2

62. $(g \circ f)(-4)$ 2

63. $(g \circ g)(2)$ 2

64. $(f \circ f)(-2)$ 2

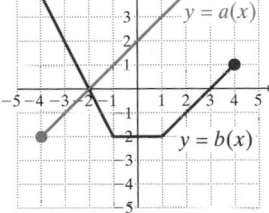

For Exercises 65–80, approximate each function value from the graph, if possible. **(See Example 4.)**

65. $a(-3)$ -1

66. $a(1)$ 3

67. $b(-1)$ -2

68. $b(3)$ 0

69. $(a - b)(-1)$ 3

70. $(a + b)(0)$ 0

71. $(b \cdot a)(1)$ -6

72. $(a \cdot b)(2)$ -4

73. $(b \circ a)(0)$ -1

74. $(a \circ b)(-2)$ 2

75. $(a \circ b)(-4)$ 4

76. $(b \circ a)(-3)$ -2

77. $\left(\dfrac{b}{a}\right)(3)$ 0

78. $\left(\dfrac{a}{b}\right)(4)$ 4

79. $(a \circ a)(-2)$ 2

80. $(b \circ b)(1)$ 0

 Writing   Translating Expression   Geometry   Scientific Calculator   Video   NS&E

81. The cost in dollars of producing x toy cars is $C(x) = 2.2x + 1$. The revenue received is $R(x) = 5.98x$. To calculate profit, subtract the cost from the revenue.

a. Write and simplify a function P that represents profit in terms of x. $P(x) = 3.78x - 1$

b. Find the profit of producing 50 toy cars. $188

82. The cost in dollars of producing x lawn chairs is $C(x) = 2.5x + 10.1$. The revenue for selling x lawn chairs is $R(x) = 6.99x$. To calculate profit, subtract the cost from the revenue.

a. Write and simplify a function P that represents profit in terms of x. $P(x) = 4.49x - 10.1$

b. Find the profit in producing 100 lawn chairs. $438.90

83. The functions defined by $D(t) = 0.925t + 26.958$ and $R(t) = 0.725t + 20.558$ approximate the amount of child support (in billions of dollars) that was due and the amount of child support actually received in the United States since 2000. In each case, $t = 0$ corresponds to the year 2000.

Difference Between Child Support Due and Child Support Paid, United States

Year ($t = 0$ corresponds to 2000)

Source: U.S. Bureau of the Census

a. Find the function F defined by $F(t) = D(t) - R(t)$. What does F represent in the context of this problem? $F(t) = 0.2t + 6.4$;
F represents the amount of child support (in billion dollars) not paid.

b. Find $F(4)$. What does this function value represent in the context of this problem?

$F(4) = 7.2$ means that in 2004, $7.2 billion of child support was not paid.

84. The rural and urban populations in the South (in the United States) between the years 1900 and 1970 can be modeled by the following:

$$r(t) = -3.497t^2 + 266.2t + 20{,}220$$

$$u(t) = 0.0566t^3 + 0.952t^2 + 177.8t + 4593$$

The variable t represents the number of years since 1900, $r(t)$ represents the rural population in thousands, and $u(t)$ represents the urban population in thousands.

Rural and Urban Populations in the South, United States, 1900–1970

Year ($t = 0$ corresponds to 1900)

Source: Historical Abstract of the United States

a. Find the function T defined by $T(t) = r(t) + u(t)$. What does the function T represent in the context of this problem? $T(t) = 0.0566t^3 - 2.545t^2 + 444t + 24{,}813$; $T(t)$ is the total population of the South (in thousands).

b. Use the function T to approximate the total population in the South for the year 1940.   42,123.4 thousand

85. Joe rides a bicycle and his wheels revolve at 80 revolutions per minute (rpm). Therefore, the total number of revolutions, r, is given by $r(t) = 80t$, where t is the time in minutes. For each revolution of the wheels of the bike, he travels approximately 7 ft. Therefore, the total distance he travels, D, depends on the total number of revolutions, r, according to the function $D(r) = 7r$.

a. Find $(D \circ r)(t)$ and interpret its meaning in the context of this problem.
$(D \circ r)(t) = 560t$; This function represents the total distance Joe travels as a function of time that he rides.

b. Find Joe's total distance in feet after 10 min.   5600 ft

86. The area of a square is given by the function $a(x) = x^2$, where x is the length of the sides of the square. If carpeting costs $9.95 per square yard, then the cost, C, to carpet a square room is given by $C(a) = 9.95a$, where a is the area of the room in square yards.

a. Find $(C \circ a)(x)$ and interpret its meaning in the context of this problem. $(C \circ a)(x) = 9.95x^2$; This function represents the total cost to carpet a square room where the dimensions of the room are x yd by x yd.

b. Find the cost to carpet a square room if its floor dimensions are 15 yd by 15 yd. $2238.75

Variation

1. Definition of Direct and Inverse Variation

In this section, we introduce the concept of variation. Direct and inverse variation models can show how one quantity varies in proportion to another.

DEFINITION   **Direct and Inverse Variation**

Let k be a nonzero constant real number. Then the following statements are equivalent:

1. y varies **directly** as x. $\left.\begin{array}{c} \\ \\ \end{array}\right\}$ $y = kx$
   y is directly proportional to x.

2. y varies **inversely** as x. $\left.\begin{array}{c} \\ \\ \end{array}\right\}$ $y = \dfrac{k}{x}$
   y is inversely proportional to x.

Note: The value of k is called the constant of variation.

For a car traveling 30 mph, the equation $d = 30t$ indicates that the distance traveled is *directly proportional* to the time of travel. For positive values of k, when two variables are directly related, as one variable increases, the other variable will also increase. Likewise, if one variable decreases, the other will decrease. In the equation $d = 30t$, the longer the time of the trip, the greater the distance traveled. The shorter the time of the trip, the shorter the distance traveled.

    For positive values of k, when two variables are *inversely related*, as one variable increases, the other will decrease, and vice versa. Consider a car traveling between Toronto and Montreal, a distance of 500 km. The time required to make the trip is inversely proportional to the speed of travel: $t = 500/r$. As the rate of speed, r, increases, the quotient $500/r$ will decrease. Thus, the time will decrease. Similarly, as the rate of speed decreases, the trip will take longer.

2. Translations Involving Variation

The first step in using a variation model is to write an English phrase as an equivalent mathematical equation.

Example 1   Translating to a Variation Model

Write each expression as an equivalent mathematical model.

a. The circumference of a circle varies directly as the radius.

b. At a constant temperature, the volume of a gas varies inversely as the pressure.

c. The length of time of a meeting is directly proportional to the *square* of the number of people present.

Classroom Examples: p. 609, Exercises 12 and 14

Solution:

a. Let C represent circumference and r represent radius. The variables are directly related, so use the model $C = kr$.

b. Let V represent volume and P represent pressure. Because the variables are inversely related, use the model $V = \frac{k}{P}$.

c. Let t represent time, and let N be the number of people present at a meeting. Because t is directly related to N^2, use the model $t = kN^2$.

Skill Practice Write each expression as an equivalent mathematical model.

1. The distance, d, driven in a particular time varies directly with the speed of the car, s.
2. The weight of an individual kitten, w, varies inversely with the number of kittens in the litter, n.
3. The value of v varies inversely as the square root of b.

Sometimes a variable varies directly as the product of two or more other variables. In this case, we have joint variation.

DEFINITION   Joint Variation

Let k be a nonzero constant real number. Then the following statements are equivalent:

y varies **jointly** as w and z.

y is jointly proportional to w and z. $\left.\begin{array}{c}\\\\\end{array}\right\}$ $y = kwz$

Classroom Examples: p. 609,
Exercises 18 and 22

Example 2   **Translating to a Variation Model**

Write each expression as an equivalent mathematical model.

a. y varies jointly as u and the square root of v.

b. The gravitational force of attraction between two planets varies jointly as the product of their masses and inversely as the square of the distance between them.

Solution:

a. $y = ku\sqrt{v}$

b. Let m_1 and m_2 represent the masses of the two planets. Let F represent the gravitational force of attraction and d represent the distance between the planets.

The variation model is $F = \dfrac{km_1m_2}{d^2}$

Answers

1. $d = ks$ 2. $w = \dfrac{k}{n}$

3. $v = \dfrac{k}{\sqrt{b}}$ 4. $q = kuv$

5. $x = \dfrac{ky^2}{z}$

Skill Practice Write each expression as an equivalent mathematical model.

4. The value of q varies jointly as u and v.

5. The value of x varies directly as the square of y and inversely as z.

3. Applications of Variation

Consider the variation models $y = kx$ and $y = \frac{k}{x}$. In either case, if values for x and y are known, we can solve for k. Once k is known, we can use the variation equation to find y if x is known, or to find x if y is known. This concept is the basis for solving many problems involving variation.

PROCEDURE Finding a Variation Model

Step 1 Write a general variation model that relates the variables given in the problem. Let k represent the constant of variation.

Step 2 Solve for k by substituting known values of the variables into the model from step 1.

Step 3 Substitute the value of k into the original variation model from step 1.

Example 3 Solving an Application Involving Direct Variation

Classroom Examples: p. 609, Exercises 24 and 32

The variable z varies directly as w. When w is 16, z is 56.

a. Write a variation model for this situation. Use k as the constant of variation.

b. Solve for the constant of variation.

c. Find the value of z when w is 84.

Solution:

a. $z = kw$

b. $z = kw$

$56 = k(16)$ Substitute known values for z and w. Then solve for the unknown value of k.

$\dfrac{56}{16} = \dfrac{k(16)}{16}$ To isolate k, divide both sides by 16.

$\dfrac{7}{2} = k$ Simplify $\dfrac{56}{16}$ to $\dfrac{7}{2}$.

c. With the value of k known, the variation model can now be written as $z = \dfrac{7}{2}w$.

$z = \dfrac{7}{2}(84)$ To find z when $w = 84$, substitute $w = 84$ into the equation.

$z = 294$

Skill Practice The variable t varies directly as the square of v. When v is 8, t is 32.

6. Write a variation model for this relationship.

7. Solve for the constant of variation.

8. Find t when $v = 10$.

Answers

6. $t = kv^2$ 7. $\dfrac{1}{2}$ 8. 50

Classroom Example: p. 610,
Exercise 42

Example 4   Solving an Application Involving Direct Variation

The speed of a racing canoe in still water varies directly as the square root of the length of the canoe.

   a. If a 16-ft canoe can travel 6.2 mph in still water, find a variation model that relates the speed of a canoe to its length.

   b. Find the speed of a 25-ft canoe.

Solution:

   a. Let s represent the speed of the canoe and L represent the length. The general variation model is $s = k\sqrt{L}$. To solve for k, substitute the known values for s and L.

$$s = k\sqrt{L}$$

$$6.2 = k\sqrt{16} \qquad \text{Substitute } s = 6.2 \text{ mph and } L = 16 \text{ ft.}$$

$$6.2 = k \cdot 4$$

$$\frac{6.2}{4} = \frac{4k}{4} \qquad \text{Solve for } k.$$

$$k = 1.55$$

$$s = 1.55\sqrt{L} \qquad \text{Substitute } k = 1.55 \text{ into the model } s = k\sqrt{L}.$$

   b. $s = 1.55\sqrt{L}$

$$= 1.55\sqrt{25} \qquad \text{Find the speed when } L = 25 \text{ ft.}$$

$$= 7.75 \text{ mph} \qquad \text{The speed is 7.75 mph.}$$

Skill Practice

   9. The amount of water needed by a mountain hiker varies directly as the time spent hiking. The hiker needs 2.4 L for a 4-hr hike. How much water will be needed for a 5-hr hike?

Classroom Example: p. 611,
Exercise 50

Example 5   Solving an Application Involving Inverse Variation

The loudness of sound measured in decibels (dB) varies inversely as the square of the distance between the listener and the source of the sound. If the loudness of sound is 17.92 dB at a distance of 10 ft from a home theater speaker, what is the decibel level 20 ft from the speaker?

Solution:

Let L represent the loudness of sound in decibels and d represent the distance in feet. The inverse relationship between decibel level and the square of the distance is modeled by

Answer

9. 3 L

$$L = \frac{k}{d^2}$$

$$17.92 = \frac{k}{(10)^2} \qquad \text{Substitute } L = 17.92 \text{ dB and } d = 10 \text{ ft.}$$

$$17.92 = \frac{k}{100}$$

$$(17.92)100 = \frac{k}{100} \cdot 100 \qquad \text{Solve for } k \text{ (clear fractions).}$$

$$k = 1792$$

$$L = \frac{1792}{d^2} \qquad \text{Substitute } k = 1792 \text{ into the original model } L = \frac{k}{d^2}.$$

With the value of k known, we can find L for any value of d.

$$L = \frac{1792}{(20)^2} \qquad \text{Find the loudness when } d = 20 \text{ ft.}$$

$$= 4.48 \text{ dB} \qquad \text{The loudness is 4.48 dB.}$$

Notice that the loudness of sound is 17.92 dB at a distance 10 ft from the speaker. When the distance from the speaker is increased to 20 ft, the decibel level decreases to 4.48 dB. This is consistent with an inverse relationship. For $k > 0$, as one variable is increased, the other is decreased. It also seems reasonable that the further one moves away from the source of a sound, the softer the sound becomes.

Skill Practice

10. The yield on a bond varies inversely as the price. The yield on a particular bond is 5% when the price is $100. Find the yield when the price is $125.

Example 6 Solving an Application Involving Joint Variation

Classroom Example: p. 611, Exercise 58

The kinetic energy of an object varies jointly as the weight of the object at sea level and as the square of its velocity. During a hurricane, a 0.5-lb stone traveling at 60 mph has 81 J (joules) of kinetic energy. Suppose the wind speed doubles to 120 mph. Find the kinetic energy.

Solution:

Let E represent the kinetic energy, let w represent the weight, and let v represent the velocity of the stone. The variation model is

$$E = kwv^2$$

$$81 = k(0.5)(60)^2 \qquad \text{Substitute } E = 81 \text{ J}, w = 0.5 \text{ lb, and } v = 60 \text{ mph.}$$

$$81 = k(0.5)(3600) \qquad \text{Simplify exponents.}$$

$$81 = k(1800)$$

$$\frac{81}{1800} = \frac{k(1800)}{1800} \qquad \text{Divide by 1800.}$$

$$0.045 = k \qquad \text{Solve for } k.$$

Answer

10. 4%

With the value of k known, the model $E = kwv^2$ can now be written as $E = 0.045wv^2$. We now find the kinetic energy of a 0.5-lb stone traveling at 120 mph.

$$E = 0.045(0.5)(120)^2$$
$$= 324$$

The kinetic energy of a 0.5-lb stone traveling at 120 mph is 324 J.

Skill Practice

11. The amount of simple interest earned in an account varies jointly as the interest rate and time of the investment. An account earns $72 in 4 years at 2% interest. How much interest would be earned in 3 years at a rate of 5%?

Answer

11. $135

In Example 6, when the velocity increased by 2 times, the kinetic energy increased by 4 times (note that $324 \text{ J} = 4 \cdot 81 \text{ J}$). This factor of 4 occurs because the kinetic energy is proportional to the *square* of the velocity. When the velocity increased by 2 times, the kinetic energy increased by 2^2 times.

Section 8.5   Practice Exercises

Boost *your* GRADE at ALEKS.com!

- Practice Problems
- Self-Tests
- NetTutor

- e-Professors
- Videos

For additional exercises, see Classroom Activities 8.5A–8.5C in the *Instructor's Resource Manual* at www.mhhe.com/moh.

Study Skills Exercise

1. Define the key terms.

    a. direct variation   **b. inverse variation**   **c. joint variation**

Review Exercises

For Exercises 2–7, refer to the functions defined below.

$$f(x) = x^2 \qquad g(x) = x - 2 \qquad h(x) = \sqrt{2 - x}$$

Find the indicated functions or function values.

2. $(f + g)(2)$ 4

3. $(f \circ g)(x)$ $x^2 - 4x + 4$

4. $(g - f)(3)$ -8

5. $(g \circ f)(x)$ $x^2 - 2$

6. $(f \cdot g)(x)$ $x^3 - 2x^2$

7. $\left(\dfrac{g}{h}\right)(1)$ -1

Concept 1: Definition of Direct and Inverse Variation

8. In the equation $r = kt$, does r vary directly or inversely with t?   Directly

9. In the equation $w = \dfrac{k}{v}$, does w vary directly or inversely with v?   Inversely

10. In the equation $P = \dfrac{k \cdot c}{v}$, does P vary directly or inversely as v?   Inversely

Concept 2: Translations Involving Variation

For Exercises 11–22, write a variation model. Use k as the constant of variation. **(See Examples 1–2.)**

11. T varies directly as q. $T = kq$

12. W varies directly as z. $W = kz$

13. b varies inversely as c. $b = \dfrac{k}{c}$

14. m varies inversely as t. $m = \dfrac{k}{t}$

15. Q is directly proportional to x and inversely proportional to y. $Q = \dfrac{kx}{y}$

16. d is directly proportional to p and inversely proportional to n. $d = \dfrac{kp}{n}$

17. c varies jointly as s and t. $c = kst$

18. w varies jointly as p and f. $w = kpf$

19. L varies jointly as w and the square root of v. $L = kw\sqrt{v}$

20. q varies jointly as v and the square root of w. $q = kv\sqrt{w}$

21. x varies directly as the square of y and inversely as z. $x = \dfrac{ky^2}{z}$

22. a varies directly as n and inversely as the square of d. $a = \dfrac{kn}{d^2}$

Concept 3: Applications of Variation

For Exercises 23–28, find the constant of variation, k. **(See Example 3.)**

23. y varies directly as x and when x is 4, y is 18. $k = \dfrac{9}{2}$

24. m varies directly as x and when x is 8, m is 22. $k = \dfrac{11}{4}$

25. p varies inversely as q and when q is 16, p is 32. $k = 512$

26. T varies inversely as x and when x is 40, T is 200. $k = 8000$

27. y varies jointly as w and v. When w is 50 and v is 0.1, y is 8.75. $k = 1.75$

28. N varies jointly as t and p. When t is 1 and p is 7.5, N is 330. $k = 44$

Solve Exercises 29–40 using the steps found on page 605. **(See Example 3.)**

29. x varies directly as p. If $x = 50$ when $p = 10$, find x when p is 14. $x = 70$

30. y is directly proportional to z. If $y = 12$ when $z = 36$, find y when z is 21. $y = 7$

31. b is inversely proportional to c. If b is 4 when c is 3, find b when $c = 2$. $b = 6$

32. q varies inversely as w. If q is 8 when w is 50, find q when w is 125. $q = 3.2$

33. Z varies directly as the square of w. If $Z = 14$ when $w = 4$, find Z when $w = 8$. $Z = 56$

34. m varies directly as the square of x. If $m = 200$ when $x = 20$, find m when x is 32. $m = 512$

35. Q varies inversely as the square of p. If $Q = 4$ when $p = 3$, find Q when $p = 2$. $Q = 9$

36. z is inversely proportional to the square of t. If $z = 15$ when $t = 4$, find z when $t = 10$. $z = 2.4$

37. L varies jointly as a and the square root of b. If $L = 72$ when $a = 8$ and $b = 9$, find L when $a = \frac{1}{2}$ and $b = 36$. $L = 9$

38. Y varies jointly as the cube of x and the square root of w. $Y = 128$ when $x = 2$ and $w = 16$. Find Y when $x = \frac{1}{2}$ and $w = 64$. $Y = 4$

39. B varies directly as m and inversely as n. $B = 20$ when $m = 10$ and $n = 3$. Find B when $m = 15$ and $n = 12$. $B = \dfrac{15}{2}$

40. R varies directly as s and inversely as t. $R = 14$ when $s = 2$ and $t = 9$. Find R when $s = 4$ and $t = 3$. $R = 84$

 Writing   Translating Expression   Geometry   Scientific Calculator   Video   NS&E

For Exercises 41–58, use a variation model to solve for the unknown value. **(See Examples 4–6.)**

41. The weight of a person's heart varies directly as the person's actual weight. For a 150-lb man, his heart would weigh 0.75 lb.

   a. Approximate the weight of a 184-lb man's heart. The heart weighs 0.92 lb.

   b. How much does your heart weigh?
   Answers will vary.

42. The number of calories, C, in beer varies directly with the number of ounces, n. If 12 oz of beer contains 153 calories, how many calories are in 40 oz of beer?   There are 510 calories in 40 oz of beer.

43. The amount of medicine that a physician prescribes for a patient varies directly as the weight of the patient. A physician prescribes 3 g of a medicine for a 150-lb person.

   a. How many grams should be prescribed for a 180-lb person?   3.6 g

   b. How many grams should be prescribed for a 225-lb person?   4.5 g

   c. How many grams should be prescribed for a 120-lb person?   2.4 g

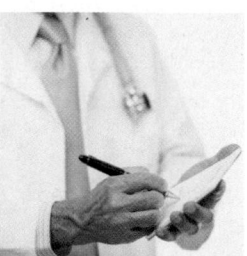

44. The number of turkeys needed for a banquet is directly proportional to the number of guests that must be fed. Master Chef Rico knows that he needs to cook 3 turkeys to feed 42 guests.

   a. How many turkeys should he cook to feed 70 guests?   5 turkeys

   b. How many turkeys should he cook to feed 140 guests?   10 turkeys

   c. How many turkeys should be cooked to feed 700 guests at an inaugural ball?   50 turkeys

   d. How many turkeys should be cooked for a wedding with 100 guests?   8 turkeys; Note that the answer was rounded up, because it would be better for the chef to have too much food than too little.

45. The unit cost of producing CDs is inversely proportional to the number of CDs produced. If 5000 CDs are produced, the cost per CD is $0.48.

   a. What would be the unit cost if 6000 CDs were produced? $0.40

   b. What would be the unit cost if 8000 CDs were produced? $0.30

   c. What would be the unit cost if 2400 CDs were produced? $1.00

46. An author self-publishes a book and finds that the number of books she can sell per month varies inversely as the price of the book. The author can sell 1500 books per month when the price is set at $8 per book.

   a. How many books would she expect to sell if the price were $12?   1000 books

   b. How many books would she expect to sell if the price were $15?   800 books

   c. How many books would she expect to sell if the price were $6?   2000 books

 Writing   Translating Expression   Geometry   Scientific Calculator   Video   NS&E

47. The amount of pollution entering the atmosphere over a given time varies directly as the number of people living in an area. If 80,000 people cause 56,800 tons of pollutants, how many tons enter the atmosphere in a city with a population of 500,000?   355,000 tons

48. The area of a picture projected on a wall varies directly as the square of the distance from the projector to the wall. If a 10-ft distance produces a 16-ft^2 picture, what is the area of a picture produced when the projection unit is moved to a distance 20 ft from the wall?
64 ft^2

49. The stopping distance of a car varies directly as the square of the speed of the car. If a car traveling at 40 mph has a stopping distance of 109 ft, find the stopping distance of a car that is traveling at 25 mph. (Round your answer to one decimal place.)   42.6 ft

50. The intensity of a light source varies inversely as the square of the distance from the source. If the intensity is 48 lumens at a distance of 5 ft, what is the intensity when the distance is 8 ft?   18.75 lumens

51. The power in an electric circuit varies jointly as the current and the square of the resistance. If the power is 144 W (watts) when the current is 4 A (amperes) and the resistance is 6 Ω, find the power when the current is 3 A and the resistance is 10 Ω.   300 W

52. Some body-builders claim that, within safe limits, the number of repetitions that a person can complete on a given weight-lifting exercise is inversely proportional to the amount of weight lifted. Roxanne can bench press 45 lb for 15 repetitions.

a. How many repetitions can Roxanne bench with 60 lb of weight?   11 complete repetitions

b. How many repetitions can Roxanne bench with 75 lb of weight?   9 repetitions

c. How many repetitions can Roxanne bench with 100 lb of weight?   6 complete repetitions

53. The current in a wire varies directly as the voltage and inversely as the resistance. If the current is 9 A when the voltage is 90 V (volts) and the resistance is 10 Ω (ohms), find the current when the voltage is 185 V and the resistance is 10 Ω.   18.5 A

54. The resistance of a wire varies directly as its length and inversely as the square of its diameter. A 40-ft wire 0.1 in. in diameter has a resistance of 4 Ω. What is the resistance of a 50-ft wire with a diameter of 0.2 in.?   1.25 Ω

55. The weight of a medicine ball varies directly as the cube of its radius. A ball with a radius of 3 in. weighs 4.32 lb. How much would a medicine ball weigh if its radius is 5 in.?   20 lb

56. The area of an equilateral triangle varies directly as the square of the length of the sides. For an equilateral triangle with 7-cm sides, the area is 21.22 cm^2. What is the area of an equilateral triangle with 17-cm sides? Round to the nearest whole unit.
125 cm^2

57. The amount of simple interest earned in an account varies jointly as the amount of principal invested and the amount of time the money is invested. If $2500 in principal earns $500 in interest after 4 years, then how much interest will be earned on $7000 invested for 10 years? $3500

58. The amount of simple interest earned in an account varies jointly as the amount of principal invested and the amount of time the money is invested. If $6000 in principal earns $840 in interest after 2 years, then how much interest will be earned on $4500 invested for 8 years? $2520

 Writing   Translating Expression   Geometry   Scientific Calculator   Video   NS&E

Group Activity

Deciphering a Coded Message

Materials: A calculator

Estimated time: 20–25 minutes

Group Size: 4 (two pairs)

Cryptography is the study of coding and decoding messages. One type of coding process assigns a number to each letter of the alphabet and to the space character. For example:

A	B	C	D	E	F	G	H	I	J	K	L	M	N
1	2	3	4	5	6	7	8	9	10	11	12	13	14

O	P	Q	R	S	T	U	V	W	X	Y	Z	space
15	16	17	18	19	20	21	22	23	24	25	26	27

According to the numbers assigned to each letter, the message "*Decimals have a point*" would be coded as follows:

D E C I M A L S _ H A V E _ A _ P O I N T

4 5 3 9 13 1 12 19 27 8 1 22 5 27 1 27 16 15 9 14 20

Now suppose each letter is encoded by applying a function such as $f(x) = 2x + 5$, where x is the numerical value of each letter. For example:

The letter "a" would be coded as: $f(1) = 2(1) + 5 = 7$

The letter "b" would be coded as: $f(2) = 2(2) + 5 = 9$

Using this encoding function, we have

Message:	D	E	C	I	M	A	L	S	_	H	A	V	E	_	A	_	P	O	I	N	T
Original:	4	5	3	9	13	1	12	19	27	8	1	22	5	27	1	27	16	15	9	14	20
Coded Form:	13	15	11	23	31	7	29	43	59	21	7	49	15	59	7	59	37	35	23	33	45

To decode this message, the receiver would need to reverse the operations assigned by $f(x) = 2x + 5$. Since the function f multiplies x by 2 and then adds 5, we can reverse this process by subtracting 5 and dividing by 2. This is represented by $g(x) = \frac{x - 5}{2}$.

1. a. One pair of students will encode the follow message according to $f(x) = 4x + 2$.

MATH IS THE KEY TO THE SCIENCES
54, 6, 82, 34, 110, 38, 78, 110, 82, 34, 22, 110, 46, 22, 102, 110, 82, 62, 110, 82, 34, 22, 110, 78, 14, 38, 22, 58, 14, 22, 78

b. The second pair of students will encode the follow message according to $f(x) = 3x - 1$.

MATH IS NOT A SPECTATOR SPORT
38, 2, 59, 23, 80, 26, 56, 80, 41, 44, 59, 80, 2, 80, 56, 47, 14, 8, 59, 2, 59, 44, 53, 80, 56, 47, 44, 53, 59

2. With each message encoded, the pairs will exchange papers. Each pair will then decode the message.

Instructor Note: This activity would be a great place to use the *Table* feature on a graphing calculator.

Chapter 8   Summary

Section 8.1   Introduction to Relations

Key Concepts

A set of ordered pairs (x, y) is called a **relation in x and y.**

The **domain** of a relation is the set of first components in the ordered pairs in the relation. The **range** of a relation is the set of second components in the ordered pairs.

Examples

Example 1

Let $A = \{(0, 0), (1, 1), (2, 4), (3, 9), (-1, 1), (-2, 4)\}$.

Domain of A: $\{0, 1, 2, 3, -1, -2\}$

Range of A: $\{0, 1, 4, 9\}$

Example 2

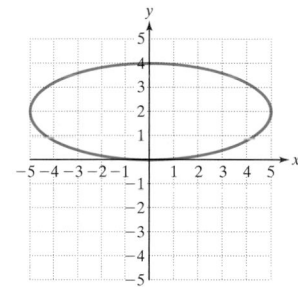

Domain: $[-5, 5]$
Range: $[0, 4]$

Section 8.2   Introduction to Functions

Key Concepts

Given a relation in x and y, we say "y is a **function** of x" if, for each element x in the domain, there is exactly one value of y in the range.

Note: This means that no two ordered pairs may have the same first coordinate and different second coordinates.

The Vertical Line Test for Functions

Consider a relation defined by a set of points (x, y) in a rectangular coordinate system. The graph defines y as a function of x if no vertical line intersects the graph in more than one point.

Examples

Example 1

Function $\{(1, 3), (2, 5), (6, 3)\}$
Not a function $\{(1, 3), (2, 5), (1, 4)\}$

Example 2

Function

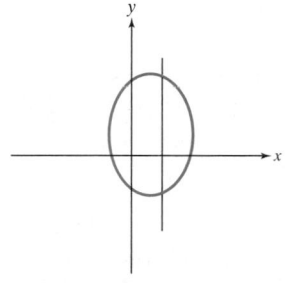

Not a function

Function Notation

$f(x)$ is the value of the function f at x.

The domain of a function defined by $y = f(x)$ is the set of x-values that when substituted into the function produces a real number. In particular,

- Exclude values of x that make the denominator of a fraction zero.
- Exclude values of x that make the expression within a square root negative.

Example 3

Given $f(x) = -3x^2 + 5x$, find $f(-2)$.

$$f(-2) = -3(-2)^2 + 5(-2)$$
$$= -12 - 10$$
$$= -22$$

Example 4

Find the domain.

1. $f(x) = \dfrac{x + 4}{x - 5}$; Domain: $(-\infty, 5) \cup (5, \infty)$

2. $f(x) = \sqrt{x - 3}$; Domain: $[3, \infty)$

3. $f(x) = 3x^2 - 5$; Domain: $(-\infty, \infty)$

Section 8.3 Graphs of Functions

Key Concepts

A function of the form $f(x) = mx + b\ (m \neq 0)$ is a **linear function**. Its graph is a line with slope m and y-intercept $(0, b)$.

A function of the form $f(x) = k$ is a **constant function**. Its graph is a horizontal line.

A function of the form $f(x) = ax^2 + bx + c\ (a \neq 0)$ is a **quadratic function**. Its graph is a **parabola**.

Graphs of basic functions:

    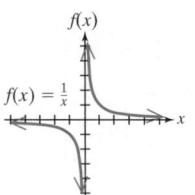

The x-intercepts of a function are determined by finding the real solutions to the equation $f(x) = 0$.

The y-intercept of a function is at $f(0)$.

Examples

Example 1

$$f(x) = 2x - 3 \qquad\qquad f(x) = 3$$

  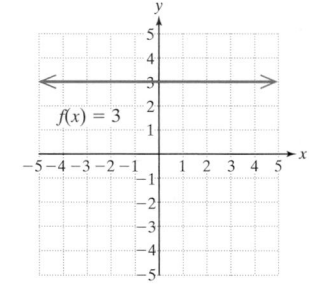

Example 2

Find the x- and y-intercepts for the function pictured.

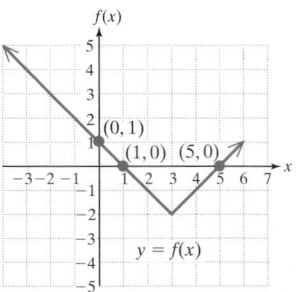

$f(x) = 0$, when $x = 1$ and $x = 5$.

The x-intercepts are $(1, 0)$ and $(5, 0)$.

$f(0) = 1$. The y-intercept is $(0, 1)$.

Section 8.4   Algebra of Functions and Composition

Key Concepts

The Algebra of Functions

Given two functions f and g, the functions
$f + g, f - g, f \cdot g$, and $\dfrac{f}{g}$ are defined as

$(f + g)(x) = f(x) + g(x)$

$(f - g)(x) = f(x) - g(x)$

$(f \cdot g)(x) = f(x) \cdot g(x)$

$\left(\dfrac{f}{g}\right)(x) = \dfrac{f(x)}{g(x)}$ provided $g(x) \neq 0$

Composition of Functions

The **composition** of f and g, denoted $f \circ g$, is defined by the rule

$(f \circ g)(x) = f(g(x))$ provided that $g(x)$ is in the domain of f

The **composition** of g and f, denoted $g \circ f$, is defined by the rule

$(g \circ f)(x) = g(f(x))$ provided that $f(x)$ is in the domain of g

Examples

Example 1

Let $g(x) = 5x + 1$ and $h(x) = x^3$. Find:

1. $(g + h)(3) = g(3) + h(3) = 16 + 27 = 43$
2. $(g \cdot h)(-1) = g(-1) \cdot h(-1) = (-4) \cdot (-1) = 4$
3. $(g - h)(x) = 5x + 1 - x^3$
4. $\left(\dfrac{g}{h}\right)(x) = \dfrac{5x + 1}{x^3}$

Example 2

Find $(f \circ g)(x)$ and $(g \circ f)(x)$ given the functions defined by $f(x) = 4x + 3$ and $g(x) = 7x$.

$(f \circ g)(x) = f(g(x))$

$\qquad = f(7x)$

$\qquad = 4(7x) + 3$

$\qquad = 28x + 3$

$(g \circ f)(x) = g(f(x))$

$\qquad = g(4x + 3)$

$\qquad = 7(4x + 3)$

$\qquad = 28x + 21$

Section 8.5   Variation

Key Concepts

Direct Variation

y varies directly as x.
y is directly proportional to x. $\Big\}$ $y = kx$

Inverse Variation

y varies inversely as x.
y is inversely proportional to x. $\Big\}$ $y = \dfrac{k}{x}$

Examples

Example 1

t varies directly as the square root of x.

$t = k\sqrt{x}$

Example 2

W is inversely proportional to the cube of x.

$W = \dfrac{k}{x^3}$

Joint Variation

y varies jointly as w and z.
y is jointly proportional to w and z. $\left.\right\}$ $y = kwz$

Steps to Find a Variation Model

1. Write a general variation model that relates the variables given in the problem. Let k represent the constant of variation.
2. Solve for k by substituting known values of the variables into the model from step 1.
3. Substitute the value of k into the original variation model from step 1.

Example 3

y is jointly proportional to x and the square of z.

$y = kxz^2$

Example 4

C varies directly as the square root of d and inversely as t. If $C = 12$ when d is 9 and t is 6, find C if d is 16 and t is 12.

Step 1. $C = \dfrac{k\sqrt{d}}{t}$

Step 2. $12 = \dfrac{k\sqrt{9}}{6} \Rightarrow 12 = \dfrac{k \cdot 3}{6} \Rightarrow k = 24$

Step 3. $C = \dfrac{24\sqrt{d}}{t} \Rightarrow C = \dfrac{24\sqrt{16}}{12} \Rightarrow C = 8$

Chapters 8   Review Exercises

Section 8.1

For Exercises 1–4, find the domain and range.

1. $\left\{\left(\dfrac{1}{3}, 10\right), \left(6, -\dfrac{1}{2}\right), \left(\dfrac{1}{4}, 4\right), \left(7, \dfrac{2}{5}\right)\right\}$ Domain: $\left\{\dfrac{1}{3}, 6, \dfrac{1}{4}, 7\right\}$; range: $\left\{10, -\dfrac{1}{2}, 4, \dfrac{2}{5}\right\}$

2.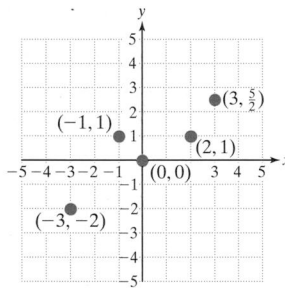

Domain: $\{-3, -1, 0, 2, 3\}$;
range: $\left\{-2, 0, 1, \dfrac{5}{2}\right\}$

3.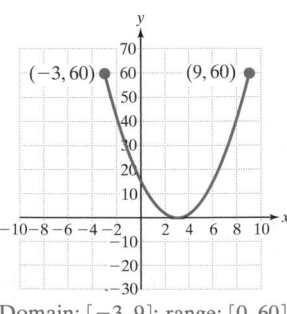

Domain: $[-3, 9]$; range: $[0, 60]$

4.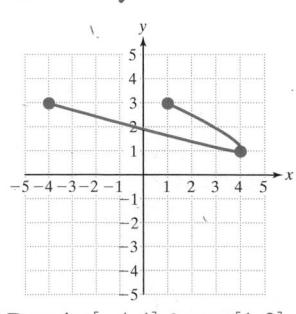

Domain: $[-4, 4]$; range: $[1, 3]$

Section 8.2

5. Sketch a relation that is *not* a function. (Answers may vary.)

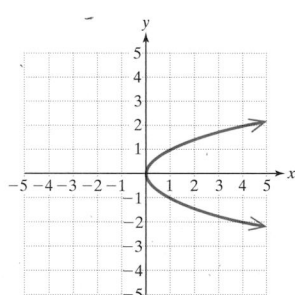

6. Sketch a relation that *is* a function. (Answers may vary.)

For Exercises 7–12:

a. Determine whether the relation defines y as a function of x.

b. Find the domain.

c. Find the range.

7. a. Not a function
b. $[1, 3]$
c. $[-4, 4]$

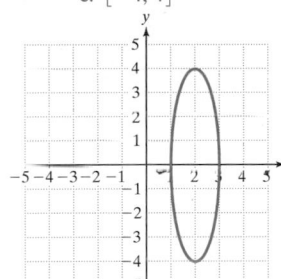

8. a. Function
b. $(-\infty, \infty)$
c. $(-\infty, 0.35]$

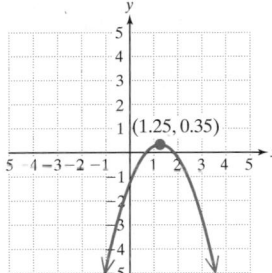

(1.25, 0.35)

9. $\{(1, 3), (2, 3), (3, 3), (4, 3)\}$
a. Function   b. $\{1, 2, 3, 4\}$
c. $\{3\}$

10. $\{(0, 2), (0, 3), (4, 4), (0, 5)\}$
a. Not a function
b. $\{0, 4\}$ c. $\{2, 3, 4, 5\}$

11.

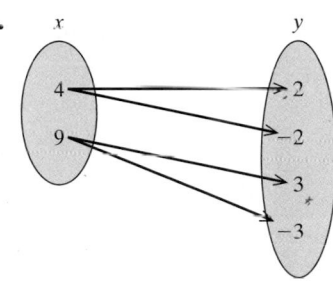

a. Not a function
b. $\{4, 9\}$
c. $\{2, -2, 3, -3\}$

12.

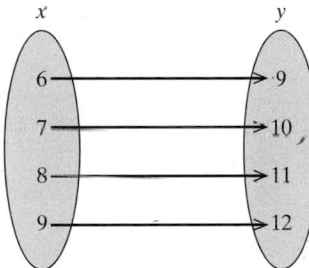

a. Function
b. $\{6, 7, 8, 9\}$
c. $\{9, 10, 11, 12\}$

For Exercises 13–20, find the function values given $f(x) = 6x^2 - 4$.

13. $f(0)$ -4

14. $f(1)$ 2

15. $f(-1)$ 2

16. $f(t)$ $6t^2 - 4$

17. $f(b)$ $6b^2 - 4$

18. $f(\pi)$ $6\pi^2 - 4$

19. $f(a)$ $6a^2 - 4$

20. $f(-2)$ 20

For Exercises 21–24, write the domain of each function in interval notation.

21. $g(x) = 7x^3 + 1$
$(-\infty, \infty)$

22. $h(x) = \dfrac{x + 10}{x - 11}$
$(-\infty, 11) \cup (11, \infty)$

23. $k(x) = \sqrt{x - 8}$
$[8, \infty)$

24. $w(x) = \sqrt{x + 2}$
$[-2, \infty)$

25. Anita is a waitress and makes $6 per hour plus tips. Her tips average $5 per table. In one 8-hr shift, Anita's pay can be described by $p(x) = 48 + 5x$, where x represents the number of tables she waits on. Determine how much Anita will earn if she waits on

a. 10 tables   **b.** 15 tables   **c.** 20 tables
$98 $123 $148

Section 8.3

For Exercises 26–31, sketch the functions from memory.

26. $h(x) = x$

27. $f(x) - x^2$

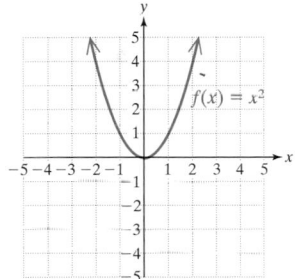

$f(x) = x^2$

28. $g(x) = x^3$

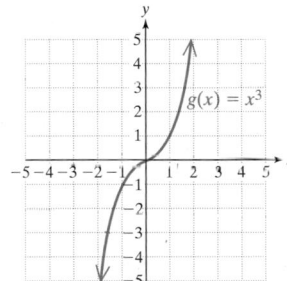

$g(x) = x^3$

29. $w(x) = |x|$

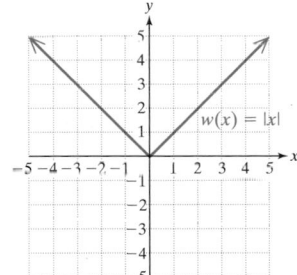

$w(x) = |x|$

30. $s(x) = \sqrt{x}$

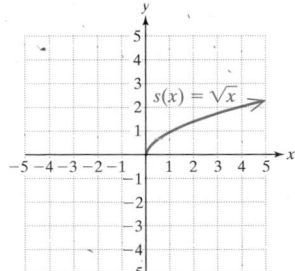

$s(x) = \sqrt{x}$

31. $r(x) = \dfrac{1}{x}$

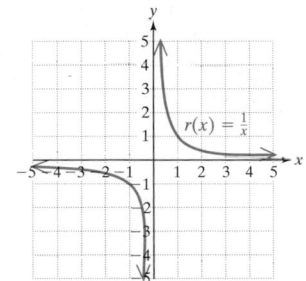

$r(x) = \frac{1}{x}$

Writing   Translating Expression   Geometry   Scientific Calculator   Video   NS&E

For Exercises 32–33, sketch the functions.

32. $q(x) = 3$

33. $k(x) = 2x + 1$

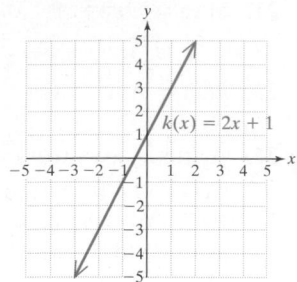

34. Given: $s(x) = (x - 2)^2$

    a. Find $s(4), s(-3), s(2), s(1)$, and $s(0)$.
      $s(4) = 4, s(-3) = 25, s(2) = 0, s(1) = 1, s(0) = 4$
    b. What is the domain of s?
      $(-\infty, \infty)$

35. Given: $r(x) = 2\sqrt{x - 4}$

    a. Find $r(2), r(4), r(5)$, and $r(8)$.
      $r(2)$ is not a real number, $r(4) = 0, r(5) = 2, r(8) = 4$
    b. What is the domain of r?
      $[4, \infty)$

36. Given: $h(x) = \dfrac{3}{x - 3}$

    a. Find $h(-3), h(0), h(2)$, and $h(5)$.
      $h(-3) = -\dfrac{1}{2}$, $h(0) = -1, h(2) = -3, h(5) = \dfrac{3}{2}$
    b. What is the domain of h?
      $(-\infty, 3) \cup (3, \infty)$

37. Given: $k(x) = -|x + 3|$

    a. Find $k(-5), k(-4), k(-3)$, and $k(2)$.
      $k(-5) = -2, k(-4) = -1, k(-3) = 0, \ k(2) = -5$
    b. What is the domain of k?
      $(-\infty, \infty)$

For Exercises 38–39, find the x- and y-intercepts.

38. $p(x) = 4x - 7$ x-intercept: $\left(\dfrac{7}{4}, 0\right)$; y-intercept: $(0, -7)$

39. $q(x) = -2x + 9$ x-intercept: $\left(\dfrac{9}{2}, 0\right)$; y-intercept: $(0, 9)$

40. The function defined by $b(t) = 0.7t + 4.5$ represents the per capita consumption of bottled water in the United States since 1985. The values of $b(t)$ are measured in gallons, and $t = 0$ corresponds to the year 1985. (*Source:* U.S. Department of Agriculture)

    a. Evaluate $b(0)$ and $b(7)$ and interpret the results in the context of this problem. $b(0) = 4.5$.
In 1985 consumption was 4.5 gal of bottled water per capita. $b(7) = 9.4$.
In 1992 consumption was 9.4 gal of bottled water per capita.
    b. Determine the slope and interpret its meaning in the context of this problem.
      $m = 0.7$. Consumption increased at a rate of 0.7 gal/year.

For Exercises 41–46, refer to the graph.

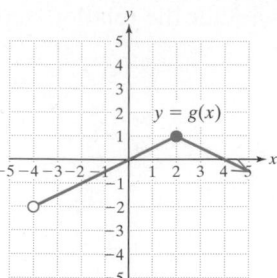

41. Find $g(-2)$. -1 **42.** Find $g(4)$. 0

43. For what value(s) of x is $g(x) = 0$? $x = 0$ and $x = 4$

44. For what value(s) of x is $g(x) = 4$?
    There are no values of x for which $g(x) = 4$.

45. Write the domain of g. $(-4, \infty)$

46. Write the range of g. $(-\infty, 1]$

Section 8.4

For Exercises 47–54, refer to the functions defined here.
$$f(x) = x - 7 \qquad g(x) = -2x^3 - 8x$$
$$m(x) = x^2 \qquad n(x) = \dfrac{1}{x - 2}$$

Find the indicated functions.

47. $(f - g)(x)$
    $(f - g)(x) = 2x^3 + 9x - 7$

48. $(f + g)(x)$
    $(f + g)(x) = -2x^3 - 7x - 7$

49. $(f \cdot n)(x)$
    $(f \cdot n)(x) = \dfrac{x - 7}{x - 2}, x \neq 2$

50. $(f \cdot m)(x)$
    $(f \cdot m)(x) = x^3 - 7x^2$

51. $\left(\dfrac{f}{g}\right)(x)$
    $\left(\dfrac{f}{g}\right)(x) = \dfrac{x - 7}{-2x^3 - 8x}, x \neq 0$

52. $\left(\dfrac{g}{f}\right)(x)$
    $\left(\dfrac{g}{f}\right)(x) = \dfrac{-2x^3 - 8x}{x - 7}, x \neq 7$

53. $(m \circ f)(x)$
$(m \circ f)(x) = (x - 7)^2$ or $x^2 - 14x + 49$

54. $(n \circ f)(x)$
    $(n \circ f)(x) = \dfrac{1}{x - 9}, x \neq 9$

For Exercises 55–58, refer to the functions defined for Exercises 47–54. Find the function values, if possible.

55. $(m \circ g)(-1)$ 100

56. $(n \circ g)(-1)$ $\dfrac{1}{8}$

57. $(f \circ g)(4)$ -167

58. $(g \circ f)(8)$ -10

59. Given $f(x) = 2x + 1$ and $g(x) = x^2$

    a. Find $(g \circ f)(x)$. $(2x + 1)^2$ or $4x^2 + 4x + 1$

    b. Find $(f \circ g)(x)$. $2x^2 + 1$

    c. Based on your answers to part (a), is $f \circ g$ equal to $g \circ f$?   No, $f \circ g \neq g \circ f$

 Writing   Translating Expression   Geometry   Scientific Calculator   Video   NS E

For Exercises 60–65, refer to the graph. Approximate the function values, if possible.

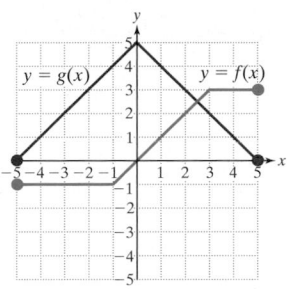

60. $\left(\dfrac{f}{g}\right)(1)$ $\dfrac{1}{4}$

61. $(f \cdot g)(-2)$ -3

62. $(f + g)(-4)$ 0

63. $(f - g)(2)$ -1

64. $(g \circ f)(-3)$ 4

65. $(f \circ g)(4)$ 1

Section 8.5

66. The force applied to a spring varies directly with the distance that the spring is stretched.

   a. Write a variation model using k as the constant of variation. $F = kd$

   b. When 6 lb of force is applied, the spring stretches 2 ft. Find k. $k = 3$

   c. How much force is required to stretch the spring 4.2 ft?   12.6 lb

67. Suppose y varies inversely with the cube of x, and $y = 9$ when $x = 2$. Find y when $x = 3$. $y = \dfrac{8}{3}$,

68. Suppose y varies jointly with x and the square root of z, and $y = 3$ when $x = 3$ and $z = 4$. Find y when $x = 8$ and $z = 9$. $y = 12$

69. The distance, d, that one can see to the horizon varies directly as the square root of the height above sea level. If a person 25 m above sea level can see 30 km, how far can a person see if she is 64 m above sea level?   48 km

---

Chapter 8   Test

For Exercises 1–2, **a.** determine if the relation defines y as a function of x, **b.** identify the domain, and **c.** identify the range.

1.
  a. Not a function
  b. $\{-3, -1, 1, 3\}$
  c. $\{-2, -1, 1, 3\}$

2.
  a. Function
  b. $(-\infty, \infty)$
  c. $(-\infty, 0]$

3. Explain how to find the x- and y-intercepts of the graph defined by $y = f(x)$.
To find the x-intercept(s), solve for the real solutions of the equation $f(x) = 0$. To find the y-intercept, find $f(0)$.

For Exercises 4–7, graph the functions.

4. $f(x) = -3x - 1$

5. $k(x) = -2$

6. $p(x) = x^2$

7. $w(x) = |x|$

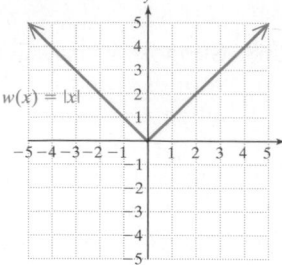

For Exercises 8–10, write the domain in interval notation.

8. $f(x) = \dfrac{x - 5}{x + 7}$ $(-\infty, -7) \cup (-7, \infty)$

9. $f(x) = \sqrt{x + 7}$ $[-7, \infty)$

10. $h(x) = (x + 7)(x - 5)$ $(-\infty, \infty)$

11. Given: $r(x) = x^2 - 2x + 1$

a. Find $r(-2)$, $r(0)$, and $r(3)$.
$r(-2) = 9$, $r(0) = 1$, $r(3) = 4$

b. What is the domain of r?
$(-\infty, \infty)$

12. The function defined by $s(t) = 1.6t + 36$ approximates the per capita consumption of soft drinks in the United States since 1985. The values of $s(t)$ are measured in gallons, and $t = 0$ corresponds to the year 1985. (Source: U.S. Department of Agriculture) Evaluate $s(0)$ and $s(7)$ and interpret the results in the context of this problem.
$s(0) = 36$. In 1985 the per capita consumption was 36 gal.
$s(7) = 47.2$. In 1992 the per capita consumption was 47.2 gal.

For Exercises 13–20, refer to the graph.

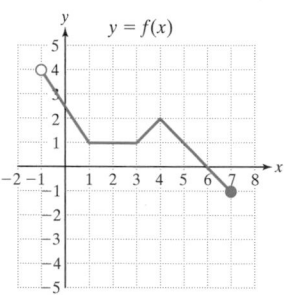

13. Find $f(1)$. 1

14. Find $f(4)$. 2

15. Write the domain of f. $(-1, 7]$

16. Write the range of f. $[-1, 4)$

17. Answer true or false. The value $y = 5$ is in the range of f. False

18. Find the x-intercept. $(6, 0)$

19. For what value(s) of x is $f(x) = 0$? $x = 6$

20. For what value(s) of x is $f(x) = 1$? All x in the interval $[1, 3]$ and $x = 5$

For Exercises 21–24, determine if the function is constant, linear, quadratic, or none of these.

21. $f(x) = -3x^2$
Quadratic

22. $g(x) = -3x$
Linear

23. $h(x) = -3$
Constant

24. $k(x) = -\dfrac{3}{x}$
None of these

25. Find the x- and y-intercepts for $f(x) = \dfrac{3}{4}x + 9$.
x-intercept: $(-12, 0)$; y-intercept: $(0, 9)$

For Exercises 26–34, refer to these functions.

$$f(x) = x - 4 \qquad g(x) = x^2 + 2 \qquad h(x) = \frac{1}{x}$$

Find the indicated functions or function values.

26. $\left(\dfrac{f}{g}\right)(x)$ $\left(\dfrac{f}{g}\right)(x) = \dfrac{x - 4}{x^2 + 2}$

27. $(h \cdot g)(x)$ $(h \cdot g)(x) = \dfrac{x^2 + 2}{x}, x \neq 0$

28. $(g \circ f)(x)$ $(g \circ f)(x) = x^2 - 8x + 18$

29. $(h \circ f)(x)$ $(h \circ f)(x) = \dfrac{1}{x - 4}, x \neq 4$

30. $(f - g)(7)$ -48

31. $(h + f)(2)$ $-\dfrac{3}{2}$

32. $(h \circ g)(4)$ $\dfrac{1}{18}$

33. $(g \circ f)(0)$ 18

34. $\left(\dfrac{g}{f}\right)(x)$ $\left(\dfrac{g}{f}\right)(x) = \dfrac{x^2 + 2}{x - 4}, x \neq 4$

35. The amount of medication prescribed for a patient varies directly as the patient's weight. If a 160-lb person is prescribed 6 mL of a medicine, then how much medicine would be prescribed to a 220-lb person? 8.25 mL

36. The number of drinks sold at a concession stand varies inversely as price. If the price is set at \$1.25 per drink, then 400 drinks are sold. If the price is set at \$2.50 per drink, then how many drinks are sold? 200 drinks are sold.

 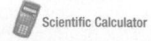

Chapters 1–8 Cumulative Review Exercises

For Exercises 1–2, simplify the expression.

1. $\dfrac{5 - 2^3 \div 4 + 7}{-1 - 3(4 - 1)}$ -1

2. $4[-3x - 5(y - 2x) + 3] - 7(6y + x)$

$21x - 62y + 12$

For Exercises 3–4, solve the equation.

3. $\dfrac{2x - 3}{6} - \dfrac{x + 1}{4} = -2$ $\{-15\}$

4. $w - (3 + 2w) + 5 = -w - 5$ $\{\ \}$

5. Solve the inequality. $-3x + 2 \le 11$ $[-3, \infty)$

6. Find the x- and y-intercepts of $3x - 5y = 10$. Then graph the line. x-intercept: $\left(\dfrac{10}{3}, 0\right)$

y-intercept: $(0, -2)$

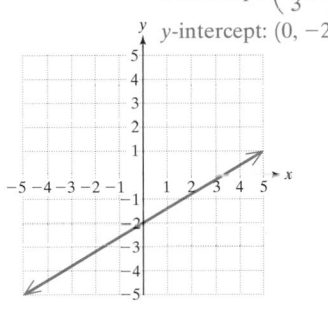

7. Find the slope of the line that passes through the point $(4, -5)$ and $(-6, -3)$. $m = -\dfrac{1}{5}$

8. Find the slope of the line $5x - 2y = -10$. $m = \dfrac{5}{2}$

For Exercises 9–10, solve the system of equations.

9. $\begin{aligned} 4x - y &= 9 \\ x + 2y &= 0 \end{aligned}$ $\{(2, -1)\}$

10. $\begin{aligned} x - 2y + z &= 1 \\ 3x + y - 2z &= -22 \\ 4x \quad\quad + z &= -11 \end{aligned}$

$\{(-4, 0, 5)\}$

11. Simplify. $\left(\dfrac{3x^2y}{9x^3y^{-2}}\right)^{-2}$ $\dfrac{9x^2}{y^6}$

For Exercises 12–13, perform the indicated operation.

12. $(5x^2 - 6x) + (-2x + 7)$ $5x^2 - 8x + 7$

13. $(5x^2 - 6x)(-2x + 7)$ $-10x^3 + 47x^2 - 42x$

For Exercises 14–15, factor completely.

14. $2x^2 + 7x + 3$ $(2x + 1)(x + 3)$

15. $5x^2 - 80$ $5(x - 4)(x + 4)$

16. Add. $\dfrac{5}{x - 5} + \dfrac{x}{x + 1}$ $\dfrac{x^2 + 5}{(x - 5)(x + 1)}$

17. Divide. $\dfrac{x^2 + 3x}{x - 2} \div \dfrac{x^4 + 3x^3}{x^2 - 4}$ $\dfrac{x + 2}{x^2}$

18. Determine the domain and range of the function.

$$\{(2, 4), (-1, 4), (9, 2), (-6, 8)\}$$

Domain: $\{2, -1, 9, -6\}$

Range: $\{4, 2, 8\}$

19. Determine the domain of $f(x) = \dfrac{x - 5}{x}$.

$(-\infty, 0) \cup (0, \infty)$

20. Find $(f \circ g)(x)$ for $f(x) = x^2 - 6$ and $g(x) = x + 1$.

$(f \circ g)(x) = x^2 + 2x - 5$

More Equations and Inequalities

9

Chapter 9

In this chapter we will solve different types of inequalities including polynomial, rational, and absolute value inequalities.

Are You Prepared?

To prepare for this section, practice solving linear inequalities in one variable that were first presented in Section 2.8. Match the inequality on the left with the correct solution set on the right.

1. $5(x + 1) > 20$ b
2. $9x + 1 \le -x + 31$ g
3. $2x + 5 < 4x + 11$ f
4. $5(2x + 1) < -x + 38$ a
5. $7 \ge -x + 10$ e
6. $2(x + 2) \ge -2$ c
7. $-7x + 8 \ge 29$ d
8. $-4x + 32 > 44$ h

a. $(-\infty, 3)$
b. $(3, \infty)$
c. $[-3, \infty)$
d. $(-\infty, -3]$
e. $[3, \infty)$
f. $(-3, \infty)$
g. $(-\infty, 3]$
h. $(-\infty, -3)$

Section 9.1	Compound Inequalities

Concepts

1. Union and Intersection of Sets
2. Solving Compound Inequalities: And
3. Solving Inequalities of the Form $a < x < b$
4. Solving Compound Inequalities: Or
5. Applications of Compound Inequalities

1. Union and Intersection of Sets

In Chapter 2 we graphed linear inequalities and expressed the solution sets in interval notation and in set-builder notation. In this chapter we will solve **compound inequalities** that involve the union or intersection of two or more inequalities.

> **DEFINITION** *A* Union *B* and *A* Intersection *B*
>
> The **union** of sets A and B, denoted $A \cup B$, is the set of elements that belong to set A or to set B or to both sets A and B.
>
> The **intersection** of two sets A and B, denoted $A \cap B$, is the set of elements common to both A and B.

The concepts of the union and intersection of two sets are illustrated in Figures 9-1 and 9-2.

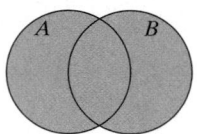

$A \cup B$
A union B
The elements in A *or* B *or* both

Figure 9-1

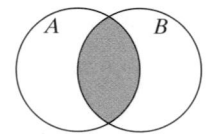

$A \cap B$
A intersection B
The elements in A *and* B

Figure 9-2

Classroom Example: p. 632, Exercise 8

Example 1	Finding the Union and Intersection of Sets

Given the sets: $A = \{a, b, c, d, e, f\}$ $B = \{a, c, e, g, i, k\}$ $C = \{g, h, i, j, k\}$

Find: **a.** $A \cup B$ **b.** $A \cap B$ **c.** $A \cap C$

Solution:

a. $A \cup B = \{a, b, c, d, e, f, g, i, k\}$ The union of A and B includes all the elements of A along with all the elements of B. Notice that the elements a, c, and e are not listed twice.

b. $A \cap B = \{a, c, e\}$ The intersection of A and B includes only those elements that are common to both sets.

c. $A \cap C = \{ \ \}$ (the empty set)   Because A and C share no common elements, the intersection of A and C is the empty set (also called the null set).

> **TIP:** The empty set may be denoted by the symbol { } or by the symbol ∅.

Skill Practice Given: $A = \{r, s, t, u, v, w\}$ $B = \{s, v, w, y, z\}$ $C = \{x, y, z\}$
Find: **1.** $B \cup C$ **2.** $A \cap B$ **3.** $A \cap C$

Answers

1. $\{s, v, w, x, y, z\}$ **2.** $\{s, v, w\}$ **3.** $\{ \ \}$

Classroom Examples: p. 632, Exercises 10 and 12

Example 2 Finding the Union and Intersection of Sets

Given the sets: $A = \{x \mid x < 3\}$ $B = \{x \mid x \geq -2\}$ $C = \{x \mid x \geq 5\}$

Graph the following sets. Then express each set in interval notation.

a. $A \cap B$ **b.** $A \cup C$

Solution:

It is helpful to visualize the graphs of individual sets on the number line before taking the union or intersection.

a. Graph of $A = \{x \mid x < 3\}$

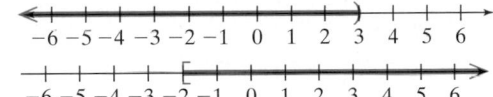

Graph of $B = \{x \mid x \geq -2\}$

Graph of $A \cap B$ (the "overlap")

Interval notation: $[-2, 3)$

Note that the set $A \cap B$ represents the real numbers greater than or equal to -2 and less than 3. This relationship can be written more concisely as a compound inequality: $-2 \leq x < 3$. We can interpret this inequality as "x is between -2 and 3, including $x = -2$."

b. Graph of $A = \{x \mid x < 3\}$

Graph of $C = \{x \mid x \geq 5\}$

Graph of $A \cup C$

Interval notation: $(-\infty, 3) \cup [5, \infty)$ $A \cup C$ includes all elements from set A along with the elements from set C.

Skill Practice Given the sets: $A = \{x \mid x \geq -1\}$, $B = \{x \mid x < 4\}$, and $C = \{x \mid x \geq 9\}$, determine the union or intersection and express the answer in interval notation.

4. $A \cap B$ **5.** $B \cup C$

In example 3, we find the union and intersection of sets expressed in interval notation.

Example 3 Finding the Union and Intersection of Two Intervals

Classroom Example: p. 632, Exercise 22

Find the union or intersection as indicated. Write the answer in interval notation.

a. $(-\infty, -2) \cup [\ 4, 3)$ **b.** $(-\infty, -2) \cap [-4, 3)$

Solution:

a. $(-\infty, -2) \cup [-4, 3)$ To find the union, graph each interval separately. The union is the collection of real numbers that lie in the first interval, the second interval, or both intervals.

Answers

4. $[-1, 4)$ **5.** $(-\infty, 4) \cup [9, \infty)$

$(-\infty, -2)$

$[-4, 3)$

The union consists of all real numbers in the red interval along with the real numbers in the blue interval: $(-\infty, 3)$

The union is $(-\infty, 3)$.

b. $(-\infty, -2) \cap [-4, 3)$

$(-\infty, -2)$

$[-4, 3)$

The intersection is the "overlap" of the two intervals: $[-4, -2)$.

The intersection is $[-4, -2)$.

Skill Practice Find the union or intersection. Write the answer in interval notation.

6. $(-\infty, -5] \cup (-7, 0)$ **7.** $(-\infty, -5] \cap (-7, 0)$

2. Solving Compound Inequalities: And

The solution to two inequalities joined by the word *and* is the intersection of their solution sets. The solution to two inequalities joined by the word *or* is the union of their solution sets.

> **PROCEDURE Solving a Compound Inequality**
>
> **Step 1** Solve and graph each inequality separately.
>
> **Step 2** • If the inequalities are joined by the word *and*, find the intersection of the two solution sets.
>
> • If the inequalities are joined by the word *or*, find the union of the two solution sets.
>
> **Step 3** Express the solution set in interval notation or in set-builder notation.

As you work through the examples in this section, remember that multiplying or dividing an inequality by a negative factor reverses the direction of the inequality sign.

Classroom Example: p. 632, Exercise 28

Instructor Note: If students are struggling with the issue of when to reverse the inequality symbol, some examples using numbers may help:

$2 < 5$ but $-2 > -5$

$-4 < -2$ but $4 > 2$

Answers

6. $(-\infty, 0)$ **7.** $(-7, -5]$

Example 4 Solving a Compound Inequality: And

Solve the compound inequality.

$$-2x < 6 \quad \text{and} \quad x + 5 \leq 7$$

Solution:

$-2x < 6$	and	$x + 5 \leq 7$

Solve each inequality separately.

$$\frac{-2x}{-2} > \frac{6}{-2} \quad \text{and} \quad x \leq 2$$

Reverse the first inequality sign.

$$x > -3 \quad \text{and} \quad x \leq 2$$

$\{x \mid x > -3\}$

$\{x \mid x \le 2\}$

Identify the intersection of the solution sets: $\{x \mid -3 < x \le 2\}$

The solution is $\{x \mid -3 < x \le 2\}$, or equivalently in interval notation, $(-3, 2]$.

Skill Practice Solve the compound inequality.

8. $5x + 2 \ge -8$ and $-4x > -24$

Example 5 Solving a Compound Inequality: And

Classroom Example: p. 633, Exercise 36

Solve the compound inequality.

$$4.4a + 3.1 < -12.3 \quad \text{and} \quad -2.8a + 9.1 < -6.3$$

Solution:

$4.4a + 3.1 < -12.3$	and	$-2.8a + 9.1 < -6.3$
$4.4a < -15.4$	and	$-2.8a < -15.4$

Solve each inequality separately.

$$\frac{4.4a}{4.4} < \frac{-15.4}{4.4} \quad \text{and} \quad \frac{-2.8a}{-2.8} > \frac{-15.4}{-2.8}$$

Reverse the second inequality sign.

$$a < -3.5 \quad \text{and} \quad a > 5.5$$

$\{a \mid a < -3.5\}$

$\{a \mid a > 5.5\}$

The intersection of the solution sets is the empty set: $\{\ \}$

There are no real numbers that are simultaneously less than -3.5 and greater than 5.5. There is no solution.

The solution set is $\{\ \}$.

Skill Practice Solve the compound inequality.

9. $3.2y - 2.4 > 16.8$ and $-4.1y \ge 8.2$

Classroom Example: p. 633,
Exercise 34

Example 6 **Solving a Compound Inequality: And**

Solve the compound inequality.

$$-\frac{2}{3}x \le 6 \quad \text{and} \quad -\frac{1}{2}x < 1$$

Solution:

$$-\frac{2}{3}x \le 6 \qquad \text{and} \qquad -\frac{1}{2}x < 1$$

$$-\frac{3}{2}\left(-\frac{2}{3}x\right) \ge -\frac{3}{2}(6) \quad \text{and} \quad -2\left(-\frac{1}{2}x\right) > -2(1) \qquad \text{Solve each inequality separately.}$$

$$x \ge -9 \qquad \text{and} \qquad x > -2$$

$\{x \mid x \ge -9\}$

$\{x \mid x > -2\}$

Identify the intersection of the solution sets:
$\{x \mid x > -2\}$

The solution set is $\{x \mid x > -2\}$, or in interval notation, $(-2, \infty)$.

Skill Practice Solve the compound inequality.

10. $-\frac{1}{4}z < \frac{5}{8}$ and $\frac{1}{2}z + 1 \ge 3$

3. Solving Inequalities of the Form $a < x < b$

Instructor Note: Remind students
that a "three-part" inequality is used
to imply that x is *between* two
values. Show them why the
following statements fail to do this.

$$-5 > x < 4$$
$$-6 < x > 8$$
$$5 < x < -2$$

An inequality of the form $a < x < b$ is a type of compound inequality, one that defines two simultaneous conditions on x.

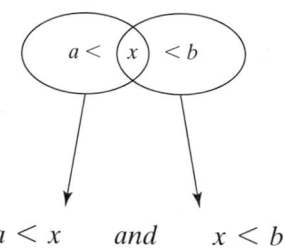

$$a < x \quad \text{and} \quad x < b$$

The solution set to the compound inequality $a < x < b$ is the *intersection* of the solution sets to the inequalities $a < x$ and $x < b$.

Classroom Example: p. 633,
Exercise 44

Example 7 **Solving an Inequality of the Form $a < x < b$**

Solve the inequality. $-4 < 3x + 5 \le 10$

Solution:

$$-4 < 3x + 5 \quad \text{and} \quad 3x + 5 \le 10 \qquad \text{Set up the intersection of two inequalities.}$$

Answer
10. $\{z \mid z \ge 4\}$; $[4, \infty)$

$$-9 < 3x \qquad \text{and} \qquad 3x \le 5 \qquad \text{Solve each inequality.}$$

$$\frac{-9}{3} < \frac{3x}{3} \qquad \text{and} \qquad \frac{3x}{3} \le \frac{5}{3}$$

$$-3 < x \qquad \text{and} \qquad x \le \frac{5}{3} \qquad \begin{array}{l}\text{Recall } -3 < x \text{ is the same as} \\ x > -3.\end{array}$$

$$-3 < x \le \frac{5}{3} \qquad \qquad \begin{array}{l}\text{Identify the intersection of} \\ \text{the solution sets.}\end{array}$$

The solution is $\{x \mid -3 < x \le \frac{5}{3}\}$, or equivalently in interval notation, $(-3, \frac{5}{3}]$.

Skill Practice Solve the inequality.

11. $-6 \le 2x - 5 < 1$

To solve an inequality of the form $a < x < b$, we can also work with the inequality as a "three-part" inequality and isolate x. This is demonstrated in Example 8.

Example 8 Solving an Inequality of the Form $a < x < b$

Classroom Example: p. 633, Exercise 48

Solve the inequality. $\quad 2 \ge \dfrac{p - 2}{-3} \ge -1$

Solution:

$$2 \ge \frac{p - 2}{-3} \ge -1 \qquad \begin{array}{l}\text{Isolate the variable in the} \\ \text{middle part.}\end{array}$$

$$-3(2) \le -3\left(\frac{p - 2}{-3}\right) \le -3(-1) \qquad \begin{array}{l}\text{Multiply all three parts by } -3. \text{ Remember} \\ \text{to reverse the inequality signs.}\end{array}$$

$$-6 \le p - 2 \le 3 \qquad \text{Simplify.}$$

$$-6 + 2 \le p - 2 + 2 \le 3 + 2 \qquad \text{Add 2 to all three parts to isolate } p.$$

$$-4 \le p \le 5$$

The solution is $\{p \mid -4 \le p \le 5\}$, or equivalently in interval notation $[-4, 5]$.

Skill Practice Solve the inequality.

12. $8 > \dfrac{t + 4}{-2} > -5$

4. Solving Compound Inequalities: Or

In Examples 9 and 10, we solve compound inequalities that involve inequalities joined by the word "or." In such a case, the solution to the compound inequality is the union of the solution sets of the individual inequalities.

Answers

11. $\{x \mid -\frac{1}{2} \le x < 3\}; [-\frac{1}{2}, 3)$
12. $\{t \mid -20 < t < 6\}; (-20, 6)$

Classroom Example: p. 633,
Exercise 56

Example 9 Solving a Compound Inequality: Or

Solve the compound inequality.

$$-3y - 5 > 4 \quad \text{or} \quad 4 - y \leq 6$$

Solution:

$$-3y - 5 > 4 \qquad \text{or} \qquad 4 - y \leq 6$$

$$-3y > 9 \qquad \text{or} \qquad -y \leq 2 \qquad \text{Solve each inequality separately.}$$

$$\frac{-3y}{-3} < \frac{9}{-3} \qquad \text{or} \qquad \frac{-y}{-1} \geq \frac{2}{-1} \qquad \text{Reverse the inequality signs.}$$

$$y < -3 \qquad \text{or} \qquad y \geq -2$$

 $\{y \mid y < -3\}$

$\{y \mid y \geq -2\}$

Identify the union of the solution sets:
$\{y \mid y < -3 \text{ or } y \geq -2\}$

The solution is $\{y \mid y < -3 \text{ or } y \geq -2\}$ or, equivalently in interval notation, $(-\infty, -3) \cup [-2, \infty)$.

Skill Practice Solve the compound inequality.

13. $-10t - 8 \geq 12$ or $3t - 6 > 3$

Classroom Example: p. 634,
Exercise 62

Example 10 Solving a Compound Inequality: Or

Solve the compound inequality.

$$4x + 3 < 16 \quad \text{or} \quad -2x < 3$$

Solution:

$$4x + 3 < 16 \qquad \text{or} \qquad -2x < 3$$

$$4x < 13 \qquad \text{or} \qquad x > -\frac{3}{2} \qquad \text{Solve each inequality separately.}$$

$$x < \frac{13}{4} \qquad \text{or} \qquad x > -\frac{3}{2}$$

$\{x \mid x < \frac{13}{4}\}$

$\frac{13}{4}$

$\{x \mid x > -\frac{3}{2}\}$

$-\frac{3}{2}$

Identify the union of the solution sets.

Answer

13. $\{t \mid t \leq -2 \text{ or } t > 3\}$;
$(-\infty, -2] \cup (3, \infty)$

The union of the solution sets is $\{x\,|\,x \text{ is a real number}\}$, or equivalently, $(-\infty, \infty)$.

Skill Practice Solve the compound inequality.

14. $x - 7 > -2$ or $-6x > -48$

5. Applications of Compound Inequalities

Compound inequalities are used in many applications, as shown in Examples 11 and 12.

Example 11 Translating Compound Inequalities

Classroom Example: p. 634, Exercise 76

The normal level of thyroid-stimulating hormone (TSH) for adults ranges from 0.4 to 4.8 microunits per milliliter (μU/mL), inclusive. Let x represent the amount of TSH measured in microunits per milliliter.

   a. Write an inequality representing the normal range of TSH, inclusive.

   b. Write a compound inequality representing abnormal TSH levels.

Solution:

   a. $0.4 \le x \le 4.8$ **b.** $x < 0.4$ or $x > 4.8$

Skill Practice The length of a normal human pregnancy, w, is from 37 to 41 weeks, inclusive.

15. Write an inequality representing the normal length of a pregnancy.

16. Write a compound inequality representing an abnormal length for a pregnancy.

> **TIP:**
> - In mathematics, the word "between" means strictly between two values. That is, the endpoints are *excluded*.
>   <u>Example:</u> x is between 4 and 10 $\Rightarrow$ (4, 10).
> - If the word "inclusive" is added to the statement, then we *include* the endpoints.
>   <u>Example:</u> x is between 4 and 10, inclusive $\Rightarrow$ [4, 10].

Example 12 Translating and Solving a Compound Inequality

Classroom Example: p. 635, Exercise 80

The sum of a number and 4 is between -5 and 12. Find all such numbers.

Solution:

Let x represent a number.

$$-5 < x + 4 < 12 \qquad \text{Translate the inequality.}$$

$$-5 - 4 < x + 4 - 4 < 12 - 4 \qquad \text{Subtract 4 from all three parts of the inequality.}$$

$$-9 < x < 8$$

The number may be any real number between -9 and 8: $\{x\,|\,-9 < x < 8\}$.

Skill Practice

17. The sum of twice a number and 11 is between 21 and 31. Find all such numbers.

Answers

14. $\{x\,|\,x \text{ is a real number}\}$; $(-\infty, \infty)$
15. $37 \le w \le 41$
16. $w < 37$ or $w > 41$
17. Any real number between 5 and 10: $\{n\,|\,5 < n < 10\}$

Section 9.1   Practice Exercises

Boost *your* GRADE at
ALEKS.com!

ALEKS®
version 3.0

- Practice Problems
- Self-Tests
- NetTutor

- e-Professors
- Videos

For additional exercises, see Classroom Activities
9.1A–9.1D in the *Instructor's Resource Manual*
at www.mhhe.com/moh.

Study Skills Exercise

1. Define the key terms.

   a. compound inequality   **b. intersection**   **c. union**

Review Exercises

For Exercises 2–6, solve the linear inequality. Write the solution in interval notation.

2. $-6u + 8 > 2$ $(-\infty, 1)$ 3. $2 - 3z \geq -4$ $(-\infty, 2]$ 4. $-12 \leq \frac{3}{4}p$ $[-16, \infty)$

5. $5 > \frac{1}{3}w$ $(-\infty, 15)$ 6. $-3x + 5 < -2x + 1$ $(4, \infty)$

Concept 1: Union and Intersection of Sets

7. Given: $M = \{-3, -1, 1, 3, 5\}$ and
   $N = \{-4, -3, -2, -1, 0\}$. **(See Example 1.)**

   List the elements of the following sets:

   a. $M \cap N$ **b.** $M \cup N$
   $\{-3, -1\}$ $\{-4, -3, -2, -1, 0, 1, 3, 5\}$

8. Given: $P = \{a, b, c, d, e, f, g, h, i\}$ and
   $Q = \{a, e, i, o, u\}$.

   List the elements of the following sets.

   a. $P \cap Q$ **b.** $P \cup Q$
   $\{a, e, i\}$ $\{a, b, c, d, e, f, g, h, i, o, u\}$

For Exercises 9–20, refer to the sets $A, B, C,$ and D. Determine the union or intersection as indicated. Express the answer in interval notation, if possible. **(See Example 2.)**

$A = \{x \mid x < -4\}, B = \{x \mid x > 2\}, C = \{x \mid x \geq -7\}, D = \{x \mid 0 \leq x < 5\}$

9. $A \cap C$ $[-7, -4)$

10. $B \cap C$ $(2, \infty)$

11. $A \cup B$ $(-\infty, -4) \cup (2, \infty)$

12. $A \cup D$ $(-\infty, -4) \cup [0, 5)$

13. $A \cap B$ $\{ \}$

14. $A \cap D$ $\{ \}$

15. $B \cup C$ $[-7, \infty)$

16. $B \cup D$ $[0, \infty)$

17. $C \cap D$ $[0, 5)$

18. $B \cap D$ $(2, 5)$

19. $C \cup D$ $[-7, \infty)$

20. $A \cup C$ $(-\infty, \infty)$

For Exercises 21–26, find the intersection and union of sets as indicated. Write the answers in interval notation.
(See Example 3.)

21. **a.** $(-2, 5) \cap [-1, \infty)$ $[-1, 5)$

   b. $(-2, 5) \cup [-1, \infty)$ $(-2, \infty)$

22. **a.** $(-\infty, 4) \cap [-1, 5)$ $[-1, 4)$

   b. $(-\infty, 4) \cup [-1, 5)$ $(-\infty, 5)$

23. **a.** $\left(-\frac{5}{2}, 3\right) \cap \left(-1, \frac{9}{2}\right)$ $(-1, 3)$

   b. $\left(-\frac{5}{2}, 3\right) \cup \left(-1, \frac{9}{2}\right)$ $\left(-\frac{5}{2}, \frac{9}{2}\right)$

24. **a.** $(-3.4, 1.6) \cap (-2.2, 4.1)$
   $(-2.2, 1.6)$

   b. $(-3.4, 1.6) \cup (-2.2, 4.1)$
   $(-3.4, 4.1)$

25. **a.** $(-4, 5] \cap (0, 2]$ $(0, 2]$

   b. $(-4, 5] \cup (0, 2]$ $(-4, 5]$

26. **a.** $[-1, 5) \cap (0, 3)$ $(0, 3)$

   b. $[-1, 5) \cup (0, 3)$ $[-1, 5)$

Concept 2: Solving Compound Inequalities: And

For Exercises 27–36, solve the inequality and graph the solution. Write the answer in interval notation. **(See Examples 4–6.)**

27. $y - 7 \geq -9$ and $y + 2 \leq 5$ $[-2, 3]$

28. $a + 6 > -2$ and $5a < 30$ $(-8, 6)$

29. $2t + 7 < 19$ and $5t + 13 > 28$ (3, 6)

30. $5p + 2p \geq -21$ and $-9p + 3p \geq -24$ [-3, 4]

31. $2.1k - 1.1 \leq 0.6k + 1.9$ and

$0.3k - 1.1 < -0.1k + 0.9$ $(-\infty, 2]$

32. $0.6w + 0.1 > 0.3w - 1.1$ and

$2.3w + 1.5 \geq 0.3w + 6.5$ $[2.5, \infty)$

33. $\frac{2}{3}(2p - 1) \geq 10$ and $\frac{4}{5}(3p + 4) \geq 20$ $[8, \infty)$

34. $\frac{5}{2}(a + 2) < -6$ and $\frac{3}{4}(a - 2) < 1$ $\left(-\infty, -\frac{22}{5}\right)$

35. $-2 < -x - 12$ and $-14 < 5(x - 3) + 6x$ { }

36. $-8 \geq -3y - 2$ and $3(y - 7) + 16 > 4y$ { }

Concept 3: Solving Inequalities of the Form $a < x < b$

37. Write $-4 \leq t < \frac{3}{4}$ as two separate inequalities.
$-4 \leq t$ and $t < \frac{3}{4}$

38. Write $-2.8 < y \leq 15$ as two separate inequalities.
$-2.8 < y$ and $y \leq 15$

39. Explain why $6 < x < 2$ has no solution.
The statement $6 < x < 2$ is equivalent to $6 < x$ and $x < 2$.
However, no real number is greater than 6 and also less than 2.

40. Explain why $4 < t < 1$ has no solution.
The statement $4 < t < 1$ is equivalent to $4 < t$ and $t < 1$.
However, no real number is greater than 4 and also less than 1.

41. Explain why $-5 > y > -2$ has no solution.
The statement $-5 > y > -2$ is equivalent to $-5 > y$ and $y > -2$.
However, no real number is less than -5 and also greater than -2.

42. Explain why $-3 > w > -1$ has no solution.
The statement $-3 > w > -1$ is equivalent to $-3 > w$ and $w > -1$.
However, no real number is less than -3 and also greater than -1.

For Exercises 43–54, solve the inequality and graph the solution set. Write the answer in interval notation. **(See Examples 7–8.)**

43. $0 \leq 2b - 5 < 9$ $\left[\frac{5}{2}, 7\right)$

44. $-6 < 3k - 9 \leq 0$ (1, 3]

45. $-1 < \frac{a}{6} \leq 1$ $(-6, 6]$

46. $-3 \leq \frac{1}{2}x < 0$ $[-6, 0)$

47. $-\frac{2}{3} < \frac{y - 4}{-6} < \frac{1}{3}$ (2, 8)

48. $\frac{1}{3} > \frac{t - 4}{-3} > -2$ (3, 10)

49. $5 \leq -3x - 2 \leq 8$ $\left[-\frac{10}{3}, -\frac{7}{3}\right]$

50. $-1 < -2x + 4 \leq 5$ $\left[-\frac{1}{2}, \frac{5}{2}\right)$

51. $12 > 6x + 3 \geq 0$ $\left[-\frac{1}{2}, \frac{3}{2}\right)$

52. $-4 \geq 2x - 5 > -7$ $\left(-1, \frac{1}{2}\right]$

53. $-0.2 < 2.6 + 7t < 4$ $(-0.4, 0.2)$

54. $-1.5 < 0.1x \leq 8.1$ $(-15, 81]$

Concept 4: Solving Compound Inequalities: Or

For Exercises 55–64, solve the inequality and graph the solution set. Write the answer in interval notation. **(See Examples 9–10.)**

55. $2y - 1 \geq 3$ or $y < -2$ $(-\infty, -2) \cup [2, \infty)$

56. $x < 0$ or $3x + 1 \geq 7$ $(-\infty, 0) \cup [2, \infty)$

57. $1 > 6z - 8$ or $8z - 6 \leq 10$ $(-\infty, 2]$

58. $22 > 4t - 10$ or $7 > 2t - 5$ $(-\infty, 8)$

59. $5(x - 1) \geq -5$ or $5 - x \leq 11$ $[-6, \infty)$

60. $-p + 7 \geq 10$ or $3(p - 1) \leq 12$ $(-\infty, 5]$

 Writing Translating Expression Geometry Scientific Calculator Video NS&E

61. $\frac{5}{3}v \le 5$ or $-v - 6 < 1$ $(-\infty, \infty)$

62. $\frac{3}{8}u + 1 > 0$ or $-2u \ge -4$ $(-\infty, \infty)$

63. $0.5w + 5 < 2.5w - 4$ or $0.3w \le -0.1w - 1.6$ $(-\infty, -4] \cup (4.5, \infty)$

-4 4.5

64. $1.25a + 3 \le 0.5a - 6$ or $2.5a - 1 \ge 9 - 1.5a$ $(-\infty, -12] \cup [2.5, \infty)$

-12 2.5

Mixed Exercises

For Exercises 65–74, solve the inequality. Write the answer in interval notation.

65. a. $3x - 5 < 19$ and $-2x + 3 < 23$ $(-10, 8)$
b. $3x - 5 < 19$ or $-2x + 3 < 23$ $(-\infty, \infty)$

66. a. $0.5(6x + 8) > 0.8x - 7$ and $4(x + 1) < 7.2$ $(-5, 0.8)$
b. $0.5(6x + 8) > 0.8x - 7$ or $4(x + 1) < 7.2$ $(-\infty, \infty)$

67. a. $8x - 4 \ge 6.4$ or $0.3(x + 6) \le -0.6$ $(-\infty, -8] \cup [1.3, \infty)$
b. $8x - 4 \ge 6.4$ and $0.3(x + 6) \le -0.6$ $\{ \}$

68. a. $-2r + 4 \le -8$ or $3r + 5 \le 8$ $(-\infty, 1] \cup [6, \infty)$
b. $-2r + 4 \le -8$ and $3r + 5 \le 8$ $\{ \}$

69. $-4 \le \frac{2 - 4x}{3} < 8$ $\left(-\frac{11}{2}, \frac{7}{2}\right]$

70. $-1 < \frac{3 - x}{2} \le 0$ $[3, 5)$

71. $5 \ge -4(t - 3) + 3t$ or
$6 < 12t + 8(4 - t)$ $\left(-\frac{13}{2}, \infty\right)$

72. $3 > -(w - 3) + 4w$ or
$-5 \ge -3(w - 5) + 6w$ $(-\infty, 0)$

73. $\frac{-x + 3}{2} > \frac{4 + x}{5}$ or $\frac{1 - x}{4} > \frac{2 - x}{3}$
$(-\infty, 1) \cup (5, \infty)$

74. $\frac{y - 7}{-3} < \frac{1}{4}$ or $\frac{y + 1}{-2} > -\frac{1}{3}$
$\left(-\infty, -\frac{1}{3}\right) \cup \left(\frac{25}{4}, \infty\right)$

Concept 5: Applications of Compound Inequalities

75. The normal number of white blood cells for human blood is between 4800 and 10,800 cells per cubic millimeter, inclusive. Let x represent the number of white blood cells per cubic millimeter. **(See Example 11.)**

   a. Write an inequality representing the normal range of white blood cells per cubic millimeter. $4800 \le x \le 10,800$

   b. Write a compound inequality representing abnormal levels of white blood cells per cubic millimeter. $x < 4800$ or $x > 10,800$

76. Normal hemoglobin levels in human blood for adult males are between 13 and 16 grams per deciliter (g/dL), inclusive. Let x represent the level of hemoglobin measured in grams per deciliter.

   a. Write an inequality representing normal hemoglobin levels for adult males. $13 \le x \le 16$

   b. Write a compound inequality representing abnormal levels of hemoglobin for adult males.
   $x < 13$ or $x > 16$

77. The normal number of platelets in human blood is between 200,000 and 350,000 platelets per cubic millimeter, inclusive. Let x represent the number of platelets per cubic millimeter.

   a. Write an inequality representing a normal platelet count per cubic millimeter. $200,000 \le x \le 350,000$

   b. Write a compound inequality representing abnormal platelet counts per cubic millimeter.
   $x < 200,000$ or $x > 350,000$

78. Normal hemoglobin levels in human blood for adult females are between 12 and 15 g/dL, inclusive. Let x represent the level of hemoglobin measured in grams per deciliter.

   a. Write an inequality representing normal hemoglobin levels for adult females. $12 \le x \le 15$

   b. Write a compound inequality representing abnormal levels of hemoglobin for adult females.
   $x < 12$ or $x > 15$

 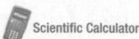

79. Twice a number is between -3 and 12. Find all such numbers. **(See Example 12.)**   All real numbers between $-\dfrac{3}{2}$ and 6

80. The difference of a number and 6 is between 0 and 8. Find all such numbers.   All real numbers between 6 and 14

81. One plus twice a number is either greater than 5 or less than -1. Find all such numbers.   All real numbers greater than 2 or less than -1

82. One-third of a number is either less than -2 or greater than 5. Find all such numbers.   All real numbers less than -6 or greater than 15

83. Amy knows from reading her syllabus in intermediate algebra that the average of her chapter tests accounts for 80% (0.8) of her overall course grade. She also knows that the final exam counts as 20% (0.2) of her grade.

    a. Suppose that the average of Amy's chapter tests is 92%. Determine the range of grades that she would need on her final exam to get an "A" in the class. (Assume that a grade of "A" is obtained if Amy's overall average is 90% or better.)   Amy would need 82% or better on her final exam.

    b. Determine the range of grades that Amy would need on her final exam to get a "B" in the class. (Assume that a grade of "B" is obtained if Amy's overall average is at least 80% but less than 90%.)
    If Amy scores at least 32% and less than 82% on her final exam she will receive a "B" in the class.

84. Robert knows from reading his syllabus in intermediate algebra that the average of his chapter tests accounts for 60% (0.6) of his overall course grade. He also knows that the final exam counts as 40% (0.4) of his grade.

    a. Suppose that the average of Robert's chapter tests is 89%. Determine the range of grades that he would need on his final exam to get an "A" in the class. (Assume that a grade of "A" is obtained if Robert's overall average is 90% or better.)   Robert would need 91.5% or better on his final.

    b. Determine the range of grades that Robert would need on his final exam to get a "B" in the class. (Assume that a grade of "B" is obtained if Robert's overall average is at least 80% but less than 90%.)
    If Robert scores at least 66.5% and less than 91.5% on his final exam he will receive a "B" in the class.

85. The average high and low temperatures for Vancouver, British Columbia, in January are 5.6°C and 0°C, respectively. The formula relating Celsius temperatures to Fahrenheit temperatures is given by $C = \frac{5}{9}(F - 32)$. Convert the inequality $0.0° \le C \le 5.6°$ to an equivalent inequality using Fahrenheit temperatures.
$32° \le F \le 42.08°$

86. For a day in July, the temperatures in Austin, Texas, ranged from 20°C to 29°C. The formula relating Celsius temperatures to Fahrenheit temperatures is given by $C = \frac{5}{9}(F - 32)$. Convert the inequality $20° \le C \le 29°$ to an equivalent inequality using Fahrenheit temperatures.
$68° \le F \le 84.2°$

Polynomial and Rational Inequalities

Section 9.2

1. Solving Quadratic and Polynomial Inequalities

In this section, we will expand our study of solving inequalities.

    Quadratic inequalities are inequalities that can be written in one of the following forms:

$$ax^2 + bx + c \ge 0 \qquad ax^2 + bx + c \le 0$$
$$ax^2 + bx + c > 0 \qquad ax^2 + bx + c < 0 \qquad \text{where } a \ne 0$$

Recall from Section 8.3 that the graph of a quadratic function defined by $f(x) = ax^2 + bx + c$ is a parabola that opens upward or downward.

- The inequality $ax^2 + bx + c > 0$ is asking "For what values of x is the function positive (above the x-axis)?"

- The inequality $ax^2 + bx + c < 0$ is asking "For what values of x is the function negative (below the x-axis)?"

The graph of a quadratic function can be used to answer these questions.

Concepts

1. Solving Quadratic and Polynomial Inequalities
2. Solving Rational Inequalities

Classroom Example: p. 642, Exercise 10

Example 1 Using a Graph to Solve a Quadratic Inequality

Use the graph of $f(x) = x^2 - 6x + 5$ in Figure 9-3 to solve the inequalities.

a. $x^2 - 6x + 5 < 0$ **b.** $x^2 - 6x + 5 > 0$

Solution:

From Figure 9-3, we see that the graph of $f(x) = x^2 - 6x + 5$ is a parabola opening upward. The function factors as $f(x) = (x - 1)(x - 5)$. The x-intercepts are $(1, 0)$ and $(5, 0)$, and the y-intercept is $(0, 5)$.

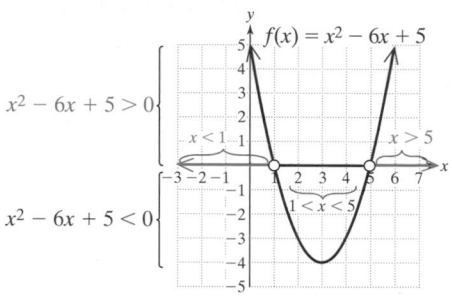

Figure 9-3

a. The solution to $x^2 - 6x + 5 < 0$ is the set of real numbers, x, for which $f(x) < 0$. Graphically, this is the set of all x values corresponding to the points where the parabola is below the x-axis (shown in red).

$$x^2 - 6x + 5 < 0 \quad \text{for } \{x \mid 1 < x < 5\} \text{ or equivalently, } (1, 5)$$

b. The solution to $x^2 - 6x + 5 > 0$ is the set of real numbers, x, for which $f(x) > 0$. This is the set of x values where the parabola is above the x-axis (shown in blue).

$$x^2 - 6x + 5 > 0 \quad \text{for } \{x \mid x < 1 \quad \text{or} \quad x > 5\} \quad \text{or} \quad (-\infty, 1) \cup (5, \infty)$$

Skill Practice Refer to the graph of $f(x) = x^2 + 3x - 4$ to solve the inequalities.

1. $x^2 + 3x - 4 > 0$
2. $x^2 + 3x - 4 < 0$

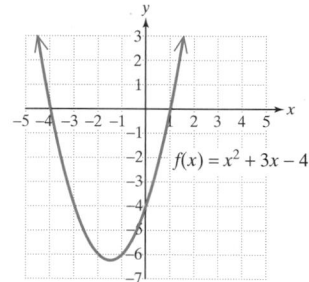

TIP: The inequalities in Example 1 are strict inequalities. Therefore, $x = 1$ and $x = 5$ (where $f(x) = 0$) are not included in the solution set. However, the corresponding inequalities using the symbols $\leq$ and $\geq$ *do* include the values where $f(x) = 0$.

The solution to $x^2 - 6x + 5 \leq 0$ is $\{x \mid 1 \leq x \leq 5\}$ or equivalently, $[1, 5]$.

The solution to $x^2 - 6x + 5 \geq 0$ is $\{x \mid x \leq 1 \text{ or } x \geq 5\}$ or $(-\infty, 1] \cup [5, \infty)$.

Answers

1. $\{x \mid x < -4 \text{ or } x > 1\}$;
$(-\infty, -4) \cup (1, \infty)$
2. $\{x \mid -4 < x < 1\}$; $(-4, 1)$

Notice that $x = 1$ and $x = 5$ are the boundaries of the solution set to the inequalities in Example 1. These values are the solutions to the related equation $x^2 - 6x + 5 = 0$.

DEFINITION Boundary Points

The **boundary points** of an inequality consist of the real solutions to the related equation and the points where the inequality is undefined.

Testing points in intervals bounded by these points is the basis of the **test point method** to solve inequalities.

PROCEDURE Solving Inequalities by Using the Test Point Method

Step 1 Find the boundary points of the inequality.

Step 2 Plot the boundary points on the number line. This divides the number line into intervals.

Step 3 Select a test point from each interval and substitute it into the original inequality.
- If a test point makes the original inequality true, then that interval is part of the solution set.

Step 4 Test the boundary points in the original inequality.
- If the original inequality is strict ($<$ or $>$), do not include the boundary points in the solution set.
- If the original inequality is defined using $\leq$ or $\geq$, then include the boundary points that are well defined within the inequality.

Note: Any boundary point that makes an expression within the inequality undefined must *always* be excluded from the solution set.

Classroom Example: p. 643, Exercise 16

Example 2 Solving a Quadratic Inequality by Using the Test Point Method

Solve the inequality by using the test point method.

$$2x^2 + 5x < 12$$

Solution:

$2x^2 + 5x < 12$ **Step 1:** Find the boundary points. Because polynomials are defined for all values of x, the only boundary points are the real solutions to the related equation.

$2x^2 + 5x = 12$ Solve the related equation.

$2x^2 + 5x - 12 = 0$

$(2x - 3)(x + 4) = 0$

$x = \frac{3}{2} \qquad x = -4$ The boundary points are $\frac{3}{2}$ and -4.

Step 2: Plot the boundary points.

Step 3: Select a test point from each interval.

Test $x = -5$

$2x^2 + 5x < 12$

$2(-5)^2 + 5(-5) \overset{?}{<} 12$

$50 - 25 \overset{?}{<} 12$

$25 \overset{?}{<} 12$ False

Test $x = 0$

$2x^2 + 5x < 12$

$2(0)^2 + 5(0) \overset{?}{<} 12$

$0 \overset{?}{<} 12$

$0 \overset{?}{<} 12$ True

Test $x = 2$

$2x^2 + 5x < 12$

$2(2)^2 + 5(2) \overset{?}{<} 12$

$8 + 10 \overset{?}{<} 12$

$18 \overset{?}{<} 12$ False

Step 4: Test the boundary points. The strict inequality excludes values of x for which $2x^2 + 5x = 12$. Therefore, the boundary points are *not* included in the solution set.

The solution is $\{x \mid -4 < x < \frac{3}{2}\}$ or equivalently in interval notation $(-4, \frac{3}{2})$.

Skill Practice Solve the inequality.

3. $x^2 + x > 6$

Graph $Y_1 = 2x^2 + 5x$ and $Y_2 = 12$.
Notice that $Y_1 < Y_2$ for $\{x \mid -4 < x < \frac{3}{2}\}$.

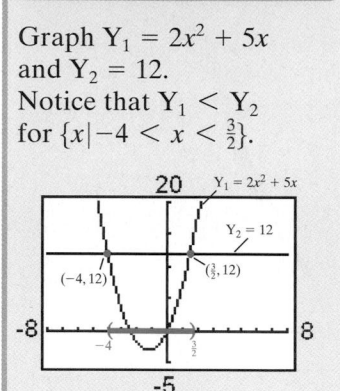

Classroom Example: p. 643, Exercise 24

| **Example 3** | Solving a Polynomial Inequality by Using the Test Point Method |

Solve the inequality by using the test point method.

$$x(x - 2)(x + 4)^2(x - 4) > 0$$

Solution:

$x(x - 2)(x + 4)^2(x - 4) > 0$

$x(x - 2)(x + 4)^2(x - 4) = 0$ **Step 1:** Find the boundary points.

$x = 0 \qquad x = 2 \qquad x = -4 \qquad x = 4$

Step 2: Plot the boundary points.

Step 3: Select a test point from each interval.

Test $x = -5$: $-5(-5 - 2)(-5 + 4)^2(-5 - 4) \overset{?}{>} 0$ $-315 \overset{?}{>} 0$ False

Test $x = -1$: $-1(-1 - 2)(-1 + 4)^2(-1 - 4) \overset{?}{>} 0$ $-135 \overset{?}{>} 0$ False

Test $x = 1$: $1(1 - 2)(1 + 4)^2(1 - 4) \overset{?}{>} 0$ $75 \overset{?}{>} 0$ True

Test $x = 3$: $3(3 - 2)(3 + 4)^2(3 - 4) \overset{?}{>} 0$ $-147 \overset{?}{>} 0$ False

Test $x = 5$: $5(5 - 2)(5 + 4)^2(5 - 4) \overset{?}{>} 0$ $1215 \overset{?}{>} 0$ True

Answer

3. $(-\infty, -3) \cup (2, \infty)$

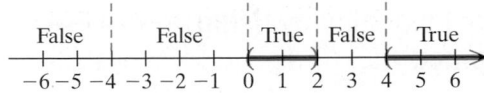

False   False   True   False   True

Step 4: The boundary points are not included because the inequality, $>$, is strict.

The solution is $\{x \mid 0 < x < 2 \text{ or } x > 4\}$ or, equivalently in interval notation, $(0, 2) \cup (4, \infty)$.

Skill Practice Solve the inequality.

   4. $t(t - 5)(t + 2)^2 > 0$

Calculator Connections

Graph $Y_1 = x(x - 2)(x + 4)^2(x - 4)$. Y_1 is positive (above the x-axis) for $\{x \mid 0 < x < 2 \text{ or } x > 4\}$ or equivalently $(0, 2) \cup (4, \infty)$.

$Y_1 = x(x - 2)(x + 4)^2(x - 4)$

TIP: In Example 3, one side of the inequality is factored, and the other side is zero. For inequalities written in this form, we can use a sign chart to determine the sign of each factor. Then the sign of the product (bottom row) is easily determined.

Sign of x	$- \; - \; -$	$- \; - \; - \; - \; -$	$+ \; +$	$+ \; +$	$+ \; + \; +$
Sign of $(x - 2)$	$- \; - \; -$	$- \; - \; - \; - \; -$	$- \; -$	$+ \; +$	$+ \; + \; +$
Sign of $(x + 4)^2$	$+ \; + \; +$	$+ \; + \; + \; + \; +$	$+ \; +$	$+ \; +$	$+ \; + \; +$
Sign of $(x - 4)$	$- \; - \; -$	$- \; - \; - \; - \; -$	$- \; -$	$- \; -$	$+ \; + \; +$
Sign of $x(x - 2)(x + 4)^2(x - 4)$	$- \; - \; -$	$- \; - \; - \; - \; -$	$+ \; +$	$- \; -$	$+ \; + \; +$

$\qquad\qquad\qquad -4 \qquad\qquad 0 \qquad 2 \qquad 4$

The solution to the inequality $x(x - 2)(x + 4)^2(x - 4) > 0$ includes the intervals in which the product is positive (shown in blue). The boundary points for those intervals are not included.

The solution is $(0, 2) \cup (4, \infty)$.

---

2. Solving Rational Inequalities

The test point method can be used to solve rational inequalities. A **rational inequality** is an inequality in which one or more terms is a rational expression. The solution set to a rational inequality must exclude all values of the variable that make the inequality undefined. That is, exclude all values that make the denominator equal to zero for any rational expression in the inequality.

Answer

   4. $(-\infty, -2) \cup (-2, 0) \cup (5, \infty)$

Classroom Example: p. 644,
Exercise 42

Example 4   Solving a Rational Inequality by Using the Test Point Method

Solve the inequality. $\dfrac{3}{x-1} > 0$

Solution:

$$\frac{3}{x-1} > 0$$

Step 1: Find the boundary points. Note that the inequality is undefined for $x = 1$, so $x = 1$ is a boundary point. To find any other boundary points, solve the related equation.

$$\frac{3}{x-1} = 0$$

$$(x-1) \cdot \left(\frac{3}{x-1}\right) = (x-1) \cdot 0$$

Clear fractions.

$$3 = 0$$

There is no solution to the related equation.

The only boundary point is $x = 1$.

I   II

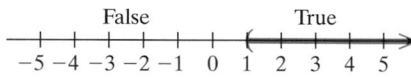

Step 2: Plot boundary points.

Test $x = 0$:   **Test $x = 2$:**   **Step 3:** Select test points.

$$\frac{3}{(0)-1} \overset{?}{>} 0$$ $$\frac{3}{(2)-1} \overset{?}{>} 0$$

$$\frac{3}{-1} \overset{?}{>} 0 \text{ False}$$ $$\frac{3}{1} > 0 \text{ True}$$

    False   True

Step 4: The boundary point $x = 1$ cannot be included in the solution set because it is undefined in the original inequality.

The solution is $\{x \mid x > 1\}$ or equivalently in interval notation, $(1, \infty)$.

Skill Practice Solve the inequality.

5. $\dfrac{-5}{y+2} < 0$

TIP: Using a sign chart we see that the quotient of the factors 3 and $(x - 1)$ is positive on the interval $(1, \infty)$.

Therefore, the solution to the inequality $\dfrac{3}{x-1} > 0$ is $(1, \infty)$.

Sign of 3	+ + +	+ + +
Sign of $(x - 1)$	– – –	+ + +
Sign of $\dfrac{3}{x-1}$	– – –	+ + +

1
(Undefined)

Answer

5. $(-2, \infty)$

The solution to the inequality $\dfrac{3}{x-1} > 0$ can be confirmed from the graph of the

related rational function, $f(x) = \dfrac{3}{x-1}$ (see Figure 9-4).

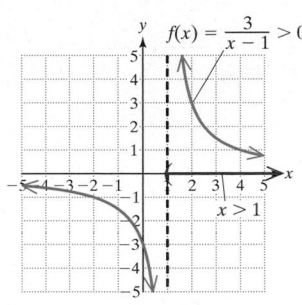

- The graph is above the x-axis where $f(x) = \dfrac{3}{x-1} > 0$ for $x > 1$ (shaded red).

- Also note that $x = 1$ cannot be included in the solution set because 1 is not in the domain of f.

Figure 9-4

Example 5   **Solving a Rational Inequality by Using the Test Point Method**

Classroom Example: p. 644, Exercise 52

Solve the inequality by using the test point method. $\dfrac{x+2}{x-4} \le 3$

Solution:

$\dfrac{x+2}{x-4} \le 3$ **Step 1:** Find the boundary points. Note that the inequality is undefined for $x - 4$. Therefore, $x = 4$ is automatically a boundary point. To find any other boundary points, solve the related equation.

$$\frac{x+2}{x-4} = 3$$

$$(x-4)\left(\frac{x+2}{x-4}\right) = (x-4)(3) \qquad \text{Clear fractions.}$$

$$x + 2 = 3(x-4) \qquad\qquad \text{Solve for } x.$$

$$x + 2 = 3x - 12$$

$$-2x = -14$$

$$x = 7$$

The solution to the related equation is $x = 7$, and the inequality is undefined for $x = 4$. Therefore, the boundary points are $x = 4$ and $x = 7$.

       I   II   III   **Step 2:** Plot boundary points.

       Step 3: Select test points.

Test $x = 0$ **Test $x = 5$**   **Test $x = 8$**

$\dfrac{x+2}{x-4} \le 3$ $\dfrac{x+2}{x-4} \le 3$ $\dfrac{x+2}{x-4} \le 3$

$\dfrac{0+2}{0-4} \overset{?}{\le} 3$ $\dfrac{5+2}{5-4} \overset{?}{\le} 3$ $\dfrac{8+2}{8-4} \overset{?}{\le} 3$

$-\dfrac{1}{2} \overset{?}{\le} 3$ True $\dfrac{7}{1} \overset{?}{\le} 3$ False $\dfrac{10}{4} \overset{?}{\le} 3$

                                                    $\dfrac{5}{2} \overset{?}{\le} 3$ True

Test $x = 4$:

$$\frac{x + 2}{x - 4} \le 3$$

$$\frac{4 + 2}{4 - 4} \overset{?}{\le} 3$$

$$\frac{6}{0} \overset{?}{\le} 3 \quad \text{Undefined}$$

Test $x = 7$:

$$\frac{x + 2}{x - 4} \le 3$$

$$\frac{7 + 2}{7 - 4} \overset{?}{\le} 3$$

$$\frac{9}{3} \overset{?}{\le} 3 \quad \text{True}$$

Step 4: Test the boundary points.

The boundary point $x = 4$ cannot be included in the solution set, because it is undefined in the inequality. The boundary point $x = 7$ makes the original inequality true and must be included in the solution set.

The solution is $\{x \mid x < 4 \text{ or } x \ge 7\}$, or equivalently in interval notation, $(-\infty, 4) \cup [7, \infty)$.

Skill Practice Solve the inequality.

6. $\dfrac{x - 5}{x + 4} \le -1$

Answer

6. $\left(-4, \dfrac{1}{2}\right]$

Section 9.2   Practice Exercises

Boost *your* GRADE at ALEKS.com!

- Practice Problems
- Self-Tests
- NetTutor

- e-Professors
- Videos

For additional exercises, see Classroom Activities 9.2A–9.2C in the *Instructor's Resource Manual* at www.mhhe.com/moh.

Study Skills Exercise

1. Define the key terms.

   a. quadratic inequality   **b. boundary points**   **c. test point method**   **d. rational inequality**

Review Exercises

For Exercises 2–8, solve the compound inequalities. Write the solutions in interval notation.

2. $6x - 10 > 8$ or $8x + 2 < 5$ $\left(-\infty, \dfrac{3}{8}\right) \cup (3, \infty)$ 3. $3(a - 1) + 2 > 0$ or $2a > 5a + 12$ $(-\infty, -4) \cup \left(\dfrac{1}{3}, \infty\right)$

4. $5(k - 2) > -25$ and $7(1 - k) > 7$ $(-3, 0)$ 5. $2y + 4 \ge 10$ and $5y - 3 \le 13$ $\left[3, \dfrac{16}{5}\right]$

6. $0 < 3(x + 1) \le 4$ $(-1, \frac{1}{3}]$ 7. $6 \ge 4 - 2x \ge -2$ $[-1, 3]$ 8. $-4 > 5 - x > -6$ $(9, 11)$

Concept 1: Solving Quadratic and Polynomial Inequalities

For Exercises 9–12, estimate from the graph the intervals for which the inequality is true. (See Example 1.)

9.

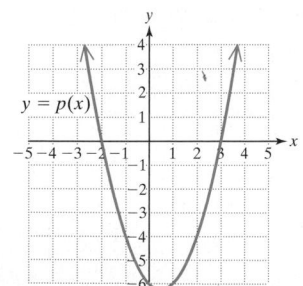

a. $p(x) > 0$
$(-\infty, -2) \cup (3, \infty)$
c. $p(x) \le 0$ $[-2, 3]$

b. $p(x) < 0$
$(-2, 3)$
d. $p(x) \ge 0$ $(-\infty, -2] \cup [3, \infty)$

10.

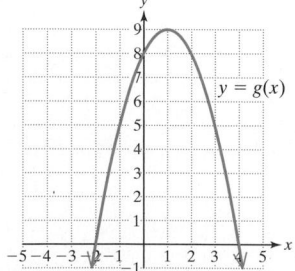

a. $g(x) > 0$
$(-2, 4)$
c. $g(x) \le 0$
$(-\infty, -2] \cup [4, \infty)$

b. $g(x) < 0$
$(-\infty, -2) \cup (4, \infty)$
d. $g(x) \ge 0$ $[-2, 4]$

Writing   Translating Expression   Geometry   Scientific Calculator   Video   NSE

11.

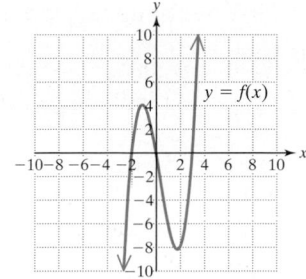

$y = f(x)$

a. $f(x) > 0$
$(-2, 0) \cup (3, \infty)$

b. $f(x) < 0$
$(-\infty, -2) \cup (0, 3)$

c. $f(x) \leq 0$
$(-\infty, -2] \cup [0, 3]$

d. $f(x) \geq 0$
$[-2, 0] \cup [3, \infty)$

12.

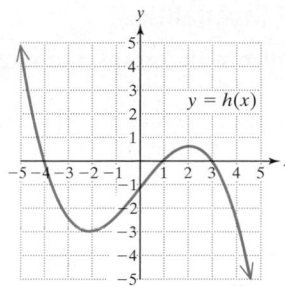

$y = h(x)$

a. $h(x) > 0$
$(-\infty, -4) \cup (1, 3)$

b. $h(x) < 0$
$(-4, 1) \cup (3, \infty)$

c. $h(x) \leq 0$
$[-4, 1] \cup [3, \infty)$

d. $h(x) \geq 0$
$(-\infty, -4] \cup [1, 3]$

For Exercises 13–18, solve the equation and related inequalities. **(See Examples 2–3.)**

13. a. $3(4 - x)(2x + 1) = 0$ $\{4, -\frac{1}{2}\}$

   b. $3(4 - x)(2x + 1) < 0$ $(-\infty, -\frac{1}{2}) \cup (4, \infty)$

   c. $3(4 - x)(2x + 1) > 0$ $(-\frac{1}{2}, 4)$

14. a. $5(y + 6)(3 - 5y) = 0$ $\{-6, \frac{3}{5}\}$

   b. $5(y + 6)(3 - 5y) < 0$ $(-\infty, -6) \cup (\frac{3}{5}, \infty)$

   c. $5(y + 6)(3 - 5y) > 0$ $(-6, \frac{3}{5})$

15. a. $x^2 + 7x = 30$ $\{-10, 3\}$

   b. $x^2 + 7x < 30$ $(-10, 3)$

   c. $x^2 + 7x > 30$ $(-\infty, -10) \cup (3, \infty)$

16. a. $q^2 - 4q = 5$ $\{5, -1\}$

   b. $q^2 - 4q \leq 5$ $[-1, 5]$

   c. $q^2 - 4q \geq 5$ $(-\infty, -1] \cup [5, \infty)$

17. a. $2p(p - 2) = p + 3$ $\left\{-\frac{1}{2}, 3\right\}$

   b. $2p(p - 2) \leq p + 3$ $\left[-\frac{1}{2}, 3\right]$

   c. $2p(p - 2) \geq p + 3$
   $\left(-\infty, -\frac{1}{2}\right] \cup [3, \infty)$

18. a. $3w(w + 4) = 10 - w$ $\left\{\frac{2}{3}, -5\right\}$

   b. $3w(w + 4) < 10 - w$ $\left(-5, \frac{2}{3}\right)$

   c. $3w(w + 4) > 10 - w$
   $(-\infty, -5) \cup \left(\frac{2}{3}, \infty\right)$

For Exercises 19–36, solve the polynomial inequality. Write the answer in interval notation. **(See Examples 2–3.)**

19. $(t - 7)(t - 1) < 0$
$(1, 7)$

20. $(p - 4)(p - 2) > 0$
$(-\infty, 2) \cup (4, \infty)$

21. $-6(4 + 2x)(5 - x) > 0$
$(-\infty, -2) \cup (5, \infty)$

22. $-8(2t + 5)(6 - t) < 0$ $\left(-\frac{5}{2}, 6\right)$

23. $m(m + 1)^2(m + 5) \leq 0$
$[-5, 0]$

24. $w^2(3 - w)(w + 2) \geq 0$
$[-2, 3]$

25. $a^2 - 12a \leq -32$
$[4, 8]$

26. $w^2 + 20w \geq -64$
$(-\infty, -16] \cup [-4, \infty)$

27. $5x^2 - 4x - 1 > 0$
$\left(-\infty, -\frac{1}{5}\right) \cup (1, \infty)$

28. $x^2 + x \leq 6$ $[-3, 2]$

29. $b^2 - 121 < 0$ $(-11, 11)$

30. $c^2 - 25 < 0$ $(-5, 5)$

31. $3p(p - 2) - 3 \geq 2p$
$\left(-\infty, -\frac{1}{3}\right] \cup [3, \infty)$

32. $2t(t + 3) - t \leq 12$ $\left[-4, \frac{3}{2}\right]$

33. $x^3 - x^2 \leq 12x$ $(-\infty, -3] \cup [0, 4]$

34. $x^3 + 36 > 4x^2 + 9x$
$(-3, 3) \cup (4, \infty)$

35. $w^3 + w^2 > 4w + 4$
$(-2, -1) \cup (2, \infty)$

36. $2p^3 - 5p^2 \leq 3p$ $\left(-\infty, -\frac{1}{2}\right] \cup [0, 3]$

Concept 2: Solving Rational Inequalities

For Exercises 37–40, estimate from the graph the intervals for which the inequality is true.

37.

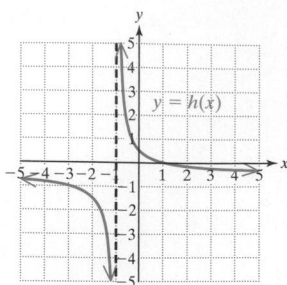

a. $h(x) \geq 0$
$(-1, 1]$
b. $h(x) \leq 0$
$(-\infty, -1) \cup [1, \infty)$
c. $h(x) < 0$
$(-\infty, -1) \cup (1, \infty)$
d. $h(x) > 0$
$(-1, 1)$

38.

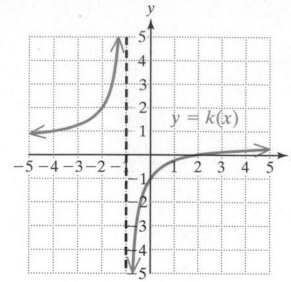

a. $k(x) \leq 0$
$(-1, 2]$
b. $k(x) \geq 0$
$(-\infty, -1) \cup [2, \infty)$
c. $k(x) > 0$
$(-\infty, -1) \cup (2, \infty)$
d. $k(x) < 0$
$(-1, 2)$

39.

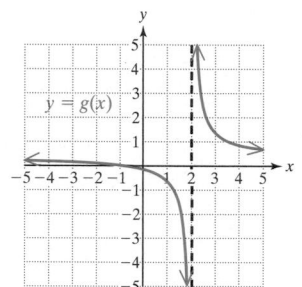

a. $g(x) > 0$
$(-\infty, -1) \cup (2, \infty)$
b. $g(x) < 0$
$(-1, 2)$
c. $g(x) \leq 0$
$[-1, 2)$
d. $g(x) \geq 0$
$(-\infty, -1] \cup (2, \infty)$

40.

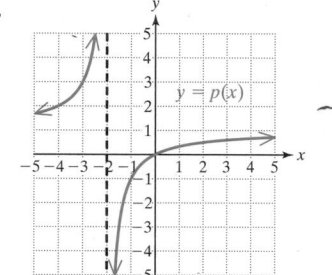

a. $p(x) > 0$
$(-\infty, -2) \cup (0, \infty)$
b. $p(x) < 0$
$(-2, 0)$
c. $p(x) \leq 0$
$(-2, 0]$
d. $p(x) \geq 0$
$(-\infty, -2) \cup [0, \infty)$

For Exercises 41–44, solve the equation and related inequalities. **(See Examples 4–5.)**

41. a. $\dfrac{10}{x - 5} = 5$ {7}

b. $\dfrac{10}{x - 5} < 5$
$(-\infty, 5) \cup (7, \infty)$

c. $\dfrac{10}{x - 5} > 5$ $(5, 7)$

42. a. $\dfrac{8}{a + 1} = 4$ {1}

b. $\dfrac{8}{a + 1} > 4$ $(-1, 1)$

c. $\dfrac{8}{a + 1} < 4$
$(-\infty, -1) \cup (1, \infty)$

43. a. $\dfrac{z + 2}{z - 6} = -3$ {4}

b. $\dfrac{z + 2}{z - 6} \leq -3$ $[4, 6)$

c. $\dfrac{z + 2}{z - 6} \geq -3$
$(-\infty, 4] \cup (6, \infty)$

44. a. $\dfrac{w - 8}{w + 6} = 2$ {−20}

b. $\dfrac{w - 8}{w + 6} \leq 2$
$(-\infty, -20] \cup (-6, \infty)$

c. $\dfrac{w - 8}{w + 6} \geq 2$ $[-20, -6)$

For Exercises 45–56, solve the rational inequality. Write the answer in interval notation. **(See Examples 4–5.)**

45. $\dfrac{2}{x - 1} \geq 0$ $(1, \infty)$

46. $\dfrac{-3}{x + 2} \leq 0$ $(-2, \infty)$

47. $\dfrac{b + 4}{b - 4} > 0$
$(-\infty, -4) \cup (4, \infty)$

48. $\dfrac{a + 1}{a - 3} < 0$ $(-1, 3)$

49. $\dfrac{3}{2x - 7} < -1$ $\left(2, \dfrac{7}{2}\right)$

50. $\dfrac{8}{4x + 9} > 1$ $\left(-\dfrac{9}{4}, -\dfrac{1}{4}\right)$

51. $\dfrac{x + 1}{x - 5} \geq 4$ $(5, 7]$

52. $\dfrac{x - 2}{x + 6} \leq 5$
$(-\infty, -8] \cup (-6, \infty)$

53. $\dfrac{1}{x} \leq 2$ $(-\infty, 0) \cup \left[\dfrac{1}{2}, \infty\right)$

54. $\dfrac{1}{x} \geq 3$ $\left(0, \dfrac{1}{3}\right]$

55. $\dfrac{(x + 2)^2}{x} > 0$ $(0, \infty)$

56. $\dfrac{(x - 3)^2}{x} < 0$ $(-\infty, 0)$

Mixed Exercises

For Exercises 57–76, identify the inequality as one of the following types: linear, quadratic, rational, or polynomial (degree > 2). Then solve the inequality and write the answer in interval notation.

57. $2y^2 - 8 \le 24$
Quadratic; $[-4, 4]$

58. $8p^2 - 18 > 0$
Quadratic; $(-\infty, -\frac{3}{2}) \cup (\frac{3}{2}, \infty)$

59. $(5x + 2)^2 > 4$
Quadratic; $\left(-\infty, -\frac{4}{5}\right) \cup (0, \infty)$

60. $(7x - 4)^2 < 9$ Quadratic; $\left(\frac{1}{7}, 1\right)$

61. $4(x - 2) < 6x - 3$ Linear; $(-\frac{5}{2}, \infty)$

62. $-7(3 - y) > 4 + 2y$ Linear; $(5, \infty)$

63. $\dfrac{2x + 3}{x + 1} \le 2$
Rational; $(-\infty, -1)$

64. $\dfrac{5x - 1}{x + 3} \ge 5$
Rational; $(-\infty, -3)$

65. $4x^3 - 40x^2 + 100x > 0$
Polynomial (degree > 2); $(0, 5) \cup (5, \infty)$

66. $2y^3 - 12y^2 + 18y < 0$
Polynomial (degree > 2); $(-\infty, 0)$

67. $2p^3 > 4p^2$
Polynomial (degree > 2); $(2, \infty)$

68. $w^3 \le 5w^2$
Polynomial (degree > 2); $(-\infty, 5]$

69. $-3(x + 4)^2(x - 5) \ge 0$
Polynomial (degree > 2); $(-\infty, 5]$

70. $5x(x - 2)(x - 6)^2 \ge 0$
Polynomial (degree > 2); $(-\infty, 0] \cup [2, \infty]$

71. $x^2 - 4 < 0$
Quadratic; $(-2, 2)$

72. $y^2 - 9 > 0$
Quadratic; $(-\infty, -3) \cup (3, \infty)$

73. $\dfrac{a + 2}{a - 5} \ge 0$ Rational; $(-\infty, -2] \cup (5, \infty)$

74. $\dfrac{t + 1}{t - 2} \le 0$ Rational; $[-1, 2)$

75. $2 \ge t - 3$ Linear; $(-\infty, 5]$

76. $-5p + 8 < p$ Linear; $\left(\frac{4}{3}, \infty\right)$

Expanding Your Skills

The solution to an inequality is often one or more intervals on the real number line. Sometimes, however, the solution to an inequality may be a single point on the number line, the empty set, or the set of all real numbers. We call these "special case" solution sets.

For Exercises 77–92, solve the inequalities involving "special case" solution sets.

77. $x^2 + 10x + 25 \ge 0$
$(-\infty, \infty)$

78. $x^2 + 6x + 9 < 0$
$\{\,\}$

79. $x^2 + 2x + 1 < 0$
$\{\,\}$

80. $x^2 + 8x + 16 \ge 0$
$(-\infty, \infty)$

81. $x^4 + 3x^2 \le 0$ $\{0\}$

82. $x^4 + 2x^2 \le 0$ $\{0\}$

83. $x^2 + 12x + 36 < 0$
$\{\,\}$

84. $x^2 + 12x + 36 \ge 0$
$(-\infty, \infty)$

85. $x^2 + 3x + 5 < 0$
$\{\,\}$

86. $2x^2 + 3x + 3 > 0$
$(-\infty, \infty)$

87. $-5x^2 + x < 1$
$(-\infty, \infty)$

88. $-3x^2 - x > 6$
$\{\,\}$

89. $x^2 + 22x + 121 > 0$
$(-\infty, -11) \cup (-11, \infty)$

90. $y^2 - 24y + 144 > 0$
$(-\infty, 12) \cup (12, \infty)$

91. $4t^2 - 12t \le -9$
$\left\{\frac{3}{2}\right\}$

92. $4t^2 - 12t > -9$
$\left(-\infty, \frac{3}{2}\right) \cup \left(\frac{3}{2}, \infty\right)$

Graphing Calculator Exercises

93. To solve the inequality $\dfrac{x}{x - 2} > 0$ enter Y_1 as $x/(x - 2)$ and determine where the graph is above the x-axis. Write the solution in interval notation. $(-\infty, 0) \cup (2, \infty)$

94. To solve the inequality $\dfrac{x}{x - 2} < 0$ enter Y_1 as $x/(x - 2)$ and determine where the graph is below the x-axis. Write the solution in interval notation. $(0, 2)$

95. To solve the inequality $x^2 - 1 < 0$, enter Y_1 as $x^2 - 1$ and determine where the graph is below the x-axis. Write the solution in interval notation. $(-1, 1)$

96. To solve the inequality $x^2 - 1 > 0$, enter Y_1 as $x^2 - 1$ and determine where the graph is above the x-axis. Write the solution in interval notation. $(-\infty, -1) \cup (1, \infty)$

For Exercises 97–100, determine the solution by graphing the inequalities.

97. $x^2 + 10x + 25 \le 0$ $\{-5\}$

98. $-x^2 + 10x - 25 \ge 0$ $\{5\}$

99. $\dfrac{8}{x^2 + 2} < 0$ $\{\,\}$

100. $\dfrac{-6}{x^2 + 3} > 0$ $\{\,\}$

 Writing   Translating Expression   Geometry   Scientific Calculator   Video   NS E

Section 9.3 Absolute Value Equations

1. Solving Absolute Value Equations

An equation of the form $|x| = a$ is called an **absolute value equation**. The solution includes all real numbers whose absolute value equals a. For example, the solutions to the equation $|x| = 4$ are 4 as well as -4, because $|4| = 4$ and $|-4| = 4$. In Chapter 1, we introduced a geometric interpretation of $|x|$. The absolute value of a number is its distance from zero on the number line (Figure 9-5). Therefore, the solutions to the equation $|x| = 4$ are the values of x that are 4 units away from zero.

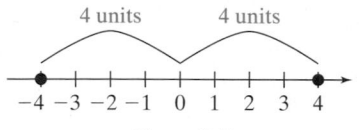

Figure 9-5

PROCEDURE Solving Absolute Value Equations of the Form $|x| = a$

If a is a real number, then

- If $a \geq 0$, the solutions to the equation $|x| = a$ are $x = a$ and $x = -a$.
- If $a < 0$, there is no solution to the equation $|x| = a$.

To solve an absolute value equation of the form $|x| = a$ $(a \geq 0)$, rewrite the equation as $x = a$ or $x = -a$.

Classroom Examples: p. 652, Exercises 8, 14, and 16

Example 1 Solving Absolute Value Equations

Solve the absolute value equations.

  a. $|x| = 5$ **b.** $|w| - 2 = 12$ **c.** $|p| = 0$ **d.** $|x| = -6$

Solution:

a. $|x| = 5$ The equation is in the form $|x| = a$, where $a = 5$.

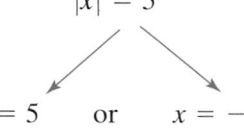

$x = 5$ or $x = -5$ Rewrite the equation as $x = a$ or $x = -a$.

The solution set is $\{5, -5\}$.

b. $|w| - 2 = 12$ Isolate the absolute value to write the equation in the form $|w| = a$.

       $|w| = 14$

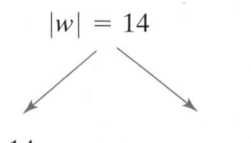

$w = 14$ or $w = -14$ Rewrite the equation as $w = a$ or $w = -a$.

The solution set is $\{14, -14\}$.

c.

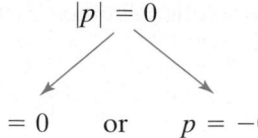

$|p| = 0$

$p = 0$ or $p = -0$ Rewrite as two equations. Notice that the second equation $p = -0$ is the same as the first equation. Intuitively, $p = 0$ is the only number whose absolute value equals 0.

The solution set is $\{0\}$.

d. $|x| = -6$ This equation is of the form $|x| = a$, but a is negative. There is no number whose absolute value is negative.

No solution, $\{\ \}$

Skill Practice Solve the absolute value equations.

1. $|y| = 7$ **2.** $|v| + 6 = 10$ **3.** $|w| = 0$ **4.** $|z| = -12$

We have solved absolute value equations of the form $|x| = a$. Notice that x can represent any algebraic quantity. For example, to solve the equation $|2w - 3| = 5$, we still rewrite the absolute value equation as two equations. In this case, we set the quantity $2w - 3$ equal to 5 and to -5, respectively.

$$|2w - 3| = 5$$

$2w - 3 = 5$ or $2w - 3 = -5$

PROCEDURE   Solving an Absolute Value Equation

Step 1   Isolate the absolute value. That is, write the equation in the form $|x| = a$, where a is a real number.

Step 2   If $a < 0$, there is no solution.

Step 3   Otherwise, if $a \geq 0$, rewrite the absolute value equation as $x = a$ or $x = -a$.

Step 4   Solve the individual equations from step 3.

Step 5   Check the answers in the original absolute value equation.

Example 2   Solving an Absolute Value Equation

Solve the equation. $|2w - 3| = 5$

Solution:

$|2w - 3| = 5$ The equation is already in the form $|x| = a$, where $x = 2w - 3$.

$2w - 3 = 5$ or $2w - 3 = -5$ Rewrite as two equations.

$2w = 8$ or $2w = -2$ Solve each equation.

$w = 4$ or $w = -1$

Classroom Example: p. 652, Exercise 18

Answers

1. $\{7, -7\}$
2. $\{4, -4\}$
3. $\{0\}$ **4.** $\{\ \}$

Check: $w = 4$ Check: $w = -1$ Check the solutions in the original
$|2w - 3| = 5$ $|2w - 3| = 5$ equation.

$|2(4) - 3| \overset{?}{=} 5$ $|2(-1) - 3| \overset{?}{=} 5$

$|8 - 3| \overset{?}{=} 5$ $|-2 - 3| \overset{?}{=} 5$

$|5| \overset{?}{=} 5 ✔$ $|-5| \overset{?}{=} 5 ✔$

The solution set is $\{4, -1\}$.

Skill Practice Solve the equation.

5. $|4x + 1| = 9$

Calculator Connections

To confirm the answers to Example 2,
graph $Y_1 = \text{abs}(2x - 3)$ and $Y_2 = 5$.
The solutions to the equation $|2x - 3| = 5$
are the x-coordinates of the points of
intersection $(4, 5)$ and $(-1, 5)$.

Classroom Example: p. 652,
Exercise 32

Example 3 Solving an Absolute Value Equation

Solve the equation. $|2c - 5| + 6 = 2$

Solution:

$|2c - 5| + 6 = 2$

$|2c - 5| = -4$ Isolate the absolute value. The equation is in the
                     form $|x| = a$, where $x = 2c - 5$ and $a = -4$.
                     Because $a < 0$, there is no solution.

Avoiding Mistakes

Always isolate the absolute value
first. Otherwise you will get
answers that do not check.

No solution, $\{\ \}$ There are no numbers c that will make an absolute
                          value equal to a negative number.

Skill Practice Solve the equation.

6. $|3z + 10| + 3 = 1$

Calculator Connections

The graphs of $Y_1 = \text{abs}(2x - 5) + 6$ and
$Y_2 = 2$ do not intersect.
      Therefore, there is no solution to the
equation $|2x - 5| + 6 = 2$.

Answers

5. $\left\{2, -\dfrac{5}{2}\right\}$ **6.** $\{\ \}$

Example 4 Solving an Absolute Value Equation

Solve the equation. $-2\left|\dfrac{2}{5}p + 3\right| - 7 = -19$

Classroom Example: p. 652, Exercise 38

Solution:

$$-2\left|\frac{2}{5}p + 3\right| - 7 = -19$$

$$-2\left|\frac{2}{5}p + 3\right| = -12 \qquad \text{Isolate the absolute value.}$$

$$\frac{-2\left|\frac{2}{5}p + 3\right|}{-2} = \frac{-12}{-2}$$

$$\left|\frac{2}{5}p + 3\right| = 6$$

$\frac{2}{5}p + 3 = 6$	or	$\frac{2}{5}p + 3 = -6$	Rewrite as two equations.
$2p + 15 = 30$	or	$2p + 15 = -30$	Multiply by 5 to clear fractions.
$2p = 15$	or	$2p = -45$	
$p = \frac{15}{2}$	or	$p = -\frac{45}{2}$	Both solutions check in the original equation.

The solution set is $\left\{\dfrac{15}{2}, -\dfrac{45}{2}\right\}$.

Skill Practice Solve the equation.

7. $3\left|\dfrac{3}{2}a + 1\right| + 2 = 14$

Example 5 Solving an Absolute Value Equation

Solve the equation. $6.9 = |4.1 - p| + 6.9$

Classroom Example: p. 652, Exercise 34

Solution:

$6.9 = |4.1 - p| + 6.9$

$|4.1 - p| + 6.9 = 6.9$ First write the absolute value on the left. Then subtract 6.9 from both sides to write the equation in the form $|x| = a$.

$|4.1 - p| = 0$ Isolate the absolute value.

$4.1 - p = 0$ or $4.1 - p = -0$ Rewrite as two equations. Notice that the equations are the same.

$-p = -4.1$ Subtract 4.1 from both sides.

Answer

7. $\left\{2, -\dfrac{10}{3}\right\}$

$$p = 4.1$$

<u>Check:</u> $p = 4.1$

$$|4.1 - p| + 6.9 = 6.9$$

$$|4.1 - 4.1| + 6.9 \overset{?}{=} 6.9$$

$$|0| + 6.9 \overset{?}{=} 6.9$$

The solution set is {4.1}.

$$6.9 \overset{?}{=} 6.9 ✔$$

Skill Practice Solve the equation.

8. $-3.5 = |1.2 + x| - 3.5$

2. Solving Equations Containing Two Absolute Values

Some equations have two absolute values such as $|x| = |y|$. If two quantities have the same absolute value, then the quantities are equal or the quantities are opposites.

> **PROPERTY** **Equality of Absolute Values**
>
> $|x| = |y|$ implies that $x = y$ or $x = -y$.

Classroom Example: p. 652, Exercise 42

Example 6 Solving an Equation Having Two Absolute Values

Solve the equation. $|2w - 3| = |5w + 1|$

Solution:

$$|2w - 3| = |5w + 1|$$

$2w - 3 = 5w + 1$	or	$2w - 3 = -(5w + 1)$	Rewrite as two equations, $x = y$ or $x = -y$.
$2w - 3 = 5w + 1$	or	$2w - 3 = -5w - 1$	Solve for w.
$-3w - 3 = 1$	or	$7w - 3 = -1$	
$-3w = 4$	or	$7w = 2$	
$w = -\dfrac{4}{3}$	or	$w = \dfrac{2}{7}$	Both values check in the original equation.

> **Avoiding Mistakes**
>
> To take the opposite of the quantity $5w + 1$, use parentheses and apply the distributive property.

The solution set is $\left\{ -\dfrac{4}{3}, \dfrac{2}{7} \right\}$.

Skill Practice Solve the equation.

9. $|3 - 2x| = |3x - 1|$

Answers

8. $\{-1.2\}$ **9.** $\left\{ \dfrac{4}{5}, -2 \right\}$

Example 7 Solving an Equation Having Two Absolute Values

Solve the equation. $|x - 4| = |x + 8|$

Classroom Example: p. 652, Exercise 48

Solution:

$|x - 4| = |x + 8|$

$x - 4 = x + 8$ or $x - 4 = -(x + 8)$ Rewrite as two equations, $x = y$ or $x = -y$.

$-4 = 8$ or $x - 4 = -x - 8$ Solve for x.

$\uparrow$ $2x - 4 = -8$

contradiction

$2x = -4$

$x = -2$ $x = -2$ checks in the original equation.

The solution set is $\{-2\}$.

Skill Practice Solve the equation.

10. $|4t + 3| = |4t - 5|$

Answer

10. $\left\{\dfrac{1}{4}\right\}$

Calculator Connections

Graph $Y_1 = \text{abs}(x - 4)$ and $Y_2 = \text{abs}(x + 8)$. There is one point of intersection at $(-2, 6)$. Therefore, the solution to $|x - 4| = |x + 8|$ is -2.

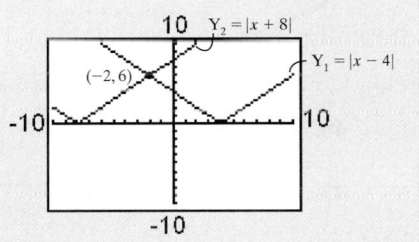

Section 9.3 **Practice Exercises**

Boost *your* GRADE at ALEKS.com!

ALEKS version 3.0

• Practice Problems
• Self-Tests
• NetTutor
• e-Professors
• Videos

For additional exercises, see Classroom Activities 9.3A–9.3B in the *Instructor's Resource Manual* at www.mhhe.com/moh.

Study Skills Exercise

1. Define the key term **absolute value equation**.

Review Exercises

For Exercises 2–6, solve the inequalities. Write the answers in interval notation.

2. $x^2 - 3x - 10 \le 0$ $[-2, 5]$ **3.** $x^2 - 1 \ge 0$ $(-\infty, -1] \cup [1, \infty)$

4. $\dfrac{4}{y - 4} \ge 3$ $\left(4, \dfrac{16}{3}\right]$ **5.** $\dfrac{3}{t + 1} \le 2$ $(-\infty, -1) \cup \left[\dfrac{1}{2}, \infty\right)$ **6.** $x^3 - 7x^2 - 8x > 0$ $(-1, 0) \cup (8, \infty)$

Concept 1: Solving Absolute Value Equations

For Exercises 7–38, solve the absolute value equations. (See Examples 1–5.)

7. $|p| = 7$
$\{7, -7\}$

8. $|q| = 10$
$\{10, -10\}$

9. $|x| + 5 = 11$
$\{6, -6\}$

10. $|x| - 3 = 20$
$\{23, -23\}$

11. $|y| = \sqrt{2}$
$\{\sqrt{2}, -\sqrt{2}\}$

12. $|y| = \sqrt{5}$
$\{\sqrt{5}, -\sqrt{5}\}$

13. $|w| - 3 = -5$
$\{\}$

14. $|w| + 4 = -8$
$\{\}$

15. $|3q| = 0$ $\{0\}$

16. $|4p| = 0$ $\{0\}$

17. $|3x - 4| = 8$ $\left\{4, -\dfrac{4}{3}\right\}$

18. $|4x + 1| = 6$ $\left\{\dfrac{5}{4}, -\dfrac{7}{4}\right\}$

19. $5 = |2x - 4|$ $\left\{\dfrac{9}{2}, -\dfrac{1}{2}\right\}$

20. $10 = |3x + 7|$
$\left\{1, -\dfrac{17}{3}\right\}$

21. $\left|\dfrac{7z}{3} - \dfrac{1}{3}\right| + 3 = 6$
$\left\{\dfrac{10}{7}, -\dfrac{8}{7}\right\}$

22. $\left|\dfrac{w}{2} + \dfrac{3}{2}\right| - 2 = 7$
$\{15, -21\}$

23. $|0.2x - 3.5| = -5.6$
$\{\}$

24. $|1.81 + 2x| = -2.2$
$\{\}$

25. $1 = -4 + \left|2 - \dfrac{1}{4}w\right|$
$\{-12, 28\}$

26. $-12 = -6 - |6 - 2x|$
$\{0, 6\}$

27. $10 = 4 + |2y + 1|$
$\left\{\dfrac{5}{2}, -\dfrac{7}{2}\right\}$

28. $-1 = -|5x + 7|$
$\left\{-\dfrac{6}{5}, -\dfrac{8}{5}\right\}$

29. $-2|3b - 7| - 9 = -9$
$\dfrac{7}{3}$ ₊ ₉ ₊₉

30. $-3|5x + 1| + 4 = 4$
$\left\{-\dfrac{1}{5}\right\}$

31. $-2|x + 3| = 5$ $\{\}$

32. $-3|x - 5| = 7$ $\{\}$ $= 0$

33. $0 = |6x - 9|$
$\left\{\dfrac{3}{2}\right\}$

34. $7 = |4k - 6| + 7$
$\left\{\dfrac{3}{2}\right\}$

35. $\left|-\dfrac{1}{5} - \dfrac{1}{2}k\right| = \dfrac{9}{5}$ $\left\{-4, \dfrac{16}{5}\right\}$

36. $\left|-\dfrac{1}{6} - \dfrac{2}{9}h\right| = \dfrac{1}{2}$
$\left\{-3, \dfrac{3}{2}\right\}$

37. $-3|2 - 6x| + 5 = -10$
$\left\{-\dfrac{1}{2}, \dfrac{7}{6}\right\}$

38. $5|1 - 2x| - 7 = 3$
$\left\{-\dfrac{1}{2}, \dfrac{3}{2}\right\}$

Concept 2: Solving Equations Containing Two Absolute Values

For Exercises 39–52, solve the absolute value equations. (See Examples 6–7.)

39. $|4x - 2| = |-8|$ $\left\{\dfrac{5}{2}, -\dfrac{3}{2}\right\}$

40. $|3x + 5| = |-5|$ $\left\{0, -\dfrac{10}{3}\right\}$

41. $|4w + 3| = |2w - 5|$ $\left\{-4, \dfrac{1}{3}\right\}$

42. $|3y + 1| = |2y - 7|$ $\left\{-8, \dfrac{6}{5}\right\}$

43. $|2y + 5| = |7 - 2y|$ $\left\{\dfrac{1}{2}\right\}$

44. $|9a + 5| = |9a - 1|$ $\left\{-\dfrac{2}{9}\right\}$

45. $\left|\dfrac{4w - 1}{6}\right| = \left|\dfrac{2w}{3} + \dfrac{1}{4}\right|$ $\left\{-\dfrac{1}{16}\right\}$

46. $\left|\dfrac{3p + 2}{4}\right| = \left|\dfrac{1}{2}p - 2\right|$ $\left\{-10, \dfrac{6}{5}\right\}$

47. $|2h - 6| = |2h + 5|$ $\left\{\dfrac{1}{4}\right\}$

48. $|6n - 7| = |4 - 6n|$ $\left\{\dfrac{11}{12}\right\}$

49. $|3.5m - 1.2| = |8.5m + 6|$
$\{-1.44, -0.4\}$

50. $|11.2n + 9| = |7.2n - 2.1|$
$\{-2.775, -0.375\}$

51. $|4x - 3| = -|2x - 1|$ $\{\}$

52. $-|3 - 6y| = |8 - 2y|$ $\{\}$

Expanding Your Skills

53. Write an absolute value equation whose solution is the set of real numbers 6 units from zero on the number line. $|x| = 6$

54. Write an absolute value equation whose solution is the set of real numbers $\dfrac{7}{2}$ units from zero on the number line. $|x| = \dfrac{7}{2}$

55. Write an absolute value equation whose solution is the set of real numbers $\dfrac{4}{3}$ units from zero on the number line. $|x| = \dfrac{4}{3}$

56. Write an absolute value equation whose solution is the set of real numbers 9 units from zero on the number line. $|x| = 9$

Graphing Calculator Exercises

For Exercises 57–62, enter the left side of the equation as Y_1 and enter the right side of the equation as Y_2. Then use the *Intersect* feature to approximate the x-values where the two graphs intersect (if they intersect).

57. $|4x - 3| = 5$ $\left\{2, -\dfrac{1}{2}\right\}$

58. $|x - 4| = 3$ $\{7, 1\}$

59. $|8x + 1| + 8 = 1$ $\{\}$

60. $|3x - 2| + 4 = 2$ $\{\}$

61. $|x - 3| = |x + 2|$ $\left\{\dfrac{1}{2}\right\}$

62. $|x + 4| = |x - 2|$ $\{-1\}$

Absolute Value Inequalities

Section 9.4

1. Solving Absolute Value Inequalities by Definition

Concepts

In Section 9.3, we studied absolute value equations in the form $|x| = a$. In this section, we will solve absolute value *inequalities*. An inequality in any of the forms $|x| < a$, $|x| \le a$, $|x| > a$, or $|x| \ge a$ is called an **absolute value inequality**.

Recall that an absolute value represents distance from zero on the real number line. Consider the following absolute value equation and inequalities.

1. Solving Absolute Value Inequalities by Definition

2. Solving Absolute Value Inequalities by the Test Point Method

3. Translating to an Absolute Value Expression

1. $|x| = 3$
   $x = 3$ or $x = -3$

Solution:

The set of all points 3 units from zero on the number line

2. $|x| > 3$
   $x < -3$ or $x > 3$

Solution:

The set of all points more than 3 units from zero

3. $|x| < 3$
   $-3 < x < 3$

Solution:

The set of all points less than 3 units from zero

PROCEDURE **Solving Absolute Value Equations and Inequalities**

Let a be a real number such that $a > 0$. Then

Equation/ Inequality	Solution (Equivalent Form)	Graph
$\lvert x \rvert = a$	$x = -a$ or $x = a$	
$\lvert x \rvert > a$	$x < -a$ or $x > a$	
$\lvert x \rvert < a$	$-a < x < a$	

Instructor Note:
$|x| = a$ means that x is "a" units away from 0.
$|x| > a$ means that x is more than "a" units away from 0.
$|x| < a$ means that x is less than "a" units away from 0.

To solve an absolute value inequality, first isolate the absolute value and then rewrite the absolute value inequality in its equivalent form.

Classroom Example: p. 661, Exercise 12

Example 1   Solving an Absolute Value Inequality

Solve the inequality. $|3w + 1| - 4 < 7$

Solution:

$$|3w + 1| - 4 < 7$$

$$|3w + 1| < 11 \longleftarrow \text{Isolate the absolute value first.}$$

The inequality is in the form $|x| < a$, where $x = 3w + 1$.

$$-11 < 3w + 1 < 11 \qquad \text{Rewrite in the equivalent form } -a < x < a.$$

$$-12 < 3w < 10 \qquad \text{Solve for } w.$$

$$-4 < w < \frac{10}{3}$$

TIP: Recall that a strict inequality (using the symbols $>$ and $<$) will have parentheses at the endpoints of the interval form of the solution.

The solution is $\{w \mid -4 < w < \frac{10}{3}\}$, or equivalently in interval notation, $(-4, \frac{10}{3})$.

Skill Practice   Solve the inequality. Write the solution in interval notation.

1. $|2t + 5| + 2 \leq 11$

Calculator Connections

Graph $Y_1 = \text{abs}(3x + 1) - 4$ and $Y_2 = 7$. On the given display window, $Y_1 < Y_2$ (Y_1 is below Y_2) for $-4 < x < \frac{10}{3}$.

Classroom Example: p. 661, Exercise 32

Example 2   Solving an Absolute Value Inequality

Solve the inequality. $3 \leq 1 + \left|\frac{1}{2}t - 5\right|$

Solution:

$$3 \leq 1 + \left|\frac{1}{2}t - 5\right|$$

$$1 + \left|\frac{1}{2}t - 5\right| \geq 3 \qquad \text{Write the inequality with the absolute value on the left.}$$

$$\left|\frac{1}{2}t - 5\right| \geq 2 \qquad \text{Isolate the absolute value.}$$

The inequality is in the form $|x| \geq a$, where $x = \frac{1}{2}t - 5$.

TIP: It is generally easier to solve an absolute value inequality if the absolute value appears on the left-hand side of the inequality.

$$\frac{1}{2}t - 5 \leq -2 \qquad \text{or} \qquad \frac{1}{2}t - 5 \geq 2 \qquad \begin{array}{l} \text{Rewrite in the equivalent form} \\ x \leq -a \text{ or } x \geq a. \end{array}$$

Answer

1. $[-7, 2]$

$$\frac{1}{2}t \le 3 \quad \text{or} \quad \frac{1}{2}t \ge 7 \qquad \text{Solve the compound inequality.}$$

$$2\left(\frac{1}{2}t\right) \le 2(3) \quad \text{or} \quad 2\left(\frac{1}{2}t\right) \ge 2(7) \qquad \text{Clear fractions.}$$

$$t \le 6 \quad \text{or} \quad t \ge 14$$

The solution is $\{t \,|\, t \le 6 \text{ or } t \ge 14\}$ or, equivalently in interval notation, $(-\infty, 6] \cup [14, \infty)$.

Skill Practice Solve the inequality. Write the solution in interval notation.

2. $5 < 1 + \left|\dfrac{1}{3}c - 1\right|$

Calculator Connections

Graph $Y_1 = \text{abs}((1/2)x - 5) + 1$ and $Y_2 = 3$. On the given display window, $Y_1 \ge Y_2$ for $x \le 6$ or $x \ge 14$.

By definition, the absolute value of a real number will always be nonnegative. Therefore, the absolute value of any expression will always be greater than a negative number. Similarly, an absolute value can never be less than a negative number. Let a represent a positive real number. Then

- The solution to the inequality $|x| > -a$ is all real numbers, $(-\infty, \infty)$.
- There is no solution to the inequality $|x| < -a$.

Example 3   Solving Absolute Value Inequalities

Solve the inequalities.

a. $|3d - 5| + 7 < 4$ **b.** $|3d - 5| + 7 > 4$

Solution:

a. $|3d - 5| + 7 < 4$ Isolate the absolute value. An absolute value

$\qquad |3d - 5| < -3$ expression cannot be less than a negative number. Therefore, there is no solution.

No solution, $\{\,\}$

b. $|3d - 5| + 7 > 4$ Isolate the absolute value. The inequality is in

$\qquad |3d - 5| > -3$ the form $|x| > a$, where a is negative. An absolute value of any real number is greater than a negative number. Therefore, the

All real numbers, $(-\infty, \infty)$ solution is all real numbers.

Skill Practice Solve the inequalities.

3. $|4p + 2| + 6 < 2$ **4.** $|4p + 2| + 6 > 2$

Classroom Examples: pp. 661–662, Exercises 38 and 40

Answers
2. $(-\infty, -9) \cup (15, \infty)$
3. $\{\,\}$
4. All real numbers; $(-\infty, \infty)$

Classroom Examples: pp. 661–662, Exercises 26, 42, and 44

Example 4 Solving Absolute Value Inequalities

Solve the inequalities.

a. $|4x + 2| \geq 0$ **b.** $|4x + 2| > 0$ **c.** $|4x + 2| \leq 0$

Solution:

a. $|4x + 2| \geq 0$ ←— The absolute value is already isolated.

The absolute value of any real number is nonnegative. Therefore, the solution is all real numbers, $(-\infty, \infty)$.

b. $|4x + 2| > 0$

An absolute value will be greater than zero at all points *except where it is equal to zero.* That is, the point(s) for which $|4x + 2| = 0$ must be excluded from the solution set.

$|4x + 2| = 0$

$4x + 2 = 0$ or $4x + 2 = -0$ The second equation is the same as the first.

$4x = -2$

$x = -\dfrac{1}{2}$ Therefore, exclude $x = -\frac{1}{2}$ from the solution.

The solution is $\{x \mid x \neq -\frac{1}{2}\}$ or equivalently in interval notation, $(-\infty, -\frac{1}{2}) \cup (-\frac{1}{2}, \infty)$.

c. $|4x + 2| \leq 0$

An absolute value of a number cannot be less than zero. However, it can be *equal* to zero. Therefore, the only solutions to this inequality are the solutions to the related equation:

$|4x + 2| = 0$ From part (b), we see that the solution set is $\left\{-\dfrac{1}{2}\right\}$.

Skill Practice Solve the inequalities.

5. $|3x - 1| \geq 0$ **6.** $|3x - 1| > 0$

Answers

5. $(-\infty, \infty)$

6. $\left\{x \mid x \neq \dfrac{1}{3}\right\}$ or $\left(-\infty, \dfrac{1}{3}\right) \cup \left(\dfrac{1}{3}, \infty\right)$

2. Solving Absolute Value Inequalities by the Test Point Method

For the problems in Examples 1 and 2, the absolute value inequality was converted to an equivalent compound inequality. However, sometimes students have difficulty setting up the appropriate compound inequality. To avoid this problem, you may want to use the test point method to solve absolute value inequalities.

PROCEDURE **Solving Inequalities by Using the Test Point Method**

Step 1 Find the boundary points of the inequality. (Boundary points are the real solutions to the related equation and points where the inequality is undefined.)

Step 2 Plot the boundary points on the number line. This divides the number line into intervals.

Step 3 Select a test point from each interval and substitute it into the original inequality.
- If a test point makes the original inequality true, then that interval is part of the solution set.

Step 4 Test the boundary points in the original inequality.
- If the original inequality is strict ($<$ or $>$), do not include the boundary points in the solution set.
- If the original inequality is defined using $\leq$ or $\geq$, then include the boundary points that are well defined within the inequality.

Note: Any boundary point that makes an expression within the inequality undefined must *always* be excluded from the solution set.

To demonstrate the use of the test point method, we will repeat the absolute value inequalities from Examples 1 and 2. Notice that regardless of the method used, the absolute value is always isolated *first* before any further action is taken.

Example 5 **Solving an Absolute Value Inequality by the Test Point Method**

Classroom Example: p. 662, Exercise 48

Solve the inequality by using the test point method. $|3w + 1| - 4 < 7$

Solution:

$|3w + 1| - 4 < 7$

$|3w + 1| < 11 \longleftarrow$ Isolate the absolute value.

$|3w + 1| = 11$ **Step 1:** Solve the related equation.

$$3w + 1 = 11 \quad \text{or} \quad 3w + 1 = -11$$
$$3w = 10 \quad \text{or} \quad 3w = -12$$

Write as an equivalent system of two equations.

$$w = \frac{10}{3} \quad \text{or} \quad w = -4$$

These are the only boundary points.

Step 2: Plot the boundary points.

Step 3: Select a test point from each interval.

Test $w = -5$:

$$|3(-5) + 1| - 4 \overset{?}{<} 7$$

$$|-14| - 4 \overset{?}{<} 7$$

$$14 - 4 \overset{?}{<} 7$$

$$10 \overset{?}{<} 7 \text{ False}$$

Test $w = 0$:

$$|3(0) + 1| - 4 \overset{?}{<} 7$$

$$|1| - 4 \overset{?}{<} 7$$

$$-3 \overset{?}{<} 7 \text{ True}$$

Test $w = 4$:

$$|3(4) + 1| - 4 \overset{?}{<} 7$$

$$|13| - 4 \overset{?}{<} 7$$

$$13 - 4 \overset{?}{<} 7$$

$$9 \overset{?}{<} 7 \text{ False}$$

False True False

$$-6 \ -5 \ -4 \ -3 \ -2 \ -1 \ \ 0 \ \ 1 \ \ 2 \ \ 3 \ \ 4 \ \ 5 \ \ 6$$
$$\tfrac{10}{3}$$

Step 4: Because the original inequality is a strict inequality, the boundary points (where equality occurs) are not included.

The solution is $\{w \mid -4 < w < \frac{10}{3}\}$ or, equivalently in interval notation, $(-4, \frac{10}{3})$.

Skill Practice Solve the inequality.

7. $6 + |3t - 4| \le 10$

Classroom Example: p. 662, Exercise 46

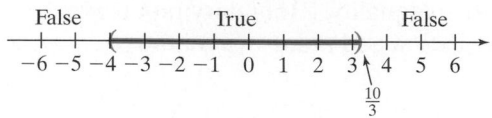 **Example 6** **Solving an Absolute Value Inequality by the Test Point Method**

Solve the inequality by using the test point method. $3 \le 1 + \left| \dfrac{1}{2}t - 5 \right|$

Solution:

$$3 \le 1 + \left| \frac{1}{2}t - 5 \right|$$

$$1 + \left| \frac{1}{2}t - 5 \right| \ge 3 \qquad \text{Write the inequality with the absolute value on the left.}$$

$$\left| \frac{1}{2}t - 5 \right| \ge 2 \longleftarrow \qquad \text{Isolate the absolute value.}$$

$$\left| \frac{1}{2}t - 5 \right| = 2 \qquad \textbf{Step 1: } \text{Solve the related equation.}$$

$$\frac{1}{2}t - 5 = 2 \qquad \text{or} \qquad \frac{1}{2}t - 5 = -2 \qquad \text{Write as an equivalent system of two equations.}$$

$$\frac{1}{2}t = 7 \qquad \text{or} \qquad \frac{1}{2}t = 3$$

$$t = 14 \qquad \text{or} \qquad t = 6 \qquad \text{These are the boundary points.}$$

$$\overset{\text{I}}{\rule{0pt}{0pt}} \quad \big| \quad \overset{\text{II}}{\rule{0pt}{0pt}} \quad \big| \quad \overset{\text{III}}{\rule{0pt}{0pt}}$$
$$6 \qquad\quad 14$$

Step 2: Plot the boundary points.

Step 3: Select a test point from each interval.

Answer

7. $\left[0, \dfrac{8}{3} \right]$

Test $t = 0$:

$3 \overset{?}{\leq} 1 + \left| \dfrac{1}{2}(0) - 5 \right|$

$3 \overset{?}{\leq} 1 + |0 - 5|$

$3 \overset{?}{\leq} 1 + |-5|$

$3 \overset{?}{\leq} 6$ True

Test $t = 10$:

$3 \overset{?}{\leq} 1 + \left| \dfrac{1}{2}(10) - 5 \right|$

$3 \overset{?}{\leq} 1 + |5 - 5|$

$3 \overset{?}{\leq} 1 + |0|$

$3 \overset{?}{\leq} 1$ False

Test $t = 16$:

$3 \overset{?}{\leq} 1 + \left| \dfrac{1}{2}(16) - 5 \right|$

$3 \overset{?}{\leq} 1 + |8 - 5|$

$3 \overset{?}{\leq} 1 + |3|$

$3 \overset{?}{\leq} 4$ True

Step 4: The original inequality uses the sign $\geq$. Therefore, the boundary points (where equality occurs) must be part of the solution set.

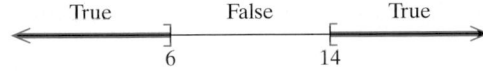

The solution is $\{t \mid t \leq 6 \text{ or } t \geq 14\}$ or, equivalently in interval notation, $(-\infty, 6] \cup [14, \infty)$.

Skill Practice   Solve the inequality.

8. $\left| \dfrac{1}{2}c + 4 \right| + 1 > 6$

3. Translating to an Absolute Value Expression

Absolute value expressions can be used to describe distances. The distance between c and d is given by $|c - d|$. For example, the distance between -2 and 3 on the number line is $|(-2) - 3| = 5$ as expected.

Example 7   Expressing Distances with Absolute Value

Write an absolute value inequality to represent the following phrases.

a. All real numbers x, whose distance from zero is greater than 5 units

b. All real numbers x, whose distance from -7 is less than 3 units

Classroom Example: p. 662, Exercise 52

Solution:

a. All real numbers x, whose distance from zero is greater than 5 units

$|x - 0| > 5$ or simply $|x| > 5$

b. All real numbers x, whose distance from -7 is less than 3 units

$|x - (-7)| < 3$ or simply $|x + 7| < 3$

Skill Practice   Write an absolute value inequality to represent the following phrases.

9. All real numbers whose distance from zero is greater than 10 units

10. All real numbers whose distance from 4 is less than 6 units

Answers

8. $(-\infty, -18) \cup (2, \infty)$

9. $|x| > 10$

10. $|x - 4| < 6$

Absolute value expressions can also be used to describe boundaries for measurement error.

Classroom Example: p. 662, Exercise 56

Example 8 **Expressing Measurement Error with Absolute Value**

Latoya measured a certain compound on a scale in the chemistry lab at school. She measured 8 g of the compound, but the scale is only accurate to ± 0.1 g. Write an absolute value inequality to express an interval for the true mass, x, of the compound she measured.

Solution:

Because the scale is only accurate to ± 0.1 g, the true mass, x, of the compound may deviate by as much as 0.1 g above or below 8 g. This may be expressed as an absolute value inequality:

$$|x - 8.0| \leq 0.1 \quad \text{or equivalently} \quad 7.9 \leq x \leq 8.1$$

Skill Practice

11. Vonzell molded a piece of metal in her machine shop. She measured the thickness at 12 mm. Her machine is accurate to ± 0.05 mm. Write an absolute value inequality to express an interval for the true measurement of the thickness, t, of the metal.

Answer

11. $|t - 12| \leq 0.05$

Section 9.4 Practice Exercises

Study Skills Exercise

1. Define the key term **absolute value inequality**.

Review Exercises

For Exercises 2–4, solve the equations.

2. $|10x - 6| = -5$ $\{\}$

3. $2 = |5 - 7x| + 1$ $\left\{\dfrac{4}{7}, \dfrac{6}{7}\right\}$

4. $|3x - 12| + 4 = 6 - 2$ $\{4\}$

For Exercises 5–8, solve the inequalities and graph the solution set. Write the solution in interval notation.

5. $-15 < 3w - 6 \leq -9$ $(-3, -1]$

6. $5 - 2y \leq 1$ and $3y + 2 \geq 14$ $[4, \infty)$

7. $m - 7 \leq -5$ or $m - 7 \geq -10$ $(-\infty, \infty)$

8. $3b - 2 < 7$ or $b - 2 > 4$ $(-\infty, 3) \cup (6, \infty)$

Concepts 1 and 2: Solving Absolute Value Inequalities

For Exercises 9–20, solve the equations and inequalities. For each inequality, graph the solution set and express the solution in interval notation. **(See Examples 1–6.)**

9. a. $|x| = 5$ {−5, 5}

b. $|x| > 5$ $(-\infty, -5) \cup (5, \infty)$

c. $|x| < 5$ $(-5, 5)$

10. a. $|a| = 4$ {4, −4}

b. $|a| > 4$ $(-\infty, -4) \cup (4, \infty)$

c. $|a| < 4$ $(-4, 4)$

11. a. $|x - 3| = 7$ {10, −4}

b. $|x - 3| > 7$ $(-\infty, -4) \cup (10, \infty)$

c. $|x - 3| < 7$ $(-4, 10)$

12. a. $|w + 2| = 6$ {4, −8}

b. $|w + 2| > 6$ $(-\infty, -8) \cup (4, \infty)$

c. $|w + 2| < 6$ $(-8, 4)$

13. a. $|p| = -2$ { }

b. $|p| > -2$ $(-\infty, \infty)$

c. $|p| < -2$ { }

14. a. $|x| = -14$ { }

b. $|x| > -14$ $(-\infty, \infty)$

c. $|x| < -14$ { }

15. a. $|y + 1| = -6$ { }

b. $|y + 1| > -6$ $(-\infty, \infty)$

c. $|y + 1| < -6$ { }

16. a. $|z - 4| = -3$ { }

b. $|z - 4| > -3$ $(-\infty, \infty)$

c. $|z - 4| < -3$ { }

17. a. $|x| = 0$ {0}

b. $|x| > 0$ $(-\infty, 0) \cup (0, \infty)$

c. $|x| < 0$ { }

18. a. $|p + 3| = 0$ {−3}

b. $|p + 3| > 0$ $(-\infty, -3) \cup (-3, \infty)$

c. $|p + 3| < 0$ { }

19. a. $|k - 7| = 0$ {7}

b. $|k - 7| > 0$ $(-\infty, 7) \cup (7, \infty)$

c. $|k - 7| < 0$ { }

20. a. $|2x + 4| + 3 = 2$ { }

b. $|2x + 4| + 3 > 2$ $(-\infty, \infty)$

c. $|2x + 4| + 3 < 2$ { }

For Exercises 21–50, solve the absolute value inequalities. Graph the solution set and write the solution in interval notation. **(See Examples 1–6.)**

21. $|x| > 6$ $(-\infty, -6) \cup (6, \infty)$

22. $|x| \le 6$ $[-6, 6]$

23. $|t| \le 3$ $[-3, 3]$

24. $|p| > 3$ $(-\infty, 3) \cup (3, \infty)$

25. $|y + 2| \ge 0$ $(-\infty, \infty)$

26. $0 \le |7n + 2|$ $(-\infty, \infty)$

27. $5 \le |2x - 1|$ $(-\infty, -2] \cup [3, \infty)$

28. $|x - 2| \ge 7$ $(-\infty, -5] \cup [9, \infty)$

29. $|k - 7| < -3$ { }

30. $|h + 2| < -9$ { }

31. $\left|\dfrac{w - 2}{3}\right| - 3 \le 1$ $[-10, 14]$

32. $\left|\dfrac{x + 3}{2}\right| - 2 \ge 4$ $(-\infty, -15] \cup [9, \infty)$

33. $12 \le |9 - 4y| - 2$ $\left(-\infty, -\dfrac{5}{4}\right] \cup \left[\dfrac{23}{4}, \infty\right)$

34. $5 > |2m - 7| + 4$ $(3, 4)$

35. $4 > -1 + \left|\dfrac{2x + 1}{4}\right|$ $\left(-\dfrac{21}{2}, \dfrac{19}{2}\right)$

36. $9 \ge 2 + \left|\dfrac{x - 4}{5}\right|$ $[-31, 39]$

37. $8 < |4 - 3x| + 12$ $(-\infty, \infty)$

38. $-16 < |5x - 1| - 1$ $(-\infty, \infty)$

39. $5 - |2m + 1| > 5$　{ }

40. $3 - |5x + 3| > 3$　{ }

41. $|p + 5| \leq 0$　{−5}

　　　−5

42. $|y + 1| - 4 \leq -4$　{−1}

43. $|z - 6| + 5 > 5$　$(-\infty, 6) \cup (6, \infty)$

44. $|2c - 1| - 4 > -4$　$\left(-\infty, \frac{1}{2}\right) \cup \left(\frac{1}{2}, \infty\right)$

　　　　　　　　−1　　　　　　　　　　　　　　　　　　　　6　　　　　　　　　　　　　　　　　$\frac{1}{2}$

45. $5|2y - 6| + 3 \geq 13$　$(-\infty, 2] \cup [4, \infty)$

46. $7|y + 1| - 3 \geq 11$　$(-\infty, -3] \cup [1, \infty)$

47. $-3|6 - t| + 1 > -5$　$(4, 8)$

　　　　　2　　　4　　　　　　　　　　　　　　−3　　　1　　　　　　　　　　　　　　4　　　8

48. $-4|8 - x| + 2 > -14$　$(4, 12)$

49. $|0.02x + 0.06| - 0.1 < 0.05$

　　　　$(-10.5, 4.5)$

50. $|0.05x - 0.04| - 0.01 < 0.11$

　　　　$(-1.6, 3.2)$

　　　　4　　12　　　　　　　　　　　　　　　−10.5　　4.5　　　　　　　　　　　−1.6　　3.2

↔ Concept 3: Translating to an Absolute Value Expression

For Exercises 51–54, write an absolute value inequality equivalent to the expression given. **(See Example 7.)**

51. All real numbers whose distance from 0 is greater than 7　$|x| > 7$

52. All real numbers whose distance from −3 is less than 4
$|x + 3| < 4$

53. All real numbers whose distance from 2 is at most 13　$|x - 2| \leq 13$

54. All real numbers whose distance from 0 is at least 6
$|x| \geq 6$

55. A 32-oz jug of orange juice may not contain exactly 32 oz of juice. The possibility of measurement error exists when the jug is filled in the factory. If the maximum measurement error is ±0.05 oz, write an absolute value inequality representing the range of volumes, x, in which the orange juice jug may be filled. **(See Example 8.)**　$|x - 32| \leq 0.05$

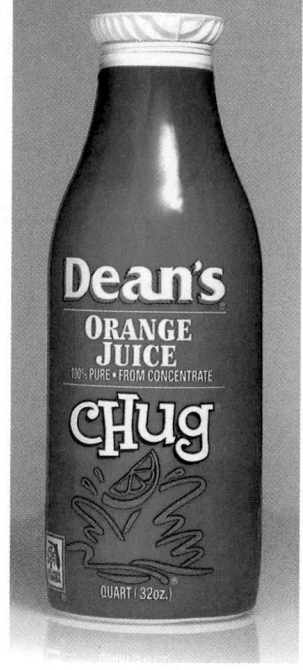

56. The length of a board is measured to be 32.3 in. The maximum measurement error is ±0.2 in. Write an absolute value inequality that represents the range for the length of the board, x.　$|x - 32.3| \leq 0.2$

57. A bag of potato chips states that its weight is $6\frac{3}{4}$ oz. The maximum measurement error is $\pm\frac{1}{8}$ oz. Write an absolute value inequality that represents the range for the weight, x, of the bag of chips.　$\left|x - 6\frac{3}{4}\right| \leq \frac{1}{8}$

58. A $\frac{7}{8}$-in. bolt varies in length by at most $\pm\frac{1}{16}$ in. Write an absolute value inequality that represents the range for the length, x, of the bolt.　$\left|x - \frac{7}{8}\right| \leq \frac{1}{16}$

59. The width, w, of a bolt is supposed to be 2 cm but may have a 0.01-cm margin of error. Solve $|w - 2| \leq 0.01$, and interpret the solution to the inequality in the context of this problem.
$1.99 \leq w \leq 2.01$ or, equivalently in interval notation, [1.99, 2.01]. This means that the actual width of the bolt could be between 1.99 cm and 2.01 cm inclusive.

60. In the 2008 election, Barak Obama was projected to receive 70% of the votes with a margin of error of 3%. Solve $|p - 0.70| \leq 0.03$, and interpret the solution to the inequality in the context of this problem.
$0.67 \leq p \leq 0.73$ or, equivalently in interval notation, [0.67, 0.73]. This means that the percentage of votes received by Obama was projected to be between 67% and 73% inclusive.

Expanding Your Skills

For Exercises 61–64, match the graph with the inequality.

61.

　　　　−3　　　　　　5　　　b

62.

　　　　　　　　　　4　　6　　d

63.

　　　　−2　　　　　6　　a

64.

　　　　　　　1　　　5　　c

a. $|x - 2| < 4$　　**b.** $|x - 1| > 4$　　**c.** $|x - 3| < 2$　　**d.** $|x - 5| > 1$

Graphing Calculator Exercises

To solve an absolute value inequality by using a graphing calculator, let Y_1 equal the left side of the inequality and let Y_2 equal the right side of the inequality. Graph both Y_1 and Y_2 on a standard viewing window and use an *Intersect* feature to approximate the intersection of the graphs. To solve $Y_1 > Y_2$, determine all x-values where the graph of Y_1 is above the graph of Y_2. To solve $Y_1 < Y_2$, determine all x-values where the graph of Y_1 is below the graph of Y_2.

For Exercises 65–74, solve the inequalities using a graphing calculator.

65. $|x + 2| > 4$ $(-\infty, -6) \cup (2, \infty)$

66. $|3 - x| > 6$ $(-\infty, -3) \cup (9, \infty)$

67. $\left|\dfrac{x + 1}{3}\right| < 2$ $(-7, 5)$

68. $\left|\dfrac{x - 1}{4}\right| < 1$ $(-3, 5)$

69. $|x - 5| < -3$ $\{\}$

70. $|x + 2| < -2$ $\{\}$

71. $|2x + 5| > -4$ $(-\infty, \infty)$

72. $|1 - 2x| > -4$ $(-\infty, \infty)$

73. $|6x + 1| \le 0$ $\left\{-\dfrac{1}{6}\right\}$

74. $|3x - 4| \le 0$ $\left\{\dfrac{4}{3}\right\}$

Problem Recognition Exercises

Equations and Inequalities

For Exercises 1–24, identify the category for each equation or inequality (choose from the list here). Then solve the equation or inequality. Express the solution in interval notation where appropriate.

- Linear
- Quadratic
- Polynomial (degree greater than 2)
- Rational
- Absolute value

1. $z^2 + 10z + 9 > 0$
Quadratic;
$(-\infty, -9) \cup (-1, \infty)$

2. $5a - 2 = 6(a + 4)$ Linear; $\{-26\}$

3. $\dfrac{x - 4}{2x + 4} \ge 1$
Rational; $[-8, -2)$

4. $4x^2 - 7x = 2$
Quadratic; $\{-\frac{1}{4}, 2\}$

5. $|3x - 1| + 4 < 6$
Absolute value; $(-\frac{1}{3}, 1)$

6. $2t^2 - t + 1 < 0$
Quadratic; $\{\}$

7. $\dfrac{1}{2}p - \dfrac{2}{3} < \dfrac{1}{6}p - 4$
Linear; $(-\infty, -10)$

8. $p^2 + 3p \le 4$
Quadratic; $[-4, 1]$

9. $3y^2 + y - 2 \ge 0$
Quadratic;
$(-\infty, -1] \cup [\frac{2}{3}, \infty)$

10. $\dfrac{x + 6}{x + 4} = 7$
Rational; $\{-\frac{11}{3}\}$

11. $3(2x - 4) \ge 1 - (x - 3)$
Linear; $\left[\dfrac{16}{7}, \infty\right)$

12. $|6x + 5| + 3 = 2$
Absolute value; $\{\}$

13. $(x - 3)(2x + 1)(x + 5) \ge 0$
Polynomial; $[-5, -\frac{1}{2}] \cup [3, \infty)$

14. $-x^2 - x - 3 \le 0$
Quadratic; $(-\infty, \infty)$

15. $\dfrac{-6}{y - 2} < 2$
Rational; $(-\infty, -1) \cup (2, \infty)$

16. $x^2 - 5 = 4x$
Quadratic; $\{-1, 5\}$

17. $\left|\dfrac{x}{4} + 2\right| + 6 > 6$
Absolute value; $(-\infty, -8) \cup (-8, \infty)$

18. $x^2 - 36 < 0$
Quadratic; $(-6, 6)$

19. $3y^3 + 5y^2 - 12y - 20 = 0$
Polynomial; $\{2, -2, -\frac{5}{3}\}$

20. $|8 - 2x| = 16$
Absolute value; $\{12, -4\}$

21. $5b - 10 - 3b = 3(b - 2) - 4$
Linear; $\{0\}$

22. $\dfrac{x}{x - 5} \ge 0$
Rational; $(-\infty, 0] \cup (5, \infty)$

23. $|6x + 1| = |5 + 6x|$
Absolute value; $\{-\frac{1}{3}\}$

24. $4x(x - 5)^2(2x + 3) < 0$
Polynomial; $(-\frac{3}{2}, 0)$

 Writing   Translating Expression   Geometry   Scientific Calculator   Video   NS E

Section 9.5 **Linear and Compound Inequalities in Two Variables**

Concepts

1. Graphing Linear Inequalities in Two Variables
2. Compound Linear Inequalities in Two Variables
3. Graphing a Feasible Region

1. Graphing Linear Inequalities in Two Variables

A **linear inequality in two variables** x and y is an inequality that can be written in one of the following forms: $ax + by < c$, $ax + by > c$, $ax + by \leq c$, or $ax + by \geq c$, provided a and b are not both zero.

A solution to a linear inequality in two variables is an ordered pair that makes the inequality true. For example, solutions to the inequality $x + y < 6$ are ordered pairs (x, y) such that the sum of the x- and y-coordinates is less than 6. This inequality has an infinite number of solutions, and therefore it is convenient to express the solution set as a graph.

To graph a linear inequality in two variables, we will follow these steps.

> **PROCEDURE** Graphing a Linear Inequality in Two Variables
>
> **Step 1** Solve for y, if possible.
> **Step 2** Graph the related equation. Draw a dashed line if the inequality is strict, $<$ or $>$. Otherwise, draw a solid line.
> **Step 3** Shade above or below the line as follows:
> - Shade *above* the line if the inequality is of the form $y > ax + b$ or $y \geq ax + b$.
> - Shade *below* the line if the inequality is of the form $y < ax + b$ or $y \leq ax + b$.
>
> *Note:* A dashed line indicates that the line is *not* included in the solution set. A solid line implies that the line *is* included in the solutions set.

This process is demonstrated in Example 1.

Classroom Example: p. 672, Exercise 18

Instructor Note: Introduce this concept by asking students to determine if a given ordered pair is a solution to the inequality. For example, ask students to test $(3, 1)$, $(-1, 4)$, and $(-4, -1)$ in Example 1.

Answer

1.

Example 1 Graphing a Linear Inequality in Two Variables

Graph the solution set. $\qquad -3x + y \leq 1$

Solution:

$$-3x + y \leq 1$$

$$y \leq 3x + 1 \qquad\qquad \text{Solve for } y.$$

Next graph the line defined by the related equation $y = 3x + 1$.

Because the inequality is of the form $y \leq ax + b$, the solution to the inequality is the region *below* the line $y = 3x + 1$. See Figure 9-6.

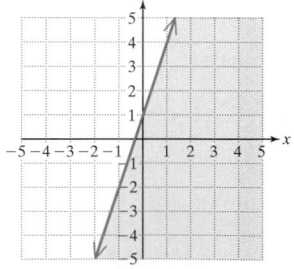

Figure 9-6

Skill Practice Graph the solution set.

1. $2x + y \geq -4$

After graphing the solution to a linear inequality, we can verify that we have shaded the correct side of the line by using test points. In Example 1, we can pick an arbitrary ordered pair within the shaded region. Then substitute the x- and y-coordinates in the original inequality. If the result is a true statement, then that ordered pair is a solution to the inequality and suggests that other points from the same region are also solutions.

For example, the point $(0, 0)$ lies within the shaded region (Figure 9-7).

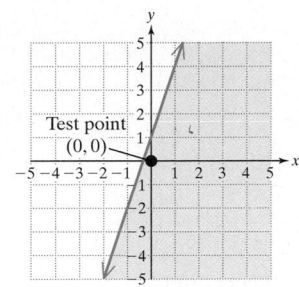

Figure 9-7

$$-3x + y \leq 1 \qquad \text{Substitute } (0, 0) \text{ in the original inequality.}$$
$$-3(0) + (0) \overset{?}{\leq} 1$$
$$0 + 0 \overset{?}{\leq} 1 \quad \checkmark \text{ True} \qquad \text{The point } (0, 0) \text{ from the shaded region is a solution.}$$

In Example 2, we will graph the solution set to a strict inequality. A strict inequality uses the symbol $<$ or $>$. In such a case, the boundary line will be drawn as a dashed line. This indicates that the boundary itself is *not* part of the solution set.

Example 2   Graphing a Linear Inequality in Two Variables

Classroom Example: p. 672, Exercise 24

Graph the solution set. $-4y < 5x$

Solution:

$$-4y < 5x$$

$$\frac{-4y}{-4} > \frac{5x}{-4} \qquad \text{Solve for } y. \text{ Recall that when we divide both sides by a negative number, reverse the inequality sign.}$$

$$y > -\frac{5}{4}x$$

Instructor Note: Consider drawing an analogy between shading the number line when expressing the solution to a single variable inequality. With an inequality in two variables, we shade part of a plane.

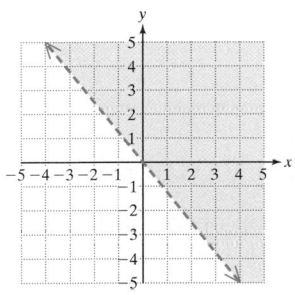

Figure 9-8

Graph the line defined by the related equation, $y = -\frac{5}{4}x$. The boundary line is drawn as a dashed line because the inequality is strict. Also note that the line passes through the origin.

Because the inequality is of the form $y > ax + b$, the solution to the inequality is the region *above* the line. See Figure 9-8.

Skill Practice Graph the solution set.

2. $-3y < x$

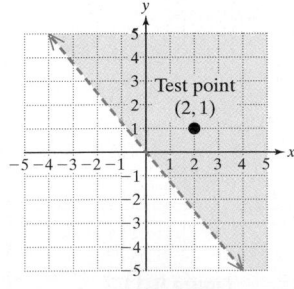

Figure 9-9

In Example 2, we cannot use the origin as a test point, because the point $(0, 0)$ is on the boundary line. Be sure to select a test point strictly within the shaded region. In this case, we choose $(2, 1)$. See Figure 9-9.

Answer

2.

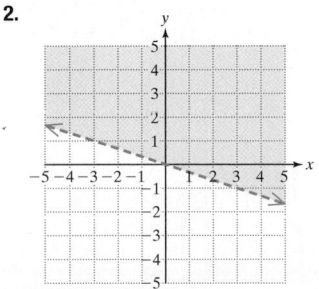

$$-4y < 5x$$

$$-4(1) \overset{?}{<} 5(2) \qquad \text{Substitute } (2, 1) \text{ in the original inequality.}$$

$$-4 \overset{?}{<} 10 \ \checkmark \ \text{True} \qquad \text{The point } (2, 1) \text{ from the shaded region is a solution to the original inequality.}$$

In Example 3, we encounter a situation in which we cannot solve for the y-variable.

Classroom Example: p. 672, Exercise 28

Example 3   Graphing a Linear Inequality in Two Variables

Graph the solution set. $4x \geq -12$

Solution:

$$4x \geq -12$$

$$x \geq -3$$

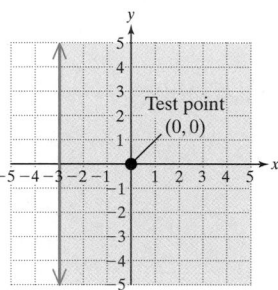

Figure 9-10

In this inequality, there is no y-variable. However, we can simplify the inequality by solving for x.

Graph the related equation $x = -3$. This is a vertical line. The boundary is drawn as a solid line, because the inequality is not strict, $\geq$.

To shade the appropriate region, refer to the inequality, $x \geq -3$. The points for which x is greater than -3 are to the right of $x = -3$. Therefore, shade the region to the *right* of the line (Figure 9-10).

Selecting a test point such as $(0, 0)$ from the shaded region indicates that we have shaded the correct side of the line.

$$4x \geq -12 \qquad \text{Substitute } x = 0.$$

$$4(0) \overset{?}{\geq} -12 \ \checkmark \qquad \text{True}$$

Skill Practice Graph the solution set.

3. $-2x \geq 2$

---

2. Compound Linear Inequalities in Two Variables

Some applications require us to find the union or intersection of the solutions of two or more linear inequalities.

Classroom Example: p. 674, Exercise 46

Example 4   Graphing a Compound Linear Inequality

Graph the solution set of the compound inequality.

$$y > \tfrac{1}{2}x + 1 \quad \text{and} \quad x + y < 1$$

Answer

3.

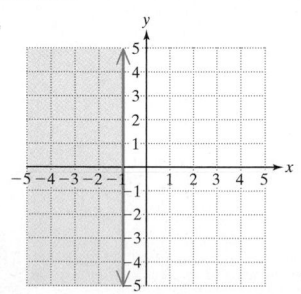

Solution:

Solve each inequality for y.

First inequality

$$y > \tfrac{1}{2}x + 1$$

The inequality is of the form $y > ax + b$. Shade *above* the boundary line. See Figure 9-11.

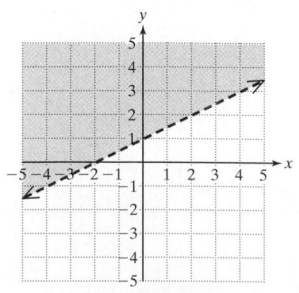

Figure 9-11

Second inequality

$x + y < 1$

$\quad y < -x + 1$

The inequality is of the form $y < ax + b$. Shade *below* the boundary line. See Figure 9-12.

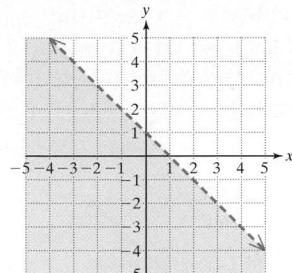

Figure 9-12

The region bounded by the inequalities is the region above the line $y = \frac{1}{2}x + 1$ and below the line $y = -x + 1$. This is the intersection or "overlap" of the two regions (shown in purple in Figure 9-13).

The intersection is the solution set to the system of inequalities. See Figure 9-14.

Figure 9-13

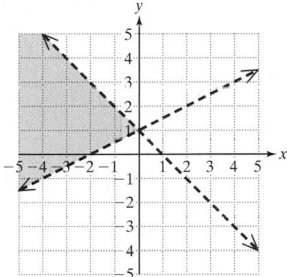

Figure 9-14

Skill Practice Graph the solution set.

4. $x - 3y > 3$ and $y < -2x + 4$

Example 5 demonstrates the union of the solution sets of two linear inequalities.

Example 5 Graphing a Compound Linear Inequality

Classroom Example: p. 674, Exercise 44

Graph the solution set of the compound incquality.

$$3y \leq 6 \quad \text{or} \quad y - x \leq 0$$

Solution:

First inequality	Second inequality
$3y \leq 6$	$y - x \leq 0$
$y \leq 2$	$y \leq x$

The graph of $y \leq 2$ is the region on and below the horizontal line $y = 2$. See Figure 9-15.

Figure 9-15

Answer

4.

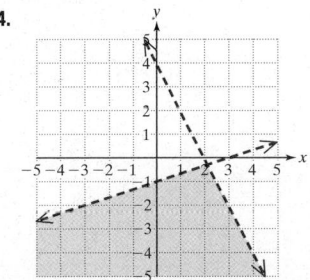

The inequality $y \leq x$ is of the form $y \leq ax + b$. Graph a solid line and the region below the line. See Figure 9-16.

The solution to the compound inequality $3y \leq 6$ or $y - x \leq 0$ is the union of these regions. See Figure 9-17.

Figure 9-16

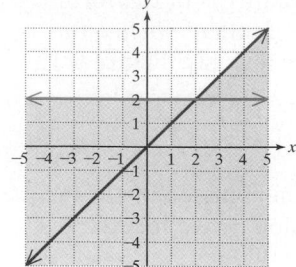

Figure 9-17

Skill Practice Graph the solution set.

5. $2y \leq 4$ or $y \leq x + 1$

Classroom Example: p. 674, Exercise 50

Example 6 **Graphing Compound Linear Inequalities**

Describe the region of the plane defined by the system of inequalities.

$$x \leq 0 \quad \text{and} \quad y \geq 0$$

Solution:

$x \leq 0$ $x \leq 0$ on the y-axis and in the second and third quadrants.

$y \geq 0$ $y \geq 0$ on the x-axis and in the first and second quadrants.

The intersection of these regions is the set of points in the second quadrant (with the boundary included).

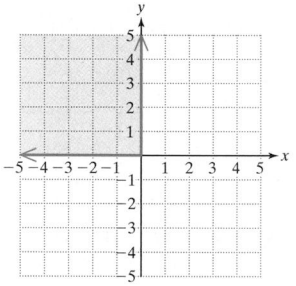

Skill Practice Graph the region defined by the system of inequalities.

6. $x \leq 0$ and $y \leq 0$

Answers

5.

6.

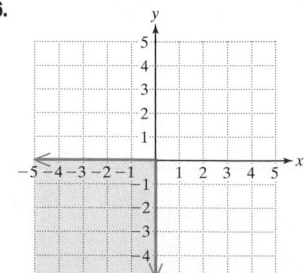

3. Graphing a Feasible Region

When two variables are related under certain constraints, a system of linear inequalities can be used to show a region of feasible values for the variables.

The feasible region represents the ordered pairs that are true for each inequality in the system.

Classroom Example: p. 676, Exercise 62

Example 7	Graphing a Feasible Region

Susan has two tests on Friday: one in chemistry and one in psychology. Because the two classes meet in consecutive hours, she has no study time between tests. Susan estimates that she has a maximum of 12 hr of study time before the tests, and she must divide her time between chemistry and psychology.

Let x represent the number of hours Susan spends studying chemistry.

Let y represent the number of hours Susan spends studying psychology.

a. Find a set of inequalities to describe the constraints on Susan's study time.

b. Graph the constraints to find the feasible region defining Susan's study time.

Solution:

a. Because Susan cannot study chemistry or psychology for a negative period of time, we have $x \geq 0$ and $y \geq 0$. Furthermore, her total time studying cannot exceed 12 hr. $x + y \leq 12$.

A system of inequalities that defines the constraints on Susan's study time is:

$$x \geq 0$$

$$y \geq 0$$

$$x + y \leq 12$$

b. The first two conditions $x \geq 0$ and $y \geq 0$ represent the set of points in the first quadrant. The third condition $x + y \leq 12$ represents the set of points below and including the line $x + y = 12$ (Figure 9-18).

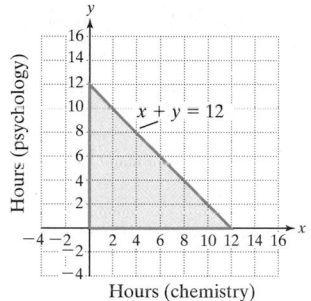

Figure 9-18

Discussion:

1. Refer to the feasible region drawn in Example 7(b). Is the ordered pair $(8, 5)$ part of the feasible region?

No. The ordered pair $(8, 5)$ indicates that Susan spent 8 hr studying chemistry and 5 hr studying psychology. This is a total of 13 hr, which exceeds the constraint that Susan only had 12 hr to study. The point $(8, 5)$ lies outside the feasible region, above the line $x + y = 12$ (Figure 9-19).

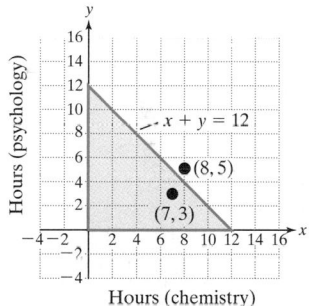

Figure 9-19

2. Is the ordered pair $(7, 3)$ part of the feasible region?

Yes. The ordered pair $(7, 3)$ indicates that Susan spent 7 hr studying chemistry and 3 hr studying psychology.

This point lies within the feasible region and satisfies all three constraints.

$$x \geq 0 \longrightarrow \qquad 7 \geq 0 \qquad \text{True}$$

$$y \geq 0 \longrightarrow \qquad 3 \geq 0 \qquad \text{True}$$

$$x + y \leq 12 \longrightarrow (7) + (3) \leq 12 \qquad \text{True}$$

Notice that the ordered pair $(7, 3)$ corresponds to a point where Susan is not making full use of the 12 hr of study time.

3. Suppose there was one additional constraint imposed on Susan's study time. She knows she needs to spend at least twice as much time studying chemistry as she does studying psychology. Graph the feasible region with this additional constraint.

Figure 9-20

Because the time studying chemistry must be at least twice the time studying psychology, we have $x \geq 2y$.

This inequality may also be written as $y \leq \frac{1}{2}x$.

Figure 9-20 shows the first quadrant with the constraint $y \leq \frac{1}{2}x$.

4. At what point in the feasible region is Susan making the most efficient use of her time for both classes?

First and foremost, Susan must make use of *all* 12 hr. This occurs for points along the line $x + y = 12$. Susan will also want to study for both classes with approximately twice as much time devoted to chemistry. Therefore, Susan will be deriving the maximum benefit at the point of intersection of the line

$x + y = 12$ and the line $y = \frac{1}{2}x$.

Using the substitution method, replace $y = \frac{1}{2}x$ into the equation $x + y = 12$.

$x + \frac{1}{2}x = 12$

$2x + x = 24$ Clear fractions.

$3x = 24$

$x = 8$ Solve for x.

$y = \dfrac{(8)}{2}$ To solve for y, substitute $x = 8$ into the equation $y = \frac{1}{2}x$.

$y = 4$

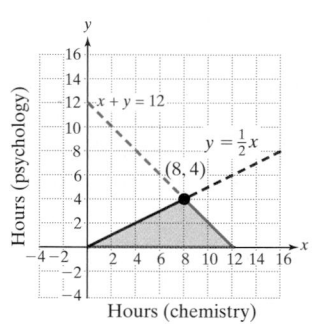

Therefore, Susan should spend 8 hr studying chemistry and 4 hr studying psychology.

Skill Practice

7. A local pet rescue group has a total of 30 cages that can be used to hold cats and dogs. Let x represent the number of cages used for cats, and let y represent the number used for dogs.

   a. Write a set of inequalities to express the fact that the number of cat and dog cages cannot be negative.

   b. Write an inequality to describe the constraint on the total number of cages for cats and dogs.

   c. Graph the system of inequalities to find the feasible region describing the available cages.

Answer

7a. $x \geq 0$ and $y \geq 0$

  b. $x + y \leq 30$

  c.

Section 9.5   Practice Exercises

Study Skills Exercise

1. Define the key term **linear inequality in two variables**.

Review Exercises

For Exercises 2–5, solve the inequalities.

2. $5 < x + 1$ and $-2x + 6 \geq -6$ $(4, 6]$

3. $5 - x \leq 4$ and $6 > 3x - 3$ $[1, 3)$

4. $4 - y < 3y + 12$ or $-2(y + 3) \geq 12$
$(-\infty, -9] \cup (-2, \infty)$

5. $-2x < 4$ or $3x - 1 \leq -13$
$(-\infty, -4] \cup (-2, \infty)$

Concept 1:   Graphing Linear Inequalities in Two Variables

For Exercises 6–9, determine if the given point is a solution to the inequality.

6. $2x - y > 8$

    a. $(3, -5)$ Yes

    b. $(-1, -10)$ No

    c. $(4, -2)$ Yes

    d. $(0, 0)$ No

7. $3y + x < 5$

    a. $(-1, 7)$ No

    b. $(5, 0)$ No

    c. $(0, 0)$ Yes

    d. $(2, -3)$ Yes

8. $y \leq -2$

    a. $(5, -3)$ Yes

    b. $(-4, -2)$ Yes

    c. $(0, 0)$ No

    d. $(3, 2)$ No

9. $x \geq 5$

    a. $(4, 5)$ No

    b. $(5, -1)$ Yes

    c. $(8, 8)$ Yes

    d. $(0, 0)$ No

10. When should you use a dashed line to graph the solution to a linear inequality?
Use a dashed line when the inequality is strict ($<$ or $>$).

For Exercises 11–16, decide which inequality symbol should be used ($<, >, \geq, \leq$) by looking at the graph.

11.

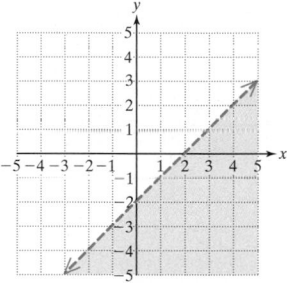

$x - y \underline{\;>\;} 2$

12.

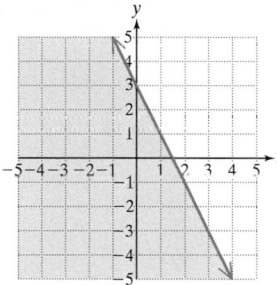

$y \underline{\;\leq\;} -2x + 3$

13.

$y \underline{\;\geq\;} -4$

14.

$x \underline{\;<\;} 3$

15.

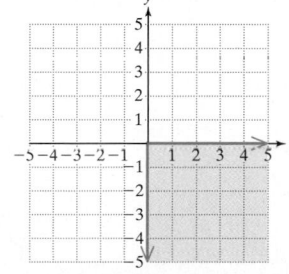

$x \underline{\;\geq\;} 0$ and $y \underline{\;\leq\;} 0$

16.

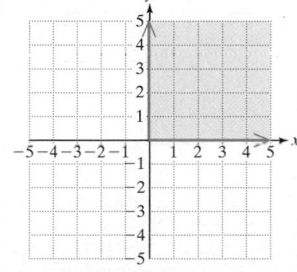

$x \underline{\;\geq\;} 0$ and $y \underline{\;\geq\;} 0$

Writing   ⟷ Translating Expression   ◁ Geometry   ▦ Scientific Calculator   ◉ Video   NS&E

For Exercises 17–40, graph the solution set. **(See Examples 1–3.)**

17. $x - 2y > 4$

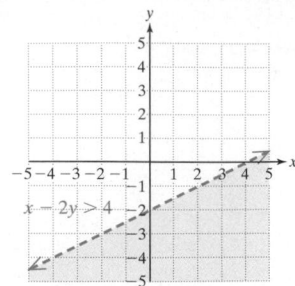

18. $x - 3y \geq 6$

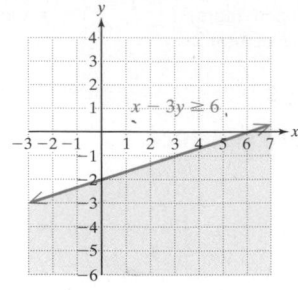

19. $5x - 2y < 10$

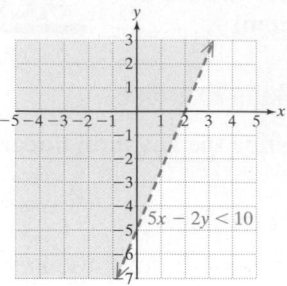

20. $x - 3y < 8$

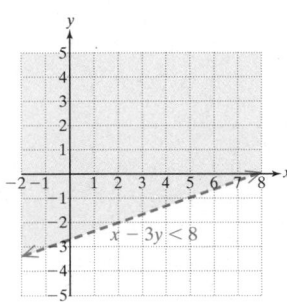

21. $2x \leq -6y + 12$

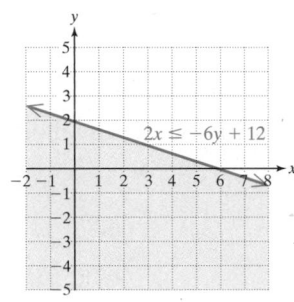

22. $4x < 3y + 12$

23. $2y \leq 4x$

24. $-6x < 2y$

25. $y \geq -2$

26. $y \geq 5$

27. $4x < 5$

28. $x + 6 < 7$

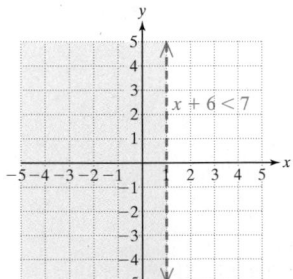

29. $y \geq \dfrac{2}{5}x - 4$

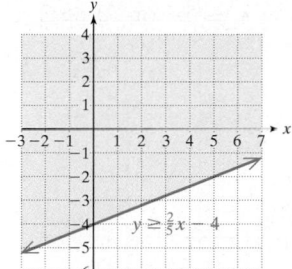

30. $y \geq -\dfrac{5}{2}x - 4$

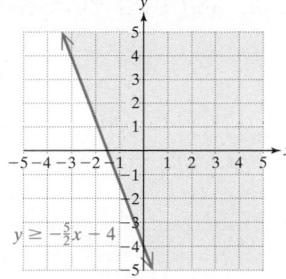

31. $y \leq \dfrac{1}{3}x + 6$

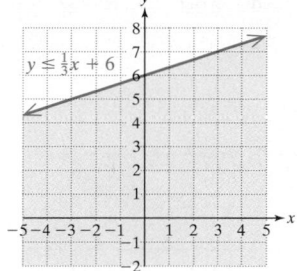

32. $y \leq -\dfrac{1}{4}x + 2$

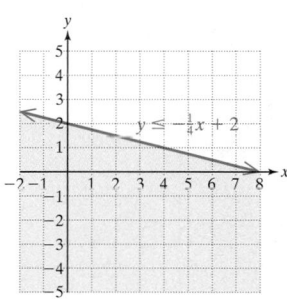

33. $y - 5x > 0$

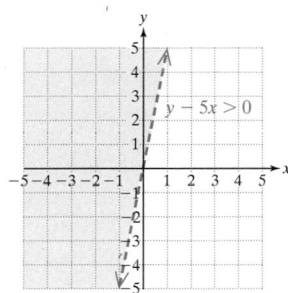

34. $y - \dfrac{1}{2}x > 0$

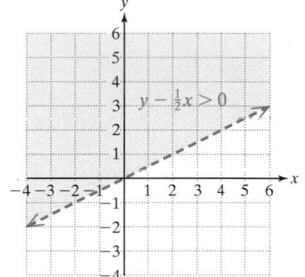

35. $\dfrac{x}{5} + \dfrac{y}{4} < 1$

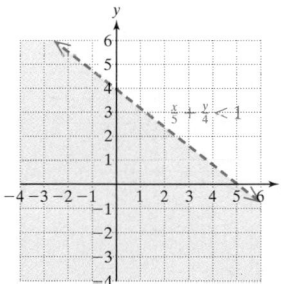

36. $x + \dfrac{y}{2} \geq 2$

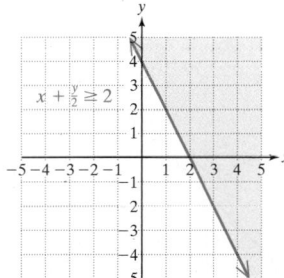

37. $0.1x + 0.2y \leq 0.6$

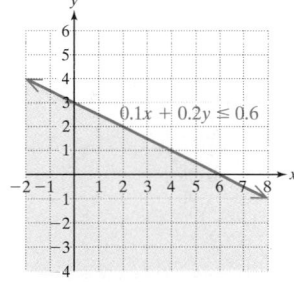

38. $0.3x - 0.2y < 0.6$

39. $x \leq -\dfrac{2}{3}y$

40. $x \geq -\dfrac{5}{4}y$

 Writing   ⟵⟶ Translating Expression   Geometry   Scientific Calculator   Video   NS&E

Concept 2: Compound Linear Inequalities in Two Variables

For Exercises 41–55, graph the solution set of each compound inequality. **(See Examples 4–6.)**

41. $y < 4$ and $y > -x + 2$

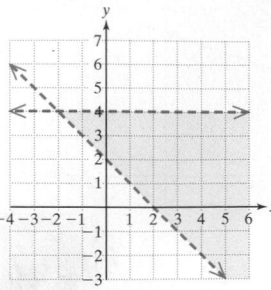

42. $y < 3$ and $x + 2y < 6$

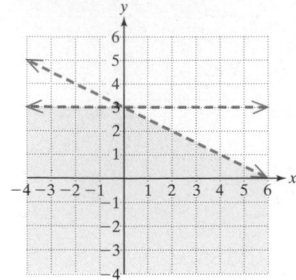

43. $2x + y \leq 5$ or $x \geq 3$

44. $x + 3y \geq 3$ or $x \leq -2$

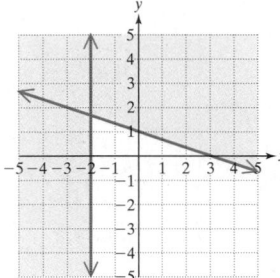

45. $x + y < 3$ and $4x + y < 6$

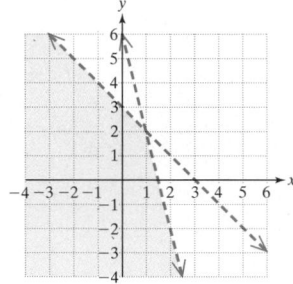

46. $x + y < 4$ and $3x + y < 9$

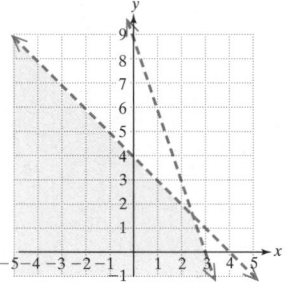

47. $2x - y \leq 2$ or $2x + 3y \geq 6$

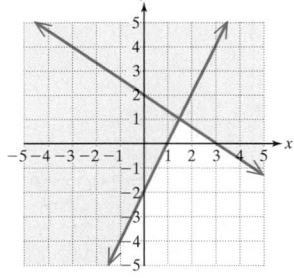

48. $3x + 2y \geq 4$ or $x - y \leq 3$

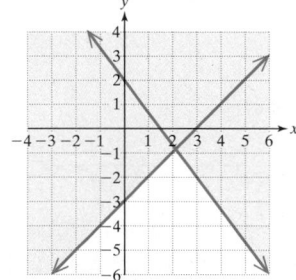

49. $x > 4$ and $y < 2$

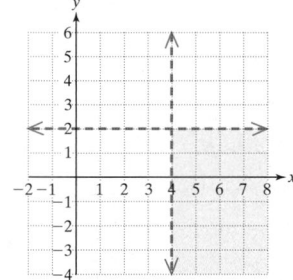

50. $x < 3$ and $y > 4$

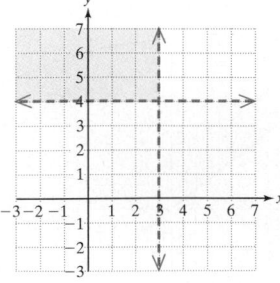

51. $x \leq -2$ or $y \leq 0$

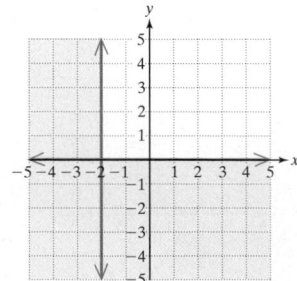

52. $x \geq 0$ or $y \geq -3$

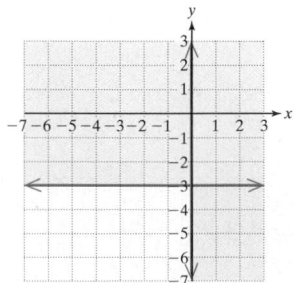

53. $x > 0$ and $x + y < 6$ **54.** $x < 0$ and $x + y < 2$ **55.** $y \leq 0$ or $x - y \leq -4$

  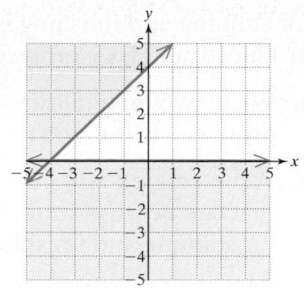

Concept 3: Graphing a Feasible Region

For Exercises 56–59, graph the feasible regions.

56. $x + y \leq 3$ and

$x \geq 0, y \geq 0$

57. $x - y \leq 2$ and

$x \geq 0, y \geq 0$

58. $x \geq 0, y \geq 0$

$x + y \leq 8$ and

$3x + 5y \leq 30$

59. $x \geq 0, y \geq 0$

$x + y \leq 5$ and

$x + 2y \leq 6$

   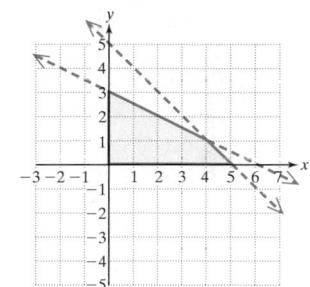

60. Suppose Sue has 50 ft of fencing with which she can build a rectangular dog run. Let x represent the length of the dog run and let y represent the width.

   a. Write an inequality representing the fact that the total perimeter of the dog run is at most 50 ft. $2x + 2y \leq 50$

   b. Sketch part of the solution set for this inequality that represents all possible values for the length and width of the dog run. (*Hint:* Note that both the length and the width must be positive.)

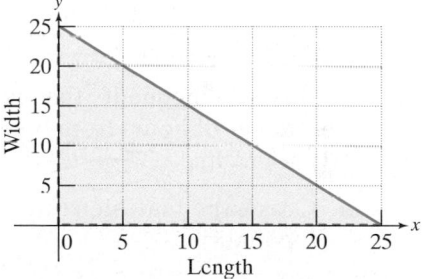

61. Suppose Rick has 40 ft of fencing with which he can build a rectangular garden. Let x represent the length of the garden and let y represent the width.

   a. Write an inequality representing the fact that the total perimeter of the garden is at most 40 ft. $2x + 2y \leq 40$

   b. Sketch part of the solution set for this inequality that represents all possible values for the length and width of the garden. (*Hint:* Note that both the length and the width must be positive.)

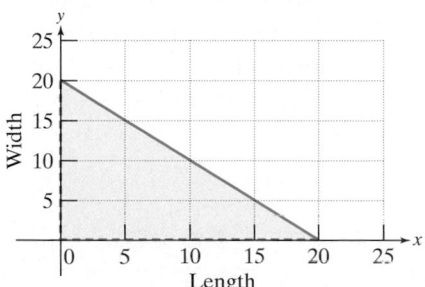

Writing   Translating Expression   Geometry   Scientific Calculator   Video   NS&E

62. A manufacturer produces two models of desks. Model A requires 4 hr to stain and finish and 3 hr to assemble. Model B requires 3 hr to stain and finish and 1 hr to assemble. The total amount of time available for staining and finishing is 24 hr and for assembling is 12 hr. Let x represent the number of Model A desks produced, and let y represent the number of Model B desks produced.

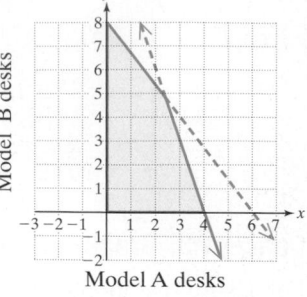

a. Write two inequalities that express the fact that the number of desks to be produced cannot be negative. $x \geq 0, y \geq 0$

b. Write an inequality in terms of the number of Model A and Model B desks that can be produced if the total time
for staining and finishing is at most 24 hr. $4x + 3y \leq 24$

c. Write an inequality in terms of the number of Model A and Model B desks that can be produced if the total time for assembly is no more than 12 hr.
$3x + y \leq 12$

d. Graph the feasible region formed by graphing the preceding inequalities.

e. Is the point $(3, 1)$ in the feasible region? What does the point $(3, 1)$ represent in the context of this problem?   Yes; The point $(3, 1)$ represents 3 Model A desks and 1 Model B desk produced.

f. Is the point $(5, 4)$ in the feasible region? What does the point $(5, 4)$ represent in the context of this problem?   No; The point $(5, 4)$ represents 5 Model A desks and 4 Model B desks produced. Producing this combination of desks would exceed the number of available hours for staining and finishing and for assembly.

63. In scheduling two drivers for delivering pizza, James needs to have at least 65 hr scheduled this week. His two drivers, Karen and Todd, are not allowed to get overtime, so each one can work at most 40 hr. Let x represent the number of hours that Karen can be scheduled, and let y represent the number of hours Todd can be scheduled. **(See Example 7.)**

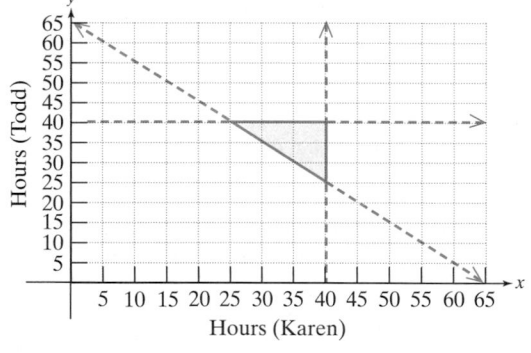

a. Write two inequalities that express the fact that Karen and Todd cannot work a negative number of hours.
$x \geq 0, y \geq 0$

b. Write two inequalities that express the fact that neither Karen nor Todd is allowed overtime (i.e., each driver can have at most 40 hr). $x \leq 40, y \leq 40$

c. Write an inequality that expresses the fact that the total number of hours from both Karen and Todd needs to be at least 65 hr. $x + y \geq 65$

d. Graph the feasible region formed by graphing the inequalities.

e. Is the point $(35, 40)$ in the feasible region? What does the point $(35, 40)$ represent in the context of this problem?   Yes; The point $(35, 40)$ means that Karen works 35 hr and Todd works 40 hr.

f. Is the point $(20, 40)$ in the feasible region? What does the point $(20, 40)$ represent in the context of this problem?   No; The point $(20, 40)$ means that Karen works 20 hr and Todd works 40 hr. This does not satisfy the constraint that there must be at least 65 hr total.

Group Activity

Recognizing Inequality Types

Estimated time: 20–25 minutes

Group Size: 3

For each exercise, solve the equation in part (a). Then determine how the solution sets differ for parts (b)–(e). Use interval notation to express your answers to the inequalities.

1. a. $2x - 3 = 15$ $\{9\}$

   b. $2x - 3 > 15$ $(9, \infty)$

   c. $2x - 3 < 15$ $(-\infty, 9)$

   d. $2x - 3 \leq 15$ $(-\infty, 9]$

   e. $2x - 3 \geq 15$ $[9, \infty)$

2. a. $|2x - 3| = 15$ $\{-6, 9\}$

   b. $|2x - 3| > 15$ $(-\infty, -6) \cup (9, \infty)$

   c. $|2x - 3| < 15$ $(-6, 9)$

   d. $|2x - 3| \leq 15$ $[-6, 9]$

   e. $|2x - 3| \geq 15$ $(-\infty, -6] \cup [9, \infty)$

3. a. $2x^2 - 3 = 15$ $\{-3, 3\}$

   b. $2x^2 - 3 > 15$ $(-\infty, -3) \cup (3, \infty)$

   c. $2x^2 - 3 < 15$ $(-3, 3)$

   d. $2x^2 - 3 \leq 15$ $[-3, 3]$

   e. $2x^2 - 3 \geq 15$ $(-\infty, -3] \cup [3, \infty)$

4. a. $\dfrac{3}{x - 6} = 3$ $\{7\}$

   b. $\dfrac{3}{x - 6} > 3$ $(6, 7)$

   c. $\dfrac{3}{x - 6} < 3$ $(-\infty, 6) \cup (7, \infty)$

   d. $\dfrac{3}{x - 6} \leq 3$ $(-\infty, 6) \cup [7, \infty)$

   e. $\dfrac{3}{x - 6} \geq 3$ $(6, 7]$

5. a. $x^2 + 12x + 36 = 0$ $\{-6\}$

   b. $x^2 + 12x + 36 > 0$
   $(-\infty, -6) \cup (-6, \infty)$

   c. $x^2 + 12x + 36 < 0$ $\{\ \}$

   d. $x^2 + 12x + 36 \leq 0$ $\{-6\}$

   e. $x^2 + 12x + 36 \geq 0$ (∞, ∞)

6. a. $|x - 3| = -6$ $\{\ \}$

   b. $|x - 3| > -6$ $(-\infty, \infty)$

   c. $|x - 3| < -6$ $\{\ \}$

   d. $|x - 3| \leq -6$ $\{\ \}$

   e. $|x - 3| \geq -6$ $(-\infty, \infty)$

Chapter 9   Summary

Key Concepts

$A \cup B$ is the **union** of A and B. This is the set of elements that belong to set A or set B or both sets A and B.

$A \cap B$ is the **intersection** of A and B. This is the set of elements common to both A and B.

- Solve two or more inequalities joined by *and* by finding the intersection of their solution sets.
- Solve two or more inequalities joined by *or* by finding the union of their solution sets.

Example 2

$$-7x + 3 \geq -11 \quad \text{and} \quad 1 - x < 4.5$$
$$-7x \geq -14 \quad \text{and} \quad -x < 3.5$$
$$x \leq 2 \quad \text{and} \quad x > -3.5$$

$x \leq 2$

$x > -3.5$

The solution is $\{x \mid -3.5 < x \leq 2\}$ or equivalently $(-3.5, 2]$.

Inequalities of the form $a < x < b$:

The inequality $a < x < b$ is represented by

 or, in interval notation, (a, b).

Examples

Example 1

Union   **Intersection**

            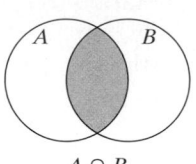

$A \cup B$ $A \cap B$

Example 3

$$5y + 1 \geq 6 \quad \text{or} \quad 2y - 5 \leq -11$$
$$5y \geq 5 \quad \text{or} \quad 2y \leq -6$$
$$y \geq 1 \quad \text{or} \quad y \leq -3$$

$y \geq 1$

$y \leq -3$

The solution is $\{y \mid y \geq 1 \text{ or } y \leq -3\}$ or equivalently $(-\infty, -3] \cup [1, \infty)$.

Example 4

Solve.

$$-13 \leq 3x - 1 < 5$$
$$-13 + 1 \leq 3x - 1 + 1 < 5 + 1$$
$$-12 \leq 3x < 6$$
$$\frac{-12}{3} \leq \frac{3x}{3} < \frac{6}{3}$$
$$-4 \leq x < 2$$

Interval notation: $[-4, 2)$

Section 9.2   Polynomial and Rational Inequalities

Key Concepts

The Test Point Method to Solve Polynomial and

Rational Inequalities

1. Find the boundary points of the inequality. (Boundary points are the real solutions to the related equation and points where the inequality is undefined.)
2. Plot the boundary points on the number line. This divides the number line into intervals.
3. Select a test point from each interval and substitute it into the original inequality.
   - If a test point makes the original inequality true, then that interval is part of the solution set.
4. Test the boundary points in the original inequality.
   - If the original inequality is strict ($<$ or $>$), do not include the boundary points in the solution set.
   - If the original inequality is defined using $\leq$ or $\geq$, then include the boundary points that are well defined within the inequality.

Note: Any boundary point that makes an expression within the inequality undefined must *always* be excluded from the solution set.

Example 1

$4x^2 - 7x - 2 < 0$

$(4x + 1)(x - 2) = 0$ Related equation

$4x + 1 = 0 \quad x - 2 = 0$

$x = -\dfrac{1}{4} \quad x = 2$ The boundaries are $-\dfrac{1}{4}$ and 2.

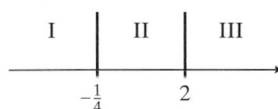

Interval I: Test $x = -1$: $4(-1)^2 - 7(-1) - 2 \overset{?}{<} 0$ False

Interval II: Test $x = 0$: $4(0)^2 - 7(0) - 2 \overset{?}{<} 0$ True

Interval III: Test $x = 3$: $4(3)^2 - 7(3) - 2 \overset{?}{<} 0$ False

The strict inequality excludes the boundary points as solutions.

False   True   False   The solution is $\left(-\dfrac{1}{4}, 2\right)$.

Examples

Example 2

$\dfrac{28}{2x - 3} \leq 4$ The inequality is undefined for $x = \dfrac{3}{2}$. Find other possible boundary points by solving the related equation.

$\dfrac{28}{2x - 3} = 4$ Related equation

$(2x - 3) \cdot \dfrac{28}{2x - 3} = (2x - 3) \cdot 4$

$28 = 8x - 12$

$40 = 8x$

$x = 5$

The boundaries are $x = \dfrac{3}{2}$ and $x = 5$.

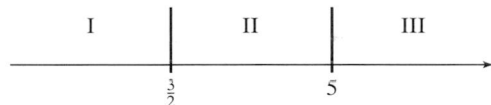

Interval I: Test $x = 1$: $\dfrac{28}{2(1) - 3} \overset{?}{\leq} 4$ True

Interval II: Test $x = 2$: $\dfrac{28}{2(2) - 3} \overset{?}{\leq} 4$ False

Interval III: Test $x = 6$: $\dfrac{28}{2(6) - 3} \overset{?}{\leq} 4$ True

The boundary point $x = \dfrac{3}{2}$ is not included because $\dfrac{28}{2x - 3}$ is undefined there. The boundary $x = 5$ does check in the original inequality.

The solution is $\left(-\infty, \dfrac{3}{2}\right) \cup [5, \infty)$.

Section 9.3   Absolute Value Equations

Key Concepts

The equation $|x| = a$ is an absolute value equation. For $a \geq 0$, the solution to the equation $|x| = a$ is $x = a$ or $x = -a$.

Steps to Solve an Absolute Value Equation

1. Isolate the absolute value to write the equation in the form $|x| = a$.
2. If $a < 0$, there is no solution.
3. Otherwise, rewrite the equation $|x| = a$ as $x = a$ or $x = -a$.
4. Solve the equations from step 3.
5. Check answers in the original equation.

The equation $|x| = |y|$ implies $x = y$ or $x = -y$.

Examples

Example 1

$$|2x - 3| + 5 = 10$$

$$|2x - 3| = 5 \qquad \text{Isolate the absolute value.}$$

$$2x - 3 = 5 \quad \text{or} \quad 2x - 3 = -5$$

$$2x = 8 \quad \text{or} \quad 2x = -2$$

$$x = 4 \quad \text{or} \quad x = -1$$

The solution set is $\{4, -1\}$.

Example 2

$$|x + 2| + 5 = 1$$

$$|x + 2| = -4 \qquad \text{There is no solution, } \{ \ \}.$$

Example 3

$$|2x - 1| = |x + 4|$$

$$2x - 1 = x + 4 \quad \text{or} \quad 2x - 1 = -(x + 4)$$

$$x = 5 \qquad \text{or} \quad 2x - 1 = -x - 4$$

$$\text{or} \qquad 3x = -3$$

$$\text{or} \qquad x = -1$$

The solution set is $\{5, -1\}$.

Section 9.4 — Absolute Value Inequalities

Key Concepts

Solutions to Absolute Value Inequalities

For $a > 0$, we have:

$|x| > a \Rightarrow x < -a$ or $x > a$

$|x| < a \Rightarrow -a < x < a$

Test Point Method to Solve Inequalities

1. Find the boundary points of the inequality. (Boundary points are the real solutions to the related equation and points where the inequality is undefined.)
2. Plot the boundary points on the number line. This divides the number line into intervals.
3. Select a test point from each interval and substitute it into the original inequality.
   - If a test point makes the original inequality true, then that interval is part of the solution set.
4. Test the boundary points in the original inequality.
   - If the original inequality is strict ($<$ or $>$), do not include the boundary in the solution set.
   - If the original inequality is defined using $\leq$ or $\geq$, then include the boundary points that are well defined within the inequality.

Note: Any boundary point that makes an expression within the inequality undefined must *always* be excluded from the solution set.

If *a* is *negative* (*a* < 0), then

1. $|x| < a$ has no solution.
2. $|x| > a$ is true for all real numbers.

Examples

Example 1

$$|5x - 2| < 12$$

$$-12 < 5x - 2 < 12$$

$$-10 < 5x < 14$$

$$-2 < x < \frac{14}{5}$$

The solution is $\left(-2, \dfrac{14}{5}\right)$.

Example 2

$|x - 3| + 2 \geq 7$

$\qquad |x - 3| \geq 5 \qquad$ Isolate the absolute value.

$\qquad |x - 3| = 5 \qquad$ Solve the related equation.

$x - 3 = 5$ or $x - 3 = -5$

$\qquad x = 8$ or $\qquad x = -2 \qquad$ Boundary points

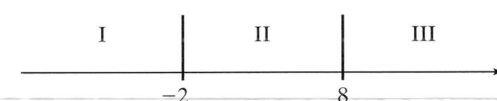

Interval I: Test $x = -3$: $|(-3) - 3| + 2 \overset{?}{\geq} 7$ True

Interval II: Test $x = 0$: $|(0) - 3| + 2 \overset{?}{\geq} 7$ False

Interval III: Test $x = 9$: $|(9) - 3| + 2 \overset{?}{\geq} 7$ True

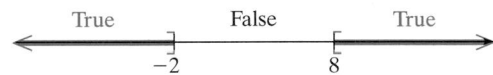

The solution is $(-\infty, -2] \cup [8, \infty)$.

Example 3

$|x + 5| > -2$

The solution is all real numbers because an absolute value will always be greater than a negative number.

$(-\infty, \infty)$

Section 9.5 — Linear and Compound Inequalities in Two Variables

Key Concepts

A **linear inequality in two variables** is an inequality of the form $ax + by < c$, $ax + by > c$, $ax + by \leq c$, or $ax + by \geq c$.

Graphing a Linear Inequality in Two Variables

1. Solve for y, if possible.
2. Graph the related equation. Draw a dashed line if the inequality is strict, $<$ or $>$. Otherwise, draw a solid line.
3. Shade above or below the line according to the following convention.

   - Shade *above* the line if the inequality is of the form $y > ax + b$ or $y \geq ax + b$.
   - Shade *below* the line if the inequality is of the form $y < ax + b$ or $y \leq ax + b$.

   You can use test points to check that you have shaded the correct region. Select an ordered pair from the proposed solution set and substitute the values of x and y in the original inequality. If the test point produces a true statement, then you have shaded the correct region.

   The union or intersection of two or more linear inequalities is the union or intersection of the solution sets.

Examples

Example 1

Graph the solution to the inequality $2x - y < 4$. Graph the related equation, $y = 2x - 4$, with a dashed line.

Solve for y: $2x - y < 4$

$$-y < -2x + 4$$
$$y > 2x - 4$$

Shade above the line.

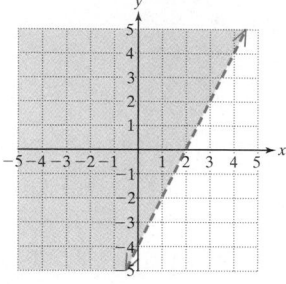

Example 2

Graph.

$x < 0$ and $y > 2$

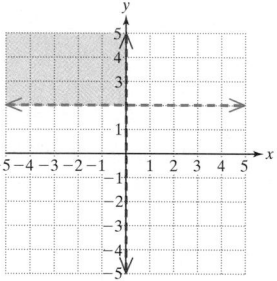

Example 3

Graph.

$x \leq 0$ or $y \geq 2$

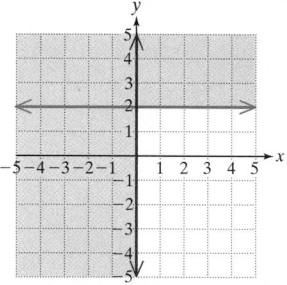

Chapter 9   Review Exercises

Section 9.1

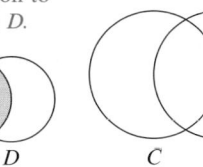 **1.** Explain the difference between the union and intersection of two sets. You may use the sets C and D in the following diagram to provide an example.

$C \cap D$ is the set of elements common to both sets C and D.

$C \cup D$ is the set of elements in either set C, set D, or both sets.

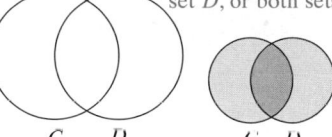

     C D C D C D

Let $X = \{x \mid x \geq -10\}$, $Y = \{x \mid x < 1\}$, $Z = \{x \mid x > -1\}$, and $W = \{x \mid x \leq -3\}$. For Exercises 2–7, find the intersection or union of the sets X, Y, Z, and W. Write the answers in interval notation.

2. $X \cap Y$ $[-10, 1)$

3. $X \cup Y$ $(-\infty, \infty)$

4. $Y \cup Z$ $(-\infty, \infty)$

5. $Y \cap Z$ $(-1, 1)$

6. $Z \cup W$
$(-\infty, -3] \cup (-1, \infty)$

7. $Z \cap W$ $\{\}$

For Exercises 8–13, solve the compound inequalities. Write the solutions in interval notation.

8. $4m > -11$ and $4m - 3 \leq 13$ $\left(-\dfrac{11}{4}, 4\right]$

9. $4n - 7 < 1$ and $7 + 3n \geq -8$ $[-5, 2)$

10. $\dfrac{2}{3}t - 3 \leq 1$ or $\dfrac{3}{4}t - 2 > 7$ $(-\infty, 6] \cup (12, \infty)$

11. $2(3x + 1) < -10$ or $3(2x - 4) \geq 0$
$(-\infty, -2) \cup [2, \infty)$

12. $2 \geq -(b - 2) - 5b \geq -6$ $\left[0, \dfrac{4}{3}\right]$

13. $-4 \leq \dfrac{1}{2}(x - 1) < -\dfrac{3}{2}$ $[-7, -2)$

 14. Normal levels of total cholesterol vary according to age. For adults between 25 and 40 yr old, the normal range is generally accepted to be between 140 and 225 mg/dL (milligrams per deciliter), inclusive.

    a. Write an inequality representing the normal range for total cholesterol for adults between 25 and 40 yr old. $140 \leq x \leq 225$

    b. Write a compound inequality representing abnormal ranges for total cholesterol for adults between 25 and 40 yr old.
    $x < 140$ or $x > 225$

 15. Normal levels of total cholesterol vary according to age. For adults younger than 25 yr old, the normal range is generally accepted to be between 125 and 200 mg/dL, inclusive.

    a. Write an inequality representing the normal range for total cholesterol for adults younger than 25 yr old. $125 \leq x \leq 200$

    b. Write a compound inequality representing abnormal ranges for total cholesterol for adults younger than 25 yr old.
    $x < 125$ or $x > 200$

Section 9.2

 16. Solve the equation and inequalities. How do your answers to parts (a), (b), and (c) relate to the graph of $g(x) = x^2 - 4$?

    a. $x^2 - 4 = 0$ $(-2, 0)$ and $(2, 0)$ are the x-intercepts.

    b. $x^2 - 4 < 0$
    On the interval $(-2, 2)$ the graph is below the x-axis.

    c. $x^2 - 4 > 0$
    On the intervals $(-\infty, -2)$ and $(2, \infty)$ the graph is above the x-axis.

$g(x) = x^2 - 4$

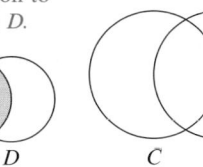 **17.** Solve the equation and inequalities. How do your answers to parts (a), (b), (c), and (d) relate to the graph of $k(x) = \dfrac{4x}{(x - 2)}$?

    a. $\dfrac{4x}{x - 2} = 0$ $x = 0$; $(0, 0)$ is the x-intercept.

    b. For which values is $k(x)$ undefined?
    $x = 2$ is the vertical asymptote.

    c. $\dfrac{4x}{x - 2} \geq 0$
    On the intervals $(-\infty, 0]$ and $(2, \infty)$ the graph is on or above the x-axis.

    d. $\dfrac{4x}{x - 2} \leq 0$
    On the interval $[0, 2)$ the graph is on or below the x-axis.

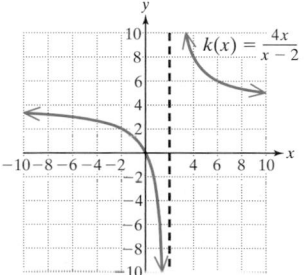

$k(x) = \dfrac{4x}{x - 2}$

For Exercises 18–29, solve the inequalities. Write the answers in interval notation.

18. $w^2 - 4w - 12 < 0$
$(-2, 6)$

19. $t^2 + 6t + 9 \geq 0$
$(-\infty, \infty)$

20. $\dfrac{12}{x + 2} \leq 6$
$(-\infty, -2) \cup [0, \infty)$

21. $\dfrac{8}{p - 1} \geq -4$
$(-\infty, -1] \cup (1, \infty)$

22. $3y(y - 5)(y + 2) > 0$ $\quad (-2, 0) \cup (5, \infty)$

23. $-3c(c + 2)(2c - 5) < 0$ $\quad (-2, 0) \cup \left(\dfrac{5}{2}, \infty\right)$

24. $-x^2 - 4x \geq 3$
$[-3, -1]$

25. $y^2 + 4y > 5$
$(-\infty, -5) \cup (1, \infty)$

26. $\dfrac{w + 1}{w - 3} > 1$ $\quad (3, \infty)$

27. $\dfrac{2a}{a + 3} \leq 2$ $\quad (-3, \infty)$

28. $t^2 + 10t + 25 \leq 0$
$\{-5\}$

29. $-x^2 - 4x < 4$
$(-\infty, -2) \cup (-2, \infty)$

Section 9.3

For Exercises 30–41, solve the absolute value equations.

30. $|x| = 10$
$\{10, -10\}$

31. $|x| = 17$
$\{17, -17\}$

32. $|8.7 - 2x| = 6.1$
$\{1.3, 7.4\}$

33. $|5.25 - 5x| = 7.45$
$\{-0.44, 2.54\}$

34. $16 = |x + 2| + 9$
$\{5, -9\}$

35. $5 = |x - 2| + 4$
$\{3, 1\}$

36. $|4x - 1| + 6 = 4$
$\{ \}$

37. $|3x - 1| + 7 = 3$
$\{ \}$

38. $\left|\dfrac{7x - 3}{5}\right| + 4 = 4$ $\quad \left\{\dfrac{3}{7}\right\}$

39. $\left|\dfrac{4x + 5}{-2}\right| - 3 = -3$ $\quad \left\{-\dfrac{5}{4}\right\}$

40. $|3x - 5| = |2x + 1|$ $\quad \left\{6, \dfrac{4}{5}\right\}$

41. $|8x + 9| = |8x - 1|$ $\quad \left\{-\dfrac{1}{2}\right\}$

42. Which absolute value expression represents the distance between 3 and -2 on the number line?

$$|3 - (-2)| \qquad |-2 - 3|$$

Both expressions give the distance between 3 and -2.

Section 9.4

43. Write the compound inequality $x < -5$ or $x > 5$ as an absolute value inequality. $\quad |x| > 5$

44. Write the compound inequality $-4 < x < 4$ as an absolute value inequality. $\quad |x| < 4$

For Exercises 45–46, write an absolute value inequality that represents the solution sets graphed here.

45. $|x| < 6$

46. $|x| > \dfrac{2}{3}$

For Exercises 47–60, solve the absolute value inequalities. Graph the solution set and write the solution in interval notation.

47. $|x + 6| \geq 8$
$(-\infty, -14] \cup [2, \infty)$

48. $|x + 8| \leq 3$
$[-11, -5]$

49. $2|7x - 1| + 4 > 4$ $\quad \left(-\infty, \dfrac{1}{7}\right) \cup \left(\dfrac{1}{7}, \infty\right)$

50. $4|5x + 1| - 3 > -3$ $\quad \left(-\infty, -\dfrac{1}{5}\right) \cup \left(-\dfrac{1}{5}, \infty\right)$

51. $|3x + 4| - 6 \leq -4$ $\quad \left[-2, -\dfrac{2}{3}\right]$

52. $|5x - 3| + 3 \leq 6$ $\quad \left[0, \dfrac{6}{5}\right]$

53. $\left|\dfrac{x}{2} - 6\right| < 5$ $\quad (2, 22)$

54. $\left|\dfrac{x}{3} + 2\right| < 2$ $\quad (-12, 0)$

55. $|4 - 2x| + 8 \geq 8$
$(-\infty, \infty)$

56. $|9 + 3x| + 1 \geq 1$
$(-\infty, \infty)$

57. $-2|5.2x - 7.8| < 13$
$(-\infty, \infty)$

58. $-|2.5x + 15| < 7$
$(-\infty, \infty)$

59. $|3x - 8| < -1$
$\{ \}$

60. $|x + 5| < -4$
$\{ \}$

61. State one possible situation in which an absolute value inequality will have no solution. If an absolute value is less than a negative number, there will be no solution.

62. State one possible situation in which an absolute value inequality will have a solution of all real numbers. If an absolute value is greater than a negative number, then all real numbers are solutions.

63. The Neilsen ratings estimated that the percent, p, of the television viewing audience watching *American Idol* was 20% with a 3% margin of error. Solve the inequality $|p - 0.20| \leq 0.03$ and interpret the answer in the context of this problem. $0.17 \leq p \leq 0.23$ or, equivalently in interval notation, $[0.17, 0.23]$. This means that the actual percentage of viewers is estimated to be between 17% and 23% inclusive.

 Writing Translating Expression Geometry Scientific Calculator Video NS&E

64. The length, L, of a screw is supposed to be $3\frac{3}{8}$ in. Due to variation in the production equipment, there is a $\frac{1}{4}$-in. margin of error. Solve the inequality $|L - 3\frac{3}{8}| \leq \frac{1}{4}$ and interpret the answer in the context of this problem. $3\frac{1}{8} \leq L \leq 3\frac{5}{8}$ or, equivalently in interval notation, $[3\frac{1}{8}, 3\frac{5}{8}]$. This means that the actual length of the screw may be between $3\frac{1}{8}$ in. and $3\frac{5}{8}$ in., inclusive.

Section 9.5

For Exercises 65–72, solve the inequalities by graphing.

65. $2x > -y + 5$

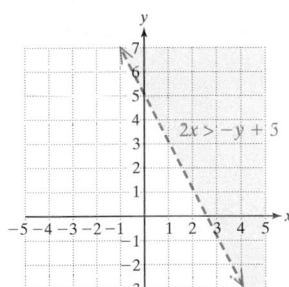

66. $2x \leq -8 - 3y$

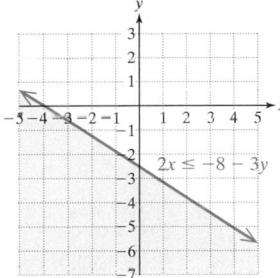

67. $y \geq -\frac{2}{3}x + 3$

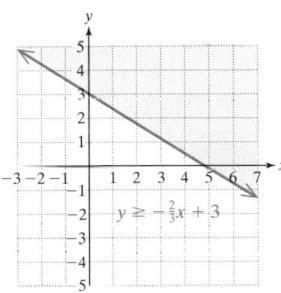

68. $y > \frac{3}{4}x - 2$

69. $x > -3$

70. $x \leq 2$

71. $x \geq \frac{1}{2}y$

72. $x < \frac{2}{5}y$

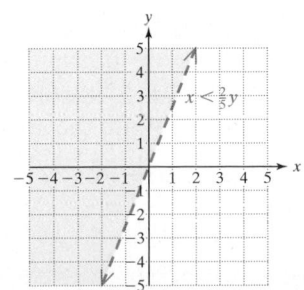

For Exercises 73–76, graph the system of inequalities.

73. $2x - y > -2$ and $2x - y \leq 2$

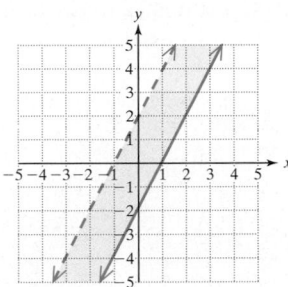

74. $3x + y \geq 6$ or $3x + y < -6$

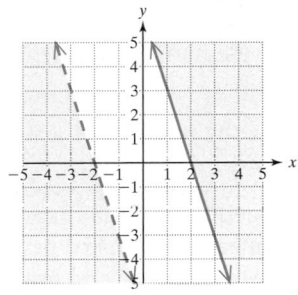

75. $y \geq x$, or $y \leq -x$

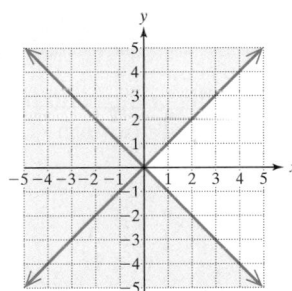

76. $x \geq 0$, $y \geq 0$, and $y \leq -\frac{2}{3}x + 4$

 Writing   ⇔ Translating Expression   Geometry   Scientific Calculator   Video   NS&E

77. Suppose a farmer has 100 acres of land on which to grow oranges and grapefruit. Furthermore, because of demand from his customers, he wants to plant at least 4 times as many acres of orange trees as grapefruit trees.

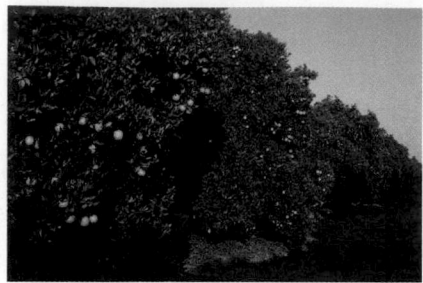

Let x represent the number of acres of orange trees.

Let y represent the number of acres of grapefruit trees.

a. Write two inequalities that express the fact that the farmer cannot use a negative number of acres to plant orange and grapefruit trees.
$x \geq 0, y \geq 0$

b. Write an inequality that expresses the fact that the total number of acres used for growing orange and grapefruit trees is at most 100.
$x + y \leq 100$

c. Write an inequality that expresses the fact that the farmer wants to plant at least 4 times as many orange trees as grapefruit trees.
$x \geq 4y$

d. Sketch the inequalities in parts (a)–(c) to find the feasible region for the farmer's distribution of orange and grapefruit trees.

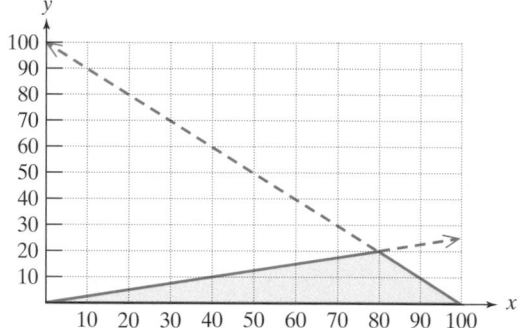

Chapter 9   Test

For Exercises 1–5, solve the compound inequalities. Write the answers in interval notation.

1. $-2 \leq 3x - 1 \leq 5$ $\left[-\frac{1}{3}, 2\right]$

2. $-\frac{3}{5}x - 1 \leq 8$ or $-\frac{2}{3}x \geq 16$
$(-\infty, -24] \cup [-15, \infty)$

3. $-2x - 3 > -3$ and $x + 3 \geq 0$ $[-3, 0)$

4. $5x + 1 \leq 6$ or $2x + 4 > -6$ $(-\infty, \infty)$

5. $2x - 3 > 1$ and $x + 4 < -1$
$\{\ \}$

6. The normal range in humans of the enzyme adenosine deaminase (ADA), is between 9 and 33 IU (international units), inclusive. Let x represent the ADA level in international units.

a. Write an inequality representing the normal range for ADA. $9 \leq x \leq 33$

b. Write a compound inequality representing abnormal ranges for ADA. $x < 9$ or $x > 33$

For Exercises 7–12, solve the polynomial and rational inequalities.

7. $50 - 2a^2 > 0$
$(-5, 5)$

8. $y^3 + 3y^2 - 4y - 12 < 0$
$(-\infty, -3) \cup (-2, 2)$

9. $5x^2 - 2x + 2 < 0$
$\{\ \}$

10. $t^2 + 22t + 121 \leq 0$
$\{-11\}$

11. $\dfrac{2x - 1}{x - 6} \leq 0$ $\left[\frac{1}{2}, 6\right)$

12. $\dfrac{3}{w + 3} > 2$ $\left(-3, -\frac{3}{2}\right)$

For Exercises 13–14, solve the absolute value equations.

13. $\left|\dfrac{1}{2}x + 3\right| - 4 = 4$ $\{10, -22\}$

14. $|3x + 4| = |x - 12|$ $\{-8, 2\}$

For Exercises 15–18, solve the absolute value inequalities. Write the answers in interval notation.

15. $|3 - 2x| + 6 < 2$
$\{\ \}$

16. $|3x - 8| > 9$
$\left(-\infty, -\dfrac{1}{3}\right) \cup \left(\dfrac{17}{3}, \infty\right)$

 Writing   Translating Expression   Geometry   Scientific Calculator   Video   NS&E

17. $|0.4x + 0.3| - 0.2 < 7$ ($-18.75, 17.25$)

18. $|7 - 3x| + 1 > -3$ ($-\infty, \infty$)

19. The mass of a small piece of metal is measured to be 15.41 g. If the measurement error is at most ±0.01 g, write an absolute value inequality that represents the possible mass, x, of the piece of metal. $|x - 15.41| \leq 0.01$

20. Graph the solution to the inequality $2x - 5y \geq 10$.

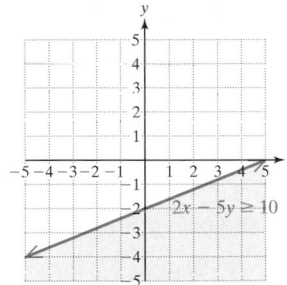

For Exercises 21–22, graph the solution to the compound inequality.

21. $x + y < 3$ and
$3x - 2y > -6$

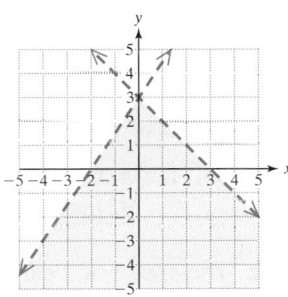

22. $5x \leq 5$ or $x + y \leq 0$

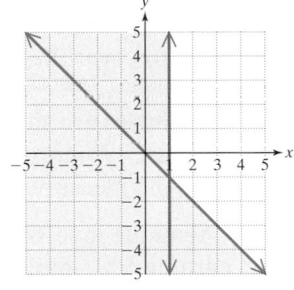

23. After menopause, women are at higher risk for hip fractures as a result of low calcium. As early as their teen years, women need at least 1200 mg of calcium per day (the USDA recommended daily allowance). One 8-oz glass of skim milk contains 300 mg of calcium, and one Antacid (regular strength) contains 400 mg of calcium. Let x represent the number of 8-oz glasses of milk that a woman drinks per day. Let y represent the number of Antacid tablets (regular strength) that a woman takes per day.

   a. Write two inequalities that express the fact that the number of glasses of milk and the number of Antacid taken each day cannot be negative. $x \geq 0, y \geq 0$

   b. Write a linear inequality in terms of x and y for which the daily calcium intake is at least 1200 mg. $300x + 400y \geq 1200$

   c. Graph the inequalities.

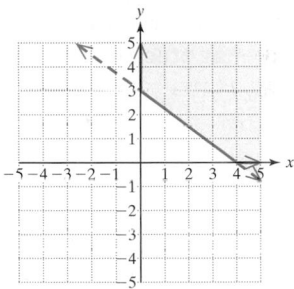

Chapters 1–9   Cumulative Review Exercises

1. Perform the indicated operations.

$$(2x - 3)(x - 4) - (x - 5)^2 \quad x^2 - x - 13$$

2. Solve. $\quad -9m + 3 = 2m(m - 4)$
$\left\{ -\dfrac{3}{2}, 1 \right\}$

For Exercises 3–4, solve the equation and inequalities. Write the solution to the inequalities in interval notation.

3. a. $2|3 - p| - 4 = 2$ $\{0, 6\}$

   b. $2|3 - p| - 4 < 2$ $(0, 6)$

   c. $2|3 - p| - 4 > 2$ $(-\infty, 0) \cup (6, \infty)$

 Writing   Translating Expression   Geometry   Scientific Calculator   Video

4. a. $\left|\dfrac{y-2}{4}\right| - 6 = -3$ {14, −10}

b. $\left|\dfrac{y-2}{4}\right| - 6 < -3$ (−10, 14)

c. $\left|\dfrac{y-2}{4}\right| - 6 > -3$ (−∞, −10) ∪ (14, ∞)

5. Graph the inequality. $4x - y > 12$

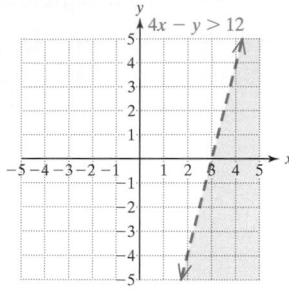

6. The time in minutes required for a rat to run through a maze depends on the number of trials, n, that the rat has practiced.

$$t(n) = \dfrac{3n + 15}{n + 1} \qquad n \geq 1$$

$t(1) = 9$. After one trial the rat requires 9 min to complete the maze. $t(50) = 3.24$. After 50 trials the rat requires

a. Find $t(1), t(50)$, and $t(500)$, and interpret the results in the context of this problem. Round to 2 decimal places, if necessary.

3.24 min to complete the maze. $t(500) = 3.02$. After 500 trials the rat requires 3.02 min to complete the maze.

b. Does there appear to be a limiting time in which the rat can complete the maze?
The limiting time is 3 min.

c. How many trials are required so that the rat is able to finish the maze in under 5 min?
More than 5 trials

7. a. Solve the inequality. $2x^2 + x - 10 \geq 0$
$\left(-\infty, -\dfrac{5}{2}\right] \cup [2, \infty)$

b. How does the answer in part (a) relate to the graph of the function $f(x) = 2x^2 + x - 10$?

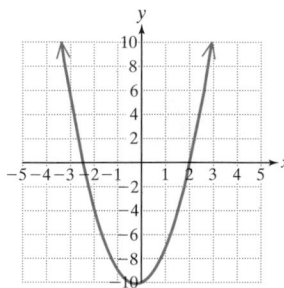

On these intervals, the graph is on or above the x-axis.

8. Shade the region defined by the compound inequality.

$$3x + y \leq -2 \quad \text{or} \quad y \geq 1$$

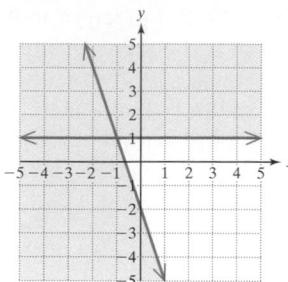

9. Simplify the expression.

$$2 - 3(x - 5) + 2[4 - (2x + 6)]$$
$-7x + 13$

10. a. Divide the polynomials.

$$\dfrac{2x^4 - x^3 + 5x - 7}{x^2 + 2x - 1}$$

Identify the quotient and remainder.
Quotient: $2x^2 - 5x + 12$; remainder: $-24x + 5$

b. Check your answer by multiplying.

11. The area of a trapezoid is given by $A = \frac{1}{2}h(b_1 + b_2)$.

a. Solve for b_1. $b_1 = \dfrac{2A - hb_2}{h}$ or $b_1 = \dfrac{2A}{h} - b_2$

b. Find b_1 when $h = 4$ cm, $b_2 = 6$ cm, and $A = 32$ cm^2.   10 cm

12. The speed of a car varies inversely as the time to travel a fixed distance. A car traveling the speed limit of 60 mph travels between two points in 10 sec. How fast is a car moving if it takes only 8 sec to cover the same distance?   75 mph

13. Two angles are supplementary. One angle measures 9° more than twice the other angle. Find the measures of the angles.   57°, 123°

14. Chemique invests $3000 less in an account earning 5% simple interest than she does in an account earning 6.5% simple interest. At the end of one year, she earns a total $770 in interest. Find the amount invested in each account.
$8000 in the 6.5% account; $5000 in the 5% account

15. Determine algebraically whether the lines are parallel, perpendicular, or neither.   Neither

$$4x - 2y = 5$$
$$-3x + 6y = 10$$

16. Find the x- and y-intercepts and slope (if they exist) of the lines. Then graph the lines.

a. $3x + 5 = 8$

b. $\dfrac{1}{2}x + y = 4$

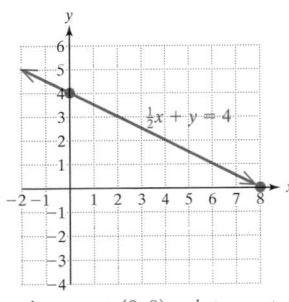

x-intercept $(1, 0)$; no
y-intercept; undefined slope

x-intercept $(8, 0)$; y-intercept
$(0, 4)$; slope $-\dfrac{1}{2}$

17. Find an equation of the line with slope $-\dfrac{2}{3}$ passing through the point $(4, -7)$. Write the final answer in slope-intercept form.
$y = -\dfrac{2}{3}x - \dfrac{13}{3}$

18. Solve the system of equations. $\{(-1, 3, -2)\}$

$$3x + y = z + 2$$
$$y = 1 - 2x$$
$$3z = -2y$$

19. Simplify. $\left(\dfrac{5x^2y^5}{30x^{-2}y^0}\right)^{-1}$ $\dfrac{6}{x^4y^5}$

20. Against a headwind, a plane can travel 6240 mi in 13 hr. On the return trip flying with the same wind, the plane can fly 6240 mi in 12 hr. Find the wind speed and the speed of the plane in still air.
Plane: 500 mph; wind: 20 mph

21. The profit that a company makes manufacturing computer desks is given by

$$P(x) = -\tfrac{1}{5}(x - 20)(x - 650) \qquad x \geq 0$$

where x is the number of desks produced and $P(x)$ is the profit in dollars.

a. Is this function constant, linear, or quadratic?
Quadratic

b. Find $P(0)$ and interpret the result in the context of this problem. $P(0) = -2600$. The company will lose $2600 if no desks are produced.

c. Find the values of x where $P(x) = 0$. Interpret the results in the context of this problem.
$P(x) = 0$ for $x = 20$ and $x = 650$. The company will break even ($0 profit) when 20 desks or 650 desks are produced.

22. Factor the expression. $3x^3 - 6x^2 - 12x + 24$
$3(x - 2)^2(x + 2)$

23. Simplify completely. $\dfrac{x^{-1} - y^{-1}}{y^{-2} - x^{-2}}$ $-\dfrac{xy}{x + y}$

24. Divide. $\dfrac{a^3 + 64}{16 - a^2} \div \dfrac{a^3 - 4a^2 + 16a}{a^2 - 3a - 4}$ $-\dfrac{a + 1}{a}$

25. Perform the indicated operations.
$$\dfrac{1}{x^2 - 7x + 10} + \dfrac{1}{x^2 + 8x - 20}$$
$\dfrac{2x + 5}{(x - 5)(x - 2)(x + 10)}$

 Writing   Translating Expression   Geometry   Scientific Calculator   Video   NS&E

Radicals and Complex Numbers

10

CHAPTER OUTLINE

Chapter 10

In this chapter, we study radical expressions. This includes operations on square roots, cube roots, fourth roots, and so on. We also revisit the Pythagorean theorem and its applications as well as introduce the set of complex numbers.

Are You Prepared?

Take a minute to review your knowledge of square roots and operations on polynomials. These skills will help you be successful in this chapter.

   For Exercises 1–10, perform the indicated operations. Then write the letter corresponding to each answer in the space at the bottom of the page.

1. $(4x - 3)(x + 5)$ **2.** $4x^2(3x^2 + 5x + 1)$ **3.** $(4x - 3)(4x + 3)$ **4.** $(4x - 3)^2$

5. $\sqrt{4}$ **6.** 4^2 **7.** $\sqrt{-4}$ **8.** $\sqrt{10^2 - 6^2}$

9. $(-3x^4 + 9x^2 - 15x) - (-3x^4 - 7x^2 + 9x + 9)$ **10.** $(2x)(6x^3)$

R 16	N $16x^2 - 9$	I $16x^2 - 24x + 9$	M 8
Y $16x^2 - 24x - 9$	A not a real number	E $12x^4 + 20x^3 + 4x^2$	U 2
G $4x^2 + 17x - 15$	B $12x^4$		

In this chapter, we also introduce a new type of number called an

<u>I</u> <u>M</u> <u>A</u> <u>G</u> <u>I</u> <u>N</u> <u>A</u> <u>R</u> <u>Y</u>   <u>N</u> <u>U</u> <u>M</u> <u>B</u> <u>E</u> <u>R</u>.
4 8 7 1 4 3 7 6 9   3 5 8 10 2 6

Section 10.1 Definition of an *n*th Root

Concepts

1. Definition of a Square Root
2. Definition of an *n*th Root
3. Roots of Variable Expressions
4. Pythagorean Theorem
5. Radical Functions

1. Definition of a Square Root

The reverse operation to squaring a number is to find its square roots. For example, finding a square root of 36 is equivalent to asking, "what number when squared equals 36?"

One obvious answer to this question is 6 because $(6)^2 = 36$, but -6 will also work, because $(-6)^2 = 36$.

> **DEFINITION Square Root**
>
> b is a **square root** of a if $b^2 = a$.

Classroom Example: p. 700, Exercise 4

> **Example 1 Identifying Square Roots**
>
> Identify the square roots of the real numbers.
>
> **a.** 25 **b.** 49 **c.** 0 **d.** -9
>
> **Solution:**
>
> **a.** 5 is a square root of 25 because $(5)^2 = 25$.
>
> -5 is a square root of 25 because $(-5)^2 = 25$.
>
> **b.** 7 is a square root of 49 because $(7)^2 = 49$.
>
> -7 is a square root of 49 because $(-7)^2 = 49$.
>
> **c.** 0 is a square root of 0 because $(0)^2 = 0$.
>
> **d.** There are no real numbers that when squared will equal a negative number; therefore, there are no real-valued square roots of -9.
>
> **Skill Practice** Identify the square roots of the real numbers.
>
> **1.** 64 **2.** 16 **3.** 1 **4.** -100

> **TIP:**
> - All positive real numbers have two real-valued square roots (one positive and one negative).
> - Zero has only one square root, which is zero itself.
> - A negative number has no real-valued square roots.

Recall from Section 1.3 that the positive square root of a real number can be denoted with a **radical sign** $\sqrt{}$.

> **DEFINITION Positive and Negative Square Roots**
>
> Let a represent a positive real number. Then
>
> **1.** $\sqrt{a}$ is the *positive* square root of a. The positive square root is also called the **principal square root**.
>
> **2.** $-\sqrt{a}$ is the *negative* square root of a.
>
> **3.** $\sqrt{0} = 0$

Answers

1. -8 and 8
2. -4 and 4
3. -1 and 1
4. No real-valued square roots

Example 2 **Simplifying Square Roots**

Classroom Example: p. 700, Exercise 14

Simplify the square roots.

a. $\sqrt{36}$ **b.** $\sqrt{\dfrac{4}{9}}$ **c.** $\sqrt{0.04}$

Solution:

a. $\sqrt{36}$ denotes the positive square root of 36.

$\sqrt{36} = 6$

b. $\sqrt{\dfrac{4}{9}}$ denotes the positive square root of $\dfrac{4}{9}$.

$\sqrt{\dfrac{4}{9}} = \dfrac{2}{3}$

c. $\sqrt{0.04}$ denotes the positive square root of 0.04.

$\sqrt{0.04} = 0.2$ *Note:* $(0.2)(0.2) = 0.04$

Skill Practice Simplify the square roots.

5. $\sqrt{81}$ **6.** $\sqrt{\dfrac{36}{49}}$ **7.** $\sqrt{0.09}$

The numbers $36, \frac{4}{9}$, and 0.04 are **perfect squares** because their square roots are rational numbers.

Radicals that cannot be simplified to rational numbers are irrational numbers. Recall that an irrational number cannot be written as a terminating or repeating decimal. For example, the symbol $\sqrt{13}$ is used to represent the *exact* value of the square root of 13. The symbol $\sqrt{42}$ is used to represent the *exact* value of the square root of 42. These values can be approximated by a rational number by using a calculator.

$$\sqrt{13} \approx 3.605551275 \qquad \sqrt{42} \approx 6.480740698$$

Calculator Connections

Use a calculator to approximate the values of $\sqrt{13}$ and $\sqrt{42}$.

```
√(13)
        3.605551275
√(42)
        6.480740698
```

TIP: Before using a calculator to evaluate a square root, try estimating the value first.

$\sqrt{13}$ must be a number between 3 and 4 because $\sqrt{9} < \sqrt{13} < \sqrt{16}$.

$\sqrt{42}$ must be a number between 6 and 7 because $\sqrt{36} < \sqrt{42} < \sqrt{49}$.

A negative number cannot have a real number as a square root because no real number when squared is negative. For example, $\sqrt{-25}$ is *not* a real number because there is no real number b for which $(b)^2 = -25$.

Answers

5. 9 **6.** $\dfrac{6}{7}$ **7.** 0.3

Classroom Examples: p. 700, Exercises 10, 12, and 18

Example 3 Simplifying Square Roots

Simplify the square roots, if possible.

a. $\sqrt{-144}$ **b.** $-\sqrt{144}$ **c.** $\sqrt{-0.01}$ **d.** $-\sqrt{\dfrac{1}{9}}$

Solution:

a. $\sqrt{-144}$ is *not* a real number.

b. $-\sqrt{144}$

$$= -1 \cdot \sqrt{144}$$
$$= -1 \cdot \quad 12$$
$$= -12$$

> **TIP:** For the expression $-\sqrt{144}$, the factor of -1 is *outside* the radical.

c. $\sqrt{-0.01}$ is *not* a real number.

d. $-\sqrt{\dfrac{1}{9}}$

$$= -1 \cdot \sqrt{\dfrac{1}{9}}$$
$$= -1 \cdot \dfrac{1}{3}$$
$$= -\dfrac{1}{3}$$

Skill Practice Simplify the square roots, if possible.

8. $\sqrt{-81}$ **9.** $-\sqrt{64}$ **10.** $-\sqrt{0.25}$ **11.** $\sqrt{-\dfrac{1}{4}}$

2. Definition of an *n*th Root

Finding a square root of a number is the reverse process of squaring a number. This concept can be extended to finding a third root (called a cube root), a fourth root, and in general an **nth root**.

> **DEFINITION** *n*th Root
>
> b is an nth root of a if $b^n = a$.
>
> Example: 2 is a fourth root of 16 because $2^4 = 16$.

    The radical sign $\sqrt{}$ is used to denote the principal square root of a number. The symbol $\sqrt[n]{}$ is used to denote the principal nth root of a number. In the expression $\sqrt[n]{a}$, n is called the **index** of the radical, and a is called the **radicand**. For a square root, the index is 2, but it is usually not written ($\sqrt[2]{a}$ is denoted simply as $\sqrt{a}$). A radical with an index of 3 is called a **cube root**, denoted by $\sqrt[3]{a}$.

Answers

8. Not a real number   **9.** -8
10. -0.5 **11.** Not a real number

> **PROPERTY** $\sqrt[n]{a}$
>
> 1. If $n > 1$ is an *even* integer and $a > 0$, then $\sqrt[n]{a}$ is the principal (positive) *n*th root of *a*.
> 2. If $n > 1$ is an *odd* integer, then $\sqrt[n]{a}$ is the *n*th root of *a*.
> 3. If $n > 1$ is an integer, then $\sqrt[n]{0} = 0$.

For the purpose of simplifying radicals, it is helpful to know the following powers.

Perfect Squares	Perfect Cubes	Perfect Fourth Powers	Perfect Fifth Powers
$1^2 = 1$	$1^3 = 1$	$1^4 = 1$	$1^5 = 1$
$2^2 = 4$	$2^3 = 8$	$2^4 = 16$	$2^5 = 32$
$3^2 = 9$	$3^3 = 27$	$3^4 = 81$	$3^5 = 243$
$4^2 = 16$	$4^3 = 64$	$4^4 = 256$	$4^5 = 1024$
$5^2 = 25$	$5^3 = 125$	$5^4 = 625$	$5^5 = 3125$

Instructor Note: Students are acquainted with the perfect square integers 1, 4, 9. . . . They may need to familiarize themselves with the perfect cubes, 4th powers, etc.

Example 4 **Identifying the *n*th Root of a Real Number**

Simplify the expressions, if possible.

a. $\sqrt{4}$ **b.** $\sqrt[3]{64}$ **c.** $\sqrt[5]{-32}$ **d.** $\sqrt[4]{81}$

e. $\sqrt[6]{1,000,000}$ **f.** $\sqrt{-100}$ **g.** $\sqrt[4]{-16}$

Classroom Examples: p. 700, Exercises 24, 32, and 34

Solution:

a. $\sqrt{4} - 2$ because $(2)^2 = 4$

b. $\sqrt[3]{64} = 4$ because $(4)^3 = 64$

c. $\sqrt[5]{-32} = -2$ because $(-2)^5 = -32$

d. $\sqrt[4]{81} = 3$ because $(3)^4 = 81$

e. $\sqrt[6]{1,000,000} = 10$ because $(10)^6 = 1,000,000$

f. $\sqrt{-100}$ is not a real number.   No real number when squared equals -100.

g. $\sqrt[4]{-16}$ is not a real number.   No real number when raised to the fourth power equals -16.

Calculator Connections

Topic: Approximating *n*th Roots

A calculator can be used to approximate *n*th roots by using the $\sqrt[n]{}$ function. On most calculators, the index is entered first.

```
3ˣʃ(64)
                    4
5ˣʃ(-32)
                   -2
6ˣʃ(1000000)
                   10
```

Skill Practice Simplify if possible.

12. $\sqrt[4]{16}$ **13.** $\sqrt[3]{1000}$ **14.** $\sqrt[5]{-1}$ **15.** $\sqrt[5]{32}$

16. $\sqrt[5]{100,000}$ **17.** $\sqrt{-36}$ **18.** $\sqrt[3]{-27}$

Examples 4(f) and 4(g) illustrate that an *n*th root of a negative quantity is not a real number if the index is even. This is because no real number raised to an even power is negative.

3. Roots of Variable Expressions

Finding an *n*th root of a variable expression is similar to finding an *n*th root of a numerical expression. For roots with an even index, however, particular care must be taken to obtain a nonnegative result.

Answers
12. 2   **13.** 10   **14.** -1
15. 2   **16.** 10
17. Not a real number   **18.** -3

> **DEFINITION** $\sqrt[n]{a^n}$
>
> **1.** If n is a positive *odd* integer, then $\sqrt[n]{a^n} = a$.
>
> **2.** If n is a positive *even* integer, then $\sqrt[n]{a^n} = |a|$.

The absolute value bars are necessary for roots with an even index because the variable a may represent a positive quantity or a negative quantity. By using absolute value bars, $\sqrt[n]{a^n} = |a|$ is nonnegative and represents the principal nth root of a^n.

Classroom Examples: p. 700,
Exercises 40 and 42

> **Example 5**   Simplifying Expressions of the Form $\sqrt[n]{a^n}$
>
> Simplify the expressions.
>
> **a.** $\sqrt[4]{(-3)^4}$ **b.** $\sqrt[5]{(-3)^5}$ **c.** $\sqrt{(x+2)^2}$ **d.** $\sqrt[3]{(a+b)^3}$ **e.** $\sqrt{y^4}$
>
> **Solution:**
>
> **a.** $\sqrt[4]{(-3)^4} = |-3| = 3$ Because this is an *even*-indexed root, absolute value bars are necessary to make the answer positive.
>
> **b.** $\sqrt[5]{(-3)^5} = -3$ This is an *odd*-indexed root, so absolute value bars are not necessary.
>
> **c.** $\sqrt{(x+2)^2} = |x+2|$ Because this is an *even*-indexed root, absolute value bars are necessary. The sign of the quantity $x+2$ is unknown; however, $|x+2| \geq 0$ regardless of the value of x.
>
> **d.** $\sqrt[3]{(a+b)^3} = a+b$ This is an *odd*-indexed root, so absolute value bars are not necessary.
>
> **e.** $\sqrt{y^4} = \sqrt{(y^2)^2}$
>
> $= |y^2|$ Because this is an even-indexed root, use absolute value bars.
>
> $= y^2$ However, because y^2 is nonnegative, the absolute value bars are not necessary.
>
> **Skill Practice** Simplify the expressions.
>
> **19.** $\sqrt{(-4)^2}$ **20.** $\sqrt[3]{(-4)^3}$ **21.** $\sqrt{(y+9)^2}$ **22.** $\sqrt[3]{(t+1)^3}$ **23.** $\sqrt[4]{v^8}$

If n is an even integer, then $\sqrt[n]{a^n} = |a|$; however, if the variable a is assumed to be *nonnegative*, then the absolute value bars may be dropped. That is, $\sqrt[n]{a^n} = a$ provided $a \geq 0$. In many examples and exercises, we will make the assumption that the variables within a radical expression are positive real numbers. In such a case, the absolute value bars are not needed to evaluate $\sqrt[n]{a^n}$.

In Chapter 6 you became familiar with the patterns associated with perfect squares and perfect cubes. In general, any expression raised to an even power is a perfect square. An expression raised to a power that is a multiple of three is a perfect cube.

Perfect Squares	**Perfect Cubes**
$(x^1)^2 = x^2$	$(x^1)^3 = x^3$
$(x^2)^2 = x^4$	$(x^2)^3 = x^6$
$(x^3)^2 = x^6$	$(x^3)^3 = x^9$
$(x^4)^2 = x^8$	$(x^4)^3 = x^{12}$

Answers
19. 4   **20.** -4 **21.** $|y+9|$
22. $t+1$ **23.** v^2

These patterns may be extended to higher powers.

Example 6 Simplifying *n*th Roots

Simplify the expressions. Assume that all variables are positive real numbers.

a. $\sqrt{y^8}$ **b.** $\sqrt[3]{27a^3}$ **c.** $\sqrt[5]{\dfrac{a^5}{b^5}}$ **d.** $-\sqrt[4]{\dfrac{81x^4y^8}{16}}$

Solution:

a. $\sqrt{y^8} = \sqrt{(y^4)^2} = y^4$ **b.** $\sqrt[3]{27a^3} = \sqrt[3]{(3a)^3} = 3a$

c. $\sqrt[5]{\dfrac{a^5}{b^5}} = \sqrt[5]{\left(\dfrac{a}{b}\right)^5} = \dfrac{a}{b}$ **d.** $-\sqrt[4]{\dfrac{81x^4y^8}{16}} = -\sqrt[4]{\left(\dfrac{3xy^2}{2}\right)^4} = -\dfrac{3xy^2}{2}$

Skill Practice Simplify the expressions. Assume all variables represent positive real numbers.

24. $\sqrt{t^6}$ **25.** $\sqrt[3]{64y^{12}}$ **26.** $\sqrt[4]{\dfrac{x^4}{y^4}}$ **27.** $-\sqrt[5]{\dfrac{32a^5}{b^{10}}}$

Classroom Examples: p. 701, Exercises 66 and 70

TIP: In Example 6, the variables are assumed to represent positive numbers. Therefore, absolute value bars are not necessary in the simplified form.

4. Pythagorean Theorem

In Section 6.8, we used the Pythagorean theorem in several applications. For the triangle shown in Figure 10-1, the **Pythagorean theorem** may be stated as $a^2 + b^2 = c^2$. In this formula, *a* and *b* are the legs of the right triangle, and *c* is the hypotenuse.

Example 7 Applying the Pythagorean Theorem

Use the Pythagorean theorem and the definition of the principal square root to find the length of the unknown side.

Solution:

Label the sides of the triangle.

$a^2 + b^2 = c^2$	Apply the Pythagorean theorem.
$(5)^2 + b^2 = (13)^2$	
$25 + b^2 = 169$	Simplify.
$b^2 = 169 - 25$	Isolate b^2.
$b^2 = 144$	By definition, *b* must be one of the square roots of 144. Because *b* represents the length of a side of a triangle, choose the positive square root of 144.
$b = 12$	

The third side is 12 ft long.

Skill Practice Use the Pythagorean theorem and the definition of the principal square root to find the length of the unknown side of the right triangle.

28.

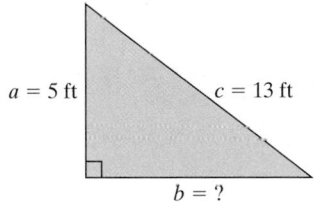

Figure 10-1

Classroom Example: p. 701, Exercise 78

Answers

24. t^3 **25.** $4y^4$ **26.** $\dfrac{x}{y}$

27. $-\dfrac{2a}{b^2}$ **28.** 9 cm

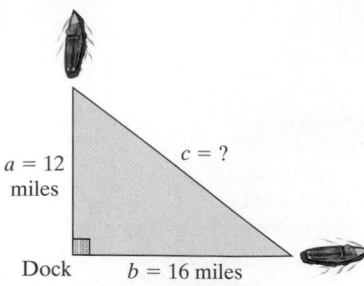

Figure 10-2

Example 8   Applying the Pythagorean Theorem

Two boats leave a dock at 12:00 noon. One travels due north at 6 mph, and the other travels due east at 8 mph (Figure 10-2). How far apart are the two boats after 2 hr?

Solution:

The boat traveling north travels a distance of (6 mph)(2 hr) = 12 mi. The boat traveling east travels a distance of (8 mph)(2 hr) = 16 mi. The course of the boats forms a right triangle where the hypotenuse represents the distance between them.

$$a^2 + b^2 = c^2$$

$$(12)^2 + (16)^2 = c^2 \qquad \text{Apply the Pythagorean theorem.}$$

$$144 + 256 = c^2 \qquad \text{Simplify.}$$

$$400 = c^2$$

$$\sqrt{400} = c \qquad \text{By definition, } c \text{ must be one of the square roots of}$$
$$\qquad\qquad\qquad 400. \text{ Choose the positive square root of } 400 \text{ to}$$
$$20 = c \qquad \text{represent the distance between the two boats.}$$

The boats are 20 mi apart.

Skill Practice

29. Two cars leave from the same place at the same time. One travels west at 40 mph, and the other travels north at 30 mph. How far apart are they after 2 hr?

5. Radical Functions

If n is an integer greater than 1, then a function written in the form $f(x) = \sqrt[n]{x}$ is called a **radical function**. Note that if n is an even integer, then the function will be a real number only if the radicand is nonnegative. Therefore, the domain is restricted to nonnegative real numbers, or equivalently, $[0, \infty)$. If n is an odd integer, then the domain is all real numbers.

Example 9   Determining the Domain of Radical Functions

For each function, write the domain in interval notation.

   a. $g(t) = \sqrt[4]{t - 2}$ **b.** $h(a) = \sqrt[3]{a - 3}$ **c.** $k(x) = \sqrt{3 - 5x} + 2$

Solution:

   a. $g(t) = \sqrt[4]{t - 2}$ The index is even. The radicand must be nonnegative.

        $t - 2 \geq 0$ Set the radicand greater than or equal to zero.

           $t \geq 2$ Solve for t.

   The domain is $[2, \infty)$.

   b. $h(a) = \sqrt[3]{a - 3}$ The index is odd; therefore, the domain is all real numbers.

   The domain is $(-\infty, \infty)$.

c. $k(x) = \sqrt{3 - 5x} + 2$ The index is even; therefore, the radicand must be nonnegative.

$3 - 5x \geq 0$ Set the radicand greater than or equal to zero.

$-5x \geq -3$ Solve for x.

$\dfrac{-5x}{-5} \leq \dfrac{-3}{-5}$ Reverse the inequality sign.

$x \leq \dfrac{3}{5}$

The domain is $(-\infty, \frac{3}{5}]$.

Skill Practice For each function, write the domain in interval notation.

30. $f(x) - \sqrt{x + 5}$ **31.** $g(t) = \sqrt[3]{t - 9}$ **32.** $h(a) = \sqrt{1 - 2a}$

Calculator Connections

We can graph the functions defined in Example 9. The graphs support the answers we obtained for the domain of each function.

$g(t) = \sqrt[4]{t - 2}$ $h(a) = \sqrt[3]{a - 3}$ $k(x) = \sqrt{3 - 5x} + 2$

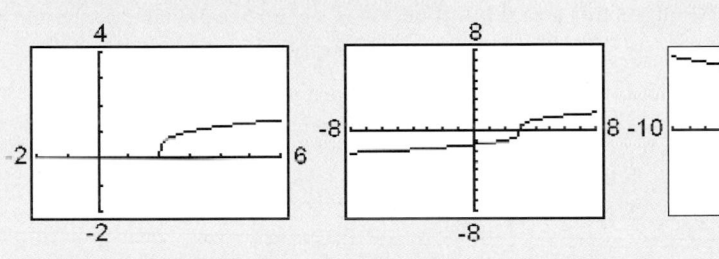

Answers

30. $[-5, \infty)$ **31.** $(-\infty, \infty)$

32. $(-\infty, \frac{1}{2}]$

Section 10.1   Practice Exercises

Boost *your* GRADE at ALEKS.com!

ALEKS version 3.0

- Practice Problems
- Self-Tests
- NetTutor
- e-Professors
- Videos

For additional exercises, see Classroom Activities 10.1A–10.1D in the *Instructor's Resource Manual* at www.mhhe.com/moh.

Study Skills Exercise

1. Define the key terms.

    a. square root   **b.** radical sign   **c.** principal square root   **d.** perfect square

    e. *n*th root   **f.** index   **g.** radicand   **h.** cube root

    i. pythagorean theorem   **j.** radical function

Concept 1: Definition of a Square Root

2. Simplify the expression $\sqrt[3]{8}$. Explain how you can check your answer. $\sqrt[3]{8} = 2$ because $2^3 = 8$.

 Writing   Translating Expression   Geometry   Scientific Calculator   Video   NS&E

3. a. Find the square roots of 64. **(See Example 1.)**
    8, −8
  b. Find $\sqrt{64}$.   8

  c. Explain the difference between the answers in part (a) and part (b).
There are two square roots for every positive number. $\sqrt{64}$ identifies the positive square root.

5. a. What is the principal square root of 81?   9

  b. What is the negative square root of 81?   −9

4. a. Find the square roots of 121.   11, −11
  b. Find $\sqrt{121}$.   11

  c. Explain the difference between the answers in part (a) and part (b).
There are two square roots for every positive number. $\sqrt{121}$ identifies the positive square root.

6. a. What is the principal square root of 100?   10

  b. What is the negative square root of 100?   −10

7. Using the definition of a square root, explain why $\sqrt{-36}$ is not a real number.   There is no real number b such that $b^2 = -36$.

For Exercises 8–19, evaluate the roots without using a calculator. Identify those that are not real numbers. **(See Examples 2–3.)**

8. $\sqrt{25}$ 5

9. $\sqrt{49}$ 7

10. $-\sqrt{25}$ −5

11. $-\sqrt{49}$ −7

12. $\sqrt{-25}$
Not a real number

13. $\sqrt{-49}$
Not a real number

14. $\sqrt{\dfrac{100}{121}}$ $\dfrac{10}{11}$

15. $\sqrt{\dfrac{64}{9}}$ $\dfrac{8}{3}$

16. $\sqrt{0.64}$ 0.8

17. $\sqrt{0.81}$ 0.9

18. $-\sqrt{0.0144}$ −0.12

19. $-\sqrt{0.16}$ −0.4

Concept 2: Definition of an *n*th Root

20. Using the definition of an *n*th root, explain why $\sqrt[4]{-16}$ is not a real number.   There is no real number b such that $b^4 = -16$.

For Exercises 21–38, evaluate the roots without using a calculator. Identify those that are not real numbers. **(See Example 4.)**

21. a. $\sqrt{64}$ 8
  b. $\sqrt[3]{64}$ 4
  c. $-\sqrt{64}$ −8
  d. $-\sqrt[3]{64}$ −4
  e. $\sqrt{-64}$ Not a real number
  f. $\sqrt[3]{-64}$ −4

22. a. $\sqrt{16}$ 4
  b. $\sqrt[4]{16}$ 2
  c. $-\sqrt{16}$ −4
  d. $-\sqrt[4]{16}$ −2
  e. $\sqrt{-16}$ Not a real number
  f. $\sqrt[4]{-16}$ Not a real number

23. $\sqrt[3]{-27}$ −3

24. $\sqrt[3]{-125}$ −5

25. $\sqrt[3]{\dfrac{1}{8}}$ $\dfrac{1}{2}$

26. $\sqrt[5]{\dfrac{1}{32}}$ $\dfrac{1}{2}$

27. $\sqrt[5]{32}$ 2

28. $\sqrt[4]{1}$ 1

29. $\sqrt[3]{-\dfrac{125}{64}}$ $-\dfrac{5}{4}$

30. $\sqrt[3]{-\dfrac{8}{27}}$ $-\dfrac{2}{3}$

31. $\sqrt[4]{-1}$
Not a real number

32. $\sqrt[6]{-1}$
Not a real number

33. $\sqrt[6]{1,000,000}$ 10

34. $\sqrt[4]{10,000}$ 10

35. $-\sqrt[3]{0.008}$ −0.2

36. $-\sqrt[4]{0.0016}$ −0.2

37. $\sqrt[4]{0.0625}$ 0.5

38. $\sqrt[3]{0.064}$ 0.4

Concept 3: Roots of Variable Expressions

For Exercises 39–58, simplify the radical expressions. **(See Example 5.)**

39. $\sqrt{a^2}$ $|a|$

40. $\sqrt[4]{a^4}$ $|a|$

41. $\sqrt[3]{a^3}$ a

42. $\sqrt[5]{a^5}$ a

43. $\sqrt[6]{a^6}$ $|a|$

44. $\sqrt[7]{a^7}$ a

45. $\sqrt{(x+1)^2}$ $|x+1|$

46. $\sqrt[3]{(y+3)^3}$ $y+3$

47. $\sqrt{x^2 y^4}$ $|x|y^2$

48. $\sqrt[3]{(u+v)^3}$ $u+v$

49. $-\sqrt[3]{\dfrac{x^3}{y^3}},\ y \neq 0$ $-\dfrac{x}{y}$

50. $\sqrt[4]{\dfrac{a^4}{b^8}},\ b \neq 0$ $\dfrac{|a|}{b^2}$

51. $\dfrac{2}{\sqrt[4]{x^4}}$, $x \neq 0$ $\dfrac{2}{|x|}$ **52.** $\sqrt{(-5)^2}$ 5   **53.** $\sqrt[3]{(-92)^3}$ -92 **54.** $\sqrt[6]{(50)^6}$ 50

55. $\sqrt[10]{(-2)^{10}}$ 2   **56.** $\sqrt[5]{(-2)^5}$ -2 **57.** $\sqrt[7]{(-923)^7}$ -923 **58.** $\sqrt[6]{(-417)^6}$ 417

For Exercises 59–74, simplify the expressions. Assume all variables are positive real numbers. **(See Example 6.)**

59. $\sqrt{x^2y^4}$ xy^2 **60.** $\sqrt{16p^2}$ $4p$ **61.** $\sqrt{\dfrac{a^6}{b^2}}$ $\dfrac{a^3}{b}$ **62.** $\sqrt{\dfrac{w^2}{z^4}}$ $\dfrac{w}{z^2}$

63. $-\sqrt{\dfrac{25}{q^2}}$ $-\dfrac{5}{q}$ **64.** $-\sqrt{\dfrac{p^6}{81}}$ $-\dfrac{p^3}{9}$ **65.** $\sqrt{9x^2y^4z^2}$ $3xy^2z$ **66.** $\sqrt{4a^4b^2c^6}$ $2a^2bc^3$

67. $\sqrt{\dfrac{h^2k^4}{16}}$ $\dfrac{hk^2}{4}$ **68.** $\sqrt{\dfrac{4x^2}{y^8}}$ $\dfrac{2x}{y^4}$ **69.** $-\sqrt[3]{\dfrac{t^3}{27}}$ $-\dfrac{t}{3}$ **70.** $\sqrt[4]{\dfrac{16}{w^4}}$ $\dfrac{2}{w}$

71. $\sqrt[5]{32y^{10}}$ $2y^2$ **72.** $\sqrt[3]{64x^6y^3}$ $4x^2y$ ⊙ **73.** $\sqrt[6]{64p^{12}q^{18}}$ $2p^2q^3$ **74.** $\sqrt[4]{16r^{12}s^8}$ $2r^3s^2$

Concept 4: Pythagorean Theorem

For Exercises 75–78, find the length of the third side of each triangle by using the Pythagorean theorem. **(See Example 7.)**

75.

76.

77.

78.

For Exercises 79–82, use the Pythagorean theorem.

79. Roberto and Sherona began running from the same place at the same time. They ran along two different paths that formed right angles with each other. Roberto ran 4 mi and stopped, while Sherona ran 3 mi and stopped. How far apart were they when they stopped? **(See Example 8.)**

They were 5 mi apart.

80. Leine and Laura began hiking from their campground. Laura headed south while Leine headed east. Laura walked 12 mi and Leine walked 5 mi. How far apart were they when they stopped walking?   They were 13 mi apart.

81. Two mountain bikers take off from the same place at the same time. One travels north at 4 mph, and the other travels east at 3 mph. How far apart are they after 5 hr?   They are 25 mi apart.

82. Professor Ortiz leaves campus on her bike, heading west at 12 ft/sec. Professor Wilson leaves campus at the same time and walks south at 5 ft/sec. How far apart are they after 40 sec?

They are 520 ft apart.

Concept 5: Radical Functions

For Exercises 83–86, evaluate the function for the given values of *x*. Then write the domain of the function in interval notation. **(See Example 9.)**

83. $h(x) = \sqrt{x - 2}$

   a. $h(0)$ Not a real number

   b. $h(1)$ Not a real number

   c. $h(2)$ 0

   d. $h(3)$ 1

   e. $h(6)$ 2

   Domain: $[2, \infty)$

84. $k(x) = \sqrt{x + 1}$

   a. $k(-3)$ Not a real number

   b. $k(-2)$ Not a real number

   c. $k(-1)$ 0

   d. $k(0)$ 1

   e. $k(3)$ 2

   Domain: $[-1, \infty)$

85. $g(x) = \sqrt[3]{x - 2}$

   a. $g(-6)$ -2

   b. $g(1)$ -1

   c. $g(2)$ 0

   d. $g(3)$ 1

   Domain: $(-\infty, \infty)$

86. $f(x) = \sqrt[3]{x + 1}$

   a. $f(-9)$ -2

   b. $f(-2)$ -1

   c. $f(0)$ 1

   d. $f(7)$ 2

   Domain: $(-\infty, \infty)$

 Writing   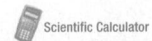 Translating Expression   Geometry   Scientific Calculator   Video   NS&E

For each function defined in Exercises 87–94, write the domain in interval notation. **(See Example 9.)**

87. $f(x) = \sqrt{5 - 2x}$
$\left(-\infty, \frac{5}{2}\right]$

88. $g(x) = \sqrt{3 - 4x}$
$\left(-\infty, \frac{3}{4}\right]$

89. $k(x) = \sqrt[3]{4x - 7}$
$(-\infty, \infty)$

90. $R(x) = \sqrt[3]{x + 1}$
$(-\infty, \infty)$

91. $M(x) = \sqrt{x - 5} + 3$
$[5, \infty)$

92. $N(x) = \sqrt{x + 3} - 1$
$[-3, \infty)$

93. $F(x) = \sqrt[3]{x + 7} - 2$
$(-\infty, \infty)$

94. $G(x) = \sqrt[3]{x - 10} + 4$
$(-\infty, \infty)$

For Exercises 95–98, find the domain of the function. Then match the function with its graph.

95. $p(x) = \sqrt{1 - x}$
$(-\infty, 1]$; b

96. $q(x) = \sqrt{x + 5}$
$[-5, \infty)$; a

97. $T(x) = \sqrt{x - 10}$
$[10, \infty)$; d

98. $R(x) = \sqrt[3]{x + 1}$
$(-\infty, \infty)$; c

a.

b.

c.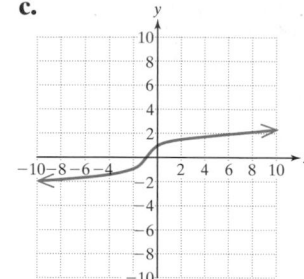

d.

Mixed Exercises

For Exercises 99–102, write the English phrase as an algebraic expression.

99. The sum of q and the square of p $q + p^2$

100. The product of 11 and the cube root of x $11\sqrt[3]{x}$

101. The quotient of 6 and the cube root of x $\dfrac{6}{\sqrt[3]{x}}$

102. The difference of y and the principal square root of x
$y - \sqrt{x}$

103. If a square has an area of 64 in.^{2}, then what are the lengths of the sides?   8 in.

$s = ?$

$A = 64$ in.^{2} $s = ?$

104. If a square has an area of 121 m^2, then what are the lengths of the sides?   11 m

$s = ?$

$A = 121$ m^2 $s = ?$

Graphing Calculator Exercises

For Exercises 105–112, use a calculator to evaluate the expressions to four decimal places.

105. $\sqrt{69}$ 8.3066

106. $\sqrt{5798}$ 76.1446

107. $2 + \sqrt[3]{5}$ 3.7100

108. $3 - 2\sqrt[4]{10}$ −0.5566

109. $7\sqrt[4]{25}$ 15.6525

110. $-3\sqrt[3]{9}$ −6.2403

111. $\dfrac{3 - \sqrt{19}}{11}$ −0.1235

112. $\dfrac{5 + 2\sqrt{15}}{12}$ 1.0622

113. Graph $h(x) = \sqrt{x - 2}$. Use the graph to confirm the domain found in Exercise 83.

114. Graph $k(x) = \sqrt{x + 1}$. Use the graph to confirm the domain found in Exercise 84.

115. Graph $g(x) = \sqrt[3]{x - 2}$. Use the graph to confirm the domain found in Exercise 85.

116. Graph $f(x) = \sqrt[3]{x + 1}$. Use the graph to confirm the domain found in Exercise 86.

Rational Exponents

1. Definition of $a^{1/n}$ and $a^{m/n}$

In Sections 5.1–5.3, the properties for simplifying expressions with integer exponents were presented. In this section, the properties are expanded to include expressions with rational exponents. We begin by defining expressions of the form $a^{1/n}$.

> **DEFINITION** $a^{1/n}$
>
> Let a be a real number, and let n be an integer such that $n > 1$. If $\sqrt[n]{a}$ is a real number, then
>
> $$a^{1/n} = \sqrt[n]{a}$$

Concepts

1. **Definition of $a^{1/n}$ and $a^{m/n}$**
2. **Converting Between Rational Exponents and Radical Notation**
3. **Properties of Rational Exponents**
4. **Applications Involving Rational Exponents**

Example 1   **Evaluating Expressions of the Form $a^{1/n}$**

Convert the expression to radical form and simplify, if possible.

a. $(-8)^{1/3}$ **b.** $81^{1/4}$ **c.** $-100^{1/2}$ **d.** $(-100)^{1/2}$ **e.** $16^{-1/2}$

Solution:

a. $(-8)^{1/3} = \sqrt[3]{-8} = -2$

b. $81^{1/4} = \sqrt[4]{81} = 3$

c. $-100^{1/2} = -1 \cdot 100^{1/2}$ The exponent applies only to the base of 100.

$\qquad = -1\sqrt{100}$

$\qquad = -10$

d. $(-100)^{1/2}$ is not a real number because $\sqrt{-100}$ is not a real number.

e. $16^{-1/2} = \dfrac{1}{16^{1/2}}$ Write the expression with a positive exponent.

$\qquad\qquad\qquad$ Recall that $b^{-n} = \dfrac{1}{b^n}$.

$\qquad = \dfrac{1}{\sqrt{16}}$

$\qquad = \dfrac{1}{4}$

Skill Practice   Convert the expression to radical form and simplify, if possible.

1. $(-64)^{1/3}$ **2.** $16^{1/4}$ **3.** $-36^{1/2}$ **4.** $(-36)^{1/2}$ **5.** $64^{-1/3}$

Classroom Examples: p. 708, Exercises 10, 14, and 18

If $\sqrt[n]{a}$ is a real number, then we can define an expression of the form $a^{m/n}$ in such a way that the multiplication property of exponents still holds true. For example:

$$16^{3/4} \nearrow (16^{1/4})^3 = (\sqrt[4]{16})^3 = (2)^3 = 8$$
$$\searrow (16^3)^{1/4} = \sqrt[4]{16^3} = \sqrt[4]{4096} = 8$$

Answers

1. -4 **2.** 2 **3.** -6

4. Not a real number   **5.** $\dfrac{1}{4}$

> **DEFINITION** $a^{m/n}$
>
> Let a be a real number, and let m and n be positive integers such that m and n share no common factors and $n > 1$. If $\sqrt[n]{a}$ is a real number, then
>
> $$a^{m/n} = (a^{1/n})^m = (\sqrt[n]{a})^m \qquad \text{and} \qquad a^{m/n} = (a^m)^{1/n} = \sqrt[n]{a^m}$$

The rational exponent in the expression $a^{m/n}$ is essentially performing two operations. The numerator of the exponent raises the base to the mth power. The denominator takes the nth root.

Classroom Example: p. 708, Exercise 26

| **Example 2** | **Evaluating Expressions of the Form $a^{m/n}$** |

Convert each expression to radical form and simplify.

a. $8^{2/3}$ **b.** $100^{5/2}$ **c.** $\left(\dfrac{1}{25}\right)^{3/2}$ **d.** $4^{-3/2}$ **e.** $(-81)^{3/4}$

Solution:

Calculator Connections

A calculator can be used to confirm the results of Example 2(a)–2(c).

```
(8)^(2/3)
                4
(100)^(5/2)
           100000
(1/25)^(3/2)
             .008
```

a. $8^{2/3} = (\sqrt[3]{8})^2$ Take the cube root of 8 and square the result.

$\quad\quad\; = (2)^2$ Simplify.

$\quad\quad\; = 4$

b. $100^{5/2} = (\sqrt{100})^5$ Take the square root of 100 and raise the result to the fifth power.

$\quad\quad\quad\; = (10)^5$ Simplify.

$\quad\quad\quad\; = 100{,}000$

c. $\left(\dfrac{1}{25}\right)^{3/2} = \left(\sqrt{\dfrac{1}{25}}\right)^3$ Take the square root of $\dfrac{1}{25}$ and cube the result.

$\quad\quad\quad\;\; = \left(\dfrac{1}{5}\right)^3$ Simplify.

$\quad\quad\quad\;\; = \dfrac{1}{125}$

d. $4^{-3/2} = \left(\dfrac{1}{4}\right)^{3/2} = \dfrac{1}{4^{3/2}}$ Write the expression with positive exponents.

$\quad\quad\quad\; = \dfrac{1}{(\sqrt{4})^3}$ Take the square root of 4 and cube the result.

$\quad\quad\quad\; = \dfrac{1}{2^3}$ Simplify.

$\quad\quad\quad\; = \dfrac{1}{8}$

e. $(-81)^{3/4}$ is not a real number because $\sqrt[4]{-81}$ is not a real number.

Skill Practice Convert each expression to radical form and simplify.

6. $9^{3/2}$ **7.** $8^{5/3}$ **8.** $\left(\dfrac{1}{27}\right)^{4/3}$ **9.** $32^{-4/5}$ **10.** $(-4)^{3/2}$

2. Converting Between Rational Exponents and Radical Notation

Example 3   **Using Radical Notation and Rational Exponents**

Classroom Examples: p. 708, Exercises 52 and 54

Convert each expression to radical notation. Assume all variables represent positive real numbers.

a. $a^{3/5}$ **b.** $(5x^2)^{1/3}$ **c.** $3y^{1/4}$ **d.** $z^{-3/4}$

Solution:

a. $a^{3/5} = \sqrt[5]{a^3}$ or $\left(\sqrt[5]{a}\right)^3$

b. $(5x^2)^{1/3} = \sqrt[3]{5x^2}$

c. $3y^{1/4} = 3\sqrt[4]{y}$ Note that the coefficient 3 is not raised to the $\frac{1}{4}$ power.

d. $z^{-3/4} = \dfrac{1}{z^{3/4}} = \dfrac{1}{\sqrt[4]{z^3}}$

Skill Practice Convert each expression to radical notation. Assume all variables represent positive real numbers.

11. $t^{4/5}$ **12.** $(2y^3)^{1/4}$ **13.** $10p^{1/2}$ **14.** $q^{-2/3}$

Example 4   **Using Radical Notation and Rational Exponents**

Classroom Examples: p. 709, Exercises 62 and 64

Convert each expression to an equivalent expression by using rational exponents. Assume that all variables represent positive real numbers.

a. $\sqrt[4]{b^3}$ **b.** $\sqrt{7a}$ **c.** $7\sqrt{a}$

Solution:

a. $\sqrt[4]{b^3} = b^{3/4}$ **b.** $\sqrt{7a} = (7a)^{1/2}$ **c.** $7\sqrt{a} = 7a^{1/2}$

Skill Practice Convert to an equivalent expression using rational exponents. Assume all variables represent positive real numbers.

15. $\sqrt[3]{x^2}$ **16.** $\sqrt{5y}$ **17.** $5\sqrt{y}$

3. Properties of Rational Exponents

In Sections 5.1–5.3, several properties and definitions were introduced to simplify expressions with integer exponents. These properties also apply to rational exponents.

Answers

6. 27   **7.** 32   **8.** $\dfrac{1}{81}$

9. $\dfrac{1}{16}$ **10.** Not a real number

11. $\sqrt[5]{t^4}$ **12.** $\sqrt[4]{2y^3}$ **13.** $10\sqrt{p}$

14. $\dfrac{1}{\sqrt[3]{q^2}}$ **15.** $x^{2/3}$ **16.** $(5y)^{1/2}$

17. $5y^{1/2}$

SUMMARY Definitions and Properties of Exponents

Let a and b be nonzero real numbers. Let m and n be rational numbers such that a^m, a^n, and b^m are real numbers.

Description	Property	Example
1. Multiplying like bases	$a^m a^n = a^{m+n}$	$x^{1/3} x^{4/3} = x^{5/3}$
2. Dividing like bases	$\dfrac{a^m}{a^n} = a^{m-n}$	$\dfrac{x^{3/5}}{x^{1/5}} = x^{2/5}$
3. The power rule	$(a^m)^n = a^{mn}$	$(2^{1/3})^{1/2} = 2^{1/6}$
4. Power of a product	$(ab)^m = a^m b^m$	$(9y)^{1/2} = 9^{1/2} y^{1/2} = 3y^{1/2}$
5. Power of a quotient	$\left(\dfrac{a}{b}\right)^m = \dfrac{a^m}{b^m}$	$\left(\dfrac{4}{25}\right)^{1/2} = \dfrac{4^{1/2}}{25^{1/2}} = \dfrac{2}{5}$

Description	Definition	Example
1. Negative exponents	$a^{-m} = \left(\dfrac{1}{a}\right)^m = \dfrac{1}{a^m}$	$(8)^{-1/3} = \left(\dfrac{1}{8}\right)^{1/3} = \dfrac{1}{2}$
2. Zero exponent	$a^0 = 1$	$5^0 = 1$

Classroom Examples: p. 709, Exercises 68, 76, and 82

Example 5 Simplifying Expressions with Rational Exponents

Use the properties of exponents to simplify the expressions. Assume all variables represent positive real numbers.

a. $y^{2/5} y^{3/5}$ **b.** $\dfrac{6a^{-1/2}}{a^{3/2}}$ **c.** $\left(\dfrac{s^{1/2} t^{1/3}}{w^{3/4}}\right)^4$

Solution:

a. $y^{2/5} y^{3/5} = y^{(2/5)+(3/5)}$ Multiply like bases by adding exponents.

$= y^{5/5}$ Simplify.

$= y$

b. $\dfrac{6a^{-1/2}}{a^{3/2}}$ Divide like bases by subtracting exponents.

$= 6a^{(-1/2)-(3/2)}$ Simplify: $-\dfrac{4}{2} = -2$

$= 6a^{-2}$

$= \dfrac{6}{a^2}$ Simplify the negative exponent.

c. $\left(\dfrac{s^{1/2} t^{1/3}}{w^{3/4}}\right)^4 = \dfrac{s^{(1/2)\cdot 4} t^{(1/3)\cdot 4}}{w^{(3/4)\cdot 4}}$ Apply the power rule. Multiply exponents.

$= \dfrac{s^2 t^{4/3}}{w^3}$ Simplify.

Skill Practice Use the properties of exponents to simplify the expressions. Assume all variables represent positive real numbers.

18. $x^{1/2} \cdot x^{3/4}$ **19.** $\dfrac{4k^{-2/3}}{k^{1/3}}$ **20.** $\left(\dfrac{a^{1/3} b^{1/2}}{c^{5/8}}\right)^6$

Answers

18. $x^{5/4}$ **19.** $\dfrac{4}{k}$ **20.** $\dfrac{a^2 b^3}{c^{15/4}}$

4. Applications Involving Rational Exponents

Example 6 Applying Rational Exponents

Suppose P dollars in principal is invested in an account that earns interest annually. If after t years the investment grows to A dollars, then the annual rate of return r on the investment is given by

$$r = \left(\frac{A}{P}\right)^{1/t} - 1$$

Find the annual rate of return on $5000 which grew to $6894.21 after 6 yr.

Classroom Example: p. 709, Exercise 92

Solution:

$$r = \left(\frac{A}{P}\right)^{1/t} - 1$$

$$= \left(\frac{6894.21}{5000}\right)^{1/6} - 1 \quad \text{where } A = \$6894.21, P = \$5000, \text{ and } t = 6$$

$$\approx 0.055 \text{ or } 5.5\%$$

The annual rate of return is 5.5%.

Skill Practice

21. The formula for the radius of a sphere is

$$r = \left(\frac{3V}{4\pi}\right)^{1/3}$$

where V is the volume. Find the radius of a sphere whose volume is 113.04 in.^{3} (Use 3.14 for π.)

Answer

21. 3 in.

Section 10.2 Practice Exercises

Boost *your* **GRADE at ALEKS.com!**

ALEKS
version 3.0

- Practice Problems
- Self-Tests
- NetTutor

- e-Professors
- Videos

For additional exercises, see Classroom Activities 10.2A–10.2C in the *Instructor's Resource Manual* at www.mhhe.com/moh.

For the exercises in this set, assume that all variables represent positive real numbers unless otherwise stated.

Study Skills Exercises

1. Before you do your homework for this section, go back to Sections 5.1–5.3 and review the properties of exponents. Do several problems from the Section 5.3 exercises. This will help you with the concepts in Section 10.2.

2. Define the key terms.

   a. $a^{1/n}$ **b.** $a^{m/n}$

Review Exercises

3. Given: $\sqrt[3]{27}$

   a. Identify the index.   3

   b. Identify the radicand.   27

4. Given: $\sqrt{18}$

   a. Identify the index.   2

   b. Identify the radicand.   18

 Writing   Translating Expression   Geometry   Scientific Calculator   Video   NS&E

For Exercises 5–8, evaluate the radicals.

5. $\sqrt{25}$ 5

6. $\sqrt[3]{8}$ 2

7. $\sqrt[4]{81}$ 3

8. $(\sqrt[4]{16})^3$ 8

Concept 1: Definition of $a^{1/n}$ and $a^{m/n}$

For Exercises 9–20, convert the expressions to radical form and simplify. **(See Example 1.)**

9. $144^{1/2}$ 12

10. $16^{1/4}$ 2

11. $-144^{1/2}$ -12

12. $-16^{1/4}$ -2

13. $(-144)^{1/2}$
Not a real number

14. $(-16)^{1/4}$
Not a real number

15. $(-64)^{1/3}$ -4

16. $(-32)^{1/5}$ -2

17. $(25)^{-1/2}$ $\frac{1}{5}$

18. $(27)^{-1/3}$ $\frac{1}{3}$

19. $-49^{-1/2}$ $-\frac{1}{7}$

20. $-64^{-1/2}$ $-\frac{1}{8}$

21. Explain how to interpret the expression $a^{m/n}$ as a radical. $a^{m/n} = \sqrt[n]{a^m}$; The numerator of the exponent represents the power of the base. The denominator of the exponent represents the index of the radical.

22. Explain why $(\sqrt[3]{8})^4$ is easier to evaluate than $\sqrt[3]{8^4}$.
$(\sqrt[3]{8})^4$ works within the parentheses first. Taking the root first results in a smaller number that must be raised to the fourth power. $\sqrt[3]{8^4}$ takes the fourth power of 8 first. This results in a larger number whose cube root may be difficult to identify.

For Exercises 23–26, simplify the expression, if possible. **(See Example 2.)**

23. a. $16^{3/4}$ 8
b. $-16^{3/4}$ -8
c. $(-16)^{3/4}$
Not a real number
d. $16^{-3/4}$ $\frac{1}{8}$
e. $-16^{-3/4}$ $-\frac{1}{8}$
f. $(-16)^{-3/4}$
Not a real number

24. a. $81^{3/4}$ 27
b. $-81^{3/4}$ -27
c. $(-81)^{3/4}$
Not a real number
d. $81^{-3/4}$ $\frac{1}{27}$
e. $-81^{-3/4}$ $-\frac{1}{27}$
f. $(-81)^{-3/4}$
Not a real number

25. a. $25^{3/2}$ 125
b. $-25^{3/2}$ -125
c. $(-25)^{3/2}$
Not a real number
d. $25^{-3/2}$ $\frac{1}{125}$
e. $-25^{-3/2}$ $-\frac{1}{125}$
f. $(-25)^{-3/2}$
Not a real number

26. a. $4^{3/2}$ 8
b. $-4^{3/2}$ -8
c. $(-4)^{3/2}$
Not a real number
d. $4^{-3/2}$ $\frac{1}{8}$
e. $-4^{-3/2}$ $-\frac{1}{8}$
f. $(-4)^{-3/2}$
Not a real number

For Exercises 27–50, simplify the expression. **(See Example 2.)**

27. $64^{-3/2}$ $\frac{1}{512}$

28. $81^{-3/2}$ $\frac{1}{729}$

29. $243^{3/5}$ 27

30. $1^{5/3}$ 1

31. $-27^{-4/3}$ $-\frac{1}{81}$

32. $-16^{-5/4}$ $-\frac{1}{32}$

33. $\left(\frac{100}{9}\right)^{-3/2}$ $\frac{27}{1000}$

34. $\left(\frac{49}{100}\right)^{-1/2}$ $\frac{10}{7}$

35. $(-4)^{-3/2}$ Not a real number

36. $(-49)^{-3/2}$ Not a real number

37. $(-8)^{1/3}$ -2

38. $(-9)^{1/2}$ Not a real number

39. $-8^{1/3}$ -2

40. $-9^{1/2}$ -3

41. $\frac{1}{36^{-1/2}}$ 6

42. $\frac{1}{16^{-1/2}}$ 4

43. $\frac{1}{1000^{-1/3}}$ 10

44. $\frac{1}{81^{-3/4}}$ 27

45. $\left(\frac{1}{8}\right)^{2/3} + \left(\frac{1}{4}\right)^{1/2}$ $\frac{3}{4}$

46. $\left(\frac{1}{8}\right)^{-2/3} + \left(\frac{1}{4}\right)^{-1/2}$ 6

47. $\left(\frac{1}{16}\right)^{-3/4} - \left(\frac{1}{49}\right)^{-1/2}$ 1

48. $\left(\frac{1}{16}\right)^{1/4} - \left(\frac{1}{49}\right)^{1/2}$ $\frac{5}{14}$

49. $\left(\frac{1}{4}\right)^{1/2} + \left(\frac{1}{64}\right)^{-1/3}$ $\frac{9}{2}$

50. $\left(\frac{1}{36}\right)^{1/2} + \left(\frac{1}{64}\right)^{-5/6}$ $\frac{193}{6}$

Concept 2: Converting Between Rational Exponents and Radical Notation

For Exercises 51–58, convert each expression to radical notation. **(See Example 3.)**

51. $q^{2/3}$ $\sqrt[3]{q^2}$

52. $t^{3/5}$ $\sqrt[5]{t^3}$

53. $6y^{3/4}$ $6\sqrt[4]{y^3}$

54. $8b^{4/9}$ $8\sqrt[9]{b^4}$

55. $(x^2y)^{1/3}$ $\sqrt[3]{x^2y}$

56. $(c^2d)^{1/6}$ $\sqrt[6]{c^2d}$

57. $(qr)^{-1/5}$ $\frac{1}{\sqrt[5]{qr}}$

58. $(7x)^{-1/4}$ $\frac{1}{\sqrt[4]{7x}}$

For Exercises 59–66, write each expression by using rational exponents rather than radical notation. **(See Example 4.)**

59. $\sqrt[3]{x}$ $\quad x^{1/3}$

60. $\sqrt[4]{a}$ $\quad a^{1/4}$

61. $10\sqrt{b}$ $\quad 10b^{1/2}$

62. $-2\sqrt[3]{t}$ $\quad -2t^{1/3}$

 63. $\sqrt[3]{y^2}$ $\quad y^{2/3}$

64. $\sqrt[6]{z^5}$ $\quad z^{5/6}$

65. $\sqrt[4]{a^2b^3}$ $\quad (a^2b^3)^{1/4}$

66. $\sqrt{abc}$ $\quad (abc)^{1/2}$

Concept 3: Properties of Rational Exponents

For Exercises 67–90, simplify the expressions by using the properties of rational exponents. Write the final answer using positive exponents only. **(See Example 5.)**

67. $x^{1/4}x^{-5/4}$ $\quad \dfrac{1}{x}$

68. $2^{2/3}2^{-5/3}$ $\quad \dfrac{1}{2}$

69. $\dfrac{p^{5/3}}{p^{2/3}}$ $\quad p$

70. $\dfrac{q^{5/4}}{q^{1/4}}$ $\quad q$

71. $(y^{1/5})^{10}$ $\quad y^2$

72. $(x^{1/2})^8$ $\quad x^4$

73. $6^{-1/5}6^{3/5}$ $\quad 6^{2/5}$

74. $a^{-1/3}a^{2/3}$ $\quad a^{1/3}$

75. $\dfrac{4t^{-1/3}}{t^{4/3}}$ $\quad \dfrac{4}{t^{5/3}}$

76. $\dfrac{5s^{-1/3}}{s^{5/3}}$ $\quad \dfrac{5}{s^2}$

77. $(a^{1/3}a^{1/4})^{12}$ $\quad a^7$

78. $(x^{2/3}x^{1/2})^6$ $\quad x^7$

79. $(5a^2c^{-1/2}d^{1/2})^2$ $\quad \dfrac{25a^4d}{c}$

80. $(2x^{-1/3}y^2z^{5/3})^3$ $\quad \dfrac{8y^6z^5}{x}$

81. $\left(\dfrac{x^{-2/3}}{y^{-3/4}}\right)^{12}$ $\quad \dfrac{y^9}{x^8}$

82. $\left(\dfrac{m^{-1/4}}{n^{-1/2}}\right)^{-4}$ $\quad \dfrac{m}{n^2}$

83. $\left(\dfrac{16w^{-2}z}{2wz^{-8}}\right)^{1/3}$ $\quad \dfrac{2z^3}{w}$

84. $\left(\dfrac{50p^{-1}q}{2pq^{-3}}\right)^{1/2}$ $\quad \dfrac{5q^2}{p}$

85. $(25x^2y^4z^6)^{1/2}$ $\quad 5xy^2z^3$

86. $(8a^6b^3c^9)^{2/3}$ $\quad 4a^4b^2c^6$

87. $(x^2y^{-1/3})^6(x^{1/2}yz^{2/3})^2$
$x^{13}z^{4/3}$

88. $(a^{-1/3}b^{1/2})^4(a^{-1/2}b^{3/5})^{10}$
$\dfrac{b^8}{a^{19/3}}$

89. $\left(\dfrac{x^{3m}y^{2m}}{z^{5m}}\right)^{1/m}$ $\quad \dfrac{x^3y^2}{z^5}$

90. $\left(\dfrac{a^{4n}b^{3n}}{c^n}\right)^{1/n}$ $\quad \dfrac{a^4b^3}{c}$

Concept 4: Applications Involving Rational Exponents

91. If P dollars in principal grows to A dollars after t years with annual interest, then the interest rate is given by $r = \left(\dfrac{A}{P}\right)^{1/t} - 1$. **(See Example 6.)**

    a. In one account, $10,000 grows to $16,802 after 5 yr. Compute the interest rate. Round your answer to a tenth of a percent.   10.9%

    b. In another account $10,000 grows to $18,000 after 7 yr. Compute the interest rate. Round your answer to a tenth of a percent.   8.8%

    c. Which account produced a higher average yearly return?   The account in part (a).

92. If the area A of a square is known, then the length of its sides, s, can be computed by the formula $s = A^{1/2}$.

    a. Compute the length of the sides of a square having an area of 100 in.^{2} 10 in.

    b. Compute the length of the sides of a square having an area of 72 in.^{2} Round your answer to the nearest 0.1 in.   8.5 in.

93. The radius r of a sphere of volume V is given by $r = \left(\dfrac{3V}{4\pi}\right)^{1/3}$. Find the radius of a sphere having a volume of 85 in.^{3} Round your answer to the nearest 0.1 in.   2.7 in.

94. Is $(a + b)^{1/2}$ the same as $a^{1/2} + b^{1/2}$? If not, give a counterexample.   Not the same. For example: $(9 + 16)^{1/2} = (25)^{1/2} = 5$
$9^{1/2} + 16^{1/2} = 3 + 4 = 7$

 Writing   Translating Expression   Geometry   Scientific Calculator   Video   NSE

Expanding Your Skills

For Exercises 95–106, write the expression using rational exponents. Then simplify and convert back to radical notation. Assume that all variables represent positive real numbers.

Example: $\sqrt[15]{x^{10}}$ $\xrightarrow[\text{exponents}]{\text{Rational}}$ $x^{10/15}$ $\xrightarrow{\text{Simplify}}$ $x^{2/3}$ $\xrightarrow[\text{notation}]{\text{Radical}}$ $\sqrt[3]{x^2}$

95. $\sqrt[6]{y^3}$ $\sqrt{y}$

96. $\sqrt[4]{w^2}$ $\sqrt{w}$

97. $\sqrt[12]{z^3}$ $\sqrt[4]{z}$

98. $\sqrt[18]{t^3}$ $\sqrt[6]{t}$

99. $\sqrt[9]{x^6}$ $\sqrt[3]{x^2}$

100. $\sqrt[12]{p^9}$ $\sqrt[4]{p^3}$

101. $\sqrt[6]{x^3y^6}$ $y\sqrt{x}$

102. $\sqrt[8]{m^2p^8}$ $p\sqrt[4]{m}$

103. $\sqrt{16x^8y^6}$ $4x^4y^3$

104. $\sqrt{81a^{12}b^{20}}$ $9a^6b^{10}$

105. $\sqrt[3]{8x^3y^7z^8}$ $2xy^2z^2\sqrt[3]{yz^2}$

106. $\sqrt[3]{64m^5n^9p}$ $4mn^3\sqrt[3]{m^2p}$

For Exercises 107–110, write the expression as a single radical.

107. $\sqrt{\sqrt[3]{x}}$ $\sqrt[6]{x}$

108. $\sqrt[3]{\sqrt{x}}$ $\sqrt[6]{x}$

109. $\sqrt[5]{\sqrt[3]{w}}$ $\sqrt[15]{w}$

110. $\sqrt[3]{\sqrt[4]{w}}$ $\sqrt[12]{w}$

For Exercises 111–118, use a calculator to approximate the expressions. Round to four decimal places, if necessary.

111. $9^{1/2}$ 3

112. $125^{-1/3}$ 0.2

113. $50^{-1/4}$ 0.3761

114. $(172)^{3/5}$ 21.9441

115. $\sqrt[3]{5^2}$ 2.9240

116. $\sqrt[4]{6^3}$ 3.8337

117. $\sqrt{10^3}$ 31.6228

118. $\sqrt[3]{16}$ 2.5198

Section 10.3   Simplifying Radical Expressions

Concepts

1. Multiplication Property of Radicals
2. Simplifying Radicals by Using the Multiplication Property of Radicals
3. Simplifying Radicals by Using the Order of Operations

1. Multiplication Property of Radicals

You may have already noticed certain properties of radicals involving a product or quotient.

> **PROPERTY   Multiplication Property of Radicals**
>
> Let a and b represent real numbers such that $\sqrt[n]{a}$ and $\sqrt[n]{b}$ are both real. Then
> $$\sqrt[n]{ab} = \sqrt[n]{a} \cdot \sqrt[n]{b}$$

The multiplication property of radicals follows from the property of rational exponents.

$$\sqrt[n]{ab} = (ab)^{1/n} = a^{1/n}b^{1/n} = \sqrt[n]{a} \cdot \sqrt[n]{b}$$

The multiplication property of radicals indicates that a product within a radicand can be written as a product of radicals, provided the roots are real numbers. For example:

$$\sqrt{144} = \sqrt{16} \cdot \sqrt{9}$$

The reverse process is also true. A product of radicals can be written as a single radical provided the roots are real numbers and they have the same indices.

$$\sqrt{3} \cdot \sqrt{12} = \sqrt{36}$$

2. Simplifying Radicals by Using the Multiplication Property of Radicals

In algebra, it is customary to simplify radical expressions.

DEFINITION Simplified Form of a Radical

Consider any radical expression where the radicand is written as a product of prime factors. The expression is in *simplified form* if all the following conditions are met:

1. The radicand has no factor raised to a power greater than or equal to the index.
2. The radicand does not contain a fraction.
3. There are no radicals in the denominator of a fraction.

For example, the following radicals are not simplified.

1. The expression $\sqrt[3]{x^5}$ fails condition 1.

2. The expression $\sqrt{\dfrac{1}{4}}$ fails condition 2.

3. The expression $\dfrac{1}{\sqrt[3]{8}}$ fails condition 3.

The expressions $\sqrt{x^2}$, $\sqrt{x^4}$, $\sqrt{x^6}$, and $\sqrt{x^8}$ are not simplified because they fail condition 1 (the exponents are not less than the index). However, each radicand is a perfect square and is easily simplified for $x \geq 0$.

$$\sqrt{x^2} = x$$
$$\sqrt{x^4} = x^2$$
$$\sqrt{x^6} = x^3$$
$$\sqrt{x^8} = x^4$$

However, how is an expression such as $\sqrt{x^9}$ simplified? This and many other radical expressions are simplified by using the multiplication property of radicals. We demonstrate the process in Examples 1–4.

Example 1 Using the Multiplication Property to Simplify a Radical Expression

Classroom Example: p. 715, Exercise 10

Simplify the expression for $x \geq 0$. $\sqrt{x^9}$

Solution:

The expression $\sqrt{x^9}$ is equivalent to $\sqrt{x^8 \cdot x}$.

$$\sqrt{x^9} = \sqrt{x^8 \cdot x}$$
$$= \sqrt{x^8} \cdot \sqrt{x} \qquad \text{Apply the multiplication property of radicals.}$$
$$\qquad\qquad\quad \text{Note that } x^8 \text{ is a perfect square because } x^8 = (x^4)^2.$$
$$= x^4\sqrt{x} \qquad \text{Simplify.}$$

Instructor Note: Try giving students a visual representation of simplifying a radical.

$\sqrt{x^9}$
$= \sqrt{(x \cdot x) \cdot (x \cdot x) \cdot (x \cdot x) \cdot (x \cdot x) \cdot x}$
$= x^4 \sqrt{x}$

Skill Practice Simplify the expression. Assume $a \geq 0$.

1. $\sqrt{a^{11}}$

Answer

1. $a^5\sqrt{a}$

In Example 1, the expression x^9 is not a perfect square. Therefore, to simplify $\sqrt{x^9}$, it was necessary to write the expression as the product of the largest perfect square and a remaining or "left-over" factor: $\sqrt{x^9} = \sqrt{x^8} \cdot x$. This process also applies to simplifying nth roots, as shown in Example 2.

Classroom Examples: p. 715, Exercises 14 and 16

Example 2 Using the Multiplication Property to Simplify Radical Expressions

Simplify each expression. Assume all variables represent positive real numbers.

a. $\sqrt[4]{b^7}$ **b.** $\sqrt[3]{w^7 z^9}$

Solution:

The goal is to rewrite each radicand as the product of the greatest perfect square (perfect cube, perfect fourth power, and so on) and a leftover factor.

a. $\sqrt[4]{b^7} = \sqrt[4]{b^4 \cdot b^3}$ b^4 is the greatest perfect fourth power in the radicand.

$= \sqrt[4]{b^4} \cdot \sqrt[4]{b^3}$ Apply the multiplication property of radicals.

$= b\sqrt[4]{b^3}$ Simplify.

b. $\sqrt[3]{w^7 z^9} = \sqrt[3]{(w^6 z^9) \cdot (w)}$ $w^6 z^9$ is the greatest perfect cube in the radicand.

$= \sqrt[3]{w^6 z^9} \cdot \sqrt[3]{w}$ Apply the multiplication property of radicals.

$= w^2 z^3 \sqrt[3]{w}$ Simplify.

Skill Practice Simplify the expressions. Assume all variables represent positive real numbers.

2. $\sqrt[4]{v^{25}}$ **3.** $\sqrt[3]{p^{17} q^{10}}$

Classroom Example: p. 715, Exercise 18

Each expression in Example 2 involves a radicand that is a product of variable factors. If a numerical factor is present, sometimes it is necessary to factor the coefficient before simplifying the radical.

Calculator Connections

A calculator can be used to support the solution to Example 3. The decimal approximation for $\sqrt{56}$ and $2\sqrt{14}$ agree for the first 10 digits. This in itself does not make $\sqrt{56} = 2\sqrt{14}$. It is the multiplication property of radicals that guarantees that the expressions are equal.

```
√(56)
        7.483314774
2*√(14)
        7.483314774
```

Example 3 Using the Multiplication Property to Simplify a Radical

Simplify the expression. $\sqrt{56}$

Solution:

$\sqrt{56} = \sqrt{2^3 \cdot 7}$ Factor the radicand.

$= \sqrt{(2^2) \cdot (2 \cdot 7)}$ 2^2 is the greatest perfect square in the radicand.

$= \sqrt{2^2} \cdot \sqrt{2 \cdot 7}$ Apply the multiplication property of radicals.

$= 2\sqrt{14}$ Simplify.

$$\begin{array}{r} 2\,\lfloor 56 \\ 2\,\lfloor 28 \\ 2\,\lfloor 14 \\ 7 \end{array}$$

Skill Practice Simplify.

4. $\sqrt{24}$

Answers

2. $v^6 \sqrt[4]{v}$ **3.** $p^5 q^3 \sqrt[3]{p^2 q}$ **4.** $2\sqrt{6}$

Example 4 **Using the Multiplication Property to Simplify Radicals**

Classroom Examples: p. 715, Exercises 22 and 32

Simplify the expressions. Assume that all variables represent positive real numbers.

a. $6\sqrt{50}$ **b.** $\sqrt[3]{40x^3y^5z^7}$

Solution:

a. $6\sqrt{50} = 6\sqrt{5^2 \cdot 2}$ Factor the radicand.

$= 6 \cdot \sqrt{5^2} \cdot \sqrt{2}$ Apply the multiplication property of radicals.

$= 6 \cdot 5 \cdot \sqrt{2}$ Simplify.

$= 30\sqrt{2}$ Simplify.

b. $\sqrt[3]{40x^3y^5z^7}$

$= \sqrt[3]{2^3 5 x^3 y^5 z^7}$ Factor the radicand.

$= \sqrt[3]{(2^3 x^3 y^3 z^6) \cdot (5y^2 z)}$ $2^3 x^3 y^3 z^6$ is the greatest perfect cube.

$= \sqrt[3]{2^3 x^3 y^3 z^6} \cdot \sqrt[3]{5y^2 z}$ Apply the multiplication property of radicals.

$= 2xyz^2 \sqrt[3]{5y^2 z}$ Simplify.

$$\begin{array}{r|l} 2 & 40 \\ 2 & 20 \\ 2 & 10 \\ & 5 \end{array}$$

Skill Practice Simplify. Assume that $a > 0$ and $b > 0$.

5. $5\sqrt{18}$ **6.** $\sqrt[4]{32a^{10}b^{19}}$

TIP: To simplify the numerical factor within a radical, we can also write the factor as the product of the greatest perfect square (cube, etc.) and a "leftover" factor.

Example: $\sqrt{50} = \sqrt{25 \cdot 2} = 5\sqrt{2}$ **Example:** $\sqrt[3]{40} = \sqrt[3]{8 \cdot 5} = 2\sqrt[3]{5}$

$\uparrow$ $\uparrow$

Greatest perfect square factor of 50   Greatest perfect cube factor of 40

---

3. Simplifying Radicals by Using the Order of Operations

Often a radical can be simplified by applying the order of operations. In Examples 5 and 6, the first step will be to simplify the expression within the radicand.

Example 5 **Using the Order of Operations to Simplify Radicals**

Classroom Examples: p. 715, Exercises 36 and 40

Use the order of operations to simplify the expressions. Assume $a > 0$.

a. $\sqrt{\dfrac{a^7}{a^3}}$ **b.** $\sqrt[3]{\dfrac{3}{81}}$

Solution:

a. $\sqrt{\dfrac{a^7}{a^3}}$ The radicand contains a fraction. However, the fraction can be reduced to lowest terms.

$= \sqrt{a^4}$

$= a^2$ Simplify the radical.

Answers

5. $15\sqrt{2}$ **6.** $2a^2 b^4 \sqrt[4]{2a^2 b^3}$

b. $\sqrt[3]{\dfrac{3}{81}}$ The radical contains a fraction that can be simplified.

$= \sqrt[3]{\dfrac{1}{27}}$ Reduce to lowest terms.

$= \dfrac{1}{3}$ Simplify.

Skill Practice Use the order of operations to simplify the expressions. Assume $v > 0$.

7. $\sqrt{\dfrac{v^{21}}{v^5}}$ **8.** $\sqrt[5]{\dfrac{64}{2}}$

Classroom Example: p. 715, Exercise 42

Example 6   **Applying the Order of Operations**

Use the order of operations to simplify. $\dfrac{7\sqrt{50}}{10}$

Solution:

$\dfrac{7\sqrt{50}}{10} = \dfrac{7\sqrt{25 \cdot 2}}{10}$ 25 is the greatest perfect square in the radicand.

$= \dfrac{7 \cdot 5\sqrt{2}}{10}$ Simplify the radical.

$= \dfrac{7 \cdot \overset{1}{\cancel{5}}\sqrt{2}}{\underset{2}{\cancel{10}}}$ Simplify the fraction to lowest terms.

$= \dfrac{7\sqrt{2}}{2}$

Avoiding Mistakes

The expression $\frac{7\sqrt{2}}{2}$ cannot be simplified further because one factor of 2 is in the radicand and the other is outside the radical.

Skill Practice Simplify.

9. $\dfrac{2\sqrt{300}}{30}$

Answers

7. v^8 **8.** 2   **9.** $\dfrac{2\sqrt{3}}{3}$

Section 10.3   Practice Exercises

For the exercises in this set, assume that all variables represent positive real numbers unless otherwise stated.

Study Skills Exercise

1. The final exam is just around the corner. Your old tests and quizzes provide good material to study for the final exam. Use your old tests to make a list of the concepts on which you need to concentrate. Ask your professor for help if there are still concepts that you do not understand.

 Writing   Translating Expression   Geometry   Scientific Calculator   Video   NS&E

Review Exercises

For Exercises 2–4, simplify the expression. Write the answer with positive exponents only.

2. $(a^2b^{-4})^{1/2}\left(\dfrac{a}{b^{-3}}\right)$ $\quad a^2b$

3. $\left(\dfrac{p^4}{q^{-6}}\right)^{-1/2}(p^3q^{-2})$ $\quad \dfrac{p}{q^5}$

4. $(x^{1/3}y^{5/6})^{-6}$ $\quad \dfrac{1}{x^2y^5}$

5. Write $x^{4/7}$ in radical notation. $\quad \sqrt[7]{x^4}$

6. Write $y^{2/5}$ in radical notation. $\quad \sqrt[5]{y^2}$

7. Write $\sqrt{y^9}$ by using rational exponents. $\quad y^{9/2}$

8. Write $\sqrt[3]{x^2}$ by using rational exponents. $\quad x^{2/3}$

Concept 2: Simplifying Radicals by Using the Multiplication Property of Radicals

For Exercises 9–32, simplify the radicals. **(See Examples 1–4.)**

9. $\sqrt{x^5}$ $\quad x^2\sqrt{x}$

10. $\sqrt{p^{15}}$ $\quad p^7\sqrt{p}$

11. $\sqrt[3]{q^7}$ $\quad q^2\sqrt[3]{q}$

12. $\sqrt[3]{r^{17}}$ $\quad r^5\sqrt[3]{r^2}$

13. $\sqrt{a^5b^4}$ $\quad a^2b^2\sqrt{a}$

14. $\sqrt{c^9d^6}$ $\quad c^4d^3\sqrt{c}$

15. $-\sqrt[4]{x^8y^{13}}$ $\quad -x^2y^3\sqrt[4]{y}$

16. $-\sqrt[4]{p^{16}q^{17}}$ $\quad -p^4q^4\sqrt[4]{q}$

17. $\sqrt{28}$ $\quad 2\sqrt{7}$

18. $\sqrt{63}$ $\quad 3\sqrt{7}$

19. $\sqrt{20}$ $\quad 2\sqrt{5}$

20. $\sqrt{50}$ $\quad 5\sqrt{2}$

21. $5\sqrt{18}$ $\quad 15\sqrt{2}$

22. $2\sqrt{24}$ $\quad 4\sqrt{6}$

23. $\sqrt[3]{54}$ $\quad 3\sqrt[3]{2}$

24. $\sqrt[3]{250}$ $\quad 5\sqrt[3]{2}$

25. $\sqrt{25ab^3}$ $\quad 5b\sqrt{ab}$

26. $\sqrt{64m^5n^{20}}$ $\quad 8m^2n^{10}\sqrt{m}$

27. $\sqrt[3]{40x^7}$ $\quad 2x^2\sqrt[3]{5x}$

28. $\sqrt[3]{81y^{17}}$ $\quad 3y^5\sqrt[3]{3y^2}$

29. $\sqrt[3]{-16x^6yz^3}$ $\quad -2x^2z\sqrt[3]{2y}$

30. $\sqrt[3]{-192a^6bc^2}$ $\quad -4a^2\sqrt[3]{3bc^2}$

31. $\sqrt[4]{80w^4z^7}$ $\quad 2wz\sqrt[4]{5z^3}$

32. $\sqrt[4]{32p^8qr^5}$ $\quad 2p^2r\sqrt[4]{2qr}$

Concept 3: Simplifying Radicals by Using the Order of Operations

For Exercises 33–44, simplify the radicals. **(See Examples 5–6.)**

33. $\sqrt{\dfrac{x^3}{x}}$ $\quad x$

34. $\sqrt{\dfrac{y^5}{y}}$ $\quad y^2$

35. $\sqrt{\dfrac{p^7}{p^3}}$ $\quad p^2$

36. $\sqrt{\dfrac{q^{11}}{q^5}}$ $\quad q^3$

37. $\sqrt{\dfrac{50}{2}}$ $\quad 5$

38. $\sqrt{\dfrac{98}{2}}$ $\quad 7$

39. $\sqrt[3]{\dfrac{3}{24}}$ $\quad \dfrac{1}{2}$

40. $\sqrt[3]{\dfrac{2}{250}}$ $\quad \dfrac{1}{5}$

41. $\dfrac{5\sqrt[3]{16}}{6}$ $\quad \dfrac{5\sqrt[3]{2}}{3}$

42. $\dfrac{7\sqrt{18}}{9}$ $\quad \dfrac{7\sqrt{2}}{3}$

43. $\dfrac{5\sqrt[3]{72}}{12}$ $\quad \dfrac{5\sqrt[3]{9}}{6}$

44. $\dfrac{3\sqrt[3]{250}}{10}$ $\quad \dfrac{3\sqrt[3]{2}}{2}$

Mixed Exercises

For Exercises 45–72, simplify the radicals.

45. $\sqrt{80}$ $\quad 4\sqrt{5}$

46. $\sqrt{108}$ $\quad 6\sqrt{3}$

47. $-6\sqrt{75}$ $\quad -30\sqrt{3}$

48. $-8\sqrt{8}$ $\quad -16\sqrt{2}$

49. $\sqrt{25x^4y^3}$ $\quad 5x^2y\sqrt{y}$

50. $\sqrt{125p^3q^2}$ $\quad 5pq\sqrt{5p}$

51. $\sqrt[3]{27x^2y^3z^4}$ $\quad 3yz\sqrt[3]{x^2z}$

52. $\sqrt[3]{108a^3bc^2}$ $\quad 3a\sqrt[3]{4bc^2}$

53. $\sqrt{\dfrac{12w^5}{3w}}$ $\quad 2w^2$

54. $\sqrt{\dfrac{64x^9}{4x^3}}$ $\quad 4x^3$

55. $\sqrt{\dfrac{3y^3}{300y^{15}}}$ $\quad \dfrac{1}{10y^6}$

56. $\sqrt{\dfrac{4h}{100h^5}}$ $\quad \dfrac{1}{5h^2}$

57. $\sqrt[3]{\dfrac{16a^2b}{2a^2b^4}}$ $\quad \dfrac{2}{b}$

58. $\sqrt[3]{\dfrac{-27a^4}{8a}}$ $\quad -\dfrac{3a}{2}$

59. $\sqrt{2^3a^{14}b^8c^{31}d^{22}}$ $\quad 2a^7b^4c^{15}d^{11}\sqrt{2c}$

60. $\sqrt{7^5u^{12}v^{20}w^{65}x^{80}}$ $\quad 49u^6v^{10}w^{32}x^{40}\sqrt{7w}$

61. $\sqrt{18a^6b^3}$ $\quad 3a^3b\sqrt{2b}$

62. $\sqrt{72m^5n^2}$ $\quad 6m^2n\sqrt{2m}$

63. $-5a\sqrt{12a^3b^4c}$ $\quad -10a^2b^2\sqrt{3ac}$

64. $-7y\sqrt{75xy^5z^6}$ $\quad -35y^3z^3\sqrt{3xy}$

65. $\sqrt{7x^5y}$ $\quad x^2\sqrt{7xy}$

66. $\sqrt{10pq^7}$ $\quad q^3\sqrt{10pq}$

67. $\sqrt{54a^4b^2}$ $\quad 3a^2b\sqrt{6}$

68. $\sqrt{48r^6s^2}$ $\quad 4r^3s\sqrt{3}$

69. $\dfrac{2\sqrt{27}}{3}$ $\quad 2\sqrt{3}$

70. $\dfrac{7\sqrt{24}}{2}$ $\quad 7\sqrt{6}$

71. $\dfrac{3\sqrt{125}}{20}$ $\quad \dfrac{3\sqrt{5}}{4}$

72. $\dfrac{10\sqrt{63}}{12}$ $\quad \dfrac{5\sqrt{7}}{2}$

 Writing Translating Expression Geometry Scientific Calculator Video NS&E

↔ For Exercises 73–76, write a mathematical expression for the English phrase and simplify.

73. The quotient of 1 and the cube root of w^6

$\dfrac{1}{\sqrt[3]{w^6}}$ simplifies to $\dfrac{1}{w^2}$

74. The principal square root of the quotient of h^2 and 49

$\sqrt{\dfrac{h^2}{49}}$ simplifies to $\dfrac{h}{7}$

75. The principal square root of the quantity k raised to the third power $\sqrt{k^3}$ simplifies to $k\sqrt{k}$

76. The cube root of $2x^4$

$\sqrt[3]{2x^4}$ simplifies to $x\sqrt[3]{2x}$

For Exercises 77–80, determine the length of the third side of the right triangle. Write the answer as a simplified radical.

77.

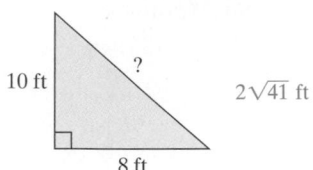

10 ft   ?

8 ft $2\sqrt{41}$ ft

78.

?   4 in.

12 in. $4\sqrt{10}$ in.

79.

?   18 m

12 m $6\sqrt{5}$ m

80.

3 cm   7 cm

? $2\sqrt{10}$ cm

81. On a baseball diamond, the bases are 90 ft apart. Find the exact distance from home plate to second base. Then round to the nearest tenth of a foot.

The distance is $90\sqrt{2}$ ft or approximately 127.3 ft.

2nd base

90 ft

90 ft

Home plate

82. Linda is at the beach flying a kite. The kite is directly over a sand castle 60 ft away from Linda. If 100 ft of kite string is out (ignoring any sag in the string), how high is the kite? (Assume that Linda is 5 ft tall.) See figure.

The kite is 85 ft high.

100 ft

60 ft

5 ft

Expanding Your Skills

83. Tom has to travel from town A to town C across a small mountain range. He can travel one of two routes. He can travel on a four-lane highway from A to B and then from B to C at an average speed of 55 mph. Or he can travel on a two-lane road directly from town A to town C, but his average speed will be only 35 mph. If Tom is in a hurry, which route will take him to town C faster?

The path from A to B and B to C is faster.

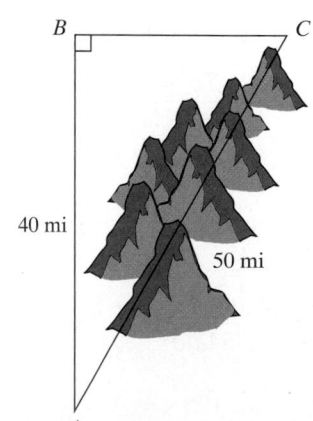

B   C

40 mi

50 mi

A

84. One side of a rectangular pasture is 80 ft in length. The diagonal distance is 110 yd. If fencing costs $3.29 per foot, how much will it cost to fence the pasture?

It will cost approximately $2633.

110 yd   80 ft

 Writing   Translating Expression   Geometry   Scientific Calculator   Video   NS&E

Addition and Subtraction of Radicals

Section 10.4

1. Addition and Subtraction of Radicals

Concept

1. Addition and Subtraction of Radicals

> **DEFINITION** *Like* Radicals
>
> Two radical terms are called *like* **radicals** if they have the same index and same radicand.

Like radicals can be added or subtracted by using the distributive property.

$$\underset{\text{Same radicand}}{\underset{\uparrow \qquad \uparrow}{3\sqrt{x} + 7\sqrt{x}}} = \overset{\text{Distributive property}}{\overbrace{(3 + 7)}}\sqrt{x} = 10\sqrt{x}$$

Same index

Example 1 Adding and Subtracting Radicals

Classroom Example: p. 720, Exercise 20

Add or subtract as indicated.

a. $6\sqrt{11} - 2\sqrt{11}$ **b.** $\sqrt{3} + \sqrt{3}$

Solution:

a. $6\sqrt{11} - 2\sqrt{11}$

  $= (6 - 2)\sqrt{11}$ Apply the distributive property.

  $= 4\sqrt{11}$ Simplify.

b. $\sqrt{3} + \sqrt{3}$

  $= 1\sqrt{3} + 1\sqrt{3}$ Note that $\sqrt{3} = 1\sqrt{3}$.

  $= (1 + 1)\sqrt{3}$ Apply the distributive property.

  $= 2\sqrt{3}$ Simplify.

Avoiding Mistakes

The process of adding *like* radicals with the distributive property is similar to adding *like* terms. The end result is that the numerical coefficients are added and the radical factor is unchanged.

$$\sqrt{3} + \sqrt{3} = 1\sqrt{3} + 1\sqrt{3} = 2\sqrt{3}$$

Be careful: $\sqrt{3} + \sqrt{3} \neq \sqrt{6}$

In general: $\sqrt{x} + \sqrt{y} \neq \sqrt{x + y}$

Skill Practice Add or subtract as indicated.

1. $5\sqrt{6} - 8\sqrt{6}$ **2.** $\sqrt{10} + \sqrt{10}$

Answers

1. $-3\sqrt{6}$ **2.** $2\sqrt{10}$

Classroom Example: p. 721,
Exercise 30

Example 2 Adding and Subtracting Radicals

Add or subtract as indicated.

a. $-2\sqrt[3]{ab} + 7\sqrt[3]{ab} - \sqrt[3]{ab}$ b. $\frac{1}{4}x\sqrt{3y} - \frac{3}{2}x\sqrt{3y}$

Solution:

a. $-2\sqrt[3]{ab} + 7\sqrt[3]{ab} - \sqrt[3]{ab}$

   $= (-2 + 7 - 1)\sqrt[3]{ab}$ Apply the distributive property.

   $= 4\sqrt[3]{ab}$ Simplify.

b. $\frac{1}{4}x\sqrt{3y} - \frac{3}{2}x\sqrt{3y}$

   $= \left(\frac{1}{4} - \frac{3}{2}\right)x\sqrt{3y}$ Apply the distributive property.

   $= \left(\frac{1}{4} - \frac{6}{4}\right)x\sqrt{3y}$ Get a common denominator.

   $= -\frac{5}{4}x\sqrt{3y}$ Simplify.

Skill Practice Add or subtract as indicated.

3. $5\sqrt[3]{xy} - 3\sqrt[3]{xy} + 7\sqrt[3]{xy}$

4. $\frac{5}{6}y\sqrt{2} + \frac{1}{4}y\sqrt{2}$

Example 3 shows that it is often necessary to simplify radicals before adding or subtracting.

Classroom Examples: p. 721,
Exercises 38 and 60

Example 3 Adding and Subtracting Radicals

Simplify the radicals and add or subtract as indicated. Assume all variables represent positive real numbers.

a. $3\sqrt{8} + \sqrt{2}$ b. $8\sqrt{x^3y^2} - 3y\sqrt{x^3}$

c. $\sqrt{50x^2y^5} - 13y\sqrt{2x^2y^3} + xy\sqrt{98y^3}$

Solution:

a. $3\sqrt{8} + \sqrt{2}$ The radicands are different. Try simplifying the radicals first.

   $= 3 \cdot 2\sqrt{2} + \sqrt{2}$ Simplify: $\sqrt{8} = \sqrt{2^3} = 2\sqrt{2}$

   $= 6\sqrt{2} + \sqrt{2}$

   $= (6 + 1)\sqrt{2}$ Apply the distributive property.

   $= 7\sqrt{2}$ Simplify.

Answers

3. $9\sqrt[3]{xy}$ 4. $\frac{13}{12}y\sqrt{2}$

b. $8\sqrt{x^3y^2} - 3y\sqrt{x^3}$ — The radicands are different. Simplify the radicals first.

$= 8xy\sqrt{x} - 3xy\sqrt{x}$ — Simplify $\sqrt{x^3y^2} = xy\sqrt{x}$ and $\sqrt{x^3} = x\sqrt{x}$.

$= (8 - 3)xy\sqrt{x}$ — Apply the distributive property.

$= 5xy\sqrt{x}$ — Simplify.

c. $\sqrt{50x^2y^5} - 13y\sqrt{2x^2y^3} + xy\sqrt{98y^3}$ — Simplify each radical.

$$\begin{cases} \sqrt{50x^2y^5} = \sqrt{25 \cdot 2x^2y^5} \\ \qquad = 5xy^2\sqrt{2y} \\ -13y\sqrt{2x^2y^3} = -13xy^2\sqrt{2y} \\ xy\sqrt{98y^3} = xy\sqrt{49 \cdot 2y^3} \\ \qquad = 7xy^2\sqrt{2y} \end{cases}$$

$= 5xy^2\sqrt{2y} - 13xy^2\sqrt{2y} + 7xy^2\sqrt{2y}$

$= (5 - 13 + 7)xy^2\sqrt{2y}$ — Apply the distributive property.

$= -xy^2\sqrt{2y}$

Skill Practice Simplify the radicals and add or subtract as indicated. Assume all variables represent positive real numbers.

5. $\sqrt{75} + 2\sqrt{3}$
6. $4\sqrt{a^2b} - 6a\sqrt{b}$
7. $-3\sqrt{2y^3} + 5y\sqrt{18y} - 2\sqrt{50y^3}$

In some cases, when two radicals are added, the resulting sum must be written in factored form. This is demonstrated in Example 4.

Example 4 Adding Radical Expressions

Classroom Example: p. 721, Exercise 58

Add the radicals. Assume that $x \geq 0$. $3\sqrt{2x^2} + \sqrt{8}$

Solution:

$3\sqrt{2x^2} + \sqrt{8}$

$= 3x\sqrt{2} + 2\sqrt{2}$ — Simplify each radical. Notice that the radicands are the same, but the terms are not *like* terms. The first term has a factor of x and the second does not.

$= (3x + 2)\sqrt{2}$ — Apply the distributive property. The expression cannot be simplified further because $3x$ and 2 are not *like* terms.

Skill Practice Add the radicals. Assume that $y \geq 0$.

8. $4\sqrt{45} - \sqrt{5y^4}$

Answers

5. $7\sqrt{3}$ **6.** $-2a\sqrt{b}$
7. $2y\sqrt{2y}$ **8.** $(12 - y^2)\sqrt{5}$

Section 10.4 Practice Exercises

For the exercises in this set, assume that all variables represent positive real numbers, unless otherwise stated.

Study Skills Exercise

1. Define the key term *like* radicals.

Review Exercises

For Exercises 2–5, simplify the radicals.

2. $\sqrt[3]{-16s^4t^9}$ $-2st^3\sqrt[3]{2s}$ **3.** $-\sqrt[4]{x^7y^4}$ $-xy\sqrt[4]{x^3}$ **4.** $\sqrt{36a^2b^3}$ $6ab\sqrt{b}$ **5.** $\sqrt[3]{\dfrac{7b^8}{56b^2}}$ $\dfrac{b^2}{2}$

6. Write $(4x^2)^{1/3}$ in radical notation. $\sqrt[3]{4x^2}$

7. Write $\sqrt[4]{x^3y}$ using rational exponents. $(x^3y)^{1/4}$

8. Simplify. $32^{-1/5}$ $\dfrac{1}{2}$

For Exercises 9–10, simplify the expressions. Write the answer with positive exponents only.

9. $y^{2/3}y^{1/4}$ $y^{11/12}$

10. $(x^{1/2}y^{-3/4})^{-4}$ $\dfrac{y^3}{x^2}$

Concept 1: Addition and Subtraction of Radicals

For Exercises 11–12, determine if the radical terms are *like*.

11. a. $\sqrt{2}$ and $\sqrt[3]{2}$ Not *like* radicals

b. $\sqrt{2}$ and $3\sqrt{2}$ *Like* radicals

c. $\sqrt{2}$ and $\sqrt{5}$ Not *like* radicals

12. a. $7\sqrt[3]{x}$ and $\sqrt[3]{x}$ *Like* radicals

b. $\sqrt[3]{x}$ and $\sqrt[4]{x}$ Not *like* radicals

c. $2\sqrt[4]{x}$ and $x\sqrt[4]{2}$ Not *like* radicals

13. Explain the similarities between the pairs of expressions.

a. $7\sqrt{5} + 4\sqrt{5}$ and $7x + 4x$ Both expressions can be simplified by using the distributive property.

b. $-2\sqrt{6} - 9\sqrt{3}$ and $-2x - 9y$ Neither expression can be simplified because the terms do not contain *like* radicals or *like* terms.

14. Explain the similarities between the pairs of expressions.

a. $-4\sqrt{3} + 5\sqrt{3}$ and $-4z + 5z$ Both expressions can be simplified by using the distributive property.

b. $13\sqrt{7} - 18$ and $13a - 18$ Neither expression can be simplified because the terms do not contain *like* radicals or *like* terms.

For Exercises 15–32, add or subtract the radical expressions, if possible. **(See Examples 1–2.)**

15. $3\sqrt{5} + 6\sqrt{5}$ $9\sqrt{5}$

16. $5\sqrt{a} + 3\sqrt{a}$ $8\sqrt{a}$

17. $3\sqrt[3]{tw} - 2\sqrt[3]{tw} + \sqrt[3]{tw}$ $2\sqrt[3]{tw}$

18. $6\sqrt[3]{7} - 2\sqrt[3]{7} + \sqrt[3]{7}$ $5\sqrt[3]{7}$

19. $6\sqrt{10} - \sqrt{10}$ $5\sqrt{10}$

20. $13\sqrt{11} - \sqrt{11}$ $12\sqrt{11}$

21. $\sqrt[4]{3} + 7\sqrt[4]{3} - \sqrt[4]{14}$ $8\sqrt[4]{3} - \sqrt[4]{14}$

22. $2\sqrt{11} + 3\sqrt{13} + 5\sqrt{11}$ $7\sqrt{11} + 3\sqrt{13}$

23. $8\sqrt{x} + 2\sqrt{y} - 6\sqrt{x}$ $2\sqrt{x} + 2\sqrt{y}$

24. $10\sqrt{10} - 8\sqrt{10} + \sqrt{2}$ $2\sqrt{10} + \sqrt{2}$

25. $\sqrt[3]{ab} + a\sqrt[3]{b}$ Cannot be simplified further

26. $x\sqrt[4]{y} - y\sqrt[4]{x}$ Cannot be simplified further

27. $\sqrt[4]{2t} + \sqrt[3]{2t}$ Cannot be simplified further

28. $\sqrt[4]{5c} + \sqrt[3]{5c}$ Cannot be simplified further

29. $\dfrac{5}{6}z\sqrt[3]{6} + \dfrac{7}{9}z\sqrt[3]{6}$ $\dfrac{29}{18}z\sqrt[3]{6}$

30. $\frac{3}{4}a\sqrt[4]{b} + \frac{1}{6}a\sqrt[4]{b}$ $\frac{11}{12}a\sqrt[4]{b}$ **31.** $0.81x\sqrt{y} - 0.11x\sqrt{y}$ $0.7x\sqrt{y}$ **32.** $7.5\sqrt{pq} - 6.3\sqrt{pq}$ $1.2\sqrt{pq}$

33. Explain the process for adding the two radicals. Then find the sum. $3\sqrt{2} + 7\sqrt{50}$ Simplify each radical: $3\sqrt{2} + 35\sqrt{2}$. Then add *like* radicals: $38\sqrt{2}$

34. Explain the process for subtracting two radicals. Then find the difference. $\sqrt{12x} - \sqrt{75x}$ Simplify each radical: $2\sqrt{3x} - 5\sqrt{3x}$. Then subtract *like* radicals: $-3\sqrt{3x}$

For Exercises 35–64, add or subtract the radical expressions as indicated. **(See Examples 3–4.)**

35. $\sqrt{36} + \sqrt{81}$ 15   **36.** $3\sqrt{80} - 5\sqrt{45}$ $-3\sqrt{5}$ **37.** $2\sqrt{12} + \sqrt{48}$ $8\sqrt{3}$ **38.** $5\sqrt{32} + 2\sqrt{50}$ $30\sqrt{2}$

39. $4\sqrt{7} + \sqrt{63} - 2\sqrt{28}$ $3\sqrt{7}$ **40.** $8\sqrt{3} - 2\sqrt{27} + \sqrt{75}$ $7\sqrt{3}$ **41.** $5\sqrt{18} + \sqrt{32} - 4\sqrt{50}$ $-\sqrt{2}$ **42.** $7\sqrt{72} - \sqrt{8} + 4\sqrt{50}$ $60\sqrt{2}$

43. $\sqrt[3]{81} - \sqrt[3]{24}$ $\sqrt[3]{3}$ **44.** $17\sqrt[3]{81} - 2\sqrt[3]{24}$ $47\sqrt[3]{3}$ **45.** $3\sqrt{2a} - \sqrt{8a} - \sqrt{72a}$ $-5\sqrt{2a}$ **46.** $\sqrt{12t} - \sqrt{27t} + 5\sqrt{3t}$ $4\sqrt{3t}$

47. $2s^2\sqrt[3]{s^2t^6} + 3t^2\sqrt[3]{8s^8}$ $8s^2t^2\sqrt[3]{s^2}$ **48.** $4\sqrt[3]{x^4} - 2x\sqrt[3]{x}$ $2x\sqrt[3]{x}$ **49.** $7\sqrt[3]{x^4} - x\sqrt[3]{x}$ $6x\sqrt[3]{x}$ **50.** $6\sqrt[3]{y^{10}} - 3y^2\sqrt[3]{y^4}$ $3y^3\sqrt[3]{y}$

51. $5p\sqrt{20p^2} + p^2\sqrt{80}$ $14p^2\sqrt{5}$ **52.** $2q\sqrt{48q^2} - \sqrt{27q^4}$ $5q^2\sqrt{3}$ **53.** $\sqrt[3]{a^2b} - \sqrt[3]{8a^2b}$ $-\sqrt[3]{a^2b}$ **54.** $w\sqrt{80} - 3\sqrt{125w^2}$ $-11w\sqrt{5}$

55. $5x\sqrt{x} + 6\sqrt{x}$ $(5x + 6)\sqrt{x}$ **56.** $9y^2\sqrt{2} + 4\sqrt{2}$ $(9y^2 + 4)\sqrt{2}$ **57.** $\sqrt{50x^2} - 3\sqrt{8}$ $(5x - 6)\sqrt{2}$ **58.** $\sqrt{9x^3} - \sqrt{25x}$ $(3x - 5)\sqrt{x}$

59. $11\sqrt[3]{54cd^3} - 2\sqrt[3]{2cd^3} + d\sqrt[3]{16c}$ $33d\sqrt[3]{2c}$ **60.** $x\sqrt[3]{64x^5y^2} - x^2\sqrt[3]{x^2y^2} + 5\sqrt[3]{x^8y^2}$ $8x^2\sqrt[3]{x^2y^2}$

61. $\frac{3}{2}ab\sqrt{24a^3} + \frac{4}{3}\sqrt{54a^5b^2} - a^2b\sqrt{150a}$ $2a^2b\sqrt{6a}$ **62.** $mn\sqrt{72n} + \frac{2}{3}n\sqrt{8m^2n} - \frac{5}{6}\sqrt{50m^2n^3}$ $\frac{19}{6}mn\sqrt{2n}$

63. $x\sqrt[3]{16} - 2\sqrt[3]{27x} + \sqrt[3]{54x^3}$ $5x\sqrt[3]{2} - 6\sqrt[3]{x}$ **64.** $5\sqrt[4]{y^5} - 2y\sqrt[4]{y} + \sqrt[4]{16y^7}$ $3y\sqrt[4]{y} + 2y\sqrt[4]{y^3}$

Mixed Exercises

For Exercises 65–70, answer true or false. If an answer is false, explain why or give a counterexample.

65. $\sqrt{x} + \sqrt{y} = \sqrt{x + y}$ False; $\sqrt{9} + \sqrt{16} \neq \sqrt{9 + 16}$; $7 \neq 5$ **66.** $\sqrt{x} + \sqrt{x} = 2\sqrt{x}$ True   **67.** $5\sqrt[3]{x} + 2\sqrt[3]{x} = 7\sqrt[3]{x}$ True

68. $6\sqrt{x} + 5\sqrt[3]{x} = 11\sqrt{x}$ False; radicals must have the same index.   **69.** $\sqrt{y} + \sqrt{y} = \sqrt{2y}$ False; $\sqrt{y} + \sqrt{y} = 2\sqrt{y} \neq \sqrt{2y}$ **70.** $\sqrt{c^2 + d^2} = c + d$ False; $\sqrt{3^2 + 4^2} \neq 3 + 4$; $5 \neq 7$

For Exercises 71–74, write the English phrase as an algebraic expression. Simplify each expression.

71. The sum of the principal square root of 48 and the principal square root of 12 $\sqrt{48} + \sqrt{12}$ simplifies to $6\sqrt{3}$

72. The sum of the cube root of 16 and the cube root of 2 $\sqrt[3]{16} + \sqrt[3]{2}$ simplifies to $3\sqrt[3]{2}$

73. The difference of 5 times the cube root of x^6 and the square of x $5\sqrt[3]{x^6} - x^2$ simplifies to $4x^2$

74. The sum of the cube of y and the principal fourth root of y^{12} $y^3 + \sqrt[4]{y^{12}}$ simplifies to $2y^3$

For Exercises 75–78, write an English phrase that translates the mathematical expression. (Answers may vary.)

75. $\sqrt{18} - 5^2$ The difference of the principal square root of 18 and the square of 5

76. $4^3 - \sqrt[3]{4}$ The difference of the cube of 4 and the cube root of 4

77. $\sqrt[4]{x} + y^3$ The sum of the principal fourth root of x and the cube of y

78. $a^4 + \sqrt{a}$ The sum of the fourth power of a and the principal square root of a

For Exercises 79–80, find the exact value of the perimeter, and then approximate the value to one decimal place.

79.

$2\sqrt{6}$ cm

$2\sqrt{24}$ cm

$\sqrt{54}$ cm

$9\sqrt{6}$ cm ≈ 22.0 cm

80.

$\sqrt{75}$ ft

$\sqrt{3}$ ft

$\sqrt{27}$ ft

$9\sqrt{3}$ ft ≈ 15.6 ft

Writing   Translating Expression   Geometry   Scientific Calculator   Video   NS&E

81. The figure has perimeter $14\sqrt{2}$ ft. Find the value of x. $x = 2\sqrt{2}$ ft

$\sqrt{50}$ ft

x

82. The figure has perimeter $12\sqrt{7}$ cm. Find the value of x. $x = 2\sqrt{7}$ cm

$\sqrt{112}$ cm

x

Expanding Your Skills

83. a. An irregularly shaped garden is shown in the figure. All distances are expressed in yards. Find the perimeter. *Hint:* Use the Pythagorean theorem to find the length of each side. Write the final answer in radical form. $10\sqrt{5}$ yd

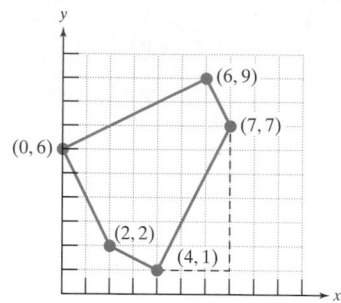

b. Approximate your answer to two decimal places.   22.36 yd

c. If edging costs $1.49 per foot and sales tax is 6%, find the total cost of edging the garden. $105.95

Section 10.5   Multiplication of Radicals

Concepts

1. Multiplication Property of Radicals
2. Expressions of the Form $(\sqrt[n]{a})^n$
3. Special Case Products
4. Multiplying Radicals with Different Indices

1. Multiplication Property of Radicals

In this section, we will learn how to multiply radicals by using the multiplication property of radicals first introduced in Section 10.3.

> **PROPERTY**   **The Multiplication Property of Radicals**
>
> Let a and b represent real numbers such that $\sqrt[n]{a}$ and $\sqrt[n]{b}$ are both real. Then
>
> $$\sqrt[n]{ab} = \sqrt[n]{a} \cdot \sqrt[n]{b}$$

To multiply two radical expressions, we use the multiplication property of radicals along with the commutative and associative properties of multiplication.

Classroom Examples: p. 728, Exercises 12 and 22

Example 1   **Multiplying Radical Expressions**

Multiply each expression and simplify the result. Assume all variables represent positive real numbers.

a. $(3\sqrt{2})(5\sqrt{6})$ **b.** $(2x\sqrt{y})(-7\sqrt{xy})$ **c.** $(15c\sqrt[3]{cd})\left(\dfrac{1}{3}\sqrt[3]{cd^2}\right)$

Solution:

a. $(3\sqrt{2})(5\sqrt{6})$

$= (3 \cdot 5)(\sqrt{2} \cdot \sqrt{6})$ Commutative and associative properties of multiplication

$= 15\sqrt{12}$ Multiplication property of radicals

$= 15\sqrt{2^2 3}$

$= 15 \cdot 2\sqrt{3}$ Simplify the radical.

$= 30\sqrt{3}$

 Writing   Translating Expression   Geometry   Scientific Calculator   Video   NS&E

b. $(2x\sqrt{y})(-7\sqrt{xy})$

$\quad = (2x)(-7)(\sqrt{y} \cdot \sqrt{xy})$ Commutative and associative properties of multiplication

$\quad = -14x\sqrt{xy^2}$ Multiplication property of radicals

$\quad = -14xy\sqrt{x}$ Simplify the radical.

c. $(15c\sqrt[3]{cd})\left(\dfrac{1}{3}\sqrt[3]{cd^2}\right)$

$\quad = \left(15c \cdot \dfrac{1}{3}\right)(\sqrt[3]{cd} \cdot \sqrt[3]{cd^2})$ Commutative and associative properties of multiplication

$\quad = 5c\sqrt[3]{c^2d^3}$ Multiplication property of radicals

$\quad = 5cd\sqrt[3]{c^2}$ Simplify the radical.

Skill Practice Multiply the expressions and simplify the results. Assume all variables represent positive real numbers.

  1. $(4\sqrt{6})(-2\sqrt{3})$

  2. $(3ab\sqrt{b})(-2\sqrt{ab})$

  3. $(2\sqrt[3]{4ab})(5\sqrt[3]{2a^2b})$

When multiplying radical expressions with more than one term, we use the distributive property.

Example 2   **Multiplying Radical Expressions**

Multiply. $3\sqrt{11}(2 + \sqrt{11})$

Solution:

$3\sqrt{11}(2 + \sqrt{11})$

$\quad = 3\sqrt{11} \cdot (2) + 3\sqrt{11} \cdot \sqrt{11}$ Apply the distributive property.

$\quad = 6\sqrt{11} + 3\sqrt{11^2}$ Multiplication property of radicals

$\quad = 6\sqrt{11} + 3 \cdot 11$ Simplify the radical.

$\quad = 6\sqrt{11} + 33$

Skill Practice Multiply.

  4. $5\sqrt{5}(2\sqrt{5} - 2)$

Classroom Example: p. 728, Exercise 30

Answers

1. $-24\sqrt{2}$ **2.** $-6ab^2\sqrt{a}$

3. $20a\sqrt[3]{b^2}$ **4.** $50 - 10\sqrt{5}$

Classroom Examples: p. 728,
Exercises 36 and 42

Example 3 Multiplying Radical Expressions

Multiply.

a. $(\sqrt{5} + 3\sqrt{2})(2\sqrt{5} - \sqrt{2})$ **b.** $(-10a\sqrt{b} + 7b)(a\sqrt{b} + 2b)$

Solution:

a. $(\sqrt{5} + 3\sqrt{2})(2\sqrt{5} - \sqrt{2})$

$= 2\sqrt{5^2} - \sqrt{10} + 6\sqrt{10} - 3\sqrt{2^2}$ Apply the distributive property.

$= 2 \cdot 5 + 5\sqrt{10} - 3 \cdot 2$ Simplify radicals and

$= 10 + 5\sqrt{10} - 6$ combine *like* radicals.

$= 4 + 5\sqrt{10}$ Combine *like* terms.

b. $(-10a\sqrt{b} + 7b)(a\sqrt{b} + 2b)$

$= -10a^2\sqrt{b^2} - 20ab\sqrt{b} + 7ab\sqrt{b} + 14b^2$ Apply the distributive property.

$= -10a^2b - 13ab\sqrt{b} + 14b^2$ Simplify and combine *like* terms.

Skill Practice Multiply.

5. $(2\sqrt{3} - 3\sqrt{10})(\sqrt{3} + 2\sqrt{10})$ **6.** $(x\sqrt{y} + y)(3x\sqrt{y} - 2y)$

Classroom Example: p. 728,
Exercise 44

Example 4 Multiplying Radical Expressions

Multiply. $(2\sqrt{x} + \sqrt{y})(6 - \sqrt{x} + 8\sqrt{y})$

Solution:

$(2\sqrt{x} + \sqrt{y})(6 - \sqrt{x} + 8\sqrt{y})$

$= 12\sqrt{x} - 2\sqrt{x^2} + 16\sqrt{xy} + 6\sqrt{y} - \sqrt{xy} + 8\sqrt{y^2}$ Apply the distributive property.

$= 12\sqrt{x} - 2x + 16\sqrt{xy} + 6\sqrt{y} - \sqrt{xy} + 8y$ Simplify the radicals.

$= 12\sqrt{x} - 2x + 15\sqrt{xy} + 6\sqrt{y} + 8y$ Combine *like* terms.

Skill Practice Multiply.

7. $(\sqrt{t} + 3\sqrt{w})(4 - \sqrt{t} - \sqrt{w})$

Answers

5. $-54 + \sqrt{30}$
6. $3x^2y + xy\sqrt{y} - 2y^2$
7. $4\sqrt{t} - t - 4\sqrt{tw} + 12\sqrt{w} - 3w$

2. Expressions of the Form $(\sqrt[n]{a})^n$

Instructor Note: Ask students if $(\sqrt{x})^2 = \sqrt{x^2}$ is always true, sometimes true, or never true.

The multiplication property of radicals can be used to simplify an expression of the form $(\sqrt{a})^2$, where $a \geq 0$.

$$(\sqrt{a})^2 = \sqrt{a} \cdot \sqrt{a} = \sqrt{a^2} = a \qquad \text{where } a \geq 0$$

This logic can be applied to nth roots. If $\sqrt[n]{a}$ is a real number, then $(\sqrt[n]{a})^n = a$.

Example 5 **Simplifying Radical Expressions**

Classroom Example: p. 728, Exercise 46

Simplify the expressions. Assume all variables represent positive real numbers.

a. $(\sqrt{11})^2$ **b.** $(\sqrt[5]{z})^5$ **c.** $(\sqrt[3]{pq})^3$

Solution:

a. $(\sqrt{11})^2 = 11$ **b.** $(\sqrt[5]{z})^5 = z$ **c.** $(\sqrt[3]{pq})^3 = pq$

Skill Practice Simplify.

8. $(\sqrt{14})^2$ **9.** $(\sqrt[7]{q})^7$ **10.** $(\sqrt[5]{3z})^5$

3. Special Case Products

From Examples 2–4, you may have noticed a similarity between multiplying radical expressions and multiplying polynomials.

In Section 5.6 we learned that the square of a binomial results in a perfect square trinomial:

$$(a + b)^2 = a^2 + 2ab + b^2$$

$$(a - b)^2 = a^2 - 2ab + b^2$$

The same patterns occur when squaring a radical expression with two terms.

Example 6 **Squaring a Two-Term Radical Expression**

Classroom Example: p. 728, Exercise 60

Square the radical expressions. Assume all variables represent positive real numbers.

a. $(\sqrt{d} + 3)^2$ **b.** $(5\sqrt{y} - \sqrt{2})^2$

Solution:

a. $(\sqrt{d} + 3)^2$ This expression is in the form $(a + b)^2$, where $a = \sqrt{d}$ and $b = 3$.

$\qquad a^2 + 2ab + b^2$

$= (\sqrt{d})^2 + 2(\sqrt{d})(3) + (3)^2$ Apply the formula $(a + b)^2 = a^2 + 2ab + b^2$.

$= d + 6\sqrt{d} + 9$ Simplify.

TIP: The product $(\sqrt{d} + 3)^2$ can also be found by using the distributive property.

$$(\sqrt{d} + 3)^2 = (\sqrt{d} + 3)(\sqrt{d} + 3)$$

Answers

8. 14   **9.** q **10.** $3z$

b. $(5\sqrt{y} - \sqrt{2})^2$ This expression is in the form $(a - b)^2$, where $a = 5\sqrt{y}$ and $b = \sqrt{2}$.

$$a^2 - 2ab + b^2$$

$$= (5\sqrt{y})^2 - 2(5\sqrt{y})(\sqrt{2}) + (\sqrt{2})^2$$ Apply the formula $(a - b)^2 = a^2 - 2ab + b^2$.

$$= 25y - 10\sqrt{2y} + 2$$ Simplify.

Skill Practice Square the radical expressions. Assume all variables represent positive real numbers.

11. $(\sqrt{a} - 5)^2$ **12.** $(4\sqrt{x} + \sqrt{3})^2$

Recall from Section 5.6 that the product of two conjugate binomials results in a difference of squares.

$$(a + b)(a - b) = a^2 - b^2$$

The same pattern occurs when multiplying two conjugate radical expressions.

Classroom Example: p. 728, Exercise 62

Example 7   **Multiplying Conjugate Radical Expressions**

Multiply the radical expressions. Assume all variables represent positive real numbers.

a. $(\sqrt{3} + 2)(\sqrt{3} - 2)$ **b.** $\left(\dfrac{1}{3}\sqrt{s} - \dfrac{3}{4}\sqrt{t}\right)\left(\dfrac{1}{3}\sqrt{s} + \dfrac{3}{4}\sqrt{t}\right)$

Solution:

a. $(\sqrt{3} + 2)(\sqrt{3} - 2)$ The expression is in the form $(a + b)(a - b)$, where $a = \sqrt{3}$ and $b = 2$.

TIP: The product $(\sqrt{3} + 2)(\sqrt{3} - 2)$ can also be found by using the distributive property.

$$(\sqrt{3} + 2)(\sqrt{3} - 2)$$

$$\overset{a^2 - b^2}{= (\sqrt{3})^2 - (2)^2}$$ Apply the formula $(a + b)(a - b) = a^2 - b^2$.

$$= 3 - 4$$ Simplify.

$$= -1$$

b. $\left(\dfrac{1}{3}\sqrt{s} - \dfrac{3}{4}\sqrt{t}\right)\left(\dfrac{1}{3}\sqrt{s} + \dfrac{3}{4}\sqrt{t}\right)$ This expression is in the form $(a - b)(a + b)$, where $a = \dfrac{1}{3}\sqrt{s}$ and $b = \dfrac{3}{4}\sqrt{t}$.

$$\overset{a^2 - b^2}{= \left(\dfrac{1}{3}\sqrt{s}\right)^2 - \left(\dfrac{3}{4}\sqrt{t}\right)^2}$$ Apply the formula $(a + b)(a - b) = a^2 - b^2$.

$$= \dfrac{1}{9}s - \dfrac{9}{16}t$$ Simplify.

Skill Practice Multiply the conjugates. Assume all variables represent positive real numbers.

13. $(\sqrt{5} + 3)(\sqrt{5} - 3)$ **14.** $\left(\dfrac{1}{2}\sqrt{a} + \dfrac{2}{5}\sqrt{b}\right) \cdot \left(\dfrac{1}{2}\sqrt{a} - \dfrac{2}{5}\sqrt{b}\right)$

Answers

11. $a - 10\sqrt{a} + 25$

12. $16x + 8\sqrt{3x} + 3$

13. -4 **14.** $\dfrac{1}{4}a - \dfrac{4}{25}b$

4. Multiplying Radicals with Different Indices

The product of two radicals can be simplified provided the radicals have the same index. If the radicals have different indices, then we can use the properties of rational exponents to obtain a common index.

Example 8   Multiplying Radicals with Different Indices

Multiply the expressions. Write the answers in radical form.

a. $\sqrt[3]{5} \cdot \sqrt[4]{5}$ **b.** $\sqrt[3]{7} \cdot \sqrt{2}$

Solution:

a. $\sqrt[3]{5} \cdot \sqrt[4]{5}$

$\quad = 5^{1/3}5^{1/4}$ Rewrite each expression with rational exponents.

$\quad = 5^{(1/3)+(1/4)}$ Because the bases are equal, we can add the exponents.

$\quad = 5^{(4/12)+(3/12)}$ Write the fractions with a common denominator.

$\quad = 5^{7/12}$ Simplify the exponent.

$\quad = \sqrt[12]{5^7}$ Rewrite the expression as a radical.

b. $\sqrt[3]{7} \cdot \sqrt{2}$

$\quad = 7^{1/3}2^{1/2}$ Rewrite each expression with rational exponents.

$\quad = 7^{2/6}2^{3/6}$ Write the rational exponents with a common denominator.

$\quad = (7^2 2^3)^{1/6}$ Apply the power rule of exponents.

$\quad = \sqrt[6]{7^2 2^3}$ Rewrite the expression as a single radical.

$\quad = \sqrt[6]{392}$ Simplify.

Skill Practice Multiply the expressions. Write the answers in radical form. Assume all variables represent positive real numbers.

15. $\sqrt{x} \cdot \sqrt[3]{x}$ **16.** $\sqrt[4]{a^3} \cdot \sqrt[3]{b}$

Classroom Examples: p. 729, Exercises 92 and 98

Answers
15. $\sqrt[6]{x^5}$ **16.** $\sqrt[12]{a^9 b^4}$

Section 10.5   Practice Exercises

For the exercises in this set, assume that all variables represent positive real numbers, unless otherwise stated.

Review Exercises

For Exercises 1–3, simplify the radicals.

1. $\sqrt[3]{-16x^5y^6z^7}$ **2.** $-\sqrt{20a^2b^3c}$ **3.** $\sqrt{\dfrac{8y^3z^5}{y}}$ $2yz^2\sqrt{2z}$

$\quad -2xy^2z^2\sqrt[3]{2x^2z}$ $\quad -2ab\sqrt{5bc}$

For Exercises 4–6, simplify the expressions. Write the answer with positive exponents only.

4. $x^{1/3}y^{1/4}x^{-1/6}y^{1/3}$ $x^{1/6}y^{7/12}$ **5.** $p^{1/8}q^{1/2}p^{-1/4}q^{3/2}$ $\dfrac{q^2}{p^{1/8}}$ **6.** $\dfrac{b^{1/4}}{b^{3/2}}$ $\dfrac{1}{b^{5/4}}$

 Writing   Translating Expression   Geometry   Scientific Calculator   Video   NS&E

For Exercises 7–8, add or subtract as indicated.

7. $-2\sqrt[3]{7} + 4\sqrt[3]{7}$ $2\sqrt[3]{7}$

8. $4\sqrt{8x^3} - x\sqrt{50x}$ $3x\sqrt{2x}$

Concept 1: Multiplication Property of Radicals

For Exercises 9–44, multiply the radical expressions. **(See Examples 1–4.)**

9. $\sqrt[3]{7} \cdot \sqrt[3]{3}$ $\sqrt[3]{21}$

10. $\sqrt[4]{6} \cdot \sqrt[4]{2}$ $\sqrt[4]{12}$

11. $\sqrt{2} \cdot \sqrt{10}$ $2\sqrt{5}$

12. $\sqrt[3]{4} \cdot \sqrt[3]{12}$ $2\sqrt[3]{6}$

13. $\sqrt[4]{16} \cdot \sqrt[4]{64}$ $4\sqrt[4]{4}$

14. $\sqrt{5x^3} \cdot \sqrt{10x^4}$ $5x^3\sqrt{2x}$

15. $(4\sqrt[3]{4})(2\sqrt[3]{5})$ $8\sqrt[3]{20}$

16. $(2\sqrt{5})(3\sqrt{7})$ $6\sqrt{35}$

17. $(8a\sqrt{b})(-3\sqrt{ab})$ $-24ab\sqrt{a}$

18. $(p\sqrt[4]{q^3})(\sqrt[4]{pq})$ $pq\sqrt[4]{p}$

19. $\sqrt{30} \cdot \sqrt{12}$ $6\sqrt{10}$

20. $\sqrt{20} \cdot \sqrt{54}$ $6\sqrt{30}$

21. $\sqrt{6x} \cdot \sqrt{12x}$ $6x\sqrt{2}$

22. $(\sqrt{3ab^2})(\sqrt{21a^2b})$ $3ab\sqrt{7ab}$

23. $\sqrt{5a^3b^2} \cdot \sqrt{20a^3b^3}$ $10a^3b^2\sqrt{b}$

24. $\sqrt[3]{m^2n^2} \cdot \sqrt[3]{48m^4n^2}$
$2m^2n\sqrt[3]{6n}$

25. $(4\sqrt{3xy^3})(-2\sqrt{6x^3y^2})$
$-24x^2y^2\sqrt{2y}$

26. $(2\sqrt[4]{3x})(4\sqrt[4]{27x^6})$
$24x\sqrt[4]{x^3}$

27. $(\sqrt[3]{4a^2b})(\sqrt[3]{2ab^3})(\sqrt[3]{54a^2b})$
$6ab\sqrt[3]{2a^2b^2}$

28. $(\sqrt[3]{9x^3y})(\sqrt[3]{6xy})(\sqrt[3]{8x^2y^5})$
$6x^2y^2\sqrt[3]{2y}$

29. $\sqrt{3}(4\sqrt{3} - 6)$
$12 - 6\sqrt{3}$

30. $3\sqrt{5}(2\sqrt{5} + 4)$ $30 + 12\sqrt{5}$

31. $\sqrt{2}(\sqrt{6} - \sqrt{3})$ $2\sqrt{3} - \sqrt{6}$

32. $\sqrt{5}(\sqrt{3} + \sqrt{7})$ $\sqrt{15} + \sqrt{35}$

33. $-\dfrac{1}{3}\sqrt{x}(6\sqrt{x} + 7)$ $-2x - \dfrac{7}{3}\sqrt{x}$

34. $-\dfrac{1}{2}\sqrt{y}(8 - 3\sqrt{y})$ $-4\sqrt{y} + \dfrac{3}{2}y$

35. $(\sqrt{3} + 2\sqrt{10})(4\sqrt{3} - \sqrt{10})$
$-8 + 7\sqrt{30}$

36. $(8\sqrt{7} - \sqrt{5})(\sqrt{7} + 3\sqrt{5})$
$41 + 23\sqrt{35}$

37. $(\sqrt{x} + 4)(\sqrt{x} - 9)$
$x - 5\sqrt{x} - 36$

38. $(\sqrt{w} - 2)(\sqrt{w} - 9)$
$w - 11\sqrt{w} + 18$

39. $(\sqrt[3]{y} + 2)(\sqrt[3]{y} - 3)$
$\sqrt[3]{y^2} - \sqrt[3]{y} - 6$

40. $(4 + \sqrt[5]{p})(5 + \sqrt[5]{p})$
$20 + 9\sqrt[5]{p} + \sqrt[5]{p^2}$

41. $(\sqrt{a} - 3\sqrt{b})(9\sqrt{a} - \sqrt{b})$
$9a - 28\sqrt{ab} + 3b$

42. $(11\sqrt{m} + 4\sqrt{n})(\sqrt{m} + \sqrt{n})$
$11m + 15\sqrt{mn} + 4n$

43. $(\sqrt{p} + 2\sqrt{q})(8 + 3\sqrt{p} - \sqrt{q})$
$8\sqrt{p} + 3p + 5\sqrt{pq} + 16\sqrt{q} - 2q$

44. $(5\sqrt{s} - \sqrt{t})(\sqrt{s} + 5 + 6\sqrt{t})$
$5s + 25\sqrt{s} + 29\sqrt{st} - 5\sqrt{t} - 6t$

Concept 2: Expressions of the Form $(\sqrt[n]{a})^n$

For Exercises 45–52, simplify the expressions. Assume all variables represent positive real numbers. **(See Example 5.)**

45. $(\sqrt{15})^2$ 15

46. $(\sqrt{58})^2$ 58

47. $(\sqrt{3y})^2$ $3y$

48. $(\sqrt{19yz})^2$ $19yz$

49. $(\sqrt[3]{6})^3$ 6

50. $(\sqrt[5]{24})^5$ 24

51. $\sqrt{709} \cdot \sqrt{709}$ 709

52. $\sqrt{401} \cdot \sqrt{401}$ 401

Concept 3: Special Case Products

53. a. Write the formula for the product of two conjugates. $(x + y)(x - y) =$ $x^2 - y^2$

b. Multiply $(x + 5)(x - 5)$. $x^2 - 25$

54. a. Write the formula for squaring a binomial.
$(x + y)^2 =$ $x^2 + 2xy + y^2$

b. Multiply $(x + 5)^2$. $x^2 + 10x + 25$

For Exercises 55–66, multiply the special products. **(See Examples 6–7.)**

55. $(\sqrt{13} + 4)^2$ $29 + 8\sqrt{13}$

56. $(6 - \sqrt{11})^2$ $47 - 12\sqrt{11}$

57. $(\sqrt{p} - \sqrt{7})^2$ $p - 2\sqrt{7p} + 7$

58. $(\sqrt{q} + \sqrt{2})^2$ $q + 2\sqrt{2q} + 2$

59. $(\sqrt{2a} - 3\sqrt{b})^2$ $2a - 6\sqrt{2ab} + 9b$

60. $(\sqrt{3w} + 4\sqrt{z})^2$ $3w + 8\sqrt{3wz} + 16z$

61. $(\sqrt{3} + x)(\sqrt{3} - x)$ $3 - x^2$

62. $(y + \sqrt{6})(y - \sqrt{6})$ $y^2 - 6$

63. $(\sqrt{6} + \sqrt{2})(\sqrt{6} - \sqrt{2})$ 4

64. $(\sqrt{15} + \sqrt{5})(\sqrt{15} - \sqrt{5})$ 10

65. $\left(\dfrac{2}{3}\sqrt{x} + \dfrac{1}{2}\sqrt{y}\right)\left(\dfrac{2}{3}\sqrt{x} - \dfrac{1}{2}\sqrt{y}\right)$ $\dfrac{4}{9}x - \dfrac{1}{4}y$

66. $\left(\dfrac{1}{4}\sqrt{s} + \dfrac{1}{5}\sqrt{t}\right)\left(\dfrac{1}{4}\sqrt{s} - \dfrac{1}{5}\sqrt{t}\right)$ $\dfrac{1}{16}s - \dfrac{1}{25}t$

 Writing   Translating Expression   Geometry   Scientific Calculator   Video   NS E

For Exercises 67–68, multiply the expressions.

67. a. $(\sqrt{3} + \sqrt{x})(\sqrt{3} - \sqrt{x})$ $3 - x$
   b. $(\sqrt{3} + \sqrt{x})(\sqrt{3} + \sqrt{x})$ $3 + 2\sqrt{3x} + x$
   c. $(\sqrt{3} - \sqrt{x})(\sqrt{3} - \sqrt{x})$ $3 - 2\sqrt{3x} + x$

68. a. $(\sqrt{5} + \sqrt{y})(\sqrt{5} - \sqrt{y})$ $5 - y$
   b. $(\sqrt{5} + \sqrt{y})(\sqrt{5} + \sqrt{y})$ $5 + 2\sqrt{5y} + y$
   c. $(\sqrt{5} - \sqrt{y})(\sqrt{5} - \sqrt{y})$ $5 - 2\sqrt{5y} + y$

Mixed Exercises

For Exercises 69–76, identify each statement as true or false. If an answer is false, explain why.

69. $\sqrt{3} \cdot \sqrt{2} = \sqrt{6}$ True

70. $\sqrt{5} \cdot \sqrt[3]{2} = \sqrt{10}$
   False; the radicals have different indices.

71. $(x - \sqrt{5})^2 = x - 5$
   False; $(x - \sqrt{5})^2 = x^2 - 2x\sqrt{5} + 5$

72. $3(2\sqrt{5x}) = 6\sqrt{5x}$ True

73. $5(3\sqrt{4x}) = 15\sqrt{20x}$
   False; 5 is multiplied by 3 only.

74. $\dfrac{\sqrt{5x}}{5} = \sqrt{x}$ False; $\dfrac{\sqrt{5}}{5} \neq 1$

75. $\dfrac{3\sqrt{x}}{3} = \sqrt{x}$ True

76. $(\sqrt{t} - 1)(\sqrt{t} + 1) = t - 1$ True

For Exercises 77–84, perform the indicated operations.

77. $(-\sqrt{6x})^2$ $6x$

78. $(-\sqrt{8a})^2$ $8a$

79. $(\sqrt{3x + 1})^2$ $3x + 1$

80. $(\sqrt{x - 1})^2$ $x - 1$

81. $(\sqrt{x + 3} - 4)^2$
   $x + 19 - 8\sqrt{x + 3}$

82. $(\sqrt{x + 1} + 3)^2$
   $x + 10 + 6\sqrt{x + 1}$

83. $(\sqrt{2t - 3} + 5)^2$
   $2t + 10\sqrt{2t - 3} + 22$

84. $(\sqrt{3w - 2} - 4)^2$
   $3w - 8\sqrt{3w - 2} + 14$

For Exercises 85–88, find the exact area.

85.

$\sqrt{40}$ ft

$3\sqrt{2}$ ft

$12\sqrt{5}$ ft^2

86.
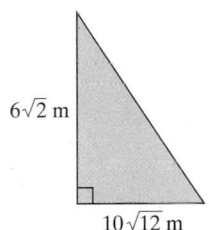
$6\sqrt{2}$ m

$10\sqrt{12}$ m

$60\sqrt{6}$ m^2

87.
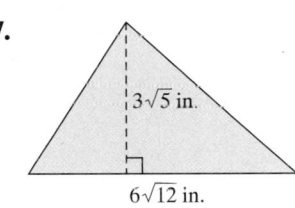
$3\sqrt{5}$ in.

$6\sqrt{12}$ in.

$18\sqrt{15}$ in.^{2}

88.
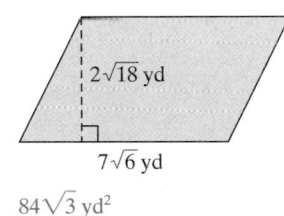
$2\sqrt{18}$ yd

$7\sqrt{6}$ yd

$84\sqrt{3}$ yd^2

Concept 4: Multiplying Radicals with Different Indices

For Exercises 89–100, multiply or divide the radicals with different indices. Write the answers in radical form and simplify. **(See Example 8.)**

89. $\sqrt{x} \cdot \sqrt[4]{x}$ $\sqrt[4]{x^3}$

90. $\sqrt[3]{y} \cdot \sqrt{y}$ $\sqrt[6]{y^5}$

91. $\sqrt[5]{2z} \cdot \sqrt[3]{2z}$ $\sqrt[15]{(2z)^8}$

92. $\sqrt[3]{5w} \cdot \sqrt[4]{5w}$ $\sqrt[12]{(5w)^7}$

93. $\sqrt[3]{p^2} \cdot \sqrt{p^3}$ $p^2\sqrt[6]{p}$

94. $\sqrt[4]{q^3} \cdot \sqrt[3]{q^2}$ $q\sqrt[12]{q^5}$

95. $\dfrac{\sqrt{u^3}}{\sqrt[3]{u}}$ $u\sqrt[6]{u}$

96. $\dfrac{\sqrt{v^5}}{\sqrt[4]{v}}$ $v^2\sqrt[4]{v}$

97. $\sqrt[3]{x} \cdot \sqrt[6]{y}$ $\sqrt[6]{x^2y}$

98. $\sqrt{a} \cdot \sqrt[6]{b}$ $\sqrt[6]{a^3b}$

99. $\sqrt[4]{8} \cdot \sqrt{3}$
   $\sqrt[4]{2^3 \cdot 3^2}$ or $\sqrt[4]{72}$

100. $\sqrt{11} \cdot \sqrt[6]{2}$
   $\sqrt[6]{11^3 \cdot 2}$ or $\sqrt[6]{2662}$

Expanding Your Skills

For Exercises 101–106, multiply.

101. $\sqrt[3]{2xy} \cdot \sqrt[4]{5xy}$
   $\sqrt[12]{2^4 5^3 x^7 y^7}$

102. $\sqrt{6ab} \cdot \sqrt[3]{7ab}$
   $\sqrt[6]{2^3 3^3 7^2 a^5 b^5}$

103. $\sqrt[3]{4m^2n} \cdot \sqrt{6mn}$
   $2m\sqrt[6]{3^3 2mn^5}$

104. $\sqrt[4]{5xy^3} \cdot \sqrt[3]{10x^2y}$
   $y\sqrt[12]{2^4 5^7 x^{11} y}$

105. $(\sqrt[3]{a} + \sqrt[3]{b})(\sqrt[3]{a^2} - \sqrt[3]{ab} + \sqrt[3]{b^2})$
   $a + b$

106. $(\sqrt[3]{a} - \sqrt[3]{b})(\sqrt[3]{a^2} + \sqrt[3]{ab} + \sqrt[3]{b^2})$
   $a - b$

 Writing   Translating Expression   Geometry   Scientific Calculator   Video   NS&E

Problem Recognition Exercises

Simplifying Radical Expressions

For Exercises 1–20, simplify the expressions.

1. a. $\sqrt{24}$ $2\sqrt{6}$
  b. $\sqrt[3]{24}$ $2\sqrt[3]{3}$

2. a. $\sqrt{54}$ $3\sqrt{6}$
  b. $\sqrt[3]{54}$ $3\sqrt[3]{2}$

3. a. $\sqrt{200y^6}$ $10y^3\sqrt{2}$
  b. $\sqrt[3]{200y^6}$ $2y^2\sqrt[3]{25}$

4. a. $\sqrt{32z^{15}}$ $4z^7\sqrt{2z}$
  b. $\sqrt[3]{32z^{15}}$ $2z^5\sqrt[3]{4}$

5. a. $\sqrt{80}$ $4\sqrt{5}$
  b. $\sqrt[3]{80}$ $2\sqrt[3]{10}$
  c. $\sqrt[4]{80}$ $2\sqrt[4]{5}$

6. a. $\sqrt{48}$ $4\sqrt{3}$
  b. $\sqrt[3]{48}$ $2\sqrt[3]{6}$
  c. $\sqrt[4]{48}$ $2\sqrt[4]{3}$

7. a. $\sqrt{x^5y^6}$ $x^2y^3\sqrt{x}$
  b. $\sqrt[3]{x^5y^6}$ $xy^2\sqrt[3]{x^2}$
  c. $\sqrt[4]{x^5y^6}$ $xy\sqrt[4]{xy^2}$

8. a. $\sqrt{a^{10}b^{12}}$ a^5b^6
  b. $\sqrt[3]{a^{10}b^{12}}$ $a^3b^4\sqrt[3]{a}$
  c. $\sqrt[4]{a^{10}b^{12}}$ $a^2b^3\sqrt[4]{a^2}$

9. a. $\sqrt[3]{32s^5t^6}$ $2st^2\sqrt[3]{4s^2}$
  b. $\sqrt[4]{32s^5t^6}$ $2st\sqrt[4]{2st^2}$
  c. $\sqrt[5]{32s^5t^6}$ $2st\sqrt[5]{t}$

10. a. $\sqrt[3]{96v^7w^{20}}$ $2v^2w^6\sqrt[3]{12vw^2}$
  b. $\sqrt[4]{96v^7w^{20}}$ $2vw^5\sqrt[4]{6v^3}$
  c. $\sqrt[5]{96v^7w^{20}}$ $2vw^4\sqrt[5]{3v^2}$

11. a. $\sqrt{5} + \sqrt{5}$ $2\sqrt{5}$
  b. $\sqrt{5} \cdot \sqrt{5}$ 5

12. a. $\sqrt{10} + \sqrt{10}$ $2\sqrt{10}$
  b. $\sqrt{10} \cdot \sqrt{10}$ 10

13. a. $2\sqrt{6} - 5\sqrt{6}$ $-3\sqrt{6}$
  b. $2\sqrt{6} \cdot 5\sqrt{6}$ 60

14. a. $3\sqrt{7} - 10\sqrt{7}$ $-7\sqrt{7}$
  b. $3\sqrt{7} \cdot 10\sqrt{7}$ 210

15. a. $\sqrt{8} + \sqrt{2}$ $3\sqrt{2}$
  b. $\sqrt{8} \cdot \sqrt{2}$ 4

16. a. $\sqrt{12} + \sqrt{3}$ $3\sqrt{3}$
  b. $\sqrt{12} \cdot \sqrt{3}$ 6

17. a. $5\sqrt{18} - 4\sqrt{8}$ $7\sqrt{2}$
  b. $5\sqrt{18} \cdot 4\sqrt{8}$
  240

18. a. $\sqrt{50} - \sqrt{72}$ $-\sqrt{2}$
  b. $\sqrt{50} \cdot \sqrt{72}$
  60

19. a. $4\sqrt[3]{24} + 6\sqrt[3]{3}$ $14\sqrt[3]{3}$
  b. $4\sqrt[3]{24} \cdot 6\sqrt[3]{3}$
  $48\sqrt[3]{9}$

20. a. $2\sqrt[3]{54} - 5\sqrt[3]{2}$ $\sqrt[3]{2}$
  b. $2\sqrt[3]{54} \cdot 5\sqrt[3]{2}$
  $30\sqrt[3]{4}$

Section 10.6   Division of Radicals and Rationalization

Concepts

1. **Simplified Form of a Radical**
2. **Division Property of Radicals**
3. **Rationalizing the Denominator—One Term**
4. **Rationalizing the Denominator—Two Terms**

1. Simplified Form of a Radical

Recall that for a radical expression to be in simplified form the following three conditions must be met.

> **DEFINITION   Simplified Form of a Radical**
>
> Consider any radical expression in which the radicand is written as a product of prime factors. The expression is in simplified form if all the following conditions are met:
>
> 1. The radicand has no factor raised to a power greater than or equal to the index.
> 2. The radicand does not contain a fraction.
> 3. No radicals are in the denominator of a fraction.

In the previous sections, we have concentrated on the first condition in the simplification process. Next, we will demonstrate how to satisfy the second and third conditions involving radicals and fractions.

2. Division Property of Radicals

The multiplication property of radicals makes it possible to write a product within a radical to be separated as a product of radicals. We now state a similar property for radicals involving quotients.

PROPERTY   Division Property of Radicals

Let a and b represent real numbers such that $\sqrt[n]{a}$ and $\sqrt[n]{b}$ are both real. Then,

$$\sqrt[n]{\frac{a}{b}} = \frac{\sqrt[n]{a}}{\sqrt[n]{b}} \quad b \neq 0$$

The division property of radicals indicates that a quotient within a radicand can be written as a quotient of radicals provided the roots are real numbers. For example:

$$\sqrt{\frac{25}{36}} = \frac{\sqrt{25}}{\sqrt{36}}$$

The reverse process is also true. A quotient of radicals can be written as a single radical provided that the roots are real numbers and that they have the same index.

$$\text{Same index} \longrightarrow \frac{\sqrt[3]{125}}{\sqrt[3]{8}} = \sqrt[3]{\frac{125}{8}}$$

In Examples 1 and 2, we will apply the division property of radicals to simplify radical expressions.

Example 1 **Using the Division Property to Simplify Radicals**

Classroom Example: p. 738, Exercise 16

Use the division property of radicals to simplify the expressions. Assume the variables represent positive real numbers.

a. $\sqrt{\dfrac{a^6}{b^4}}$ **b.** $\sqrt[3]{\dfrac{81y^5}{x^3}}$

Solution:

a. $\sqrt{\dfrac{a^6}{b^4}}$ The radicand contains an irreducible fraction.

$= \dfrac{\sqrt{a^6}}{\sqrt{b^4}}$ Apply the division property to rewrite as a quotient of radicals.

$= \dfrac{a^3}{b^2}$ Simplify the radicals.

b. $\sqrt[3]{\dfrac{81y^5}{x^3}}$ The radicand contains an irreducible fraction.

$= \dfrac{\sqrt[3]{81y^5}}{\sqrt[3]{x^3}}$ Apply the division property to rewrite as a quotient of radicals.

$= \dfrac{\sqrt[3]{3^4 \cdot y^5}}{\sqrt[3]{x^3}}$ Factor the radicand in the numerator to simplify the radical.

$= \dfrac{3y\sqrt[3]{3y^2}}{x}$ Simplify the radicals in the numerator and the denominator. The expression is simplified because it now satisfies all conditions.

Skill Practice   Simplify the expressions.

1. $\sqrt{\dfrac{x^4}{y^{10}}}$ **2.** $\sqrt[3]{\dfrac{w^7}{64}}$

Classroom Example: p. 738, Exercise 20

Example 2   **Using the Division Property to Simplify a Radical**

Use the division property of radicals to simplify the expression. Assume the variables represent positive real numbers.

$$\frac{\sqrt[4]{8p^7}}{\sqrt[4]{p^3}}$$

Solution:

$\dfrac{\sqrt[4]{8p^7}}{\sqrt[4]{p^3}}$ There is a radical in the denominator of the fraction.

$= \sqrt[4]{\dfrac{8p^7}{p^3}}$ Apply the division property to write the quotient under a single radical.

$= \sqrt[4]{8p^4}$ Simplify the fraction.

$= p\sqrt[4]{8}$ Simplify the radical.

Skill Practice   Simplify the expression.

3. $\dfrac{\sqrt[3]{16y^4}}{\sqrt[3]{y}}$

3. Rationalizing the Denominator—One Term

The third condition restricts radicals from the denominator of an expression. The process to remove a radical from the denominator is called **rationalizing the denominator**. In many cases, rationalizing the denominator creates an expression that is computationally simpler. For example,

$$\frac{6}{\sqrt{3}} = 2\sqrt{3} \qquad \text{and} \qquad \frac{-2}{2 + \sqrt{6}} = 2 - \sqrt{6}$$

Answers

1. $\dfrac{x^2}{y^5}$ **2.** $\dfrac{w^2\sqrt[3]{w}}{4}$ **3.** $2y\sqrt[3]{2}$

We will demonstrate the process to rationalize the denominator as two separate cases:

- Rationalizing the denominator (one term)
- Rationalizing the denominator (two terms involving square roots)

To begin the first case, recall that the nth root of a perfect nth power simplifies completely.

$$\sqrt{x^2} = x \qquad x \geq 0$$
$$\sqrt[3]{x^3} = x$$
$$\sqrt[4]{x^4} = x \qquad x \geq 0$$
$$\sqrt[5]{x^5} = x$$
$$\cdots$$

Therefore, to rationalize a radical expression, use the multiplication property of radicals to create an nth root of an nth power.

Example 3 **Rationalizing Radical Expressions**

Classroom Example: p. 738, Exercise 26

Fill in the missing radicand to rationalize the radical expressions. Assume all variables represent positive real numbers.

a. $\sqrt{a} \cdot \sqrt{?} = \sqrt{a^2} = a$ **b.** $\sqrt[3]{y} \cdot \sqrt[3]{?} = \sqrt[3]{y^3} = y$

c. $\sqrt[4]{2z^3} \cdot \sqrt[4]{?} = \sqrt[4]{2^4 z^4} = 2z$

Solution:

a. $\sqrt{a} \cdot \sqrt{?} = \sqrt{a^2} = a$ What multiplied by $\sqrt{a}$ will equal $\sqrt{a^2}$?

    $\sqrt{a} \cdot \sqrt{a} = \sqrt{a^2} = a$

b. $\sqrt[3]{y} \cdot \sqrt[3]{?} = \sqrt[3]{y^3} = y$ What multiplied by $\sqrt[3]{y}$ will equal $\sqrt[3]{y^3}$?

    $\sqrt[3]{y} \cdot \sqrt[3]{y^2} = \sqrt[3]{y^3} = y$

c. $\sqrt[4]{2z^3} \cdot \sqrt[4]{?} = \sqrt[4]{2^4 z^4} = 2z$ What multiplied by $\sqrt[4]{2z^3}$ will equal $\sqrt[4]{2^4 z^4}$?

    $\sqrt[4]{2z^3} \cdot \sqrt[4]{2^3 z} = \sqrt[4]{2^4 z^4} = 2z$

Skill Practice Fill in the missing radicand to rationalize the radical expression.

4. $\sqrt{7} \cdot \sqrt{?}$ **5.** $\sqrt[5]{t^2} \cdot \sqrt[5]{?}$ **6.** $\sqrt[3]{5x^2} \cdot \sqrt[3]{?}$

     To rationalize the denominator of a radical expression, multiply the numerator and denominator by an appropriate expression to create an nth root of an nth power in the denominator.

Answers

4. 7   **5.** t^3 **6.** $5^2 x$

Classroom Example: p. 738,
Exercise 42

Example 4   Rationalizing the Denominator—One Term

Simplify the expression. $\dfrac{5}{\sqrt[3]{a}}$ $a \neq 0$

Solution:

To remove the radical from the denominator, a cube root of a perfect cube is needed in the denominator. Multiply numerator and denominator by $\sqrt[3]{a^2}$ because $\sqrt[3]{a} \cdot \sqrt[3]{a^2} = \sqrt[3]{a^3} = a$.

$\dfrac{5}{\sqrt[3]{a}} = \dfrac{5}{\sqrt[3]{a}} \cdot \dfrac{\sqrt[3]{a^2}}{\sqrt[3]{a^2}}$ Multiplying by $\dfrac{\sqrt[3]{a^2}}{\sqrt[3]{a^2}}$ is the same as multiplying by 1.

$= \dfrac{5\sqrt[3]{a^2}}{\sqrt[3]{a^3}}$ Multiply the radicals.

$= \dfrac{5\sqrt[3]{a^2}}{a}$ Simplify.

Skill Practice Simplify the expression. Assume $y > 0$.

7. $\dfrac{2}{\sqrt[4]{y}}$

Classroom Example: p. 738,
Exercise 38

Example 5   Rationalizing the Denominator—One Term

Simplify the expression. $\sqrt{\dfrac{y^5}{7}}$

Solution:

$\sqrt{\dfrac{y^5}{7}}$ The radical contains an irreducible fraction.

$= \dfrac{\sqrt{y^5}}{\sqrt{7}}$ Apply the division property of radicals.

$= \dfrac{y^2\sqrt{y}}{\sqrt{7}}$ Simplify the radical in the numerator.

$= \dfrac{y^2\sqrt{y}}{\sqrt{7}} \cdot \dfrac{\sqrt{7}}{\sqrt{7}}$ Rationalize the denominator.
    Note: $\sqrt{7} \cdot \sqrt{7} = \sqrt{7^2} = 7$.

$= \dfrac{y^2\sqrt{7y}}{\sqrt{7^2}}$

$= \dfrac{y^2\sqrt{7y}}{7}$ Simplify.

> **Avoiding Mistakes**
>
> A factor within a radicand cannot be simplified with a factor outside the radicand. For example, $\dfrac{\sqrt{7y}}{7}$ cannot be simplified.

Skill Practice Simplify the expression.

8. $\sqrt{\dfrac{8}{3}}$

Answers

7. $\dfrac{2\sqrt[4]{y^3}}{y}$ 8. $\dfrac{2\sqrt{6}}{3}$

Example 6 **Rationalizing the Denominator—One Term**

Classroom Example: p. 738, Exercise 52

Simplify the expression. $\dfrac{15}{\sqrt[3]{25s}}$

Solution:

$\dfrac{15}{\sqrt[3]{25s}}$

$= \dfrac{15}{\sqrt[3]{5^2 s}} \cdot \dfrac{\sqrt[3]{5s^2}}{\sqrt[3]{5s^2}}$ Because $25 = 5^2$, one additional factor of 5 is needed to form a perfect cube. Two additional factors of s are needed to make a perfect cube. Multiply numerator and denominator by $\sqrt[3]{5s^2}$.

$= \dfrac{15\sqrt[3]{5s^2}}{\sqrt[3]{5^3 s^3}}$

$= \dfrac{15\sqrt[3]{5s^2}}{5s}$ Simplify the perfect cube.

$= \dfrac{\overset{3}{\cancel{15}}\sqrt[3]{5s^2}}{\underset{1}{\cancel{5}s}}$ Reduce to lowest terms.

$= \dfrac{3\sqrt[3]{5s^2}}{s}$

Skill Practice Simplify the expression.

9. $\dfrac{18}{\sqrt[3]{3y^2}}$

TIP: In the expression $\dfrac{15\sqrt[3]{5s^2}}{5s}$, the factor of 15 and the factor of 5 may be reduced because both are outside the radical.

$\dfrac{15\sqrt[3]{5s^2}}{5s} = \dfrac{15}{5} \cdot \dfrac{\sqrt[3]{5s^2}}{s}$

$= \dfrac{3\sqrt[3]{5s^2}}{s}$

4. Rationalizing the Denominator—Two Terms

Example 7 demonstrates how to rationalize a two-term denominator involving square roots.

First recall from the multiplication of polynomials that the product of two conjugates results in a difference of squares.

$$(a + b)(a - b) = a^2 - b^2$$

If either a or b has a square root factor, the expression will simplify without a radical. That is, the expression is *rationalized*. For example:

$$(2 + \sqrt{6})(2 - \sqrt{6}) = (2)^2 - (\sqrt{6})^2$$
$$= 4 - 6$$
$$= -2$$

Answer

9. $\dfrac{6\sqrt[3]{9y}}{y}$

Classroom Example: p. 739, Exercise 66

Example 7 Rationalizing the Denominator—Two Terms

Simplify the expression by rationalizing the denominator. $\dfrac{-2}{2 + \sqrt{6}}$

Solution:

$$\dfrac{-2}{2 + \sqrt{6}}$$

$$= \dfrac{(-2)}{(2 + \sqrt{6})} \cdot \dfrac{(2 - \sqrt{6})}{(2 - \sqrt{6})}$$

Multiply the numerator and denominator by the conjugate of the denominator. Multiplying by $\dfrac{2 - \sqrt{6}}{2 - \sqrt{6}}$ is the same as multiplying by 1.

conjugates

> **Avoiding Mistakes**
>
> When constructing the conjugate of an expression, change only the sign between the terms (not the sign of the leading term).

$$= \dfrac{-2(2 - \sqrt{6})}{(2)^2 - (\sqrt{6})^2}$$

In the denominator, apply the formula $(a + b)(a - b) = a^2 - b^2$.

$$= \dfrac{-2(2 - \sqrt{6})}{4 - 6}$$

Simplify.

$$= \dfrac{-2(2 - \sqrt{6})}{-2}$$

$$= \dfrac{-\cancel{2}(2 - \sqrt{6})}{-\cancel{2}}$$

$$= 2 - \sqrt{6}$$

Skill Practice Simplify by rationalizing the denominator.

10. $\dfrac{8}{3 + \sqrt{5}}$

Classroom Example: p. 739, Exercise 74

Example 8 Rationalizing the Denominator—Two Terms

Rationalize the denominator. $\dfrac{4 + \sqrt{x}}{\sqrt{x} - 7}$

Solution:

$$\dfrac{(4 + \sqrt{x})}{(\sqrt{x} - 7)} \cdot \dfrac{(\sqrt{x} + 7)}{(\sqrt{x} + 7)}$$

Multiply numerator and denominator by the conjugate of the denominator.

$$= \dfrac{(4)(\sqrt{x}) + (4)(7) + (\sqrt{x})(\sqrt{x}) + (\sqrt{x})(7)}{(\sqrt{x})^2 - (7)^2}$$

Apply the distributive property.

$$= \dfrac{4\sqrt{x} + 28 + x + 7\sqrt{x}}{x - 49}$$

Multiply the radicals.

$$= \dfrac{x + 11\sqrt{x} + 28}{x - 49}$$

Simplify.

Skill Practice Rationalize the denominator.

11. $\dfrac{\sqrt{y} - 4}{8 - \sqrt{y}}$

Answers

10. $6 - 2\sqrt{5}$

11. $\dfrac{y + 4\sqrt{y} - 32}{64 - y}$

Example 9 Rationalizing the Denominator—Two Terms

Classroom Example: p. 739, Exercise 80

Rationalize the denominator. $\dfrac{3\sqrt{2} + 2\sqrt{5}}{\sqrt{2} - 4\sqrt{5}}$

Solution:

$\dfrac{(3\sqrt{2} + 2\sqrt{5})}{(\sqrt{2} - 4\sqrt{5})} \cdot \dfrac{(\sqrt{2} + 4\sqrt{5})}{(\sqrt{2} + 4\sqrt{5})}$ Multiply numerator and denominator by the conjugate of the denominator.

$= \dfrac{(3\sqrt{2}) \cdot (\sqrt{2}) + (3\sqrt{2})(4\sqrt{5}) + (2\sqrt{5})(\sqrt{2}) + (2\sqrt{5})(4\sqrt{5})}{(\sqrt{2})^2 - (4\sqrt{5})^2}$ Apply the distributive property.

$= \dfrac{6 + 12\sqrt{10} + 2\sqrt{10} + 40}{2 - 80}$ Multiply the radicals.

$= \dfrac{46 + 14\sqrt{10}}{-78} \quad \text{or} \quad -\dfrac{46 + 14\sqrt{10}}{78}$

$= -\dfrac{\overset{1}{2}(23 + 7\sqrt{10})}{\underset{39}{78}}$ Factor and simplify.

$= -\dfrac{23 + 7\sqrt{10}}{39}$

Skill Practice Rationalize the denominator.

12. $\dfrac{5\sqrt{2} - 2\sqrt{5}}{\sqrt{2} - \sqrt{5}}$

Answer

12. $-\sqrt{10}$

Section 10.6 Practice Exercises

For the exercises in this set, assume that all variables represent positive real numbers unless otherwise stated.

Study Skills Exercise

1. Define the key term **rationalizing the denominator**.

Review Exercises

2. Simplify. $(4x^2y^4)^{1/2}(64y^{-3})^{1/3}$ $8xy$

For Exercises 3–10, perform the indicated operations.

3. $2y\sqrt{45} + 3\sqrt{20y^2}$
$12y\sqrt{5}$

4. $3x\sqrt{72x} - 9\sqrt{50x^3}$
$-27x\sqrt{2x}$

5. $(-6\sqrt{y} + 3)(3\sqrt{y} + 1)$
$-18y + 3\sqrt{y} + 3$

6. $(\sqrt{w} + 12)(2\sqrt{w} - 4)$
$2w + 20\sqrt{w} - 48$

7. $(8 - \sqrt{t})^2$
$64 - 16\sqrt{t} + t$

8. $(\sqrt{p} + 4)^2$
$p + 8\sqrt{p} + 16$

9. $(\sqrt{2} + \sqrt{7})(\sqrt{2} - \sqrt{7})$
-5

10. $(\sqrt{3} + 5)(\sqrt{3} - 5)$
-22

Concept 2: Division Property of Radicals

For Exercises 11–22, simplify using the division property of radicals. Assume all variables represent positive real numbers. **(See Examples 1–2.)**

11. $\sqrt{\dfrac{49x^4}{y^6}}$ $\dfrac{7x^2}{y^3}$

12. $\sqrt{\dfrac{100p^2}{q^8}}$ $\dfrac{10p}{q^4}$

13. $\sqrt{\dfrac{8a^2}{x^6}}$ $\dfrac{2a\sqrt{2}}{x^3}$

14. $\sqrt{\dfrac{4w^3}{25y^4}}$ $\dfrac{2w\sqrt{w}}{5y^2}$

15. $\sqrt[3]{\dfrac{-16j^3}{k^3}}$ $\dfrac{-2j\sqrt[3]{2}}{k}$

16. $\sqrt[5]{\dfrac{32x}{y^{10}}}$ $\dfrac{2\sqrt[5]{x}}{y^2}$

17. $\dfrac{\sqrt{72ab^5}}{\sqrt{8ab}}$ $3b^2$

18. $\dfrac{\sqrt{6x^3}}{\sqrt{24x}}$ $\dfrac{x}{2}$

19. $\dfrac{\sqrt[4]{3b^3}}{\sqrt[4]{48b^{11}}}$ $\dfrac{1}{2b^2}$

20. $\dfrac{\sqrt[3]{128wz^8}}{\sqrt[3]{2wz^2}}$ $4z^2$

21. $\dfrac{\sqrt{3yz^2}}{\sqrt{w^4}}$ $\dfrac{z\sqrt{3y}}{w^2}$

22. $\dfrac{\sqrt{50x^3z}}{\sqrt{9y^4}}$ $\dfrac{5x\sqrt{2xz}}{3y^2}$

Concept 3: Rationalizing the Denominator—One Term

The radical expressions in Exercises 23–30 have radicals in the denominator. Fill in the missing radicands to rationalize the denominators. **(See Example 3.)**

23. $\dfrac{x}{\sqrt{5}} = \dfrac{x}{\sqrt{5}} \cdot \dfrac{\sqrt{?}}{\sqrt{?}}$ $\dfrac{\sqrt{5}}{\sqrt{5}}$

24. $\dfrac{2}{\sqrt{x}} = \dfrac{2}{\sqrt{x}} \cdot \dfrac{\sqrt{?}}{\sqrt{?}}$ $\dfrac{\sqrt{x}}{\sqrt{x}}$

25. $\dfrac{7}{\sqrt[3]{x}} = \dfrac{7}{\sqrt[3]{x}} \cdot \dfrac{\sqrt[3]{?}}{\sqrt[3]{?}}$ $\dfrac{\sqrt[3]{x^2}}{\sqrt[3]{x^2}}$

26. $\dfrac{5}{\sqrt[4]{y}} = \dfrac{5}{\sqrt[4]{y}} \cdot \dfrac{\sqrt[4]{?}}{\sqrt[4]{?}}$ $\dfrac{\sqrt[4]{y^3}}{\sqrt[4]{y^3}}$

27. $\dfrac{8}{\sqrt{3z}} = \dfrac{8}{\sqrt{3z}} \cdot \dfrac{\sqrt{??}}{\sqrt{??}}$ $\dfrac{\sqrt{3z}}{\sqrt{3z}}$

28. $\dfrac{10}{\sqrt{7w}} = \dfrac{10}{\sqrt{7w}} \cdot \dfrac{\sqrt{??}}{\sqrt{??}}$ $\dfrac{\sqrt{7w}}{\sqrt{7w}}$

29. $\dfrac{1}{\sqrt[4]{8a^2}} = \dfrac{1}{\sqrt[4]{8a^2}} \cdot \dfrac{\sqrt[4]{??}}{\sqrt[4]{??}}$ $\dfrac{\sqrt[4]{2a^2}}{\sqrt[4]{2a^2}}$

30. $\dfrac{1}{\sqrt[3]{9b^2}} = \dfrac{1}{\sqrt[3]{9b^2}} \cdot \dfrac{\sqrt[3]{??}}{\sqrt[3]{??}}$ $\dfrac{\sqrt[3]{3b}}{\sqrt[3]{3b}}$

For Exercises 31–58, rationalize the denominator. **(See Examples 4–6.)**

31. $\dfrac{1}{\sqrt{3}}$ $\dfrac{\sqrt{3}}{3}$

32. $\dfrac{1}{\sqrt{7}}$ $\dfrac{\sqrt{7}}{7}$

33. $\sqrt{\dfrac{1}{x}}$ $\dfrac{\sqrt{x}}{x}$

34. $\sqrt{\dfrac{1}{z}}$ $\dfrac{\sqrt{z}}{z}$

35. $\dfrac{6}{\sqrt{2y}}$ $\dfrac{3\sqrt{2y}}{y}$

36. $\dfrac{9}{\sqrt{3t}}$ $\dfrac{3\sqrt{3t}}{t}$

37. $\sqrt{\dfrac{a^3}{2}}$ $\dfrac{a\sqrt{2a}}{2}$

38. $\sqrt{\dfrac{b^3}{3}}$ $\dfrac{b\sqrt{3b}}{3}$

39. $\dfrac{6}{\sqrt{8}}$ $\dfrac{3\sqrt{2}}{2}$

40. $\dfrac{2}{\sqrt{48}}$ $\dfrac{\sqrt{3}}{6}$

41. $\dfrac{3}{\sqrt[3]{2}}$ $\dfrac{3\sqrt[3]{4}}{2}$

42. $\dfrac{2}{\sqrt[3]{7}}$ $\dfrac{2\sqrt[3]{49}}{7}$

43. $\dfrac{-6}{\sqrt[4]{x}}$ $\dfrac{-6\sqrt[4]{x^3}}{x}$

44. $\dfrac{-2}{\sqrt[5]{y}}$ $\dfrac{-2\sqrt[5]{y^4}}{y}$

45. $\dfrac{7}{\sqrt[3]{4}}$ $\dfrac{7\sqrt[3]{2}}{2}$

46. $\dfrac{1}{\sqrt[3]{9}}$ $\dfrac{\sqrt[3]{3}}{3}$

47. $\sqrt[3]{\dfrac{4}{w^2}}$ $\dfrac{\sqrt[3]{4w}}{w}$

48. $\sqrt[3]{\dfrac{5}{z^2}}$ $\dfrac{\sqrt[3]{5z}}{z}$

49. $\sqrt[4]{\dfrac{16}{3}}$ $\dfrac{2\sqrt[4]{27}}{3}$

50. $\sqrt[4]{\dfrac{81}{8}}$ $\dfrac{3\sqrt[4]{2}}{2}$

51. $\dfrac{2}{\sqrt[3]{4x^2}}$ $\dfrac{\sqrt[3]{2x}}{x}$

52. $\dfrac{6}{\sqrt[3]{3y^2}}$ $\dfrac{2\sqrt[3]{9y}}{y}$

53. $\dfrac{8}{7\sqrt{24}}$ $\dfrac{2\sqrt{6}}{21}$

54. $\dfrac{5}{3\sqrt{50}}$ $\dfrac{\sqrt{2}}{6}$

55. $\dfrac{1}{\sqrt{x^7}}$ $\dfrac{\sqrt{x}}{x^4}$

56. $\dfrac{1}{\sqrt{y^5}}$ $\dfrac{\sqrt{y}}{y^3}$

57. $\dfrac{2}{\sqrt{8x^5}}$ $\dfrac{\sqrt{2x}}{2x^3}$

58. $\dfrac{6}{\sqrt{27t^7}}$ $\dfrac{2\sqrt{3t}}{3t^4}$

Concept 4: Rationalizing the Denominator—Two Terms

59. What is the conjugate of $\sqrt{2} - \sqrt{6}$?
$\sqrt{2} + \sqrt{6}$

60. What is the conjugate of $\sqrt{11} + \sqrt{5}$?
$\sqrt{11} - \sqrt{5}$

61. What is the conjugate of $\sqrt{x} + 23$?
$\sqrt{x} - 23$

62. What is the conjugate of $17 - \sqrt{y}$?
$17 + \sqrt{y}$

 Writing   Translating Expression   Geometry   Scientific Calculator   Video   NS&E

For Exercises 63–82, rationalize the denominators. **(See Examples 7–9.)**

63. $\dfrac{4}{\sqrt{2}+3}$

$\dfrac{4\sqrt{2}-12}{-7}$ or $\dfrac{-4\sqrt{2}+12}{7}$

64. $\dfrac{6}{4-\sqrt{3}}$ $\dfrac{24+6\sqrt{3}}{13}$

65. $\dfrac{8}{\sqrt{6}-2}$ $4\sqrt{6}+8$

66. $\dfrac{-12}{\sqrt{5}-3}$ $3\sqrt{5}+9$

67. $\dfrac{\sqrt{7}}{\sqrt{3}+2}$ $-\sqrt{21}+2\sqrt{7}$

68. $\dfrac{\sqrt{8}}{\sqrt{3}+1}$ $\sqrt{6}-\sqrt{2}$

69. $\dfrac{-1}{\sqrt{p}+\sqrt{q}}$ $\dfrac{-\sqrt{p}+\sqrt{q}}{p-q}$

70. $\dfrac{6}{\sqrt{a}-\sqrt{b}}$ $\dfrac{6\sqrt{a}+6\sqrt{b}}{a-b}$

71. $\dfrac{x-5}{\sqrt{x}+\sqrt{5}}$ $\sqrt{x}-\sqrt{5}$

72. $\dfrac{y-2}{\sqrt{y}-\sqrt{2}}$ $\sqrt{y}+\sqrt{2}$

73. $\dfrac{\sqrt{w}+2}{9-\sqrt{w}}$ $\dfrac{w+11\sqrt{w}+18}{81-w}$

74. $\dfrac{10-\sqrt{t}}{\sqrt{t}-6}$ $\dfrac{-t+4\sqrt{t}+60}{t-36}$

75. $\dfrac{3\sqrt{x}-\sqrt{y}}{\sqrt{y}+\sqrt{x}}$ $\dfrac{4\sqrt{xy}-3x-y}{y-x}$

76. $\dfrac{2\sqrt{a}+\sqrt{b}}{\sqrt{b}-\sqrt{a}}$ $\dfrac{3\sqrt{ab}+2a+b}{b-a}$

77. $\dfrac{3\sqrt{10}}{2+\sqrt{10}}$ $5-\sqrt{10}$

78. $\dfrac{4\sqrt{7}}{3+\sqrt{7}}$ $6\sqrt{7}-14$

79. $\dfrac{2\sqrt{3}+\sqrt{7}}{3\sqrt{3}-\sqrt{7}}$ $\dfrac{5+\sqrt{21}}{4}$

80. $\dfrac{5\sqrt{2}-\sqrt{5}}{5\sqrt{2}+\sqrt{5}}$ $\dfrac{11-2\sqrt{10}}{9}$

81. $\dfrac{\sqrt{5}+4}{2-\sqrt{5}}$ $-6\sqrt{5}-13$

82. $\dfrac{3+\sqrt{2}}{\sqrt{2}-5}$ $\dfrac{17+8\sqrt{2}}{-23}$ or $\dfrac{-17-8\sqrt{2}}{23}$

Mixed Exercises

For Exercises 83–86, write the English phrase as an algebraic expression. Then simplify the expression.

83. 16 divided by the cube root of 4 $\dfrac{16}{\sqrt[3]{4}}$ simplifies to $8\sqrt[3]{2}$

84. 21 divided by the principal fourth root of 27 $\dfrac{21}{\sqrt[4]{27}}$ simplifies to $7\sqrt[4]{3}$

85. 4 divided by the difference of x and the principal square root of 2 $\dfrac{4}{x-\sqrt{2}}$ simplifies to $\dfrac{4x+4\sqrt{2}}{x^2-2}$

86. 8 divided by the sum of y and the principal square root of 3 $\dfrac{8}{y+\sqrt{3}}$ simplifies to $\dfrac{8y-8\sqrt{3}}{y^2-3}$

87. The time $T(x)$ (in seconds) for a pendulum to make one complete swing back and forth is approximated by

$$T(x) = 2\pi\sqrt{\dfrac{x}{32}}$$

where x is the length of the pendulum in feet.

Determine the exact time required for one swing for a pendulum that is 1 ft long. Then approximate the time to the nearest hundredth of a second. $\dfrac{\pi\sqrt{2}}{4}$ sec ≈ 1.11 sec

88. An object is dropped off a building x meters tall. The time $T(x)$ (in seconds) required for the object to hit the ground is given by

$$T(x) = \sqrt{\dfrac{10x}{49}}$$

Find the exact time required for the object to hit the ground if it is dropped off the First National Plaza Building in Chicago, a height of 230 m. Then round the time to the nearest hundredth of a second. $\dfrac{10\sqrt{23}}{7}$ sec ≈ 6.85 sec

Expanding Your Skills

For Exercises 89–94, simplify each term of the expression. Then add or subtract as indicated.

89. $\dfrac{\sqrt{6}}{2}+\dfrac{1}{\sqrt{6}}$ $\dfrac{2\sqrt{6}}{3}$

90. $\dfrac{1}{\sqrt{7}}+\sqrt{7}$ $\dfrac{8\sqrt{7}}{7}$

91. $\sqrt{15}-\sqrt{\dfrac{3}{5}}+\sqrt{\dfrac{5}{3}}$ $\dfrac{17\sqrt{15}}{15}$

92. $\sqrt{\dfrac{6}{2}}-\sqrt{12}+\sqrt{\dfrac{2}{6}}$ $\dfrac{-2\sqrt{3}}{3}$

93. $\sqrt[3]{25}+\dfrac{3}{\sqrt[3]{5}}$ $\dfrac{8\sqrt[3]{25}}{5}$

94. $\dfrac{1}{\sqrt[3]{4}}+\sqrt[3]{54}$ $\dfrac{7\sqrt[3]{2}}{2}$

For Exercises 95–102, rationalize the numerator by multiplying both numerator and denominator by the conjugate of the numerator.

95. $\dfrac{\sqrt{3}+6}{2}$ $\quad \dfrac{-33}{2\sqrt{3}-12}$ 96. $\dfrac{\sqrt{7}-2}{5}$ $\quad \dfrac{3}{5\sqrt{7}+10}$ 97. $\dfrac{\sqrt{a}-\sqrt{b}}{\sqrt{a}+\sqrt{b}}$ $\quad \dfrac{a-b}{a+2\sqrt{ab}+b}$ 98. $\dfrac{\sqrt{p}+\sqrt{q}}{\sqrt{p}-\sqrt{q}}$ $\quad \dfrac{p-q}{p-2\sqrt{pq}+q}$

99. $\dfrac{\dfrac{\sqrt{5+3h}-\sqrt{5}}{h}}{\dfrac{3}{\sqrt{5+3h}+\sqrt{5}}}$ 100. $\dfrac{\dfrac{\sqrt{7+2h}-\sqrt{7}}{h}}{\dfrac{2}{\sqrt{7+2h}+\sqrt{7}}}$ 101. $\dfrac{\dfrac{\sqrt{4+5h}-2}{h}}{\dfrac{5}{\sqrt{4+5h}+2}}$ 102. $\dfrac{\dfrac{\sqrt{9+4h}-3}{h}}{\dfrac{4}{\sqrt{9+4h}+3}}$

Section 10.7 | Solving Radical Equations

1. Solutions to Radical Equations

An equation with one or more radicals containing a variable is called a **radical equation**. For example, $\sqrt[3]{x}=5$ is a radical equation. Recall that $(\sqrt[n]{a})^n=a$, provided $\sqrt[n]{a}$ is a real number. The basis of solving a radical equation is to eliminate the radical by raising both sides of the equation to a power equal to the index of the radical.

To solve the equation $\sqrt[3]{x}=5$, cube both sides of the equation.

$$\sqrt[3]{x}=5$$
$$(\sqrt[3]{x})^3=(5)^3$$
$$x=125$$

By raising each side of a radical equation to a power equal to the index of the radical, a new equation is produced. Note, however, that some of (or all) the solutions to the new equation may *not* be solutions to the original radical equation. For this reason, it is necessary to *check all potential solutions* in the original equation. For example, consider the equation $x=4$. By squaring both sides we produce a quadratic equation.

Instructor Note: Give students this Memory Device: Extraneous solutions are *Extra* solutions that don't fit the original problem.

Square both sides.
$$x=4$$
$$(x)^2=(4)^2 \quad \longleftarrow \quad$$ Squaring both sides produces a quadratic equation.
$$x^2=16 \quad \longleftarrow \quad$$ Solving this equation, we find two solutions.
$$x^2-16=0$$
$$(x-4)(x+4)=0$$
$$x=4 \quad \text{or} \quad x \ne -4$$

However, the solution -4 does not check in the original equation.

(-4 does not check and is called an **extraneous solution**.)

PROCEDURE Solving a Radical Equation

Step 1 Isolate the radical. If an equation has more than one radical, choose one of the radicals to isolate.

Step 2 Raise each side of the equation to a power equal to the index of the radical.

Step 3 Solve the resulting equation. If the equation still has a radical, repeat steps 1 and 2.

***Step 4** Check the potential solutions in the original equation.

*Extraneous solutions can arise only when both sides of the equation are raised to an *even power*. Therefore, an equation with odd-index roots will not have an extraneous solution. However, it is still recommended that you check *all* potential solutions regardless of the type of root.

---

2. Solving Radical Equations Involving One Radical

Example 1 Solving an Equation Containing One Radical

Classroom Example: p. 747, Exercise 12

Solve the equation. $\sqrt{p} + 5 = 9$

Solution:

$$\sqrt{p} + 5 = 9$$

$$\sqrt{p} = 4 \qquad \text{Isolate the radical.}$$

$$(\sqrt{p})^2 = 4^2 \qquad \text{Because the index is 2, square both sides.}$$

$$p = 16$$

$\underline{\text{Check}}: p = 16 \qquad \text{Check } p = 16 \text{ as a potential solution.}$

$$\sqrt{p} + 5 = 9$$

$$\sqrt{16} + 5 \overset{?}{=} 9$$

$$4 + 5 \overset{?}{=} 9 ✔ \qquad \text{True, 16 is a solution to the original equation.}$$

The solution set is $\{16\}$.

Skill Practice Solve.

1. $\sqrt{x} - 3 = 2$

Example 2 Solving an Equation Containing One Radical

Classroom Example: p. 747, Exercise 18

Solve the equation. $\sqrt[3]{w - 1} - 2 = 2$

Solution:

$$\sqrt[3]{w - 1} - 2 = 2$$

$$\sqrt[3]{w - 1} = 4 \qquad \text{Isolate the radical.}$$

$$(\sqrt[3]{w - 1})^3 = (4)^3 \qquad \text{Because the index is 3, cube both sides.}$$

$$w - 1 = 64 \qquad \text{Simplify.}$$

$$w = 65$$

$\underline{\text{Check}}: w = 65$

$$\sqrt[3]{65 - 1} - 2 \overset{?}{=} 2 \qquad \text{Check } w = 65 \text{ as a potential solution.}$$

$$\sqrt[3]{64} - 2 \overset{?}{=} 2$$

$$4 - 2 \overset{?}{=} 2 ✔ \qquad \text{True, 65 is a solution to the original equation.}$$

The solution set is $\{65\}$.

Skill Practice Solve.
2. $\sqrt[3]{t + 2} + 5 = 3$

Answers
1. $\{25\}$ 2. $\{-10\}$

Classroom Example: p. 747, Exercise 26

Example 3 Solving an Equation Containing One Radical

Solve the equation. $7 = (x + 3)^{1/4} + 9$

Solution:

$$7 = (x + 3)^{1/4} + 9$$

$$7 = \sqrt[4]{x + 3} + 9 \qquad \text{Note that } (x + 3)^{1/4} = \sqrt[4]{x + 3}.$$

$$-2 = \sqrt[4]{x + 3} \qquad \text{Isolate the radical.}$$

$$(-2)^4 = (\sqrt[4]{x + 3})^4 \qquad \text{Because the index is 4, raise both sides to the fourth power.}$$

$$16 = x + 3$$

$$x = 13 \qquad \text{Solve for } x.$$

$\underline{\text{Check}}$: $x = 13$

$$7 = \sqrt[4]{x + 3} + 9$$

$$7 \stackrel{?}{=} \sqrt[4]{(13) + 3} + 9$$

$$7 \stackrel{?}{=} \sqrt[4]{16} + 9$$

$$7 \stackrel{?}{=} 2 + 9 \text{ (false)} \qquad \text{13 is } not \text{ a solution to the original equation.}$$

The equation $7 = \sqrt[4]{x + 3} + 9$ has no solution.

The solution set is the empty set, $\{\ \}$.

TIP: After isolating the radical in Example 3, the equation shows a fourth root equated to a negative number:

$$-2 = \sqrt[4]{x + 3}$$

By definition, a principal fourth root of any real number must be nonnegative. Therefore, there can be no real solution to this equation.

Skill Practice Solve.

3. $3 = 6 + (x - 1)^{1/4}$

Classroom Example: p. 747, Exercise 42

Example 4 Solving an Equation Containing One Radical

Solve the equation. $y + 2\sqrt{4y - 3} = 3$

Solution:

$$y + 2\sqrt{4y - 3} = 3$$

$$2\sqrt{4y - 3} = 3 - y \qquad \text{Isolate the radical term.}$$

$$(2\sqrt{4y - 3})^2 = (3 - y)^2 \qquad \text{Because the index is 2, square both sides.}$$

$$4(4y - 3) = 9 - 6y + y^2 \qquad \text{Note that } (2\sqrt{4y - 3})^2 = 2^2(\sqrt{4y - 3})^2 \text{ and } (3 - y)^2 = (3 - y)(3 - y) = 9 - 6y + y^2.$$

$$16y - 12 = 9 - 6y + y^2$$

$$0 = y^2 - 22y + 21 \qquad \text{The equation is quadratic. Set one side equal to zero. Write the other side in descending order.}$$

$$0 = (y - 21)(y - 1) \qquad \text{Factor.}$$

$$y - 21 = 0 \quad \text{or} \quad y - 1 = 0 \qquad \text{Set each factor equal to zero.}$$

$$y = 21 \quad \text{or} \quad y = 1 \qquad \text{Solve.}$$

Avoiding Mistakes

Be sure to square the binomial, not the individual terms.

Answer

3. $\{\ \}$ (The value 82 does not check.)

Check: $y = 21$

$$y + 2\sqrt{4y - 3} = 3$$

$$21 + 2\sqrt{4(21) - 3} \overset{?}{=} 3$$

$$21 + 2\sqrt{81} \overset{?}{=} 3$$

$$21 + 18 \overset{?}{=} 3$$

$$39 \overset{?}{=} 3 \text{ False}$$

Check: $y = 1$

$$y + 2\sqrt{4y - 3} = 3$$

$$1 + 2\sqrt{4(1) - 3} \overset{?}{=} 3$$

$$1 + 2\sqrt{1} \overset{?}{=} 3$$

$$1 + 2 \overset{?}{=} 3$$

$$3 \overset{?}{=} 3 \checkmark \text{ True}$$

The solution set is {1} (the value 21 does not check).

Skill Practice Solve.

   4. $3\sqrt{x - 1} + 5 = x$

3. Solving Radical Equations Involving More than One Radical

Example 5 Solving an Equation with Two Radicals

Solve the equation.

$$\sqrt[3]{2x - 4} = \sqrt[3]{1 - 8x}$$

Classroom Example: p. 748, Exercise 46

Solution:

$\sqrt[3]{2x - 4} = \sqrt[3]{1 - 8x}$	
$(\sqrt[3]{2x - 4})^3 = (\sqrt[3]{1 - 8x})^3$	Because the index is 3, cube both sides.
$2x - 4 = 1 - 8x$	Simplify.
$10x - 4 = 1$	Solve the resulting equation.
$10x = 5$	
$x = \dfrac{1}{2}$	Solve for x.

Check: $x = \frac{1}{2}$

$$\sqrt[3]{2x - 4} = \sqrt[3]{1 - 8x}$$

$$\sqrt[3]{2\left(\frac{1}{2}\right) - 4} \overset{?}{=} \sqrt[3]{1 - 8\left(\frac{1}{2}\right)}$$

$$\sqrt[3]{1 - 4} \overset{?}{=} \sqrt[3]{1 - 4}$$

$$\sqrt[3]{-3} \overset{?}{=} \sqrt[3]{-3} \checkmark \text{ (True)}$$

Therefore, $\frac{1}{2}$ is a solution to the original equation.

The solution set is $\left\{\dfrac{1}{2}\right\}$.

Skill Practice Solve.

   5. $\sqrt[5]{2y - 1} = \sqrt[5]{10y + 3}$

Answers

4. {17} (The value 2 does not check.)

5. $\left\{-\dfrac{1}{2}\right\}$

Classroom Example: p. 748, Exercise 58

Example 6   Solving an Equation with Two Radicals

Solve the equation. $\sqrt{3m+1} - \sqrt{m+4} = 1$

Solution:

$$\sqrt{3m+1} - \sqrt{m+4} = 1$$

$$\sqrt{3m+1} = \sqrt{m+4} + 1 \qquad \text{Isolate one of the radicals.}$$

$$(\sqrt{3m+1})^2 = (\sqrt{m+4} + 1)^2 \qquad \text{Square both sides.}$$

$$3m+1 = m+4 + 2\sqrt{m+4} + 1$$

$$\textit{Note: } (\sqrt{m+4} + 1)^2$$
$$= (\sqrt{m+4})^2 + 2(1)\sqrt{m+4} + (1)^2$$
$$= m+4 + 2\sqrt{m+4} + 1$$

TIP: In Example 6, we divided the equation by 2 because all coefficients were divisible by 2. This made the coefficients smaller before we squared both sides of the equation a second time.

$$3m+1 = m+5 + 2\sqrt{m+4} \qquad \text{Combine } \textit{like} \text{ terms.}$$

$$2m-4 = 2\sqrt{m+4} \qquad \text{Isolate the radical again.}$$

$$m-2 = \sqrt{m+4} \qquad \text{Divide both sides by 2.}$$

$$(m-2)^2 = (\sqrt{m+4})^2 \qquad \text{Square both sides again.}$$

$$m^2 - 4m + 4 = m+4 \qquad \text{The resulting equation is quadratic.}$$

$$m^2 - 5m = 0 \qquad \text{Set one side equal to zero.}$$

$$m(m-5) = 0 \qquad \text{Factor.}$$

$$m = 0 \qquad \text{or} \qquad m = 5$$

Check: $m = 0$ Check: $m = 5$

$$\sqrt{3(0)+1} - \sqrt{(0)+4} \overset{?}{=} 1 \qquad\qquad \sqrt{3(5)+1} - \sqrt{(5)+4} = 1$$

$$\sqrt{1} - \sqrt{4} \overset{?}{=} 1 \qquad\qquad\qquad \sqrt{16} - \sqrt{9} \overset{?}{=} 1$$

$$1 - 2 \overset{?}{=} 1 \quad \text{(False)} \qquad\qquad\qquad 4 - 3 \overset{?}{=} 1 \; ✔$$

The solution set is $\{5\}$ (the value 0 does not check).

Answer

6. $\{1, 5\}$

Skill Practice Solve.

6. $\sqrt{3c+1} - \sqrt{c-1} = 2$

4. Applications of Radical Equations and Functions

Example 7 **Applying a Radical Equation in Geometry**

Classroom Example: p. 748, Exercise 68

For a pyramid with a square base, the length of a side of the base b is given by

$$b = \sqrt{\frac{3V}{h}}$$

where V is the volume and h is the height.

The Pyramid of the Pharoah Khufu (known as the Great Pyramid) at Giza has a square base (Figure 10-3). If the distance around the bottom of the pyramid is 921.6 m and the height is 146.6 m, what is the volume of the pyramid?

Figure 10-3

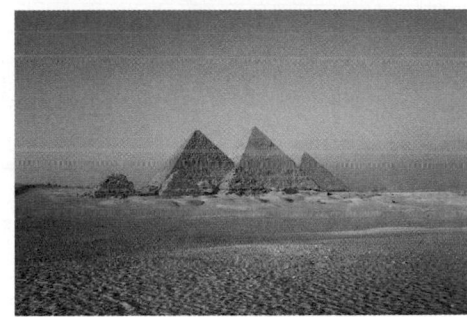

Solution:

The length of a side b (in meters) is given by $\dfrac{921.6}{4} = 230.4$ m.

$$b = \sqrt{\frac{3V}{h}}$$

$$230.4 = \sqrt{\frac{3V}{146.6}} \qquad \text{Substitute } b = 230.4 \text{ and } h = 146.6.$$

$$(230.4)^2 = \left(\sqrt{\frac{3V}{146.6}}\right)^2 \qquad \text{Because the index is 2, square both sides.}$$

$$53,084.16 = \frac{3V}{146.6} \qquad \text{Simplify.}$$

$$(53,084.16)(146.6) = \frac{3V}{146.6}(146.6) \qquad \text{Multiply both sides by 146.6.}$$

$$(53,084.16)(146.6) = 3V$$

$$\frac{(53,084.16)(146.6)}{3} = \frac{3V}{3} \qquad \text{Divide both sides by 3.}$$

$$2,594,046 \approx V$$

The volume of the Great Pyramid at Giza is approximately 2,594,046 m^3.

Skill Practice

7. The length of the legs, s, of an isosceles right triangle is $s = \sqrt{2A}$, where A is the area. If the legs of the triangle are 9 in., find the area.

Answer

7. 40.5 in.^{2}

Classroom Example: p. 749, Exercise 70

Example 8 Applying a Radical Function

On a certain surface, the speed $s(x)$ (in miles per hour) of a car before the brakes were applied can be approximated from the length of its skid marks x (in feet) by

$$s(x) = 3.8\sqrt{x} \qquad x \geq 0 \quad \text{See Figure 10-4.}$$

Speed of Car Based on Length of Skid Marks

Figure 10-4

a. Find the speed of a car before the brakes were applied if its skid marks are 361 ft long.

b. How long would you expect the skid marks to be if the car had been traveling the speed limit of 50 mph? (Round to the nearest foot.)

Solution:

a. $s(x) = 3.8\sqrt{x}$

$s(361) = 3.8\sqrt{361}$ Substitute $x = 361$.

$ = 3.8(19)$

$ = 72.2$

If the skid marks are 361 ft, the car was traveling approximately 72.2 mph before the brakes were applied.

b. $s(x) = 3.8\sqrt{x}$

$50 = 3.8\sqrt{x}$ Substitute $s(x) = 50$ and solve for x.

$\dfrac{50}{3.8} = \sqrt{x}$ Isolate the radical.

$\left(\dfrac{50}{3.8}\right)^2 = x$

$x \approx 173$

If the car had been going the speed limit (50 mph), then the length of the skid marks would have been approximately 173 ft.

Skill Practice When an object is dropped from a height of 64 ft, the time $t(x)$ (in seconds) it takes to reach a height x (in feet) is given by

$$t(x) = \frac{1}{4}\sqrt{64 - x}$$

8. Find the time to reach a height of 28 ft from the ground.

9. What is the height after 1 sec?

Answers

8. $\dfrac{3}{2}$ sec   9. 48 ft

Section 10.7 Practice Exercises

Study Skills Exercise

1. Define the key terms.

    a. radical equation   **b. extraneous solution**

Review Exercises

2. Identify the equation as linear or quadratic. Then solve the equation.

    a. $2x + 3 = 23$ Linear; $\{10\}$ **b.** $2x^2 - 9x = 5$ Quadratic; $\left\{-\dfrac{1}{2}, 5\right\}$

For Exercises 3–6, simplify the radical expressions. Assume all variables represent positive real numbers.

3. $\sqrt{\dfrac{9w^3}{16}}$ $\dfrac{3w\sqrt{w}}{4}$ **4.** $\sqrt{\dfrac{a^2}{3}}$ $\dfrac{a\sqrt{3}}{3}$ **5.** $\sqrt[3]{54c^4}$ $3c\sqrt[3]{2c}$ **6.** $\sqrt{\dfrac{49}{5t^3}}$ $\dfrac{7\sqrt{5t}}{5t^2}$

For Exercises 7–10, simplify each expression. Assume all radicands represent positive real numbers.

7. $(\sqrt{4x - 6})^2$ $4x - 6$ **8.** $(\sqrt{5y + 2})^2$ $5y + 2$ **9.** $(\sqrt[3]{9p + 7})^3$ $9p + 7$ **10.** $(\sqrt[3]{4t + 13})^3$ $4t + 13$

Concept 2: Solving Radical Equations Involving One Radical

For Exercises 11–26, solve the equations. **(See Examples 1–3.)**

11. $\sqrt{x} + 4 = 6$ $\{4\}$ **12.** $\sqrt{x} + 2 = 8$ $\{36\}$ **13.** $\sqrt{5y + 1} = 4$ $\{3\}$ **14.** $\sqrt{9z - 5} - 2 = 9$ $\{14\}$

15. $6 = \sqrt{2z \quad 3}$ 3 $\{42\}$ **16.** $4 - \sqrt{8 + 3a} - 1$ $\left\{\dfrac{17}{3}\right\}$ **17.** $\sqrt[3]{x - 2} - 3 = 0$ $\{29\}$ **18.** $\sqrt[3]{2x - 5} - 2 = 0$ $\left\{\dfrac{13}{2}\right\}$

19. $(15 - w)^{1/3} + 5 = 0$ $\{140\}$ **20.** $(k + 18)^{1/3} + 2 = 0$ $\{-26\}$ **21.** $3 + \sqrt{x - 16} = 0$ $\{\ \}$ (The value 25 does not check.)   **22.** $12 + \sqrt{2x + 1} = 0$ $\{\ \}$ (The value $\frac{143}{2}$ does not check.)

23. $2\sqrt{6a + 7} - 2a = 0$ $\{7\}$ (The value -1 does not check.)   **24.** $2\sqrt{3 - w} - w = 0$ $\{2\}$ (The value -6 does not check.)   **25.** $(2x - 5)^{1/4} = -1$ $\{\ \}$ (The value 3 does not check.)   **26.** $(x + 16)^{1/4} = -4$ $\{\ \}$ (The value 240 does not check.)

For Exercises 27–30, assume all variables represent positive real numbers.

27. Solve for V: $\quad r = \sqrt[3]{\dfrac{3V}{4\pi}}$ $V = \dfrac{4\pi r^3}{3}$ **28.** Solve for V: $\quad r = \sqrt{\dfrac{V}{h\pi}}$ $V = \pi r^2 h$

29. Solve for h^2: $\quad r = \pi\sqrt{r^2 + h^2}$ $h^2 = \dfrac{r^2 - \pi^2 r^2}{\pi^2}$ or $h^2 = \dfrac{r^2}{\pi^2} - r^2$ **30.** Solve for d: $\quad s = 1.3\sqrt{d}$ $d = \dfrac{s^2}{1.69}$

For Exercises 31–36, square the expression as indicated.

31. $(a + 5)^2$ **32.** $(b + 7)^2$ **33.** $(\sqrt{5a} - 3)^2$

  $a^2 + 10a + 25$ $b^2 + 14b + 49$ $5a - 6\sqrt{5a} + 9$

34. $(2 + \sqrt{b})^2$ **35.** $(\sqrt{r - 3} + 5)^2$ **36.** $(2 - \sqrt{2t - 4})^2$

  $4 + 4\sqrt{b} + b$ $r + 22 + 10\sqrt{r - 3}$ $2t - 4\sqrt{2t - 4}$

For Exercises 37–42, solve the radical equations, if possible. **(See Example 4.)**

37. $\sqrt{a^2 + 2a + 1} = a + 5$ **38.** $\sqrt{b^2 - 5b - 8} = b + 7$ **39.** $\sqrt{25w^2 - 2w - 3} = 5w - 4$

  $\{-3\}$ $\{-3\}$ $\{\ \}$ (The value $\frac{1}{2}$ does not check.)

40. $\sqrt{4p^2 - 2p + 1} = 2p - 3$ **41.** $4\sqrt{p - 2} - 2 = -p$ **42.** $x - 3\sqrt{x - 5} = 5$

  $\{\ \}$ (The value $\frac{4}{5}$ does not check.) $\{2\}$ (The value 18 does not check.) $\{5, 14\}$

Concept 3: Solving Radical Equations Involving More than One Radical

For Exercises 43–66, solve the radical equations, if possible. **(See Examples 5–6.)**

43. $\sqrt[4]{h+4} = \sqrt[4]{2h-5}$
{9}

44. $\sqrt[4]{3b+6} = \sqrt[4]{7b-6}$
{3}

45. $\sqrt[3]{5a+3} - \sqrt[3]{a-13} = 0$
{−4}

46. $\sqrt[3]{k-8} - \sqrt[3]{4k+1} = 0$
{−3}

47. $\sqrt{5a-9} = \sqrt{5a} - 3$ $\left\{\dfrac{9}{5}\right\}$

48. $\sqrt{8+b} = 2 + \sqrt{b}$
{1}

49. $\sqrt{2h+5} - \sqrt{2h} = 1$ {2}

50. $\sqrt{3k-5} - \sqrt{3k} = -1$ {3}

51. $\sqrt{t-9} - \sqrt{t} = 3$
{ } (The value 9 does not check.)

52. $\sqrt{y-16} - \sqrt{y} = 4$
{ } (The value 16 does not check.)

53. $6 = \sqrt{x^2+3} - x$ $\left\{-\dfrac{11}{4}\right\}$

54. $2 = \sqrt{y^2+5} - y$ $\left\{\dfrac{1}{4}\right\}$

55. $\sqrt{3t-7} = 2 - \sqrt{3t+1}$
{ } (The value $\frac{8}{3}$ does not check.)

56. $\sqrt{p-6} = \sqrt{p+2} - 4$
{ } (The value 7 does not check.)

57. $\sqrt{z+1} + \sqrt{2z+3} = 1$
{−1} (The value 3 does not check.)

58. $\sqrt{2y+6} = \sqrt{7-2y} + 1$
$\left\{\frac{3}{2}\right\}$ (The value −1 does not check.)

59. $\sqrt{6m+7} - \sqrt{3m+3} = 1$
$\left\{\dfrac{1}{3}, -1\right\}$

60. $\sqrt{5w+1} - \sqrt{3w} = 1$
{0, 3}

61. $2 + 2\sqrt{2t+3} + 2\sqrt{3t-5} = 0$
{ } (The values 3 and 23 do not check.)

62. $6 + 3\sqrt{3x+1} + 3\sqrt{x-1} = 0$
{ } (The values 5 and 1 do not check.)

63. $3\sqrt{y-3} = \sqrt{4y+3}$ {6}

64. $\sqrt{5x-8} = 2\sqrt{x-1}$ {4}

65. $\sqrt{p+7} = \sqrt{2p} + 1$
{2} (The value 18 does not check.)

66. $\sqrt{t} = \sqrt{t-12} + 2$ {16}

Concept 4: Applications of Radical Equations and Functions

67. If an object is dropped from an initial height h, its velocity at impact with the ground is given by

$$v = \sqrt{2gh}$$

where g is the acceleration due to gravity and h is the initial height. **(See Example 7.)**

a. Find the initial height (in feet) of an object if its velocity at impact is 44 ft/sec. (Assume that the acceleration due to gravity is $g = 32$ ft/sec^2.)   30.25 ft

b. Find the initial height (in meters) of an object if its velocity at impact is 26 m/sec. (Assume that the acceleration due to gravity is $g = 9.8$ m/sec^2.) Round to the nearest tenth of a meter.   34.5 m

68. The time T (in seconds) required for a pendulum to make one complete swing back and forth is approximated by

$$T = 2\pi\sqrt{\dfrac{L}{g}}$$

where g is the acceleration due to gravity and L is the length of the pendulum (in feet).

a. Find the length of a pendulum that requires 1.36 sec to make one complete swing back and forth. (Assume that the acceleration due to gravity is $g = 32$ ft/sec^2.) Round to the nearest tenth of a foot.   1.5 ft

b. Find the time required for a pendulum to complete one swing back and forth if the length of the pendulum is 4 ft. (Assume that the acceleration due to gravity is $g = 32$ ft/sec^2.) Round to the nearest tenth of a second.   2.2 sec

69. The airline cost for x thousand passengers to travel round trip from New York to Atlanta is given by

$$C(x) = \sqrt{0.3x+1}$$

where $C(x)$ is measured in millions of dollars and $x \geq 0$. **(See Example 8.)**

a. Find the airline's cost for 10,000 passengers ($x = 10$) to travel from New York to Atlanta. $2 million

b. If the airline charges $320 per passenger, find the profit made by the airline for flying 10,000 passengers from New York to Atlanta. $1.2 million

c. Approximate the number of passengers who traveled from New York to Atlanta if the total cost for the airline was $4 million.   50,000 passengers

 Writing   Translating Expression   Geometry   Scientific Calculator   Video   NS&E

70. The time $t(d)$ in seconds it takes an object to drop d meters is given by

$$t(d) = \sqrt{\dfrac{d}{4.9}}$$

   a. Approximate the height of the Texas Commerce Tower in Houston if it takes an object 7.89 sec to drop from the top. Round to the nearest meter. 305 m

   b. Approximate the height of the Willis Tower in Chicago if it takes an object 9.51 sec to drop from the top. Round to the nearest meter. 443 m

Expanding Your Skills

 71. The number of hours needed to cook a turkey that weighs x pounds can be approximated by

$$t(x) = 0.90\sqrt[5]{x^3}$$

where $t(x)$ is the time in hours and x is the weight of the turkey in pounds.

   a. Find the weight of a turkey that cooked for 4 hr. Round to the nearest pound. 12 lb

   b. Find $t(18)$ and interpret the result. Round to the nearest tenth of an hour.
     $t(18) = 5.1$. An 18-lb turkey will take about 5.1 hr to cook.

 For Exercises 72–75, use the Pythagorean theorem to find a, b, or c.

   72. Find b when $a = 2$ and $c = y$. $b = \sqrt{y^2 - 4}$ **73.** Find b when $a = h$ and $c = 5$. $b = \sqrt{25 - h^2}$

   74. Find a when $b = x$ and $c = 8$. $a = \sqrt{64 - x^2}$ **75.** Find a when $b = 14$ and $c = k$. $a = \sqrt{k^2 - 196}$

Graphing Calculator Exercises

76. Graph Y_1 and Y_2 on a viewing window defined by $-10 \le x \le 40$ and $-5 \le y \le 10$.

$$Y_1 = \sqrt{2x} \quad \text{and} \quad Y_2 = 8$$

Use an *Intersect* feature to approximate the x-coordinate of the point of intersection of the two graphs. How does the point of intersection relate to the solution to the equation $\sqrt{2x} = 8$? The x-coordinate of the point of intersection is the solution to the equation.

77. Graph Y_1 and Y_2 on a viewing window defined by $-10 \le x \le 20$ and $5 \le y \le 10$.

$$Y_1 = \sqrt{4x} \quad \text{and} \quad Y_2 = 6$$

Use an *Intersect* feature to approximate the x-coordinate of the point of intersection of the two graphs. How does the point of intersection relate to the solution to the equation $\sqrt{4x} = 6$? The x-coordinate of the point of intersection is the solution to the equation.

78. Refer to Exercise 44. Graph Y_1 and Y_2 on a viewing window defined by $-5 \le x \le 20$ and $-1 \le y \le 4$.

$$Y_1 = \sqrt[4]{3x + 6} \quad \text{and} \quad Y_2 = \sqrt[4]{7x - 6}$$

Use an *Intersect* feature to approximate the x-coordinate of the point of intersection of the two graphs to support your solution to Exercise 44.

79. Refer to Exercise 43. Graph Y_1 and Y_2 on a viewing window defined by $-5 \le x \le 20$ and $-1 \le y \le 4$.

$$Y_1 = \sqrt[4]{x + 4} \quad \text{and} \quad Y_2 = \sqrt[4]{2x - 5}$$

Use an *Intersect* feature to approximate the x-coordinate of the point of intersection of the two graphs to support your solution to Exercise 43.

Section 10.8	Complex Numbers

Concepts

1. **Definition of *i***
2. **Powers of *i***
3. **Definition of a Complex Number**
4. **Addition, Subtraction, and Multiplication of Complex Numbers**
5. **Division and Simplification of Complex Numbers**

1. Definition of *i*

In Section 10.1, we learned that there are no real-valued square roots of a negative number. For example, $\sqrt{-9}$ is not a real number because no real number when squared equals -9. However, the square roots of a negative number are defined over another set of numbers called the **imaginary numbers**. The foundation of the set of imaginary numbers is the definition of the imaginary number *i*.

DEFINITION *i*

$$i = \sqrt{-1}$$

Note: From the definition of *i*, it follows that $i^2 = -1$.

Instructor Note: Since $i = \sqrt{-1}$, and $\sqrt{-1}$ is not real, *i* is not a real number.

Using the imaginary number *i*, we can define the square root of any negative real number.

DEFINITION $\sqrt{-b}$ for $b > 0$

Let *b* be a real number such that $b > 0$. Then $\sqrt{-b} = i\sqrt{b}$.

Classroom Examples: p. 758, Exercises 12, 14, and 16

Example 1	Simplifying Expressions in Terms of *i*

Simplify the expressions in terms of *i*.

a. $\sqrt{-64}$ **b.** $\sqrt{-50}$ **c.** $-\sqrt{-4}$ **d.** $\sqrt{-29}$

Solution:

a. $\sqrt{-64} = i\sqrt{64}$

$\qquad = 8i$

b. $\sqrt{-50} = i\sqrt{50}$

$\qquad = i\sqrt{5^2 \cdot 2}$

$\qquad = 5i\sqrt{2}$

c. $-\sqrt{-4} = -1 \cdot \sqrt{-4}$

$\qquad = -1 \cdot 2i$

$\qquad = -2i$

d. $\sqrt{-29} = i\sqrt{29}$

> **Avoiding Mistakes**
>
> In an expression such as $i\sqrt{29}$, the *i* is often written in front of the square root. The expression $\sqrt{29}\,i$ is also correct, but may be misinterpreted as $\sqrt{29i}$ (with *i* incorrectly placed under the radical).

Skill Practice Simplify the expressions in terms of *i*.

1. $\sqrt{-81}$ **2.** $\sqrt{-20}$ **3.** $-\sqrt{-36}$ **4.** $\sqrt{-7}$

The multiplication and division properties of radicals were presented in Sections 10.3 and 10.5 as follows:

If *a* and *b* represent real numbers such that $\sqrt[n]{a}$ and $\sqrt[n]{b}$ are both real, then

$$\sqrt[n]{ab} = \sqrt[n]{a} \cdot \sqrt[n]{b} \qquad \text{and} \qquad \sqrt[n]{\frac{a}{b}} = \frac{\sqrt[n]{a}}{\sqrt[n]{b}} \qquad b \neq 0$$

Answers

1. $9i$ **2.** $2i\sqrt{5}$ **3.** $-6i$ **4.** $i\sqrt{7}$

The conditions that $\sqrt[n]{a}$ and $\sqrt[n]{b}$ must both be real numbers prevent us from applying the multiplication and division properties of radicals for square roots with a negative radicand. Therefore, to multiply or divide radicals with a negative radicand, first write the radical in terms of the imaginary number i. This is demonstrated in Example 2.

Example 2 Simplifying a Product or Quotient in Terms of i

Classroom Examples: p. 758, Exercises 22, 24, and 30

Simplify the expressions.

a. $\dfrac{\sqrt{-100}}{\sqrt{-25}}$ b. $\sqrt{-25} \cdot \sqrt{-9}$ c. $\sqrt{-5} \cdot \sqrt{-5}$

Solution:

a. $\dfrac{\sqrt{-100}}{\sqrt{-25}}$

$= \dfrac{10i}{5i}$ Simplify each radical in terms of i *before* dividing.

$= 2$

b. $\sqrt{-25} \cdot \sqrt{-9}$

$= 5i \cdot 3i$ Simplify each radical in terms of i first *before* multiplying.

$= 15i^2$ Multiply.

$= 15(-1)$ Recall that $i^2 = -1$.

$= -15$ Simplify.

c. $\sqrt{-5} \cdot \sqrt{-5}$

$= i\sqrt{5} \cdot i\sqrt{5}$

$= i^2 \cdot (\sqrt{5})^2$

$= -1 \cdot 5$

$= -5$

Skill Practice Simplify the expressions.

5. $\dfrac{\sqrt{-36}}{\sqrt{-9}}$ 6. $\sqrt{-16} \cdot \sqrt{-49}$ 7. $\sqrt{-2} \cdot \sqrt{-2}$

Avoiding Mistakes

In Example 2, we wrote the radical expressions in terms of i first, before multiplying or dividing. If we had mistakenly applied the multiplication or division property first, we would have obtained an incorrect answer.

Correct: $\sqrt{-25} \cdot \sqrt{-9}$

$= (5i)(3i) = 15i^2$

$= 15(-1) = -15$

↑ correct

Be careful: $\sqrt{-25} \cdot \sqrt{-9}$ $\sqrt{-25}$ and $\sqrt{-9}$ are not real numbers. Therefore, the multiplication property of radicals cannot be applied.

$\neq \sqrt{225} = 15$

↑ (incorrect answer)

Answers

5. 2   6. -28 7. -2

2. Powers of i

From the definition of $i = \sqrt{-1}$, it follows that

$$i = i$$

$$i^2 = -1$$

$$i^3 = -i \qquad \text{because } i^3 = i^2 \cdot i = (-1)i = -i$$

$$i^4 = 1 \qquad \text{because } i^4 = i^2 \cdot i^2 = (-1)(-1) = 1$$

$$i^5 = i \qquad \text{because } i^5 = i^4 \cdot i = (1)i = i$$

$$i^6 = -1 \qquad \text{because } i^6 = i^4 \cdot i^2 = (1)(-1) = -1$$

This pattern of values $i, -1, -i, 1, i, -1, -i, 1, \ldots$ continues for all subsequent powers of i. Table 10-1 lists several powers of i.

Table 10-1 **Powers of i**

$i^1 = i$	$i^5 = i$	$i^9 = i$
$i^2 = -1$	$i^6 = -1$	$i^{10} = -1$
$i^3 = -i$	$i^7 = -i$	$i^{11} = -i$
$i^4 = 1$	$i^8 = 1$	$i^{12} = 1$

To simplify higher powers of i, we can decompose the expression into multiples of i^4 ($i^4 = 1$) and write the remaining factors as i, i^2, or i^3.

Classroom Examples: p. 758, Exercises 34, 36, and 42

Example 3   **Simplifying Powers of i**

Simplify the powers of i.

a. i^{13} **b.** i^{18} **c.** i^{107} **d.** i^{32}

Solution:

a. $i^{13} = (i^{12}) \cdot (i)$ Write the exponent as a multiple of 4 and a remainder.

$\quad = (i^4)^3 \cdot (i)$

$\quad = (1)^3(i)$ Recall that $i^4 = 1$.

$\quad = i$ Simplify.

b. $i^{18} = (i^{16}) \cdot (i^2)$ Write the exponent as a multiple of 4 and a remainder.

$\quad = (i^4)^4 \cdot (i^2)$

$\quad = (1)^4 \cdot (-1)$ $i^4 = 1$ and $i^2 = -1$

$\quad = -1$ Simplify.

c. $i^{107} = (i^{104}) \cdot (i^3)$ Write the exponent as a multiple of 4 and a remainder.

$\quad = (i^4)^{26}(i^3)$

$\quad = (1)^{26}(-i)$ $i^4 = 1$ and $i^3 = -i$

$\quad = -i$ Simplify.

d. $i^{32} = (i^4)^8$

$\quad\quad = (1)^8 \quad i^4 = 1$

$\quad\quad = 1 \quad\quad$ Simplify.

Skill Practice Simplify the powers of i.

8. i^{45} **9.** i^{22} **10.** i^{31} **11.** i^{80}

3. Definition of a Complex Number

We have already learned the definitions of the integers, rational numbers, irrational numbers, and real numbers. In this section, we define the complex numbers.

DEFINITION   Complex Number

A **complex number** is a number of the form $a + bi$, where a and b are real numbers and $i = \sqrt{-1}$.

Notes:

- If $b = 0$, then the complex number $a + bi$ is a real number.
- If $b \neq 0$, then we say that $a + bi$ is an imaginary number.
- The complex number $a + bi$ is said to be written in standard form. The quantities a and b are called the real and imaginary parts (respectively) of the complex number.
- The complex numbers $a - bi$ and $a + bi$ are called **conjugates**.

From the definition of a complex number, it follows that all real numbers are complex numbers and all imaginary numbers are complex numbers. Figure 10-5 illustrates the relationship among the sets of numbers we have learned so far.

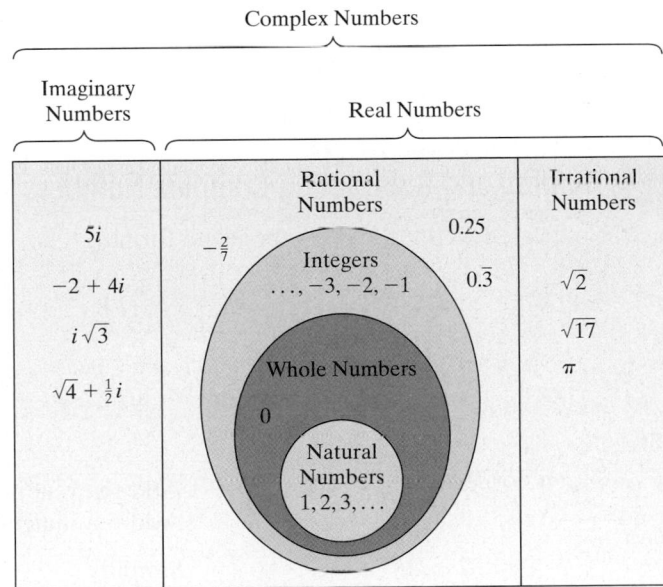

Figure 10-5

Classroom Examples: p. 758, Exercises 46, 48, and 50

Example 4 **Identifying the Real and Imaginary Parts of a Complex Number**

Identify the real and imaginary parts of the complex numbers.

a. $-8 + 2i$ **b.** $\dfrac{3}{2}$ **c.** $-1.75i$

Solution:

a. $-8 + 2i$ -8 is the real part, and 2 is the imaginary part.

b. $\dfrac{3}{2} = \dfrac{3}{2} + 0i$ Rewrite $\frac{3}{2}$ in the form $a + bi$.
$\frac{3}{2}$ is the real part, and 0 is the imaginary part.

c. $-1.75i$

$= 0 + -1.75i$ Rewrite $-1.75i$ in the form $a + bi$.
0 is the real part, and -1.75 is the imaginary part.

Skill Practice Identify the real and imaginary parts of the complex numbers.

12. $22 - 14i$ **13.** -50 **14.** $15i$

TIP: Example 4(b) illustrates that a real number is also a complex number.

$$\dfrac{3}{2} = \dfrac{3}{2} + 0i$$

Example 4(c) illustrates that an imaginary number is also a complex number.

$$-1.75i = 0 + -1.75i$$

4. Addition, Subtraction, and Multiplication of Complex Numbers

The operations of addition, subtraction, and multiplication of real numbers also apply to imaginary numbers. To add or subtract complex numbers, combine the real parts and combine the imaginary parts. The commutative, associative, and distributive properties that apply to real numbers also apply to complex numbers.

Classroom Example: p. 758, Exercise 56

Example 5 **Adding and Subtracting Complex Numbers**

Add or subtract as indicated. Write the answers in the form $a + bi$.

a. $(1 - 5i) + (-3 + 7i)$ **b.** $\left(-\dfrac{1}{4} + \dfrac{3}{5}i\right) - \left(\dfrac{1}{2} - \dfrac{1}{10}i\right)$

Solution:

       real parts

a. $(1 - 5i) + (-3 + 7i) = (1 + -3) + (-5 + 7)i$ Add the real parts.
Add the imaginary parts.

       imaginary parts

$= -2 + 2i$ Simplify.

Answers

12. real: 22; imaginary: -14
13. real: -50; imaginary: 0
14. real: 0; imaginary: 15

b. $\left(-\dfrac{1}{4} + \dfrac{3}{5}i\right) - \left(\dfrac{1}{2} - \dfrac{1}{10}i\right) = -\dfrac{1}{4} + \dfrac{3}{5}i - \dfrac{1}{2} + \dfrac{1}{10}i$ Apply the distributive property.

$$= \left(-\dfrac{1}{4} - \dfrac{1}{2}\right) + \left(\dfrac{3}{5} + \dfrac{1}{10}\right)i$$ Add real parts. Add imaginary parts.

$$= \left(-\dfrac{1}{4} - \dfrac{2}{4}\right) + \left(\dfrac{6}{10} + \dfrac{1}{10}\right)i$$ Get common denominators.

$$= -\dfrac{3}{4} + \dfrac{7}{10}i$$ Simplify.

Skill Practice Perform the indicated operations.

15. $\left(\dfrac{1}{2} - \dfrac{1}{4}i\right) + \left(\dfrac{3}{5} + \dfrac{2}{3}i\right)$ **16.** $(-6 + 11i) - (-9 - 12i)$

Example 6   **Multiplying Complex Numbers**

Multiply the complex numbers. Write the answers in the form $a + bi$.

  a. $(10 - 5i)(2 + 3i)$ **b.** $(1.2 + 0.5i)(1.2 - 0.5i)$

Classroom Examples: p. 758, Exercises 66 and 68

Solution:

a. $(10 - 5i)(2 + 3i)$

$$= (10)(2) + (10)(3i) + (-5i)(2) + (-5i)(3i)$$ Apply the distributive property.

$$= 20 + 30i - 10i - 15i^2$$

$$= 20 + 20i - (15)(-1)$$ Recall $i^2 = -1$.

$$= 20 + 20i + 15$$

$$= 35 + 20i$$ Write in the form $a + bi$.

b. $(1.2 + 0.5i)(1.2 - 0.5i)$

The expressions $(1.2 + 0.5i)$ and $(1.2 - 0.5i)$ are conjugates. The product is a difference of squares.

$$(a + b)(a - b) = a^2 - b^2$$

$$(1.2 + 0.5i)(1.2 - 0.5i) = (1.2)^2 - (0.5i)^2$$ Apply the formula, where $a = 1.2$ and $b = 0.5i$.

$$= 1.44 - 0.25i^2$$

$$= 1.44 - 0.25(-1)$$ Recall $i^2 = -1$.

$$= 1.44 + 0.25$$

$$= 1.69 + 0i$$

Skill Practice Multiply.

17. $(4 - 6i)(2 - 3i)$ **18.** $(1.5 + 0.8i)(1.5 - 0.8i)$

Answers

15. $\dfrac{11}{10} + \dfrac{5}{12}i$ **16.** $3 + 23i$

17. $-10 - 24i$ **18.** $2.89 + 0i$

5. Division and Simplification of Complex Numbers

The product of a complex number and its conjugate is a real number. For example:

$$(5 + 3i)(5 - 3i) = 25 - 9i^2$$
$$= 25 - 9(-1)$$
$$= 25 + 9$$
$$= 34$$

To divide by a complex number, multiply the numerator and denominator by the conjugate of the denominator. This produces a real number in the denominator so that the resulting expression can be written in the form $a + bi$.

Classroom Example: p. 759, Exercise 82

Example 7 **Dividing by a Complex Number**

Divide the complex numbers and write the answer in the form $a + bi$.

$$\frac{4 - 3i}{5 + 2i}$$

Instructor Note: In Example 7 point out that $\dfrac{(5 - 2i)}{(5 - 2i)} = 1$.

Solution:

$\dfrac{4 - 3i}{5 + 2i}$ Multiply the numerator and denominator by the conjugate of the denominator:

$$\frac{(4 - 3i)}{(5 + 2i)} \cdot \frac{(5 - 2i)}{(5 - 2i)} = \frac{(4)(5) + (4)(-2i) + (-3i)(5) + (-3i)(-2i)}{(5)^2 - (2i)^2}$$

$$= \frac{20 - 8i - 15i + 6i^2}{25 - 4i^2} \qquad \text{Simplify numerator and denominator.}$$

$$= \frac{20 - 23i + 6(-1)}{25 - 4(-1)} \qquad \text{Recall } i^2 = -1.$$

$$= \frac{20 - 23i - 6}{25 + 4}$$

$$= \frac{14 - 23i}{29} \qquad \text{Simplify.}$$

$$= \frac{14}{29} - \frac{23}{29}i \qquad \text{Write in the form } a + bi.$$

TIP: In Example 7, we asked for the answer in the form $a + bi$. However, if the second term is negative, we often leave an answer in terms of subtraction: $\frac{14}{29} - \frac{23}{29}i$. This is the same as $\frac{14}{29} + \left(-\frac{23}{29}i\right)$.

Skill Practice Divide the complex numbers. Write the answer in the form $a + bi$.

19. $\dfrac{2 + i}{3 - 2i}$

Example 8	**Simplifying a Complex Number**

Simplify the complex number. $\dfrac{6 + \sqrt{-18}}{9}$

Classroom Example: p. 759, Exercise 94

Solution:

$\dfrac{6 + \sqrt{-18}}{9} = \dfrac{6 + i\sqrt{18}}{9}$ Write the radical in terms of i.

$= \dfrac{6 + 3i\sqrt{2}}{9}$ Simplify $\sqrt{18} = 3\sqrt{2}$.

$= \dfrac{3(2 + i\sqrt{2})}{9}$ Factor the numerator.

$= \dfrac{\overset{1}{\cancel{3}}(2 + i\sqrt{2})}{\underset{3}{\cancel{9}}}$ Simplify.

$= \dfrac{2 + i\sqrt{2}}{3}$ or $\dfrac{2}{3} + \dfrac{\sqrt{2}}{3}i$ Write in the form $a + bi$.

Skill Practice Simplify the complex number.

20. $\dfrac{8 - \sqrt{-24}}{6}$

Answer

20. $\dfrac{4 - i\sqrt{6}}{3}$ or $\dfrac{4}{3} - \dfrac{\sqrt{6}}{3}i$

Section 10.8   Practice Exercises

Boost *your* GRADE at ALEKS.com!

ALEKS® version 3.0

- Practice Problems
- Self-Tests
- NetTutor
- e-Professors
- Videos

For additional exercises, see Classroom Activities 10.8A–10.8D in the *Instructor's Resource Manual* at www.mhhe.com/moh.

Study Skills Exercise

1. Define the key terms.

    a. imaginary numbers   **b.** *i*   **c. complex number**   **d. conjugate**

Review Exercises

For Exercises 2–4, perform the indicated operations.

2. $-2\sqrt{5} - 3\sqrt{50} + \sqrt{125}$
    $3\sqrt{5} - 15\sqrt{2}$

3. $(3 - \sqrt{x})(3 + \sqrt{x})$
    $9 - x$

4. $(\sqrt{5} + \sqrt{2})^2$
    $7 + 2\sqrt{10}$

For Exercises 5–7, solve the equations.

5. $\sqrt[3]{3p + 7} - \sqrt[3]{2p - 1} = 0$
    $\{-8\}$

6. $\sqrt{9t + 10} + 18 = 10$
    $\{\ \}$ (The value 6 does not check.)

7. $\sqrt{4a + 29} = 2\sqrt{a} + 5$
    $\left\{\dfrac{1}{25}\right\}$

8. Rationalize the denominator. $\dfrac{2}{\sqrt{x} - 3}$ $\dfrac{2\sqrt{x} + 6}{x - 9}$

Concept 1: Definition of *i*

9. Simplify the expressions $\sqrt{-1}$ and $-\sqrt{1}$.
    $\sqrt{-1} = i$ and $-\sqrt{1} = -1$

10. Simplify i^2.
    $i^2 = -1$

 Writing   Translating Expression   Geometry   Scientific Calculator   Video   NS&E

For Exercises 11–30, simplify the expressions. **(See Examples 1–2.)**

11. $\sqrt{-144}$
$12i$

12. $\sqrt{-81}$
$9i$

13. $\sqrt{-3}$
$i\sqrt{3}$

14. $\sqrt{-17}$
$i\sqrt{17}$

15. $\sqrt{-20}$
$2i\sqrt{5}$

16. $\sqrt{-75}$
$5i\sqrt{3}$

17. $(2\sqrt{-25})(3\sqrt{-4})$
-60

18. $(-4\sqrt{-9})(-3\sqrt{-1})$
-36

19. $7\sqrt{-63} - 4\sqrt{-28}$
$13i\sqrt{7}$

20. $7\sqrt{-3} - 4\sqrt{-27}$
$-5i\sqrt{3}$

21. $\sqrt{-7} \cdot \sqrt{-7}$
-7

22. $\sqrt{-11} \cdot \sqrt{-11}$
-11

23. $\sqrt{-9} \cdot \sqrt{-16}$
-12

24. $\sqrt{-25} \cdot \sqrt{-36}$
-30

25. $\sqrt{-15} \cdot \sqrt{-6}$
$-3\sqrt{10}$

26. $\sqrt{-12} \cdot \sqrt{-50}$
$-10\sqrt{6}$

27. $\dfrac{\sqrt{-50}}{\sqrt{25}}$ $i\sqrt{2}$

28. $\dfrac{\sqrt{-27}}{\sqrt{9}}$ $i\sqrt{3}$

29. $\dfrac{\sqrt{-90}}{\sqrt{-10}}$ 3

30. $\dfrac{\sqrt{-125}}{\sqrt{-45}}$ $\dfrac{5}{3}$

Concept 2: Powers of *i*

For Exercises 31–42, simplify the powers of *i*. **(See Example 3.)**

31. i^7 $-i$

32. i^{38} -1

33. i^{64} 1

34. i^{75} $-i$

35. i^{41} i

36. i^{25} i

37. i^{52} 1

38. i^0 1

39. i^{23} $-i$

40. i^{103} $-i$

41. i^6 -1

42. i^{82} -1

Concept 3: Definition of a Complex Number

43. What is the conjugate of a complex number $a + bi$? $a - bi$

44. True or false?

a. Every real number is a complex number. True **b.** Every complex number is a real number. False

For Exercises 45–52, identify the real and imaginary parts of the complex number. **(See Example 4.)**

45. $-5 + 12i$
Real: -5; imaginary: 12

46. $22 - 16i$
Real: 22; imaginary: -16

47. $-6i$
Real: 0; imaginary: -6

48. $10i$
Real: 0; imaginary: 10

49. 35
Real: 35; imaginary: 0

50. -1
Real: -1; imaginary: 0

51. $\dfrac{3}{5} + i$
Real: $\dfrac{3}{5}$; imaginary: 1

52. $-\dfrac{1}{2} - \dfrac{1}{4}i$
Real: $-\dfrac{1}{2}$; imaginary: $-\dfrac{1}{4}$

Concept 4: Addition, Subtraction, and Multiplication of Complex Numbers

For Exercises 53–76, perform the indicated operations. Write the answer in the form $a + bi$. **(See Examples 5–6.)**

53. $(2 - i) + (5 + 7i)$ $7 + 6i$

54. $(5 - 2i) + (3 + 4i)$ $8 + 2i$

55. $\left(\dfrac{1}{2} + \dfrac{2}{3}i\right) - \left(\dfrac{1}{5} - \dfrac{5}{6}i\right)$ $\dfrac{3}{10} + \dfrac{3}{2}i$

56. $\left(\dfrac{11}{10} - \dfrac{7}{5}i\right) - \left(-\dfrac{2}{5} + \dfrac{3}{5}i\right)$ $\dfrac{3}{2} - 2i$

57. $(1 + 3i) + (4 - 3i)$ $5 + 0i$

58. $(-2 + i) + (1 - i)$ $-1 + 0i$

59. $(2 + 3i) - (1 - 4i) + (-2 + 3i)$
$-1 + 10i$

60. $(2 + 5i) - (7 - 2i) + (-3 + 4i)$
$-8 + 11i$

61. $(8i)(3i)$ $-24 + 0i$

62. $(2i)(4i)$ $-8 + 0i$

63. $6i(1 - 3i)$ $18 + 6i$

64. $-i(3 + 4i)$ $4 - 3i$

65. $(2 - 10i)(3 + 2i)$
$26 - 26i$

66. $(4 + 7i)(2 - 3i)$
$29 + 2i$

67. $(-5 + 2i)(5 + 2i)$
$-29 + 0i$

68. $(4 - 11i)(4 + 11i)$
$137 + 0i$

69. $(4 + 5i)^2$
$-9 + 40i$

70. $(3 - 2i)^2$ $5 - 12i$

71. $(2 + i)(3 - 2i)(4 + 3i)$
$35 + 20i$

72. $(3 - i)(3 + i)(4 - i)$
$40 - 10i$

73. $(-4 - 6i)^2$ $-20 + 48i$

74. $(-3 - 5i)^2$ $-16 + 30i$

75. $\left(-\dfrac{1}{2} - \dfrac{3}{4}i\right)\left(-\dfrac{1}{2} + \dfrac{3}{4}i\right)$
$\dfrac{13}{16} + 0i$

76. $\left(-\dfrac{2}{3} + \dfrac{1}{6}i\right)\left(-\dfrac{2}{3} - \dfrac{1}{6}i\right)$
$\dfrac{17}{36} + 0i$

Concept 5: Division and Simplification of Complex Numbers

For Exercises 77–90, divide the complex numbers. Write the answer in the form $a + bi$. **(See Example 7.)**

77. $\dfrac{2}{1 + 3i}$ $\dfrac{1}{5} - \dfrac{3}{5}i$ **78.** $\dfrac{-2}{3 + i}$ $-\dfrac{3}{5} + \dfrac{1}{5}i$ **79.** $\dfrac{-i}{4 - 3i}$ $\dfrac{3}{25} - \dfrac{4}{25}i$ **80.** $\dfrac{3 - 3i}{1 - i}$ $3 + 0i$

81. $\dfrac{5 + 2i}{5 - 2i}$ $\dfrac{21}{29} + \dfrac{20}{29}i$ **82.** $\dfrac{7 + 3i}{4 - 2i}$ $\dfrac{11}{10} + \dfrac{13}{10}i$ **83.** $\dfrac{3 + 7i}{-2 - 4i}$ $-\dfrac{17}{10} - \dfrac{1}{10}i$ **84.** $\dfrac{-2 + 9i}{-1 - 4i}$ $-2 - i$

85. $\dfrac{13i}{-5 - i}$ $-\dfrac{1}{2} - \dfrac{5}{2}i$ **86.** $\dfrac{15i}{-2 - i}$ $-3 - 6i$ **87.** $\dfrac{2 + 3i}{6i}$ $\dfrac{1}{2} - \dfrac{1}{3}i$ (*Hint:* The denominator can be written as $0 + 6i$. Therefore, the conjugate is $0 - 6i$, or simply $-6i$.)

88. $\dfrac{4 - i}{2i}$ $-\dfrac{1}{2} - 2i$ **89.** $\dfrac{-10 + i}{i}$ $1 + 10i$ **90.** $\dfrac{-6 - i}{-i}$ $1 - 6i$

For Exercises 91–98, simplify the complex numbers. Write the answer in the form $a + bi$. **(See Example 8.)**

91. $\dfrac{2 + \sqrt{-16}}{8}$ $\dfrac{1}{4} + \dfrac{1}{2}i$ **92.** $\dfrac{6 - \sqrt{-4}}{4}$ $\dfrac{3}{2} - \dfrac{1}{2}i$ **93.** $\dfrac{-6 + \sqrt{-72}}{6}$ $-1 + i\sqrt{2}$ **94.** $\dfrac{-20 + \sqrt{-500}}{10}$ $-2 + i\sqrt{5}$

95. $\dfrac{-8 - \sqrt{-48}}{4}$ $-2 - i\sqrt{3}$ **96.** $\dfrac{-18 - \sqrt{-72}}{3}$ $-6 - 2i\sqrt{2}$ **97.** $\dfrac{-5 + \sqrt{-50}}{10}$ $-\dfrac{1}{2} + \dfrac{\sqrt{2}}{2}i$ **98.** $\dfrac{14 + \sqrt{-98}}{7}$ $2 + i\sqrt{2}$

Expanding Your Skills

For Exercises 99–102, determine if the complex number is a solution to the equation.

99. $x^2 - 4x + 5 = 0$; $2 + i$ Yes   **100.** $x^2 - 6x + 25 = 0$; $3 - 4i$ Yes

101. $x^2 + 12 = 0$; $-2i\sqrt{3}$ Yes   **102.** $x^2 + 18 = 0$; $3i\sqrt{2}$ Yes

Group Activity

Margin of Error of Survey Results

Materials: Calculator

Estimated time: 20 minutes

Group Size: 3

Instructor Note: You might want to have students begin collecting data a week or so before assigning this activity.

The members of the class will conduct a survey to estimate the percentage of the college population that answers "yes" to the several survey questions asked.

1. The members of the class will decide on three "Yes or No" questions that they will use to perform a survey. For example, here are some possible questions.

"Do you study more than 10 hr a week?"

"Do you work more than 25 hr a week?"

"Are you taking more than 10 credit hours?"

 Writing   Translating Expression   Geometry   Scientific Calculator   Video   NS&E

List the questions here:

a. _____   Answers will vary.

b. _____

c. _____

2. Each student in the class will survey 20 people and record the number of "yes" responses in the table.

Question	Number of "Yes" Responses
1	
2	
3	

3. The instructor will then pool the results obtained from each student to get the total number of people surveyed by the whole class. Record the number of people surveyed (sample size) and the number of "yes" responses for each question in the table. Once the data are entered into the table, compute the percent, p, of "yes" responses in the fourth column. Write this value in decimal form. Round the values of p to three decimal places. (*Note:* For now, leave the last column blank.)

Question	Sample Size	Number of "Yes" Responses	Percent "Yes" Responses, p	Margin of Error, E
1				
2				
3				

4. The value of p represents the percent (written in decimal form) of people in the *sample* who answered "yes." However, the percentage of people in the entire college population who would answer "yes" is unknown. The value of p is only an *estimate*. Statisticians often compute a margin of error associated with such an estimate by using the following formula.

$$E = 1.96 \sqrt{\frac{p(1-p)}{n}}$$ where E is the margin of error.
                                              n is the sample size.
                                              p is the percent (in decimal form) of "yes" responses.

Compute the margin of error for each of the three questions. Round the values of E to three decimal places. Record the results in the table.

5. The margin of error computed in step 4 is associated with what statisticians call a 95% level of confidence. To interpret the results, a statistician would say "With 95% confidence, the researcher estimates the percentage of "yes" responses from the entire college population to be between $p \pm E$."

Interpret the results from each of the three questions.

Chapter 10   Summary

Section 10.1   Definition of an *n*th root

Key Concepts

b is an **nth root** of *a* if $b^n = a$.

The expression $\sqrt{a}$ represents the principal square root of *a*.

The expression $\sqrt[n]{a}$ represents the principal *n*th root of *a*.

$\sqrt[n]{a^n} = |a|$ if *n* is even.

$\sqrt[n]{a^n} = a$ if *n* is odd.

$\sqrt[n]{a}$ is not a real number if $a < 0$ and *n* is even.

$f(x) = \sqrt[n]{x}$ defines a **radical function**.

The Pythagorean Theorem

$a^2 + b^2 = c^2$

Examples

Example 1

2 is a square root of 4.

-2 is a square root of 4.

-3 is a cube root of -27.

Example 2

$\sqrt{36} = 6$ $\sqrt[3]{-64} = -4$

Example 3

$\sqrt[4]{(x + 3)^4} = |x + 3|$ $\sqrt[5]{(x + 3)^5} = x + 3$

Example 4

$\sqrt[4]{-16}$ is not a real number.

Example 5

For $g(x) = \sqrt{x}$ the domain is $[0, \infty)$.

For $h(x) = \sqrt[3]{x}$ the domain is $(-\infty, \infty)$.

Example 6

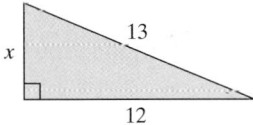

$x^2 + 12^2 = 13^2$

$x^2 + 144 = 169$

$x^2 = 25$

$x = \sqrt{25}$

$x = 5$

Section 10.2   Rational Exponents

Key Concepts

Let a be a real number and n be an integer such that $n > 1$. If $\sqrt[n]{a}$ exists, then

$$a^{1/n} = \sqrt[n]{a}$$

$$a^{m/n} = \left(\sqrt[n]{a}\right)^{m} = \sqrt[n]{a^{m}}$$

All properties of integer exponents hold for rational exponents, provided the roots are real-valued.

Examples

Example 1

$$121^{1/2} = \sqrt{121} = 11$$

Example 2

$$27^{2/3} = \left(\sqrt[3]{27}\right)^{2} = (3)^{2} = 9$$

Example 3

$p^{1/3} \cdot p^{1/4}$	$\dfrac{x^{4/3}}{x^{1/3}}$	$(y^{-1/2})^6$
$= p^{1/3 + 1/4}$	$= x^{4/3 - 1/3}$	$= y^{(-1/2)(6)}$
$= p^{4/12 + 3/12}$	$= x^{3/3}$	$= y^{-3}$
$= p^{7/12}$	$= x$	$= \dfrac{1}{y^{3}}$

Section 10.3   Simplifying Radical Expressions

Key Concepts

Let a and b represent real numbers such that $\sqrt[n]{a}$ and $\sqrt[n]{b}$ are both real. Then

$$\sqrt[n]{ab} = \sqrt[n]{a} \cdot \sqrt[n]{b} \qquad \text{Multiplication property}$$

A radical expression whose radicand is written as a product of prime factors is in simplified form if all the following conditions are met:

1. The radicand has no factor raised to a power greater than or equal to the index.
2. The radicand does not contain a fraction.
3. No radicals are in the denominator of a fraction.

Examples

Example 1

$$\sqrt{12} = \sqrt{4 \cdot 3}$$
$$= \sqrt{4} \cdot \sqrt{3}$$
$$= 2\sqrt{3}$$

Example 2

$$\sqrt[3]{16x^5y^7}$$
$$= \sqrt[3]{2^4x^5y^7}$$
$$= \sqrt[3]{2^3x^3y^6 \cdot 2x^2y}$$
$$= \sqrt[3]{2^3x^3y^6} \cdot \sqrt[3]{2x^2y}$$
$$= 2xy^2\sqrt[3]{2x^2y}$$

Section 10.4   Addition and Subtraction of Radicals

Key Concepts

Like **radicals** have radical factors with the same index and the same radicand.

Use the distributive property to add and subtract *like* radicals.

Examples

Example 1

$2x\sqrt{7} - 5x\sqrt{7} + x\sqrt{7}$

$= (2 - 5 + 1)x\sqrt{7}$

$= -2x\sqrt{7}$

Example 2

$x\sqrt[4]{16x} - 3\sqrt[4]{x^5}$

$= 2x\sqrt[4]{x} - 3x\sqrt[4]{x}$

$= (2 - 3)x\sqrt[4]{x}$

$= -x\sqrt[4]{x}$

Section 10.5   Multiplication of Radicals

Key Concepts

The Multiplication Property of Radicals

If $\sqrt[n]{a}$ and $\sqrt[n]{b}$ are real numbers, then

$$\sqrt[n]{a} \cdot \sqrt[n]{b} = \sqrt[n]{ab}$$

To multiply or divide radicals with different indices, convert to rational exponents and use the properties of exponents.

Examples

Example 1

$3\sqrt{2}(\sqrt{2} + 5\sqrt{7} - \sqrt{6})$

$= 3\sqrt{4} + 15\sqrt{14} - 3\sqrt{12}$

$= 3 \cdot 2 + 15\sqrt{14} - 3 \cdot 2\sqrt{3}$

$= 6 + 15\sqrt{14} - 6\sqrt{3}$

Example 2

$\sqrt{p} \cdot \sqrt[5]{p^2}$

$= p^{1/2} \cdot p^{2/5}$

$= p^{5/10} \cdot p^{4/10}$

$= p^{9/10}$

$= \sqrt[10]{p^9}$

Section 10.6   Division of Radicals and Rationalization

Key Concepts

The Division Property of Radicals

If $\sqrt[n]{a}$ and $\sqrt[n]{b}$ are real numbers, then

$$\sqrt[n]{\frac{a}{b}} = \frac{\sqrt[n]{a}}{\sqrt[n]{b}} \qquad b \neq 0$$

The process of removing a radical from the denominator of an expression is called **rationalizing the denominator**.

- Rationalizing a denominator with one term

- Rationalizing a denominator with two terms involving square roots

Examples

Example 1

Simplify.

$$\sqrt{\frac{4x^5}{y^4}}$$

$$= \frac{\sqrt{4x^5}}{\sqrt{y^4}}$$

$$= \frac{2x^2\sqrt{x}}{y^2}$$

Example 2

Rationalize the denominator.

$$\frac{4}{\sqrt[3]{t}}$$

$$= \frac{4}{\sqrt[3]{t}} \cdot \frac{\sqrt[3]{t^2}}{\sqrt[3]{t^2}}$$

$$= \frac{4\sqrt[3]{t^2}}{\sqrt[3]{t^3}} = \frac{4\sqrt[3]{t^2}}{t}$$

Example 3

Rationalize the denominator.

$$\frac{\sqrt{2} - 3\sqrt{x}}{\sqrt{x} - \sqrt{2}}$$

$$= \frac{(\sqrt{2} - 3\sqrt{x})}{(\sqrt{x} - \sqrt{2})} \cdot \frac{(\sqrt{x} + \sqrt{2})}{(\sqrt{x} + \sqrt{2})}$$

$$= \frac{\sqrt{2} \cdot \sqrt{x} + \sqrt{2} \cdot \sqrt{2} - 3\sqrt{x} \cdot \sqrt{x} - 3\sqrt{x} \cdot \sqrt{2}}{(\sqrt{x})^2 - (\sqrt{2})^2}$$

$$= \frac{\sqrt{2x} + 2 - 3x - 3\sqrt{2x}}{x - 2}$$

$$= \frac{-3x - 2\sqrt{2x} + 2}{x - 2}$$

Section 10.7   Solving Radical Equations

Key Concepts

Steps to Solve a Radical Equation

1. Isolate the radical. If an equation has more than one radical, choose one of the radicals to isolate.
2. Raise each side of the equation to a power equal to the index of the radical.
3. Solve the resulting equation. If the equation still has a radical, repeat steps 1 and 2.
4. Check the potential solutions in the original equation.

Example

Example 1

Solve:

$$\sqrt{b - 5} - \sqrt{b + 3} = 2$$

$$\sqrt{b - 5} = \sqrt{b + 3} + 2$$

$$(\sqrt{b - 5})^2 = (\sqrt{b + 3} + 2)^2$$

$$b - 5 = b + 3 + 4\sqrt{b + 3} + 4$$

$$b - 5 = b + 7 + 4\sqrt{b + 3}$$

$$-12 = 4\sqrt{b + 3}$$

$$-3 = \sqrt{b + 3}$$

$$(-3)^2 = (\sqrt{b + 3})^2$$

$$9 = b + 3$$

$$6 = b$$

Check:

$$\sqrt{6 - 5} - \sqrt{6 + 3} \overset{?}{=} 2$$

$$\sqrt{1} - \sqrt{9} \overset{?}{=} 2$$

$$1 - 3 \overset{?}{=} 2 \qquad \text{(false)}$$

No solution, { }

Section 10.8 Complex Numbers

Key Concepts

$i = \sqrt{-1}$ and $i^2 = -1$

For a real number $b > 0$, $\sqrt{-b} = i\sqrt{b}$

A **complex number** is in the form $a + bi$, where a and b are real numbers. The value a is called the real part, and b is called the imaginary part.

To add or subtract complex numbers, combine the real parts and combine the imaginary parts.

Multiply complex numbers by using the distributive property.

Divide complex numbers by multiplying the numerator and denominator by the **conjugate** of the denominator.

Examples

Example 1

$\sqrt{-4} \cdot \sqrt{-9}$

$= (2i)(3i)$

$= 6i^2$

$= -6$

Example 2

$(3 - 5i) - (2 + i) + (3 - 2i)$

$= 3 - 5i - 2 - i + 3 - 2i$

$= 4 - 8i$

Example 3

$(1 + 6i)(2 + 4i)$

$= 2 + 4i + 12i + 24i^2$

$= 2 + 16i + 24(-1)$

$= -22 + 16i$

Example 4

$\dfrac{3}{2 - 5i}$

$= \dfrac{3}{(2 - 5i)} \cdot \dfrac{(2 + 5i)}{(2 + 5i)}$

$= \dfrac{6 + 15i}{4 - 25i^2}$

$= \dfrac{6 + 15i}{4 + 25}$

$= \dfrac{6 + 15i}{29}$

$= \dfrac{6}{29} + \dfrac{15}{29}i$

Chapter 10   Review Exercises

For the exercises in this set, assume that all variables represent positive real numbers unless otherwise stated.

Section 10.1

1. True or false?

   a. The principal nth root of an even-indexed root is always positive.
      False; $\sqrt{0} = 0$ is not positive.
   b. The principal nth root of an odd-indexed root is always positive.   False; $\sqrt[3]{-8} = -2$

2. Explain why $\sqrt{(-3)^2} \neq -3$. $\sqrt{(-3)^2} = \sqrt{9} = 3$

3. For $a > 0$ and $b > 0$, are the following statements true or false?

   a. $\sqrt{a^2 + b^2} = a + b$ False

   b. $\sqrt{(a + b)^2} = a + b$ True

For Exercises 4–6, simplify the radicals.

4. $\sqrt{\dfrac{50}{32}}$ $\dfrac{5}{4}$ 5. $\sqrt[4]{625}$ 5 6. $\sqrt{(-6)^2}$ 6

7. Evaluate the function values for $f(x) = \sqrt{x - 1}$.

   a. $f(10)$ 3 b. $f(1)$ 0 c. $f(8)$ $\sqrt{7}$

   d. Write the domain of f in interval notation.
      $[1, \infty)$
8. Evaluate the function values for $g(t) = \sqrt{5 + t}$.

   a. $g(-5)$ 0 b. $g(-4)$ 1 c. $g(4)$ 3

   d. Write the domain of g in interval notation.
      $[-5, \infty)$
9. Write the English expression as an algebraic expression: Four more than the quotient of the cube root of $2x$ and the principal fourth root of $2x$.
   $\dfrac{\sqrt[3]{2x}}{\sqrt[4]{2x}} + 4$

For Exercises 10–11, simplify the expression. Assume that x and y represent *any* real number.

10. a. $\sqrt{x^2}$ $|x|$ b. $\sqrt[3]{x^3}$ x

    c. $\sqrt[4]{x^4}$ $|x|$ d. $\sqrt[5]{(x + 1)^5}$ $x + 1$

11. a. $\sqrt{4y^2}$ $2|y|$ b. $\sqrt[3]{27y^3}$ $3y$

    c. $\sqrt[100]{y^{100}}$ $|y|$ d. $\sqrt[101]{y^{101}}$ y

12. Use the Pythagorean theorem to find the length of the third side of the triangle.   8 cm

17 cm

15 cm

Section 10.2

13. Are the properties of exponents the same for rational exponents and integer exponents? Give an example. (Answers may vary.)   Yes, provided the expressions are defined. For example: $x^5 \cdot x^3 = x^8$ and $x^{1/5} \cdot x^{2/5} = x^{3/5}$

14. In the expression $x^{m/n}$ what does n represent?
    n represents the root.

15. Explain the process of eliminating a negative exponent from an algebraic expression.   Take the reciprocal of the base and change the exponent to positive.

For Exercises 16–21, simplify the expressions. Write the answer with positive exponents only.

16. $(-125)^{1/3}$ -5 17. $16^{-1/4}$ $\dfrac{1}{2}$

18. $\left(\dfrac{1}{16}\right)^{-3/4} - \left(\dfrac{1}{8}\right)^{-2/3}$ 4 19. $(b^{1/2} \cdot b^{1/3})^{12}$
    b^{10}

20. $\left(\dfrac{x^{-1/4}y^{-1/3}z^{3/4}}{2^{1/3}x^{-1/3}y^{2/3}}\right)^{-12}$ 21. $\left(\dfrac{a^{12}b^{-4}c^7}{a^3b^2c^4}\right)^{1/3}$ $\dfrac{a^3c}{b^2}$
    $\dfrac{16y^{12}}{xz^9}$

For Exercises 22–23, rewrite the expressions by using rational exponents.

22. $\sqrt[4]{x^3}$ $x^{3/4}$ 23. $\sqrt[3]{2y^2}$ $(2y^2)^{1/3}$

For Exercises 24–26, use a calculator to approximate the expressions to four decimal places.

24. $10^{1/3}$ 25. $17.8^{2/3}$ 26. $\sqrt[5]{147^4}$
    2.1544   6.8173   54.1819

Section 10.3

27. List the criteria for a radical expression to be simplified.   See page 711.

For Exercises 28–31, simplify the radicals.

28. $\sqrt{108}$ $6\sqrt{3}$ 29. $\sqrt[4]{x^5yz^4}$ $xz\sqrt[4]{xy}$

30. $-2\sqrt[3]{250a^3b^{10}}$ 31. $\sqrt[3]{\dfrac{-16a^4}{2ab^3}}$ $-\dfrac{2a}{b}$
    $-10ab^3\sqrt[3]{2b}$

32. Write an English phrase that describes the following mathematical expressions: (Answers may vary.)

a. $\sqrt{\dfrac{2}{x}}$ The principal square root of the quotient of 2 and x **b.** $(x + 1)^3$ The cube of the sum of x and 1

33. An engineering firm made a mistake when building a $\frac{1}{4}$-mi bridge in the Florida Keys. The bridge was made without adequate expansion joints to prevent buckling during the heat of summer. During mid-June, the bridge expanded 1.5 ft, causing a vertical bulge in the middle. Calculate the height of the bulge h in feet. (*Note:* 1 mi = 5280 ft.) Round to the nearest foot.
31 ft

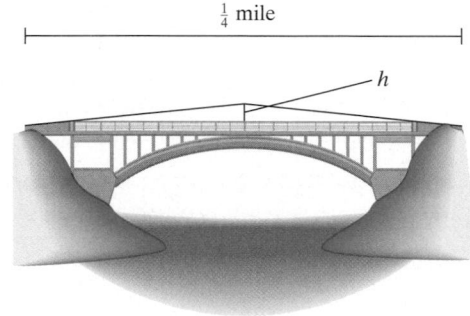

$\frac{1}{4}$ mile

Section 10.4

34. Complete the following statement: Radicals may be added or subtracted if ...
they are *like* radicals.

For Exercises 35–38, determine whether the radicals may be combined, and explain your answer.

35. $\sqrt[3]{2x} - 2\sqrt{2x}$ Cannot be combined; the indices are different.
36. $2 + \sqrt{x}$ Cannot be combined; one term has a radical, but the other does not.
37. $\sqrt[4]{3xy} + 2\sqrt[4]{3xy}$ Can be combined: $3\sqrt[4]{3xy}$
38. $-4\sqrt{32} + 7\sqrt{50}$ Can be added after simplifying: $19\sqrt{2}$

For Exercises 39–42, add or subtract as indicated.

39. $4\sqrt{7} - 2\sqrt{7} + 3\sqrt{7}$ $5\sqrt{7}$

40. $2\sqrt[3]{64} + 3\sqrt[3]{54} - 16$ $9\sqrt[3]{2} - 8$

41. $\sqrt{50} + 7\sqrt{2} - \sqrt{8}$ $10\sqrt{2}$

42. $x\sqrt[3]{16x^2} - 4\sqrt[3]{2x^5} + 5x\sqrt[3]{54x^2}$ $13x\sqrt[3]{2x^2}$

For Exercises 43–44, answer true or false. If an answer is false, explain why. Assume all variables represent positive real numbers.

43. $5 + 3\sqrt{x} = 8\sqrt{x}$ False; 5 and $3\sqrt{x}$ are not *like* radicals.

44. $\sqrt{y} + \sqrt{y} = \sqrt{2y}$ False; $\sqrt{y} + \sqrt{y} = 2\sqrt{y}$ (add the coefficients).

Section 10.5

For Exercises 45–56, multiply the radicals and simplify the answer.

45. $\sqrt{3} \cdot \sqrt{12}$ 6   **46.** $\sqrt[4]{4} \cdot \sqrt[4]{8}$ $2\sqrt[4]{2}$

47. $-2\sqrt{3}(\sqrt{7} - 3\sqrt{11})$ $-2\sqrt{21} + 6\sqrt{33}$ **48.** $-3\sqrt{5}(2\sqrt{3} - \sqrt{5})$ $-6\sqrt{15} + 15$

49. $(2\sqrt{x} - 3)(2\sqrt{x} + 3)$ $4x - 9$ **50.** $(\sqrt{y} + 4)(\sqrt{y} - 4)$ $y - 16$

51. $(\sqrt{7y} - \sqrt{3x})^2$ $7y - 2\sqrt{21xy} + 3x$ **52.** $(2\sqrt{3w} + 5)^2$ $12w + 20\sqrt{3w} + 25$

53. $(-\sqrt{z} - \sqrt{6})(2\sqrt{z} + 7\sqrt{6})$ $-2z - 9\sqrt{6z} - 42$

54. $(3\sqrt{a} - \sqrt{5})(\sqrt{a} + 2\sqrt{5})$ $3a + 5\sqrt{5a} - 10$

55. $\sqrt[3]{u} \cdot \sqrt{u^5}$ $u^2\sqrt[6]{u^5}$ **56.** $\sqrt{2} \cdot \sqrt[4]{w^3}$ $\sqrt[4]{4w^3}$

Section 10.6

For Exercises 57–60, simplify the radicals.

57. $\sqrt{\dfrac{3y^5}{25x^6}}$ $\dfrac{y^2\sqrt{3y}}{5x^3}$ **58.** $\sqrt[3]{\dfrac{-16x^7y^6}{z^9}}$ $\dfrac{-2x^2y^2\sqrt[3]{2x}}{z^3}$

59. $\dfrac{\sqrt{324w^7}}{\sqrt{4w^3}}$ $9w^2$ **60.** $\dfrac{\sqrt[3]{3t^{14}}}{\sqrt[3]{192t^2}}$ $\dfrac{t^4}{4}$

For Exercises 61–68, rationalize the denominator.

61. $\sqrt{\dfrac{7}{2y}}$ $\dfrac{\sqrt{14y}}{2y}$ **62.** $\sqrt{\dfrac{5}{3w}}$ $\dfrac{\sqrt{15w}}{3w}$

63. $\dfrac{4}{\sqrt[3]{9p^2}}$ $\dfrac{4\sqrt[3]{3p}}{3p}$ **64.** $\dfrac{-2}{\sqrt[3]{2x}}$ $-\dfrac{\sqrt[3]{4x^2}}{x}$

65. $\dfrac{-5}{\sqrt{15} + \sqrt{10}}$ $\sqrt{10} - \sqrt{15}$ **66.** $\dfrac{-6}{\sqrt{7} + \sqrt{5}}$ $3\sqrt{5} - 3\sqrt{7}$

67. $\dfrac{t - 3}{\sqrt{t} - \sqrt{3}}$ $\sqrt{t} + \sqrt{3}$ **68.** $\dfrac{w - 7}{\sqrt{w} - \sqrt{7}}$ $\sqrt{w} + \sqrt{7}$

69. Write the mathematical expression as an English phrase. (Answers may vary.)

$\dfrac{\sqrt{2}}{x^2}$ The quotient of the principal square root of 2 and the square of x

Section 10.7

Solve the radical equations in Exercises 70–77, if possible.

70. $\sqrt{2y} = 7$ $\left\{\dfrac{49}{2}\right\}$ **71.** $\sqrt{a - 6} - 5 = 0$ $\{31\}$

72. $\sqrt[3]{2w - 3} + 5 = 2$ $\{-12\}$

 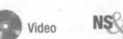

73. $\sqrt[4]{p + 12} - \sqrt[4]{5p - 16} = 0$ {7}

74. $\sqrt{t} + \sqrt{t - 5} = 5$ {9}

75. $\sqrt{8x + 1} = -\sqrt{x - 13}$
{ } (The value −2 does not check.)

76. $\sqrt{2m^2 + 4} - \sqrt{9m} = 0$ $\left\{\frac{1}{2}, 4\right\}$

77. $\sqrt{x + 2} = 1 - \sqrt{2x + 5}$
{−2} (The value 2 does not check.)

78. A tower is supported by stabilizing wires. Find the exact length of each wire, and then round to the nearest tenth of a meter. $6\sqrt{5}$ m ≈ 13.4 m

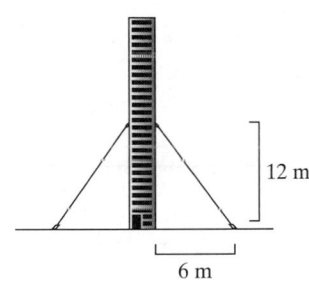

12 m

6 m

79. The velocity, $v(d)$, of an ocean wave depends on the water depth d as the wave approaches land.

$$v(d) = \sqrt{32d}$$

where $v(d)$ is in feet per second and d is in feet.

a. Find $v(20)$ and interpret its value. Round to one decimal place. $v(20)$ ≈ 25.3 ft/sec. When the water depth is 20 ft, a wave travels about 25.3 ft/sec.

b. Find the depth of the water at a point where a wave is traveling at 16 ft/sec. 8 ft

Section 10.8

80. Define a complex number.
$a + bi$, where a and b are real numbers and $i = \sqrt{-1}$

81. Define an imaginary number. $a + bi$, where $b \neq 0$

82. Consider the following expressions.

$$\frac{3}{4 + 6i} \quad \text{and} \quad \frac{3}{\sqrt{4} + \sqrt{6}}$$

Compare the process of dividing by a complex number to the process of rationalizing the denominator. In each case we simplify the expression by multiplying the numerator and denominator by the conjugate of the denominator.

For Exercises 83–86, rewrite the expressions in terms of i.

83. $\sqrt{-16}$ $4i$

84. $-\sqrt{-5}$ $-i\sqrt{5}$

85. $\sqrt{-75} \cdot \sqrt{-3}$ −15

86. $\dfrac{-\sqrt{-24}}{\sqrt{6}}$ −2i

For Exercises 87–90, simplify the powers of i.

87. i^{38} −1

88. i^{101} i

89. i^{19} $-i$

90. $i^{1000} + i^{1002}$ 0

For Exercises 91–94, perform the indicated operations. Write the final answer in the form $a + bi$.

91. $(-3 + i) - (2 - 4i)$
−5 + 5i

92. $(1 + 6i)(3 - i)$
9 + 17i

93. $(4 - 3i)(4 + 3i)$
25 + 0i

94. $(5 - i)^2$
24 − 10i

For Exercises 95–96, write the expressions in the form $a + bi$, and determine the real and imaginary parts.

95. $\dfrac{17 - 4i}{-4}$ $-\dfrac{17}{4} + i$;
real part: $-\dfrac{17}{4}$;
imaginary part: 1

96. $\dfrac{-16 - 8i}{8}$ −2 − i;
real part: −2;
imaginary part: −1

For Exercises 97–100, divide and simplify. Write the final answer in the form $a + bi$.

97. $\dfrac{2 - i}{3 + 2i}$ $\dfrac{4}{13} - \dfrac{7}{13}i$

98. $\dfrac{10 + 5i}{2 - i}$ 3 + 4i

99. $\dfrac{5 + 3i}{-2i}$ $-\dfrac{3}{2} + \dfrac{5}{2}i$

100. $\dfrac{4i}{4 - i}$ $-\dfrac{4}{17} + \dfrac{16}{17}i$

For Exercises 101–102, simplify the expression.

101. $\dfrac{-8 + \sqrt{-40}}{12}$
$-\dfrac{2}{3} + \dfrac{\sqrt{10}}{6}i$

102. $\dfrac{6 - \sqrt{-144}}{3}$ 2 − 4i

Writing   Translating Expression   Geometry   Scientific Calculator   Video   NS&E

Chapter 10 Test

1. a. What is the principal square root of 36?   6

   b. What is the negative square root of 36? -6

2. Which of the following are real numbers?

   a. $-\sqrt{100}$ Real   **b.** $\sqrt{-100}$ Not real

   c. $-\sqrt[3]{1000}$ Real   **d.** $\sqrt[3]{-1000}$ Real

3. Simplify.

   a. $\sqrt[3]{y^3}$ y **b.** $\sqrt[4]{y^4}$ $|y|$

For Exercises 4–11, simplify the radicals. Assume that all variables represent positive numbers.

4. $\sqrt[4]{81}$ 3

5. $\sqrt{\dfrac{16}{9}}$ $\dfrac{4}{3}$

6. $\sqrt[3]{32}$ $2\sqrt[3]{4}$

7. $\sqrt{a^4b^3c^5}$ $a^2bc^2\sqrt{bc}$

8. $\sqrt{18x^5y^3z^4}$ $3x^2yz^2\sqrt{2xy}$ **9.** $\sqrt{\dfrac{32w^6}{2w}}$ $4w^2\sqrt{w}$

10. $\sqrt[3]{\dfrac{x^6}{125y^3}}$ $\dfrac{x^2}{5y}$ **11.** $\dfrac{2\sqrt{72}}{8}$ $\dfrac{3\sqrt{2}}{2}$

12. a. Evaluate the function values $f(-8)$, $f(-6)$, $f(-4)$, and $f(-2)$ for $f(x) = \sqrt{-2x - 4}$.
   $f(-8) = 2\sqrt{3}$; $f(-6) = 2\sqrt{2}$; $f(-4) = 2$; $f(-2) = 0$
   b. Write the domain of f in interval notation.
   $(-\infty, -2]$

13. Use a calculator to evaluate $\dfrac{-3 - \sqrt{5}}{17}$ to four decimal places. -0.3080

For Exercises 14–15, simplify the expressions. Assume that all variables represent positive numbers.

14. $-27^{1/3}$ -3 **15.** $8^{2/3} \cdot \left(\dfrac{25x^4y^6}{z^2}\right)^{1/2}$ $\dfrac{20x^2y^3}{z}$

For Exercises 16–17, use rational exponents to multiply or divide. Write the final answer in radical form.

16. $\sqrt[6]{7} \cdot \sqrt{y}$ $\sqrt[6]{7y^3}$ **17.** $\dfrac{\sqrt[3]{10}}{\sqrt[4]{10}}$ $\sqrt[12]{10}$

18. Add or subtract as indicated. $3\sqrt{5}$
$$3\sqrt{5} + 4\sqrt{5} - 2\sqrt{20}$$

For Exercises 19–20, multiply the radicals.

19. $3\sqrt{x}(\sqrt{2} - \sqrt{5})$ $3\sqrt{2x} - 3\sqrt{5x}$

20. $(2\sqrt{5} - 3\sqrt{x})(4\sqrt{5} + \sqrt{x})$ $40 - 10\sqrt{5x} - 3x$

For Exercises 21–22, rationalize the denominator. Assume $x > 0$.

21. $\dfrac{-2}{\sqrt[3]{x}}$ $\dfrac{-2\sqrt[3]{x^2}}{x}$ **22.** $\dfrac{\sqrt{x} + 2}{3 - \sqrt{x}}$ $\dfrac{x + 6 + 5\sqrt{x}}{9 - x}$

23. Rewrite the expressions in terms of i.

   a. $\sqrt{-8}$ $2i\sqrt{2}$ **b.** $2\sqrt{-16}$ $8i$ **c.** $\dfrac{2 + \sqrt{-8}}{4}$ $\dfrac{1}{2} + \dfrac{\sqrt{2}}{2}i$

For Exercises 24–30, perform the indicated operations and simplify completely. Write the final answer in the form $a + bi$.

24. $(3 - 5i) - (2 + 6i)$ $1 - 11i$ **25.** $(4 + i)(8 + 2i)$ $30 + 16i$

26. $\sqrt{-16} \cdot \sqrt{-49}$ -28 **27.** $(4 - 7i)^2$ $-33 - 56i$

28. $(2 - 10i)(2 + 10i)$ 104 **29.** $\dfrac{3 - 2i}{3 - 4i}$ $\dfrac{17}{25} + \dfrac{6}{25}i$

30. $\dfrac{6i}{3 - 5i}$ $-\dfrac{15}{17} + \dfrac{9}{17}i$

31. If the volume V of a sphere is known, the radius of the sphere can be computed by
$$r(V) = \sqrt[3]{\dfrac{3V}{4\pi}}.$$
Find $r(10)$ to two decimal places. Interpret the meaning in the context of the problem.
$r(10) \approx 1.34$; the radius of a sphere of volume 10 cubic units is approximately 1.34 units.

32. A patio 20 ft wide has a slanted roof, as shown in the picture. Find the length of the roof if there is an 8-in. overhang. Round the answer to the nearest foot.   21 ft

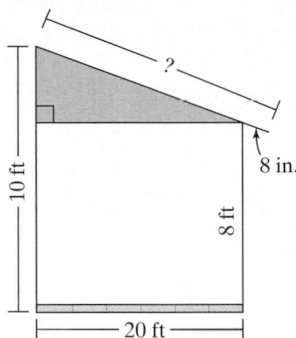

For Exercises 33–35, solve the radical equation.

33. $\sqrt[3]{2x + 5} = -3$ $\{-16\}$

34. $\sqrt{5x + 8} = \sqrt{5x - 1} + 1$ $\left\{\dfrac{17}{5}\right\}$

35. $\sqrt{t + 7} - \sqrt{2t - 3} = 2$ $\{2\}$ (The value 42 does not check.)

Chapters 1–10   Cumulative Review Exercises

1. Simplify the expression.
$6^2 - 2[5 - 8(3 - 1) + 4 \div 2]$ 54

2. Simplify the expression.
$3x - 3(-2x + 5) - 4y + 2(3x + 5) - y$
$15x - 5y - 5$

3. Solve. $9(2y + 8) = 20 - (y + 5)$ $\{-3\}$

For Exercises 4–7, solve the inequalities. Write the answers in interval notation, if possible.

4. $2a - 4 < -14$
$(-\infty, -5)$

5. $11 \geq -x + 2 > 5$
$[-9, -3)$

6. $|9 - 4x| + 4 < 2$ $\{\ \}$

7. $x^2 + 2x - 3 \geq 0$
$(-\infty, -3] \cup [1, \infty)$

8. Write an equation of the line that is parallel to the line $2x + y = 9$ and passes through the point $(3, -1)$. Write the answer in slope-intercept form. $y = -2x + 5$

9. Write an equation of a line parallel to the y-axis passing through the point $(-5, 8)$. $x = -5$

10. Solve the system of equations by using the addition method.

$$2x - 3y = 0$$
$$-4x + 3y = -1$$ $\left\{\left(\dfrac{1}{2}, \dfrac{1}{3}\right)\right\}$

11. Determine if $(2, -2, \frac{1}{2})$ is a solution to the system.

$$2x + y - 4z = 0$$
$$x - y + 2z = 5$$
$$3x + 2y + 2z = 4$$

$(2, -2, \frac{1}{2})$ is not a solution.

12. Bennette and Pepe are landscapers and have to dig a ditch in which to put underground piping for a sprinkler system. Bennette can dig 40 yd of ditch in 3 hr and Pepe can dig 40 yd of ditch in 5 hr. How long will it take them to dig 40 yd together?   Together it will take them $1\frac{7}{8}$ hr.

13. Given the function defined by $f(x) = 4x - 2$.

a. Find $f(-2)$, $f(0)$, $f(4)$, and $f(\frac{1}{2})$.
$f(-2) = -10$; $f(0) = -2$; $f(4) = 14$; $f\left(\dfrac{1}{2}\right) = 0$
b. Write the ordered pairs that correspond to the function values in part (a).
$(-2, -10), (0, -2), (4, 14), \left(\dfrac{1}{2}, 0\right)$
c. Graph $y = f(x)$.

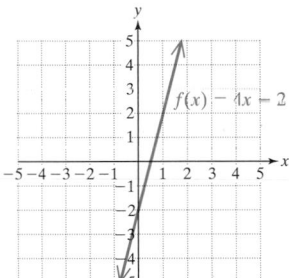

14. Simplify the expression. Write the final answer with positive exponents only. $a^6 b^{12} c^4$

$$\left(\frac{a^{3/2} b^{-1/4} c^{1/3}}{ab^{-5/4} c^0}\right)^{12}$$

 Writing   Translating Expression   Geometry   Scientific Calculator   Video   NS&E

15. Multiply or divide as indicated, and write the answer in scientific notation.

    a. $(3.5 \times 10^7)(4 \times 10^{-12})$ 1.4×10^{-4}

    b. $\dfrac{6.28 \times 10^5}{2.0 \times 10^{-4}}$ 3.14×10^9

16. Multiply the polynomials $(2x + 5)(x - 3)$. What is the degree of the product?
$2x^2 - x - 15$; 2nd degree

17. Perform the indicated operations and simplify.
$\sqrt{3}(\sqrt{5} + \sqrt{6} + \sqrt{3})$ $\sqrt{15} + 3\sqrt{2} + 3$

18. Divide. $(x^2 - x - 12) \div (x + 3)$ $x - 4$

19. Simplify and subtract. $\sqrt[4]{\dfrac{1}{16}} - \sqrt[3]{\dfrac{8}{27}}$ $-\dfrac{1}{6}$

20. Simplify. $\sqrt[3]{\dfrac{54c^4}{cd^3}}$ $\dfrac{3c\sqrt[3]{2}}{d}$

21. Add. $4\sqrt{45b^3} + 5b\sqrt{80b}$ $32b\sqrt{5b}$

22. Solve. $\dfrac{5}{y - 2} - \dfrac{3}{y - 4} = \dfrac{6}{y^2 - 6y + 8}$ $\{10\}$

23. Add. $\dfrac{3}{x^2 + 5x} + \dfrac{-2}{x^2 - 25}$ $\dfrac{x - 15}{x(x + 5)(x - 5)}$

24. Divide. $\dfrac{a + 10}{2a^2 - 11a - 6} \div \dfrac{a^2 + 12a + 20}{6 - a}$ $\dfrac{-1}{(2a + 1)(a + 2)}$

25. Perform the indicated operations.
$(-5x^2 - 4x + 8) - (3x - 5)^2$ $-14x^2 + 26x - 17$

26. Simplify. $\dfrac{-4}{\sqrt{3} - \sqrt{5}}$ $2\sqrt{3} + 2\sqrt{5}$

27. Divide. $\dfrac{4}{3 - 5i}$ $\dfrac{6}{17} + \dfrac{10}{17}i$

28. Solve. $12x^2 + 4x - 21 = 0$ $\left\{\dfrac{7}{6}, -\dfrac{3}{2}\right\}$

29. Factor. $x^2 + 6x + 9 - y^2$ $(x + 3 - y)(x + 3 + y)$

30. Factor. $x^6 + 8$ $(x^2 + 2)(x^4 - 2x^2 + 4)$

 Writing   Translating Expression   Geometry   Scientific Calculator   Video   NS&E

Quadratic Equations and Functions

11

CHAPTER OUTLINE

Chapter 11

In Chapter 11, we revisit quadratic equations. We have already learned how to solve quadratic equations by factoring and applying the zero product rule. Now we present two additional techniques that can be used to solve a quadratic equation even if the quadratic polynomial is not factorable.

Are You Prepared?

To prepare for this chapter, we recommend that you review how to solve quadratic equations by using the zero product rule and how to simplify radical expressions. Match the answers to the exercises below to the letter on the right. Then write the letter in the appropriate space at the bottom of the page to define an important vocabulary word.

Solve.

1. $x^2 - 9 = 0$

2. $x^2 - 6x + 8 = 0$

3. $3x(x + 1) = 60$

Simplify.

4. $\dfrac{-5 \pm \sqrt{50}}{10}$ **5.** $\dfrac{7 \pm 21i}{7}$ **6.** $\dfrac{2 \pm \sqrt{-12}}{4}$

7. Determine the x-intercept(s). $f(x) = x^2 - 6x + 5$

8. Determine the y-intercept. $f(x) = x^2 - 6x + 5$

A function defined by $f(x) = ax^2 + bx + c$ $(a \neq 0)$ is called a

<u>Q</u> <u>U</u> <u>A</u> <u>D</u> <u>R</u> <u>A</u> <u>T</u> <u>I</u> <u>C</u> function.
 2   1   6   5   8   6   4   7   3

Answers

D $1 \pm 3i$

A $\dfrac{1}{2} \pm \dfrac{\sqrt{3}}{2}i$

C $\{4, -5\}$

U $\{-3, 3\}$

T $\dfrac{-1 \pm \sqrt{2}}{2}$

Q $\{2, 4\}$

R $(0, 5)$

I $(1, 0)$ and $(5, 0)$

Section 11.1 Square Root Property and Completing the Square

Concepts

1. Solving Quadratic Equations by Using the Square Root Property
2. Solving Quadratic Equations by Completing the Square
3. Literal Equations

1. Solving Quadratic Equations by Using the Square Root Property

In Section 6.7 we learned how to solve a quadratic equation by factoring and applying the zero product rule. For example:

$$x^2 = 81$$

$$x^2 - 81 = 0 \qquad \text{Set one side equal to zero.}$$

$$(x - 9)(x + 9) = 0 \qquad \text{Factor.}$$

$$x - 9 = 0 \quad \text{or} \quad x + 9 = 0 \qquad \text{Set each factor equal to zero.}$$

$$x = 9 \quad \text{or} \qquad x = -9$$

The solution set is $\{9, -9\}$.

It is important to note that the zero product rule can only be used if the equation is factorable. In this section and Section 11.2, we will learn how to solve quadratic equations, factorable and nonfactorable.

The first technique utilizes the **square root property**.

Instructor Note: Emphasize to students that k must be a constant.

> **PROPERTY** The Square Root Property
>
> For any real number, k, if $x^2 = k$, then $x = \sqrt{k}$ or $x = -\sqrt{k}$.
>
> *Note:* The solution may also be written as $\pm\sqrt{k}$, read "plus or minus the square root of k."

Classroom Example: p. 780, Exercise 2

Example 1 Solving a Quadratic Equation by Using the Square Root Property

Use the square root property to solve the equation.

$$x^2 = 81$$

Solution:

$$x^2 = 81 \qquad \text{The equation is in the form } x^2 = k.$$

$$x = \pm\sqrt{81} \qquad \text{Apply the square root property.}$$

$$x = \pm 9$$

The solution set is $\{9, -9\}$.   Notice that the solutions are the same as those found by applying the zero product rule.

Skill Practice Solve by using the square root property.

1. $a^2 = 49$

For a quadratic equation, $ax^2 + bx + c = 0$, if $b = 0$, then the equation is easily solved by using the square root property. This is demonstrated in Example 2.

Answer

1. $\{\pm 7\}$

Example 2   Solving a Quadratic Equation by Using the Square Root Property

Classroom Example: p. 780, Exercise 6

Use the square root property to solve the equation.

$$3x^2 + 75 = 0$$

Solution:

$3x^2 + 75 = 0$ Rewrite the equation to fit the form $x^2 = k$.

$3x^2 = -75$

$x^2 = -25$ The equation is now in the form $x^2 = k$.

$x = \pm\sqrt{-25}$ Apply the square root property.

$= \pm 5i$

> **Avoiding Mistakes**
>
> A common mistake is to forget the $\pm$ symbol when solving the equation $x^2 = k$:
>
> $$x = \pm\sqrt{k}$$

Check: $x = 5i$

$3x^2 + 75 = 0$

$3(5i)^2 + 75 \overset{?}{=} 0$

$3(25i^2) + 75 \overset{?}{=} 0$

$3(-25) + 75 \overset{?}{=} 0$

$-75 + 75 \overset{?}{=} 0$ ✔

Check: $x = -5i$

$3x^2 + 75 = 0$

$3(-5i)^2 + 75 \overset{?}{=} 0$

$3(25i^2) + 75 \overset{?}{=} 0$

$3(-25) + 75 \overset{?}{=} 0$

$-75 + 75 \overset{?}{=} 0$ ✔

The solution set is $\{\pm 5i\}$.

Skill Practice Solve using the square root property.

2. $8x^2 + 72 = 0$

Example 3   Solving a Quadratic Equation by Using the Square Root Property

Classroom Example: p. 781, Exercise 10

Use the square root property to solve the equation.

$$(w + 3)^2 = 20$$

Solution:

$(w + 3)^2 = 20$ The equation is in the form $x^2 = k$, where $x = (w + 3)$.

$w + 3 = \pm\sqrt{20}$ Apply the square root property.

$w + 3 = \pm\sqrt{2^2 \cdot 5}$ Simplify the radical.

$w + 3 = \pm 2\sqrt{5}$

$w = -3 \pm 2\sqrt{5}$ Solve for w.

The solution set is $\{-3 \pm 2\sqrt{5}\}$.

Skill Practice Solve using the square root property.

3. $(t - 5)^2 = 18$

Answers

2. $\{\pm 3i\}$ **3.** $\{5 \pm 3\sqrt{2}\}$

2. Solving Quadratic Equations by Completing the Square

In Example 3 we used the square root property to solve an equation where the square of a binomial was equal to a constant.

$$(w + 3)^2 = 20$$

Square of a · · · Constant
binomial

The square of a binomial is the factored form of a perfect square trinomial. For example:

Perfect Square Trinomial	**Factored Form**
$x^2 + 10x + 25$ ⟶	$(x + 5)^2$
$t^2 - 6t + 9$ ⟶	$(t - 3)^2$
$p^2 - 14p + 49$ ⟶	$(p - 7)^2$

For a perfect square trinomial with a leading coefficient of 1, the constant term is the square of one-half the linear term coefficient. For example:

$$x^2 + 10x + 25$$

$$[\tfrac{1}{2}(10)]^2$$

In general an expression of the form $x^2 + bx + n$ is a perfect square trinomial if $n = (\tfrac{1}{2}b)^2$. The process to create a perfect square trinomial is called **completing the square**.

Classroom Examples: p. 781, Exercises 22 and 32

Example 4 Completing the Square

Determine the value of n that makes the polynomial a perfect square trinomial. Then factor the expression as the square of a binomial.

a. $x^2 + 12x + n$ **b.** $x^2 - 26x + n$

c. $x^2 + 11x + n$ **d.** $x^2 - \dfrac{4}{7}x + n$

Solution:

The expressions are in the form $x^2 + bx + n$. The value of n equals the square of one-half the linear term coefficient $(\tfrac{1}{2}b)^2$.

a. $x^2 + 12x + n$

$x^2 + 12x + 36$ $n = [\tfrac{1}{2}(12)]^2 = (6)^2 = 36$

$(x + 6)^2$ Factored form

b. $x^2 - 26x + n$

$x^2 - 26x + 169$ $n = [\tfrac{1}{2}(-26)]^2 = (-13)^2 = 169$

$(x - 13)^2$ Factored form

c. $x^2 + 11x + n$

$x^2 + 11x + \dfrac{121}{4}$ $n = [\tfrac{1}{2}(11)]^2 = (\tfrac{11}{2})^2 = \tfrac{121}{4}$

$\left(x + \dfrac{11}{2}\right)^2$ Factored form

d. $x^2 - \dfrac{4}{7}x + n$

$x^2 - \dfrac{4}{7}x + \dfrac{4}{49}$ $n = [\frac{1}{2}(-\frac{4}{7})]^2 = (-\frac{2}{7})^2 = \frac{4}{49}$

$\left(x - \dfrac{2}{7}\right)^2$ Factored form

Skill Practice Determine the value of n that makes the polynomial a perfect square trinomial. Then factor.

4. $x^2 + 20x + n$ **5.** $y^2 - 16y + n$

6. $a^2 - 5a + n$ **7.** $w^2 + \dfrac{7}{3}w + n$

The process of completing the square can be used to write a quadratic equation $ax^2 + bx + c = 0$ $(a \neq 0)$ in the form $(x - h)^2 = k$. Then the square root property can be used to solve the equation. The following steps outline the procedure.

PROCEDURE   **Solving a Quadratic Equation $ax^2 + bx + c = 0$ by Completing the Square and Applying the Square Root Property**

Step 1 Divide both sides by a to make the leading coefficient 1.

Step 2 Isolate the variable terms on one side of the equation.

Step 3 Complete the square.
- Add the square of one-half the linear term coefficient to both sides, $(\frac{1}{2}b)^2$.
- Factor the resulting perfect square trinomial.

Step 4 Apply the square root property and solve for x.

Example 5   **Solving a Quadratic Equation by Completing the Square and Applying the Square Root Property**

Classroom Example: p. 781, Exercise 40

Solve by completing the square and applying the square root property.

$$x^2 - 6x + 13 = 0$$

Solution:

$x^2 - 6x + 13 = 0$ **Step 1:** Since the leading coefficient a is equal to 1, we do not have to divide by a. We can proceed to step 2.

$x^2 - 6x = -13$ **Step 2:** Isolate the variable terms on one side.

$x^2 - 6x + 9 = -13 + 9$ **Step 3:** To complete the square, add $[\frac{1}{2}(-6)]^2 = 9$ to both sides of the equation.

$(x - 3)^2 = -4$ Factor the perfect square trinomial.

Instructor Note: It may help if you discuss the connection between degree and the anticipated number of solutions. With degree two, we expect to see two solutions (including multiplicities).

Answers

4. $n = 100$; $(x + 10)^2$

5. $n = 64$; $(y - 8)^2$

6. $n = \dfrac{25}{4}$; $\left(a - \dfrac{5}{2}\right)^2$

7. $n = \dfrac{49}{36}$; $\left(w + \dfrac{7}{6}\right)^2$

$$x - 3 = \pm\sqrt{-4}$$

Step 4: Apply the square root property.

$$x - 3 = \pm 2i$$

Simplify the radical.

$$x = 3 \pm 2i$$

Solve for x.

The solutions are imaginary numbers and can be written as $3 + 2i$ and $3 - 2i$. The solution set is $\{3 \pm 2i\}$.

Skill Practice Solve by completing the square and applying the square root property.

8. $z^2 - 4z + 26 = 0$

Classroom Example: p. 781, Exercise 48

| Example 6 | Solving a Quadratic Equation by Completing the Square and Applying the Square Root Property |

Solve by completing the square and applying the square root property.

$$2m^2 + 10m = 3$$

Solution:

$$2m^2 + 10m = 3$$

The variable terms are already isolated on one side of the equation.

$$\frac{2m^2}{2} + \frac{10m}{2} = \frac{3}{2}$$

Divide by the leading coefficient, 2.

$$m^2 + 5m = \frac{3}{2}$$

$$m^2 + 5m + \frac{25}{4} = \frac{3}{2} + \frac{25}{4}$$

Add $[\frac{1}{2}(5)]^2 = (\frac{5}{2})^2 = \frac{25}{4}$ to both sides.

$$\left(m + \frac{5}{2}\right)^2 = \frac{6}{4} + \frac{25}{4}$$

Factor the left side and write the terms on the right with a common denominator.

$$\left(m + \frac{5}{2}\right)^2 = \frac{31}{4}$$

$$m + \frac{5}{2} = \pm\sqrt{\frac{31}{4}}$$

Apply the square root property.

$$m = -\frac{5}{2} \pm \frac{\sqrt{31}}{2}$$

Subtract $\frac{5}{2}$ from both sides and simplify the radical.

The solution set is $\left\{-\frac{5}{2} \pm \frac{\sqrt{31}}{2}\right\}$. The solutions are irrational numbers.

TIP: The solutions to Example 6 can also be written as:

$$\frac{-5 \pm \sqrt{31}}{2}$$

Skill Practice Solve by completing the square and applying the square root property.

9. $4x^2 + 12x = 5$

Answers

8. $\{2 \pm i\sqrt{22}\}$

9. $\left\{-\frac{3}{2} \pm \frac{\sqrt{14}}{2}\right\}$

Example 7 **Solving a Quadratic Equation by Completing the Square and Applying the Square Root Property**

Classroom Example: p. 781, Exercise 54

Solve by completing the square and applying the square root property.

$$2x(2x - 10) = -30 + 6x$$

Instructor Note: Dividing through by "*a*" is a trouble spot for students. Be sure they understand that *all* terms must be divided by "*a*."

Solution:

$$2x(2x - 10) = -30 + 6x$$

$$4x^2 - 20x = -30 + 6x \qquad \text{Clear parentheses.}$$

$$4x^2 - 26x + 30 = 0 \qquad \text{Write the equation in the form } ax^2 + bx + c = 0.$$

$$\frac{4x^2}{4} - \frac{26x}{4} + \frac{30}{4} = \frac{0}{4} \qquad \textbf{Step 1:} \quad \text{Divide both sides by the leading coefficient 4.}$$

$$x^2 - \frac{13}{2}x + \frac{15}{2} = 0$$

$$x^2 - \frac{13}{2}x - = -\frac{15}{2} \qquad \textbf{Step 2:} \quad \text{Isolate the variable terms on one side.}$$

$$x^2 - \frac{13}{2}x + \frac{169}{16} = -\frac{15}{2} + \frac{169}{16} \qquad \textbf{Step 3:} \quad \text{Add } [\frac{1}{2}(-\frac{13}{2})]^2 = (-\frac{13}{4})^2 = \frac{169}{16} \text{ to both sides.}$$

$$\left(x - \frac{13}{4}\right)^2 = -\frac{120}{16} + \frac{169}{16} \qquad \text{Factor the perfect square trinomial. Rewrite the right-hand side with a common denominator.}$$

$$\left(x - \frac{13}{4}\right)^2 = \frac{49}{16}$$

$$x - \frac{13}{4} - \pm\sqrt{\frac{49}{16}} \qquad \textbf{Step 4:} \quad \text{Apply the square root property.}$$

$$x - \frac{13}{4} = \pm\frac{7}{4} \qquad \text{Simplify the radical.}$$

$$x = \frac{13}{4} \pm \frac{7}{4}$$

$$x = \frac{13}{4} + \frac{7}{4} = \frac{20}{4} = 5$$

$$x = \frac{13}{4} - \frac{7}{4} = \frac{6}{4} = \frac{3}{2}$$

The solution set is $\left\{5, \frac{3}{2}\right\}$. The solutions are rational numbers.

TIP: In general, if the solutions to a quadratic equation are rational numbers, the equation can be solved by factoring and using the zero product rule. Consider the equation from Example 7.

$$2x(2x - 10) = -30 + 6x$$
$$4x^2 - 20x = -30 + 6x$$
$$4x^2 - 26x + 30 = 0$$
$$2(2x^2 - 13x + 15) = 0$$
$$2(x - 5)(2x - 3) = 0$$
$$x = 5 \quad \text{or} \quad x = \frac{3}{2}$$

Avoiding Mistakes

If the terms are *like* terms, be sure to combine them.

Skill Practice Solve by completing the square and applying the square root property.

10. $2y(y - 1) = 3 - y$

Answer

10. $\left\{\frac{3}{2}, -1\right\}$

3. Literal Equations

Classroom Example: p. 782, Exercise 56

| **Example 8** | Solving a Literal Equation |

Ignoring air resistance, the distance d (in meters) that an object falls in t sec is given by the equation

$$d = 4.9t^2 \qquad \text{where } t \geq 0$$

a. Solve the equation for t. Do not rationalize the denominator.

b. Using the equation from part (a), determine the amount of time required for an object to fall 500 m. Round to the nearest second.

Solution:

a. $d = 4.9t^2$

$\dfrac{d}{4.9} = t^2$ Isolate the quadratic term. The equation is in the form $t^2 = k$.

$t = \pm\sqrt{\dfrac{d}{4.9}}$ Apply the square root property.

$= \sqrt{\dfrac{d}{4.9}}$ Because t represents time, $t \geq 0$. We reject the negative solution.

b. $t = \sqrt{\dfrac{d}{4.9}}$

$= \sqrt{\dfrac{500}{4.9}}$ Substitute $d = 500$.

$t \approx 10.1$

The object will require approximately 10.1 sec to fall 500 m.

Skill Practice The formula for the area of a circle is $A = \pi r^2$, where r is the radius.

Answers

11. $r = \sqrt{\dfrac{A}{\pi}}$

12. The radius is $\sqrt{5} \approx 2.24$ cm.

11. Solve for r. (Do not rationalize the denominator.)

12. Use the equation from Skill Practice exercise 11 to find the radius for an area of 15.7 cm^2. (Use 3.14 for π and round to 2 decimal places.)

Section 11.1 Practice Exercises

Study Skills Exercise

1. Define the key terms.

     a. square root property   **b. completing the square**

Concept 1: Solving Quadratic Equations by Using the Square Root Property

For Exercises 2–17, solve the equations by using the square root property. **(See Examples 1–3.)**

2. $x^2 = 100$ $\{\pm 10\}$ **3.** $y^2 = 4$ $\{\pm 2\}$ **4.** $a^2 = 5$ $\{\pm\sqrt{5}\}$ **5.** $k^2 - 7 = 0$ $\{\pm\sqrt{7}\}$

6. $3v^2 + 33 = 0$ $\{\pm i\sqrt{11}\}$ **7.** $-2m^2 = 50$ $\{\pm 5i\}$ **8.** $(p - 5)^2 = 9$ $\{8, 2\}$ **9.** $(q + 3)^2 = 4$ $\{-1, -5\}$

 Writing   Translating Expression   Geometry   Scientific Calculator   Video   NS E

10. $(3x - 2)^2 - 5 = 0$
$\left\{\dfrac{2 \pm \sqrt{5}}{3}\right\}$

11. $(2y + 3)^2 - 7 = 0$
$\left\{\dfrac{-3 \pm \sqrt{7}}{2}\right\}$

12. $(h - 4)^2 = -8$
$\{4 \pm 2i\sqrt{2}\}$

13. $(t + 5)^2 = -18$
$\{-5 \pm 3i\sqrt{2}\}$

14. $6p^2 - 3 = 2$ $\left\{\pm\dfrac{\sqrt{30}}{6}\right\}$

15. $15 = 4 + 3w^2$ $\left\{\pm\dfrac{\sqrt{33}}{3}\right\}$

16. $\left(x - \dfrac{3}{2}\right)^2 + \dfrac{7}{4} = 0$
$\left\{\dfrac{3}{2} \pm \dfrac{\sqrt{7}}{2}i\right\}$

17. $\left(m + \dfrac{4}{5}\right)^2 + \dfrac{3}{25} = 0$
$\left\{-\dfrac{4}{5} \pm \dfrac{\sqrt{3}}{5}i\right\}$

18. Given the equation $x^2 = k$, match the following statements.

    a. If $k > 0$, then _____

    b. If $k < 0$, then _____

    c. If $k = 0$, then _____
    a. ii   b. iii   c. i

    i. there will be one real solution.

    ii. there will be two real solutions.

    iii. there will be two imaginary solutions.

19. State two methods that can be used to solve the equation $x^2 - 36 = 0$. Then solve the equation by using both methods.   1. Factoring and applying the zero product rule. 2. Applying the square root property. $\{\pm 6\}$

20. Explain the difference between solving the equations: $x = \sqrt{16}$ and $x^2 = 16$.   The equation $x = \sqrt{16}$ has only one solution, 4, because the symbol $\sqrt{\ }$ gives only the principal square root. The equation $x^2 = 16$ has two solutions, $\pm\sqrt{16}$ that simplify to 4 and -4.

Concept 2: Solving Quadratic Equations by Completing the Square

For Exercises 21–32, find the value of n so that the expression is a perfect square trinomial. Then factor the trinomial.
(See Example 4.)

21. $x^2 - 6x + n$
$n = 9; (x - 3)^2$

22. $x^2 + 12x + n$
$n = 36; (x + 6)^2$

23. $t^2 + 8t + n$
$n = 16; (t + 4)^2$

24. $v^2 - 18v + n$
$n = 81; (v - 9)^2$

25. $c^2 - c + n$
$n = \dfrac{1}{4}; \left(c - \dfrac{1}{2}\right)^2$

26. $x^2 + 9x + n$
$n = \dfrac{81}{4}; \left(x + \dfrac{9}{2}\right)^2$

27. $y^2 + 5y + n$
$n = \dfrac{25}{4}; \left(y + \dfrac{5}{2}\right)^2$

28. $a^2 - 7a + n$
$n = \dfrac{49}{4}; \left(a - \dfrac{7}{2}\right)^2$

29. $b^2 + \dfrac{2}{5}b + n$
$n = \dfrac{1}{25}; \left(b + \dfrac{1}{5}\right)^2$

30. $m^2 - \dfrac{2}{7}m + n$
$n = \dfrac{1}{49}; \left(m - \dfrac{1}{7}\right)^2$

31. $p^2 - \dfrac{2}{3}p + n$
$n = \dfrac{1}{9}; \left(p - \dfrac{1}{3}\right)^2$

32. $w^2 + \dfrac{3}{4}w + n$
$n = \dfrac{9}{64}; \left(w + \dfrac{3}{8}\right)^2$

33. Summarize the steps used in solving a quadratic equation by completing the square and applying the square root property.   See page 777.

34. What types of quadratic equations can be solved by completing the square and applying the square root property?   All quadratic equations

For Exercises 35–54, solve the quadratic equation by completing the square and applying the square root property.
(See Examples 5–7.)

35. $t^2 + 8t + 15 = 0$
$\{-3, -5\}$

36. $m^2 + 6m + 8 = 0$
$\{-4, -2\}$

37. $x^2 + 6x = -16$
$\{-3 \pm i\sqrt{7}\}$

38. $x^2 - 4x = -15$
$\{2 \pm i\sqrt{11}\}$

39. $p^2 + 4p + 6 = 0$
$\{-2 \pm i\sqrt{2}\}$

40. $q^2 + 2q + 2 = 0$
$\{-1 \pm i\}$

41. $-3y - 10 = -y^2$
$\{5, -2\}$

42. $-24 = -2y^2 + 2y$
$\{4, -3\}$

43. $2a^2 + 4a + 5 = 0$
$\left\{-1 \pm \dfrac{\sqrt{6}}{2}i\right\}$

44. $3a^2 + 6a - 7 = 0$
$\left\{-1 \pm \dfrac{\sqrt{30}}{3}\right\}$

45. $9x^2 - 36x + 40 = 0$
$\left\{2 \pm \dfrac{2}{3}i\right\}$

46. $9y^2 - 12y + 5 = 0$
$\left\{\dfrac{2}{3} \pm \dfrac{1}{3}i\right\}$

47. $25p^2 - 10p = 2$
$\left\{\dfrac{1}{5} \pm \dfrac{\sqrt{3}}{5}\right\}$

48. $9n^2 - 6n = 1$
$\left\{\dfrac{1}{3} \pm \dfrac{\sqrt{2}}{3}\right\}$

49. $(2w + 5)(w - 1) = 2$
$\left\{-\dfrac{3}{4} \pm \dfrac{\sqrt{65}}{4}\right\}$

50. $(3p - 5)(p + 1) = -3$
$\left\{\dfrac{1}{3} \pm \dfrac{\sqrt{7}}{3}\right\}$

51. $n(n - 4) = 7$
$\{2 \pm \sqrt{11}\}$

52. $m(m + 10) = 2$
$\{-5 \pm 3\sqrt{3}\}$

53. $2x(x + 6) = 14$
$\{1, -7\}$

54. $3x(x - 2) = 24$
$\{-2, 4\}$

Concept 3: Literal Equations

55. The distance (in feet) that an object falls in t sec is given by the equation $d = 16t^2$, where $t \geq 0$.

    a. Solve the equation for t. **(See Example 8.)** $t = \dfrac{\sqrt{d}}{4}$

    b. Using the equation from part (a), determine the amount of time required for an object to fall 1024 ft.
    8 sec

 Writing   Translating Expression   Geometry   Scientific Calculator   Video   NS&E

56. The volume of a can that is 4 in. tall is given by the equation $V = 4\pi r^2$, where r is the radius of the can, measured in inches.

   a. Solve the equation for r. Do not rationalize the denominator. $r = \frac{1}{2}\sqrt{\frac{V}{\pi}}$

   b. Using the equation from part (a), determine the radius of a can with volume of 12.56 in.^{3} Use 3.14 for π.
   1 in.

For Exercises 57–62, solve for the indicated variable.

57. $A = \pi r^2$ for r $(r > 0)$ $r = \sqrt{\frac{A}{\pi}}$ or $r = \frac{\sqrt{A\pi}}{\pi}$ **58.** $E = mc^2$ for c $(c > 0)$ $c = \sqrt{\frac{E}{m}}$ or $c = \frac{\sqrt{Em}}{m}$

 59. $a^2 + b^2 + c^2 = d^2$ for a $(a > 0)$ **60.** $a^2 + b^2 = c^2$ for b $(b > 0)$ $b = \sqrt{c^2 - a^2}$
   $a = \sqrt{d^2 - b^2 - c^2}$

61. $V = \frac{1}{3}\pi r^2 h$ for r $(r > 0)$ $r = \sqrt{\frac{3V}{\pi h}}$ or $r = \frac{\sqrt{3V\pi h}}{\pi h}$ **62.** $V = \frac{1}{3}s^2 h$ for s $(s > 0)$ $s = \sqrt{\frac{3V}{h}}$ or $s = \frac{\sqrt{3Vh}}{h}$

63. A corner shelf is to be made from a triangular piece of plywood, as shown in the diagram. Find the distance x that the shelf will extend along the walls. Assume that the walls are at right angles. Round the answer to a tenth of a foot.
   4.2 ft

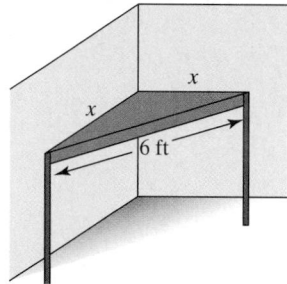

64. The volume of a box with a square bottom and a height of 4 in. is given by $V(x) = 4x^2$, where x is the length (in inches) of the sides of the bottom of the box.

   a. If the volume of the box is 289 in.^{3}, find the dimensions of the box.   8.5 in. by 8.5 in. by 4 in.

   b. Are there two possible answers to part (a)? Why or why not?
   One answer only. A length cannot be represented by a negative number.

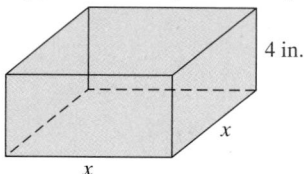

65. A square has an area of 50 in.^{2} What are the lengths of the sides? (Round to one decimal place.)   7.1 in.

66. The amount of money A in an account with an interest rate r compounded annually is given by

$$A = P(1 + r)^t$$

where P is the initial principal and t is the number of years the money is invested.

   a. If a $10,000 investment grows to $11,664 after 2 yr, find the interest rate.   8%

   b. If a $6000 investment grows to $7392.60 after 2 yr, find the interest rate.   11%

   c. Jamal wants to invest $5000. He wants the money to grow to at least $6500 in 2 yr to cover the cost of his son's first year at college. What interest rate does Jamal need for his investment to grow to $6500 in 2 yr? Round to the nearest hundredth of a percent.   14.02%

67. A textbook company has discovered that the profit for selling its books is given by

$$P(x) = -\frac{1}{8}x^2 + 5x$$

where x is the number of textbooks produced (in thousands) and $P(x)$ is the corresponding profit (in thousands of dollars). The graph of the function is shown at the right.

   a. Approximate the number of books required to make a profit of $20,000. [*Hint:* Let $P(x) = 20$. Then complete the square to solve for x.] Round to one decimal place.   4.5 thousand textbooks or 35.5 thousand textbooks

   b. Why are there two answers to part (a)? Profit increases to a point as more books are produced. Beyond that point, the market is "flooded," and profit decreases. There are two points at which the profit is $20,000. Producing 4.5 thousand books makes the same profit using fewer resources as producing 35.5 thousand books.

 Writing   Translating Expression   Geometry   Scientific Calculator   Video   NS&E

68. If we ignore air resistance, the distance (in feet) that an object travels in free fall can be approximated by $d(t) = 16t^2$, where t is the time in seconds after the object was dropped.

   a. If the CN Tower in Toronto is 1815 ft high, how long will it take an object to fall from the top of the building? Round to one decimal place.   10.7 sec

   b. If the Renaissance Tower in Dallas is 886 ft high, how long will it take an object to fall from the top of the building? Round to one decimal place.   7.4 sec

Quadratic Formula   Section 11.2

1. Derivation of the Quadratic Formula

If we solve a general quadratic equation $ax^2 + bx + c = 0 \,(a \neq 0)$ by completing the square and using the square root property, the result is a formula that gives the solutions for x in terms of a, b, and c.

$$ax^2 + bx + c = 0$$
Begin with a quadratic equation in standard form.

$$\frac{ax^2}{a} + \frac{bx}{a} + \frac{c}{a} = \frac{0}{a}$$
Divide by the leading coefficient.

$$x^2 + \frac{b}{a}x + \frac{c}{a} = 0$$

$$x^2 + \frac{b}{a}x = -\frac{c}{a}$$
Isolate the terms containing x.

$$x^2 + \frac{b}{a}x + \left(\frac{1}{2}\cdot\frac{b}{a}\right)^2 = \left(\frac{1}{2}\cdot\frac{b}{a}\right)^2 - \frac{c}{a}$$
Add the square of $\frac{1}{2}$ the linear term coefficient to both sides of the equation.

$$\left(x + \frac{b}{2a}\right)^2 = \frac{b^2}{4a^2} - \frac{c}{a}$$
Factor the left side as a perfect square.

$$\left(x + \frac{b}{2a}\right)^2 = \frac{b^2 - 4ac}{4a^2}$$
Combine fractions on the right side by getting a common denominator.

$$x + \frac{b}{2a} = \pm\sqrt{\frac{b^2 - 4ac}{4a^2}}$$
Apply the square root property.

$$x + \frac{b}{2a} = \frac{\pm\sqrt{b^2 - 4ac}}{2a}$$
Simplify the denominator.

$$x = -\frac{b}{2a} \pm \frac{\sqrt{b^2 - 4ac}}{2a}$$
Subtract $\frac{b}{2a}$ from both sides.

$$x = \frac{-b \pm \sqrt{b^2 - 4ac}}{2a}$$
Combine fractions.

The solutions to the equation $ax^2 + bx + c = 0$ for x in terms of the coefficients a, b, and c are given by the **quadratic formula**.

Concepts

1. Derivation of the Quadratic Formula
2. Solving Quadratic Equations by Using the Quadratic Formula
3. Using the Quadratic Formula in Applications
4. Discriminant
5. Mixed Review: Methods to Solve a Quadratic Equation

Instructor Note: Consider solving a quadratic equation with numerical coefficients such as $2x^2 + 3x + 5 = 0$ first. Then show the students the same steps using a, b, and c as coefficients.

TIP: When applying the quadratic formula, note that a, b, and c are constants. The variable is x.

 Writing   Translating Expression   Geometry   Scientific Calculator   Video   NS E

> **FORMULA** **The Quadratic Formula**
>
> For a quadratic equation of the form $ax^2 + bx + c = 0$ $(a \neq 0)$ the solutions are
>
> $$x = \frac{-b \pm \sqrt{b^2 - 4ac}}{2a}$$

The quadratic formula gives us another technique to solve a quadratic equation. This method will work regardless of whether the equation is factorable or not factorable.

2. Solving Quadratic Equations by Using the Quadratic Formula

Classroom Example: p. 795, Exercise 16

Example 1 **Solving a Quadratic Equation by Using the Quadratic Formula**

Solve the quadratic equation by using the quadratic formula.

$$2x^2 - 3x = 5$$

Solution:

$$2x^2 - 3x = 5$$

$$2x^2 - 3x - 5 = 0 \qquad \text{Write the equation in the form } ax^2 + bx + c = 0.$$

$$a = 2, \qquad b = -3, \qquad c = -5 \qquad \text{Identify } a, b, \text{ and } c.$$

> **Avoiding Mistakes**
> - The term, $-b$, represents the *opposite* of b.
> - Remember to write the *entire* numerator over $2a$.

$$x = \frac{-b \pm \sqrt{b^2 - 4ac}}{2a} \qquad \text{Apply the quadratic formula.}$$

$$= \frac{-(-3) \pm \sqrt{(-3)^2 - 4(2)(-5)}}{2(2)} \qquad \text{Substitute } a = 2, b = -3, \text{ and } c = -5.$$

$$= \frac{3 \pm \sqrt{9 + 40}}{4} \qquad \text{Simplify.}$$

$$= \frac{3 \pm \sqrt{49}}{4}$$

$$= \frac{3 \pm 7}{4} \qquad\qquad x = \frac{3 + 7}{4} = \frac{10}{4} = \frac{5}{2}$$

$$x = \frac{3 - 7}{4} = \frac{-4}{4} = -1$$

The solution set is $\left\{ \dfrac{5}{2}, -1 \right\}$. Both solutions check in the original equation.

Skill Practice Solve the equation by using the quadratic formula.

1. $6x^2 - 5x = 4$

Answer

1. $\left\{ -\dfrac{1}{2}, \dfrac{4}{3} \right\}$

Example 2 Solving a Quadratic Equation by Using the Quadratic Formula

Classroom Example: p. 795, Exercise 22

Solve the quadratic equation by using the quadratic formula.

$$-x(x - 6) = 11$$

Solution:

$$-x(x - 6) = 11$$

$$-x^2 + 6x - 11 = 0 \qquad \text{Write the equation in the form } ax^2 + bx + c = 0.$$

$$-1(-x^2 + 6x - 11) = -1(0) \qquad \text{If the leading coefficient of the}$$
$$x^2 - 6x + 11 = 0 \qquad \text{quadratic polynomial is negative, we suggest multiplying both sides of the equation by } -1. \text{ Although this is not mandatory, it is generally easier to simplify the quadratic formula when the value of } a \text{ is positive.}$$

$$a = 1, b = -6, \text{ and } c = 11 \qquad \text{Identify } a, b, \text{ and } c.$$

$$x = \frac{-b \pm \sqrt{b^2 - 4ac}}{2a} \qquad \text{Apply the quadratic formula.}$$

$$= \frac{-(-6) \pm \sqrt{(-6)^2 - 4(1)(11)}}{2(1)} \qquad \text{Substitute } a = 1, b = -6, \text{ and } c = 11.$$

$$= \frac{6 \pm \sqrt{36 - 44}}{2} \qquad \text{Simplify.}$$

$$= \frac{6 \pm \sqrt{-8}}{2}$$

$$= \frac{6 \pm 2i\sqrt{2}}{2} \qquad \text{Simplify the radical.}$$

$$= \frac{2(3 \pm i\sqrt{2})}{2} \qquad \text{Factor the numerator.}$$

$$= \frac{2(3 \pm i\sqrt{2})}{2} \qquad \text{Simplify the fraction to lowest terms.}$$

$$= 3 \pm i\sqrt{2} \qquad \begin{aligned} & x = 3 + i\sqrt{2} \qquad \text{The solutions are} \\ & \qquad\qquad\qquad\quad \text{imaginary numbers.} \\ & x = 3 - i\sqrt{2} \end{aligned}$$

The solution set is $\{3 \pm i\sqrt{2}\}$.

Avoiding Mistakes

When identifying a, b, and c, use the coefficients only, not the variable.

Avoiding Mistakes

Always simplify the radical completely before trying to reduce the fraction to lowest terms.

Skill Practice Solve the equation by using the quadratic formula.

2. $y(y + 4) = -12$

Answer

2. $\{-2 \pm 2i\sqrt{2}\}$

3. Using the Quadratic Formula in Applications

Classroom Example: p. 795, Exercise 42

Example 3 Using the Quadratic Formula in an Application

A delivery truck travels south from Hartselle, Alabama, to Birmingham, Alabama, along Interstate 65. The truck then heads east to Atlanta, Georgia, along Interstate 20. The distance from Birmingham to Atlanta is 8 mi less than twice the distance from Hartselle to Birmingham. If the straight-line distance from Hartselle to Atlanta is 165 mi, find the distance from Hartselle to Birmingham and from Birmingham to Atlanta. (Round the answers to the nearest mile.)

Solution:

The motorist travels due south and then due east. Therefore, the three cities form the vertices of a right triangle (Figure 11-1).

Let x represent the distance between Hartselle and Birmingham.

Then $2x - 8$ represents the distance between Birmingham and Atlanta.

Use the Pythagorean theorem to establish a relationship among the three sides of the triangle.

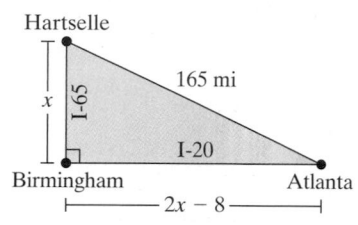

Figure 11-1

$$(x)^2 + (2x - 8)^2 = (165)^2$$

$$x^2 + 4x^2 - 32x + 64 = 27{,}225$$

$$5x^2 - 32x - 27{,}161 = 0 \qquad \text{Write the equation in the form } ax^2 + bx + c = 0.$$

$$a = 5 \qquad b = -32 \qquad c = -27{,}161 \qquad \text{Identify } a, b, \text{ and } c.$$

$$x = \frac{-(-32) \pm \sqrt{(-32)^2 - 4(5)(-27{,}161)}}{2(5)} \qquad \text{Apply the quadratic formula.}$$

$$= \frac{32 \pm \sqrt{1024 + 543{,}220}}{10} \qquad \text{Simplify.}$$

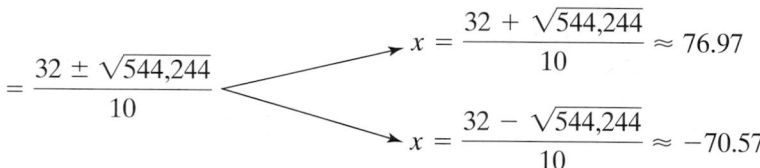

$$= \frac{32 \pm \sqrt{544{,}244}}{10}$$

$$x = \frac{32 + \sqrt{544{,}244}}{10} \approx 76.97$$

$$x = \frac{32 - \sqrt{544{,}244}}{10} \approx -70.57$$

We reject the negative solution because distance cannot be negative. Rounding to the nearest whole unit, we have $x = 77$. Therefore, $2x - 8 = 2(77) - 8 = 146$.

The distance between Hartselle and Birmingham is 77 mi, and the distance between Birmingham and Atlanta is 146 mi.

Skill Practice

3. Steve and Tammy leave a campground, hiking on two different trails. Steve heads south and Tammy heads east. By lunchtime they are 9 mi apart. Steve walked 3 mi more than twice as many miles as Tammy. Find the distance each person hiked. (Round to the nearest tenth of a mile.)

Answer

3. Tammy hiked 2.8 mi, and Steve hiked 8.6 mi.

| Example 4 | Analyzing a Quadratic Function |

Classroom Example: p. 796, Exercise 48

A model rocket is launched straight upward from the side of a 144-ft cliff (Figure 11-2). The initial velocity is 112 ft/sec. The height of the rocket $h(t)$ is given by

$$h(t) = -16t^2 + 112t + 144$$

where $h(t)$ is measured in feet and t is the time in seconds. Find the time(s) at which the rocket is 208 ft above the ground.

Solution:

$$h(t) = -16t^2 + 112t + 144$$

$$208 = -16t^2 + 112t + 144 \qquad \text{Substitute 208 for } h(t).$$

$$16t^2 - 112t + 64 = 0 \qquad \text{Write the equation in the form } at^2 + bt + c = 0.$$

$$\frac{16t^2}{16} - \frac{112t}{16} + \frac{64}{16} = \frac{0}{16} \qquad \text{Divide by 16. This makes the coefficients smaller, and it is less cumbersome to solve.}$$

$$t^2 - 7t + 4 = 0 \qquad \text{The equation is not factorable. Apply the quadratic formula.}$$

$$t = \frac{-(-7) \pm \sqrt{(-7)^2 - 4(1)(4)}}{2(1)} \qquad \text{Let } a = 1, b = -7, \text{ and } c = 4.$$

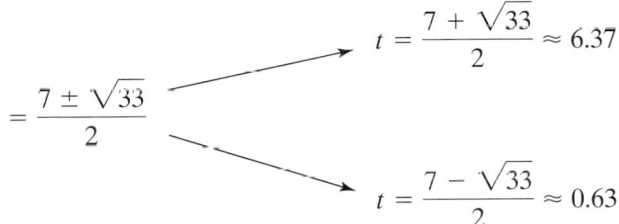

$$= \frac{7 \pm \sqrt{33}}{2}$$

$$t = \frac{7 + \sqrt{33}}{2} \approx 6.37$$

$$t = \frac{7 - \sqrt{33}}{2} \approx 0.63$$

The rocket will reach a height of 208 ft after approximately 0.63 sec (on the way up) and after 6.37 sec (on the way down).

Skill Practice

4. A rocket is launched from the top of a 96-ft building with an initial velocity of 64 ft/sec. The height $h(t)$ of the rocket is given by $h(t) = -16t^2 + 64t + 96$. Find the time it takes for the rocket to hit the ground. [Hint: $h(t) = 0$ when the object hits the ground.]

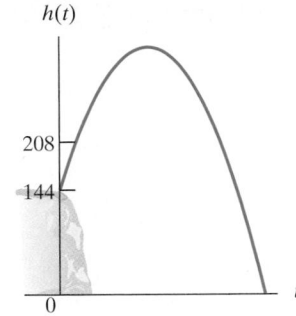

Figure 11-2

4. Discriminant

The radicand within the quadratic formula is the expression $b^2 - 4ac$. This is called the **discriminant**. The discriminant can be used to determine the number of solutions to a quadratic equation as well as whether the solutions are rational, irrational, or imaginary numbers.

Answer

4. $2 + \sqrt{10} \approx 5.16$ sec

Instructor Note: You can sketch a graph to show that we cannot have one real solution and one imaginary solution to a quadratic equation with real coefficients.

PROCEDURE   **Using the Discriminant to Determine the Number and Type of Solutions to a Quadratic Equation**

Consider the equation $ax^2 + bx + c = 0$, where a, b, and c are rational numbers and $a \neq 0$. The expression $b^2 - 4ac$ is called the *discriminant*. Furthermore,

- If $b^2 - 4ac > 0$, then there will be two real solutions.

    a. If $b^2 - 4ac$ is a perfect square, the solutions will be rational numbers.
    b. If $b^2 - 4ac$ is not a perfect square, the solutions will be irrational numbers.

- If $b^2 - 4ac < 0$, then there will be two imaginary solutions.
- If $b^2 - 4ac = 0$, then there will be one rational solution.

Classroom Examples: p. 796, Exercises 50, 52, 54, and 56

Example 5   **Using the Discriminant**

Use the discriminant to determine the type and number of solutions for each equation.

a. $2x^2 - 5x + 9 = 0$ **b.** $3x^2 = -x + 2$

c. $-2x(2x - 3) = -1$ **d.** $3.6x^2 = -1.2x - 0.1$

Solution:

For each equation, first write the equation in standard form $ax^2 + bx + c = 0$. Then determine the discriminant.

Equation	Discriminant	Solution Type and Number
a. $2x^2 - 5x + 9 = 0$	$b^2 - 4ac$ $= (-5)^2 - 4(2)(9)$ $= 25 - 72$ $= -47$	Because $-47 < 0$, there will be two imaginary solutions.
b. $3x^2 = -x + 2$ $3x^2 + x - 2 = 0$	$b^2 - 4ac$ $= (1)^2 - 4(3)(-2)$ $= 1 - (-24)$ $= 25$	$25 > 0$ and 25 is a perfect square. There will be two rational solutions.
c. $-2x(2x - 3) = -1$ $-4x^2 + 6x = -1$ $-4x^2 + 6x + 1 = 0$	$b^2 - 4ac$ $= (6)^2 - 4(-4)(1)$ $= 36 - (-16)$ $= 52$	$52 > 0$, but 52 is *not* a perfect square. There will be two irrational solutions.
d. $3.6x^2 = -1.2x - 0.1$ $3.6x^2 + 1.2x + 0.1 = 0$	$b^2 - 4ac$ $= (1.2)^2 - 4(3.6)(0.1)$ $= 1.44 - 1.44$ $= 0$	Because the discriminant equals 0, there will be only one rational solution.

Skill Practice Use the discriminant to determine the type and number of solutions for the equation.

5. $3y^2 + y + 3 = 0$

6. $4t^2 = 6t - 2$

7. $3t(t + 1) = 9$

8. $\dfrac{2}{3}x^2 - \dfrac{2}{3}x + \dfrac{1}{6} = 0$

With the discriminant we can determine the number of real-valued solutions to the equation $ax^2 + bx + c = 0$, and thus the number of x-intercepts to the function $f(x) = ax^2 + bx + c$. The following illustrations show the graphical interpretation of the three cases of the discriminant.

$f(x) = x^2 - 4x + 3$

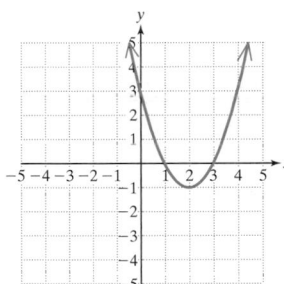

Use $x^2 - 4x + 3 = 0$ to find the value of the discriminant.

$$b^2 - 4ac = (-4)^2 - 4(1)(3)$$
$$= 4$$

Since the discriminant is positive, there are two real solutions to the quadratic equation. Therefore, there are two x-intercepts to the corresponding quadratic function, $(1, 0)$ and $(3, 0)$.

$f(x) = x^2 - x + 1$

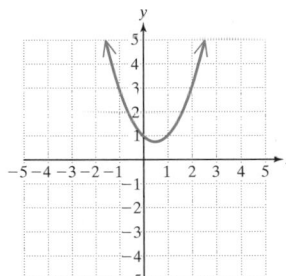

Use $x^2 - x + 1 = 0$ to find the value of the discriminant.

$$b^2 - 4ac = (-1)^2 - 4(1)(1)$$
$$= -3$$

Since the discriminant is negative, there are no real solutions to the quadratic equation. Therefore, there are no x-intercepts to the corresponding quadratic function.

$f(x) = x^2 - 2x + 1$

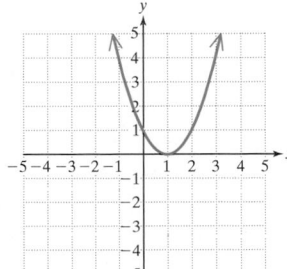

Use $x^2 - 2x + 1 = 0$ to find the value of the discriminant.

$$b^2 - 4ac = (-2)^2 - 4(1)(1)$$
$$= 0$$

Since the discriminant is zero, there is one real solution to the quadratic equation. Therefore, there is one x-intercept to the corresponding quadratic function, $(1, 0)$.

Answers

5. -35; two imaginary solutions

6. 4; two rational solutions

7. 117; two irrational solutions

8. 0; one rational solution

Classroom Example: p. 796,
Exercise 64

Example 6 Finding *x*- and *y*-Intercepts of a Quadratic Function

Given $f(x) = x^2 - 3x + 1$.

a. Find the discriminant and use it to determine if there are any *x*-intercepts.

b. Find the *x*-intercept(s), if they exist.

c. Find the *y*-intercept.

Solution:

a. $a = 1$, $b = -3$, and $c = 1$.

The discriminant is $b^2 - 4ac = (-3)^2 - 4(1)(1)$

$$= 9 - 4$$

$$= 5$$

Since $5 > 0$, there are two *x*-intercepts.

b. The *x*-intercepts are given by the real solutions to the equation $f(x) = 0$. In this case, we have

$f(x) = x^2 - 3x + 1 = 0$

$x^2 - 3x + 1 = 0$ The equation is in the form
                                       $ax^2 + bx + c = 0$.

$x = \dfrac{3 \pm \sqrt{(-3)^2 - (4)(1)(1)}}{2(1)}$ Apply the quadratic formula.

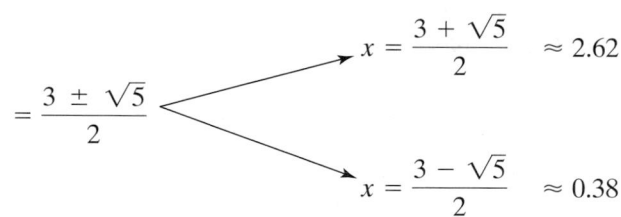

$= \dfrac{3 \pm \sqrt{5}}{2}$ $x = \dfrac{3 + \sqrt{5}}{2} \approx 2.62$

$x = \dfrac{3 - \sqrt{5}}{2} \approx 0.38$

The solutions are $\dfrac{3 + \sqrt{5}}{2}$ and $\dfrac{3 - \sqrt{5}}{2}$. Therefore, the *x*-intercepts are

$\left(\dfrac{3 + \sqrt{5}}{2}, 0 \right)$ and $\left(\dfrac{3 - \sqrt{5}}{2}, 0 \right)$.

c. To find the *y*-intercept, evaluate $f(0)$.

$f(0) = (0)^2 - 3(0) + 1 = 1$

The *y*-intercept is located at $(0, 1)$.

The parabola is shown in the graph with the *x*- and *y*-intercepts labeled.

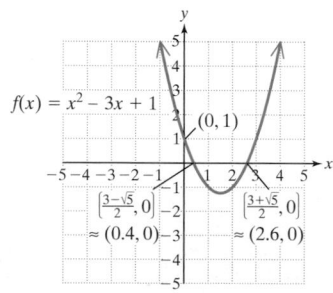

Skill Practice Given $f(x) = x^2 + 5x + 2$,

9. Find the discriminant and use it to determine if there are any *x*-intercepts.

10. Find the *x*- and *y*-intercepts.

Answers

9. 17, there are two *x*-intercepts.

10. *x*-intercepts: $\left(\dfrac{-5 + \sqrt{17}}{2}, 0 \right)$,

$\left(\dfrac{-5 - \sqrt{17}}{2}, 0 \right)$

y-intercept: $(0, 2)$

Example 7   **Finding *x*- and *y*-Intercepts of a Quadratic Function**

Classroom Example: p. 796, Exercise 66

Given $f(x) = x^2 + x + 2,$

a. Find the discriminant and use it to determine if there are any *x*-intercepts.

b. Find the *x*-intercept(s), if they exist.

c. Find the *y*-intercept.

Solution:

a. $a = 1, b = 1,$ and $c = 2.$

The discriminant is $b^2 - 4ac = (1)^2 - 4(1)(2)$

$$= 1 - 8$$

$$= -7$$

Since $-7 < 0,$ there are no *x*-intercepts.

b. There are no *x*-intercepts.

c. $f(0) = (0)^2 + (0) + 2$

$$= 2$$

The *y*-intercept is located at $(0, 2).$

The parabola is shown. *Note:* the graph does not intersect the *x*-axis.

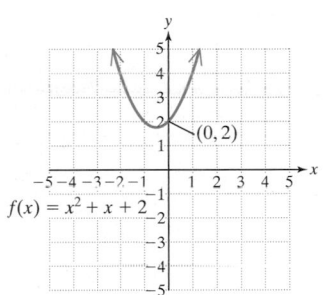

Skill Practice Given $f(x) = 2x^2 \quad 3x + 5,$

11. Find the discriminant and use it to determine if there are any *x*-intercepts.

12. Find the *x*- and *y*-intercepts.

5. Mixed Review: Methods to Solve a Quadratic Equation

Three methods have been presented to solve quadratic equations.

SUMMARY   Methods to Solve a Quadratic Equation

Factor and use the zero product rule (Section 6.7).	
• This method works well if you can factor the equation easily.	Example: $x^2 + 8x + 15 = 0$ factors as $(x + 3)(x + 5) = 0$
Use the square root property. Complete the square if necessary (Section 11.1). This method is particularly good if	
• the equation is of the form $ax^2 + c = 0$ or • the equation is of the form $x^2 + bx + c = 0$, where b is even.	Examples: $4x^2 + 9 = 0$ $x^2 + 10x - 3 = 0$
Quadratic Formula (Section 11.2)	
• This method works in all cases—just be sure to write the equation in the form $ax^2 + bx + c = 0$ before applying the formula.	Example: $7x^2 - 3x + 11 = 0$

Answers

11. $-31,$ there are no *x*-intercepts.

12. $(0, 5)$

Before solving a quadratic equation, take a minute to analyze it first. Each problem must be evaluated individually before choosing the most efficient method to find its solutions.

Classroom Example: p. 797, Exercise 72

Example 8   Solving a Quadratic Equation by Using Any Method

Solve the equation by using any method.

$$(x + 3)^2 + x^2 - 9x = 8$$

Solution:

$$(x + 3)^2 + x^2 - 9x = 8$$

$$x^2 + 6x + 9 + x^2 - 9x - 8 = 0 \qquad \text{Clear parentheses and write the equation in the form } ax^2 + bx + c = 0.$$

$$2x^2 - 3x + 1 = 0 \qquad \text{This equation is factorable.}$$

$$(2x - 1)(x - 1) = 0 \qquad \text{Factor.}$$

$$2x - 1 = 0 \quad \text{or} \quad x - 1 = 0 \qquad \text{Apply the zero product rule.}$$

$$x = \tfrac{1}{2} \quad \text{or} \quad x = 1 \qquad \text{Solve for } x.$$

The solution set is $\{\tfrac{1}{2}, 1\}$.

This equation could have been solved by using any of the three methods, but factoring was the most efficient method.

Skill Practice Solve using any method.

13. $2t(t - 1) + t^2 = 5$

Classroom Example: p. 797, Exercise 74

Example 9   Solving a Quadratic Equation by Using Any Method

Solve the equation by using any method.

$$x^2 + 5 = -2x$$

Solution:

$$x^2 + 2x + 5 = 0 \qquad \text{The equation does not factor.}$$

$$x^2 + 2x = -5 \qquad \text{Because } a = 1 \text{ and } b \text{ is even, we can easily complete the square.}$$

$$x^2 + 2x + 1 = -5 + 1 \qquad \text{Add } [\tfrac{1}{2}(2)]^2 = 1^2 = 1 \text{ to both sides.}$$

$$(x + 1)^2 = -4$$

$$x + 1 = \pm\sqrt{-4} \qquad \text{Apply the square root property.}$$

$$x = -1 \pm 2i \qquad \text{Solve for } x.$$

The solution set is $\{-1 \pm 2i\}$.

This equation could also have been solved by using the quadratic formula.

Answers

13. $\left\{-1, \dfrac{5}{3}\right\}$

14. $\{2 \pm i\sqrt{3}\}$

Skill Practice Solve using any method.

14. $x^2 - 4x = -7$

Example 10 Solving a Quadratic Equation by Using Any Method

Classroom Example: p. 797, Exercise 82

Solve the equation by using any method. $\dfrac{1}{4}x^2 - \dfrac{1}{2}x + \dfrac{1}{3} = 0$

Solution:

$12 \cdot \left(\dfrac{1}{4}x^2 - \dfrac{1}{2}x + \dfrac{1}{3} \right) = 12 \cdot (0)$ Clear fractions.

$3x^2 - 6x + 4 = 0$ The equation is in the form $ax^2 + bx + c = 0$.
The left-hand side does not factor.

$a = 3, b = -6,$ and $c = 4$

$x = \dfrac{-(-6) \pm \sqrt{(-6)^2 - 4(3)(4)}}{2(3)}$ Apply the quadratic formula.

$= \dfrac{6 \pm \sqrt{-12}}{6}$ Simplify.

$= \dfrac{6 \pm 2i\sqrt{3}}{6}$ Simplify the radical.

$= \dfrac{\overset{1}{2}(3 \pm i\sqrt{3})}{\underset{3}{6}}$ Factor and simplify.

$= \dfrac{3 \pm i\sqrt{3}}{3}$

$= \dfrac{3}{3} \pm \dfrac{\sqrt{3}}{3}i$ Write in the form $a \pm bi$.

$= 1 \pm \dfrac{\sqrt{3}}{3}i$ Simplify.

The solution set is $\left\{ 1 \pm \dfrac{\sqrt{3}}{3}i \right\}$.

Avoiding Mistakes

Do not try to "cancel" the 3 in the denominator with the terms in the numerator. Only common *factors* can be reduced.

Skill Practice Solve using any method.

15. $\dfrac{1}{5}x^2 - \dfrac{4}{5}x + \dfrac{1}{2} = 0$

Answer

15. $\left\{ \dfrac{4 \pm \sqrt{6}}{2} \right\}$

Classroom Example: p. 797,
Exercise 86

Example 11 **Solving a Quadratic Equation by Using Any Method**

Solve the equation by using any method. $9p^2 - 11 = 0$

Solution:

$9p^2 - 11 = 0$	Because $b = 0$, use the square root property.
$9p^2 = 11$	Isolate the variable term.
$p^2 = \dfrac{11}{9}$	The equation is in the form $x^2 = k$.
$p = \pm\sqrt{\dfrac{11}{9}}$	Apply the square root property.
$p = \pm\dfrac{\sqrt{11}}{3}$	Simplify the radical.

The solution set is $\left\{ \pm\dfrac{\sqrt{11}}{3} \right\}$.

Skill Practice Solve using any method.

16. $4y^2 - 13 = 0$

Answer

16. $\left\{ \pm\dfrac{\sqrt{13}}{2} \right\}$

Section 11.2 Practice Exercises

Study Skills Exercise

1. Define the key terms.

   a. quadratic formula   **b. discriminant**

Review Exercises

2. Use substitution to determine if $x = -3 + \sqrt{5}$ is a solution to $x^2 + 6x + 4 = 0$.   Yes

For Exercises 3–6, simplify the expression.

3. $\dfrac{16 - \sqrt{320}}{4}$
   $4 - 2\sqrt{5}$

4. $\dfrac{18 + \sqrt{180}}{3}$
   $6 + 2\sqrt{5}$

5. $\dfrac{14 - \sqrt{-147}}{7}$
   $2 - i\sqrt{3}$

6. $\dfrac{10 - \sqrt{-175}}{5}$
   $2 - i\sqrt{7}$

Concept 2: Solving Quadratic Equations by Using the Quadratic Formula

7. What form should a quadratic equation be in so that the quadratic formula can be applied?   The form
   $ax^2 + bx + c = 0$

8. Write the quadratic formula from memory. $x = \dfrac{-b \pm \sqrt{b^2 - 4ac}}{2a}$

 Writing   Translating Expression   Geometry   Scientific Calculator   Video   NS&E

For Exercises 9–34, solve the equation by using the quadratic formula. **(See Examples 1–2.)**

9. $x^2 + 11x - 12 = 0$ $\{-12, 1\}$

10. $5x^2 - 14x - 3 = 0$ $\left\{-\frac{1}{5}, 3\right\}$

11. $9y^2 - 2y + 5 = 0$ $\left\{\frac{1}{9} \pm \frac{2\sqrt{11}}{9}i\right\}$

12. $2t^2 + 3t - 7 = 0$ $\left\{\frac{-3 \pm \sqrt{65}}{4}\right\}$

13. $12p^2 - 4p + 5 = 0$ $\left\{\frac{1}{6} \pm \frac{\sqrt{14}}{6}i\right\}$

14. $-5n^2 + 4n - 6 = 0$ $\left\{\frac{2}{5} \pm \frac{\sqrt{26}}{5}i\right\}$

15. $-z^2 = -2z - 35$ $\{7, -5\}$

16. $12x^2 - 5x = 2$ $\left\{\frac{2}{3}, -\frac{1}{4}\right\}$

17. $y^2 + 3y = 8$ $\left\{\frac{-3 \pm \sqrt{41}}{2}\right\}$

18. $k^2 + 4 = 6k$ $\{3 \pm \sqrt{5}\}$

19. $25x^2 - 20x + 4 = 0$ $\left\{\frac{2}{5}\right\}$

20. $9y^2 = -12y - 4$ $\left\{-\frac{2}{3}\right\}$

21. $w(w - 6) = -14$ $\{3 \pm i\sqrt{5}\}$

22. $m(m + 6) = -11$ $\{-3 \pm i\sqrt{2}\}$

23. $(x + 2)(x - 3) = 1$ $\left\{\frac{1 \pm \sqrt{29}}{2}\right\}$

24. $3y(y + 1) - 7y(y + 2) = 6$ $\left\{-\frac{3}{4}, -2\right\}$

25. $-4a^2 - 2a + 3 = 0$ $\left\{\frac{-1 \pm \sqrt{13}}{4}\right\}$

26. $-2m^2 - 5m + 3 = 0$ $\left\{-3, \frac{1}{2}\right\}$

27. $\frac{1}{2}y^2 + \frac{2}{3} = -\frac{2}{3}y$ $\left\{-\frac{2}{3} \pm \frac{2\sqrt{2}}{3}i\right\}$

28. $\frac{2}{3}p^2 - \frac{1}{6}p + \frac{1}{2} = 0$ $\left\{\frac{1}{8} \pm \frac{\sqrt{47}}{8}i\right\}$

29. $\frac{1}{5}h^2 + h + \frac{3}{5} = 0$ $\left\{\frac{-5 \pm \sqrt{13}}{2}\right\}$

(*Hint:* Clear fractions first.)

30. $\frac{1}{4}w^2 + \frac{7}{4}w + 1 = 0$ $\left\{\frac{-7 \pm \sqrt{33}}{2}\right\}$

31. $0.01x^2 + 0.06x + 0.08 = 0$
(*Hint:* Clear decimals first.)
$\{-2, -4\}$

32. $0.5y^2 - 0.7y + 0.2 = 0$
$\left\{\frac{2}{5}, 1\right\}$

33. $0.3t^2 + 0.7t - 0.5 = 0$
$\left\{\frac{-7 \pm \sqrt{109}}{6}\right\}$

34. $0.01x^2 + 0.04x - 0.07 = 0$
$\{-2 \pm \sqrt{11}\}$

For Exercises 35–38, factor the expression. Then use the zero product rule and the quadratic formula to solve the equation. There should be three solutions to each equation.

35. a. Factor. $x^3 - 27$ $(x - 3)(x^2 + 3x + 9)$

   b. Solve. $x^3 - 27 = 0$ $\left\{3, -\frac{3}{2} \pm \frac{3\sqrt{3}}{2}i\right\}$

36. a. Factor. $64x^3 + 1$ $(4x + 1)(16x^2 - 4x + 1)$

   b. Solve. $64x^3 + 1 = 0$ $\left\{-\frac{1}{4}, \frac{1}{8} \pm \frac{\sqrt{3}}{8}i\right\}$

37. a. Factor. $3x^3 - 6x^2 + 6x$ $3x(x^2 - 2x + 2)$

   b. Solve. $3x^3 - 6x^2 + 6x = 0$ $\{0, 1 \pm i\}$

38. a. Factor. $5x^3 + 5x^2 + 10x$ $5x(x^2 + x + 2)$

   b. Solve. $5x^3 + 5x^2 + 10x = 0$ $\left\{0, -\frac{1}{2} \pm \frac{\sqrt{7}}{2}i\right\}$

39. The volume of a cube is 27 ft³. Find the lengths of the sides. The length of each side is 3 ft.

40. The volume of a rectangular box is 64 ft³. If the width is 3 times longer than the height, and the length is 9 times longer than the height, find the dimensions of the box.

The dimensions are $1\frac{1}{3}$ ft by 4 ft by 12 ft.

Concept 3: Using the Quadratic Formula in Applications

41. The hypotenuse of a right triangle measures 4 in. One leg of the triangle is 2 in. longer than the other leg. Find the lengths of the legs of the triangle. Round to one decimal place. **(See Example 3.)** The legs are approximately 1.6 in. and 3.6 in.

42. The length of one leg of a right triangle is 1 cm more than twice the length of the other leg. The hypotenuse measures 6 cm. Find the lengths of the legs. Round to one decimal place. The legs are approximately 2.3 cm and 5.6 cm.

43. The hypotenuse of a right triangle is 10.2 m long. One leg is 2.1 m shorter than the other leg. Find the lengths of the legs. Round to one decimal place. The legs are approximately 8.2 m and 6.1 m.

44. The hypotenuse of a right triangle is 17 ft long. One leg is 3.4 ft longer than the other leg. Find the lengths of the legs. The legs are approximately 10.2 ft and 13.6 ft.

45. The fatality rate (in fatalities per 100 million vehicle miles driven) can be approximated for drivers x years old according to the function, $F(x) = 0.0036x^2 - 0.35x + 9.2$. (*Source:* U.S. Department of Transportation)

   a. Approximate the fatality rate for drivers 16 yr old. Approximately 4.5 fatalities per 100 million miles driven

   b. Approximate the fatality rate for drivers 40 yr old. Approximately 1 fatality per 100 million miles driven

   c. Approximate the fatality rate for drivers 80 yr old. Approximately 4.2 fatalities per 100 million miles driven

   d. For what age(s) is the fatality rate approximately 2.5? For drivers 26 yr old and 71 yr old

46. The braking distance (in feet) of a car going v mph is given by

$$d(v) = \frac{v^2}{20} + v \qquad v \geq 0$$

   a. Find the speed for a braking distance of 150 ft. Round to the nearest mile per hour. 46 mph

   b. Find the speed for a braking distance of 100 ft. Round to the nearest mile per hour. 36 mph

47. Mitch throws a baseball straight up in the air from a cliff that is 48 ft high. The initial velocity is 48 ft/sec. The height (in feet) of the object after t sec is given by $h(t) = -16t^2 + 48t + 48$. Find the time at which the height of the object is 64 ft.
(See Example 4.)
The times are $\dfrac{3 + \sqrt{5}}{2}$ sec ≈ 2.62 sec or $\dfrac{3 - \sqrt{5}}{2}$ sec ≈ 0.38 sec.

48. An astronaut on the moon throws a rock into the air from the deck of a spacecraft that is 8 m high. The initial velocity of the rock is 2.4 m/sec. The height (in meters) of the rock after t sec is given by $h(t) = -0.8t^2 + 2.4t + 8$. Find the time at which the height of the rock is 6 m.
The rock is 6 m high after $\dfrac{3 + \sqrt{19}}{2}$ sec ≈ 3.68 sec.

Concept 4: Discriminant

For Exercises 49–56,

   a. Write the equation in the form $ax^2 + bx + c = 0,\ a > 0$.

   b. Find the value of the discriminant.

   c. Use the discriminant to determine the number and type of solutions. **(See Example 5.)**

49. $x^2 + 2x = -1$ a. $x^2 + 2x + 1 = 0$ b. 0   c. 1 rational solution

50. $12y - 9 = 4y^2$ a. $4y^2 - 12y + 9 = 0$ b. 0   c. 1 rational solution

51. $19m^2 = 8m$ a. $19m^2 - 8m + 0 = 0$ b. 64   c. 2 rational solutions

52. $2n - 5n^2 = 0$ a. $5n^2 - 2n + 0 = 0$ b. 4   c. 2 rational solutions

53. $5p^2 - 21 = 0$ a. $5p^2 + 0p - 21 = 0$ b. 420   c. 2 irrational solutions

54. $3k^2 = 7$ a. $3k^2 + 0k - 7 = 0$ b. 84   c. 2 irrational solutions

55. $4n(n - 2) - 5n(n - 1) = 4$ a. $n^2 + 3n + 4 = 0$ b. −7   c. 2 imaginary solutions

56. $(2x + 1)(x - 3) = -9$ a. $2x^2 - 5x + 6 = 0$ b. −23   c. 2 imaginary solutions

For Exercises 57–62, determine the discriminant. Then use the discriminant to determine the number of x-intercepts for the function.

57. $f(x) = x^2 - 6x + 5$ Discriminant: 16; two x-intercepts

58. $g(x) = -x^2 - 4x - 3$ Discriminant: 4; two x-intercepts

59. $h(x) = 4x^2 + 12x + 9$ Discriminant: 0; one x-intercept

60. $k(x) = 25x^2 - 10x + 1$ Discriminant: 0; one x-intercept

61. $p(x) = 2x^2 + 3x + 6$ Discriminant: −39; no x-intercepts

62. $m(x) = 3x^2 + 4x + 7$ Discriminant: −68; no x-intercepts

For Exercises 63–68, find the x- and y-intercepts of the quadratic function. **(See Examples 6–7.)**

63. $f(x) = x^2 - 5x + 3$ x-intercepts: $\left(\dfrac{5 + \sqrt{13}}{2}, 0\right), \left(\dfrac{5 - \sqrt{13}}{2}, 0\right)$; y-intercept: $(0, 3)$

64. $g(x) = 2x^2 + 7x + 2$ x-intercepts: $\left(\dfrac{-7 - \sqrt{33}}{4}, 0\right), \left(\dfrac{-7 + \sqrt{33}}{4}, 0\right)$; y-intercept: $(0, 2)$

65. $g(x) = -x^2 + x - 1$ x-intercepts: none; y-intercept: $(0, -1)$

66. $f(x) = 2x^2 + x + 5$ x-intercepts: none; y-intercept: $(0, 5)$

67. $p(x) = 2x^2 + 5x - 2$ x-intercepts: $\left(\dfrac{-5 - \sqrt{41}}{4}, 0\right), \left(\dfrac{-5 + \sqrt{41}}{4}, 0\right)$; y-intercept: $(0, -2)$

68. $h(x) = 3x^2 + 2x - 2$ x-intercepts: $\left(\dfrac{-1 - \sqrt{7}}{3}, 0\right), \left(\dfrac{-1 + \sqrt{7}}{3}, 0\right)$; y-intercept: $(0, -2)$

 Writing   Translating Expression   Geometry   Scientific Calculator   Video   NS&E

Concept 5: Mixed Review: Methods to Solve a Quadratic Equation

For Exercises 69–86, solve the quadratic equation by using any method. **(See Examples 8–11.)**

69. $a^2 + 3a + 4 = 0$ $\left\{-\dfrac{3}{2} \pm \dfrac{\sqrt{7}}{2}i\right\}$

70. $4z^2 + 7z = 0$ $\left\{0, -\dfrac{7}{4}\right\}$

71. $(x - 2)^2 + 2x^2 - 13x = 10$ $\left\{-\dfrac{1}{3}, 6\right\}$

72. $(x - 3)^2 + 3x^2 - 5x = 12$ $\left\{-\dfrac{1}{4}, 3\right\}$

73. $4y^2 + 8y - 5 = 0$ $\left\{-\dfrac{5}{2}, \dfrac{1}{2}\right\}$

74. $k^2 - 4k = -13$ $\{2 \pm 3i\}$

75. $\left(x + \dfrac{1}{2}\right)^2 + 4 = 0$ $\left\{-\dfrac{1}{2} \pm 2i\right\}$

76. $(2y + 3)^2 = 9$ $\{0, -3\}$

77. $2y(y - 3) = -1$ $\left\{\dfrac{3 \pm \sqrt{7}}{2}\right\}$

78. $w(w - 5) = 4$ $\left\{\dfrac{5 \pm \sqrt{41}}{2}\right\}$

79. $(2t + 5)(t - 1) = (t - 3)(t + 8)$ $\{1 + 3i\sqrt{2}\}$

80. $(b - 1)(b + 4) = (3b + 2)(b + 1)$ $\left\{-\dfrac{1}{2} \pm \dfrac{\sqrt{11}}{2}i\right\}$

81. $\dfrac{1}{8}x^2 - \dfrac{1}{2}x + \dfrac{1}{4} = 0$ $\{2 \pm \sqrt{2}\}$

82. $\dfrac{1}{6}x^2 - \dfrac{1}{2}x + \dfrac{1}{4} = 0$ $\left\{\dfrac{3 \pm \sqrt{3}}{2}\right\}$

83. $32z^2 - 20z - 3 = 0$ $\left\{-\dfrac{1}{8}, \dfrac{3}{4}\right\}$

84. $8k^2 \quad 14k + 3 = 0$ $\left\{\dfrac{3}{2}, \dfrac{1}{4}\right\}$

85. $3p^2 - 27 = 0$ $\{3, -3\}$

86. $5h^2 - 120 = 0$ $\{\pm 2\sqrt{6}\}$

Sometimes students shy away from completing the square and using the square root property to solve a quadratic equation. However, sometimes this process leads to a simple solution. For Exercises 87–88, solve the equations two ways.

a. Solve the equation by completing the square and applying the square root property.

b. Solve the equation by applying the quadratic formula.

c. Which technique was easier for you?

87. $x^2 + 6x = 5$
a. $\{-3 \pm \sqrt{14}\}$
b. $\{-3 \pm \sqrt{14}\}$
c. Answers will vary.

88. $x^2 - 10x = -27$
a. $\{5 \pm i\sqrt{2}\}$
b. $\{5 \pm i\sqrt{2}\}$
c. Answers will vary.

Expanding Your Skills

89. An artist has been commissioned to make a stained glass window in the shape of a regular octagon. The octagon must fit inside an 18-in. square space. See the figure.

a. Let x represent the length of each side of the octagon. Verify that the legs of the small triangles formed by the corners of the square can be expressed as $\dfrac{18 - x}{2}$.

b. Use the Pythagorean theorem to set up an equation in terms of x that represents the relationship between the legs of the triangle and the hypotenuse. $x^2 = \left(\dfrac{18 - x}{2}\right)^2 + \left(\dfrac{18 - x}{2}\right)^2$

c. Simplify the equation by clearing parentheses and clearing fractions. $x^2 + 36x - 324 = 0$

d. Solve the resulting quadratic equation by using the quadratic formula. Use a calculator and round your answers to the nearest tenth of an inch. 7.5 in., −43.5 in.

e. There are two solutions for x. Which one is appropriate and why? 7.5 in. is appropriate; the other solution is negative.

 Writing   Translating Expression   Geometry   Scientific Calculator   Video NS&E

90. The maximum slope of a handicap ramp is $\frac{1}{12}$. This means that for every 1 in. of rise, the run is 12 in. A ramp needs to be built from the parking area of an apartment complex to the front door of an apartment. There is a total rise of 42 in. from the parking area to the door. The management makes two ramps with a landing area between the ramps.

   a. Assume that the ramps have a slope $\frac{1}{12}$. Find the values of x and y using similar triangles.
      $x = 360$ in. and $y = 144$ in.
   b. Find the length of each ramp (pictured in red). Round to the nearest tenth of an inch.
      The ramps are 361.2 in. and 144.5 in.

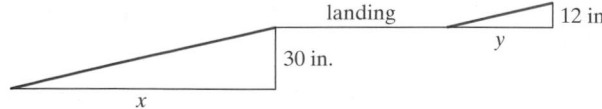

Graphing Calculator Exercises

91. Graph $Y_1 = x^3 - 27$. Compare the x-intercepts with the solutions to the equation $x^3 - 27 = 0$ found in Exercise 35.

92. Graph $Y_1 = 64x^3 + 1$. Compare the x-intercepts with the solutions to the equation $64x^3 + 1 = 0$ found in Exercise 36.

93. Graph $Y_1 = 3x^3 - 6x^2 + 6x$. Compare the x-intercepts with the solutions to the equation $3x^3 - 6x^2 + 6x = 0$ found in Exercise 37.

94. Graph $Y_1 = 5x^3 + 5x^2 + 10x$. Compare the x-intercepts with the solutions to the equation $5x^3 + 5x^2 + 10x = 0$ found in Exercise 38.

Section 11.3   Equations in Quadratic Form

Concepts

1. Solving Equations by Using Substitution
2. Solving Equations Reducible to a Quadratic

1. Solving Equations by Using Substitution

We have learned to solve a variety of different types of equations, including linear, radical, rational, and polynomial equations. Sometimes, however, it is necessary to use a quadratic equation as a tool to solve other types of equations.

In Example 1, we will solve the equation $(2x^2 - 5)^2 - 16(2x^2 - 5) + 39 = 0$. Notice that the terms in the equation are written in descending order by degree. Furthermore, the first two terms have the same base, $2x^2 - 5$, and the exponent on the first term is exactly double the exponent on the second term. The third term is a constant. An equation in this pattern is called **quadratic in form**.

$$\overset{\text{exponent is double}}{\overbrace{\qquad}} \qquad \overset{\text{third term is constant}}{\Big\downarrow}$$
$$(2x^2 - 5)^2 - 16(2x^2 - 5)^1 + 39 = 0.$$

To solve this equation we will use substitution as demonstrated in Example 1.

Classroom Example: p. 802, Exercise 12

Example 1   Solving an Equation in Quadratic Form

Solve the equation. $(2x^2 - 5)^2 - 16(2x^2 - 5) + 39 = 0$

Solution:

$(2x^2 - 5)^2 - 16(2x^2 - 5) + 39 = 0$ Once the substitution is made, the equation becomes quadratic in the variable u.

Substitute $u = (2x^2 - 5)$.

$u^2 \quad - \quad 16u \quad + 39 = 0$ The equation is in the form $au^2 + bu + c = 0$.

 Writing   Translating Expression   Geometry   Scientific Calculator   Video   NS&E

$$(u - 13)(u - 3) = 0 \qquad \text{Factor.}$$

$$u = 13 \quad \text{or} \quad u = 3 \qquad \text{Apply the zero product rule.}$$

Reverse substitute.

$$2x^2 - 5 = 13 \quad \text{or} \quad 2x^2 - 5 = 3 \qquad \text{Reverse substitute.}$$

$$2x^2 = 18 \quad \text{or} \quad 2x^2 = 8$$

$$x^2 = 9 \quad \text{or} \quad x^2 = 4 \qquad \text{Write the equations in the form } x^2 = k.$$

$$x = \pm\sqrt{9} \quad \text{or} \quad x = \pm\sqrt{4} \qquad \text{Apply the square root property.}$$

$$= \pm 3 \quad \text{or} \quad = \pm 2$$

The solution set is $\{3, -3, 2, -2\}$.   All solutions check in the original equation.

Skill Practice Solve the equation.

1. $(3t^2 - 10)^2 + 5(3t^2 - 10) - 14 = 0$

Avoiding Mistakes

When using substitution, it is critical to reverse substitute to solve the equation in terms of the original variable.

For an equation written in descending order, notice that u was set equal to the variable factor on the middle term. This is generally the case.

Example 2   Solving an Equation in Quadratic Form

Solve the equation. $p^{2/3} - 2p^{1/3} = 8$

Classroom Example: p. 802, Exercise 16

Solution:

$$p^{2/3} - 2p^{1/3} = 8$$

$$p^{2/3} - 2p^{1/3} - 8 = 0 \qquad \text{Set the equation equal to zero.}$$

$$(p^{1/3})^2 - 2(p^{1/3})^1 - 8 = 0 \qquad \text{Make the substitution } u = p^{1/3}.$$

Substitute $u = p^{1/3}$.

$$u^2 \quad - \quad 2u \quad - 8 = 0 \qquad \begin{array}{l}\text{Then the equation is in the form} \\ au^2 + bu + c = 0.\end{array}$$

$$(u - 4)(u + 2) = 0 \qquad \text{Factor.}$$

$$u = 4 \quad \text{or} \quad u = -2 \qquad \text{Apply the zero product rule.}$$

Reverse substitute.

$$p^{1/3} = 4 \quad \text{or} \quad p^{1/3} = -2$$

$$\sqrt[3]{p} = 4 \quad \text{or} \quad \sqrt[3]{p} = -2 \qquad \begin{array}{l}\text{The equations are radical} \\ \text{equations.}\end{array}$$

$$(\sqrt[3]{p})^3 = (4)^3 \quad \text{or} \quad (\sqrt[3]{p})^3 = (-2)^3 \qquad \text{Cube both sides.}$$

$$p = 64 \quad \text{or} \quad p = -8$$

The solution set is $\{64, -8\}$.   All solutions check in the original equation.

Skill Practice Solve the equation.

2. $y^{2/3} - y^{1/3} = 12$

Answers

1. $\{1, -1, 2, -2\}$ **2.** $\{64, -27\}$

Classroom Example: p. 802,
Exercise 20

Example 3 Solving an Equation in Quadratic Form

Solve the equation. $\quad x - \sqrt{x} - 12 = 0$

Solution:

The equation can be solved by first isolating the radical and then squaring both sides (this is left as an exercise—see Exercise 24). However, this equation is also quadratic in form. By writing $\sqrt{x}$ as $x^{1/2}$, we see that the exponent on the first term is exactly double the exponent on the middle term.

$$x^1 - x^{1/2} - 12 = 0$$

$$(x^{1/2})^2 - (x^{1/2})^1 - 12 = 0 \qquad \text{Let } u = x^{1/2}.$$

$$u^2 - u - 12 = 0$$

$$(u - 4)(u + 3) = 0 \qquad \text{Factor.}$$

$$u = 4 \quad \text{or} \quad u = -3 \qquad \text{Solve for } u.$$

$$x^{1/2} = 4 \quad \text{or} \quad x^{1/2} = -3 \qquad \text{Reverse substitute.}$$

$$\sqrt{x} = 4 \quad \text{or} \quad \sqrt{x} \ne -3 \qquad \text{Solve each equation for } x. \text{ Recall that the}$$

$$x = 16 \qquad\qquad\qquad\qquad \text{principal square root of a number cannot}$$
$$\text{equal } -3.$$

The solution set is $\{16\}$. $\qquad$ The value 16 checks in the original equation.

> **Avoiding Mistakes**
>
> Recall from Section 10.7 that when each side of an equation is raised to an even power, we must check the potential solutions.

Skill Practice Solve the equation.

3. $z - \sqrt{z} - 2 = 0$

2. Solving Equations Reducible to a Quadratic

Some equations are reducible to a quadratic equation. In Example 4, we solve a polynomial equation by factoring. The resulting factors are quadratic.

Classroom Example: p. 802,
Exercise 26

Example 4 Solving a Polynomial Equation

Solve the equation. $\quad 4x^4 + 7x^2 - 2 = 0$

Solution:

$$4x^4 + 7x^2 - 2 = 0 \qquad \text{This is a polynomial equation.}$$

$$(4x^2 - 1)(x^2 + 2) = 0 \qquad \text{Factor.}$$

$$4x^2 - 1 = 0 \text{ or } x^2 + 2 = 0 \qquad \text{Set each factor equal to zero. Notice}$$
$$\text{that the two equations are quadratic.}$$

$$x^2 = \frac{1}{4} \qquad \text{or} \quad x^2 = -2 \qquad \text{Each can be solved by the square}$$
$$\text{root property.}$$

$$x = \pm\sqrt{\frac{1}{4}} \quad \text{or} \quad x = \pm\sqrt{-2} \qquad \text{Apply the square root property.}$$

$$x = \pm\frac{1}{2} \qquad \text{or} \quad x = \pm i\sqrt{2} \qquad \text{Simplify the radicals.}$$

The solution set is $\left\{ \dfrac{1}{2}, -\dfrac{1}{2}, i\sqrt{2}, -i\sqrt{2} \right\}$.

Skill Practice Solve the equation.

4. $9x^4 + 35x^2 - 4 = 0$

Answers

3. $\{4\}$ (The value 1 does not check.)

4. $\left\{ \pm\dfrac{1}{3}, \pm 2i \right\}$

Example 5 Solving a Rational Equation

Classroom Example: p. 803, Exercise 34

Solve the equation. $\dfrac{3y}{y+2} - \dfrac{2}{y-1} = 1$

Solution:

$\dfrac{3y}{y+2} - \dfrac{2}{y-1} = 1$ 　　This is a rational equation. The LCD is $(y+2)(y-1)$.
Also note that the restrictions on y are $y \neq -2$ and $y \neq 1$.

$\left(\dfrac{3y}{y+2} - \dfrac{2}{y-1}\right) \cdot (y+2)(y-1) = 1 \cdot (y+2)(y-1)$ 　　Multiply both sides by the LCD.

$\dfrac{3y}{\cancel{y+2}} \cdot \cancel{(y+2)}(y-1) - \dfrac{2}{\cancel{y-1}} \cdot (y+2)\cancel{(y-1)} = 1 \cdot (y+2)(y-1)$

$3y(y-1) - 2(y+2) = (y+2)(y-1)$ 　　Clear fractions.

$3y^2 - 3y - 2y - 4 = y^2 - y + 2y - 2$ 　　Apply the distributive property.

$3y^2 - 5y - 4 = y^2 + y - 2$ 　　The equation is quadratic.

$2y^2 - 6y - 2 = 0$ 　　Write the equation in descending order.

$\dfrac{2y^2}{2} - \dfrac{6y}{2} - \dfrac{2}{2} = \dfrac{0}{2}$ 　　Each coefficient in the equation is divisible by 2. Therefore, if we divide both sides by 2, the coefficients in the equation are smaller. This will make it easier to apply the quadratic formula.

$y^2 - 3y - 1 = 0$

$y = \dfrac{(3) \pm \sqrt{(-3)^2 - 4(1)(-1)}}{2(1)}$ 　　Apply the quadratic formula.

$= \dfrac{3 \pm \sqrt{9+4}}{2}$

$= \dfrac{3 \pm \sqrt{13}}{2}$ ⟨ $y = \dfrac{3 + \sqrt{13}}{2}$

$y = \dfrac{3 - \sqrt{13}}{2}$ 　　Both solutions check.

The solution set is $\left\{ \dfrac{3 + \sqrt{13}}{2}, \dfrac{3 - \sqrt{13}}{2} \right\}$.

Skill Practice Solve the equation.

5. $\dfrac{t}{2t-1} - \dfrac{1}{t+4} = 1$

Answer

5. $\left\{ \dfrac{-5 \pm 3\sqrt{5}}{2} \right\}$

Section 11.3 Practice Exercises

Study Skills Exercise

1. What is meant by an equation in **quadratic form**?

An equation is in quadratic form if it can be written as $au^2 + bu + c = 0$ where u represents an algebraic expression.

Review Exercises

For Exercises 2–7, solve the quadratic equations.

2. $16 = (2x - 3)^2$ $\left\{\frac{7}{2}, -\frac{1}{2}\right\}$

3. $\left(x - \frac{3}{2}\right)^2 = \frac{7}{4}$ $\left\{\frac{3}{2} \pm \frac{\sqrt{7}}{2}\right\}$

4. $n(n - 6) = -13$ $\{3 \pm 2i\}$

5. $x(x + 8) = -16$ $\{-4\}$

6. $6k^2 + 7k = 6$ $\left\{\frac{-7 \pm \sqrt{193}}{12}\right\}$

7. $2x^2 - 8x - 44 = 0$ $\{2 \pm \sqrt{26}\}$

Concept 1: Solving Equations by Using Substitution

8. a. Solve the quadratic equation by factoring. $u^2 - 2u - 24 = 0$ $\{6, -4\}$

   b. Solve the equation by using substitution. $(x - 5)^2 - 2(x - 5) - 24 = 0$ $\{11, 1\}$

9. a. Solve the quadratic equation by factoring. $u^2 + 10u + 24 = 0$ $\{-4, -6\}$

   b. Solve the equation by using substitution. $(y^2 + 5y)^2 + 10(y^2 + 5y) + 24 = 0$ $\{-4, -1, -2, -3\}$

10. a. Solve the quadratic equation by factoring. $u^2 - 2u - 35 = 0$ $\{7, -5\}$

   b. Solve the equation by using substitution. $(w^2 - 6w)^2 - 2(w^2 - 6w) - 35 = 0$ $\{7, -1, 5, 1\}$

For Exercises 11–24, solve the equation by using substitution. **(See Examples 1–3.)**

11. $(x^2 - 2x)^2 + 2(x^2 - 2x) = 3$ $\{1 \pm i\sqrt{2}, 1 \pm \sqrt{2}\}$

12. $(x^2 + x)^2 - 8(x^2 + x) = -12$ $\{-2, 1, -3, 2\}$

13. $(y^2 - 4y)^2 - (y^2 - 4y) = 20$ $\{5, -1, 2\}$

14. $(w^2 - 2w)^2 - 11(w^2 - 2w) = -24$ $\{4, -2, 3, -1\}$

15. $m^{2/3} - m^{1/3} - 6 = 0$ $\{27, -8\}$

16. $2n^{2/3} + 7n^{1/3} - 15 = 0$ $\left\{\frac{27}{8}, -125\right\}$

17. $2t^{2/5} + 7t^{1/5} + 3 = 0$ $\left\{-\frac{1}{32}, -243\right\}$

18. $p^{2/5} + p^{1/5} - 2 = 0$ $\{-32, 1\}$

19. $y + 6\sqrt{y} = 16$ $\{4\}$ (The value 64 does not check.)

20. $p - 8\sqrt{p} = -15$ $\{25, 9\}$

21. $2x + 3\sqrt{x} - 2 = 0$ $\left\{\frac{1}{4}\right\}$ (The value 4 does not check.)

22. $3t + 5\sqrt{t} - 2 = 0$ $\left\{\frac{1}{9}\right\}$ (The value 4 does not check.)

23. $16\left(\frac{x + 6}{4}\right)^2 + 8\left(\frac{x + 6}{4}\right) + 1 = 0$ $\{-7\}$

24. $9\left(\frac{x + 3}{2}\right)^2 - 6\left(\frac{x + 3}{2}\right) + 1 = 0$ $\left\{-\frac{7}{3}\right\}$

25. In Example 3, we solved the equation $x - \sqrt{x} - 12 = 0$ by using substitution. Now solve this equation by first isolating the radical and then squaring both sides. Don't forget to check the potential solutions in the original equation. Do you obtain the same solution as in Example 3? $\{16\}$; yes

Concept 2: Solving Equations Reducible to a Quadratic

For Exercises 26–36, solve the equations. **(See Examples 4–5.)**

26. $t^4 + t^2 - 12 = 0$ $\{\pm\sqrt{3}, \pm 2i\}$

27. $w^4 + 4w^2 - 45 = 0$ $\{\pm 3i, \pm\sqrt{5}\}$

28. $x^2(9x^2 + 7) = 2$ $\left\{\pm\frac{\sqrt{2}}{3}, \pm i\right\}$

29. $y^2(4y^2 + 17) = 15$ $\left\{\pm\frac{\sqrt{3}}{2}, \pm i\sqrt{5}\right\}$

30. $\frac{y}{10} - 1 = -\frac{12}{5y}$ $\{4, 6\}$

31. $1 + \frac{5}{x} = -\frac{3}{x^2}$ $\left\{\frac{-5 \pm \sqrt{13}}{2}\right\}$

32. $\dfrac{x+5}{x} + \dfrac{x}{2} = \dfrac{x+19}{4x}$ $\left\{-1, -\dfrac{1}{2}\right\}$ **33.** $\dfrac{3x}{x+1} - \dfrac{2}{x-3} = 1$ $\left\{\dfrac{9 \pm \sqrt{73}}{4}\right\}$ **34.** $\dfrac{2t}{t-3} - \dfrac{1}{t+4} = 1$ $\{-3 \pm i\sqrt{6}\}$

35. $\dfrac{x}{2x-1} = \dfrac{1}{x-2}$ $\{2 \pm \sqrt{3}\}$ **36.** $\dfrac{z}{3z+2} = \dfrac{2}{z+1}$ $\left\{\dfrac{5 \pm \sqrt{41}}{2}\right\}$

Mixed Exercises

For Exercises 37–60, solve the equations.

37. $x^4 - 16 = 0$ $\{\pm 2, \pm 2i\}$ **38.** $t^4 - 625 = 0$ $\{\pm 5, \pm 5i\}$ **39.** $(4x+5)^2 + 3(4x+5) + 2 = 0$
$\left\{-\dfrac{7}{4}, -\dfrac{3}{2}\right\}$

40. $2(5x+3)^2 - (5x+3) - 28 = 0$ **41.** $4m^4 - 9m^2 + 2 = 0$ **42.** $x^4 - 7x^2 + 12 = 0$
$\left\{-\dfrac{13}{10}, \dfrac{1}{5}\right\}$ $\left\{\dfrac{1}{2}, -\dfrac{1}{2}, \sqrt{2}, -\sqrt{2}\right\}$ $\{2, -2, \sqrt{3}, -\sqrt{3}\}$

43. $x^6 - 9x^3 + 8 = 0$ **44.** $x^6 - 26x^3 - 27 = 0$ **45.** $\sqrt{x^2 + 20} = 3\sqrt{x}$ $\{5, 4\}$
$\left\{2, 1, -1 \pm i\sqrt{3}, -\dfrac{1}{2} \pm \dfrac{\sqrt{3}}{2}i\right\}$ $\left\{3, -1, -\dfrac{3}{2} \pm \dfrac{3\sqrt{3}}{2}i, \dfrac{1}{2} \pm \dfrac{\sqrt{3}}{2}i\right\}$

46. $\sqrt{x^2 + 60} = 4\sqrt{x}$ $\{6, 10\}$ **47.** $\sqrt{4t+1} = t + 1$ $\{0, 2\}$ **48.** $\sqrt{t+10} = t + 4$
$\{-1\}$ (The value -6 does not check.)

49. $2\left(\dfrac{t-4}{3}\right)^2 - \left(\dfrac{t-4}{3}\right) - 3 = 0$ **50.** $\left(\dfrac{x+1}{5}\right)^2 - 3\left(\dfrac{x+1}{5}\right) - 10 = 0$ **51.** $x^{2/3} + x^{1/3} = 20$ $\{64, -125\}$
$\left\{1, \dfrac{17}{2}\right\}$ $\{24, -11\}$

52. $x^{2/5} - 3x^{1/5} = -2$ $\{32, 1\}$ **53.** $m^4 + 2m^2 - 8 = 0$ $\{\pm\sqrt{2}, \pm 2i\}$ **54.** $2c^4 + c^2 - 1 = 0$ $\left\{\pm\dfrac{\sqrt{2}}{2}, \pm i\right\}$

55. $a^3 + 16a - a^2 - 16 = 0$ $\{\pm 4i, 1\}$ **56.** $b^3 + 9b - b^2 - 9 = 0$ $\{\pm 3i, 1\}$ **57.** $x^3 + 5x - 4x^2 - 20 = 0$
(*Hint:* Factor by grouping first.) $\{4, \pm i\sqrt{5}\}$

58. $y^3 + 8y - 3y^2 - 24 = 0$ **59.** $\left(\dfrac{2}{x-3}\right)^2 + 8\left(\dfrac{2}{x-3}\right) + 12 = 0$ **60.** $\left(\dfrac{5}{x+1}\right)^2 - 6\left(\dfrac{5}{x+1}\right) - 16 = 0$
$\{3, \pm 2i\sqrt{2}\}$ $\left\{\dfrac{8}{3}, 2\right\}$ $\left\{-\dfrac{7}{2}, -\dfrac{3}{8}\right\}$

Graphing Calculator Exercises

61. **a.** Solve the equation $x^4 + 4x^2 + 4 = 0$. $\{\pm i\sqrt{2}\}$

   b. How many solutions are real and how many solutions are imaginary?
   Two imaginary solutions; no real solutions
   c. How many x-intercepts do you anticipate for the function defined by $y = x^4 + 4x^2 + 4$?   No x-intercepts

   d. Graph $Y_1 = x^4 + 4x^2 + 4$ on a standard viewing window.

62. **a.** Solve the equation $x^4 - 2x^2 + 1 = 0$. $\{1, -1\}$

   b. How many solutions are real and how many solutions are imaginary?
   Two real solutions; no imaginary solutions
   c. How many x-intercepts do you anticipate for the function defined by $y = x^4 - 2x^2 + 1$?   Two x-intercepts

   d. Graph $Y_1 = x^4 - 2x^2 + 1$ on a standard viewing window.

63. **a.** Solve the equation $x^4 - x^3 - 6x^2 = 0$. $\{0, 3, -2\}$

   b. How many solutions are real and how many solutions are imaginary?
   Three real solutions; no imaginary solutions
   c. How many x-intercepts do you anticipate for the function defined by $y = x^4 - x^3 - 6x^2$?   Three x-intercepts

   d. Graph $Y_1 = x^4 - x^3 - 6x^2$ on a standard viewing window.

64. **a.** Solve the equation $x^4 - 10x^2 + 9 = 0$. $\{\pm 1, \pm 3\}$

   b. How many solutions are real and how many solutions are imaginary?
   Four real solutions; no imaginary solutions
   c. How many x-intercepts do you anticipate for the function defined by $y = x^4 - 10x^2 + 9$?   Four x-intercepts

   d. Graph $Y_1 = x^4 - 10x^2 + 9$ on a standard viewing window.

 Writing   Translating Expression   Geometry   Scientific Calculator   Video   NS&E

Problem Recognition Exercises

Quadratic and Quadratic Type Equations

For Exercises 1–4, solve each equation by

a. Completing the square and applying the square root property.

b. Using the quadratic formula.

1. $x^2 + 10x + 3 = 0$
$\{-5 \pm \sqrt{22}\}$

2. $v^2 - 16v + 5 = 0$
$\{8 \pm \sqrt{59}\}$

3. $3t^2 + t + 4 = 0$
$\left\{-\dfrac{1}{6} \pm \dfrac{\sqrt{47}}{6}i\right\}$

4. $4y^2 + 3y + 5 = 0$
$\left\{-\dfrac{3}{8} \pm \dfrac{\sqrt{71}}{8}i\right\}$

In Exercises 5–24, we have presented all types of equations that you have learned up to this point. For each equation,

a. First determine the type of equation that is presented. Choose from: linear equation, quadratic equation, quadratic in form, rational equation, or radical equation.

b. Solve the equation by using a suitable method.

5. $t^2 + 5t - 14 = 0$ a. Quadratic
b. $\{2, -7\}$

6. $a^2 - 9a + 20 = 0$ a. Quadratic
b. $\{4, 5\}$

7. $a^4 - 10a^2 + 9 = 0$ a. Quadratic form
b. $\{-3, -1, 1, 3\}$

8. $x^4 - 3x^2 - 4 = 0$
a. Quadratic form
b. $\{2, -2, i, -i\}$

9. $x - 3x^{1/2} - 4 = 0$
a. Quadratic form (or radical)
b. $\{16\}$ (The value 1 does not check.)

10. $x^2 - 9x - 2 = 0$ a. Quadratic
b. $\left\{\dfrac{9 \pm \sqrt{89}}{2}\right\}$

11. $8b(b + 1) + 2(3b - 4) = 4b(2b + 3)$
a. Linear
b. $\{4\}$

12. $6x(x + 1) - 3(x + 4) = 3x(2x + 5)$
a. Linear
b. $\{-1\}$

13. $5a(a + 6) = 10(3a - 1)$
a. Quadratic
b. $\{\pm i\sqrt{2}\}$

14. $4x(x + 3) = 6(2x - 4)$
a. Quadratic
b. $\{\pm i\sqrt{6}\}$

15. $\dfrac{t}{t + 5} + \dfrac{3}{t - 4} = \dfrac{17}{t^2 + t - 20}$
a. Rational
b. $\{2, -1\}$

16. $\dfrac{v}{v + 4} + \dfrac{12}{v^2 + 7v + 12} = \dfrac{5}{v + 3}$
a. Rational
b. $\{-2, 4\}$

17. $c^2 - 20c - 1 = 0$
a. Quadratic
b. $\{10 \pm \sqrt{101}\}$

18. $d^2 + 18d + 4 = 0$
a. Quadratic
b. $\{-9 \pm \sqrt{77}\}$

19. $2u(u - 3) = 4(2 - u)$ a. Quadratic
b. $\left\{\dfrac{1 \pm \sqrt{17}}{2}\right\}$

20. $3y(y + 2) = 9(y + 1)$ a. Quadratic
b. $\left\{\dfrac{1 \pm \sqrt{13}}{2}\right\}$

21. $\sqrt{2b + 3} = b$ a. Radical
b. $\{3\}$ (The value -1 does not check.)

22. $\sqrt{5t + 6} = t$
a. Radical
b. $\{6\}$ (The value -1 does not check.)

23. $x^{2/3} + 2x^{1/3} - 15 = 0$
a. Quadratic form (or radical)
b. $\{-125, 27\}$

24. $y^{2/3} + 5y^{1/3} + 4 = 0$
a. Quadratic form (or radical)
b. $\{-64, -1\}$

Section 11.4 | Graphs of Quadratic Functions

Concepts

1. Quadratic Functions of the Form $f(x) = x^2 + k$

2. Quadratic Functions of the Form $f(x) = (x - h)^2$

3. Quadratic Functions of the Form $f(x) = ax^2$

4. Quadratic Functions of the Form $f(x) = a(x - h)^2 + k$

In Section 8.3, we defined a quadratic function as a function of the form $f(x) = ax^2 + bx + c$ ($a \neq 0$). We also learned that the graph of a quadratic function is a **parabola**. In this section, we will learn how to graph parabolas.

A parabola opens upward if $a > 0$ (Figure 11-3) and opens downward if $a < 0$ (Figure 11-4). If a parabola opens upward, the **vertex** is the lowest point on the graph. If a parabola opens downward, the **vertex** is the highest point on the graph. The **axis of symmetry** is the vertical line that passes through the vertex.

Figure 11-3

Figure 11-4

 Writing   Translating Expression   Geometry   Scientific Calculator   Video   NS&E

1. Quadratic Functions of the Form $f(x) = x^2 + k$

One technique for graphing a function is to plot a sufficient number of points on the graph until the general shape and defining characteristics can be determined. Then sketch a curve through the points.

Example 1 **Graphing Quadratic Functions of the Form $f(x) = x^2 + k$**

Classroom Example: p. 813, Exercise 12

Graph the functions f, g, and h on the same coordinate system.

$$f(x) = x^2 \qquad g(x) = x^2 + 1 \qquad h(x) = x^2 - 2$$

Solution:

Several function values for f, g, and h are shown in Table 11-1 for selected values of x. The corresponding graphs are pictured in Figure 11-5.

Table 11-1

x	$f(x) = x^2$	$g(x) = x^2 + 1$	$h(x) = x^2 - 2$
-3	9	10	7
-2	4	5	2
-1	1	2	-1
0	0	1	-2
1	1	2	-1
2	4	5	2
3	9	10	7

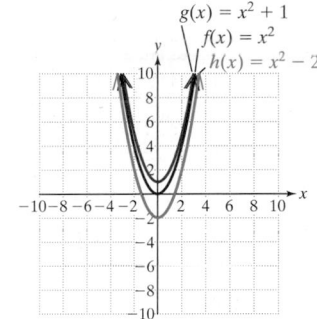

Figure 11-5

Skill Practice Refer to the graph of $f(x) = x^2 + k$ to determine the value of k.

1.

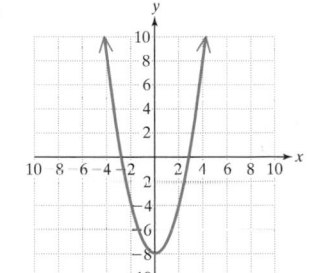

Notice that the graphs of $g(x) = x^2 + 1$ and $h(x) = x^2 - 2$ take on the same shape as $f(x) = x^2$. However, the y values of g are 1 greater than the y values of f. Hence, the graph of $g(x) = x^2 + 1$ is the same as the graph of $f(x) = x^2$ shifted *up* 1 unit. Likewise the y-values of h are 2 less than those of f. The graph of $h(x) = x^2 - 2$ is the same as the graph of $f(x) = x^2$ shifted *down* 2 units.

The functions in Example 1 illustrate the following properties of quadratic functions of the form $f(x) = x^2 + k$.

Answer

1. $k = -8$

PROPERTY Graphs of $f(x) = x^2 + k$

If $k > 0$, then the graph of $f(x) = x^2 + k$ is the same as the graph of $y = x^2$ shifted *up* k units.

If $k < 0$, then the graph of $f(x) = x^2 + k$ is the same as the graph of $y = x^2$ shifted *down* $|k|$ units.

Calculator Connections

Try experimenting with a graphing calculator by graphing functions of the form $y = x^2 + k$ for several values of k.

Classroom Example: p. 813,
Exercise 14

Example 2 Graphing Quadratic Functions of the Form $f(x) = x^2 + k$

Sketch the functions defined by

a. $m(x) = x^2 - 4$ **b.** $n(x) = x^2 + \dfrac{7}{2}$

TIP: For more accuracy in the graph, plot one or two points near the vertex and use the symmetry of the curve to find additional points on the graph.

Solution:

a. $m(x) = x^2 - 4$

$m(x) = x^2 + (-4)$

Because $k = -4$, the graph is obtained by shifting the graph of $y = x^2$ down $|-4|$ units (Figure 11-6).

b. $n(x) = x^2 + \dfrac{7}{2}$

Because $k = \frac{7}{2}$, the graph is obtained by shifting the graph of $y = x^2$ up $\frac{7}{2}$ units (Figure 11-7).

Figure 11-6

Figure 11-7

Answer

2.

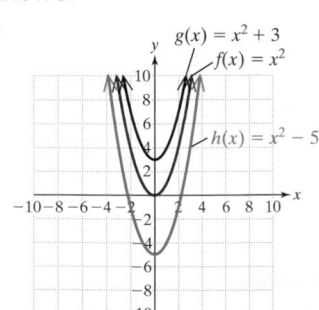

Skill Practice

2. Graph the functions f, g, and h on the same coordinate system.

$f(x) = x^2$ $g(x) = x^2 + 3$ $h(x) = x^2 - 5$

2. Quadratic Functions of the Form $f(x) = (x - h)^2$

The graph of $f(x) = x^2 + k$ represents a vertical shift (up or down) of the function $y = x^2$. Example 3 shows that functions of the form $f(x) = (x - h)^2$ represent a horizontal shift (left or right) of the function $y = x^2$.

Example 3 **Graphing Quadratic Functions of the Form**
$$f(x) = (x - h)^2$$

Classroom Example: p. 814, Exercise 20

Graph the functions $f, g,$ and h on the same coordinate system.
$$f(x) = x^2 \qquad g(x) = (x + 1)^2 \qquad h(x) = (x - 2)^2$$

Solution:

Several function values for $f, g,$ and h are shown in Table 11-2 for selected values of x. The corresponding graphs are pictured in Figure 11-8.

Table 11-2

x	$f(x) = x^2$	$g(x) = (x + 1)^2$	$h(x) = (x - 2)^2$
-4	16	9	36
-3	9	4	25
-2	4	1	16
-1	1	0	9
0	0	1	4
1	1	4	1
2	4	9	0
3	9	16	1
4	16	25	4
5	25	36	9

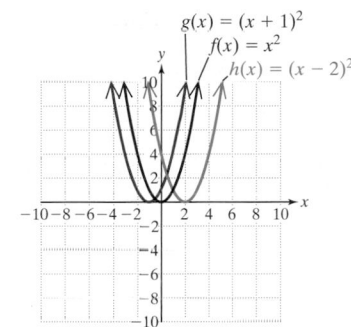

Figure 11-8

Skill Practice Refer to the graph of $f(x) = (x - h)^2$ to determine the value of h.

3.

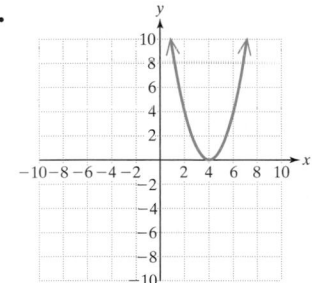

Example 3 illustrates the following properties of quadratic functions of the form $f(x) = (x - h)^2$.

Answer

3. $h = 4$

> **PROPERTY   Graphs of $f(x) = (x - h)^2$**
>
> If $h > 0$, then the graph of $f(x) = (x - h)^2$ is the same as the graph of $y = x^2$ shifted h units to the *right*.
>
> If $h < 0$, then the graph of $f(x) = (x - h)^2$ is the same as the graph of $y = x^2$ shifted $|h|$ units to the *left*.

From Example 3 we have

$$h(x) = (x - 2)^2 \qquad \text{and} \qquad g(x) = (x + 1)^2$$

$$g(x) = [x - (-1)]^2$$

$y = x^2$ shifted 2 units to the right $y = x^2$ shifted $|-1|$ unit to the left

Classroom Example: p. 814, Exercise 26

Example 4   Graphing Functions of the Form $f(x) = (x - h)^2$

Sketch the functions p and q.

a. $p(x) = (x - 7)^2$ **b.** $q(x) = (x + 1.6)^2$

Solution:

a. $p(x) = (x - 7)^2$

Because $h = 7 > 0$, shift the graph of $y = x^2$ to the *right* 7 units (Figure 11-9).

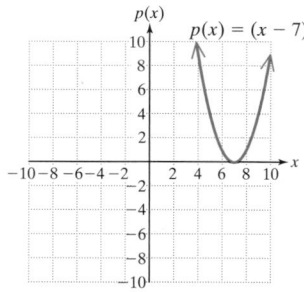

Figure 11-9

b. $q(x) = (x + 1.6)^2$

$q(x) = [x - (-1.6)]^2$

Because $h = -1.6 < 0$, shift the graph of $y = x^2$ to the *left* 1.6 units (Figure 11-10).

Figure 11-10

Answer

4.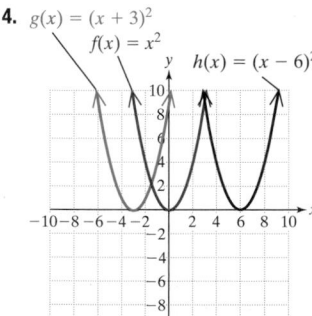

Skill Practice

4. Graph the functions $f, g,$ and h on the same coordinate system.

$$f(x) = x^2$$
$$g(x) = (x + 3)^2$$
$$h(x) = (x - 6)^2$$

3. Quadratic Functions of the Form $f(x) = ax^2$

Examples 5 and 6 investigate functions of the form $f(x) = ax^2$ $(a \neq 0)$.

Example 5 Graphing Functions of the Form $f(x) = ax^2$

Classroom Example: p. 814, Exercise 32

Graph the functions $f, g,$ and h on the same coordinate system.

$$f(x) = x^2 \qquad g(x) = 2x^2 \qquad h(x) = \frac{1}{2}x^2$$

Solution:

Several function values for $f, g,$ and h are shown in Table 11-3 for selected values of x. The corresponding graphs are pictured in Figure 11-11.

Table 11-3

x	$f(x) = x^2$	$g(x) = 2x^2$	$h(x) = \frac{1}{2}x^2$
-3	9	18	$\frac{9}{2}$
-2	4	8	2
-1	1	2	$\frac{1}{2}$
0	0	0	0
1	1	2	$\frac{1}{2}$
2	4	8	2
3	9	18	$\frac{9}{2}$

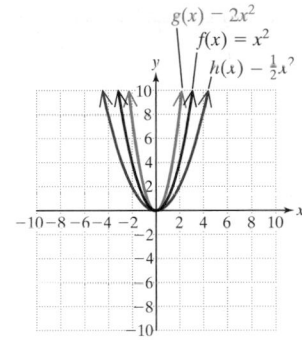

Figure 11-11

Skill Practice

5. Graph the functions $f, g,$ and h on the same coordinate system.

$f(x) = x^2$

$g(x) = 3x^2$

$h(x) = \dfrac{1}{3}x^2$

In Example 5, the function values defined by $g(x) = 2x^2$ are twice those of $f(x) = x^2$. The graph of $g(x) = 2x^2$ is the same as the graph of $f(x) = x^2$ *stretched vertically* by a factor of 2 (the graph appears narrower than $f(x) = x^2$).

In Example 5, the function values defined by $h(x) = \frac{1}{2}x^2$ are one-half those of $f(x) = x^2$. The graph of $h(x) = \frac{1}{2}x^2$ is the same as the graph of $f(x) = x^2$ *shrunk vertically* by a factor of $\frac{1}{2}$ (the graph appears wider than $f(x) = x^2$).

Answer

5.

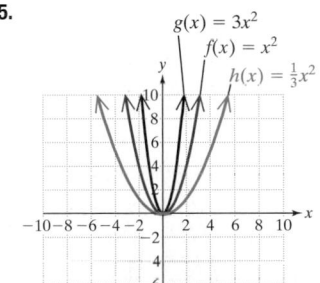

Example 6 Graphing Functions of the Form $f(x) = ax^2$

Graph the functions $f, g,$ and h on the same coordinate system.

$$f(x) = -x^2 \qquad g(x) = -3x^2 \qquad h(x) = -\frac{1}{3}x^2$$

Classroom Example: p. 814,
Exercise 34

Solution:

Several function values for f, g, and h are shown in Table 11-4 for selected values of x. The corresponding graphs are pictured in Figure 11-12.

Table 11-4

x	$f(x) = -x^2$	$g(x) = -3x^2$	$h(x) = -\frac{1}{3}x^2$
-3	-9	-27	-3
-2	-4	-12	$-\frac{4}{3}$
-1	-1	-3	$-\frac{1}{3}$
0	0	0	0
1	-1	-3	$-\frac{1}{3}$
2	-4	-12	$-\frac{4}{3}$
3	-9	-27	-3

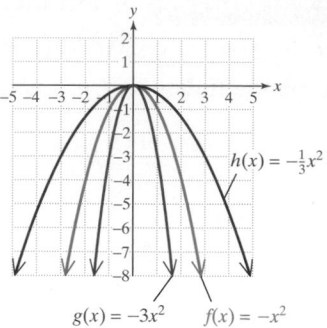

Figure 11-12

Skill Practice

6. Graph the functions f, g, and h on the same coordinate system.

$$f(x) = -x^2 \qquad g(x) = -2x^2 \qquad h(x) = -\frac{1}{2}x^2$$

Example 6 illustrates that if the coefficient of the square term is negative, the parabola opens downward. The graph of $g(x) = -3x^2$ is the same as the graph of $f(x) = -x^2$ with a *vertical stretch* by a factor of $|-3|$. The graph of $h(x) = -\frac{1}{3}x^2$ is the same as the graph of $f(x) = -x^2$ with a *vertical shrink* by a factor of $|-\frac{1}{3}|$.

PROPERTY   Graphs of $f(x) = ax^2$

1. If $a > 0$, the parabola opens upward. Furthermore,
   - If $0 < a < 1$, then the graph of $f(x) = ax^2$ is the same as the graph of $y = x^2$ with a *vertical shrink* by a factor of a.
   - If $a > 1$, then the graph of $f(x) = ax^2$ is the same as the graph of $y = x^2$ with a *vertical stretch* by a factor of a.

2. If $a < 0$, the parabola opens downward. Furthermore,
   - If $0 < |a| < 1$, then the graph of $f(x) = ax^2$ is the same as the graph of $y = -x^2$ with a *vertical shrink* by a factor of $|a|$.
   - If $|a| > 1$, then the graph of $f(x) = ax^2$ is the same as the graph of $y = -x^2$ with a *vertical stretch* by a factor of $|a|$.

Answer

6.

$f(x) = -x^2$
$g(x) = -2x^2$
$h(x) = -\frac{1}{2}x^2$

4. Quadratic Functions of the Form $f(x) = a(x - h)^2 + k$

We can summarize our findings from Examples 1–6 by graphing functions of the form $f(x) = a(x - h)^2 + k$ $(a \neq 0)$.

The graph of $y = x^2$ has its vertex at the origin $(0, 0)$. The graph of $f(x) = a(x - h)^2 + k$ is the same as the graph of $y = x^2$ shifted to the right or left h units and shifted up or down k units. Therefore, the vertex is shifted from $(0, 0)$ to (h, k). The axis of symmetry is the vertical line through the vertex. Therefore, the axis of symmetry must be the line $x = h$.

PROPERTY   Graphs of $f(x) = a(x - h)^2 + k$

1. The vertex is located at (h, k).
2. The axis of symmetry is the line $x = h$.
3. If $a > 0$, the parabola opens upward, and k is the **minimum value** of the function.
4. If $a < 0$, the parabola opens downward, and k is the **maximum value** of the function.

Example 7   **Graphing a Function of the Form $f(x) = a(x - h)^2 + k$**

Classroom Example: p. 816, Exercise 62

Given the function defined by

$$f(x) = 2(x - 3)^2 + 4$$

a. Identify the vertex.

b. Sketch the function.

c. Identify the axis of symmetry.

d. Identify the maximum or minimum value of the function.

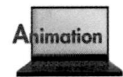

Solution:

a. The function is in the form $f(x) = a(x - h)^2 + k$, where $a = 2$, $h = 3$, and $k = 4$. Therefore, the vertex is $(3, 4)$.

b. The graph of f is the same as the graph of $y = x^2$ shifted to the right 3 units, shifted up 4 units, and stretched vertically by a factor of 2 (Figure 11-13).

c. The axis of symmetry is the line $x = 3$.

d. Because $a > 0$, the function opens upward. Therefore, the minimum function value is 4. Notice that the minimum value is the minimum y-value on the graph.

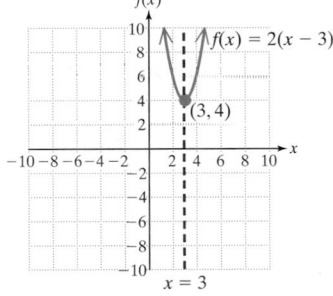

Figure 11-13

Skill Practice

7. Given the function defined by $g(x) = 3(x + 1)^2 - 3$
   a. Identify the vertex.
   b. Sketch the graph.
   c. Identify the axis of symmetry.
   d. Identify the maximum or minimum value of the function.

Answer

7. a. Vertex: $(-1, -3)$
   b.

   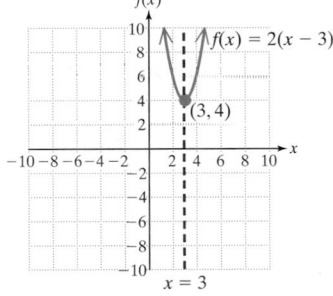

   c. Axis of symmetry: $x = -1$
   d. Minimum value: -3

Topic: Using the Maximum and Minimum Features

Some graphing calculators have *Minimum* and *Maximum* features that enable the user to approximate the minimum and maximum values of a function.

Classroom Example: p. 816, Exercise 60

Example 8   Graphing a Function of the Form $f(x) = a(x - h)^2 + k$

Given the function defined by

$$g(x) = -(x + 2)^2 - \frac{7}{4}$$

a. Identify the vertex.

b. Sketch the function.

c. Identify the axis of symmetry.

d. Identify the maximum or minimum value of the function.

Solution:

a. $g(x) = -(x + 2)^2 - \dfrac{7}{4}$

$$= -1[x - (-2)]^2 + \left(-\frac{7}{4}\right)$$

The function is in the form $g(x) = a(x - h)^2 + k$, where $a = -1$, $h = -2$, and $k = -\frac{7}{4}$. Therefore, the vertex is $\left(-2, -\frac{7}{4}\right)$.

b. The graph of g is the same as the graph of $y = x^2$ shifted to the left 2 units, shifted down $\frac{7}{4}$ units, and opening downward (Figure 11-14).

c. The axis of symmetry is the line $x = -2$.

d. The parabola opens downward, so the maximum function value is $-\frac{7}{4}$.

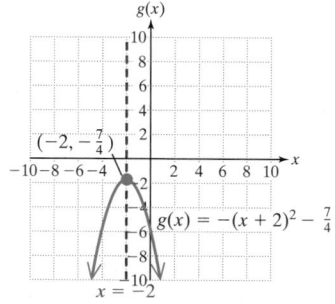

Figure 11-14

Skill Practice

8. Given the function defined by $h(x) = -\dfrac{1}{2}(x - 4)^2 + 2$

a. Identify the vertex.

b. Sketch the graph.

c. Identify the axis of symmetry.

d. Identify the maximum or minimum value of the function.

Answer

8. a. Vertex: (4, 2)

b.

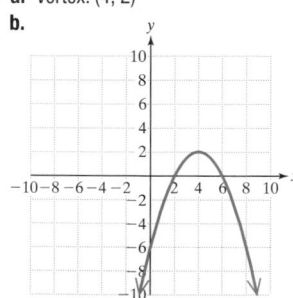

c. Axis of symmetry: $x = 4$

d. Maximum value: 2

Section 11.4 Practice Exercises

Study Skills Exercise

1. Define the key terms.

   a. parabola   b. vertex   c. axis of symmetry

   d. maximum value   e. minimum value

Review Exercises

For Exercises 2–8, solve the equations.

2. $x^2 + x - 5 = 0$
   $\left\{ \dfrac{-1 \pm \sqrt{21}}{2} \right\}$

3. $(y - 3)^2 = -4$
   $\{3 \pm 2i\}$

4. $\sqrt{2a + 2} = a + 1$
   $\{1, -1\}$

5. $5t(t - 2) = -3$
   $\left\{ \dfrac{5 \pm \sqrt{10}}{5} \right\}$

6. $2z^2 - 3z - 9 = 0$
   $\left\{ -\dfrac{3}{2}, 3 \right\}$

7. $x^{2/3} + 5x^{1/3} + 6 = 0$
   $\{-27, -8\}$

8. $m^2(m^2 + 6) = 27$
   $\{\pm\sqrt{3}, \pm 3i\}$

Concept 1: Quadratic Functions of the Form $f(x) = x^2 + k$

 9. Describe how the value of k affects the graph of a function defined by $f(x) = x^2 + k$.
   The value of k shifts the graph of $y = x^2$ vertically.

For Exercises 10–17, graph the functions. **(See Examples 1–2.)**

10. $g(x) = x^2 + 1$

11. $f(x) = x^2 + 2$

12. $p(x) = x^2 - 3$

 13. $q(x) = x^2 - 4$

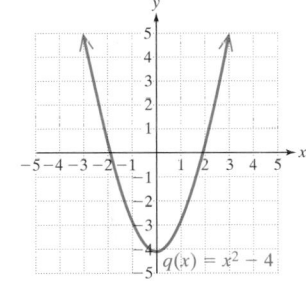

14. $T(x) = x^2 + \dfrac{3}{4}$

15. $S(x) = x^2 + \dfrac{3}{2}$

16. $M(x) = x^2 - \dfrac{5}{4}$

17. $n(x) = x^2 - \dfrac{1}{3}$

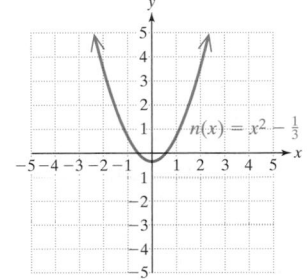

Concept 2: Quadratic Functions of the Form $f(x) = (x - h)^2$

 18. Describe how the value of h affects the graph of a function defined by $f(x) = (x - h)^2$.
   The value of h shifts the graph of $y = x^2$ horizontally.

For Exercises 19–26, graph the functions. **(See Examples 3–4.)**

19. $r(x) = (x + 1)^2$

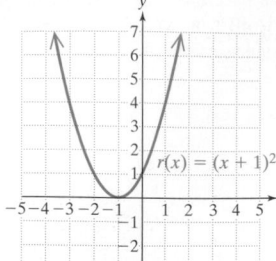

20. $h(x) = (x + 2)^2$

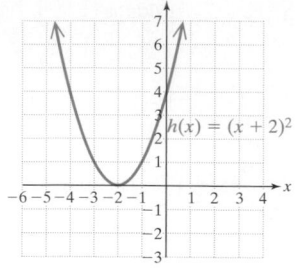

21. $k(x) = (x - 3)^2$

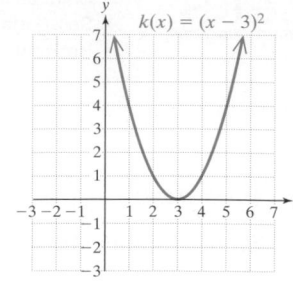

22. $L(x) = (x - 4)^2$

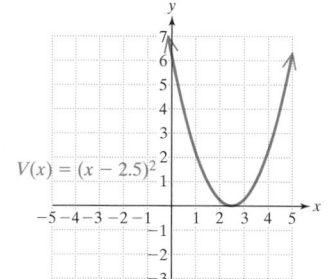

23. $A(x) = \left(x + \dfrac{3}{4}\right)^2$

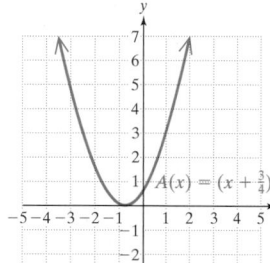

24. $r(x) = \left(x + \dfrac{3}{2}\right)^2$

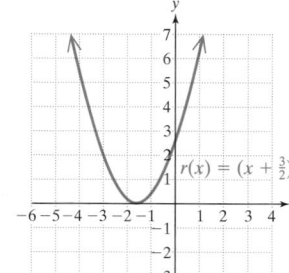

25. $W(x) = (x - 1.25)^2$

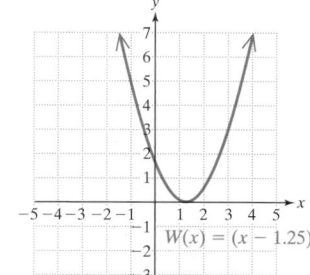

26. $V(x) = (x - 2.5)^2$

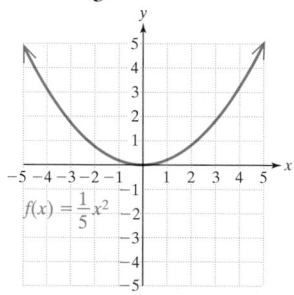

Concept 3: Quadratic Functions of the Form $f(x) = ax^2$

27. Describe how the value of a affects the graph of a function defined by $f(x) = ax^2$, where $a \neq 0$.
The value of a vertically stretches or shrinks the graph of $y = x^2$.

28. How do you determine whether the graph of a function defined by $h(x) = ax^2 + bx + c$ $(a \neq 0)$ opens upward or downward? If $a > 0$, the parabola opens upward; if $a < 0$, the parabola opens downward.

For Exercises 29–36, graph the functions. **(See Examples 5–6.)**

29. $f(x) = 4x^2$

30. $g(x) = 3x^2$

31. $h(x) = \dfrac{1}{4}x^2$

32. $f(x) = \dfrac{1}{5}x^2$

33. $c(x) = -x^2$

34. $g(x) = -4x^2$

35. $v(x) = -\dfrac{1}{5}x^2$

36. $f(x) = -\dfrac{1}{4}x^2$

Concept 4: Quadratic Functions of the Form $f(x) = a(x - h)^2 + k$

For Exercises 37–44, match the function with its graph.

37. $f(x) = -\dfrac{1}{4}x^2$ d

38. $g(x) = (x + 3)^2$ c

39. $k(x) = (x - 3)^2$ g

40. $h(x) = \dfrac{1}{4}x^2$ h

41. $t(x) = x^2 + 2$ a

42. $m(x) = x^2 - 4$ f

43. $p(x) = (x + 1)^2 - 3$ e

44. $n(x) = -(x - 2)^2 + 3$ b

a.

b.

c.

d.

e.

f.

g.

h.
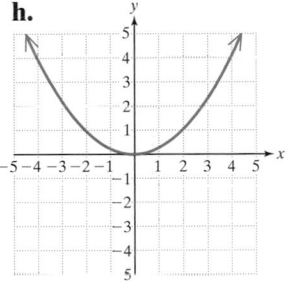

For Exercises 45–64, graph the parabola and the axis of symmetry. Label the coordinates of the vertex, and write the equation of the axis of symmetry. **(See Examples 7–8.)**

45. $y = (x - 3)^2 + 2$

46. $y = (x - 2)^2 + 3$

47. $y = (x + 1)^2 - 3$

48. $y = (x + 3)^2 - 1$

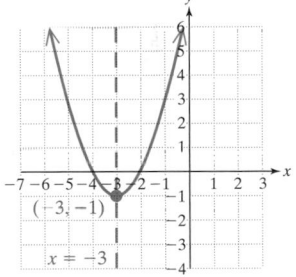

49. $y = -(x - 4)^2 - 2$

50. $y = -(x - 2)^2 - 4$

51. $y = -(x + 3)^2 + 3$

52. $y = -(x + 2)^2 + 2$

 Writing Translating Expression Geometry Scientific Calculator Video NS&E

53. $y = (x + 1)^2 + 1$ **54.** $y = (x - 4)^2 - 4$ **55.** $y = 3(x - 1)^2$ **56.** $y = -3(x - 1)^2$

   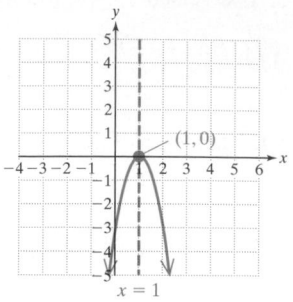

57. $y = -4x^2 + 3$ **58.** $y = 4x^2 + 3$ **59.** $y = 2(x + 3)^2 - 1$ **60.** $y = -2(x + 3)^2 - 1$

   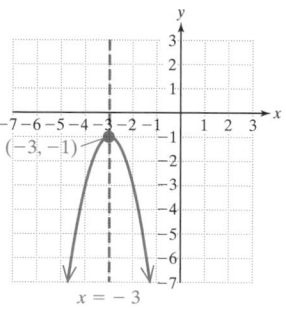

61. $y = -\dfrac{1}{4}(x - 1)^2 + 2$ **62.** $y = \dfrac{1}{4}(x - 1)^2 + 2$ **63.** $y = \dfrac{1}{3}(x - 2)^2 + 1$ **64.** $y = -\dfrac{1}{3}(x - 2)^2 + 1$

   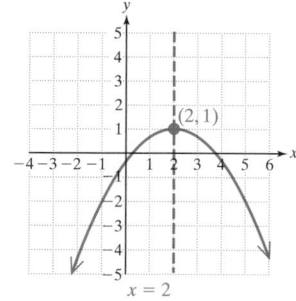

65. Compare the graphs of the following equations to the graph of $y = x^2$.

a. $y = x^2 + 3$
   $y = x^2 + 3$ is $y = x^2$ shifted up 3 units.

b. $y = (x + 3)^2$
   $y = (x + 3)^2$ is $y = x^2$ shifted left 3 units.

c. $y = 3x^2$
   $y = 3x^2$ is $y = x^2$ with a vertical stretch.

66. Compare the graphs of the following equations to the graph of $y = x^2$.

a. $y = (x - 2)^2$
   $y = (x - 2)^2$ is $y = x^2$ shifted right 2 units.

b. $y = 2x^2$
   $y = 2x^2$ is $y = x^2$ with a vertical stretch.

c. $y = x^2 - 2$
   $y = x^2 - 2$ is $y = x^2$ shifted down 2 units.

For Exercises 67–78, write the coordinates of the vertex and determine if the vertex is a maximum point or a minimum point. Then write the maximum or minimum value.

67. $f(x) = 4(x - 6)^2 - 9$
Vertex $(6, -9)$; minimum point;
minimum value: -9

68. $g(x) = 3(x - 4)^2 - 7$
Vertex $(4, -7)$; minimum point;
minimum value: -7

69. $p(x) = -\dfrac{2}{5}(x - 2)^2 + 5$
Vertex $(2, 5)$; maximum point;
maximum value: 5

70. $h(x) = -\dfrac{3}{7}(x - 5)^2 + 10$
Vertex $(5, 10)$; maximum point;
maximum value: 10

71. $k(x) = \dfrac{1}{2}(x + 8)^2$
Vertex $(-8, 0)$; minimum point;
minimum value: 0

72. $m(x) = \dfrac{2}{9}(x + 11)^2$
Vertex $(-11, 0)$; minimum point;
minimum value: 0

73. $n(x) = -6x^2 + \dfrac{21}{4}$ Vertex $\left(0, \dfrac{21}{4}\right)$;
maximum point; maximum value: $\dfrac{21}{4}$

74. $q(x) = -4x^2 + \dfrac{1}{6}$ Vertex $\left(0, \dfrac{1}{6}\right)$;
maximum point; maximum value: $\dfrac{1}{6}$

75. $A(x) = 2(x - 7)^2 - \dfrac{3}{2}$
Vertex $\left(7, -\dfrac{3}{2}\right)$; minimum point;
minimum value: $-\dfrac{3}{2}$

76. $B(x) = 5(x - 3)^2 - \dfrac{1}{4}$ Vertex $\left(3, -\dfrac{1}{4}\right)$;
minimum point; minimum value: $-\dfrac{1}{4}$

77. $F(x) = 7x^2$
Vertex $(0, 0)$; minimum point;
minimum value: 0

78. $G(x) = -7x^2$
Vertex $(0, 0)$; maximum point;
maximum value: 0

79. True or false: The function defined by $g(x) = -5x^2$ has a maximum value but no minimum value.   True

80. True or false: The function defined by $f(x) = 2(x - 5)^2$ has a maximum value but no minimum value.   False

81. True or false: If the vertex $(-2, 8)$ represents a minimum point, then the minimum value is -2.   False

82. True or false: If the vertex $(-2, 8)$ represents a maximum point, then the maximum value is 8.   True

Expanding Your Skills

83. A suspension bridge is 120 ft long. Its supporting cable hangs in a shape that resembles a parabola. The function defined by $H(x) = \frac{1}{90}(x - 60)^2 + 30$ (where $0 \le x \le 120$) approximates the height of the supporting cable a distance of x ft from the end of the bridge (see figure).

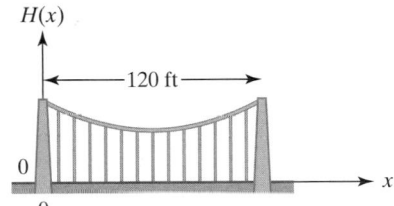

  a. What is the location of the vertex of the parabolic cable? $(60, 30)$

  b. What is the minimum height of the cable?   30 ft

  c. How high are the towers at either end of the supporting cable?   70 ft

84. A 50-m bridge over a crevasse is supported by a parabolic arch. The function defined by $f(x) = -0.16(x - 25)^2 + 100$ (where $0 \le x \le 50$) approximates the height of the supporting arch x meters from the end of the bridge (see figure).

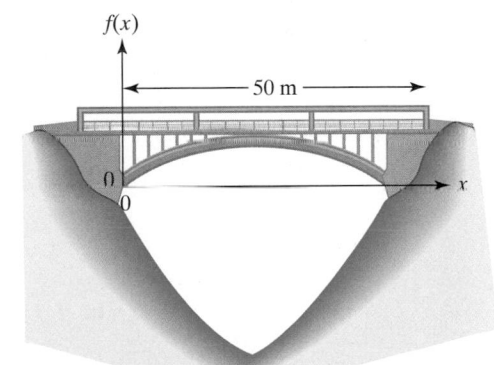

  a. What is the location of the vertex of the arch? $(25, 100)$

  b. What is the maximum height of the arch (relative to the origin)?   100 m

85. The staging platform for a fireworks display is 6 ft above ground, and the mortars leave the platform at 96 ft/sec. The height of the mortars, $h(t)$, can be modeled by

$h(t) = -16(t - 3)^2 + 150$, where t is the time in seconds after launch.

  a. If the fuses are set for 3 sec after launch, at what height will the fireworks explode?
The fireworks will explode at a height of 150 ft.

  b. Will the fireworks explode at their maximum height? Explain.
Yes, because the ordered pair $(3, 150)$ is the vertex.

 Writing   Translating Expression   Geometry   Scientific Calculator   Video   NS&E

Section 11.5   Vertex of a Parabola: Applications and Modeling

Classroom Example: p. 825, Exercise 18

1. Writing a Quadratic Function in the Form $f(x) = a(x - h)^2 + k$

The graph of a quadratic function is a parabola, and if the function is written in the form $f(x) = a(x - h)^2 + k$ $(a \neq 0)$, then the vertex is at (h, k). A quadratic function can be written in the form $f(x) = a(x - h)^2 + k$ $(a \neq 0)$ by completing the square. The process is similar to the steps outlined in Section 11.1 except that all algebraic manipulations are performed on the right-hand side of the equation.

Example 1   Writing a Quadratic Function in the Form $f(x) = a(x - h)^2 + k$ $(a \neq 0)$

Given: $f(x) = x^2 + 8x + 13$

a. Write the function in the form $f(x) = a(x - h)^2 + k$.

b. Identify the vertex, axis of symmetry, and minimum function value.

Solution:

a. $f(x) = x^2 + 8x + 13$

Rather than dividing by the leading coefficient on both sides, we will factor out the leading coefficient from the variable terms on the right-hand side.

$= 1(x^2 + 8x) + 13$

$= 1(x^2 + 8x \quad\quad) + 13$

Next, complete the square on the expression within the parentheses: $[\frac{1}{2}(8)]^2 = 16$.

Avoiding Mistakes

Do not factor out the leading coefficient from the constant term.

$= 1(x^2 + 8x + 16 - 16) + 13$

Rather than add 16 to both sides of the function, we *add and subtract* 16 within the parentheses on the right-hand side. This has the effect of adding 0 to the right-hand side.

$= 1(x^2 + 8x + 16) - 16 + 13$

Use the associative property of addition to regroup terms and isolate the perfect square trinomial within the parentheses.

$= (x + 4)^2 - 3$

Factor and simplify.

b. $f(x) = (x + 4)^2 - 3$

The vertex is $(-4, -3)$.

The axis of symmetry is $x = -4$.

Because $a > 0$, the parabola opens upward.

The minimum value is -3 (Figure 11-15).

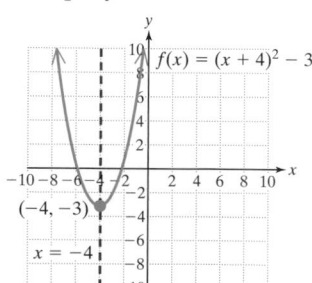

Figure 11-15

Skill Practice

1. Given: $f(x) = x^2 + 8x - 1$
   a. Write the equation in the form $f(x) = a(x - h)^2 + k$.
   b. Identify the vertex, axis of symmetry, and minimum value of the function.

Example 2 Analyzing a Quadratic Function

Classroom Example: p. 825, Exercise 22

Given: $f(x) = -2x^2 + 12x - 16$

a. Write the function in the form $f(x) = a(x - h)^2 + k$.

b. Find the vertex, axis of symmetry, and maximum function value.

c. Find the x- and y-intercepts.

d. Sketch the graph of the function.

Solution:

a. $f(x) = -2x^2 + 12x - 16$

To find the vertex, write the function in the form $f(x) = a(x - h)^2 + k$.

$= -2(x^2 - 6x \quad\quad) - 16$

If the leading coefficient is not 1, factor the coefficient from the variable terms.

$= -2(x^2 - 6x + 9 - 9) - 16$

Add and subtract the quantity $[\frac{1}{2}(-6)]^2 = 9$ within the parentheses.

$= -2(x^2 - 6x + 9) + (-2)(-9) - 16$

To remove the term -9 from the parentheses, we must first apply the distributive property. When -9 is removed from the parentheses, it carries with it a factor of -2.

$= -2(x - 3)^2 + 18 - 16$

Factor and simplify.

$= -2(x - 3)^2 + 2$

> **TIP:** We do not divide by -2 because we are rewriting the expression $-2x^2 + 12x - 16$ and not solving an equation.

b. $f(x) = -2(x - 3)^2 + 2$

The vertex is $(3, 2)$. The axis of symmetry is $x = 3$. Because $a < 0$, the parabola opens downward and the maximum value is 2.

c. The y intercept is given by $f(0) = -2(0)^2 + 12(0) - 16 = -16$.

The y-intercept is $(0, -16)$.

To find the x-intercept(s), find the real solutions to the equation $f(x) = 0$.

$f(x) = -2x^2 + 12x - 16$

$0 = -2x^2 + 12x - 16$ Substitute $f(x) = 0$.

$0 = -2(x^2 - 6x + 8)$ Factor.

$0 = -2(x - 4)(x - 2)$

$x = 4$ or $x = 2$

The x-intercepts are $(4, 0)$ and $(2, 0)$.

d. Using the information from parts (a)–(c), sketch the graph (Figure 11-16).

> **TIP:** When a quadratic function has two x-intercepts, the vertex is located halfway between the two x-intercepts.

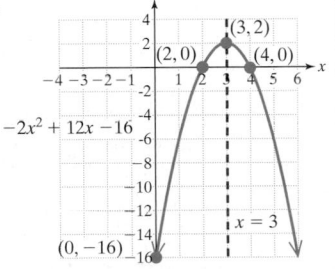

$f(x) = -2x^2 + 12x - 16$

Figure 11-16

Skill Practice

2. Given: $g(x) = -x^2 + 6x - 5$
   a. Write the equation in the form $g(x) = a(x - h)^2 + k$.
   b. Identify the vertex, axis of symmetry, and maximum value of the function.
   c. Determine the x- and y-intercepts.
   d. Graph the function.

2. Vertex Formula

Completing the square and writing a quadratic function in the form $f(x) = a(x - h)^2 + k$ $(a \neq 0)$ is one method to find the vertex of a parabola. Another method is to use the vertex formula. The **vertex formula** can be derived by completing the square on $f(x) = ax^2 + bx + c$ $(a \neq 0)$.

$f(x) = ax^2 + bx + c \qquad (a \neq 0)$

$$= a\left(x^2 + \frac{b}{a}x \qquad\qquad\right) + c \qquad \text{Factor } a \text{ from the variable terms.}$$

$$= a\left(x^2 + \frac{b}{a}x + \frac{b^2}{4a^2} - \frac{b^2}{4a^2}\right) + c \qquad \text{Add and subtract } [\tfrac{1}{2}(b/a)]^2 = b^2/(4a^2) \text{ within the parentheses.}$$

Instructor Note: It can be interesting to let students know that calculus also provides a technique to find the vertex of the parabola.

$$= a\left(x^2 + \frac{b}{a}x + \frac{b^2}{4a^2}\right) + (a)\left(-\frac{b^2}{4a^2}\right) + c \qquad \text{Apply the distributive property and remove the term } -b^2/(4a^2) \text{ from the parentheses.}$$

$$= a\left(x + \frac{b}{2a}\right)^2 - \frac{b^2}{4a} + c \qquad \text{Factor the trinomial and simplify.}$$

$$= a\left(x + \frac{b}{2a}\right)^2 + c - \frac{b^2}{4a} \qquad \text{Apply the commutative property of addition to reverse the last two terms.}$$

$$= a\left(x + \frac{b}{2a}\right)^2 + \frac{4ac}{4a} - \frac{b^2}{4a} \qquad \text{Obtain a common denominator.}$$

$$= a\left(x + \frac{b}{2a}\right)^2 + \frac{4ac - b^2}{4a}$$

$$= a\left[x - \left(-\frac{b}{2a}\right)\right]^2 + \frac{4ac - b^2}{4a}$$

Answer

2. a. $g(x) = -(x - 3)^2 + 4$
  b. Vertex: $(3, 4)$; axis of symmetry: $x = 3$; maximum value: 4
  c. x-intercepts: $(5, 0)$ and $(1, 0)$; y-intercept: $(0, -5)$
  d.

$f(x) = a(x \qquad - \qquad h)^2 \qquad + \qquad k$

The function is in the form $f(x) = a(x - h)^2 + k$, where

$$h = \frac{-b}{2a} \qquad \text{and} \qquad k = \frac{4ac - b^2}{4a}$$

Therefore, the vertex is $\left(\dfrac{-b}{2a}, \dfrac{4ac - b^2}{4a}\right)$

Although the y-coordinate of the vertex is given by $\dfrac{4ac - b^2}{4a}$, it is usually easier to determine the x-coordinate of the vertex first and then find y by evaluating the function at $x = -b/(2a)$.

> **FORMULA** The Vertex Formula
>
> For $f(x) = ax^2 + bx + c$ $(a \neq 0)$, the vertex is given by
>
> $$\left(\frac{-b}{2a}, \frac{4ac - b^2}{4a}\right) \quad \text{or} \quad \left(\frac{-b}{2a}, f\left(\frac{-b}{2a}\right)\right)$$

3. Determining the Vertex and Intercepts of a Quadratic Function

Example 3 Determining the Vertex and Intercepts of a Quadratic Function

Classroom Example: p. 826, Exercise 46

Given: $h(x) = x^2 - 2x + 5$

a. Use the vertex formula to find the vertex.

b. Find the x- and y-intercepts.

c. Sketch the function.

Solution:

a. $h(x) = x^2 - 2x + 5$

$a = 1 \quad b = -2 \quad c = 5$ Identify a, b, and c.

The x-coordinate of the vertex is $\dfrac{-b}{2a} = \dfrac{-(-2)}{2(1)} = 1$.

The y-coordinate of the vertex is $h(1) = (1)^2 - 2(1) + 5 = 4$.

The vertex is $(1, 4)$.

b. The y-intercept is given by $h(0) = (0)^2 - 2(0) + 5 = 5$.

The y-intercept is $(0, 5)$.

To find the x-intercept(s), find the real solutions to the equation $h(x) = 0$.

$h(x) = x^2 - 2x + 5$

$0 = x^2 - 2x + 5$ This quadratic equation is not factorable. Apply the quadratic formula: $a = 1, b = -2, c = 5$.

$$x = \frac{-(-2) \pm \sqrt{(-2)^2 - 4(1)(5)}}{2(1)}$$

$$= \frac{2 \pm \sqrt{4 - 20}}{2(1)}$$

$$= \frac{2 \pm \sqrt{-16}}{2}$$

$$= \frac{2 \pm 4i}{2}$$

$$= 1 \pm 2i$$

The solutions to the equation $h(x) = 0$ are not real numbers. Therefore, there are no x-intercepts.

c.

Because $a > 0$, the parabola opens up.

$h(x) = x^2 - 2x + 5$

$(0, 5)$

$(1, 4)$

Figure 11-17

> **TIP:** The location of the vertex and the direction that the parabola opens can be used to determine whether the function has any x-intercepts.
>
> Given $h(x) = x^2 - 2x + 5$, the vertex $(1, 4)$ is *above* the x-axis. Furthermore, because $a > 0$, the parabola opens upward. Therefore, it is not possible for the graph to cross the x-axis (Figure 11-17).

Skill Practice

3. Given: $f(x) = x^2 + 4x + 6$

   a. Use the vertex formula to find the vertex of the parabola.

   b. Determine the x- and y-intercepts.

   c. Sketch the graph.

4. Applications and Modeling of Quadratic Functions

Classroom Example: p. 826, Exercise 56

> **Example 4** Applying a Quadratic Function

The crew from Extravaganza Entertainment launches fireworks at an angle of 60° from the horizontal. The height of one particular type of display can be approximated by:

$$h(t) = -16t^2 + 128\sqrt{3}t$$

where $h(t)$ is measured in feet and t is measured in seconds.

   a. How long will it take the fireworks to reach their maximum height? Round to the nearest second.

   b. Find the maximum height. Round to the nearest foot.

Answer

3. a. Vertex: $(-2, 2)$

   b. x-intercepts: none;
      y-intercepts: $(0, 6)$

   c.

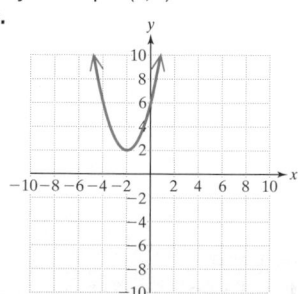

Solution:

$$h(t) = -16t^2 + 128\sqrt{3}t$$

This parabola opens downward; therefore, the maximum height of the fireworks will occur at the vertex of the parabola.

$a = -16$ $b = 128\sqrt{3}$ $c = 0$ Identify a, b, and c, and apply the vertex formula.

The x-coordinate of the vertex is

$$\frac{-b}{2a} = \frac{-128\sqrt{3}}{2(-16)} = \frac{-128\sqrt{3}}{-32} \approx 6.9$$

The y-coordinate of the vertex is approximately

$$h(6.9) = -16(6.9)^2 + 128\sqrt{3}(6.9) \approx 768$$

The vertex is $(6.9, 768)$.

a. The fireworks will reach their maximum height in 6.9 sec.

b. The maximum height is 768 ft.

Skill Practice

4. An object is launched into the air with an initial velocity of 48 ft/sec from the top of a building 288 ft high. The height $h(t)$ of the object after t seconds is given by

$$h(t) = -16t^2 + 48t + 288$$

a. Find the time it takes for the object to reach its maximum height.

b. Find the maximum height.

In Section 3.5 we wrote a linear model given two points. Now we will learn how to write a quadratic model of a parabola given three points by using a system of equations and the standard form of a parabola: $y = ax^2 + bx + c$.

This process involves substituting the x- and y-coordinates of the three given points into the quadratic model. Then we solve the resulting system of three equations (Section 4.5).

Example 5 **Writing a Quadratic Model**

Classroom Example: p. 827, Exercise 62

Write an equation of a parabola that passes through the points $(1, -1), (-1, -5)$, and $(2, 4)$.

Solution:

Substitute $(1, -1)$ into the equation
$y = ax^2 + bx + c$ $\longrightarrow$ $(-1) = a(1)^2 + b(1) + c$
$-1 = a + b + c$
$a + b + c = -1$

Substitute $(-1, -5)$ into the equation
$y = ax^2 + bx + c$ $\longrightarrow$ $(-5) = a(-1)^2 + b(-1) + c$
$-5 = a - b + c$
$a - b + c = -5$

Substitute $(2, 4)$ into the equation
$y = ax^2 + bx + c$ $\longrightarrow$ $(4) = a(2)^2 + b(2) + c$
$4 = 4a + 2b + c$
$4a + 2b + c = 4$

Solve the system:
$\boxed{\text{A}}$ $a + b + c = -1$
$\boxed{\text{B}}$ $a - b + c = -5$
$\boxed{\text{C}}$ $4a + 2b + c = 4$

Answer
4. a. 1.5 sec **b.** 324 ft

Notice that the *c*-variables all have a coefficient of 1. Therefore, we choose to eliminate the *c*-variable.

$$
\begin{array}{ll}
\boxed{A} & a + b + c = -1 \longrightarrow \qquad a + b + c = -1 \\
\boxed{B} & a - b + c = -5 \xrightarrow{\text{Multiply by } -1.} \dfrac{-a + b - c = \;\; 5}{} \\
& \qquad\qquad\qquad\qquad\qquad\quad 2b \;\;\;\;\; = \;\; 4 \\
& \qquad\qquad\qquad\qquad\qquad\quad\;\; b = \;\; 2 \quad \boxed{D}
\end{array}
$$

$$
\begin{array}{ll}
\boxed{B} & a - \;\; b + c = -5 \longrightarrow \qquad a - \;\; b + c = -5 \\
\boxed{C} & 4a + 2b + c = \;\;\; 4 \xrightarrow{\text{Multiply by } -1.} \dfrac{-4a - 2b - c = -4}{} \\
& \qquad\qquad\qquad\qquad\qquad\;\; -3a - 3b \;\;\;\;\; = -9 \quad \boxed{E}
\end{array}
$$

Substitute *b* with 2 in equation $\boxed{E}$:
$$
\begin{aligned}
-3a - 3(2) &= -9 \\
-3a - 6 &= -9 \\
-3a &= -3 \\
a &= 1
\end{aligned}
$$

Substitute *a* and *b* in equation $\boxed{A}$ to solve for *c*:
$$
\begin{aligned}
(1) + (2) + c &= -1 \\
3 + c &= -1 \\
c &= -4
\end{aligned}
$$

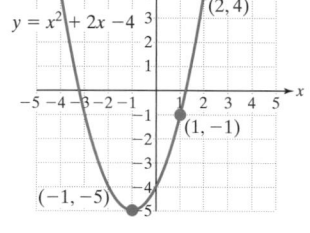

$y = x^2 + 2x - 4$

(2, 4)

(1, −1)

(−1, −5)

Figure 11-18

Substitute $a = 1$, $b = 2$, and $c = -4$ in the standard form of the parabola for the final answer.

$$
y = ax^2 + bx + c
$$

$$
y = (1)x^2 + (2)x + (-4) \longrightarrow y = x^2 + 2x - 4
$$

A graph $y = x^2 + 2x - 4$ is shown in Figure 11-18. Notice that the graph of the function passes through the points $(1, -1)$, $(-1, -5)$, and $(2, 4)$.

Skill Practice

Answer

5. $a = -1$, $b = -1$, $c = 3$;
$y = -x^2 - x + 3$

5. Write an equation of the parabola that passes through the points $(1, 1)$, $(-2, 1)$, and $(3, -9)$.

Section 11.5 Practice Exercises

Study Skills Exercise

1. Write the **vertex formula**.

For $f(x) = ax^2 + bx + c$, the vertex (h, k) is given by $\left(\dfrac{-b}{2a}, \dfrac{4ac - b^2}{4a} \right)$ or $\left(\dfrac{-b}{2a}, f\left(\dfrac{-b}{2a} \right) \right)$.

Review Exercises

2. How does the graph of $f(x) = -2x^2$ compare with the graph of $y = x^2$?
The graph of *f* is the graph of $y = x^2$ but opening downward and stretched vertically by a factor of 2.

3. How does the graph of $p(x) = \frac{1}{4}x^2$ compare with the graph of $y = x^2$?
The graph of *p* is the graph of $y = x^2$ shrunk vertically by a factor of $\frac{1}{4}$.

4. How does the graph of $Q(x) = x^2 - \frac{8}{3}$ compare with the graph of $y = x^2$?
The graph of *Q* is the graph of $y = x^2$ shifted down $\frac{8}{3}$ units.

5. How does the graph of $r(x) = x^2 + 7$ compare with the graph of $y = x^2$?
The graph of *r* is the graph of $y = x^2$ shifted up 7 units.

 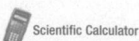

6. How does the graph of $s(x) = (x - 4)^2$ compare with the graph of $y = x^2$?
The graph of s is the graph of $y = x^2$ shifted to the right 4 units.

7. How does the graph of $t(x) = (x + 10)^2$ compare with the graph of $y = x^2$?
The graph of t is the graph of $y = x^2$ shifted to the left 10 units.

8. Find the coordinates of the vertex of the parabola defined by $g(x) = 2(x + 3)^2 - 4$. $(-3, -4)$

For Exercises 9–16, find the value of n to complete the square. Factor the resulting trinomial.

9. $x^2 - 8x + n$
$16; (x - 4)^2$

10. $x^2 + 4x + n$
$4; (x + 2)^2$

11. $y^2 + 7y + n$ $\frac{49}{4}; \left(y + \frac{7}{2}\right)^2$

12. $a^2 - a + n$ $\frac{1}{4}; \left(a - \frac{1}{2}\right)^2$

13. $b^2 + \frac{2}{9}b + n$

$\frac{1}{81}; \left(b + \frac{1}{9}\right)^2$

14. $m^2 - \frac{2}{7}m + n$

$\frac{1}{49}; \left(m - \frac{1}{7}\right)^2$

15. $t^2 - \frac{1}{3}t + n$ $\frac{1}{36}; \left(t - \frac{1}{6}\right)^2$

16. $p^2 + \frac{1}{4}p + n$ $\frac{1}{64}; \left(p + \frac{1}{8}\right)^2$

Concept 1: Writing a Quadratic Function in the Form $f(x) = a(x - h)^2 + k$

For Exercises 17–28, write the function in the form $f(x) = a(x - h)^2 + k$ by completing the square. Then identify the vertex. **(See Examples 1–2.)**

17. $g(x) = x^2 - 8x + 5$
$g(x) = (x - 4)^2 - 11; (4, -11)$

18. $h(x) = x^2 + 4x + 5$
$h(x) = (x + 2)^2 + 1; (-2, 1)$

19. $n(x) = 2x^2 + 12x + 13$
$n(x) = 2(x + 3)^2 - 5; (-3, -5)$

20. $f(x) = 4x^2 + 16x + 19$
$f(x) = 4(x + 2)^2 + 3; (-2, 3)$

21. $p(x) = -3x^2 + 6x - 5$
$p(x) = -3(x - 1)^2 - 2; (1, -2)$

22. $q(x) = -2x^2 + 12x - 11$
$q(x) = -2(x - 3)^2 + 7; (3, 7)$

23. $k(x) = x^2 + 7x - 10$
$k(x) = \left(x + \frac{7}{2}\right)^2 - \frac{89}{4}; \left(-\frac{7}{2}, -\frac{89}{4}\right)$

24. $m(x) = x^2 - x - 8$
$m(x) = \left(x - \frac{1}{2}\right)^2 - \frac{33}{4}; \left(\frac{1}{2}, -\frac{33}{4}\right)$

25. $F(x) = 5x^2 + 10x + 1$
$F(x) = 5(x + 1)^2 - 4; (-1, -4)$

26. $G(x) = 4x^2 + 4x - 7$
$G(x) = 4\left(x + \frac{1}{2}\right)^2 - 8; \left(-\frac{1}{2}, -8\right)$

27. $P(x) = -2x^2 + x$
$P(x) = -2\left(x - \frac{1}{4}\right)^2 + \frac{1}{8}; \left(\frac{1}{4}, \frac{1}{8}\right)$

28. $Q(x) = -3x^2 + 12x$
$Q(x) = -3(x - 2)^2 + 12; (2, 12)$

Concept 2: Vertex Formula

For Exercises 29–40, find the vertex by using the vertex formula. **(See Example 3.)**

29. $Q(x) = x^2 - 4x + 7$
$(2, 3)$

30. $T(x) = x^2 - 8x + 17$
$(4, 1)$

31. $r(x) = -3x^2 - 6x - 5$
$(-1, -2)$

32. $s(x) = -2x^2 - 12x - 19$
$(-3, -1)$

33. $N(x) = x^2 + 8x + 1$
$(-4, -15)$

34. $M(x) = x^2 + 6x - 5$
$(-3, -14)$

35. $m(x) = \frac{1}{2}x^2 + x + \frac{5}{2}$ $(-1, 2)$

36. $n(x) = \frac{1}{2}x^2 + 2x + 3$ $(-2, 1)$

37. $k(x) = -x^2 + 2x + 2$ $(1, 3)$

38. $h(x) = -x^2 + 4x - 3$ $(2, 1)$

39. $A(x) = -\frac{1}{3}x^2 + x$ $\left(\frac{3}{2}, \frac{3}{4}\right)$

40. $B(x) = -\frac{2}{3}x^2 - 2x$ $\left(-\frac{3}{2}, \frac{3}{2}\right)$

For Exercises 41–44, find the vertex two ways:

a. by completing the square and writing in the form $f(x) = a(x - h)^2 + k$.

b. by using the vertex formula.

41. $p(x) = x^2 + 8x + 1$
$(-4, -15)$

42. $F(x) = x^2 + 4x - 2$
$(-2, -6)$

43. $f(x) = 2x^2 + 4x + 6$
$(-1, 4)$

44. $g(x) = 3x^2 + 12x + 9$
$(-2, -3)$

Concept 3: Determining the Vertex and Intercepts of a Quadratic Function

For Exercises 45–52

a. Find the vertex.

b. Find the y-intercept.

c. Find the x-intercept(s), if they exist.

d. Use this information to graph the function. **(See Examples 2–3.)**

 Writing   Translating Expression   Geometry   Scientific Calculator   Video   NS&E

45. $y = x^2 + 2x - 3$

a. $(-1, -4)$ b. $(0, -3)$

c. $(1, 0), (-3, 0)$

d.

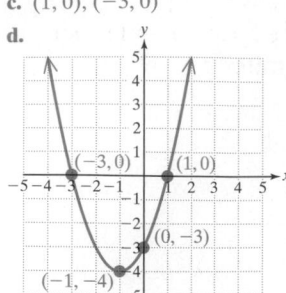

46. $y = x^2 + 4x + 3$

a. $(-2, -1)$ b. $(0, 3)$

c. $(-1, 0), (-3, 0)$

d.

 47. $y = 2x^2 - 2x + 4$

a. $\left(\frac{1}{2}, \frac{7}{2}\right)$ b. $(0, 4)$

c. No x-intercepts

d.

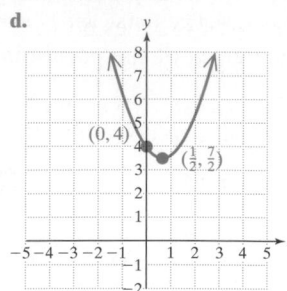

48. $y = 2x^2 - 12x + 19$

a. $(3, 1)$ b. $(0, 19)$

c. No x-intercepts

d.

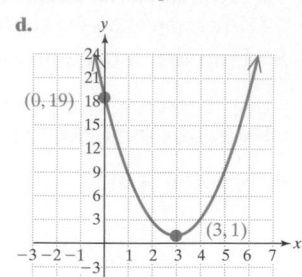

49. $y = -x^2 + 3x - \dfrac{9}{4}$

a. $\left(\frac{3}{2}, 0\right)$ b. $\left(0, -\frac{9}{4}\right)$ c. $\left(\frac{3}{2}, 0\right)$

d.

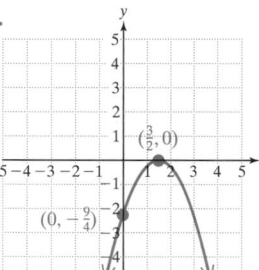

50. $y = -x^2 - \dfrac{3}{2}x - \dfrac{9}{16}$

a. $\left(-\frac{3}{4}, 0\right)$ b. $\left(0, -\frac{9}{16}\right)$ c. $\left(-\frac{3}{4}, 0\right)$

d.

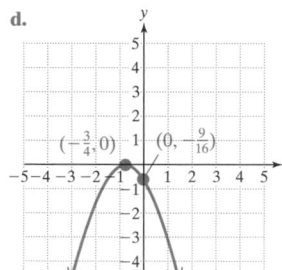

51. $y = -x^2 - 2x + 3$

a. $(-1, 4)$ b. $(0, 3)$

c. $(1, 0), (-3, 0)$

d.

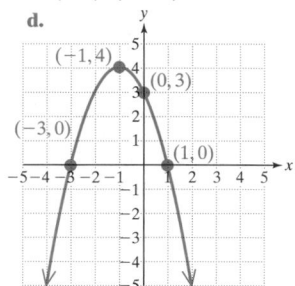

52. $y = -x^2 - 4x$

a. $(-2, 4)$ b. $(0, 0)$

c. $(0, 0), (-4, 0)$

d.

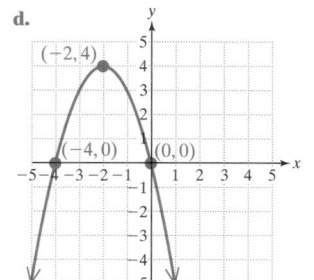

Concept 4: Applications and Modeling of Quadratic Functions

53. Mia sells used MP3 players. The average cost to package MP3 players is given by the equation $C(x) = 2x^2 - 40x + 2200$, where x is the number of MP3 players she packages in a week. How many players must she package to minimize her average cost? Mia must package 10 MP3 players.

54. Ben sells used iPods. The average cost to package iPods is given by the equation $C(x) = 3x^2 - 120x + 1300$, where x is the number of iPods packaged per month. Determine the number of iPods that Ben needs to package to minimize the average cost. Ben needs to package 20 iPods per month.

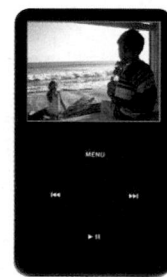

55. A set of fireworks mortar shells is launched from the staging platform at 100 ft/sec from an initial height of 8 ft above the ground. The height of the fireworks, $h(t)$, can be modeled by

$$h(t) = -16t^2 + 100t + 8, \text{ where } t \text{ is the time in seconds after launch. (See Example 4.)}$$

a. What is the maximum height that the shells can reach before exploding? 164.25 ft

b. For how many seconds after launch would the fuses need to be set so that the mortar shells would in fact explode at the maximum height 3.125 sec

56. A baseball player throws a ball, and the height of the ball (in feet) can be approximated by

$$y(x) = -0.011x^2 + 0.577x + 5$$

where x is the horizontal position of the ball measured in feet from the origin.

a. For what value of x will the ball reach its highest point? Round to the nearest foot. 26 ft

b. What is the maximum height of the ball? Round to the nearest tenth of a foot. 12.6 ft

 Writing Translating Expression 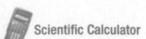 Geometry Scientific Calculator Video NS&E

57. Gas mileage depends in part on the speed of the car. The gas mileage of a subcompact car is given by $m(x) = -0.04x^2 + 3.6x - 49$, where $20 \le x \le 70$ represents the speed in miles per hour and $m(x)$ is given in miles per gallon.

  a. At what speed will the car get the maximum gas mileage?   45 mph

  b. What is the maximum gas mileage?   32 mpg

58. Gas mileage depends in part on the speed of the car. The gas mileage of a luxury car is given by $L(x) = -0.015x^2 + 1.44x - 21$, where $25 \le x \le 70$ represents the speed in miles per hour and $L(x)$ is given in miles per gallon.

  a. At what speed will the car get the maximum gas mileage?   48 mph

  b. What is the maximum gas mileage? Round to the nearest whole unit.   14 mpg

59. Tetanus bacillus bacterium is cultured to produce tetanus toxin used in an inactive form for the tetanus vaccine. The amount of toxin produced per batch increases with time and then becomes unstable. The amount of toxin (in grams) as a function of time t (in hours) can be approximated by:

$$b(t) = -\frac{1}{1152}t^2 + \frac{1}{12}t$$

  a. How many hours will it take to produce the maximum yield?   48 hr

  b. What is the maximum yield?   2 g

60. The bacterium *Pseudomonas aeruginosa* is cultured with an initial population of 10^4 active organisms. The population of active bacteria increases up to a point, and then due to a limited food supply and an increase of waste products, the population of living organisms decreases. Over the first 48 hr, the population can be approximated by:

$$P(t) = -1718.75t^2 + 82{,}500t + 10{,}000$$

where $0 \le t \le 48$

  a. Find the time required for the population to reach its maximum value.   24 hr

  b. What is the maximum population?
  1,000,000 organisms

For Exercises 61–66, use the standard form of a parabola given by $y = ax^2 + bx + c$ to write an equation of a parabola that passes through the given points. **(See Example 5.)**

61. (0, 4), (1, 0), and (−1, −10)
$a = -9, b = 5, c = 4;$
$y = -9x^2 + 5x + 4$

62. (0, 3), (3, 0), (−1, 8)
$a = 1, b = -4, c = 3;$
$y = x^2 - 4x + 3$

63. (2, 1), (−2, 5), and (1, −4)
$a = 2, b = -1, c = -5;$
$y = 2x^2 - x - 5$

64. (1, 2), (−1, −6), and (2, −3)
$a = -3, b = 4, c = 1;$
$y = -3x^2 + 4x + 1$

65. (2, −4), (1, 1), and (−1, −7)
$a = -3, b = 4, c = 0;$
$y = -3x^2 + 4x$

66. (1, 4), (−1, 6), and (2, 18)
$a = 5, b = -1, c = 0;$
$y = 5x^2 - x$

Expanding Your Skills

67. A farmer wants to fence a rectangular corral adjacent to the side of a barn; however, she has only 200 ft of fencing and wants to enclose the largest possible area. See the figure.

  a. If x represents the length of the corral and y represents the width, explain why the dimensions of the corral are subject to the constraint $2x + y = 200$.
  The sum of the sides must equal the total amount of fencing.

  b. The area of the corral is given by $A = xy$. Use the constraint equation from part (a) to express A as a function of x, where $0 < x < 100$.
  $A = x(200 - 2x)$

  c. Use the function from part (b) to find the dimensions of the corral that will yield the maximum area. [*Hint:* Find the vertex of the function from part (b).]   50 ft by 100 ft

68. A veterinarian wants to construct two equal-sized pens of maximum area
out of 240 ft of fencing. See the figure.

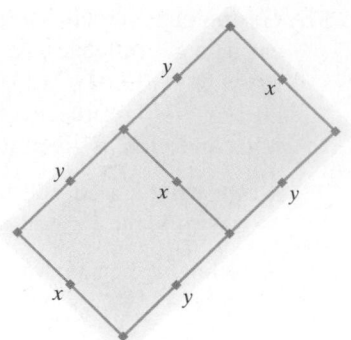

   a. If x represents the length of each pen and y represents the width of each
pen, explain why the dimensions of the pens are subject to the constraint $3x + 4y = 240$.
     The sum of the sides must equal the total amount of fencing.

   b. The area of each individual pen is given by $A = xy$. Use the constraint
equation from part (a) to express A as a function of x, where
$0 < x < 80$. $A = x\left(60 - \dfrac{3}{4}x\right)$

   c. Use the function from part (b) to find the dimensions of an individual
pen that will yield the maximum area. [*Hint:* Find the vertex of the
function from part (b).] 30 ft by 40 ft

Graphing Calculator Exercises

For Exercises 69–74, graph the functions in Exercises 45–50 on a graphing calculator. Use the *Max* or *Min* feature
to approximate the vertex.

69. $Y_1 = x^2 + 2x - 3$ (Exercise 45)

70. $Y_1 = x^2 + 4x + 3$ (Exercise 46)

71. $Y_1 = 2x^2 - 2x + 4$ (Exercise 47)

72. $Y_1 = 2x^2 - 12x + 19$ (Exercise 48)

73. $Y_1 = -x^2 + 3x - \dfrac{9}{4}$ (Exercise 49)

74. $Y_1 = -x^2 - \dfrac{3}{2}x - \dfrac{9}{16}$ (Exercise 50)

Group Activity

Creating a Quadratic Model of the Form $y = a(x - h)^2 + k$

Estimated time: 20 minutes

Group Size: 3

The table below has data points taken from an experiment involving the path of a softball that is thrown from
right field to third base. The values of t represent the time in seconds after the ball was released, and y represents
the height of the ball in feet.

Time (sec) t	0	0.2	0.4	0.6	0.8	1.0	1.2	1.4	1.6	1.8	2.0
Height (ft) y	5	11	16	19	21	22	21	19	16	12	6

1. Graph the points defined by (t, y) in the table.

2. Select a point that you think best represents the vertex of the
parabola. Label this point (h, k).

$(h, k) = $ _____(1, 22)_____

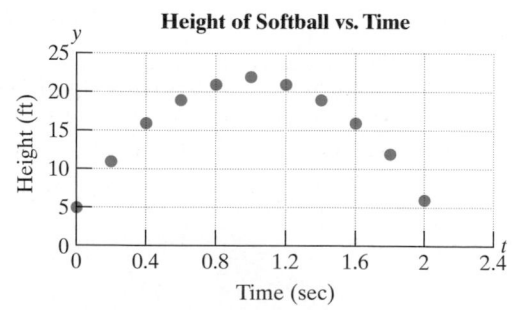

Height of Softball vs. Time

3. Substitute the values of h and k into the formula $y = a(t - h)^2 + k$, and write the equation here.

$$y = a(t - \underline{}1\underline{})^2 + \underline{}22\underline{}$$

4. Choose a different point (t, y) from the graph. Substitute these values into the equation in step 3 and then solve for a.

Answers will vary based on the choices for (h, k) and (t, y). However, a should be close to -16.

5. Substitute the values of h, k, and a that you found in steps 2 and 4 into the equation $y = a(t - h)^2 + k$.

Answers will vary, but should be close to $y = -16(t - 1)^2 + 22$.

6. Use the function found in step 5 to approximate the height of the ball after 0.7 sec.

Answers should be close to 20.56 ft.

7. Use the function found in step 5 to approximate the height of the ball after 1.8 sec. How well does this value match the observed value of 12 ft?

Answers will vary, but should be close to the observed value of 12 ft.

Chapter 11 Summary

Section 11.1 Square Root Property and Completing the Square

Key Concepts

The **square root property** states that

If $x^2 = k$ then $x = \pm\sqrt{k}$

Follow these steps to solve a quadratic equation in the form $ax^2 + bx + c = 0$ $(a \neq 0)$ by completing the square and applying the square root property:

1. Divide both sides by a to make the leading coefficient 1.
2. Isolate the variable terms on one side of the equation.
3. Complete the square: Add the square of one-half the linear term coefficient to both sides of the equation. Then factor the resulting perfect square trinomial.
4. Apply the square root property and solve for x.

Examples

Example 1

$(x - 5)^2 = -13$

$x - 5 = \pm\sqrt{-13}$ (square root property)

$x = 5 \pm i\sqrt{13}$

The solution set is $\{5 \pm i\sqrt{13}\}$.

Example 2

$2x^2 - 12x - 16 = 0$

$\dfrac{2x^2}{2} - \dfrac{12x}{2} - \dfrac{16}{2} = \dfrac{0}{2}$

$x^2 - 6x - 8 = 0$

$x^2 - 6x = 8$

$x^2 - 6x + 9 = 8 + 9$ *Note:* $[\tfrac{1}{2}(-6)]^2 = 9$

$(x - 3)^2 = 17$

$x - 3 = \pm\sqrt{17}$

$x = 3 \pm \sqrt{17}$

The solution set is $\{3 \pm \sqrt{17}\}$.

Section 11.2 Quadratic Formula

Key Concepts

The solutions to a quadratic equation
$ax^2 + bx + c = 0$ $(a \neq 0)$ are given by the **quadratic formula**

$$x = \frac{-b \pm \sqrt{b^2 - 4ac}}{2a}$$

The **discriminant** of a quadratic equation $ax^2 + bx + c = 0$ is $b^2 - 4ac$. If a, b, and c are rational numbers, then

1. If $b^2 - 4ac > 0$, then there will be two real solutions. Moreover,
   a. If $b^2 - 4ac$ is a perfect square, the solutions will be rational numbers.
   b. If $b^2 - 4ac$ is not a perfect square, the solutions will be irrational numbers.
2. If $b^2 - 4ac < 0$, then there will be two imaginary solutions.
3. If $b^2 - 4ac = 0$, then there will be one rational solution.

Three methods to solve a quadratic equation are

1. Factoring and applying the zero product rule.
2. Completing the square and applying the square root property.
3. Using the quadratic formula.

Example

Example 1

$$3x^2 - 2x + 4 = 0$$

$$a = 3 \qquad b = -2 \qquad c = 4$$

$$x = \frac{-(-2) \pm \sqrt{(-2)^2 - 4(3)(4)}}{2(3)}$$

$$= \frac{2 \pm \sqrt{4 - 48}}{6}$$

$$= \frac{2 \pm \sqrt{-44}}{6} \qquad \text{The discriminant is } -44. \text{ Therefore, there will be two imaginary solutions.}$$

$$= \frac{2 \pm 2i\sqrt{11}}{6}$$

$$= \frac{\overset{1}{2}(1 \pm i\sqrt{11})}{\underset{3}{6}}$$

$$= \frac{1 \pm i\sqrt{11}}{3}$$

$$= \frac{1}{3} \pm \frac{\sqrt{11}}{3}i$$

The solution set is $\left\{ \dfrac{1}{3} \pm \dfrac{\sqrt{11}}{3}i \right\}$.

Section 11.3 Equations in Quadratic Form

Key Concepts

Substitution can be used to solve equations that are in quadratic form.

Example

Example 1

$$x^{2/3} - x^{1/3} - 12 = 0 \quad \text{Let } u = x^{1/3}.$$

$$u^2 - u - 12 = 0$$

$$(u - 4)(u + 3) = 0$$

$$u = 4 \qquad \text{or} \qquad u = -3$$

$$x^{1/3} = 4 \qquad \text{or} \qquad x^{1/3} = -3$$

$$x = 64 \qquad \text{or} \qquad x = -27 \quad \text{Cube both sides.}$$

The solution set is $\{64, -27\}$.

Section 11.4   Graphs of Quadratic Functions

Key Concepts

A quadratic function of the form $f(x) = x^2 + k$ shifts the graph of $y = x^2$ up k units if $k > 0$ and down $|k|$ units if $k < 0$.

A quadratic function of the form $f(x) = (x - h)^2$ shifts the graph of $y = x^2$ right h units if $h > 0$ and left $|h|$ units if $h < 0$.

The graph of a quadratic function of the form $f(x) = ax^2$ is a parabola that opens upward when $a > 0$ and opens downward when $a < 0$. If $|a| > 1$, the graph of $y = x^2$ is stretched vertically by a factor of $|a|$. If $0 < |a| < 1$, the graph of $y = x^2$ is shrunk vertically by a factor of $|a|$.

A quadratic function of the form $f(x) = a(x - h)^2 + k$ has vertex (h, k). If $a > 0$, the vertex represents the minimum point. If $a < 0$, the vertex represents the maximum point.

Examples

Example 1

Example 2

Example 3

Example 4

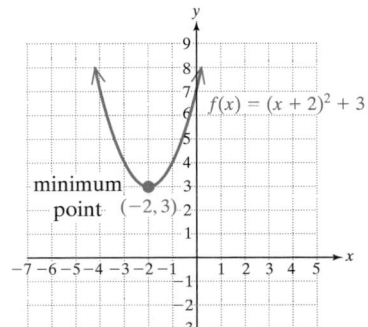

| **Section 11.5** | **Vertex of a Parabola: Applications and Modeling** |

Key Concepts

Completing the square is a technique used to write a quadratic function $f(x) = ax^2 + bx + c$ $(a \neq 0)$ in the form $f(x) = a(x - h)^2 + k$ for the purpose of identifying the vertex (h, k).

Examples

Example 1

$$f(x) = 3x^2 + 6x + 11$$
$$= 3(x^2 + 2x \qquad\quad) + 11$$
$$= 3(x^2 + 2x + 1 - 1) + 11$$
$$= 3(x^2 + 2x + 1) - 3 + 11$$
$$= 3(x + 1)^2 + 8$$
$$= 3[x - (-1)]^2 + 8$$

The vertex is $(-1, 8)$. Because $a = 3 > 0$, the parabola opens upward and the vertex $(-1, 8)$ is a minimum point.

The **vertex formula** finds the vertex of a quadratic function $f(x) = ax^2 + bx + c$ $(a \neq 0)$.

The vertex is

$$\left(\frac{-b}{2a}, \frac{4ac - b^2}{4a}\right) \quad \text{or} \quad \left(\frac{-b}{2a}, f\left(\frac{-b}{2a}\right)\right)$$

Example 2

$$f(x) = 3x^2 + 6x + 11$$
$$a = 3 \qquad b = 6 \qquad c = 11$$
$$x = \frac{-6}{2(3)} = -1$$
$$f(-1) = 3(-1)^2 + 6(-1) + 11 = 8$$

The vertex is $(-1, 8)$.

Chapter 11   Review Exercises

Section 11.1

For Exercises 1–8, solve the equations by using the square root property.

1. $x^2 = 5$ $\{\pm\sqrt{5}\}$

2. $2y^2 = -8$ $\{\pm 2i\}$

3. $a^2 = 81$ $\{\pm 9\}$

4. $3b^2 = -19$ $\left\{\pm\dfrac{\sqrt{57}}{3}i\right\}$

5. $(x - 2)^2 = 72$
$\{2 \pm 6\sqrt{2}\}$

6. $(2x - 5)^2 = -9$ $\left\{\dfrac{5}{2} \pm \dfrac{3}{2}i\right\}$

7. $(3y - 1)^2 = 3$ $\left\{\dfrac{1 \pm \sqrt{3}}{3}\right\}$

8. $3(m - 4)^2 = 15$
$\{4 \pm \sqrt{5}\}$

9. The length of each side of an equilateral triangle is 10 in. Find the height of the triangle. Round the answer to the nearest tenth of an inch.
$5\sqrt{3}$ in. ≈ 8.7 in.

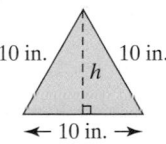
10 in.   10 in.
h
← 10 in. →

10. Use the square root property to find the length of the sides of a square whose area is 81 in².
9 in.

11. Use the square root property to find the length of the sides of a square whose area is 150 in². Round the answer to the nearest tenth of an inch. $5\sqrt{6}$ in. ≈ 12.2 in.

For Exercises 12–15, find the value of n so that the expression is a perfect square trinomial. Then factor the trinomial.

12. $x^2 + 16x + n$
$n = 64; (x + 8)^2$

13. $x^2 - 9x + n$
$n = \dfrac{81}{4}; \left(x - \dfrac{9}{2}\right)^2$

14. $y^2 + \dfrac{1}{2}y + n$
$n = \dfrac{1}{16}; \left(y + \dfrac{1}{4}\right)^2$

15. $z^2 - \dfrac{2}{5}z + n$
$n = \dfrac{1}{25}; \left(z - \dfrac{1}{5}\right)^2$

For Exercises 16–21, solve the equation by completing the square and applying the square root property.

16. $w^2 + 4w + 13 = 0$
$\{-2 \pm 3i\}$

17. $4y^2 - 8y - 20 = 0$
$\{1 \pm \sqrt{6}\}$

18. $2x^2 = 12x + 6$
$\{3 \pm 2\sqrt{3}\}$

19. $-t^2 + 8t - 25 = 0$
$\{4 \pm 3i\}$

20. $3x^2 + 2x = 1$
$\left\{\dfrac{1}{3}, -1\right\}$

21. $b^2 + \dfrac{7}{2}b = 2$
$\left\{\dfrac{1}{2}, -4\right\}$

22. Solve for r. $V = \pi r^2 h$ $(r > 0)$ $r = \sqrt{\dfrac{V}{\pi h}}$ or $r = \dfrac{\sqrt{V\pi h}}{\pi h}$

23. Solve for s. $A = 6s^2$ $(s > 0)$ $s = \sqrt{\dfrac{A}{6}}$ or $s = \dfrac{\sqrt{6A}}{6}$

Section 11.2

24. Explain how the discriminant can determine the type and number of solutions to a quadratic equation with rational coefficients. See page 788.

For Exercises 25–30, determine the type (rational, irrational, or imaginary) and number of solutions for the equations by using the discriminant.

25. $x^2 - 5x = -6$
Two rational solutions

26. $2y^2 = -3y$
Two rational solutions

27. $z^2 + 23 = 17z$
Two irrational solutions

28. $a^2 + a + 1 = 0$
Two imaginary solutions

29. $10b + 1 = -25b^2$
One rational solution

30. $3x^2 + 15 = 0$
Two imaginary solutions

For Exercises 31–38, solve the equations by using the quadratic formula.

31. $y^2 - 4y + 1 = 0$
$\{2 \pm \sqrt{3}\}$

32. $m^2 - 5m + 25 = 0$
$\left\{\dfrac{5}{2} \pm \dfrac{5\sqrt{3}}{2}i\right\}$

33. $6a(a - 1) = 10 + a$
$\left\{2, -\dfrac{5}{6}\right\}$

34. $3x(x - 3) = x - 8$
$\left\{2, \dfrac{4}{3}\right\}$

35. $b^2 - \dfrac{4}{25} = \dfrac{3}{5}b$
$\left\{\dfrac{4}{5}, -\dfrac{1}{5}\right\}$

36. $k^2 + 0.4k = 0.05$
$\left\{\dfrac{1}{10}, -\dfrac{1}{2}\right\}$

37. $-32 + 4x - x^2 = 0$
$\{2 \pm 2i\sqrt{7}\}$

38. $8y - y^2 - 10$
$\{4 \pm \sqrt{6}\}$

For Exercises 39–42, solve using any method.

39. $3x^2 - 4x = 6$
$\left\{\dfrac{2 \pm \sqrt{22}}{3}\right\}$

40. $\dfrac{w}{8} - \dfrac{2}{w} = \dfrac{3}{4}$
$\{8, -2\}$

41. $y^2 + 14y = -46$
$\{-7 \pm \sqrt{3}\}$

42. $(a + 1)^2 = 11$
$\{-1 \pm \sqrt{11}\}$

43. The landing distance that a certain plane will travel on a runway is determined by the initial landing speed at the instant the plane touches down. The function D relates landing distance in feet to initial landing speed s:

$$D(s) = \dfrac{1}{10}s^2 - 3s + 22 \text{ for } s \geq 50$$

where s is in feet per second.

 Writing   ← → Translating Expression   Geometry   Scientific Calculator   Video   NS&E

a. Find the landing distance for a plane traveling 150 ft/sec at touchdown. 1822 ft

b. If the landing speed is too fast, the pilot may run out of runway. If the speed is too slow, the plane may stall. Find the maximum initial landing speed of a plane for a runway that is 1000 ft long. Round to one decimal place. 115 ft/s

44. The recent population of Kenya (in thousands) can be approximated by $P(t) = 4.62t^2 + 564.6t + 13,128$, where t is the number of years since 1974.

    a. If this trend continues, approximate the number of people in Kenya for the year 2025. ≈53,939 thousand

    b. In what year after 1974 will the population of Kenya reach 50 million? (*Hint:* 50 million equals 50,000 thousand.) 2021

45. A custom-built kitchen island is in the shape of a rectangle. The length is 1 ft more than twice the width. If the area is 22.32 ft², determine the dimensions of the island.
The dimensions are approximately 3.1 ft by 7.2 ft.

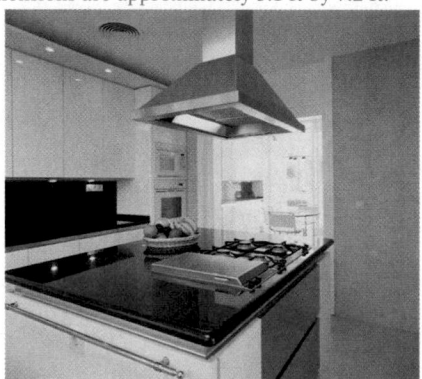

46. Lincoln, Nebraska, Kansas City, Missouri, and Omaha, Nebraska, form the vertices of a right triangle. The distance between Lincoln and Kansas City is 10 mi more than 3 times the distance between Lincoln and Omaha. If the distance from Omaha and Kansas City is 167 mi, find the distance between Lincoln and Omaha. Round to the nearest mile.
The distance between Lincoln and Omaha is approximately 50 mi.

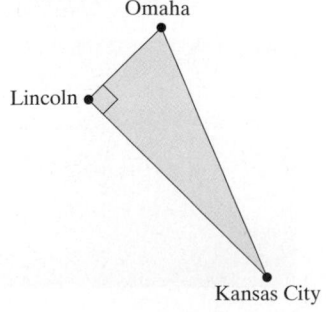

Section 11.3

For Exercises 47–56, solve the equations by using substitution, if necessary.

47. $x - 4\sqrt{x} - 21 = 0$ {49} (The value 9 does not check.)

48. $n - 6\sqrt{n} + 8 = 0$ {4, 16}

49. $y^4 - 11y^2 + 18 = 0$ {±3, ±√2}

50. $2m^4 - m^2 - 3 = 0$ $\left\{\pm\dfrac{\sqrt{6}}{2}, \pm i\right\}$

51. $t^{2/5} + t^{1/5} - 6 = 0$ {−243, 32}

52. $p^{2/5} - 3p^{1/5} + 2 = 0$ {32, 1}

53. $\dfrac{2t}{t + 1} + \dfrac{-3}{t - 2} = 1$ {3 ± √10}

54. $\dfrac{1}{m - 2} - \dfrac{m}{m + 3} = 2$ $\left\{\dfrac{1 \pm \sqrt{181}}{6}\right\}$

55. $(x^2 + 5)^2 + 2(x^2 + 5) - 8 = 0$ {±3i, ±i√3}

56. $(x^2 - 3)^2 - 5(x^2 - 3) + 4 = 0$ {±√7, ±2}

Section 11.4

For Exercises 57–64, graph the functions.

57. $g(x) = x^2 - 5$ **58.** $f(x) = x^2 + 3$

  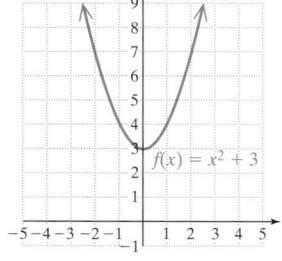

59. $h(x) = (x - 5)^2$ **60.** $k(x) = (x + 3)^2$

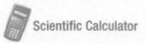 Writing   ⟷ Translating Expression   ◁ Geometry   Scientific Calculator   ● Video   NS&E

61. $m(x) = -2x^2$

62. $n(x) = -4x^2$

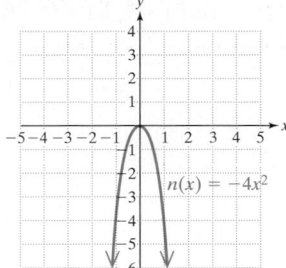

63. $p(x) = -2(x - 5)^2 - 5$ **64.** $q(x) = -4(x + 3)^2 + 3$

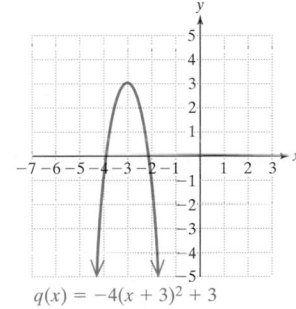

For Exercises 65–66, write the coordinates of the vertex of the parabola and determine if the vertex is a maximum point or a minimum point. Then write the maximum or the minimum value.

65. $t(x) = \dfrac{1}{3}(x - 4)^2 + \dfrac{5}{3}$ $\left(4, \dfrac{5}{3}\right)$ is the minimum point

The minimum value is $\dfrac{5}{3}$.

66. $s(x) = -\dfrac{5}{7}(x - 1)^2 - \dfrac{1}{7}$ $\left(1, -\dfrac{1}{7}\right)$ is the maximum point.

The maximum value is $-\dfrac{1}{7}$.

For Exercises 67–68, write the equation of the axis of symmetry of the parabola.

67. $a(x) = -\dfrac{3}{2}\left(x + \dfrac{2}{11}\right)^2 - \dfrac{4}{13}$ $x = -\dfrac{2}{11}$

68. $w(x) = -\dfrac{4}{3}\left(x - \dfrac{3}{16}\right)^2 + \dfrac{2}{9}$ $x = \dfrac{3}{16}$

Section 11.5

For Exercises 69–72, write the function in the form $f(x) = a(x - h)^2 + k$ by completing the square. Then write the coordinates of the vertex.

69. $z(x) = x^2 - 6x + 7$

$z(x) = (x - 3)^2 - 2; (3, -2)$

70. $b(x) = x^2 - 4x - 44$

$b(x) = (x - 2)^2 - 48; (2, -48)$

71. $p(x) = -5x^2 - 10x - 13$

$p(x) = -5(x + 1)^2 - 8; (-1, -8)$

72. $q(x) = -3x^2 - 24x - 54$

$q(x) = -3(x + 4)^2 - 6; (-4, -6)$

For Exercises 73–76, find the coordinates of the vertex of each parabola by using the vertex formula.

73. $f(x) = -2x^2 + 4x - 17$ $(1, -15)$

74. $g(x) = -4x^2 - 8x + 3$ $(-1, 7)$

75. $m(x) = 3x^2 - 3x + 11$ $\left(\dfrac{1}{2}, \dfrac{41}{4}\right)$

76. $n(x) = 3x^2 + 2x - 7$ $\left(-\dfrac{1}{3}, -\dfrac{22}{3}\right)$

77. For the quadratic equation $y = \dfrac{3}{4}x^2 - 3x$,

  a. Write the coordinates of the vertex. $(2, -3)$

  b. Find the x- and y-intercepts. $(0, 0)$, $(4, 0)$

  c. Use this information to sketch a graph of the parabola.

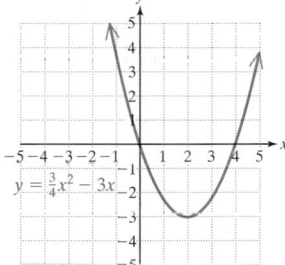

78. For the quadratic equation $y = -(x + 2)^2 + 4$,

  a. Write the coordinates of the vertex. $(-2, 4)$

  b. Find the x- and y-intercepts. $(0, 0)$ $(-4, 0)$

  c. Use this information to sketch a graph of the parabola.

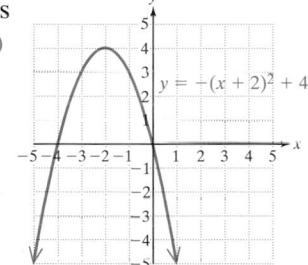

79. The height $h(t)$ (in feet) of a projectile fired vertically into the air from the ground is given by the equation $h(t) = -16t^2 + 96t$, where t represents the number of seconds that the projectile has been in the air.

  a. How long will it take the projectile to reach its maximum height?   3 sec

  b. What is the maximum height?   144 ft

80. The weekly profit, $P(x)$ (in dollars), for a catering service is given by $P(x) = -0.053x^2 + 15.9x + 7.5$. In this context, x is the number of meals prepared.

  a. Find the number of meals that should be prepared to obtain the maximum profit.   150 meals

  b. What is the maximum profit? $1200

 Writing   Translating Expression   Geometry   Scientific Calculator   Video   NS&E

81. Write an equation of a parabola that passes through the points $(-3, -4)$, $(-2, -5)$, and $(1, 4)$ $a = 1, b = 4, c = -1; y = x^2 + 4x - 1$

82. Write an equation of a parabola that passes through the points $(4, 18)$, $(-2, 12)$, and $(-1, 8)$ $a = 1, b = -1, c = 6; y = x^2 - x + 6$

Chapter 11   Test

For Exercises 1–3, solve the equation by using the square root property.

1. $(x + 3)^2 = 25$ $\{2, -8\}$

2. $(p - 2)^2 = 12$ $\{2 \pm 2\sqrt{3}\}$

3. $(m + 1)^2 = -1$ $\{-1 \pm i\}$

4. Find the value of n so that the expression is a perfect square trinomial. Then factor the trinomial $d^2 + 11d + n$. $n = \dfrac{121}{4}; \left(d + \dfrac{11}{2}\right)^2$

For Exercises 5–6, solve the equation by completing the square and applying the square root property.

5. $2x^2 + 12x - 36 = 0$ $\{-3 \pm 3\sqrt{3}\}$

6. $2x^2 = 3x - 7$ $\left\{\dfrac{3}{4} \pm \dfrac{\sqrt{47}}{4}i\right\}$

For Exercises 7–8,

   a. Write the equation in standard form $ax^2 + bx + c = 0$.

   b. Identify $a, b,$ and c.

   c. Find the discriminant.

   d. Determine the number and type (rational, irrational, or imaginary) of solutions.

7. $x^2 - 3x = -12$

a. $x^2 - 3x + 12 = 0$
b. $a = 1, b = -3, c = 12$
c. -39
d. Two imaginary solutions

8. $y(y - 2) = -1$

a. $y^2 - 2y + 1 = 0$
b. $a = 1, b = -2, c = 1$
c. 0
d. One rational solution

For Exercises 9–10, solve the equation by using the quadratic formula.

9. $3x^2 - 4x + 1 = 0$ $\left\{1, \dfrac{1}{3}\right\}$

10. $x(x + 6) = -11 - x$ $\left\{\dfrac{-7 \pm \sqrt{5}}{2}\right\}$

11. The base of a triangle is 3 ft less than twice the height. The area of the triangle is 14 ft². Find the base and the height. Round the answers to the nearest tenth of a foot.
The height is approximately 4.6 ft and the base is 6.2 ft.

12. A circular garden has an area of approximately 450 ft². Find the radius. Round the answer to the nearest tenth of a foot.
The radius is approximately 12.0 ft.

For Exercises 13–17, solve the equation.

13. $x - \sqrt{x} - 6 = 0$
$\{9\}$ (The value 4 does not check.)

14. $y^{2/3} + 2y^{1/3} = 8$
$\{8, -64\}$

15. $(3y - 8)^2 - 13(3y - 8) + 30 = 0$ $\left\{\dfrac{11}{3}, 6\right\}$

16. $p^4 - 15p^2 = -54$
$\{\pm\sqrt{6}, \pm 3\}$

17. $3 = \dfrac{y}{2} - \dfrac{1}{y + 1}$
$\left\{\dfrac{5 \pm \sqrt{57}}{2}\right\}$

18. Find the vertex of $y = x^2 - 6x - 8$ two ways,

   a. By completing the square.

   b. By using the vertex formula.   The vertex is $(3, -17)$.

For Exercises 19–21, graph the functions.

19. $h(x) = x^2 - 4$

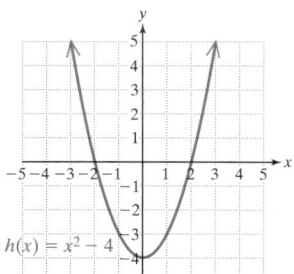

20. $f(x) = (x - 4)^2$

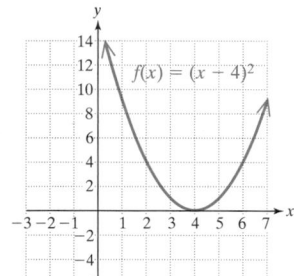

21. $g(x) = \dfrac{1}{2}(x + 2)^2 - 3$

 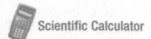

22. A child launches a toy rocket from the ground. The height of the rocket can be determined by its horizontal distance from the launch pad x by

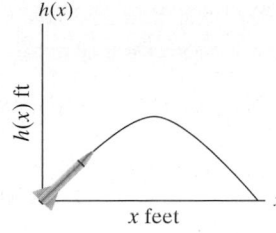

$$h(x) = -\frac{x^2}{256} + x$$

where x and $h(x)$ are in feet. How many feet from the launch pad will the rocket hit the ground?

The rocket will hit the ground 256 ft away.

23. The recent population of India (in millions) can be approximated by $P(t) = 0.135t^2 + 12.6t + 600$, where $t = 0$ corresponds to the year 1974.

  a. If this trend continues, approximate the number of people in India in the year 2014.
  1320 million

  b. Approximate the year in which the population of India reached 1 billion (1000 million). (Round to the nearest year.)
  1999

24. Explain the relationship between the graphs of $y = x^2$ and $y = x^2 - 2$.   The graph of $y = x^2 - 2$ is the graph of $y = x^2$ shifted down 2 units.

25. Explain the relationship between the graphs of $y = x^2$ and $y = (x + 3)^2$.   The graph of $y = (x + 3)^2$ is the graph of $y = x^2$ shifted 3 units to the left.

26. Explain the relationship between the graphs of $y = 4x^2$ and $y = -4x^2$.   The graph of $y = -4x^2$ is the graph of $y = 4x^2$ opening downward instead of upward.

27. Given the function defined by

$$f(x) = -(x - 4)^2 + 2$$

  a. Identify the vertex of the parabola. $(4, 2)$

  b. Does this parabola open upward or downward?
  Downward

  c. Does the vertex represent the maximum or minimum point of the function?   Maximum point

  d. What is the maximum or minimum value of the function f?   The maximum value is 2.

  e. Write an equation for the axis of symmetry.
  $x = 4$

28. For the function defined by $g(x) = 2x^2 - 20x + 51$, find the vertex by using two methods.

  a. Complete the square to write $g(x)$ in the form $g(x) = a(x - h)^2 + k$. Identify the vertex.
  $g(x) = 2(x - 5)^2 + 1; (5, 1)$

  b. Use the vertex formula to find the vertex.
  $(5, 1)$

29. Given: $f(x) = x^2 + 4x - 12$

  a. Write the equation for the function in the form $f(x) = a(x - h)^2 + k$.
  $f(x) = (x + 2)^2 - 16$

  b. Determine the vertex.
  Vertex: $(-2, -16)$

  c. Find the x- and y-intercepts.
  x-intercepts: $(-6, 0)$ and $(2, 0)$; y-intercept: $(0, -12)$

  d. Determine the maximum or minimum value.
  The minimum value is -16.

  e. Write an equation for the axis of symmetry.
  $x = -2$

30. A farmer has 400 ft of fencing with which to enclose a rectangular field. The field is situated such that one of its sides is adjacent to a river and requires no fencing. The area of the field (in square feet) can be modeled by

$$A(x) = -\frac{x^2}{2} + 200x$$

where x is the length of the side parallel to the river (measured in feet).

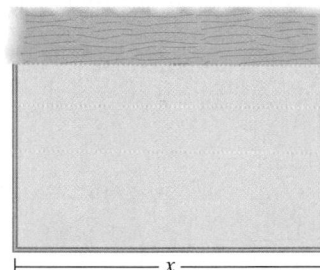

  a. Determine the value of x that maximizes the area of the field.   200 ft

  b. Determine the maximum area that can be enclosed.   20,000 ft^2

Chapters 1–11   Cumulative Review Exercises

1. Given: $A = \{2, 4, 6, 8, 10\}$ and $B = \{2, 8, 12, 16\}$

   a. Find $A \cup B$.   **b.** Find $A \cap B$.

   $\{2, 4, 6, 8, 10, 12, 16\}$ $\{2, 8\}$

2. Perform the indicated operations and simplify.

$$(2x^2 - 5) - (x + 3)(5x - 2)$$

$-3x^2 - 13x + 1$

3. Simplify completely. $4^0 - \left(\dfrac{1}{2}\right)^{-3} - 81^{1/2}$ -16

4. Perform the indicated operations. Write the answer in scientific notation: 1.8×10^{10}

$$(3.0 \times 10^{12})(6.0 \times 10^{-3})$$

5. a. Factor completely. $x^3 + 2x^2 - 9x - 18$

   $(x + 2)(x + 3)(x - 3)$

   b. Divide by using long division. Identify the quotient and remainder.

$$(x^3 + 2x^2 - 9x - 18) \div (x - 3)$$

   Quotient: $x^2 + 5x + 6$; remainder: 0

6. Multiply. $(\sqrt{x} - \sqrt{2})(\sqrt{x} + \sqrt{2})$ $x - 2$

7. Simplify. $\dfrac{4}{\sqrt{2x}}$ $\dfrac{2\sqrt{2x}}{x}$

8. Jacques invests a total of $10,000 in two mutual funds. After 1 yr, one fund produced 12% growth, and the other lost 3%. Find the amount invested in each fund if the total investment grew by $900.

   $8000 in 12% account; $2000 in 3% account

9. Solve the system of equations. $\{(8, 7)\}$

$$\frac{1}{9}x - \frac{1}{3}y = -\frac{13}{9}$$

$$x - \frac{1}{2}y = \frac{9}{2}$$

10. An object is fired straight up into the air from an initial height of 384 ft with an initial velocity of 160 ft/sec. The height in feet is given by

$$h(t) = -16t^2 + 160t + 384$$

   where t is the time in seconds after launch.

   a. Find the height of the object after 3 sec.
   720 ft

   b. Find the height of the object after 7 sec.
   720 ft

   c. Find the time required for the object to hit the ground.   12 sec

11. Solve. $(x - 3)^2 + 16 = 0$ $\{3 \pm 4i\}$

12. Solve. $2x^2 + 5x - 1 = 0$ $\left\{\dfrac{-5 \pm \sqrt{33}}{4}\right\}$

13. Find the value of n so that the expression is a perfect square trinomial. Then factor the trinomial $x^2 + 10x + n$. $n = 25; (x + 5)^2$

14. Factor completely. $2x^3 + 250$

   $2(x + 5)(x^2 - 5x + 25)$

15. Graph the equation. $3x - 5y = 10$

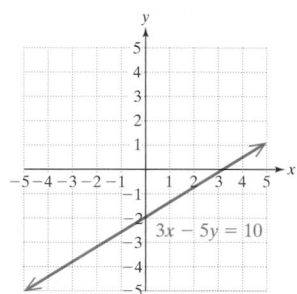

16. a. Find the x-intercepts of the function defined by $g(x) = 2x^2 - 9x + 10$. $\left(\dfrac{5}{2}, 0\right), (2, 0)$

   b. What is the y-intercept? $(0, 10)$

17. Explain why this relation is *not* a function.
The domain element 3 has more than one corresponding range element.

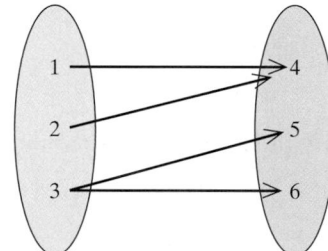

18. Graph the function defined by $f(x) = \dfrac{1}{x}$.

19. The quantity y varies directly as x and inversely as z. If $y = 15$ when $x = 50$ and $z = 10$, find y when $x = 65$ and $z = 5$. $y = 39$

20. The total number of flights (including passenger flights and cargo flights) at a large airport can be approximated by $F(x) = 300{,}000 + 0.008x$, where x is the number of passengers.

   a. Is this function linear, quadratic, constant, or other?   Linear

   b. Find the y-intercept and interpret its meaning in the context of this problem. $(0, 300{,}000)$. If there are no passengers, the airport runs 300,000 flights per year.

   c. What is the slope of the function and what does the slope mean in the context of this problem? $m = 0.008$ or $m = \frac{8}{1000}$. There are eight additional flights per 1000 passengers.

21. Let $m(x) = \sqrt{x} + 4$ and $n(x) = x^2 + 2$. Find

   a. The domain of m **b.** The domain of n
     $[-4, \infty)$ $(-\infty, \infty)$

22. Consider the function $y = f(x)$ graphed here. Find

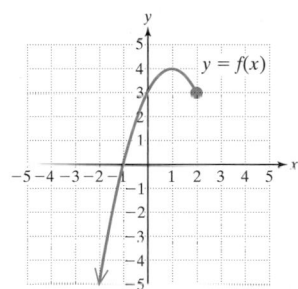

   a. The domain $(-\infty, 2]$ **b.** The range $(-\infty, 4]$

   c. $f(1)$ 4   **d.** $f(0)$ 3

   e. For what value(s) of x is $f(x) = 0$? $x = -1$

23. Solve. $\sqrt{8x + 5} = \sqrt{2x} + 2$ $\left\{\frac{1}{18}, \frac{1}{2}\right\}$

24. Solve for f. $\dfrac{1}{p} + \dfrac{1}{q} = \dfrac{1}{f}$ $f = \dfrac{pq}{p + q}$

25. Solve. $\dfrac{15}{t^2 - 2t - 8} = \dfrac{1}{t - 4} + \dfrac{2}{t + 2}$ $\{7\}$

26. Simplify. $\dfrac{y - \dfrac{4}{y - 3}}{y - 4}$ $\dfrac{y + 1}{y - 3}$

27. Given the function defined by $f(x) = 2(x - 3)^2 + 1$

   a. Write the coordinates of the vertex. $(3, 1)$

   b. Does the graph of the function open upward or downward?   Upward

   c. Write the coordinates of the y-intercept. $(0, 19)$

   d. Find the x-intercepts, if possible.   No x-intercept

   e. Sketch the function.

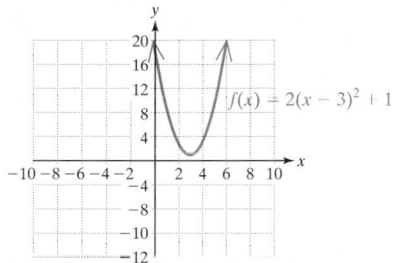

28. Find the vertex of the parabola.   Vertex: $(8, -62)$

$$f(x) = x^2 - 16x + 2$$

29. **a.** Solve the inequality. $2x^2 + x - 10 \geq 0$
     $\left(-\infty, -\dfrac{5}{2}\right] \cup [2, \infty)$

   b. How does the answer in part (a) relate to the graph of the function $f(x) = 2x^2 + x - 10$?

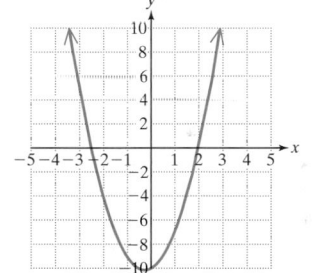

   On these intervals, the graph is on or above the x-axis

30. Solve the inequality. $\dfrac{8}{x - 3} \leq 4$ $(-\infty, 3) \cup [5, \infty)$

Exponential and Logarithmic Functions and Applications

12

Chapter 12

This chapter is devoted to the study of exponential and logarithmic functions. These functions are used to study many naturally occurring phenomena such as population growth, exponential decay of radioactive matter, and growth of investments.

Are You Prepared?

To prepare yourself for this chapter, practice evaluating the expressions with exponents. Use the clues to fill in the boxes labeled A–H. Then fill in the remaining part of the grid so that every row, every column, and every 2 × 3 box contains the digits 1 through 6.

A. Value of x in the equation $5^x = 25$.

B. Value of x in the equation $3^x = 81$.

C. Value of x in the equation $8^{1/x} = 2$.

D. Real value of x in the equation $x^4 = 16$ (assume that $x > 0$).

E. Absolute value of x in the equation $2^x = \dfrac{1}{16}$.

F. Value of x in the equation $2^x = 64$.

G. Value of x in the equation $5^0 = x$.

H. Value of x in the equation $e^0 = x$.

5	1	ᴮ4	ᶜ3	6	2
3	ꜰ6	2	1	4	5
ᴳ1	5	3	6	ᴰ2	4
ᴬ2	4	6	5	1	3
6	2	5	ᴱ4	3	1
4	3	ᴴ1	2	5	6

Concepts

1. Introduction to Inverse Functions
2. Definition of a One-to-One Function
3. Finding an Equation of the Inverse of a Function
4. Definition of the Inverse of a Function

Avoiding Mistakes

f^{-1} denotes the inverse of a function. The -1 does not represent an exponent.

1. Introduction to Inverse Functions

In Section 8.2, we defined a function as a set of ordered pairs (x, y) such that for every element x in the domain, there corresponds exactly one element y in the range. For example, the function f relates the weight of a package of deli meat, x, to its cost, y.

$$f = \{(1, 4), (2.5, 10), (4, 16)\}$$

That is, 1 lb of meat sells for $4, 2.5 lb sells for $10, and 4 lb sells for $16. Now suppose we create a new function in which the values of x and y are interchanged. The new function, called the *inverse of f*, denoted f^{-1}, relates the price of meat, x, to its weight, y.

$$f^{-1} = \{(4, 1), (10, 2.5), (16, 4)\}$$

Notice that interchanging the x- and y-values has the following outcome. The domain of f is the same as the range of f^{-1}, and the range of f is the domain of f^{-1}.

2. Definition of a One-to-One Function

A necessary condition for a function f to have an inverse function is that no two ordered pairs in f have different x-coordinates and the same y-coordinate. A function that satisfies this condition is called a **one-to-one function**. The function relating the weight of a package of meat to its price is a one-to-one function. However, consider the function g defined by

$$g = \{(1, 4), (2, 3), (-2, 4)\}$$

same y

different x

This function is not one-to-one because the range element 4 has two different x-coordinates, 1 and -2. Interchanging the x- and y-values produces a relation that violates the definition of a function.

$$\{(4, 1), (3, 2), (4, -2)\}$$

same x

different y

This relation is not a function because for $x = 4$ there are two different y-values, $y = 1$ and $y = -2$.

In Section 8.2, you learned the vertical line test to determine visually if a graph represents a function. Similarly, we use a **horizontal line test** to determine whether a function is one-to-one.

PROPERTY Using the Horizontal Line Test

Consider a function defined by a set of points (x, y) in a rectangular coordinate system. Then y is a *one-to-one* function of x if no horizontal line intersects the graph in more than one point.

To understand the horizontal line test, consider the functions f and g.

$$f = \{(1, 4), (2.5, 10), (4, 16)\} \qquad g = \{(1, 4), (2, 3), (-2, 4)\}$$

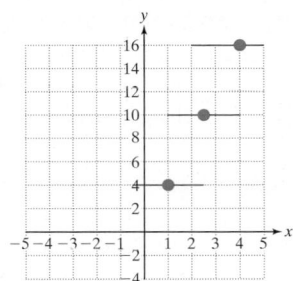

This function is one-to-one. No horizontal line intersects more than once.

This function is *not* one-to-one. A horizontal line intersects more than once.

 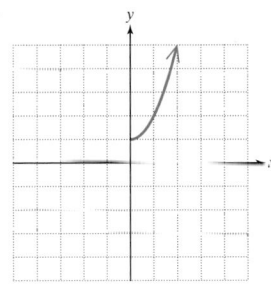

Example 1 **Identifying a One-to-One Function**

Classroom Examples: p. 849, Exercises 18 and 20

For each function, determine if the function is one-to-one.

a.

b.

Solution:

a. Function is not one-to-one. A horizontal line intersects in more than one point.

b. Function is one-to-one. No horizontal line intersects more than once.

 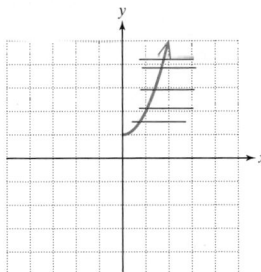

Skill Practice For each function determine if the function is one-to-one.

1.

2.

 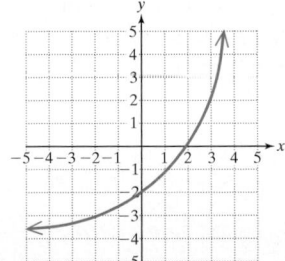

Answers

1. Not one-to-one
2. One-to-one

3. Finding an Equation of the Inverse of a Function

For a one-to-one function defined by $y = f(x)$, the inverse is a function $y = f^{-1}(x)$ that performs the inverse operations in the reverse order. For example, the function defined by $f(x) = 2x + 1$ multiplies x by 2 and then adds 1. Therefore, the inverse function must *subtract* 1 from x and *divide* by 2. We have

$$f^{-1}(x) = \frac{x - 1}{2} \qquad \text{The expression } f^{-1}(x) \text{ is read as "}f\text{ inverse of }x\text{."}$$

To facilitate the process of finding an equation of the inverse of a one-to-one function, we offer the following steps.

PROCEDURE **Finding an Equation of an Inverse of a Function**

For a one-to-one function defined by $y = f(x)$, the equation of the inverse can be found as follows:

Step 1 Replace $f(x)$ by y.

Step 2 Interchange x and y.

Step 3 Solve for y.

Step 4 Replace y by $f^{-1}(x)$.

Classroom Example: p. 849, Exercise 24

Example 2 **Finding an Equation of the Inverse of a Function**

Find the inverse. $\quad f(x) = 2x + 1$

Solution:

Foremost, we know the graph of f is a nonvertical line. Therefore, $f(x) = 2x + 1$ defines a one-to-one function. To find the inverse we have

Instructor Note: It is important for students to check to see if the function is one-to-one. If it is not one-to-one, the function does not have an inverse function.

$$y = 2x + 1 \qquad \textbf{Step 1:} \quad \text{Replace } f(x) \text{ by } y.$$

$$x = 2y + 1 \qquad \textbf{Step 2:} \quad \text{Interchange } x \text{ and } y.$$

$$x - 1 = 2y \qquad \textbf{Step 3:} \quad \text{Solve for } y. \text{ Subtract 1 from both sides.}$$

$$\frac{x - 1}{2} = y \qquad\qquad \text{Divide both sides by 2.}$$

$$f^{-1}(x) = \frac{x - 1}{2} \qquad \textbf{Step 4:} \quad \text{Replace } y \text{ by } f^{-1}(x).$$

Skill Practice Find the inverse.

3. $f(x) = 4x + 6$

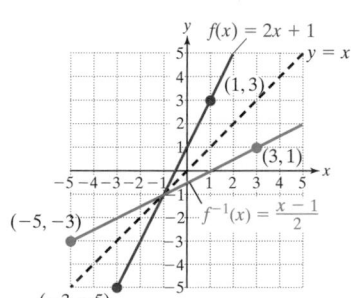

Figure 12-1

The key step in determining the equation of the inverse of a function is to interchange x and y. By so doing, a point (a, b) on f corresponds to a point (b, a) on f^{-1}. For this reason, the graphs of f and f^{-1} are symmetric with respect to the line $y = x$ (Figure 12-1). Notice that the point $(-3, -5)$ of the function f corresponds to the point $(-5, -3)$ of f^{-1}. Likewise, $(1, 3)$ of f corresponds to $(3, 1)$ of f^{-1}.

Answer

3. $f^{-1}(x) = \dfrac{x - 6}{4}$

Example 3 Finding an Equation of the Inverse of a Function

Classroom Example: p. 849, Exercise 28

Find the inverse of the one-to-one function. $g(x) = \sqrt[3]{5x} - 4$

Solution:

$y = \sqrt[3]{5x} - 4$	**Step 1:**	Replace $g(x)$ by y.
$x = \sqrt[3]{5y} - 4$	**Step 2:**	Interchange x and y.
$x + 4 = \sqrt[3]{5y}$	**Step 3:**	Solve for y. Add 4 to both sides.
$(x + 4)^3 = (\sqrt[3]{5y})^3$		To eliminate the cube root, cube both sides.
$(x + 4)^3 = 5y$		Simplify the right side.
$\dfrac{(x + 4)^3}{5} = y$		Divide both sides by 5.
$g^{-1}(x) = \dfrac{(x + 4)^3}{5}$	**Step 4:**	Replace y by $g^{-1}(x)$.

Skill Practice Find the inverse.

4. $h(x) = \sqrt[3]{2x - 1}$

The graphs of g and g^{-1} from Example 3 are shown in Figure 12-2. Once again we see that the graphs of a function and its inverse are symmetric with respect to the line $y = x$.

For a function that is not one-to-one, sometimes we can restrict its domain to create a new function that is one-to-one. This is demonstrated in Example 4.

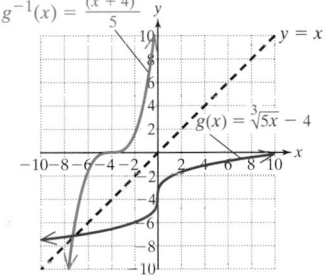

Figure 12-2

Example 4 Finding the Equation of an Inverse of a Function with a Restricted Domain

Classroom Example: p. 849, Exercise 32

Given the function defined by $m(x) = x^2 + 4$ for $x \geq 0$, find an equation defining m^{-1}.

Solution:

From Section 11.4, we know that $y = x^2 + 4$ is a parabola with vertex at $(0, 4)$ (Figure 12-3). The graph represents a function that is not one-to-one. However, with the restriction on the domain $x \geq 0$, the graph of $m(x) = x^2 + 4$, $x \geq 0$, consists of only the "right" branch of the parabola (Figure 12-4). This *is* a one-to-one function.

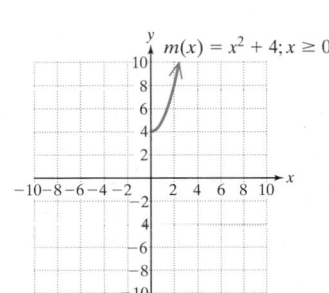

Figure 12-3   **Figure 12-4**

Answer

4. $h^{-1}(x) = \dfrac{x^3 + 1}{2}$

To find the inverse, we have

$$y = x^2 + 4 \qquad x \ge 0$$ **Step 1:** Replace $m(x)$ by y.

$$x = y^2 + 4 \qquad y \ge 0$$ **Step 2:** Interchange x and y. Notice that the restriction $x \ge 0$ becomes $y \ge 0$.

$$x - 4 = y^2 \qquad y \ge 0$$ **Step 3:** Solve for y. Subtract 4 from both sides.

$$\sqrt{x - 4} = y \qquad y \ge 0$$ Apply the square root property. Notice that we obtain the *positive* square root of $x - 4$ because of the restriction $y \ge 0$.

$$m^{-1}(x) = \sqrt{x - 4}$$ **Step 4:** Replace y by $m^{-1}(x)$. Notice that the domain of m^{-1} has the same values as the range of m.

Figure 12-5 shows the graphs of m and m^{-1}.

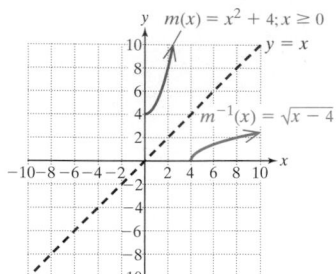

Figure 12-5

Skill Practice Find the inverse.

5. $g(x) = x^2 - 2 \qquad x \ge 0$

4. Definition of the Inverse of a Function

> **DEFINITION   Inverse Function**
>
> If f is a one-to-one function represented by ordered pairs of the form (x, y), then the **inverse function**, denoted f^{-1}, is the set of ordered pairs determined by interchanging the coordinates, denoted by (y, x).

An important relationship between a function and its inverse is shown in Figure 12-6.

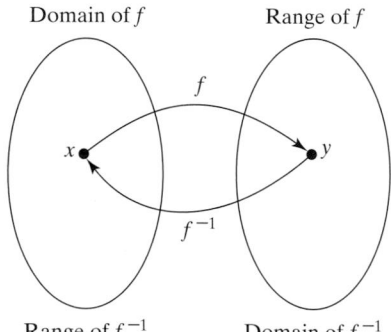

Figure 12-6

Recall that the domain of f is the range of f^{-1} and the range of f is the domain of f^{-1}. The operations performed by f are reversed by f^{-1}. This leads to the inverse function property.

Answer

5. $g^{-1}(x) = \sqrt{x + 2}$

Instructor Note: Ask students to verify the answer from Example 4 by showing that $(m \circ m^{-1})(x) = (m^{-1} \circ m)(x) = x.$

> **PROPERTY** Inverse Function Property
>
> If f is a one-to-one function, then g is the inverse of f if and only if
>
> $$(f \circ g)(x) = x \qquad \text{for all } x \text{ in the domain of } g$$
>
> and
>
> $$(g \circ f)(x) = x \qquad \text{for all } x \text{ in the domain of } f$$
>
> Recall that composition of functions was first introduced in Section 8.4.

Example 5 **Composing a Function with Its Inverse**

Show that the functions are inverses.

$$f(x) = 2x + 1 \qquad g(x) = \frac{x - 1}{2}$$

Classroom Example: p. 850, Exercise 54

Solution:

To show that the functions f and g are inverses, confirm that $(f \circ g)(x) = x$ and $(g \circ f)(x) = x.$

$$(f \circ g)(x) = f(g(x)) \qquad\qquad (g \circ f)(x) = g(f(x))$$

$$= f\!\left(\frac{x - 1}{2}\right) \qquad\qquad = g(2x + 1)$$

$$= 2\!\left(\frac{x - 1}{2}\right) + 1 \qquad\qquad = \frac{(2x + \cancel{1}) - \cancel{1}}{2}$$

$$= x - 1 + 1 \qquad\qquad = \frac{2x}{2}$$

$$= x \checkmark \qquad\qquad = x \checkmark$$

The functions f and g are inverses because $(f \circ g)(x) = x$ and $(g \circ f)(x) = x.$ This also confirms our solution to Example 2.

Skill Practice Show that the functions are inverses.

6. $f(x) = 3x - 2$ and $g(x) = \dfrac{x + 2}{3}$

Answer

6. $(f \circ g)(x) = f(g(x))$

$$= 3\!\left(\frac{x + 2}{3}\right) - 2 = x$$

$(g \circ f)(x) = g(f(x))$

$$= \frac{3x - 2 + 2}{3} = x$$

Section 12.1 Practice Exercises

Study Skills Exercise

1. Define the key terms.

   a. inverse function   **b. one-to-one function**   **c. horizontal line test**

Review Exercises

2. Write the domain and range of the relation $\{(3, 4), (5, -2), (6, 1), (3, 0)\}$.
Domain: $\{3, 5, 6\}$; range: $\{4, -2, 1, 0\}$

For Exercises 3–8, determine the functions, using f and g as given. **(See Section 8.4.)** $f(x) = 2x^2 + x + 2$ $g(x) = 3x - 1$

3. $(f + g)(x)$ $2x^2 + 4x + 1$

4. $(g - f)(x)$ $-2x^2 + 2x - 3$

5. $(f \cdot g)(x)$ $6x^3 + x^2 + 5x - 2$

6. $\left(\dfrac{g}{f}\right)(x)$ $\dfrac{3x - 1}{2x^2 + x + 2}$

7. $(f \circ g)(x)$ $18x^2 - 9x + 3$

8. $(g \circ f)(x)$ $6x^2 + 3x + 5$

Concept 1: Introduction to Inverse Functions

For Exercises 9–12, write the inverse function for each function.

9. $g = \{(3, 5), (8, 1), (-3, 9), (0, 2)\}$
$g^{-1} = \{(5, 3), (1, 8), (9, -3), (2, 0)\}$

10. $f = \{(-6, 2), (-9, 0), (-2, -1), (3, 4)\}$
$f^{-1} = \{(2, -6), (0, -9), (-1, -2), (4, 3)\}$

11. $r = \{(a, 3), (b, 6), (c, 9)\}$
$r^{-1} = \{(3, a), (6, b), (9, c)\}$

12. $s = \{(-1, x), (-2, y), (-3, z)\}$
$s^{-1} = \{(x, -1), (y, -2), (z, -3)\}$

Concept 2: Definition of a One-to-One Function

13. The table relates a state, x, to the number of representatives in the House of Representatives, y, for a recent year. Does this relation define a one-to-one function? If so, write a function defining the inverse as a set of ordered pairs.   The function is not one-to-one.

State x	Number of Representatives y
Colorado	7
California	53
Texas	32
Louisiana	7
Pennsylvania	19

14. The table relates a city, x, to its average January temperature, y. Does this relation define a one-to-one function? If so, write a function defining the inverse as a set of ordered pairs.   The function is not one-to-one.

City x	Temperature y (°C)
Gainesville, Florida	13.6
Keene, New Hampshire	-6.0
Wooster, Ohio	-4.0
Rock Springs, Wyoming	-6.0
Lafayette, Louisiana	10.9

For Exercises 15–20, determine if the function is one-to-one by using the horizontal line test. (See Example 1.)

15.

Yes

16.

No

17.

No

18.

No

19.

Yes

20.

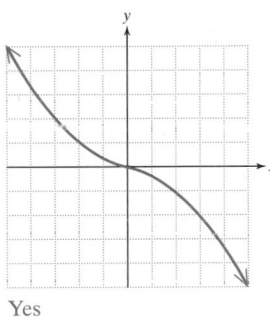

Yes

Concept 3: Finding an Equation of the Inverse of a Function

For Exercises 21–32, write an equation of the inverse for each one-to-one function as defined. (See Examples 2–4.)

21. $h(x) = x + 4$
$h^{-1}(x) = x - 4$

22. $k(x) = x - 3$
$k^{-1}(x) = x + 3$

23. $m(x) = \frac{1}{3}x - 2$
$m^{-1}(x) = 3(x + 2)$

24. $n(x) = 4x + 2$
$n^{-1}(x) = \frac{x - 2}{4}$

25. $p(x) = -x + 10$
$p^{-1}(x) = -x + 10$

26. $q(x) = -x - \frac{2}{3}$
$q^{-1}(x) = -x - \frac{2}{3}$

27. $f(x) = x^3 + 1$
$f^{-1}(x) = \sqrt[3]{x - 1}$

28. $g(x) = \sqrt[3]{x} + 2$
$g^{-1}(x) = (x - 2)^3$

29. $g(x) = \sqrt[3]{2x - 1}$
$g^{-1}(x) = \frac{x^3 + 1}{2}$

30. $f(x) = x^3 - 4$
$f^{-1}(x) = \sqrt[3]{x + 4}$

31. $g(x) = x^2 + 9 \quad x \geq 0$
$g^{-1}(x) = \sqrt{x - 9}$

32. $m(x) = x^2 - 1 \quad x \geq 0$
$m^{-1}(x) = \sqrt{x + 1}$

33. The function defined by $f(x) = 0.3048x$ converts a length of x feet into $f(x)$ meters.

    a. Find the equivalent length in meters for a 4-ft board and a 50-ft wire. 1.2192 m, 15.24 m

    b. Find an equation defining $y = f^{-1}(x)$. $f^{-1}(x) = \frac{x}{0.3048}$

    c. Use the inverse function from part (b) to find the equivalent length in feet for a 1500-m race in track and field. Round to the nearest tenth of a foot. 4921.3 ft

34. The function defined by $s(x) = 1.47x$ converts a speed of x mph to $s(x)$ ft/sec.

    a. Find the equivalent speed in feet per second for a car traveling 60 mph. 88.2 ft/sec

    b. Find an equation defining $y = s^{-1}(x)$. $s^{-1}(x) = \frac{x}{1.47}$

    c. Use the inverse function from part (b) to find the equivalent speed in miles per hour for a train traveling 132 ft/sec. Round to the nearest tenth. 89.8 mph

For Exercises 35–41, answer true or false.

35. The function defined by $y = 2$ has an inverse function defined by $x = 2$. False

36. The domain of any one-to-one function is the same as the domain of its inverse. False

37. All linear functions with a nonzero slope have an inverse function. True

 Writing   Translating Expression   Geometry   Scientific Calculator   Video   NS&E

38. The function defined by $g(x) = |x|$ is one-to-one.   False

39. The function defined by $k(x) = x^2$ is one-to-one.   False

40. The function defined by $h(x) = |x|$ for $x \geq 0$ is one-to-one.   True

41. The function defined by $L(x) = x^2$ for $x \geq 0$ is one-to-one.   True

42. Explain how the domain and range of a one-to-one function and its inverse are related.   The domain of a one-to-one function is the same as the range of its inverse. The range of a one-to-one function is the same as the domain of its inverse.

43. If $(0, b)$ is the y-intercept of a one-to-one function, what is the x-intercept of its inverse? $(b, 0)$

44. If $(a, 0)$ is the x-intercept of a one-to-one function, what is the y-intercept of its inverse? $(0, a)$

45. **a.** Find the domain and range of the function defined by $f(x) = \sqrt{x - 1}$.
Domain $[1, \infty)$, range $[0, \infty)$
b. Find the domain and range of the function defined by $f^{-1}(x) = x^2 + 1, x \geq 0$.
Domain $[0, \infty)$, range $[1, \infty)$

46. **a.** Find the domain and range of the function defined by $g(x) = x^2 - 4, x \leq 0$.
Domain $(-\infty, 0]$, range $[-4, \infty)$
b. Find the domain and range of the function defined by $g^{-1}(x) = -\sqrt{x + 4}$.
Domain $[-4, \infty)$, range $(-\infty, 0]$

For Exercises 47–50, the graph of $y = f(x)$ is given.

a. State the domain of f.   **b.** State the range of f.

c. State the domain of f^{-1}.   **d.** State the range of f^{-1}.

e. Graph the function defined by $y = f^{-1}(x)$. The line $y = x$ is provided for your reference.

47.

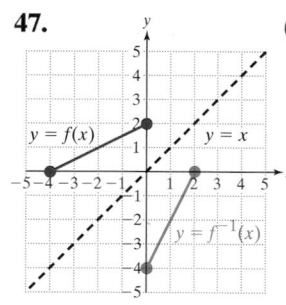

a. $[-4, 0]$ b. $[0, 2]$
c. $[0, 2]$ d. $[-4, 0]$

48.

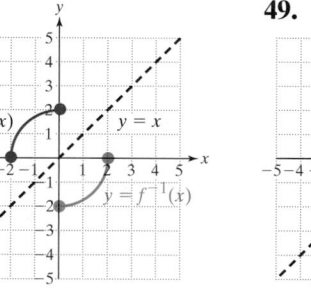

a. $[-2, 0]$ b. $[0, 2]$
c. $[0, 2]$ d. $[-2, 0]$

49.

a. $[0, 2]$ b. $[0, 4]$
c. $[0, 4]$ d. $[0, 2]$

50.

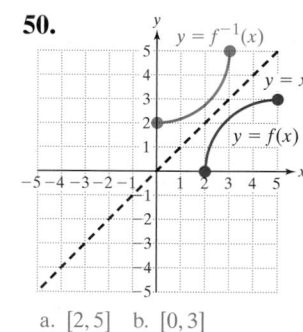

a. $[2, 5]$ b. $[0, 3]$
c. $[0, 3]$ d. $[2, 5]$

Concept 4: Definition of the Inverse of a Function

For Exercises 51–56, verify that f and g are inverse functions by showing that

a. $(f \circ g)(x) = x$ **b.** $(g \circ f)(x) = x$ **(See Example 5.)**

51. $f(x) = 6x + 1$ and $g(x) = \dfrac{x - 1}{6}$
a. $(f \circ g)(x) = 6\left(\dfrac{x - 1}{6}\right) + 1 = x$ b. $(g \circ f)(x) = \dfrac{(6x + 1) - 1}{6} = x$

52. $f(x) = 5x - 2$ and $g(x) = \dfrac{x + 2}{5}$
a. $(f \circ g)(x) = 5\left(\dfrac{x + 2}{5}\right) - 2 = x$ b. $(g \circ f)(x) = \dfrac{(5x - 2) + 2}{5} = x$

53. $f(x) = \dfrac{\sqrt[3]{x}}{2}$ and $g(x) = 8x^3$
a. $(f \circ g)(x) = \dfrac{\sqrt[3]{8x^3}}{2} = x$ b. $(g \circ f)(x) = 8\left(\dfrac{\sqrt[3]{x}}{2}\right)^3 = x$

54. $f(x) = \dfrac{\sqrt[3]{x}}{3}$ and $g(x) = 27x^3$
a. $(f \circ g)(x) = \dfrac{\sqrt[3]{27x^3}}{3} = x$ b. $(g \circ f)(x) = 27\left(\dfrac{\sqrt[3]{x}}{3}\right)^3 = x$

55. $f(x) = x^2 + 1, x \geq 0$, and $g(x) = \sqrt{x - 1}, x \geq 1$
a. $(f \circ g)(x) = (\sqrt{x - 1})^2 + 1 = x$
b. $(g \circ f)(x) = \sqrt{(x^2 + 1) - 1} = x$

56. $f(x) = x^2 - 3, x \geq 0$, and $g(x) = \sqrt{x + 3}, x \geq -3$
a. $(f \circ g)(x) = (\sqrt{x + 3})^2 - 3 = x$
b. $(g \circ f)(x) = \sqrt{(x^2 - 3) + 3} = x$

Writing   Translating Expression   Geometry   Scientific Calculator   Video   NS E

Expanding Your Skills

For Exercises 57–66, write an equation of the inverse of the one-to-one function.

57. $q(x) = \sqrt{x + 4}$
$q^{-1}(x) = x^2 - 4, \quad x \geq 0$

58. $v(x) = \sqrt{x + 16}$
$v^{-1}(x) = x^2 - 16, \quad x \geq 0$

59. $z(x) = -\sqrt{x + 4}$
$z^{-1}(x) = x^2 - 4, \quad x \leq 0$

60. $u(x) = -\sqrt{x + 16}$
$u^{-1}(x) = x^2 - 16, \quad x \leq 0$

61. $f(x) = \dfrac{x - 1}{x + 1}$

$f^{-1}(x) = \dfrac{x + 1}{1 - x}$

62. $p(x) = \dfrac{3 - x}{x + 3}$

$p^{-1}(x) = \dfrac{3 - 3x}{x + 1}$

63. $t(x) = \dfrac{2}{x - 1}$

$t^{-1}(x) = \dfrac{x + 2}{x}$

64. $w(x) = \dfrac{4}{x + 2}$

$w^{-1}(x) = \dfrac{4 - 2x}{x}$

65. $n(x) = x^2 + 9 \quad x \leq 0$
$n^{-1}(x) = -\sqrt{x - 9}$

66. $g(x) = x^2 - 1 \quad x \leq 0$
$g^{-1}(x) = -\sqrt{x + 1}$

Graphing Calculator Exercises

For Exercises 67–70, use a graphing calculator to graph each function on the standard viewing window. Use the graph of the function to determine if the function is one-to-one on the interval $-10 \leq x \leq 10$. If the function is one-to-one, find its inverse and graph both functions on the standard viewing window.

67. $f(x) = \sqrt[3]{x + 5} \quad f^{-1}(x) = x^3 - 5$

68. $k(x) = x^3 - 4 \quad k^{-1}(x) = \sqrt[3]{x + 4}$

69. $g(x) = 0.5x^3 - 2 \quad g^{-1}(x) = \sqrt[3]{2x + 4}$

70. $m(x) = 3x - 4 \quad m^{-1}(x) = \dfrac{x + 4}{3}$

Exponential Functions

1. Definition of an Exponential Function

The concept of a function was first introduced in Section 2.6. Since then we have learned to recognize several categories of functions, including constant, linear, rational, and quadratic functions. In this section and the next, we will define two new types of functions called exponential and logarithmic functions.

To introduce the concept of an exponential function, consider the following salary plans for a new job. Plan A pays $1 million for a month's work. Plan B starts with 2¢ on the first day, and every day thereafter the salary is doubled.

At first glance, the million-dollar plan appears to be more favorable. Look, however, at Table 12-1, which shows the daily payments for 30 days under plan B.

Concepts

1. **Definition of an Exponential Function**
2. **Approximating Exponential Expressions with a Calculator**
3. **Graphs of Exponential Functions**
4. **Applications of Exponential Functions**

Table 12-1

Day	Payment	Day	Payment	Day	Payment
1	2¢	11	$20.48	21	$20,971.52
2	4¢	12	$40.96	22	$41,943.04
3	8¢	13	$81.92	23	$83,886.08
4	16¢	14	$163.84	24	$167,772.16
5	32¢	15	$327.68	25	$335,544.32
6	64¢	16	$655.36	26	$671,088.64
7	$1.28	17	$1310.72	27	$1,342,177.28
8	$2.56	18	$2621.44	28	$2,684,354.56
9	$5.12	19	$5242.88	29	$5,368,709.12
10	$10.24	20	$10,485.76	30	$10,737,418.24

 Writing Translating Expression Geometry Scientific Calculator Video NS&E

Instructor Note: Ask students: What would happen if we created a relation $y = b^x$ and b was negative?

Notice that the salary on the 30th day for plan B is over $10 million. Taking the sum of the payments, we see the total salary for the 30-day period is $21,474,836.46.

The daily salary for plan B can be represented by the function $y = 2^x$, where x is the number of days on the job and y is the salary (in cents) for that day. An interesting feature of this function is that for every positive 1-unit change in x, the y-value doubles. The function $y = 2^x$ is called an exponential function.

DEFINITION Exponential Function

Let b be any real number such that $b > 0$ and $b \neq 1$. Then for any real number x, a function of the form $y = b^x$ is called an **exponential function**.

An exponential function is recognized as a function with a constant base and exponent, x. Notice that the base of an exponential function must be a positive real number not equal to 1.

2. Approximating Exponential Expressions with a Calculator

Up to this point, we have evaluated exponential expressions with integer exponents and rational exponents, for example, $4^3 = 64$ and $4^{1/2} = \sqrt{4} = 2$. However, how do we evaluate an exponential expression with an irrational exponent such as 4^π? In such a case, the exponent is a nonterminating and nonrepeating decimal. The value of 4^π can be thought of as the limiting value of a sequence of approximations using rational exponents:

$$4^{3.14} \approx 77.7084726$$

$$4^{3.141} \approx 77.81627412$$

$$4^{3.1415} \approx 77.87023095$$

$$\vdots$$

$$4^\pi \approx 77.88023365$$

An exponential expression can be evaluated at all rational numbers and at all irrational numbers. Therefore, the domain of an exponential function is all real numbers.

Classroom Example: p. 858, Exercise 18

Example 1 Approximating Exponential Expressions with a Calculator

Approximate the value of the expression using a calculator. Round the answers to four decimal places.

a. $8^{\sqrt{3}}$ **b.** $5^{-\sqrt{17}}$ **c.** $\sqrt{10}^{\sqrt{2}}$

Solution:

Calculator Connections

On a calculator, use the ⌃ , **yˣ** , or **xʸ** key to approximate an expression with an irrational exponent.

   a. $8^{\sqrt{3}} \approx 36.6604$ **b.** $5^{-\sqrt{17}} \approx 0.0013$

   c. $\sqrt{10}^{\sqrt{2}} \approx 5.0946$

```
8^√(3)
          36.66044576
5^-√(17)
          .00131242
(√(10))^√(2)
          5.09456117
```

Skill Practice Approximate the value of the expressions. Round the answers to 4 decimal places.

   1. 9^{π} **2.** $15^{\sqrt{5}}$ **3.** $\sqrt{7}^{\sqrt{3}}$

3. Graphs of Exponential Functions

The functions defined by $f(x) = 2^x$, $g(x) = (\tfrac{1}{2})^x$, $h(x) = 3^x$, and $k(x) = 5^x$ are all examples of exponential functions. Example 2 illustrates the two general shapes of exponential functions.

Example 2   Graphing an Exponential Function

Graph the functions f and g.

   a. $f(x) = 2^x$ **b.** $g(x) = (\tfrac{1}{2})^x$

Classroom Examples: p. 859, Exercises 36 and 38

Solution:

Table 12-2 shows several function values for $f(x)$ and $g(x)$ for both positive and negative values of x. The graphs are shown in Figure 12-7.

Table 12-2

x	$f(x) = 2^x$	$g(x) = (\tfrac{1}{2})^x$
-4	$\frac{1}{16}$	16
-3	$\frac{1}{8}$	8
-2	$\frac{1}{4}$	4
-1	$\frac{1}{2}$	2
0	1	1
1	2	$\frac{1}{2}$
2	4	$\frac{1}{4}$
3	8	$\frac{1}{8}$
4	16	$\frac{1}{16}$

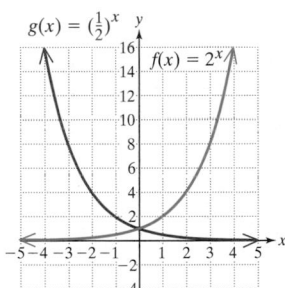

Figure 12-7

Skill Practice Graph the functions f and g on the same grid.

   4. $f(x) = 3^x$ **5.** $g(x) = \left(\dfrac{1}{3}\right)^x$

Answers

1. 995.0416   **2.** 426.4028
3. 5.3936
4–5.

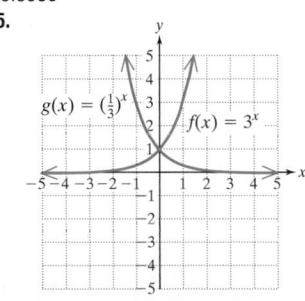

The graphs in Figure 12-7 illustrate several important features of exponential functions.

PROPERTY   Graphs of $f(x) = b^x$

The graph of an exponential function defined by $f(x) = b^x$ ($b > 0$ and $b \neq 1$) has the following properties.

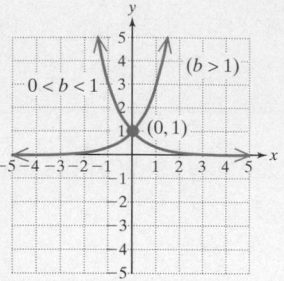

1. If $b > 1$, f is an *increasing* exponential function, sometimes called an **exponential growth function**.

   If $0 < b < 1$, f is a *decreasing* exponential function, sometimes called an **exponential decay function**.

2. The domain is the set of all real numbers, $(-\infty, \infty)$.

3. The range is $(0, \infty)$.

4. The line $y = 0$ (x-axis) is a horizontal asymptote.

5. The function passes through the point $(0, 1)$ because $f(0) = b^0 = 1$.

These properties indicate that the graph of an exponential function is an increasing function if the base is greater than 1. Furthermore, the base affects the rate of increase. Consider the graphs of $f(x) = 2^x$, $h(x) = 3^x$, and $k(x) = 5^x$ (Figure 12-8). For every positive 1-unit change in x, $f(x) = 2^x$ increases by 2 times, $h(x) = 3^x$ increases by 3 times, and $k(x) = 5^x$ increases by 5 times (Table 12-3).

Table 12-3

x	$f(x) = 2^x$	$h(x) = 3^x$	$k(x) = 5^x$
-3	$\frac{1}{8}$	$\frac{1}{27}$	$\frac{1}{125}$
-2	$\frac{1}{4}$	$\frac{1}{9}$	$\frac{1}{25}$
-1	$\frac{1}{2}$	$\frac{1}{3}$	$\frac{1}{5}$
0	1	1	1
1	2	3	5
2	4	9	25
3	8	27	125

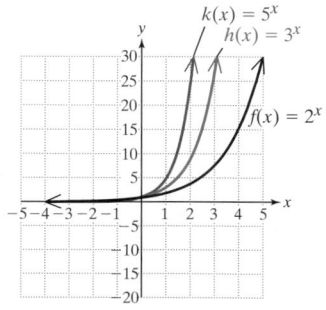

Figure 12-8

The graph of an exponential function is a *decreasing function* if the base is between 0 and 1. Consider the graphs of $g(x) = \left(\frac{1}{2}\right)^x$, $m(x) = \left(\frac{1}{3}\right)^x$, and $n(x) = \left(\frac{1}{5}\right)^x$ (Table 12-4 and Figure 12-9).

Table 12-4

x	$g(x) = \left(\frac{1}{2}\right)^x$	$m(x) = \left(\frac{1}{3}\right)^x$	$n(x) = \left(\frac{1}{5}\right)^x$
-3	8	27	125
-2	4	9	25
-1	2	3	5
0	1	1	1
1	$\frac{1}{2}$	$\frac{1}{3}$	$\frac{1}{5}$
2	$\frac{1}{4}$	$\frac{1}{9}$	$\frac{1}{25}$
3	$\frac{1}{8}$	$\frac{1}{27}$	$\frac{1}{125}$

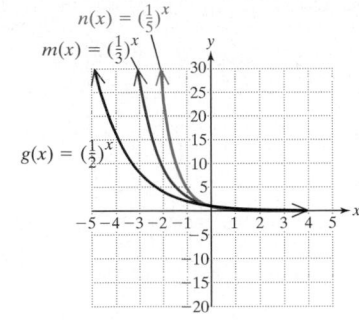

Figure 12-9

4. Applications of Exponential Functions

Exponential growth and decay can be found in a variety of real world phenomena; for example,

* Population growth can often be modeled by an exponential function.
* The growth of an investment under compound interest increases exponentially.
* The mass of a radioactive substance decreases exponentially with time.
* The temperature of a cup of coffee decreases exponentially as it approaches room temperature.

A substance that undergoes radioactive decay is said to be radioactive. The *half-life* of a radioactive substance is the amount of time it takes for one-half of the original amount of the substance to change into something else. That is, after each half-life the amount of the original substance decreases by one-half.

In 1898, Marie Curie discovered the highly radioactive element radium. She shared the 1903 Nobel Prize in physics for her research on radioactivity and was awarded the 1911 Nobel Prize in chemistry for her discovery of radium and polonium. Radium 226 (an isotope of radium) has a half-life of 1620 years and decays into radon 222 (a radioactive gas).

Marie and Pierre Curie

| **Example 3** | **Applying an Exponential Decay Function** |

Classroom Example: p. 859, Exercise 44

In a sample originally having 1 g of radium 226, the amount of radium 226 present after t years is given by

$$A(t) = \left(\tfrac{1}{2}\right)^{t/1620}$$

where $A(t)$ is the amount of radium in grams and t is the time in years.

a. How much radium 226 will be present after 1620 yr?

b. How much radium 226 will be present after 3240 yr?

c. How much radium 226 will be present after 4860 yr?

Solution:

$$A(t) = \left(\frac{1}{2}\right)^{t/1620}$$

a. $A(1620) = \left(\frac{1}{2}\right)^{1620/1620}$ Substitute $t = 1620$.

$$= \left(\frac{1}{2}\right)^{1}$$

$$= 0.5$$

After 1620 yr (1 half-life), 0.5 g remains.

b. $A(3240) = \left(\frac{1}{2}\right)^{3240/1620}$ Substitute $t = 3240$.

$$= \left(\frac{1}{2}\right)^{2}$$

$$= 0.25$$

After 3240 yr (2 half-lives), the amount of the original substance is reduced by one-half, 2 times: 0.25 g remains.

c. $A(4860) = \left(\frac{1}{2}\right)^{4860/1620}$ Substitute $t = 4860$.

$$= \left(\frac{1}{2}\right)^{3}$$

$$= 0.125$$

After 4860 yr (3 half-lives), the amount of the original substance is reduced by one-half, 3 times: 0.125 g remains.

Skill Practice Cesium 137 is a radioactive metal with a short half-life of 30 years. In a sample originally having 1 g of cesium 137, the amount, $A(t)$ (in grams), of cesium 137 present after t years is given by

$$A(t) = \left(\frac{1}{2}\right)^{t/30}$$

6. How much cesium 137 will be present after 30 years?

7. How much cesium 137 will be present after 90 years?

Exponential functions are often used to model population growth. Suppose the initial value of a population at some time $t = 0$ is P_0. If the rate of increase of a population is r, then after t years, the population $P(t)$ is given by

$$P(t) = P_0(1 + r)^t$$

Answers

6. 0.5 g

7. 0.125 g

Example 4 Applying an Exponential Growth Function

Classroom Example: p. 860, Exercise 48

The population of the Bahamas in 2008 was estimated at 321,000 with an annual rate of increase of 1.39%.

a. Find a mathematical model that relates the population of the Bahamas as a function of the number of years since 2008.

b. If the annual rate of increase remains the same, use this model to predict the population of the Bahamas in the year 2016. Round to the nearest thousand.

Solution:

a. The initial population is $P_0 = 321{,}000$, and the rate of increase is 1.39%.

$P(t) = P_0(1 + r)^t$ Substitute $P_0 = 321{,}000$ and $r = 0.0139$.

    $= 321{,}000(1 + 0.0139)^t$

    $= 321{,}000(1.0139)^t$ Here $t = 0$ corresponds to the year 2008.

b. Because the initial population ($t = 0$) corresponds to the year 2008, we use $t = 8$ to find the population in the year 2016.

$P(8) = 321{,}000(1.0139)^8$

    $\approx 358{,}000$ The population in the year 2016 will be approximately 358,000.

Skill Practice The population of Colorado in 2000 was approximately 3,700,000 with an annual increase of 2%.

8. Find a mathematical model that relates the population of Colorado as a function of the number of years since 2000.

9. Use this model to predict the population of Colorado in 2016. Round to the nearest thousand.

Answers

8. $P(t) = 3{,}700{,}000(1.02)^t$

9. Approximately 5,079,000

Section 12.2 Practice Exercises

Study Skills Exercise

1. Define the key terms.

    a. exponential function   **b.** exponential growth function   **c.** exponential decay function

Review Exercises

For Exercises 2–8, refer to the set $A = \{(3, 0), (2, -2), (5, 1), (12, 3)\}$.

2. Write the domain of the relation, A. $\{3, 2, 5, 12\}$

3. Write the range of the relation, A. $\{0, -2, 1, 3\}$

4. Does A represent a function?   Yes

5. Does A represent a one-to-one function?   Yes

6. Find the inverse of A^{-1}. $\{(0, 3), (-2, 2), (1, 5), (3, 12)\}$

7. Write the domain of A^{-1}. $\{0, -2, 1, 3\}$

8. Write the range of A^{-1}. $\{3, 2, 5, 12\}$

 Writing   Translating Expression   Geometry   Scientific Calculator   Video   NS&E

For Exercises 9–16, evaluate the expression without the use of a calculator.

9. 5^2 25

10. 2^{-3} $\frac{1}{8}$

11. 10^{-3} $\frac{1}{1000}$

12. 3^4 81

13. $36^{1/2}$ 6

14. $27^{1/3}$ 3

15. $16^{3/4}$ 8

16. $8^{2/3}$ 4

Concept 2: Approximating Exponential Expressions with a Calculator

For Exercises 17–24, evaluate the expression by using a calculator. Round to 4 decimal places. **(See Example 1.)**

17. $5^{1.1}$ 5.8731

18. $2^{\sqrt{3}}$ 3.3220

19. 10^{π} 1385.4557

20. $3^{4.8}$ 195.0662

21. $36^{-\sqrt{2}}$ 0.0063

22. $27^{-0.5126}$ 0.1846

23. $16^{-0.04}$ 0.8950

24. $8^{-0.61}$ 0.2813

25. Solve for x.

    a. $3^x = 9$
      $x = 2$

    b. $3^x = 27$
      $x = 3$

    c. Between what two consecutive integers must the solution to $3^x = 11$ lie?   Between 2 and 3

26. Solve for x.

    a. $5^x = 125$
      $x = 3$

    b. $5^x = 625$
      $x = 4$

    c. Between what two consecutive integers must the solution to $5^x = 130$ lie?   Between 3 and 4

27. Solve for x.

    a. $2^x = 16$
      $x = 4$

    b. $2^x = 32$
      $x = 5$

    c. Between what two consecutive integers must the solution to $2^x = 30$ lie?   Between 4 and 5

28. Solve for x.

    a. $4^x = 16$
      $x = 2$

    b. $4^x = 64$
      $x = 3$

    c. Between what two consecutive integers must the solution to $4^x = 20$ lie?   Between 2 and 3

29. For $f(x) = \left(\frac{1}{5}\right)^x$ find $f(0), f(1), f(2), f(-1),$ and $f(-2)$. $f(0) = 1, f(1) = \frac{1}{5}, f(2) = \frac{1}{25}, f(-1) = 5, f(-2) = 25$

30. For $g(x) = \left(\frac{2}{3}\right)^x$ find $g(0), g(1), g(2), g(-1),$ and $g(-2)$. $g(0) = 1, g(1) = \frac{2}{3}, g(2) = \frac{4}{9}, g(-1) = \frac{3}{2}, g(-2) = \frac{9}{4}$

31. For $h(x) = 3^x$ use a calculator to find $h(0), h(1), h(-1), h\left(\sqrt{2}\right),$ and $h(\pi)$. Round to two decimal places.
$h(0) = 1, h(1) = 3, h(-1) = \frac{1}{3}, h(\sqrt{2}) \approx 4.73, h(\pi) \approx 31.54$

32. For $k(x) = 5^x$ use a calculator to find $k(0), k(1), k(-1), k(\pi),$ and $k\left(\sqrt{2}\right)$. Round to two decimal places.
$k(0) = 1, k(1) = 5, k(-1) = \frac{1}{5}, k(\pi) \approx 156.99, k(\sqrt{2}) \approx 9.74$

Concept 3: Graphs of Exponential Functions

33. How do you determine whether the graph of $f(x) = b^x$ $(b > 0, b \neq 1)$ is increasing or decreasing?
If $b > 1$, the graph is increasing. If $0 < b < 1$, the graph is decreasing.

34. For $f(x) = b^x$ $(b > 0, b \neq 1)$, find $f(0)$. $f(0) = b^0 = 1$

Graph the functions defined in Exercises 35–42. Plot at least three points for each function. **(See Example 2.)**

35. $f(x) = 4^x$

36. $g(x) = 6^x$

37. $m(x) = \left(\dfrac{1}{8}\right)^x$

38. $n(x) = \left(\dfrac{1}{3}\right)^x$

39. $h(x) = 2^{x+1}$

40. $k(x) = 5^{x-1}$

41. $g(x) = 5^{-x}$

42. $f(x) = 2^{-x}$

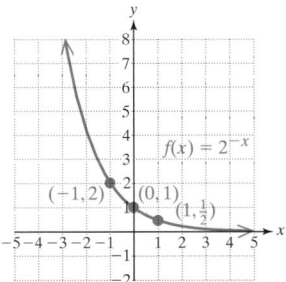

Concept 4: Applications of Exponential Functions

43. The half-life of the element radon (Rn 86) is 3.8 days. In a sample originally containing 1 g of radon, the amount left after t days is given by $A(t) = (0.5)^{t/3.8}$. (Round to two decimal places, if necessary.) **(See Example 3.)**

   a. How much radon will be present after 7.6 days?   0.25 g

   b. How much radon will be present after 10 days? ≈ 0.16 g

44. Nobelium, an element discovered in 1958, has a half-life of 10 min under certain conditions. In a sample containing 1 g of nobelium, the amount left after t min is given by $A(t) = (0.5)^{t/10}$. (Round to three decimal places.)

   a. How much nobelium is left after 5 min? ≈ 0.707 g

   b. How much nobelium is left after 1 hr? ≈ 0.016 g

 Writing   Translating Expression   Geometry   Scientific Calculator   Video   NS&E

45. Once an antibiotic is introduced to bacteria, the number of bacteria decreases exponentially. For example, beginning with 1 million bacteria, the amount present t days from the time penicillin is introduced is given by the function $A(t) = 1,000,000(2)^{-t/5}$. Rounding to the nearest thousand, determine how many bacteria are present after

   a. 2 days   **b.** 1 week   **c.** 2 weeks
       758,000   379,000   144,000

46. Once an antibiotic is introduced to bacteria, the number of bacteria decreases exponentially. For example, beginning with 1 million bacteria, the amount present t days from the time streptomycin is introduced is given by the function $A(t) = 1,000,000(2)^{-t/10}$. Rounding to the nearest thousand, determine how many bacteria are present after

   a. 5 days   **b.** 1 week   **c.** 2 weeks
       707,000   616,000   379,000

47. The population of Bangladesh was 153,000,000 in 2009 with an annual growth rate of 1.25%. **(See Example 4.)**

   a. Find a mathematical model that relates the population of Bangladesh as a function of the number of years after 2009. $P(t) = 153,000,000(1.0125)^t$

   b. If the annual rate of increase remains the same, use this model to predict the population of Bangladesh in the year 2050. Round to the nearest million. $P(41) \approx 255,000,000$

48. The population of Fiji was 908,000 in 2009 with an annual growth rate of 0.07%.

   a. Find a mathematical model that relates the population of Fiji as a function of the number of years after 2009. $P(t) = 908,000(1.0007)^t$

   b. If the annual rate of increase remains the same, use this model to predict the population of Fiji in the year 2050. Round to the nearest thousand. $P(41) \approx 934,000$

49. Suppose $1000 is initially invested in an account and the value of the account grows exponentially. If the investment doubles in 7 yr, then the amount in the account t years after the initial investment is given by $A(t)$.

$$A(t) = 1000(2)^{t/7}$$

   a. Find the amount in the account after 5 yr. $1640.67

   b. Find the amount in the account after 10 yr. $2691.80

   c. Find $A(0)$ and $A(7)$ and interpret the answers in the context of this problem. $A(0) = 1000$. The initial amount of the investment is $1000. $A(7) = 2000$. The amount of the investment doubles in 7 yr.

50. Suppose $1500 is initially invested in an account and the value of the account grows exponentially. If the investment doubles in 8 yr, then the amount in the account t years after the initial investment is given by $A(t)$.

$$A(t) = 1500(2)^{t/8}$$

   a. Find the amount in the account after 5 yr. $2313.32

   b. Find the amount in the account after 10 yr. $3567.62

   c. Find $A(0)$ and $A(8)$ and interpret the answers in the context of this problem. $A(0) = 1500$. The initial amount of the investment is $1500. $A(8) = 3000$. The amount of the investment doubles in 8 yr.

Graphing Calculator Exercises

For Exercises 51–58, graph the functions on your calculator to support your solutions to the indicated exercises.

51. $f(x) = 4^x$ **52.** $g(x) = 6^x$ **53.** $m(x) = \left(\frac{1}{8}\right)^x$ **54.** $n(x) = \left(\frac{1}{3}\right)^x$
(see Exercise 35)   (see Exercise 36)   (see Exercise 37)   (see Exercise 38)

55. $h(x) = 2^{x+1}$ **56.** $k(x) = 5^{x-1}$ **57.** $g(x) = 5^{-x}$ **58.** $f(x) = 2^{-x}$
(see Exercise 39)   (see Exercise 40)   (see Exercise 41)   (see Exercise 42)

 Writing   Translating Expression   Geometry   Scientific Calculator   Video   NSE

Logarithmic Functions

1. Definition of a Logarithmic Function

Consider the following equations in which the variable is located in the exponent of an expression. In some cases the solution can be found by inspection because the constant on the right-hand side of the equation is a perfect power of the base.

Equation		Solution
$5^x = 5$	$\longrightarrow$	$x = 1$
$5^x = 20$	$\longrightarrow$	$x = ?$
$5^x = 25$	$\longrightarrow$	$x = 2$
$5^x = 60$	$\longrightarrow$	$x = ?$
$5^x = 125$	$\longrightarrow$	$x = 3$

The equation $5^x = 20$ cannot be solved by inspection. However, we might suspect that x is between 1 and 2. Similarly, the solution to the equation $5^x = 60$ is between 2 and 3. To solve an exponential equation for an unknown exponent, we must use a new type of function called a logarithmic function.

> **DEFINITION** Logarithm Function
>
> If x and b are positive real numbers such that $b \neq 1$, then $y = \log_b x$ is called the **logarithmic function** with base b and
>
> $$y = \log_b x \quad \text{is equivalent to} \quad b^y = x$$
>
> *Note:* In the expression $y = \log_b x$, y is called the **logarithm**, b is called the **base**, and x is called the **argument**.

The expression $y = \log_b x$ is equivalent to $b^y = x$ and indicates that *the logarithm y is the exponent to which b must be raised to obtain x.* The expression $y = \log_b x$ is called the logarithmic form of the equation, and the expression $b^y = x$ is called the exponential form of the equation.

The definition of a logarithmic function suggests a close relationship with an exponential function of the same base. In fact, a logarithmic function is the inverse of the corresponding exponential function. For example, the following steps find the inverse of the exponential function defined by $f(x) = b^x$.

$f(x) = b^x$

$\quad y = b^x \qquad$ Replace $f(x)$ by y.

$\quad x = b^y \qquad$ Interchange x and y.

$\quad y = \log_b x \qquad$ Solve for y using the definition of a logarithmic function.

$f^{-1}(x) = \log_b x \qquad$ Replace y by $f^{-1}(x)$.

The concept of a logarithm is new and unfamiliar. Therefore, it is often advantageous to rewrite a logarithm in its exponential form.

Example 1 Converting from Logarithmic Form to Exponential Form

Rewrite the logarithmic equations in exponential form.

a. $\log_2 32 = 5$ **b.** $\log_{10}\left(\dfrac{1}{1000}\right) = -3$ **c.** $\log_5 1 = 0$

Concepts

1. Definition of a Logarithmic Function
2. Evaluating Logarithmic Expressions
3. The Common Logarithmic Function
4. Graphs of Logarithmic Functions
5. Applications of the Common Logarithmic Function

Instructor Note: Emphasize to students that, like the notation $f(x)$, we are not multiplying log times x. We read $\log_b x$ as log, base b, of x.

Classroom Examples: p. 870, Exercises 14 and 16

Solution:

Logarithmic Form		Exponential Form
a. $\log_2 32 = 5$	$\Leftrightarrow$	$2^5 = 32$
b. $\log_{10}\left(\dfrac{1}{1000}\right) = -3$	$\Leftrightarrow$	$10^{-3} = \dfrac{1}{1000}$
c. $\log_5 1 = 0$	$\Leftrightarrow$	$5^0 = 1$

Skill Practice Rewrite the logarithmic equations in exponential form.

1. $\log_3 9 = 2$ **2.** $\log_{10}\left(\dfrac{1}{100}\right) = -2$ **3.** $\log_8 1 = 0$

2. Evaluating Logarithmic Expressions

Classroom Examples: p. 870,
Exercises 36 and 46

Example 2 Evaluating Logarithmic Expressions

Evaluate the logarithmic expressions.

a. $\log_8 64$ **b.** $\log_5\left(\dfrac{1}{125}\right)$ **c.** $\log_{1/2}\left(\dfrac{1}{8}\right)$

Solution:

a. $\log_8 64$ is the exponent to which 8 must be raised to obtain 64.

$y = \log_8 64$	Let y represent the value of the logarithm.
$8^y = 64$	Rewrite the expression in exponential form.
$8^y = 8^2$	
$y = 2$	Therefore, $\log_8 64 = 2$.

b. $\log_5\left(\frac{1}{125}\right)$ is the exponent to which 5 must be raised to obtain $\frac{1}{125}$.

$y = \log_5\left(\dfrac{1}{125}\right)$	Let y represent the value of the logarithm.
$5^y = \dfrac{1}{125}$	Rewrite the expression in exponential form.
$5^y = \dfrac{1}{5^3} = 5^{-3}$	
$y = -3$	Therefore, $\log_5\left(\dfrac{1}{125}\right) = -3$.

c. $\log_{1/2}\left(\frac{1}{8}\right)$ is the exponent to which $\frac{1}{2}$ must be raised to obtain $\frac{1}{8}$.

$y = \log_{1/2}\left(\dfrac{1}{8}\right)$	Let y represent the value of the logarithm.
$\left(\dfrac{1}{2}\right)^y = \dfrac{1}{8}$	Rewrite the expression in exponential form.
$\left(\dfrac{1}{2}\right)^y = \left(\dfrac{1}{2}\right)^3$	
$y = 3$	Therefore, $\log_{1/2}\left(\dfrac{1}{8}\right) = 3$.

Skill Practice Evaluate the logarithmic expressions.

4. $\log_{10} 1000$ **5.** $\log_4\left(\dfrac{1}{16}\right)$ **6.** $\log_{1/3} 3$

Answers

1. $3^2 = 9$ **2.** $10^{-2} = \dfrac{1}{100}$

3. $8^0 = 1$ **4.** 3

5. -2 **6.** -1

Example 3 Evaluating Logarithmic Expressions

Classroom Examples: p. 870, Exercises 48 and 50

Evaluate the logarithmic expressions.

a. $\log_b b$ **b.** $\log_c c^7$ **c.** $\log_3 \sqrt[4]{3}$

Solution:

a. $\log_b b$ is the exponent to which b must be raised to obtain b.

$y = \log_b b$ Let y represent the value of the logarithm.

$b^y = b$ Rewrite the expression in exponential form.

$y = 1$ Therefore, $\log_b b = 1$.

b. $\log_c c^7$ is the exponent to which c must be raised to obtain c^7.

$y = \log_c c^7$ Let y represent the value of the logarithm.

$c^y = c^7$ Rewrite the expression in exponential form.

$y = 7$ Therefore, $\log_c c^7 - 7$.

c. $\log_3 \sqrt[4]{3} = \log_3 3^{1/4}$ is the exponent to which 3 must be raised to obtain $3^{1/4}$.

$y = \log_3 3^{1/4}$ Let y represent the value of the logarithm.

$3^y = 3^{1/4}$ Rewrite the expression in exponential form.

$y = \dfrac{1}{4}$ Therefore, $\log_3 \sqrt[4]{3} = \frac{1}{4}$.

Skill Practice Evaluate the logarithmic expressions.

7. $\log_x x$ **8.** $\log_b b^{10}$ **9.** $\log_5 \sqrt[3]{5}$

3. The Common Logarithmic Function

The logarithmic function with base 10 is called the **common logarithmic function** and is denoted by $y = \log x$. Notice that the base is not explicitly written but is understood to be 10. That is, $y = \log_{10} x$ is written simply as $y = \log x$.

Example 4 Evaluating Common Logarithms

Classroom Examples: p. 870, Exercises 52 and 56

Evaluate the logarithmic expressions.

a. $\log 100,000$ **b.** $\log 0.01$

Solution:

a. $\log 100,000$ is the exponent to which 10 must be raised to obtain 100,000.

$y = \log 100,000$ Let y represent the value of the logarithm.

$10^y = 100,000$ Rewrite the expression in exponential form.

$10^y = 10^5$

$y = 5$ Therefore, $\log 100,000 = 5$.

Answers

7. 1 **8.** 10 **9.** $\dfrac{1}{3}$

b. log 0.01 is the exponent to which 10 must be raised to obtain 0.01 or $\frac{1}{100}$.

$y = \log 0.01$	Let y represent the value of the logarithm.
$10^y = 0.01$	Rewrite the expression in exponential form.
$10^y = 10^{-2}$	Note that $0.01 = \frac{1}{100}$ or 10^{-2}.
$y = -2$	Therefore, $\log 0.01 = -2$.

Skill Practice Evaluate the logarithmic expressions.

10. log 1,000,000   **11.** log 0.0001

On most calculators the ⎡**LOG**⎤ key is used to compute logarithms with base 10. This is demonstrated in Example 5.

Classroom Examples: p. 871, Exercises 60 and 68

Example 5   **Evaluating Common Logarithms on a Calculator**

Evaluate the common logarithms. Round the answers to four decimal places.

   a. log 420   **b.** $\log\left(8.2 \times 10^9\right)$ **c.** log 0.0002

> **TIP:** On a scientific calculator, you may need to enter the logarithmic function and argument in reverse order. For example: 420 ⎡**LOG**⎤.

Solution:

a. $\log 420 \approx 2.6232$

b. $\log\left(8.2 \times 10^9\right) \approx 9.9138$

c. $\log 0.0002 \approx -3.6990$

Skill Practice Evaluate the common logarithms. Round answers to four decimal places.

12. log 1200   **13.** $\log\left(6.3 \times 10^5\right)$ **14.** log 0.00025

4. Graphs of Logarithmic Functions

In Section 12.2 we studied the graphs of exponential functions. In this section, we will graph logarithmic functions. First, recall that $f(x) = \log_b x$ is the inverse of $g(x) = b^x$. Therefore, the graph of $y = f(x)$ is symmetric to the graph of $y = g(x)$ about the line $y = x$, as shown in Figures 12-10 and 12-11.

Figure 12-10

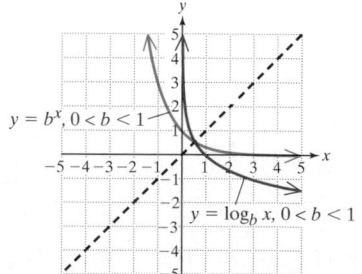

Figure 12-11

From Figures 12-10 and 12-11, we see that the range of $y = b^x$ is the set of positive real numbers. As expected, the domain of its inverse, the logarithmic function $y = \log_b x$, is also the set of positive real numbers. Therefore, the **domain of the logarithmic function** $y = \log_b x$ is the set of positive real numbers.

Answers

10. 6   **11.** -4
12. ≈ 3.0792 **13.** ≈ 5.7993
14. ≈ -3.6021

Example 6 **Graphing Logarithmic Functions**

Classroom Examples: pp. 871–872, Exercises 76, 78

Graph the logarithmic functions.

a. $y = \log_2 x$ **b.** $y = \log_{1/4} x$

Solution:

A logarithmic function is the inverse of an exponential function with the same base. For this reason, we can reverse the coordinates of the ordered pairs on an exponential function to obtain ordered pairs on the related logarithmic function. For example, to graph the function $y = \log_2 x$ reverse the coordinates of the ordered pairs from its inverse function, $y = 2^x$.

a. Exponential function   Logarithmic function

x	$y = 2^x$
-3	$\frac{1}{8}$
-2	$\frac{1}{4}$
-1	$\frac{1}{2}$
0	1
1	2
2	4
3	8

x	$y = \log_2 x$
$\frac{1}{8}$	-3
$\frac{1}{4}$	-2
$\frac{1}{2}$	-1
1	0
2	1
4	2
8	3

Reverse the order.

Figure 12-12

The graph of $y = \log_2 x$ is shown in Figure 12-12.

b. Exponential function   Logarithmic function

x	$y = \left(\frac{1}{4}\right)^x$
-3	64
-2	16
-1	4
0	1
1	$\frac{1}{4}$
2	$\frac{1}{16}$
3	$\frac{1}{64}$

x	$y = \log_{1/4} x$
64	-3
16	-2
4	-1
1	0
$\frac{1}{4}$	1
$\frac{1}{16}$	2
$\frac{1}{64}$	3

Reverse the order.

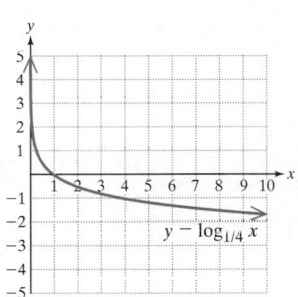

Figure 12-13

The graph of $y = \log_{1/4} x$ is shown in Figure 12-13.

Skill Practice Graph.

15. $y = \log_3 x$ **16.** $y = \log_{1/2} x$

Answers

15–16.

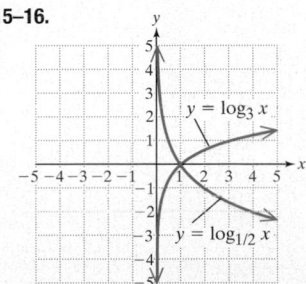

The general shape and important features of exponential and logarithmic functions are summarized as follows.

SUMMARY   Graphs of Exponential and Logarithmic Functions

Exponential Functions	Logarithmic Functions

Domain: $(-\infty, \infty)$	Domain: $(0, \infty)$
Range: $(0, \infty)$	Range: $(-\infty, \infty)$
Horizontal asymptote: $y = 0$	Vertical asymptote: $x = 0$
Passes through $(0, 1)$	Passes through $(1, 0)$
If $b > 1$, the function is increasing.	If $b > 1$, the function is increasing.
If $0 < b < 1$, the function is decreasing.	If $0 < b < 1$, the function is decreasing.

Notice that the roles of x and y are interchanged for the functions $y = b^x$ and $b^y = x$. Therefore, it is not surprising that the domain and range are reversed between exponential and logarithmic functions. Moreover, an exponential function passes through $(0, 1)$, whereas a logarithmic function passes through $(1, 0)$. An exponential function has a horizontal asymptote at $y = 0$, whereas a logarithmic function has a vertical asymptote at $x = 0$.

When graphing a logarithmic equation, it is helpful to know its domain.

Classroom Examples: p. 872,
Exercises 82 and 84

Example 7   Identifying the Domain of a Logarithmic Function

Find the domain of the functions.

  a. $f(x) = \log(4 - x)$ **b.** $g(x) = \log(2x + 6)$

Solution:

The domain of the function $y = \log_b x$ is the set of all positive real numbers. That is, the argument x must be greater than zero: $x > 0$.

a. $f(x) = \log(4 - x)$	The argument is $4 - x$.
$4 - x > 0$	The argument of the logarithm must be greater than zero.
$-x > -4$	Solve for x.
$x < 4$	Divide by -1 and reverse the inequality sign.

The domain is $(-\infty, 4)$.

b. $g(x) = \log (2x + 6)$ The argument is $2x + 6$.

$$2x + 6 > 0$$ The argument of the logarithm must be greater than zero.

$$2x > -6$$

$$x > -3$$

The domain is $(-3, \infty)$.

Skill Practice Find the domain of the functions.

17. $f(x) = \log_3 (x + 7)$ **18.** $g(x) = \log (4 - 8x)$

Calculator Connections

The graphs of $Y_1 = \log (4 - x)$ and $Y_2 = \log (2x + 6)$ are shown here and can be used to confirm the solutions to Example 7. Notice that each function has a vertical asymptote at the value of x where the argument equals zero.

---

5. Applications of the Common Logarithmic Function

Example 8   **Applying a Common Logarithm to Compute pH**

Classroom Example: p. 872, Exercise 92

The pH (hydrogen potential) of a solution is defined as

$$pH = -\log [H^+]$$

where $[H^+]$ represents the concentration of hydrogen ions in moles per liter (mol/L). The pH scale ranges from 0 to 14. The midpoint of this range, 7, represents a neutral solution. Values below 7 are progressively more acidic, and values above 7 are progressively more alkaline. Based on the equation $pH = -\log [H^+]$, a 1-unit change in pH means a 10-fold change in hydrogen ion concentration.

a. Normal rain has a pH of 5.6. However, in some areas of the northeastern United States the rainwater is more acidic. What is the pH of a rain sample for which the concentration of hydrogen ions is 0.0002 mol/L?

b. Find the pH of household ammonia if the concentration of hydrogen ions is 1.0×10^{-11} mol/L.

Solution:

a. $pH = -\log [H^+]$

     $= -\log (0.0002)$ Substitute $[H^+] = 0.0002$.

     ≈ 3.7 The pH of the rain sample is 3.7. (To compare this value with a familiar substance, note that the pH of orange juice is roughly 3.5.)

Answers

17. Domain: $(-7, \infty)$

18. Domain: $\left(-\infty, \dfrac{1}{2}\right)$

b. $\text{pH} = -\log [\text{H}^+]$

$\qquad = -\log (1.0 \times 10^{-11})$ Substitute $[\text{H}^+] = 1.0 \times 10^{-11}$.

$\qquad = -\log (10^{-11})$

$\qquad = -(-11)$

$\qquad = 11$ The pH of household ammonia is 11.

Skill Practice

19. A new all-natural shampoo on the market claims its hydrogen ion concentration is 5.88×10^{-7} mol/L. Use the formula $\text{pH} = -\log [\text{H}^+]$ to calculate the pH level of the shampoo.

Classroom Example: p. 873, Exercise 94

Example 9   Applying a Logarithmic Function to a Memory Model

One method of measuring a student's retention of material after taking a course is to retest the student at specified time intervals after the course has been completed. A student's score on a calculus test t months after completing a course in calculus is approximated by

$$S(t) = 85 - 25 \log (t + 1)$$

where t is the time in months after completing the course and $S(t)$ is the student's score as a percent.

a. What was the student's score at $t = 0$?

b. What was the student's score after 2 months?

c. What was the student's score after 1 yr?

Solution:

a. $S(t) = 85 - 25 \log (t + 1)$

$\quad S(0) = 85 - 25 \log (0 + 1)$ Substitute $t = 0$.

$\qquad = 85 - 25 \log 1$ $\log 1 = 0$ because $10^0 = 1$.

$\qquad = 85 - 25(0)$

$\qquad = 85 - 0$

$\qquad = 85$ The student's score at the time the course was completed was 85%.

b. $S(t) = 85 - 25 \log (t + 1)$

$\quad S(2) = 85 - 25 \log (2 + 1)$

$\qquad = 85 - 25 \log 3$ Use a calculator to approximate $\log 3$.

$\qquad \approx 73.1$ The student's score dropped to 73.1%.

Answer

19. $\text{pH} \approx 6.23$

c. $S(t) = 85 - 25 \log (t + 1)$

$S(12) = 85 - 25 \log (12 + 1)$

$\qquad = 85 - 25 \log 13 \qquad$ Use a calculator to approximate $\log 13$.

$\qquad \approx 57.2 \qquad\qquad$ The student's score dropped to 57.2%.

Skill Practice The memory model for a student's score on a statistics test t months after completion of the course in statistics is approximated by

$$S(t) = 92 - 28 \log (t + 1)$$

20. What was the student's score at the time the course was completed $(t = 0)$?

21. What was her score after 1 month?

22. What was the score after 2 months?

Answers

20. 92   **21.** 83.6   **22.** 78.6

Section 12.3   Practice Exercises

Boost *your* GRADE at
mathzone.com!

ALEKS version 3.0

- Practice Problems
- Self-Tests
- NetTutor

- e-Professors
- Videos

For additional exercises, see Classroom Activities
12.3A–12.3C in the *Instructor's Resource Manual*
at www.mhhe.com/moh.

Study Skills Exercise

1. Define the key terms.

   a. logarithmic function   **b. logarithm**   **c. base of a logarithm**

   d. argument   **e. common logarithmic function**   **f. domain of a logarithmic function**

Review Exercises

2. For which graph of $y = b^x$ is $0 < b < 1$?   ii   **i.**   **ii.**

3. For which graph of $y = b^x$ is $b > 1$?   i

 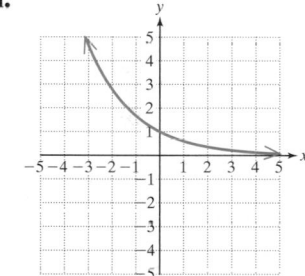

4. Let $f(x) = 6^x$. $f(-2) = \dfrac{1}{36}, f(-1) = \dfrac{1}{6}, f(0) = 1, f(1) = 6, f(2) = 36$

   a. Find $f(-2), f(-1), f(0), f(1),$ and $f(2)$.

   b. Graph $y = f(x)$.

5. Let $s(x) = \left(\dfrac{2}{5}\right)^x$. $s(-2) = \dfrac{25}{4}, s(-1) = \dfrac{5}{2}, s(0) = 1, s(1) = \dfrac{2}{5}, s(2) = \dfrac{4}{25}$

   a. Find $s(-2), s(-1), s(0), s(1),$ and $s(2)$.

   b. Graph $y = s(x)$.

 Writing   Translating Expression   Geometry   Scientific Calculator   Video   NS&E

6. Let $r(x) = \left(\dfrac{3}{4}\right)^x$. Find $r(-2), r(-1), r(0)$, $r(1)$, and $r(2)$.

$r(-2) = \dfrac{16}{9}, r(-1) = \dfrac{4}{3}, r(0) = 1, r(1) = \dfrac{3}{4}, r(2) = \dfrac{9}{16}$

7. Let $g(x) = 3^x$. Find $g(-2), g(-1), g(0)$, $g(1)$, and $g(2)$.

$g(-2) = \dfrac{1}{9}, g(-1) = \dfrac{1}{3}, g(0) = 1, g(1) = 3, g(2) = 9$

Concept 1: Definition of a Logarithmic Function

8. For the equation $y = \log_b x$, identify the base, the argument, and the logarithm.
The base is b, x is the argument, y is the logarithm.

9. Rewrite the equation in exponential form. $y = \log_b x$ $b^y = x$

10. Write the equation in logarithmic form. $b^y = x$ $\log_b x = y$

For Exercises 11–22, write the equation in exponential form. **(See Example 1.)**

11. $\log_5 625 = 4$ $5^4 = 625$
12. $\log_{125} 25 = \dfrac{2}{3}$ $125^{2/3} = 25$
13. $\log_{10}(0.0001) = -4$ $10^{-4} = 0.0001$
14. $\log_{25}\left(\dfrac{1}{5}\right) = -\dfrac{1}{2}$ $25^{-1/2} = \dfrac{1}{5}$

15. $\log_6 36 = 2$ $6^2 = 36$
16. $\log_2 128 = 7$ $2^7 = 128$
17. $\log_b 15 = x$ $b^x = 15$
18. $\log_b 82 = y$ $b^y = 82$

19. $\log_3 5 = x$ $3^x = 5$
20. $\log_2 7 = x$ $2^x = 7$
21. $\log_{1/4} x = 10$ $\left(\dfrac{1}{4}\right)^{10} = x$
22. $\log_{1/2} x = 6$ $\left(\dfrac{1}{2}\right)^6 = x$

For Exercises 23–34, write the equation in logarithmic form.

23. $3^x = 81$ $\log_3 81 = x$
24. $10^3 = 1000$ $\log_{10} 1000 = 3$
25. $5^2 = 25$ $\log_5 25 = 2$
26. $8^{1/3} = 2$ $\log_8 2 = \dfrac{1}{3}$

27. $7^{-1} = \dfrac{1}{7}$ $\log_7\left(\dfrac{1}{7}\right) = -1$
28. $8^{-2} = \dfrac{1}{64}$ $\log_8\left(\dfrac{1}{64}\right) = -2$
29. $b^x = y$ $\log_b y = x$
30. $b^y = x$ $\log_b x = y$

31. $e^x = y$ $\log_e y = x$
32. $e^y = x$ $\log_e x = y$
33. $\left(\dfrac{1}{3}\right)^{-2} = 9$ $\log_{1/3} 9 = -2$
34. $\left(\dfrac{5}{2}\right)^{-1} = \dfrac{2}{5}$ $\log_{5/2}\left(\dfrac{2}{5}\right) = -1$

Concept 2: Evaluating Logarithmic Expressions

For Exercises 35–50, evaluate the logarithms without the use of a calculator. **(See Examples 2–3.)**

35. $\log_7 49$ 2
36. $\log_3 81$ 4
37. $\log_{10} 0.1$ -1
38. $\log_2\left(\dfrac{1}{16}\right)$ -4

39. $\log_{16} 4$ $\dfrac{1}{2}$
40. $\log_8 2$ $\dfrac{1}{3}$
41. $\log_{7/2} 1$ 0
42. $\log_{1/2} 2$ -1

43. $\log_3 3^5$ 5
44. $\log_9 9^3$ 3
45. $\log_{10} 10$ 1
46. $\log_7 1$ 0

47. $\log_a a^3$ 3
48. $\log_r r^4$ 4
49. $\log_x \sqrt{x}$ $\dfrac{1}{2}$
50. $\log_y \sqrt[3]{y}$ $\dfrac{1}{3}$

Concept 3: The Common Logarithmic Function

For Exercises 51–58, evaluate the common logarithm without the use of a calculator. **(See Example 4.)**

51. $\log 10$ 1
52. $\log 100$ 2
53. $\log 1000$ 3

54. $\log 10,000$ 4
55. $\log (1.0 \times 10^6)$ 6
56. $\log 0.1$ -1

57. $\log 0.01$ -2
58. $\log 0.001$ -3

For Exercises 59–70, use a calculator to approximate the logarithms. Round to four decimal places. **(See Example 5.)**

59. $\log 6$ 0.7782

60. $\log 18$ 1.2553

61. $\log \pi$ 0.4971

62. $\log \left(\dfrac{1}{8}\right)$ −0.9031

63. $\log \left(\dfrac{1}{32}\right)$ −1.5051

64. $\log \sqrt{5}$ 0.3495

65. $\log 0.0054$ −2.2676

66. $\log 0.0000062$ −5.2076

67. $\log (3.4 \times 10^5)$
    5.5315

68. $\log (4.78 \times 10^9)$
    9.6794

69. $\log (3.8 \times 10^{-8})$
    −7.4202

70. $\log (2.77 \times 10^{-4})$
    −3.5575

71. Given: $\log 10 = 1$ and $\log 100 = 2$

   a. Estimate $\log 93$.   Slightly less than 2

   b. Estimate $\log 12$.   Slightly more than 1

   c. Evaluate the logarithms in parts (a) and (b) on a calculator and compare to your estimates. $\log 93 \approx 1.9685$, $\log 12 \approx 1.0792$

72. Given: $\log \left(\dfrac{1}{10}\right) = -1$ and $\log 1 = 0$

   a. Estimate $\log \left(\dfrac{9}{10}\right)$.   Slightly less than 0

   b. Estimate $\log \left(\dfrac{1}{5}\right)$.   Slightly more than −1

   c. Evaluate the logarithms in parts (a) and (b) on a calculator and compare to your estimates. $\log \left(\dfrac{9}{10}\right) \approx -0.0458$, $\log \left(\dfrac{1}{5}\right) \approx -0.6990$

Concept 4: Graphs of Logarithmic Functions

73. Let $f(x) = \log_4 x$. $f\left(\dfrac{1}{64}\right) = -3, f\left(\dfrac{1}{16}\right) = -2, f\left(\dfrac{1}{4}\right) = -1,$

   a. Find the values of $f\left(\dfrac{1}{64}\right), f\left(\dfrac{1}{16}\right), f\left(\dfrac{1}{4}\right), f(1),$

   $f(4), f(16),$ and $f(64)$. $f(1) = 0, f(4) = 1, f(16) = 2, f(64) = 3$

   b. Graph $y = f(x)$. **(See Example 6.)**

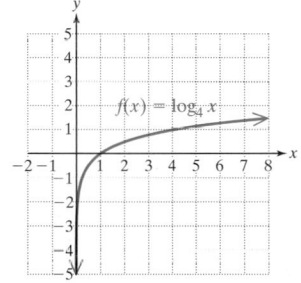

74. Let $g(x) = \log_2 x$. $g\left(\dfrac{1}{8}\right) = -3, g\left(\dfrac{1}{4}\right) = -2, g\left(\dfrac{1}{2}\right) = -1,$

   a. Find the values of $g\left(\dfrac{1}{8}\right), g\left(\dfrac{1}{4}\right), g\left(\dfrac{1}{2}\right), g(1), g(2),$

   $g(4),$ and $g(8)$. $g(1) = 0, g(2) = 1, g(4) = 2, g(8) = 3$

   b. Graph $y = g(x)$.

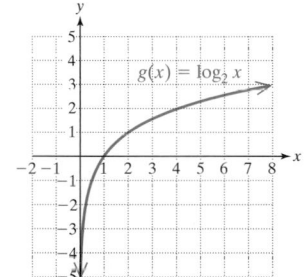

Graph the logarithmic functions in Exercises 75–78 by writing the function in exponential form and making a table of points.

75. $y = \log_3 x$ $3^y = x$

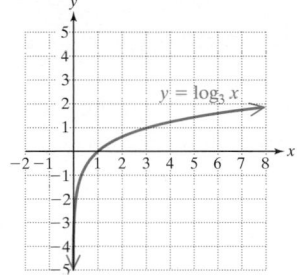

x	y
$\frac{1}{9}$	−2
$\frac{1}{3}$	−1
1	0
3	1
9	2

76. $y = \log_5 x$ $5^y = x$

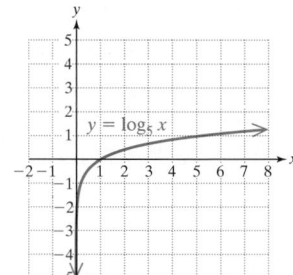

x	y
$\frac{1}{25}$	−2
$\frac{1}{5}$	−1
1	0
5	1
25	2

 Writing   Translating Expression   Geometry   Scientific Calculator   Video   NS&E

77. $y = \log_{1/2} x$ **(See Example 6.)** $\left(\dfrac{1}{2}\right)^y = x$

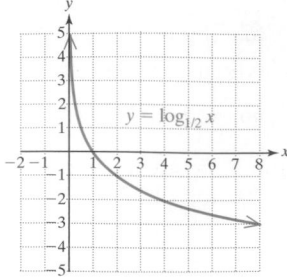

x	y
4	-2
2	-1
1	0
$\frac{1}{2}$	1
$\frac{1}{4}$	2

78. $y = \log_{1/3} x$ $\left(\dfrac{1}{3}\right)^y = x$

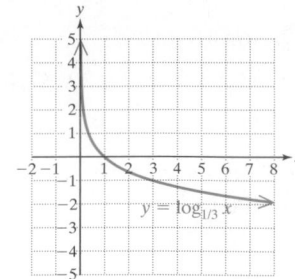

x	y
9	-2
3	-1
1	0
$\frac{1}{3}$	1
$\frac{1}{9}$	2

For Exercises 79–90, find the domain of the function and express the domain in interval notation. **(See Example 7.)**

79. $y = \log_7 (x - 5)$ $(5, \infty)$

80. $y = \log (x - 4)$ $(4, \infty)$

81. $g(x) = \log (2 - x)$ $(-\infty, 2)$

82. $f(x) = \log (1 - x)$ $(-\infty, 1)$

83. $y = \log (3x - 1)$ $\left(\dfrac{1}{3}, \infty\right)$

84. $y = \log_3 (2x + 1)$ $\left(-\dfrac{1}{2}, \infty\right)$

85. $y = \log_3 (x + 1.2)$ $(-1.2, \infty)$

86. $y = \log\left(x - \dfrac{1}{2}\right)$ $\left(\dfrac{1}{2}, \infty\right)$

87. $k(x) = \log (4 - 2x)$ $(-\infty, 2)$

88. $h(x) = \log (6 - 2x)$ $(-\infty, 3)$

89. $y = \log x^2$ $(-\infty, 0) \cup (0, \infty)$

90. $y = \log (x^2 + 1)$ $(-\infty, \infty)$

Concept 5: Applications of the Common Logarithmic Function

For Exercises 91–92, use the formula pH $= -\log[H^+]$, where $[H^+]$ represents the concentration of hydrogen ions in moles per liter. Round to two decimal places. **(See Example 8.)**

91. Normally, the level of hydrogen ions in the blood is approximately 4.47×10^{-8} mol/L. Find the pH level of blood. ≈ 7.35

92. The normal pH level for streams and rivers is between 6.5 and 8.5. A high level of bacteria in a particular stream caused environmentalists to test the water. The level of hydrogen ions was found to be 0.006 mol/L. What is the pH level of the stream? ≈ 2.22

93. A graduate student in education is doing research to compare the effectiveness of two different teaching techniques designed to teach vocabulary to sixth-graders. The first group of students (group 1) was taught with method I, in which the students worked individually to complete the assignments in a workbook. The second group (group 2) was taught with method II, in which the students worked cooperatively in groups of four to complete the assignments in the same workbook.

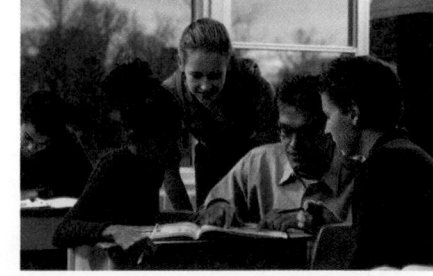

None of the students knew any of the vocabulary words before the study began. After completing the assignments in the workbook, the students were then tested on the vocabulary at 1-month intervals to assess how much material they had retained over time. The students' average score t months after completing the assignments are given by the following functions:

 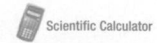

Method I: $S_1(t) = 91 - 30 \log (t + 1)$, where t is the time in months and $S_1(t)$ is the average score of students in group 1.

Method II: $S_2(t) = 88 - 15 \log (t + 1)$, where t is the time in months and $S_2(t)$ is the average score of students in group 2.

a. Complete the table to find the average scores for each group of students after the indicated number of months. Round to one decimal place. **(See Example 9.)**

t (months)	0	1	2	6	12	24
$S_1(t)$	91	82.0	76.7	65.6	57.6	49.1
$S_2(t)$	88	83.5	80.8	75.3	71.3	67.0

b. Based on the table of values, what were the average scores for each group immediately after completion of the assigned material $(t = 0)$?   Group 1: 91; Group 2: 88

c. Based on the table of values, which teaching method helped students retain the material better for a long time?   Method II

94. Generally, the more money a company spends on advertising, the higher the sales. Let a represent the amount of money spent on advertising (in $100s). Then the amount of money in sales $S(a)$ (in $1000s) is given by

$$S(a) = 10 + 20 \log (a + 1) \text{ where } a \geq 0.$$

$S(11) = 31.6$. If the company spends $1100 on advertising, $31,600 is returned in sales. $S(21) = 36.8$. If the company spends $2100 on advertising, $36,800 is returned in sales. $S(31) = 40.1$. If the company spends $3100 on advertising, $40,100 is returned in sales.

a. The value of $S(1) \approx 16.0$ means that if $100 is spent on advertising, $16,000 is returned in sales. Find the values of $S(11)$, $S(21)$, and $S(31)$. Round to one decimal place. Interpret the meaning of each function value in the context of this problem.

b. The graph of $y = S(a)$ is shown here. Use the graph and your answers from part (a) to explain why the money spent in advertising becomes less "efficient" as it is used in larger amounts.
Although more money spent on advertising increases sales, the rate of increase in sales decreases.

Graphing Calculator Exercises

For Exercises 95–100, graph the function on an appropriate viewing window. From the graph, identify the domain of the function and the location of the vertical asymptote.

95. $y = \log (x + 6)$
Domain: $(-6, \infty)$; asymptote: $x = -6$

96. $y = \log (2x + 4)$
Domain: $(-2, \infty)$; asymptote: $x = -2$

97. $y = \log (0.5x - 1)$
Domain: $(2, \infty)$; asymptote: $x = 2$

98. $y = \log (x + 8)$
Domain: $(-8, \infty)$; asymptote: $x = -8$

99. $y = \log (2 - x)$
Domain: $(-\infty, 2)$; asymptote: $x = 2$

100. $y = \log (3 - x)$
Domain: $(-\infty, 3)$; asymptote: $x = 3$

 Writing Translating Expression Geometry Scientific Calculator Video NS&E

Problem Recognition Exercises

Identifying Graphs of Functions

Match the function with the appropriate graph.

1. $g(x) = 3^x$　e

2. $f(x) = \log x$　l

3. $h(x) = x^2$　j

4. $k(x) = -2x - 3$　g

5. $L(x) = |x|$　c

6. $m(x) = \sqrt{x}$　a

7. $B(x) = 3$　k

8. $A(x) = -x^2$　b

9. $n(x) = \sqrt[3]{x}$　i

10. $p(x) = x^3$　h

11. $q(x) = \dfrac{1}{x}$　f

12. $r(x) = x$　d

a.

b.

c.

d.

e.

f.

g.

h.

i.

j.

k.

l.

 Writing　 Translating Expression　 Geometry　Scientific Calculator　Video　NS&E

Properties of Logarithms

1. Properties of Logarithms

You have already been exposed to certain properties of logarithms that follow directly from the definition. Recall

$$y = \log_b x \quad \text{is equivalent to} \quad b^y = x \quad \text{for } x > 0, b > 0, \text{ and } b \neq 1$$

The following properties follow directly from the definition.

Property	Explanation
1. $\log_b 1 = 0$	Exponential form: $b^0 = 1$
2. $\log_b b = 1$	Exponential form: $b^1 = b$
3. $\log_b b^p = p$	Exponential form: $b^p = b^p$
4. $b^{\log_b x} = x$	Logarithmic form: $\log_b x = \log_b x$

Example 1 **Applying the Properties of Logarithms to Simplify Expressions**

Use the properties of logarithms to simplify the expressions. Assume that all variable expressions within the logarithms represent positive real numbers.

a. $\log_8 8 + \log_8 1$ **b.** $10^{\log (x+2)}$ **c.** $\log_{1/2} \left(\frac{1}{2}\right)^x$

Solution:

a. $\log_8 8 + \log_8 1 = 1 + 0 = 1$ Properties 2 and 1

b. $10^{\log (x+2)} = x + 2$ Property 4

c. $\log_{1/2} \left(\frac{1}{2}\right)^x = x$ Property 3

Skill Practice Use the properties of logarithms to simplify the expressions.

1. $\log_5 1 + \log_5 5$ **2.** $15^{\log_{15} 7}$ **3.** $\log_{1/3} \left(\frac{1}{3}\right)^c$

Classroom Examples: p. 881, Exercises 22 and 24

Three additional properties are useful when simplifying logarithmic expressions. The first is the product property for logarithms.

PROPERTY   Product Property of Logarithms

Let b, x, and y be positive real numbers where $b \neq 1$. Then

$$\log_b (xy) = \log_b x + \log_b y$$

The logarithm of a product equals the sum of the logarithms of the factors.

Answers
1. 1   **2.** 7   **3.** c

Proof:

Let $M = \log_b x$, which implies $b^M = x$.

Let $N = \log_b y$, which implies $b^N = y$.

Then $xy = b^M b^N = b^{M+N}$.

Writing the expression $xy = b^{M+N}$ in logarithmic form, we have,

$$\log_b (xy) = M + N$$

$$\log_b (xy) = \log_b x + \log_b y \checkmark$$

To demonstrate the product property for logarithms, simplify the following expressions by using the order of operations.

$$\log_3 (3 \cdot 9) \overset{?}{=} \log_3 3 + \log_3 9$$

$$\log_3 27 \overset{?}{=} 1 + 2$$

$$3 \overset{?}{=} 3 \checkmark \text{ True}$$

PROPERTY   Quotient Property of Logarithms

Let b, x, and y be positive real numbers where $b \neq 1$. Then

$$\log_b \left(\frac{x}{y} \right) = \log_b x - \log_b y$$

The logarithm of a quotient equals the difference of the logarithms of the numerator and denominator.

The proof of the quotient property for logarithms is similar to the proof of the product property and is omitted here. To demonstrate the quotient property for logarithms, simplify the following expressions by using the order of operations.

$$\log \left(\frac{1,000,000}{100} \right) \overset{?}{=} \log (1,000,000) - \log (100)$$

$$\log (10,000) \overset{?}{=} 6 - 2$$

$$4 \overset{?}{=} 4 \checkmark \text{ True}$$

PROPERTY   Power Property of Logarithms

Let b and x be positive real numbers where $b \neq 1$. Let p be any real number. Then

$$\log_b x^p = p \log_b x$$

To demonstrate the power property for logarithms, simplify the following expressions by using the order of operations.

$$\log_4 4^2 \overset{?}{=} 2 \log_4 4$$

$$2 \overset{?}{=} 2 \cdot 1$$

$$2 \overset{?}{=} 2 \checkmark \text{ True}$$

The properties of logarithms are summarized in the box.

SUMMARY **Properties of Logarithms**

Let b, x, and y be positive real numbers where $b \neq 1$, and let p be a real number. Then the following properties of logarithms are true.

1. $\log_b 1 = 0$ **5.** $\log_b (xy) = \log_b x + \log_b y$ **Product property for logarithms**

2. $\log_b b = 1$ **6.** $\log_b \left(\dfrac{x}{y} \right) = \log_b x - \log_b y$ **Quotient property for logarithms**

3. $\log_b b^p = p$ **7.** $\log_b x^p = p \log_b x$ **Power property for logarithms**

4. $b^{\log_b x} = x$

---

2. Expanded Logarithmic Expressions

In many applications, it is advantageous to expand a logarithm into a sum or difference of simpler logarithms.

Example 2 **Writing a Logarithmic Expression in Expanded Form**

Classroom Example: p. 882, Exercise 52

Write the expression as the sum or difference of logarithms of x, y, and z. Assume all variables represent positive real numbers.

$$\log_3 \left(\frac{xy^3}{z^2} \right)$$

Solution:

$\log_3 \left(\dfrac{xy^3}{z^2} \right)$

$= \log_3 (xy^3) - \log_3 z^2$ Quotient property for logarithms (property 6)

$= [\log_3 x + \log_3 y^3] - \log_3 z^2$ Product property for logarithms (property 5)

$= \log_3 x + 3 \log_3 y - 2 \log_3 z$ Power property for logarithms (property 7)

Skill Practice Write the expression as the sum or difference of logarithms of a, b, and c. Assume all variables represent positive real numbers.

4. $\log_5 \left(\dfrac{a^2 b^3}{c} \right)$

Example 3 **Writing a Logarithmic Expression in Expanded Form**

Classroom Example: p. 882, Exercise 56

Write the expression as the sum or difference of logarithms of x and y. Assume all variables represent positive real numbers.

$$\log \left(\frac{\sqrt{x} + y}{10} \right)$$

Answer

4. $2 \log_5 a + 3 \log_5 b - \log_5 c$

Solution:

$$\log\left(\frac{\sqrt{x+y}}{10}\right)$$

$$= \log(\sqrt{x+y}) - \log 10 \qquad \text{Quotient property for logarithms (property 6)}$$

$$= \log(x+y)^{1/2} - 1 \qquad \text{Write } \sqrt{x+y} \text{ as } (x+y)^{1/2} \text{ and simplify } \log 10 = 1.$$

$$= \frac{1}{2}\log(x+y) - 1 \qquad \text{Power property for logarithms (property 7)}$$

Skill Practice Write the expression as the sum or difference of logarithms of a and b. Assume $a > b$.

5. $\log\dfrac{(a-b)^2}{\sqrt{10}}$

Classroom Example: p. 882, Exercise 58

| Example 4 | **Writing a Logarithmic Expression in Expanded Form** |

Write the expression as the sum or difference of logarithms of x, y, and z. Assume all variables represent positive real numbers.

$$\log_b \sqrt[5]{\frac{x^4}{yz^3}}$$

Solution:

$$\log_b \sqrt[5]{\frac{x^4}{yz^3}}$$

$$= \log_b\left(\frac{x^4}{yz^3}\right)^{1/5} \qquad \qquad \text{Write } \sqrt[5]{\frac{x^4}{yz^3}} \text{ as } \left(\frac{x^4}{yz^3}\right)^{1/5}.$$

Instructor Note: For Example 4, some students may simplify using the rules of exponents first.

$$\log_b\left(\frac{x^{4/5}}{y^{1/5}z^{3/5}}\right)$$

$$= \frac{1}{5}\log_b\left(\frac{x^4}{yz^3}\right) \qquad \qquad \text{Power property for logarithms (property 7)}$$

$$= \frac{1}{5}\left[\log_b x^4 - \log_b(yz^3)\right] \qquad \text{Quotient property for logarithms (property 6)}$$

$$= \frac{1}{5}\left[\log_b x^4 - (\log_b y + \log_b z^3)\right] \qquad \text{Product property for logarithms (property 5)}$$

$$= \frac{1}{5}\left[\log_b x^4 - \log_b y - \log_b z^3\right] \qquad \text{Distributive property}$$

$$= \frac{1}{5}\left[4\log_b x - \log_b y - 3\log_b z\right] \qquad \text{Power property for logarithms (property 7)}$$

$$\text{or} \quad \frac{4}{5}\log_b x - \frac{1}{5}\log_b y - \frac{3}{5}\log_b z$$

Skill Practice Write the expression as the sum or difference of logarithms of a, b, and c. Assume all variables represent positive real numbers.

6. $\log_3 \sqrt[4]{\dfrac{a}{bc^5}}$

Answers

5. $2\log(a-b) - \dfrac{1}{2}$

6. $\dfrac{1}{4}\log_3 a - \dfrac{1}{4}\log_3 b - \dfrac{5}{4}\log_3 c$

3. Single Logarithmic Expressions

In some applications, it is necessary to write a sum or difference of logarithms as a single logarithm.

Example 5 Writing a Sum or Difference of Logarithms as a Single Logarithm

Classroom Example: p. 882, Exercise 64

Rewrite the expression as a single logarithm, and simplify the result, if possible.

$$\log_2 560 - \log_2 7 - \log_2 5$$

Solution:

$$\log_2 560 - \log_2 7 - \log_2 5$$

$$= \log_2 560 - (\log_2 7 + \log_2 5) \qquad \text{Factor out } -1 \text{ from the last two terms.}$$

$$= \log_2 560 - \log_2 (7 \cdot 5) \qquad \text{Product property for logarithms (property 5)}$$

$$= \log_2 \left(\frac{560}{7 \cdot 5} \right) \qquad \text{Quotient property for logarithms (property 6)}$$

$$= \log_2 16 \qquad \text{Simplify inside parentheses.}$$

$$= 4$$

Skill Practice Write the expression as a single logarithm, and simplify the result, if possible.

7. $\log_3 54 + \log_3 10 - \log_3 20$

Example 6 Writing a Sum or Difference of Logarithms as a Single Logarithm

Classroom Example: p. 882, Exercise 68

Rewrite the expression as a single logarithm, and simplify the result, if possible. Assume all variable expressions within the logarithms represent positive real numbers.

$$2 \log x - \frac{1}{2} \log y + 3 \log z$$

Solution:

$$2 \log x - \frac{1}{2} \log y + 3 \log z$$

$$= \log x^2 - \log y^{1/2} + \log z^3 \qquad \text{Power property for logarithms (property 7)}$$

$$= \log x^2 + \log z^3 - \log y^{1/2} \qquad \text{Group terms with positive coefficients.}$$

$$= \log (x^2 z^3) - \log y^{1/2} \qquad \text{Product property for logarithms (property 5)}$$

$$= \log \left(\frac{x^2 z^3}{y^{1/2}} \right) \quad \text{or} \quad \log \left(\frac{x^2 z^3}{\sqrt{y}} \right) \qquad \text{Quotient property for logarithms (property 6)}$$

Skill Practice Write the expression as a single logarithm, and simplify, if possible.

8. $3 \log x + \frac{1}{3} \log y - 2 \log z$

Answers

7. 3   **8.** $\log \left(\dfrac{x^3 \sqrt[3]{y}}{z^2} \right)$

When a plant or animal dies, it no longer ingests carbon from the atmosphere. The amount of stable carbon 12 remains unchanged from the time of death, but the carbon 14 begins to decay. Because the rate of decay is constant, a tissue sample can be dated by comparing the percent of carbon 14 still present to the percentage of carbon 14 assumed to be in its original living state.

The age of a tissue sample is a function of the percent of carbon 14 still present in the organism according to the following model:

$$A(p) = \frac{\ln p}{-0.000121}$$

where $A(p)$ is the age in years and p is the percentage (in decimal form) of carbon 14 still present.

Classroom Example: p. 895,
Exercise 62

Example 8 Applying the Natural Logarithmic Function to Radioactive Decay

Using the formula

$$A(p) = \frac{\ln p}{-0.000121}$$

a. Find the age of a bone that has 72% of its initial carbon 14.

b. Find the age of the Iceman, a body uncovered in the mountains of northern Italy in 1991. Samples of his hair revealed that 52.7% of the original carbon 14 was present after his death.

Solution:

a. $A(p) = \dfrac{\ln p}{-0.000121}$

   $A(0.72) = \dfrac{\ln 0.72}{-0.000121}$ Substitute 0.72 for p.

   ≈ 2715 years

b. $A(p) = \dfrac{\ln p}{-0.000121}$

   $A(0.527) = \dfrac{\ln 0.527}{-0.000121}$ Substitute 0.527 for p.

   ≈ 5300 years   The body of the Iceman is approximately 5300 yr old.

Skill Practice

12. Use the formula

$$A(p) = \frac{\ln p}{-0.000121}$$

(where $A(p)$ is the age in years and p is the percent of carbon 14 still present) to determine the age of a human skull that has 90% of its initial carbon 14.

Answer

12. ≈ 871 yr

Section 12.5 Practice Exercises

Boost *your* GRADE at
ALEKS.com!

 ALEKS version 3.0

- Practice Problems
- Self-Tests
- NetTutor

- e-Professors
- Videos

For additional exercises, see Classroom Activities
12.5A–12.5E in the *Instructor's Resource Manual*
at www.mhhe.com/moh.

Study Skills Exercise

1. Define the key terms.

   a. *e*

   b. continuously compounded interest

   c. natural logarithmic function

   d. change-of-base formula

Review Exercises

For Exercises 2–3, write the expression as a single logarithm. Assume that all variables represent positive real numbers.

2. $\log_5 x + 3 \log_5 y - \log_5 z$ $\log_5\left(\dfrac{xy^3}{z}\right)$

3. $\log_3 a - 5 \log_3 c + \dfrac{1}{2} \log_3 d$ $\log_3\left(\dfrac{a\sqrt{d}}{c^5}\right)$

For Exercises 4–5, write the expression as the sum or difference of logarithms of *x*, *y*, and *z*. Assume that all variables represent positive real numbers.

4. $\log\left(\dfrac{\sqrt{x}}{yz^4}\right)$ $\dfrac{1}{2}\log x - \log y - 4 \log z$

5. $\log_6 \sqrt[4]{\dfrac{xy^2}{z^3}}$ $\dfrac{1}{4}\log_6 x + \dfrac{1}{2}\log_6 y - \dfrac{3}{4}\log_6 z$

Concept 1: The Irrational Number *e*

6. From memory, write a decimal approximation of the number *e*, correct to three decimal places.   2.718

 For Exercises 7–10, graph the equation by completing the table and plotting points. Identify the domain. Round to two decimal places when necessary. **(See Example 1.)**

7. $y = e^{x+1}$

x	y
−4	0.05
−3	0.14
−2	0.37
−1	1
0	2.72
1	7.39

Domain: $(-\infty, \infty)$

8. $y = e^{x+2}$

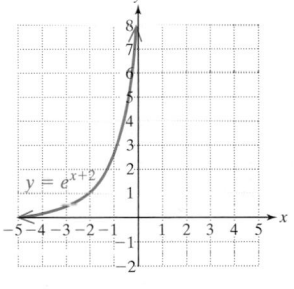

x	y
−5	0.05
−4	0.14
−3	0.37
−2	1
−1	2.72
0	7.39

Domain: $(-\infty, \infty)$

9. $y = e^x + 2$

x	y
−2	2.14
−1	2.37
0	3
1	4.72
2	9.39
3	22.09

Domain: $(-\infty, \infty)$

10. $y = e^x - 1$

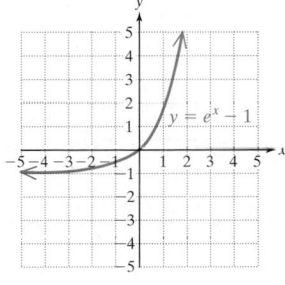

x	y
−4	−0.98
−3	−0.95
−2	−0.86
−1	−0.63
0	0
1	1.72

Domain: $(-\infty, \infty)$

Concept 2: Computing Compound Interest

 In Exercises 11–16, use the model

$$A(t) = P\left(1 + \frac{r}{n}\right)^{nt}$$

for interest compounded n times per year. Use the model $A(t) = Pe^{rt}$ for interest compounded continuously.

11. Suppose an investor deposits $10,000 in a certificate of deposit for 5 yr for which the interest is compounded monthly. Find the total amount of money in the account for the following interest rates. Compare your answers and comment on the effect of interest rate on an investment. **(See Example 2.)**

    $12,209.97 $13,488.50 $14,898.46 $16,050.09

  a. $r = 4.0\%$ **b.** $r = 6.0\%$ **c.** $r = 8.0\%$ **d.** $r = 9.5\%$

  An investment grows more rapidly at higher interest rates.

12. Suppose an investor deposits $5000 in a certificate of deposit for 8 yr for which the interest is compounded quarterly. Find the total amount of money in the account for the following interest rates. Compare your answers and comment on the effect of interest rate on an investment.

    $7152.26 $7740.30 $8711.07 $10,190.52

  a. $r = 4.5\%$ **b.** $r = 5.5\%$ **c.** $r = 7.0\%$ **d.** $r = 9.0\%$

  An investment grows more rapidly at higher interest rates.

13. Suppose an investor deposits $8000 in a savings account for 10 yr at 4.5% interest. Find the total amount of money in the account for the following compounding options. Compare your answers. How does the number of compound periods per year affect the total investment?

  a. Compounded annually $12,423.76

  b. Compounded quarterly $12,515.01

  c. Compounded monthly $12,535.94

  d. Compounded daily $12,546.15

  e. Compounded continuously $12,546.50

  More money is earned at a greater number of compound periods per year.

14. Suppose an investor deposits $15,000 in a savings account for 8 yr at 5.0% interest. Find the total amount of money in the account for the following compounding options. Compare your answers. How does the number of compound periods per year affect the total investment?

  a. Compounded annually $22,161.83

  b. Compounded quarterly $22,321.96

  c. Compounded monthly $22,358.78

  d. Compounded daily $22,376.76

  e. Compounded continuously $22,377.37

  More money is earned at a greater number of compound periods per year.

15. Suppose an investor deposits $5000 in an account earning 6.5% interest compounded continuously. Find the total amount in the account for the following time periods. How does the length of time affect the amount of interest earned?

    $6920.15 $9577.70 $13,255.84 $18,346.48 $35,143.44

  a. 5 yr   **b.** 10 yr   **c.** 15 yr   **d.** 20 yr   **e.** 30 yr

  More money is earned over a longer period of time.

16. Suppose an investor deposits $10,000 in an account earning 6.0% interest compounded continuously. Find the total amount in the account for the following time periods. How does the length of time affect the amount of interest earned?

    $13,498.59 $18,221.19 $24,596.03 $33,201.17 $60,496.47

  a. 5 yr   **b.** 10 yr   **c.** 15 yr   **d.** 20 yr   **e.** 30 yr

  More money is earned over a longer period of time.

Concept 3: The Natural Logarithmic Function

For Exercises 17–20, graph the equation by completing the table and plotting the points. Identify the domain. Round to two decimal places when necessary. **(See Example 3.)**

17. $y = \ln(x - 2)$

x	y
2.25	−1.39
2.50	−0.69
2.75	−0.29
3	0
4	0.69
5	1.10
6	1.39

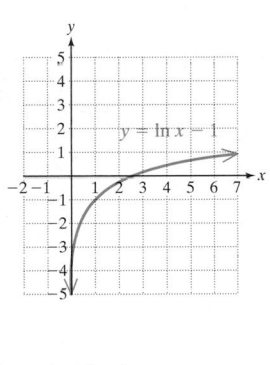

Domain: $(2, \infty)$

18. $y = \ln(x - 1)$

x	y
1.25	−1.39
1.50	−0.69
1.75	−0.29
2	0
3	0.69
4	1.10
5	1.39

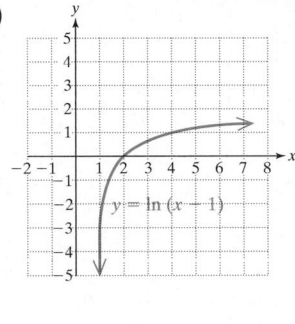

Domain: $(1, \infty)$

19. $y = \ln x - 1$

x	y
0.25	−2.39
0.5	−1.69
0.75	−1.29
1	−1.00
2	−0.31
3	0.10
4	0.39

Domain: $(0, \infty)$

20. $y = \ln x + 2$

x	y
0.25	0.61
0.5	1.31
0.75	1.71
1	2.00
2	2.69
3	3.10
4	3.39

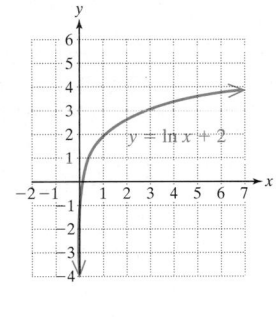

Domain: $(0, \infty)$

21. a. Graph $f(x) = 10^x$ and $g(x) = \log x$.

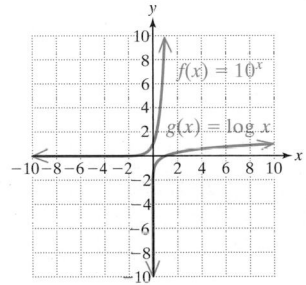

b. Identify the domain and range of *f*.
 Domain: $(-\infty, \infty)$; range: $(0, \infty)$
c. Identify the domain and range of *g*.
 Domain: $(0, \infty)$; range: $(-\infty, \infty)$

22. a. Graph $f(x) = e^x$ and $g(x) = \ln x$.

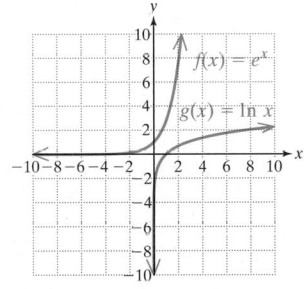

b. Identify the domain and range of *f*.
 Domain: $(-\infty, \infty)$; range: $(0, \infty)$
c. Identify the domain and range of *g*.
 Domain: $(0, \infty)$; range: $(-\infty, \infty)$

For Exercises 23–30, simplify the expressions. Assume all variables represent positive real numbers. **(See Example 4.)**

23. $\ln e$ 1

24. $\ln e^2$ 2

25. $\ln 1$ 0

26. $e^{\ln x}$ x

27. $\ln e^{-6}$ −6

28. $\ln e^{(5-3x)}$ 5 − 3x

29. $e^{\ln(2x+3)}$ 2x + 3

30. $e^{\ln 4}$ 4

 Writing   Translating Expression   Geometry   Scientific Calculator   Video   NS&E

For Exercises 31–38, write the expression as a single logarithm. Assume all variables represent positive real numbers. **(See Example 5.)**

31. $6 \ln p + \dfrac{1}{3} \ln q$ $\ln (p^6 \sqrt[3]{q})$

32. $2 \ln w + \ln z$ $\ln (w^2 z)$

33. $\dfrac{1}{2} (\ln x - 3 \ln y)$ $\ln \sqrt{\dfrac{x}{y^3}}$

34. $\dfrac{1}{3} (4 \ln a - \ln b)$ $\ln \sqrt[3]{\dfrac{a^4}{b}}$

35. $2 \ln a - \ln b - \dfrac{1}{3} \ln c$ $\ln \left(\dfrac{a^2}{b \sqrt[3]{c}} \right)$

36. $-\ln x + 3 \ln y - \ln z$ $\ln \left(\dfrac{y^3}{xz} \right)$

37. $4 \ln x - 3 \ln y - \ln z$ $\ln \left(\dfrac{x^4}{y^3 z} \right)$

38. $\dfrac{1}{2} \ln c + \ln a - 2 \ln b$ $\ln \left(\dfrac{\sqrt{c} \cdot a}{b^2} \right)$

For Exercises 39–46, write the expression as a sum and/or difference of $\ln a$, $\ln b$, and $\ln c$. Assume all variables represent positive real numbers. **(See Example 6.)**

39. $\ln \left(\dfrac{a}{b} \right)^2$ $2 \ln a - 2 \ln b$

40. $\ln \sqrt[3]{\dfrac{a}{b}}$ $\dfrac{1}{3} \ln a - \dfrac{1}{3} \ln b$

41. $\ln (b^2 \cdot e)$ $2 \ln b + 1$

42. $\ln (\sqrt{c} \cdot e)$ $\dfrac{1}{2} \ln c + 1$

43. $\ln \left(\dfrac{a^4 \sqrt{b}}{c} \right)$ $4 \ln a + \dfrac{1}{2} \ln b - \ln c$

44. $\ln \left(\dfrac{\sqrt{ab}}{c^3} \right)$ $\dfrac{1}{2} \ln a + \dfrac{1}{2} \ln b - 3 \ln c$

45. $\ln \left(\dfrac{ab}{c^2} \right)^{1/5}$ $\dfrac{1}{5} \ln a + \dfrac{1}{5} \ln b - \dfrac{2}{5} \ln c$

46. $\ln \sqrt{2ab}$ $\dfrac{1}{2} \ln 2 + \dfrac{1}{2} \ln a + \dfrac{1}{2} \ln b$

Concept 4: Change-of-Base Formula

47. a. Evaluate $\log_6 200$ by computing $\dfrac{\log 200}{\log 6}$ to four decimal places.   2.9570

    b. Evaluate $\log_6 200$ by computing $\dfrac{\ln 200}{\ln 6}$ to four decimal places.   2.9570

    c. How do your answers to parts (a) and (b) compare?   They are the same.

48. a. Evaluate $\log_8 120$ by computing $\dfrac{\log 120}{\log 8}$ to four decimal places.   2.3023

    b. Evaluate $\log_8 120$ by computing $\dfrac{\ln 120}{\ln 8}$ to four decimal places.   2.3023

    c. How do your answers to parts (a) and (b) compare?   They are the same.

For Exercises 49–60, use the change-of-base formula to approximate the logarithms to four decimal places. Check your answers by using the exponential key on your calculator. **(See Example 7.)**

49. $\log_2 7$ 2.8074

50. $\log_3 5$ 1.4650

51. $\log_8 24$ 1.5283

52. $\log_4 17$ 2.0437

53. $\log_8 0.012$ -2.1269

54. $\log_7 0.251$ -0.7104

55. $\log_9 1$ 0

56. $\log_2 \left(\dfrac{1}{5} \right)$ -2.3219

57. $\log_4 \left(\dfrac{1}{100} \right)$ -3.3219

58. $\log_5 0.0025$ -3.7227

59. $\log_7 0.0006$ -3.8124

60. $\log_2 0.24$ -2.0589

Writing   Translating Expression   Geometry   Scientific Calculator   Video   NSⓔ

Concept 5: Applications of the Natural Logarithmic Function

Under continuous compounding, the amount of time *t* in years required for an investment to double is a function of the interest rate *r* according to the formula:

$$t = \frac{\ln 2}{r}$$

Use the formula for Exercises 61–63. **(See Example 8.)**

61. a. If you invest $5000, how long will it take the investment to reach $10,000 if the interest rate is 4.5%? Round to one decimal place.   15.4 yr

b. If you invest $5000, how long will it take the investment to reach $10,000 if the interest rate is 10%? Round to one decimal place.   6.9 yr

c. Using the doubling time found in part (b), how long would it take a $5000 investment to reach $20,000 if the interest rate is 10%?   13.8 yr

62. a. If you invest $3000, how long will it take the investment to reach $6000 if the interest rate is 5.5%? Round to one decimal place.   12.6 yr

b. If you invest $3000, how long will it take the investment to reach $6000 if the interest rate is 8%? Round to one decimal place.   8.7 yr

c. Using the doubling time found in part (b), how long would it take a $3000 investment to reach $12,000 if the interest rate is 8%?   17.4 yr

63. a. If you invest $4000, how long will it take the investment to reach $8000 if the interest rate is 3.5%? Round to one decimal place.   19.8 yr

b. If you invest $4000, how long will it take the investment to reach $8000 if the interest rate is 5%? Round to one decimal place.   13.9 yr

c. Using the doubling time found in part (b), how long would it take a $4000 investment to reach $16,000 if the interest rate is 5%?   27.8 yr

64. On August 31, 1854, an epidemic of cholera was discovered in London, England, resulting from a contaminated community water pump at Broad Street. By the end of September more than 600 citizens who drank water from the pump had died.

The cumulative number of deaths from cholera in the 1854 London epidemic can be approximated by

$$D(t) = 91 + 160 \ln (t + 1)$$

where *t* is the number of days after the start of the epidemic (*t* = 0 corresponds to September 1, 1854).

a. Approximate the total number of deaths as of September 1 (*t* = 0).   91 deaths

b. Approximate the total number of deaths as of September 5, September 10, and September 20.
Sept. 5: 349 deaths; Sept. 10: 459 deaths; Sept. 20: 570 deaths

Graphing Calculator Exercises

65. a. Graph the function defined by $f(x) = \log_3 x$ by graphing $Y_1 = \dfrac{\log x}{\log 3}$.

b. Graph the function defined by $f(x) = \log_3 x$ by graphing $Y_2 = \dfrac{\ln x}{\ln 3}$.

c. Does it appear that $Y_1 = Y_2$ on the standard viewing window?
They appear to be the same.

 Writing   Translating Expression   Geometry   Scientific Calculator   Video   NS E

66. a. Graph the function defined by $f(x) = \log_7 x$ by graphing $Y_1 = \dfrac{\log x}{\log 7}$.

b. Graph the function defined by $f(x) = \log_7 x$ by graphing $Y_2 = \dfrac{\ln x}{\ln 7}$.

c. Does it appear that $Y_1 = Y_2$ on the standard viewing window?
They appear to be the same.

For Exercises 67–69, graph the functions on your calculator.

67. Graph $s(x) = \log_{1/2} x$ **68.** Graph $y = e^{x-2}$ **69.** Graph $y = e^{x-1}$

Problem Recognition Exercises

Logarithmic and Exponential Forms

Fill out the table by writing the exponential expressions in logarithmic form, and the logarithmic expressions in exponential form. Use the fact that:

$$y = \log_b x \quad \text{is equivalent to} \quad b^y = x$$

	Exponential Form	Logarithmic Form
1.	$2^5 = 32$	$\log_2 32 = 5$
2.	$3^4 = 81$	$\log_3 81 = 4$
3.	$z^y = x$	$\log_z x = y$
4.	$b^c = a$	$\log_b a = c$
5.	$10^3 = 1000$	$\log 1000 = 3$
6.	$10^1 = 10$	$\log 10 = 1$
7.	$e^a = b$	$\ln b = a$
8.	$e^q = p$	$\ln p = q$
9.	$\left(\frac{1}{2}\right)^2 = \frac{1}{4}$	$\log_{1/2}\left(\frac{1}{4}\right) = 2$
10.	$\left(\frac{1}{3}\right)^{-2} = 9$	$\log_{1/3} 9 = -2$
11.	$10^{-2} = 0.01$	$\log 0.01 = -2$
12.	$10^x = 4$	$\log 4 = x$
13.	$e^0 = 1$	$\ln 1 = 0$
14.	$e^1 = e$	$\ln e = 1$
15.	$25^{1/2} = 5$	$\log_{25} 5 = \frac{1}{2}$
16.	$16^{1/4} = 2$	$\log_{16} 2 = \frac{1}{4}$
17.	$e^t = s$	$\ln s = t$
18.	$e^r = w$	$\ln w = r$
19.	$15^{-2} = \frac{1}{225}$	$\log_{15}\left(\frac{1}{225}\right) = -2$
20.	$3^{-1} = p$	$\log_3 p = -1$

 Writing   Translating Expression   Geometry   Scientific Calculator   Video   NS&E

Logarithmic and Exponential Equations and Applications

1. Solving Logarithmic Equations

Equations containing one or more logarithms are called **logarithmic equations**. For example:

$$\log_3(2x + 5) = 1 \quad \text{and} \quad \log_4 x = 1 - \log_4(x - 3)$$

To solve equations involving logarithms of first degree, we use the following guidelines.

PROCEDURE Solving Logarithmic Equations

Step 1 Isolate the logarithms on one side of the equation.
Step 2 Write a sum or difference of logarithms as a single logarithm.
Step 3 Rewrite the equation in step 2 in exponential form.
Step 4 Solve the resulting equation from step 3.
Step 5 Check all solutions to verify that they are within the domain of the logarithmic expressions in the original equation.

Example 1 Solving a Logarithmic Equation

Solve the equation. $\log_3(2x + 5) = 1$

Solution:

$\log_3(2x + 5) = 1$	This equation has a single logarithm isolated on the left-hand side.
$2x + 5 = 3^1$	Write the logarithm in its equivalent exponential form.
$2x + 5 = 3$	Solve the resulting equation.
$2x = -2$	
$x = -1$	Check: $x = -1$

$$\log_3(2x + 5) = 1$$
$$\log_3[2(-1) + 5] \overset{?}{=} 1$$
$$\log_3(3) \overset{?}{=} 1 \;\checkmark$$

The solution set is $\{-1\}$.

Skill Practice Solve the equation.

  1. $\log_6(5x - 4) = 2$

Classroom Example: p. 906, Exercise 22

Answer

1. $\{8\}$

Classroom Example: p. 906, Exercise 30

Example 2 Solving a Logarithmic Equation

Solve the equation. $\log_4 x = 1 - \log_4(x - 3)$

Solution:

$$\log_4 x = 1 - \log_4(x - 3)$$

$$\log_4 x + \log_4(x - 3) = 1 \qquad \text{Isolate the logarithms on one side of the equation.}$$

$$\log_4[x(x - 3)] = 1 \qquad \text{Write as a single logarithm.}$$

$$\log_4(x^2 - 3x) = 1 \qquad \text{Simplify inside the parentheses.}$$

$$x^2 - 3x = 4^1 \qquad \text{Write the equation in exponential form.}$$

$$x^2 - 3x - 4 = 0 \qquad \text{The resulting equation is quadratic.}$$

$$(x - 4)(x + 1) = 0 \qquad \text{Factor.}$$

$$x = 4 \quad \text{or} \quad x = -1 \qquad \text{Apply the zero product rule.}$$

Notice that -1 is *not* a solution because $\log_4 x$ is not defined at $x = -1$. However, $x = 4$ *is* defined in both expressions $\log_4 x$ and $\log_4(x - 3)$. We can substitute $x = 4$ into the original equation to show that it checks.

Instructor Note: It is very important that students realize that there is a possibility of extraneous solutions for logarithmic equations.

Check: $x = 4$

$$\log_4 x = 1 - \log_4(x - 3)$$

$$\log_4 4 \overset{?}{=} 1 - \log_4(4 - 3)$$

$$1 \overset{?}{=} 1 - \log_4 1$$

$$1 \overset{?}{=} 1 - 0 \ \checkmark \ \text{True}$$

The solution set is $\{4\}$. (The value -1 does not check.)

Skill Practice Solve the equation.

2. $\log_3(x - 8) = 2 - \log_3 x$

Classroom Example: p. 906, Exercise 14

Example 3 Solving a Logarithmic Equation

Solve the equation. $\log(x + 300) = 3.7$

Solution:

$$\log(x + 300) = 3.7 \qquad \text{The equation has a single logarithm that is already isolated.}$$

$$10^{3.7} = x + 300 \qquad \text{Write the equation in exponential form.}$$

$$10^{3.7} - 300 = x \qquad \text{Solve for } x.$$

$$x = 10^{3.7} - 300$$

$$\approx 4711.87$$

Answer

2. $\{9\}$ (The value -1 does not check.)

Check: $x = 10^{3.7} - 300$

$$\log(x + 300) = 3.7$$

$$\log[(10^{3.7} - 300) + 300] \overset{?}{=} 3.7$$

$$\log(10^{3.7} - 300 + 300) \overset{?}{=} 3.7$$

$$\log 10^{3.7} \overset{?}{=} 3.7$$

$$3.7 \overset{?}{=} 3.7 \; ✔ \; \text{True}$$

Check the exact value of x in the original equation.

Property 3 of logarithms:
$\log_b b^p = p$

The solution $10^{3.7} - 300$ checks.

The solution set is $\{10^{3.7} - 300\}$.

Skill Practice Solve the equation.

3. $\log(p + 6) = 1.3$

The following property is another useful tool to solve a logarithmic equation. This is demonstrated in Example 4.

> **PROPERTY** **Equivalence of Logarithmic Expressions**
>
> Let x, y, and b represent real numbers such that $x > 0$, $y > 0$, $b > 0$, and $b \neq 1$. Then
>
> $$\log_b x = \log_b y \quad \text{implies} \quad x = y$$

Example 4 Solving a Logarithmic Equation

Solve the equation.

$$\ln(x + 2) + \ln(x - 1) = \ln(9x - 17)$$

Classroom Example: p. 906, Exercise 34

Solution:

$$\ln(x + 2) + \ln(x - 1) = \ln(9x - 17)$$

$$\ln[(x + 2)(x - 1)] = \ln(9x - 17)$$

Write the logarithms on the left-hand side as a single logarithm.

$$\ln(x^2 + x - 2) = \ln(9x - 17)$$

Simplify.

$$x^2 + x - 2 = 9x - 17$$

Use the equivalence property of logarithms. That is, equate the arguments of each log.

$$x^2 - 8x + 15 = 0$$

Solve the resulting quadratic equation.

$$(x - 5)(x - 3) = 0$$

$$x = 5 \quad \text{or} \quad x = 3$$

Answer

3. $\{10^{1.3} - 6\}$

The solutions 5 and 3 are both within the domain of the logarithmic functions in the original equation. Both solutions check.

The solution set is $\{5, 3\}$.

Skill Practice Solve the equation.

4. $\ln(t - 3) + \ln(t - 1) = \ln(2t - 5)$

2. Solving Exponential Equations

An equation with one or more exponential expressions is called an **exponential equation**. The following property is often useful in solving exponential equations.

> **PROPERTY** Equivalence of Exponential Expressions
>
> Let x, y, and b be real numbers such that $b > 0$ and $b \neq 1$. Then
>
> $$b^x = b^y \qquad \text{implies} \qquad x = y$$

The equivalence of exponential expressions indicates that if two exponential expressions of the same base are equal, their exponents must be equal.

Classroom Example: p. 906, Exercise 46

Example 5 Solving an Exponential Equation

Solve the equation. $\qquad 4^{2x-9} = 64$

Solution:

$$4^{2x-9} = 64$$

$$4^{2x-9} = 4^3 \qquad \text{Write both sides with a common base.}$$

$$2x - 9 = 3 \qquad \text{If } b^x = b^y, \text{ then } x = y.$$

$$2x = 12 \qquad \text{Solve for } x.$$

$$x = 6$$

To check, substitute $x = 6$ into the original equation.

$$4^{2(6)-9} \stackrel{?}{=} 64$$

$$4^{12-9} \stackrel{?}{=} 64$$

$$4^3 \stackrel{?}{=} 64 \; \checkmark \; \text{True}$$

The solution set is $\{6\}$.

Skill Practice Solve the equation.

5. $2^{3x+1} = 8$

Answers

4. $\{4\}$ (The value 2 does not check.)

5. $\left\{ \dfrac{2}{3} \right\}$

Example 6 **Solving an Exponential Equation**

Classroom Example: p. 906, Exercise 50

Solve the equation. $(2^x)^{x+3} = \dfrac{1}{4}$

Solution:

$$(2^x)^{x+3} = \frac{1}{4}$$

$2^{x^2+3x} = 2^{-2}$ Apply the multiplication property of exponents. Write both sides of the equation with a common base.

$x^2 + 3x = -2$ If $b^x = b^y$, then $x = y$.

$x^2 + 3x + 2 = 0$ The resulting equation is quadratic.

$(x + 2)(x + 1) = 0$ Solve for x.

$x = -2$ or $x = -1$ Both solutions check.

The solution set is $\{-2, -1\}$.

Skill Practice Solve the equation.

6. $(3^x)^{x-5} = \dfrac{1}{81}$

Example 7 **Solving an Exponential Equation by Taking a Logarithm on Both Sides**

Classroom Example: p. 906, Exercise 56

Solve the equation. $4^x = 25$

Solution:

Because 25 cannot be written as an integral power of 4, we cannot easily use the property that if $b^x = b^y$, then $x = y$. Instead, we can take a logarithm of any base on both sides of the equation. Then by applying the power property of logarithms, the unknown exponent can be written as a factor.

$4^x = 25$

$\log 4^x = \log 25$ Take the common logarithm of both sides.

$x \log 4 = \log 25$ Apply the power property of logarithms to express the exponent as a factor. This is now a linear equation in x.

$\dfrac{x \, \cancel{\log 4}}{\cancel{\log 4}} = \dfrac{\log 25}{\log 4}$ Solve for x.

$x = \dfrac{\log 25}{\log 4}$ or approximately 2.322.

The solution set is $\left\{ \dfrac{\log 25}{\log 4} \right\}$.

Skill Practice Solve the equation.

7. $5^x = 32$

Calculator Connections

Graph $Y_1 = 4^x$ and $Y_2 = 25$. An *Intersect* feature can be used to find the x-coordinate where $Y_1 = Y_2$.

Answers

6. $\{1, 4\}$

7. $\left\{ \dfrac{\log 32}{\log 5} \right\}$ or $\left\{ \dfrac{\ln 32}{\ln 5} \right\}$

TIP: The equation from Example 7 is written in the form $b^x =$ constant. In this special case, we also have the option of rewriting the equation in its corresponding logarithmic form to solve for x.

$$4^x = 25$$

$$x = \log_4 25$$

$$= \frac{\ln 25}{\ln 4} \qquad \text{(Change-of-base formula)}$$

PROCEDURE   Solving Exponential Equations

Step 1 Isolate one of the exponential expressions in the equation.

Step 2 Take a logarithm on both sides of the equation. (The natural logarithmic function or the common logarithmic function is often used so that the final answer can be approximated with a calculator.)

Step 3 Use the power property of logarithms (property 7) to write exponents as factors. Recall: $\log_b M^p = p \log_b M$.

Step 4 Solve the resulting equation from step 3.

Classroom Example: p. 906, Exercise 62

Example 8 Solving an Exponential Equation by Taking a Logarithm on Both Sides

Solve the equation. $e^{-3.6x} = 9.74$

Solution:

$$e^{-3.6x} = 9.74$$

$$\ln e^{-3.6x} = \ln 9.74 \qquad$$ The exponential expression has a base of e, so it is convenient to take the natural logarithm of both sides.

$$(-3.6x) \ln e = \ln 9.74 \qquad$$ Use the power property of logarithms.

$$-3.6x = \ln 9.74 \qquad$$ Simplify (recall that $\ln e = 1$).

$$x = \frac{\ln 9.74}{-3.6} \approx -0.632$$

The solution set is $\left\{ -\dfrac{\ln 9.74}{3.6} \right\}$.

Skill Practice Solve the equation.

8. $e^{-0.2t} = 7.52$

Answer

8. $\left\{ \dfrac{\ln 7.52}{-0.2} \right\}$

Example 9   **Solving an Exponential Equation by Taking a Logarithm on Both Sides**

Classroom Example: p. 906, Exercise 66

Solve the equation. $2^{x+3} = 7^x$

Solution:

$$2^{x+3} = 7^x$$

$$\ln 2^{(x+3)} = \ln 7^x \qquad \text{Take the natural logarithm of both sides.}$$

$$(x+3)\ln 2 = x \ln 7 \qquad \text{Use the power property of logarithms.}$$

$$x(\ln 2) + 3(\ln 2) = x \ln 7 \qquad \text{Apply the distributive property.}$$

$$x(\ln 2) - x(\ln 7) = -3 \ln 2 \qquad \text{Collect } x\text{-terms on one side.}$$

$$x(\ln 2 - \ln 7) = -3 \ln 2 \qquad \text{Factor out } x.$$

$$\frac{x(\ln 2 - \ln 7)}{(\ln 2 - \ln 7)} = \frac{-3 \ln 2}{\ln 2 - \ln 7} \qquad \text{Solve for } x.$$

$$x = \frac{-3 \ln 2}{\ln 2 - \ln 7} \approx 1.66$$

The solution set is $\left\{ -\dfrac{3 \ln 2}{\ln 2 - \ln 7} \right\}$.

Skill Practice   Solve the equation.

9. $3^x = 8^{x+2}$

TIP: The exponential equation $2^{x+3} = 7^x$ could have been solved by taking a logarithm of *any* base on both sides of the equation.

3. Applications

Example 10   **Applying an Exponential Function to World Population**

Classroom Example: p. 907, Exercise 76

The population of the world was estimated to have reached 6.5 billion in April 2006. The population growth rate for the world is estimated to be 1.4%. (*Source:* U.S. Census Bureau)

$$P(t) = 6.5(1.014)^t$$

represents the world population in billions as a function of the number of years after April 2006 ($t = 0$ represents April 2006).

a. Use the function to estimate the world population in April 2010.

b. Use the function to estimate the amount of time after April 2006 required for the world population to reach 13 billion.

Solution:

a. $P(t) = 6.5(1.014)^t$

$P(4) = 6.5(1.014)^4 \qquad$ The year 2010 corresponds to $t = 4$.

$\approx 6.87 \qquad$ In 2010, the world's population will be approximately 6.87 billion.

Answer

9. $\left\{ \dfrac{2 \ln 8}{\ln 3 - \ln 8} \right\}$

b. $P(t) = 6.5(1.014)^t$

$13 = 6.5(1.014)^t$ Substitute $P(t) = 13$ and solve for t.

$\dfrac{13}{6.5} = \dfrac{\cancel{6.5}(1.014)^t}{\cancel{6.5}}$ Isolate the exponential expression on one side of the equation.

$2 = 1.014^t$

$\ln 2 = \ln 1.014^t$ Take the natural logarithm of both sides.

$\ln 2 = t \ln 1.014$ Use the power property of logarithms.

$\dfrac{\ln 2}{\ln 1.014} = \dfrac{t \cancel{\ln 1.014}}{\cancel{\ln 1.014}}$ Solve for t.

$t = \dfrac{\ln 2}{\ln 1.014} \approx 50$ The population will reach 13 billion (double the April 2006 value) approximately 50 yr after 2006.

Note: It has taken thousands of years for the world's population to reach 6.5 billion. However, with a growth rate of 1.4%, it will take only 50 years to gain an additional 6.5 billion, if this trend continues.

Skill Practice Use the population function from Example 10.

10. Estimate the world population in April 2020.

11. Estimate the year in which the world population will reach 9 billion.

On Friday, April 25, 1986, a nuclear accident occurred at the Chernobyl nuclear reactor, resulting in radioactive contaminates being released into the atmosphere. The most hazardous isotopes released in this accident were ^{137}Cs (cesium 137), ^{131}I (iodine 131), and ^{90}Sr (strontium 90). People living close to Chernobyl (in Ukraine) were at risk of radiation exposure from inhalation, from absorption through the skin, and from food contamination. Years after the incident, scientists have seen an increase in the incidence of thyroid disease among children living in the contaminated areas. Because iodine is readily absorbed in the thyroid gland, scientists suspect that radiation from iodine 131 is the cause.

Classroom Example: p. 908, Exercise 82

Example 11 **Applying an Exponential Equation to Radioactive Decay**

The half-life of radioactive iodine, ^{131}I, is 8.04 days. If 10 g of iodine 131 is initially present, then the amount of radioactive iodine still present after t days is approximated by

$$A(t) = 10e^{-0.0862t}$$

where t is the time in days.

a. Use the model to approximate the amount of ^{131}I still present after 2 weeks. Round to the nearest 0.1 g.

b. How long will it take for the amount of ^{131}I to decay to 0.5 g? Round to the nearest 0.1 day.

Answers

10. Approximately 7.9 billion
11. The year 2029

Solution:

a. $A(t) = 10e^{-0.0862t}$

$A(14) = 10e^{-0.0862(14)}$ Substitute $t = 14$ (2 weeks).

$\approx 3.0 \text{ g}$ There was 3.0 g still present after 2 weeks.

b.

$A(t) = 10e^{-0.0862t}$

$0.5 = 10e^{-0.0862t}$ Substitute $A = 0.5$.

$\dfrac{0.5}{10} = \dfrac{\cancel{10}e^{-0.0862t}}{\cancel{10}}$ Isolate the exponential expression.

$0.05 = e^{-0.0862t}$

$\ln 0.05 = \ln e^{-0.0862t}$ Take the natural logarithm of both sides.

$\ln 0.05 = -0.0862t$ The resulting equation is linear.

$\dfrac{\ln 0.05}{-0.0862} = \dfrac{\cancel{-0.0862}t}{\cancel{-0.0862}}$ Solve for t.

$t = \dfrac{\ln 0.05}{-0.0862} \approx 34.8 \text{ days}$ It will take 34.8 days for 10 g of ^{131}I to decay to 0.5 g.

Skill Practice Radioactive strontium 90 (^{90}Sr) has a half-life of 28 yr. If 100 g of strontium 90 is initially present, the amount left after t years is approximated by

$$A(t) = 100e^{-0.0248t}$$

12. Find the amount of ^{90}Sr present after 85 yr.

13. How long will it take for the amount of ^{90}Sr to decay to 40 g?

Answers

12. 12.1 g   **13.** 36.9 years

Section 12.6   Practice Exercises

Boost *your* GRADE at ALEKS.com!

- Practice Problems
- Self-Tests
- NetTutor

- e-Professors
- Videos

For additional exercises, see Classroom Activities 12.6A–12.6C in the *Instructor's Resource Manual* at www.mhhe.com/moh.

Study Skills Exercise

1. Define the key terms.

     a. logarithmic equation   **b. exponential equation**

Review Exercises

For Exercises 2–6, write the expression as a single logarithm. Assume all variables represent positive real numbers.

2. $\log_b (x - 1) + \log_b (x + 2)$ $\log_b [(x - 1)(x + 2)]$

3. $\log_b x + \log_b (2x + 3)$ $\log_b [x(2x + 3)]$

4. $\log_b x - \log_b (1 - x)$ $\log_b \left(\dfrac{x}{1 - x}\right)$

5. $\log_b (x + 2) - \log_b (3x - 5)$ $\log_b \left(\dfrac{x + 2}{3x - 5}\right)$

6. $2 \log_b x - \log_b (x + 1)$ $\log_b \left(\dfrac{x^2}{x + 1}\right)$

 Writing   Translating Expression   Geometry   Scientific Calculator   Video   NS&E

Concept 1: Solving Logarithmic Equations

For Exercises 7–38, solve the logarithmic equations. **(See Examples 1–4.)**

7. $\log_3 x = 2$ {9}

8. $\log_4 x = 9$ {4^9}

9. $\log p = 42$ {10^{42}}

10. $\log q = \dfrac{1}{2}$ {$\sqrt{10}$}

11. $\ln x = 0.08$ {$e^{0.08}$}

12. $\ln x = 19$ {e^{19}}

13. $\log (x + 40) = -9.2$ {$10^{-9.2} - 40$}

14. $\log (z - 3) = -6.7$ {$10^{-6.7} + 3$}

15. $\log_x 25 = 2$ $(x > 0)$ {5}

16. $\log_x 100 = 2$ $(x > 0)$ {10}

17. $\log_b 10{,}000 = 4$ $(b > 0)$ {10}

18. $\log_b e^3 = 3$ $(b > 0)$ {e}

19. $\log_y 5 = \dfrac{1}{2}$ $(y > 0)$ {25}

20. $\log_b 8 = \dfrac{1}{2}$ $(b > 0)$ {64}

21. $\log_4 (c + 5) = 3$ {59}

22. $\log_5 (a - 4) = 2$ {29}

23. $\log_5 (4y + 1) = 1$ {1}

24. $\log_6 (5t - 2) = 1$ $\left\{\dfrac{8}{5}\right\}$

25. $\ln (1 - x) = 0$ {0}

26. $\log_4 (2 - x) = 1$ {-2}

27. $\log_3 8 - \log_3 (x + 5) = 2$ $\left\{-\dfrac{37}{9}\right\}$

28. $\log_2 (x + 3) - \log_2 (x + 2) = 1$ {-1}

29. $\log_2 (h - 1) + \log_2 (h + 1) = 3$ {3} (The value -3 does not check.)

30. $\log_3 k + \log_3 (2k + 3) = 2$ $\left\{\dfrac{3}{2}\right\}$ (The value -3 does not check.)

31. $\log (x + 2) = \log (3x - 6)$ {4}

32. $\log x = \log (1 - x)$ $\left\{\dfrac{1}{2}\right\}$

33. $\ln x - \ln (4x - 9) = 0$ {3}

34. $\ln (x + 5) - \ln x = \ln (4x)$ $\left\{\dfrac{5}{4}\right\}$; (The value -1 does not check.)

35. $\log_5 (3t + 2) - \log_5 t = \log_5 4$ {2}

36. $\log (6y - 7) + \log y = \log 5$ $\left\{\dfrac{5}{3}\right\}$ (The value $-\dfrac{1}{2}$ does not check.)

37. $\log (4m) = \log 2 + \log (m - 3)$ { } (The value -3 does not check.)

38. $\log (-h) + \log 3 = \log (2h - 15)$ { } (The value 3 does not check.)

Concept 2: Solving Exponential Equations

For Exercises 39–54, solve the exponential equation by using the property that $b^x = b^y$ implies $x = y$, for $b > 0$ and $b \neq 1$. **(See Examples 5–6.)**

39. $5^x = 625$ {4}

40. $3^x = 81$ {4}

41. $2^{-x} = 64$ {-6}

42. $6^{-x} = 216$ {-3}

43. $36^x = 6$ $\left\{\dfrac{1}{2}\right\}$

44. $343^x = 7$ $\left\{\dfrac{1}{3}\right\}$

45. $4^{2x-1} = 64$ {2}

46. $5^{3x-1} = 125$ $\left\{\dfrac{4}{3}\right\}$

47. $81^{3x-4} = \dfrac{1}{243}$ $\left\{\dfrac{11}{12}\right\}$

48. $4^{2x-7} = \dfrac{1}{128}$ $\left\{\dfrac{7}{4}\right\}$

49. $\left(\dfrac{2}{3}\right)^{-x+4} = \dfrac{8}{27}$ {1}

50. $\left(\dfrac{1}{4}\right)^{3x+2} = \dfrac{1}{64}$ $\left\{\dfrac{1}{3}\right\}$

51. $16^{-x+1} = 8^{5x}$ $\left\{\dfrac{4}{19}\right\}$

52. $27^{(1/3)x} = \left(\dfrac{1}{9}\right)^{2x-1}$ $\left\{\dfrac{2}{5}\right\}$

53. $(4^x)^{x+1} = 16$ {$-2, 1$}

54. $(3^x)^{x+2} = \dfrac{1}{3}$ {-1}

For Exercises 55–74, solve the exponential equation by taking the logarithm of both sides. **(See Examples 7–9.)**

55. $8^a = 21$ $\left\{\dfrac{\ln 21}{\ln 8}\right\}$

56. $6^y = 39$ $\left\{\dfrac{\ln 39}{\ln 6}\right\}$

57. $e^x = 8.1254$ {$\ln 8.1254$}

58. $e^x = 0.3151$ {$\ln 0.3151$}

59. $10^t = 0.0138$ {$\log 0.0138$}

60. $10^p = 16.8125$ {$\log 16.8125$}

61. $e^{0.07h} = 15$ $\left\{\dfrac{\ln 15}{0.07}\right\}$

62. $e^{0.03k} = 4$ $\left\{\dfrac{\ln 4}{0.03}\right\}$

63. $e^{1.2t} = 3$ $\left\{\dfrac{\ln 3}{1.2}\right\}$

64. $e^{1.5t} = 7$ $\left\{\dfrac{\ln 7}{1.5}\right\}$

65. $3^{x+1} = 5^x$ $\left\{\dfrac{\ln 3}{\ln 5 - \ln 3}\right\}$

66. $2^{x-1} = 7^x$ $\left\{\dfrac{\ln 2}{\ln 2 - \ln 7}\right\}$

67. $2^{x+2} = 6^x$ $\left\{\dfrac{2 \ln 2}{\ln 6 - \ln 2}\right\}$

68. $5^{x-2} = 3^x$ $\left\{\dfrac{2 \ln 5}{\ln 5 - \ln 3}\right\}$

69. $32e^{0.04m} = 128$ $\left\{\dfrac{\ln 4}{0.04}\right\}$

70. $8e^{0.05n} = 160$ $\left\{\dfrac{\ln 20}{0.05}\right\}$

71. $6e^{x/3} = 125$ $\left\{3 \ln\left(\dfrac{125}{6}\right)\right\}$

72. $8e^{x/5} = 155$ $\left\{5 \ln\left(\dfrac{155}{8}\right)\right\}$

73. $5^{x-2} - 4 = 16$ $\left\{\dfrac{\ln 20}{\ln 5} + 2\right\}$

74. $2^{x+4} + 17 = 50$ $\left\{\dfrac{\ln 33}{\ln 2} - 4\right\}$

Concept 3: Applications

75. The population of China can be modeled by the function

$$P(t) = 1237(1.0095)^t$$

where $P(t)$ is in millions and t is the number of years since 1998. **(See Example 10.)**

 a. Using this model, what was the population in the year 2002?   ≈1285 million (or 1,285,000,000) people

 b. Predict the population in the year 2016.   ≈1466.5 million (or 1,466,500,000) people

 c. If this growth rate continues, in what year will the population reach 2 billion people (2 billion is 2000 million)?   The year 2049 ($t \approx 50.8$)

76. The population of Delhi, India, can be modeled by the function

$$P(t) = 9817(1.031)^t$$

where $P(t)$ is in thousands and t is the number of years since 2001.

 a. Using this model, predict the population in the year 2018.   16,496 thousand (or 16,496,000) people

 b. If this growth rate continues, in what year will the population reach 15 million (15 million is 15,000 thousand)?   The year 2015 ($t \approx 13.9$)

77. The growth of a certain bacteria in a culture is given by the model

$$A(t) = 500e^{0.0277t}$$

where $A(t)$ is the number of bacteria and t is time in minutes.

 a. What is the initial number of bacteria?   500 bacteria

 b. What is the population after 10 min?   ≈660 bacteria

 c. How long will it take for the population to double (that is, reach 1000)?   ≈25 min

78. The population of the bacteria *Salmonella typhimurium* is given by the model

$$A(t) = 300e^{0.01733t}$$

where $A(t)$ is the number of bacteria and t is time in minutes.

 a. What is the initial number of bacteria?   300 bacteria

 b. What is the population after 10 min?   ≈357 bacteria

 c. How long will it take for the population to double?   ≈40 min

79. Suppose $5000 is invested at 7% interest compounded continuously. How long will it take for the investment to grow to $10,000? Use the model $A(t) = Pe^{rt}$ and round to the nearest tenth of a year.
It will take 9.9 yr for the investment to double.

80. Suppose $2000 is invested at 10% interest compounded continuously. How long will it take for the investment to triple? Use the model $A(t) = Pe^{rt}$ and round to the nearest year.
It will take 11 yr for the investment to triple.

81. Phosphorus 32 (^{32}P) has a half-life of approximately 14 days. If 10 g of ^{32}P is present initially, then the amount of phosphorus 32 still present after t days is given by $A(t) = 10(0.5)^{t/14}$. **(See Example 11.)**

 a. Find the amount of phosphorus 32 still present after 5 days. Round to the nearest tenth of a gram.   7.8 g

 b. Find the amount of time necessary for the amount of ^{32}P to decay to 4 g. Round to the nearest tenth of a day.
   18.5 days

 Writing Translating Expression Geometry   Scientific Calculator   Video   NS&E

82. Polonium 210 (^{210}Po) has a half-life of approximately 138.6 days. If 4 g of ^{210}Po is present initially, then the amount of polonium 210 still present after t days is given by $A(t) = 4e^{-0.005t}$.

   a. Find the amount of polonium 210 still present after 50 days. Round to the nearest tenth of a gram.   3.1 g

   b. Find the amount of time necessary for the amount of ^{210}P to decay to 0.5 g. Round to the nearest tenth of a day.   415.9 days

The decibel level of sound can be found by the equation $D = 10 \log\left(\dfrac{I}{I_0}\right)$, where I is the intensity of the sound and I_0 is the intensity of the least audible sound that an average person can hear. Generally I_0 is found as 10^{-12} watt per square meter (W/m^2). Use this information to answer Exercises 83–84.

83. Given that heavy traffic has a decibel level of 89.3 and that $I_0 = 10^{-12}$, find the intensity of the sound of heavy traffic.   The intensity of sound of heavy traffic is $10^{-3.07}$ W/m^2.

84. Given that normal conversation has a decibel level of 65 and $I_0 = 10^{-12}$, find the intensity of the sound of normal conversation.   The intensity of sound of normal conversation is $10^{-5.5}$ W/m^2.

85. Suppose you save $10,000 from working an extra job. Rather than spending the money, you decide to save the money for retirement by investing in a mutual fund that averages 12% per year. How long will it take for this money to grow to $1,000,000? Use the model $A(t) = Pe^{rt}$ and round to the nearest tenth of a year. It will take 38.4 yr.

86. The model $A = Pe^{rt}$ is used to compute the total amount of money in an account after t years at an interest rate r, compounded continuously. The value P is the initial principal. Find the amount of time required for the investment to double as a function of the interest rate. (*Hint:* Substitute $A = 2P$ and solve for t.) $t = \dfrac{\ln 2}{r}$

Expanding Your Skills

87. The isotope of plutonium of mass 238 (written ^{238}Pu) is used to make thermoelectric power sources for spacecraft. The heat and electric power derived from such units have made the Voyager, Gallileo, and Cassini missions to the outer reaches of our solar system possible. The half-life of ^{238}Pu is 87.7 yr.

   Suppose a space probe was launched in the year 2002 with 2.0 kg of ^{238}Pu. Then the amount of ^{238}Pu available to power the spacecraft decays over time according to

   $$P(t) = 2e^{-0.0079t}$$

   where $t \geq 0$ is the number of years since 2002 and $P(t)$ is the amount of plutonium still present (in kilograms).

   a. Suppose the space probe is due to arrive at Pluto in the year 2045. How much plutonium will remain when the spacecraft reaches Pluto? Round to two decimal places.   1.42 kg

   b. If 1.5 kg of ^{238}Pu is required to power the spacecraft's data transmitter, will there be enough power in the year 2045 for us to receive close-up images of Pluto?   No

88. ^{99m}Tc is a radionuclide of technetium that is widely used in nuclear medicine. Although its half-life is only 6 hr, the isotope is continuously produced via the decay of its longer-lived parent ^{99}Mo (molybdenum 99) whose half-life is approximately 3 days. The ^{99}Mo generators (or "cows") are sold to hospitals in which the ^{99m}Tc can be "milked" as needed over a period of a few weeks. Once separated from its parent, the ^{99m}Tc may be chemically incorporated into a variety of imaging agents, each of which is designed to be taken up by a specific target organ within the body. Special cameras, sensitive to the gamma rays emitted by the technetium, are then used to record a "picture" (similar in appearance to an X-ray film) of the selected organ.

   Suppose a technician prepares a sample of ^{99m}Tc-pyrophosphate to image the heart of a patient suspected of having had a mild heart attack. If the injection contains 10 millicuries (mCi) of ^{99m}Tc at 1:00 P.M., then the amount of technetium still present is given by

   $$T(t) = 10e^{-0.1155t}$$

 Writing   Translating Expression   Geometry   Scientific Calculator   Video   NS&E

where $t > 0$ represents the time in hours after 1:00 P.M. and $T(t)$ represents the amount of ^{99m}Tc (in millicuries) still present.

a. How many millicuries of ^{99m}Tc will remain at 4:20 P.M. when the image is recorded? Round to the nearest tenth of a millicurie.   6.8 mCi

b. How long will it take for the radioactive level of the ^{99m}Tc to reach 2 mCi? Round to the nearest tenth of an hour.   13.9 hr

For Exercises 89–92, solve the equations.

89. $(\log x)^2 - 2 \log x - 15 = 0$
(*Hint:* Let $u = \log x$.) $\{10^5, 10^{-3}\}$

90. $(\log_2 z)^2 - 3 \log_2 z - 4 = 0$ $\left\{16, \dfrac{1}{2}\right\}$

91. $(\log_3 w)^2 + 5 \log_3 w + 6 = 0$ $\left\{\dfrac{1}{27}, \dfrac{1}{9}\right\}$

92. $(\ln x)^2 - 2 \ln x = 0$ $\{1, e^2\}$

Graphing Calculator Exercises

93. Graph $Y_1 = 8^x$ and $Y_2 = 21$ on a window where $0 \le x \le 5$ and $0 \le y \le 40$. Use the graph and an *Intersect* feature to support your answer to Exercise 55.

94. Graph $Y_1 = 6^x$ and $Y_2 = 39$ on a window where $0 \le x \le 5$ and $0 \le y \le 50$. Use the graph and an *Intersect* feature to support your answer to Exercise 56.

Group Activity

Creating a Population Model

Materials: A computer with Internet access and a calculator

Estimated time: 15–20 minutes

Group Size: 3

Answers will vary.

1. Go to a website such as http://www.census.gov/ and determine the population of your state for the year 2000, and then for another year after that time. For example, the population of Florida in the year 2000 was approximately 16,050,000. Florida's population in 2006 was approximately 18,090,000.

2. Let the variable t represent the number of years since the year 2000. Therefore, $t = 0$ represents the year 2000, $t = 1$ represents the year 2001, and so on. Write your data from step 1 as ordered pairs. For example: (0, 16050000) and (6, 18090000). (_____ , _____) (_____ , _____)

3. Population growth can be modeled by an exponential function of the form:

$P(t) = P_0 e^{kt}$ 　 where P_0 is the initial population for $t = 0$

$P(t)$ is the population at time, t

k is the growth constant

Substitute the population for the year 2000 into the model for P_0, and write the function here:

$P(t) = $ _____ e^{kt} 　 [For example: $P(t) = 16{,}050{,}000e^{kt}$]

 Writing 　 Translating Expression 　 Geometry 　 Scientific Calculator 　 Video 　 NS&E

4. Substitute the population value and t value from the second ordered pair into the function for $P(t)$ and t, respectively.   [For example: $18{,}090{,}000 = 16{,}050{,}000e^{k(6)}$]

5. Solve the equation from step 4 for the value of k. Round k to five decimal places.

6. Substitute the values of P_0 and k in the original model, $P(t) = P_0 e^{kt}$, and write the function here:

   $P(t) = $ _____

   You should now have a function that models the population of your state as a function of the time in years since 2000.

7. Assuming that the population follows this trend, predict the population of your state in the year 2015.

8. Assuming that the population follows this trend, predict the population of your state in the year 2050.

Instructor Note: As a follow-up, you might ask students if the growth rate can continue indefinitely. You can ask students to predict the number of years it will take so that each person in your state will have only 1 m^2 of land area.

Chapter 12   Summary

Section 12.1   Inverse Functions

Key Concepts

Horizontal Line Test

Consider a function defined by a set of points (x, y) in a rectangular coordinate system. Then y is a one-to-one function of x if no horizontal line intersects the graph in more than one point.

Examples

Example 1

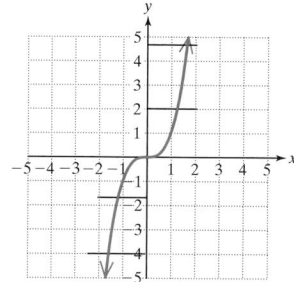

The function is one-to-one because it passes the horizontal line test.

Finding an Equation of the Inverse of a Function

For a one-to-one function defined by $y = f(x)$, the equation of the inverse can be found as follows:

1. Replace $f(x)$ by y.
2. Interchange x and y.
3. Solve for y.
4. Replace y by $f^{-1}(x)$.

The graphs defined by $y = f(x)$ and $y = f^{-1}(x)$ are symmetric with respect to the line $y = x$.

Definition of an Inverse Function

If f is a one-to-one function represented by ordered pairs of the form (x, y), then the inverse function, denoted f^{-1}, is the set of ordered pairs (y, x).

Inverse Function Property

If f is a one-to-one function, then g is the inverse of f if and only if $(f \circ g)(x) = x$ for all x in the domain of g, and $(g \circ f)(x) = x$ for all x in the domain of f.

Example 2

Find the inverse of the one-to-one function defined by $f(x) = 3 - x^3$.

1. $y = 3 - x^3$
2. $x = 3 - y^3$
3. $\quad x - 3 = -y^3$

$\quad\quad -x + 3 = y^3$

$\quad\quad \sqrt[3]{-x + 3} = y$

4. $f^{-1}(x) = \sqrt[3]{-x + 3}$

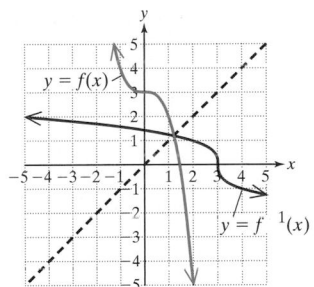

Example 3

Verify that the functions defined by $f(x) = x - 1$ and $g(x) = x + 1$ are inverses.

$(f \circ g)(x) = f(x + 1) = (x + 1) - 1 = x$

$(g \circ f)(x) = g(x - 1) = (x - 1) + 1 = x$

Section 12.2   Exponential Functions

Key Concepts

A function $y = b^x$ $(b > 0, b \neq 1)$ is an **exponential function**.

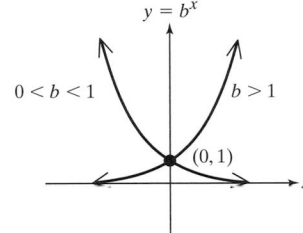

The domain is $(-\infty, \infty)$.

The range is $(0, \infty)$.

The line $y = 0$ (x-axis) is a horizontal asymptote.

The y-intercept is $(0, 1)$.

Example

Example 1

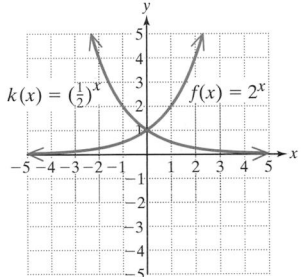

Section 12.3 Logarithmic Functions

Key Concepts

The function $y = \log_b x$ is a **logarithmic function**.

$$y = \log_b x \iff b^y = x \quad (x > 0, b > 0, b \neq 1)$$

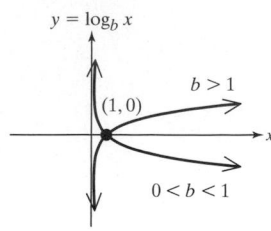

For $y = \log_b x$, the domain is $(0, \infty)$.

The range is $(-\infty, \infty)$.

The line $x = 0$ (y-axis) is a vertical asymptote.

The x-intercept is $(1, 0)$.

The function $y = \log x$ is the **common logarithmic function** (base 10).

Examples

Example 1

$\log_4 64 = 3 \quad$ because $4^3 = 64$

Example 2

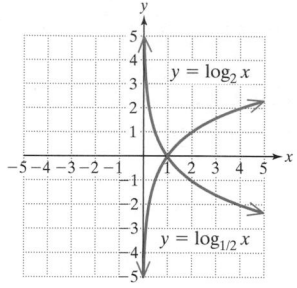

Example 3

$\log 10{,}000 = 4 \quad$ because $10^4 = 10{,}000$

Section 12.4 Properties of Logarithms

Key Concepts

Let b, x, and y be positive real numbers where $b \neq 1$, and let p be a real number. Then the following properties are true.

1. $\log_b 1 = 0$
2. $\log_b b = 1$
3. $\log_b b^p = p$
4. $b^{\log_b x} = x$
5. $\log_b (xy) = \log_b x + \log_b y$
6. $\log_b \left(\dfrac{x}{y}\right) = \log_b x - \log_b y$
7. $\log_b x^p = p \log_b x$

Examples

Example 1

1. $\log_5 1 = 0$
2. $\log_6 6 = 1$
3. $\log_4 4^7 = 7$
4. $2^{\log_2 5} = 5$
5. $\log (5x) = \log 5 + \log x$
6. $\log_7 \left(\dfrac{z}{10}\right) = \log_7 z - \log_7 10$
7. $\log x^5 = 5 \log x$

The **properties of logarithms** can be used to write multiple logarithms as a single logarithm.

Example 2

$\log x - \dfrac{1}{2} \log y - 3 \log z$

$= \log x - (\log y^{1/2} + \log z^3)$

$= \log x - \log (\sqrt{y} z^3)$

$= \log \left(\dfrac{x}{\sqrt{y} z^3} \right)$

The **properties of logarithms** can be used to write a single logarithm as a sum or difference of logarithms.

Example 3

$\log \sqrt[3]{\dfrac{x}{y^2}}$

$= \dfrac{1}{3} \log \left(\dfrac{x}{y^2} \right)$

$= \dfrac{1}{3} (\log x - \log y^2)$

$= \dfrac{1}{3} (\log x - 2 \log y)$

$= \dfrac{1}{3} \log x - \dfrac{2}{3} \log y$

Section 12.5   **The Irrational Number e and Change of Base**

Key Concepts

The function $y = e^x$ is the exponential function with base e.

    The **natural logarithm function** $y = \ln x$ is the logarithm function with base e.

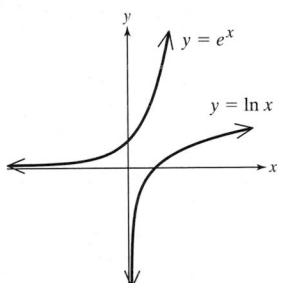

Change-of-Base Formula

$\log_b x = \dfrac{\log_a x}{\log_a b}$ $a > 0, a \neq 1, b > 0, b \neq 1$

Examples

Example 1

Use a calculator to approximate the value of the expressions.

$e^{7.5} \approx 1808.0424$

$e^{-\pi} \approx 0.0432$

$\ln 107 \approx 4.6728$

$\ln \left(\dfrac{1}{\sqrt{2}} \right) \approx -0.3466$

Example 2

$\log_3 59 = \dfrac{\log 59}{\log 3} \approx 3.7115$

Section 12.6 Logarithmic and Exponential Equations and Applications

Key Concepts

Guidelines to Solve Logarithmic Equations

1. Isolate the logarithms on one side of the equation.
2. Write a sum or difference of logarithms as a single logarithm.
3. Rewrite the equation in step 2 in exponential form.
4. Solve the resulting equation from step 3.
5. Check all solutions to verify that they are within the domain of the logarithmic expressions in the equation.

The equivalence of exponential expressions can be used to solve **exponential equations**.

If $b^x = b^y$, then $x = y$

Guidelines to Solve Exponential Equations

1. Isolate one of the exponential expressions in the equation.
2. Take a logarithm of both sides of the equation.
3. Use the power property of logarithms to write exponents as factors.
4. Solve the resulting equation from step 3.

Examples

Example 1

$\log(3x - 1) + 1 = \log(2x + 1)$

Step 1: $\log(3x - 1) - \log(2x + 1) = -1$

Step 2: $\log\left(\dfrac{3x - 1}{2x + 1}\right) = -1$

Step 3: $10^{-1} = \dfrac{3x - 1}{2x + 1}$

Step 4: $\dfrac{1}{10} = \dfrac{3x - 1}{2x + 1}$

$2x + 1 = 10(3x - 1)$

$2x + 1 = 30x - 10$

$-28x = -11$

$x = \dfrac{11}{28}$ The solution checks.

Step 5: The solution set is $\left\{\dfrac{11}{28}\right\}$.

Example 2

$5^{2x} = 125$

$5^{2x} = 5^3$ implies that $2x = 3$

$x = \dfrac{3}{2}$

The solution set is $\left\{\dfrac{3}{2}\right\}$.

Example 3

$4^{x+1} - 2 = 1055$

Step 1: $4^{x+1} = 1057$

Step 2: $\ln 4^{x+1} = \ln 1057$

Step 3: $(x + 1)\ln 4 = \ln 1057$

Step 4: $x + 1 = \dfrac{\ln 1057}{\ln 4}$

$x = \dfrac{\ln 1057}{\ln 4} - 1 \approx 4.023$

The solution set is $\left\{\dfrac{\ln 1057}{\ln 4} - 1\right\}$.

Chapter 12   Review Exercises

Section 12.1

For Exercises 1–2, determine if the function is one-to-one by using the horizontal line test.

1.   No

2.   Yes

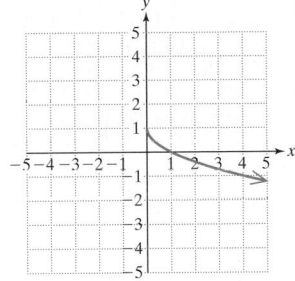

For Exercises 3–6, write the inverse for each one-to-one function.

3. $\{(3,5),(2,9),(0,-1),(4,1)\}$

$\{(5,3),(9,2),(-1,0),(1,4)\}$

4. $q(x) = \dfrac{3}{4}x - 2$ $q^{-1}(x) = \dfrac{4}{3}(x+2)$

5. $f(x) = (x-1)^3$

$f^{-1}(x) = \sqrt[3]{x} + 1$

6. $n(x) = \dfrac{4}{x-2}$ $n^{-1}(x) = \dfrac{2x+4}{x}$

$(f \circ g)(x) = 5\left(\dfrac{1}{5}x + \dfrac{2}{5}\right) - 2 = x + 2 - 2 = x$

7. Verify that the functions defined by $f(x) = 5x - 2$ and $g(x) = \dfrac{1}{5}x + \dfrac{2}{5}$ are inverses by showing that $(f \circ g)(x) = x$ and $(g \circ f)(x) = x$.

$(g \circ f)(x) = \dfrac{1}{5}(5x - 2) + \dfrac{2}{5} = x - \dfrac{2}{5} + \dfrac{2}{5} = x$

8. Graph the functions q and q^{-1} from Exercise 4 on the same grid. What can you say about the relationship between these two graphs?

The graphs are symmetric about the line $y = x$.

9. a. Find the domain and range of the function defined by $h(x) = \sqrt{x+1}$.

Domain: $[-1, \infty)$; range: $[0, \infty)$

b. Find the domain and range of the function defined by $k(x) = x^2 - 1$, $x \geq 0$.

Domain: $[0, \infty)$ range: $[-1, \infty)$

10. Determine the inverse of the function $p(x) = \sqrt{x} + 2$. $p^{-1}(x) = (x-2)^2, x \geq 2$

Section 12.2

For Exercises 11–18, evaluate the exponential expressions. Use a calculator and round to three decimal places, if necessary.

11. 4^5 1024

12. 6^{-2} $\dfrac{1}{36} \approx 0.028$

13. $8^{1/3}$ 2

14. $\left(\dfrac{1}{100}\right)^{-1/2}$ 10

15. 2^{π} 8.825

16. $5^{\sqrt{3}}$ 16.242

17. $(\sqrt{7})^{1/2}$ 1.627

18. $\left(\dfrac{3}{4}\right)^{4/3}$ 0.681

For Exercises 19–22, graph the functions.

19. $f(x) = 3^x$

20. $g(x) = \left(\dfrac{1}{4}\right)^x$

21. $h(x) = 5^{-x}$

22. $k(x) = \left(\dfrac{2}{5}\right)^{-x}$

23. a. Does the graph of $y = b^x, b > 0, b \neq 1$, have a vertical or a horizontal asymptote?

Horizontal

b. Write an equation of the asymptote. $y = 0$

24. Background radiation is radiation that we are exposed to from naturally occurring sources including the soil, the foods we eat, and the sun. Background radiation varies depending on where we live. A typical background radiation level is 150 millirems (mrem) per year. (A rem is a measure of energy produced from radiation.) Suppose a substance emits 30,000 mrem per year and has a half-life of 5 yr. The function defined by

$$A(t) = 30{,}000\left(\frac{1}{2}\right)^{t/5}$$

gives the radiation level (in millirems) of this substance after t years.

a. What is the radiation level after 5 yr?
15,000 mrem

b. What is the radiation level after 15 yr?
3750 mrem

c. Will the radiation level of this substance be below the background level of 150 mrem after 50 yr?   Yes

Section 12.3

For Exercises 25–32, evaluate the logarithms without using a calculator.

25. $\log_3\left(\dfrac{1}{27}\right)$ -3 **26.** $\log_5 1$ 0

27. $\log_7 7$ 1   **28.** $\log_2 2^8$ 8

29. $\log_2 16$ 4   **30.** $\log_3 81$ 4

31. $\log 100{,}000$ 5   **32.** $\log_8\left(\dfrac{1}{8}\right)$ -1

For Exercises 33–34, graph the logarithmic functions.

33. $q(x) = \log_3 x$ **34.** $r(x) = \log_{1/2} x$

        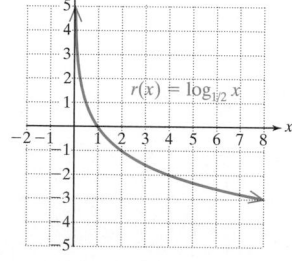

35. a. Does the graph of $y = \log_b x$ have a vertical or a horizontal asymptote?   Vertical asymptote

b. Write an equation of the asymptote. $x = 0$

36. Acidity of a substance is measured by its pH. The pH can be calculated by the formula $pH = -\log[H^+]$, where $[H^+]$ is the hydrogen ion concentration.

a. What is the pH of a fruit with a hydrogen ion concentration of 0.00316 mol/L? Round to one decimal place.   2.5

b. What is the pH of an antacid tablet with $[H^+] = 3.16 \times 10^{-10}$? Round to one decimal place.   9.5

Section 12.4

For Exercises 37–40, evaluate the logarithms without using a calculator.

37. $\log_8 8$ 1   **38.** $\log_{11} 11^6$ 6

39. $\log_{1/2} 1$ 0   **40.** $12^{\log_{12} 7}$ 7

41. Complete the properties. Assume $x, y,$ and b are positive real numbers such that $b \neq 1$.

a. $\log_b(xy) = \log_b x + \log_b y$

b. $\log_b x - \log_b y = \log_b\left(\dfrac{x}{y}\right)$

c. $\log_b x^p = p \log_b x$

42. Complete the properties. Assume x and b are positive real numbers such that $b \neq 1$.

a. $\log_b b =$ 1

b. $\log_b b^x =$ x

c. $\log_b 1 =$ 0

For Exercises 43–46, write the logarithmic expressions as a single logarithm and simplify if possible.

43. $\dfrac{1}{4}(\log_b y - 4\log_b z + 3\log_b x)$ $\log_b\left(\dfrac{\sqrt[4]{x^3 y}}{z}\right)$

44. $\dfrac{1}{2}\log_3 a + \dfrac{1}{2}\log_3 b - 2\log_3 c - 4\log_3 d$ $\log_3\left(\dfrac{\sqrt{ab}}{c^2 d^4}\right)$

45. $\log 540 - 3\log 3 - 2\log 2$ $\log 5$

46. $-\log_4 18 + \log_4 6 + \log_4 3 - \log_4 1$ 0

47. Which of the following is equivalent to $\dfrac{2\log 7}{\log 7 + \log 6}$?   b

a. $\dfrac{\log 7}{\log 6}$ **b.** $\dfrac{\log 49}{\log 42}$ **c.** $\log\left(\dfrac{7}{6}\right)$

48. Which of the following is equivalent to $\dfrac{\log 8^{-3}}{\log 2 + \log 4}$? a

   a. -3 **b.** $-3 \log\left(\dfrac{4}{3}\right)$ **c.** $\dfrac{-3 \log 4}{\log 3}$

Section 12.5

For Exercises 49–56, use a calculator to approximate the expressions to four decimal places.

49. e^5 148.4132

50. $e^{\sqrt{7}}$ 14.0940

51. $32e^{0.008}$ 32.2570

52. $58e^{-0.0125}$ 57.2795

53. $\ln 6$ 1.7918

54. $\ln\left(\dfrac{1}{9}\right)$ −2.1972

55. $\log 22$ 1.3424

56. $\log e^3$ 1.3029

For Exercises 57–60, use the change-of-base formula to approximate the logarithms to four decimal places.

57. $\log_2 10$ 3.3219

58. $\log_9 80$ 1.9943

59. $\log_5 0.26$ −0.8370

60. $\log_4 0.0062$ −3.6668

61. An investor wants to deposit \$20,000 in an account for 10 yr at 5.25% interest. Compare the amount she would have if her money were invested with the following different compounding options. Use

$$A(t) = P\left(1 + \frac{r}{n}\right)^{nt}$$

for interest compounded n times per year and $A(t) = Pe^{rt}$ for interest compounded continuously.

   a. Compounded annually   \$33,361.92

   b. Compounded quarterly   \$33,693.90

   c. Compounded monthly   \$33,770.48

   d. Compounded continuously   \$33,809.18

62. To measure a student's retention of material at the end of a course, researchers give the student a test on the material every month for 24 months after the course is over. The student's average score t months after completing the course is given by

$$S(t) = 75e^{-0.5t} + 20$$

where $S(t)$ is the test score.

   a. Find $S(0)$ and interpret the result.
   $S(0) = 95$; the student's score is 95 at the end of the course.

   b. Find $S(6)$ and interpret the result.
   $S(6) \approx 23.7$; the student's score is 23.7 after 6 months.

   c. Find $S(12)$ and interpret the result.
   $S(12) \approx 20.2$; the student's score is 20.2 after 1 yr.

For Exercises 63–70, identify the domain. Write the answer in interval notation.

63. $f(x) = e^x$ $(-\infty, \infty)$

64. $g(x) = e^{x+6}$ $(-\infty, \infty)$

65. $h(x) = e^{x-3}$ $(-\infty, \infty)$

66. $k(x) = \ln x$ $(0, \infty)$

67. $q(x) = \ln(x + 5)$
   $(-5, \infty)$

68. $p(x) = \ln(x - 7)$
   $(7, \infty)$

69. $r(x) = \ln(3x - 4)$
   $\left(\dfrac{4}{3}, \infty\right)$

70. $w(x) = \ln(5 - x)$
   $(-\infty, 5)$

Section 12.6

For Exercises 71–88, solve the equations.

71. $\log_5 x = 3$ $\{125\}$

72. $\log_7 x = -2$ $\left\{\dfrac{1}{49}\right\}$

73. $\log_6 y = 3$ $\{216\}$

74. $\log_3 y = \dfrac{1}{12}$ $\{3^{1/12}\}$

75. $\log(2w - 1) = 3$ $\left\{\dfrac{1001}{2}\right\}$

76. $\log_2(3w + 5) = 5$ $\{9\}$

77. $-1 + \log p = -\log(p - 3)$
   $\{5\}$ (The value -2 does not check.)

78. $\log_4(2 + t) - 3 = \log_4(3 - 5t)$ $\left\{\dfrac{190}{321}\right\}$

79. $4^{3x+5} = 16$ $\{-1\}$

80. $5^{7x} = 625$ $\left\{\dfrac{4}{7}\right\}$

81. $4^a = 21$ $\left\{\dfrac{\ln 21}{\ln 4}\right\}$

82. $5^a = 18$ $\left\{\dfrac{\ln 18}{\ln 5}\right\}$

83. $e^{-x} = 0.1$
   $\{-\ln 0.1\}$

84. $e^{-2x} = 0.06$
   $\left\{-\dfrac{\ln 0.06}{2}\right\}$

85. $10^{2n} = 1512$
   $\left\{\dfrac{\log 1512}{2}\right\}$

86. $10^{-3m} = \dfrac{1}{821}$ $\left\{\dfrac{\log 821}{3}\right\}$

87. $2^{x+3} = 7^x$
   $\left\{\dfrac{3 \ln 2}{\ln 7 - \ln 2}\right\}$

88. $14^{x-5} = 6^x$
   $\left\{\dfrac{5 \ln 14}{\ln 14 - \ln 6}\right\}$

89. Radioactive iodine (^{131}I) is used to treat patients with a hyperactive (overactive) thyroid. The half-life of radioactive iodine is 8.04 days. If a patient is given an initial dose of 2 μg, then the amount of iodine in the body after t days is approximated by

$$A(t) = 2e^{-0.0862t}$$

where t is the time in days and $A(t)$ is the amount (in micrograms) of ^{131}I remaining.

a. How much radioactive iodine is present after a week? Round to two decimal places.   1.09 μg

b. How much radioactive iodine is present after 30 days? Round to two decimal places.   0.15 μg

c. How long will it take for the level of radioactive iodine to reach 0.5 μg?   16.08 days

90. The growth of a certain bacteria in a culture is given by the model $A(t) = 150e^{0.007t}$, where $A(t)$ is the number of bacteria and t is time in minutes.

a. What is the initial number of bacteria?
150 bacteria

b. What is the population after $\frac{1}{2}$ hr?
$\approx$ 185 bacteria

c. How long will it take for the population to double? $\approx$ 99 min

 91. The value of a car is depreciated with time according to

$$V(t) = 15{,}000e^{-0.15t}$$

where $V(t)$ is the value in dollars and t is the time in years.

a. Find $V(0)$ and interpret the result in the context of this problem.
$V(0) = 15{,}000$; the initial value of the car is $15,000.

b. Find $V(10)$ and interpret the result in the context of this problem. Round to the nearest dollar.
$V(10) = 3347$; the value of the car after 10 years is $3347.

c. Find the time required for the value of the car to drop to $5000. Round to the nearest tenth of a year.   7.3 yr

Chapter 12   Test

1. Explain how to determine graphically if a function is one-to-one.   A function is one-to-one if it passes the horizontal line test.

2. Which of the functions is one-to-one?   b

a.

b.

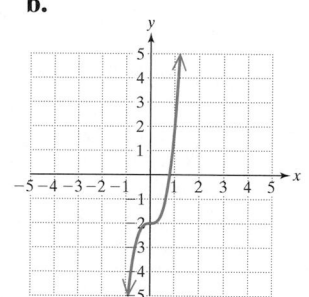

3. Write an equation of the inverse of the one-to-one function defined by $f(x) = \frac{1}{4}x + 3$.
$f^{-1}(x) = 4x - 12$

4. Write an equation of the inverse of the function defined by $g(x) = (x - 1)^2$, $x \geq 1$.
$g^{-1}(x) = \sqrt{x} + 1$

5. Given the graph of the function $y = p(x)$, graph its inverse $p^{-1}(x)$.

 6. Use a calculator to approximate the expression to four decimal places.

a. $10^{2/3}$ 4.6416   **b.** $3^{\sqrt{10}}$ 32.2693   **c.** 8^{π} 687.2913

7. Graph $f(x) = 4^{x-1}$.

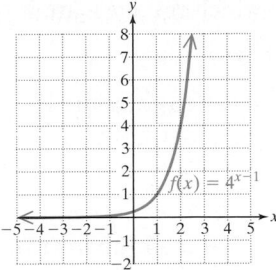

8. a. Write in logarithmic form. $16^{3/4} = 8$ $\log_{16} 8 = \dfrac{3}{4}$

   b. Write in exponential form. $\log_x 31 = 5$
   $x^5 = 31$

9. Graph $g(x) = \log_3 x$.

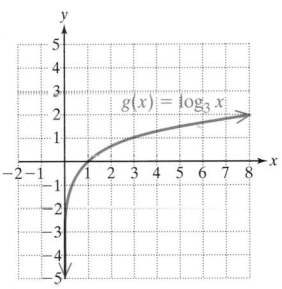

10. Complete the change-of-base formula: $\dfrac{\log_a n}{\log_a b}$
   $\log_b n =$ _____

11. Use a calculator to approximate the expression to four decimal places:

   a. $\log 21$ **b.** $\log_4 13$ **c.** $\log_{1/2} 6$
   1.3222   1.8502   −2.5850

12. Using the properties of logarithms, expand and simplify. Assume all variables represent positive real numbers.

   a. $-\log_3\left(\dfrac{3}{9x}\right)$ $1 + \log_3 x$ **b.** $\log\left(\dfrac{1}{10^5}\right)$ -5

13. Write as a single logarithm. Assume all variables represent positive real numbers.

   a. $\dfrac{1}{2}\log_b x + 3\log_b y$ **b.** $\log a - 4\log a$
   $\log_b(\sqrt{x}y^3)$ $\log\left(\dfrac{1}{a^3}\right)$ or $-\log a^3$

14. Use a calculator to approximate the expression to four decimal places, if necessary.

   a. $e^{1/2}$ 1.6487   **b.** e^{-3} 0.0498

   c. $\ln\left(\dfrac{1}{3}\right)$ −1.0986   **d.** $\ln e$ 1

15. Identify the graphs as $y = e^x$ or $y = \ln x$.

   a. $y = \ln x$ **b.** $y = e^x$

   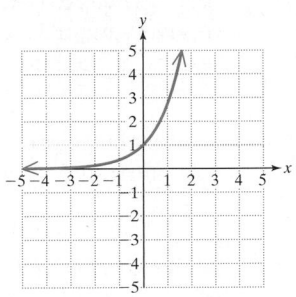

16. Researchers found that t months after taking a course, students remembered $p\%$ of the material according to

$$p(t) = 92 - 20\ln(t+1)$$

where $0 < t < 24$ is the time in months.

   a. Find $p(4)$ and interpret the results.
   $p(4) \approx 59.8$; 59.8% of the material is retained after 4 months.
   b. Find $p(12)$ and interpret the results.
   $p(12) \approx 40.7$; 40.7% of the material is retained after 1 yr.
   c. Find $p(0)$ and interpret the results.
   $p(0) = 92$; 92% of the material is retained at the end of the course.

17. The function $A(x) = 283e^{0.00015262(x)}$ represents the mean online enrollment, $A(x)$, for institutions having an overall enrollment of x students.

   a. Evaluate $A(10,000)$ and interpret the meaning in the context of this problem.
   $A(10,000) \approx 1300$. The mean online enrollment for an institution of 10,000 students is approximately 1300 students.
   b. Evaluate $A(20,000)$ and interpret the meaning in the context of this problem.
   $A(20,000) \approx 5990$. The mean online enrollment for an institution of 20,000 students is approximately 5990 students.

18. A certain bacterial culture grows according to

$$P(t) = \frac{1,500,000}{1 + 5000e^{-0.8t}}$$

where P is the population of the bacteria and t is the time in hours.

   a. Find $P(0)$ and interpret the result. Round to the nearest whole number.
   $P(0) = 300$; there are 300 bacteria initially.
   b. How many bacteria will be present after 6 hr?
   35,588 bacteria
   c. How many bacteria will be present after 12 hr?
   1,120,537 bacteria
   d. How many bacteria will be present after 18 hr?
   1,495,831 bacteria

For Exercises 19–26, solve the exponential and logarithmic equations.

19. $\log x + \log(x - 21) - 2$
   {25} (The value −4 does not check.)

20. $\log_{1/2} x = -5$ {32}

 Writing   Translating Expression   Geometry   Scientific Calculator   Video   NS&E

21. $\ln(x + 7) = 2.4$ $\{e^{2.4} - 7\}$

22. $3^{x+4} = \dfrac{1}{27}$ $\{-7\}$

23. $4^x = 50$ $\left\{\dfrac{\ln 50}{\ln 4}\right\}$

24. $e^{2.4x} = 250$ $\left\{\dfrac{\ln 250}{2.4}\right\}$

25. $68 = 10 + 2^{x-3}$ $\left\{\dfrac{\ln 58}{\ln 2} + 3\right\}$

26. $4^{x+7} = 5^x$ $\left\{\dfrac{7\ln 4}{\ln 5 - \ln 4}\right\}$

27. Atmospheric pressure P decreases exponentially with altitude x according to

$$P(x) = 760e^{-0.000122x}$$

where $P(x)$ is the pressure measured in millimeters of mercury (mm Hg) and x is the altitude measured in meters.

a. Find $P(2500)$ and interpret the result. Round to one decimal place. $P(2500) = 560.2$; at 2500 m the atmospheric pressure is 560.2 mm Hg.

b. Find the pressure at sea level.   760 mm Hg

c. Find the altitude at which the pressure is 633 mm Hg.   1498.8 m

28. Use the formula $A(t) = Pe^{rt}$ to compute the value of an investment under continuous compounding.

a. If $2000 is invested at 7.5% compounded continuously, find the value of the investment after 5 yr. $2909.98

b. How long will it take the investment to double? Round to two decimal places.   9.24 yr to double

---

Chapters 1–12   Cumulative Review Exercises

1. Simplify completely.

$$\dfrac{8 - 4 \cdot 2^2 + 15 \div 5}{|-3 + 7|} \quad -\dfrac{5}{4}$$

2. Divide. $\dfrac{-8p^2 + 4p^3 + 6p^5}{8p^2}$ $-1 + \dfrac{p}{2} + \dfrac{3p^3}{4}$

3. Divide $(t^4 - 13t^2 + 36) \div (t - 2)$. Identify the quotient and remainder.
Quotient: $t^3 + 2t^2 - 9t - 18$; remainder: 0

4. Simplify. $\sqrt{x^2 - 6x + 9}$ $|x - 3|$

5. Simplify. $\dfrac{4}{\sqrt[3]{40}}$ $\dfrac{2\sqrt[3]{25}}{5}$

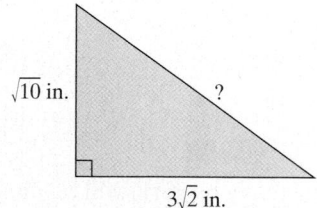

6. Find the length of the missing side. $2\sqrt{7}$ in.

$\sqrt{10}$ in.   ?

$3\sqrt{2}$ in.

7. Simplify. Write the answer with positive exponents only.

$$\dfrac{2^{2/5}c^{-1/4}d^{1/5}}{2^{-8/5}c^{3/4}d^{1/10}} \quad \dfrac{4d^{1/10}}{c}$$

8. Find the area of the rectangle.
$(\sqrt{15} - \sqrt{6} + \sqrt{30} - 2\sqrt{3})$ m²

$(\sqrt{5} - \sqrt{2})$ m

$(\sqrt{3} + \sqrt{6})$ m

9. Perform the indicated operation.

$$\dfrac{4 - 3i}{2 + 5i} \quad -\dfrac{7}{29} - \dfrac{26}{29}i$$

10. Solve. $2x(x - 7) = x - 18$ $\left\{6, \dfrac{3}{2}\right\}$

11. How many liters of pure alcohol must be mixed with 8 L of 20% alcohol to bring the concentration up to 50% alcohol?   4.8 L

12. Bank robbers leave the scene of a crime and head north through winding mountain roads to their hideaway. Their average rate of speed is 40 mph. The police leave 6 min later in pursuit. If the police car averages 50 mph traveling the same route, how long will it take the police to catch the bank robbers?   24 min

13. Solve the system. $\{(7, -1)\}$

$$5x + 10y = 25$$
$$-2x + 6y = -20$$

14. Solve. $-2[w - 3(w + 1)] = 4 - 7(w + 3)$ $\left\{-\dfrac{23}{11}\right\}$

15. Solve for x. $ax - c = bx + d$ $x = \dfrac{c + d}{a - b}$

16. Solve for t. $s = \dfrac{1}{2}gt^2$ $t \geq 0$ $t = \dfrac{\sqrt{2sg}}{g}$

17. Solve. $3w(w - 2) = 6 + 2w$ $\left\{\dfrac{4 \pm \sqrt{34}}{3}\right\}$

18. Find the x-intercepts of the function defined by $f(x) = |x - 5| - 2$. $(7, 0), (3, 0)$

19. Let $f(t) = 6$, $g(t) = -5t$, and $h(t) = 2t^2$. Find

    a. $(f \cdot g)(t)$ **b.** $(g \circ h)(t)$ **c.** $(h - g)(t)$
    $-30t$ $-10t^2$ $2t^2 + 5t$

20. Solve. $|2q - 5| = |2q + 5|$ $\{0\}$

21. a. Find an equation of the line parallel to the y-axis and passing through the point $(2, 6)$.
    $x = 2$
    b. Find an equation of the line perpendicular to the y-axis and passing through the point $(2, 6)$.
    $y = 6$
    c. Find an equation of the line perpendicular to the line $2x + y = 4$ and passing through the point $(2, 6)$. Write the answer in slope-intercept form. $y = \dfrac{1}{2}x + 5$

22. The smallest angle in a triangle measures one-half the largest angle. The smallest angle measures $20°$ less than the middle angle. Find the measures of all three angles. $40°, 80°, 60°$

23. Solve the system. $\{(-2, 3, -1)\}$

$$2x - 3y + z = -14$$
$$-x + y - 5z = 10$$
$$3x - 4y = -18$$

24. Find the domain. $f(x) = \sqrt{2x - 1}$. $\left[\dfrac{1}{2}, \infty\right)$

25. Find $f^{-1}(x)$, given $f(x) = 5x - \dfrac{2}{3}$. $f^{-1}(x) = \dfrac{1}{5}x + \dfrac{2}{15}$

26. The volume of a gas varies directly as its temperature and inversely with pressure. At a temperature of 100 kelvins (K) and a pressure of 10 newtons per square meter (N/m^2), the gas occupies a volume of 30 m^3. Find the volume at a temperature of 200 K and pressure of 15 N/m^2.
40 m^3

27. Perform the indicated operations. $\dfrac{-x^2 + 5x - 25}{(2x + 1)(x - 2)}$

$$\dfrac{5x - 10}{x^2 - 4x + 4} \div \dfrac{5x^2 - 125}{25 - 5x} \cdot \dfrac{x^3 + 125}{10x + 5}$$

28. Perform the indicated operations. $1 + x$

$$\dfrac{x}{x - y} + \dfrac{y}{y - x} + x$$

29. Given the equation

$$\dfrac{2}{x - 4} = \dfrac{5}{x + 2}$$

    a. Are there any restrictions on x for which the rational expressions are undefined?
    Yes; $x \neq 4$, $x \neq -2$
    b. Solve the equation. $\{8\}$

    c. Solve the related inequality. $(-\infty, -2) \cup (4, 8]$

$$\dfrac{2}{x - 4} \geq \dfrac{5}{x + 2}$$

    Write the answer in interval notation.

30. Two more than 3 times the reciprocal of a number is $\dfrac{5}{4}$ less than the number. Find all such numbers.   The numbers are $-\dfrac{3}{4}$, 4.

31. Solve. $\sqrt{-x} = x + 6$
    $\{-4\}$ (The value -9 does not check.)

32. Solve the inequality $2|x - 3| + 1 > -7$. Write the answer in interval notation. $(-\infty, \infty)$

33. Four million *Escherichia coli (E. coli)* bacteria are present in a laboratory culture. An antibacterial agent is introduced and the population of bacteria decreases by one-half every 6 hr according to

$$P(t) = 4{,}000{,}000\left(\dfrac{1}{2}\right)^{1/6} \qquad t \geq 0$$

where t is the time in hours.

    a. Find the population of bacteria after 6, 12, 18, 24, and 30 hr. $P(6) = 2{,}000{,}000$,
$P(12) = 1{,}000{,}000$, $P(18) = 500{,}000$, $P(24) = 250{,}000$, $P(30) = 125{,}000$
    b. Predict the time required for the population to decrease to 15,625 bacteria.   48 hr

34. Evaluate the expressions without a calculator.

    a. $\log_7 49$ 2   **b.** $\log_4\left(\dfrac{1}{64}\right)$ -3

    c. $\log 1{,}000{,}000$ 6   **d.** $\ln e^3$ 3

35. Use a calculator to approximate the expressions to four decimal places.

  a. $\pi^{4.7}$ 217.0723   **b.** e^{π} 23.1407

  c. $(\sqrt{2})^{-5}$ 0.1768   **d.** $\log 5362$ 3.7293

  e. $\ln 0.67$ -0.4005 **f.** $\log_4 37$ 2.6047

36. Solve. $5^2 = 125^x$ $\left\{\dfrac{2}{3}\right\}$

37. Solve. $e^x = 100$ $\{\ln 100\}$

38. Solve. $\log_3 (x + 6) - 3 = -\log_3 x$

  $\{3\}$ (The value -9 does not check.)

39. Write the following expression as a single logarithm.

$$\frac{1}{2} \log z - 2 \log x - 3 \log y \quad \log\left(\frac{\sqrt{z}}{x^2 y^3}\right)$$

40. Write the following expression as a sum or difference of logarithms

$$\ln \sqrt[3]{\frac{x^2}{y}} \quad \frac{2}{3} \ln x - \frac{1}{3} \ln y$$

Conic Sections

CHAPTER OUTLINE

Chapter 13

In this chapter, we present several new types of graphs, called conic sections. These include the parabola, the circle, the ellipse, and the hyperbola. These shapes are found in a variety of applications. For example, a reflecting telescope has a mirror whose cross section is in the shape of a parabola, and planetary orbits are modeled by ellipses.

Are You Prepared?

To prepare yourself for this chapter, review the process of completing the square. For Exercises 1–6 below, find the value of k that makes the trinomial a perfect square trinomial. Then factor the trinomial. Find the answer at the right and then record the corresponding letter in the space at the bottom of the page.

Answers

1. $x^2 + 6x + k$ 2. $x^2 - 8x + k$

3. $x^2 - 7x + k$ 4. $x^2 + 3x + k$

5. $x^2 - \dfrac{2}{5}x + k$ 6. $x^2 - \dfrac{1}{4}x + k$

I $\dfrac{49}{4}; \left(x - \dfrac{7}{2}\right)^2$ **O** $\dfrac{9}{4}; \left(x + \dfrac{3}{2}\right)^2$

C $\dfrac{1}{25}; \left(x - \dfrac{1}{5}\right)^2$ **N** $\dfrac{1}{64}; \left(x - \dfrac{1}{8}\right)^2$

S $9; (x + 3)^2$ **T** $16; (x - 4)^2$

7. Plot the points $(3, 1)$, $(7, 1)$, and $(7, 6)$. Use the Pythagorean theorem to determine the distance between the points $(3, 1)$ and $(7, 6)$ and choose the correct answer.

   A. 4   **B.** 5   **C.** $\sqrt{29}$ **D.** 3   **E.** $\sqrt{41}$

The parabola, ellipse, hyperbola, are all

$$\underset{5}{\text{C}}\ \underset{4}{\text{O}}\ \underset{6}{\text{N}}\ \underset{3}{\text{I}}\ \underset{5}{\text{C}}\qquad \underset{1}{\text{S}}\ \underset{7}{\text{E}}\ \underset{5}{\text{C}}\ \underset{2}{\text{T}}\ \underset{3}{\text{I}}\ \underset{4}{\text{O}}\ \underset{6}{\text{N}}\ \underset{1}{\text{S}}$$

Section 13.1   Distance Formula, Midpoint Formula, and Circles

Concepts

1. Distance Formula
2. Circles
3. Writing an Equation of a Circle
4. Midpoint Formula

1. Distance Formula

Suppose we are given two points (x_1, y_1) and (x_2, y_2) in a rectangular coordinate system. The distance between the two points can be found by using the Pythagorean theorem (Figure 13-1).

First draw a right triangle with the distance d as the hypotenuse. The length of the horizontal leg a is $|x_2 - x_1|$, and the length of the vertical leg b is $|y_2 - y_1|$. From the Pythagorean theorem we have

$$d^2 = a^2 + b^2$$
$$= (x_2 - x_1)^2 + (y_2 - y_1)^2$$
$$d = \pm\sqrt{(x_2 - x_1)^2 + (y_2 - y_1)^2}$$
$$= \sqrt{(x_2 - x_1)^2 + (y_2 - y_1)^2}$$

Because distance is positive, reject the negative value.

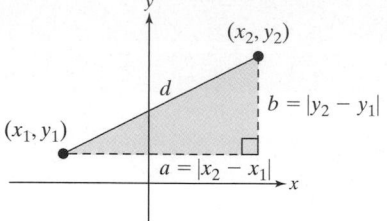

Figure 13-1

FORMULA   The Distance Formula

The distance d between the points (x_1, y_1) and (x_2, y_2) is

$$d = \sqrt{(x_2 - x_1)^2 + (y_2 - y_1)^2}$$

Classroom Example: p. 929,
Exercise 2

Example 1   Finding the Distance Between Two Points

Find the distance between the points $(-2, 3)$ and $(4, -1)$ (Figure 13-2).

Solution:

$(-2, 3)$ and $(4, -1)$

(x_1, y_1) and (x_2, y_2) Label the points.

$$d = \sqrt{(x_2 - x_1)^2 + (y_2 - y_1)^2}$$
$$= \sqrt{[(4) - (-2)]^2 + [(-1) - (3)]^2}$$ Apply the distance formula.
$$= \sqrt{(6)^2 + (-4)^2}$$
$$= \sqrt{36 + 16}$$
$$= \sqrt{52}$$
$$= \sqrt{2^2 \cdot 13}$$
$$= 2\sqrt{13}$$

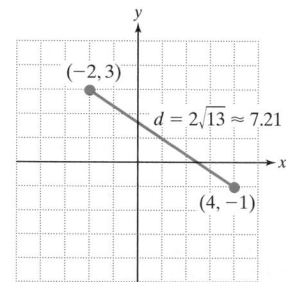

Figure 13-2

Skill Practice

1. Find the distance between the points $(-4, -2)$ and $(2, -5)$.

Answer

1. $3\sqrt{5}$

TIP: The order in which the points are labeled does not affect the result of the distance formula. For example, if the points in Example 1 had been labeled in reverse, the distance formula would still yield the same result:

$$(-2, 3) \quad \text{and} \quad (4, -1) \qquad d = \sqrt{(x_2 - x_1)^2 + (y_2 - y_1)^2}$$
$$(x_2, y_2) \quad \text{and} \quad (x_1, y_1) \qquad = \sqrt{[(-2) - (4)]^2 + [3 - (-1)]^2}$$
$$= \sqrt{(-6)^2 + (4)^2}$$
$$= \sqrt{36 + 16}$$
$$= \sqrt{52}$$
$$= 2\sqrt{13}$$

2. Circles

A **circle** is defined as the set of all points in a plane that are equidistant from a fixed point called the **center**. The fixed distance from the center is called the **radius** and is denoted by r, where $r > 0$.

Suppose a circle is centered at the point (h, k) and has radius, r (Figure 13-3). The distance formula can be used to derive an equation of the circle.

Let (x, y) be any arbitrary point on the circle. Then, by definition, the distance between (h, k) and (x, y) must be r.

$$\sqrt{(x - h)^2 + (y - k)^2} = r$$
$$(x - h)^2 + (y - k)^2 = r^2 \qquad \text{Square both sides.}$$

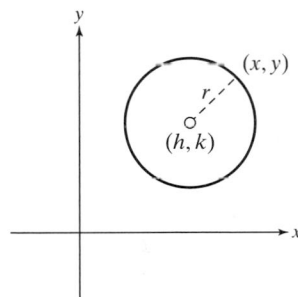

Figure 13-3

FORMULA Standard Equation of a Circle

The **standard equation of a circle**, centered at (h, k) with radius r, is given by

$$(x - h)^2 + (y - k)^2 = r^2 \qquad \text{where } r > 0.$$

Note: If a circle is centered at the origin $(0, 0)$, then $h = 0$ and $k = 0$, and the equation simplifies to $x^2 + y^2 = r^2$.

Example 2 Graphing a Circle

Find the center and radius of the circle. Then graph the circle.

$$(x - 3)^2 + (y + 4)^2 = 36$$

Solution:

$$(x - 3)^2 + (y + 4)^2 = 36$$
$$(x - 3)^2 + [y - (-4)]^2 = (6)^2$$
$$h = 3, k = -4, \text{ and } r = 6$$

The center is $(3, -4)$ and the radius is 6. To graph the circle, first locate the center. From the center, mark points 6 units to the right, left, above, and below the center. Then sketch the circle through these four points (Figure 13-4).

Note that the center of the circle is not actually part of the circle. It is drawn as an open dot for reference.

Figure 13-4

Classroom Example: p. 930, Exercise 28

Animation

Answer

2. Center: $(-1, 2)$; radius: 3

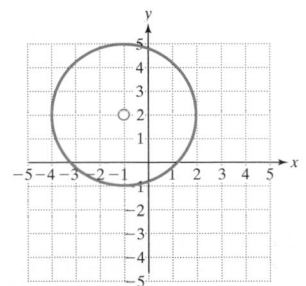

Skill Practice Find the center and radius of the circle. Then graph the circle.

2. $(x + 1)^2 + (y - 2)^2 = 9$

Calculator Connections

Graphing calculators are designed to graph *functions*, in which y is written in terms of x. A circle is not a function. However, it can be graphed as the union of two functions—one representing the top semicircle and the other representing the bottom semicircle.

Solving for y in Example 2, we have

$$(x - 3)^2 + (y + 4)^2 = 36$$

Graph these functions as Y_1 and Y_2, using a square viewing window.

$$(y + 4)^2 = 36 - (x - 3)^2$$

$$y + 4 = \pm\sqrt{36 - (x - 3)^2}$$

$$y = -4 \pm \sqrt{36 - (x - 3)^2}$$

$$Y_1 = -4 + \sqrt{36 - (x - 3)^2}$$

$$Y_2 = -4 - \sqrt{36 - (x - 3)^2}$$

Instructor Note: Ask students why a circle is not a function.

Notice that the image from the calculator does not show the upper and lower semicircles connecting at their endpoints, when in fact the semicircles should "hook up." This is due to the calculator's limited resolution.

Classroom Examples: p. 931, Exercises 36 and 38

Example 3   Graphing a Circle

Find the center and radius of each circle. Then graph the circle.

a. $x^2 + \left(y - \dfrac{10}{3}\right)^2 = \dfrac{25}{9}$ **b.** $x^2 + y^2 = 10$

Solution:

a. $x^2 + \left(y - \dfrac{10}{3}\right)^2 = \dfrac{25}{9}$

$$(x - 0)^2 + \left(y - \dfrac{10}{3}\right)^2 = \left(\dfrac{5}{3}\right)^2$$

The center is $\left(0, \dfrac{10}{3}\right)$ and the radius is $\dfrac{5}{3}$ (Figure 13-5).

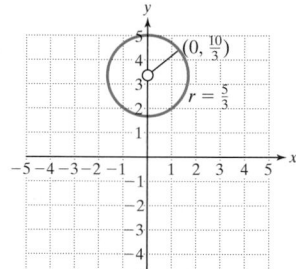

Figure 13-5

b. $x^2 + y^2 = 10$

$(x - 0)^2 + (y - 0)^2 = (\sqrt{10})^2$

The center is $(0, 0)$ and the radius is
$\sqrt{10} \approx 3.16$ (Figure 13-6).

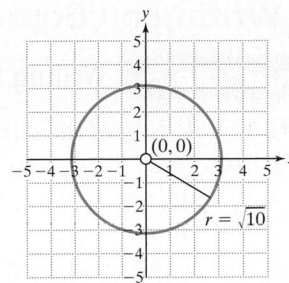

Figure 13-6

Skill Practice Find the center and radius of the circle. Then graph the circle.

3. $\left(x + \dfrac{7}{2}\right)^2 + y^2 = \dfrac{9}{4}$

Sometimes it is necessary to complete the square to write an equation of a circle in standard form.

| **Example 4** | **Writing the Equation of a Circle in the Form $(x - h)^2 + (y - k)^2 = r^2$** |

Classroom Example: p. 931, Exercise 40

Identify the center and radius of the circle given by the equation
$x^2 + y^2 + 2x - 16y + 61 = 0$.

Solution:

$x^2 + y^2 + 2x - 16y + 61 = 0$ To identify the center and radius, write the equation in the form $(x - h)^2 + (y - k)^2 = r^2$.

$(x^2 + 2x \quad) + (y^2 - 16y \quad) = -61$ Group the x terms and group the y terms. Move the constant to the right-hand side.

$(x^2 + 2x + 1) + (y^2 - 16y + 64) = -61 + 1 + 64$

- Complete the square on x. Add $[\frac{1}{2}(2)]^2 = 1$ to both sides of the equation.
- Complete the square on y. Add $[\frac{1}{2}(-16)]^2 = 64$ to both sides of the equation.

$(x + 1)^2 + (y - 8)^2 = 4$ Factor and simplify.

$[x - (-1)]^2 + (y - 8)^2 = 2^2$

The center is $(-1, 8)$ and the radius is 2.

Skill Practice

4. Identify the center and radius of the circle given by the equation
$$x^2 + y^2 - 10x + 4y - 7 = 0$$

Answers

3. Center: $\left(-\dfrac{7}{2}, 0\right)$; radius: $\dfrac{3}{2}$

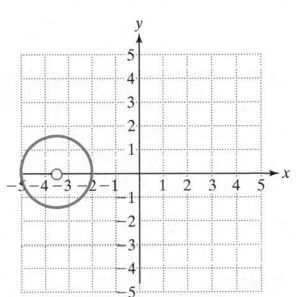

4. Center: $(5, -2)$; radius: 6

3. Writing an Equation of a Circle

Classroom Example: p. 932, Exercise 54

Example 5 Writing an Equation of a Circle

Write an equation of the circle shown in Figure 13-7.

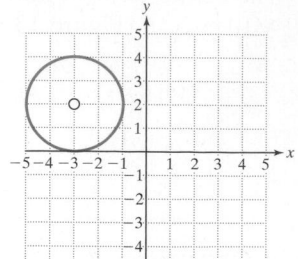

Solution:

The center is at $(-3, 2)$; therefore, $h = -3$ and $k = 2$. From the graph, $r = 2$.

$$(x - h)^2 + (y - k)^2 = r^2$$
$$[x - (-3)]^2 + (y - 2)^2 = (2)^2$$
$$(x + 3)^2 + (y - 2)^2 = 4$$

Figure 13-7

Avoiding Mistakes

Be sure that you *subtract* both coordinates of the center, when substituting the coordinates into the standard form of a circle.

Skill Practice

5. Write an equation for a circle whose center is $(6, -1)$ and whose radius is 8.

4. Midpoint Formula

Consider two points in the coordinate plane and the line segment determined by the points. It is sometimes necessary to determine the point that is halfway between the endpoints of the segment. This point is called the *midpoint*. If the coordinates of the endpoints are represented by (x_1, y_1) and (x_2, y_2), then the midpoint of the segment is given by the following formula.

TIP: The midpoint of a line segment is found by taking the *average* of the x-coordinates and the *average* of the y-coordinates of the endpoints.

Midpoint formula: $\left(\dfrac{x_1 + x_2}{2}, \dfrac{y_1 + y_2}{2} \right)$

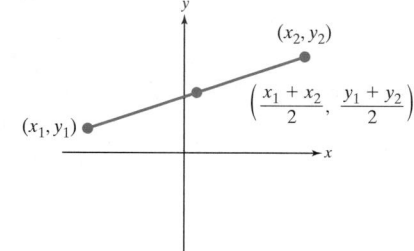

FORMULA   The Midpoint Formula

The midpoint of the segment with endpoints (x_1, y_1) and (x_2, y_2) is given by $\left(\dfrac{x_1 + x_2}{2}, \dfrac{y_1 + y_2}{2} \right)$.

Classroom Example: p. 933, Exercise 64

Example 6 Finding the Midpoint of a Segment

Find the midpoint of the line segment with the given endpoints.

a. $(-4, 6)$ and $(8, 1)$ **b.** $(-1.2, -3.1)$ and $(-6.6, 1.2)$

Solution:

a. $(-4, 6)$ and $(8, 1)$

$\left(\dfrac{-4 + 8}{2}, \dfrac{6 + 1}{2} \right)$ Apply the midpoint formula.

$\left(2, \dfrac{7}{2} \right)$ Simplify.

Avoiding Mistakes

Always remember that the midpoint of a line segment is a *point*. The answer should be an ordered pair, (x, y).

Answer

5. $(x - 6)^2 + (y + 1)^2 = 64$

The midpoint of the segment is $(2, \frac{7}{2})$.

b. $(-1.2, -3.1)$ and $(-6.6, 1.2)$

$\left(\dfrac{-1.2 + (-6.6)}{2}, \dfrac{-3.1 + 1.2}{2}\right)$ Apply the midpoint formula.

$(-3.9, -0.95)$ Simplify.

Skill Practice Find the midpoint of the line segment with the given endpoints.

6. $(5, 6)$ and $(-10, 4)$ **7.** $(-2.6, -6.3)$ and $(1.2, 4.1)$

Example 7   **Applying the Midpoint Formula**

Find the center of the circle in Figure 13-8 given that the endpoints of a diameter are $(-2, 3)$ and $(4, 1)$.

Solution:

Because the midpoint of a diameter of a circle is the center of the circle, apply the midpoint formula.

$(-2, 3)$ and $(4, 1)$

(x_1, y_1) and (x_2, y_2)

$\left(\dfrac{x_1 + x_2}{2}, \dfrac{y_1 + y_2}{2}\right)$

$\left(\dfrac{-2 + 4}{2}, \dfrac{3 + 1}{2}\right)$ Apply the midpoint formula.

$(1, 2)$ Simplify.

The center of the circle is $(1, 2)$.

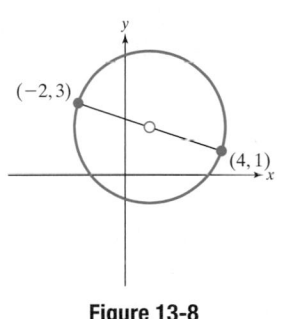

Figure 13-8

Classroom Example: p. 933, Exercise 72

Skill Practice

8. Find the center of the circle given that the endpoints of a diameter are $(3, 2)$ and $(7, 10)$.

Answers

6. $\left(-\dfrac{5}{2}, 5\right)$ **7.** $(-0.7, -1.1)$

8. $(5, 6)$

Section 13.1   Practice Exercises

Boost *your* GRADE at ALEKS.com!   **ALEKS** version 3.0

- Practice Problems
- Self-Tests
- NetTutor

- e-Professors
- Videos

For additional exercises, see Classroom Activities 13.1A–13.1D in the *Instructor's Resource Manual* at www.mhhe.com/moh.

Study Skills Exercise

1. Define the key terms.

  a. distance formula   **b. circle**   **c. center of a circle**

  d. radius   **e. standard equation of a circle**   **f. midpoint formula**

Concept 1: Distance Formula

For Exercises 2–16, use the distance formula to find the distance between the two points. **(See Example 1.)**

2. $(-2, 7)$ and $(4, -5)$ $6\sqrt{5}$ **3.** $(1, 10)$ and $(-2, 4)$ $3\sqrt{5}$ **4.** $(0, 5)$ and $(-3, 8)$ $3\sqrt{2}$

 Writing   Translating Expression   Geometry   Scientific Calculator   Video   NS&E

5. (6, 7) and (3, 2) $\sqrt{34}$

6. $\left(\dfrac{2}{3}, \dfrac{1}{5}\right)$ and $\left(-\dfrac{5}{6}, \dfrac{3}{10}\right)$ $\dfrac{\sqrt{226}}{10}$

7. $\left(-\dfrac{1}{2}, \dfrac{5}{8}\right)$ and $\left(-\dfrac{3}{2}, \dfrac{1}{4}\right)$ $\dfrac{\sqrt{73}}{8}$

8. (4, 13) and (4, −6)   19

9. (−2, 5) and (−2, 9)   4

10. (8, −6) and (−2, −6)   10

11. (7, 2) and (15, 2)   8

12. (−6, −2) and (−3, −5) $3\sqrt{2}$

13. (−1, −5) and (−5, −9) $4\sqrt{2}$

14. $(3\sqrt{5}, 2\sqrt{7})$ and $(-\sqrt{5}, -3\sqrt{7})$
$\sqrt{255}$

15. $(4\sqrt{6}, -2\sqrt{2})$ and $(2\sqrt{6}, \sqrt{2})$
$\sqrt{42}$

16. (6, 0) and (0, −1) $\sqrt{37}$

17. Explain how to find the distance between 5 and −7 on the y-axis.
Subtract 5 and −7. This becomes 5 − (−7) = 12.

18. Explain how to find the distance between 15 and −37 on the x-axis.
Subtract 15 and −37. This becomes 15 − (−37) = 52.

19. Find the values of y such that the distance between the points (4, 7) and (−4, y) is 10 units. $y = 13, y = 1$

20. Find the values of x such that the distance between the points (−4, −2) and (x, 3) is 13 units. $x = 8, x = -16$

21. Find the values of x such that the distance between the points (x, 2) and (4, −1) is 5 units. $x = 0, x = 8$

22. Find the values of y such that the distance between the points (−5, 2) and (3, y) is 10 units. $y = 8, y = -4$

For Exercises 23–26, determine if the three points define the vertices of a right triangle.

23. (−3, 2), (−2, −4), and (3, 3)   Yes

24. (1, −2), (−2, 4), and (7, 1)   Yes

25. (−3, −2), (4, −3), and (1, 5)   No

26. (1, 4), (5, 3), and (2, 0)   No

Concept 2: Circles

For Exercises 27–47, identify the center and radius of the circle and then graph the circle. Complete the square, if necessary. **(See Examples 2–4.)**

27. $(x - 4)^2 + (y + 2)^2 = 9$

28. $(x - 3)^2 + (y + 1)^2 = 16$

29. $(x + 1)^2 + (y + 1)^2 = 1$

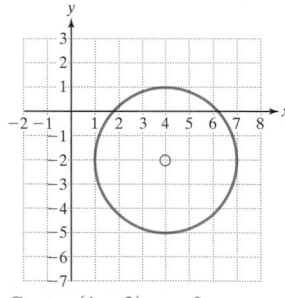
Center (4, −2); $r = 3$

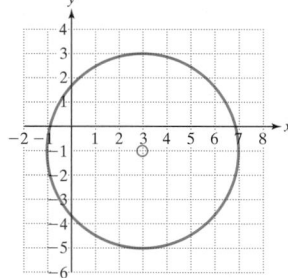
Center (3, −1); $r = 4$

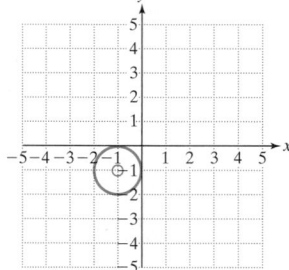
Center (−1, −1); $r = 1$

30. $(x - 4)^2 + (y - 4)^2 = 4$

31. $x^2 + (y - 2)^2 = 4$

32. $(x + 1)^2 + y^2 = 1$

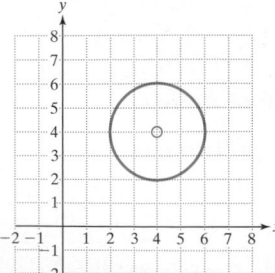
Center (4, 4); $r = 2$

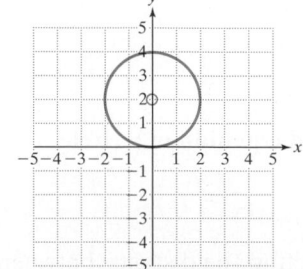
Center (0, 2); $r = 2$

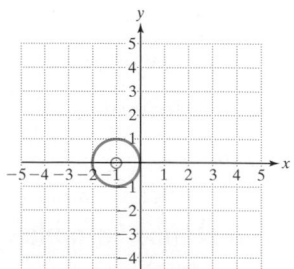
Center (−1, 0); $r = 1$

33. $(x - 3)^2 + y^2 = 8$

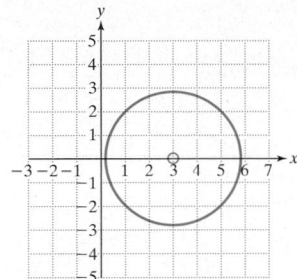

Center $(3, 0)$; $r = 2\sqrt{2}$

34. $x^2 + (y + 2)^2 = 20$

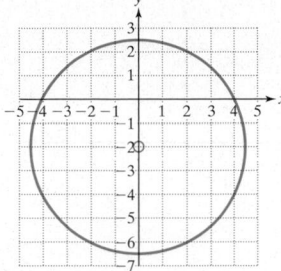

Center $(0, -2)$; $r = 2\sqrt{5}$

35. $x^2 + y^2 = 6$

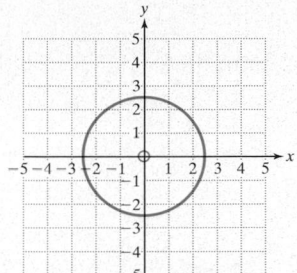

Center $(0, 0)$; $r = \sqrt{6}$

36. $x^2 + y^2 = 15$

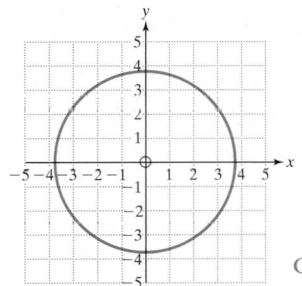

Center $(0, 0)$; $r = \sqrt{15}$

37. $\left(x + \dfrac{4}{5}\right)^2 + y^2 = \dfrac{64}{25}$

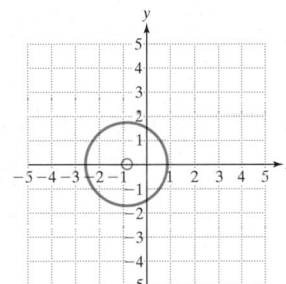

Center $\left(-\dfrac{4}{5}, 0\right)$; $r = \dfrac{8}{5}$

38. $x^2 + \left(y - \dfrac{5}{2}\right)^2 = \dfrac{9}{4}$

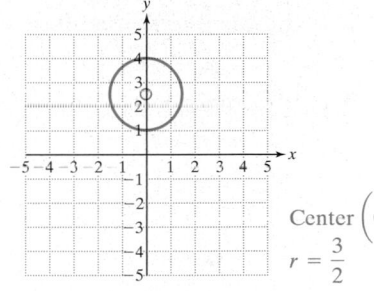

Center $\left(0, \dfrac{5}{2}\right)$; $r = \dfrac{3}{2}$

39. $x^2 + y^2 - 2x - 6y - 26 = 0$

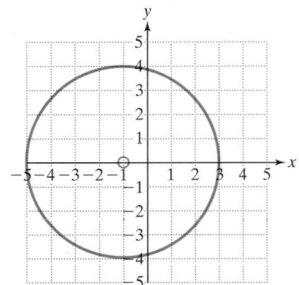

Center $(1, 3)$; $r = 6$

40. $x^2 + y^2 + 4x - 8y + 16 = 0$

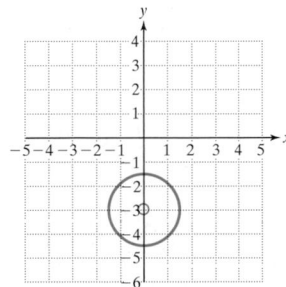

Center $(-2, 4)$; $r = 2$

41. $x^2 + y^2 - 6y + 5 = 0$

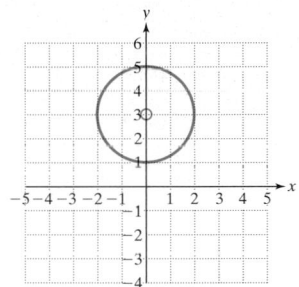

Center: $(0, 3)$; $r = 2$

42. $x^2 + 2x + y^2 - 15 = 0$

Center: $(-1, 0)$; $r = 4$

43. $x^2 + y^2 + 6y + \dfrac{65}{9} = 0$

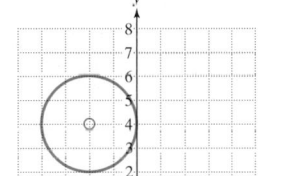

Center $(0, -3)$; $r = \dfrac{4}{3}$

44. $x^2 + y^2 - 12x + 12y + 71 = 0$

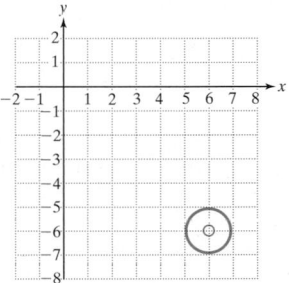

Center: $(6, -6)$; $r = 1$

45. $x^2 + y^2 + 2x + 4y - 4 = 0$ **46.** $2x^2 + 2y^2 = 32$ **47.** $3x^2 + 3y^2 = 3$

        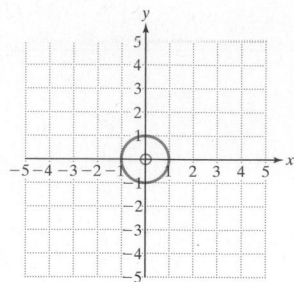

Center: $(-1, -2)$; $r = 3$ Center: $(0, 0)$; $r = 4$ Center: $(0, 0)$; $r = 1$

Concept 3: Writing an Equation of a Circle

48. If the diameter of a circle is 10 ft, what is the radius?   5 ft

For Exercises 49–54, write an equation that represents the graph of the circle. **(See Example 5.)**

49.

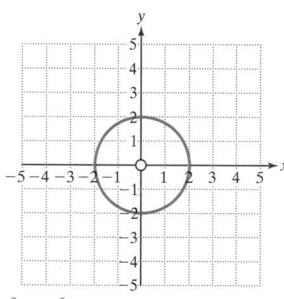

$x^2 + y^2 = 4$

50.

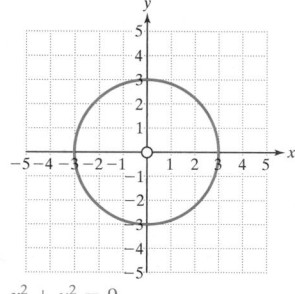

$x^2 + y^2 = 9$

51.

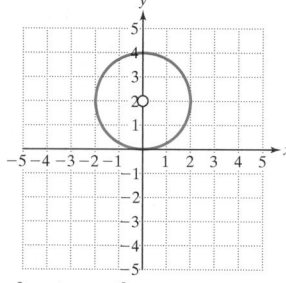

$x^2 + (y - 2)^2 = 4$

52.

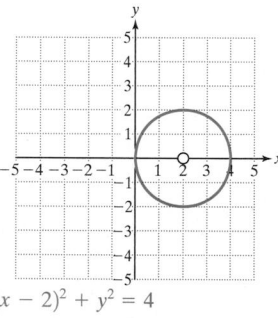

$(x - 2)^2 + y^2 = 4$

53.

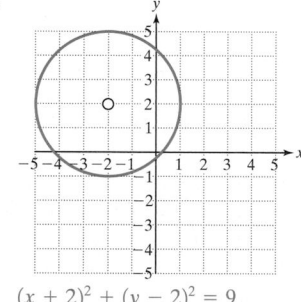

$(x + 2)^2 + (y - 2)^2 = 9$

54.

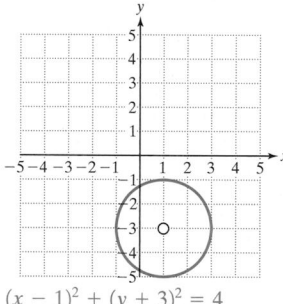

$(x - 1)^2 + (y + 3)^2 = 4$

55. Write an equation of a circle centered at the origin with a radius of 7.
$x^2 + y^2 = 49$

56. Write an equation of a circle centered at the origin with a radius of 12.
$x^2 + y^2 = 144$

57. Write an equation of a circle centered at $(-3, -4)$ with a diameter of 12.
$(x + 3)^2 + (y + 4)^2 = 36$

58. Write an equation of a circle centered at $(5, -1)$ with a diameter of 8. $(x - 5)^2 + (y + 1)^2 = 16$

 Writing   ↔ Translating Expression   Geometry   Scientific Calculator   Video

Concept 4: Midpoint Formula

For Exercises 59–62, find the midpoint of the line segment. Check your answers by plotting the midpoint on the graph.

59.

$(1, 2)$

60.

$(2, -3)$

61.

$(-1, 0)$

62.

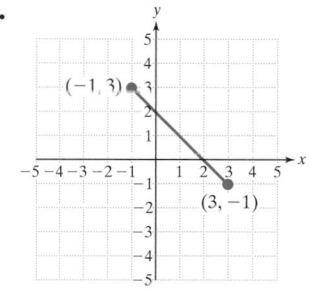

$(1, 1)$

For Exercises 63–70, find the midpoint of the line segment between the two given points. **(See Example 6.)**

63. $(4, 0)$ and $(-6, 12)$ $(-1, 6)$

64. $(-7, 2)$ and $(-3, -2)$ $(-5, 0)$

65. $(-3, 8)$ and $(3, -2)$ $(0, 3)$

66. $(0, 5)$ and $(4, -5)$ $(2, 0)$

67. $(5, 2)$ and $(-6, 1)$ $\left(-\dfrac{1}{2}, \dfrac{3}{2}\right)$

68. $(-9, 3)$ and $(0, -4)$ $\left(-\dfrac{9}{2}, -\dfrac{1}{2}\right)$

69. $(-2.4, -3.1)$ and $(1.6, 1.1)$
$(-0.4, -1)$

70. $(0.8, 5.3)$ and $(-4.2, 7.1)$
$(-1.7, 6.2)$

71. Find the center of a circle if a diameter of the circle has endpoints $(-1, 2)$ and $(3, 4)$. **(See Example 7.)** $(1, 3)$

72. Find the center of a circle if a diameter of the circle has endpoints $(-3, 3)$ and $(7, -1)$. $(2, 1)$

73. Two courier trucks leave the warehouse to make deliveries. One travels 20 mi north and 30 mi east. The other truck travels 5 mi south and 50 mi east. If the two drivers want to meet for lunch at a restaurant at a point halfway between them, where should they meet relative to the warehouse?
(*Hint:* Label the warehouse as the origin, and find the coordinates of the restaurant. See the figure.)

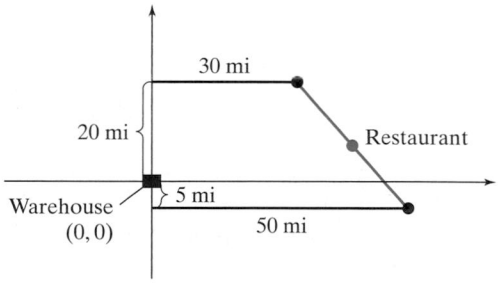

$(40, 7\frac{1}{2})$; they should meet 40 mi east, $7\frac{1}{2}$ mi north of the warehouse.

74. A map of a hiking area is drawn so that the Visitor Center is at the origin of a rectangular grid. Two hikers are located at positions $(-1, 1)$ and $(-3, -2)$ with respect to the Visitor Center where all units are in miles. A campground is located exactly halfway between the hikers. What are the coordinates of the campground? $\left(-2, -\dfrac{1}{2}\right)$

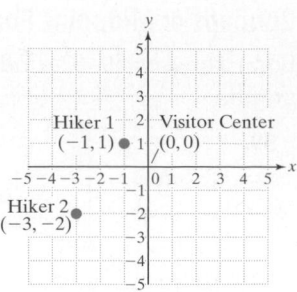

Expanding Your Skills

75. Write an equation of a circle that has the points $(-2, 3)$ and $(2, 3)$ as endpoints of a diameter. $x^2 + (y - 3)^2 = 4$

76. Write an equation of a circle that has the points $(-1, 3)$ and $(-1, -3)$ as endpoints of a diameter. $(x + 1)^2 + y^2 = 9$

77. Write an equation of a circle whose center is $(4, 4)$ and is tangent to the x- and y-axes. (*Hint:* Sketch the circle first.) $(x - 4)^2 + (y - 4)^2 = 16$

78. Write an equation of a circle whose center is $(-3, 3)$ and is tangent to the x- and y-axes. (*Hint:* Sketch the circle first.) $(x + 3)^2 + (y - 3)^2 = 9$

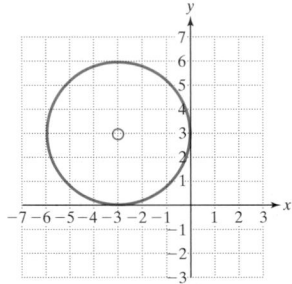

79. Write an equation of a circle whose center is $(1, 1)$ and that passes through the point $(-4, 3)$. $(x - 1)^2 + (y - 1)^2 = 29$

80. Write an equation of a circle whose center is $(-3, -1)$ and that passes through the point $(5, -2)$. $(x + 3)^2 + (y + 1)^2 = 65$

Graphing Calculator Exercises

For Exercises 81–86, graph the circles from the indicated exercise on a square viewing window, and approximate the center and the radius from the graph.

81. $(x - 4)^2 + (y + 2)^2 = 9$ (Exercise 27)

82. $(x - 3)^2 + (y + 1)^2 = 16$ (Exercise 28)

83. $x^2 + (y - 2)^2 = 4$ (Exercise 31)

84. $(x + 1)^2 + y^2 = 1$ (Exercise 32)

85. $x^2 + y^2 = 6$ (Exercise 35)

86. $x^2 + y^2 = 15$ (Exercise 36)

 Writing   Translating Expression   Geometry   Scientific Calculator   Video   NS&E

More on the Parabola

1. Introduction to Conic Sections

Recall that the graph of a second-degree equation of the form $y = ax^2 + bx + c$ ($a \neq 0$) is a parabola. In Section 13.1 we learned that the graph of $(x - h)^2 + (y - k)^2 = r^2$ is a circle. These and two other types of figures called ellipses and hyperbolas are called **conic sections**. Conic sections derive their names because each is the intersection of a plane and a double-napped cone.

Instructor Note: Three-dimensional models of the conic sections can really help students visualize these intersections more clearly.

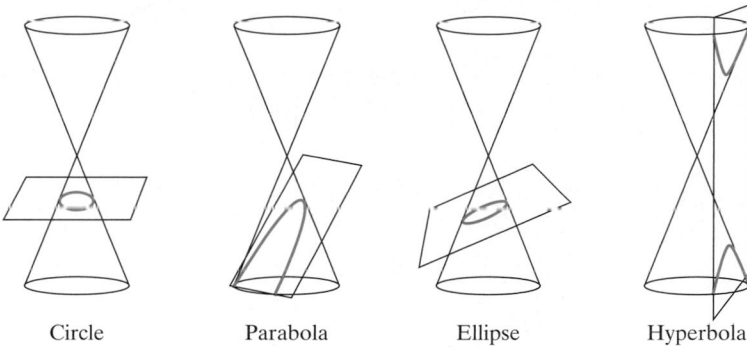

Circle   Parabola   Ellipse   Hyperbola

2. Parabola—Vertical Axis of Symmetry

A **parabola** is defined by a set of points in a plane that are equidistant from a fixed line (called the directrix) and a fixed point (called the focus) not on the directrix (Figure 13-9). Parabolas have numerous real-world applications. For example, a flashlight has a mirror with the cross section in the shape of a parabola. The bulb is located at the focus. The light hits the mirror and is reflected outward parallel to the sides of the cylinder. This forms a beam of light (Figure 13-10).

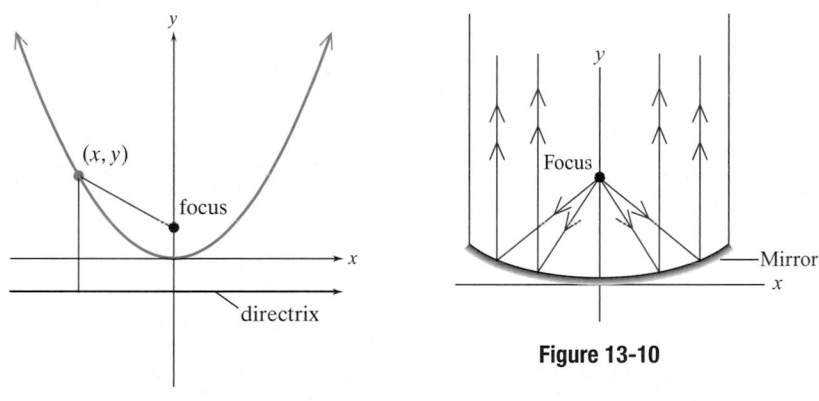

Figure 13-10

Figure 13-9

The graph of the solutions to the quadratic equation $y = ax^2 + bx + c$ is a parabola. We graphed parabolas of this type in Section 11.4. Recall that the **vertex** is the highest or the lowest point of a parabola. The **axis of symmetry** of the parabola is a line that passes through the vertex and is perpendicular to the directrix (Figure 13-11).

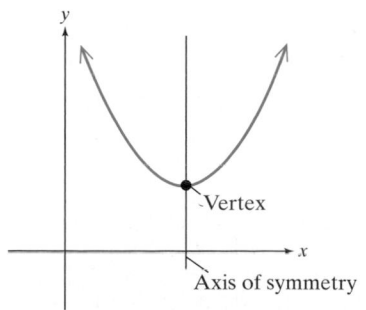

Figure 13-11

> **FORMULA** **Standard Form of the Equation of a Parabola—Vertical Axis of Symmetry**
>
> The standard form of the equation of a parabola with vertex (h, k) and vertical axis of symmetry is
>
> $$y = a(x - h)^2 + k \qquad \text{where } a \neq 0$$
>
> If $a > 0$, the parabola opens upward; and if $a < 0$, the parabola opens downward.
>
> The axis of symmetry is given by $x = h$.

In Section 11.5, we learned that it is sometimes necessary to complete the square to write the equation of a parabola in standard form.

Classroom Example: p. 942, Exercise 14

Example 1 **Graphing a Parabola by First Completing the Square**

Given the equation of the parabola $y = -2x^2 + 4x + 1$,

a. Write the equation in standard form $y = a(x - h)^2 + k$.

b. Identify the vertex and axis of symmetry. Determine if the parabola opens upward or downward.

c. Graph the parabola.

Solution:

a. Complete the square to write the equation in the form $y = a(x - h)^2 + k$.

$y = -2x^2 + 4x + 1$

$y = -2(x^2 - 2x) + 1$	Factor out -2 from the variable terms.
$y = -2(x^2 - 2x + 1 - 1) + 1$	Add and subtract the quantity $\left[\frac{1}{2}(-2)\right]^2 = 1$.
$y = -2(x^2 - 2x + 1) + (-2)(-1) + 1$	Remove the -1 term from within the parentheses by first applying the distributive property. When -1 is removed from the parentheses, it carries with it the factor of -2 from outside the parentheses.
$y = -2(x - 1)^2 + 2 + 1$	
$y = -2(x - 1)^2 + 3$	

The equation is in the form $y = a(x - h)^2 + k$ where $a = -2$, $h = 1$, and $k = 3$.

b. The vertex is $(1, 3)$. Because a is negative, the parabola opens downward. The axis of symmetry is $x = 1$.

c. To graph the parabola, we know that its orientation is downward. Furthermore, we know the vertex is $(1, 3)$. To find other points on the parabola, select several values of x and solve for y. Recall that the y-intercept is found by substituting $x = 0$ and solving for y.

x	y	
1	3	← Vertex
0	1	← y-intercept
−1	−5	
2	1	
3	−5	

Choose x. Solve for y.

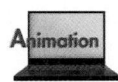
Animation

Notice that the points $(2, 1)$ and $(3, -5)$ are the mirror images of the points $(0, 1)$ and $(-1, -5)$ around the axis of symmetry, $x = 1$. For this reason, once we plot several points on one side of the axis of symmetry, the points on the other side automatically follow as mirror images.

Skill Practice Given the equation of the parabola $y = 2x^2 + 4x + 3$,

1. Write the equation in standard form.
2. Identify the vertex and axis of symmetry.
3. Graph the parabola.

3. Parabola—Horizontal Axis of Symmetry

We have seen that the graph of a parabola $y = ax^2 + bx + c$ opens upward if $a > 0$ and downward if $a < 0$. A parabola can also open to the left or right. In such a case, the "roles" of x and y are essentially interchanged in the equation. Thus, the graph of $x = ay^2 + by + c$ opens to the right if $a > 0$ (Figure 13-12) and to the left if $a < 0$ (Figure 13-13).

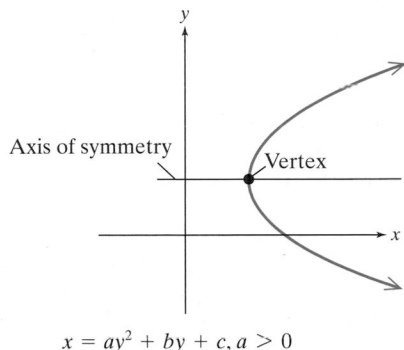

$x = ay^2 + by + c, a > 0$

Figure 13-12

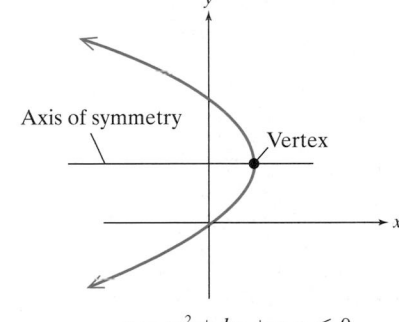

$x = ay^2 + by + c, a < 0$

Figure 13-13

Answers

1. $y = 2(x + 1)^2 + 1$
2. Vertex: $(-1, 1)$; axis of symmetry: $x = -1$
3.

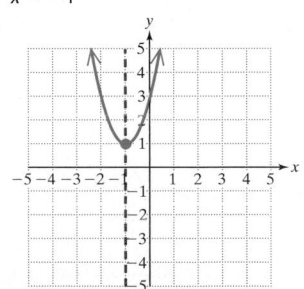

FORMULA   Standard Form of the Equation of a Parabola— Horizontal Axis of Symmetry

The standard form of the equation of a parabola with vertex (h, k) and horizontal axis of symmetry is

$$x = a(y - k)^2 + h \qquad \text{where } a \neq 0$$

If $a > 0$, the parabola opens to the right and if $a < 0$, the parabola opens to the left.

The axis of symmetry is given by $y = k$.

Classroom Example: p. 943,
Exercise 18

Example 2 Graphing a Parabola with a Horizontal Axis of Symmetry

Given the equation of the parabola $x = 4y^2$,

a. Determine the coordinates of the vertex and the equation of the axis of symmetry.

b. Use the value of a to determine if the parabola opens to the right or left.

c. Plot several points and graph the parabola.

Solution:

a. The equation can be written in the form $x = a(y - k)^2 + h$:
$$x = 4(y - 0)^2 + 0$$

Therefore, $h = 0$ and $k = 0$.

The vertex is $(0, 0)$. The axis of symmetry is $y = 0$ (the x-axis).

b. Because a is positive, the parabola opens to the right.

c. The vertex of the parabola is $(0, 0)$. To find other points on the graph, select values for y and solve for x.

TIP: For Example 2, the x-axis is the axis of symmetry. Therefore, once we find points on the parabola above the axis of symmetry, their mirror images will be points on the parabola below the axis of symmetry.

x	y	
0	0	← Vertex
4	1	
4	−1	
16	2	
16	−2	

Solve for x.   Choose y.

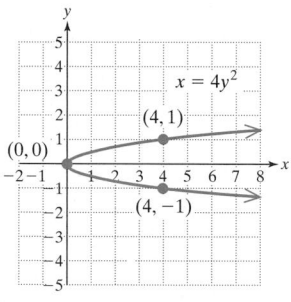

Answers

4. Vertex: $(1, 0)$; axis of symmetry: $y = 0$
5. Parabola opens left.
6.

Skill Practice Given the equation $x = -y^2 + 1$,

4. Identify the vertex and the axis of symmetry.

5. Determine if the parabola opens to the right or to the left.

6. Graph the parabola.

Calculator Connections

Graphing calculators are designed to graph functions, where y is written as a function of x. The parabola from Example 2 is not a function. It can be graphed, however, as the union of two functions, one representing the top branch and the other representing the bottom branch.

Solving for y in Example 2, we have:

Graph these functions as Y_1 and Y_2.

$x = 4y^2$

$y^2 = \dfrac{x}{4}$

$y = \pm\sqrt{\dfrac{x}{4}}$

$y = \pm\dfrac{\sqrt{x}}{2}$

$Y_1 = \dfrac{\sqrt{x}}{2}$ and $Y_2 = -\dfrac{\sqrt{x}}{2}$

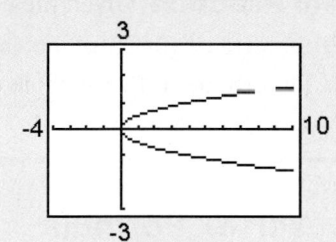

| **Example 3** | **Graphing a Parabola by First Completing the Square** |

Classroom Example: p. 943, Exercise 22

Given the equation of the parabola $x = -y^2 + 8y - 14$,

a. Write the equation in standard form $x = a(y - k)^2 + h$.

b. Identify the vertex and axis of symmetry. Determine if the parabola opens to the right or left.

c. Graph the parabola.

Solution:

a. Complete the square to write the equation in the form $x = a(y - k)^2 + h$.

$x = -y^2 + 8y - 14$

$x = -1(y^2 - 8y) - 14$ Factor out -1 from the variable terms.

$x = -1(y^2 - 8y + 16 - 16) - 14$ Add and subtract the quantity $\left[\frac{1}{2}(-8)\right]^2 = 16$.

$x = -1(y^2 - 8y + 16) + (-1)(-16) - 14$ Remove the -16 term from within the parentheses by first applying the distributive property. When -16 is removed from the parentheses, it carries with it the factor of -1 from outside the parentheses.

$x = -1(y - 4)^2 + 16 - 14$

$x = -1(y - 4)^2 + 2$

The equation is in the form $x = a(y - k)^2 + h$, where $a = -1$, $h = 2$, and $k = 4$.

b. The vertex is $(2, 4)$. Because a is negative, the parabola opens to the left. The axis of symmetry is $y = 4$.

c.

x	y	
2	4	← Vertex
1	5	
1	3	
−2	6	
−2	2	

↑ Solve for x. ↑ Choose y.

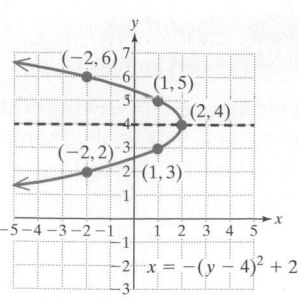

Skill Practice Given the equation of the parabola $x = y^2 + 4y + 7$,

7. Determine the coordinates of the vertex.

8. Determine if the parabola opens to the right or to the left.

9. Graph the parabola.

4. Vertex Formula

From Section 11.5, we learned that the vertex formula can also be used to find the vertex of a parabola.

For a parabola defined by $y = ax^2 + bx + c$,

- The x-coordinate of the vertex is given by $x = \frac{-b}{2a}$.
- The y-coordinate of the vertex is found by substituting this value for x into the original equation and solving for y.

For a parabola defined by $x = ay^2 + by + c$,

- The y-coordinate of the vertex is given by $y = \frac{-b}{2a}$.
- The x-coordinate of the vertex is found by substituting this value for y into the original equation and solving for x.

Classroom Example: p. 943, Exercise 28

Example 4 Finding the Vertex of a Parabola by Using the Vertex Formula

Find the vertex by using the vertex formula. $x = y^2 + 4y + 5$

Solution:

$x = y^2 + 4y + 5$ The parabola is in the form $x = ay^2 + by + c$.

$a = 1 \qquad b = 4 \qquad c = 5$ Identify a, b, and c.

The y-coordinate of the vertex is given by $y = \dfrac{-b}{2a} = \dfrac{-(4)}{2(1)} = -2$.

The x-coordinate of the vertex is found by substitution:
$$x = (-2)^2 + 4(-2) + 5 = 1.$$

The vertex is $(1, -2)$.

Skill Practice Find the vertex by using the vertex formula.

10. $x = -4y^2 + 12y$

Answers

7. Vertex: $(3, -2)$
8. Parabola opens right.
9.

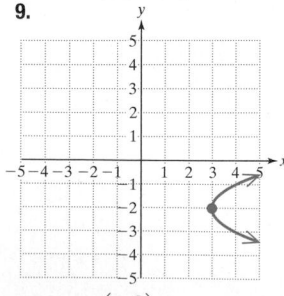

10. Vertex: $\left(9, \dfrac{3}{2}\right)$

Example 5   **Find a Vertex of a Parabola by Using the Vertex Formula**

Classroom Example: p. 943, Exercise 30

Find the vertex by using the vertex formula. $y = \dfrac{1}{2}x^2 - 3x + \dfrac{5}{2}$

Solution:

$y = \dfrac{1}{2}x^2 - 3x + \dfrac{5}{2}$ The parabola is in the form $y = ax^2 + bx + c$.

$a = \dfrac{1}{2}$ $b = -3$ $c = \dfrac{5}{2}$ Identify a, b, and c.

The x-coordinate of the vertex is given by $x = \dfrac{-b}{2a} = \dfrac{-(-3)}{2\left(\dfrac{1}{2}\right)} = 3$.

The y-coordinate of the vertex is found by substitution.

$$y = \dfrac{1}{2}(3)^2 - 3(3) + \dfrac{5}{2}$$

$$= \dfrac{9}{2} - 9 + \dfrac{5}{2}$$

$$= \dfrac{14}{2} - 9$$

$$= 7 - 9$$

$$= -2$$

The vertex is $(3, -2)$.

Skill Practice Find the vertex by using the vertex formula.

11. $y = \dfrac{3}{4}x^2 + 3x + 5$

Answer

11. $(-2, 2)$

Section 13.2   Practice Exercises

Study Skills Exercise

  1. Define the key terms.

     a. conic sections   **b. parabola**   **c. axis of symmetry**   **d. vertex**

Review Exercises

  2. Determine the distance between the points $(1, 1)$ and $(2, -2)$. $\sqrt{10}$

  3. Determine the distance from the origin to the point $(4, -3)$.   5

  4. Determine the distance between the points $(11, 3)$ and $(5, 3)$.   6

 Writing   Translating Expression   Geometry   Scientific Calculator   Video   NS&E

For Exercises 5–6, identify the center and radius of the circle and then graph the circle.

5. $x^2 + (y + 1)^2 = 16$

Center: (0, −1); radius: 4

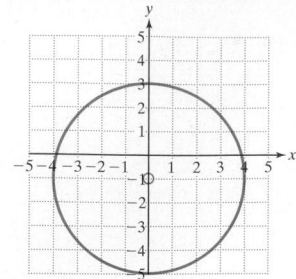

6. $(x − 3)^2 + y^2 = 4$

Center: (3, 0); radius: 2

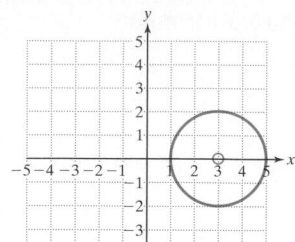

7. Find the midpoint of the line segment between the points (7, −3) and (4, 5).

$\left(\dfrac{11}{2}, 1\right)$

8. Find the midpoint of the line segment between the points (−3, 0) and (−1, 9).

$\left(−2, \dfrac{9}{2}\right)$

Concept 2: Parabola—Vertical Axis of Symmetry

For Exercises 9–16, use the equation of the parabola in standard form $y = a(x − h)^2 + k$ to determine the coordinates of the vertex and the equation of the axis of symmetry (complete the square if necessary). Then graph the parabola. **(See Example 1.)**

9. $y = (x + 2)^2 + 1$

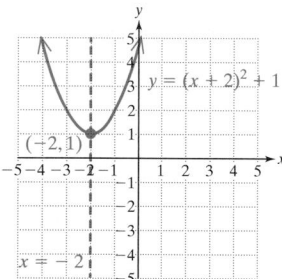

10. $y = (x − 1)^2 + 1$

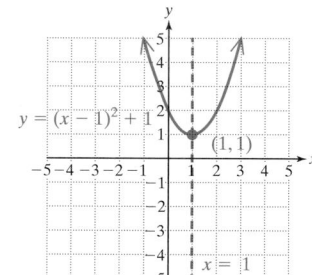

11. $y = x^2 − 4x + 3$

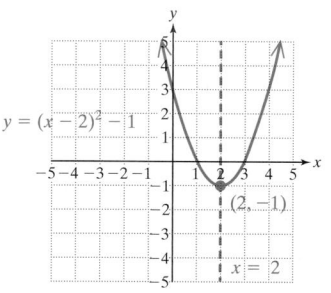

12. $y = x^2 + 6x + 5$

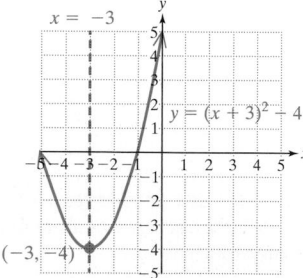

13. $y = −2x^2 + 8x$

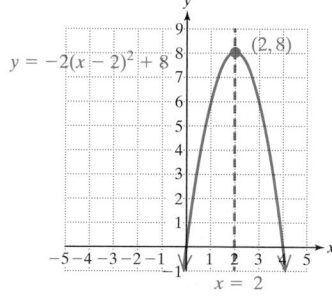

14. $y = −3x^2 − 6x$

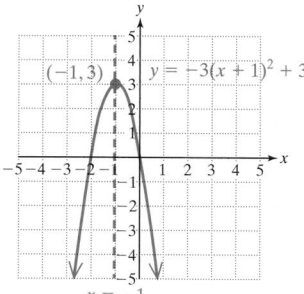

15. $y = −x^2 − 3x + 2$

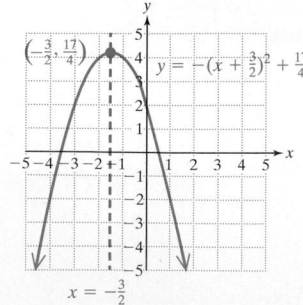

16. $y = −x^2 + x − 4$

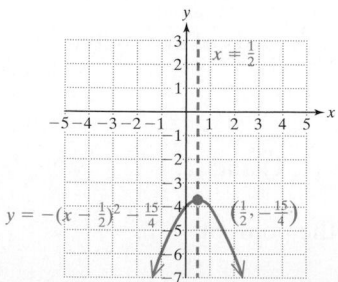

Concept 3: Parabola—Horizontal Axis of Symmetry

For Exercises 17–24, use the equation of the parabola in standard form $x = a(y - k)^2 + h$ to determine the coordinates of the vertex and the axis of symmetry (complete the square if necessary). Then graph the parabola. **(See Examples 2–3.)**

17. $x = y^2 - 3$

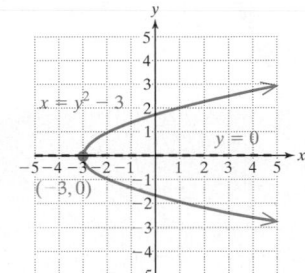

18. $x = y^2 + 1$

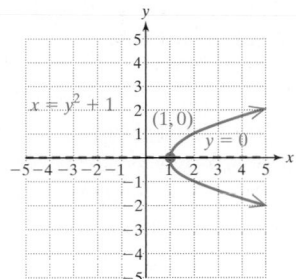

19. $x = -(y - 3)^2 - 3$

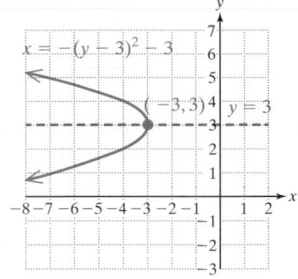

20. $x = -2(y + 2)^2 + 1$

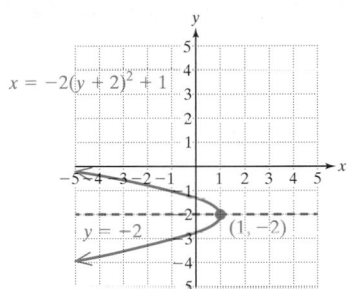

21. $x = -y^2 + 4y - 4$

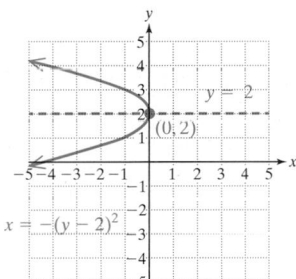

22. $x = -4y^2 - 4y - 2$

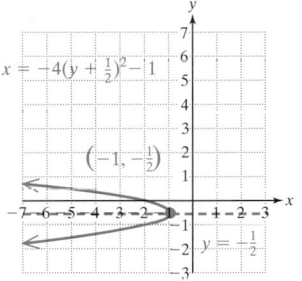

23. $x = y^2 - 2y + 2$

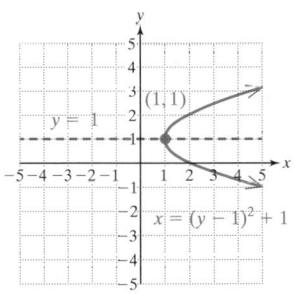

24. $x = y^2 + 4y + 1$

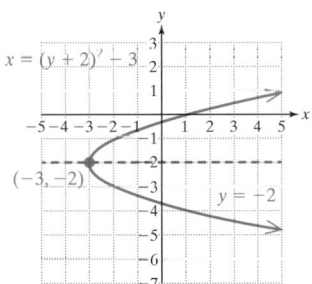

Concept 4: Vertex Formula

For Exercises 25–33, determine the vertex by using the vertex formula. **(See Examples 4–5.)**

25. $y = x^2 - 4x + 3$ $(2, -1)$

26. $y = x^2 + 6x - 2$ $(-3, -11)$

27. $x = y^2 + 2y + 6$ $(5, -1)$

28. $x = y^2 - 8y + 3$ $(-13, 4)$

29. $y = -\dfrac{1}{4}x^2 + x + \dfrac{3}{4}$ $\left(2, \dfrac{7}{4}\right)$

30. $y = -\dfrac{1}{2}x^2 - x + \dfrac{1}{2}$ $(-1, 1)$

31. $y = x^2 - 3x + 2$ $\left(\dfrac{3}{2}, -\dfrac{1}{4}\right)$

32. $x = -2y^2 + 16y + 1$ $(33, 4)$

33. $x = -3y^2 - 6y + 7$ $(10, -1)$

  ✏ Writing ↔ Translating Expression ◁ Geometry 🖩 Scientific Calculator ● Video NS⚙E

34. Ricardo has a satellite dish for his television. The cross sections of the satellite dish are parabolic in shape. A cross section through the vertex can be described by the equation

$$d(x) = \frac{2}{25}x^2 - \frac{2}{5}x$$

where $d(x)$ is the depth of the dish (in feet) at a distance of x ft from the edge of the dish. How deep is the satellite dish?

The satellite dish is $\frac{1}{2}$ ft deep.

35. Water from an outdoor fountain is projected outward from a jet on the side wall of the fountain. The water follows a parabolic path, and can be modeled by $h(x) = -x^2 + 10x - 3$. In this function, $h(x)$ represents the height of the water, x ft from the jet. Find the maximum height of the water.

The maximum height of the water is 22 ft.

Mixed Exercises

36. Explain how to determine whether a parabola opens upward, downward, left, or right.

For a parabola whose equation is written in the form $y = a(x - h)^2 + k$, if $a > 0$, the parabola opens upward; if $a < 0$, the parabola opens downward. For a parabola written in the form $x = a(y - k)^2 + h$, if $a > 0$, the parabola opens right; if $a < 0$, the parabola opens left.

37. Explain how to determine whether a parabola has a vertical or horizontal axis of symmetry.

A parabola whose equation is in the form $y = a(x - h)^2 + k$ has a vertical axis of symmetry. A parabola whose equation is in the form $x = a(y - k)^2 + h$ has a horizontal axis of symmetry.

For Exercises 38–49, use the equation of the parabola first to determine whether the axis of symmetry is vertical or horizontal. Then determine if the parabola opens upward, downward, left, or right.

38. $y = (x - 2)^2 + 3$ Vertical axis of symmetry; opens upward

39. $y = (x - 4)^2 + 2$ Vertical axis of symmetry; opens upward

40. $y = -2(x + 1)^2 - 4$ Vertical axis of symmetry; opens downward

41. $y = -3(x + 2)^2 - 1$ Vertical axis of symmetry; opens downward

42. $x = y^2 + 4$ Horizontal axis of symmetry; opens right

43. $x = y^2 - 2$ Horizontal axis of symmetry; opens right

44. $x = -(y + 3)^2 + 2$ Horizontal axis of symmetry; opens left

45. $x = -2(y - 1)^2 - 3$ Horizontal axis of symmetry; opens left

46. $y = -2x^2 - 5$ Vertical axis of symmetry; opens downward

47. $y = -x^2 + 3$ Vertical axis of symmetry; opens downward

48. $x = 2y^2 + 3y - 2$ Horizontal axis of symmetry; opens right

49. $x = y^2 - 5y + 1$ Horizontal axis of symmetry; opens right

---

Section 13.3 The Ellipse and Hyperbola

Concepts

1. **Standard Form of an Equation of an Ellipse**
2. **Standard Form of an Equation of a Hyperbola**

1. Standard Form of an Equation of an Ellipse

In this section, we will study the two remaining conic sections: the ellipse and the hyperbola. An **ellipse** is the set of all points (x, y) such that the sum of the distances between (x, y) and two distinct points is a constant. The fixed points are called the foci (plural of *focus*) of the ellipse.

To visualize an ellipse, consider the following application. Suppose Sonya wants to cut an elliptical rug from a rectangular rug to avoid a stain made by the family dog. She places two tacks along the center horizontal line. Then she ties the ends of a slack piece of rope to each tack. With the rope pulled tight, she traces out a curve. This curve is an ellipse, and the tacks are located at the foci of the ellipse (Figure 13-14).

 Writing   Translating Expression   Geometry   Scientific Calculator   Video NS&E

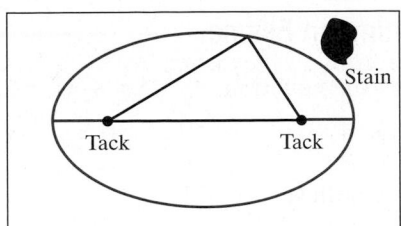

Figure 13-14

We will first graph ellipses that are centered at the origin.

FORMULA   Standard Form of an Equation of an Ellipse Centered at the Origin

An ellipse with the center at the origin has the equation $\dfrac{x^2}{a^2} + \dfrac{y^2}{b^2} = 1$, where a and b are positive real numbers. In the standard form of the equation, the right side must equal 1.

To graph an ellipse centered at the origin, find the x- and y-intercepts.

To find the x-intercepts, let $y = 0$.

$$\frac{x^2}{a^2} + \frac{0}{b^2} = 1$$

$$\frac{x^2}{a^2} = 1$$

$$x^2 = a^2$$

$$x = \pm\sqrt{a^2}$$

$$x = \pm a$$

The x-intercepts are $(a, 0)$ and $(-a, 0)$. See Figure 13-15.

To find the y-intercepts, let $x = 0$.

$$\frac{0}{a^2} + \frac{y^2}{b^2} = 1$$

$$\frac{y^2}{b^2} = 1$$

$$y^2 = b^2$$

$$y = \pm\sqrt{b^2}$$

$$y = \pm b$$

The y-intercepts are $(0, b)$ and $(0, -b)$. See Figure 13-15.

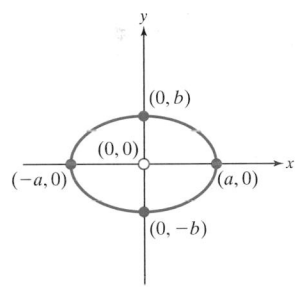

Figure 13-15

Example 1   **Graphing an Ellipse**

Graph the ellipse given by the equation. $\dfrac{x^2}{9} + \dfrac{y^2}{4} = 1$

Solution:

The equation can be written as $\dfrac{x^2}{3^2} + \dfrac{y^2}{2^2} = 1$;

therefore, $a = 3$ and $b = 2$.

Graph the intercepts $(3, 0), (-3, 0), (0, 2), (0, -2)$ and sketch the ellipse.

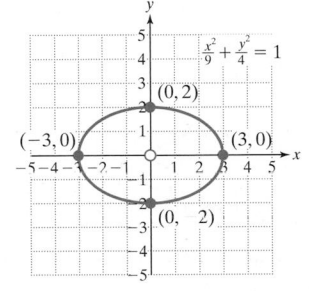

Skill Practice

1. Graph the ellipse given by the equation $\dfrac{x^2}{4} + \dfrac{y^2}{16} = 1$.

Answer

1.

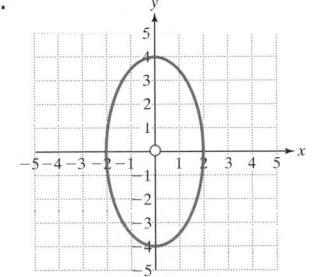

Example 2 **Graphing an Ellipse**

Graph the ellipse given by the equation. $25x^2 + y^2 = 25$

Solution:

$25x^2 + y^2 = 25$ Divide both sides by 25.

$$\frac{25x^2}{25} + \frac{y^2}{25} = \frac{25}{25}$$

$$x^2 + \frac{y^2}{25} = 1$$

The equation can then be written as $\dfrac{x^2}{1^2} + \dfrac{y^2}{5^2} = 1$;

therefore, $a = 1$ and $b = 5$.

Graph the intercepts $(1, 0), (-1, 0), (0, 5),$ and $(0, -5)$ and sketch the ellipse.

Skill Practice

2. Graph the ellipse given by the equation $x^2 + 9y^2 = 9$.

A circle is a special case of an ellipse where $a = b$. Therefore, it is not surprising that we graph an ellipse centered at the point (h, k) in much the same way we graph a circle.

Example 3 **Graphing an Ellipse Whose Center Is Not at the Origin**

Graph the ellipse given by the equation. $\dfrac{(x - 1)^2}{16} + \dfrac{(y + 3)^2}{4} = 1$

Solution:

Just as we would find the center of a circle, we see that the center of the ellipse is $(1, -3)$. Now we can use the values of a and b to help us plot four strategic points to define the curve.

The equation can be written as $\dfrac{(x - 1)^2}{(4)^2} + \dfrac{(y + 3)^2}{(2)^2} = 1.$

From this, we have $a = 4$ and $b = 2$. To sketch the curve, locate the center at $(1, -3)$. Then move $a = 4$ units to the left and right of the center and plot two points. Similarly, move $b = 2$ units up and down from the center and plot two points.

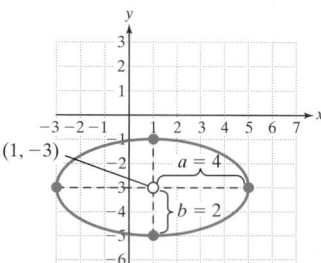

Skill Practice

3. Graph the ellipse $\dfrac{(x + 1)^2}{4} + \dfrac{(y - 4)^2}{9} = 1.$

Answers

2.

3.

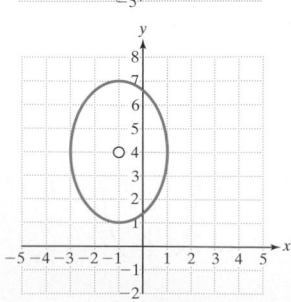

2. Standard Form of an Equation of a Hyperbola

A **hyperbola** is the set of all points (x, y) such that the absolute value of the *difference* of the distances between (x, y) and two distinct points is a constant. The fixed points are called the foci of the hyperbola. The graph of a hyperbola has two parts, called branches. A hyperbola has two vertices that lie on an axis of symmetry called the **transverse axis**. For the hyperbolas studied here, the transverse axis is either horizontal or vertical.

Instructor Note: Students may think that a hyperbola is two parabolas. Emphasize that they are not the same curves. The curvature on the branches of a hyperbola is different than that of a parabola.

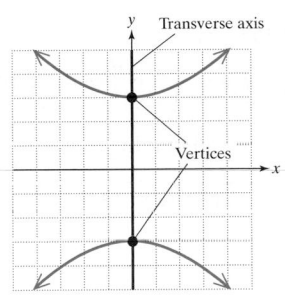

Instructor Note: Ask students if either form of hyperbola would pass the vertical line test.

FORMULA **Standard Forms of an Equation of a Hyperbola with Center at the Origin**

Let a and b represent positive real numbers.

Horizontal transverse axis:

The standard form of an equation of a hyperbola with a *horizontal transverse axis* and center at the origin is given by $\dfrac{x^2}{a^2} - \dfrac{y^2}{b^2} = 1$.

Note: The x term is positive. The branches of the hyperbola open left and right.

Vertical transverse axis:

The standard form of an equation of a hyperbola with a *vertical transverse axis* and center at the origin is given by $\dfrac{y^2}{b^2} - \dfrac{x^2}{a^2} = 1$.

Note: The y term is positive. The branches of the hyperbola open up and down.

In the standard forms of an equation of a hyperbola, the right side must equal 1.

To graph a hyperbola centered at the origin, first construct a reference rectangle. Draw this rectangle by using the points (a, b), $(-a, b)$, $(a, -b)$, and $(-a, -b)$. Asymptotes lie on the diagonals of the rectangle. The branches of the hyperbola are drawn to approach the asymptotes.

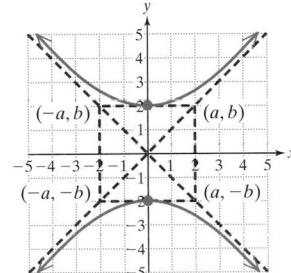

Example 4 Graphing a Hyperbola

Graph the hyperbola given by the equation. $\dfrac{x^2}{36} - \dfrac{y^2}{9} = 1$

   a. Determine whether the transverse axis is horizontal or vertical.

   b. Draw the reference rectangle and asymptotes.

   c. Graph the hyperbola and label the vertices.

Solution:

   a. Since the x-term is positive, the transverse axis is horizontal.

   b. The equation can be written $\dfrac{x^2}{6^2} - \dfrac{y^2}{3^2} = 1$;

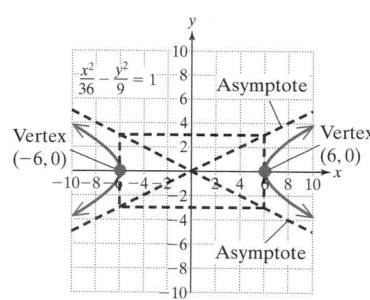

      therefore, $a = 6$ and $b = 3$. Graph the reference rectangle from the points $(6, 3), (6, -3), (-6, 3), (-6, -3)$.

   c. The vertices are $(-6, 0)$ and $(6, 0)$.

Skill Practice

   4. Graph the hyperbola $x^2 - \dfrac{y^2}{9} = 1$.

Example 5 Graphing a Hyperbola

Graph the hyperbola given by the equation. $y^2 - 4x^2 - 16 = 0$

   a. Write the equation in standard form to determine whether the transverse axis is horizontal or vertical.

   b. Draw the reference rectangle and asymptotes.

   c. Graph the hyperbola and label the vertices.

Solution:

   a. $y^2 - 4x^2 - 16 = 0$

$$y^2 - 4x^2 = 16 \qquad \text{Isolate the constant term on the right.}$$

$$\frac{y^2}{16} - \frac{4x^2}{16} = \frac{16}{16} \qquad \text{Divide by 16 to make the constant term 1.}$$

$$\frac{y^2}{16} - \frac{x^2}{4} = 1$$

Since the y term is positive, the transverse axis is vertical.

   b. The equation can be written $\dfrac{y^2}{4^2} - \dfrac{x^2}{2^2} = 1$;

      therefore, $a = 2$ and $b = 4$. Graph the reference rectangle from the points $(2, 4)$, $(2, -4), (-2, 4), (-2, -4)$.

   c. The vertices are $(0, 4)$ and $(0, -4)$.

Skill Practice

   5. Graph the hyperbola $9y^2 - 4x^2 = 36$.

Answers

4.

5.

Section 13.3 Practice Exercises

Study Skills Exercise

1. Define the key terms.

   a. ellipse   b. hyperbola   c. transverse axis of a hyperbola

Review Exercises

2. Write the standard form of a circle with center at (h, k) and radius, r. $(x - h)^2 + (y - k)^2 = r^2$

For Exercises 3–4, identify the center and radius of the circle.

3. $x^2 + y^2 - 16x + 12y = 0$ Center: $(8, -6)$; radius: 10

4. $x^2 + y^2 + 4x + 4y - 1 = 0$ Center: $(-2, -2)$; radius: 3

For Exercises 5–6, identify the vertex and the axis of symmetry.

5. $y = 3(x + 3)^2 - 1$ Vertex: $(-3, -1)$; $x = -3$

6. $x = -\dfrac{1}{4}(y - 1)^2 - 6$ Vertex: $(-6, 1)$; $y = 1$

7. Write an equation for a circle whose center has coordinates $\left(\dfrac{1}{2}, \dfrac{5}{2}\right)$ with radius equal to $\dfrac{1}{2}$. $\left(x - \dfrac{1}{2}\right)^2 + \left(y - \dfrac{5}{2}\right)^2 = \dfrac{1}{4}$

8. Write the equation for the circle centered at the origin and with radius equal to $\dfrac{1}{8}$. $x^2 + y^2 = \dfrac{1}{64}$

Concept 1: Standard Form of an Equation of an Ellipse

For Exercises 9–16, find the x- and y-intercepts and graph the ellipse. **(See Examples 1–2.)**

 9. $\dfrac{x^2}{4} + \dfrac{y^2}{9} = 1$

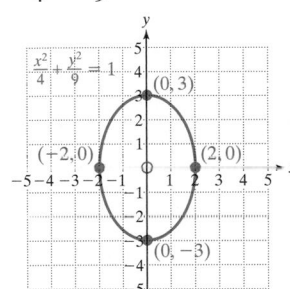

10. $\dfrac{x^2}{16} + \dfrac{y^2}{25} = 1$

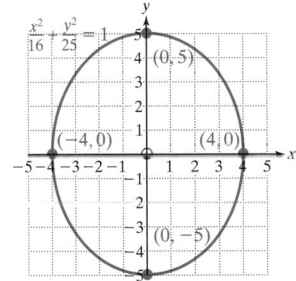

11. $\dfrac{x^2}{16} + \dfrac{y^2}{9} = 1$

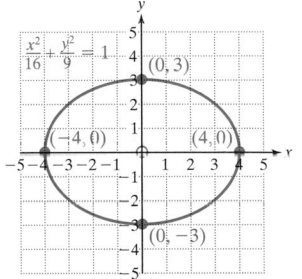

12. $\dfrac{x^2}{36} + \dfrac{y^2}{4} = 1$

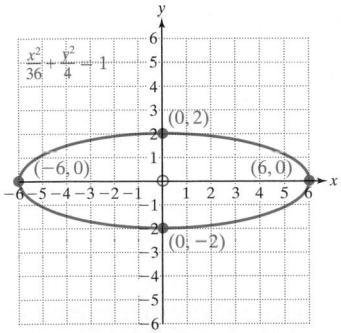

13. $4x^2 + y^2 = 4$

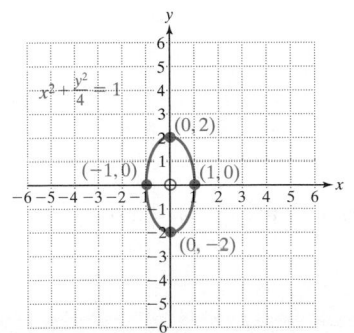

14. $9x^2 + y^2 = 36$

15. $x^2 + 25y^2 - 25 = 0$

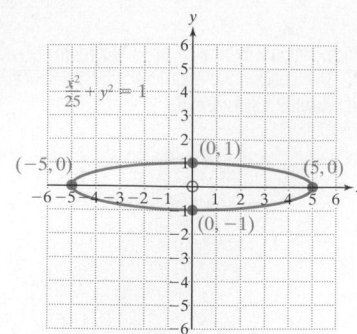

16. $4x^2 + 9y^2 = 144$

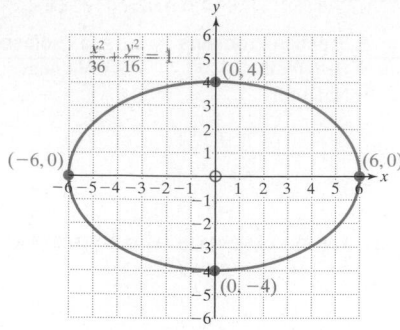

For Exercises 17–24, identify the center (h, k) of the ellipse. Then graph the ellipse. **(See Example 3.)**

17. $\dfrac{(x-4)^2}{4} + \dfrac{(y-5)^2}{9} = 1$

Center: $(4, 5)$

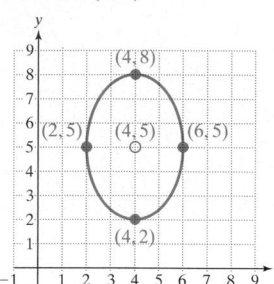

18. $\dfrac{(x+2)^2}{9} + \dfrac{(y-1)^2}{16} = 1$

Center: $(-2, 1)$

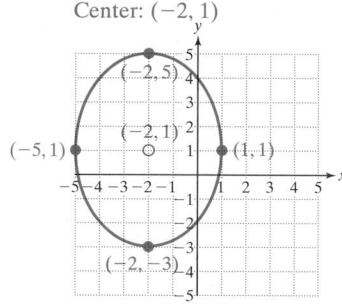

19. $\dfrac{(x+1)^2}{25} + \dfrac{(y-2)^2}{9} = 1$

Center: $(-1, 2)$

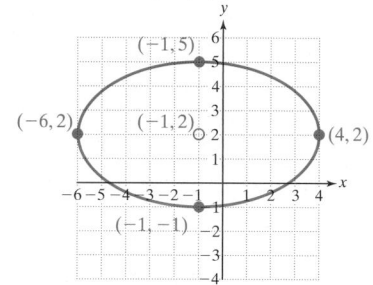

20. $\dfrac{(x-4)^2}{25} + \dfrac{(y+1)^2}{16} = 1$

Center: $(4, -1)$

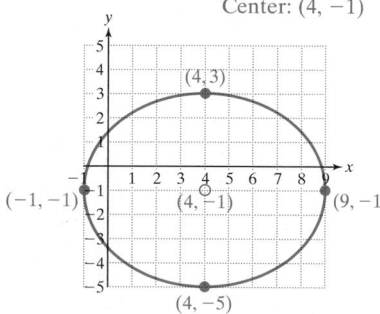

21. $\dfrac{(x-2)^2}{9} + (y+3)^2 = 1$

Center: $(2, -3)$

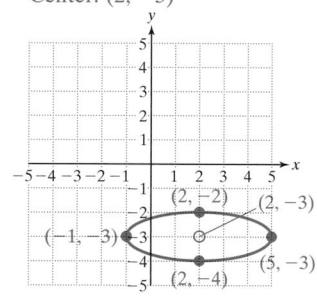

22. $(x-5)^2 + \dfrac{(y-3)^2}{4} = 1$

Center: $(5, 3)$

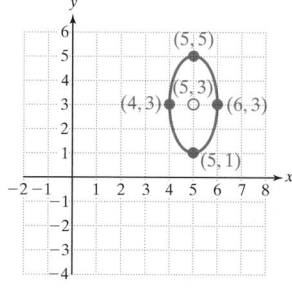

23. $\dfrac{x^2}{36} + \dfrac{(y-1)^2}{25} = 1$

Center: $(0, 1)$

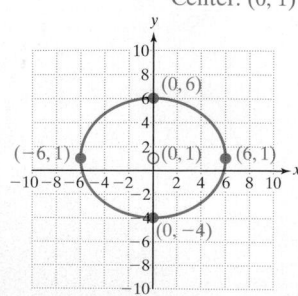

24. $\dfrac{(x+5)^2}{4} + \dfrac{y^2}{16} = 1$ Center: $(-5, 0)$

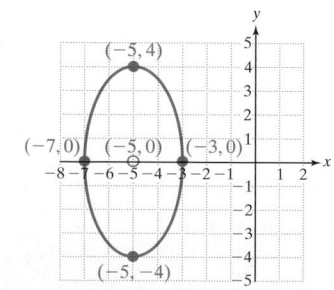

Animation

/ Writing ⟷ Translating Expression ◁ Geometry ▤ Scientific Calculator Video NS&E

Concept 2: Standard Form of an Equation of a Hyperbola

For Exercises 25–32, determine whether the transverse axis is horizontal or vertical.

25. $\dfrac{y^2}{6} - \dfrac{x^2}{18} = 1$
Vertical

26. $\dfrac{y^2}{10} - \dfrac{x^2}{4} = 1$
Vertical

27. $\dfrac{x^2}{20} - \dfrac{y^2}{15} = 1$
Horizontal

28. $\dfrac{x^2}{12} - \dfrac{y^2}{9} = 1$
Horizontal

 29. $x^2 - y^2 = 12$
Horizontal

30. $x^2 - y^2 = 15$
Horizontal

31. $x^2 - 3y^2 = -9$
Vertical

32. $2x^2 - y^2 = -10$
Vertical

For Exercises 33–40, use the equation in standard form to graph the hyperbola. Label the vertices of the hyperbola.
(See Examples 4–5.)

33. $\dfrac{x^2}{25} - \dfrac{y^2}{16} = 1$

34. $\dfrac{x^2}{9} - \dfrac{y^2}{36} = 1$

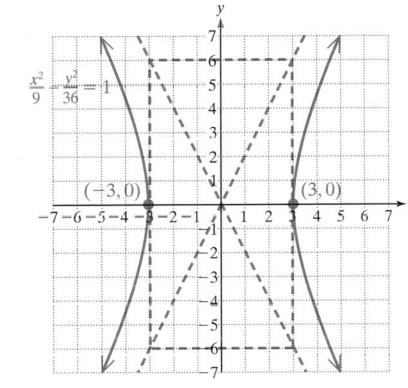

35. $\dfrac{y^2}{4} - \dfrac{x^2}{4} = 1$

36. $\dfrac{y^2}{9} - \dfrac{x^2}{9} = 1$

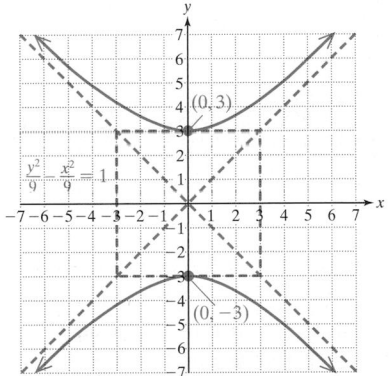

37. $36x^2 - y^2 = 36$

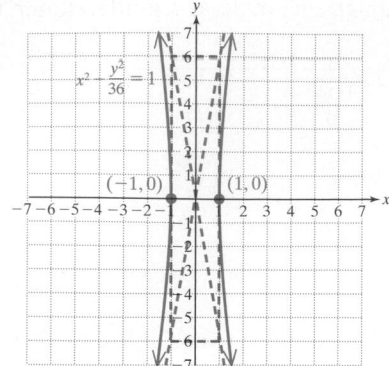

38. $x^2 - 25y^2 = 25$

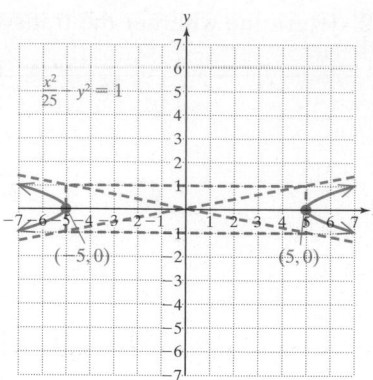

39. $y^2 - 4x^2 - 16 = 0$

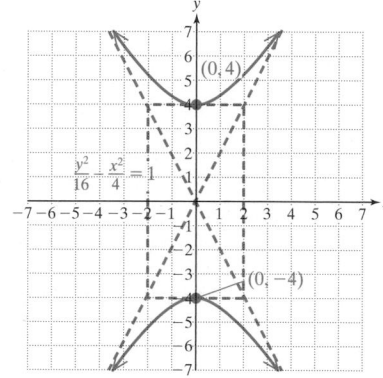

40. $y^2 - 4x^2 - 36 = 0$

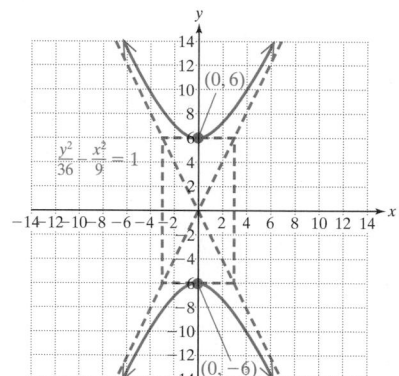

Mixed Exercises

For Exercises 41–52, determine if the equation represents an ellipse or a hyperbola.

41. $\dfrac{x^2}{6} - \dfrac{y^2}{10} = 1$
Hyperbola

42. $\dfrac{x^2}{14} + \dfrac{y^2}{2} = 1$
Ellipse

43. $\dfrac{y^2}{4} + \dfrac{x^2}{16} = 1$
Ellipse

44. $\dfrac{x^2}{5} + \dfrac{y^2}{10} = 1$
Ellipse

45. $4x^2 + y^2 = 16$
Ellipse

46. $-3x^2 - 4y^2 = -36$
Ellipse

47. $-y^2 + 2x^2 = -10$
Hyperbola

48. $x^2 - y^2 = -1$
Hyperbola

49. $5x^2 + y^2 - 10 = 0$
Ellipse

50. $5x^2 - 3y^2 = 15$
Hyperbola

51. $y^2 - 6x^2 = 6$
Hyperbola

52. $3x^2 + 5y^2 = 15$
Ellipse

Expanding Your Skills

53. An arch for a tunnel is in the shape of a semiellipse. The distance between vertices is 120 ft, and the height to the top of the arch is 50 ft. Find the height of the arch 10 ft from the center. Round to the nearest foot.
The height 10 ft from the center is approximately 49 ft.

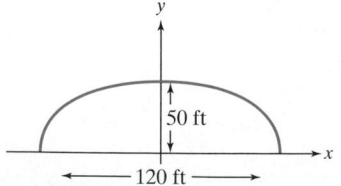

54. A bridge over a gorge is supported by an arch in the shape of a semiellipse. The length of the bridge is 400 ft, and the height is 100 ft. Find height of the arch 50 ft from the center. Round to the nearest foot.
The height 50 ft from the center is approximately 97 ft.

In Exercises 55–58, graph the hyperbola centered at (h, k) by following these guidelines. First locate the center. Then draw the reference rectangle relative to the center (h, k). Using the reference rectangle as a guide, sketch the hyperbola. Label the center and vertices.

55. $\dfrac{(x-1)^2}{9} - \dfrac{(y+2)^2}{4} = 1$

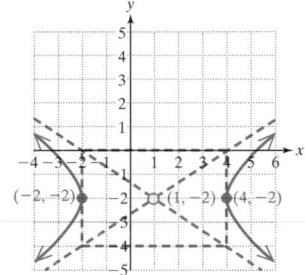

56. $\dfrac{(x+2)^2}{16} - \dfrac{(y-3)^2}{4} = 1$

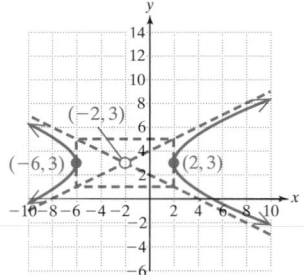

57. $\dfrac{(y-1)^2}{4} - (x+3)^2 = 1$

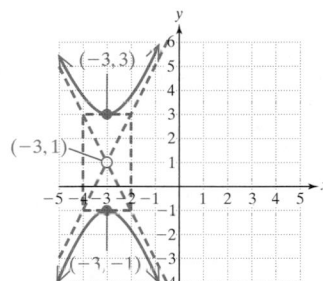

58. $(y+2)^2 - \dfrac{(x+3)^2}{4} = 1$

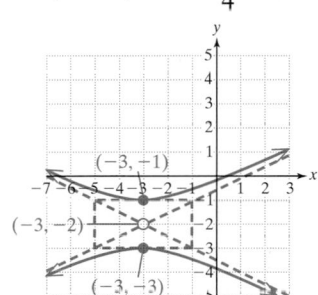

Problem Recognition Exercises

Formulas and Conic Sections

For Exercises 1–8, identify the formula.

1. $(x-h)^2 + (y-k)^2 = r^2$
Standard equation
of a circle

2. $\dfrac{x^2}{a^2} + \dfrac{y^2}{b^2} = 1$
Ellipse centered at
the origin

3. $\sqrt{(x_2 - x_1)^2 + (y_2 - y_1)^2}$
Distance between
two points

4. $\left(\dfrac{x_1 + x_2}{2}, \dfrac{y_1 + y_2}{2}\right)$
Midpoint between two points

5. $y = a(x - h)^2 + k$
Parabola with vertical axis
of symmetry

6. $\dfrac{x^2}{a^2} - \dfrac{y^2}{b^2} = 1$
Hyperbola with horizontal
transverse axis

7. $\dfrac{y^2}{b^2} - \dfrac{x^2}{a^2} = 1$
Hyperbola with vertical
transverse axis

8. $x = a(y - k)^2 + h$
Parabola with horizontal
axis of symmetry

For Exercises 9–28, identify the equation as representing a circle, parabola, ellipse, or hyperbola.

9. $y = -2(x - 3)^2 + 4$
Parabola

10. $y = \dfrac{1}{2}(x + 2)^2 - 3$
Parabola

11. $(x + 3)^2 + (y + 2)^2 = 4$
Circle

12. $(x - 2)^2 + (y - 4)^2 = 9$ Circle

13. $\dfrac{x^2}{9} - \dfrac{y^2}{9} = 1$ Hyperbola

14. $\dfrac{x^2}{4} - \dfrac{y^2}{1} = 1$ Hyperbola

15. $x^2 + y^2 - 2x + 4y - 4 = 0$
Circle

16. $x^2 + y^2 + 6x + 8 = 0$
Circle

17. $x = (y + 2)^2 - 4$
Parabola

 Writing   Translating Expression   Geometry   Scientific Calculator   Video NS&E

18. $x = -(y - 2)^2 - 1$
Parabola

19. $\dfrac{x^2}{9} + \dfrac{y^2}{16} = 1$
Ellipse

20. $\dfrac{x^2}{25} + \dfrac{y^2}{4} = 1$
Ellipse

21. $x^2 + y^2 = 15$
Circle

22. $\dfrac{x^2}{4} - \dfrac{y^2}{2} = 1$
Hyperbola

23. $y = (x - 6)^2 + 4$
Parabola

24. $\dfrac{(x + 1)^2}{2} + \dfrac{(y + 1)^2}{5} = 1$
Ellipse

25. $\dfrac{y^2}{3} - \dfrac{x^2}{3} = 1$
Hyperbola

26. $3x^2 + 3y^2 = 1$
Circle

27. $\dfrac{x^2}{9} + \dfrac{y^2}{12} = 1$ Ellipse

28. $x = (y + 2)^2 - 5$ Parabola

Section 13.4   Nonlinear Systems of Equations in Two Variables

Concepts

1. Solving Nonlinear Systems of Equations by the Substitution Method
2. Solving Nonlinear Systems of Equations by the Addition Method

1. Solving Nonlinear Systems of Equations by the Substitution Method

Recall that a linear equation in two variables x and y is an equation that can be written in the form $Ax + By = C$, where A and B are not both zero. In Sections 4.1–4.3, we solved systems of linear equations in two variables by using the graphing method, the substitution method, and the addition method. In this section, we will solve *nonlinear* systems of equations by using the same methods. A **nonlinear system of equations** is a system in which at least one of the equations is nonlinear.

Graphing the equations in a nonlinear system helps to determine the number of solutions and to approximate the coordinates of the solutions. The substitution method is used most often to solve a nonlinear system of equations analytically.

Classroom Example: p. 959, Exercise 18

Example 1   Solving a Nonlinear System of Equations

Given the system
$$x - 7y = -25$$
$$x^2 + y^2 = 25$$

a. Solve the system by graphing.

b. Solve the system by the substitution method.

Solution:

a. $x - 7y = -25$ is a line (the slope-intercept form is $y = \frac{1}{7}x + \frac{25}{7}$).

$x^2 + y^2 = 25$ is a circle centered at the origin with radius 5.

From Figure 13-16, we appear to have two solutions $(-4, 3)$ and $(3, 4)$.

Figure 13-16

b. To use the substitution method, isolate one of the variables from one of the equations. We will solve for x in the first equation.

$\boxed{A}$ $\qquad x - 7y = -25 \xrightarrow{\text{Solve for } x.} x = 7y - 25$

$\boxed{B}$ $\qquad x^2 + y^2 = 25$

$\boxed{B}$ $(7y - 25)^2 + y^2 = 25$ $\qquad$ Substitute $(7y - 25)$ for x in the second equation.

$49y^2 - 350y + 625 + y^2 = 25$ $\qquad$ The resulting equation is quadratic in y.

$50y^2 - 350y + 600 = 0$ $\qquad$ Set the equation equal to zero.

$50(y^2 - 7y + 12) = 0$ $\qquad$ Factor.

$50(y - 3)(y - 4) = 0$

$y = 3 \quad$ or $\quad y = 4$

For each value of y, find the corresponding x value from the equation $x = 7y - 25$.

$y = 3$: $\quad x = 7(3) - 25 = -4$ $\qquad$ The solution point is $(-4, 3)$.

$y = 4$: $\quad x = 7(4) - 25 = 3$ $\qquad$ The solution point is $(3, 4)$.
$\qquad\qquad\qquad\qquad\qquad\qquad\qquad$ (See Figure 13-16.)

The solution set is $\{(-4, 3), (3, 4)\}$.

Skill Practice Given the system

$$2x + y = 5$$
$$x^2 + y^2 = 50$$

1. Solve the system by graphing.

2. Solve the system by the substitution method.

Example 2 **Solving a Nonlinear System by the Substitution Method**

Classroom Example: p. 960, Exercise 24

Given the system $\qquad y = \sqrt{x}$
$\qquad\qquad\qquad\quad x^2 + y^2 = 20$

a. Sketch the graphs.

b. Solve the system by the substitution method.

Solution:

a. $\quad y = \sqrt{x} \qquad$ is one of the six basic functions graphed in Section 2.7.

$x^2 + y^2 = 20 \qquad$ is a circle centered at the origin with radius $\sqrt{20} \approx 4.5$.

From Figure 13-17, we see that there is one solution.

Figure 13-17

Answers

1.

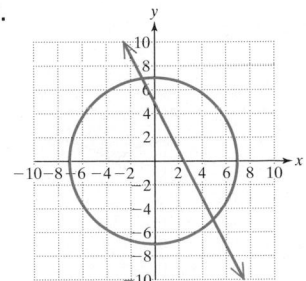

The solutions appear to be $(-1, 7)$ and $(5, -5)$.

2. $\{(-1, 7), (5, -5)\}$

b. To use the substitution method, we will substitute $y = \sqrt{x}$ into equation $\boxed{B}$.

$\boxed{A}$ $y = \sqrt{x}$

$\boxed{B}$ $x^2 + y^2 = 20$

$\boxed{B}$ $x^2 + (\sqrt{x})^2 = 20$ Substitute $y = \sqrt{x}$ into the second equation.

         $x^2 + x = 20$

       $x^2 + x - 20 = 0$ Set the second equation equal to zero.

     $(x + 5)(x - 4) = 0$ Factor.

$x \cancel{=} -5$ or $x = 4$ Reject $x = -5$ because it is not in the domain of $y = \sqrt{x}$.

Substitute $x = 4$ into the equation $y = \sqrt{x}$.

If $x = 4$, then $y = \sqrt{4} = 2$.   The solution set is $\{(4, 2)\}$.

Skill Practice   Given the system

$$y = \sqrt{2x}$$
$$x^2 + y^2 = 8$$

3. Sketch the graphs.

4. Solve the system by using the substitution method.

Calculator Connections

Graph the equations from Example 2 to confirm your solution to the system of equations. Use an *Intersect* feature to approximate the point of intersection. Recall that the circle must be entered into the calculator as two functions:

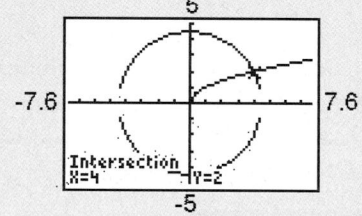

$$Y_1 = \sqrt{20 - x^2}$$
$$Y_2 = -\sqrt{20 - x^2}$$
$$Y_3 = \sqrt{x}$$

Classroom Example: p. 960, Exercise 26

Answers

3.

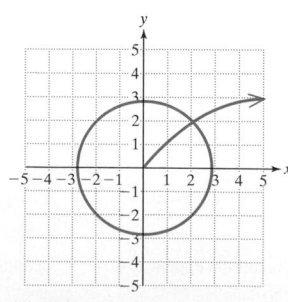

4. $\{(2, 2)\}$

Example 3   Solving a Nonlinear System by the Substitution Method

Solve the system by using the substitution method. $y = \sqrt[3]{x}$

                                        $y = x$

Solution:

$\boxed{A}$ $y = \sqrt[3]{x}$

$\boxed{B}$ $y = x$

     $\sqrt[3]{x} = x$ Because y is isolated in both equations, we can equate the expressions for y.

   $(\sqrt[3]{x})^3 = (x)^3$ To solve the radical equation, raise both sides to the third power.

$x = x^3$	This is a third-degree polynomial equation.
$0 = x^3 - x$	Set the equation equal to zero.
$0 = x(x^2 - 1)$	Factor out the GCF.
$0 = x(x + 1)(x - 1)$	Factor completely.

$$x = 0 \quad \text{or} \quad x = -1 \quad \text{or} \quad x = 1$$

For each value of x, find the corresponding y-value from either original equation. We will use equation $\boxed{B}$: $y = x$.

If $x = 0$, then $y = 0$.   The solution point is $(0, 0)$.

If $x = -1$, then $y = -1$.   The solution point is $(-1, -1)$.

If $x = 1$, then $y = 1$.   The solution point is $(1, 1)$.

The solution set is $\{(0, 0), (-1, -1), (1, 1)\}$.

Skill Practice Solve the system by using the substitution method.

5. $y = \sqrt[3]{9x}$
    $y = x$

2. Solving Nonlinear Systems of Equations by the Addition Method

The substitution method is used most often to solve a system of nonlinear equations. In some situations, however, the addition method offers an efficient means of finding a solution. Example 4 demonstrates that we can eliminate a variable from both equations provided the terms containing the corresponding variables are *like* terms.

Example 4   Solving a Nonlinear System of Equations by the Addition Method

Classroom Example: p. 960, Exercise 34

Solve the system. $2x^2 + y^2 = 17$
                $x^2 + 2y^2 = 22$

Solution:

$\boxed{A}$ $2x^2 + y^2 = 17$ Notice that the y^2 terms are *like* in each equation.

$\boxed{B}$ $x^2 + 2y^2 = 22$ To eliminate the y^2 terms, multiply the first equation by -2.

$\boxed{A}$ $2x^2 + y^2 = 17$ $\xrightarrow{\text{Multiply by } -2.}$ $-4x^2 - 2y^2 = -34$

$\boxed{B}$ $x^2 + 2y^2 = 22$ $\xrightarrow{}$ $\underline{x^2 + 2y^2 = 22}$

$ -3x^2 = -12$ Eliminate the y^2 term.

$$\frac{-3x^2}{-3} = \frac{-12}{-3}$$

$$x^2 = 4$$

$$x = \pm 2$$

TIP: In Example 4, the x^2 terms are also *like* in both equations. We could have eliminated the x^2 terms by multiplying equation $\boxed{B}$ by -2.

Answer

5. $\{(0, 0), (3, 3), (-3, -3)\}$

Substitute each value of x into one of the original equations to solve for y. We will use equation $\boxed{A}$: $2x^2 + y^2 = 17$.

$x = 2$: $\boxed{A}$ $\quad 2(2)^2 + y^2 = 17$

$$8 + y^2 = 17$$

$$y^2 = 9$$

$$y = \pm 3 \quad \text{The solution points are } (2, 3) \text{ and } (2, -3).$$

$x = -2$: $\boxed{A}$ $\quad 2(-2)^2 + y^2 = 17$

$$8 + y^2 = 17$$

$$y^2 = 9$$

$$y = \pm 3 \quad \text{The solution points are } (-2, 3) \text{ and } (-2, -3).$$

The solution set is $\{(2, 3), (2, -3), (-2, 3), (-2, -3)\}$.

> **TIP:** When equations are difficult to graph, the solutions to a system can be checked by substituting the ordered pairs into both equations.

Skill Practice Solve the system by using the addition method.

6. $x^2 - y^2 = 24$
$\quad 3x^2 + y^2 = 76$

> **TIP:** It is important to note that the addition method can be used only if two equations share a pair of *like* terms. The substitution method is effective in solving a wider range of systems of equations. The system in Example 4 could also have been solved by using substitution.
>
> $\boxed{A} \qquad 2x^2 + y^2 = 17 \xrightarrow{\text{Solve for } y^2.} y^2 = 17 - 2x^2$
>
> $\boxed{B} \qquad x^2 + 2y^2 = 22$
>
> $\boxed{B} \quad x^2 + 2(17 - 2x^2) = 22 \qquad\qquad x = 2: \quad y^2 = 17 - 2(2)^2$
>
> $\qquad\quad x^2 + 34 - 4x^2 = 22 \qquad\qquad\qquad\qquad\quad y^2 = 9$
>
> $\qquad\qquad\qquad -3x^2 = -12 \qquad\qquad\qquad\qquad\quad y = \pm 3 \quad \text{The solutions are}$
> $\qquad\qquad\qquad\qquad\qquad\qquad\qquad\qquad\qquad\qquad\qquad\qquad\qquad (2, 3) \text{ and } (2, -3).$
>
> $\qquad\qquad\qquad\quad x^2 = 4$
>
> $\qquad\qquad\qquad\quad x = \pm 2 \longrightarrow x = -2: \quad y^2 = 17 - 2(-2)^2$
>
> $\qquad\qquad\qquad\qquad\qquad\qquad\qquad\qquad\qquad\qquad y^2 = 9$
>
> $\qquad\qquad\qquad\qquad\qquad\qquad\qquad\qquad\qquad\qquad y = \pm 3 \quad \text{The solutions are}$
> $\qquad\qquad\qquad\qquad\qquad\qquad\qquad\qquad\qquad\qquad\qquad\qquad\qquad (-2, 3) \text{ and } (-2, -3).$

Answer

6. $\{(5, 1), (5, -1), (-5, 1), (-5, -1)\}$

Section 13.4 Practice Exercises

Study Skills Exercise

1. Define the key term **nonlinear system of equations**.

 Writing $\quad$ Translating Expression $\quad$ Geometry $\quad$ Scientific Calculator $\quad$ Video $\quad$ NS&E

Review Exercises

2. Write the distance formula between two points (x_1, y_1) and (x_2, y_2) from memory. $d = \sqrt{(x_2 - x_1)^2 + (y_2 - y_1)^2}$

3. Find the distance between the two points $(8, -1)$ and $(1, -8)$. $7\sqrt{2}$

4. Write an equation representing the set of all points 2 units from the point $(-1, 1)$. $(x + 1)^2 + (y - 1)^2 = 4$

5. Write an equation representing the set of all points 8 units from the point $(-5, 3)$. $(x + 5)^2 + (y - 3)^2 = 64$

6. Write the formula for the midpoint between the points (x_1, y_1) and (x_2, y_2). $\left(\dfrac{x_1 + x_2}{2}, \dfrac{y_1 + y_2}{2}\right)$

7. Find the midpoint of the segment with the endpoints $(3, -9)$ and $(-4, 2)$. $\left(-\dfrac{1}{2}, -\dfrac{7}{2}\right)$

8. Find the midpoint of the segment with the endpoints $(2.4, 1.8)$ and $(-1.6, -5.2)$. $(0.4, -1.7)$

Concept 1: Solving Nonlinear Systems of Equations by the Substitution Method

For Exercises 9–16, use sketches to explain.

9. How many points of intersection are possible between a line and a parabola?   Zero, one, or two

10. How many points of intersection are possible between a line and a circle?   Zero, one, or two

 11. How many points of intersection are possible between two distinct circles?   Zero, one, or two

12. How many points of intersection are possible between two distinct parabolas of the form $y = ax^2 + bx + c$, $a \neq 0$?   Zero, one, or two

13. How many points of intersection are possible between a circle and a parabola?   Zero, one, two, three, or four

14. How many points of intersection are possible between two distinct lines?   Zero or one

15. How many points of intersection are possible with an ellipse and a hyperbola?   Zero, one, two, three, or four

16. How many points of intersection are possible with an ellipse and a parabola?   Zero, one, two, three, or four

For Exercises 17–22, sketch each system of equations. Then solve the system by the substitution method. **(See Example 1.)**

17. $y = x + 3$
    $x^2 + y = 9$ $\{(-3, 0), (2, 5)\}$

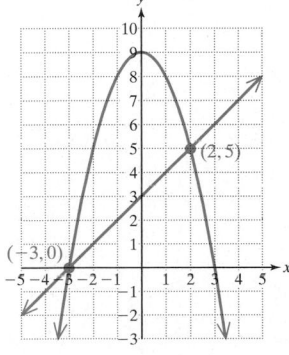

18. $y = x - 2$
    $x^2 + y = 4$ $\{(-3, -5), (2, 0)\}$

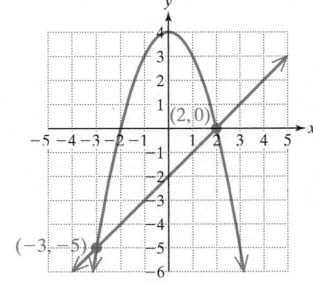

19. $x^2 + y^2 = 1$
    $y = x + 1$ $\{(0, 1), (-1, 0)\}$

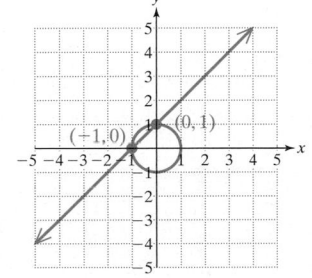

20. $x^2 + y^2 = 25$

$y = 2x$ $\{(\sqrt{5}, 2\sqrt{5}),$
$(\ -\sqrt{5},\ -2\sqrt{5})\}$

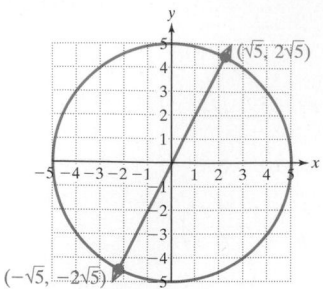

21. $x^2 + y^2 = 6$

$y = x^2$ $\{(\sqrt{2}, 2), (-\sqrt{2}, 2)\}$

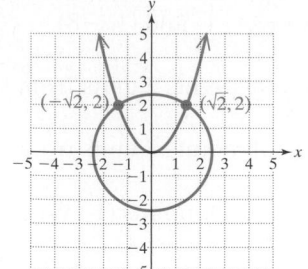

22. $x^2 + y^2 = 12$

$y = x^2$ $\{(\sqrt{3}, 3), (-\sqrt{3}, 3)\}$

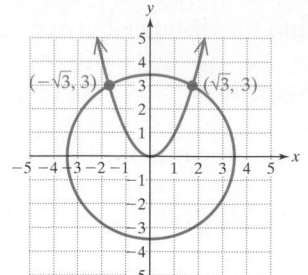

For Exercises 23–31, solve the system by the substitution method. **(See Examples 2–3.)**

23. $x^2 + y^2 = 20$

     $y = \sqrt{x}$ $\{(4, 2)\}$

24. $x^2 + y^2 = 30$

     $y = \sqrt{x}$ $\{(5, \sqrt{5})\}$

25. $y = x^2$

     $y = -\sqrt{x}$ $\{(0, 0)\}$

26. $y = -x^2$

     $y = -\sqrt{x}$ $\{(0, 0), (1, -1)\}$

27. $y = x^2$

     $y = (x - 3)^2$ $\left\{\left(\dfrac{3}{2}, \dfrac{9}{4}\right)\right\}$

28. $y = (x + 4)^2$

     $y = x^2$ $\{(-2, 4)\}$

29. $y = x^2 + 6x$

     $y = 4x$ $\{(0, 0), (-2, -8)\}$

30. $y = 3x^2 - 6x$

     $y = 3x$ $\{(0, 0), (3, 9)\}$

31. $x^2 - 5x + y = 0$

     $y = 3x + 1$ $\{(1, 4)\}$

Concept 2: Solving Nonlinear Systems of Equations by the Addition Method

For Exercises 32–48, solve the system of nonlinear equations by the addition method if appropriate. **(See Example 4.)**

32. $x^2 + y^2 = 13$

     $x^2 - y^2 = 5$
$\{(3, 2), (3, -2), (-3, 2), (-3, -2)\}$

33. $4x^2 - y^2 = 4$

     $4x^2 + y^2 = 4$ $\{(1, 0), (-1, 0)\}$

34. $9x^2 + 4y^2 = 36$

     $x^2 + y^2 = 9$ $\{(0, 3), (0, -3)\}$

35. $x^2 + y^2 = 4$

     $2x^2 + y^2 = 8$ $\{(2, 0), (-2, 0)\}$

36. $3x^2 + 4y^2 = 16$

     $2x^2 - 3y^2 = 5$
$\{(2, 1), (-2, 1), (2, -1), (-2, -1)\}$

37. $2x^2 - 5y^2 = -2$

     $3x^2 + 2y^2 = 35$
$\{(3, 2), (-3, 2), (3, -2), (-3, -2)\}$

38. $x^2 + y^2 = 169$

     $12x - 5y = 0$ $\{(5, 12), (-5, -12)\}$

39. $x^2 + y^2 = 100$

     $4y - 3x = 0$ $\{(8, 6), (-8, -6)\}$

40. $\dfrac{x^2}{4} + \dfrac{y^2}{9} = 1$

     $x^2 + y^2 = 4$ $\{(2, 0), (-2, 0)\}$

41. $\dfrac{x^2}{16} + \dfrac{y^2}{4} = 1$

     $x^2 + y^2 = 4$ $\{(0, -2), (0, 2)\}$

42. $\dfrac{x^2}{10} + \dfrac{y^2}{10} = 1$

     $2x^2 + y^2 = 11$
$\{(1, 3), (1, -3), (-1, 3), (-1, -3)\}$

43. $2y = -x + 2$

     $x^2 + 4y^2 = 4$ $\{(2, 0), (0, 1)\}$

44. $2y = -3x - 6$

     $9x^2 + 4y^2 = 36$ $\{(-2, 0), (0, -3)\}$

45. $x^2 - xy = -4$

     $2x^2 - xy = 12$ $\{(4, 5), (-4, -5)\}$

46. $x^2 - xy = 3$

     $2x^2 + xy = 6$ $\{(\sqrt{3}, 0), (-\sqrt{3}, 0)\}$

47. $3x^2 + 2xy = 4$

     $x^2 - xy = 3$

     $\left\{\left(-\sqrt{2}, \dfrac{\sqrt{2}}{2}\right), \left(\sqrt{2}, -\dfrac{\sqrt{2}}{2}\right)\right\}$

48. $x^2 - 3xy = 8$

     $x^2 + xy = 4$ $\left\{\left(-\sqrt{5}, \dfrac{\sqrt{5}}{5}\right), \left(\sqrt{5}, -\dfrac{\sqrt{5}}{5}\right)\right\}$

Expanding Your Skills

49. The sum of two numbers is 7. The sum of the squares of the numbers is 25. Find the numbers.
3 and 4

50. The sum of the squares of two numbers is 100. The sum of the numbers is 2. Find the numbers.
−6 and 8

51. The sum of the squares of two numbers is 32. The difference of the squares of the numbers is 18. Find the numbers.   5 and $\sqrt{7}$, −5 and $\sqrt{7}$, 5 and $-\sqrt{7}$, or −5 and $-\sqrt{7}$

52. The sum of the squares of two numbers is 24. The difference of the squares of the numbers is 8. Find the numbers.   4 and $2\sqrt{2}$, −4 and $2\sqrt{2}$, 4 and $-2\sqrt{2}$, or −4 and $-2\sqrt{2}$

Graphing Calculator Exercises

For Exercises 53–56, use the *Intersect* feature to approximate the solutions to the system.

53. $y = x + 3$ (Exercise 17)

$x^2 + y = 9$

54. $y = x - 2$ (Exercise 18)

$x^2 + y = 4$

55. $y = x^2$ (Exercise 25)

$y = -\sqrt{x}$

56. $y = -x^2$ (Exercise 26)

$y = -\sqrt{x}$

For Exercises 57–58, graph the system on a square viewing window. What can be said about the solution to the system?

57. $x^2 + y^2 = 4$

$y = x^2 + 3$ { }

58. $x^2 + y^2 = 16$

$y = -x^2 - 5$ { }

Nonlinear Inequalities and Systems of Inequalities

Section 13.5

1. Nonlinear Inequalities in Two Variables

In Section 9.5 we graphed the solution sets to linear inequalities in two variables, such as $y \leq 2x + 1$. This involved graphing the related equation (a line in the xy-plane) and then shading the appropriate region above or below the line. See Figure 13-18. In this section, we will employ the same technique to solve nonlinear inequalities in two variables.

Concepts

1. Nonlinear Inequalities in Two Variables
2. Systems of Nonlinear Inequalities in Two Variables

Figure 13-18

 Writing   Translating Expression   Geometry   Scientific Calculator   Video NS&E

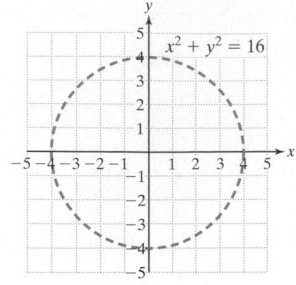

Figure 13-19

Example 1 Graphing a Nonlinear Inequality in Two Variables

Graph the solution set of the inequality $x^2 + y^2 < 16$.

Solution:

The related equation $x^2 + y^2 = 16$ is a circle of radius 4, centered at the origin. Graph the related equation by using a dashed curve because the points satisfying the equation $x^2 + y^2 = 16$ are not part of the solution to the strict inequality $x^2 + y^2 < 16$. See Figure 13-19.

Notice that the dashed curve separates the xy-plane into two regions, one "inside" the circle, the other "outside" the circle. Select a test point from each region and test the point in the original inequality.

Test Point "Inside": (0, 0)	**Test Point "Outside": (4, 4)**
$x^2 + y^2 < 16$	$x^2 + y^2 < 16$
$(0)^2 + (0)^2 \overset{?}{<} 16$	$(4)^2 + (4)^2 \overset{?}{<} 16$
$0 \overset{?}{<} 16$ True	$32 \overset{?}{<} 16$ False

The inequality $x^2 + y^2 < 16$ is true at the test point $(0, 0)$. Therefore, the solution set is the region "inside" the circle. See Figure 13-20.

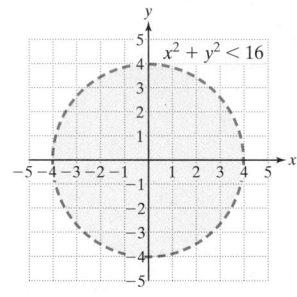

Figure 13-20

Skill Practice

1. Graph the solution set of the inequality $x^2 + y^2 \geq 9$.

Example 2 Graphing a Nonlinear Inequality in Two Variables

Graph the solution set of the inequality $9y^2 \geq 36 + 4x^2$.

Solution:

First graph the related equation $9y^2 = 36 + 4x^2$. Notice that the equation can be written in the standard form of a hyperbola.

$$9y^2 = 36 + 4x^2$$

$$9y^2 - 4x^2 = 36 \qquad \text{Subtract } 4x^2 \text{ from both sides.}$$

$$\frac{9y^2}{36} - \frac{4x^2}{36} = \frac{36}{36} \qquad \text{Divide both sides by 36.}$$

$$\frac{y^2}{4} - \frac{x^2}{9} = 1$$

Answer

1.

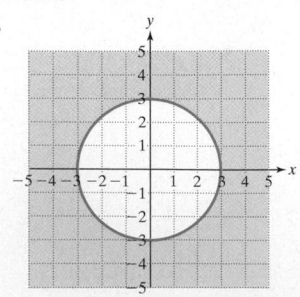

Graph the hyperbola as a solid curve, because the original inequality includes equality. See Figure 13-21.

The hyperbola divides the xy-plane into three regions: a region above the upper branch, a region between the branches, and a region below the lower branch. Select a test point from each region.

$$9y^2 \geq 36 + 4x^2$$

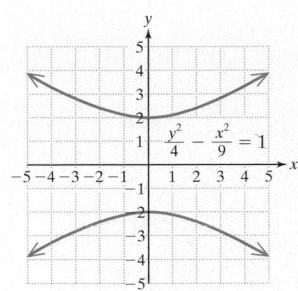

Figure 13-21

Test: (0, 3)	**Test: (0, 0)**	**Test: (0, −3)**
$9(3)^2 \overset{?}{\geq} 36 + 4(0)^2$	$9(0)^2 \overset{?}{\geq} 36 + 4(0)^2$	$9(-3)^2 \overset{?}{\geq} 36 + 4(0)^2$
$81 \overset{?}{\geq} 36$ True	$0 \overset{?}{\geq} 36$ False	$81 \overset{?}{\geq} 36$ True

Shade the regions above the top branch and below the bottom branch of the hyperbola. See Figure 13-22.

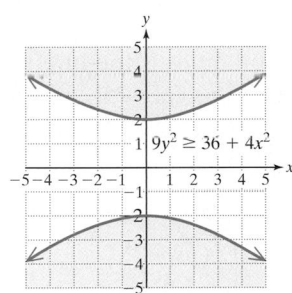

Figure 13-22

Skill Practice

2. Graph the solution set of the inequality $9x^2 < 144 - 16y^2$.

2. Systems of Nonlinear Inequalities in Two Variables

In Section 9.5 we solved systems of nonlinear equations in two variables. The solution set for such a system is the set of ordered pairs that satisfy both equations simultaneously. We will now solve systems of nonlinear inequalities in two variables. Similarly, the solution set is the set of all ordered pairs that simultaneously satisfy each inequality. To solve a system of inequalities, we will graph the solution to each individual inequality and then take the intersection of the solution sets.

Example 3 **Graphing a System of Nonlinear Inequalities in Two Variables**

Graph the solution set.

$$y > e^x$$
$$y < -x^2 + 4$$

Classroom Example: p. 968, Exercise 40

Answer

2.

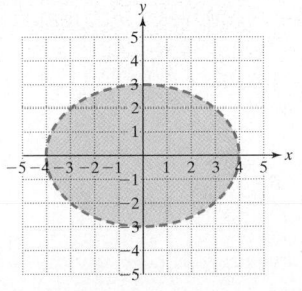

Solution:

The solution to $y > e^x$ is the set of points above the curve $y = e^x$. See Figure 13-23.
The solution to $y < -x^2 + 4$ is the set of points below the parabola $y = -x^2 + 4$.
See Figure 13-24.

Figure 13-23

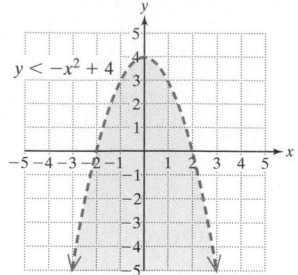

Figure 13-24

The solution to the system of inequalities is the intersection of the solution sets
of the individual inequalities. See Figure 13-25.

Figure 13-25

Answer

3.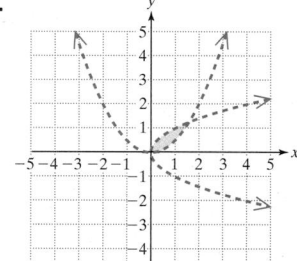

Skill Practice

3. Graph the solution set.

$$y > \frac{1}{2}x^2$$
$$x > y^2$$

Section 13.5 | Practice Exercises

Review Exercises

For Exercises 1–12, match the equation with its graph.

1. $y = \left(\frac{1}{3}\right)^x$ k

2. $y = 4x - 1$ g

3. $y = -4x^2$ e

4. $y = e^x$ h

5. $y = x^3$ i

6. $\dfrac{x^2}{4} + \dfrac{y^2}{9} = 1$ f

7. $\dfrac{x^2}{4} - \dfrac{y^2}{9} = 1$ j

8. $y = \dfrac{1}{x}$ c

 Writing   Translating Expression   Geometry   Scientific Calculator   Video   NS&E

9. $y = \log_2(x)$ a   **10.** $y = \sqrt{x}$ b   **11.** $(x + 2)^2 + (y - 1)^2 = 4$ d **12.** $x = -y^2$ l

a.

b.

c.

d.

e.

f.

g.

h.

i.

j.

k.

l.
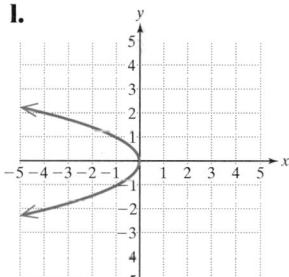

Concept 1: Nonlinear Inequalities in Two Variables

13. True or false? The point $(2, 3)$ satisfies the inequality $-x^2 + y^3 > 1$. True

14. True or false? The point $(4, -2)$ satisfies the inequality $4x^2 - 2x + 1 + y^2 < 3$. False

15. True or false? The point $(5, 4)$ satisfies the system of inequalities. False

$$\frac{x^2}{36} + \frac{y^2}{25} < 1$$

$$x^2 + y^2 \geq 4$$

16. True or false? The point $(1, -2)$ satisfies the system of inequalities. True

$$y < x^2$$

$$y > x^2 - 4$$

 Writing   Translating Expression Geometry Scientific Calculator Video   NS&E

17. a. Graph the solution set for $x^2 + y^2 \le 9$.

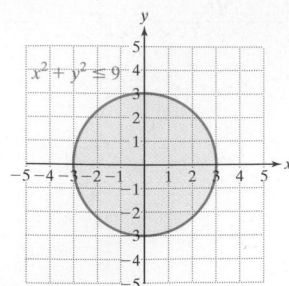

b. Describe the solution set for the inequality $x^2 + y^2 \ge 9$.
The set of points on and "outside" the circle $x^2 + y^2 = 9$

c. Describe the solution set for the equation $x^2 + y^2 = 9$
The set of points on the circle $x^2 + y^2 = 9$

18. a. Graph the solution set for $\dfrac{x^2}{4} + \dfrac{y^2}{9} \ge 1$.

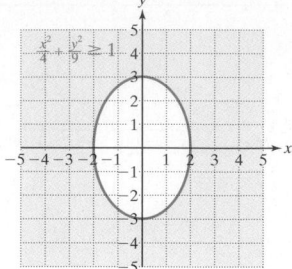

b. Describe the solution set for the inequality $\dfrac{x^2}{4} + \dfrac{y^2}{9} \le 1$. The set of points on and "inside" the ellipse $\dfrac{x^2}{4} + \dfrac{y^2}{9} = 1$

c. Describe the solution set for the equation $\dfrac{x^2}{4} + \dfrac{y^2}{9} = 1$ The set of points on the ellipse $\dfrac{x^2}{4} + \dfrac{y^2}{9} = 1$

19. a. Graph the solution set for $y \ge x^2 + 1$.

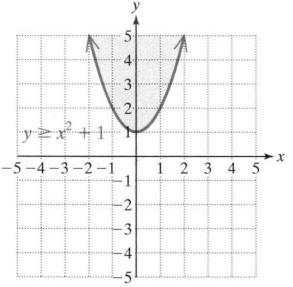

b. How would the solution change for the strict inequality $y > x^2 + 1$? The parabola $y = x^2 + 1$ would be drawn as a dashed curve.

20. a. Graph the solution set for $\dfrac{x^2}{4} - \dfrac{y^2}{9} \le 1$.

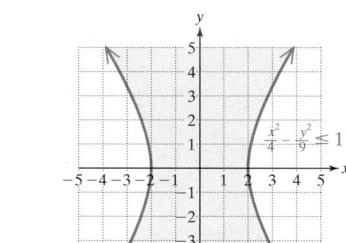

b. How would the solution change for the strict inequality $\dfrac{x^2}{4} - \dfrac{y^2}{9} < 1$? The hyperbola $\dfrac{x^2}{4} - \dfrac{y^2}{9} = 1$ would be drawn as a dashed curve.

21. A weak earthquake occurred in northern California roughly 4 mi south and 3 mi east of Sunol, California. The quake could be felt 25 mi away. Suppose the origin of a map is placed at the center of Sunol with the positive x-axis pointing east and the positive y-axis pointing north. Find an inequality that describes the points on the map for which the earthquake could be felt.
$(x - 3)^2 + (y + 4)^2 \le 625$

22. A coordinate system is placed at the center of a town with the positive x-axis pointing east, and the positive y-axis pointing north. A cell tower is located 2 mi west and 4 mi north of the center of town. If the tower has a 30-mi range, write an inequality that represents the points on the map serviced by this tower.
$(x + 2)^2 + (y - 4)^2 \le 900$

For Exercises 23–37, graph the solution set. **(See Examples 1–2.)**

23. $2x + y \geq 1$

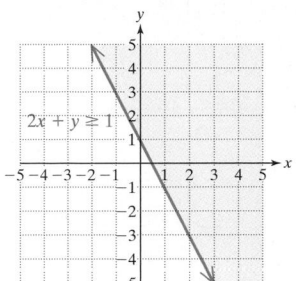

24. $3x + 2y \geq 6$

25. $x \leq y^2$

26. $y \leq -x^2$

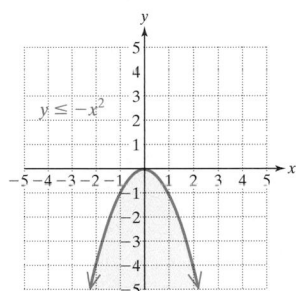

27. $(x - 1)^2 + (y + 2)^2 > 9$

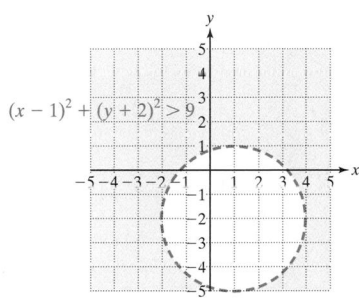

28. $(x + 1)^2 + (y - 4)^2 > 1$

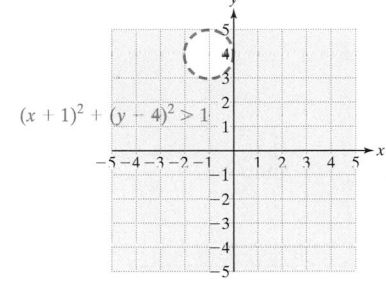

29. $x + y^2 \geq 4$

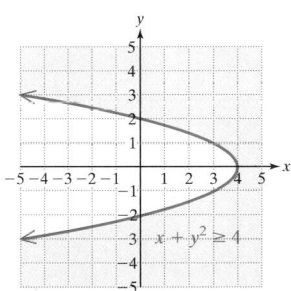

30. $x^2 + 2x + y - 1 \leq 0$

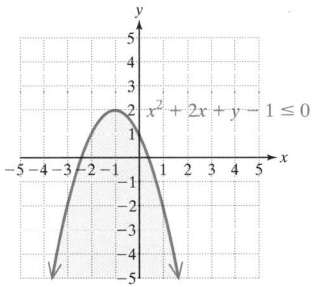

31. $9x^2 - y^2 > 9$

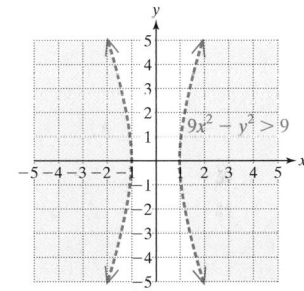

32. $y^2 - 4x^2 \leq 4$

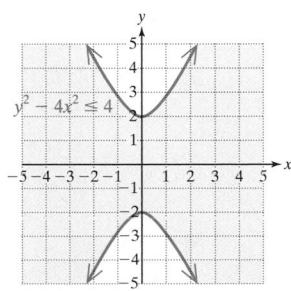

33. $x^2 + 16y^2 \leq 16$

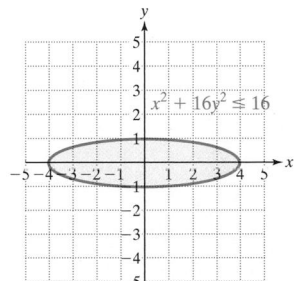

34. $4x^2 + y^2 \leq 4$

 Writing   ⟷ Translating Expression   ◢ Geometry   🖩 Scientific Calculator   ● Video   NS&E

35. $y \leq \ln x$

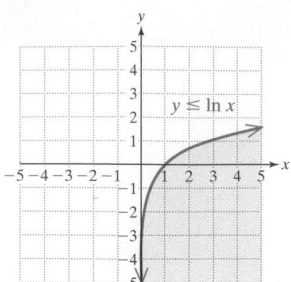

36. $y \leq \log x$

37. $y > 5^x$

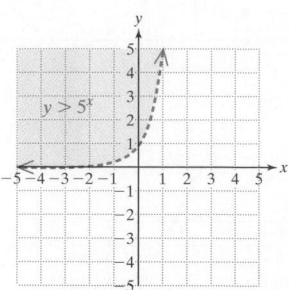

Concept 2: Systems of Nonlinear Inequalities in Two Variables

For Exercises 38–51, graph the solution set to the system of inequalities. **(See Example 3.)**

38. $y < \sqrt{x}$
$x > 1$

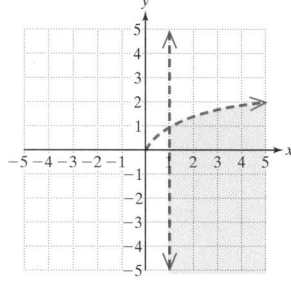

39. $y \geq \sqrt{x}$
$x \geq 0$

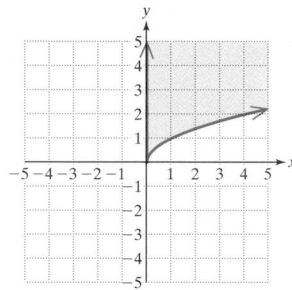

40. $\dfrac{x^2}{36} + \dfrac{y^2}{25} < 1$
$x^2 + y^2 \geq 4$

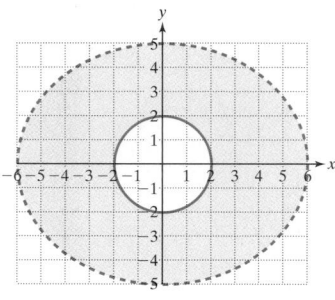

41. $x^2 - y^2 \geq 1$
$x \leq 0$

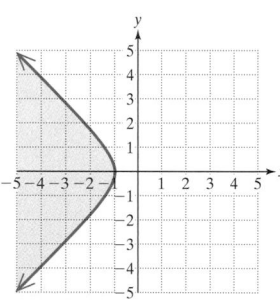

42. $y < x^2$
$y > x^2 - 4$

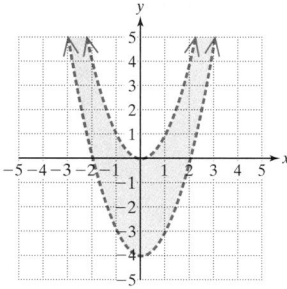

43. $y^2 - x^2 \geq 1$
$y \geq 0$

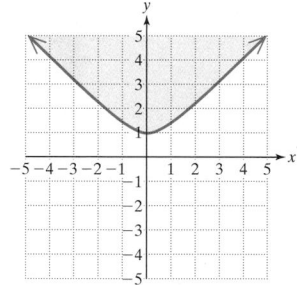

44. $y < \dfrac{1}{x}$
$y > 0$
$y < x$

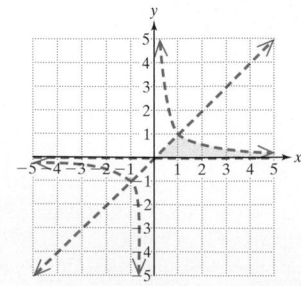

45. $y > x^3$
$y < 8$
$x > 0$

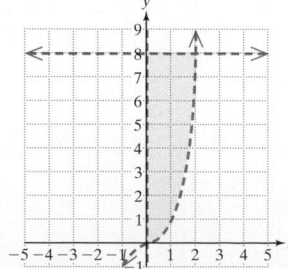

46. $x^2 + y^2 \geq 25$
$x^2 + y^2 \leq 9$
$\{\ \}$

 Writing   Translating Expression   Geometry   Scientific Calculator   Video   NS E

47. $\dfrac{x^2}{4} + \dfrac{y^2}{25} \geq 1$

$x^2 + \dfrac{y^2}{4} \leq 1$ { }

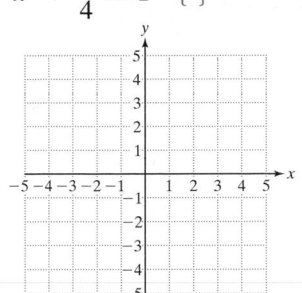

48. $x < -(y-1)^2 + 3$

$x + y > 2$

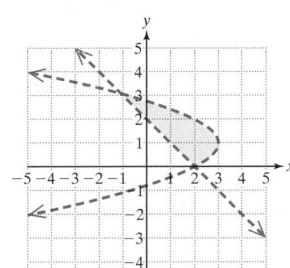

49. $x > (y-2)^2 + 1$

$x - y < 1$

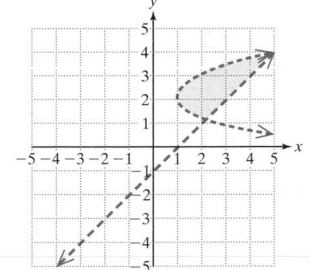

50. $x^2 + y^2 < 25$

$y < \dfrac{4}{3}x$

$y > -\dfrac{4}{3}x$

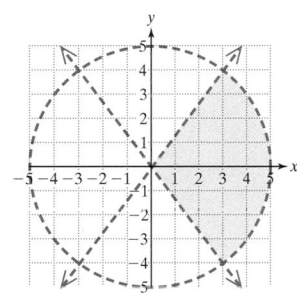

51. $y < e^x$

$y > 1$

$x < 2$

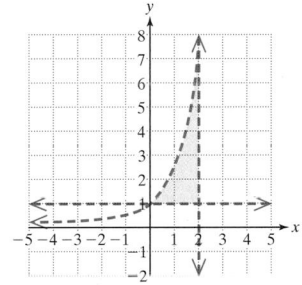

Expanding Your Skills

For Exercises 52–55, graph the compound inequalities.

52. $x^2 + y^2 \leq 36$ or $x + y \geq 0$

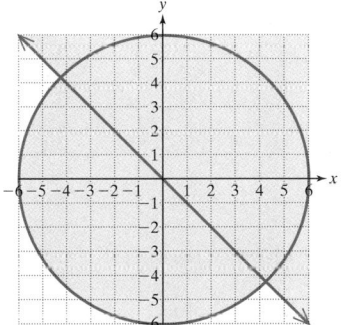

53. $y \leq -x^2 + 4$ or $y \geq x^2 - 4$

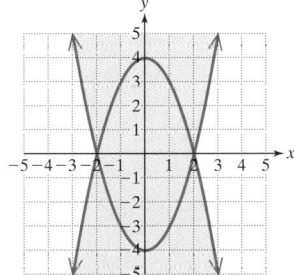

54. $y + 1 \geq x^2$ or $y + 1 \leq -x^2$

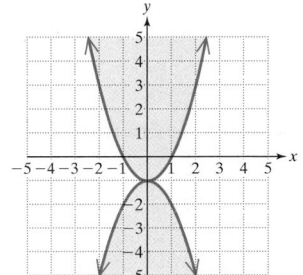

55. $(x+2)^2 + (y+3)^2 \leq 4$ or $x \geq y^2$

 Writing   Translating Expression   Geometry   Scientific Calculator   Video   NS&E

Group Activity

Investigating the Graphs of Conic Sections on a Calculator

Materials: Graphing Calculator

Estimated time: 15 minutes

Group Size: 3

1. a. Given $x^2 + y^2 = 25$, use analytical methods to determine the x- and y-intercepts.

    x-intercepts: $\underline{\quad (-5, 0), (5, 0) \quad}$ y-intercepts: $\underline{\quad (0, -5), (0, 5) \quad}$

b. Solve the equation for y: $x^2 + y^2 = 25$. (*Hint:* When taking the square root of both sides of the equation, don't forget the $\pm$.)

    $Y_1 = \underline{\quad Y_1 = \sqrt{25 - x^2} \quad}$

    $Y_2 = \underline{\quad Y_2 = -\sqrt{25 - x^2} \quad}$

c. Graph the two functions from part (b) on a graphing calculator. Use a window defined by $-7.6 \le x \le 7.6$ and $-5 \le y \le 5$.

d. Does it look like the functions graphed on the calculator intersect with the x-axis? Why do the x-intercepts not show up in the graph? If you relied solely on your calculator to find the x-intercepts, do you think that you would always get reliable results?   No, the calculator has limited resolution.

2. a. Given $(x + 1)^2 - \dfrac{y^2}{9} = 1$, use analytical methods to find the x- and y-intercepts.

    x-intercepts: $\underline{\quad (-2, 0), (0, 0) \quad}$ y-intercepts: $\underline{\quad (0, 0) \quad}$

b. Solve the equation for y. $(x + 1)^2 - \dfrac{y^2}{9} = 1$

    $Y_1 = \underline{\quad Y_1 = \sqrt{9(x + 1)^2 - 9} \quad}$

    $Y_2 = \underline{\quad Y_2 = -\sqrt{9(x + 1)^2 - 9} \quad}$

c. Graph the two functions from part (b) on a graphing calculator. Use a window defined by $-7.6 \le x \le 7.6$ and $-5 \le y \le 5$.

d. Does it look like the functions graphed on the calculator intersect with the x-axis? Why do the x-intercepts not show up in the graph? If you relied solely on your calculator to find the x-intercepts, do you think that you would always get reliable results?   No, the calculator has limited resolution.

3. Solve the equation for y and graph the functions on a graphing calculator. Use a window defined by $-7.6 \le x \le 7.6$ and $-5 \le y \le 5$.

    a. $\dfrac{x^2}{4} + \dfrac{y^2}{16} = 1$ $Y_1 = \underline{\quad Y_1 = \sqrt{16 - 4x^2} \quad}$

                           $Y_2 = \underline{\quad Y_2 = -\sqrt{16 - 4x^2} \quad}$

    b. What are the x-intercepts for the equation $\dfrac{x^2}{4} + \dfrac{y^2}{16} = 1$?

    x-intercepts: $\underline{\quad (-2, 0), (2, 0) \quad}$

Chapter 13   Summary

Section 13.1   Distance Formula, Midpoint Formula, and Circles

Key Concepts

The **distance between two points** (x_1, y_1) and (x_2, y_2) is

$$d = \sqrt{(x_2 - x_1)^2 + (y_2 - y_1)^2}$$

Examples

Example 1

Find the distance between two points.

$(5, -2)$ and $(-1, -6)$

$$
\begin{aligned}
d &= \sqrt{(-1 - 5)^2 + [-6 - (-2)]^2} \\
&= \sqrt{(-6)^2 + (-4)^2} \\
&= \sqrt{36 + 16} \\
&= \sqrt{52} = 2\sqrt{13}
\end{aligned}
$$

The standard equation of a **circle** with center (h, k) and radius r is

$$(x - h)^2 + (y - k)^2 = r^2$$

Example 2

Find the center and radius of the circle.

$$x^2 + y^2 - 8x + 6y = 0$$
$$(x^2 - 8x + 16) + (y^2 + 6y + 9) = 16 + 9$$
$$(x - 4)^2 + (y + 3)^2 = 25$$

The center is $(4, -3)$ and the radius is 5.

The midpoint between two points is found by using the formula:

$$\left(\frac{x_1 + x_2}{2}, \frac{y_1 + y_2}{2} \right)$$

Example 3

Find the midpoint between $(-3, 1)$ and $(5, 7)$.

$$\left(\frac{-3 + 5}{2}, \frac{1 + 7}{2} \right) = (1, 4)$$

Section 13.2   More on the Parabola

Key Concepts

A **parabola** is the set of points in a plane that are equidistant from a fixed line (called the directrix) and a fixed point (called the focus) not on the directrix.

The standard form of an equation of a parabola with **vertex** (h, k) and vertical **axis of symmetry** is

$$y = a(x - h)^2 + k \qquad \text{where } a \neq 0$$

- The equation of the axis of symmetry is $x = h$.
- If $a > 0$, the parabola opens upward.
- If $a < 0$, the parabola opens downward.

The standard form of an equation of a parabola with vertex (h, k) and horizontal axis of symmetry is

$$x = a(y - k)^2 + h \qquad \text{where } a \neq 0$$

- The equation of the axis of symmetry is $y = k$.
- If $a > 0$, the parabola opens to the right.
- If $a < 0$, the parabola opens to the left.

Examples

Example 1

Given the parabola $y = (x - 2)^2 + 1$,

The vertex is $(2, 1)$.

The axis of symmetry is $x = 2$.

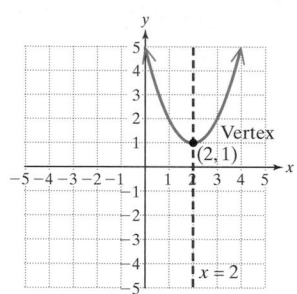

Example 2

Given the parabola $x = -\dfrac{1}{4}y^2 + 1$,

determine the coordinates of the vertex and the equation of the axis of symmetry.

$$x = -\frac{1}{4}(y - 0)^2 + 1$$

The vertex is $(1, 0)$.

The axis of symmetry is $y = 0$.

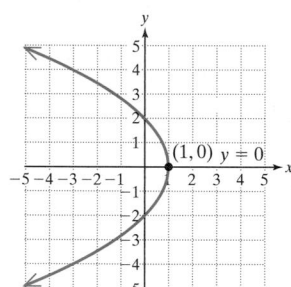

Section 13.3   The Ellipse and Hyperbola

Key Concepts

An **ellipse** is the set of all points (x, y) such that the sum of the distances between (x, y) and two distinct points (called foci) is constant.

Standard Form of an Ellipse with Center at the Origin

An ellipse with the center at the origin has the equation

$$\frac{x^2}{a^2} + \frac{y^2}{b^2} = 1$$

where a and b are positive real numbers.

For an ellipse centered at the origin, the x-intercepts are given by $(a, 0)$ and $(-a, 0)$, and the y-intercepts are given by $(0, b)$ and $(0, -b)$.

A **hyperbola** is the set of all points (x, y) such that the absolute value of the difference of the distances between (x, y) and two distinct points is a constant. The fixed points are called the foci of the hyperbola.

Standard Forms of an Equation of a Hyperbola

Let a and b represent positive real numbers.

Horizontal Transverse Axis. The standard form of an equation of a hyperbola with a horizontal transverse axis and center at the origin is given by

$$\frac{x^2}{a^2} - \frac{y^2}{b^2} = 1$$

Vertical Transverse Axis. The standard form of an equation of a hyperbola with a vertical transverse axis and center at the origin is given by

$$\frac{y^2}{b^2} - \frac{x^2}{a^2} = 1$$

Examples

Example 1

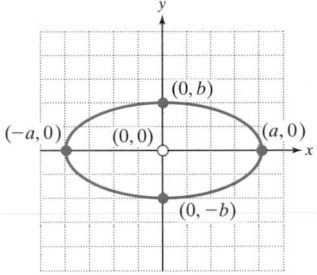

Example 2

$$\frac{x^2}{25} + \frac{y^2}{9} = 1$$

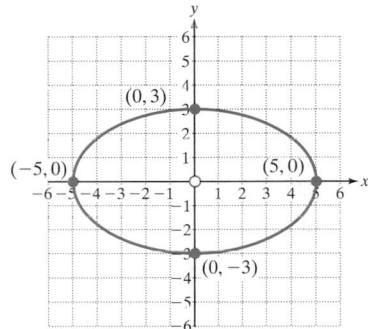

Example 3

$$\frac{x^2}{4} - \frac{y^2}{16} = 1$$

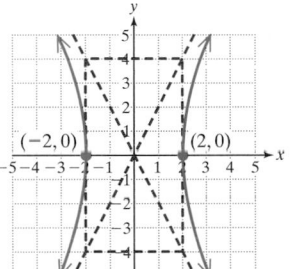

Example 4

$$\frac{y^2}{4} - \frac{x^2}{16} = 1$$

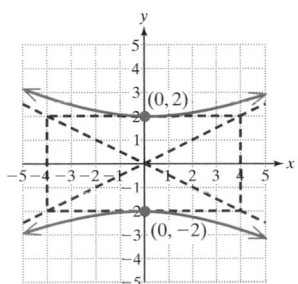

Section 13.4 Nonlinear Systems of Equations in Two Variables

Key Concepts

A **nonlinear system of equations** can be solved by graphing or by the substitution method.

$$2x^2 + y^2 = 15$$
$$x^2 - y = 0$$

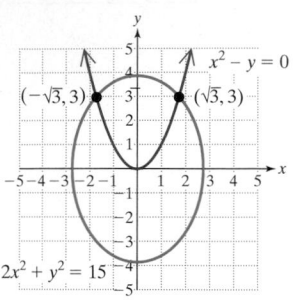

Example

Example 1

$\boxed{A}$ $\quad 2x^2 + y^2 = 15$

$\boxed{B}$ $\quad x^2 - y = 0$ Solve for y: $y = x^2$

$\boxed{A}$ $2x^2 + (x^2)^2 = 15$ Substitute in first equation.

$\quad\quad 2x^2 + x^4 = 15$

$\quad x^4 + 2x^2 - 15 = 0$

$(x^2 + 5)(x^2 - 3) = 0$

$x^2 + 5 = 0 \quad\quad$ or $\quad\quad x^2 - 3 = 0$

$\cancel{x^2 = -5} \quad\quad$ or $\quad\quad\quad x^2 = 3$

$\quad\quad\quad\quad\quad\quad\quad\quad\quad\quad x = \pm\sqrt{3}$

If $x = \sqrt{3}$ then $y = (\sqrt{3})^2 = 3$.

If $x = -\sqrt{3}$ then $y = (-\sqrt{3})^2 = 3$.

Points of intersection are $(\sqrt{3}, 3)$ and $(-\sqrt{3}, 3)$.

The solution set is $\{(\sqrt{3}, 3), (-\sqrt{3}, 3)\}$.

Section 13.5   Nonlinear Inequalities and Systems of Inequalities

Key Concepts

Graph a nonlinear inequality by using the test point method. That is, graph the related equation. Then choose test points in each region to determine where the inequality is true.

Example 1

$y \geq x^2$

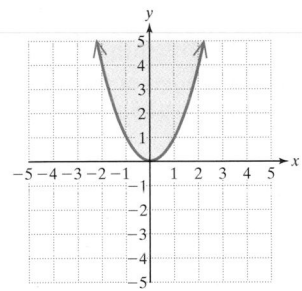

Graph a system of nonlinear inequalities by finding the intersection of the solution sets. That is, graph the solution set for each individual inequality, then take the intersection.

Examples

Example 2

$x^2 + y^2 < 4$

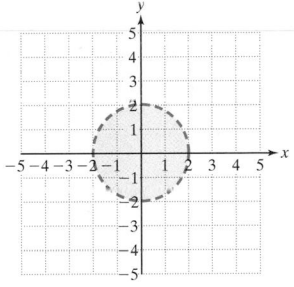

Example 3

$x \geq 0, \qquad y > x^2, \qquad$ and $\qquad x^2 + y^2 < 4$

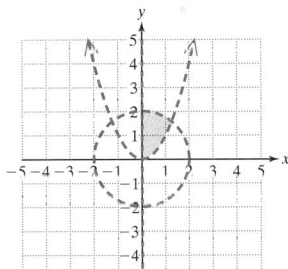

Chapter 13   Review Exercises

Section 13.1

For Exercises 1–4, find the distance between the two points by using the distance formula.

1. $(-6, 3)$ and $(0, 1)$
$2\sqrt{10}$

2. $(4, 13)$ and $(-1, 5)$
$\sqrt{89}$

3. Find x such that $(x, 5)$ is 5 units from $(2, 9)$.
$x = 5$ or $x = -1$

4. Find x such that $(-3, 4)$ is 3 units from $(x, 1)$.
$x = -3$

For Exercises 5–8, find the center and the radius of the circle.

5. $(x - 12)^2 + (y - 3)^2 = 16$ Center $(12, 3); r = 4$

6. $(x + 7)^2 + (y - 5)^2 = 81$ Center $(-7, 5); r = 9$

7. $(x + 3)^2 + (y + 8)^2 = 20$ Center $(-3, -8); r = 2\sqrt{5}$

8. $(x - 1)^2 + (y + 6)^2 = 32$ Center $(1, -6); r = 4\sqrt{2}$

9. A stained glass window is in the shape of a circle with a 16-in. diameter. Find an equation of the circle relative to the origin for each of the following graphs.

a.

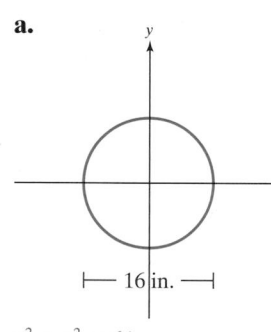

$x^2 + y^2 = 64$

b.

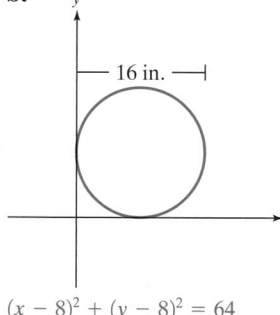

$(x - 8)^2 + (y - 8)^2 = 64$

For Exercises 10–13, write the equation of the circle in standard form by completing the square.

10. $x^2 + y^2 + 12x - 10y + 51 = 0$
$(x + 6)^2 + (y - 5)^2 = 10$

11. $x^2 + y^2 + 4x + 16y + 60 = 0$
$(x + 2)^2 + (y + 8)^2 = 8$

12. $x^2 + y^2 - x - 4y + \dfrac{1}{4} = 0$
$\left(x - \dfrac{1}{2}\right)^2 + (y - 2)^2 = 4$

13. $x^2 + y^2 - 6x - \dfrac{2}{3}y + \dfrac{1}{9} = 0$
$(x - 3)^2 + \left(y - \dfrac{1}{3}\right)^2 = 9$

14. Write an equation of a circle with center at the origin and a diameter of 7 m.
$x^2 + y^2 = \dfrac{49}{4}$

15. Write an equation of a circle with center $(0, 2)$ and radius 3 m.
$x^2 + (y - 2)^2 = 9$

For Exercises 16–17, find the midpoint of the segment with the given endpoints.

16. $(-3, 1)$ and $(-5, -5)$
$(-4, -2)$

17. $(0, 9)$ and $(-2, 7)$
$(-1, 8)$

Section 13.2

For Exercises 18–21, determine whether the axis of symmetry is vertical or horizontal and if the parabola opens upward, downward, left, or right.

18. $y = -2(x - 3)^2 + 2$
Vertical axis of symmetry; parabola opens downward

19. $x = 3(y - 9)^2 + 1$
Horizontal axis of symmetry; parabola opens right

20. $x = -(y + 4)^2 - 8$
Horizontal axis of symmetry; parabola opens left

21. $y = (x + 3)^2 - 10$
Vertical axis of symmetry; parabola opens upward

For Exercises 22–25, determine the coordinates of the vertex and the equation of the axis of symmetry. Then use this information to graph the parabola.

22. $x = -(y - 1)^2$

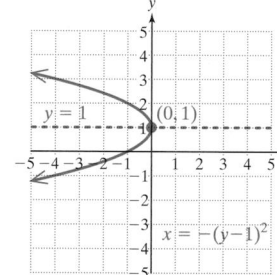

23. $y = (x + 2)^2$

24. $y = -\dfrac{1}{4}x^2$

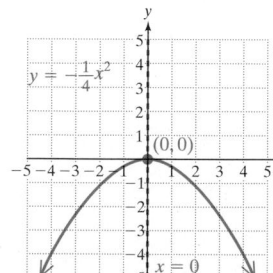

25. $x = 2y^2 - 1$

For Exercises 26–29, write the equation in standard form $y = a(x - h)^2 + k$ or $x = a(y - k)^2 + h$. Then identify the vertex and axis of symmetry.

26. $y = x^2 - 6x + 5$ $y = (x - 3)^2 - 4$; vertex: $(3, -4)$;
axis of symmetry: $x = 3$

27. $x = y^2 + 4y + 2$ $x = (y + 2)^2 - 2$; vertex: $(-2, -2)$;
axis of symmetry: $y = -2$

28. $x = -4y^2 + 4y$ $x = -4\left(y - \dfrac{1}{2}\right)^2 + 1$; vertex: $\left(1, \dfrac{1}{2}\right)$; axis
of symmetry: $y = \dfrac{1}{2}$

29. $y = -2x^2 - 2x$
$y = -2\left(x + \dfrac{1}{2}\right)^2 + \dfrac{1}{2}$; vertex: $\left(-\dfrac{1}{2}, \dfrac{1}{2}\right)$; axis of symmetry: $x = -\dfrac{1}{2}$

Section 13.3

For Exercises 30–31, identify the x- and y-intercepts. Then graph the ellipse.

30. $\dfrac{x^2}{9} + \dfrac{y^2}{25} = 1$

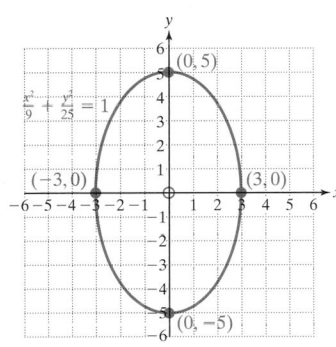

31. $x^2 + 4y^2 = 36$

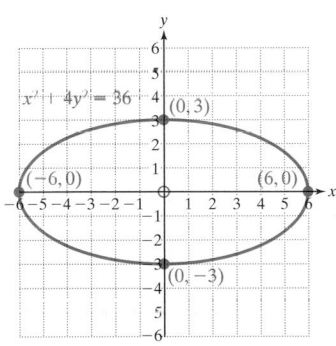

For Exercises 32–33, identify the center of the ellipse and graph the ellipse.

32. $\dfrac{(x - 5)^2}{4} + \dfrac{(y + 3)^2}{16} = 1$ Center: $(5, -3)$

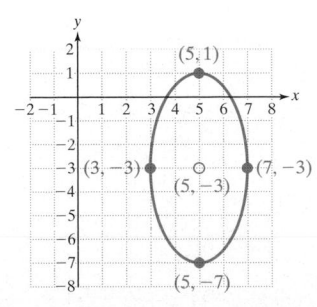

33. $\dfrac{x^2}{25} + \dfrac{(y - 2)^2}{9} = 1$ Center: $(0, 2)$

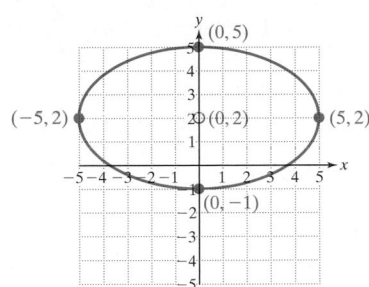

For Exercises 34–37, determine whether the transverse axis is horizontal or vertical.

34. $\dfrac{x^2}{12} - \dfrac{y^2}{16} = 1$ Horizontal

35. $\dfrac{y^2}{9} - \dfrac{x^2}{9} = 1$ Vertical

36. $y^2 - 8x^2 = 16$ Vertical

37. $3x^2 - y^2 = 18$ Horizontal

For Exercises 38–39, graph the hyperbola by first drawing the reference rectangle and the asymptotes. Label the vertices.

38. $\dfrac{x^2}{4} - y^2 = 1$

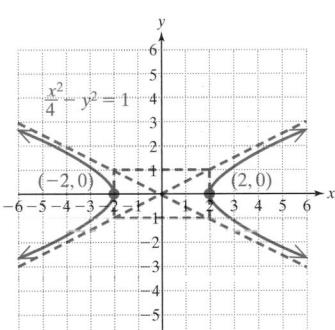

39. $y^2 - x^2 = 16$

 Writing   ⟷ Translating Expression   ◁ Geometry   📱 Scientific Calculator   💿 Video   NS☍E

For Exercises 40–43, identify the equations as representing an ellipse or a hyperbola.

40. $\dfrac{x^2}{4} - \dfrac{y^2}{9} = 1$ Hyperbola   **41.** $\dfrac{x^2}{16} + \dfrac{y^2}{9} = 1$ Ellipse

42. $\dfrac{x^2}{4} + \dfrac{y^2}{1} = 1$ **43.** $\dfrac{y^2}{1} - \dfrac{x^2}{16} = 1$
Ellipse   Hyperbola

Section 13.4

For Exercises 44–47,

   a. Identify each equation as representing a line, a parabola, a circle, an ellipse, or a hyperbola.

   b. Graph both equations on the same coordinate system.

   c. Solve the system analytically and verify the answers from the graph.

44. $3x + 2y = 10$ a. Line and parabola

$y = x^2 - 5$ b.

c. $\left\{\left(\dfrac{5}{2}, \dfrac{5}{4}\right), (-4, 11)\right\}$

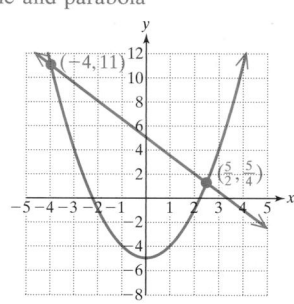

45. $4x + 2y = 10$ a. Line and parabola

$y = x^2 - 10$ b.

c. $\{(-5, 15), (3, -1)\}$

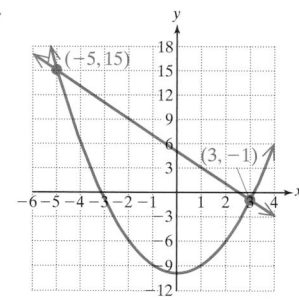

46. $x^2 + y^2 = 9$ a. Circle and line

$2x + y = 3$ b.

c. $\left\{(0, 3), \left(\dfrac{12}{5}, -\dfrac{9}{5}\right)\right\}$

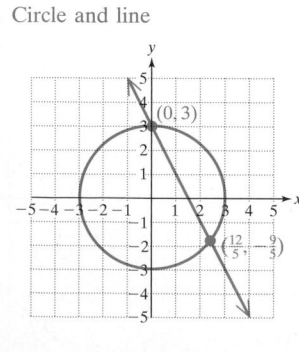

47. $x^2 + y^2 = 16$ a. Circle and line

$x - 2y = 8$ b.

c. $\left\{(0, -4), \left(\dfrac{16}{5}, -\dfrac{12}{5}\right)\right\}$

For Exercises 48–53, solve the system of nonlinear equations by using either the substitution method or the addition method.

48. $x^2 + 2y^2 = 8$ **49.** $x^2 + 4y^2 = 29$

$2x - y = 2$ $\left\{(0, -2), \left(\dfrac{16}{9}, \dfrac{14}{9}\right)\right\}$ $x - y = -4$ $\left\{\left(-\dfrac{7}{5}, \dfrac{13}{5}\right), (-5, -1)\right\}$

50. $x - y = 4$ **51.**

$y^2 = 2x$ $y = x^2$
$\{(8, 4), (2, -2)\}$ $6x^2 - y^2 = 8$ $\{(2, 4), (-2, 4), (\sqrt{2}, 2), (-\sqrt{2}, 2)\}$

52. $x^2 + y^2 = 10$ **53.** $x^2 + y^2 = 61$

$x^2 + 9y^2 = 18$ $x^2 - y^2 = 11$
$\{(3, 1), (3, -1),$ $\{(6, 5), (-6, 5),$
$(-3, 1), (-3, -1)\}$ $(6, -5), (-6, -5)\}$

Section 13.5

For Exercises 54−59, graph the solution set to the inequality.

54. $\dfrac{x^2}{16} + \dfrac{y^2}{81} < 1$ **55.** $\dfrac{x^2}{25} + \dfrac{y^2}{4} > 1$

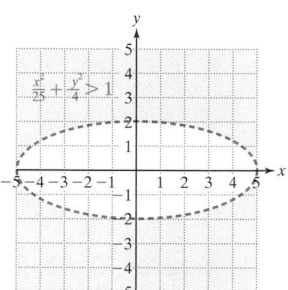

56. $(x - 3)^2 + (y + 1)^2 \geq 9$

 Writing   ↔ Translating Expression   Geometry   Scientific Calculator   Video   NS&E

57. $(x + 2)^2 + (y + 1)^2 \leq 4$

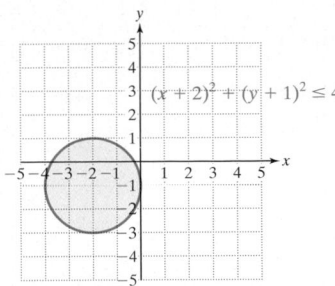

For Exercises 60–61, graph the solution set to the system of nonlinear inequalities.

60. $y > 2^x$

$x^2 + y^2 < 4$

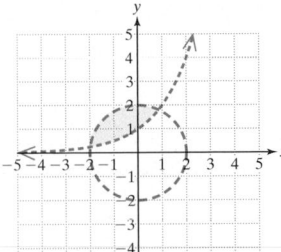

61. $y < x^2$

$x^2 + y^2 < 9$

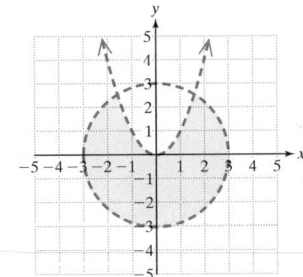

58. $y > (x - 1)^2$

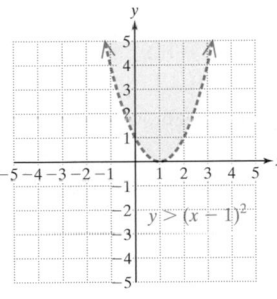

59. $x^2 - \dfrac{y^2}{4} \leq 1$

Chapter 13   Test

1. Use the distance formula to find the distance between the two points $(-5, 19)$ and $(-3, 13)$.
$2\sqrt{10}$

2. Determine the center and radius of the circle.

$$\left(x - \frac{5}{6}\right)^2 + \left(y + \frac{1}{3}\right)^2 = \frac{25}{49}$$

Center: $\left(\frac{5}{6}, -\frac{1}{3}\right)$; $r = \frac{5}{7}$

3. Determine the center and radius of the circle.
Center: $(0, 2)$; $r = 3$

$$x^2 + y^2 - 4y - 5 = 0$$

4. Let $(0, 4)$ be the center of a circle that passes through the point $(-2, 5)$.

   a. What is the radius of the circle? $\sqrt{5}$

   b. Write the equation of the circle in standard form. $x^2 + (y - 4)^2 = 5$

5. Find the center of the circle that has a diameter with endpoints $(7.3, -1.2)$ and $(0.3, 5.1)$.
The center is the midpoint $(3.8, 1.95)$.

6. Determine the vertex and the equation of the axis of symmetry. Then graph the parabola.

$$x = -(y - 2)^2 + 3$$

7. Write the equation in standard form $y = a(x - h)^2 + k$, and graph the parabola.

$y = x^2 + 4x + 5$

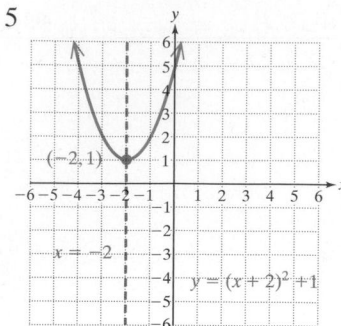

8. Graph the ellipse.

$$\frac{x^2}{16} + \frac{y^2}{49} = 1$$

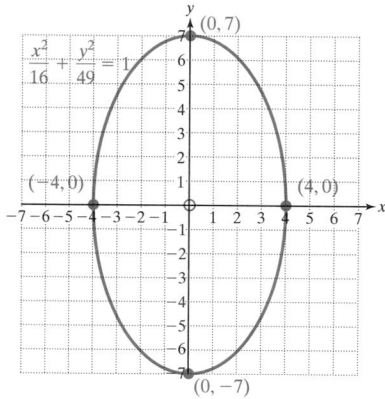

9. Graph the ellipse.

$$\frac{(x + 4)^2}{25} + (y - 3)^2 = 1$$

10. Graph the hyperbola.

$$y^2 - \frac{x^2}{4} = 1$$

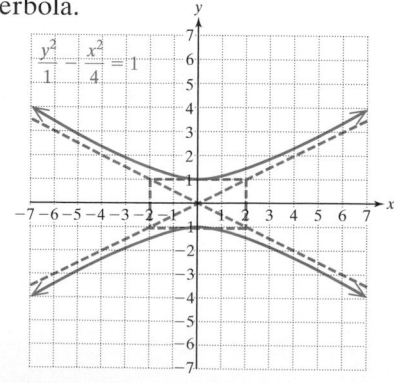

For Exercises 11–12, solve the system and identify the correct graph.

11. $16x^2 + 9y^2 = 144$

$4x - 3y = -12$

$\{(-3, 0), (0, 4)\};$ graph b

12. $x^2 + 4y^2 = 4$

$4x - 3y = -12$

$\{\ \};$ graph a

a.

b.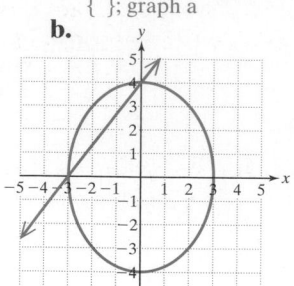

13. Describe the circumstances in which a nonlinear system of equations can be solved by using the addition method. The addition method can be used if the equations have corresponding *like* terms.

14. Solve the system by using either the substitution method or the addition method. $\{(2, 0), (-2, 0)\}$

$$25x^2 + 4y^2 = 100$$
$$25x^2 - 4y^2 = 100$$

For Exercises 15–18, graph the solution set.

15. $x \le y^2 + 1$

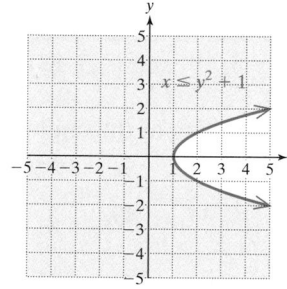

16. $y \ge -\frac{1}{3}x + 1$

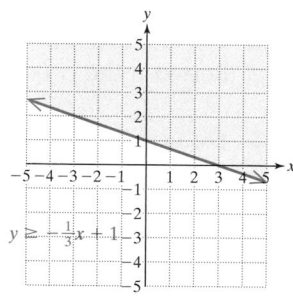

17. $x < y^2 + 1$

$$y > -\frac{1}{3}x + 1$$

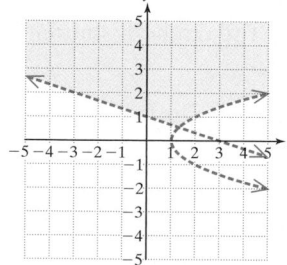

18. $y < \sqrt{x}$

$$y > x - 2$$
$$x > 0$$

Chapters 1–13   Cumulative Review Exercises

1. Solve. $5(2y - 1) = 2y - 4 + 8y - 1$
   $\{x \mid x \text{ is a real number}\}$

2. Solve the inequality. Graph the solution and write the solution in interval notation.

   $$4(x - 1) + 2 > 3x + 8 - 2x$$

   $\left(\dfrac{10}{3}, \infty\right)$ 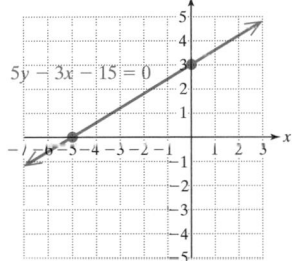

3. The product of two integers is 150. If one integer is 5 less than twice the other, find the integers.
   10, 15

4. For $5y - 3x - 15 = 0$:

   a. Find the x- and y-intercepts.
   $(-5, 0), (0, 3)$

   b. Find the slope.
   $m = \dfrac{3}{5}$

   c. Graph the line.

5. Find the slope and y-intercept of $3x - 4y = 6$.
   slope: $\dfrac{3}{4}$; y-intercept: $\left(0, -\dfrac{3}{2}\right)$

6. A collection of dimes and quarters has a total value of \$2.45. If there are 17 coins, how many of each type are there?   12 dimes, 5 quarters

7. Solve the system. $\{(2, -3, 1)\}$

   $$\begin{aligned} x + y \quad\;\; &= -1 \\ 2x \quad\; - z &= 3 \\ y + 2z &= -1 \end{aligned}$$

8. Solve the system. $\left\{\left(\dfrac{5}{2}, \dfrac{3}{2}\right)\right\}$

   $$4x - 2y = 7$$
   $$-3x + 5y = 0$$

9. Solve the system. $\{\ \}$

   $$y = -\dfrac{1}{2}x + 2$$
   $$x + 2y = 12$$

10. For $f(x) = 3x - x^2 - 12$, find the function values $f(0), f(-1), f(2),$ and $f(4)$.
    $f(0) = -12; f(-1) = -16; f(2) = -10; f(4) = -16$

11. Solve the inequality. $x^2 + 6x < -8$ $(-4, -2)$

12. The quantity z varies jointly as y and as the square of x. If z is 80 when x is 5 and y is 2, find z when $x = 2$ and $y = 5$. $z = 32$

13. For $f(x) = \sqrt{x + 1}$ and $g(x) = x^2 + 6$, find $(g \circ f)(x)$. $(g \circ f)(x) = x + 7; x \geq -1$

14. a. Find the value of the expression $x^3 + x^2 + x + 1$ for $x = -2$. -5

    b. Factor the expression $x^3 + x^2 + x + 1$ and find the value when x is -2. $(x + 1)(x^2 + 1); -5$

    c. Compare the values for parts (a) and (b).
    They are the same.

15. Factor completely. $x^2 - y^2 - 6x - 6y$
    $(x + y)(x - y - 6)$

16. Multiply. $(x - 4)(x^2 + 2x + 1)$ $x^3 - 2x^2 - 7x - 4$

17. Solve. $2x(x - 7) = x - 18$ $\left\{6, \dfrac{3}{2}\right\}$

18. Simplify. $\dfrac{3a^2 - a - 2}{3a^2 + 8a + 4}$ $\dfrac{a - 1}{a + 2}$

19. Subtract. $\dfrac{2}{x + 3} - \dfrac{x}{x - 2}$ $\dfrac{-x^2 - x - 4}{(x + 3)(x - 2)}$

20. Solve. $\dfrac{2}{x + 3} - \dfrac{x}{x - 2} = \dfrac{-4}{x^2 + x - 6}$ $\{0, -1\}$

21. Solve the radical equations.

    a. $\sqrt{2x - 5} = -3$ $\{\ \}$

    b. $\sqrt[3]{2x - 5} = -3$ $\{-11\}$

For Exercises 22–23, perform the indicated operations with complex numbers.

22. $6i(4 + 5i)$ $-30 + 24i$

23. $\dfrac{3}{4 - 5i}$ $\dfrac{12}{41} + \dfrac{15}{41}i$

24. Find the length of the missing side. $2\sqrt{7}$ m

25. An automobile starts from rest and accelerates at a constant rate for 10 sec. The distance, $d(t)$, in feet traveled by the car is given by

$$d(t) = 4.4t^2$$

where $0 \leq t \leq 10$ is the time in seconds.

   a. How far has the car traveled after 2, 3, and 4 sec, respectively?   17.6 ft; 39.6 ft; 70.4 ft

   b. How long will it take for the car to travel 281.6 ft?   8 sec

26. Solve the equation $125w^3 + 1 = 0$ by factoring and using the quadratic formula. (*Hint:* You will find one real solution and two imaginary solutions.) $\left\{-\dfrac{1}{5}, \dfrac{1}{10} \pm \dfrac{\sqrt{3}}{10}i\right\}$

27. Solve. $\dfrac{x}{x+2} - \dfrac{3}{x-1} = \dfrac{1}{x^2 + x - 2}$ $\{2 \pm \sqrt{11}\}$

28. Find the coordinates of the vertex of the parabola defined by $f(x) = x^2 + 10x - 11$ by completing the square. $(-5, -36)$

29. Graph the quadratic function defined by $g(x) = -x^2 - 2x + 3$.

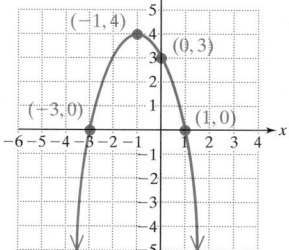

   a. Label the x-intercepts. $(-3, 0), (1, 0)$

   b. Label the y-intercept. $(0, 3)$

   c. Label the vertex. $(-1, 4)$

30. Solve the inequality and write the answer in interval notation. $(-1, 19)$

$$|x - 9| - 3 < 7$$

31. Solve the inequality: $|2x - 5| \geq 4$ $\left(-\infty, \dfrac{1}{2}\right] \cup \left[\dfrac{9}{2}, \infty\right)$

32. Write the expression in logarithmic form. $8^{5/3} = 32$ $\log_8 32 = \frac{5}{3}$

33. Solve. $5^2 = 125^x$ $\left\{\dfrac{2}{3}\right\}$

34. For $h(x) = x^3 - 1$, find $h^{-1}(x)$. $h^{-1}(x) = \sqrt[3]{x + 1}$

35. Write an equation representing the set of all points 4 units from the point $(0, 5)$. $x^2 + (y - 5)^2 = 16$

36. Graph the ellipse. $\dfrac{x^2}{4} + \dfrac{y^2}{25} = 1$

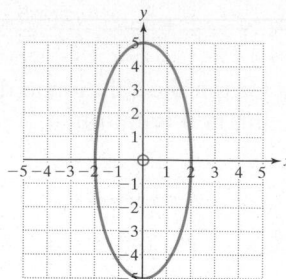

37. Determine the center of the circle, given the endpoints of a diameter. $\left(-\dfrac{1}{2}, 0\right)$

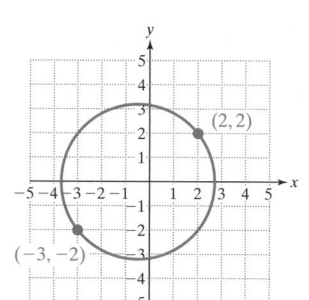

38. Solve the system of nonlinear equations. $\{(0, -4)\}$

$$x^2 + y^2 = 16$$
$$y = -x^2 - 4$$

39. Graph the solution set.

$$y^2 - x^2 < 1$$

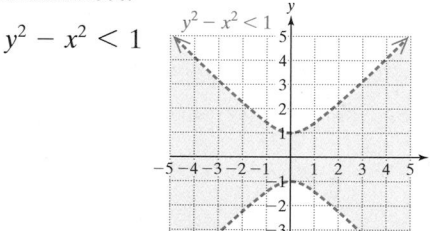

40. Graph the solution set to this system.

$$y > \left(\dfrac{1}{2}\right)^x$$
$$x < 0$$

 Writing   Translating Expression   Geometry   Scientific Calculator   Video   NS&E

Binomial Expansions, Sequences, and Series

14

CHAPTER OUTLINE

Chapter 14

We begin this chapter by learning how to expand expressions of the form $(a + b)^n$. Then we study a new type of function called a sequence. A sequence is a progression of terms, and the sum of the terms in a sequence is called a series. We will study arithmetic and geometric sequences. These are sequences in which successive terms differ by a fixed constant or by a fixed ratio.

Are You Prepared?

To practice working with sequences, try Exercises 1–8. In each case, fill in the blanks with the next three terms that follow the given pattern.

1. 1, 4, 7, 10, ___13___ , ___16___ , ___19___

2. 6, −2, −10, −18, ___−26___ , ___−34___ , ___−42___

3. 3, 6, 12, 24, ___48___ , ___96___ , ___192___

4. 9, 3, 1, $\frac{1}{3}$, ___$\frac{1}{9}$___ , ___$\frac{1}{27}$___ , ___$\frac{1}{81}$___

5. 1, 4, 9, 16, ___25___ , ___36___ , ___49___

6. −4, 12, −36, 108, ___−324___ , ___972___ , ___−2916___

7. $x^7, x^6y, x^5y^2, x^4y^3$, ___$x^3y^4$___ , ___$x^2y^5$___ , ___$xy^6$___

8. $a^9, a^8b, a^7b^2, a^6b^3$, ___$a^5b^4$___ , ___$a^4b^5$___ , ___$a^3b^6$___

9. Expand the expression. $(a + b)^2 = $ ___$a^2 + 2ab + b^2$___

10. Expand the expression. $(a + b)^3 = $ ___$a^3 + 3a^2b + 3ab^2 + b^3$___

11. Based on your answers to Exercises 9 and 10, how many terms are in the expansion of $(a + b)^n$? ___$n + 1$___

Section 14.1	**Binomial Expansions**

1. Binomial Expansions and Pascal's Triangle

In Section 5.6 we learned how to square a binomial.

$$(a + b)^2 = a^2 + 2ab + b^2$$

The expression $a^2 + 2ab + b^2$ is called the **binomial expansion** of $(a + b)^2$. To expand $(a + b)^3$, we can find the product $(a + b)(a + b)^2$.

$$(a + b)(a + b)^2 = (a + b)(a^2 + 2ab + b^2)$$

$$= a^3 + 2a^2b + ab^2 + a^2b + 2ab^2 + b^3$$

$$= a^3 + 3a^2b + 3ab^2 + b^3$$

Similarly, to expand $(a + b)^4$, we can multiply $(a + b)$ by $(a + b)^3$. Using this method, we can expand several powers of $(a + b)$ to find the following pattern:

$$(a + b)^0 = 1$$
$$(a + b)^1 = a + b$$
$$(a + b)^2 = a^2 + 2ab + b^2$$
$$(a + b)^3 = a^3 + 3a^2b + 3ab^2 + b^3$$
$$(a + b)^4 = a^4 + 4a^3b + 6a^2b^2 + 4ab^3 + b^4$$
$$(a + b)^5 = a^5 + 5a^4b + 10a^3b^2 + 10a^2b^3 + 5ab^4 + b^5$$

Notice that the exponents on a decrease from left to right, while the exponents on b increase from left to right. Also observe that for each term, the sum of the exponents is equal to the exponent to which $(a + b)$ is raised. Finally, notice that the number of terms in the expansion is exactly 1 more than the power to which $(a + b)$ is raised. For example, the expansion of $(a + b)^4$ has five terms, and the expansion of $(a + b)^5$ has six terms.

With these guidelines in mind, we know that $(a + b)^6$ will contain seven terms involving

$$a^6 \quad a^5b \quad a^4b^2 \quad a^3b^3 \quad a^2b^4 \quad ab^5 \quad b^6$$

We can complete the expansion of $(a + b)^6$ if we can determine the correct coefficients of each term.

If we write the coefficients for several expansions of $(a + b)^n$, where $n \geq 0$, we have a triangular array of numbers.

$$(a + b)^0 = 1$$
$$(a + b)^1 = 1a + 1b$$
$$(a + b)^2 = 1a^2 + 2ab + 1b^2$$
$$(a + b)^3 = 1a^3 + 3a^2b + 3ab^2 + 1b^3$$
$$(a + b)^4 = 1a^4 + 4a^3b + 6a^2b^2 + 4ab^3 + 1b^4$$
$$(a + b)^5 = 1a^5 + 5a^4b + 10a^3b^2 + 10a^2b^3 + 5ab^4 + 1b^5$$

```
              1
            1   1
          1   2   1
        1   3   3   1
      1   4   6   4   1
    1   5  10  10   5   1
```

Each row begins and ends with a 1, and each entry in between is the sum of the two entries from the line above. For example, in the last row, $5 = 1 + 4$, $10 = 4 + 6$, and so on. This triangular array of coefficients for a binomial expansion is called **Pascal's triangle**, named after French mathematician Blaise Pascal (1623–1662).

$$
\begin{array}{c}
1 \\
1 \quad 1 \\
1 \quad 2 \quad 1 \\
1 \quad 3 \quad 3 \quad 1 \\
1 \quad 4 \quad 6 \quad 4 \quad 1 \\
1 \quad 5 \quad 10 \quad 10 \quad 5 \quad 1 \\
1 \quad 6 \quad 15 \quad 20 \quad 15 \quad 6 \quad 1
\end{array}
$$

By using the pattern shown in Pascal's triangle, the coefficients corresponding to $(a + b)^6$ would be 1, 6, 15, 20, 15, 6, 1. By inserting the coefficients, the sum becomes

$$(a + b)^6 = 1a^6 + 6a^5b + 15a^4b^2 + 20a^3b^3 + 15a^2b^4 + 6ab^5 + 1b^6$$

2. Factorial Notation

Although Pascal's triangle provides an easy method to find the coefficients of $(a + b)^n$, it is impractical for large values of n. A more efficient method to find the coefficients of a binomial expansion involves **factorial notation**.

DEFINITION $n!$

Let n be a positive integer. Then $n!$ (read as "n factorial") is defined as the product of integers from 1 through n. That is,

$$n! = n(n - 1)(n - 2) \cdots (2)(1)$$

Note: We define $0! = 1$.

| **Example 1** | **Evaluating Factorial Notation** |

Evaluate the expressions.

  a. 4!   **b.** 10!   **c.** 0!

Solution:

  a. $4! = 4 \cdot 3 \cdot 2 \cdot 1 = 24$

  b. $10! = 10 \cdot 9 \cdot 8 \cdot 7 \cdot 6 \cdot 5 \cdot 4 \cdot 3 \cdot 2 \cdot 1 = 3,628,800$

  c. $0! = 1$ by definition

Skill Practice Evaluate the expressions.

  1. 3!   **2.** 8!   **3.** 1!

Classroom Example: p. 990, Exercise 12

Calculator Connections

Most calculators have a $\boxed{!}$ function. Try evaluating the expressions from Example 1 on a calculator:

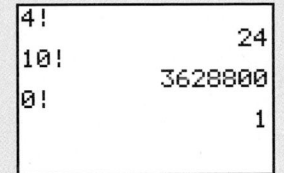

Answers

  1. 6   **2.** 40,320   **3.** 1

Sometimes factorial notation is used with other operations such as multiplication and division.

Classroom Example: p. 990,
Exercise 26

Calculator Connections

To evaluate the expressions from Example 2 on a calculator, use parentheses around the factors in the denominator.

```
4!/(4!*0!)
              1
4!/(3!*1!)
              4
4!/(2!*2!)
              6
```

Example 2   Evaluating Expressions with Factorials

Evaluate the expressions.

a. $\dfrac{4!}{4! \cdot 0!}$ b. $\dfrac{4!}{3! \cdot 1!}$ c. $\dfrac{4!}{2! \cdot 2!}$ d. $\dfrac{4!}{1! \cdot 3!}$ e. $\dfrac{4!}{0! \cdot 4!}$

Solution:

a. $\dfrac{4!}{4! \cdot 0!} = \dfrac{(4 \cdot 3 \cdot 2 \cdot 1)}{(4 \cdot 3 \cdot 2 \cdot 1) \cdot (1)} = \dfrac{4 \cdot 3 \cdot 2 \cdot 1}{4 \cdot 3 \cdot 2 \cdot 1 \cdot 1} = 1$

b. $\dfrac{4!}{3! \cdot 1!} = \dfrac{(4 \cdot 3 \cdot 2 \cdot 1)}{(3 \cdot 2 \cdot 1) \cdot (1)} = \dfrac{4 \cdot 3 \cdot 2 \cdot 1}{3 \cdot 2 \cdot 1 \cdot 1} = 4$

c. $\dfrac{4!}{2! \cdot 2!} = \dfrac{(4 \cdot 3 \cdot 2 \cdot 1)}{(2 \cdot 1) \cdot (2 \cdot 1)} = \dfrac{4 \cdot 3 \cdot 2 \cdot 1}{2 \cdot 1 \cdot 2 \cdot 1} = 6$

d. $\dfrac{4!}{1! \cdot 3!} = \dfrac{(4 \cdot 3 \cdot 2 \cdot 1)}{(1) \cdot (3 \cdot 2 \cdot 1)} = \dfrac{4 \cdot 3 \cdot 2 \cdot 1}{1 \cdot 3 \cdot 2 \cdot 1} = 4$

e. $\dfrac{4!}{0! \cdot 4!} = \dfrac{(4 \cdot 3 \cdot 2 \cdot 1)}{(1) \cdot (4 \cdot 3 \cdot 2 \cdot 1)} = \dfrac{4 \cdot 3 \cdot 2 \cdot 1}{1 \cdot 4 \cdot 3 \cdot 2 \cdot 1} = 1$

Skill Practice Evaluate.

4. $\dfrac{5!}{5!0!}$ 5. $\dfrac{5!}{4!1!}$ 6. $\dfrac{5!}{3!2!}$

3. The Binomial Theorem

Notice from Example 2 that the values of

$$\dfrac{4!}{4! \cdot 0!} \qquad \dfrac{4!}{3! \cdot 1!} \qquad \dfrac{4!}{2! \cdot 2!} \qquad \dfrac{4!}{1! \cdot 3!} \qquad \text{and} \qquad \dfrac{4!}{0! \cdot 4!}$$

correspond to the values $1, 4, 6, 4, 1$, which are the coefficients for the expansion of $(a + b)^4$. Generalizing this pattern, we see the coefficients for the terms in the expansion of $(a + b)^n$ are given by

$$\dfrac{n!}{r! \cdot (n - r)!}$$

where r corresponds to the exponent on the factor of a and $(n - r)$ corresponds to the exponent on the factor of b. Using this formula for the coefficients in a binomial expansion results in the **binomial theorem**.

Answers

4. 1   **5.** 5   **6.** 10

> **DEFINITION** The Binomial Theorem
>
> For any positive integer n,
>
> $$(a + b)^n = \frac{n!}{n! \cdot 0!} a^n + \frac{n!}{(n-1)! \cdot 1!} a^{(n-1)}b + \frac{n!}{(n-2)! \cdot 2!} a^{(n-2)}b^2$$
> $$+ \cdots + \frac{n!}{0! \cdot n!} b^n$$

Example 3 Applying the Binomial Theorem

Write out the first three terms of the expansion of $(a + b)^{10}$.

Classroom Example: p. 990, Exercise 30

Solution:

The first three terms of $(a + b)^{10}$ are

$$\frac{10!}{10! \cdot 0!} a^{10} + \frac{10!}{9! \cdot 1!} a^9 b + \frac{10!}{8! \cdot 2!} a^8 b^2$$

$$= \frac{10!}{10! \cdot 1} a^{10} + \frac{10 \cdot 9!}{9! \cdot 1!} a^9 b + \frac{10 \cdot 9 \cdot 8!}{8! \cdot 2 \cdot 1} a^8 b^2$$

$$= a^{10} + 10a^9 b + 45a^8 b^2$$

> **TIP:** When applying the binomial theorem, exponents on a and b must add up to n.

Skill Practice

7. Write out the first three terms of $(x + y)^5$.

Example 4 Applying the Binomial Theorem

Use the binomial theorem to expand $(2m + 7)^3$.

Classroom Example: p. 990, Exercise 40

Solution:

This expression is of the form $(a + b)^3$, where $a = 2m$ and $b = 7$. Applying the binomial theorem we have

$$(a + b)^3 = \frac{3!}{3! \cdot 0!} a^3 + \frac{3!}{2! \cdot 1!} a^2 b + \frac{3!}{1! \cdot 2!} ab^2 + \frac{3!}{0! \cdot 3!} b^3$$

$$= \frac{3!}{3! \cdot 0!} (2m)^3 + \frac{3!}{2! \cdot 1!} (2m)^2(7) + \frac{3!}{1! \cdot 2!} (2m)(7)^2 + \frac{3!}{0! \cdot 3!} (7)^3$$

$$= 1 \cdot (8m^3) + 3 \cdot (4m^2)(7) + 3 \cdot (2m)(49) + 1 \cdot (343)$$

$$= 8m^3 + 84m^2 + 294m + 343$$

> **TIP:** The values of
> $$\frac{n!}{r! \cdot (n-r)!}$$
> can also be found by using Pascal's triangle.
>
> ```
>       1
>      1 1
>     1 2 1
>    1 3 3 1
> ```

Skill Practice

8. Use the binomial theorem to expand $(3y + 4)^3$.

Answers

7. $x^5 + 5x^4 y + 10x^3 y^2$
8. $27y^3 + 108y^2 + 144y + 64$

Classroom Example: p. 990, Exercise 42

Example 5 Applying the Binomial Theorem

Use the binomial theorem to expand $(3x^2 - 5y)^4$.

Solution:

Write $(3x^2 - 5y)^4$ as $[(3x^2) + (-5y)]^4$. In this case, the expressions $3x^2$ and $-5y$ may be substituted for a and b in the expansion of $(a + b)^4$.

$$(a + b)^4 = \frac{4!}{4! \cdot 0!}a^4 + \frac{4!}{3! \cdot 1!}a^3b + \frac{4!}{2! \cdot 2!}a^2b^2 + \frac{4!}{1! \cdot 3!}ab^3 + \frac{4!}{0! \cdot 4!}b^4$$

$$= \frac{4!}{4! \cdot 0!}(3x^2)^4 + \frac{4!}{3! \cdot 1!}(3x^2)^3(-5y) + \frac{4!}{2! \cdot 2!}(3x^2)^2(-5y)^2$$

$$+ \frac{4!}{1! \cdot 3!}(3x^2)(-5y)^3 + \frac{4!}{0! \cdot 4!}(-5y)^4$$

$$= 1 \cdot (81x^8) + 4 \cdot (27x^6)(-5y) + 6 \cdot (9x^4)(25y^2) + 4 \cdot (3x^2)(-125y^3)$$

$$+ 1 \cdot (625y^4)$$

$$= 81x^8 - 540x^6y + 1350x^4y^2 - 1500x^2y^3 + 625y^4$$

TIP: The values of $\dfrac{n!}{r! \cdot (n-r)!}$ can also be found by using Pascal's triangle.

```
        1
      1   1
    1   2   1
  1   3   3   1
1   4   6   4   1
```

Skill Practice

9. Use the binomial theorem to expand $(2a - 3b^2)^4$.

The binomial theorem may also be used to find a specific term in a binomial expansion.

Classroom Example: p. 990, Exercise 46

Example 6 Finding a Specific Term in a Binomial Expansion

Find the fourth term of the expansion $(a + b)^{13}$.

Solution:

There are 14 terms in the expansion of $(a + b)^{13}$. The first term will have variable factors $a^{13}b^0$. The second term will have variable factors $a^{12}b^1$. The third term will have $a^{11}b^2$, and the fourth term will have $a^{10}b^3$. Hence, the fourth term is

$$\frac{13!}{10! \cdot 3!}a^{10}b^3 = 286a^{10}b^3$$

Skill Practice

10. Find the 4th term of $(x + y)^8$.

From Example 6, we see that for the kth term in the expansion $(a + b)^n$, where k is an integer greater than zero, the variable factors are $a^{n-(k-1)}$ and b^{k-1}. Therefore, to find the kth term of $(a + b)^n$, we can make the following generalization.

PROCEDURE Finding a Specific Term in a Binomial Expansion

Let n and k be positive integers such that $k \leq n$. Then the kth term in the expansion of $(a + b)^n$ is given by

$$\frac{n!}{[n - (k - 1)]! \cdot (k - 1)!} \cdot a^{n-(k-1)} \cdot b^{k-1}$$

Answers

9. $16a^4 - 96a^3b^2 + 216a^2b^4 - 216ab^6 + 81b^8$

10. $56x^5y^3$

Example 7 **Finding a Specific Term in a Binomial Expansion**

Find the sixth term of $(p^3 + 2w)^8$.

Classroom Example: p. 990, Exercise 48

Solution:

Apply the formula.

$$\frac{n!}{[n - (k - 1)]! \cdot (k - 1)!} \cdot a^{n-(k-1)} \cdot b^{k-1} \quad \text{with } n = 8, k = 6, a = p^3, \text{ and } b = 2w$$

$$\frac{8!}{[8 - (6 - 1)]! \cdot (6 - 1)!} \cdot (p^3)^{8-(6-1)} \cdot (2w)^{6-1}$$

$$= \frac{8!}{(3)! \cdot (5)!} \cdot (p^3)^3 \cdot (2w)^5$$

$$= 56 \cdot (p^9) \cdot (32w^5)$$

$$= 1792p^9w^5$$

Skill Practice

11. Find the 5th term of $(t - m^2)^8$.

Answer

11. $70t^4m^8$

Section 14.1 Practice Exercises

Study Skills Exercise

1. Define the key terms.

    a. binomial expansion   **b. Pascal's triangle**   **c. factorial notation**   **d. binomial theorem**

Concept 1: Binomial Expansions and Pascal's Triangle

For Exercises 2–7, expand the binomials. Use Pascal's triangle to find the coefficients.

2. $(x + y)^4$
$x^4 + 4x^3y + 6x^2y^2 + 4xy^3 + y^4$

3. $(a + b)^3$
$a^3 + 3a^2b + 3ab^2 + b^3$

4. $(4 + p)^3$
$64 + 48p + 12p^2 + p^3$

5. $(1 + g)^4$
$1 + 4g + 6g^2 + 4g^3 + g^4$

6. $(a^2 + b)^6$
$a^{12} + 6a^{10}b + 15a^8b^2 + 20a^6b^3 + 15a^4b^4 + 6a^2b^5 + b^6$

7. $(p + q^2)^7$
$p^7 + 7p^6q^2 + 21p^5q^4 + 35p^4q^6 + 35p^3q^8 + 21p^2q^{10} + 7pq^{12} + q^{14}$

For Exercises 8–9, rewrite each binomial of the form $(a - b)^n$ as $[a + (-b)]^n$. Then expand the binomials. Use Pascal's triangle to find the coefficients.

8. $(p^2 - w)^3$
$p^6 - 3p^4w + 3p^2w^2 - w^3$

9. $(5 - u^3)^4$
$625 - 500u^3 + 150u^6 - 20u^9 + u^{12}$

10. For $a > 0$ and $b > 0$, what happens to the signs of the terms when expanding the binomial $(a - b)^n$ compared with $(a + b)^n$?
The signs alternate on the terms of the expression $(a - b)^n$. The signs for the expression $(a + b)^n$ are all positive.

Concept 2: Factorial Notation

For Exercises 11–14, evaluate the expression. **(See Example 1.)**

11. $5!$ 120

12. $3!$ 6

13. $0!$ 1

14. $1!$ 1

15. True or false: $0! \neq 1!$ False

16. True or false: $n!$ is defined for negative integers. False

17. True or false: $n! = n$ for $n = 1$ and 2. True

18. Show that $9! = 9 \cdot 8!$
$9! = 9 \cdot (8 \cdot 7 \cdot 6 \cdot 5 \cdot 4 \cdot 3 \cdot 2 \cdot 1) = 9 \cdot 8!$

19. Show that $6! = 6 \cdot 5!$
$6! = 6 \cdot (5 \cdot 4 \cdot 3 \cdot 2 \cdot 1) = 6 \cdot 5!$

20. Show that $8! = 8 \cdot 7!$
$8! = 8 \cdot (7 \cdot 6 \cdot 5 \cdot 4 \cdot 3 \cdot 2 \cdot 1) = 8 \cdot 7!$

For Exercises 21–28, evaluate the expression. **(See Example 2.)**

21. $\dfrac{8!}{4!}$ 1680

22. $\dfrac{7!}{5!}$ 42

23. $\dfrac{3!}{0!}$ 6

24. $\dfrac{4!}{0!}$ 24

25. $\dfrac{8!}{3! \cdot 5!}$ 56

26. $\dfrac{6!}{2! \cdot 4!}$ 15

27. $\dfrac{4!}{0! \cdot 4!}$ 1

28. $\dfrac{6!}{0! \cdot 6!}$ 1

Concept 3: The Binomial Theorem

For Exercises 29–32, find the first three terms of the expansion. **(See Example 3.)**

29. $(m + n)^{11}$
$m^{11} + 11m^{10}n + 55m^9n^2$

30. $(p + q)^9$
$p^9 + 9p^8q + 36p^7q^2$

31. $(u^2 - v)^{12}$
$u^{24} - 12u^{22}v + 66u^{20}v^2$

32. $(r - s^2)^8$
$r^8 - 8r^7s^2 + 28r^6s^4$

33. How many terms are in the expansion of $(a + b)^8$? 9 terms

34. How many terms are in the expansion of $(x + y)^{13}$? 14 terms

For Exercises 35–44, use the binomial theorem to expand the binomials. **(See Examples 4–5.)**

35. $(s + t)^6$
$s^6 + 6s^5t + 15s^4t^2 + 20s^3t^3$
$+ 15s^2t^4 + 6st^5 + t^6$

36. $(h + k)^4$
$h^4 + 4h^3k + 6h^2k^2 + 4hk^3 + k^4$

37. $(b - 3)^3$
$b^3 - 9b^2 + 27b - 27$

38. $(c - 2)^5$
$c^5 - 10c^4 + 40c^3 - 80c^2 + 80c - 32$

39. $(2x + y)^4$
$16x^4 + 32x^3y + 24x^2y^2 + 8xy^3 + y^4$

40. $(p + 3q)^3$
$p^3 + 9p^2q + 27pq^2 + 27q^3$

41. $(c^2 - d)^7$
$c^{14} - 7c^{12}d + 21c^{10}d^2 - 35c^8d^3$
$+ 35c^6d^4 - 21c^4d^5 + 7c^2d^6 - d^7$

42. $(u - v^3)^6$
$u^6 - 6u^5v^3 + 15u^4v^6 - 20u^3v^9$
$+ 15u^2v^{12} - 6uv^{15} + v^{18}$

43. $\left(\dfrac{a}{2} - b\right)^5$
$\dfrac{1}{32}a^5 - \dfrac{5}{16}a^4b + \dfrac{5}{4}a^3b^2 - \dfrac{5}{2}a^2b^3 + \dfrac{5}{2}ab^4 - b^5$

44. $\left(\dfrac{s}{3} + t\right)^5$
$\dfrac{1}{243}s^5 + \dfrac{5}{81}s^4t + \dfrac{10}{27}s^3t^2 + \dfrac{10}{9}s^2t^3 + \dfrac{5}{3}st^4 + t^5$

For Exercises 45–50, find the indicated term of the binomial expansion. **(See Examples 6–7.)**

45. $(m - n)^{11}$; sixth term
$-462m^6n^5$

46. $(p - q)^9$; fourth term
$-84p^6q^3$

47. $(u^2 - v)^{12}$; fifth term
$495u^{16}v^4$

48. $(2r - s^2)^8$; sixth term
$-448r^3s^{10}$

49. $(5f + g)^9$; 10th term
g^9

50. $(4m + n)^{10}$; 11th term
n^{10}

Section 14.2   Sequences and Series

Concepts

1. Finite and Infinite Sequences
2. Series

1. Finite and Infinite Sequences

In day-to-day life, we think of a sequence as a set of items with some order or pattern. In mathematics, a sequence is a list of terms that correspond to the set of positive integers.

For example, suppose Justine is allowed to choose between two salary plans. Plan A offers \$48,000 as a starting salary with a 5% raise each year. Plan B offers

 Writing   Translating Expression   Geometry   Scientific Calculator   Video NS E

$50,000 with a $2000 raise each year. Then the following sequences represent the salaries for each plan for the first 5 yr:

Plan A: $48,000 $50,400 $52,920 $55,566 $58,344.30

Plan B: $50,000 $52,000 $54,000 $56,000 $58,000

By studying sequences we can see that Plan A yields a better salary if Justine plans to stay in the job for at least 5 yr.

These sequences are called *finite sequences* because they have a finite number of terms. The sequence 1, 4, 9, 16, 25, . . . is called an *infinite sequence* because it continues indefinitely.

Because the terms in a sequence are related to the set of positive integers, we give a formal definition of finite and infinite sequences, using the language of functions.

DEFINITION Finite and Infinite Sequences

An **infinite sequence** is a function whose domain is the set of positive integers. A **finite sequence** is a function whose domain is the set of the first n positive integers.

For any positive integer n, the value of the sequence is denoted by a_n (read as "a sub n"). The values $a_1, a_2, a_3, . . .$ are called the **terms of the sequence**. The expression a_n defines the **nth term** (or general term) **of the sequence**.

Example 1   Listing the Terms of a Sequence

Classroom Example: p. 996, Exercise 8

List the terms of the following sequences.

a. $a_n = 3n^2 - 4; \quad 1 \le n \le 4$ **b.** $a_n = 3 \cdot 2^n$

Solution:

a. The domain is restricted to the first four positive integers, indicating that the sequence is finite.

n	a_n
1	$3(1)^2 - 4 = -1$
2	$3(2)^2 - 4 = 8$
3	$3(3)^2 - 4 = 23$
4	$3(4)^2 - 4 = 44$

The sequence is $-1, 8, 23, 44$.

b. The sequence $a_n = 3 \cdot 2^n$ has no restrictions on its domain; therefore, it is an infinite sequence.

n	a_n
1	$3 \cdot 2^1 = 6$
2	$3 \cdot 2^2 = 12$
3	$3 \cdot 2^3 = 24$
4	$3 \cdot 2^4 = 48$

The sequence is $6, 12, 24, 48, . . .$

. . .

Skill Practice List the terms of the sequences.

1. $a_n = n^3 - 2 \quad 1 \le n \le 3$ **2.** $a_n = \left(\dfrac{2}{3}\right)^n$

Answers

1. $-1, 6, 25$ **2.** $\dfrac{2}{3}, \dfrac{4}{9}, \dfrac{8}{27}, . . .$

Calculator Connections

If the nth term of a sequence is known, a *Seq* function on a graphing calculator can quickly display a list of terms. It is necessary to enter the formula for the nth term, the independent variable, the starting value for n, the ending value for n, and the increment for n.

$$\text{Seq}(a_n, n, \text{begin, end, increment})$$

The first four terms of the sequence $a_n = 3 \cdot 2^n$ from Example 1(b) are shown.

```
seq(3*2^n,n,1,4,
1)
       {6 12 24 48}
```

Sometimes the terms of a sequence may have alternating signs. Such a sequence is called an **alternating sequence**.

Classroom Example: p. 996, Exercise 14

Example 2   Listing the Terms of an Alternating Sequence

List the first four terms of each alternating sequence.

a. $a_n = (-1)^n \cdot \dfrac{1}{n}$ **b.** $a_n = (-1)^{n+1} \cdot \left(\dfrac{2}{3}\right)^n$

Solution:

a.

n	a_n	
1	$(-1)^1 \cdot \dfrac{1}{1} = -1$	The first four terms are $-1, \frac{1}{2}, -\frac{1}{3}, \frac{1}{4}$.
2	$(-1)^2 \cdot \dfrac{1}{2} = \dfrac{1}{2}$	
3	$(-1)^3 \cdot \dfrac{1}{3} = -\dfrac{1}{3}$	
4	$(-1)^4 \cdot \dfrac{1}{4} = \dfrac{1}{4}$	

TIP: Notice that the factor $(-1)^n$ makes the even-numbered terms positive and the odd-numbered terms negative.

b.

n	a_n	
1	$(-1)^{1+1} \cdot \left(\dfrac{2}{3}\right)^1 = (-1)^2 \cdot \left(\dfrac{2}{3}\right) = \dfrac{2}{3}$	
2	$(-1)^{2+1} \cdot \left(\dfrac{2}{3}\right)^2 = (-1)^3 \cdot \left(\dfrac{4}{9}\right) = -\dfrac{4}{9}$	
3	$(-1)^{3+1} \cdot \left(\dfrac{2}{3}\right)^3 = (-1)^4 \cdot \left(\dfrac{8}{27}\right) = \dfrac{8}{27}$	
4	$(-1)^{4+1} \cdot \left(\dfrac{2}{3}\right)^4 = (-1)^5 \cdot \left(\dfrac{16}{81}\right) = -\dfrac{16}{81}$	

TIP: Notice that the factor $(-1)^{n+1}$ makes the odd-numbered terms positive and the even-numbered terms negative.

The first four terms are $\frac{2}{3}, -\frac{4}{9}, \frac{8}{27}, -\frac{16}{81}$.

Skill Practice List the first four terms of each alternating sequence.

3. $a_n = (-1)^n \left(\dfrac{1}{2}\right)^n$ **4.** $a_n = (-1)^{n+1} \left(\dfrac{2}{n}\right)$

Answers

3. $-\dfrac{1}{2}, \dfrac{1}{4}, -\dfrac{1}{8}, \dfrac{1}{16}$

4. $2, -1, \dfrac{2}{3}, -\dfrac{1}{2}$

In Examples 1 and 2, we were given the formula for the *n*th term of a sequence and asked to list several terms of the sequence. We now consider the reverse process. Given several terms of the sequence, we will find a formula for the *n*th term. To do so, look for a pattern that establishes each term as a function of the term number.

Example 3 | **Finding the *n*th Term of a Sequence**

Classroom Examples: p. 996, Exercises 24 and 30

Find a formula for the *n*th term of the sequence.

a. $\dfrac{1}{2}, \dfrac{2}{3}, \dfrac{3}{4}, \dfrac{4}{5}, \ldots$ **b.** $-2, 4, -6, 8, -10, \ldots$ **c.** $\dfrac{1}{2}, \dfrac{1}{4}, \dfrac{1}{8}, \dfrac{1}{16}, \ldots$

Solution:

a. For each term in the sequence, the numerator is equal to the term number, and the denominator is equal to 1 more than the term number. Therefore, the *n*th term may be given by

$$a_n = \frac{n}{n+1}$$

b. The odd-numbered terms are negative, and the even-numbered terms are positive. The factor $(-1)^n$ will produce the required alternation of signs. The numbers 2, 4, 6, 8, 10, ... are equal to 2(1), 2(2), 2(3), 2(4), 2(5), ... Therefore, the *n*th term may be given by

$$a_n = (-1)^n \cdot 2n$$

c. The denominators are consecutive powers of 2. The sequence can be written as

$$\frac{1}{2^1}, \frac{1}{2^2}, \frac{1}{2^3}, \frac{1}{2^4}, \ldots$$

Therefore, the *n*th term may be given by

$$a_n = \frac{1}{2^n}$$

Skill Practice Find a formula for the *n*th term of the sequence.

5. $\dfrac{1}{3}, \dfrac{1}{9}, \dfrac{1}{27}, \dfrac{1}{81}, \ldots$ **6.** $-1, 4, -9, 16, -25, \ldots$ **7.** $\dfrac{3}{2}, \dfrac{4}{3}, \dfrac{5}{4}, \dfrac{6}{5}, \dfrac{7}{6}, \ldots$

TIP: The first few terms of a sequence are not sufficient to define the sequence uniquely. For example, consider the sequence

$$\frac{1}{2}, \frac{1}{4}, \frac{1}{8}, \ldots$$

The following formulas both produce the first three terms, but differ at the fourth term:

$$a_n = \frac{1}{2^n} \quad \text{and} \quad b_n = \frac{1}{n^2 - n + 2}$$

$$a_4 = \frac{1}{16} \quad \text{whereas} \quad b_4 = \frac{1}{14}$$

To define a sequence uniquely, the *n*th term must be provided.

Answers

5. $a_n = \dfrac{1}{3^n}$ **6.** $a_n = (-1)^n n^2$

7. $a_n = \dfrac{n+2}{n+1}$

Classroom Example: p. 997,
Exercise 36

| **Example 4** | **Using a Sequence in an Application** |

A child drops a ball from a height of 4 ft. With each bounce, the ball rebounds to 50% of its height. Write a sequence whose terms represent the heights from which the ball falls (begin with the initial height from which the ball was dropped).

Solution:

The ball first drops 4 ft and then rebounds to a new height of 0.50(4 ft) = 2 ft. Similarly, it falls from 2 ft and rebounds 0.50(2 ft) = 1 ft. Repeating this process, we have

$$4, 2, 1, \frac{1}{2}, \frac{1}{4}, \frac{1}{8}, \cdots$$

The nth term can be represented by $a_n = 4 \cdot (0.50)^{n-1}$.

Skill Practice

8. The first swing of a pendulum measures 30°. If each swing that follows is 25% less, list the first three terms of this sequence.

2. Series

In many mathematical applications it is important to find the sum of the terms of a sequence. For example, suppose that the yearly interest earned in an account over a 4-yr period is given by the sequence

$$\$250, \quad \$265, \quad \$278.25, \quad \$292.16$$

The sum of the terms gives the total interest earned

$$\$250 + \$265 + \$278.25 + \$292.16 = \$1085.41$$

By adding the terms of a sequence, we obtain a series.

Calculator Connections

The sum of a finite series may be found on a graphing calculator if the nth term of the corresponding sequence is known. The calculator takes the sum of a sequence by using the *Sum* and *Seq* functions.

```
sum(seq(n^3,n,1,
4,1))
            100
```

DEFINITION   Series

The indicated sum of the terms of a sequence is called a **series**.

As with a sequence, a series may be a finite or an infinite sum of terms.

A convenient notation used to denote the sum of a set of terms is called **sigma notation**. The Greek letter Σ (sigma) is used to indicate sums. For example, the sum of the first four terms of the sequence defined by $a_n = n^3$ are denoted by

$$\sum_{n=1}^{4} n^3$$

This is read as "the sum from n equals 1 to 4 of n^3" and is simplified as

$$\sum_{n=1}^{4} n^3 = (1)^3 + (2)^3 + (3)^3 + (4)^3$$
$$= 1 + 8 + 27 + 64$$
$$= 100$$

In this example, the letter n is called the **index of summation**. Many times, the letters i, j, and k are also used for the index of summation.

Answer

8. 30°, 22.5°, 16.875°

Example 5 Finding a Sum from Sigma Notation

Classroom Example: p. 997, Exercise 46

Find the sum. $\displaystyle\sum_{i=1}^{3}(-1)^{i+1}\cdot(3i+4)$

Solution:

$$\sum_{i=1}^{3}(-1)^{i+1}\cdot(3i+4)=(-1)^{1+1}\cdot[3(1)+4]+(-1)^{2+1}\cdot[3(2)+4]$$
$$+(-1)^{3+1}\cdot[3(3)+4]$$
$$=(-1)^{2}\cdot(7)+(-1)^{3}\cdot(10)+(-1)^{4}\cdot(13)$$
$$=7-10+13$$
$$=10$$

Avoiding Mistakes

The letter i is used as a variable for the index of summation. In this context, it does not represent an imaginary number.

Skill Practice Find the sum.

9. $\displaystyle\sum_{i=1}^{4}(-1)^{i}(4i-3)$

Example 6 Converting to Summation Notation

Classroom Example: p. 997, Exercise 62

Write the series in summation notation.

a. $\dfrac{2}{3}+\dfrac{4}{9}+\dfrac{8}{27}+\dfrac{16}{81}$ Use n as the index of summation.

b. $1-\dfrac{1}{2}+\dfrac{1}{3}-\dfrac{1}{4}+\dfrac{1}{5}-\dfrac{1}{6}$ Use j as the index of summation.

Solution:

a. The sum can be written as

$$\left(\frac{2}{3}\right)^{1}+\left(\frac{2}{3}\right)^{2}+\left(\frac{2}{3}\right)^{3}+\left(\frac{2}{3}\right)^{4}$$

Taking n from 1 to 4, we have

$$\sum_{n=1}^{4}\left(\frac{2}{3}\right)^{n}$$

b. The even-numbered terms are negative. The factor $(-1)^{j+1}$ is negative for even values of j. Therefore, the series can be written as

$$\sum_{j=1}^{6}(-1)^{j+1}\cdot\frac{1}{j}$$

Skill Practice Write the series in summation notation.

10. $\dfrac{1}{4}+\dfrac{1}{16}+\dfrac{1}{64}+\dfrac{1}{256}$ **11.** $\dfrac{1}{2}-\dfrac{1}{4}+\dfrac{1}{6}-\dfrac{1}{8}+\dfrac{1}{10}$

Answers

9. 8   **10.** $\displaystyle\sum_{i=1}^{4}\frac{1}{4^{i}}$

11. $\displaystyle\sum_{i=1}^{5}(-1)^{i+1}\frac{1}{2i}$

Section 14.2 Practice Exercises

Boost *your* GRADE at
ALEKS.com!

 ALEKS®
version 3.0

- Practice Problems
- Self-Tests
- NetTutor

- e-Professors
- Videos

For additional exercises, see Classroom Activities
14.2A–14.2C in the *Instructor's Resource Manual*
at www.mhhe.com/moh.

Study Skills Exercise

1. Define the key terms.

   a. infinite sequence   b. finite sequence   c. terms of a sequence

   d. *n*th term of a sequence   e. alternating sequence   f. series

   g. sigma notation   h. index of summation

Review Exercises

For Exercises 2–4, evaluate the expression.

2. $9!$ 362,880

3. $\dfrac{8!}{2! \cdot 6!}$ 28

4. $\dfrac{7!}{7! \cdot 0!}$ 1

For Exercises 5–6, expand the binomial.

5. $(2x + z)^4$ $16x^4 + 32x^3z + 24x^2z^2 + 8xz^3 + z^4$

6. $(4m - 3t)^3$ $64m^3 - 144m^2t + 108mt^2 - 27t^3$

Concept 1: Finite and Infinite Sequences

For Exercises 7–18, list the terms of each sequence. **(See Examples 1–2.)**

7. $a_n = 3n + 1,\quad 1 \le n \le 4$ $4, 7, 10, 13$

8. $a_n = -2n + 3,\quad 1 \le n \le 4$ $1, -1, -3, -5$

9. $a_n = \sqrt{n + 2},\quad 1 \le n \le 4$ $\sqrt{3}, 2, \sqrt{5}, \sqrt{6}$

10. $a_n = \sqrt{n - 1},\quad 1 \le n \le 4$ $0, 1, \sqrt{2}, \sqrt{3}$

11. $a_n = (-1)^n \dfrac{n + 1}{n + 2},\quad 1 \le n \le 4$ $-\dfrac{2}{3}, \dfrac{3}{4}, -\dfrac{4}{5}, \dfrac{5}{6}$

12. $a_n = (-1)^n \dfrac{n - 1}{n + 2},\quad 1 \le n \le 4$ $0, \dfrac{1}{4}, -\dfrac{2}{5}, \dfrac{1}{2}$

13. $a_n = (-1)^{n+1} (n^2 - 1),\quad 1 \le n \le 4$ $0, -3, 8, -15$

14. $a_n = (-1)^{n+1} (n^2),\quad 1 \le n \le 4$ $1, -4, 9, -16$

15. $a_n = n^2 - n,\quad 1 \le n \le 4$ $0, 2, 6, 12$

16. $a_n = n(n^2 - 1),\quad 1 \le n \le 4$ $0, 6, 24, 60$

17. $a_n = (-1)^n 3^n,\quad 1 \le n \le 4$ $-3, 9, -27, 81$

18. $a_n = (-1)^n n,\quad 1 \le n \le 4$ $-1, 2, -3, 4$

19. If the *n*th term of a sequence is $a_n = (-1)^n \cdot n^2$, which terms are positive and which are negative? When n is odd, the term is negative. When n is even, the term is positive.

20. If the *n*th term of a sequence is $a_n = (-1)^{n-1} \cdot \frac{1}{n}$, which terms are positive and which are negative? When n is odd, the term is positive. When n is even, the term is negative.

For Exercises 21–32, find a formula for the *n*th term of the sequence. Answers may vary. **(See Example 3.)**

21. $2, 4, 6, 8, \ldots$
    $a_n = 2n$

22. $3, 6, 9, 12, \ldots$
    $a_n = 3n$

23. $1, 3, 5, 7, \ldots$
    $a_n = 2n - 1$

24. $3, 5, 7, 9, \ldots$
    $a_n = 2n + 1$

25. $1, \dfrac{1}{4}, \dfrac{1}{9}, \dfrac{1}{16}, \ldots$
    $a_n = \dfrac{1}{n^2}$

26. $\dfrac{1}{2}, \dfrac{2}{3}, \dfrac{3}{4}, \dfrac{4}{5}, \ldots$
    $a_n = \dfrac{n}{n + 1}$

27. $1, -1, 1, -1, \ldots$
    $a_n = (-1)^{n+1}$

28. $-1, 1, -1, 1, \ldots$
    $a_n = (-1)^n$

29. $-2, 4, -8, 16, \ldots$
    $a_n = (-1)^n 2^n$

30. $3, -9, 27, -81, \ldots$
    $a_n = (-1)^{n+1} 3^n$

31. $\dfrac{3}{5}, \dfrac{3}{25}, \dfrac{3}{125}, \dfrac{3}{625}, \ldots$
    $a_n = \dfrac{3}{5^n}$

32. $\dfrac{1}{4}, \dfrac{1}{16}, \dfrac{1}{64}, \dfrac{1}{256}, \ldots$
    $a_n = \dfrac{1}{4^n}$

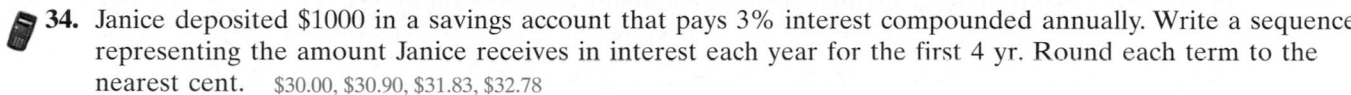

33. Edmond borrowed $500. To pay off the loan, he agreed to pay 2% of the balance plus $50 each month. Write a sequence representing the amount Edmond will pay each month for the next 4 months. Round each term to the nearest cent. $60, $58.80, $57.62, $56.47

34. Janice deposited $1000 in a savings account that pays 3% interest compounded annually. Write a sequence representing the amount Janice receives in interest each year for the first 4 yr. Round each term to the nearest cent. $30.00, $30.90, $31.83, $32.78

35. A certain bacteria culture doubles its size each day. If there are 25,000 bacteria on the first day, write a sequence representing the population each day for the first week (7 days).   **(See Example 4.)**
25,000; 50,000; 100,000; 200,000; 400,000; 800,000; 1,600,000

36. A radioactive chemical decays by one-half of its amount each week. If there is 16 g of the chemical in week 1, write a sequence representing the amount present each week for 2 months (8 weeks).
$16, 8, 4, 2, 1, \frac{1}{2}, \frac{1}{4}, \frac{1}{8}$ (grams)

Concept 2: Series

37. What is the difference between a sequence and a series?
A sequence is an ordered list of terms. A series is the sum of the terms of a sequence.

38. a. Identify the index of summation for the series. $\displaystyle\sum_{k=1}^{7}(k^2+1)$ k

b. How many terms does this series have?   7

For Exercises 39–54, find the sums. **(See Example 5.)**

39. $\displaystyle\sum_{i=1}^{4}(3i^2)$ 90

40. $\displaystyle\sum_{i=1}^{4}(2i^2)$ 60

41. $\displaystyle\sum_{j=0}^{4}\left(\frac{1}{2}\right)^j$ $\frac{31}{16}$

42. $\displaystyle\sum_{j=0}^{4}\left(\frac{1}{3}\right)^j$ $\frac{121}{81}$

43. $\displaystyle\sum_{i=1}^{6}5$ 30

44. $\displaystyle\sum_{i=1}^{7}3$ 21

45. $\displaystyle\sum_{j=1}^{4}(-1)^j(5j)$ 10

46. $\displaystyle\sum_{j=1}^{4}(-1)^j(4j)$ 8

47. $\displaystyle\sum_{i=1}^{4}\frac{i+1}{i}$ $\frac{73}{12}$

48. $\displaystyle\sum_{i=2}^{5}\frac{i-1}{i}$ $\frac{163}{60}$

49. $\displaystyle\sum_{j=1}^{3}(j+1)(j+2)$ 38

50. $\displaystyle\sum_{j=1}^{3}j(j+2)$ 26

51. $\displaystyle\sum_{k=1}^{7}(-1)^k$ -1

52. $\displaystyle\sum_{k=0}^{5}(-1)^{k+1}$ 0

53. $\displaystyle\sum_{k=1}^{5}k^2$ 55

54. $\displaystyle\sum_{k=1}^{5}2^k$ 62

For Exercises 55–64, write the series in summation notation. **(See Example 6.)**

55. $1+2+3+4+5+6$ $\displaystyle\sum_{n=1}^{6}n$

56. $1-2+3-4+5-6$ $\displaystyle\sum_{n=1}^{6}(-1)^{n+1}n$

57. $4+4+4+4+4$ $\displaystyle\sum_{i=1}^{5}4$

58. $8+8+8+8+8$ $\displaystyle\sum_{i=1}^{5}8$

59. $4+8+12+16+20$ $\displaystyle\sum_{j=1}^{5}4j$

60. $3+6+9+12+15$ $\displaystyle\sum_{j=1}^{5}3j$

61. $\frac{1}{3}-\frac{1}{9}+\frac{1}{27}-\frac{1}{81}$ $\displaystyle\sum_{k=1}^{4}(-1)^{k+1}\frac{1}{3^k}$

62. $\frac{1}{2}-\frac{1}{4}+\frac{1}{8}-\frac{1}{16}$ $\displaystyle\sum_{k=1}^{4}(-1)^{k+1}\frac{1}{2^k}$

63. $x+x^2+x^3+x^4+x^5$ $\displaystyle\sum_{n=1}^{5}x^n$

64. $y^2+y^4+y^6+y^8+y^{10}$ $\displaystyle\sum_{n=1}^{5}y^{2n}$

Expanding Your Skills

Some sequences are defined by a recursion formula, which defines each term of a sequence in terms of one or more of its preceding terms. For example, if $a_1 = 5$ and $a_n = 2a_{n-1} + 1$ for $n > 1$, then the terms of the sequence are 5, 11, 23, 47, ... In this case, each term after the first is one more than twice the term before it.

For Exercises 65–68, list the first five terms of the sequence.

65. $a_1 = -3$, $a_n = a_{n-1} + 5$ for $n > 1$
    $-3, 2, 7, 12, 17$

66. $a_1 = 10$, $a_n = a_{n-1} - 3$ for $n > 1$
    $10, 7, 4, 1, -2$

67. $a_1 = 5$, $a_n = 4a_{n-1} + 1$ for $n > 1$
    $5, 21, 85, 341, 1365$

68. $a_1 = -2$, $a_n = -3a_{n-1} + 4$ for $n > 1$
    $-2, 10, -26, 82, -242$

69. A famous sequence in mathematics is called the Fibonacci sequence, named after the Italian mathematician Leonardo Fibonacci of the thirteenth century. The Fibonacci sequence is defined by

$$a_1 = 1$$

$$a_2 = 1$$

$$a_n = a_{n-1} + a_{n-2} \quad \text{for } n > 2$$

This definition implies that beginning with the third term, each term is the sum of the preceding two terms. Write out the first 10 terms of the Fibonacci sequence. $1, 1, 2, 3, 5, 8, 13, 21, 34, 55$

Section 14.3   Arithmetic Sequences and Series

Concepts

1. Arithmetic Sequences
2. Arithmetic Series

1. Arithmetic Sequences

In this section and the next, we will study two special types of sequences and series. The first is called an arithmetic sequence, for example:

$$4, 7, 10, 13, 16, \ldots$$

This sequence is an arithmetic sequence. Note the characteristic that each successive term after the first is a fixed value more than the previous term (in this case the terms differ by 3).

> **DEFINITION**   Arithmetic Sequence
>
> An **arithmetic sequence** is a sequence in which the difference between consecutive terms is constant.

The fixed difference between a term and its predecessor is called the **common difference** and is denoted by the letter d. The common difference is the difference between a term and its predecessor. That is,

$$d = a_{n+1} - a_n$$

Furthermore, if a_1 is the first term, then

$$a_1 = a_1$$

$$a_2 = a_1 + d \qquad \text{is the second term}$$

$$a_3 = a_1 + 2d \qquad \text{is the third term}$$

$$a_4 = a_1 + 3d \qquad \text{is the fourth term and so on}$$

$$\cdots$$

In general, $a_n = a_1 + (n - 1)d$.

 Writing   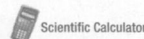 Translating Expression   Geometry   Scientific Calculator   Video   NS&E

> **FORMULA** *n*th Term of an Arithmetic Sequence
>
> The *n*th term of an arithmetic sequence is given by
>
> $$a_n = a_1 + (n - 1)d$$
>
> where a_1 is the first term of the sequence and d is the common difference.

Example 1 Writing the *n*th Term of an Arithmetic Sequence

Write the *n*th term of the sequence. $9, 2, -5, -12, \ldots$

Classroom Example: p. 1003, Exercise 20

Solution:

$$9, \quad 2, \quad -5, \quad -12, \ldots$$

$$-7 \quad -7 \quad -7$$

The common difference can be found by subtracting a term from its predecessor. $2 - 9 = -7$

With $a_1 = 9$ and $d = -7$, we have

$$a_n = 9 + (n - 1)(-7)$$
$$= 9 - 7n + 7$$
$$= -7n + 16$$

TIP: Notice that the terms of an arithmetic sequence increase or decrease linearly. In Example 1, the terms decrease by 7 for each subsequent term. This is similar to a line with a slope of -7.

Skill Practice Write the *n*th term of the sequence.

1. $-3, -1, 1, 3, 5, \ldots$

In Example 1, the common difference between terms is -7. Accordingly, each term of the sequence *decreases* by 7.

The formula $a_n = a_1 + (n - 1)d$ contains four variables: $a_n, a_1, n,$ and d. Consequently, if we know the value of three of the four variables, we can solve for the fourth.

Example 2 Finding a Specified Term of an Arithmetic Sequence

Find the ninth term of the arithmetic sequence in which $a_1 = -4$ and $a_{22} = 164$.

Classroom Example: p. 1003, Exercise 34

Solution:

To find the value of the ninth term a_9, we need to determine the value of d. To find d, substitute $a_1 = -4$, $n = 22$, and $a_{22} = 164$ into the formula $a_n = a_1 + (n - 1)d$.

$$a_n = a_1 + (n - 1)d$$
$$164 = -4 + (22 - 1)d$$
$$164 = -4 + 21d$$
$$168 = 21d$$
$$d = 8$$

Answer

1. $2n - 5$

Instructor Note: Consider showing your students the similarity between an arithmetic sequence and a linear equation in two variables. The term number, n, behaves as the independent variable, x. The common difference, d, behaves as the slope, m.

Therefore, $a_n = -4 + (n-1)(8)$

$$a_9 = -4 + (9-1)(8)$$
$$= -4 + (8)(8)$$
$$= 60$$

Skill Practice

2. Find the tenth term of the arithmetic sequence in which $a_1 = 14$ and $a_{15} = -28$.   (Hint: First find d.)

Classroom Example: p. 1003, Exercise 36

Example 3   Finding the Number of Terms in an Arithmetic Sequence

Find the number of terms of the sequence $7, 3, -1, -5, \ldots, -113$.

Solution:

To find the number of terms n, we can substitute $a_1 = 7$, $d = -4$, and $a_n = -113$ into the formula for the nth term.

$$a_n = a_1 + (n-1)d$$
$$-113 = 7 + (n-1)(-4)$$
$$-113 = 7 - 4n + 4$$
$$-113 = 11 - 4n$$
$$-124 = -4n$$
$$n = 31$$

Skill Practice   Find the number of terms of the sequence.

3. $-15, -11, -7, -3, \ldots 81$

2. Arithmetic Series

The indicated sum of an arithmetic sequence is called an **arithmetic series**. For example, the series

$$3 + 7 + 11 + 15 + 19 + 23$$

is an arithmetic series because the common difference between terms is constant (4). Adding the terms in a lengthy sum is cumbersome, so we offer the following "short cut," which is developed here. Let S represent the sum of the terms in the series.

$S = 3 + 7 + 11 + 15 + 19 + 23$	Add the terms in ascending order.
$S = 23 + 19 + 15 + 11 + 7 + 3$	Add the terms in descending order.
$2S = 26 + 26 + 26 + 26 + 26 + 26$	Adding the two series produces six terms of 26.

$$2S = 6 \cdot 26$$
$$S = \frac{6 \cdot 26}{2}$$
$$= 78$$

Answers

2. $d = -3$, $a_{10} = -13$ **3.** 25

By adding the terms in ascending and descending order, we double the sum but create a pattern that is easily added. This is true in general. To find the sum, S_n, of the first n terms of the arithmetic series $a_1 + a_2 + a_3 + \cdots + a_n$, we have

$$S_n = a_1 \qquad + (a_1 + d) + (a_1 + 2d) + \cdots + a_n \qquad \text{Ascending order}$$
$$\underline{S_n = a_n \qquad + (a_n - d) + (a_n - 2d) + \cdots + a_1} \qquad \text{Descending order}$$
$$2S_n = (a_1 + a_n) + (a_1 + a_n) + (a_1 + a_n) + \cdots + (a_1 + a_n)$$
$$2S_n = n(a_1 + a_n)$$
$$S_n = \frac{n}{2}(a_1 + a_n)$$

FORMULA Sum of an Arithmetic Series

The sum, S_n, of the first n terms of an arithmetic series is given by

$$S_n = \frac{n}{2}(a_1 + a_n)$$

where a_1 is the first term of the series and a_n is the nth term of the series.

Example 4 **Finding the Sum of an Arithmetic Series**

Find the sum of the series. $\displaystyle\sum_{i=1}^{25}(2i + 3)$

Solution:

In this series, $n = 25$. Furthermore, $a_1 = 2(1) + 3 = 5$ and $a_{25} = 2(25) + 3 = 53$. Therefore,

$$S_{25} = \frac{25}{2}(5 + 53) \qquad \text{Apply the formula } S_n = \frac{n}{2}(a_1 + a_n).$$

$$= \frac{25}{2}(58) \qquad \text{Simplify.}$$

$$= 725$$

Skill Practice Find the sum of the series.

4. $\displaystyle\sum_{i=1}^{20}(3i - 2)$

Classroom Example: p. 1003, Exercise 50

Avoiding Mistakes

When we apply the sum formula $S_n = \dfrac{n}{2}(a_1 + a_n)$ to find the sum $\displaystyle\sum_{i=1}^{n} a_n$, the index of summation, i, must begin at 1.

Answer

4. 590

Classroom Example: p. 1003,
Exercise 58

Example 5 **Finding the Sum of an Arithmetic Series**

Find the sum of the series.

$$-3 + (-5) + (-7) + \cdots + (-127)$$

Solution:

For this series, $a_1 = -3$ and $a_n = -127$. However, to determine the sum, we also need to find the value of n. The difference between the second term and its predecessor is $-5 - (-3) = -2$. Thus, $d = -2$. We have

$-127 = -3 + (n-1)(-2)$	Apply the formula $a_n = a_1 + (n-1)d$.
$-127 = -3 - 2n + 2$	Apply the distributive property.
$-127 = -1 - 2n$	Combine *like* terms.
$-126 = -2n$	Solve for n.
$n = 63$	

Using $n = 63$, $a_1 = -3$, and $a_{63} = -127$, we have

$$S_n = \frac{n}{2}(a_1 + a_n) = \frac{63}{2}[-3 + (-127)] = \frac{63}{2}(-130) = -4095$$

Skill Practice Find the sum of the series.

5. $8 + 3 + (-2) + \cdots + (-137)$

Answer

5. -1935

Section 14.3   Practice Exercises

Study Skills Exercise

1. Define the key terms.

    a. arithmetic sequence   **b. common difference**   **c. arithmetic series**

Review Exercises

2. Write the first four terms of the sequence. $c_n = \dfrac{n^2}{n+1}$ $\dfrac{1}{2}, \dfrac{4}{3}, \dfrac{9}{4}, \dfrac{16}{5}$

3. Write the first four terms of the sequence. $d_n = (-1)^n$ $-1, 1, -1, 1$

4. Find the sum. $\displaystyle\sum_{n=1}^{10}(-1)^{n+1}$ 0 **5.** Find the sum. $\displaystyle\sum_{n=1}^{5}(1-4n)$ -55

Concept 1: Arithmetic Sequences

6. Explain how to determine if a sequence is arithmetic.   A sequence is arithmetic if the difference between any term and the preceding term is constant.

For Exercises 7–12, find the common difference d for each arithmetic sequence.

7. $1, 3, 5, 7, 9, \ldots$ 2 **8.** $2, 8, 14, 20, 26, \ldots$ 6 **9.** $6, 3, 0, -3, -6, \ldots$ -3

10. $8, 3, -2, -7, -12, \ldots$ -5 **11.** $-7, -9, -11, -13, -15, \ldots$ -2 **12.** $-15, -11, -7, -3, 1, \ldots$ 4

For Exercises 13–18, write the first five terms of the arithmetic sequence.

13. $a_1 = 3, d = 5$ 3, 8, 13, 18, 23

14. $a_1 = -3, d = 2$ $-3, -1, 1, 3, 5$

15. $a_1 = 2, d = \frac{1}{2}$ $2, \frac{5}{2}, 3, \frac{7}{2}, 4$

16. $a_1 = 0, d = \frac{1}{3}$ $0, \frac{1}{3}, \frac{2}{3}, 1, \frac{4}{3}$

17. $a_1 = 2, d = -4$

$2, -2, -6, -10, -14$

18. $a_1 = 10, d = -6$ $10, 4, -2, -8, -14$

For Exercises 19–27, write the nth term of the sequence. **(See Example 1.)**

19. 0, 5, 10, 15, 20, . . .
$a_n = -5 + 5n$

20. 7, 12, 17, 22, 27, . . .
$a_n = 2 + 5n$

21. $-2, -4, -6, -8, -10, \ldots$
$a_n = -2n$

22. 1, $-3, -7, -11, -15, \ldots$
$a_n = 5 - 4n$

23. $2, \frac{5}{2}, 3, \frac{7}{2}, 4, \ldots$ $a_n = \frac{3}{2} + \frac{1}{2}n$

24. $1, \frac{4}{3}, \frac{5}{3}, 2, \frac{7}{3}, \ldots$ $a_n = \frac{2}{3} + \frac{1}{3}n$

25. 21, 17, 13, 9, 5, . . .
$a_n = 25 - 4n$

26. 9, 6, 3, 0, -3, . . .
$a_n = 12 - 3n$

27. $-8, -2, 4, 10, 16, \ldots$
$a_n = -14 + 6n$

For Exercises 28–35, find the indicated term of each arithmetic sequence. **(See Example 2.)**

28. Find the eighth term given $a_1 = -6$ and $d = -3$.
$u_8 -27$

29. Find the sixth term given $a_1 = -3$ and $d = 4$.
$u_6 = 17$

30. Find the 12th term given $a_1 = -8$ and $d = -2$.
$a_{12} = -30$

31. Find the ninth term given $a_1 = -1$ and $d = 6$.
$a_9 = 47$

32. Find the tenth term given $a_1 = 1$ and $a_7 = 31$.
$a_{10} = 46$

33. Find the seventh term given $a_1 = 0$ and $a_{10} = -45$.
$a_7 = -30$

34. Find the sixth term given $a_1 - 3$ and $a_{13} - 39$.
$a_6 = 18$

35. Find the 11th term given $a_1 - 12$ and $a_6 = -18$.
$a_{11} = -48$

For Exercises 36–43, find the number of terms, n, of each arithmetic sequence. **(See Example 3.)**

36. 2, 0, -2, . . . , -56
30

37. 8, 13, 18, . . . , 98
19

38. 1, $-3, -7, \ldots, -67$
18

39. 1, 5, 9, . . . , 85
22

40. $1, \frac{3}{4}, \frac{1}{2}, \ldots, -4$ 21

41. $2, \frac{5}{2}, 3, \ldots, 13$ 23

42. $-\frac{5}{3}, -1, -\frac{1}{3}, \ldots, \frac{37}{3}$ 22

43. $\frac{13}{3}, \frac{19}{3}, \frac{25}{3}, \ldots, \frac{73}{3}$ 11

44. If the third and fourth terms of an arithmetic sequence are 18 and 21, what are the first and second terms? $a_1 = 12, a_2 = 15$

45. If the third and fourth terms of an arithmetic sequence are -8 and -11, what are the first and second terms? $a_1 = -2, a_2 = -5$

Concept 2: Arithmetic Series

46. Explain the difference between an arithmetic sequence and an arithmetic series.
An arithmetic sequence is an ordered list of terms in which the difference between a term and its predecessor is constant. An arithmetic series is the sum of the terms in such a sequence.

For Exercises 47–60, find the sum of the arithmetic series. **(See Examples 4–5.)**

47. $\sum_{i=1}^{20} (3i + 2)$ 670

48. $\sum_{i=1}^{15} (2i - 3)$ 195

49. $\sum_{i=1}^{20} (i + 4)$ 290

50. $\sum_{i=1}^{25} (i - 3)$ 250

51. $\sum_{j=1}^{10} (4 - j)$ -15

52. $\sum_{j=1}^{10} (6 - j)$ 5

53. $\sum_{j=1}^{15} \left(\frac{2}{3}j + 1\right)$ 95

54. $\sum_{j=1}^{15} \left(\frac{1}{2}j - 2\right)$ 30

55. $4 + 8 + 12 + \cdots + 84$ 924

56. $4 + 9 + 14 + \cdots + 49$ 265

57. $6 + 8 + 10 + \cdots + 34$ 300

58. $-4 + (-3) + (-2) + \cdots + 12$ 68

59. $-3 + (-7) + (-11) + \cdots + (-39)$ -210

60. $2 + 5 + 8 + \cdots + 53$ 495

 Writing   Translating Expression   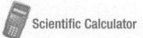 Geometry   Scientific Calculator   Video   NS&E

61. Find the sum of the first 100 positive integers.
5050

62. Find the sum of the first 50 positive even integers.
2550

 63. The seating in a certain theater is arranged so that there are 30 seats in row 1, 32 in row 2, 34 in row 3, and so on. If there are 20 rows, how many total seats are there? What is the total revenue if the average ticket price is $15 per seat and the theater is sold out? 980 seats; $14,700

64. A triangular array of dominoes has one domino in the first row, two dominoes in the second row, three dominoes in the third row, and so on. If there are 15 rows, how many dominoes are in the array? 120 dominoes

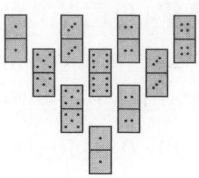

Section 14.4 Geometric Sequences and Series

Concepts

1. Geometric Sequences
2. Geometric Series

1. Geometric Sequences

The sequence 2, 4, 8, 16, 32, . . . is not an arithmetic sequence because the difference between terms is not constant. However, a different pattern exists. Notice that each term after the first is 2 times the preceding term. This sequence is called a geometric sequence.

> **DEFINITION** Geometric Sequence
>
> A **geometric sequence** is a sequence in which each term after the first term is a constant multiple of the preceding term.

The constant multiple between a term and its predecessor is called the **common ratio** and is denoted by r. The common ratio is found by dividing a term by the preceding term. That is,

$$r = \frac{a_{n+1}}{a_n}$$

For the sequence 2, 4, 8, 16, 32, . . . we have $r = \frac{4}{2} = \frac{8}{4} = \frac{16}{8} = \frac{32}{16} = 2$.

If a_1 denotes the first term of a geometric sequence, then

$$a_2 = a_1 r \qquad \text{is the second term.}$$
$$a_3 = a_1 r^2 \qquad \text{is the third term.}$$
$$a_4 = a_1 r^3 \qquad \text{is the fourth term, and so on.}$$
$$\cdots$$

This pattern gives $a_n = a_1 r^{n-1}$.

> **FORMULA** nth Term of a Geometric Sequence
>
> The nth term of a geometric sequence is given by
>
> $$a_n = a_1 r^{n-1}$$
>
> where a_1 is the first term and r is the common ratio.

 Writing   Translating Expression   Geometry   Scientific Calculator ● Video NS&E

Example 1 **Finding the *n*th Term of a Geometric Sequence**

Classroom Example: p. 1010, Exercise 20

Find the *n*th term of the sequence. **a.** $-1, 4, -16, 64, \ldots$ **b.** $12, 8, \dfrac{16}{3}, \dfrac{32}{9}, \ldots$

Solution:

a. The common ratio is found by dividing any term (after the first) by its predecessor.

$$r = \frac{4}{-1} = -4$$

With $r = -4$ and $a_1 = -1$, we have $a_n = -1(-4)^{n-1}$.

b. The common ratio is $r = \frac{8}{12} = \frac{2}{3}$. With $a_1 = 12$ and $r = \frac{2}{3}$, we have

$$a_n = 12\left(\frac{2}{3}\right)^{n-1}$$

Skill Practice Find the *n*th term of the geometric sequence.

1. $6, 12, 24, 48, \ldots$ **2.** $6, 2, \dfrac{2}{3}, \dfrac{2}{9}, \ldots$

The formula $a_n = a_1 r^{n-1}$ contains the variables $a_n, a_1, n,$ and r. If we know the value of three of the four variables, we can find the fourth.

Example 2 **Finding a Specified Term of a Geometric Sequence**

Classroom Example: p. 1010, Exercise 26

Given $a_n = 6\left(\dfrac{1}{2}\right)^{n-1}$, find a_5.

Solution:

$$a_n = 6\left(\frac{1}{2}\right)^{n-1}$$

$$a_5 = 6\left(\frac{1}{2}\right)^{5-1} = 6\left(\frac{1}{2}\right)^4 = 6\left(\frac{1}{16}\right) = \frac{3}{8}$$

Skill Practice

3. Given $a_n = 3(-2)^{n-1}$, find a_6.

Example 3 **Finding a Specified Term of a Geometric Sequence**

Classroom Example: p. 1010, Exercise 32

Find the first term of the geometric sequence where $a_5 = -162$ and $r = 3$.

Solution:

$-162 = a_1(3)^{5-1}$ Substitute $a_5 = -162, n = 5,$ and $r = 3$ into the formula $a_n = a_1 r^{n-1}$.

$-162 = a_1(3)^4$ Simplify and solve for a_1.

$-162 = a_1(81)$

$a_1 = -2$

Answers

1. $a_n = 6(2)^{n-1}$ **2.** $a_n = 6\left(\dfrac{1}{3}\right)^{n-1}$

3. -96

Skill Practice

4. Find the first term of the geometric sequence where $a_4 = \frac{25}{32}$ and $r = \frac{1}{4}$.

2. Geometric Series

The indicated sum of a geometric sequence is called a **geometric series**. For example,

$$1 + 3 + 9 + 27 + 81 + 243$$

is a geometric series. To find the sum, consider the following procedure. Let S represent the sum

$$S = 1 + 3 + 9 + 27 + 81 + 243$$

Now multiply S by the common ratio, which in this case is 3.

$$3S = 3 + 9 + 27 + 81 + 243 + 729$$

Then

$$3S - S = (3 + 9 + 27 + 81 + 243 + 729) - (1 + 3 + 9 + 27 + 81 + 243)$$

$$2S = 3 + 9 + 27 + 81 + 243 + 729 - 1 - 3 - 9 - 27 - 81 - 243$$

$$2S = 729 - 1 \qquad \text{The terms in red form a sum of zero.}$$

$$2S = 728$$

$$S = 364$$

A similar procedure can be used to find the sum S_n of the first n terms of any geometric series. Subtract rS_n from S_n.

$$S_n = a_1 \qquad + a_1 r \qquad + a_1 r^2 \qquad + \cdots + a_1 r^{n-1}$$

$$\underline{rS_n = a_1 r \qquad + a_1 r^2 \qquad + a_1 r^3 \qquad + \cdots + a_1 r^n}$$

$$S_n - rS_n = (a_1 - a_1 r) + (a_1 r - a_1 r^2) + (a_1 r^2 - a_1 r^3) + \cdots + (a_1 r^{n-1} - a_1 r^n)$$

$$S_n - rS_n = a_1 - a_1 r^n \qquad \text{The terms in red form a sum of zero.}$$

$$S_n(1 - r) = a_1(1 - r^n) \qquad \text{Factor each side of the equation.}$$

$$S_n = \frac{a_1(1 - r^n)}{1 - r} \qquad \text{Divide by } (1 - r).$$

FORMULA   Sum of a Geometric Series

The sum, S_n, of the first n terms of a geometric series $\displaystyle\sum_{i=1}^{n} a_1 r^{i-1}$ is given by

$$S_n = \frac{a_1(1 - r^n)}{1 - r}$$

where a_1 is the first term of the series, r is the common ratio, and $r \neq 1$.

Answer

4. 50

Example 4 **Finding the Sum of a Geometric Series**

Classroom Example: p. 1010, Exercise 40

Find the sum of the series. $\displaystyle\sum_{i=1}^{6} 4\left(\frac{1}{2}\right)^{i-1}$

Solution:

By expanding the terms of this series, we see that the series is geometric.

$$\sum_{i=1}^{6} 4\left(\frac{1}{2}\right)^{i-1} = 4 + 2 + 1 + \frac{1}{2} + \frac{1}{4} + \frac{1}{8}$$

We have: $a_1 = 4 \quad r = \dfrac{1}{2} \quad$ and $\quad n = 6$

$$S_n = \frac{a_1(1 - r^n)}{1 - r} = \frac{4[1 - (\frac{1}{2})^6]}{1 - \frac{1}{2}} = \frac{4(1 - \frac{1}{64})}{\frac{1}{2}} = 8\left(\frac{63}{64}\right) = \frac{63}{8}$$

Skill Practice Find the sum of the geometric series.

5. $\dfrac{1}{9} + \dfrac{1}{3} + 1 + 3 + 9 + 27$

Example 5 **Finding the Sum of a Geometric Series**

Classroom Example: p. 1010, Exercise 46

Find the sum of the series $5 + 10 + 20 + \cdots + 5120$.

Solution:

The common ratio is 2 and $a_1 = 5$. The nth term of the sequence can be written as $a_n = 5(2)^{n-1}$. To find the value of n, substitute 5120 for a_n.

$5120 = 5(2)^{n-1}$

$\dfrac{5120}{5} = \dfrac{5(2)^{n-1}}{5}$ Divide both sides by 5.

$1024 = 2^{n-1}$ To solve the exponential equation, write each side as

$2^{10} = 2^{n-1}$ a power of 2.

$10 = n - 1$ From Section 12.6, we know that if $b^x = b^y$, then $x = y$.

$n = 11$

With $a_1 = 5$, $r = 2$, and $n = 11$, we have

$$S_n = \frac{a_1(1 - r^n)}{1 - r} = \frac{5(1 - 2^{11})}{1 - 2} = \frac{5(1 - 2048)}{-1} = \frac{5(-2047)}{-1} = 10{,}235$$

Skill Practice Find the sum of the geometric series.

6. $3 + 6 + 12 + \cdots + 768$

Consider a geometric series where $|r| < 1$. For increasing values of n, r^n decreases. For example,

$\left(\dfrac{1}{2}\right)^5 = 0.03125 \qquad \left(\dfrac{1}{2}\right)^{10} \approx 0.00097656 \qquad \left(\dfrac{1}{2}\right)^{15} \approx 0.00003052$

Answers

5. $\dfrac{364}{9}$ 6. 1533

For $|r| < 1$, r^n approaches 0 as n gets larger and larger. As n approaches infinity, the sum

$$S = \frac{a_1(1 - r^n)}{1 - r} \quad \text{approaches} \quad \frac{a_1(1 - 0)}{1 - r} = \frac{a_1}{1 - r}$$

> **FORMULA   Sum of an Infinite Geometric Series**
>
> Given an infinite geometric series $a_1 + a_1r + a_1r^2 + \cdots$, with $|r| < 1$, the sum S of all terms in the series is given by
>
> $$S = \frac{a_1}{1 - r}$$
>
> *Note:* If $|r| \geq 1$, then the sum does not exist.

Classroom Example: p. 1011, Exercise 52

Example 6   Finding the Sum of an Infinite Geometric Series

Find the sum of the series.

$$1 + \frac{1}{3} + \frac{1}{9} + \frac{1}{27} + \frac{1}{81} + \cdots$$

Solution:

This is a geometric series with $a_1 = 1$ and $r = \frac{1}{3}$. Because $|r| = |\frac{1}{3}| < 1$, we have

$$S = \frac{a_1}{1 - r} = \frac{1}{1 - \frac{1}{3}} = \frac{1}{\frac{2}{3}} = \frac{3}{2}$$

The sum is $\frac{3}{2}$.

Skill Practice   Find the sum of the series.

7. $4 + 3 + \dfrac{9}{4} + \dfrac{27}{16} + \ldots$

Classroom Example: p. 1011, Exercise 58

Example 7   Using a Geometric Series in a Physics Application

A child drops a ball from a height of 4 ft. With each bounce, the ball rebounds to 50% of its original height. Determine the total distance traveled by the ball.

Solution:

The heights from which the ball drops are given by the sequence

$$4, 2, 1, \frac{1}{2}, \frac{1}{4}, \cdots$$

After the ball falls from its initial height of 4 ft, the distance traveled for every bounce thereafter is doubled (the ball travels up and down). Therefore, the total distance traveled is given by the series

$$4 + 2 \cdot 2 + 2 \cdot 1 + 2 \cdot \frac{1}{2} + 2 \cdot \frac{1}{4} + \cdots$$

Answer

7. 16

or equivalently $4 + 4 + 2 + 1 + \dfrac{1}{2} + \cdots$

The series $4 + 2 + 1 + \frac{1}{2} + \cdots$ is an infinite geometric series with $a_1 = 4$ and $r = \frac{1}{2}$.

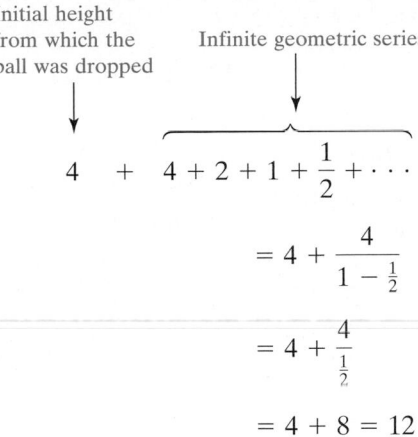

$$\underbrace{4}_{\substack{\text{Initial height} \\ \text{from which the} \\ \text{ball was dropped}}} + \overbrace{4 + 2 + 1 + \frac{1}{2} + \cdots}^{\text{Infinite geometric series}}$$

$$= 4 + \frac{4}{1 - \frac{1}{2}}$$

$$= 4 + \frac{4}{\frac{1}{2}}$$

$$= 4 + 8 = 12$$

The ball traveled a total of 12 ft.

Skill Practice

8. A child drops a ball from a height of 3 ft. With each bounce, the ball rebounds to $\frac{1}{3}$ of its original height. Determine the total distance traveled by the ball.

Answer

8. 6 ft

Section 14.4 Practice Exercises

Boost *your* GRADE at ALEKS.com!

ALEKS® VERSION 3.0

- Practice Problems
- Self-Tests
- NetTutor
- e-Professors
- Videos

For additional exercises, see Classroom Activities 14.4A–14.4C in the *Instructor's Resource Manual* at www.mhhe.com/moh.

Study Skills Exercise

1. Define the key terms.

   a. geometric sequence   **b. common ratio**   **c. geometric series**

Review Exercises

2. Determine the common difference. $7, 1, -5, -11, \ldots$ -6

3. Write an expression for the nth term of the sequence. $-4, 0, 4, 8, 12, \ldots$ $a_n = 4n - 8$

4. Find the sum of the series. $\displaystyle\sum_{i=1}^{6} (3i^2 - 4)$ 249

5. Find the fifth term of the arithmetic sequence with $a_1 = -15$ and $d = 10$. 25

Concept 1: Geometric Sequences

6. Explain how to determine if a sequence is geometric. A sequence is geometric if the ratio between each term and the preceding term is constant.

 Writing   Translating Expression   Geometry   Scientific Calculator   Video   NS&E

For Exercises 7–12, determine the common ratio, r, for the geometric sequence.

7. 5, 10, 20, 40, . . .   2

8. $-2, -1, -\dfrac{1}{2}, -\dfrac{1}{4}, \ldots$ $\dfrac{1}{2}$

9. $8, -2, \dfrac{1}{2}, -\dfrac{1}{8}, \ldots$ $-\dfrac{1}{4}$

10. 4, −12, 36, −108, . . .   −3

11. 3, −6, 12, −24, . . .   −2

12. 1, 4, 16, 64, . . .   4

For Exercises 13–18, write the first five terms of the geometric sequence.

13. $a_1 = -3, r = -2$
$-3, 6, -12, 24, -48$

14. $a_1 = -4, r = -1$
$-4, 4, -4, 4, -4$

15. $a_1 = 6, r = \dfrac{1}{2}$ $6, 3, \dfrac{3}{2}, \dfrac{3}{4}, \dfrac{3}{8}$

16. $a_1 = 8, r = \dfrac{1}{4}$ $8, 2, \dfrac{1}{2}, \dfrac{1}{8}, \dfrac{1}{32}$

17. $a_1 = -1, r = 6$
$-1, -6, -36, -216, -1296$

18. $a_1 = 2, r = -3$
$2, -6, 18, -54, 162$

For Exercises 19–24, find the nth term of each geometric sequence. **(See Example 1.)**

19. 3, 12, 48, 192, . . . $a_n = 3(4)^{n-1}$

20. 2, 6, 18, 54, . . . $a_n = 2(3)^{n-1}$

21. $-5, 15, -45, 135, \ldots$
$a_n = -5(-3)^{n-1}$

22. $-6, 12, -24, 48, \ldots$
$a_n = -6(-2)^{n-1}$

23. $\dfrac{1}{2}, 2, 8, 32, \ldots$ $a_n = \frac{1}{2}(4)^{n-1}$

24. $\dfrac{16}{3}, 4, 3, \dfrac{9}{4}, \ldots$ $a_n = \dfrac{16}{3}\left(\dfrac{3}{4}\right)^{n-1}$

For Exercises 25–34, find the indicated term of each geometric sequence. **(See Examples 2–3.)**

25. Given $a_n = 2(\frac{1}{2})^{n-1}$, find a_8.
$\dfrac{1}{64}$

26. Given $a_n = -3(\frac{1}{2})^{n-1}$, find a_8.
$-\dfrac{3}{128}$

27. Given $a_n = 4(-\frac{3}{2})^{n-1}$, find a_6.
$-\dfrac{243}{8}$

28. Given $a_n = 6(-\frac{1}{3})^{n-1}$, find a_6. $-\dfrac{2}{81}$

29. Given $a_n = -3(2)^{n-1}$, find a_5.
-48

30. Given $a_n = 5(3)^{n-1}$, find a_4.
135

31. Given $a_5 = -\frac{16}{9}$ and $r = -\frac{2}{3}$, find a_1. -9

32. Given $a_6 = \frac{5}{16}$ and $r = -\frac{1}{2}$, find a_1. -10

33. Given $a_7 = 8$ and $r = 2$, find a_1. $\dfrac{1}{8}$

34. Given $a_6 = 27$ and $r = 3$, find a_1. $\dfrac{1}{9}$

35. If the second and third terms of a geometric sequence are 16 and 64, what is the first term?
4

36. If the second and third terms of a geometric sequence are $\frac{1}{3}$ and $\frac{1}{9}$, what is the first term?
1

Concept 2: Geometric Series

37. Explain the difference between a geometric sequence and a geometric series.   A geometric sequence is an ordered list of numbers in which the ratio between each term and its predecessor is constant. A geometric series is the sum of the terms of such a sequence.

38. a. Write the series in expanded form. $\displaystyle\sum_{i=1}^{5} 4(2)^{i-1}$ $4 + 8 + 16 + 32 + 64$

b. Find the sum of the series. $\displaystyle\sum_{i=1}^{5} 4(2)^{i-1}$ 124

For Exercises 39–48, find the sum of the geometric series. **(See Examples 4–5.)**

39. $10 + 2 + \dfrac{2}{5} + \dfrac{2}{25} + \dfrac{2}{125}$
$\dfrac{1562}{125}$

40. $1 + 3 + 9 + 27 + 81 + 243$
364

41. $-2 + 1 + \left(-\dfrac{1}{2}\right) + \dfrac{1}{4} + \left(-\dfrac{1}{8}\right)$
$-\dfrac{11}{8}$

42. $\dfrac{1}{4} + (-1) + 4 + (-16) + 64$
$\dfrac{205}{4}$

43. $12 + 16 + \dfrac{64}{3} + \dfrac{256}{9} + \dfrac{1024}{27}$
$\dfrac{3124}{27}$

44. $9 + 6 + 4 + \dfrac{8}{3} + \dfrac{16}{9}$
$\dfrac{211}{9}$

45. $1 + \dfrac{2}{3} + \dfrac{4}{9} + \cdots + \dfrac{32}{243}$
$\dfrac{665}{243}$

46. $\dfrac{8}{3} + 2 + \dfrac{3}{2} + \cdots + \dfrac{243}{512}$ $\dfrac{14{,}197}{1536}$

47. $-4 + 8 + (-16) + \cdots + (-256)$ **48.** $-\dfrac{7}{3} + 7 + (-21) + \cdots + 5103$ $\dfrac{11{,}480}{3}$

-172

49. A deposit of \$1000 is made in an account that earns 5% interest compounded annually. The balance in the account after n years is given by

$$a_n = 1000(1.05)^n \quad \text{for } n \geq 1$$

   a. List the first four terms of the sequence. Round to the nearest cent.   \$1050.00, \$1102.50, \$1157.63, \$1215.51

   b. Find the balance after 10 yr, 20 yr, and 40 yr by computing a_{10}, a_{20}, and a_{40}. Round to the nearest cent.

     $a_{10} = \$1628.89$; $a_{20} = \$2653.30$; $a_{40} = \$7039.99$

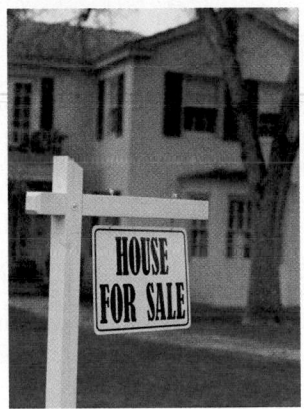

50. A home purchased for \$125,000 increases by 4% of its value each year. The value of the home after n years is given by

$$a_n = 125{,}000(1.04)^n \quad \text{for } n \geq 1$$

   a. List the first four terms of the sequence. Round to the nearest dollar.

     \$130,000, \$135,200, \$140,608, \$146,232

   b. Find the value of the home after 5 yr, 10 yr, and 20 yr by computing a_5, a_{10}, and a_{20}. Round to the nearest dollar.

     $a_5 = \$152{,}082$; $a_{10} = \$185{,}031$; $a_{20} = \$273{,}890$

For Exercises 51–56, first find the common ratio r. Then determine the sum of the infinite series, if it exists. **(See Example 6.)**

51. $1 + \dfrac{1}{6} + \dfrac{1}{36} + \dfrac{1}{216} + \cdots$ $r = \dfrac{1}{6}; \dfrac{6}{5}$

52. $-2 + \left(-\dfrac{1}{2}\right) + \left(-\dfrac{1}{8}\right) + \left(-\dfrac{1}{32}\right) + \cdots$ $r = \dfrac{1}{4}; -\dfrac{8}{3}$

53. $-3 + 1 + \left(-\dfrac{1}{3}\right) + \dfrac{1}{9} + \cdots$ $r = -\dfrac{1}{3}; -\dfrac{9}{4}$

54. $\dfrac{1}{2} + \left(-\dfrac{1}{10}\right) + \dfrac{1}{50} + \left(-\dfrac{1}{250}\right) + \cdots$ $r = -\dfrac{1}{5}; \dfrac{5}{12}$

55. $\dfrac{2}{3} + (-1) + \dfrac{3}{2} + \left(-\dfrac{9}{4}\right) + \cdots$ $r = -\dfrac{3}{2}$; sum does not exist

56. $3 + 5 + \dfrac{25}{3} + \dfrac{125}{9} + \cdots$ $r = \dfrac{5}{3}$; sum does not exist

57. Suppose \$200 million is spent by tourists at a certain resort town. Further suppose that 75% of the revenue is respent in the community and then respent over and over, each time at a rate of 75%. The series

$$200 + 200(0.75) + 200(0.75)^2 + 200(0.75)^3 + \cdots$$

gives the total amount spent (and respent) in the community. Find the sum of the infinite series. **(See Example 7.)**

The sum is \$800 million.

58. A bungee jumper jumps off a platform and stretches the cord 80 ft before rebounding upward. Each successive bounce stretches the cord 60% of its previous length. The total vertical distance traveled is given by

$$80 + 2(0.60)(80) + 2(0.60)^2(80) + 2(0.60)^3(80) + \cdots$$

After the first term, the series is an infinite geometric series. Compute the total vertical distance traveled.

The total vertical distance traveled is 320 ft.

59. A ball drops from a height of 4 ft. With each bounce, the ball rebounds to $\frac{3}{4}$ of its height. The total vertical distance traveled is given by

$$4 + 2\left(\dfrac{3}{4}\right)(4) + 2\left(\dfrac{3}{4}\right)^2(4) + 2\left(\dfrac{3}{4}\right)^3(4) + \cdots$$

After the first term, the series is an infinite geometric series. Compute the total vertical distance traveled.

The total vertical distance traveled is 28 ft.

 Writing   Translating Expression   Geometry   Scientific Calculator   Video   NS&E

60. The repeating decimal number $0.\overline{2}$ can be written as an infinite geometric series by

$$\frac{2}{10} + \frac{2}{100} + \frac{2}{1000} + \cdots$$

a. What is a_1? $\frac{2}{10}$ **b.** What is r? $\frac{1}{10}$ **c.** Find the sum of the series. $\frac{2}{9}$

61. The repeating decimal number $0.\overline{7}$ can be written as an infinite geometric series by

$$\frac{7}{10} + \frac{7}{100} + \frac{7}{1000} + \cdots$$

a. What is a_1? $\frac{7}{10}$ **b.** What is r? $\frac{1}{10}$ **c.** Find the sum of the series. $\frac{7}{9}$

Expanding Your Skills

62. The yearly salary for job A is $40,000 initially with an annual raise of $3000 per year. The yearly salary for job B is $38,000 initially with an annual raise of 6% per year.

a. Find the total earnings for job A over 20 yr. Is this an arithmetic or geometric series? $1,370,000; arithmetic

b. For job B, what is the amount of the raise after 1 yr? $2280

c. Find the total earnings for job B over 20 yr. Round to the nearest dollar. Is this an arithmetic or geometric series? $1,397,852; geometric

d. What is the difference in total salary earned over 20 yr between job A and job B? $27,852

63. a. Brook has a job that pays $48,000 the first year. She receives a 4% raise each year. Find the sum of her yearly salaries over a 20-yr period. Round to the nearest dollar. $1,429,348

b. Chamille has a job that pays $48,000 the first year. She receives a 4.5% raise each year. Find the sum of her yearly salaries over a 20-yr period. Round to the nearest dollar. $1,505,828

c. Chamille's raise each year was 0.5% higher than Brook's raise. How much more total income did Chamille receive than Brook over 20 yr? $76,480

Problem Recognition Exercises

Identifying Arithmetic and Geometric Sequences

For Exercises 1–14, determine if the sequence is arithmetic, geometric, or neither. If the sequence is arithmetic, find d. If the sequence is geometric, find r.

1. $5, -\frac{5}{2}, \frac{5}{4}, -\frac{5}{8}, \ldots$
Geometric, $r = -\frac{1}{2}$

2. $1, -\frac{3}{2}, \frac{9}{4}, -\frac{27}{8}, \ldots$
Geometric, $r = -\frac{3}{2}$

3. $\frac{1}{2}, 1, \frac{3}{2}, 2, \frac{5}{2}, \ldots$
Arithmetic, $d = \frac{1}{2}$

4. $-\frac{1}{3}, \frac{1}{3}, 1, \frac{5}{3}, \ldots$
Arithmetic, $d = \frac{2}{3}$

5. $-2, -4, -8, -16, -32, \ldots$
Geometric, $r = 2$

6. $2, 6, 18, 54, 162, \ldots$
Geometric, $r = 3$

7. $-2, -4, -6, -8, -10, \ldots$
Arithmetic, $d = -2$

8. $2, 6, 10, 14, 18, 22, \ldots$
Arithmetic, $d = 4$

9. $-2, -4, -7, -11, -16, \ldots$
Neither

10. $2, 6, 11, 17, 24, \ldots$
Neither

11. $1, 3, 1, 3, 1, \ldots$
Neither

12. $0, 1, 0, 1, 0, 1, \ldots$
Neither

13. $2, -2, 2, -2, 2, \ldots$
Geometric, $r = -1$

14. $-1, 1, -1, 1, -1, \ldots$
Geometric, $r = -1$

 Writing   Translating Expression   Geometry   Scientific Calculator   Video   NS&E

Group Activity

Investigating Mean and Standard Deviation

Materials: A computer with Internet access and a calculator

Estimated time: 15–20 minutes

Group Size: 2

To study the characteristics of a population, statisticians often use a sample or part of the population. A sample of data values is smaller and less cumbersome than data from the entire population. Furthermore, if the sample is taken randomly, the sample is generally a good representation of the population as a whole.

Once a collection of data is obtained, statisticians may compute the mean and standard deviation of the sample. The mean is the average of the data values. The standard deviation is a measure of variability and is based on finding the deviation between the given data values and the mean.

The formulas to compute sample mean (denoted by $\bar{x}$) and sample standard deviation (denoted by s) are as follows. In each case, the sample size is n, and the individual data values are denoted by $x_1, x_2, x_3, \ldots, x_n$. Notice that sometimes the summations are given without the index of summation. This is common practice in statistics. The index of summation is understood to be from 1 to n.

$$\bar{x} = \frac{\sum_{i=1}^{n} x_i}{n}$$

- Take the sum of the data values $(x_1 + x_2 + x_3 + \cdots + x_n)$ and divide by n.

$$s = \sqrt{\frac{n \cdot \Sigma(x^2) - (\Sigma x)^2}{n(n-1)}}$$

- For the first term in the numerator, square each value of x first, then take the sum and multiply by the sample size, n

- For the second term in the numerator, add the values of x first and then square the result.

1. The following data represent a sample of eight breakfast cereals and the corresponding number of calories for a 1-cup serving. Find the mean number of calories. Round to one decimal place.

   160   120   140   240   180   210   380   320 $\bar{x} = 218.8$ calories

2. Use the data from Question 1 to compute the standard deviation. Use the given chart to help you organize the calculations. Round to one decimal place. $s = 90.8$ calories

3. Select two cities in different parts of the country that have roughly the same latitude (same distance north from the equator) such as Phoenix, Arizona, and Charleston, South Carolina. Visit a website that gives the average monthly temperatures for each city for a 1-yr period. Record the data here.   Answers will vary.

Brand	x	x^2
1	160	
2	120	
3	140	
4	240	
5	180	
6	210	
7	380	
8	320	
Sum:		

	Jan.	Feb.	Mar.	Apr.	May	June	July	Aug.	Sept.	Oct.	Nov.	Dec.
City 1 temp												
City 2 temp												

4. Compute the mean and standard deviation for the average monthly temperature for each city.

Answers will vary.

5. Based on the mean and standard deviation, what conclusions can you make about the differences between the monthly temperatures of each city? Answers will vary. For example, one might expect Phoenix to have a greater standard deviation than Charleston. There is more variability in temperatures in a desert climate than on the coast.

Chapter 14 Summary

Section 14.1 Binomial Expansions

Key Concepts

For a whole number, n, the expression $n!$ (read as "n factorial") is defined as the product of integers from 1 to n, for $n \geq 1$.

$$n! = n(n-1)(n-2)\ldots(2)(1)$$

$0! = 1$ by definition

For a positive integer, n, the expression $(a+b)^n$ can be expanded using the **binomial theorem**:

$$(a+b)^n = \frac{n!}{n! \cdot 0!}a^n + \frac{n!}{(n-1)! \cdot 1!}a^{(n-1)}b$$

$$+ \frac{n!}{(n-2)! \cdot 2!}a^{(n-2)}b^2 + \cdots + \frac{n!}{0! \cdot n!}b^n$$

The coefficients of the expansion may also be found by using Pascal's triangle.

```
            1
         1     1
      1     2     1
   1     3     3     1
1     4     6     4     1
```

Let n and k be positive integers such that $k \leq n$. Then the kth term in the expansion of $(a+b)^n$ is

$$\frac{n!}{[n-(k-1)]! \cdot (k-1)!} \cdot a^{n-(k-1)} \cdot b^{k-1}$$

Examples

Example 1

$$6! = (6)(5)(4)(3)(2)(1) = 720$$

Example 2

$$\frac{7!}{2! \cdot 5!} = \frac{7 \cdot \overset{3}{\cancel{6}} \cdot \cancel{5 \cdot 4 \cdot 3 \cdot 2 \cdot 1}}{(2 \cdot 1)(\cancel{5 \cdot 4 \cdot 3 \cdot 2 \cdot 1})} = 21$$

Example 3

$$(2x - 4y)^4 = [2x + (-4y)]^4$$

$$= \frac{4!}{4! \cdot 0!}(2x)^4 + \frac{4!}{3! \cdot 1!}(2x)^3(-4y) + \frac{4!}{2! \cdot 2!}(2x)^2(-4y)^2 +$$

$$\frac{4!}{1! \cdot 3!}(2x)(-4y)^3 + \frac{4!}{0! \cdot 4!}(-4y)^4$$

$$= 1(2x)^4 + 4(2x)^3(-4y) + 6(2x)^2(-4y)^2$$

$$+ 4(2x)(-4y)^3 + 1(-4y)^4$$

$$= 16x^4 - 128x^3y + 384x^2y^2 - 512xy^3 + 256y^4$$

Example 4

The third term of $(3x + y^2)^7$ is

$$\frac{7!}{[7-(3-1)]! \cdot (3-1)!} \cdot (3x)^{7-(3-1)} \cdot (y^2)^{3-1}$$

$$= \frac{7!}{5! \cdot 2!}(3x)^5(y^2)^2$$

$$= 5103x^5y^4$$

Section 14.2 Sequences and Series

Key Concepts

An **infinite sequence** is a function whose domain is the set of positive integers.

A **finite sequence** is a function whose domain is the set of the first n positive integers.

The expression a_n defines the nth term (or general term) of a sequence.

A **series** is the sum of a sequence.

Examples

Example 1

$a_n = 8 - 3n$

$= 5, 2, -1, -4, -7, -10, \ldots$

Example 2

$a_n = (-1)^n \dfrac{n}{n+1}$ for $1 \leq n \leq 5$

$= -\dfrac{1}{2}, \dfrac{2}{3}, -\dfrac{3}{4}, \dfrac{4}{5}, -\dfrac{5}{6}$

Example 3

$\displaystyle\sum_{i=1}^{4} 5i = 5 + 10 + 15 + 20 = 50$

Section 14.3 Arithmetic Sequences and Series

Key Concepts

An **arithmetic sequence** is a sequence in which the common difference, d, between two consecutive terms is a constant.

The nth term of an arithmetic sequence is given by

$a_n = a_1 + (n-1)d$

This formula has four variables, $a_n, a_1, n,$ and d. Sometimes it is necessary to solve for one or more of the variables before the nth term can be identified.

Examples

Example 1

Write the nth term of the sequence:
$10, 8, 6, 4, \ldots$

$a_1 = 10$ (the first term)

$d = -2$ (the common difference)

$a_n = 10 + (n-1) \cdot (-2)$

$a_n = -2n + 12$

Example 2

Find the 12th term of the arithmetic sequence in which $a_1 = -6$ and $a_{20} = 51$.

$a_n = a_1 + (n-1)d$ Find d first.

$51 = -6 + (20-1)d$ Substitute known values for a_1 and a_{20}.

$57 = 19d$

$3 = d$

$a_n = -6 + (n-1) \cdot 3 \longrightarrow a_{12} = -6 + (12-1) \cdot 3$

$a_{12} = 27$

The sum of an arithmetic sequence is an **arithmetic series**. The sum of the first n terms of an arithmetic series is given by

$$S_n = \frac{n}{2}(a_1 + a_n)$$

Example 3

Find the sum. $\sum_{i=1}^{50} (3i - 1)$

$n = 50, a_1 = 2, \ a_{50} = 149$

$$S_n = \frac{n}{2}(a_1 + a_n) = \frac{50}{2}(2 + 149)$$

$$= 3775$$

Section 14.4 Geometric Sequences and Series

Key Concepts

A **geometric sequence** is a sequence in which each term after the first term is a constant multiple of the preceding term. The constant multiple is called the **common ratio**, r.

The nth term of a geometric sequence is given by

$$a_n = a_1 r^{(n-1)}$$

The sum of a geometric sequence is called a **geometric series**. The sum of the first n terms of a geometric series is given by

$$S_n = \frac{a_1(1 - r^n)}{1 - r}$$

The sum of an infinite geometric series is given by

$$S_n = \frac{a_1}{1 - r} \quad \text{provided } |r| < 1$$

Examples

Example 1

Find the common ratio: $\dfrac{8}{5}, \dfrac{6}{5}, \dfrac{9}{10}, \dfrac{27}{40}, \cdots$

$$r = \frac{6}{5} \div \frac{8}{5} = \frac{6}{5} \cdot \frac{5}{8} = \frac{30}{40} = \frac{3}{4}$$

Example 2

Find the fourth term.

$$a_n = 3\left(\frac{2}{3}\right)^{n-1} \longrightarrow a_4 = 3\left(\frac{2}{3}\right)^{4-1} = 3\left(\frac{2}{3}\right)^3 = \frac{8}{9}$$

Example 3

Find the sum. $48, 24, 12, 6, 3, \frac{3}{2}$

$a_1 = 48, r = \frac{1}{2}, n = 6$

$$S_n = \frac{a_1(1 - r^n)}{1 - r} = \frac{48[1 - (\frac{1}{2})^6]}{1 - \frac{1}{2}} = \frac{189}{2}$$

Example 4

Find the sum of the series: $4 - 2 + 1 - \frac{1}{2} + \cdots$

$a_1 = 4$ and the common ratio is $-2 \div 4 = -\frac{1}{2}$.

Since $|-\frac{1}{2}| < 1$,

$$S_n = \frac{a_1}{1 - r} = \frac{4}{1 - (-\frac{1}{2})} = \frac{4}{\frac{3}{2}} = \frac{8}{3}$$

Chapter 14 Review Exercises

Section 14.1

For Exercises 1–4, simplify the expression.

1. $8!$ 40,320   2. $5!$ 120   3. $\dfrac{12!}{10! \cdot 2!}$ 66   4. $\dfrac{9!}{6! \cdot 3!}$ 84

For Exercises 5–6, expand the binomial.

5. $(x^2 + 4)^5$ $x^{10} + 20x^8 + 160x^6 + 640x^4 + 1280x^2 + 1024$

6. $(c - 3d)^4$ $c^4 - 12c^3d + 54c^2d^2 - 108cd^3 + 81d^4$

7. Find the first three terms of the binomial expansion. $(a - 2b)^{11}$ $a^{11} - 22a^{10}b + 220a^9b^2$

8. Find the fourth term of the binomial expansion. $(x^2 + 3y)^8$ $1512x^{10}y^3$

9. Find the eighth term of the binomial expansion. $(5x - y^3)^{10}$ $-15,000x^3y^{21}$

10. Find the middle term of the binomial expansion. $(a + 2b)^6$ $160a^3b^3$

Section 14.2

For Exercises 11–14, write the terms of the sequence.

11. $a_n = -3n + 4;\ 1 \le n \le 5$ $1, -2, -5, -8, -11$

12. $a_n = -2n^3;\ 1 \le n \le 3$ $-2, -16, -54$

13. $a_n = (-1)^{n+1} \cdot \dfrac{n}{n+2};\ 1 \le n \le 4$ $\dfrac{1}{3}, -\dfrac{1}{2}, \dfrac{3}{5}, -\dfrac{2}{3}$

14. $a_n = \left(-\dfrac{2}{3}\right)^n;\ 1 \le n \le 4$ $-\dfrac{2}{3}, \dfrac{4}{9}, -\dfrac{8}{27}, \dfrac{16}{81}$

For Exercises 15–16, write a formula for the nth term of the sequence.

15. $\dfrac{1}{2}, \dfrac{2}{3}, \dfrac{3}{4}, \dfrac{4}{5}, \ldots$ $a_n = \dfrac{n}{n+1}$

16. $-\dfrac{3}{2}, \dfrac{3}{4}, -\dfrac{3}{8}, \dfrac{3}{16}, \ldots$ $a_n = (-1)^n \cdot \dfrac{3}{2^n}$

17. What is the index of summation for the series?

$$\sum_{k=1}^{7} (2n + 3) \quad k$$

18. How many terms are in the series? $\displaystyle\sum_{j=1}^{5} j^3$ 5

For Exercises 19–20, find the sum of the series.

19. $\displaystyle\sum_{i=1}^{7} 5(-1)^{i-1}$ 5   20. $\displaystyle\sum_{n=1}^{5} (-2)^n$ -22

21. Write the sum in summation notation.

$$\dfrac{4}{1} + \dfrac{5}{2} + \dfrac{6}{3} + \dfrac{7}{4} + \dfrac{8}{5} + \dfrac{9}{6} + \dfrac{10}{7} \quad \sum_{i=1}^{7} \dfrac{3+i}{i}$$

22. Study the figures and the corresponding expression for the area of each region. Write the nth term of a sequence representing the area of a region with base n.

$$a_n = n^2 + \left(\dfrac{n}{2}\right)h$$

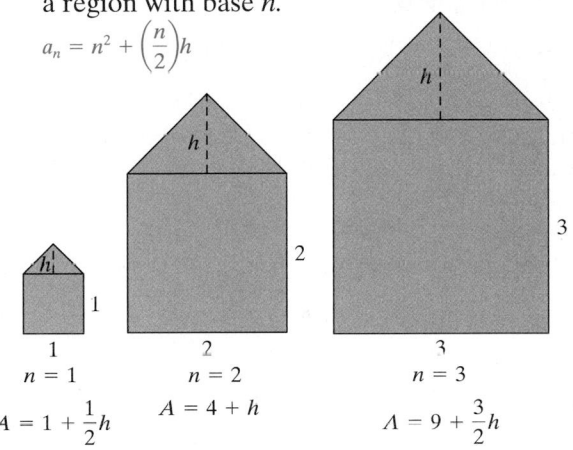

$n = 1$	$n = 2$	$n = 3$
$A = 1 + \dfrac{1}{2}h$	$A = 4 + h$	$A = 9 + \dfrac{3}{2}h$

Section 14.3

For Exercises 23–24, write the first five terms of the arithmetic sequence.

23. $a_1 = -12,\ d = 1.5$ $-12, -10.5, -9, -7.5, -6$

24. $a_1 = \dfrac{2}{3},\ d = \dfrac{1}{3}$ $\dfrac{2}{3}, 1, \dfrac{4}{3}, \dfrac{5}{3}, 2$

For Exercises 25–26, write an expression for the nth term of the sequence.

25. $1, 11, 21, 31, \ldots$ $a_n = 10n - 9$

26. $6, -8, -22, -36, \ldots$ $a_n = -14n + 20$

For Exercises 27–28, find the indicated term of the arithmetic sequence.

27. $a_n = \dfrac{1}{2} + (n - 1) \cdot \dfrac{1}{4};$ 17th term $a_{17} = \dfrac{9}{2}$

28. $a_1 = -11,\ d = -6;$ 25th term $a_{25} = -155$

For Exercises 29–30, find the number of terms.

29. $3, 8, 13, 18, \ldots, 118$ 24 terms

30. $4, 1, -2, -5 \ldots, -50$ 19 terms

 Writing   Translating Expression   Geometry   Scientific Calculator   Video   NS&E

31. Find the common difference for an arithmetic sequence, given $a_1 = -40$ and $a_{19} = 140$. $d = 10$

32. Write an expression for the nth term of the arithmetic sequence, $14, 9, 4, -1, -6, \ldots$
$a_n = -5n + 19$

For Exercises 33–36, find the sum of the arithmetic series.

33. $\displaystyle\sum_{k=1}^{40} (5 - k)$ -620

34. $\displaystyle\sum_{i=1}^{20} (0.25i + 2)$ 92.5

35. $-6 + (-4) + (-2) + \cdots + 34$ 294

36. $4 + 5 + 6 + \cdots + 109$ 5989

Section 14.4

For Exercises 37–38, find the common ratio.

37. $5, 15, 45, 135, \ldots$ $r = 3$

38. $2, 2.4, 2.88, 3.456$ $r = 1.2$

For Exercises 39–40, write the first four terms of the geometric series.

39. $a_1 = -1$ and $r = -\dfrac{1}{4}$ $-1, \dfrac{1}{4}, -\dfrac{1}{16}, \dfrac{1}{64}$

40. $a_n = 10(2)^{n-1}$ $10, 20, 40, 80$

For Exercises 41–42, write an expression for the nth term of the geometric series.

41. $-4, -8, -16, -32, \ldots$ $a_n = -4(2)^{n-1}$

42. $6, -2, \dfrac{2}{3}, -\dfrac{2}{9}, \ldots$ $a_n = 6\left(-\dfrac{1}{3}\right)^{n-1}$

43. Given $a_n = 4\left(\dfrac{2}{3}\right)^{n-1}$, find a_6. $a_6 = \dfrac{128}{243}$

44. Given $a_n = 10(3)^{n-1}$, find a_4. $a_4 = 270$

45. Given $a_7 = \dfrac{1}{16}$ and $r = \dfrac{1}{2}$, find a_1. $a_1 = 4$

46. Given $a_5 = 81$, and $r = 3$, find a_1. $a_1 = 1$

47. Find the sum of the series. $\displaystyle\sum_{n=1}^{8} 5(2)^{n-1}$ 1275

48. Find the sum of the series.
$\dfrac{1}{3} + (-1) + 3 + (-9) + \cdots + (-81)$ $-\dfrac{182}{3}$

49. Find the sum of the series.
$6 + 4 + \dfrac{8}{3} + \dfrac{16}{9} + \cdots$ 18

50. Find the sum of the series.
$10 + 2 + \dfrac{2}{5} + \dfrac{2}{25} + \cdots$ $\dfrac{25}{2}$

51. An investment of $10,000 is originally invested in a mutual fund. After 10 yr, the yearly return averaged approximately 7%. The balance on the account is given by $b_n = 10{,}000(1.07)^n$.

    a. Find the first three terms of the sequence.
$10,700, $11,449, $12,250.43

    b. Interpret the value of b_3.
The account is worth $12,250.43 after 3 yr.

    c. Find the amount in the account after 10 yr.
$19,671.51

Chapter 14   Test

For Exercises 1–2, simplify.

1. $0!$ 1

2. $\dfrac{10!}{6! \cdot 4!}$ 210

3. Write the expansion of $(a + b)^4$. Use Pascal's triangle to determine the coefficients of the expansion. $a^4 + 4a^3b + 6a^2b^2 + 4ab^3 + b^4$

4. Expand. $(3y - 2x^2)^4$
$81y^4 - 216y^3x^2 + 216y^2x^4 - 96yx^6 + 16x^8$

5. Find the sixth term. $(a - c^3)^8$ $-56a^3c^{15}$

6. Write the terms of the sequence.
$a_n = -\dfrac{3}{n + 2}; 1 \le n \le 4$ $-1, -\dfrac{3}{4}, -\dfrac{3}{5}, -\dfrac{1}{2}$

7. Find the sum. $\displaystyle\sum_{i=1}^{5} i^2 + 2$ 65

8. a. An 8-in. tomato seedling is planted on Sunday. Each day, it grows an average of 1.5 in. Write five terms representing the height of the plant each day, beginning with Sunday. $8, 9.5, 11, 12.5, 14$

    b. Write the nth term of the sequence.
$a_n = 1.5n + 6.5$

 Writing   Translating Expression   Geometry   Scientific Calculator   Video   NS&E

9. Write the series in summation notation.
$x^3 + x^6 + x^9 + x^{12}$　　$\sum\limits_{n=1}^{4} x^{3n}$

10. Find the common difference.　　$3, \dfrac{13}{4}, \dfrac{7}{2}, \dfrac{15}{4}, \ldots$
$d = \dfrac{1}{4}$

11. Find the common ratio.　　$9, 3, 1, \dfrac{1}{3}, \ldots$　　$r = \dfrac{1}{3}$

12. Given an arithmetic sequence with $a_1 = -15$ and $d = -3$,

　a. Write the first four terms of the sequence.
　　$-15, -18, -21, -24$
　b. Write an expression for the nth term of the sequence.　　$a_n = -3n - 12$

　c. Find the 40th term of the sequence.　　$a_{40} = -132$

13. Given a geometric sequence with $a_1 = 4$ and $r = -2$,

　a. Write the first four terms of the sequence.
　　$4, -8, 16, -32$
　b. Write an expression for the nth term of the sequence.　　$a_n = 4(-2)^{n-1}$

　c. Find the 10th term of the sequence.　　-2048

14. Write an expression for the nth term of the sequence.　　$\dfrac{3}{5}, \dfrac{3}{10}, \dfrac{3}{20}, \dfrac{3}{40}, \ldots$　　$a_n = \dfrac{3}{5} \cdot \left(\dfrac{1}{2}\right)^{n-1}$

15. Write an expression for the nth term of the sequence.　　$20, 18, 16, 14, \ldots$　　$a_n = -2n + 22$

16. Find the number of terms in the sequence.
$3, 10, 17, 24, \ldots, 213$　　31 terms

17. Find the number of terms in the sequence.
$1, \dfrac{2}{3}, \dfrac{4}{9}, \ldots, \dfrac{64}{729}$　　7 terms

18. Find the sum of the arithmetic series.
$\sum\limits_{i=1}^{100} (8 + 2i)$　　10,900

19. Find the sum of the geometric series.
$\sum\limits_{n=1}^{10} 8\left(\dfrac{1}{2}\right)^{n-1}$　　$\dfrac{1023}{64}$

20. Find the sum of the infinite geometric series.
$4 + 2 + 1 + \dfrac{1}{2} + \cdots$　　8

21. Given a geometric series with $a_6 = 9$ and $r = 3$, find a_1.　　$a_1 = \dfrac{1}{27}$

22. Find the 18th term of the arithmetic sequence in which $a_1 = -66$ and $a_{40} = -378$.　　$a_{18} = -202$

23. Suppose a student smokes one pack of cigarettes per day at a cost of $3.00 per pack.

　a. If the student quits smoking and puts the $3.00 saved per day in a jar, how much money will the student have saved at the end of 1 yr?　　$1095

　b. If the student takes the savings from part (a) and invests the money in a bond fund paying 6% annual interest, how much will this money be worth a year later?　　$1160.70

　c. Suppose that the student reinvests the principal and interest each year so that the money is compounded annually. The student will have:

　　end of 1 yr　$1095
　　end of 2 yr　($1095)(1.06) = $1160.70
　　end of 3 yr　($1095)(1.06)^2 = $1230.34
　　$\cdots$

　　The sequence $a_n = 1095(1.06)^{n-1}$ represents the value of the investment at the end of n years. Find the value of the investment after 30 yr. (Round to two decimal places.)　　$5933.13

　d. Now suppose that the student saves $1095 per year each year for 30 yr. Further suppose that the student invests each year's savings at 6% interest compounded annually. The following series represents the total savings plus interest over 30 yr. Find the sum.　　$86,568.71

$$\sum\limits_{n=1}^{30} 1095(1.06)^{n-1}$$

Chapters 1–14   Cumulative Review Exercises

For Exercises 1–8, simplify the expressions.

1. $(2x - 3)(x - 4) - (x - 5)^2$ $x^2 - x - 13$

2. $\dfrac{5a^2b^{-3}}{25a^{-4}b} \cdot \left(\dfrac{10c^0}{b^3}\right)^2$ $\dfrac{20a^6}{b^{10}}$

3. $64^{-2/3}$ $\dfrac{1}{16}$

4. $\dfrac{5}{\sqrt{10}}$ $\dfrac{\sqrt{10}}{2}$

5. $\dfrac{2c^2 - 3c - 20}{2c^2 - 32}$ $\dfrac{2c + 5}{2(c + 4)}$

6. $\dfrac{x^{-1} - y^{-1}}{y^{-2} - x^{-2}}$ $-\dfrac{xy}{x + y}$

7. $\log_3 81$ 4

8. $\sqrt[3]{54x^5y^{12}z^2}$ $3xy^4\sqrt[3]{2x^2z^2}$

For Exercises 9–12, perform the indicated operations.

9. $\dfrac{a^3 + 64}{16 - a^2} \div \dfrac{a^3 - 4a^2 + 16a}{a^2 - 3a - 4}$ $-\dfrac{a + 1}{a}$

10. $\dfrac{1}{x^2 - 7x + 10} + \dfrac{1}{x^2 + 8x - 20}$ $\dfrac{2x + 5}{(x - 5)(x - 2)(x + 10)}$

11. $\sqrt{50x^5} + 4x\sqrt{2x^3} - x^2\sqrt{8x}$ $7x^2\sqrt{2x}$

12. $(\sqrt{x} + 3\sqrt{y})(\sqrt{x} - 3\sqrt{y})$ $x - 9y$

13. Divide using long division or synthetic division.
$\dfrac{2x^4 - x^3 + 5x - 7}{x - 2}$ $2x^3 + 3x^2 + 6x + 17 + \dfrac{27}{x - 2}$

For Exercises 14–17, factor completely.

14. $6a^2 - 17a - 14$
$(2a - 7)(3a + 2)$

15. $75c^3 - 12c$
$3c(5c - 2)(5c + 2)$

16. $27x^3 + 64y^6$
$(3x + 4y^2)(9x^2 - 12xy^2 + 16y^4)$

17. $w^3 + 9w^2 - 4w - 36$
$(w + 9)(w - 2)(w + 2)$

For Exercises 18–25, solve the equation.

18. $\dfrac{1}{2}t - \dfrac{3}{5} = \dfrac{1}{10}t + 1$ $\{4\}$

19. $\dfrac{9}{x - 4} + \dfrac{3}{x + 2} = \dfrac{6}{x^2 - 2x - 8}$ $\{0\}$

20. $\sqrt[3]{4x + 3} - 9 = -7$ $\left\{\dfrac{5}{4}\right\}$

21. $(5y - 2)^2 + 7 = 4$ $\left\{\dfrac{2}{5} \pm \dfrac{\sqrt{3}}{5}i\right\}$

22. $c^4 - 17c^2 + 16 = 0$ $\{4, -4, 1, -1\}$

23. $|x + 5| = |3x - 2|$ $\left\{\dfrac{7}{2}, -\dfrac{3}{4}\right\}$

24. $5^{2x + 1} = 125$ $\{1\}$

25. $\log x + \log(x + 3) = 1$
$\{2\}$ (The value -5 does not check.)

26. Write the expression as a single logarithm.

$\ln x - 5\ln y + \dfrac{1}{2}\ln z$ $\ln\left(\dfrac{x\sqrt{z}}{y^5}\right)$

27. Use a calculator to approximate the value of the expression. Round to four decimal places.

$\log_7 895$ 3.4929

For Exercises 28–32, solve the inequality. Write the answer in interval notation if possible.

28. $2x - 4 < 6$ and $-3x \le 6$ $[-2, 5)$

29. $3x(x + 5)(x - 1) \ge 0$ $[-5, 0] \cup [1, \infty)$

30. $x^2 - 10x \le -25$ $\{5\}$

31. $\dfrac{3}{x + 4} \le 1$
$(-\infty, -4) \cup [-1, \infty)$

32. $|2x - 4| + 5 > 7$
$(-\infty, 1) \cup (3, \infty)$

For Exercises 33–35, graph the equation.

33. $3x - 2y = 6$

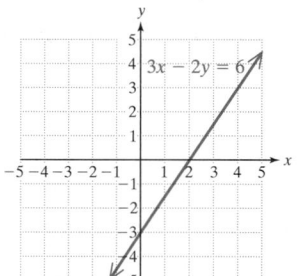

34. $(x - 2)^2 + y^2 = 9$

35. $y = 2^x$

 Writing   Translating Expression   Geometry   Scientific Calculator   Video   NS&E

36. Graph the solution set. $\dfrac{x^2}{9} + \dfrac{y^2}{25} \leq 1$

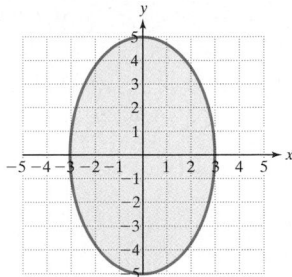

37. Given $f(x) = x^2 + 6x + 5$,

    a. Determine the x-intercepts. $(-1, 0), (-5, 0)$

    b. Determine the y-intercept. $(0, 5)$

    c. Determine the vertex of the parabola. $(-3, -4)$

38. Determine the slope and y-intercept of the line defined by $4x + y = 6$
slope -4; y-intercept $(0, 6)$

39. Write an equation of the line passing through the point $(4, -2)$ and perpendicular to the line defined by $x - 5y = 2$. $y = -5x + 18$

40. Refer to the graph of $y = f(x)$.

    a. Find $f(-1)$. 2

    b. Find $f(4)$.
    undefined

    c. For what value(s) of x is $f(x) = 3$?
    $x = 2$

    d. Write the domain in interval notation.
    $(-\infty, 4)$

    e. Write the range in interval notation.
    $(-\infty, 3]$

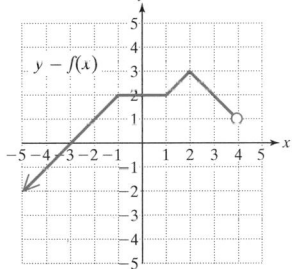

41. Given $f(x) = \sqrt{5 - x}$, write the domain of f.
$(-\infty, 5]$

For Exercises 42–43, solve the system.

42. $\begin{aligned} x &= 1 - 2y \\ 7y &= 3x - 16 \end{aligned}$ $\{(3, -1)\}$

43. $\begin{aligned} x \qquad\quad + 2z &= 7 \\ 2x + 4y \qquad &= 10 \\ -3y + 5z &= 9 \end{aligned}$ $\{(1, 2, 3)\}$

44. Given the points $(9, -4)$ and $(3, 0)$.

    a. Find the distance between the points. $2\sqrt{13}$

    b. Find the midpoint of the line segment $(6, -2)$ between the two points.

45. Given $A = \frac{1}{2}(b_1 + b_2)h$, solve for b_1. $b_1 = \dfrac{2A - hb_2}{h}$

46. The time, $t(n)$ (in minutes), required for a rat to run through a maze depends on the number of trials, n, that the rat has practiced. Find $t(9)$ and interpret its meaning in the context of this problem.

$$t(n) = \dfrac{3n + 15}{n + 1} \text{ for } n \geq 1$$

$t(9) = 4.2$; This means that it will take the rat 4.2 min if the rat has practiced 9 times.

47. The speed of a car varies inversely as the time to travel a fixed distance. A car traveling the speed limit of 60 mph travels between two points in 10 sec. How fast is a car moving if it takes only 8 sec to cover the same distance?
The car is moving 75 mph.

48. Two angles are supplementary. One angle measures 9° more than twice the other angle. Find the measures of the angles.
The angles are 57° and 123°.

49. Chemique invests $3000 less in an account earning 5% simple interest than she does in an account earning 6.5% simple interest. At the end of 1 yr, she earns a total of $770 in interest. Find the amount invested in each account.
She invested $8000 at 6.5% and $5000 at 5%.

50. Against a headwind, a plan can travel 4950 mi in 11 hr. On the return trip flying with the same wind, the plane can fly the same distance in 9 hr. Find the wind speed and the speed of the plane in still air.
The plane travels 500 mph in still air. The wind speed is 50 mph.

Additional Topics Appendix

Mean, Median, and Mode

Section A.1

1. Mean

When given a list of numerical data, it is often desirable to obtain a single number that represents the central value of the data. In this section, we discuss three such values called the mean, median, and mode.

Concepts

1. Mean
2. Median
3. Mode
4. Weighted Mean

> **DEFINITION Mean**
>
> The **mean** (or average) of a set of numbers is the sum of the values divided by the number of values. We can write this as a formula.
>
> $$\text{Mean} = \frac{\text{sum of the values}}{\text{number of values}}$$

Instructor Note: Ask students to compute the mean of their quiz scores or test scores for this class, as a warm-up exercise.

Example 1 **Finding the Mean of a Data Set**

Classroom Example: p. A-7, Exercise 10

A small business employs five workers. Their yearly salaries are

$42,000 $36,000 $45,000 $35,000 $38,000

a. Find the mean yearly salary for the five employees.

b. Suppose the owner of the business makes $218,000 per year. Find the mean salary for all six individuals (that is, include the owner's salary).

Solution:

a. Mean salary of five employees

$$= \frac{42{,}000 + 36{,}000 + 45{,}000 + 35{,}000 + 38{,}000}{5}$$

$$= \frac{196{,}000}{5} \qquad \text{Add the data values.}$$

$$= 39{,}200 \qquad \text{Divide.}$$

The mean salary for employees is $39,200.

Avoiding Mistakes

When computing a mean remember to add the data first before dividing.

b. Mean of all six individuals

$$= \frac{42{,}000 + 36{,}000 + 45{,}000 + 35{,}000 + 38{,}000 + 218{,}000}{6}$$

$$= \frac{414{,}000}{6}$$

$$= 69{,}000$$

The mean salary with the owner's salary included is $69,000.

Skill Practice Housing prices for five homes in one neighborhood are given.

$108,000 $149,000 $164,000 $118,000 $144,000

1. Find the mean of these five prices.

2. Suppose a new home is built in the neighborhood for $1.3 million ($1,300,000). Find the mean price of all six homes.

2. Median

In Example 1, you may have noticed that the mean salary was greatly affected by the unusually high value of $218,000. For this reason, you may want to use a different measure of "center" called the median. The **median** is the "middle" number in an ordered list of numbers.

PROCEDURE   Finding the Median

To compute the median of a list of numbers, first arrange the numbers in order from least to greatest.

- If the number of data values in the list is *odd*, then the median is the middle number in the list.
- If the number of data values is *even*, there is no single middle number. Therefore, the median is the mean (average) of the two middle numbers in the list.

Classroom Examples: p. A-7, Exercises 16 and 18

Example 2   Finding the Median of a Data Set

Consider the salaries of the five workers from Example 1.

$42,000 $36,000 $45,000 $35,000 $38,000

a. Find the median salary for the five workers.

b. Find the median salary including the owner's salary of $218,000.

Solution:

a. 35,000   36,000   38,000   42,000   45,000   Arrange the data in order.

Because there are five data values (an *odd* number), the median is the middle number.

The median is $38,000.

b. Now consider the scores of all six individuals (including the owner). Arrange the data in order.

35,000   36,000   38,000   42,000   45,000   218,000

There are six data values (an *even* number). The median is the average of the two middle numbers.

$$\frac{38,000 + 42,000}{2}$$ Add the two middle numbers.

$$= \frac{80,000}{2}$$ Divide.

$$= 40,000$$

The median of all six salaries is $40,000.

Answers

1. $136,600   **2.** $330,500

Skill Practice Housing prices for five homes in one neighborhood are given.

$108,000 $149,000 $164,000 $118,000 $144,000

3. Find the median price of these five houses.

4. Suppose a new home is built in the neighborhood for $1,300,000. Find the median price of all six homes. Compare this price with the mean in Skill Practice Exercise 2.

In Examples 1 and 2, the mean of all six salaries is $69,000, whereas the median is $40,000. These examples show that the median is a better representation for a central value when the data list has an unusually high (or low) value.

Example 3 Determining the Median of a Data Set

Classroom Example: p. A-8, Exercise 24

The average monthly temperatures (in °C) for the South Pole are given in the table. Find the median temperature. (*Source:* NOAA)

Jan.	Feb.	March	April	May	June	July	Aug.	Sept.	Oct.	Nov.	Dec.
−2.9	−9.5	−19.2	−20.7	−21.7	−23.0	−25.7	−26.1	−24.6	−18.9	−9.7	−3.4

Solution:

First arrange the numbers in order from least to greatest.

−26.1 −25.7 −24.6 −23.0 −21.7 −20.7 −19.2 −18.9 −9.7 −9.5 −3.4 −2.9

$$\text{Median} = \frac{-20.7 + (-19.2)}{2} = -19.95$$

There are 12 data values (an *even* number). Therefore, the median is the average of the two middle numbers. The median temperature at the South Pole is −19.95°C.

TIP: Note that the median may not be one of the original data values.

Skill Practice The gain or loss for a stock is given for an 8-day period. Find the median gain or loss.

5. −2.4   −2.0   1.25   0.6
   −1.8   −0.4   0.6   −0.9

3. Mode

A third representative value for a list of data is called the mode.

DEFINITION Mode

The **mode** of a set of data is the value or values that occur most often.
- If two values occur most often we say the data are **bimodal**.
- If more than two values occur most often, we say there is no mode.

Answers
3. $144,000   4. $146,500
5. −0.65

Classroom Example: p. A-8, Exercise 28

Example 4 Finding the Mode of a Data Set

The student-to-teacher ratio is given for elementary schools for ten selected states. For example, California has a student-to-teacher ratio of 20.6. This means that there are approximately 20.6 students per teacher in California elementary schools. (*Source:* National Center for Education Statistics)

ME	ND	WI	NH	RI	IL	IN	MS	CA	UT
12.5	13.4	14.1	14.5	14.8	16.1	16.1	16.1	20.6	21.9

Find the mode of the student-to-teacher ratio for these states.

Solution:

The data value 16.1 appears most often. Therefore, the mode is 16.1 students per teacher.

Skill Practice The monthly rainfall amounts (in inches) for Houston, Texas, are given. Find the mode. (*Source:* NOAA)

6. 4.5   3.0   3.2   3.5   5.1   6.8
  4.3   4.5   5.6   5.3   4.5   3.8

Classroom Example: p. A-8, Exercise 32

Example 5 Finding the Mode of a Data Set

Find the mode of the list of average monthly temperatures for Albany, New York. Values are in °F.

Jan.	Feb.	March	April	May	June	July	Aug.	Sept.	Oct.	Nov.	Dec.
22	25	35	47	58	66	71	69	61	49	39	26

Solution:

No data value occurs most often. There is no mode for this set of data.

Skill Practice

7. Find the mode of the weights in pounds of babies born one day at Brackenridge Hospital in Austin, Texas.
7.2   8.1   6.9   9.3   8.3   7.7   7.9   6.4   7.5

Classroom Example: p. A-9, Exercise 36

Example 6 Finding the Mode of a Data Set

The grades for a quiz in college algebra are as follows. The scores are out of a possible 10 points.

9   4   6   9   9   8   2   1   4   9
5   10   10   5   7   7   9   8   7   3
9   7   10   7   10   1   7   4   5   6

Answers
6. 4.5 in.   **7.** There is no mode.

Solution:

Sometimes arranging the data in order makes it easier to find the repeated values.

1	1	2	3	4	4	4	5	5	5
6	6	7	7	7	7	7	7	8	8
9	9	9	9	9	9	10	10	10	10

The score of 7 occurs 6 times. The score of 9 occurs 6 times. There are two modes, 7 and 9, because these scores both occur more than any other score. We say that these data are *bimodal*.

Skill Practice

8. The ages of children participating in an after-school sports program are given. Find the mode(s).

13	15	17	15	14	15	16	16
15	16	12	13	15	14	16	15
15	16	16	13	16	13	14	18

TIP: To remember the difference between median and mode, think of the *median* of a highway that goes down the *middle*. Think of the word *mode* as sounding similar to the word *most*.

4. Weighted Mean

Sometimes data values in a list appear multiple times. In such a case, we can compute a **weighted mean**. In Example 7, we demonstrate how to use a weighted mean to compute a grade point average (GPA). To compute GPA, each grade is assigned a numerical value. For example, an "A" is worth 4 points, a "B" is worth 3 points, and so on. Then each grade for a course is "weighted" by the number of credit-hours that the course is worth.

Example 7   Using a Weighted Mean to Compute GPA

Classroom Example: p. A-9, Exercise 44

At a certain college, the grades A–F are assigned numerical values as follows.

$$A = 4.0 \quad B+ = 3.5 \quad B = 3.0 \quad C+ = 2.5$$

$$C = 2.0 \quad D+ = 1.5 \quad D = 1.0 \quad F = 0.0$$

Elmer takes the following classes with the grades as shown. Determine Elmer's GPA.

Course	Grade	Number of Credit-Hours
Prealgebra	A = 4 pts	3
Study Skills	C = 2 pts	1
First Aid	B+ = 3.5 pts	2
English I	D = 1.0 pt	4

Solution:

The data in the table can be visualized as follows.

4 pts	4 pts	4 pts	2 pts	3.5 pts	3.5 pts	1 pt	1 pt	1 pt	1pt
A	A	A	C	B+	B+	D	D	D	D

       3 of these   1 of these   2 of these   4 of these

The number of grade points earned for each course is the product of the grade for the course and the number of credit-hours for the course. For example:

    Grade points for Prealgebra: (4 pts)(3 credit-hours) = 12 points

Answer

8. There are two modes, 15 and 16.

Course	Grade	Number of Credit-Hours (Weights)	Product Number of Grade Points	
Prealgebra	A = 4 pts	3	(4 pts)(3 credit-hours)	= 12 pts
Study Skills	C = 2 pts	1	(2 pts)(1 credit-hour)	= 2 pts
First Aid	B+ = 3.5 pts	2	(3.5 pts)(2 credit-hours)	= 7 pts
English I	D = 1.0 pt	4	(1 pt)(4 credit-hours)	= 4 pts
		Total hours: 10	Total grade points:	25 pts

To determine GPA, we will add the number of grade points earned for each course and then divide by the total number of credit-hours taken.

$$\text{Mean} = \frac{25}{10} = 2.5 \qquad \text{Elmer's GPA for this term is 2.5.}$$

Skill Practice

9. Clyde received the following grades for the semester. Use the numerical values assigned to grades from Example 7 to find Clyde's GPA.

Course	Grade	Credit-Hours
Math	B+	4
Science	C	3
Speech	A	3

In Example 7, notice that the value of each grade is "weighted" by the number of credit-hours. The grade of "A" for Prealgebra is weighted three times. The grade of "C" for the study skills course is weighted one time. The grade that hurt Elmer's GPA was the "D" in English. Not only did he receive a low grade, but the course was weighted heavily (4 credit-hours). In Exercise 47, we recompute Elmer's GPA with a "B" in English to see how this grade affects his GPA.

Answer

9. 3.2

Section A.1 Practice Exercises

Study Skills Exercise

1. Define the key terms.

   a. mean   **b.** median   **c.** mode   **d.** bimodal   **e.** weighted mean

Concept 1: Mean

For Exercises 2–7, find the mean of each set of numbers. **(See Example 1.)**

2. 4, 6, 5, 10, 4, 5, 8   6

3. 3, 8, 5, 7, 4, 2, 7, 4   5

4. 0, 5, 7, 4, 7, 2, 4, 3   4

5. 7, 6, 5, 10, 8, 4, 8, 6, 0   6

6. −10, −13, −18, −20, −15   −15.2

7. −22, −14, −12, −16, −15   −15.8

8. Compute the mean of your test scores for this class up to this point.   Answers will vary.

9. The flight times in hours for six flights between New York and Los Angeles are given. Find the mean flight time. Round to the nearest tenth of an hour. 5.8 hr

5.5, 6.0, 5.8, 5.8, 6.0, 5.6

10. A nurse takes the temperature of a patient every 10 min and records the temperatures as follows: 98°F, 98.4°F, 98.9°F, 100.1°F, and 99.2°F. Find the patient's mean temperature. 98.92°F

11. The number of Calories for six different chicken sandwiches and chicken salads is given in the table.

Chicken Sandwiches	Salads with Chicken
360	310
370	325
380	350
400	390
400	440
470	500

  a. What is the mean number of Calories for a chicken sandwich? Round to the nearest whole unit. 397 Cal

  b. What is the mean number of Calories for a salad with chicken? Round to the nearest whole unit. 386 Cal

  c. What is the difference in the means? There is only an 11-Cal difference in the means.

12. The heights of the players from two NBA teams are given in the table. All heights are in inches.

Philadelphia 76ers' Height (in.)	Milwaukee Bucks' Height (in.)
83	70
83	83
72	82
79	72
77	82
84	85
75	75
76	75
82	78
79	77

  a. Find the mean height for the players on the Philadelphia 76ers. 79 in.

  b. Find the mean height for the players on the Milwaukee Bucks. 77.9 in.

  c. What is the difference in the mean heights? The mean height for the 76ers is slightly higher by 1.1 in.

13. Zach received the following scores for his first four tests: 98%, 80%, 78%, 90%.

  a. Find Zach's mean test score. 86.5%

  b. Zach got a 59% on his fifth test. Find the mean of all five tests. 81%

  c. How did the low score of 59% affect the overall mean of five tests? The low score of 59% decreased Zach's average by 5.5%.

14. The prices of four steam irons are $50, $30, $25, and $45.

  a. Find the mean of these prices. $37.50

  b. An iron that costs $140 is added to the list. What is the mean of all five irons? $58.00

  c. How does the expensive iron affect the mean? By including the iron for $140, the mean increased by $20.50.

Concept 2: Median

For Exercises 15–20, find the median for each set of numbers. **(See Examples 2–3.)**

15. 16, 14, 22, 13, 20, 19, 17
17

16. 32, 35, 22, 36, 30, 31, 38
32

17. 109, 118, 111, 110, 123, 100
110.5

18. 134, 132, 120, 135, 140, 118
133

19. $-58, -55, -50, -40, -40, -55$
-52.5

20. $-82, -90, -99, -82, -88, -87$
-87.5

21. The infant mortality rates for five countries are given in the table. Find the median.
3.93 deaths per 1000

Country	Infant Mortality Rate (Deaths per 1000)
Sweden	3.93
Japan	4.10
Finland	3.82
Andorra	4.09
Singapore	3.87

22. The snowfall amounts for 5 winter months in Burlington, Vermont, are given in the table. Find the median.   16.8 in.

Month	Snowfall (in.)
November	6.6
December	18.1
January	18.8
February	16.8
March	12.4

23. Jonas Slackman played 8 golf tournaments, each with 72-holes of golf. His score for the tournaments are given. Find the median score.

$-3, -5, 1, 4, -8, 2, 8, -1$ 0

24. Andrew Strauss recorded the daily low temperature (in °C) at his home in Virginia for 8 days in January. Find the median temperature.

$5, 6, -5, 1, -4, -11, -8, -5$ −4.5°C

25. The number of passengers (in millions) on 9 leading airlines for a recent year is listed. Find the median number of passengers. (*Source: International Airline Transport Association*)

48.3, 42.4, 91.6, 86.8, 46.5, 71.2, 45.4, 56.4, 51.7
51.7 million passengers

 26. For a recent year the number of albums sold (in millions) is listed for the 10 best sellers. Find the median number of albums sold.

2.7, 3.0, 4.8, 7.4, 3.4, 2.6, 3.0, 3.0, 3.9, 3.2
3.1 million albums

Concept 3: Mode

For Exercises 27–32, find the mode(s) for each set of numbers. **(See Examples 4–6.)**

27. 4, 5, 3, 8, 4, 9, 4, 2, 1, 4   4

28. 12, 14, 13, 17, 19, 18, 19, 17, 17   17

29. $-28, -21, -24, -23, -24, -30, -21$
−21 and −24

30. $-45, -42, -40, -41, -49, -49, -42$
−42 and −49

31. 90, 89, 91, 77, 88   No mode

32. 132, 253, 553, 255, 552, 234   No mode

33. The table gives the price of seven "smart" cell phones. Find the mode. $600

Brand and Model	Price ($)
Samsung	600
Kyocera	400
Sony Ericsson	800
PalmOne	450
Motorola	300
Siemens	600

 34. The table gives the number of hazardous waste sites for selected states. Find the mode.   39

State	Number of Sites
Florida	51
New Jersey	112
Michigan	67
Wisconsin	39
California	96
Pennsylvania	94
Illinois	39
New York	90

35. The unemployment rates in percent for nine countries are given. Find the mode.

6.3%, 7.0%, 5.8%, 9.1%, 5.2%, 8.8%, 8.4%, 5.8%, 5.2%   5.2% and 5.8%

36. The list gives the number of children who were absent from class for a 11-day period. Find the mode.

4, 1, 6, 2, 4, 4, 4, 2, 2, 3, 2   2 children and 4 children

Mixed Exercises

37. Six test scores for Jonathan's history class are listed. Find the mean and median. Round to the nearest tenth if necessary. Did the mean or median give a better overall score for Jonathan's performance?

92%, 98%, 43%, 98%, 97%, 85%
Mean: 85.5%; median: 94.5%; The median gave Jonathan a better overall score.

38. Nora's math test results are listed. Find the mean and median. Round to the nearest tenth if necessary. Did the mean or median give a better overall score for Nora's performance?

52%, 85%, 89%, 90%, 83%, 89%
Mean: 81.3%; median: 87%; The median gave Nora a better overall score.

39. Listed below are monthly costs for seven health insurance companies for a self-employed person, 55 years of age, and in good health. Find the mean, median, and mode (if one exists). Round to the nearest dollar. (*Source:* eHealth Insurance Company, 2007)

$312, $225, $221, $256, $308, $280, $147

Mean: $250; median: $256; mode: There is no mode.

40. The salaries for seven Associate Professors at the University of Michigan are listed. These are salaries for 9-month contracts in 2006. Find the mean, median, and mode (if one exists). Round to the nearest dollar. (*Source:* University of Michigan, University Library Volume 2006, Issue 1)

$104,000, $107,000, $67,750, $82,500, $73,500, $88,300, $104,000
Mean: $89,579; median: $88,300; mode: $104,000

41. The prices of 10 single-family, three-bedroom homes for sale in Santa Rosa, California, are listed for a recent year. Find the mean, median, and mode (if one exists).

$850,000, $835,000, $839,000, $829,000, $850,000, $850,000, $850,000, $847,000, $1,850,000, $825,000
Mean: $942,500; median: $848,500; mode: $850,000

42. The prices of 10 single-family, three-bedroom homes for sale in Boston, Massachusetts, are listed for a recent year. Find the mean, median, and mode (if one exists).

$300,000, $2,495,000, $2,120,000, $220,000, $194,000, $391,000, $315,000, $330,000, $435,000, $250,000
Mean: $705,000; median: $322,500; mode: There is no mode.

Concept 4: Weighted Mean

For Exercises 43–46, use the following numerical values assigned to grades to compute GPA. Round each GPA to the hundredths place. **(See Example 7.)**

$$A = 4.0 \qquad B+ = 3.5 \qquad B = 3.0 \qquad C+ = 2.5$$
$$C = 2.0 \qquad D+ = 1.5 \qquad D = 1.0 \qquad F = 0.0$$

43. Compute the GPA for the following grades. Round to the nearest hundredth.   2.38

Course	Grade	Number of Credit-Hours (Weights)
Intermediate Algebra	B	4
Theater	C	1
Music Appreciation	A	3
World History	D	5

44. Compute the GPA for the following grades. Round to the nearest hundredth.   3.59

Course	Grade	Number of Credit-Hours (Weights)
General Psychology	B+	3
Beginning Algebra	A	4
Student Success	A	1
Freshman English	B	3

 Writing   Translating Expression   Geometry   Scientific Calculator   Video   NS&E

45. Compute the GPA for the following grades. Round to the nearest hundredth.   2.77

Course	Grade	Number of Credit-Hours (Weights)
Business Calculus	B+	3
Biology	C	4
Library Research	F	1
American Literature	A	3

46. Compute the GPA for the following grades. Round to the nearest hundredth.   2.73

Course	Grade	Number of Credit-Hours (Weights)
University Physics	C+	5
Calculus I	A	4
Computer Programming	D	3
Swimming	A	1

47. Refer to the table given in Example 7 on page A-5. Replace the grade of "D" in English I with a grade of "B" and compute the GPA. How did Elmer's GPA differ with a better grade in the 4-hour English class?

3.3; Elmer's GPA improved from 2.5 to 3.3.

Expanding Your Skills

48. There are 20 students enrolled in a 12th-grade math class. The graph displays the number of students by age. First complete the table, and then find the mean.

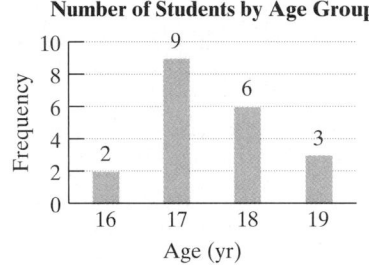

Number of Students by Age Group

Age (yr)	Number of Students	Product
16	2	32
17	9	153
18	6	108
19	3	57
Total:	20	350

The mean age is 17.5 years.

49. A survey was made in a neighborhood of 37 houses. The graph represents the number of residents who live in each house. Complete the table and determine the mean number of residents per house.

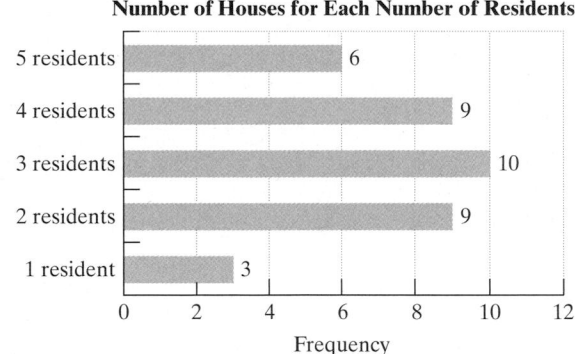

Number of Houses for Each Number of Residents

Number of Residents in Each House	Number of Houses	Product
1	3	3
2	9	18
3	10	30
4	9	36
5	6	30
Total:	37	117

The mean number of residents is approximately 3.2.

Introduction to Geometry

1. Perimeter

In this section, we present several facts and formulas that may be used throughout the text in applications of geometry. One of the most important uses of geometry involves the measurement of objects of various shapes. We begin with an introduction to perimeter, area, and volume for several common shapes and objects.

Concepts

1. **Perimeter**
2. **Area**
3. **Volume**
4. **Angles**
5. **Triangles**

100 ft

50 ft   50 ft

Perimeter — 300 ft

100 ft

Figure A-1

Ahimation

Perimeter is defined as the distance around a figure. If we were to put up a fence around a field, the perimeter would determine the amount of fencing. For example, in Figure A-1 the distance around the field is 300 ft. For a polygon (a closed figure constructed from line segments), the perimeter is the sum of the lengths of the sides. For a circle, the distance around the outside is called the **circumference**.

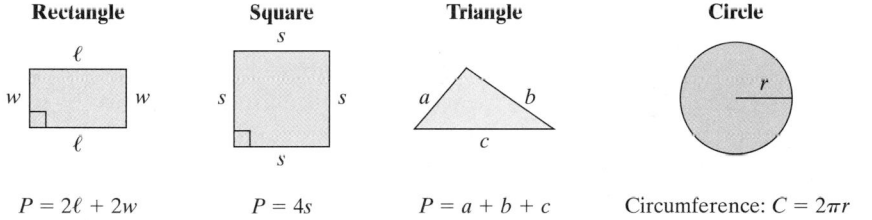

Rectangle	Square	Triangle	Circle
$P = 2\ell + 2w$	$P = 4s$	$P = a + b + c$	Circumference: $C = 2\pi r$

For a circle, r represents the length of a radius—the distance from the center to any point on the circle. The length of a diameter, d, of a circle is twice that of a radius. Thus, $d = 2r$. The number π is a constant equal to the circumference of a circle divided by the length of a diameter. That is, $\pi = \frac{C}{d}$. The value of π is often approximated by 3.14 or $\frac{22}{7}$.

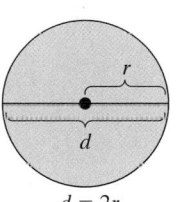

$d = 2r$

| **Example 1** | **Finding Perimeter and Circumference** |

Find the perimeter or circumference as indicated. Use 3.14 for π.

a. Perimeter of the rectangle

b. Circumference of the circle

3.1 ft

5.5 ft

6 cm

Classroom Examples: p. A-21, Exercises 4 and 10

Solution:

a. $P = 2\ell + 2w$

$= 2(5.5 \text{ ft}) + 2(3.1 \text{ ft})$ Substitute $\ell = 5.5$ ft and $w = 3.1$ ft.

$= 11 \text{ ft} + 6.2 \text{ ft}$

$= 17.2 \text{ ft}$ The perimeter is 17.2 ft.

b. $C = 2\pi r$

$\approx 2(3.14)(6 \text{ cm})$ Substitute 3.14 for π and $r = 6$ cm.

$= 6.28(6 \text{ cm})$

$= 37.68 \text{ cm}$ The circumference is 37.68 cm.

TIP: If a calculator is used to find the circumference of a circle, use the π key to get a more accurate answer.

Skill Practice

1. Find the perimeter of the square.

7.25 in.

2. Find the circumference. Use 3.14 for π.

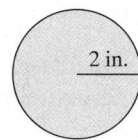

2 in.

2. Area

The **area** of a geometric figure is the number of square units that can be enclosed within the figure. In applications, we would find the area of a region if we were laying carpet or putting down sod for a lawn. For example, the rectangle shown in Figure A-2 encloses 6 square inches (6 in.^{2}).

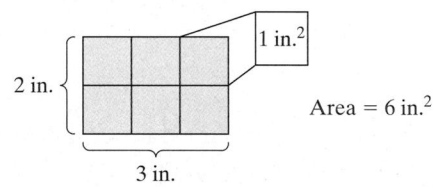

2 in.   1 in.^{2}

Area = 6 in.^{2}

3 in.

Figure A-2

The formulas used to compute the area for several common geometric shapes are given here:

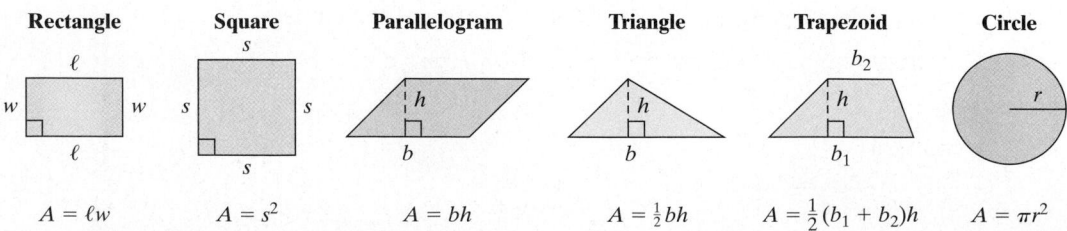

Rectangle	Square	Parallelogram	Triangle	Trapezoid	Circle
$A = \ell w$	$A = s^2$	$A = bh$	$A = \frac{1}{2}bh$	$A = \frac{1}{2}(b_1 + b_2)h$	$A = \pi r^2$

Answers

1. 29 in.   **2.** 12.56 in.

Example 2 Finding Area

Find the area.

Classroom Example: p. A-22, Exercise 18

Solution:

$A = bh$ The figure is a parallelogram.

$= (4\frac{1}{4} \text{ in.})(2\frac{1}{2} \text{ in.})$ Substitute $b = 4\frac{1}{4}$ in. and $h = 2\frac{1}{2}$ in.

$= \left(\frac{17}{4} \text{ in.}\right)\left(\frac{5}{2} \text{ in.}\right)$

$= \frac{85}{8} \text{ in.}^2 \text{ or } 10\frac{5}{8} \text{ in.}^2$

TIP: The units of area are given in square units such as square inches (in.^{2}), square feet (ft^2), square yards (yd^2), square centimeters (cm^2), and so on.

Skill Practice Find the area.

3.

Example 3 Finding Area

Find the area.

Classroom Example: p. A-22, Exercise 24

Solution:

$A = \frac{1}{2}(b_1 + b_2)h$ The figure is a trapezoid.

$= \frac{1}{2}(16 \text{ yd} + 10 \text{ yd})(3 \text{ yd})$ Substitute $b_1 = 16$ yd, $b_2 = 10$ yd, and $h = 3$ yd.

$= \frac{1}{2}(26 \text{ yd})(3 \text{ yd})$

$= (13 \text{ yd})(3 \text{ yd})$

$= 39 \text{ yd}^2$ The area is 39 yd^2.

Skill Practice Find the area.

4.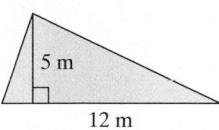

Answers

3. $\frac{9}{16}$ cm^2 4. 30 m^2

Classroom Example: p. A-22,
Exercise 22

Example 4   Finding Area of a Circle

Find the area of a circular fountain if the diameter is 50 ft. Use 3.14 for π.

Solution:

$$A = \pi r^2$$ We need the radius, which is $\frac{1}{2}$ the diameter.
$r = \frac{1}{2}(50) = 25$ ft

$$\approx (3.14)(25 \text{ ft})^2$$ Substitute 3.14 for π and $r = 25$ ft.

$$= (3.14)(625 \text{ ft}^2)$$

$$= 1962.5 \text{ ft}^2$$ The area of the fountain is 1962.5 ft^2.

Skill Practice Find the area of the circular region. Use 3.14 for π.

5.

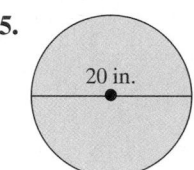

20 in.

3. Volume

The **volume** of a solid is the number of cubic units that can be enclosed within a solid. The solid shown in Figure A-3 contains 18 cubic inches (18 in.^3). In applications, volume might refer to the amount of water in a swimming pool.

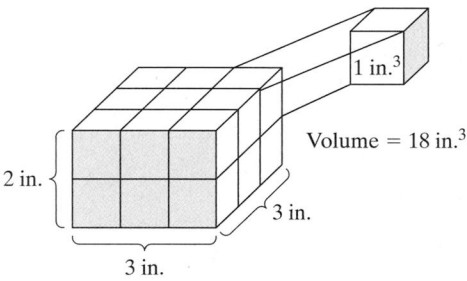

2 in.

3 in.

3 in.

1 in.^{3}

Volume = 18 in.^{3}

Figure A-3

The formulas used to compute the volume of several common solids are given here:

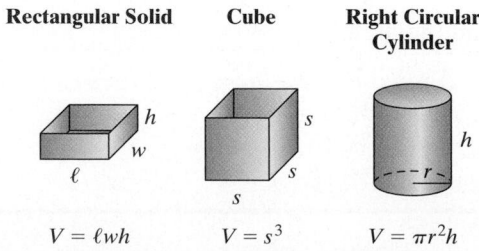

Rectangular Solid	Cube	Right Circular Cylinder
$V = \ell wh$	$V = s^3$	$V = \pi r^2 h$

Answer

5. 314 in.^{2}

TIP: Notice that the volume formulas for the three figures just shown are given by the product of the area of the base and the height of the figure:

$$V = \ell wh \qquad\qquad V = s \cdot s \cdot s \qquad\qquad V = \pi r^2 h$$

Area of   Area of   Area of
Rectangular Base   Square Base   Circular Base

Right Circular Cone   **Sphere**

$$V = \tfrac{1}{3}\pi r^2 h \qquad\qquad V = \tfrac{4}{3}\pi r^3$$

Example 5   **Finding Volume**

Find the volume.

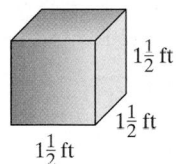

$1\tfrac{1}{2}$ ft

$1\tfrac{1}{2}$ ft

$1\tfrac{1}{2}$ ft

Classroom Example: p. A-23, Exercise 32

 Animation

Solution:

$V = s^3$ The object is a cube.

$= (1\tfrac{1}{2} \text{ ft})^3$ Substitute $s = 1\tfrac{1}{2}$ ft.

$= \left(\dfrac{3}{2} \text{ ft}\right)^3$

$= \left(\dfrac{3}{2} \text{ ft}\right)\left(\dfrac{3}{2} \text{ ft}\right)\left(\dfrac{3}{2} \text{ ft}\right)$

$= \dfrac{27}{8} \text{ ft}^3, \text{ or } 3\dfrac{3}{8} \text{ ft}^3$

TIP: The units of volume are cubic units such as cubic inches (in.^{3}), cubic feet (ft^3), cubic yards (yd^3), cubic centimeters (cm^3), and so on.

Skill Practice Find the volume.

6.

8 ft

4 ft

4 ft

Answer

6. 128 ft^3

Classroom Example: p. A-23,
Exercise 36

Example 6 Finding Volume

Find the volume. Round to the nearest whole unit.

$h = 12$ cm
$r = 4$ cm

Solution:

$V = \dfrac{1}{3}\pi r^2 h$ The object is a right circular cone.

$\approx \dfrac{1}{3}(3.14)(4 \text{ cm})^2(12 \text{ cm})$ Substitute 3.14 for π, $r = 4$ cm, and $h = 12$ cm.

$= \dfrac{1}{3}(3.14)(16 \text{ cm}^2)(12 \text{ cm})$

$= 200.96 \text{ cm}^3$

$\approx 201 \text{ cm}^3$ Round to the nearest whole unit.

Skill Practice Find the volume. Use 3.14 for π. Round to the nearest whole unit.

7. 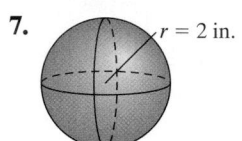 $r = 2$ in.

Classroom Example: p. A-24,
Exercise 52

Example 7 Finding Volume in an Application

An underground gas tank is in the shape of a right circular cylinder. Find the volume of the tank. Use 3.14 for π.

1 ft
10 ft

Solution:

$V = \pi r^2 h$

$\approx (3.14)(1 \text{ ft})^2(10 \text{ ft})$ Substitute 3.14 for π, $r = 1$ ft, and $h = 10$ ft.

$= (3.14)(1 \text{ ft}^2)(10 \text{ ft})$

$= 31.4 \text{ ft}^3$ The tank holds 31.4 ft^3 of gasoline.

Skill Practice

8. Find the volume of soda in the can. Use 3.14 for π. Round to the nearest whole unit.

12 cm
6 cm

Answers

7. 33 in.^{3} **8.** 339 cm^3

4. Angles

Applications involving angles and their measure come up often in the study of algebra, trigonometry, calculus, and applied sciences. The most common unit to measure an angle is the degree (°). Several angles and their corresponding degree measure are shown in Figure A-4.

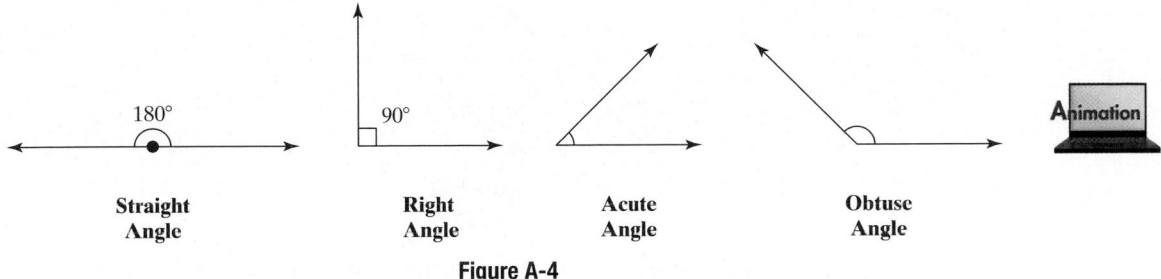

Figure A-4

- An angle that measures 90° is a **right angle** (right angles are often marked with a square or corner symbol, □).
- An angle that measures 180° is called a **straight angle**.
- An angle that measures between 0° and 90° is called an **acute angle**.
- An angle that measures between 90° and 180° is called an **obtuse angle**.
- Two angles with the same measure are **congruent angles**.

The measure of an angle will be denoted by the symbol m written in front of the angle. Therefore, the measure of $\angle A$ is denoted $m(\angle A)$.

- Two angles are **complementary** if their sum is 90°.
- Two angles are **supplementary** if their sum is 180°.

$m(\angle x) + m(\angle y) = 90°$ $m(\angle x) + m(\angle y) = 180°$

When two lines intersect, four angles are formed (Figure A-5).

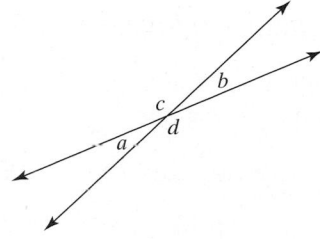

Figure A-5

In Figure A-5, $\angle a$ and $\angle b$ are a pair of **vertical angles**. Another set of vertical angles is the pair $\angle c$ and $\angle d$. An important property of vertical angles is that the measures of two vertical angles are *equal*. In the figure, $m(\angle a) = m(\angle b)$ and $m(\angle c) = m(\angle d)$.

Parallel lines are lines that lie in the same plane and do not intersect. In Figure A-6, the lines L_1 and L_2 are parallel lines. If a line intersects two parallel lines, the line forms eight angles with the parallel lines.

Figure A-6

The measures of angles 1–8 in Figure A-6 have the following special properties.

L_1 and L_2 are Parallel	Name of Angles	Property
(diagram showing angles 2, 4, 5, 7)	The following pairs of angles are called *alternate interior angles:* ∠2 and ∠7 ∠4 and ∠5	Alternate interior angles are equal in measure. $m(\angle 2) = m(\angle 7)$ $m(\angle 4) = m(\angle 5)$
(diagram showing angles 1, 3, 6, 8)	The following pairs of angles are called *alternate exterior angles:* ∠1 and ∠8 ∠3 and ∠6	Alternate exterior angles are equal in measure. $m(\angle 1) = m(\angle 8)$ $m(\angle 3) = m(\angle 6)$
(diagram showing angles 1, 2, 5, 6 and 3, 4, 7, 8)	The following pairs of angles are called *corresponding angles:* ∠1 and ∠5 ∠2 and ∠6 ∠3 and ∠7 ∠4 and ∠8	Corresponding angles are equal in measure. $m(\angle 1) = m(\angle 5)$ $m(\angle 2) = m(\angle 6)$ $m(\angle 3) = m(\angle 7)$ $m(\angle 4) = m(\angle 8)$

Classroom Examples: p. A-25, Exercises 76 and 78

Example 8 **Finding Unknown Angles in a Diagram**

Find the measure of each angle and explain how the angle is related to the given angle of 70°.

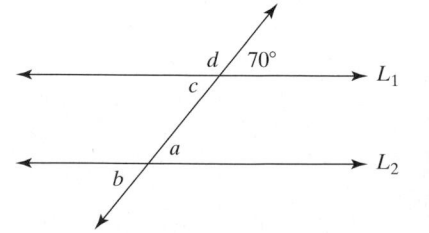

a. ∠a   **b.** ∠b

c. ∠c   **d.** ∠d

Solution:

a. $m(\angle a) = 70°$ $\angle a$ is a corresponding angle to the given angle of 70°.

b. $m(\angle b) = 70°$ $\angle b$ and the given angle of 70° are alternate exterior angles.

c. $m(\angle c) = 70°$ $\angle c$ and the given angle of 70° are vertical angles.

d. $m(\angle d) = 110°$ $\angle d$ is the supplement of the given angle of 70°.

Skill Practice Refer to the figure. Assume that lines L_1 and L_2 are parallel.

9. Given that $m(\angle 3) = 23°$, find $m(\angle 2)$, $m(\angle 4)$, $m(\angle 7)$, and $m(\angle 8)$.

5. Triangles

Triangles are categorized by the measures of the angles (Figure A-7) and by the number of congruent sides or angles (Figure A-8).

- An *acute triangle* is a triangle in which all three angles are acute.
- A **right triangle** is a triangle in which one angle is a right angle.
- An *obtuse triangle* is a triangle in which one angle is obtuse.

Acute Triangle   **Right Triangle**   **Obtuse Triangle**

Figure A-7

- An *equilateral triangle* is a triangle in which all three sides (and all three angles) are equal in measure.
- An *isosceles triangle* is a triangle in which two sides are equal in measure (the angles opposite the equal sides are also equal in measure).
- A *scalene triangle* is a triangle in which no sides (or angles) are equal in measure.

Equilateral Triangle   **Isosceles Triangle**   **Scalene Triangle**

Figure A-8

Answer

9. $m(\angle 2) = 23°$; $m(\angle 4) = 157°$;
$m(\angle 7) = 23°$; $m(\angle 8) = 157°$

The following important property is true for all triangles.

> **PROPERTY   Sum of the Angles in a Triangle**
> The sum of the measures of the angles of a triangle is 180°.

Classroom Example: p. A-26,
Exercise 98

Example 9   **Finding Unknown Angles in a Diagram**

Find the measure of each angle in the figure.

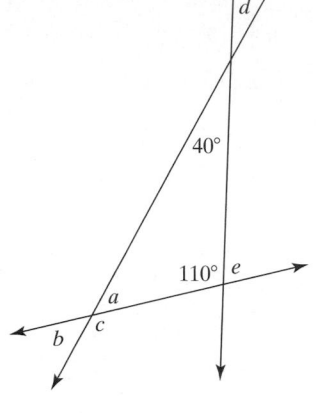

a. $\angle a$

b. $\angle b$

c. $\angle c$

d. $\angle d$

e. $\angle e$

Solution:

a. $m(\angle a) = 30°$ The sum of the angles in a triangle is 180°.

b. $m(\angle b) = 30°$ $\angle a$ and $\angle b$ are vertical angles and are equal.

c. $m(\angle c) = 150°$ $\angle c$ and $\angle a$ are supplementary angles ($\angle c$ and $\angle b$ are also supplementary).

d. $m(\angle d) = 40°$ $\angle d$ and the given angle of 40° are vertical angles.

e. $m(\angle e) = 70°$ $\angle e$ and the given angle of 110° are supplementary angles.

Skill Practice For Exercises 10–14, refer to the figure. Find the measure of the indicated angle.

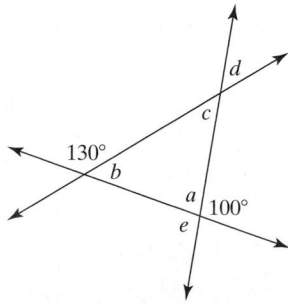

10. $\angle a$ **11.** $\angle b$ **12.** $\angle c$ **13.** $\angle d$ **14.** $\angle e$

Answers
10. 80°   **11.** 50°   **12.** 50°
13. 50°   **14.** 100°

Section A.2   Practice Exercises

Study Skills Exercise

1. Define the key terms.

   a. perimeter

   d. volume

   g. acute angle

   j. complementary angles

   m. parallel lines

   b. circumference

   e. right angle

   h. obtuse angle

   k. supplementary angles

   n. right triangle

   c. area

   f. straight angle

   i. congruent angles

   l. vertical angles

Concept 1: Perimeter

2. Identify which of the following units could be measures of perimeter.   b, e, i

   a. Square inches (in.^{2})

   d. Cubic meters (m^3)

   g. Square yards (yd^2)

   b. Meters (m)

   e. Miles (mi)

   h. Cubic inches (in.^{3})

   c. Cubic feet (ft^3)

   f. Square centimeters (cm^2)

   i. Kilometers (km)

For Exercises 3–10, find the perimeter or circumference of each figure. Use 3.14 for π. **(See Example 1.)**

3.
   32 m
   6 m
   10 m

4.
   108 cm
   22 cm
   32 cm

5.
   17.2 mi
   4.3 mi
   4.3 mi

6.
   1 ft
   0.25 ft
   0.25 ft

7.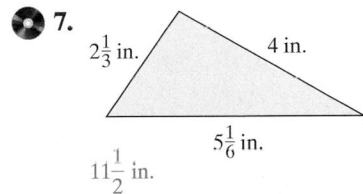
   $2\frac{1}{3}$ in.   4 in.
   $5\frac{1}{6}$ in.
   $11\frac{1}{2}$ in.

8.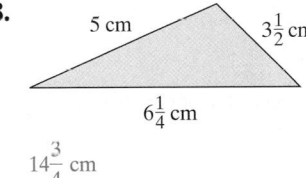
   5 cm $3\frac{1}{2}$ cm
   $6\frac{1}{4}$ cm
   $14\frac{3}{4}$ cm

9.
   10 ft
   31.4 ft

10.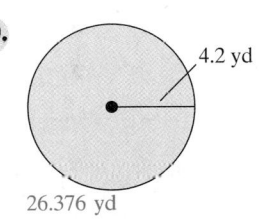
    4.2 yd
    26.376 yd

Concept 2: Area

11. Identify which of the following units could be measures of area.   a, f, g

    a. Square inches (in.^{2})

    d. Cubic meters (m^3)

    g. Square yards (yd^2)

    b. Meters (m)

    e. Miles (mi)

    h. Cubic inches (in.^{3})

    c. Cubic feet (ft^3)

    f. Square centimeters (cm^2)

    i. Kilometers (km)

12. Would you measure area or perimeter to determine the amount of carpeting needed for a room?   Area

For Exercises 13–26, find the area. Use 3.14 for π. **(See Examples 2–4.)**

13.
11 cm
3 cm
33 cm²

14.
5 ft
8 ft
40 ft²

15.
4.1 m
4.1 m
16.81 m²

16.
6.1 in.
6.1 in.
37.21 in.²

17.
6 in.
14 in.
84 in.²

18.
0.01 m
0.04 m
0.0004 m²

19.
2.3 km
8.8 km
10.12 km²

20.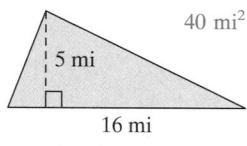
5 mi
16 mi
40 mi²

21.
4.2 ft
13.8474 ft²

22.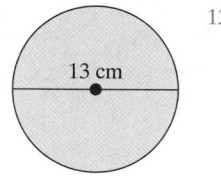
13 cm
132.665 cm²

23.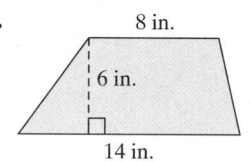
8 in.
6 in.
14 in.
66 in.²

24.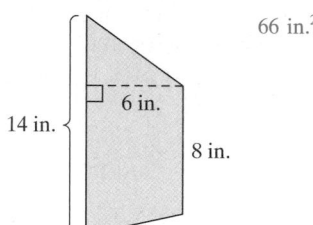
14 in.
6 in.
8 in.
66 in.²

25.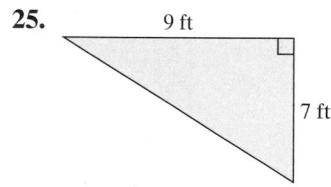
9 ft
7 ft
31.5 ft²

26.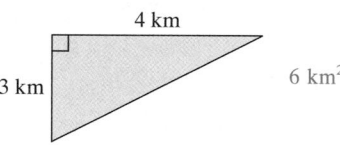
4 km
3 km
6 km²

Concept 3: Volume

27. Identify which of the following units could be measures of volume.   c, d, h

   a. Square inches (in.²)   **b.** Meters (m)   **c.** Cubic feet (ft³)

   d. Cubic meters (m³)   **e.** Miles (mi)   **f.** Square centimeters (cm²)

   g. Square yards (yd²)   **h.** Cubic inches (in.³)   **i.** Kilometers (km)

28. Would you measure perimeter, area, or volume to determine the amount of water needed to fill a swimming pool?   Volume

For Exercises 29–36, find the volume of each figure. Use 3.14 for π. **(See Examples 5–7.)**

29.
3.5 cm
8 cm
307.72 cm³

30.
2 ft
6 ft
75.36 ft³

31.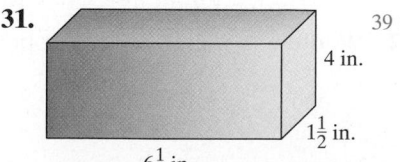
4 in.
$1\frac{1}{2}$ in.
$6\frac{1}{2}$ in.
39 in.³

32.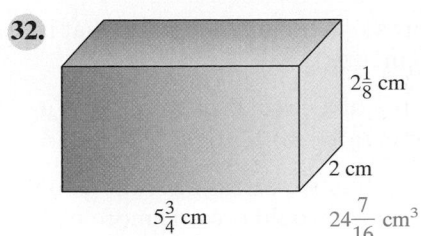

$2\frac{1}{8}$ cm

2 cm

$5\frac{3}{4}$ cm $24\frac{7}{16}$ cm³

33. 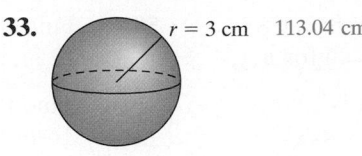 $r = 3$ cm   113.04 cm³

34. 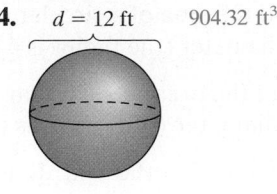 $d = 12$ ft   904.32 ft³

35.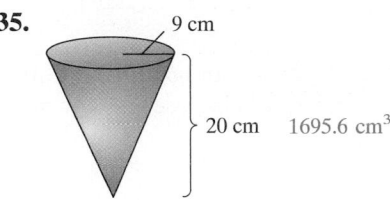

9 cm

20 cm   1695.6 cm³

36. 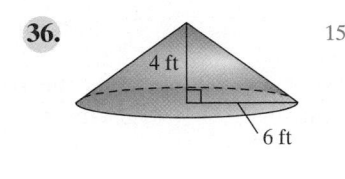   150.72 ft³

4 ft

6 ft

37. A florist sells balloons and needs to know how much helium to order. Each balloon is approximately spherical with a radius of 9 in. How much helium is needed to fill one balloon?
3052.08 in.³

38. Find the volume of a spherical ball whose radius is 2 in. Use 3.14 for π. Round to the nearest whole unit.   33 in.³

39. Find the volume of a snow cone in the shape of a right circular cone whose radius is 3 cm and whose height is 12 cm. Use 3.14 for π.
113.04 cm³

40. A landscaping supply company has a pile of gravel in the shape of a right circular cone whose radius is 10 yd and whose height is 18 yd. Find the volume of the gravel. Use 3.14 for π.   1884 yd³

Mixed Exercises: Perimeter, Area, and Volume

41. A wall measuring 20 ft by 8 ft can be painted for $40.

   a. What is the price per square foot? $0.25/ft²

   b. At this rate, how much would it cost to paint the remaining three walls that measure 20 ft by 8 ft, 16 ft by 8 ft, and 16 ft by 8 ft? $104

42. Suppose it costs $336 to carpet a 16 ft by 12 ft room.

   a. What is the price per square foot? $1.75/ft²

   b. At this rate, how much would it cost to carpet a room that is 20 ft by 32 ft? $1120

43. If you were to purchase fencing for a garden, would you measure the perimeter or area of the garden?   Perimeter

44. If you were to purchase sod (grass) for your front yard, would you measure the perimeter or area of the yard?   Area

45. How much fencing is needed to enclose a triangularly shaped garden whose sides measure 12 ft, 22 ft, and 20 ft?   54 ft

46. A regulation soccer field is 100 yd long by 60 yd wide. Find the perimeter of the field.   320 yd

47. a. An American football field is 360 ft long by 160 ft wide. What is the area of the field?
57,600 ft²

   b. How many pieces of sod, each 1 ft wide and 3 ft long, are needed to sod an entire field? (*Hint:* First find the area of a piece of sod.)
19,200 pieces

48. The Transamerica tower in San Francisco is a pyramid with triangular sides (excluding the "wings"). Each side measures 145 ft wide with a height of 853 ft. What is the area of each side?   61,842.5 ft²

49. a. Find the area of a circular pizza that is 8 in. in diameter (the radius is 4 in.). Use 3.14 for π.   50.24 in.²

    b. Find the area of a circular pizza that is 12 in. in diameter (the radius is 6 in.).   113.04 in.²

    c. Assume that the 8-in. diameter and 12-in. diameter pizzas are both the same thickness. Which would provide more pizza, two 8-in. pizzas or one 12-in. pizza?   One 12-in. pizza

50. a. Find the area of a rectangular pizza that is 12 in. by 8 in.   96 in.²

    b. Find the area of a circular pizza that has a 16-in. diameter. Use 3.14 for π.   200.96 in.²

    c. Assume that the two pizzas have the same thickness. Which would provide more pizza? Two rectangular pizzas or one circular pizza?   One circular pizza

51. Find the volume of a soup can in the shape of a right circular cylinder if its radius is 3.2 cm and its height is 9 cm. Use 3.14 for π.   289.3824 cm³

52. Find the volume of a coffee mug whose radius is 2.5 in. and whose height is 6 in. Use 3.14 for π.   117.75 in.³

Concept 4: Angles

For Exercises 53–58, answer true or false. If an answer is false, explain why.

53. The sum of the measures of two right angles equals the measure of a straight angle.   True

54. Two right angles are complementary.   False; they are supplementary.

55. Two right angles are supplementary.   True

56. Two acute angles cannot be supplementary.   True

57. Two obtuse angles cannot be supplementary.   True

58. An obtuse angle and an acute angle can be supplementary.   True

59. If possible, find two acute angles that are supplementary.   Not possible

60. If possible, find two acute angles that are complementary. Answers may vary.   For example: 30°, 60°

61. If possible, find an obtuse angle and an acute angle that are supplementary. Answers may vary.   For example: 100°, 80°

62. If possible, find two obtuse angles that are supplementary.   Not possible

63. What angle is its own complement?   45°

64. What angle is its own supplement?   90°

65. Refer to the figure.

    a. State all the pairs of vertical angles.   ∠1 and ∠3, ∠2 and ∠4

    b. State all the pairs of supplementary angles.
    ∠1 and ∠2, ∠2 and ∠3, ∠3 and ∠4, ∠1 and ∠4

    c. If the measure of ∠4 is 80°, find the measures of ∠1, ∠2, and ∠3.
    $m(\angle 1) = 100°$, $m(\angle 2) = 80°$, $m(\angle 3) = 100°$

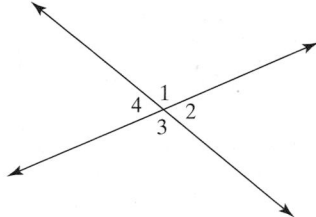

66. Refer to the figure.

    a. State all the pairs of vertical angles.
    ∠b and ∠d, ∠a and ∠c

    b. State all the pairs of supplementary angles.
    ∠a and ∠b, ∠b and ∠c, ∠c and ∠d, ∠a and ∠d

    c. If the measure of ∠a is 25°, find the measures of ∠b, ∠c, and ∠d.
    $m(\angle b) = 155°$, $m(\angle c) = 25°$, $m(\angle d) = 155°$

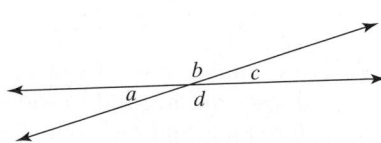

For Exercises 67–70, find the complement of each angle.

67. 33°   57°   **68.** 87°   3°   **69.** 12°   78°   **70.** 45°   45°

For Exercises 71–74, find the supplement of each angle.

71. 33°   147°   **72.** 87°   93°   **73.** 122°   58°   **74.** 90°   90°

For Exercises 75–82, refer to the figure. Assume that L_1 and L_2 are parallel lines. **(See Example 8.)**

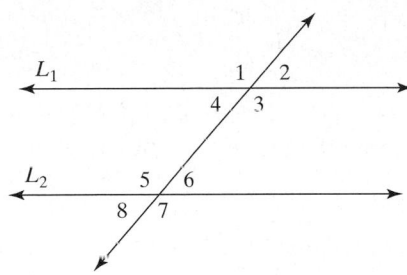

75. $m(\angle 5) = m(\angle \underline{\quad 7 \quad})$ Reason: Vertical angles have equal measures.

76. $m(\angle 5) = m(\angle \underline{\quad 3 \quad})$ Reason: Alternate interior angles have equal measures.

77. $m(\angle 5) = m(\angle \underline{\quad 1 \quad})$ Reason: Corresponding angles have equal measures.

78. $m(\angle 7) = m(\angle \underline{\quad 3 \quad})$ Reason: Corresponding angles have equal measures.

79. $m(\angle 7) = m(\angle \underline{\quad 1 \quad})$ Reason: Alternate exterior angles have equal measures.

80. $m(\angle 7) = m(\angle \underline{\quad 5 \quad})$ Reason: Vertical angles have equal measures.

81. $m(\angle 3) = m(\angle \underline{\quad 5 \quad})$ Reason: Alternate interior angles have equal measures.

82. $m(\angle 3) = m(\angle \underline{\quad 1 \quad})$ Reason: Vertical angles have equal measures.

83. Find the measure of angles a–g in the figure. Assume that L_1 and L_2 are parallel.

$m(\angle a) = 45°, m(\angle b) = 135°, m(\angle c) = 45°, m(\angle d) = 135°,$
$m(\angle e) = 45°, m(\angle f) = 135°, m(\angle g) = 45°$

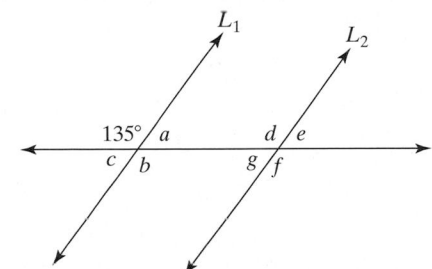

84. Find the measure of angles a–g in the figure. Assume that L_1 and L_2 are parallel.

$m(\angle a) = 65°, m(\angle b) = 115°, m(\angle c) = 115°, m(\angle d) = 65°,$
$m(\angle e) = 115°, m(\angle f) = 115°, m(\angle g) = 65°$

 Writing   Translating Expression   Geometry   Scientific Calculator   Video   NS&E

Concept 5: Triangles

For Exercises 85–88, identify the triangle as equilateral, isosceles, or scalene.

85.

6 in.   10 in.

8 in.

Scalene

86.

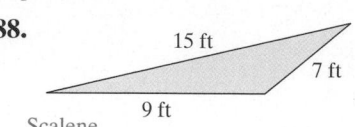

6 cm   6 cm

6 cm

Equilateral

87.

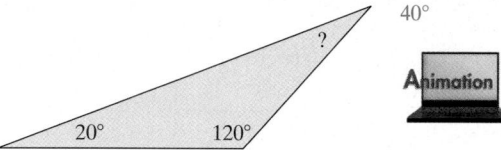

6 m   6 m

10 m

Isosceles

88.

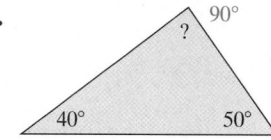

15 ft

7 ft

9 ft

Scalene

89. True or False? If a triangle is equilateral, then it is not scalene.   True

90. True or False? If a triangle is isosceles, then it is also scalene.   False; an isosceles triangle has two sides that are the same length. A scalene triangle has three sides of different length.

91. Can a triangle be both a right triangle and an obtuse triangle? Explain.   No, a 90° angle plus an angle greater than 90° would make the sum of the angles greater than 180°.

92. Can a triangle be both a right triangle and an isosceles triangle? Explain.
Yes, the sides forming the right angle can be equal.

For Exercises 93–96, find the measure of the missing angles.

93.

40°
?
20°   120°

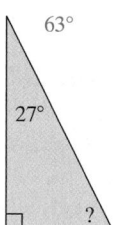

Animation

94.

90°
?
40°   50°

95.

?   37°

53°

96.

63°

27°

?

97. Refer to the figure. Find the measure of angles *a–j*. **(See Example 9.)** $m(\angle a) = 80°, m(\angle b) = 80°,$ $m(\angle c) = 100°, m(\angle d) = 100°, m(\angle e) = 65°, m(\angle f) = 115°,$ $m(\angle g) = 115°, m(\angle h) = 35°, m(\angle i) = 145°, m(\angle j) = 145°$

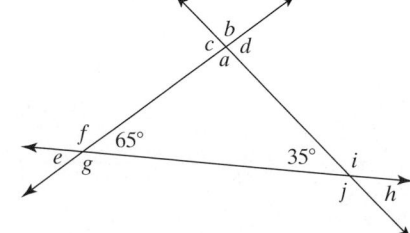

c b d
a

f 65°
e g

35° i
j h

98. Refer to the figure. Find the measure of angles *a–j*.

$m(\angle a) = 120°, m(\angle b) = 60°, m(\angle c) = 60°, m(\angle d) = 40°, m(\angle e) = 40°,$ $m(\angle f) = 140°, m(\angle g) = 140°, m(\angle h) = 160°, m(\angle i) = 20°, m(\angle j) = 160°$

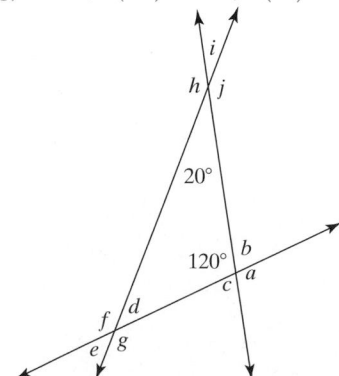

i
h j
20°
120° b
c a
f d
e g

99. Refer to the figure. Find the measure of angles
a–k. Assume that L_1 and L_2 are parallel.

$m(\angle a) = 70°, m(\angle b) = 65°, m(\angle c) = 65°, m(\angle d) = 110°, m(\angle e) = 70°,$
$m(\angle f) = 110°, m(\angle g) = 115°, m(\angle h) = 115°, m(\angle i) = 65°,$
$m(\angle j) = 70°, m(\angle k) = 65°$

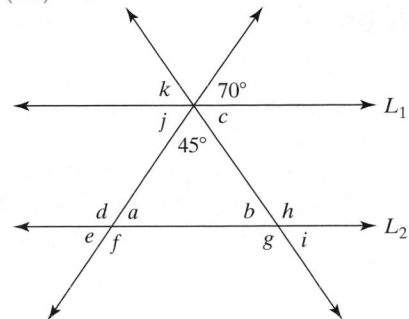

100. Refer to the figure. Find the measure of angles *a–k.*
Assume that L_1 and L_2 are parallel.

$m(\angle a) = 75°, m(\angle b) = 65°, m(\angle c) = 40°, m(\angle d) = 65°, m(\angle e) = 65°,$
$m(\angle f) = 40°, m(\angle g) = 40°, m(\angle h) = 140°, m(\angle i) = 140°,$
$m(\angle j) = 115°, m(\angle k) = 115°$

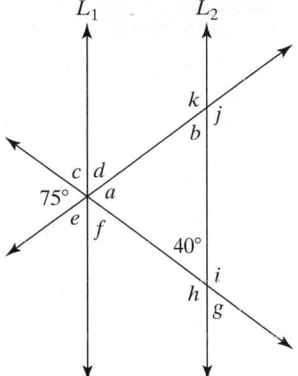

Expanding Your Skills

For Exercises 101–102, find the perimeter.

101.

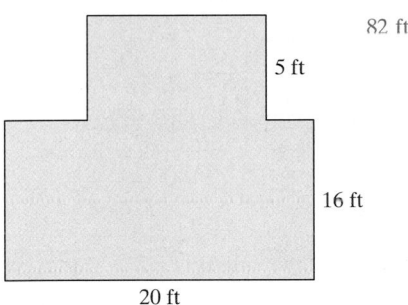

82 ft

5 ft

16 ft

20 ft

102.

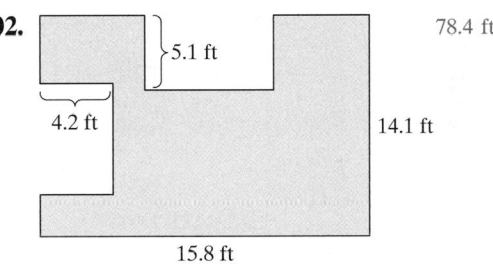

78.4 ft

5.1 ft

4.2 ft

14.1 ft

15.8 ft

For Exercises 103–106, find the area of the shaded region. Use 3.14 for π.

103.

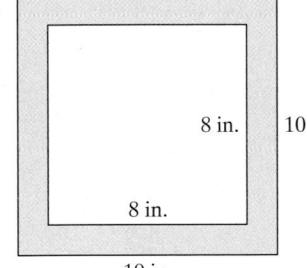

36 in.²

8 in. 10 in.

8 in.

10 in.

104.

73 ft²

3 ft   8 ft

5 ft

11 ft

105.

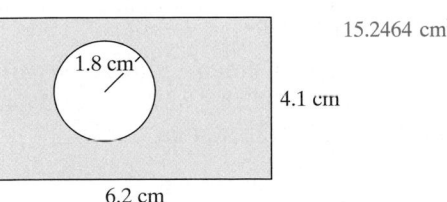

15.2464 cm²

1.8 cm

4.1 cm

6.2 cm

106.

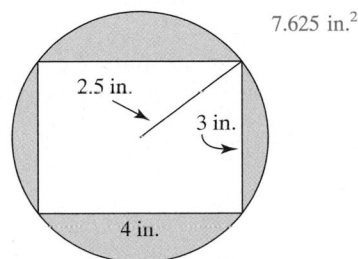

7.625 in.²

2.5 in.

3 in.

4 in.

Section A.3   Solving Systems of Linear Equations by Using Matrices

Concepts

1. Introduction to Matrices
2. Solving Systems of Linear Equations by Using the Gauss-Jordan Method

1. Introduction to Matrices

In Sections 4.2, 4.3, and 4.5, we solved systems of linear equations by using the substitution method and the addition method. We now present a third method called the Gauss-Jordan method that uses matrices to solve a linear system.

A **matrix** is a rectangular array of numbers (the plural of *matrix* is *matrices*). The rows of a matrix are read horizontally, and the columns of a matrix are read vertically. Every number or entry within a matrix is called an element of the matrix.

The **order of a matrix** is determined by the number of rows and number of columns. A matrix with m rows and n columns is an $m \times n$ (read as "m by n") matrix. Notice that with the order of a matrix, the number of rows is given first, followed by the number of columns.

Classroom Examples: p. A-35, Exercises 6, 10, and 14

Example 1   Determining the Order of a Matrix

Determine the order of each matrix.

a. $\begin{bmatrix} 2 & -4 & 1 \\ 5 & \pi & \sqrt{7} \end{bmatrix}$ **b.** $\begin{bmatrix} 1.9 \\ 0 \\ 7.2 \\ -6.1 \end{bmatrix}$ **c.** $\begin{bmatrix} 1 & 0 & 0 \\ 0 & 1 & 0 \\ 0 & 0 & 1 \end{bmatrix}$ **d.** $\begin{bmatrix} a & b & c \end{bmatrix}$

Solution:

a. This matrix has two rows and three columns. Therefore, it is a 2×3 matrix.

b. This matrix has four rows and one column. Therefore, it is a 4×1 matrix. A matrix with one column is called a **column matrix**.

c. This matrix has three rows and three columns. Therefore, it is a 3×3 matrix. A matrix with the same number of rows and columns is called a **square matrix**.

d. This matrix has one row and three columns. Therefore, it is a 1×3 matrix. A matrix with one row is called a **row matrix**.

Instructor Note: "Row" and "column" may not be familiar to some students. They need to understand that rows are horizontal and columns are vertical.

Skill Practice Determine the order of the matrix.

1. $\begin{bmatrix} -5 & 2 \\ 1 & 3 \\ 8 & 9 \end{bmatrix}$ **2.** $\begin{bmatrix} 4 & -8 \end{bmatrix}$ **3.** $\begin{bmatrix} 5 \\ 10 \\ 15 \end{bmatrix}$ **4.** $\begin{bmatrix} 2 & -0.5 \\ -1 & 6 \end{bmatrix}$

A matrix can be used to represent a system of linear equations written in standard form. To do so, we extract the coefficients of the variable terms and the constants within the equation. For example, consider the system

$$2x - y = 5$$
$$x + 2y = -5$$

The matrix **A** is called the **coefficient matrix**.

Answers

1. 3×2 **2.** 1×2
3. 3×1 **4.** 2×2

$$\mathbf{A} = \begin{bmatrix} 2 & -1 \\ 1 & 2 \end{bmatrix}$$

If we extract both the coefficients and the constants from the equations, we can construct the **augmented matrix** of the system:

$$\begin{bmatrix} 2 & -1 & 5 \\ 1 & 2 & -5 \end{bmatrix}$$

A vertical bar is inserted into an augmented matrix to designate the position of the equal signs.

Example 2 **Writing an Augmented Matrix for a System of Linear Equations**

Classroom Example: p. A-35, Exercise 18

Write the augmented matrix for each linear system.

a. $-3x - 4y = 3$
  $2x + 4y = 2$

b. $2x \quad\; - 3z = 14$
  $2y + z = 2$
  $x + y \quad\;\; = 4$

Solution:

a. $\begin{bmatrix} -3 & -4 & 3 \\ 2 & 4 & 2 \end{bmatrix}$

b. $\begin{bmatrix} 2 & 0 & -3 & 14 \\ 0 & 2 & 1 & 2 \\ 1 & 1 & 0 & 4 \end{bmatrix}$

TIP: Notice that zeros are inserted to denote the coefficient of each missing term.

Instructor Note: Discuss the difference between a "0" coefficient and a "1" as a coefficient.

Skill Practice Write the augmented matrix for each system.

5. $-x + y = 4$
  $2x - y = 1$

6. $2x - y + z = 14$
  $-3x + 4y \quad\;\; = 8$
  $x - y + 5z = 0$

Example 3 **Writing a Linear System from an Augmented Matrix**

Classroom Examples: p. A-35, Exercises 20 and 22

Write a system of linear equations represented by each augmented matrix.

a. $\begin{bmatrix} 2 & -5 & -8 \\ 4 & 1 & 6 \end{bmatrix}$

b. $\begin{bmatrix} 2 & -1 & 3 & 14 \\ 1 & 1 & -2 & -5 \\ 3 & 1 & -1 & 2 \end{bmatrix}$

c. $\begin{bmatrix} 1 & 0 & 0 & 4 \\ 0 & 1 & 0 & -1 \\ 0 & 0 & 1 & 0 \end{bmatrix}$

Solution:

a. $2x - 5y = -8$
  $4x + y = 6$

b. $2x - y + 3z = 14$
  $x + y - 2z = -5$
  $3x + y - z = 2$

c. $x + 0y + 0z = 4 \qquad x = 4$
  $0x + y + 0z = -1 \quad$ or $\quad y = -1$
  $0x + 0y + z = 0 \qquad z = 0$

Skill Practice Write a system of linear equations represented by each augmented matrix.

7. $\begin{bmatrix} 2 & 3 & 5 \\ -1 & 8 & 1 \end{bmatrix}$

8. $\begin{bmatrix} -3 & 2 & 1 & 4 \\ 14 & 1 & 0 & 20 \\ -8 & 3 & 5 & 6 \end{bmatrix}$

9. $\begin{bmatrix} 1 & 0 & 0 & -8 \\ 0 & 1 & 0 & 2 \\ 0 & 0 & 1 & 15 \end{bmatrix}$

Answers

5. $\begin{bmatrix} -1 & 1 & 4 \\ 2 & -1 & 1 \end{bmatrix}$

6. $\begin{bmatrix} 2 & -1 & 1 & 14 \\ -3 & 4 & 0 & 8 \\ 1 & -1 & 5 & 0 \end{bmatrix}$

7. $2x + 3y = 5$
  $-x + 8y = 1$

8. $-3x + 2y + z = 4$
  $14x + y \quad\;\; = 20$
  $-8x + 3y + 5z = 6$

9. $x = -8, y = 2, z = 15$

2. Solving Systems of Linear Equations by Using the Gauss-Jordan Method

We know that interchanging two equations results in an equivalent system of linear equations. Interchanging two rows in an augmented matrix results in an equivalent augmented matrix. Similarly, because each row in an augmented matrix represents a linear equation, we can perform the following elementary row operations that result in an equivalent augmented matrix.

PROPERTY   Elementary Row Operations

The following *elementary row operations* performed on an augmented matrix produce an equivalent augmented matrix:

- Interchange two rows.
- Multiply every element in a row by a nonzero real number.
- Add a multiple of one row to another row.

When we are solving a system of linear equations by any method, the goal is to write a series of simpler but equivalent systems of equations until the solution is obvious. The *Gauss-Jordan method* uses a series of elementary row operations performed on the augmented matrix to produce a simpler augmented matrix. In particular, we want to produce an augmented matrix that has 1's along the diagonal of the matrix of coefficients and 0's for the remaining entries in the matrix of coefficients. A matrix written in this way is said to be written in **reduced row echelon form**. For example, the augmented matrix from Example 3(c) is written in reduced row echelon form.

$$\left[\begin{array}{ccc|c} 1 & 0 & 0 & 4 \\ 0 & 1 & 0 & -1 \\ 0 & 0 & 1 & 0 \end{array}\right]$$

The solution to the corresponding system of equations is easily recognized as $x = 4$, $y = -1$, and $z = 0$.

Similarly, matrix **B** represents a solution of $x = a$ and $y = b$.

$$\mathbf{B} = \left[\begin{array}{cc|c} 1 & 0 & a \\ 0 & 1 & b \end{array}\right]$$

Classroom Example: p. A-36, Exercise 34

Example 4   Solving a System by Using the Gauss-Jordan Method

Solve by using the Gauss-Jordan method.

$$2x - y = 5$$
$$x + 2y = -5$$

Solution:

$$\begin{bmatrix} 2 & -1 & | & 5 \\ 1 & 2 & | & -5 \end{bmatrix}$$ Set up the augmented matrix.

$$\xrightarrow{R_1 \Leftrightarrow R_2} \begin{bmatrix} 1 & 2 & | & -5 \\ 2 & -1 & | & 5 \end{bmatrix}$$ Switch row 1 and row 2 to get a 1 in the upper left position.

$$\xrightarrow{-2R_1 + R_2 \Rightarrow R_2} \begin{bmatrix} 1 & 2 & | & -5 \\ 0 & -5 & | & 15 \end{bmatrix}$$ Multiply row 1 by -2 and add the result to row 2. This produces an entry of 0 below the upper left position.

$$\xrightarrow{-\frac{1}{5}R_2 \Rightarrow R_2} \begin{bmatrix} 1 & 2 & | & -5 \\ 0 & 1 & | & -3 \end{bmatrix}$$ Multiply row 2 by $-\frac{1}{5}$ to produce a 1 along the diagonal in the second row.

$$\xrightarrow{-2R_2 + R_1 \Rightarrow R_1} \begin{bmatrix} 1 & 0 & | & 1 \\ 0 & 1 & | & -3 \end{bmatrix}$$ Multiply row 2 by -2 and add the result to row 1. This produces a 0 in the first row, second column.

$$C = \begin{bmatrix} 1 & 0 & | & 1 \\ 0 & 1 & | & -3 \end{bmatrix}$$

The matrix C is in reduced row echelon form. From the augmented matrix, we have $x = 1$ and $y = -3$. The solution set is $\{(1, -3)\}$.

Skill Practice

10. Solve by using the Gauss-Jordan method.
$$x - 2y = -21$$
$$2x + y = -2$$

The order in which we manipulate the elements of an augmented matrix to produce reduced row echelon form was demonstrated in Example 4. In general, the order is as follows.

- First produce a 1 in the first row, first column. Then use the first row to obtain 0's in the first column below this element.
- Next, if possible, produce a 1 in the second row, second column. Use the second row to obtain 0's above and below this element.
- Next, if possible, produce a 1 in the third row, third column. Use the third row to obtain 0's above and below this element.
- The process continues until reduced row echelon form is obtained.

Answer
10. $\{(-5, 8)\}$

Classroom Example: p. A-36,
Exercise 48

Example 5 Solving a System by Using the Gauss-Jordan Method

Solve by using the Gauss-Jordan method.

$$x = -y + 5$$
$$-2x + 2z = y - 10$$
$$3x + 6y + 7z = 14$$

Solution:

First write each equation in the system in standard form.

$$x = -y + 5 \longrightarrow x + y = 5$$
$$-2x + 2z = y - 10 \longrightarrow -2x - y + 2z = -10$$
$$3x + 6y + 7z = 14 \longrightarrow 3x + 6y + 7z = 14$$

$$\begin{bmatrix} 1 & 1 & 0 & | & 5 \\ -2 & -1 & 2 & | & -10 \\ 3 & 6 & 7 & | & 14 \end{bmatrix}$$ Set up the augmented matrix.

$$2R_1 + R_2 \Rightarrow R_2 \longrightarrow$$
$$-3R_1 + R_3 \Rightarrow R_3 \longrightarrow$$
$$\begin{bmatrix} 1 & 1 & 0 & | & 5 \\ 0 & 1 & 2 & | & 0 \\ 0 & 3 & 7 & | & -1 \end{bmatrix}$$ Multiply row 1 by 2 and add the result to row 2. Multiply row 1 by −3 and add the result to row 3.

$$-1R_2 + R_1 \Rightarrow R_1 \longrightarrow$$
$$-3R_2 + R_3 \Rightarrow R_3 \longrightarrow$$
$$\begin{bmatrix} 1 & 0 & -2 & | & 5 \\ 0 & 1 & 2 & | & 0 \\ 0 & 0 & 1 & | & -1 \end{bmatrix}$$ Multiply row 2 by −1 and add the result to row 1. Multiply row 2 by −3 and add the result to row 3.

$$2R_3 + R_1 \Rightarrow R_1 \longrightarrow$$
$$-2R_3 + R_2 \Rightarrow R_2 \longrightarrow$$
$$\begin{bmatrix} 1 & 0 & 0 & | & 3 \\ 0 & 1 & 0 & | & 2 \\ 0 & 0 & 1 & | & -1 \end{bmatrix}$$ Multiply row 3 by 2 and add the result to row 1. Multiply row 3 by −2 and add the result to row 2.

From the reduced row echelon form of the matrix, we have $x = 3$, $y = 2$, and $z = -1$. The solution set is $\{(3, 2, -1)\}$.

Skill Practice Solve by using the Gauss-Jordan method.

11. $x + y + z = 2$
$x - y + z = 4$
$x + 4y + 2z = 1$

Answer
11. $\{(1, -1, 2)\}$

It is particularly easy to recognize a dependent or inconsistent system of equations from the reduced row echelon form of an augmented matrix. This is demonstrated in Examples 6 and 7.

Example 6   Solving a Dependent System by Using the Gauss-Jordan Method

Classroom Example: p. A-36, Exercise 38

Solve by using the Gauss-Jordan method.

$$x - 3y = 4$$

$$\frac{1}{2}x - \frac{3}{2}y = 2$$

Solution:

$$\begin{bmatrix} 1 & -3 & | & 4 \\ \frac{1}{2} & -\frac{3}{2} & | & 2 \end{bmatrix}$$ Set up the augmented matrix.

$$\xrightarrow{-\frac{1}{2}R_1 + R_2 \Rightarrow R_2} \begin{bmatrix} 1 & -3 & | & 4 \\ 0 & 0 & | & 0 \end{bmatrix}$$ Multiply row 1 by $-\frac{1}{2}$ and add the result to row 2.

   The second row of the augmented matrix represents the equation $0 = 0$. The system is dependent. The solution set is $\{(x, y)\,|\,x - 3y = 4\}$.

Skill Practice   Solve by using the Gauss-Jordan method.

12. $4x - 6y = 16$
      $6x - 9y = 24$

Example 7   Solving an Inconsistent System by Using the Gauss-Jordan Method

Classroom Example: p. A-36, Exercise 44

Solve by using the Gauss-Jordan method.

$$x + 3y = 2$$

$$-3x - 9y = 1$$

Solution:

$$\begin{bmatrix} 1 & 3 & | & 2 \\ -3 & -9 & | & 1 \end{bmatrix}$$ Set up the augmented matrix.

$$\xrightarrow{3R_1 + R_2 \Rightarrow R_2} \begin{bmatrix} 1 & 3 & | & 2 \\ 0 & 0 & | & 7 \end{bmatrix}$$ Multiply row 1 by 3 and add the result to row 2.

   The second row of the augmented matrix represents the contradiction $0 = 7$. The system is inconsistent. There is no solution, $\{\ \}$.

Skill Practice   Solve by using the Gauss-Jordan method.

13. $6x + 10y = 1$
      $15x + 25y = 3$

Answers

12. Infinitely many solutions;
      $\{(x, y)\,|\,4x - 6y = 16\}$;
      dependent system
13. $\{\ \}$; inconsistent system

Calculator Connections

Topic: Entering a Matrix into a Calculator

Many graphing calculators have a matrix editor in which the user defines the order of the matrix and then enters the elements of the matrix. For example, the 2×3 matrix

$$\mathbf{D} = \begin{bmatrix} 2 & -3 & | & -13 \\ 3 & 1 & | & 8 \end{bmatrix}$$

is entered as shown.

Once an augmented matrix has been entered into a graphing calculator, a *rref* function can be used to transform the matrix into reduced row echelon form.

Section A.3   Practice Exercises

Study Skills Exercise

1. Define the key terms.

   a. matrix   **b.** order of a matrix   **c.** column matrix   **d.** square matrix

   e. row matrix   **f.** coefficient matrix   **g.** augmented matrix   **h.** reduced row echelon form

Review Exercises

For Exercises 2–5, solve the system by using any method.

2. $2x - y = -9$ $\{(-2, 5)\}$
   $x + 4y = 18$

3. $x - 6y = 9$ $\left\{ \left(12, \frac{1}{2}\right) \right\}$
   $x + 2y = 13$

4. $x + y - z = 8$ $\{(6, 1, -1)\}$
   $x - 2y + z = 3$
   $x + 3y + 2z = 7$

5. $2x - y + z = -4$ $\{(1, 3, -3)\}$
   $-x + y + 3z = -7$
   $x + 3y - 4z = 22$

 Writing   Translating Expression   Geometry   Scientific Calculator   Video   NS&E

Concept 1: Introduction to Matrices

For Exercises 6–14, (**a**) determine the order of each matrix and (**b**) determine if the matrix is a row matrix, a column matrix, a square matrix, or none of these. **(See Example 1.)**

6. $\begin{bmatrix} 4 \\ 5 \\ -3 \\ 0 \end{bmatrix}$ a. 4×1
b. column matrix

7. $\begin{bmatrix} 5 \\ -1 \\ 2 \end{bmatrix}$ a. 3×1
b. column matrix

8. $\begin{bmatrix} -9 & 4 & 3 \\ -1 & -8 & 4 \\ 5 & 8 & 7 \end{bmatrix}$ a. 3×3
b. square matrix

9. $\begin{bmatrix} 3 & -9 \\ -1 & -3 \end{bmatrix}$ a. 2×2
b. square matrix

10. $\begin{bmatrix} 4 & -7 \end{bmatrix}$ a. 1×2
b. row matrix

11. $\begin{bmatrix} 0 & -8 & 11 & 5 \end{bmatrix}$ a. 1×4
b. row matrix

12. $\begin{bmatrix} 5 & -8.1 & 4.2 & 0 \\ 4.3 & -9 & 18 & 3 \end{bmatrix}$ a. 2×4
b. none of these

13. $\begin{bmatrix} \frac{1}{3} & \frac{3}{4} & 6 \\ 2 & 1 & \frac{7}{8} \end{bmatrix}$ a. 2×3
b. none of these

14. $\begin{bmatrix} 5 & 1 \\ -1 & 2 \\ 0 & 7 \end{bmatrix}$ a. 3×2
b. none of these

For Exercises 15–18, set up the augmented matrix. **(See Example 2.)**

15. $\begin{aligned} x - 2y &= -1 \\ 2x + y &= -7 \end{aligned}$ $\begin{bmatrix} 1 & -2 & | & -1 \\ 2 & 1 & | & -7 \end{bmatrix}$

16. $\begin{aligned} x - 3y &= 3 \\ 2x - 5y &= 4 \end{aligned}$ $\begin{bmatrix} 1 & -3 & | & 3 \\ 2 & -5 & | & 4 \end{bmatrix}$

17. $\begin{aligned} x - 2y &= 5 - z \\ 2x + 6y + 3z &= -2 \\ 3x - y - 2z &= 1 \end{aligned}$ $\begin{bmatrix} 1 & -2 & 1 & | & 5 \\ 2 & 6 & 3 & | & -2 \\ 3 & -1 & -2 & | & 1 \end{bmatrix}$

18. $\begin{aligned} 5x - 17 &= -2z \\ 8x + 6z &= 26 + y \\ 8x + 3y - 12z &= 24 \end{aligned}$ $\begin{bmatrix} 5 & 0 & 2 & | & 17 \\ 8 & -1 & 6 & | & 26 \\ 8 & 3 & -12 & | & 24 \end{bmatrix}$

For Exercises 19–22, write a system of linear equations represented by the augmented matrix. **(See Example 3.)**

19. $\begin{bmatrix} 4 & 3 & | & 6 \\ 12 & 5 & | & -6 \end{bmatrix}$
$\begin{aligned} 4x + 3y &= 6 \\ 12x + 5y &= -6 \end{aligned}$

20. $\begin{bmatrix} -2 & 5 & | & -15 \\ -7 & 15 & | & -45 \end{bmatrix}$
$\begin{aligned} -2x + 5y &= -15 \\ -7x + 15y &= 45 \end{aligned}$

21. $\begin{bmatrix} 1 & 0 & 0 & | & 4 \\ 0 & 1 & 0 & | & -1 \\ 0 & 0 & 1 & | & 7 \end{bmatrix}$
$x = 4, y = -1, z = 7$

22. $\begin{bmatrix} 1 & 0 & 0 & | & 0.5 \\ 0 & 1 & 0 & | & 6.1 \\ 0 & 0 & 1 & | & 3.9 \end{bmatrix}$
$x = 0.5, y = 6.1, z = 3.9$

Concept 2: Solving Systems of Linear Equations by Using the Gauss-Jordan Method

23. Given the matrix **E**

$$\mathbf{E} = \begin{bmatrix} 3 & -2 & | & 8 \\ 9 & -1 & | & 7 \end{bmatrix}$$

  a. What is the element in the second row and third column? 7

  b. What is the element in the first row and second column? -2

24. Given the matrix **F**

$$\mathbf{F} = \begin{bmatrix} 1 & 8 & | & 0 \\ 12 & -13 & | & -2 \end{bmatrix}$$

  a. What is the element in the second row and second column? -13

  b. What is the element in the first row and third column? 0

25. Given the matrix **Z**

$$\mathbf{Z} = \begin{bmatrix} 2 & 1 & | & 11 \\ 2 & -1 & | & 1 \end{bmatrix} \quad \begin{bmatrix} 1 & \frac{1}{2} & | & \frac{11}{2} \\ 2 & -1 & | & 1 \end{bmatrix}$$

write the matrix obtained by multiplying the elements in the first row by $\frac{1}{2}$.

26. Given the matrix **J**

$$\mathbf{J} = \begin{bmatrix} 1 & 1 & | & 7 \\ 0 & 3 & | & -6 \end{bmatrix} \quad \begin{bmatrix} 1 & 1 & | & 7 \\ 0 & 1 & | & -2 \end{bmatrix}$$

write the matrix obtained by multiplying the elements in the second row by $\frac{1}{3}$.

27. Given the matrix **K**

$$\mathbf{K} = \begin{bmatrix} 5 & 2 & | & 1 \\ 1 & -4 & | & 3 \end{bmatrix} \quad \begin{bmatrix} 1 & -4 & | & 3 \\ 5 & 2 & | & 1 \end{bmatrix}$$

write the matrix obtained by interchanging rows 1 and 2.

28. Given the matrix **L**

$$\mathbf{L} = \begin{bmatrix} 9 & 6 & | & 13 \\ -7 & 2 & | & 19 \end{bmatrix} \quad \begin{bmatrix} -7 & 2 & | & 19 \\ 9 & 6 & | & 13 \end{bmatrix}$$

write the matrix obtained by interchanging rows 1 and 2.

 Writing Translating Expression Geometry Scientific Calculator Video NS&E

29. Given the matrix **M**

$$\mathbf{M} = \begin{bmatrix} 1 & 5 & | & 2 \\ -3 & -4 & | & -1 \end{bmatrix} \quad \begin{bmatrix} 1 & 5 & | & 2 \\ 0 & 11 & | & 5 \end{bmatrix}$$

write the matrix obtained by multiplying the first row by 3 and adding the result to row 2.

30. Given the matrix **N**

$$\mathbf{N} = \begin{bmatrix} 1 & 3 & | & -5 \\ -2 & 2 & | & 12 \end{bmatrix} \quad \begin{bmatrix} 1 & 3 & | & -5 \\ 0 & 8 & | & 2 \end{bmatrix}$$

write the matrix obtained by multiplying the first row by 2 and adding the result to row 2.

31. Given the matrix **R**

$$\mathbf{R} = \begin{bmatrix} 1 & 3 & 0 & | & -1 \\ 4 & 1 & -5 & | & 6 \\ -2 & 0 & -3 & | & 10 \end{bmatrix} \quad \begin{bmatrix} 1 & 3 & 0 & | & -1 \\ 0 & -11 & -5 & | & 10 \\ -2 & 0 & -3 & | & 10 \end{bmatrix}$$

a. Write the matrix obtained by multiplying the first row by -4 and adding the result to row 2.

b. Using the matrix obtained from part (a), write the matrix obtained by multiplying the first row by 2 and adding the result to row 3.

$$\begin{bmatrix} 1 & 3 & 0 & | & -1 \\ 0 & -11 & -5 & | & 10 \\ 0 & 6 & -3 & | & 8 \end{bmatrix}$$

32. Given the matrix **S**

$$\mathbf{S} = \begin{bmatrix} 1 & 2 & 0 & | & 10 \\ 5 & 1 & -4 & | & 3 \\ -3 & 4 & 5 & | & 2 \end{bmatrix} \quad \begin{bmatrix} 1 & 2 & 0 & | & 10 \\ 0 & -9 & -4 & | & -47 \\ -3 & 4 & 5 & | & 2 \end{bmatrix}$$

a. Write the matrix obtained by multiplying the first row by -5 and adding the result to row 2.

b. Using the matrix obtained from part (a), write the matrix obtained by multiplying the first row by 3 and adding the result to row 3.

$$\begin{bmatrix} 1 & 2 & 0 & | & 10 \\ 0 & -9 & -4 & | & -47 \\ 0 & 10 & 5 & | & 32 \end{bmatrix}$$

For Exercises 33–48, solve the systems by using the Gauss-Jordan method. **(See Examples 4–7.)**

33. $x - 2y = -1$
$2x + y = -7$
$\{(-3, -1)\}$

34. $x - 3y = 3$
$2x - 5y = 4$
$\{(-3, -2)\}$

35. $x + 3y = 6$
$-4x - 9y = 3$
$\{(-21, 9)\}$

 36. $2x - 3y = -2$
$x + 2y = 13$
$\{(5, 4)\}$

37. $x + 3y = 3$
$4x + 12y = 12$ Infinitely many solutions; $\{(x, y) \mid x + 3y = 3\}$; dependent system

38. $2x + 5y = 1$
$-4x - 10y = -2$ Infinitely many solutions; $\{(x, y) \mid 2x + 5y = 1\}$; dependent system

39. $x - y = 4$ $\{(3, -1)\}$
$2x + y = 5$

40. $2x - y = 0$ $\{(1, 2)\}$
$x + y = 3$

41. $x + 3y = -1$
$-3x - 6y = 12$
$\{(-10, 3)\}$

42. $x + y = 4$
$2x - 4y = -4$
$\{(2, 2)\}$

43. $3x + y = -4$
$-6x - 2y = 3$
$\{\ \}$; inconsistent system

44. $2x + y = 4$
$6x + 3y = -1$
$\{\ \}$; inconsistent system

45. $x + y + z = 6$
$x - y + z = 2$
$x + y - z = 0$
$\{(1, 2, 3)\}$

46. $2x - 3y - 2z = 11$
$x + 3y + 8z = 1$
$3x - y + 14z = -2$
$\{(7, 2, -\frac{3}{2})\}$

 47. $x - 2y = 5 - z$
$2x + 6y + 3z = -10$
$3x - y - 2z = 5$
$\{(1, -2, 0)\}$

48. $5x = 10z + 15$
$x - y + 6z = 23$
$x + 3y - 12z = 13$
$\{(13, 20, 5)\}$

For Exercises 49–52, use the augmented matrices **A**, **B**, **C**, and **D** to answer true or false.

$$\mathbf{A} = \begin{bmatrix} 6 & -4 & | & 2 \\ 5 & -2 & | & 7 \end{bmatrix} \quad \mathbf{B} = \begin{bmatrix} 5 & -2 & | & 7 \\ 6 & -4 & | & 2 \end{bmatrix} \quad \mathbf{C} = \begin{bmatrix} 1 & -\frac{2}{3} & | & \frac{1}{3} \\ 5 & -2 & | & 7 \end{bmatrix} \quad \mathbf{D} = \begin{bmatrix} 5 & -2 & | & 7 \\ -12 & 8 & | & -4 \end{bmatrix}$$

49. The matrix **A** is a 2×3 matrix.
True

50. Matrix **B** is equivalent to matrix **A**.
True

51. Matrix **A** is equivalent to matrix **C**.
True

52. Matrix **B** is equivalent to matrix **D**.
True

53. What does the notation $R_2 \Leftrightarrow R_1$ mean when one is performing the Gauss-Jordan method? Interchange rows 1 and 2.

54. What does the notation $2R_3 \Rightarrow R_3$ mean when one is performing the Gauss-Jordan method? Multiply row 3 by 2. Replace row 3 with the result.

55. What does the notation $-3R_1 + R_2 \Rightarrow R_2$ mean when one is performing the Gauss-Jordan method? Multiply row 1 by -3 and add to row 2. Replace row 2 with the result.

56. What does the notation $4R_2 + R_3 \Rightarrow R_3$ mean when one is performing the Gauss-Jordan method? Multiply row 2 by 4 and add to row 3. Replace row 3 with the result.

Graphing Calculator Exercises

For Exercises 57–62, use the matrix features on a graphing calculator to express each augmented matrix in reduced row echelon form. Compare your results to the solution you obtained in the indicated exercise.

57. $\begin{bmatrix} 1 & -2 & | & -1 \\ 2 & 1 & | & -7 \end{bmatrix}$

Compare with Exercise 33.

58. $\begin{bmatrix} 1 & -3 & | & 3 \\ 2 & -5 & | & 4 \end{bmatrix}$

Compare with Exercise 34.

59. $\begin{bmatrix} 1 & 3 & | & 6 \\ -4 & -9 & | & 3 \end{bmatrix}$

Compare with Exercise 35.

60. $\begin{bmatrix} 2 & -3 & | & -2 \\ 1 & 2 & | & 13 \end{bmatrix}$

Compare with Exercise 36.

61. $\begin{bmatrix} 1 & 1 & 1 & | & 6 \\ 1 & -1 & 1 & | & 2 \\ 1 & 1 & -1 & | & 0 \end{bmatrix}$

Compare with Exercise 45.

62. $\begin{bmatrix} 2 & -3 & -2 & | & 11 \\ 1 & 3 & 8 & | & 1 \\ 3 & -1 & 14 & | & -2 \end{bmatrix}$

Compare with Exercise 46.

Determinants and Cramer's Rule

Section A.4

1. Introduction to Determinants

Associated with every square matrix is a real number called the **determinant** of the matrix. A determinant of a square matrix **A**, denoted det **A**, is written by enclosing the elements of the matrix within two vertical bars. For example,

$$\text{If} \quad \mathbf{A} = \begin{bmatrix} 2 & -1 \\ 6 & 0 \end{bmatrix} \quad \text{then} \quad \det \mathbf{A} = \begin{vmatrix} 2 & -1 \\ 6 & 0 \end{vmatrix}$$

$$\text{If} \quad \mathbf{B} = \begin{bmatrix} 0 & -5 & 1 \\ 4 & 0 & \frac{1}{2} \\ -2 & 10 & 1 \end{bmatrix} \quad \text{then} \quad \det \mathbf{B} = \begin{vmatrix} 0 & -5 & 1 \\ 4 & 0 & \frac{1}{2} \\ -2 & 10 & 1 \end{vmatrix}$$

Determinants have many applications in mathematics, including solving systems of linear equations, finding the area of a triangle, determining whether three points are collinear, and finding an equation of a line between two points.

The determinant of a 2×2 matrix is defined as follows:

Concepts

1. **Introduction to Determinants**
2. **Determinant of a 3 × 3 Matrix**
3. **Cramer's Rule**

DEFINITION Determinant of a 2 × 2 Matrix

The determinant of the matrix $\begin{bmatrix} a & b \\ c & d \end{bmatrix}$ is the real number $ad - bc$. It is written as

$$\begin{vmatrix} a & b \\ c & d \end{vmatrix} = ad - bc$$

 Writing Translating Expression Geometry Scientific Calculator Video NS&E

Classroom Example: p. A-45, Exercise 2

Example 1   Evaluating a 2 × 2 Determinant

Evaluate the determinants.

a. $\begin{vmatrix} 6 & -2 \\ 5 & \frac{1}{3} \end{vmatrix}$ **b.** $\begin{vmatrix} 2 & -11 \\ 0 & 0 \end{vmatrix}$

Solution:

a. $\begin{vmatrix} 6 & -2 \\ 5 & \frac{1}{3} \end{vmatrix}$ For this determinant, $a = 6, b = -2, c = 5,$ and $d = \frac{1}{3}$.

$$ad - bc = (6)\left(\frac{1}{3}\right) - (-2)(5)$$

$$= 2 + 10$$

$$= 12$$

TIP: Example 1(b) illustrates that the value of a determinant having a row of all zeros is 0. The same is true for a determinant having a column of all zeros.

b. $\begin{vmatrix} 2 & -11 \\ 0 & 0 \end{vmatrix}$ For this determinant, $a = 2, b = -11, c = 0, d = 0$.

$$ad - bc = (2)(0) - (-11)(0)$$

$$= 0 - 0$$

$$= 0$$

Skill Practice Evaluate the determinants.

1. $\begin{vmatrix} 2 & 8 \\ -1 & 5 \end{vmatrix}$ **2.** $\begin{vmatrix} -6 & 0 \\ 4 & 0 \end{vmatrix}$

2. Determinant of a 3 × 3 Matrix

To find the determinant of a 3×3 matrix, we first need to define the **minor** of an element of the matrix. For any element of a 3×3 matrix, the minor of that element is the determinant of the 2×2 matrix obtained by deleting the row and column in which the element resides. For example, consider the matrix

$$\begin{bmatrix} 5 & -1 & 6 \\ 0 & -7 & 1 \\ 4 & 2 & 6 \end{bmatrix}$$

The minor of the element 5 is found by deleting the first row and first column and then evaluating the determinant of the remaining 2×2 matrix:

$$\begin{bmatrix} 5 & -1 & 6 \\ 0 & -7 & 1 \\ 4 & 2 & 6 \end{bmatrix}$$ Now evaluate the determinant: $\begin{vmatrix} -7 & 1 \\ 2 & 6 \end{vmatrix} = (-7)(6) - (1)(2)$

$$= -44$$

For this matrix, the minor for the element 5 is -44.

Answers

1. 18   **2.** 0

To find the minor of the element -7, delete the second row and second column, and then evaluate the determinant of the remaining 2×2 matrix.

$$\begin{bmatrix} 5 & -1 & 6 \\ 0 & -7 & 1 \\ 4 & 2 & 6 \end{bmatrix}$$ Now evaluate the determinant: $\begin{vmatrix} 5 & 6 \\ 4 & 6 \end{vmatrix} = (5)(6) - (6)(4) = 6$

For this matrix, the minor for the element -7 is 6.

Example 2 **Determining the Minor for Elements in a 3 × 3 Matrix**

Classroom Example: p. A-46, Exercise 8

Find the minor for each element in the first column of the matrix.

$$\begin{bmatrix} 3 & 4 & -1 \\ 2 & -4 & 5 \\ 0 & 1 & 6 \end{bmatrix}$$

Solution:

For 3: $\begin{bmatrix} 3 & 4 & -1 \\ 2 & -4 & 5 \\ 0 & 1 & -6 \end{bmatrix}$ The minor is: $\begin{vmatrix} -4 & 5 \\ 1 & -6 \end{vmatrix} = (-4)(-6) - (5)(1) = 19$

For 2: $\begin{bmatrix} 3 & 4 & -1 \\ 2 & -4 & 5 \\ 0 & 1 & -6 \end{bmatrix}$ The minor is: $\begin{vmatrix} 4 & -1 \\ 1 & -6 \end{vmatrix} = (4)(-6) - (-1)(1) = -23$

For 0: $\begin{bmatrix} 3 & 4 & -1 \\ 2 & -4 & 5 \\ 0 & 1 & -6 \end{bmatrix}$ The minor is: $\begin{vmatrix} 4 & -1 \\ -4 & 5 \end{vmatrix} = (4)(5) - (-1)(-4) = 16$

Skill Practice Find the minor for the element 3.

3. $\begin{bmatrix} -1 & 8 & -6 \\ \frac{1}{2} & 3 & 2 \\ 5 & 7 & 4 \end{bmatrix}$

The determinant of a 3×3 matrix is defined as follows.

DEFINITION **Determinant of a 3 × 3 Matrix**

$$\begin{vmatrix} a_1 & b_1 & c_1 \\ a_2 & b_2 & c_2 \\ a_3 & b_3 & c_3 \end{vmatrix} = a_1 \cdot \begin{vmatrix} b_2 & c_2 \\ b_3 & c_3 \end{vmatrix} - a_2 \cdot \begin{vmatrix} b_1 & c_1 \\ b_3 & c_3 \end{vmatrix} + a_3 \cdot \begin{vmatrix} b_1 & c_1 \\ b_2 & c_2 \end{vmatrix}$$

From this definition, we see that the determinant of a 3×3 matrix can be written as

$$a_1 \cdot (\text{minor of } a_1) - a_2 \cdot (\text{minor of } a_2) + a_3 \cdot (\text{minor of } a_3)$$

Evaluating determinants in this way is called *expanding minors*.

Answer

3. $\begin{vmatrix} -1 & -6 \\ 5 & 4 \end{vmatrix} = 26$

Classroom Example: p. A-46,
Exercise 20

Example 3 Evaluating a 3 × 3 Determinant

Evaluate the determinant.
$$\begin{vmatrix} 2 & 4 & 2 \\ 1 & -3 & 0 \\ -5 & 5 & -1 \end{vmatrix}$$

Solution:

$$\begin{vmatrix} 2 & 4 & 2 \\ 1 & -3 & 0 \\ -5 & 5 & -1 \end{vmatrix} = 2 \cdot \begin{vmatrix} -3 & 0 \\ 5 & -1 \end{vmatrix} - (1) \cdot \begin{vmatrix} 4 & 2 \\ 5 & -1 \end{vmatrix} + (-5) \cdot \begin{vmatrix} 4 & 2 \\ -3 & 0 \end{vmatrix}$$

$$= 2[(-3)(-1) - (0)(5)] - 1[(4)(-1) - (2)(5)] - 5[(4)(0) - (2)(-3)]$$

$$= 2(3) - 1(-14) - 5(6)$$

$$= 6 + 14 - 30$$

$$= -10$$

Skill Practice Evaluate the determinant.

4. $$\begin{vmatrix} -2 & 4 & 9 \\ 5 & -1 & 2 \\ 1 & 1 & 6 \end{vmatrix}$$

TIP: There is another method to determine the signs for each term of the expansion. For the a_{ij} element, multiply the term by $(-1)^{i+j}$.

Although we defined the determinant of a matrix by expanding the minors of the elements in the first column, *any row or column can be used.* However, we must choose the correct sign to apply to each term in the expansion. The following array of signs is helpful.

$$\begin{array}{ccc} + & - & + \\ - & + & - \\ + & - & + \end{array}$$

The signs alternate for each row and column, beginning with + in the first row, first column.

Classroom Example: p. A-46,
Exercise 18

Example 4 Evaluating a 3 × 3 Determinant

Evaluate the determinant by expanding minors about the elements in the second row.
$$\begin{vmatrix} 2 & 4 & 2 \\ 1 & -3 & 0 \\ -5 & 5 & -1 \end{vmatrix}$$

Solution:

Signs obtained from the array of signs

$$\begin{vmatrix} 2 & 4 & 2 \\ 1 & -3 & 0 \\ -5 & 5 & -1 \end{vmatrix} = -(1) \cdot \begin{vmatrix} 4 & 2 \\ 5 & -1 \end{vmatrix} + (-3) \cdot \begin{vmatrix} 2 & 2 \\ -5 & -1 \end{vmatrix} - (0) \cdot \begin{vmatrix} 2 & 4 \\ -5 & 5 \end{vmatrix}$$

$$= -1[(4)(-1) - (2)(5)] - 3[(2)(-1) - (2)(-5)] - 0$$

$$= -1(-14) - 3(8)$$

$$= 14 - 24$$

$$= -10$$

Answer

4. -42

Skill Practice Evaluate the determinant.

5. $\begin{vmatrix} 4 & -1 & 2 \\ 3 & 6 & -8 \\ 0 & \frac{1}{2} & 5 \end{vmatrix}$

Notice that the value of the determinant obtained in Examples 3 and 4 is the same.

Calculator Connections

The determinant of a matrix can be evaluated on a graphing calculator. First use the matrix editor to enter the elements of the matrix. Then use a *det* function to evaluate the determinant. The determinant from Examples 3 and 4 is evaluated below.

```
MATRIX[A] 3 ×3
[ 2    4    2   ]
[ 1   -3    0   ]
[ -5   5   -1   ]
```

```
det([A])
               -10
```

In Example 4, the third term in the expansion of minors was zero because the element 0 when multiplied by its minor is zero. To simplify the arithmetic in evaluating a determinant of a 3×3 matrix, expand about the row or column that has the most 0 elements.

3. Cramer's Rule

In Sections 4.2, 4.3, and A.3, we learned three methods to solve a system of linear equations: the substitution method, the addition method, and the Gauss-Jordan method. In this section, we will learn another method called **Cramer's rule** to solve a system of linear equations.

PROPERTY **Cramer's Rule for a 2 × 2 System of Linear Equations**

The solution to the system
$$a_1 x + b_1 y = c_1$$
$$a_2 x + b_2 y = c_2$$

is given by $\quad x = \dfrac{\mathbf{D}_x}{\mathbf{D}} \quad$ and $\quad y = \dfrac{\mathbf{D}_y}{\mathbf{D}}$

where $\mathbf{D} = \begin{vmatrix} a_1 & b_1 \\ a_2 & b_2 \end{vmatrix}$ (and $\mathbf{D} \neq 0$) $\quad \mathbf{D}_x = \begin{vmatrix} c_1 & b_1 \\ c_2 & b_2 \end{vmatrix} \quad \mathbf{D}_y = \begin{vmatrix} a_1 & c_1 \\ a_2 & c_2 \end{vmatrix}$

- If $\mathbf{D} = 0$ and one of $\mathbf{D}_x$ or $\mathbf{D}_y$ is different from zero, then the system is inconsistent.
- If $\mathbf{D} = 0$ and both $\mathbf{D}_x$ and $\mathbf{D}_y$ equal 0, then the system is dependent.

Answer

5. 154

Classroom Example: p. A-47,
Exercise 36

Example 5 Using Cramer's Rule to Solve a 2 × 2 System of Linear Equations

Solve the system by using Cramer's rule. $3x - 5y = 11$

$-x + 3y = -5$

Solution:

For this system: $a_1 = 3$ $b_1 = -5$ $c_1 = 11$

$a_2 = -1$ $b_2 = 3$ $c_2 = -5$

$$D = \begin{vmatrix} 3 & -5 \\ -1 & 3 \end{vmatrix} = (3)(3) - (-5)(-1) = 9 - 5 = 4$$

$$D_x = \begin{vmatrix} 11 & -5 \\ -5 & 3 \end{vmatrix} = (11)(3) - (-5)(-5) = 33 - 25 = 8$$

$$D_y = \begin{vmatrix} 3 & 11 \\ -1 & -5 \end{vmatrix} = (3)(-5) - (11)(-1) = -15 + 11 = -4$$

Therefore, $x = \dfrac{D_x}{D} = \dfrac{8}{4} = 2$ $y = \dfrac{D_y}{D} = \dfrac{-4}{4} = -1$

Check the ordered pair $(2, -1)$ in both original equations.

Check: $3x - 5y = 11 \longrightarrow 3(2) - 5(-1) \overset{?}{=} 11$ ✔

$-x + 3y = -5 \longrightarrow -(2) + 3(-1) \overset{?}{=} -5$ ✔

The solution set is $\{(2, -1)\}$.

Skill Practice Solve using Cramer's rule.

6. $2x + y = 5$
$-x - 3y = 5$

TIP: Here are some memory tips to help you remember Cramer's rule.

Coefficients of
x-terms   y-terms
↓   ↓

1. The determinant **D** is the determinant of the coefficients of x and y.

$$D = \begin{vmatrix} a_1 & b_1 \\ a_2 & b_2 \end{vmatrix}$$

x-coefficients
replaced by c_1 and c_2
↓

2. The determinant D_x has the column of x-term coefficients replaced by c_1 and c_2.

$$D_x = \begin{vmatrix} c_1 & b_1 \\ c_2 & b_2 \end{vmatrix}$$

y-coefficients
replaced by c_1 and c_2
↓

3. The determinant D_y has the column of y-term coefficients replaced by c_1 and c_2.

$$D_y = \begin{vmatrix} a_1 & c_1 \\ a_2 & c_2 \end{vmatrix}$$

Answer

6. $\{(4, -3)\}$

It is important to note that the linear equations must be written in standard form to apply Cramer's rule.

Classroom Example: p. A-47, Exercise 38

Example 6 **Using Cramer's Rule to Solve a 2 × 2 System of Linear Equations**

Solve the system by using Cramer's rule. $-16y = -40x - 7$
$$40y = 24x + 27$$

Solution:

$-16y = -40x - 7 \longrightarrow 40x - 16y = -7$ Rewrite each equation
$40y = 24x + 27 \longrightarrow -24x + 40y = 27$ in standard form.

For this system: $a_1 = 40$ $b_1 = -16$ $c_1 = -7$
$$a_2 = -24 \quad b_2 = 40 \quad c_2 = 27$$

$$\mathbf{D} = \begin{vmatrix} 40 & -16 \\ -24 & 40 \end{vmatrix} = (40)(40) - (-16)(-24) = 1216$$

$$\mathbf{D}_x = \begin{vmatrix} -7 & -16 \\ 27 & 40 \end{vmatrix} = (-7)(40) - (-16)(27) = 152$$

$$\mathbf{D}_y = \begin{vmatrix} 40 & -7 \\ 24 & 27 \end{vmatrix} = (40)(27) - (-7)(-24) = 912$$

Therefore, $x = \dfrac{\mathbf{D}_x}{\mathbf{D}} = \dfrac{152}{1216} = \dfrac{1}{8}$ $y = \dfrac{\mathbf{D}_y}{\mathbf{D}} = \dfrac{912}{1216} = \dfrac{3}{4}$

The ordered pair $\left(\dfrac{1}{8}, \dfrac{3}{4}\right)$ checks in both original equations.

The solution set is $\left\{\left(\dfrac{1}{8}, \dfrac{3}{4}\right)\right\}$.

Skill Practice Solve by using Cramer's rule.

7. $9x = 12y - 8$
$30y = -18x - 7$

Cramer's rule can be used to solve a 3 × 3 system of linear equations by using a similar pattern of determinants.

PROPERTY   Cramer's Rule for a 3 × 3 System of Linear Equations

The solution to the system

$$a_1x + b_1y + c_1z = d_1$$
$$a_2x + b_2y + c_2z = d_2$$
$$a_3x + b_3y + c_3z = d_3$$

is given by $x = \dfrac{\mathbf{D}_x}{\mathbf{D}}$ $y = \dfrac{\mathbf{D}_y}{\mathbf{D}}$ and $z = \dfrac{\mathbf{D}_z}{\mathbf{D}}$

where $\mathbf{D} = \begin{vmatrix} a_1 & b_1 & c_1 \\ a_2 & b_2 & c_2 \\ a_3 & b_3 & c_3 \end{vmatrix}$ (and $\mathbf{D} \neq 0$) $\mathbf{D}_x = \begin{vmatrix} d_1 & b_1 & c_1 \\ d_2 & b_2 & c_2 \\ d_3 & b_3 & c_3 \end{vmatrix}$

$\mathbf{D}_y = \begin{vmatrix} a_1 & d_1 & c_1 \\ a_2 & d_2 & c_2 \\ a_3 & d_3 & c_3 \end{vmatrix}$ $\mathbf{D}_z = \begin{vmatrix} a_1 & b_1 & d_1 \\ a_2 & b_2 & d_2 \\ a_3 & b_3 & d_3 \end{vmatrix}$

Answer

7. $\left\{\left(-\dfrac{2}{3}, \dfrac{1}{6}\right)\right\}$

Classroom Example: p. A-47, Exercise 44

Example 7   Using Cramer's Rule to Solve a 3 × 3 System of Linear Equations

Solve the system by using Cramer's rule.

$$2x - 3y + 5z = 11$$
$$-5x + 7y - 2z = -6$$
$$9x - 2y + 3z = 4$$

Solution:

> **TIP:** In Example 7, we expanded the determinants about the first column.

$$\mathbf{D} = \begin{vmatrix} 2 & -3 & 5 \\ -5 & 7 & -2 \\ 9 & -2 & 3 \end{vmatrix} = 2 \cdot \begin{vmatrix} 7 & -2 \\ -2 & 3 \end{vmatrix} - (-5) \cdot \begin{vmatrix} -3 & 5 \\ -2 & 3 \end{vmatrix} + 9 \cdot \begin{vmatrix} -3 & 5 \\ 7 & -2 \end{vmatrix}$$

$$= 2(17) + 5(1) + 9(-29)$$

$$= -222$$

$$\mathbf{D}_x = \begin{vmatrix} 11 & -3 & 5 \\ -6 & 7 & -2 \\ 4 & -2 & 3 \end{vmatrix} = 11 \cdot \begin{vmatrix} 7 & -2 \\ -2 & 3 \end{vmatrix} - (-6) \cdot \begin{vmatrix} -3 & 5 \\ -2 & 3 \end{vmatrix} + 4 \cdot \begin{vmatrix} -3 & 5 \\ 7 & -2 \end{vmatrix}$$

$$= 11(17) + 6(1) + 4(-29)$$

$$= 77$$

$$\mathbf{D}_y = \begin{vmatrix} 2 & 11 & 5 \\ -5 & -6 & -2 \\ 9 & 4 & 3 \end{vmatrix} = 2 \cdot \begin{vmatrix} -6 & -2 \\ 4 & 3 \end{vmatrix} - (-5) \cdot \begin{vmatrix} 11 & 5 \\ 4 & 3 \end{vmatrix} + 9 \cdot \begin{vmatrix} 11 & 5 \\ -6 & -2 \end{vmatrix}$$

$$= 2(-10) + 5(13) + 9(8)$$

$$= 117$$

$$\mathbf{D}_z = \begin{vmatrix} 2 & -3 & 11 \\ -5 & 7 & -6 \\ 9 & -2 & 4 \end{vmatrix} = 2 \cdot \begin{vmatrix} 7 & -6 \\ -2 & 4 \end{vmatrix} - (-5) \cdot \begin{vmatrix} -3 & 11 \\ -2 & 4 \end{vmatrix} + 9 \cdot \begin{vmatrix} -3 & 11 \\ 7 & -6 \end{vmatrix}$$

$$= 2(16) + 5(10) + 9(-59)$$

$$= -449$$

$$x = \frac{\mathbf{D}_x}{\mathbf{D}} = \frac{77}{-222} = -\frac{77}{222}$$

$$y = \frac{\mathbf{D}_y}{\mathbf{D}} = \frac{117}{-222} = -\frac{39}{74}$$

$$z = \frac{\mathbf{D}_z}{\mathbf{D}} = \frac{-449}{-222} = \frac{449}{222}$$

The solution $\left(-\dfrac{77}{222}, -\dfrac{39}{74}, \dfrac{449}{222} \right)$ checks in each of the original equations.

The solution set is $\left\{ \left(-\dfrac{77}{222}, -\dfrac{39}{74}, \dfrac{449}{222} \right) \right\}$.

Skill Practice Solve by using Cramer's rule.

8. $x + 3y - 3z = -14$
$\quad x - 4y + \ z = 2$
$\quad x + \ y + 2z = 6$

Answer

8. $\{(-2, 0, 4)\}$

Cramer's rule may seem cumbersome for solving a 3×3 system of linear equations. However, it provides convenient formulas that can be programmed into a computer or calculator to solve for x, y, and z. Cramer's rule can also be extended to solve a 4×4 system of linear equations, a 5×5 system of linear equations, and in general an $n \times n$ system of linear equations.

Example 8   **Analyzing a Dependent System of Equations**

Classroom Example: p. A-47, Exercise 54

Solve the system. Use Cramer's rule if possible.

$$2x - 3y = 6$$
$$-6x + 9y = -18$$

Solution:

$$\mathbf{D} = \begin{vmatrix} 2 & -3 \\ -6 & 9 \end{vmatrix} = (2)(9) - (-3)(-6) = 18 - 18 = 0$$

$$\mathbf{D}_x = \begin{vmatrix} 6 & -3 \\ -18 & 9 \end{vmatrix} = (6)(9) - (-18)(-3) = 54 - 54 = 0$$

$$\mathbf{D}_y = \begin{vmatrix} 2 & 6 \\ -6 & -18 \end{vmatrix} = (2)(-18) - (-6)(-6) = -36 - (-36) = 0$$

The system is dependent. The solution set is $\{(x, y) \mid 2x - 3y = 6\}$.

Skill Practice   Solve. Use Cramer's rule if possible.

9. $x - 6y = 2$
    $2x - 12y = -2$

Answer

9. { }; inconsistent system

Section A.4   Practice Exercises

Boost _your_ GRADE at ALEKS.com!

ALEKS version 3.0

- Practice Problems
- Self-Tests
- NetTutor
- e-Professors
- Videos

For additional exercises, see Classroom Activities A.4A–A.4D in the *Instructor's Resource Manual* at www.mhhe.com/moh.

Study Skills Exercise

1. Define the key terms.

   a. determinant   **b. minor**   **c. Cramer's rule**

Concept 1:   Introduction to Determinants

For Exercises 2–7, evaluate the determinant of the 2×2 matrix. **(See Example 1.)**

2. $\begin{vmatrix} -3 & 1 \\ 5 & 2 \end{vmatrix}$ -11

3. $\begin{vmatrix} 5 & 6 \\ 4 & 8 \end{vmatrix}$ 16

4. $\begin{vmatrix} -2 & 2 \\ -3 & -5 \end{vmatrix}$ 16

5. $\begin{vmatrix} 5 & -1 \\ 1 & 0 \end{vmatrix}$ 1

6. $\begin{vmatrix} \frac{1}{2} & 3 \\ -2 & 4 \end{vmatrix}$ 8

7. $\begin{vmatrix} -3 & \frac{1}{4} \\ 8 & -2 \end{vmatrix}$ 4

 Writing   Translating Expression   Geometry   Scientific Calculator   Video   NS_E

Concept 2: Determinant of a 3 × 3 Matrix

For Exercises 8–11, evaluate the minor corresponding to the given element from matrix **A**. (See Example 2.)

$$\mathbf{A} = \begin{bmatrix} 4 & -1 & 8 \\ 2 & 6 & 0 \\ -7 & 5 & 3 \end{bmatrix}$$

8. 4   18   **9.** −1   6   **10.** 2   −43   **11.** 3   26

For Exercises 12–15, evaluate the minor corresponding to the given element from matrix **B**.

$$\mathbf{B} = \begin{bmatrix} -2 & 6 & 0 \\ 4 & -2 & 1 \\ 5 & 9 & -1 \end{bmatrix}$$

12. 6   −9   **13.** 5   6   **14.** 1   −48   **15.** 0   46

16. Construct the sign array for a 3 × 3 matrix. $\begin{bmatrix} + & - & + \\ - & + & - \\ + & - & + \end{bmatrix}$

17. Evaluate the determinant of matrix **B**, using expansion by minors. (See Exercises 3–4.)

$$\mathbf{B} = \begin{bmatrix} 0 & 1 & 2 \\ 3 & -1 & 2 \\ 3 & 2 & -2 \end{bmatrix}$$

   a. About the first column   30

   b. About the second row   30

18. Evaluate the determinant of matrix **C**, using expansion by minors.

$$\mathbf{C} = \begin{bmatrix} 4 & 1 & 3 \\ 2 & -2 & 1 \\ 3 & 1 & 2 \end{bmatrix}$$

   a. About the first row   3

   b. About the second column   3

19. When evaluating the determinant of a 3 × 3 matrix, explain the advantage of being able to choose any row or column about which to expand minors.   Choosing the row or column with the most zero elements simplifies the arithmetic when evaluating a determinant.

For Exercises 20–25, evaluate the determinant. (See Examples 3–4.)

20. $\begin{vmatrix} 8 & 2 & -4 \\ 4 & 0 & 2 \\ 3 & 0 & -1 \end{vmatrix}$ 20

21. $\begin{vmatrix} 5 & 2 & 1 \\ 3 & -6 & 0 \\ -2 & 8 & 0 \end{vmatrix}$ 12

22. $\begin{vmatrix} -2 & 1 & 3 \\ 1 & 4 & 4 \\ 1 & 0 & 2 \end{vmatrix}$ −26

23. $\begin{vmatrix} 3 & 2 & 1 \\ 1 & -1 & 2 \\ 1 & 0 & 4 \end{vmatrix}$ −15

24. $\begin{vmatrix} -5 & 4 & 2 \\ 0 & 0 & 0 \\ 3 & -1 & 5 \end{vmatrix}$ 0

25. $\begin{vmatrix} 0 & 5 & -8 \\ 0 & -4 & 1 \\ 0 & 3 & 6 \end{vmatrix}$ 0

For Exercises 26–31, evaluate the determinant.

26. $\begin{vmatrix} x & 3 \\ y & -2 \end{vmatrix}$ −2x − 3y

27. $\begin{vmatrix} a & 2 \\ b & 8 \end{vmatrix}$ 8a − 2b

28. $\begin{vmatrix} a & 5 & -1 \\ b & -3 & 0 \\ c & 3 & 4 \end{vmatrix}$ −12a − 23b − 3c

29. $\begin{vmatrix} x & 0 & 3 \\ y & -2 & 6 \\ z & -1 & 1 \end{vmatrix}$ 4x − 3y + 6z

30. $\begin{vmatrix} p & 0 & q \\ r & 0 & s \\ t & 0 & u \end{vmatrix}$ 0

31. $\begin{vmatrix} f & e & 0 \\ d & c & 0 \\ b & a & 0 \end{vmatrix}$ 0

Concept 3: Cramer's Rule

For Exercises 32–34, evaluate the determinants represented by $\mathbf{D}$, $\mathbf{D}_x$, and $\mathbf{D}_y$.

32. $x - 4y = 2$

$3x + 2y = 1$
$\mathbf{D} = 14;\ \mathbf{D}_x = 8;\ \mathbf{D}_y = -5$

33. $4x + 6y = 9$

$-2x + y = 12$
$\mathbf{D} = 16;\ \mathbf{D}_x = -63;\ \mathbf{D}_y = 66$

34. $-3x + 8y = -10$

$5x + 5y = -13$
$\mathbf{D} = -55;\ \mathbf{D}_x = 54;\ \mathbf{D}_y = 89$

For Exercises 35–40, solve the system by using Cramer's rule. **(See Examples 5–6.)**

35. $2x + y = 3$

$x - 4y = 6$ $\{(2, -1)\}$

36. $2x - y = -1$

$3x + y = 6$ $\{(1, 3)\}$

37. $4y = x - 8$

$3x = -7y + 5$ $\{(4, -1)\}$

38. $7x - 4 = -3y$

$5x = 4y + 9$ $\{(1, -1)\}$

39. $4x - 3y = 5$

$2x + 5y = 7$ $\left\{\left(\dfrac{23}{13}, \dfrac{9}{13}\right)\right\}$

40. $2x + 3y = 4$

$6x - 12y = -5$ $\left\{\left(\dfrac{11}{14}, \dfrac{17}{21}\right)\right\}$

For Exercises 41–46, solve for the indicated variable by using Cramer's rule. **(See Example 7.)**

41. $2x - y + 3z = 9$

$x + 4y + 4z = 5$ for x
$3x + 2y + 2z = 5$ $x = 1$

42. $x + 2y + 3z = 8$

$2x - 3y + z = 5$ for y
$3x - 4y + 2z = 9$ $y = -2$

43. $3x - 2y + 2z = 5$

$6x + 3y - 4z = -1$ for z
$3x - y + 2z = 4$ $z = \dfrac{1}{2}$

44. $4x + 4y - 3z = 3$

$8x + 2y + 3y = 0$ for x
$4x - 4y + 6z = -3$
$x = \dfrac{1}{4}$

45. $5x \quad + 6z = 5$

$-2x + y \quad = -6$ for y
$3y - z = 3$
$y = \dfrac{16}{41}$

46. $8x + y \quad = 1$

$7y + z = 0$ for y
$x \quad - 3z = -2$
$y = -\dfrac{17}{167}$

47. When does Cramer's rule not apply in solving a system of equations?   Cramer's rule does not apply when the determinant $\mathbf{D} = 0$.

48. How can a system be solved if Cramer's rule does not apply?   The addition method, substitution method, or Gauss-Jordan method can be used to determine if a system is inconsistent or dependent.

For Exercises 49–58, solve the system by using Cramer's rule, if possible. Otherwise, use another method. **(See Example 8.)**

49. $4x - 2y = 3$

$-2x + y = 1$ $\{\ \};$ inconsistent system

50. $6x - 6y = 5$

$x - y = 8$ $\{\ \};$ inconsistent system

51. $4x + y = 0$ $\{(0, 0)\}$

$x - 7y = 0$

52. $3x \quad 2y = 0$

$-x + 5y = 0$
$\{(0, 0)\}$

53. $x + 5y = 3$

$2x + 10y = 6$ Infinitely many solutions; $\{(x, y)\mid x + 5y = 3\};$ dependent system

54. $-2x - 10y = -4$

$x + 5y = 2$
Infinitely many solutions; $\{(x, y)\mid x + 5y = 2\};$ dependent system

55. $x \quad = 3$

$-x + 3y = 3$
$y + 2z = 4$ $\{(3, 2, 1)\}$

56. $4x \quad + z = 7$

$y \quad = 2$
$x \quad + z = 4$ $\{(1, 2, 3)\}$

57. $x + y + 8z = 3$

$2x + y + 11z = 4$
$x \quad + 3z = 0$
$\{\ \};$ inconsistent system

58. $-8x + y + z = 6$

$2x - y + z = 3$
$3x \quad - z = 0$
$\{\ \};$ inconsistent system

Writing   *Translating Expression*   *Geometry*   *Scientific Calculator*   *Video*   NS&E

Expanding Your Skills

For Exercises 59–62, solve the equation.

59. $\begin{vmatrix} 6 & x \\ 2 & -4 \end{vmatrix} = 14$

$x = -19$

60. $\begin{vmatrix} y & -2 \\ 8 & 7 \end{vmatrix} = 30$

$y = 2$

61. $\begin{vmatrix} 3 & 1 & 0 \\ 0 & 4 & -2 \\ 1 & 0 & w \end{vmatrix} = 10$

$w = 1$

62. $\begin{vmatrix} -1 & 0 & 2 \\ 4 & t & 0 \\ 0 & -5 & 3 \end{vmatrix} = -4$

$t = -12$

For Exercises 63–64, evaluate the determinant by using expansion by minors about the first column.

63. $\begin{vmatrix} 1 & 0 & 3 & 0 \\ 0 & 1 & 2 & 4 \\ -2 & 0 & 0 & 1 \\ 4 & -1 & -2 & 0 \end{vmatrix}$ 36

64. $\begin{vmatrix} 5 & 2 & 0 & 0 \\ 0 & 4 & -1 & 1 \\ -1 & 0 & 3 & 0 \\ 0 & -2 & 1 & 0 \end{vmatrix}$ 32

For Exercises 65–66, refer to the following system of four variables.

$$x + y + z + w = 0$$
$$2x \quad - z + w = 5$$
$$2x + y \quad - w = 0$$
$$y + z \quad = -1$$

65. a. Evaluate the determinant $\mathbf{D}$.   2

b. Evaluate the determinant $\mathbf{D}_x$.   −2

c. Solve for x by computing $\dfrac{\mathbf{D}_x}{\mathbf{D}}$. $x = -1$

66. a. Evaluate the determinant $\mathbf{D}_y$.   8

b. Solve for y by computing $\dfrac{\mathbf{D}_y}{\mathbf{D}}$. $y = 4$

 Writing   Translating Expression   Geometry   Scientific Calculator   Video   NS&E

Student Answer Appendix

Chapter 1

Chapter Opener Puzzle

18	+	2	+	10	=	30
÷		+		−		÷
3	×	4	−	7	=	5
−		+		+		÷
2	×	0	+	6	−	6
=		−		−		=
4	+	6	−	9	=	1

Section 1.1 Practice Exercises, pp. 17–21

3. Numerator: 7; denominator: 8; proper
5. Numerator: 9; denominator: 5; improper
7. Numerator: 6; denominator: 6; improper
9. Numerator: 12; denominator: 1; improper
11. $\frac{3}{4}$ **13.** $\frac{4}{3}$ **15.** $\frac{1}{6}$ **17.** $\frac{2}{2}$
19. $\frac{5}{2}$ or $2\frac{1}{2}$ **21.** $\frac{6}{2}$ or 3
23. The set of whole numbers includes the number 0 and the set of natural numbers does not.
25. For example: $\frac{2}{4}$ **27.** Prime **29.** Composite
31. Composite **33.** Prime **35.** $2 \times 2 \times 3 \times 3$
37. $2 \times 3 \times 7$ **39.** $2 \times 5 \times 11$ **41.** $3 \times 3 \times 3 \times 5$
43. $\frac{1}{5}$ **45.** $\frac{3}{8}$ **47.** $\frac{7}{8}$ **49.** $\frac{3}{4}$ **51.** $\frac{5}{8}$ **53.** $\frac{3}{4}$
55. False: When adding or subtracting fractions, it is necessary to have a common denominator.
57. $\frac{4}{3}$ or $1\frac{1}{3}$ **59.** $\frac{2}{3}$ **61.** $\frac{9}{2}$ or $4\frac{1}{2}$ **63.** $\frac{3}{5}$ **65.** $\frac{5}{3}$ or $1\frac{2}{3}$
67. $\frac{90}{13}$ or $6\frac{12}{13}$ **69.** $704 **71.** 4 graduated with honors.
73. 8 aprons **75.** 8 jars **77.** $\frac{3}{7}$ **79.** $\frac{1}{2}$ **81.** 30
83. 40 **85.** $\frac{7}{8}$ **87.** $\frac{3}{40}$ **89.** $\frac{3}{26}$ **91.** $\frac{29}{36}$
93. $\frac{7}{10}$ **95.** $\frac{35}{48}$ **97.** $\frac{7}{24}$ **99.** $\frac{51}{28}$ or $1\frac{23}{28}$
101. $\frac{14}{5}$ or $2\frac{4}{5}$ **103.** 46 **105.** $\frac{46}{5}$ or $9\frac{1}{5}$ **107.** $\frac{1}{6}$
109. $\frac{11}{54}$ **111.** $\frac{7}{2}$ or $3\frac{1}{2}$ **113.** $\frac{13}{8}$ or $1\frac{5}{8}$

115. $\frac{59}{12}$ or $4\frac{11}{12}$ **117.** $\frac{1}{8}$ **119.** $8\frac{19}{24}$ in. **121.** $1\frac{7}{12}$ hr
123. $2\frac{1}{4}$ lb **125.** 25 in.

Section 1.2 Calculator Connections, p. 29

1. ≈ 3.464101615 **2.** ≈ 9.949874371
3. ≈ 12.56637061 **4.** ≈ 1.772453851

Section 1.2 Practice Exercises, pp. 29–32

3. $2\frac{2}{3}$ **5.** $2\frac{5}{11}$
7.

9. a; rational **11.** b; rational **13.** a; rational
15. c; irrational **17.** a; rational **19.** a; rational
21. b; rational **23.** c; irrational
25. For example: π, $-\sqrt{2}$, $\sqrt{3}$
27. For example: $-4, -1, 0$
29. For example: $-\frac{3}{4}, \frac{1}{2}, 0.206$ **31.** $-\frac{3}{2}, -4, 0.\overline{6}, 0, 1$
33. 1 **35.** $-4, 0, 1$ **37. a.** > **b.** > **c.** < **d.** >
39. -18 **41.** 6.1 **43.** $\frac{5}{8}$ **45.** $-\frac{7}{3}$ **47.** 3
49. $-\frac{7}{3}$ **51.** 8 **53.** -72.1 **55.** 2 **57.** 1.5
59. -1.5 **61.** $\frac{3}{2}$ **63.** -10 **65.** $-\frac{1}{2}$
67. False, $|n|$ is never negative. **69.** True **71.** False
73. True **75.** False **77.** False **79.** False
81. True **83.** True **85.** False **87.** True
89. True **91.** True **93.** For all $a < 0$

Section 1.3 Calculator Connections, p. 39

1. 2 **2.** 91 **3.** 84 **4.** 12 **5.** 49 **6.** 18

7. 4 **8.** 27 **9.** 0.5

SA-1

Section 1.3 Practice Exercises, pp. 40–42

3. $-4, 5.\overline{6}, 0, 4.02, \dfrac{7}{9}$ **5.** 9.2 **7.** -19 **9.** 3

11. 4 **13.** 9 **15.** $\dfrac{5}{6}$ **17.** $\left(\dfrac{1}{6}\right)^4$ **19.** $a^3 b^2$

21. $(5c)^5$ **23. a.** x **b.** Yes, 1 **25.** $x \cdot x \cdot x$
27. $2b \cdot 2b \cdot 2b$ **29.** $10 \cdot y \cdot y \cdot y \cdot y$

31. $2 \cdot w \cdot z \cdot z$ **33.** 36 **35.** $\dfrac{1}{49}$ **37.** 0.008

39. 64 **41.** 9 **43.** 2 **45.** 12 **47.** 4 **49.** $\dfrac{1}{3}$

51. $\dfrac{5}{9}$ **53.** 20 **55.** 60 **57.** 8 **59.** 78 **61.** 0

63. $\dfrac{7}{6}$ **65.** 45 **67.** 16 **69.** 15 **71.** 19 **73.** 3

75. 39 **77.** 26 **79.** $\dfrac{5}{12}$ **81.** $\dfrac{5}{2}$ **83.** $57,600 \text{ ft}^2$

85. 21 ft^2 **87.** $3x$ **89.** $\dfrac{x}{7}$ or $x \div 7$ **91.** $2 - a$

93. $2y + x$ **95.** $4(x + 12)$ **97.** $3 - Q$
99. $2y^3; 16$ **101.** $|z - 8|; 2$ **103.** $5\sqrt{x}; 10$

105. $yz - x; 16$ **107.** 1 **109.** $\dfrac{1}{4}$

111. a. $36 \div 4 \cdot 3$ Division must be performed before
     $= 9 \cdot 3$ multiplication.
     $= 27$
b. $36 - 4 + 3$ Subtraction must be performed
     $= 32 + 3$ before addition.
     $= 35$
113. This is acceptable, provided division and multiplication are performed in order from left to right, and subtraction and addition are performed in order from left to right.

Section 1.4 Practice Exercises, pp. 48–50

3. $>$ **5.** $>$ **7.** $>$ **9.** -6 **11.** 3 **13.** 3
15. -3 **17.** -17 **19.** 7 **21.** -19 **23.** -23
25. -5 **27.** -3 **29.** 0 **31.** 0 **33.** -5
35. -3 **37.** 0 **39.** -23 **41.** -6 **43.** -3

45. 21.3 **47.** $-\dfrac{3}{14}$ **49.** $-\dfrac{1}{6}$ **51.** $-\dfrac{15}{16}$ **53.** $\dfrac{1}{20}$

55. -2.4 or $-\dfrac{12}{5}$ **57.** $\dfrac{1}{4}$ or 0.25 **59.** 0 **61.** $-\dfrac{7}{8}$

63. -1 **65.** $\dfrac{11}{9}$ **67.** -23.08 **69.** -0.002117

71. To add two numbers with different signs, subtract the smaller absolute value from the larger absolute value and apply the sign of the number with the larger absolute value.
73. -1 **75.** 10 **77.** 5 **79.** 1
81. $-6 + (-10); -16$ **83.** $-3 + 8; 5$
85. $-21 + 17; -4$ **87.** $3(-14 + 20); 18$
89. $(-7 + (-2)) + 5; -4$ **91.** $-5 + 13 + (-11); -3°\text{F}$
93. $-2 + 6 + (-5); -1$ yd or 1-yd loss
95. a. $52.23 + (-52.95)$ **b.** Yes
97. -1

Section 1.5 Calculator Connections, p. 56

1. -13 **2.** -2 **3.** 711
1–3.

```
-8+(-5)
            -13
4+(-5)+(-1)
            -2
627-(-84)
            711
```

4. -0.18 **5.** -17.7 **6.** -990 **7.** -17 **8.** 38
4–6.   7–8.

```
-0.06-0.12
            -.18
-3.2+(-14.5)
            -17.7
-472+(-518)
            -990
```

```
-12-9+4
            -17
209-108+(-63)
            38
```

Section 1.5 Practice Exercises, pp. 56–59

3. x^2 **5.** $-b + 2$ **7.** 9 **9.** -3 **11.** -12
13. 4 **15.** -2 **17.** 8 **19.** -8 **21.** 2 **23.** 6
25. 40 **27.** -40 **29.** 0 **31.** -20 **33.** -24

35. 25 **37.** -5 **39.** $-\dfrac{3}{2}$ **41.** $\dfrac{41}{24}$ **43.** $\dfrac{2}{5}$ **45.** $-\dfrac{2}{3}$

47. 9.2 **49.** -5.72 **51.** -10 **53.** -14 **55.** -51
57. -173.188 **59.** 3.243 **61.** $6 - (-7); 13$
63. $3 - 18; -15$ **65.** $-5 - (-11); 6$
67. $-1 - (-13); 12$ **69.** $-32 - 20; -52$
71. $200 + 400 + 600 + 800 - 1000; \$1000$ **73.** $152°\text{F}$
75. $19,881 \text{ m}$ **77.** 13 **79.** -9 **81.** 5 **83.** -25

85. -2 **87.** $-\dfrac{11}{30}$ **89.** $-\dfrac{29}{9}$ **91.** -2 **93.** -11

95. 2 **97.** -7 **99.** 5 **101.** 5 **103.** 3

Chapter 1 Problem Recognition Exercises, p. 59

1. Add their absolute values and apply a negative sign.
2. Subtract the smaller absolute value from the larger absolute value. Apply the sign of the number with the larger absolute value.
3. 41 **4.** 13 **5.** 31 **6.** 46 **7.** -1.3 **8.** -3.6

9. -16 **10.** -7 **11.** $-\dfrac{1}{12}$ **12.** $\dfrac{7}{24}$ **13.** -36

14. -59 **15.** -12 **16.** -50 **17.** $-\dfrac{19}{6}$ **18.** $-\dfrac{8}{5}$

19. -5 **20.** -32 **21.** 0 **22.** 0 **23.** -7.7

24. -10.5 **25.** $-\dfrac{32}{15}$ **26.** $-\dfrac{9}{8}$ **27.** -32

28. -46 **29.** 0 **30.** 0 **31.** -30 **32.** -400

Section 1.6 Calculator Connections, pp. 66–67

1. -30 **2.** -2 **3.** 625 **4.** 625 **5.** -625 **6.** -5.76
1–3.   4–6.

```
-6(5)
            -30
-5.2/2.6
            -2
(-5)(-5)(-5)(-5)
            625
```

```
(-5)^4
            625
-5^4
            -625
-2.4²
            -5.76
```

7. 5.76   **8.** -1 **9.** 4   **10.** -36

7–8.

```
(-2.4)²
                    5.76
(-1)(-1)(-1)
                     -1
```

9–10.

```
-8.4/-2.1
                      4
90/(-5)(2)
                    -36
```

Section 1.6 Practice Exercises, pp. 67–70

3. True   **5.** False   **7.** -56 **9.** 143

11. -12.76 **13.** $\dfrac{3}{4}$ **15.** 36   **17.** -36

19. $-\dfrac{27}{125}$ **21.** 0.0016   **23.** -6 **25.** $\dfrac{15}{17}$ **27.** 2

29. $-\dfrac{1}{5}$ **31.** $(-2)(-7) = 14$ **33.** $-5 \cdot 0 = 0$

35. No number multiplied by zero equals 6.
37. $(-6)(4) = -24$ **39.** 6   **41.** -6 **43.** -8
45. 8   **47.** 0   **49.** Undefined   **51.** 0   **53.** 0

55. $-\dfrac{3}{2}$ **57.** $\dfrac{3}{10}$ **59.** -2 **61.** -7.912 **63.** 0.092

65. -6 **67.** 2.1   **69.** 9   **71.** -9 **73.** $-\dfrac{64}{27}$

75. -14.28 **77.** 340   **79.** $-\dfrac{10}{9}$ **81.** $\dfrac{14}{9}$

83. -30 **85.** 96   **87.** 2   **89.** -1 **91.** $-\dfrac{4}{33}$

93. $-\dfrac{4}{7}$ **95.** -24 **97.** $-\dfrac{1}{20}$ **99.** -23 **101.** 12

103. $\dfrac{9}{7}$ **105.** Undefined   **107.** -48 **109.** -6

111. -1 **113.** 7   **115.** -4 **117.** -40 **119.** $\dfrac{7}{2}$

121. No. The first expression is equivalent to $10 \div (5x)$. The second is $10 \div 5 \cdot x$.

123. $-3.75(0.3); -1.125$ **125.** $\dfrac{16}{5} \div \left(-\dfrac{8}{9}\right); -\dfrac{18}{5}$

127. $-0.4 + 6(-0.42); -2.92$ **129.** $-\dfrac{1}{4} - 6\left(-\dfrac{1}{3}\right); \dfrac{7}{4}$

131. $3(-2) + 3 = -3$; loss of \$3
133. a. -10 **b.** 24   **c.** In part (a), we subtract; in part (b), we multiply.

Chapter 1 Problem Recognition Exercises, p. 70

1. a. -4 **b.** 32   **c.** -12 **d.** 2
2. a. 10   **b.** 14   **c.** -24 **d.** -6
3. a. -27 **b.** -324 **c.** -4 **d.** -45
4. a. 30   **b.** 24   **c.** -81 **d.** -9
5. a. 50   **b.** -15 **c.** $\dfrac{1}{2}$ **d.** 5
6. a. -5 **b.** -24 **c.** -16 **d.** -80
7. a. 64   **b.** 12   **c.** $\dfrac{1}{4}$ **d.** -20
8. a. -7 **b.** -24 **c.** -63 **d.** -18
9. a. -400 **b.** 85   **c.** -16 **d.** 75
10. a. 7   **b.** 294   **c.** $\dfrac{2}{3}$ **d.** -35

Section 1.7 Practice Exercises, pp. 80–84

3. 8   **5.** -8 **7.** $-\dfrac{9}{2}$ or -4.5 **9.** 0   **11.** $\dfrac{7}{8}$

13. $-\dfrac{4}{45}$ **15.** $-8 + 5$ **17.** $x + 8$ **19.** $4(5)$
21. $-12x$ **23.** $x + (-3); -3 + x$
25. $4p + (-9); -9 + 4p$ **27.** $x + (4 + 9); x + 13$
29. $(-5 \cdot 3)x; -15x$ **31.** $\left(\dfrac{6}{11} \cdot \dfrac{11}{6}\right)x; x$

33. $\left(-4 \cdot -\dfrac{1}{4}\right)t; t$ **35.** $(-8 + 2) + y; -6 + y$
37. $(-5 \cdot 2)x; -10x$ **39.** Reciprocal   **41.** 0
43. $30x + 6$ **45.** $-2a - 16$ **47.** $15c - 3d$

49. $-7y + 14$ **51.** $-\dfrac{2}{3}x + 4$ **53.** $\dfrac{1}{3}m - 1$

55. $-2p - 10$ **57.** $6w + 10z - 16$ **59.** $4x + 8y - 4z$
61. $6w - x + 3y$ **63.** $6 + 2x$ **65.** $24z$ **67.** $-14x$
69. $-4 - 4x$ **71.** b   **73.** i   **75.** g   **77.** d   **79.** h

81.

Term	Coefficient
$2x$	2
$-y$	-1
$18xy$	18
5	5

83.

Term	Coefficient
$-x$	-1
$8y$	8
$-9x^2y$	-9
-3	-3

85. The variable factors are different.
87. The variables are the same and raised to the same power.   **89.** For example: $5y, -2x, 6$ **91.** $-6p$

93. $-6y^2$ **95.** $7x^3y - 4$ **97.** $3t - \dfrac{7}{5}$ **99.** $-6x + 22$

101. $4w$ **103.** $-3x + 17$ **105.** $10t - 44$ **107.** -18
109. $-2t + 7$ **111.** $51a - 27$ **113.** -6

115. $4q - \dfrac{1}{3}$ **117.** $6n$ **119.** $2x + 18$

121. $32.33z - 30.81$ **123.** $-2x - 34$ **125.** $9z - 35$
127. Equivalent   **129.** Not equivalent. The terms are not *like* terms and cannot be combined.   **131.** Not equivalent; subtraction is not commutative.   **133.** Equivalent
135. a. 55   **b.** 210

Chapter 1 Review Exercises, pp. 90–92

1. Improper   **2.** Proper   **3.** Improper   **4.** Improper

5. $2 \times 2 \times 2 \times 2 \times 7$ **6.** $\dfrac{6}{5}$ **7.** $\dfrac{35}{36}$ **8.** $\dfrac{13}{16}$

9. $\dfrac{2}{7}$ **10.** $\dfrac{6}{5}$ or $1\dfrac{1}{5}$ **11.** 3   **12.** $\dfrac{17}{10}$ or $1\dfrac{7}{10}$

13. 357 million km^2 **14. a.** $7, 1$ **b.** $7, -4, 0, 1$
c. $7, 0, 1$ **d.** $7, \frac{1}{3}, -4, 0, -0.\overline{2}, 1$ **e.** $-\sqrt{3}, \pi$
f. $7, \frac{1}{3}, -4, 0, -\sqrt{3}, -0.\overline{2}, \pi, 1$ **15.** $\dfrac{1}{2}$ **16.** 6   **17.** $\sqrt{7}$

18. 0   **19.** False   **20.** False   **21.** True   **22.** True
23. True   **24.** True   **25.** False   **26.** True   **27.** True

28. $x \cdot \dfrac{2}{3}$ or $\dfrac{2}{3}x$ **29.** $\dfrac{7}{y}$ or $7 \div y$ **30.** $2 + 3b$

31. $a - 5$ **32.** $5k + 2$ **33.** $13z - 7$ **34.** 0
35. 60   **36.** 3   **37.** 4   **38.** 216   **39.** 225

40. 6   **41.** $\dfrac{1}{10}$ **42.** $\dfrac{1}{16}$ **43.** $\dfrac{27}{8}$ **44.** 13   **45.** 11

46. 7   **47.** 10   **48.** 2   **49.** 4   **50.** 15   **51.** -17

52. $\dfrac{11}{63}$ **53.** $-\dfrac{5}{22}$ **54.** $-\dfrac{14}{15}$ **55.** $-\dfrac{27}{10}$ **56.** -2.15

57. -4.28 **58.** 3   **59.** 8   **60.** 4   **61.** When a and b are both negative or when a and b have different signs and the number with the larger absolute value is negative.

62. No. He is still overdrawn by \$8.   **63.** -12 **64.** 33

65. -1 **66.** -17 **67.** $-\dfrac{29}{18}$ **68.** $-\dfrac{19}{24}$ **69.** -1.2

70. -4.25 **71.** -10.2 **72.** 12.09   **73.** $\dfrac{10}{3}$

74. $-\dfrac{17}{20}$ **75.** -1 **76.** If $a < b$ **77.** $-7 - (-18)$; 11

78. $-6 - 41$; -47 **79.** $7 - 13$; -6
80. $(20 - (-7)) - 5$; 22   **81.** $(6 + (-12)) - 21$; -27
82. $175°$F   **83.** -170 **84.** -91 **85.** -2 **86.** 3

87. $-\dfrac{1}{6}$ **88.** $-\dfrac{8}{11}$ **89.** 0   **90.** Undefined   **91.** 0

92. 2.25   **93.** $-\dfrac{3}{2}$ **94.** $\dfrac{1}{4}$ **95.** -30 **96.** 450

97. $\dfrac{1}{4}$ **98.** $-\dfrac{1}{7}$ **99.** -2 **100.** $\dfrac{18}{7}$ **101.** 17

102. 6   **103.** $-\dfrac{7}{120}$ **104.** 4.4   **105.** $-\dfrac{1}{3}$ **106.** -1

107. -2 **108.** 11   **109.** 36   **110.** -6 **111.** 70.6
112. True   **113.** False, any nonzero real number raised to an even power is positive.   **114.** True   **115.** True
116. False, the product of two negative numbers is positive.
117. True   **118.** True   **119.** For example: $2 + 3 = 3 + 2$
120. For example: $(2 + 3) + 4 = 2 + (3 + 4)$ **121.** For example: $5 + (-5) = 0$ **122.** For example: $7 + 0 = 7$
123. For example: $5 \cdot 2 = 2 \cdot 5$ **124.** For example:

$(8 \cdot 2)10 = 8(2 \cdot 10)$ **125.** For example: $3 \cdot \dfrac{1}{3} = 1$

126. For example: $8 \cdot 1 = 8$ **127.** $5x - 2y = 5x + (-2y)$, then use the commutative property of addition.
128. $3a - 9y = 3a + (-9y)$, then use the commutative property of addition.   **129.** $3y, 10x, -12, xy$
130. $3, 10, -12, 1$ **131.** $8a - b - 10$
132. $-7p - 11q + 16$ **133.** $-8z - 18$
134. $20w - 40y + 5$ **135.** $p - 2$ **136.** $-h + 14$
137. $-14q - 1$ **138.** $-5.7b + 2.4$ **139.** $4x + 24$
140. $50y + 105$

Chapter 1 Test, pp. 92–93

1. $\dfrac{15}{4}$ **2.** $\dfrac{3}{2}$ **3.** $3\dfrac{1}{16}$ **4.** $2\dfrac{3}{8}$

5. Rational, all repeating decimals are rational numbers.
6.

$$\underset{\substack{0\ 0.5}}{\overset{\substack{-2 \qquad 0 \qquad |-\frac{3}{2}| \quad |3| \quad \sqrt{16}}}{\rule{0pt}{0pt}}}$$

7. a. False   **b.** True   **c.** True   **d.** True
8. a. $(4x)(4x)(4x)$ **b.** $4 \cdot x \cdot x \cdot x$
9. a. Twice the difference of a and b
b. b subtracted from twice a

10. $\dfrac{\sqrt{c}}{d^2}$ or $\sqrt{c} \div d^2$ **11.** 6   **12.** -12 **13.** 28

14. $-\dfrac{7}{8}$ **15.** 4.66   **16.** -32 **17.** -12

18. Undefined   **19.** -28 **20.** 0   **21.** 96   **22.** $\dfrac{2}{3}$

23. -8 **24.** 9   **25.** $\dfrac{1}{3}$ **26.** The difference is $9.5°$C.

27. a. $5 + 2 + (-10) + 4$ **b.** He gained 1 yd.
28. a. Commutative property of multiplication
b. Identity property of addition   **c.** Associative property of addition   **d.** Inverse property of multiplication
e. Associative property of multiplication
29. $-12x + 2y - 4$ **30.** $-12m - 24p + 21$

31. $-6k - 8$ **32.** $-4p - 23$ **33.** $4p - \dfrac{4}{3}$

34. 5   **35.** 18   **36.** -6 **37.** -32

38. $12 - (-4)$; 16   **39.** $6 - 8$; -2 **40.** $\dfrac{10}{-12}$; $-\dfrac{5}{6}$

Chapter 2
Chapter Opener Puzzle

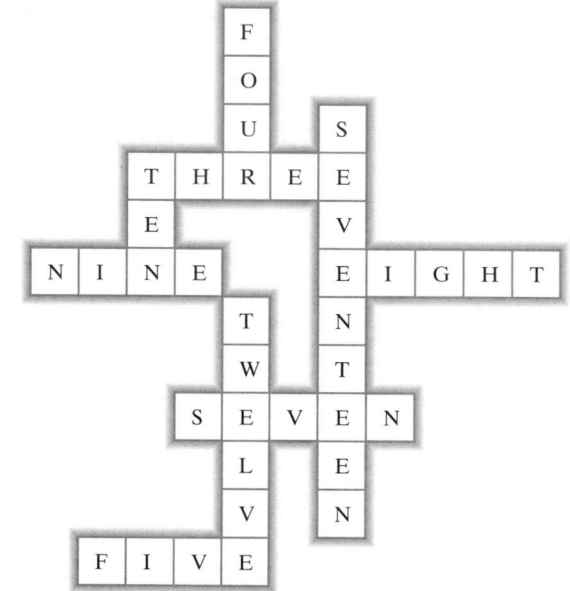

$8 \cdot \left(\dfrac{3}{8}\right) = \underline{\quad\text{three}\quad}$ $6 \cdot \left(\dfrac{2}{3}\right) = \underline{\quad\text{four}\quad}$

$100(0.17) = \underline{\text{seventeen}}$ $100(0.09) = \underline{\quad\text{nine}\quad}$

$\underline{\quad\text{five}\quad} \cdot \left(\dfrac{2}{5}\right) = 2$ $\underline{\quad\text{seven}\quad} \cdot \left(\dfrac{6}{7}\right) = 6$

$\underline{\quad\text{eight}\quad} \cdot \left(\dfrac{3}{4}\right) = 6$ $\underline{\quad\text{twelve}\quad} \cdot \left(\dfrac{5}{6}\right) = 10$

$\underline{\quad\text{ten}\quad} \cdot (0.4) = 4$

Section 2.1 Practice Exercises, pp. 105–107

3. Expression **5.** Equation **7.** Substitute the value into the equation and determine if the right-hand side is equal to the left-hand side. **9.** No **11.** Yes
13. Yes **15.** $\{-1\}$ **17.** $\{20\}$ **19.** $\{-17\}$
21. $\{-16\}$ **23.** $\{0\}$ **25.** $\{1.3\}$ **27.** $\left\{\dfrac{11}{2}\right\}$ or $\left\{5\dfrac{1}{2}\right\}$
29. $\{-2\}$ **31.** $\{-2.13\}$ **33.** $\{-3.2675\}$ **35.** $\{9\}$
37. $\{-4\}$ **39.** $\{0\}$ **41.** $\{-15\}$ **43.** $\left\{-\dfrac{4}{5}\right\}$
45. $\{-10\}$ **47.** $\{4\}$ **49.** $\{41\}$ **51.** $\{-127\}$
53. $\{-2.6\}$ **55.** $-8 + x = 42$; The number is 50.
57. $x - (-6) = 18$; The number is 12.
59. $x \cdot 7 = -63$ or $7x = -63$; The number is -9.
61. $x - 3.2 = 2.1$; The number is 5.3.
63. $\dfrac{x}{12} = \dfrac{1}{3}$; The number is 4.
65. $x + \dfrac{5}{8} = \dfrac{13}{8}$; The number is 1. **67.** $\{10\}$ **69.** $\left\{-\dfrac{1}{9}\right\}$
71. $\{-12\}$ **73.** $\left\{\dfrac{22}{3}\right\}$ **75.** $\{-36\}$ **77.** $\{16\}$ **79.** $\{2\}$
81. $\left\{-\dfrac{7}{4}\right\}$ **83.** $\{11\}$ **85.** $\{-36\}$ **87.** $\left\{\dfrac{7}{2}\right\}$ **89.** $\{4\}$
91. $\{3.6\}$ **93.** $\{0.4084\}$ **95.** Yes **97.** No **99.** Yes
101. Yes **103.** For example: $y + 9 = 15$ **105.** For example: $2p = -8$ **107.** For example: $5a + 5 = 5$
109. $\{-1\}$ **111.** $\{7\}$

Section 2.2 Practice Exercises, pp. 114–116

3. $-5z + 2$ **5.** $10p - 10$ **7.** To simplify an expression, clear parentheses and combine *like* terms. To solve an equation, use the addition, subtraction, multiplication, and division properties of equality to isolate the variable and determine the solution set.
9. $\{-3\}$ **11.** $\{-5\}$ **13.** $\{2\}$ **15.** $\{6\}$ **17.** $\left\{\dfrac{5}{2}\right\}$
19. $\{-42\}$ **21.** $\left\{-\dfrac{3}{4}\right\}$ **23.** $\{5\}$ **25.** $\{-4\}$
27. $\{-26\}$ **29.** $\{10\}$ **31.** $\{-8\}$ **33.** $\left\{-\dfrac{7}{3}\right\}$
35. $\{0\}$ **37.** $\{-3\}$ **39.** $\{-2\}$ **41.** $\left\{\dfrac{9}{2}\right\}$
43. $\left\{-\dfrac{1}{3}\right\}$ **45.** $\{10\}$ **47.** $\{-6\}$ **49.** $\{0\}$
51. $\{-2\}$ **53.** $\left\{-\dfrac{25}{4}\right\}$ **55.** $\left\{\dfrac{10}{3}\right\}$ **57.** $\{-0.25\}$
59. $\{\ \}$; contradiction **61.** $\{-15\}$; conditional equation
63. The set of real numbers; identity
65. One solution **67.** Infinitely many solutions
69. $\{7\}$ **71.** $\left\{\dfrac{1}{2}\right\}$ **73.** $\{0\}$
75. The set of real numbers **77.** $\{-46\}$ **79.** $\{2\}$
81. $\left\{\dfrac{13}{2}\right\}$ **83.** $\{-5\}$ **85.** $\{\ \}$ **87.** $\{2.205\}$
89. $\{10\}$ **91.** $\{-1\}$ **93.** $a = 15$ **95.** $a = 4$
97. For example: $5x + 2 = 2 + 5x$

Section 2.3 Practice Exercises, pp. 121–123

3. $\{-2\}$ **5.** $\{-5\}$ **7.** $\{\ \}$ **9.** 18, 36
11. 100; 1000; 10,000 **13.** 30, 60 **15.** $\{4\}$ **17.** $\{-12\}$
19. $\left\{-\dfrac{15}{4}\right\}$ **21.** $\{8\}$ **23.** $\{3\}$ **25.** $\{15\}$ **27.** $\{\ \}$
29. The set of real numbers **31.** $\{5\}$
33. $\{2\}$ **35.** $\{-15\}$ **37.** $\{6\}$ **39.** $\{3\}$
41. The set of real numbers **43.** $\{67\}$ **45.** $\{90\}$
47. $\{4\}$ **49.** $\{-3.8\}$ **51.** $\{\ \}$ **53.** $\{-0.25\}$
55. $\{-6\}$ **57.** $\left\{\dfrac{8}{3}\right\}$ or $\left\{2\dfrac{2}{3}\right\}$ **59.** $\{-9\}$ **61.** $\left\{\dfrac{1}{10}\right\}$
63. $\{-2\}$ **65.** $\{-1\}$ **67.** $\{2\}$

Chapter 2 Problem Recognition Exercises, pp. 123–124

1. Expression; $-4b + 18$ **2.** Expression; $20p - 30$
3. Equation; $\{-8\}$ **4.** Equation; $\{-14\}$
5. Equation; $\left\{\dfrac{1}{3}\right\}$ **6.** Equation; $\left\{-\dfrac{4}{3}\right\}$
7. Expression; $6z - 23$ **8.** Expression; $-x - 9$
9. Equation; $\left\{\dfrac{7}{9}\right\}$ **10.** Equation; $\left\{-\dfrac{13}{10}\right\}$
11. Equation; $\{20\}$ **12.** Equation; $\{-3\}$
13. Equation; $\left\{\dfrac{1}{2}\right\}$ **14.** Equation; $\{-6\}$
15. Expression; $\dfrac{5}{8}x + \dfrac{7}{4}$ **16.** Expression; $-26t + 18$
17. Equation; $\{\ \}$ **18.** Equation; $\{\ \}$
19. Equation; $\left\{\dfrac{23}{12}\right\}$ **20.** Equation; $\left\{\dfrac{5}{8}\right\}$
21. Equation; The set of real numbers
22. Equation; The set of real numbers
23. Equation; $\left\{\dfrac{1}{2}\right\}$ **24.** Equation; $\{0\}$
25. Expression; 0 **26.** Expression; -1
27. Expression; $2a + 13$ **28.** Expression; $8q + 3$
29. Equation; $\{10\}$ **30.** Equation; $\left\{-\dfrac{1}{20}\right\}$

Section 2.4 Practice Exercises, pp. 131–134

3. $x + 5$ **5.** $3x$ **7.** $3x + 20$ **9.** The number is -4.
11. The number is -3. **13.** The number is 5.
15. The number is -5. **17.** The number is 9.
19. a. $x + 1, x + 2$ **b.** $x - 1, x - 2$ **21.** The integers are -34 and -33. **23.** The integers are 13 and 15.
25. The sides are 14 in., 15 in., 16 in., 17 in., and 18 in.
27. The integers are 42, 44, and 46. **29.** The integers are 13, 15, and 17. **31.** The lengths of the pieces are 33 cm and 53 cm. **33.** Karen's age is 35, and Clarann's age is 23.
35. There were 201 Republicans and 232 Democrats.
37. 4.698 million watch *The Dr. Phil Show*. **39.** The Congo River is 4370 km long, and the Nile River is 6825 km.
41. The area of Africa is 30,065,000 km². The area of Asia is 44,579,000 km². **43.** They walked 12.3 mi on the first day and 8.2 mi on the second. **45.** The pieces are 6 in., 18 in., and 24 in.
47. The integers are 42, 43, and 44. **49.** Jennifer Lopez made $37 million, and U2 made $69 million. **51.** The number is 11.

53. The page numbers are 470 and 471.   **55.** The number is 10.   **57.** The deepest point in the Arctic Ocean is 5122 m.   **59.** The number is $\dfrac{7}{16}$.   **61.** The number is 2.5.

Section 2.5 Practice Exercises, pp. 139–142

3. The integers are 21 and 22.   **5.** 12.5%   **7.** 85%   **9.** 0.75   **11.** 1050.8   **13.** 885   **15.** 2200   **17.** Molly will have to pay $106.99.   **19.** Approximately 231,000 cases   **21.** 2%   **23.** Javon's taxable income was $84,000.   **25.** Aidan would earn $27 more in the CD.   **27.** Bob borrowed $1200.   **29.** The rate is 6%.   **31.** Perry needs to invest $3302.   **33. a.** $20.40 **b.** $149.60   **35.** The original price was $470.59.   **37.** The discount rate is 12%.   **39.** The original cost was $60.   **41.** The tax rate is 5%.   **43.** The original cost was $5.20 per pack.   **45.** The original price was $210,000.   **47.** Alina made $4600 that month.   **49.** Diane sold $645 over $200 worth of merchandise.

Section 2.6 Calculator Connections, p. 148

1. 140.056   **2.** 31.831   **3.** 1.273   **4.** 0.455
1–2.   3–4.

```
880/(2π)
          140.0563499
1600/(π*(4)²)
          31.83098862
```
```
20/(5π)
          1.273239545
10/(7π)
          .4547284088
```

Section 2.6 Practice Exercises, pp. 148–152

3. $\{-5\}$ **5.** $\{0\}$ **7.** $\{-2\}$ **9.** $a = P - b - c$ **11.** $y = x + z$ **13.** $q = p - 250$ **15.** $b = \dfrac{A}{h}$ **17.** $t = \dfrac{PV}{nr}$ **19.** $x = 5 + y$ **21.** $y = -3x - 19$ **23.** $y = \dfrac{-2x + 6}{3}$ or $y = -\dfrac{2}{3}x + 2$ **25.** $x = \dfrac{y + 9}{-2}$ or $x = -\dfrac{1}{2}y - \dfrac{9}{2}$ **27.** $y = \dfrac{-4x + 12}{-3}$ or $y = \dfrac{4}{3}x - 4$ **29.** $y = \dfrac{-ax + c}{b}$ or $y = -\dfrac{a}{b}x + \dfrac{c}{b}$ **31.** $t = \dfrac{A - P}{Pr}$ or $t = \dfrac{A}{Pr} - \dfrac{1}{r}$ **33.** $c = \dfrac{a - 2b}{2}$ or $c = \dfrac{a}{2} - b$ **35.** $y = 2Q - x$ **37.** $a = MS$ **39.** $R = \dfrac{P}{I^2}$

41. The length is 7 ft, and the width is 5 ft.
43. The length is 120 yd and the width is 30 yd.
45. The length is 195 m, and the width is 100 m.
47. The sides are 22 m, 22 m, and 27 m.
49. "Adjacent supplementary angles form a straight angle." The words *Supplementary* and *Straight* both begin with the same letter.   **51.** The angles are 23.5° and 66.5°.
53. The angles are 34.8° and 145.2°.
55. $x = 20$; the vertical angles measure 37°.

57. The measures of the angles are 30°, 60°, and 90°.
59. The measures of the angles are 42°, 54°, and 84°.
61. $x = 17$; the measures of the angles are 34° and 56°.

63. a. $A = lw$ **b.** $w = \dfrac{A}{l}$ **c.** The width is 29.5 ft.

65. a. $P = 2l + 2w$ **b.** $l = \dfrac{P - 2w}{2}$ **c.** The length is 103 m.

67. a. $C = 2\pi r$ **b.** $r = \dfrac{C}{2\pi}$ **c.** The radius is approximately 140 ft.   **69. a.** 415.48 m² **b.** 10,386.89 m³

Section 2.7 Practice Exercises, pp. 157–161

3. $c = \dfrac{r}{d}$ **5.** $\{4\}$ **7.** $200 - t$ **9.** $100 - x$ **11.** $3000 - y$ **13.** 53 tickets were sold at $3 and 28 tickets were sold at $2.   **15.** Josh downloaded 17 songs for $0.90 and 8 songs for $1.50.   **17.** Christopher has 5 Wii games and 15 DS games.   **19.** $x + 7$ **21.** $d + 2000$ **23.** Mix 20 oz of 50% antifreeze solution.   **25.** The pharmacist needs to use 21 mL of the 1% saline solution.   **27.** The contractor needs to mix 6.75 oz of 50% acid solution.   **29. a.** 300 mi **b.** $5x$ **c.** $5(x + 12)$ or $5x + 60$ **31.** She walks 4 mph to the lake.   **33.** Bryan hiked 6 mi up the canyon.   **35.** The plane travels 600 mph in still air.   **37.** The slower car travels 48 mph and the faster car travels 52 mph.   **39.** The speeds of the vehicles are 40 mph and 50 mph.   **41.** The rates of the boats are 20 mph and 40 mph.   **43. a.** 2 lb **b.** $0.10x$ **c.** $0.10(x + 3) = 0.10x + 0.30$ **45.** Mix 10 lb of coffee sold at $12 per pound and 40 lb of coffee sold at $8 per pound.   **47.** The boats will meet in $\frac{3}{4}$ hr (45 min).   **49.** Sam purchased 16 packages of wax and 5 bottles of sunscreen.   **51.** 2.5 quarts of 85% chlorine solution   **53.** 20 L of water must be added.   **55.** The Japanese bullet train travels 300 km/hr and the Acela Express travels 240 km/hr.

Section 2.8 Practice Exercises, pp. 172–176

3. $\{-3\}$ **5.** (graph at 5)   **7.** (graph at $\frac{5}{2}$)   **9.** (graph at 13)   **11.** (graph from 2 to 6.5)   **13.** (graph from 0 to 4)   **15.** (graph from 1 to 8)

Set-Builder Notation	Graph	Interval Notation
17. $\{x \mid x \geq 6\}$	(graph at 6)	$[6, \infty)$
19. $\{x \mid x \leq 2.1\}$	(graph at 2.1)	$(-\infty, 2.1]$
21. $\{x \mid -2 < x \leq 7\}$	(graph from −2 to 7)	$(-2, 7]$

Set-Builder Notation	Graph	Interval Notation
23. $\left\{x \mid x > \dfrac{3}{4}\right\}$	(graph at $\frac{3}{4}$)	$\left(\dfrac{3}{4}, \infty\right)$
25. $\{x \mid -1 < x < 8\}$	(graph from −1 to 8)	$(-1, 8)$
27. $\{x \mid x \leq -14\}$	(graph at −14)	$(-\infty, -14]$

Set-Builder Notation	Graph	Interval Notation
29. $\{x \mid x \geq 18\}$		$[18, \infty)$
31. $\{x \mid x < -0.6\}$		$(-\infty, -0.6)$
33. $\{x \mid -3.5 \leq x < 7.1\}$		$[-3.5, 7.1)$

35. a. $\{3\}$ **b.** $\{x \mid x > 3\}; (3, \infty)$

37. a. $\{13\}$ **b.** $\{p \mid p \leq 13\}; (-\infty, 13]$

39. a. $\{-3\}$ **b.** $\{c \mid c < -3\}; (-\infty, -3)$

41. a. $\left\{-\dfrac{3}{2}\right\}$ **b.** $\left\{z \mid z \geq -\dfrac{3}{2}\right\}; \left[-\dfrac{3}{2}, \infty\right)$

43. $(-1, 4]$ **45.** $(-3, 5)$

47. $[2, 6]$ **49.** $(-\infty, 1]$

51. $(10, \infty)$ **53.** $(3, \infty)$

55. $(-\infty, 8]$ **57.** $(2, \infty)$

59. $(-\infty, -2)$ **61.** $[14, \infty)$

63. $[-24, \infty)$ **65.** $[-3, 3)$

67. $\left(0, \dfrac{5}{2}\right)$ **69.** $(10, 12)$

71. $[-1, 4)$ **73.** $[90, \infty)$

75. $(-9, \infty)$ **77.** $\left[-\dfrac{15}{2}, \infty\right)$

79. $(-\infty, -3)$ **81.** $\left[-\dfrac{1}{3}, \infty\right)$

83. $(-3, \infty)$ **85.** $(-\infty, 7)$

87. $(-\infty, -5]$ **89.** $\left(-\infty, \dfrac{15}{4}\right]$

91. $(-\infty, -9)$ **93.** $(-3, \infty)$

95. $(-\infty, 0]$ **97.** No   **99.** Yes

101. $L \geq 10$ **103.** $w > 75$ **105.** $t \leq 72$ **107.** $L \geq 8$

109. $2 < h < 5$ **111.** More than 10.2 in. of rain is needed.

113. a. $\$1539$ **b.** 200 birdhouses cost $\$1440$. It is cheaper to purchase 200 birdhouses because the discount is greater.

115. If there were more than 145 text messages, the unlimited option would be a better deal.   **117.** Madison needs to babysit a minimum of 39.5 hr.

119. $[13, \infty)$ **121.** $[-4, \infty)$

123. $(14.5, \infty)$

Chapter 2 Review Exercises, pp. 183–186

1. a. Equation   **b.** Expression   **c.** Equation **d.** Equation   **2.** A linear equation can be written in the form $ax + b = 0, a \neq 0$.   **3. a.** No   **b.** Yes **c.** No   **d.** Yes   **4. a.** No   **b.** Yes   **5.** $\{-8\}$

6. $\{15\}$ **7.** $\left\{\dfrac{21}{4}\right\}$ **8.** $\{70\}$ **9.** $\left\{-\dfrac{21}{5}\right\}$

10. $\{-60\}$ **11.** $\left\{-\dfrac{10}{7}\right\}$ **12.** $\{27\}$

13. The number is 60.   **14.** The number is $\dfrac{7}{24}$.

15. The number is -8.   **16.** The number is -2.

17. $\{1\}$ **18.** $\left\{-\dfrac{3}{5}\right\}$ **19.** $\{2\}$ **20.** $\{-6\}$ **21.** $\{-3\}$

22. $\{18\}$ **23.** $\left\{\dfrac{3}{4}\right\}$ **24.** $\{-3\}$ **25.** $\{0\}$ **26.** $\left\{\dfrac{1}{8}\right\}$

27. $\{2\}$ **28.** $\{6\}$ **29.** A contradiction has no solution and an identity is true for all real numbers.   **30.** Identity **31.** Conditional equation   **32.** Contradiction **33.** Identity   **34.** Contradiction   **35.** Conditional equation   **36.** $\{6\}$ **37.** $\{22\}$ **38.** $\{13\}$ **39.** $\{-27\}$

40. $\{-10\}$ **41.** $\{-7\}$ **42.** $\left\{\dfrac{5}{3}\right\}$ **43.** $\left\{-\dfrac{9}{4}\right\}$

44. $\{2.5\}$ **45.** $\{-4\}$ **46.** $\{-4.2\}$ **47.** $\{2.5\}$

48. $\{-312\}$ **49.** $\{200\}$ **50.** $\{\ \}$ **51.** $\{\ \}$ **52.** The set of real numbers   **53.** The set of real numbers **54.** The number is 30.   **55.** The number is 11. **56.** The number is -7.   **57.** The number is -10. **58.** The integers are 66, 68, and 70.   **59.** The integers are 27, 28, and 29.   **60.** The sides are 25 in., 26 in., and 27 in.

61. The sides are 36 cm, 37 cm, 38 cm, 39 cm, and 40 cm.
62. The average salary was $1.07 million in 2000.
63. Indiana has 6.2 million people and Kentucky has 4.1 million.   **64.** 23.8   **65.** 28.8   **66.** 12.5%
67. 95%   **68.** 160   **69.** 1750   **70.** The dinner was $40 before tax and tip.   **71. a.** $840   **b.** $3840   **72.** He invested $12,000.   **73.** The novel originally cost $29.50.

74. $K = C + 273$ **75.** $C = K - 273$ **76.** $s = \dfrac{P}{4}$
77. $s = \dfrac{P}{3}$ **78.** $x = \dfrac{y - b}{m}$ **79.** $x = \dfrac{c - a}{b}$
80. $y = \dfrac{-2x - 2}{5}$ **81.** $b = \dfrac{Q - 4a}{4}$ or $b = \dfrac{Q}{4} - a$

82. The height is 7 m.   **83. a.** $h = \dfrac{3V}{\pi r^2}$ **b.** The height is 5.1 in.   **84.** The angles are 22°, 78°, and 80°.   **85.** The angles are 50° and 40°.   **86.** The length is 5 ft, and the width is 4 ft.   **87.** $x = 20.$ The angle measure is 65°.
88. The measure of angle y is 53°.   **89.** The truck travels 45 km/hr in bad weather and 60 km/hr in good weather.
90. Gus rides 15 mph and Winston rides 18 mph.   **91.** The cars will be 327.6 mi apart after 2.8 hr (2 hr and 48 min).
92. They meet in 2.25 hr (2 hr and 15 min).   **93.** 2 lb of 24% fat content beef is needed.   **94.** 20 lb of the 40% solder should be used.

95. $(-2, \infty)$

96. $\left(-\infty, \dfrac{1}{2}\right]$

97. $(-1, 4]$

98. a. $637   **b.** 300 plants cost $1410, and 295 plants cost $1416. 300 plants cost less.

99. $\{c | c < 17\}; (-\infty, 17)$

100. $\left\{w | w > -\dfrac{1}{3}\right\}; \left(-\dfrac{1}{3}, \infty\right)$

101. $\{x | x \le -6\}; (-\infty, -6]$

102. $\left\{y | y \le -\dfrac{14}{5}\right\}; \left(-\infty, -\dfrac{14}{5}\right]$

103. $\{a | a \ge 49\}; [49, \infty)$

104. $\{t | t < 34.5\}; (-\infty, 34.5)$

105. $\{k | k > 18\}; (18, \infty)$

106. $\left\{h | h \le \dfrac{5}{2}\right\}; \left(-\infty, \dfrac{5}{2}\right]$

107. $\{b | -3 < b \le 7\}; (-3, 7]$

108. $\{z | -6 \le z \le 5\}; [-6, 5]$

109. More than 2.5 in. is required.
110. Matthew can have at most 18 wings.

Chapter 2 Test, pp. 186–187

1. b, d   **2. a.** $5x + 7$ **b.** $\{9\}$ **3.** $\{-16\}$ **4.** $\{12\}$
5. $\left\{-\dfrac{16}{9}\right\}$ **6.** $\left\{\dfrac{7}{3}\right\}$ **7.** $\{15\}$ **8.** $\left\{\dfrac{13}{4}\right\}$ **9.** $\left\{\dfrac{20}{21}\right\}$
10. $\{\ \}$ **11.** $\{-3\}$ **12.** $\{-47\}$
13. The set of real numbers   **14.** $y = -3x - 4$
15. $r = \dfrac{C}{2\pi}$ **16.** 90   **17.** The numbers are 18 and 13.
18. The sides are 61 in., 62 in., 63 in., 64 in., and 65 in.
19. The cost was $82.00.   **20.** Each basketball ticket was $36.32, and each hockey ticket was $40.64.
21. Clarita originally borrowed $5000.   **22.** The field is 110 m long and 75 m wide.   **23.** $y = 30;$ The measures of the angles are 30°, 39°, and 111°.
24. Paula needs 30 lb of macadamia nuts.
25. One family travels 55 mph and the other travels 50 mph.
26. The measures of the angles are 32° and 58°.
27. a. $(-\infty, 0)$ **b.** $[-2, 5)$

28. $\{x | x > -2\}; (-2, \infty)$ **29.** $\{x | x \le -4\}; (-\infty, -4]$

30. $\left\{y | y > -\dfrac{3}{2}\right\}; \left(-\dfrac{3}{2}, \infty\right)$

31. $\{p | -5 \le p \le 1\}; [-5, 1]$

32. More than 26.5 in. is required.

Chapters 1–2 Cumulative Review Exercises, pp. 187–188

1. $\dfrac{1}{2}$ **2.** -7 **3.** $-\dfrac{5}{12}$ **4.** 16   **5.** 4
6. $\sqrt{5^2 - 9}; 4$ **7.** $-14 + 12; -2$ **8.** $-7x^2y, 4xy, -6$
9. $9x + 13$ **10.** $\{4\}$ **11.** $\{-7.2\}$
12. The set of real numbers   **13.** $\{-8\}$ **14.** $\left\{-\dfrac{4}{7}\right\}$
15. $\{-80\}$ **16.** The numbers are 77 and 79.   **17.** The cost before tax was $350.00.   **18.** The height is $\dfrac{41}{6}$ cm or $6\dfrac{5}{6}$ cm.
19. $\{x | x > -2\}; (-2, \infty)$ **20.** $\{x | -1 \le x \le 9\}; [-1, 9]$

Chapter 3

Chapter Opener Puzzle

THE	EQUATION	
1	2	$y = mx + b$

IS	WRITTEN	IN
3	4	5

SLOPE-INTERCEPT		FORM
6	7	8

Section 3.1 Practice Exercises, pp. 194–199

3. a. Month 10   **b.** 30   **c.** Between months 3 and 5 and between months 10 and 12   **d.** Months 8 and 9   **e.** Month 3   **f.** 80   **5. a.** On day 1 the price per share was \$89.25.   **b.** \$1.75   **c.** $-\$2.75$

7.

9.

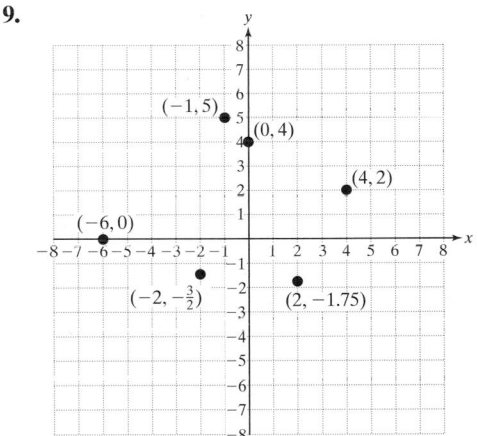

11. IV   **13.** II   **15.** III   **17.** I

19. $(0, -5)$ lies on the y-axis.

21. $\left(\frac{7}{8}, 0\right)$ is located on the x-axis.

23. $A(-4, 2)$, $B\left(\frac{1}{2}, 4\right)$, $C(3, -4)$, $D(-3, -4)$, $E(0, -3)$, $F(5, 0)$

25. a. $A(400, 200)$, $B(200, -150)$, $C(-300, -200)$, $D(-300, 250)$, $E(0, 450)$ **b.** 450 m

27. a. $(250, 225)$, $(175, 193)$, $(315, 330)$, $(220, 209)$, $(450, 570)$, $(400, 480)$, $(190, 185)$; the ordered pair $(250, 225)$ means that 250 people produce \$225 in popcorn sales.

b.

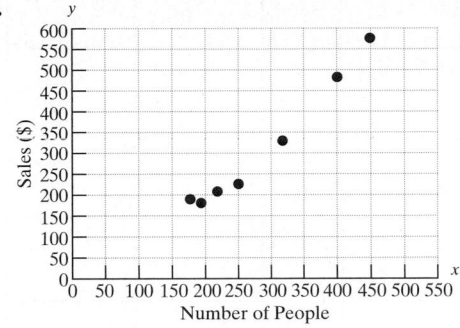

29. a. $(1, -10.2)$, $(2, -9.0)$, $(3, -2.5)$, $(4, 5.7)$, $(5, 13.0)$, $(6, 18.3)$, $(7, 20.9)$, $(8, 19.6)$, $(9, 14.8)$, $(10, 8.7)$, $(11, 2.0)$, $(12, -6.9)$.

b.

31. a.

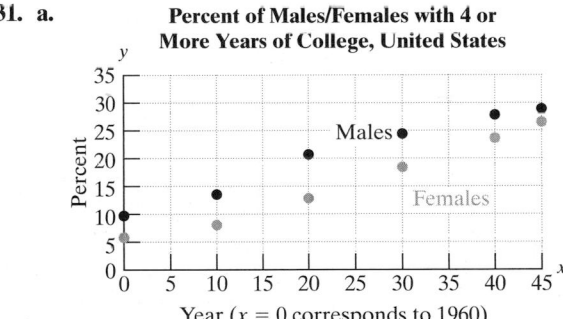

b. Increasing   **c.** Increasing

Section 3.2 Calculator Connections, pp. 207–208

1.   **2.**

3.

4.

5.

6.

7.

8.

9.

10.

11.

12.
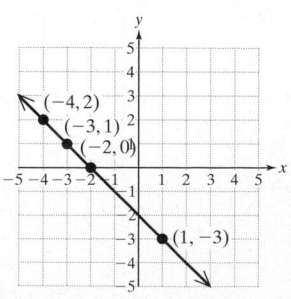

Section 3.2 Practice Exercises, pp. 208–214

3. $(2, 4)$; quadrant I   **5.** $(0, -1)$; y-axis
7. $(3, -4)$; quadrant IV   **9.** Yes   **11.** Yes   **13.** No
15. No   **17.** Yes

19.

x	y
1	-3
-2	0
-3	1
-4	2

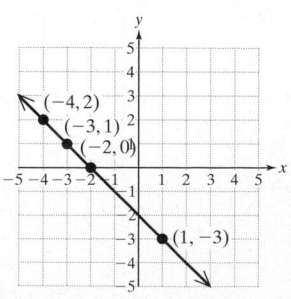

21.

x	y
-2	3
-1	0
-4	9

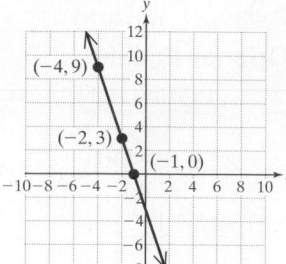

23.

x	y
0	4
2	0
3	-2

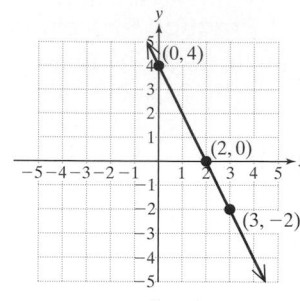

25.

x	y
0	-2
5	-5
10	-8

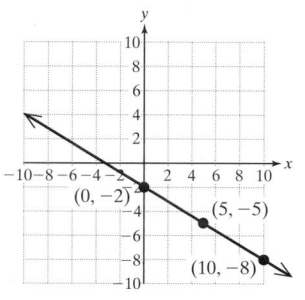

27.

x	y
0	-2
-3	-2
5	-2

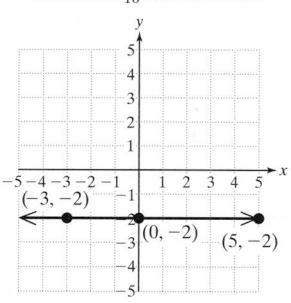

29.

x	y
3/2	-1
3/2	2
3/2	-3

31.

x	y
0	4.6
1	3.4
2	2.2

33.

35.

37.

39.

41.

43.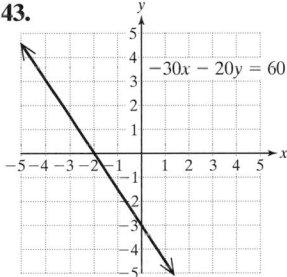

45. y-axis   **47.** x-intercept: $(-1, 0)$; y-intercept: $(0, -3)$
49. x-intercept: $(-4, 0)$; y-intercept: $(0, 1)$
51. x-intercept: $(-2, 0)$; **53.** x-intercept: $(-8, 0)$;
y-intercept: $(0, 10)$ y-intercept: $(0, 4)$
55. x-intercept: $\left(-\dfrac{9}{4}, 0\right)$; **57.** x-intercept: $\left(\dfrac{8}{3}, 0\right)$;
y-intercept: $(0, 3)$ y-intercept: $(0, 2)$

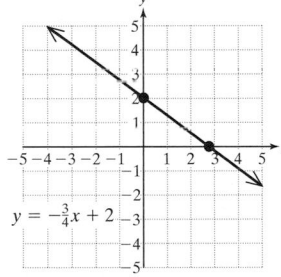

59. x-intercept: $(-4, 0)$; **61.** x-intercept: $(0, 0)$;
y-intercept: $(0, 8)$ y-intercept: $(0, 0)$

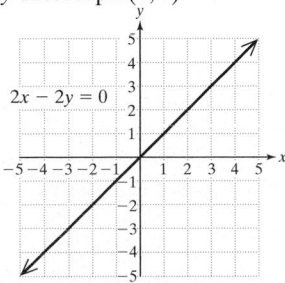

63. x-intercept: $(10, 0)$; **65.** x-intercept: $(0, 0)$;
y-intercept: $(0, 5)$ y-intercept: $(0, 0)$

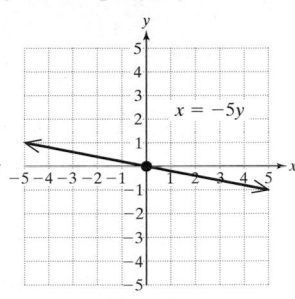

67. True
71. a. Horizontal line
c. no x-intercept;
y-intercept: $(0, -1)$

69. True
73. a. Vertical line
c. x-intercept: $(4, 0)$;
no y-intercept

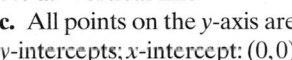

75. a. Horizontal line
c. no x-intercept;
y-intercept $(0, 3)$

77. a. Vertical line
c. All points on the y-axis are
y-intercepts; x-intercept: $(0, 0)$

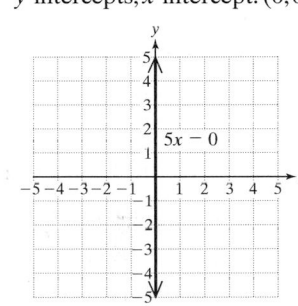

79. A horizontal line may not have an x-intercept.
A vertical line may not have a y-intercept.
81. a, b, d
83. a. $y = 11{,}190$ **b.** $x = 3$ **c.** $(1, 11{,}190)$ One year after
purchase the value of the car is \$11,190. $(3, 9140)$ Three years
after purchase the value of the car is \$9140.

Section 3.3 Practice Exercises, pp. 221–227

3. x-intercept: $(6, 0)$; **5.** x-intercept: $(0, 0)$;
y-intercept: $(0, -2)$ y-intercept: $(0, 0)$

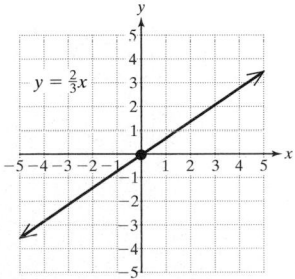

7. x-intercept: $(2, 0)$; y-intercept: $(0, 8)$

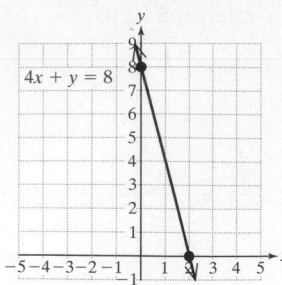

9. $m = \dfrac{1}{3}$ **11.** $m = \dfrac{6}{11}$ **13.** Undefined

15. Positive   **17.** Negative   **19.** Zero
21. Undefined   **23.** Positive   **25.** Negative

27. $m = \dfrac{1}{2}$ **29.** $m = -3$ **31.** $m = 0$

33. The slope is undefined.   **35.** $\dfrac{1}{3}$ **37.** -3

39. $\dfrac{3}{5}$ **41.** Zero   **43.** Undefined   **45.** $\dfrac{28}{5}$ **47.** $-\dfrac{7}{8}$

49. -0.45 or $-\dfrac{9}{20}$ **51.** -0.15 or $-\dfrac{3}{20}$

53. a. -2 **b.** $\dfrac{1}{2}$ **55. a.** 0 **b.** undefined

57. a. $\dfrac{4}{5}$ **b.** $-\dfrac{5}{4}$ **59. a.** undefined **b.** 0

61. Perpendicular   **63.** Parallel   **65.** Neither
67. l_1: $m = 2$, l_2: $m = 2$; parallel

69. l_1: $m = 5$, l_2: $m = -\dfrac{1}{5}$; perpendicular

71. l_1: $m = \dfrac{1}{4}$, l_2: $m = 4$; neither

73. The average rate of change is $-\$160$ per year.
75. a. $m = 45$ **b.** The number of male prisoners increased at a rate of 45 thousand per year during this time period.
77. a. 1 mi **b.** 2 mi **c.** 3 mi **d.** $m = 0.2$; The distance between a lightning strike and an observer increases by 0.2 mi for every additional second between seeing lightning and hearing thunder.

79. $m = \dfrac{3}{4}$ **81.** $m = 0$

83. For example: $(4, 0)$ and $(-2, -4)$

85. For example: $(3, -1)$ and $(1, 5)$

87.

89.

91.

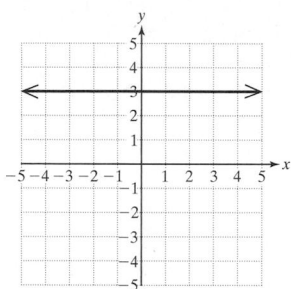

93. $\dfrac{3m - 3n}{2b}$ or $\dfrac{-3m + 3n}{-2b}$ **95.** $\left(\dfrac{c}{a}, 0\right)$

97. For example: $(7, 1)$

Section 3.4 Calculator Connections, p. 233

1. Perpendicular

2. Parallel

3. Neither

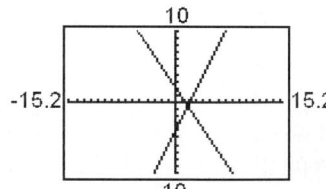

4. The lines may appear parallel; however, they are not parallel because the slopes are different.   **5.** The lines may appear to coincide on a graph; however, they are not the same line because the y-intercepts are different.

6. The line may appear to be horizontal, but it is not. The slope is 0.001 rather than 0.

Section 3.4 Practice Exercises, pp. 234–238

3. x-intercept: $(10, 0)$; y-intercept: $(0, -2)$

5. x-intercept: none; y-intercept: $(0, -3)$

7. x-intercept: $(0, 0)$; y-intercept: $(0, 0)$

9. x-intercept: $(4, 0)$; y-intercept: none

11. $m = -2$; y-intercept: $(0, 3)$ **13.** $m = 1$; y-intercept: $(0, -2)$ **15.** $m = -1$; y-intercept: $(0, 0)$

17. $m = \dfrac{3}{4}$; y-intercept: $(0, -1)$ **19.** $m = \dfrac{2}{5}$; y-intercept: $\left(0, -\dfrac{4}{5}\right)$ **21.** $m = 3$; y-intercept: $(0, -5)$

23. $m = -1$; y-intercept: $(0, 6)$ **25.** Undefined slope; no y-intercept   **27.** $m = 0$; y-intercept: $\left(0, -\dfrac{1}{4}\right)$

29. $m = \dfrac{2}{3}$; y-intercept: $(0, 0)$

31.

33.
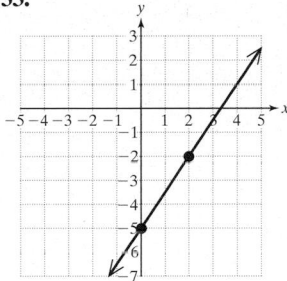

35. b   **37.** e   **39.** c

41. $y = \dfrac{1}{2}x - 3$
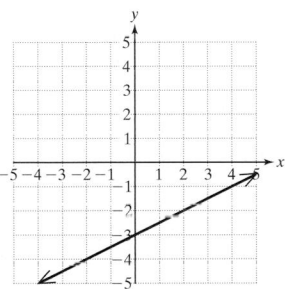

43. $y = -2x + 9$
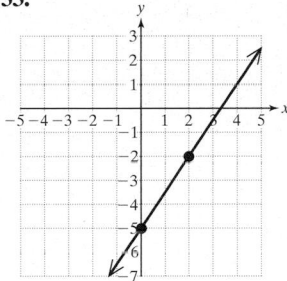

45. $y = -\dfrac{1}{2}x + \dfrac{3}{2}$

47. $y = -x$

49. $y = \dfrac{4}{5}x$

51. $y = -\dfrac{2}{3}$
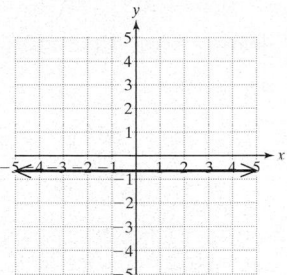

53. Perpendicular   **55.** Neither   **57.** Parallel   **59.** Perpendicular   **61.** Parallel   **63.** Perpendicular

65. Neither   **67.** Parallel   **69.** $y = -\dfrac{1}{3}x + 2$

71. $y = 10x - 19$ **73.** $y = 6x - 8$ **75.** $y = \dfrac{1}{2}x - 3$

77. $y = -11$ **79.** $y = 5x$ **81. a.** $m = 1203$; The slope represents the rate increase in cases of Lyme disease per year. **b.** $(0, 10{,}006)$; In the year 1993 there were 10,006 cases reported. **c.** $1203(17) + 10{,}006 = 30{,}457$ cases   **d.** $x = 15$; the year 2008   **83.** $y = -\dfrac{A}{B}x + \dfrac{C}{B}$; the slope is $-\dfrac{A}{B}$.

85. $m = -\dfrac{6}{7}$ **87.** $m = \dfrac{11}{8}$

Chapter 3 Problem Recognition Exercises, p. 238

1. a, c, d   **2.** b, f, h   **3.** a   **4.** f   **5.** b, f   **6.** c
7. c, d   **8.** f   **9.** e   **10.** g   **11.** b   **12.** h
13. g   **14.** e   **15.** c   **16.** b, h   **17.** e   **18.** e
19. b, f, h   **20.** c, d

Section 3.5 Practice Exercises, pp. 243–246

3.

5.
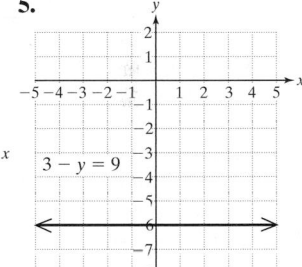

7. 9   **9.** 0   **11.** $y = 3x + 7$ or $3x - y = -7$

13. $y = -4x - 14$ or $4x + y = -14$ **15.** $y = -\dfrac{1}{2}x - \dfrac{1}{2}$ or $x + 2y = -1$ **17.** $y = 2x - 2$ or $2x - y = 2$

19. $y = -x - 4$ or $x + y = -4$

21. $y = -0.2x - 2.86$ or $20x + 100y = -286$

23. $y = -2x + 1$ **25.** $y = 2x + 4$ **27.** $y = \dfrac{1}{2}x - 1$

29. $y = 4x + 13$ or $4x - y = -13$

31. $y = -\dfrac{3}{2}x + 6$ or $3x + 2y = 12$

33. $y = -2x - 8$ or $2x + y = -8$ **35.** $y = -\frac{1}{5}x - 6$ or

$x + 5y = -30$ **37.** iv   **39.** vi   **41.** iii

43. $y = 1$ **45.** $x = 2$ **47.** $y = 2$

49. $y = \frac{1}{4}x + 8$ or $x - 4y = -32$ **51.** $y = 3x - 8$ or

$3x - y = 8$ **53.** $y = 4.5x - 25.6$ or $45x - 10y = 256$

55. $x = -6$ **57.** $y = -2$ **59.** $x = -4$

Section 3.6 Calculator Connections, p. 250

1. 13.3   **2.** −42.3

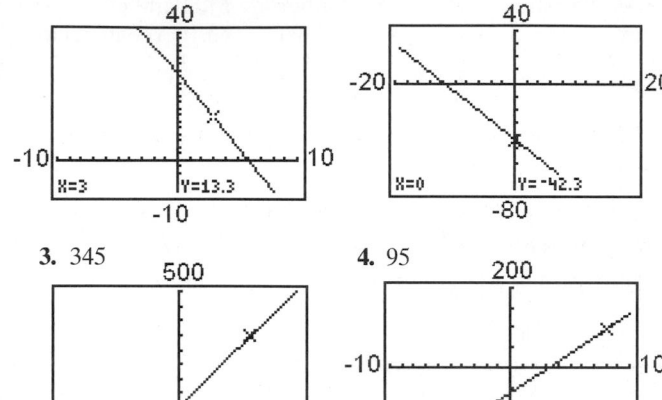

3. 345   **4.** 95

Section 3.6 Practice Exercises, pp. 250–254

3. x-intercept: $(6, 0)$; y-intercept: $(0, 5)$ **5.** x-intercept:
$(-2, 0)$; y-intercept: $(0, -4)$ **7.** x-intercept: none;
y-intercept: $(0, -9)$ **9. a.** $3.00 **b.** $7.20
c. The y-intercept is $(0, 1.6)$. This indicates that the minimum
wage was $1.60 per hour in the year 1970.   **d.** The slope is
0.14. This indicates that the minimum wage has risen
approximately $0.14 per year during this period.
11. a. $m = \frac{2}{7}$ **b.** $m = \frac{4}{7}$ **c.** $m = \frac{2}{7}$ means that Grindel's
weight increased at a rate of 2 oz in 7 days. $m = \frac{4}{7}$ means that
Frisco's weight increased at a rate of 4 oz in 7 days.
d. Frisco gained weight more rapidly.
13. a. $106.95 **b.** $201.95 **c.** $(0, 11.95)$. For 0 kilowatt-
hours used, the cost consists of only the fixed monthly tax of
$11.95.   **d.** $m = 0.095$. The cost increases by $0.095 for each
kilowatt-hour used.
15. a. $m = -1.0$ **b.** $y = -x + 1051$ **c.** The minimum
pressure was approximately 921 mb.
17. a. $m = 21.5$ **b.** The slope means that the consumption
of wind energy in the United States increased by 21.5 trillion
Btu per year. **c.** $y = 21.5x + 57$ **d.** 272 trillion Btu
19. a. $y = 0.20x + 39.99$ **b.** $47.99
21. a. $y = 90x + 105$ **b.** $1185.00
23. a. $y = 0.8x + 100$ **b.** $260.00

Chapter 3 Review Exercises, pp. 260–264

1.

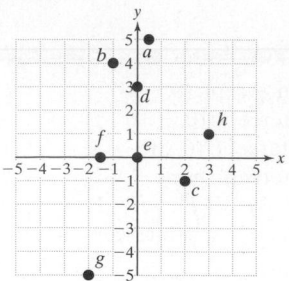

2. $A(4, -3)$; $B(-3, -2)$; $C(\frac{5}{2}, 5)$; $D(-4, 1)$; $E(-\frac{1}{2}, 0)$; $F(0, -5)$
3. III   **4.** II   **5.** IV   **6.** I   **7.** IV   **8.** III
9. x-axis   **10.** y-axis
11. a. On day 1, the price was $26.25. **b.** Day 2 **c.** $2.25
12. a. In 2003 (8 years after 1995), there was only one
space shuttle launch (this was the year that the Columbia
and its crew were lost).
b.

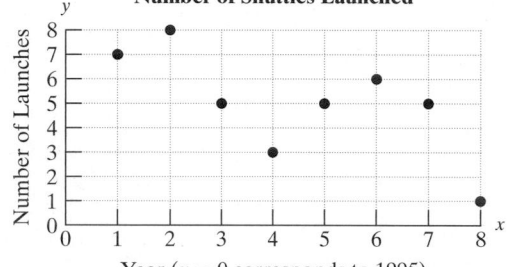

13. No   **14.** No   **15.** Yes   **16.** Yes

17.

x	y
2	1
3	4
1	−2

18.

x	y
0	2
−2	7/3
−6	3

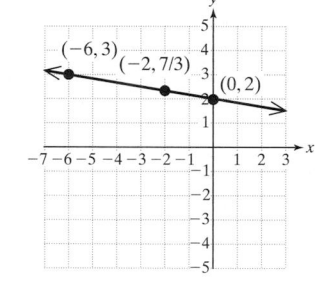

19.

x	y
0	−1
3	1
−6	−5

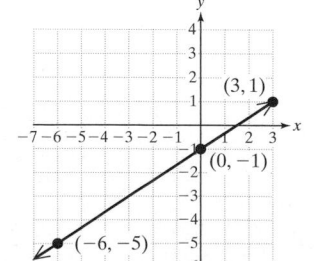

20.

x	y
0	−3
−3	3
1	−5

21.

22.

23.

24.

25. Vertical   **26.** Vertical

27. Horizontal   **28.** Horizontal

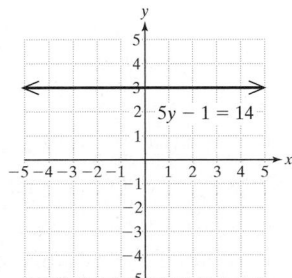

29. x-intercept: $(-3, 0)$; y-intercept: $\left(0, \dfrac{3}{2}\right)$

30. x-intercept: $(3, 0)$; y-intercept: $(0, 6)$

31. x-intercept: $(0, 0)$; y-intercept: $(0, 0)$

32. x-intercept: $(0, 0)$; y-intercept: $(0, 0)$

33. x-intercept: none; y-intercept: $(0, -4)$

34. x-intercept: none; y-intercept: $(0, 2)$

35. x-intercept: $\left(-\dfrac{5}{2}, 0\right)$; y-intercept: none

36. x-intercept: $\left(\dfrac{1}{3}, 0\right)$; y-intercept: none

37. $m = \dfrac{12}{5}$ **38.** -2 **39.** $-\dfrac{2}{3}$ **40.** 8

41. Undefined   **42.** 0   **43. a.** -5 **b.** $\dfrac{1}{5}$

44. a. 0   **b.** Undefined

45. $m_1 = \dfrac{2}{3}; m_2 = \dfrac{2}{3};$ parallel   **46.** $m_1 = 8; m_2 = 8;$ parallel

47. $m_1 = -\dfrac{5}{12}; m_2 = \dfrac{12}{5};$ perpendicular

48. $m_1 = $ undefined; $m_2 = 0;$ perpendicular

49. a. $m = 35$ **b.** The number of kilowatt-hours increased at a rate of 35 kilowatt-hours per day.

50. a. $m = -994$ **b.** The number of new cars sold in Maryland decreased at a rate of 994 cars per year.

51. $y = \dfrac{5}{2}x - 5; m = \dfrac{5}{2};$ y-intercept: $(0, -5)$

52. $y = -\dfrac{3}{4}x + 3; m = -\dfrac{3}{4};$ y-intercept: $(0, 3)$

53. $y = \dfrac{1}{3}x; m = \dfrac{1}{3};$ y-intercept: $(0, 0)$

54. $y = \dfrac{12}{5}; m = 0;$ y-intercept: $\left(0, \dfrac{12}{5}\right)$

55. $y = -\dfrac{5}{2}; m = 0;$ y-intercept: $\left(0, -\dfrac{5}{2}\right)$

56. $y = x; m = 1;$ y-intercept: $(0, 0)$ **57.** Neither

58. Perpendicular   **59.** Parallel   **60.** Parallel

61. Perpendicular   **62.** Neither

63. $y = -\frac{4}{3}x - 1$ or $4x + 3y = -3$

64. $y = 5x$ or $5x - y = 0$

65. $y = -\frac{4}{3}x - 6$ or $4x + 3y = -18$

66. $y = 5x - 3$ or $5x - y = 3$

67. For example: $y = 3x + 2$

68. For example: $5x + 2y = -4$ **69.** $m = \dfrac{y_2 - y_1}{x_2 - x_1}$

70. $y - y_1 = m(x - x_1)$ **71.** For example: $x = 6$

72. For example: $y = -5$

73. $y = -6x + 2$ or $6x + y = 2$

74. $y = \dfrac{2}{3}x + \dfrac{5}{3}$ or $2x - 3y = -5$

75. $y = \dfrac{1}{4}x - 4$ or $x - 4y = 16$ **76.** $y = -5$

77. $y = \frac{6}{5}x + 6$ or $6x - 5y = -30$

78. $y = 4x + 31$ or $4x - y = -31$

79. a. 47.8 in.   **b.** The slope is 2.4 and indicates that the average height for girls increases at a rate of 2.4 in. per year.

80. a. $y = 900x + 33{,}000$ **b.** $m = 900;$ The rate of change in starting salary per year is $900.

81. a. $y = 20x + 55$ **b.** $235

82. a. $y = 8x + 700$ **b.** $1340

Chapter 3 Test, pp. 264–266

1. a. II   **b.** IV   **c.** III   **2.** 0   **3.** 0

4. a. $(1, 368)$ In the year 2001, the total amount spent on holiday sales was $368 billion.
$(3, 389)$ $(5, 436)$, $(7, 460)$ $(8, 470)$

b.

Year ($x = 1$ represents 2001)

c. Approximately $450 billion.

5. a. No   **b.** Yes   **c.** Yes   **d.** Yes

6.

x	y
0	-2
4	-1
6	$-\frac{1}{2}$

7.

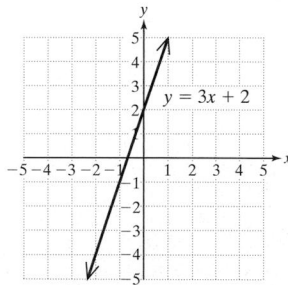

$y = 3x + 2$

8.

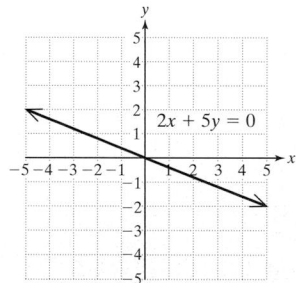

$2x + 5y = 0$

9.

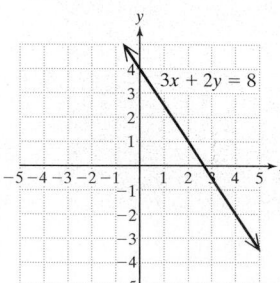

$3x + 2y = 8$

10. Horizontal

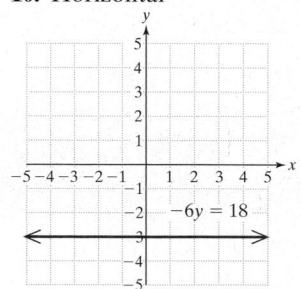

$-6y = 18$

11. Vertical

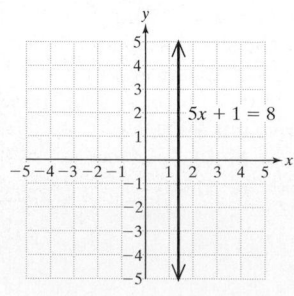

$5x + 1 = 8$

12. x-intercept: $\left(-\frac{3}{2}, 0\right)$; y-intercept: $(0, 2)$

13. x-intercept: $(0, 0)$; y-intercept: $(0, 0)$

14. x-intercept: $(4, 0)$; y-intercept: none

15. x-intercept: none; y-intercept: $(0, 3)$ **16.** $\frac{2}{5}$

17. a. $\frac{1}{3}$ **b.** $\frac{4}{3}$ **18. a.** $-\frac{1}{4}$ **b.** 4

19. a. Undefined   **b.** 0

20. a. $m = 0.6$ **b.** The cost of renting a truck increases at a rate of $0.60 per mile.   **21.** Parallel

22. Perpendicular   **23.** $y = \frac{1}{4}x + \frac{1}{2}$ or $x - 4y = -2$

24. $y = -x - 3$ or $x + y = -3$

25. $y = -\frac{7}{2}x + 15$ or $7x + 2y = 30$ **26.** $y = -6$

27. $y = -\frac{1}{3}x + 1$ or $x + 3y = 3$ **28.** $y = 3x + 8$ or

$3x - y = -8$ **29. a.** $y = 1.5x + 10$ **b.** $25

30. a. $m = 20$; The slope indicates that there is an increase of 20 thousand medical doctors per year.
b. $y = 20x + 414$ **c.** 1014 thousand or, equivalently, 1,014,000

Chapters 1–3 Cumulative Review Exercises, pp. 266-267

1. a. Rational   **b.** Rational   **c.** Irrational   **d.** Rational

2. a. $\frac{2}{3}; \frac{2}{3}$ **b.** $-5.3; 5.3$ **3.** 69   **4.** -13 **5.** 18

6. $\frac{3}{4} \div \left(-\frac{7}{8}\right); -\frac{6}{7}$ **7.** $(-2.1)(-6); 12.6$

8. The associative property of addition   **9.** $\{4\}$

10. $\{5\}$ **11.** $\left\{-\frac{9}{2}\right\}$ **12.** $\{-2\}$ **13.** 9241 mi^2

14. $a = \frac{c - b}{3}$

15.

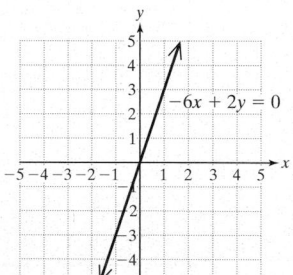

$-6x + 2y = 0$

16. x-intercept: $(-2, 0)$; y-intercept: $(0, 1)$

17. $y = -\frac{3}{2}x - 6$;   slope: $-\frac{3}{2}$; y-intercept: $(0, -6)$

18. $2x + 3 = 5$ can be written as $x = 1$, which represents a vertical line. A vertical line of the form $x = k$ ($k \neq 0$) has an x-intercept of $(k, 0)$ and no y-intercept.

19. $y = -3x + 1$ or $3x + y = 1$ **20.** $y = \frac{2}{3}x + 6$ or $2x - 3y = -18$

Chapter 4

Chapter Opener Puzzle

One drink costs $2.00 and one small popcorn costs $3.50.

Section 4.1 Calculator Connections, pp. 274–275

1. $\{(2, 1)\}$

2. $\{(6, -1)\}$

3. $\{(3, 1)\}$

4. $\{(-2, 0)\}$

5. $\{\ \}$

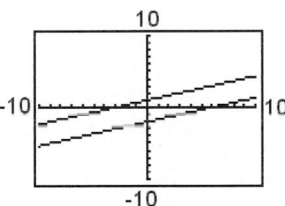

6. $\left\{(x, y) \mid y = -\dfrac{1}{4}x + 2\right\}$

Section 4.1 Practice Exercises, pp. 275–280

3. Yes **5.** No **7.** Yes **9.** No **11.** b **13.** d

15. a. **b.**

c.

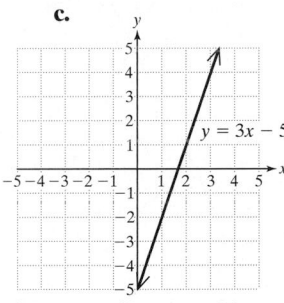

17. c **19.** a **21.** a **23.** b **25.** c

27. $\{(3, 1)\}$ **29.** $\{(1, -2)\}$

 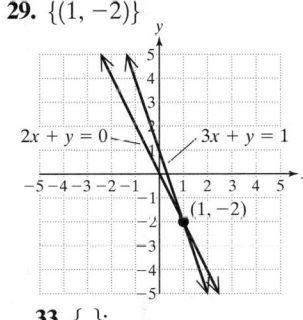

31. $\{(1, 4)\}$ **33.** $\{\ \}$; inconsistent system

  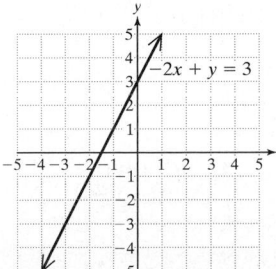

35. Infinitely many solutions; $\{(x, y) \mid -2x + y = 3\}$; dependent system **37.** $\{(-3, 6)\}$

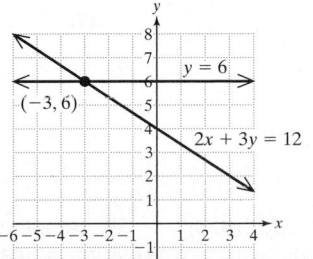

39. $\{(2, -2)\}$ **41.** { }; inconsistent system

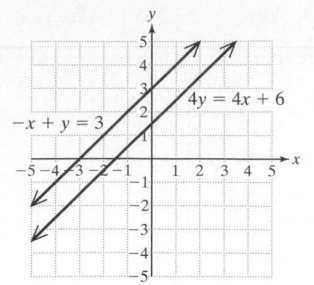

43. $\{(4, 2)\}$ **45.** $\{(1, 2)\}$

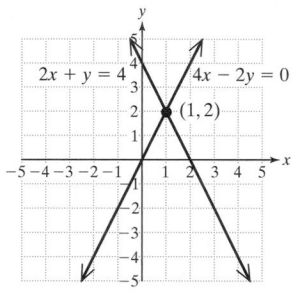

47. Infinitely many solutions; **49.** $\{(-3, -1)\}$
$\{(x, y) | y = 0.5x + 2\}$;
dependent system

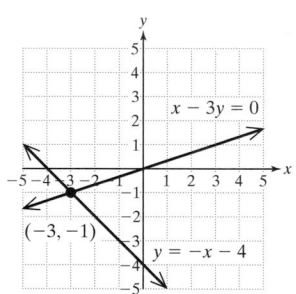

51. The same cost occurs when \$2500 of merchandise is purchased.
53. The point of intersection is below the x-axis and cannot have a positive y-coordinate.
55. For example: $4x + y = 9$; $-2x - y = -5$
57. For example: $2x + 2y = 1$

Section 4.2 Practice Exercises, pp. 288–290

1. $y = 2x - 4$; $y = 2x - 4$; coinciding lines

3. $y = -\dfrac{2}{3}x + 2$; $y = x - 5$; intersecting lines

5. $y = 4x - 4$; $y = 4x - 13$; parallel lines
7. $\{(3, -6)\}$ **9.** $\{(0, 4)\}$ **11. a.** y in the second equation is easiest to isolate because its coefficient is 1.
b. $\{(1, 5)\}$ **13.** $\{(5, 2)\}$ **15.** $\{(10, 5)\}$

17. $\left\{\left(\dfrac{1}{2}, 3\right)\right\}$ **19.** $\{(5, 3)\}$ **21.** $\{(1, 0)\}$

23. $\{(1, 4)\}$ **25.** { }; inconsistent system
27. Infinitely many solutions; $\{(x, y) | 2x - 6y = -2\}$;
dependent system   **29.** $\{(5, -7)\}$

31. $\left\{\left(-5, \dfrac{3}{2}\right)\right\}$ **33.** $\{(2, -5)\}$ **35.** $\{(-4, 6)\}$

37. $\{(0, 2)\}$ **39.** Infinitely many solutions;
$\{(x, y) | y = 0.25x + 1\}$; dependent system

41. $\{(1, 1)\}$ **43.** { }; inconsistent system
45. $\{(-1, 5)\}$ **47.** $\{(-6, -4)\}$
49. The numbers are 48 and 58.   **51.** The numbers are 13 and 39.   **53.** The angles are 165° and 15°.
55. The angles are 70° and 20°.   **57.** The angles are 42° and 48°.   **59.** For example: $(0, 3), (1, 5), (-1, 1)$

Section 4.3 Practice Exercises, pp. 297–299

3. No   **5.** Yes   **7. a.** True   **b.** False, multiply the second equation by 5.   **9. a.** x would be easier.
b. $\{(0, -3)\}$ **11.** $\{(4, -1)\}$ **13.** $\{(4, 3)\}$
15. $\{(2, 3)\}$ **17.** $\{(1, -4)\}$ **19.** $\{(1, -1)\}$

21. $\{(-4, -6)\}$ **23.** $\left\{\left(\dfrac{7}{9}, \dfrac{5}{9}\right)\right\}$
25. The system will have no solution. The lines are parallel.
27. There are infinitely many solutions. The lines coincide.
29. The system will have one solution. The lines intersect at a point whose x-coordinate is 0.
31. { }; inconsistent system   **33.** Infinitely many solutions; $\{(x, y) | x + 2y = 2\}$; dependent system
35. $\{(1, 4)\}$ **37.** $\{(-1, -2)\}$ **39.** $\{(2, 1)\}$ **41.** { }; inconsistent system   **43.** $\{(2, 3)\}$ **45.** $\{(3.5, 2.5)\}$
47. $\left\{\left(\dfrac{1}{3}, 2\right)\right\}$ **49.** $\{(-2, 5)\}$ **51.** $\left\{\left(-\dfrac{1}{2}, 1\right)\right\}$
53. $\{(0, 3)\}$ **55.** { }; inconsistent system   **57.** $\{(1, 4)\}$
59. $\{(4, 0)\}$ **61.** Infinitely many solutions;
$\{(a, b) | 9a - 2b = 8\}$; dependent system

63. $\left\{\left(\dfrac{7}{16}, -\dfrac{7}{8}\right)\right\}$ **65.** The numbers are 17 and 19.

67. The numbers are -1 and 3.   **69.** The angles are 46° and 134°.   **71.** $\{(1, 3)\}$ **73.** One line within the system of equations would have to "bend" for the system to have exactly two points of intersection. This is not possible.
75. $A = -5, B = 2$

Chapter 4 Problem Recognition Exercises, p. 300

1. Infinitely many solutions. The equations represent the same line.   **2.** No solution. The equations represent parallel lines.   **3.** One solution. The equations represent intersecting lines.   **4.** One solution. The equations represent intersecting lines.   **5.** No solution. The equations represent parallel lines.   **6.** Infinitely many solutions. The equations represent the same line.

7. $\{(5, 0)\}$ **8.** $\{(1, -7)\}$ **9.** $\{(4, -5)\}$ **10.** $\{(2, 3)\}$

11. $\{(2, 0)\}$ **12.** $\{(8, 10)\}$ **13.** $\left\{\left(2, -\dfrac{5}{7}\right)\right\}$

14. $\left\{\left(-\dfrac{14}{3}, -4\right)\right\}$ **15.** { }; inconsistent system

16. { }; inconsistent system   **17.** $\{(-1, 0)\}$
18. $\{(5, 0)\}$ **19.** Infinitely many solutions;
$\{(x, y) | y = 2x - 14\}$; dependent system
20. Infinitely many solutions; $\{(x, y) | x = 5y - 9\}$; dependent system   **21.** $\{(2200, 1000)\}$ **22.** $\{(3300, 1200)\}$

23. $\{(5, -7)\}$ **24.** $\{(2, -1)\}$ **25.** $\left\{\left(\dfrac{2}{3}, \dfrac{1}{2}\right)\right\}$

26. $\left\{\left(\dfrac{1}{4}, -\dfrac{3}{2}\right)\right\}$

Section 4.4 Practice Exercises, pp. 306–310

1. $\{(-1, 4)\}$ **3.** $\left\{\left(\frac{5}{2}, 1\right)\right\}$

5. The numbers are 4 and 16.   **7.** The angles are 80° and 10°.   **9.** It costs $8.80 to rent a video game and $5.50 to rent a DVD.   **11.** Technology stock costs $16 per share, and the mutual fund costs $11 per share.
13. Mylee bought forty 44¢ stamps and ten 61¢ stamps.
15. Shanelle invested $3500 in the 10% account and $6500 in the 7% account.   **17.** $9000 was borrowed at 6%, and $3000 was borrowed at 9%.   **19.** Invest $12,000 in the bond fund and $18,000 in the stock fund.   **21.** 15 gal of the 50% mixture should be mixed with 10 gal of the 40% mixture.   **23.** 12 gal of the 45% disinfectant solution should be mixed with 8 gal of the 30% disinfectant solution.
25. She should mix 20 mL of the 13% solution with 30 mL of the 18% solution.   **27.** The speed of the boat in still water is 6 mph, and the speed of the current is 2 mph.
29. The speed of the plane in still air is 300 mph, and the wind is 20 mph.   **31.** The speed of the plane in still air is 525 mph and the speed of the wind is 75 mph.
33. There are 17 dimes and 22 nickels.
35. a. 835 free throws and 1597 field goals   **b.** 4029 points **c.** Approximately 50 points per game   **37.** The speed of the plane in still air is 160 mph, and the wind is 40 mph.
39. $15,000 was invested in the 5.5% account, and $45,000 was invested in the 6.5% account.   **41.** 12 lb of candy should be mixed with 8 lb of nuts.   **43.** Dallas scored 30 points, and Buffalo scored 13 points.   **45.** There were 300 women and 200 men in the survey.

Section 4.5 Practice Exercises, pp. 316–318

3. { }; inconsistent system   **5.** The speeds are 65 mph and 58 mph.   **7.** $(4, 0, 2)$ is a solution.
9. $(1, 1, 1)$ is a solution.   **11.** $\{(1, -2, 4)\}$
13. $\{(-1, 2, 0)\}$ **15.** $\{(-2, -1, -3)\}$ **17.** $\{(1, -4, -2)\}$
19. $\{(1, 2, 3)\}$ **21.** $\{(-6, 1, 7)\}$ **23.** $\left\{\left(\frac{1}{2}, \frac{2}{3}, -\frac{5}{6}\right)\right\}$
25. $\left\{\left(\frac{1}{2}, 2, -\frac{1}{2}\right)\right\}$ **27.** $\{(6, -3, -2)\}$ **29.** $\{(0, 4, -4)\}$
31. $\{(1, 0, -1)\}$ **33.** $\{(-20, 8, 0)\}$ **35.** $\{(-9, 5, 5)\}$
37. Inconsistent system   **39.** $\{(1, 3, 1)\}$
41. $\left\{\left(-\frac{1}{2}, \frac{1}{3}, \frac{1}{6}\right)\right\}$ **43.** Dependent system
45. $\{(1, 0, 1)\}$ **47.** $\{(0, 0, 0)\}$ **49.** Dependent system

Section 4.6 Practice Exercises, pp. 321–323

1. $\{(-7, 0, 8)\}$ **3.** Inconsistent system   **5.** 67°, 82°, 31°
7. 25°, 56°, 99°   **9.** 10 cm, 18 cm, 27 cm   **11.** 11 in., 17 in., 26 in.   **13.** The fiber supplement has 3 g; the oatmeal has 4 g; and the cereal has 1.5 g.   **15.** Kyoki invested $2000 in bonds, $6000 in mutual funds, and $2000 in the money market account.   **17.** $1500 at 5%, $2000 at 5.5%, $1000 at 4%   **19.** 148 adult tickets, 51 children's tickets, 23 senior tickets   **21.** 24 oz peanuts, 8 oz pecans, 16 oz cashews   **23.** Vanderbilt 6100, Baylor 12,200, Pace 8900

Chapter 4 Review Exercises, pp. 331–334

1. Yes   **2.** No   **3.** No   **4.** Yes
5. Intersecting lines (the lines have different slopes)
6. Intersecting lines (the lines have different slopes)
7. Parallel lines (the lines have the same slope but different y-intercepts)   **8.** Intersecting lines (the lines have different slopes)   **9.** Coinciding lines (the lines have the same slope and same y-intercept)   **10.** Intersecting lines (the lines have different slopes)
11. $\{(0, -2)\}$

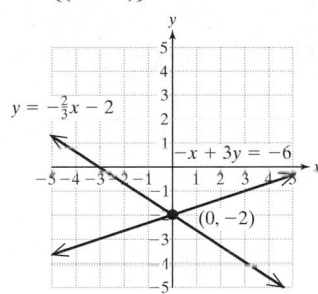

12. $\{(2, 3)\}$ **13.** Infinitely many solutions; $\{(x, y) \mid 2x + y = 5\}$; dependent system

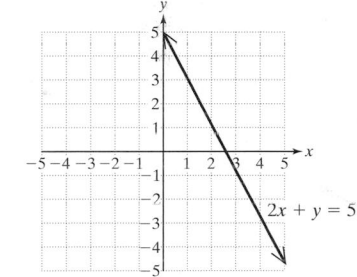

14. Infinitely many solutions; $\{(x, y) \mid -x + 5y = -5\}$; dependent system   **15.** $\{(1, -1)\}$

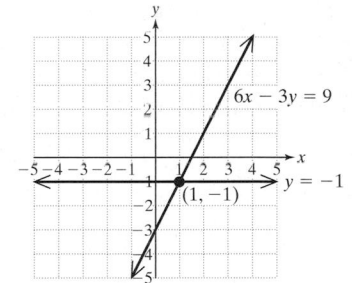

16. $\{(-1, 2)\}$ **17.** { }; inconsistent system

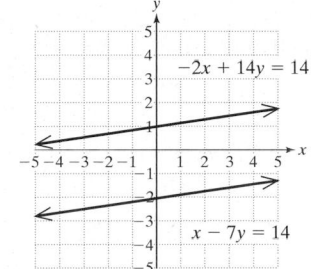

18. { }; inconsistent system

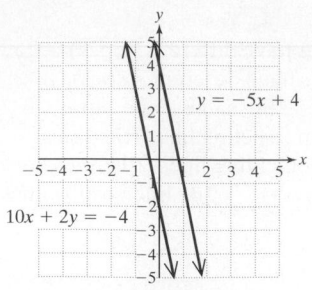

19. Using 39 minutes per month, the cost per month for each company is $9.75.

20. $\left\{\left(\dfrac{2}{3}, -2\right)\right\}$ **21.** $\{(-4, 1)\}$

22. { }; inconsistent system   **23.** Infinitely many solutions; $\{(x, y)\,|\,y = -2x + 2\}$; dependent system

24. a. x in the first equation is easiest to isolate because its coefficient is 1.   **b.** $\left\{\left(6, \dfrac{5}{2}\right)\right\}$

25. a. y in the second equation is easiest to isolate because its coefficient is 1.   **b.** $\left\{\left(\dfrac{9}{2}, 3\right)\right\}$ **26.** $\{(5, -4)\}$

27. $\{(0, 4)\}$ **28.** Infinitely many solutions; $\{(x, y)\,|\,x - 3y = 9\}$; dependent system   **29.** { }; inconsistent system   **30.** The numbers are 50 and 8.

31. The angles are $42°$ and $48°$.   **32.** The angles are $115\frac{1}{3}°$ and $64\frac{2}{3}°$.   **33.** See page 291.

34. b. $\{(-3, -2)\}$ **35. b.** $\{(2, 2)\}$ **36.** $\{(2, -1)\}$

37. $\{(-6, 2)\}$ **38.** $\left\{\left(-\dfrac{1}{2}, \dfrac{1}{3}\right)\right\}$ **39.** $\left\{\left(\dfrac{1}{4}, -\dfrac{2}{5}\right)\right\}$

40. Infinitely many solutions; $\{(x, y)\,|\,-4x - 6y = -2\}$; dependent system   **41.** { }; inconsistent system

42. $\{(-4, -2)\}$ **43.** $\{(1, 0)\}$ **44. b.** $\{(5, -3)\}$

45. b. $\{(-2, -1)\}$ **46.** There were 8 adult tickets and 52 children's tickets sold.   **47.** He should invest $75,000 at 12% and $525,000 at 4%.   **48.** 20 gal of whole milk should be mixed with 40 gal of low fat milk.

49. The speed of the boat is 18 mph, and that of the current is 2 mph.   **50.** The plane's speed in still air is 320 mph. The wind speed is 30 mph.   **51.** A hot dog costs $4.50 and a drink costs $3.50.   **52.** 3000 women and 2700 men voted.

53. The score was 72 on the first round and 82 on the second round.   **54.** $\{(2, -1, 5)\}$ **55.** Inconsistent system

56. Dependent system   **57.** $\{(-1, -2, 2)\}$

58. $\{(1, -3, -2)\}$ **59.** $\{(-1, 4, 0)\}$ **60.** 5, 12, and 13 ft

61. The pumps can drain 250, 300, and 400 gal/hr.

62. She invested $6000 in Fund A, $4000 in Fund B, and $2000 in Fund C.   **63.** The angles are $13°$, $39°$, and $128°$.

Chapter 4 Test, pp. 334–336

1. $y = -\dfrac{5}{2}x - 3; \ y = -\dfrac{5}{2}x + 3$; Parallel lines

2. $\{(3, 2)\}$

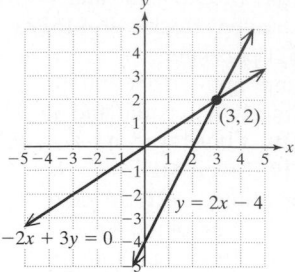

3. Infinitely many solutions; $\{(x, y)\,|\,2x + 4y = 12\}$; dependent system

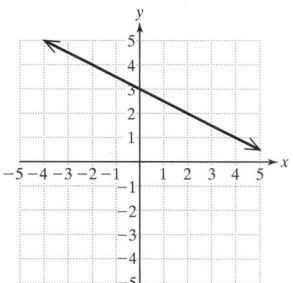

4. $\{(-2, 0)\}$ **5.** Swoopes scored 614 points and Jackson scored 597.   **6.** $\left\{\left(2, -\dfrac{1}{3}\right)\right\}$ **7.** 12 mL of the 50% acid solution should be mixed with 24 mL of the 20% solution.   **8. a.** No solution   **b.** Infinitely many solutions   **c.** One solution   **9.** $\{(-5, 4)\}$ **10.** { }

11. $\{(3, -5)\}$ **12.** $\{(-1, 2)\}$

13. Infinitely many solutions; $\{(x, y)\,|\,10x + 2y = -8\}$

14. $\{(1, -2)\}$ **15.** CDs cost $8 each and DVDs cost $11 each.   **16. a.** $18 was required.   **b.** They used 24 quarters and 12 $1 bills.   **17.** $1200 was borrowed at 10%, and $3800 was borrowed at 8%.

18. They would be the same cost for a distance of approximately 24 mi.   **19.** The plane travels 500 mph in still air, and the wind speed is 45 mph.

20. The cake has 340 calories, and the ice cream has 120 calories.   **21.** 60 mL of 10% solution and 40 mL of 25% solution.   **22.** $\{(16, -37, 9)\}$ **23.** $\{(2, -2, 5)\}$

24. { }   **25.** The sides are 5 ft, 15 ft, and 23 ft

26. $5500 was invested in Fund A. $4000 was invested in Fund B, and $2000 was invested in Fund C.   **27.** Joanne 142 orders; Kent 162 orders; Geoff 200 orders

Chapters 1–4 Cumulative Review Exercises, pp. 336–337

1. $\dfrac{11}{6}$ **2.** $\left\{-\dfrac{21}{2}\right\}$ **3.** { }   **4.** $y = \dfrac{3}{2}x - 3$

5. $x = 5z + m$ **6.** $\left[\dfrac{3}{11}, \infty\right)$

7. The angles are 37°, 33°, and 110°.   **8.** The rates of the hikers are 2 mph and 4 mph.   **9.** Jesse Ventura received approximately 762,200 votes.   **10.** 36% of the goal has been achieved.   **11.** The angles are 36.5° and 53.5°.

12. Slope: $-\dfrac{5}{3}$; y-intercept: $(0, -2)$

13. a. $-\dfrac{2}{3}$ **b.** $\dfrac{3}{2}$ **14.** $y = -3x + 3$

15. c. $\{(0, 2)\}$ **16.** $\{(0, 2)\}$

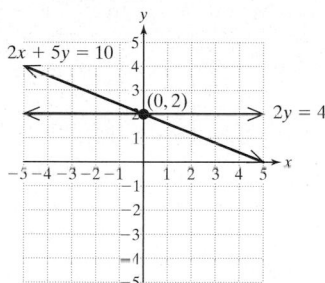

17. 20 gal of the 15% solution should be mixed with 40 gal of the 60% solution.   **18.** x is 27°; y is 63°   **19. a.** 1.4
b. Between 1920 and 1990, the winning speed in the Indianapolis 500 increased on average by 1.4 mph per year.
20. $\{(1, 0, 4)\}$

Chapter 5
Chapter Opener Puzzle

A polynomial that has two terms is called a   BINOMIAL .

Section 5.1 Calculator Connections, p. 346

1.–3.

```
(1.06)^5
         1.338225578
(1.02)^40
         2.208039664
5000(1.06)^5
         6691.127888
```

4.–6.

```
2000(1.02)^40
           4416.079327
3000(1+.06)^2
               3370.8
1000(1+.05)^3
               1157.625
```

Section 5.1 Practice Exercises, pp. 347–349

3. Base: x; exponent: 4   **5.** Base: 3; exponent: 5
7. Base: -1; exponent: 4   **9.** Base: 13; exponent: 1
11. v **13.** 1   **15.** $(-6b)^2$ **17.** $-6b^2$ **19.** $(y + 2)^4$
21. $\dfrac{-2}{t^3}$ **23.** No; $-5^2 = -25$ and $(-5)^2 = 25$

25. Yes; $-2^5 = -32$ and $(-2)^5 = -32$ **27.** Yes; $\left(\dfrac{1}{2}\right)^3 = \dfrac{1}{8}$
and $\dfrac{1}{2^3} = \dfrac{1}{8}$ **29.** Yes; $\left(\dfrac{3}{10}\right)^2 = \dfrac{9}{100}$ and $(0.3)^2 = 0.09$

31. 16   **33.** -1 **35.** $\dfrac{1}{9}$ **37.** $-\dfrac{4}{25}$ **39.** 48
41. 4   **43.** 9   **45.** 50   **47.** -100 **49.** 400
51. 1   **53.** 1   **55.** 1000   **57.** -800
59. a. $(x \cdot x \cdot x \cdot x)(x \cdot x \cdot x) = x^7$
b. $(5 \cdot 5 \cdot 5 \cdot 5)(5 \cdot 5 \cdot 5) = 5^7$ **61.** z^8 **63.** a^9
65. 4^{14} **67.** $\left(\dfrac{2}{3}\right)^4$ **69.** c^{14} **71.** x^{18}

73. a. $\dfrac{p \cdot p \cdot p \cdot p \cdot p \cdot p \cdot p \cdot p}{p \cdot p \cdot p} = p^5$
b. $\dfrac{8 \cdot 8 \cdot 8 \cdot 8 \cdot 8 \cdot 8 \cdot 8 \cdot 8}{8 \cdot 8 \cdot 8} = 8^5$

75. x^2 **77.** a^9 **79.** 7^7 **81.** 5^7 **83.** y **85.** h^4
87. 7^7 **89.** 10^9 **91.** $6x^7$ **93.** $40a^5b^5$ **95.** $13r^8s^5$
97. s^9t^{16} **99.** $-30v^8$ **101.** $16m^{20}n^{10}$ **103.** $2cd^4$
105. z^4 **107.** $\dfrac{25hjk^4}{12}$ **109.** $-8p^7q^9r^6$ **111.** $-3stu$
113. \$5724.50   **115.** \$4764.06   **117.** 201 in.^{2}
119. 268 in.^{3} **121.** x^{2n+1} **123.** p^{2m+3} **125.** z
127. r^3

Section 5.2 Practice Exercises, pp. 353–354

1. 4^9 **3.** a^{20} **5.** d^9 **7.** 7^6 **9.** When multiplying expressions with the same base, add the exponents. When raising an expression with an exponent to a power, multiply the exponents.   **11.** 5^{12} **13.** 12^6
15. y^{14} **17.** w^{25} **19.** a^{36} **21.** y^{14}
23. They are both equal to 2^6.
25. $4^{3^2} = 4^9$; $(4^3)^2 = 4^6$; the expression 4^{3^2} is greater than $(4^3)^2$.   **27.** $25w^2$ **29.** $s^4r^4t^4$
31. $\dfrac{16}{r^4}$ **33.** $\dfrac{x^5}{y^5}$ **35.** $81a^4$ **37.** $-27a^3b^3c^3$
39. $-\dfrac{64}{x^3}$ **41.** $\dfrac{a^2}{b^2}$ **43.** $6^3u^6v^{12}$ or $216\,u^6v^{12}$
45. $5x^8y^4$ **47.** $-h^{28}$ **49.** m^{12} **51.** $\dfrac{4^5}{r^5s^{20}}$ or $\dfrac{1024}{r^5s^{20}}$
53. $\dfrac{3^5p^5}{q^{15}}$ or $\dfrac{243p^5}{q^{15}}$ **55.** y^{14} **57.** x^{31} **59.** $200a^{14}b^9$
61. $16p^8q^{16}$ **63.** $-m^{35}n^{15}$ **65.** $25a^{18}b^6$ **67.** $\dfrac{4c^2d^6}{9}$
69. $\dfrac{c^{27}d^{31}}{2}$ **71.** $-\dfrac{27a^9b^3}{c^6}$ **73.** $16b^{26}$ **75.** x^{2m}
77. $125a^{6n}$ **79.** $\dfrac{m^{2b}}{n^{3b}}$ **81.** $\dfrac{3^na^{3n}}{5^nb^{4n}}$

Section 5.3 Practice Exercises, pp. 362–363

3. c^9 **5.** y **7.** 3^6 or 729   **9.** $7^4w^{28}z^8$ or $2401w^{28}z^8$
11. a. 1   **b.** 1   **13.** 1   **15.** 1   **17.** -1 **19.** 1
21. 1   **23.** -7 **25. a.** $\dfrac{1}{t^5}$ **b.** $\dfrac{1}{t^5}$ **27.** $\dfrac{343}{8}$ **29.** 25
31. $\dfrac{1}{a^3}$ **33.** $\dfrac{1}{12}$ **35.** $\dfrac{1}{16b^2}$ **37.** $\dfrac{6}{x^2}$ **39.** $\dfrac{1}{64}$
41. $-\dfrac{3}{y^4}$ **43.** $-\dfrac{1}{t^3}$ **45.** a^5 **47.** $\dfrac{x^4}{x^{-6}} = x^{4-(-6)} = x^{10}$
49. $2a^{-3} = 2 \cdot \dfrac{1}{a^3} = \dfrac{2}{a^3}$ **51.** $\dfrac{1}{x^4}$ **53.** 1   **55.** y^4
57. $\dfrac{n^{27}}{m^{18}}$ **59.** $\dfrac{81k^{24}}{j^{20}}$ **61.** $\dfrac{1}{p^6}$ **63.** $\dfrac{1}{r^3}$ **65.** a^8
67. $\dfrac{1}{y^8}$ **69.** $\dfrac{1}{7^7}$ **71.** 1   **73.** $\dfrac{1}{a^4b^6}$ **75.** $\dfrac{1}{w^{21}}$
77. $\dfrac{1}{27}$ **79.** 1   **81.** $\dfrac{1}{64x^6}$ **83.** $-\dfrac{16y^4}{z^2}$ **85.** $-\dfrac{a^{12}}{6}$
87. $80c^{21}d^{24}$ **89.** $\dfrac{9y^2}{8x^5}$ **91.** $\dfrac{4d^{16}}{c^2}$ **93.** $\dfrac{9y^2}{2x}$
95. $\dfrac{9}{20}$ **97.** $\dfrac{9}{10}$ **99.** $\dfrac{5}{4}$ **101.** $\dfrac{10}{3}$

Section 5.4 Calculator Connections, p. 367

1.–2.

```
(5.2E6)*(4.6E-3)
              23920
(2.19E-8)*(7.84E
-4)
        1.71696E-11
```

3.–4.

```
(4.76E-5)/(2.38E
9)
              2E-14
(8.5E4)/(4.0E-1)
             212500
```

5.

```
((9.6E7)*(4.0E-3
))/(2.0E-2)
          19200000
```

6.

```
((5.0E-12)*(6.4E
-5))/((1.6E-8)*(
4.0E2))
              5E-11
```

Section 5.4 Practice Exercises, pp. 368–370

3. b^{13} **5.** 10^{13} **7.** $\dfrac{1}{y^5}$ **9.** $\dfrac{x^{20}}{y^{12}}$ **11.** w^4 **13.** 10^4

15. Move the decimal point between the 2 and 3 and multiply by 10^{-10}; 2.3×10^{-10}. **17.** 5×10^4 **19.** 2.08×10^5
21. 6.01×10^6 **23.** 8×10^{-6} **25.** 1.25×10^{-4}
27. 6.708×10^{-3} **29.** 1.7×10^{-24} g **31.** $\$2.7 \times 10^{10}$
33. 6.8×10^7 gal; 1.0×10^2 miles **35.** Move the decimal point nine places to the left; $0.000\,000\,0031$. **37.** 0.00005
39. 2800 **41.** 0.000603 **43.** 2,400,000 **45.** 0.019
47. 7032 **49.** 0.000 000 000 001 g
51. 1600 calories and 2800 calories **53.** 5.0×10^4
55. 3.6×10^{11} **57.** 2.2×10^4
59. 2.25×10^{-13} **61.** 3.2×10^{14} **63.** 2.432×10^{-10}
65. 3.0×10^{13} **67.** 6.0×10^5 **69.** 1.38×10^1
71. 5.0×10^{-14} **73.** 3.75 in. **75.** $\$2.97 \times 10^{10}$
77. $\approx 5.4 \times 10^{-7}$ m **79. a.** 6.5×10^7
b. 2.3725×10^{10} days **c.** 5.694×10^{11} hr
d. 2.04984×10^{15} sec

Chapter 5 Problem Recognition Exercises, p. 370

1. t^8 **2.** 2^8 or 256 **3.** y^5 **4.** p^6 **5.** $r^4 s^8$

6. $a^3 b^9 c^6$ **7.** w^6 **8.** $\dfrac{1}{m^{16}}$ **9.** $\dfrac{x^4 z^3}{y^7}$ **10.** $\dfrac{a^3 c^8}{b^6}$

11. 1.25×10^3 **12.** 1.24×10^5 **13.** 8.0×10^8

14. 6.0×10^{-9} **15.** p^{15} **16.** p^{15} **17.** $\dfrac{1}{v^2}$

18. $c^{50} d^{40}$ **19.** 3 **20.** -4 **21.** $\dfrac{b^9}{2^{15}}$ **22.** $\dfrac{81}{y^6}$

23. $\dfrac{16y^4}{81x^4}$ **24.** $\dfrac{25d^6}{36c^2}$ **25.** $3a^7 b^5$ **26.** $64x^7 y^{11}$

27. $\dfrac{y^4}{x^8}$ **28.** $\dfrac{1}{a^{10} b^{10}}$ **29.** $\dfrac{1}{t^2}$ **30.** $\dfrac{1}{p^7}$ **31.** $\dfrac{8w^6 x^9}{27}$

32. $\dfrac{25b^8}{16c^6}$ **33.** $\dfrac{q^3 s}{r^2 t^5}$ **34.** $\dfrac{m^2 p^3 q}{n^3}$ **35.** $\dfrac{1}{y^{13}}$ **36.** w^{10}

37. $-\dfrac{1}{8a^{18} b^6}$ **38.** $\dfrac{4x^{18}}{9y^{10}}$ **39.** $\dfrac{k^8}{5h^6}$ **40.** $\dfrac{6n^{10}}{m^{12}}$

Section 5.5 Practice Exercises, pp. 376–379

3. $\dfrac{45}{x^2}$ **5.** $\dfrac{2}{t^4}$ **7.** $\dfrac{1}{3^{12}}$

9. 4.0×10^{-2} is in scientific notation in which 10 is raised to the -2 power. 4^{-2} is not in scientific notation and 4 is being raised to the -2 power. **11.** $-7x^4 + 7x^2 + 9x + 6$
13. Binomial; 10; 2 **15.** Trinomial; 2.1; 3
17. Binomial; -1; 4 **19.** Trinomial; 12; 4
21. Monomial; 23; 0 **23.** Monomial; -32; 3
25. The exponents on the x-factors are different.
27. $35x^2 y$ **29.** $8b^5 d^2 - 9d$ **31.** $4y^2 + y - 9$

33. $10.9y$ **35.** $4a - 8c$ **37.** $a - \dfrac{1}{2}b - 2$

39. $\dfrac{4}{3}z^2 - \dfrac{5}{3}$ **41.** $7.9t^3 - 3.4t^2 + 6t - 4.2$ **43.** $-4h + 5$
45. $2.3m^2 - 3.1m + 1.5$ **47.** $-3v^3 - 5v^2 - 10v - 22$
49. $-8a^3 b^2$ **51.** $-53x^3$ **53.** $-5a - 3$ **55.** $16k + 9$
57. $2m^4 - 14m$ **59.** $3s^2 - 4st - 3t^2$
61. $-2r - 3s + 3t$

63. $\dfrac{3}{4}x + \dfrac{1}{3}y - \dfrac{3}{10}$ **65.** $-\dfrac{2}{3}h^2 + \dfrac{3}{5}h - \dfrac{5}{2}$

67. $2.4x^4 - 3.1x^2 - 4.4x - 7.9$

69. $4b^3 + 12b^2 - 5b - 12$ **71.** $-\dfrac{7}{2}x^2 + 5x - 11$

73. $4y^3 + 2y^2 + 2$ **75.** $3a^2 - 3a + 5$
77. $9ab^2 - 3ab + 16a^2 b$ **79.** $4z^5 + z^4 + 9z^3 - 3z - 2$
81. $2x^4 + 11x^3 - 3x^2 + 8x - 4$
83. $-w^3 + 0.2w^2 + 3.7w - 0.7$
85. $-p^2 q - 4pq^2 + 3pq$ **87.** 0 **89.** $-5ab + 6ab^2$
91. $11y^2 - 10y - 4$ **93.** For example: $x^3 + 6$
95. For example: $8x^5$ **97.** For example: $-6x^2 + 2x + 5$

Section 5.6 Practice Exercises, pp. 386–389

3. $-2y^2$ **5.** $-8y^4$ **7.** $8uvw^2$ **9.** $7u^2 v^2 w^4$
11. $-12y$ **13.** $21p$ **15.** $12a^{14} b^8$ **17.** $-2c^{10} d^{12}$
19. $16p^2 q^2 - 24p^2 q + 40pq^2$ **21.** $-4k^3 + 52k^2 + 24k$
23. $-45p^3 q - 15p^4 q^3 + 30pq^2$ **25.** $y^2 + 19y + 90$
27. $m^2 - 14m + 24$ **29.** $12p^2 - 5p - 2$
31. $12w^2 - 32w + 16$ **33.** $p^2 - 14pw + 33w^2$
35. $12x^2 + 28x - 5$ **37.** $6a^2 - 21.5a + 18$
39. $9t^2 - 18t - 7$ **41.** $3m^2 + 28mn + 32n^2$
43. $5s^3 + 8s^2 - 7s - 6$ **45.** $27w^3 - 8$
47. $p^4 + 5p^3 - 2p^2 - 21p + 5$
49. $6a^3 - 23a^2 + 38a - 45$
51. $8x^3 - 36x^2 y + 54xy^2 - 27y^3$
53. $1.2x^2 + 7.6xy + 2.4y^2$
55. $y^2 - 36$ **57.** $9a^2 - 16b^2$ **59.** $81k^2 - 36$
61. $\dfrac{4}{9}t^2 - 9$ **63.** $u^6 - 25v^2$ **65.** $\dfrac{4}{9} - p^2$
67. $a^2 + 10a + 25$ **69.** $x^2 - 2xy + y^2$
71. $4c^2 + 20c + 25$ **73.** $9t^4 - 24st^2 + 16s^2$
75. $t^2 - 14t + 49$ **77.** $16q^2 + 24q + 9$
79. a. 36 **b.** 20 **c.** $(a + b)^2 \neq a^2 + b^2$ in general.
81. $4x^2 - 25$ **83.** $16p^2 + 40p + 25$
85. $27p^3 - 135p^2 + 225p - 125$
87. $15a^5 - 6a^2$ **89.** $49x^2 - y^2$
91. $25s^2 + 30st + 9t^2$ **93.** $21x^2 - 65xy + 24y^2$

95. $2t^2 + \dfrac{26}{3}t + 8$ **97.** $5z^3 + 23z^2 + 7z - 3$

99. $6a^3 + 11a^2 - 7a - 2$ **101.** $y^3 - 3y^2 - 6y - 20$

103. $\dfrac{1}{9}m^2 - \dfrac{2}{3}mn + n^2$ **105.** $42w^3 - 84w^2$

107. $16y^2 - 65.61$ **109.** $21c^4 + 4c^2 - 32$

111. $9.61x^2 + 27.9x + 20.25$ **113.** $k^3 - 12k^2 + 48k - 64$

115. $125x^3 + 225x^2 + 135x + 27$

117. $2y^4 + 3y^3 + 3y^2 + 5y + 3$ **119.** $6a^3 + 22a^2 - 40a$

121. $2x^3 - 13x^2 + 17x + 12$ **123.** $2x - 7$

125. $k = 10$ or -10 **127.** $k = 8$ or -8

Section 5.7 Practice Exercises, pp. 396–399

3. a. $-4a - 11b$ **b.** $5a^2 - 49ab - 10b^2$

5. a. $7x^2 + 2$ **b.** $6x^4 - 5x^3 + x^2 - 2x$

7. For example: $(5y + 1)^2 = 25y^2 + 10y + 1$

9. $-4t^3 + t - 5$ **11.** $12 + 8y + 2y^2$

13. $x^2 + 3xy - y^2$ **15.** $2y^2 + 3y - 8$

17. $-\dfrac{1}{2}p^3 + p^2 - \dfrac{1}{3}p + \dfrac{1}{6}$ **19.** $a^2 + 5a + 1 - \dfrac{5}{a}$

21. $-3s^2t + 4s - \dfrac{5}{t^2}$ **23.** $8p^2q^6 - 9p^3q^5 - 11p - \dfrac{4}{p^2q}$

25. a. Divisor $(x - 2)$; quotient $(2x^2 - 3x - 1)$; remainder (-3) **b.** Multiply the quotient and the divisor, then add the remainder. The result should equal the dividend.

27. $x + 7 + \dfrac{-9}{x + 4}$ **29.** $3y^2 + 2y + 2 + \dfrac{9}{y - 3}$

31. $-4a + 11$ **33.** $6y - 5$ **35.** $6x^2 + 4x + 5 + \dfrac{22}{3x - 2}$

37. $4a^2 - 2a + 1$ **39.** $x^2 - 2x + 2$ **41.** $x^2 + 2x + 5$

43. $x^2 - 1 + \dfrac{8}{x^2 - 2}$ **45.** $n^3 + 2n^2 + 4n + 8$

47. The divisor must be of the form $x - r$.

49. No. The divisor is not of the form $x - r$.

51. a. $x - 5$ **b.** $x^2 + 3x + 11$ **c.** 58

53. $x + 6$ **55.** $t - 4$ **57.** $5y + 10 + \dfrac{11}{y - 1}$

59. $3y^2 - 2y + 2 + \dfrac{-3}{y + 3}$ **61.** $x^2 - x - 2$

63. $a^4 + 2a^3 + 4a^2 + 8a + 16$ **65.** $x^2 + 6x + 36$

67. $4w^3 + 2w^2 + 6$ **69.** $-x^2 - 4x + 13 + \dfrac{-54}{x + 4}$

71. $2x - 1 + \dfrac{3}{x}$ **73.** $4y - 3 + \dfrac{4y + 5}{3y^2 - 2y + 5}$

75. $2x^2 + 3x - 1$ **77.** $2k^3 - 4k^2 + 1 - \dfrac{5}{k^4}$

79. $x + \dfrac{9}{5} + \dfrac{2}{x}$ **81. a.** -84 **b.** $4x^2 - 6x + 16 + \dfrac{-84}{x + 4}$

c. The values are the same.   **83.** $P(r)$ equals the remainder of $P(x) \div (x - r)$.   **85. a.** $8x + 5$ **b.** Yes

Chapter 5 Problem Recognition Exercises, p. 399

1. a. $9x^2 + 6x + 1$ **b.** $9x^2 - 1$ **c.** 2

2. a. -10 **b.** $81m^2 - 25$ **c.** $81m^2 - 90m + 25$

3. a. $2x + 4 - \dfrac{5}{x}$ **b.** $2x + 5 + \dfrac{-5}{2x - 1}$

c. $4x + 12 + \dfrac{2}{x - 1}$ **4. a.** $y - 5 + \dfrac{4}{3y}$ **b.** $y - 7 + \dfrac{46}{3y + 6}$

c. $3y - 33 + \dfrac{202}{y + 6}$ **5. a.** -30 **b.** $-10p - 50$ **c.** 0

6. a. $-8x - 32$ **b.** -20 **c.** 0 **7.** $2t^2 + t - 1$

8. $-15x^4 - 5x^3 + 10x^2$ **9.** $36z^2 - 25$

10. $9y^3 + 2y^2 - 3y + 1$ **11.** $6b^2 - 11b + 4$

12. $10a^3 + 19a^2 + 11a + 2$ **13.** $t^3 - 6t^2 + 8t + 3$

14. $2b^2 + 4b + 5$ **15.** $k^2 + 4k + 25$

16. $3x^3 + x^2 - 5$ **17.** $7t^3 - 12t^2 + 2t$

18. $-xy^2 + 2y + \dfrac{x}{7y}$ **19.** $\dfrac{11}{12}p^3 - \dfrac{1}{2}p^2 + \dfrac{1}{5}p + 5$

20. $-30.6w^6 + 15.6w^5 - 7.2w^4$ **21.** $36a^4 - 48a^2b + 16b^2$

22. $\dfrac{1}{4}z^4 - \dfrac{1}{9}$ **23.** $m^2 - 8m - 7$ **24.** $x^2 + 3x - 14$

25. $2m^4 - 8m^3 - 13m^2 + 46m - 21$ **26.** $x^2 + 4x + 16$

27. $25 - 10a - 10b + a^2 + 2ab + b^2$

28. $a^2 - x^2 + 2xy - y^2$ **29.** $4xy$

30. $a^3 - 12a^2 + 48a - 64$ **31.** $-\dfrac{1}{8}x^2 + \dfrac{1}{3}x - \dfrac{1}{6}$

32. $-\dfrac{1}{2}x^6y^4z^5w^3$

Chapter 5 Review Exercises, pp. 404–407

1. Base: 5; exponent: 3   **2.** Base: x; exponent: 4

3. Base: -2; exponent: 0   **4.** Base: y; exponent: 1

5. a. 36 **b.** 36 **c.** -36 **6. a.** 64 **b.** -64 **c.** -64

7. 5^{13} **8.** a^{11} **9.** x^9 **10.** 6^9 **11.** 10^3

12. y^6 **13.** b^8 **14.** 7^7 **15.** k **16.** 1

17. 2^8 **18.** q^6 **19.** Exponents are added only when multiplying factors with the same base. In such a case, the base does not change.   **20.** Exponents are subtracted only when dividing factors with the same base. In such a case, the base does not change.   **21.** $\$7146.10$

22. $\$22{,}050$ **23.** 7^{12} **24.** c^{12} **25.** p^{18} **26.** 9^{28}

27. $\dfrac{a^2}{b^2}$ **28.** $\dfrac{1}{3^4}$ **29.** $\dfrac{5^2}{c^4d^{10}}$ **30.** $-\dfrac{m^{10}}{4^5n^{30}}$

31. $2^4a^4b^8$ **32.** $x^{14}y^2$ **33.** $-\dfrac{3^3x^9}{5^3y^6z^3}$ **34.** $\dfrac{r^{15}}{s^{10}t^{30}}$

35. a^{11} **36.** 8^2 **37.** $4h^{14}$ **38.** $2p^{14}q^{13}$

39. $\dfrac{x^6y^2}{4}$ **40.** a^9b^6 **41.** 1   **42.** 1

43. -1 **44.** 1   **45.** 2   **46.** 1

47. $\dfrac{1}{z^5}$ **48.** $\dfrac{1}{10^4}$ **49.** $\dfrac{1}{36a^2}$ **50.** $\dfrac{6}{a^2}$

51. $\dfrac{17}{16}$ **52.** $\dfrac{10}{9}$ **53.** $\dfrac{1}{t^8}$ **54.** $\dfrac{1}{r}$ **55.** $\dfrac{2y^7}{x^6}$

56. $\dfrac{4a^6bc}{5}$ **57.** $\dfrac{n^{16}}{16m^8}$ **58.** $\dfrac{u^{15}}{27v^6}$ **59.** $\dfrac{k^{21}}{5}$ **60.** $\dfrac{h^9}{9}$

61. $\dfrac{1}{2}$ **62.** $\dfrac{5}{4}$ **63. a.** 9.74×10^7 **b.** 4.2×10^{-3} in.

64. a. $0.000\,000\,0001$ **b.** $\$256{,}000$ **65.** 9.43×10^5

66. 1.55×10^{10} **67.** 2.5×10^8 **68.** 1.638×10^3

69. $\approx 9.5367 \times 10^{13}$. This number has too many digits to fit on most calculator displays.   **70.** $\approx 1.1529 \times 10^{-12}$. This number has too many digits to fit on most calculator displays.

71. a. $\approx 5.84 \times 10^8$ mi **b.** $\approx 6.67 \times 10^4$ mph
72. a. $\approx 2.26 \times 10^8$ mi **b.** $\approx 1.07 \times 10^5$ mph
73. a. Trinomial **b.** 4 **c.** 7
74. a. Binomial **b.** 7 **c.** -5 **75.** $7x - 3$
76. $-y^2 - 14y - 2$ **77.** $14a^2 - 2a - 6$
78. $\frac{15}{2}x^3 + \frac{1}{4}x^2 + \frac{1}{2}x + 2$ **79.** $10w^4 + 2w^3 - 7w + 4$
80. $0.01b^5 + b^4 - 0.1b^3 + 0.3b + 0.33$
81. $-2x^2 - 9x - 6$ **82.** $-5x^2 - 9x - 12$
83. For example, $-5x^2 + 2x - 4$ **84.** For example,
$6x^5 + 8$ **85.** $6w + 6$ **86.** $-75x^6y^4$ **87.** $18a^8b^4$
88. $15c^4 - 35c^2 + 25c$ **89.** $-2x^3 - 10x^2 + 6x$
90. $5k^2 + k - 4$ **91.** $20t^2 + 3t - 2$
92. $6q^2 + 47q - 8$ **93.** $2a^2 + 4a - 30$
94. $49a^2 + 7a + \frac{1}{4}$ **95.** $b^2 - 8b + 16$
96. $8p^3 - 27$ **97.** $-2w^3 - 5w^2 - 5w + 4$
98. $4x^3 - 8x^2 + 11x - 4$ **99.** $12a^3 + 11a^2 - 13a - 10$
100. $b^2 - 16$ **101.** $\frac{1}{9}r^8 - s^4$ **102.** $49z^4 - 84z^2 + 36$
103. $2h^5 + h^4 - h^3 + h^2 - h + 3$ **104.** $2x^2 + 3x - 20$
105. $4y^2 - 2y$ **106.** $2a^2b - a - 3b$
107. $-3x^2 + 2x - 1$ **108.** $-\frac{z^5w^3}{2} + \frac{3zw}{4} + \frac{1}{z}$
109. $x + 2$ **110.** $2t + 5$ **111.** $p - 3 + \frac{5}{2p + 7}$
112. $a + 6 + \frac{-4}{5a - 3}$ **113.** $b^2 + 5b + 25$
114. $z + 4$ **115.** $y^2 - 4y + 2 + \frac{9y - 4}{y^2 + 3}$
116. $t^2 - 3t + 1 + \frac{-2t - 6}{3t^2 + t + 1}$ **117.** $w^2 + w - 1$

Chapter 5 Test, pp. 407–408

1. $\frac{(3 \cdot 3 \cdot 3 \cdot 3) \cdot (3 \cdot 3 \cdot 3)}{3 \cdot 3 \cdot 3 \cdot 3 \cdot 3 \cdot 3} = 3$ **2.** 9^6 **3.** q^8
4. $27a^6b^3$ **5.** $\frac{16x^4}{y^{12}}$ **6.** 1 **7.** $\frac{1}{c^3}$ **8.** 14
9. $49s^{18}t$ **10.** $\frac{4}{b^{12}}$ **11.** $\frac{16a^{12}}{9b^6}$
12. $\frac{5}{4}$ **13.** $\frac{3}{2}$ **14. a.** 4.3×10^{10} **b.** 0.000 0056
15. 8.4×10^{-9} **16.** 7.5×10^6
17. a. $2.4192 \times 10^8\,\mathrm{m}^3$ **b.** $8.83008 \times 10^{10}\,\mathrm{m}^3$
18. $5x^3 - 7x^2 + 4x + 11$ **a.** 3 **b.** 5
19. $5t^4 + 12t^3 + 7t - 19$ **20.** $24w^2 - 3w - 4$
21. $15x^3 - 7x^2 - 2x + 1$ **22.** $-10x^5 - 2x^4 + 30x^3$
23. $8a^2 - 10a + 3$ **24.** $4y^3 - 25y^2 + 37y - 15$
25. $4 - 9b^2$ **26.** $25z^2 - 60z + 36$
27. $15x^2 - x - 6$ **28.** $y^3 - 11y^2 + 32y - 12$
29. Perimeter: $12x - 2$; area: $5x^2 - 13x - 6$

30. $-3x^6 + \frac{x^4}{4} - 2x$ **31.** $-4a^2 + \frac{ab}{2} - 2$
32. $2y - 7$ **33.** $x^3 - 2x^2 + 4x - 10 + \frac{-5}{x + 2}$
34. $w^2 - 4w + 5 + \frac{-10}{2w + 3}$
35. $3x^2 + x - 12 + \frac{15}{x^2 + 4}$

Chapters 1–5 Cumulative Review Exercises, pp. 408–409

1. $-\frac{35}{2}$ **2.** 4 **3.** $5^2 - \sqrt{4}$; 23 **4.** $\left\{\frac{28}{3}\right\}$
5. $\{\ \}$ **6.** Quadrant III **7.** y-axis
8. The measures are $31°, 54°, 95°$. **9. a.** 12 in.
b. 19.5 in. **c.** 5.5 hr **10.** $\{(-3, 4)\}$
11. $[-5, \infty)$ ⟶ (number line with endpoint at -5)
12. $5x^2 - 9x - 15$ **13.** $-2y^2 - 13yz - 15z^2$
14. $16t^2 - 24t + 9$ **15.** $\frac{4}{25}a^2 - \frac{1}{9}$
16. $-4a^3b^2 + 2ab - 1$ **17.** $4m^2 + 8m + 11 + \frac{24}{m - 2}$
18. $\frac{c^2}{16d^4}$ **19.** $\frac{2b^3}{a^2}$ **20.** $M = 2.0 \times 10^{-3}$ or 0.002

Chapter 6

Chapter Opener Puzzle

5	2	6	ᴬ1	3	ᴮ4
3	ᶜ1	4	2	ᴰ6	ᴱ5
ᶠ4	6	1	5	ᴳ2	ᴴ3
ᴵ2	3	5	4	1	6
1	4	3	6	5	2
6	5	2	ᴶ3	4	1

Section 6.1 Practice Exercises, pp. 419–421

3. 7 **5.** 6 **7.** y **9.** $4w^2z$ **11.** $2xy^4z^2$
13. $(x - y)$ **15. a.** $3x - 6y$ **b.** $3(x - 2y)$
17. $4(p + 3)$ **19.** $5(c^2 - 2c + 3)$ **21.** $x^3(x^2 + 1)$
23. $t(t^3 - 4 + 8t)$ **25.** $2ab(1 + 2a^2)$ **27.** $19x^2y(2 - y^3)$
29. $6xy^5(x^2 - 3y^4z)$ **31.** The expression is prime because
it is not factorable. **33.** $7pq^2(6p^2 + 2 - p^3q^2)$
35. $t^2(t^3 + 2rt - 3t^2 + 4r^2)$ **37. a.** $-2x(x^2 + 2x - 4)$
b. $2x(-x^2 - 2x + 4)$ **39.** $-1(8t^2 + 9t + 2)$
41. $-15p^2(p + 2)$ **43.** $-3mn(m^3n - 2m + 3n)$
45. $-1(7x + 6y + 2z)$ **47.** $(a + 6)(13 - 4b)$
49. $(w^2 - 2)(8v + 1)$ **51.** $7x(x + 3)^2$
53. $(2a - b)(4a + 3c)$ **55.** $(q + p)(3 + r)$
57. $(2x + 1)(3x + 2)$ **59.** $(t + 3)(2t - 1)$
61. $(3y - 1)(2y - 3)$ **63.** $(b + 1)(b^3 - 4)$

65. $(j^2 + 5)(3k + 1)$ **67.** $(2x^6 + 1)(7w^6 - 1)$
69. $(y + x)(a + b)$ **71.** $(vw + 1)(w - 3)$
73. $5x(x^2 + y^2)(3x + 2y)$ **75.** $4b(a - b)(x - 1)$
77. $6t(t - 3)(s - t^2)$ **79.** $P = 2(l + w)$

81. $S = 2\pi r(r + h)$ **83.** $\frac{1}{7}(x^2 + 3x - 5)$

85. $\frac{1}{4}(5w^2 + 3w + 9)$ **87.** For example: $6x^2 + 9x$

89. For example: $16p^4q^2 + 8p^3q - 4p^2q$

Section 6.2 Practice Exercises, pp. 426–427

1. $4xy^5(x^2y^2 - 3x^3 + 2y^3)$ **3.** $3(t - 5)(t - 2)$
5. $(a + 2b)(x - 5)$ **7.** $(x + 8)(x + 2)$
9. $(z - 9)(z - 2)$ **11.** $(z - 6)(z + 3)$
13. $(p - 8)(p + 5)$ **15.** $(t + 10)(t - 4)$
17. Prime   **19.** $(n + 4)^2$ **21.** a   **23.** c
25. They are both correct because multiplication of
polynomials is a commutative operation.
27. The expressions are equal and both are correct.
29. Descending order   **31.** $(x - 15)(x + 2)$
33. $(w - 13)(w - 5)$ **35.** $(t + 18)(t + 4)$
37. $3(x - 12)(x + 2)$ **39.** $8p(p - 1)(p - 4)$
41. $y^2z^2(y - 6)(y - 6)$ or $y^2z^2(y - 6)^2$
43. $-(x - 4)(x - 6)$ **45.** $-5(a - 3x)(a + 2x)$
47. $-2(c + 2)(c + 1)$ **49.** $xy^3(x - 4)(x - 15)$
51. $12(p - 7)(p - 1)$ **53.** $-2(m - 10)(m - 1)$
55. $(c + 5d)(c + d)$ **57.** $(a - 2b)(a - 7b)$ **59.** Prime
61. $(q - 7)(q + 9)$ **63.** $(x + 10)^2$ **65.** $(t + 20)(t - 2)$
67. The student forgot to factor out the GCF before
factoring the trinomial further. The polynomial is not factored
completely, because $(2x - 4)$ has a common factor of 2.
69. $x^2 + 9x - 52$ **71.** $(x^2 + 1)(x^2 + 9)$
73. $(w^2 + 5)(w^2 - 3)$ **75.** $7, 5, -7, -5$
77. For example: $c = -16$

Section 6.3 Practice Exercises, pp. 435–436

1. $3ab(7ab + 4b - 5a)$ **3.** $(n - 1)(m - 2)$
5. $6(a - 7)(a + 2)$ **7.** a   **9.** b
11. $(2y + 1)(y - 2)$ **13.** $(3n + 1)(n + 4)$
15. $(5x + 1)(x - 3)$ **17.** $(4c + 1)(3c - 2)$
19. $(10w - 3)(w + 4)$ **21.** $(3q + 2)(2q - 3)$
23. Prime   **25.** $(5m + 2)(5m - 4)$
27. $(6y - 5x)(y + 4x)$ **29.** $2(m + 4)(m - 10)$
31. $y^3(2y + 1)(y + 6)$ **33.** $-(a + 17)(a - 2)$
35. $-10(4m + p)(2m - 3p)$ **37.** $(x^2 + 1)(x^2 + 9)$
39. $(w^2 + 5)(w^2 - 3)$ **41.** $(2x^2 + 3)(x^2 - 5)$
43. $-2(z - 9)(z - 1)$ **45.** $(q - 7)(q - 6)$
47. $(2t + 3)(3t - 1)$ **49.** $(2m - 5)^2$
51. Prime   **53.** $(2x - 5y)(3x - 2y)$
55. $(4m + 5n)(3m - n)$ **57.** $5(3r + 2)(2r - 1)$
59. Prime   **61.** $(2t - 5)(5t + 1)$
63. $(7w - 4)(2w + 3)$ **65.** $(a - 12)(a + 2)$
67. $(x + 5y)(x + 4y)$ **69.** $(a + 20b)(a + b)$
71. $(t - 7)(t - 3)$ **73.** $d(5d^2 + 3d - 10)$
75. $4b(b - 5)(b + 4)$ **77.** $y^2(x - 3)(x - 10)$
79. $-2u(2u + 5)(3u - 2)$ **81.** $(2x^2 + 3)(4x^2 + 1)$
83. $(5z^2 - 3)(2z^2 + 3)$
85. a. $(x - 12)(x + 2)$ **b.** $(x - 6)(x - 4)$
87. a. $(x - 6)(x + 1)$ **b.** $(x - 2)(x - 3)$

Section 6.4 Practice Exercises, pp. 442–443

1. $2(p - 3)(r + 6)$ **3.** $(y + 5)(8 + 9y)$
5. $12, 1$ **7.** $-8, -1$ **9.** $5, -4$ **11.** $9, -2$
13. $(x + 4)(3x + 1)$ **15.** $(w - 2)(4w - 1)$
17. $(x + 9)(x - 2)$ **19.** $(m + 3)(2m - 1)$
21. $(4k + 3)(2k - 3)$ **23.** $(2k - 5)^2$
25. Prime   **27.** $(3z - 5)(3z - 2)$
29. $(6y - 5z)(2y + 3z)$ **31.** $2(7y + 4)(y + 3)$
33. $-(3w - 5)(5w + 1)$ **35.** $-4(x - y)(3x - 2y)$
37. $6y(y + 1)(3y + 7)$ **39.** $(a^2 + 2)(a^2 + 3)$
41. $(3x^2 - 5)(2x^2 + 3)$ **43.** $(8p^2 - 3)(p^2 + 5)$
45. $(5p - 1)(4p - 3)$ **47.** $(3u - 2v)(2u - 5v)$
49. $(4a + 5b)(3a - b)$ **51.** $(h + 7k)(3h - 2k)$
53. Prime   **55.** $(2z - 1)(8z - 3)$ **57.** $(b - 4)^2$
59. $-5(x - 2)(x - 3)$ **61.** $(t - 3)(t + 2)$
63. Prime   **65.** $2(12x - 1)(3x + 1)$
67. $p(p + 3)(p - 9)$ **69.** $x(3x + 7)(x + 1)$
71. $2p(p - 15)(p - 4)$ **73.** $x^2(y + 3)(y + 11)$
75. $-1(k + 2)(k + 5)$ **77.** $-3(n + 6)(n - 5)$
79. $(x^2 - 2)(x^2 - 5)$ **81.** No. $(2x + 4)$ contains a
common factor of 2.

Section 6.5 Practice Exercises, pp. 449–451

3. $(3x - 1)(2x - 5)$ **5.** $5xy^5(3x - 2y)$
7. $(x + b)(a - 6)$ **9.** $(y + 10)(y - 4)$
11. $x^2 - 25$ **13.** $4p^2 - 9q^2$ **15.** $(x - 6)(x + 6)$
17. $3(w + 10)(w - 10)$ **19.** $(2a - 11b)(2a + 11b)$
21. $(7m - 4n)(7m + 4n)$ **23.** Prime
25. $(y + 2z)(y - 2z)$ **27.** $(a - b^2)(a + b^2)$

29. $(5pq - 1)(5pq + 1)$ **31.** $\left(c - \frac{1}{5}\right)\left(c + \frac{1}{5}\right)$

33. $2(5 - 4t)(5 + 4t)$ **35.** $(x + 4)(x - 4)(x^2 + 16)$
37. $(2 - z)(2 + z)(4 + z^2)$ **39.** $2(x^2 + 64)$
41. $(10xy^2 - w)(10xy^2 + w)$ **43.** $(x + 3)(x - 3)(x + 5)$
45. $(c + 5)(c - 5)(c - 1)$ **47.** $(2 + y)(x + 3)(x - 3)$
49. $(x + 2)(x - 2)(y + 3)(y - 3)$ **51.** $9x^2 + 30x + 25$
53. a. $x^2 + 4x + 4$ is a perfect square trinomial.
b. $x^2 + 4x + 4 = (x + 2)^2; x^2 + 5x + 4 = (x + 1)(x + 4)$
55. $(x + 9)^2$ **57.** $(5z - 2)^2$ **59.** $(7a + 3b)^2$
61. $(y - 1)^2$ **63.** $5(4z + 3w)^2$ **65.** $(3y + 25)(3y + 1)$
67. $2(a - 5)^2$ **69.** Prime   **71.** $(2x + y)^2$
73. $y(y - 6)$ **75.** $(2p - 5)(2p + 7)$
77. $(-t + 2)(t + 6)$ or $-(t - 2)(t + 6)$
79. $(-2b + 15)(2b + 5)$ or $-(2b - 15)(2b + 5)$
81. $(x + 6 - a)(x + 6 + a)$ **83.** $(p + q - 9)(p + q + 9)$
85. $(b - x - 2)(b + x + 2)$ **87.** $(2 + u - v)(2 - u + v)$
89. $(3a + b)(2x - y)$ **91. a.** $a^2 - b^2$ **b.** $(a - b)(a + b)$

Section 6.6 Practice Exercises, pp. 456–457

3. $5(2 - t)(2 + t)$ **5.** $(t + u)(2 + s)$
7. $(3v - 4)(v + 3)$ **9.** $-(c + 5)^2$
11. $x^3, 8, y^6, 27q^3, w^{12}, r^3s^6$ **13.** $(a + b)(a^2 - ab + b^2)$
15. $(y - 2)(y^2 + 2y + 4)$ **17.** $(1 - p)(1 + p + p^2)$
19. $(w + 4)(w^2 - 4w + 16)$
21. $(x - 10)(x^2 + 10x + 100)$ **23.** $(4t + 1)(16t^2 - 4t + 1)$
25. $(10a + 3)(100a^2 - 30a + 9)$

27. $\left(n - \frac{1}{2}\right)\left(n^2 + \frac{1}{2}n + \frac{1}{4}\right)$

29. $(5m + 2)(25m^2 - 10m + 4)$ **31.** $(x^2 - 2)(x^2 + 2)$
33. Prime   **35.** $(t + 4)(t^2 - 4t + 16)$
37. Prime   **39.** $4(b + 3)(b^2 - 3b + 9)$
41. $5(p - 5)(p + 5)$ **43.** $(\frac{1}{4} - 2h)(\frac{1}{16} + \frac{1}{2}h + 4h^2)$
45. $(x - 2)(x + 2)(x^2 + 4)$ **47.** $(q - 2)(q^2 + 2q + 4)$
$(q + 2)(q^2 - 2q + 4)$ **49.** $\left(\frac{2}{3}x - w\right)\left(\frac{2}{3}x + w\right)$
51. $(x^3 + 4y)(x^6 - 4x^3y + 16y^2)$
53. $(2x + 3)(x - 1)(x + 1)$
55. $(2x - y)(2x + y)(4x^2 + y^2)$
57. $(3y - 2)(3y + 2)(9y^2 + 4)$
59. $(a + b^2)(a^2 - ab^2 + b^4)$
61. $(2x - 5y)(2x + 5y)(4x^2 + 25y^2)$
63. $(k + 4)(k - 3)(k + 3)$ **65.** $2(t - 5)(t - 1)(t + 1)$
67. $\left(\frac{4}{5}p - \frac{1}{2}q\right)\left(\frac{16}{25}p^2 + \frac{2}{5}pq + \frac{1}{4}q^2\right)$
69. $(a^4 + b^4)(a^8 - a^4b^4 + b^8)$ **71. a.** The quotient is
$x^2 + 2x + 4$.   **b.** $(x - 2)(x^2 + 2x + 4)$
73. $x^2 + 4x + 16$ **75.** $2x + 1$

Chapter 6 Problem Recognition Exercises, pp. 458–459

1. A prime polynomial cannot be factored further.
2. Factor out the GCF.   **3.** Look for a difference of
squares: $a^2 - b^2$, a difference of cubes: $a^3 - b^3$, or a sum of
cubes: $a^3 + b^3$.   **4.** Grouping
5. a. Difference of squares   **b.** $2(a - 9)(a + 9)$
6. a. Nonperfect square trinomial   **b.** $(y + 3)(y + 1)$
7. a. None of these   **b.** $6w(w - 1)$
8. a. Difference of squares   **b.** $(2z + 3)(2z - 3)(4z^2 + 9)$
9. a. Nonperfect square trinomial   **b.** $(3t + 1)(t + 4)$
10. a. Sum of cubes   **b.** $5(r + 1)(r^2 - r + 1)$
11. a. Four terms-grouping   **b.** $(3c + d)(a - b)$
12. a. Difference of cubes   **b.** $(x - 5)(x^2 + 5x + 25)$
13. a. Sum of cubes   **b.** $(y + 2)(y^2 - 2y + 4)$
14. a. Nonperfect square trinomial   **b.** $(7p - 1)(p - 4)$
15. a. Nonperfect square trinomial   **b.** $3(q - 4)(q + 1)$
16. a. Perfect square trinomial   **b.** $-2(x - 2)^2$
17. a. None of these   **b.** $6a(3a + 2)$
18. a. Difference of cubes   **b.** $2(3 - y)(9 + 3y + y^2)$
19. a. Difference of squares   **b.** $4(t - 5)(t + 5)$
20. a. Nonperfect square trinomial   **b.** $(4t + 1)(t - 8)$
21. a. Nonperfect square trinomial   **b.** $10(c^2 + c + 1)$
22. a. Four terms-grouping   **b.** $(w - 5)(2x + 3y)$
23. a. Sum of cubes   **b.** $(x + 0.1)(x^2 - 0.1x + 0.01)$
24. a. Difference of squares   **b.** $(2q - 3)(2q + 3)$
25. a. Perfect square trinomial   **b.** $(8 + k)^2$
26. a. Four terms-grouping   **b.** $(t + 6)(s^2 + 5)$
27. a. Four terms-grouping   **b.** $(x + 1 - y)(x + 1 + y)$
28. a. Sum of cubes   **b.** $(w + y)(w^2 - wy + y^2)$
29. a. Difference of cubes   **b.** $(a - c)(a^2 + ac + c^2)$
30. a. Nonperfect square trinomial   **b.** Prime
31. a. Nonperfect square trinomial   **b.** Prime
32. a. Perfect square trinomial   **b.** $(a + 1)^2$
33. a. Perfect square trinomial   **b.** $(b + 5)^2$
34. a. Nonperfect square trinomial   **b.** $-1(t + 8)(t - 4)$
35. a. Nonperfect square trinomial   **b.** $-p(p + 4)(p + 1)$
36. a. Difference of squares   **b.** $(xy - 7)(xy + 7)$
37. a. Nonperfect square trinomial   **b.** $3(2x + 3)(x - 5)$

38. a. Nonperfect square trinomial   **b.** $2(5y - 1)(2y - 1)$
39. a. None of these   **b.** $abc^2(5ac - 7)$
40. a. Difference of squares   **b.** $2(2a - 5)(2a + 5)$
41. a. Nonperfect square trinomial   **b.** $(t + 9)(t - 7)$
42. a. Nonperfect square trinomial   **b.** $(b + 10)(b - 8)$
43. a. Four terms-grouping   **b.** $(b + y)(a - b)$
44. a. None of these   **b.** $3x^2y^4(2x + y)$
45. a. Nonperfect square trinomial   **b.** $(7u - 2v)(2u - v)$
46. a. Four term-grouping   **b.** $(y - 3 - t)(y - 3 + t)$
47. a. Nonperfect square trinomial   **b.** $2(2q^2 - 4q - 3)$
48. a. Nonperfect square trinomial   **b.** $3(3w^2 + w - 5)$
49. a. Sum of squares   **b.** Prime
50. a. Perfect square trinomial   **b.** $5(b - 3)^2$
51. a. Nonperfect square trinomial   **b.** $(3r + 1)(2r + 3)$
52. a. Nonperfect square trinomial   **b.** $(2s - 3)(2s + 5)$
53. a. Difference of squares   **b.** $(2a - 1)(2a + 1)(4a^2 + 1)$
54. a. Four terms-grouping   **b.** $(p + c)(p - 3)(p + 3)$
55. a. Perfect square trinomial   **b.** $(9u - 5v)^2$
56. a. Sum of squares   **b.** $4(x^2 + 4)$
57. a. Nonperfect square trinomial   **b.** $(x - 6)(x + 1)$
58. a. Nonperfect square trinomial   **b.** Prime
59. a. Four terms-grouping   **b.** $2(x - 3y)(a + 2b)$
60. a. Nonperfect square trinomial
b. $m(4m + 1)(2m - 3)$ **61. a.** Nonperfect square
trinomial   **b.** $x^2y(3x + 5)(7x + 2)$
62. a. Difference of squares   **b.** $2(m^2 - 8)(m^2 + 8)$
63. a. Four terms-grouping   **b.** $(4v - 3)(2u + 3)$
64. a. Four terms-grouping   **b.** $(t - 5)(4t + s)$
65. a. Perfect square trinomial   **b.** $3(2x - 1)^2$
66. a. Perfect square trinomial   **b.** $(p + q)^2$
67. a. Nonperfect square trinomial   **b.** $n(2n - 1)(3n + 4)$
68. a. Nonperfect square trinomial   **b.** $k(2k - 1)(2k + 3)$
69. a. Difference of squares   **b.** $(8 - y)(8 + y)$
70. a. Difference of squares   **b.** $b(6 - b)(6 + b)$
71. a. Nonperfect square trinomial   **b.** Prime
72. a. Nonperfect square trinomial   **b.** $(y + 4)(y + 2)$
73. a. Nonperfect square trinomial   **b.** $(c^2 - 10)(c^2 - 2)$

Section 6.7 Practice Exercises, pp. 464–466

3. $4(b - 5)(b - 6)$ **5.** $(3x - 2)(x + 4)$ **7.** $4(x^2 + 4y^2)$
9. Neither   **11.** Quadratic   **13.** Linear   **15.** $\{-3, 1\}$
17. $\left\{\frac{7}{2}, -\frac{7}{2}\right\}$ **19.** $\{-5\}$ **21.** $\left\{0, \frac{1}{5}\right\}$ **23.** The
polynomial must be factored completely.   **25.** $\{5, -3\}$
27. $\{-12, 2\}$ **29.** $\left\{4, -\frac{1}{2}\right\}$ **31.** $\left\{\frac{2}{3}, -\frac{2}{3}\right\}$ **33.** $\{6, 8\}$
35. $\left\{0, -\frac{3}{2}, 4\right\}$ **37.** $\left\{-\frac{1}{3}, 3, -6\right\}$ **39.** $\left\{0, 4, -\frac{3}{2}\right\}$
41. $\left\{0, -\frac{9}{2}, 11\right\}$ **43.** $\{0, 4, -4\}$ **45.** $\{-6, 0\}$
47. $\left\{\frac{3}{4}, -\frac{3}{4}\right\}$ **49.** $\{0, -5, -2\}$ **51.** $\left\{-\frac{14}{3}\right\}$
53. $\{5, 3\}$ **55.** $\{0, -2\}$ **57.** $\{-3\}$ **59.** $\{-3, 1\}$
61. $\left\{\frac{3}{2}\right\}$ **63.** $\left\{0, \frac{1}{3}\right\}$ **65.** $\{0, 2\}$ **67.** $\{3, -2, 2\}$
69. $\{-5, 4\}$ **71.** $\{-5, -1\}$

Chapter 6 Problem Recognition Exercises, p. 466

1. a. $(x + 7)(x - 1)$ **b.** $\{-7, 1\}$ **2. a.** $(c + 6)(c + 2)$
b. $\{-6, -2\}$ **3. a.** $(2y + 1)(y + 3)$ **b.** $\left\{-\dfrac{1}{2}, -3\right\}$
4. a. $(3x - 5)(x - 1)$ **b.** $\left\{\dfrac{5}{3}, 1\right\}$ **5. a.** $\left\{\dfrac{4}{5}, -1\right\}$
b. $(5q - 4)(q + 1)$ **6. a.** $\left\{-\dfrac{1}{3}, \dfrac{3}{2}\right\}$ **b.** $(3a + 1)(2a - 3)$
7. a. $\{-8, 8\}$ **b.** $(a + 8)(a - 8)$ **8. a.** $\{-10, 10\}$
b. $(v + 10)(v - 10)$ **9. a.** $(2b + 9)(2b - 9)$ **b.** $\left\{-\dfrac{9}{2}, \dfrac{9}{2}\right\}$
10. a. $(6t + 7)(6t - 7)$ **b.** $\left\{-\dfrac{7}{6}, \dfrac{7}{6}\right\}$
11. a. $\left\{-\dfrac{3}{2}, -\dfrac{1}{2}\right\}$ **b.** $2(2x + 3)(2x + 1)$
12. a. $\left\{-\dfrac{4}{3}, -2\right\}$ **b.** $4(3y + 4)(y + 2)$
13. a. $x(x - 10)(x + 2)$ **b.** $\{0, 10, -2\}$
14. a. $k(k + 7)(k - 2)$ **b.** $\{0, -7, 2\}$
15. a. $\{-1, 3, -3\}$ **b.** $(b + 1)(b - 3)(b + 3)$
16. a. $\{8, -2, 2\}$ **b.** $(x - 8)(x + 2)(x - 2)$
17. $(s - 3)(2s + r)$ **18.** $(2t + 1)(3t + 5u)$
19. $\left\{-\dfrac{1}{2}, 0, \dfrac{1}{2}\right\}$ **20.** $\{-5, 0, 5\}$ **21.** $\{0, 1\}$
22. $\{-3, 0\}$ **23.** $\left\{\dfrac{1}{3}\right\}$ **24.** $\left\{-\dfrac{7}{12}\right\}$
25. $(2w + 3)(4w^2 - 6w + 9)$
26. $(10q - 1)(100q^2 + 10q + 1)$ **27.** $\left\{-\dfrac{7}{5}, 1\right\}$
28. $\left\{-6, -\dfrac{1}{4}\right\}$ **29.** $\left\{-\dfrac{2}{3}, -5\right\}$ **30.** $\left\{-1, -\dfrac{1}{2}\right\}$
31. $\{3\}$ **32.** $\{0\}$ **33.** $\{-4, 4\}$ **34.** $\left\{-\dfrac{2}{3}, \dfrac{2}{3}\right\}$
35. $\{1, 6\}$ **36.** $\{-2, -12\}$

Section 6.8 Practice Exercises, pp. 471–474

3. $\left\{0, -\dfrac{2}{3}\right\}$ **5.** $\{6, -1\}$ **7.** $\left\{-\dfrac{5}{6}, 2\right\}$
9. The numbers are 7 and -7.   **11.** The numbers are 10 and -4.   **13.** The numbers are -9 and -7, or 7 and 9.
15. The numbers are 5 and 6, or -6 and -5.
17. The height of the painting is 11 ft and the width is 9 ft.
19. a. The slab is 7 m by 4 m.   **b.** The perimeter is 22 m.
21. The base is 7 ft and the height is 4 ft.
23. The bases measure 10 cm and 5 cm. The height is 8 cm.
25. The ball hits the ground in 3 sec.
27. The object is at ground level at 0 sec and 1.5 sec.
29.   **31.** $c = 25$ cm   **33.** $a = 15$ in.

35. The brace is 20 in. long.   **37.** The kite is 19 yd high.
39. The bottom of the ladder is 8 ft from the house. The distance from the top of the ladder to the ground is 15 ft.
41. The hypotenuse is 10 m.

Chapter 6 Review Exercises, pp. 480–482

1. $3a^2b$ **2.** $x + 5$ **3.** $2c(3c - 5)$ **4.** $-2yz$ or $2yz$
5. $2x(3x + x^3 - 4)$ **6.** $11w^2y^3(w - 4y^2)$
7. $t(-t + 5)$ or $-t(t - 5)$ **8.** $u(-6u - 1)$ or $-u(6u + 1)$
9. $(b + 2)(3b - 7)$ **10.** $2(5x + 9)(1 + 4x)$
11. $(w + 2)(7w + b)$ **12.** $(b - 2)(b + y)$
13. $3(4y - 3)(5y - 1)$ **14.** $a(2 - a)(3 - b)$
15. $(x - 3)(x - 7)$ **16.** $(y - 8)(y - 11)$
17. $(z - 12)(z + 6)$ **18.** $(q - 13)(q + 3)$
19. $3w(p + 10)(p + 2)$ **20.** $2m^2(m + 8)(m + 5)$
21. $-(t - 8)(t - 2)$ **22.** $-(w - 4)(w + 5)$
23. $(a + b)(a + 11b)$ **24.** $(c - 6d)(c + 3d)$
25. Different   **26.** Both negative   **27.** Both positive
28. Different   **29.** $(2y + 3)(y - 4)$
30. $(4w + 3)(w - 2)$ **31.** $(2z + 5)(5z + 2)$
32. $(4z - 3)(2z + 3)$ **33.** Prime   **34.** Prime
35. $10(w - 9)(w + 3)$ **36.** $-3(y - 8)(y + 2)$
37. $(3c - 5d)^2$ **38.** $(x + 6)^2$ **39.** $(3g + 2h)(2g + h)$
40. $(6m - n)(2m - 5n)$ **41.** $(v^2 + 1)(v^2 - 3)$
42. $(x^? + 5)(x^? + 2)$ **43.** $5, -1$ **44.** $-3, -5$
45. $(c - 2)(3c + 1)$ **46.** $(y + 3)(4y + 1)$
47. $(t + 12w)(t + w)$ **48.** $(4x^2 - 3)(x^2 + 5)$
49. $(w^2 + 5)(w^2 + 2)$ **50.** $(p - 3q)(p - 5q)$
51. $-2(4v + 3)(5v - 1)$ **52.** $10(4s - 5)(s + 2)$
53. $ab(a - 6b)(a - 4b)$ **54.** $2z^4(z + 7)(z - 3)$
55. Prime   **56.** Prime   **57.** $(7x + 10)^2$
58. $(3w - z)^2$ **59.** $(a - b)(a + b)$
60. Prime   **61.** $(a - 7)(a + 7)$
62. $(d - 8)(d + 8)$ **63.** $(10 - 9t)(10 + 9t)$
64. $(2 - 5k)(2 + 5k)$ **65.** Prime   **66.** Prime
67. $(y + 6)^2$ **68.** $(t + 8)^2$ **69.** $(3a - 2)^2$
70. $(5x - 4)^2$ **71.** $-3(v + 2)^2$ **72.** $-2(x - 5)^2$
73. $2(c^2 - 3)(c^2 + 3)$ **74.** $2(6x - y)(6x + y)$
75. $(p + 3)(p - 4)(p + 4)$
76. $(k - 2)(2 - k)(2 + k)$ or $-1(k - 2)^2(2 + k)$
77. $(a + b)(a^2 - ab + b^2)$ **78.** $(a - b)(a^2 + ab + b^2)$
79. $(4 + a)(16 - 4a + a^2)$ **80.** $(5 - b)(25 + 5b + b^2)$
81. $(p^2 + 2)(p^4 - 2p^2 + 4)$
82. $\left(q^2 - \dfrac{1}{3}\right)\left(q^4 + \dfrac{1}{3}q^2 + \dfrac{1}{9}\right)$
83. $6(x - 2)(x^2 + 2x + 4)$ **84.** $7(y + 1)(y^2 - y + 1)$
85. $x(x - 6)(x + 6)$ **86.** $q(q - 4)(q^2 + 4q + 16)$
87. $4(2h^2 + 5)$ **88.** $m(m - 8)$
89. $(x + 4)(x + 1)(x - 1)$ **90.** $5q(p^2 - 2q)(p^2 + 2q)$
91. $n(2 + n)(4 - 2n + n^2)$ **92.** $14(m - 1)(m^2 + m + 1)$
93. $(x - 3)(2x + 1) = 0$ can be solved directly by the zero product rule because it is a product of factors set equal to zero.
94. $\left\{\dfrac{1}{4}, -\dfrac{2}{3}\right\}$ **95.** $\left\{9, \dfrac{1}{2}\right\}$ **96.** $\left\{0, -3, -\dfrac{2}{5}\right\}$
97. $\left\{0, 7, \dfrac{9}{4}\right\}$ **98.** $\left\{-\dfrac{5}{7}, 2\right\}$ **99.** $\left\{-\dfrac{1}{4}, 6\right\}$
100. $\{12, -12\}$ **101.** $\{5, -5\}$ **102.** $\left\{0, \dfrac{1}{5}\right\}$
103. $\{4, 2\}$ **104.** $\left\{-\dfrac{5}{6}\right\}$ **105.** $\left\{-\dfrac{2}{3}\right\}$ **106.** $\left\{\dfrac{2}{3}, 6\right\}$
107. $\left\{\dfrac{11}{2}, -12\right\}$ **108.** $\{0, 7, 2\}$ **109.** $\{0, 2, -2\}$

110. The height is 6 ft, and the base is 13 ft.
111. The ball is at ground level at 0 and 1 sec.
112. The ramp is 13 ft long.
113. The legs are 6 ft and 8 ft; the hypotenuse is 10 ft.
114. The numbers are -8 and 8.
115. The numbers are 29 and 30, or -2 and -1.
116. The height is 4 m, and the base is 9 m.

Chapter 6 Test, p. 482

1. $3x(5x^3 - 1 + 2x^2)$ **2.** $(a - 5)(7 - a)$
3. $(6w - 1)(w - 7)$ **4.** $(13 - p)(13 + p)$
5. $(q - 8)^2$ **6.** $(2 + t)(4 - 2t + t^2)$
7. $(a + 4)(a + 8)$ **8.** $(x + 7)(x - 6)$
9. $(2y - 1)(y - 8)$ **10.** $(2z + 1)(3z + 8)$
11. $(3t - 10)(3t + 10)$ **12.** $(v + 9)(v - 9)$
13. $3(a + 6b)(a + 3b)$ **14.** $(c - 1)(c + 1)(c^2 + 1)$
15. $(y - 7)(x + 3)$ **16.** Prime   **17.** $-10(u - 2)(u - 1)$
18. $3(2t - 5)(2t + 5)$ **19.** $5(y - 5)^2$ **20.** $7q(3q + 2)$
21. $(2x + 1)(x - 2)(x + 2)$ **22.** $(y - 5)(y^2 + 5y + 25)$
23. $(mn - 9)(mn + 9)$ **24.** $16(a - 2b)(a + 2b)$
25. $(4x - 3y^2)(16x^2 + 12xy^2 + 9y^4)$ **26.** $3y(x - 4)(x + 2)$
27. $\left\{\dfrac{3}{2}, -5\right\}$ **28.** $\{0, 7\}$ **29.** $\{8, -2\}$ **30.** $\left\{\dfrac{1}{5}, -1\right\}$
31. $\{3, -3, -10\}$ **32.** The tennis court is 12 yd by 26 yd.
33. The two integers are 5 and 7, or -5 and -7.
34. The base is 12 in., and the height is 7 in.
35. The shorter leg is 5 ft.

Chapters 1–6 Cumulative Review Exercises, p. 483

1. $\dfrac{7}{5}$ **2.** $\{-3\}$ **3.** $y = \dfrac{3}{2}x - 4$

4. There are 10 quarters, 12 nickels, and 7 dimes.
5. $[-4, \infty)$ **6. a.** Yes   **b.** 1

c. $(0, 4)$ **d.** $(-4, 0)$ **e.**

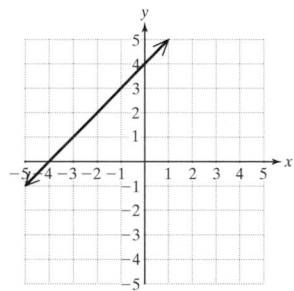

7. a. Vertical line   **b.** Undefined   **c.** $(5, 0)$
d. Does not exist   **8.** $y = 3x + 14$ **9.** $\{(5, 2)\}$
10. $\{(7, 0, -1)\}$ **11.** $-\dfrac{7}{2}y^2 - 5y - 14$
12. $8p^3 - 22p^2 + 13p + 3$ **13.** $4w^2 - 28w + 49$
14. $r^3 + 5r^2 + 15r + 40 + \dfrac{121}{r - 3}$ **15.** c^4 **16.** $\dfrac{a^4}{9b^2}$
17. 1.6×10^3 **18.** $(w - 2)(w + 2)(w^2 + 4)$
19. $(a + 5b)(2x - 3y)$ **20.** $\left\{0, \dfrac{1}{2}, -5\right\}$

Chapter 7

Chapter Opener Puzzle

$$\underbrace{p}_{4}\ \underbrace{r}_{1}\ \underbrace{o}_{2}\ \underbrace{c}_{}\ \underbrace{r}_{1}\ \underbrace{a}_{5}\ \underbrace{s}_{3}\ \underbrace{t}_{}\ \underbrace{i}_{}\ \underbrace{n}_{5}\ \underbrace{a}_{3}\ \underbrace{t}_{}\ \underbrace{i}_{2}\ \underbrace{o}_{}\ \underbrace{n}_{}$$

Section 7.1 Practice Exercises, pp. 493–496

3. a. A number $\dfrac{p}{q}$, where p and q are integers and $q \neq 0$

b. An expression $\dfrac{p}{q}$, where p and q are polynomials

and $q \neq 0$ **5.** $-\dfrac{1}{8}$ **7.** $-\dfrac{1}{2}$ **9.** Undefined

11. a. $3\frac{1}{5}$ hr or 3.2 hr   **b.** $1\frac{3}{4}$ hr or 1.75 hr

13. $k = -2$ **15.** $x = \dfrac{5}{2}, x = -8$ **17.** $m = -2, m = -3$

19. There are no restricted values.   **21.** There are no restricted values.   **23.** $t = 0$

25. For example: $\dfrac{1}{x - 2}$ **27.** For example: $\dfrac{1}{(x + 3)(x - 7)}$

29. a. $\dfrac{2}{5}$ **b.** $\dfrac{2}{5}$ **31. a.** Undefined   **b.** Undefined

33. a. $y = -2$ **b.** $\dfrac{1}{2}$ **35. a.** $t = -1$ **b.** $t - 1$

37. a. $w = 0, w = \dfrac{5}{3}$ **b.** $\dfrac{1}{3w - 5}$ **39. a.** $x = -\dfrac{2}{3}$

b. $\dfrac{3x - 2}{2}$ **41. a.** $a = -3, a = 2$ **b.** $\dfrac{a + 5}{a + 3}$

43. $\dfrac{b}{3}$ **45.** $\dfrac{3t^2}{2}$ **47.** $-\dfrac{3xy}{z^2}$ **49.** $\dfrac{1}{2}$ **51.** $\dfrac{p - 3}{p + 4}$

53. $\dfrac{1}{4(m - 11)}$ **55.** $\dfrac{2x + 1}{4x^2}$ **57.** $\dfrac{1}{4a - 5}$ **59.** $\dfrac{4}{w + 2}$

61. $\dfrac{x - 2}{3(y + 2)}$ **63.** $\dfrac{2}{x - 5}$ **65.** $a + 7$

67. Cannot simplify   **69.** $\dfrac{y + 3}{2y - 5}$ **71.** $\dfrac{3x - 2}{x + 4}$

73. $\dfrac{5}{(q + 1)(q - 1)}$ **75.** $\dfrac{c - d}{2c + d}$ **77.** $\dfrac{1}{t(t - 5)}$

79. $\dfrac{7p - 2q}{2}$ **81.** $5x + 4$ **83.** $\dfrac{x + y}{x - 4y}$

85. They are opposites.   **87.** -1 **89.** -1 **91.** $-\dfrac{1}{2}$

93. Cannot simplify   **95.** $\dfrac{5x - 6}{5x + 6}$ **97.** $-\dfrac{x + 3}{4 + x}$

99. $w - 2$ **101.** $\dfrac{z + 4}{z^2 + 4z + 16}$

Section 7.2 Practice Exercises, pp. 501–503

1. $\dfrac{3}{10}$ **3.** 2   **5.** $\dfrac{5}{2}$ **7.** $\dfrac{15}{4}$ **9.** $\dfrac{3}{2x}$ **11.** $3xy^4$

13. $\dfrac{x - 6}{8}$ **15.** $\dfrac{2}{y}$ **17.** $-\dfrac{5}{8}$ **19.** $-\dfrac{b + a}{a - b}$

21. $\dfrac{y + 1}{5}$ **23.** $\dfrac{2(x + 6)}{2x + 1}$ **25.** 6   **27.** $\dfrac{m^6}{n^2}$ **29.** $\dfrac{10}{9}$

31. $\dfrac{6}{7}$ **33.** $-m(m+n)$ **35.** $\dfrac{3p+4q}{4(p+2q)}$ **37.** $\dfrac{p}{p-1}$

39. $\dfrac{w}{2w-1}$ **41.** $\dfrac{4r}{2r+3}$ **43.** $\dfrac{5}{6}$ **45.** $\dfrac{1}{4}$

47. $\dfrac{y+9}{y-6}$ **49.** $\dfrac{t+4}{t+2}$ **51.** $\dfrac{3t+8}{t+2}$ **53.** $\dfrac{x+4}{x+1}$

55. $-\dfrac{w-3}{2}$ **57.** $\dfrac{k+6}{k+3}$ **59.** $\dfrac{2}{a}$ **61.** $2y(y+1)$

63. $x+y$ **65.** 2 **67.** $\dfrac{1}{a-2}$ **69.** $\dfrac{p+q}{2}$

Section 7.3 Practice Exercises, pp. 507–509

3. $x=1, x=-1;\ \dfrac{3}{5(x-1)}$ **5.** $\dfrac{a+5}{a+7}$ **7.** $\dfrac{2}{3y}$

9. a, b, c, d   **11.** x^5 is the greatest power of x that appears in any denominator.   **13.** 45   **15.** 48

17. 63   **19.** $9x^2y^3$ **21.** w^2y

23. $(p+3)(p-1)(p+2)$ **25.** $9t(t+1)^2$

27. $(y-2)(y+2)(y+3)$ **29.** $3-x$ or $x-3$

31. Because $(b-1)$ and $(1-b)$ are opposites, they differ by a factor of -1.

33. $\dfrac{6}{5x^2};\ \dfrac{5x}{5x^2}$ **35.** $\dfrac{24x}{30x^3};\ \dfrac{5y}{30x^3}$ **37.** $\dfrac{10}{12a^2b};\ \dfrac{a^3}{12a^2b}$

39. $\dfrac{6m-6}{(m+4)(m-1)};\ \dfrac{3m+12}{(m+4)(m-1)}$

41. $\dfrac{6x+18}{(2x-5)(x+3)};\ \dfrac{2x-5}{(2x-5)(x+3)}$

43. $\dfrac{6w+6}{(w+3)(w-8)(w+1)};\ \dfrac{w^2+3w}{(w+3)(w-8)(w+1)}$

45. $\dfrac{6p^2+12p}{(p-2)(p+2)^2};\ \dfrac{3p-6}{(p-2)(p+2)^2}$

47. $\dfrac{1}{a-4};\ \dfrac{-a}{a-4}$ or $\dfrac{-1}{4-a};\ \dfrac{a}{4-a}$

49. $\dfrac{8}{2(x-7)};\ \dfrac{-y}{2(x-7)}$ or $\dfrac{-8}{2(7-x)};\ \dfrac{y}{2(7-x)}$

51. $\dfrac{1}{a+b};\ \dfrac{-6}{a+b}$ or $\dfrac{-1}{-a-b};\ \dfrac{6}{-a-b}$

53. $\dfrac{-9}{24(3y+1)};\ \dfrac{20}{24(3y+1)}$ **55.** $\dfrac{3z+12}{5z(z+4)};\ \dfrac{5z}{5z(z+4)}$

57. $\dfrac{z^2+3z}{(z+2)(z+7)(z+3)};\ \dfrac{-3z^2-6z}{(z+2)(z+7)(z+3)};$ $\dfrac{5z+35}{(z+2)(z+7)(z+3)}$

59. $\dfrac{3p+6}{(p-2)(p^2+2p+4)(p+2)};\ \dfrac{p^3+2p^2+4p}{(p-2)(p^2+2p+4)(p+2)};$ $\dfrac{5p^3-20p}{(p-2)(p^2+2p+4)(p+2)}$

Section 7.4 Practice Exercises, pp. 516–518

1. a. $-\dfrac{1}{2}, -2, 0$, undefined, undefined

b. $(x-5)(x-2); x=5, x=2$ **c.** $\dfrac{x+1}{x-2}$

3. $\dfrac{2(2x-3)}{(x-3)(x-1)}$ **5.** $\dfrac{5}{4}$ **7.** $\dfrac{3}{8}$

9. 2 **11.** 5 **13.** $\dfrac{-2(t-2)}{t-8}$ **15.** $3x+7$

17. $m+5$ **19.** 2 **21.** $x-5$ **23.** $\dfrac{1}{r+1}$

25. $\dfrac{1}{y+7}$ **27.** $\dfrac{15x}{y}$ **29.** $\dfrac{5a+6}{4a}$ **31.** $\dfrac{2(6+x^2y)}{15xy^3}$

33. $\dfrac{2s-3t^2}{s^4t^3}$ **35.** $-\dfrac{2}{3}$ **37.** $\dfrac{19}{3(a+1)}$

39. $\dfrac{-3(k+4)}{(k-3)(k+3)}$ **41.** $\dfrac{a-4}{2a}$ **43.** $\dfrac{(x+6)(x-2)}{(x-4)(x+1)}$

45. $\dfrac{2(4a-b)}{(a+b)(a-b)}$ **47.** $\dfrac{5p-1}{3}$ or $\dfrac{-5p+1}{-3}$

49. $\dfrac{6n-1}{n-8}$ or $\dfrac{-6n+1}{8-n}$ **51.** $\dfrac{2(4x+5)}{x(x+2)}$

53. $\dfrac{3p+1}{(p-3)(p-1)}$ **55.** $\dfrac{3y}{2(2y+1)}$ **57.** $\dfrac{2(w-3)}{(w+3)(w-1)}$

59. $\dfrac{4a-13}{(a-3)(a-4)}$ **61.** $\dfrac{4x(x+1)}{(x+3)(x-2)(x+2)}$

63. $\dfrac{-y}{(y-4)(y-1)}$ **65.** $\dfrac{1}{2p+1}$ **67.** $\dfrac{2}{m-n}$

69. 0 **71.** $\dfrac{2(3x+7)}{(x+3)(x+2)}$ **73.** $\dfrac{1}{n}$ **75.** $\dfrac{5}{n+2}$

77. $n+\left(7\cdot\dfrac{1}{n}\right);\ \dfrac{n^2+7}{n}$ **79.** $\dfrac{1}{n}-\dfrac{2}{n};\ -\dfrac{1}{n}$

81. $\dfrac{-w^2}{(w+3)(w-3)(w^2-3w+9)}$

83. $\dfrac{p^2-2p+7}{(p+2)(p+3)(p-1)}$

85. $\dfrac{-m-21}{2(m+5)(m-2)}$ or $\dfrac{m+21}{2(m+5)(2-m)}$ **87.** $\dfrac{3k+5}{4k+7}$

89. $\dfrac{1}{a}$

Chapter 7 Problem Recognition Exercises, p. 519

1. $\dfrac{-2x+9}{3x+1}$ **2.** $\dfrac{1}{w-4}$ **3.** $\dfrac{y-5}{2y-3}$

4. $\dfrac{7}{(x+3)(2x-1)}$ **5.** $-\dfrac{1}{x}$ **6.** $\dfrac{1}{3}$ **7.** $\dfrac{c+3}{c}$

8. $\dfrac{x+3}{5}$ **9.** $\dfrac{a}{12b^4c}$ **10.** $\dfrac{2a-b}{a-b}$ **11.** $\dfrac{p-q}{5}$

12. 4 **13.** $\dfrac{10}{2x+1}$ **14.** $\dfrac{w+2z}{w+z}$ **15.** $\dfrac{3}{2x+5}$

16. $\dfrac{y+7}{x+a}$ **17.** $\dfrac{1}{2(a+3)}$ **18.** $\dfrac{2(3y+10)}{(y-6)(y+6)(y+2)}$

19. $(t+8)^2$ **20.** $6b+5$

Section 7.5 Practice Exercises, pp. 525–527

3. $\dfrac{1}{2a-3}$ **5.** $\dfrac{3(2k-5)}{5(k-2)}$ **7.** $\dfrac{7}{4y}$ **9.** $\dfrac{1}{2y}$

11. $\dfrac{24b}{a^3}$ **13.** $\dfrac{2r^5t^4}{s^6}$ **15.** $\dfrac{35}{2}$ **17.** $k+h$

19. $\dfrac{n+1}{2(n-3)}$ **21.** $\dfrac{2x+1}{4x+1}$ **23.** $m-7$

25. $\dfrac{2y(y-5)}{7y^2+10}$ 27. $-\dfrac{a+8}{a-2}$ or $\dfrac{a+8}{2-a}$ 29. $\dfrac{t-2}{t-4}$

31. $\dfrac{t+3}{t-5}$ 33. $\dfrac{1}{2}$ 35. $\dfrac{\frac{1}{2}+\frac{2}{3}}{5}$; $\dfrac{7}{30}$ 37. $\dfrac{3}{\frac{2}{3}+\frac{3}{4}}$; $\dfrac{36}{17}$

39. a. $\dfrac{6}{5}\,\Omega$ b. $6\,\Omega$ 41. $\dfrac{y+4x}{2y}$ 43. $\dfrac{1}{n^2+m^2}$

45. $\dfrac{2z-5}{3(z+3)}$ 47. $-\dfrac{x+1}{x-1}$ or $\dfrac{x+1}{1-x}$ 49. $\dfrac{3}{2}$

Section 7.6 Practice Exercises, pp. 535–537

3. $\dfrac{2}{4x-1}$ 5. $5(h+1)$ 7. $\dfrac{(x+4)(x-3)}{x^2}$

9. {3} 11. $\left\{\dfrac{5}{11}\right\}$ 13. $\left\{\dfrac{1}{3}\right\}$ 15. a. $z=0$

b. $5z$ c. {5} 17. $\left\{-\dfrac{200}{19}\right\}$ 19. {8} 21. $\left\{\dfrac{47}{6}\right\}$

23. {3, −1} 25. {4}

27. {5} (The value 0 does not check.) 29. {−5}

31. { } (The value 4 does not check.) 33. {4}

35. {4, −3} 37. {−4}; (The value 1 does not check.)

39. { } (The value −4 does not check.)

41. {4} (The value −6 does not check.) 43. {−25}

45. {−1} 47. The number is 8.

49. The number is −26. 51. $m=\dfrac{FK}{a}$ 53. $E=\dfrac{IR}{K}$

55. $R=\dfrac{E-Ir}{I}$ or $R=\dfrac{E}{I}-r$

57. $B=\dfrac{2A-hb}{h}$ or $B=\dfrac{2A}{h}-b$ 59. $h=\dfrac{V}{r^2\pi}$

61. $t=\dfrac{b}{x-a}$ or $t=\dfrac{-b}{a-x}$ 63. $x=\dfrac{y}{1-yz}$ or

$x=\dfrac{-y}{yz-1}$ 65. $h=\dfrac{2A}{a+b}$ 67. $R=\dfrac{R_1R_2}{R_2+R_1}$

Chapter 7 Problem Recognition Exercises, p. 538

1. $\dfrac{y-2}{2y}$ 2. {6} 3. {2} 4. $\dfrac{3a-17}{a-5}$

5. $\dfrac{4p+27}{18p^2}$ 6. $\dfrac{b(b-5)}{(b-1)(b+1)}$ 7. {5} 8. $\dfrac{2w+5}{(w+1)^2}$

9. {7} 10. {5} 11. $\dfrac{3x+14}{4(x+1)}$ 12. $\left\{\dfrac{11}{3}\right\}$

13. $\left\{\dfrac{41}{10}\right\}$ 14. $\dfrac{7-3t}{t(t-5)}$ 15. $\dfrac{8a+1}{2a-1}$

16. {5} (The value 2 does not check.)

17. {−1} (The value 3 does not check.) 18. $\dfrac{11}{12k}$

19. $\dfrac{h+9}{(h-3)(h+3)}$ 20. {7}

Section 7.7 Practice Exercises, pp. 546–550

3. Expression; $\dfrac{m^2+m+2}{(m-1)(m+3)}$ 5. Expression; $\dfrac{3}{10}$

7. Equation; {2} 9. {95} 11. {1} 13. $\left\{\dfrac{40}{3}\right\}$

15. {40} 17. {3} 19. {−1} 21. {1}

23. a. $V_f=\dfrac{V_iT_f}{T_i}$ b. $T_f=\dfrac{T_iV_f}{V_i}$

25. Toni can drive 297 mi on 9 gal of gas.
27. They would produce 1536 lb. 29. 5 oz contains 12 g of carbohydrate. 31. The minimum length is 20 ft.
33. $x=4$ cm; $y=5$ cm 35. $x=3.75$ cm; $y=4.5$ cm
37. The height of the pole is 7 m. 39. The light post is 24 ft high. 41. The speed of the boat is 20 mph.
43. The plane flies 210 mph in still air. 45. He runs 8 mph and bikes 16 mph. 47. Floyd walks 4 mph and Rachel walks 2 mph. 49. Sergio rode 12 mph and walked 3 mph. 51. $5\frac{5}{11}$ $(5.\overline{45})$ min 53. $22\frac{2}{9}$ $(22.\overline{2})$ min
55. 48 hr 57. $3\frac{1}{3}$ $(3.\overline{3})$ days 59. There are 40 smokers and 140 nonsmokers. 61. There are 240 men and 200 women.

Chapter 7 Review Exercises pp. 556–558

1. a. $-\dfrac{2}{9}$, $-\dfrac{1}{10}$, 0, $-\dfrac{5}{6}$, undefined b. $t=-9$

2. a. $-\dfrac{1}{5}$, $-\dfrac{1}{2}$, undefined, 0, $\dfrac{1}{7}$ b. $k=5$

3. a, c, d 4. $x=\dfrac{5}{2}$, $x=3$; $\dfrac{1}{2x-5}$

5. $h=-\dfrac{1}{3}$, $h=-7$; $\dfrac{1}{3h+1}$ 6. $a=2$, $a=-2$; $\dfrac{4a-1}{a-2}$

7. $w=4$, $w=-4$; $\dfrac{2w+3}{w-4}$ 8. $z=4$; $-\dfrac{z}{2}$

9. $k=0$, $k=5$; $-\dfrac{3}{2k}$ 10. $b=-3$; $\dfrac{b-1}{2}$

11. $m=-1$; $\dfrac{m-5}{3}$ 12. $n=-3$; $\dfrac{1}{n+3}$

13. $p=-7$; $\dfrac{1}{p+7}$ 14. y^2 15. $\dfrac{u^2}{2}$ 16. $v+2$

17. $\dfrac{3}{2(x-5)}$ 18. $\dfrac{c(c+1)}{2(c+5)}$ 19. $\dfrac{q-2}{4}$

20. $-2t(t-5)$ 21. $4s(s-4)$ 22. $\dfrac{1}{7}$

23. $\dfrac{1}{n-2}$ 24. $-\dfrac{1}{6}$ 25. $\dfrac{1}{m+3}$ 26. $\dfrac{-1}{(x+3)(x+2)}$

27. $-\dfrac{2y-1}{y+1}$ 28. LCD = $10ab$; $\dfrac{4b}{10ab}$; $\dfrac{3a}{10ab}$

29. LCD = $12xy$; $\dfrac{21y}{12xy}$; $\dfrac{22x}{12xy}$ 30. LCD = x^2y^5; $\dfrac{y}{x^2y^5}$; $\dfrac{3x}{x^2y^5}$

31. LCD = ab^3c^2; $\dfrac{5c^2}{ab^3c^2}$; $\dfrac{3b^3}{ab^3c^2}$

32. LCD = $(p+2)(p-4)$; $\dfrac{5p-20}{(p+2)(p-4)}$; $\dfrac{p^2+2p}{(p+2)(p-4)}$

33. LCD = $q(q+8)$; $\dfrac{6q+48}{q(q+8)}$; $\dfrac{q}{q(q+8)}$

34. LCD = $(n+3)(n-3)(n+2)$
35. LCD = $(m+4)(m-4)(m+3)$
36. $c-2$ or $2-c$ 37. $3-x$ or $x-3$ 38. 2
39. 2 40. $a+5$ 41. $x-7$
42. $\dfrac{-y-18}{(y-9)(y+9)}$ or $\dfrac{y+18}{(9-y)(y+9)}$

43. $\dfrac{t^2 + 2t + 3}{(2 - t)(2 + t)}$ **44.** $\dfrac{m + 8}{3m(m + 2)}$ **45.** $\dfrac{3(r - 4)}{2r(r + 6)}$

46. $\dfrac{p}{(p + 4)(p + 5)}$ **47.** $\dfrac{q}{(q + 5)(q + 4)}$ **48.** $\dfrac{1}{2}$

49. $\dfrac{1}{3}$ **50.** $\dfrac{a - 4}{a - 2}$ **51.** $\dfrac{3(z + 5)}{z(z - 5)}$ **52.** $\dfrac{w}{2}$ **53.** $\dfrac{8}{y}$

54. $y - x$ **55.** $-(b + a)$ **56.** $-\dfrac{2p + 7}{2p}$

57. $-\dfrac{k + 10}{k + 4}$ **58.** $\{-8\}$ **59.** $\{-2\}$ **60.** $\{0\}$

61. $\{2\}$ **62.** $\{-2\}$ **63.** $\{-1\}$ (The value 3 does not check.)   **64.** $\{\ \}$ (The value 2 does not check.)
65. $\{-11, 1\}$ **66.** The number is 4.

67. $h = \dfrac{3V}{\pi r^2}$ **68.** $b = \dfrac{2A}{h}$ **69.** $\left\{\dfrac{6}{5}\right\}$ **70.** $\left\{\dfrac{96}{5}\right\}$

71. It contains 10 g of fat.   **72.** Ed travels at 60 mph, and Bud travels at 70 mph.   **73.** Together the pumps would fill the pool in 16.8 min.   **74.** $x = 11; y = 26$

Chapter 7 Test, p. 558

1. a. $x = 2$ **b.** $-\dfrac{x + 1}{6}$ **2. a.** $a = 6, a = -2, a = 0$

b. $\dfrac{7}{a + 2}$ **3.** b, c, d   **4. a.** $15(x + 3)$ **b.** $3x^2y^2$

5. $\dfrac{y + 7}{3(y + 3)(y + 1)}$ **6.** $-\dfrac{b + 3}{5}$ **7.** $y - 6$

8. $\dfrac{x + 7}{8(x - 5)}$ **9.** $\dfrac{1}{4}$ **10.** $\dfrac{1}{w + 1}$ **11.** $\dfrac{t + 4}{t + 2}$

12. $\dfrac{x(x + 5)}{(x + 4)(x - 2)}$ **13.** $\dfrac{1}{m + 4}$ **14.** $\left\{\dfrac{8}{5}\right\}$ **15.** $\{2\}$

16. $\{1\}$ **17.** $\{\ \}$ (The value 4 does not check.)
18. $\{-5\}$ (The value 2 does not check.)

19. $r = \dfrac{2A}{C}$ **20.** $\{-8\}$ **21.** $1\frac{1}{4}$ (1.25) cups of carrots
22. The speed of the current is 5 mph.   **23.** It would take the second printer 3 hr to do the job working alone.
24. $a = 5.6; b = 12$

Chapters 1–7 Cumulative Review Exercises, p. 559

1. 32   **2.** 7   **3.** $\left\{\dfrac{10}{9}\right\}$

4.

Set-Builder Notation	Graph	Interval Notation
$\{x \mid x \geq -1\}$	⊢———→ -1	$[-1, \infty)$
$\{x \mid x < 5\}$	←———→ 5	$(-\infty, 5)$

5. The width is 17 m and the length is 35 m.

6. The base is 10 in. and the height is 8 in.   **7.** $\dfrac{x^2yz^{17}}{2}$

8. a. $6x + 4$ **b.** $2x^2 + x - 3$ **9.** $(5x - 3)^2$

10. $(2c + 1)(5d - 3)$ **11.** $x = 5, x = -\dfrac{1}{2}$

12. $\{(1, -4)\}$ **13.** $\dfrac{1}{5(x + 4)}$ **14.** -3

15. $\{1\}$ **16.** $\left\{-\dfrac{7}{2}\right\}$

17. a. x-intercept: $(-4, 0)$; y-intercept: $(0, 2)$
b. x-intercept: $(0, 0)$; y-intercept: $(0, 0)$

18. a. $m = -\dfrac{7}{5}$ **b.** $m = -\dfrac{2}{3}$ **c.** $m = 4$ **d.** $m = -\dfrac{1}{4}$

19. $y = 5x - 3$ **20.** One large popcorn costs $3.50, and one drink costs $1.50.

Chapter 8

Chapter Opener Puzzle

The set of first components of a

R E L A T I O N
10 4 3 13 2 14 8 1

is called the D O M A I N.
6 5 12 11 7 9

Section 8.1 Practice Exercises, pp. 567–570

3. a. {(Alabama, 15.3), (Florida, 20.2), (Massachusetts, 13.4), (California, 18.8), (Minnesota, 7.9)}   **b.** Domain: {Alabama, Florida, Massachusetts, California, Minnesota}; range: {15.3, 20.2, 13.4, 18.8, 7.9}   **5. a.** {(USSR, 1961), (USA, 1962), (Poland, 1978), (Vietnam, 1980), (Cuba, 1980)}
b. Domain: {USSR, USA, Poland, Vietnam, Cuba}; range: {1961, 1962, 1978, 1980}
7. a. {(A, 1), (A, 2), (B, 2), (C, 3), (D, 5), (E, 4)}
b. Domain: {A, B, C, D, E}; range: {1, 2, 3, 4, 5}
9. a. {(6, A), (6, B), (6, C)}   **b.** Domain: {6}; range: {A, B, C}
11. a. {(−4, 1), (0, 3), (1, −1), (3, 0)}
b. Domain: {−4, 0, 1, 3}; range: {−1, 0, 1, 3}
13. a. {(−4, 4), (1, 1), (2, 1), (3, 1), (4, −2)}
b. Domain: {−4, 1, 2, 3, 4}; range: {−2, 1, 4}
15. Domain: $[0, 4]$; range: $[-2, 2]$ **17.** Domain: $[-5, 3]$; range: $[-2.1, 2.8]$ **19.** Domain: $(-\infty, 2]$; range: $(-\infty, \infty)$
21. Domain: $(-\infty, \infty)$; range: $(-\infty, \infty)$ **23.** Domain: $\{-3\}$; range: $(-\infty, \infty)$ **25.** Domain: $(-\infty, 2)$; range: $[-1.3, \infty)$
27. Domain: $\{-3, -1, 1, 3\}$; range: $\{0, 1, 2, 3\}$
29. Domain: $[-4, 5)$; range: $\{-2, 1, 3\}$ **31. a.** 2.85
b. 9.33   **c.** Dec.   **d.** Nov.   **e.** 7.63   **f.** {Jan., Feb., Mar., Apr., May, June, July, Aug., Sept., Oct., Nov., Dec.}
33. a. 31.876 million or 31,876,000   **b.** The year 2012
35. a. For example: {(Julie, New York), (Peggy, Florida), (Stephen, Kansas), (Pat, New York)}   **b.** Domain: {Julie, Peggy, Stephen, Pat}; range: {New York, Florida, Kansas}
37. $y = 2x - 1$ **39.** $y = x^2$

Section 8.2 Practice Exercises, pp. 578–582

3. a. {(−2, −4), (−1, −1), (0, 0), (1, −1), (2, −4)}
b. $\{-2, -1, 0, 1, 2\}$ **c.** $\{-4, -1, 0\}$ **5.** Function
7. Not a function   **9.** Function   **11.** Not a function
13. Function   **15.** Not a function   **17.** -11 **19.** 1
21. 2   **23.** $6t - 2$ **25.** 7   **27.** 4   **29.** 4
31. $6x + 4$ **33.** $-4x^2 - 8x + 1$ **35.** $-\pi^2 + 4\pi + 1$
37. 7   **39.** $-6a - 2$ **41.** $|-c - 2|$ **43.** 1   **45.** 7

47. -18.8 **49.** -7 **51.** 2π **53.** -5 **55.** 4
57. a. 3   **b.** 1   **c.** 1   **d.** $x = -3$ **e.** $x = 0, x = 2$
f. $(-\infty, 3]$ **g.** $(-\infty, 5]$ **59. a.** 3   **b.** $H(4)$ is not defined
because 4 is not in the domain of H.   **c.** 4   **d.** $x = -3$ and
$x = 2$ **e.** All x on the interval $[-2, 1]$ **f.** $[-4, 4)$ **g.** $[2, 5)$
61. $\{-3, -7, -\frac{3}{2}, 1.2\}$ **63.** $\{6, 0\}$
65. $x = -3$ and $x = 12$ **67.** $x = 6$ and $x = 1$ **69.** -3

71. The domain is the set of all real numbers for which the
denominator is not zero. Set the denominator equal to zero,
and solve the resulting equation. The solution(s) to the
equation must be excluded from the domain. In this case,
setting $x - 2 = 0$ indicates that $x = 2$ must be excluded from
the domain. The domain is $(-\infty, 2) \cup (2, \infty)$.
73. $(-\infty, -6) \cup (-6, \infty)$ **75.** $(-\infty, 0) \cup (0, \infty)$
77. $(-\infty, \infty)$ **79.** $[-7, \infty)$ **81.** $[3, \infty)$ **83.** $(-\infty, \frac{1}{2}]$
85. $(-\infty, \infty)$ **87.** $(-\infty, \infty)$ **89. a.** $h(1) = 64$
and $h(1.5) = 44$ **b.** $h(1) = 64$ means that after 1 sec, the
height of the ball is 64 ft. $h(1.5) = 44$ means that after 1.5
sec, the height of the ball is 44 ft.   **91. a.** $d(1) = 11.5$ and
$d(1.5) = 17.25$ **b.** $d(1) = 11.5$ means that after 1 hr, the
distance traveled is 11.5 mi. $d(1.5) = 17.25$ means that after
1.5 hr, the distance traveled is 17.25 mi.   **93. a.** $f(1) \approx 1.44$
means in 2001 there were approximately 1.44 million violent
crimes.   **b.** $f(5) \approx 1.39$ means in 2005 there were approximately
1.39 million violent crimes.   **c.** In 2000 and 2002 ($x = 0$ and $x = 2$)
there were approximately 1.425 million violent crimes.
95. $f(x) = 2x + 3$ **97.** $f(x) = |x| - 10$ **99.** $(-2, \infty)$

Section 8.2 Graphing Calculator Exercises, p. 582

101.

102.

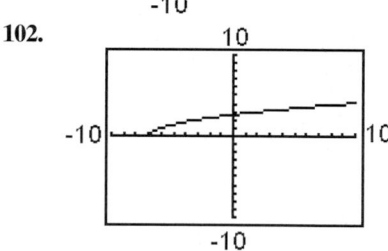

Section 8.3 Practice Exercises, pp. 590–594

3. a. Yes   **b.** $\{7, 2, -5\}$ **c.** $\{3\}$
5. $f(3) = 9$ means that 9 lb of force is required to stretch
the spring 3 in. $f(10) = 30$ means that 30 lb of force is
required to stretch the spring 10 in.   **7.** horizontal
9. Domain $(-\infty, \infty)$; range $\{2\}$

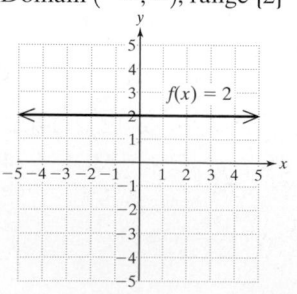

11.

x	$f(x)$	x	$f(x)$
-2	$-\frac{1}{2}$	$\frac{1}{4}$	4
-1	-1	$\frac{1}{2}$	2
$-\frac{1}{2}$	-2	1	1
$-\frac{1}{4}$	-4	2	$\frac{1}{2}$

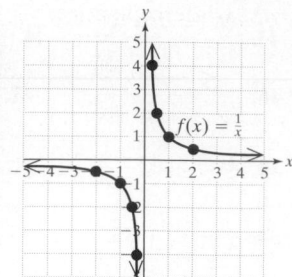

13.

x	$h(x)$
-2	-8
-1	-1
0	0
1	1
2	8

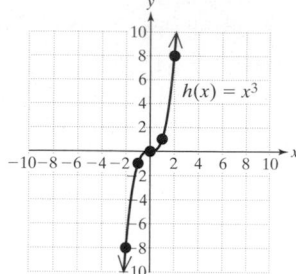

15.

x	$q(x)$
-2	4
-1	1
0	0
1	1
2	4

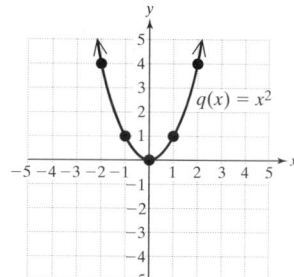

17. Quadratic   **19.** Linear   **21.** Constant
23. None of these   **25.** Linear   **27.** None of these
29. x-intercept: $(2, 0)$; y-intercept: $(0, -10)$

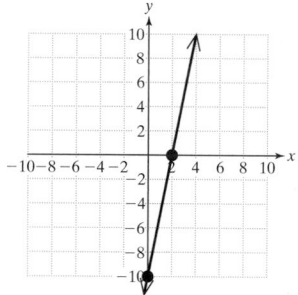

31. x-intercept: $\left(\frac{5}{6}, 0\right)$; y-intercept: $(0, 5)$

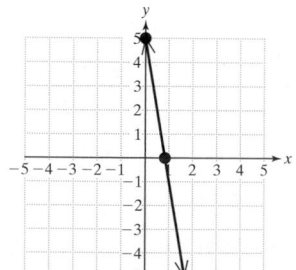

33. x-intercept: none; y-intercept: $(0, 18)$

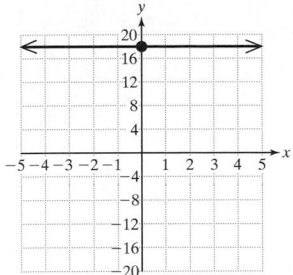

35. x-intercept: $(-3, 0)$; y-intercept: $(0, 2)$

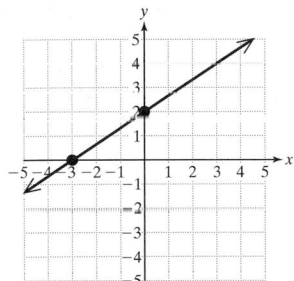

37. a. $x = -1$ **b.** $f(0) = 1$ **39. a.** $x = -2$ and $x = 2$
b. $f(0) = -2$ **41. a.** None **b.** $f(0) = 2$
43. a. $(-\infty, \infty)$ **b.** $(0, 0)$ **c.** vi   **45. a.** $(-\infty, \infty)$
b. $(0, 1)$ **c.** viii   **47. a.** $[-1, \infty)$ **b.** $(0, 1)$ **c.** vii

49. a. $(-\infty, 3) \cup (3, \infty)$ **b.** $\left(0, -\dfrac{1}{3}\right)$ **c.** ii

51. a. $(-\infty, \infty)$ **b.** $(0, 2)$ **c.** iv   **53. a.** Linear
b. $G(90) = 82.5$. This means that if the student gets a 90%
score on her final exam, then her overall course average is
82.5%. **c.** $G(50) = 72.5$. This means that if the student gets a
50% score on her final exam, then her overall course average
is 72.5%.

Section 8.3 Graphing Calculator Exercises, p. 594

55.

56.

57.

58.

59.

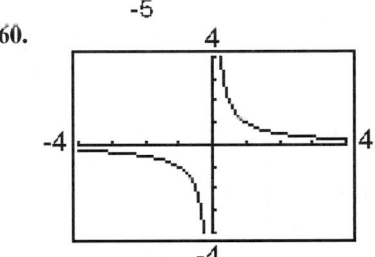

60.

61. x-intercept: $(8, 0)$; y-intercept: $(0, 1)$ **62.** x-intercept:
$(-6, 0)$; y-intercept: $(0, -3)$ **63.** x-intercept: $(-5, 0)$;
y-intercept: $(0, 4)$ **64.** x-intercept: $(2, 0)$; y-intercept: $(0, -7)$

Chapter 8 Problem Recognition Exercises, p. 595

1. a, c, d, f, g   **2.** a, b, d, f, h   **3.** 4   **4.** 2
5. $\{0, 1, \frac{1}{2}, -3, 2\}$ **6.** $\{4, 3, 6, 1, 10\}$ **7.** $[-2, 4]$

8. $[0, \infty)$ **9.** 0   **10.** $\left(\dfrac{9}{5}, 0\right)$ **11.** $(0, -1), (0, 1)$

12. 1   **13.** c   **14.** d   **15.** 3

Section 8.4 Practice Exercises, pp. 600–602

3. $(f + g)(x) = 2x^2 + 5x + 4$
5. $(g - f)(x) = 2x^2 + 3x - 4$
7. $(f \cdot h)(x) = x^3 + 4x^2 + x + 4$
9. $(g \cdot f)(x) = 2x^3 + 12x^2 + 16x$

11. $\left(\dfrac{h}{f}\right)(x) = \dfrac{x^2 + 1}{x + 4}, x \neq -4$

13. $\left(\dfrac{f}{g}\right)(x) = \dfrac{x + 4}{2x^2 + 4x}, x \neq 0, x \neq -2$

15. $(f \circ g)(x) = 2x^2 + 4x + 4$
17. $(g \circ f)(x) = 2x^2 + 20x + 48$

19. $(k \circ h)(x) = \dfrac{1}{x^2 + 1}$

21. $(k \circ g)(x) = \dfrac{1}{2x^2 + 4x}, x \neq 0, x \neq -2$ **23.** No

25. $(f \circ g)(x) = 25x^2 - 15x + 1; (g \circ f)(x) = 5x^2 - 15x + 5$
27. $(f \circ g)(x) = |x^3 - 1|; (g \circ f)(x) = |x|^3 - 1$
29. $(h \circ h)(x) = 25x - 24$ **31.** 0   **33.** -64 **35.** 2

37. 1   **39.** $\dfrac{1}{64}$ **41.** 0   **43.** Not a real number

45. $\dfrac{4}{9}$ **47.** -2 **49.** 2   **51.** 0   **53.** 1   **55.** 0

57. Undefined   **59.** -1 **61.** 2   **63.** 2   **65.** -1
67. -2 **69.** 3   **71.** -6 **73.** -1 **75.** 4
77. 0   **79.** 2   **81. a.** $P(x) = 3.78x - 1$ **b.** \$188
83. a. $F(t) = 0.2t + 6.4$; F represents the amount of child
support (in billion dollars) not paid.   **b.** $F(4) = 7.2$ means
that in 2004, \$7.2 billion of child support was not paid.
85. a. $(D \circ r)(t) = 560t$; This function represents the total
distance Joe travels as a function of time that he rides.
b. 5600 ft

Section 8.5 Practice Exercises, pp. 608–611

3. $x^2 - 4x + 4$ **5.** $x^2 - 2$ **7.** -1 **9.** Inversely

11. $T = kq$ **13.** $b = \dfrac{k}{c}$ **15.** $Q = \dfrac{kx}{y}$ **17.** $c = kst$

19. $L = kw\sqrt{v}$ **21.** $x = \dfrac{ky^2}{z}$ **23.** $k = \dfrac{9}{2}$

25. $k = 512$ **27.** $k = 1.75$ **29.** $x = 70$ **31.** $b = 6$

33. $Z = 56$ **35.** $Q = 9$ **37.** $L = 9$ **39.** $B = \dfrac{15}{2}$

41. a. The heart weighs 0.92 lb.   **b.** Answers will vary.
43. a. 3.6 g   **b.** 4.5 g   **c.** 2.4 g   **45. a.** \$0.40   **b.** \$0.30
c. \$1.00   **47.** 355,000 tons   **49.** 42.6 ft   **51.** 300 W
53. 18.5 A   **55.** 20 lb   **57.** \$3500

Chapter 8 Review Exercises, pp. 616–619

1. Domain; $\left\{\dfrac{1}{3}, 6, \dfrac{1}{4}, 7\right\}$; range; $\left\{10, -\dfrac{1}{2}, 4, \dfrac{2}{5}\right\}$

2. Domain; $\{-3, -1, 0, 2, 3\}$; range; $\left\{-2, 0, 1, \dfrac{5}{2}\right\}$

3. Domain; $[-3, 9]$; range; $[0, 60]$ **4.** Domain; $[-4, 4]$;
range; $[1, 3]$

5.

6.
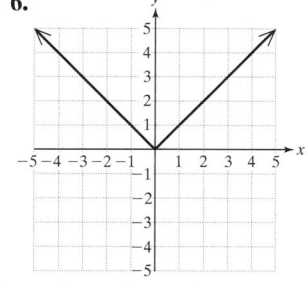

7. a. Not a function   **b.** $[1, 3]$ **c.** $[-4, 4]$
8. a. Function   **b.** $(-\infty, \infty)$ **c.** $(-\infty, 0.35]$
9. a. Function   **b.** $\{1, 2, 3, 4\}$ **c.** $\{3\}$
10. a. Not a function   **b.** $\{0, 4\}$ **c.** $\{2, 3, 4, 5\}$
11. a. Not a function   **b.** $\{4, 9\}$ **c.** $\{2, -2, 3, -3\}$
12. a. Function   **b.** $\{6, 7, 8, 9\}$ **c.** $\{9, 10, 11, 12\}$
13. -4 **14.** 2   **15.** 2   **16.** $6t^2 - 4$ **17.** $6b^2 - 4$
18. $6\pi^2 - 4$ **19.** $6a^2 - 4$ **20.** 20   **21.** $(-\infty, \infty)$
22. $(-\infty, 11) \cup (11, \infty)$ **23.** $[8, \infty)$ **24.** $[-2, \infty)$
25. a. \$98   **b.** \$123   **c.** \$148

26.

27.

28.

29.

30.

31.

32.

33.
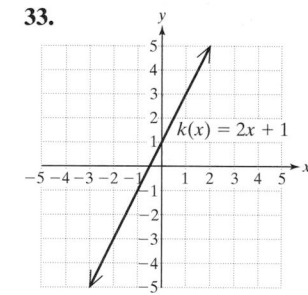

34. a. $s(4) = 4$, $s(-3) = 25$, $s(2) = 0$, $s(1) = 1$, $s(0) = 4$
b. $(-\infty, \infty)$ **35. a.** $r(2)$ is not a real number,
$r(4) = 0$, $r(5) = 2$, $r(8) = 4$ **b.** $[4, \infty)$
36. a. $h(-3) = -\dfrac{1}{2}$, $h(0) = -1$, $h(2) = -3$, $h(5) = \dfrac{3}{2}$
b. $(-\infty, 3) \cup (3, \infty)$
37. a. $k(-5) = -2$, $k(-4) = -1$, $k(-3) = 0$,
$k(2) = -5$ **b.** $(-\infty, \infty)$ **38.** x-intercept: $\left(\dfrac{7}{4}, 0\right)$;
y-intercept: $(0, -7)$
39. x-intercept: $\left(\dfrac{9}{2}, 0\right)$; y-intercept: $(0, 9)$

40. a. $b(0) = 4.5$. In 1985 consumption was 4.5 gal of bottled
water per capita. $b(7) = 9.4$. In 1992 consumption was 9.4 gal of
bottled water per capita.   **b.** $m = 0.7$. Consumption
increased at a rate of 0.7 gal/year.
41. -1 **42.** 0   **43.** $x = 0$ and $x = 4$
44. There are no values of x for which $g(x) = 4$.
45. $(-4, \infty)$ **46.** $(-\infty, 1]$ **47.** $(f - g)(x) = 2x^3 + 9x - 7$

48. $(f + g)(x) = -2x^3 - 7x - 7$

49. $(f \cdot n)(x) = \dfrac{x - 7}{x - 2}, x \neq 2$

50. $(f \cdot m)(x) = x^3 - 7x^2$

51. $\left(\dfrac{f}{g}\right)(x) = \dfrac{x - 7}{-2x^3 - 8x}; x \neq 0$

52. $\left(\dfrac{g}{f}\right)(x) = \dfrac{-2x^3 - 8x}{x - 7}, x \neq 7$

53. $(m \circ f)(x) = (x - 7)^2$ or $x^2 - 14x + 49$

54. $(n \circ f)(x) = \dfrac{1}{x - 9}, x \neq 9$ **55.** 100 **56.** $\dfrac{1}{8}$

57. -167 **58.** -10 **59. a.** $(2x + 1)^2$ or $4x^2 + 4x + 1$

b. $2x^2 + 1$ **c.** No, $f \circ g \neq g \circ f$ **60.** $\dfrac{1}{4}$ **61.** -3

62. 0 **63.** -1 **64.** 4 **65.** 1 **66. a.** $F = kd$

b. $k = 3$ **c.** 12.6 lb **67.** $y = \dfrac{8}{3}$ **68.** $y = 12$ **69.** 48 km

Chapter 8 Test, pp. 619–620

1. a. Not a function **b.** $\{-3, -1, 1, 3\}$

c. $\{-2, -1, 1, 3\}$ **2. a.** Function **b.** $(-\infty, \infty)$

c. $(-\infty, 0]$ **3.** To find the x-intercept(s), solve for the real solutions of the equation $f(x) = 0$. To find the y-intercept, find $f(0)$.

4.

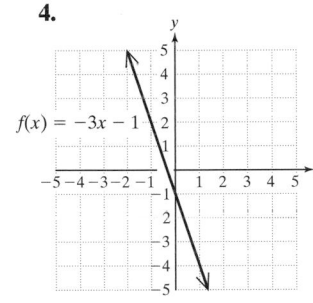

$f(x) = -3x - 1$

5.

$k(x) = -2$

6.

$p(x) = x^2$

7.

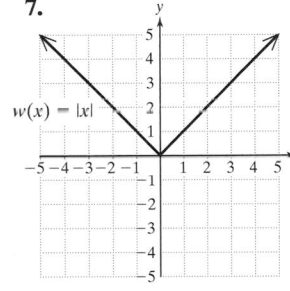

$w(x) = |x|$

8. $(-\infty, -7) \cup (-7, \infty)$ **9.** $[-7, \infty)$ **10.** $(-\infty, \infty)$

11. a. $r(-2) = 9, r(0) = 1, r(3) = 4$ **b.** $(-\infty, \infty)$

12. $s(0) = 36$. In 1985 the per capita consumption was 36 gal. $s(7) = 47.2$. In 1992 the per capita consumption was 47.2 gal. **13.** 1 **14.** 2 **15.** $(-1, 7]$ **16.** $[-1, 4)$

17. False **18.** $(6, 0)$ **19.** $x = 6$ **20.** All x in the interval $[1, 3]$ and $x = 5$ **21.** Quadratic **22.** Linear

23. Constant **24.** None of these

25. x-intercept: $(-12, 0)$; y-intercept: $(0, 9)$

26. $\left(\dfrac{f}{g}\right)(x) = \dfrac{x - 4}{x^2 + 2}$ **27.** $(h \cdot g)(x) = \dfrac{x^2 + 2}{x}, x \neq 0$

28. $(g \circ f)(x) = x^2 - 8x + 18$ **29.** $(h \circ f)(x) = \dfrac{1}{x - 4}, x \neq 4$

30. -48 **31.** $-\dfrac{3}{2}$ **32.** $\dfrac{1}{18}$ **33.** 18

34. $\left(\dfrac{g}{f}\right)(x) = \dfrac{x^2 + 2}{x - 4}, x \neq 4$ **35.** 8.25 mL

36. 200 drinks are sold.

Chapters 1–8 Cumulative Review Exercises, p. 621

1. -1 **2.** $21x - 62y + 12$ **3.** $\{-15\}$ **4.** $\{\ \}$

5. $[-3, \infty)$ **6.** x-intercept: $\left(\dfrac{10}{3}, 0\right)$ y-intercept: $(0, -2)$

7. $m = -\dfrac{1}{5}$ **8.** $m = \dfrac{5}{2}$ **9.** $\{(2, -1)\}$ **10.** $\{(-4, 0, 5)\}$

11. $\dfrac{9x^2}{y^6}$ **12.** $5x^2 - 8x + 7$ **13.** $-10x^3 + 47x^2 - 42x$

14. $(2x + 1)(x + 3)$ **15.** $5(x - 4)(x + 4)$

16. $\dfrac{x^2 + 5}{(x - 5)(x + 1)}$ **17.** $\dfrac{x + 2}{x^2}$ **18.** Domain: $\{2, -1, 9, -6\}$

Range: $\{4, 2, 8\}$ **19.** $(-\infty, 0) \cup (0, \infty)$

20. $(f \circ g)(x) = x^2 + 2x - 5$

Chapter 9

Chapter Opener Puzzle

1. b **2.** g **3.** f **4.** a **5.** e **6.** c **7.** d **8.** h

Section 9.1 Practice Exercises, pp. 632–635

3. $(-\infty, 2]$ **5.** $(-\infty, 15)$ **7. a.** $\{-3, -1\}$

b. $\{-4, -3, -2, -1, 0, 1, 3, 5\}$ **9.** $[-7, -4)$

11. $(-\infty, -4) \cup (2, \infty)$ **13.** $\{\ \}$ **15.** $[-7, \infty)$

17. $[0, 5)$ **19.** $[-7, \infty)$ **21. a.** $[-1, 5)$ **b.** $(-2, \infty)$

23. a. $(-1, 3)$ **b.** $\left(-\dfrac{5}{2}, \dfrac{9}{2}\right)$ **25. a.** $(0, 2]$ **b.** $(-4, 5]$

27. $[-2, 3]$

29. $(3, 6)$

31. $(-\infty, 2]$

33. $[8, \infty)$

35. $\{\ \}$ **37.** $-4 \leq t$ and $t < \dfrac{3}{4}$ **39.** The statement $6 < x < 2$ is equivalent to $6 < x$ and $x < 2$. However, no real number is greater than 6 and also less than 2.

41. The statement $-5 > y > -2$ is equivalent to $-5 > y$ and $y > -2$. However, no real number is less than -5 and also greater than -2.

43. $\left[\dfrac{5}{2}, 7\right)$

45. $(-6, 6]$

47. $(2, 8)$

49. $\left[-\dfrac{10}{3}, -\dfrac{7}{3}\right]$

51. $\left[-\dfrac{1}{2}, \dfrac{3}{2}\right)$

53. $(-0.4, 0.2)$

55. $(-\infty, -2) \cup [2, \infty)$

57. $(-\infty, 2]$

59. $[-6, \infty)$

61. $(-\infty, \infty)$

63. $(-\infty, -4] \cup (4.5, \infty)$

65. a. $(-10, 8)$ **b.** $(-\infty, \infty)$
67. a. $(-\infty, -8] \cup [1.3, \infty)$ **b.** $\{\,\}$
69. $\left(-\dfrac{11}{2}, \dfrac{7}{2}\right]$ **71.** $\left(-\dfrac{13}{2}, \infty\right)$ **73.** $(-\infty, 1) \cup (5, \infty)$
75. a. $4800 \le x \le 10{,}800$ **b.** $x < 4800$ or $x > 10{,}800$
77. a. $200{,}000 \le x \le 350{,}000$
b. $x < 200{,}000$ or $x > 350{,}000$
79. All real numbers between $-\dfrac{3}{2}$ and 6
81. All real numbers greater than 2 or less than -1
83. a. Amy would need 82% or better on her final exam.
b. If Amy scores at least 32% and less than 82% on her final exam she will receive a "B" in the class.
85. $32° \le F \le 42.08°$

Section 9.2 Practice Exercises, pp. 642–645

3. $(-\infty, -4) \cup \left(\dfrac{1}{3}, \infty\right)$ **5.** $\left[3, \dfrac{16}{5}\right]$ **7.** $[-1, 3]$
9. a. $(-\infty, -2) \cup (3, \infty)$ **b.** $(-2, 3)$ **c.** $[-2, 3]$
d. $(-\infty, -2] \cup [3, \infty)$ **11. a.** $(-2, 0) \cup (3, \infty)$
b. $(-\infty, -2) \cup (0, 3)$ **c.** $(-\infty, -2] \cup [0, 3]$
d. $[-2, 0] \cup [3, \infty)$ **13. a.** $\{4, -\tfrac{1}{2}\}$ **b.** $(-\infty, -\tfrac{1}{2}) \cup (4, \infty)$
c. $(-\tfrac{1}{2}, 4)$ **15. a.** $\{-10, 3\}$ **b.** $(-10, 3)$
c. $(-\infty, -10) \cup (3, \infty)$ **17. a.** $\left\{-\dfrac{1}{2}, 3\right\}$ **b.** $\left[-\dfrac{1}{2}, 3\right]$
c. $\left(-\infty, -\dfrac{1}{2}\right] \cup [3, \infty)$ **19.** $(1, 7)$
21. $(-\infty, -2) \cup (5, \infty)$ **23.** $[-5, 0]$ **25.** $[4, 8]$
27. $\left(-\infty, -\dfrac{1}{5}\right) \cup (1, \infty)$ **29.** $(-11, 11)$
31. $\left(-\infty, -\dfrac{1}{3}\right] \cup [3, \infty)$ **33.** $(-\infty, -3] \cup [0, 4]$
35. $(-2, -1) \cup (2, \infty)$ **37. a.** $(-1, 1]$
b. $(-\infty, -1) \cup [1, \infty)$ **c.** $(-\infty, -1) \cup (1, \infty)$ **d.** $(-1, 1)$
39. a. $(-\infty, -1) \cup (2, \infty)$ **b.** $(-1, 2)$ **c.** $[-1, 2)$
d. $(-\infty, -1] \cup (2, \infty)$ **41. a.** $\{7\}$ **b.** $(-\infty, 5) \cup (7, \infty)$
c. $(5, 7)$ **43. a.** $\{4\}$ **b.** $[4, 6)$ **c.** $(-\infty, 4] \cup (6, \infty)$
45. $(1, \infty)$ **47.** $(-\infty, -4) \cup (4, \infty)$
49. $\left(2, \dfrac{7}{2}\right)$ **51.** $(5, 7]$ **53.** $(-\infty, 0) \cup \left[\dfrac{1}{2}, \infty\right)$

55. $(0, \infty)$ **57.** Quadratic; $[-4, 4]$
59. Quadratic; $(-\infty, -\tfrac{4}{5}) \cup (0, \infty)$ **61.** Linear; $(-\tfrac{5}{2}, \infty)$
63. Rational; $(-\infty, -1)$ **65.** Polynomial (degree > 2);
$(0, 5) \cup (5, \infty)$ **67.** Polynomial (degree > 2); $(2, \infty)$
69. Polynomial (degree > 2); $(-\infty, 5]$
71. Quadratic; $(-2, 2)$
73. Rational; $(-\infty, -2] \cup (5, \infty)$ **75.** Linear; $(-\infty, 5]$
77. $(-\infty, \infty)$ **79.** $\{\,\}$ **81.** $\{0\}$ **83.** $\{\,\}$ **85.** $\{\,\}$
87. $(-\infty, \infty)$ **89.** $(-\infty, -11) \cup (-11, \infty)$ **91.** $\{\tfrac{3}{2}\}$

Section 9.2 Graphing Calculator Exercises, p. 645

93. $(-\infty, 0) \cup (2, \infty)$

94. $(0, 2)$

95. $(-1, 1)$

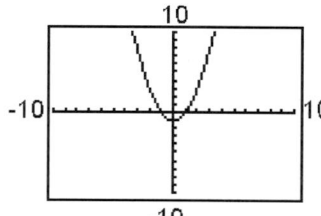

96. $(-\infty, -1) \cup (1, \infty)$

97. $\{-5\}$

98. {5}

99. { }

100. { }

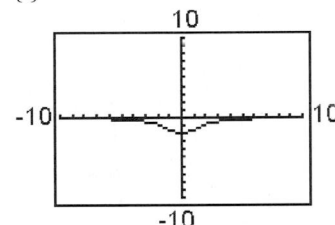

Section 9.3 Practice Exercises, pp. 651–652

3. $(-\infty, -1] \cup [1, \infty)$ **5.** $(-\infty, \ 1) \cup \left[\dfrac{1}{2}, \infty\right)$

7. $\{7, -7\}$ **9.** $\{6, -6\}$ **11.** $\{\sqrt{2}, -\sqrt{2}\}$ **13.** { }

15. $\{0\}$ **17.** $\left\{4, -\dfrac{4}{3}\right\}$ **19.** $\left\{\dfrac{9}{2}, -\dfrac{1}{2}\right\}$ **21.** $\left\{\dfrac{10}{7}, -\dfrac{8}{7}\right\}$

23. { }   **25.** $\{-12, 28\}$ **27.** $\left\{\dfrac{5}{2}, -\dfrac{7}{2}\right\}$ **29.** $\left\{\dfrac{7}{3}\right\}$

31. { }   **33.** $\left\{\dfrac{3}{2}\right\}$ **35.** $\left\{-4, \dfrac{16}{5}\right\}$ **37.** $\left\{-\dfrac{1}{2}, \dfrac{7}{6}\right\}$

39. $\left\{\dfrac{5}{2}, -\dfrac{3}{2}\right\}$ **41.** $\left\{-4, \dfrac{1}{3}\right\}$ **43.** $\left\{\dfrac{1}{2}\right\}$ **45.** $\left\{-\dfrac{1}{16}\right\}$

47. $\left\{\dfrac{1}{4}\right\}$ **49.** $\{-1.44, -0.4\}$ **51.** { }   **53.** $|x| = 6$

55. $|x| = \dfrac{4}{3}$

Section 9.3 Graphing Calculator Exercises, p. 652

57. $\left\{2, -\dfrac{1}{2}\right\}$

58. {7, 1}

59. { }

60. { }

61. $\left\{\dfrac{1}{2}\right\}$

62. $\{-1\}$

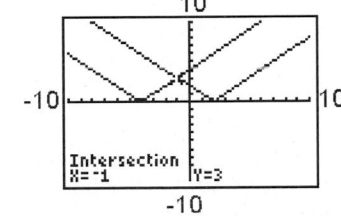

Section 9.4 Practice Exercises, pp. 660–662

3. $\left\{\dfrac{4}{7}, \dfrac{6}{7}\right\}$ **5.** $(-3, -1]$ ⟶ with marks at -3 and -1

7. $(-\infty, \infty)$ **9. a.** $\{-5, 5\}$

b. $(-\infty, -5) \cup (5, \infty)$ with marks at -5 and 5

c. $(-5, 5)$ with marks at -5 and 5 **11. a.** $\{10, -4\}$

b. $(-\infty, -4) \cup (10, \infty)$ with marks at -4 and 10

c. $(-4, 10)$ with marks at -4 and 10

13. a. $\{\ \}$ **b.** $(-\infty, \infty)$

c. $\{\ \}$ **15. a.** $\{\ \}$

b. $(-\infty, \infty)$ **c.** $\{\ \}$

17. a. $\{0\}$ **b.** $(-\infty, 0) \cup (0, \infty)$ with mark at 0

c. $\{\ \}$ **19. a.** $\{7\}$

b. $(-\infty, 7) \cup (7, \infty)$ with mark at 7 **c.** $\{\ \}$

21. $(-\infty, -6) \cup (6, \infty)$ with marks at -6 and 6

23. $[-3, 3]$ with marks at -3 and 3

25. $(-\infty, \infty)$

27. $(-\infty, -2] \cup [3, \infty)$ with marks at -2 and 3

29. $\{\ \}$ **31.** $[-10, 14]$ with marks at -10 and 14

33. $\left(-\infty, -\dfrac{5}{4}\right] \cup \left[\dfrac{23}{4}, \infty\right)$ with marks at $-\dfrac{5}{4}$ and $\dfrac{23}{4}$

35. $\left(-\dfrac{21}{2}, \dfrac{19}{2}\right)$ with marks at $-\dfrac{21}{2}$ and $\dfrac{19}{2}$

37. $(-\infty, \infty)$

39. $\{\ \}$ **41.** $\{-5\}$ with mark at -5

43. $(-\infty, 6) \cup (6, \infty)$ with mark at 6

45. $(-\infty, 2] \cup [4, \infty)$ with marks at 2 and 4

47. $(4, 8)$ with marks at 4 and 8

49. $(-10.5, 4.5)$ with marks at -10.5 and 4.5

51. $|x| > 7$ **53.** $|x - 2| \le 13$ **55.** $|x - 32| \le 0.05$

57. $\left| x - 6\dfrac{3}{4} \right| \le \dfrac{1}{8}$

59. $1.99 \le w \le 2.01$ or, equivalently in interval notation, $[1.99, 2.01]$. This means that the actual width of the bolt could be between 1.99 cm and 2.01 cm inclusive.   **61.** b   **63.** a

Section 9.4 Graphing Calculator Exercises, p. 663

65. $(-\infty, -6) \cup (2, \infty)$

66. $(-\infty, -3) \cup (9, \infty)$

67. $(-7, 5)$

68. $(-3, 5)$

69. $\{\ \}$

70. $\{\ \}$

71. $(-\infty, \infty)$

72. $(-\infty, \infty)$

73. $\left\{ -\dfrac{1}{6} \right\}$

74. $\left\{ \dfrac{4}{3} \right\}$

Chapter 9 Problem Recognition Exercises, p. 663

1. Quadratic; $(-\infty, -9) \cup (-1, \infty)$ **2.** Linear; $\{-26\}$

3. Rational; $[-8, -2)$ **4.** Quadratic; $\{-\frac{1}{4}, 2\}$

5. Absolute value, $(-\frac{1}{3}, 1)$ **6.** Quadratic; $\{\ \}$

7. Linear; $(-\infty, -10)$ **8.** Quadratic; $[-4, 1]$

9. Quadratic; $(-\infty, -1] \cup [\frac{2}{3}, \infty)$ **10.** Rational; $\{-\frac{11}{3}\}$

11. Linear; $\left[\dfrac{16}{7}, \infty \right)$ **12.** Absolute value; $\{\ \}$

13. Polynomial; $[-5, -\frac{1}{2}] \cup [3, \infty)$ **14.** Quadratic; $(-\infty, \infty)$

15. Rational; $(-\infty, -1) \cup (2, \infty)$ **16.** Quadratic; $\{-1, 5\}$

17. Absolute value; $(-\infty, -8) \cup (-8, \infty)$

18. Quadratic; $(-6, 6)$ **19.** Polynomial; $\{2, -2, -\frac{5}{3}\}$

20. Absolute value; $\{12, -4\}$ **21.** Linear; $\{0\}$

22. Rational; $(-\infty, 0] \cup (5, \infty)$ **23.** Absolute value; $\{-\frac{1}{2}\}$

24. Polynomial; $(-\frac{3}{2}, 0)$

Section 9.5 Practice Exercises, pp. 671–676

3. $[1, 3)$ **5.** $(-\infty, -4] \cup (-2, \infty)$ **7. a.** No **b.** No
c. Yes **d.** Yes   **9. a.** No **b.** Yes **c.** Yes **d.** No
11. $>$ **13.** $\geq$ **15.** $\geq, \leq$

17.

19.

21.

23.

25.

27.

29.

31.

33.

35.

37.

39.

41.

43.

45.

47.

49.

51.

53.

55.

57.

59.

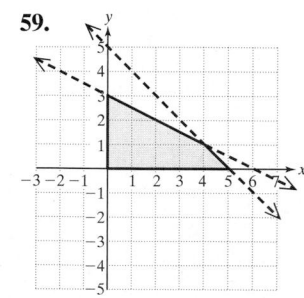

61. a. $2x + 2y \leq 40$

b.

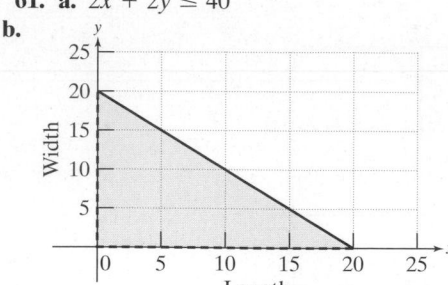

63. a. $x \geq 0, y \geq 0$ **b.** $x \leq 40, y \leq 40$ **c.** $x + y \geq 65$

d.

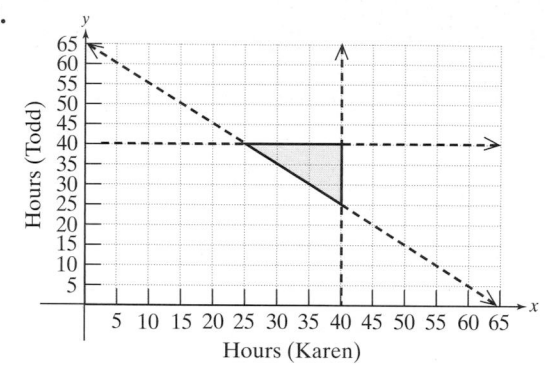

e. Yes; The point $(35, 40)$ means that Karen works 35 hr and Todd works 40 hr.   **f.** No; The point $(20, 40)$ means that Karen works 20 hr and Todd works 40 hr. This does not satisfy the constraint that there must be at least 65 hr total.

Chapter 9 Review Exercises, pp. 683–686

1. $C \cap D$ is the set of elements common to both sets C and D.

$C \cup D$ is the set of elements in either set C, set D, or both sets.

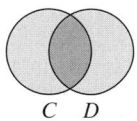

2. $[-10, 1)$ **3.** $(-\infty, \infty)$ **4.** $(-\infty, \infty)$ **5.** $(-1, 1)$

6. $(-\infty, -3] \cup (-1, \infty)$ **7.** $\{\}$ **8.** $\left(-\dfrac{11}{4}, 4\right]$

9. $[-5, 2)$ **10.** $(-\infty, 6] \cup (12, \infty)$

11. $(-\infty, -2) \cup [2, \infty)$ **12.** $\left[0, \dfrac{4}{3}\right]$ **13.** $[-7, -2)$

14. a. $140 \leq x \leq 225$ **b.** $x < 140$ or $x > 225$

15. a. $125 \leq x \leq 200$ **b.** $x < 125$ or $x > 200$

16. a. $(-2, 0)$ and $(2, 0)$ are the x-intercepts.   **b.** On the interval $(-2, 2)$ the graph is below the x-axis.   **c.** On the intervals $(-\infty, -2)$ and $(2, \infty)$ the graph is above the x-axis.

17. a. $x = 0$; $(0, 0)$ is the x-intercept.   **b.** $x = 2$ is the vertical asymptote.   **c.** On the intervals $(-\infty, 0]$ and $(2, \infty)$ the graph is on or above the x-axis.   **d.** On the interval $[0, 2)$ the graph is on or below the x-axis.   **18.** $(-2, 6)$

19. $(-\infty, \infty)$ **20.** $(-\infty, -2) \cup [0, \infty)$

21. $(-\infty, -1] \cup (1, \infty)$ **22.** $(-2, 0) \cup (5, \infty)$

23. $(-2, 0) \cup \left(\dfrac{5}{2}, \infty\right)$ **24.** $[-3, -1]$

25. $(-\infty, -5) \cup (1, \infty)$ **26.** $(3, \infty)$ **27.** $(-3, \infty)$

28. $\{-5\}$ **29.** $(-\infty, -2) \cup (-2, \infty)$ **30.** $\{10, -10\}$
31. $\{17, -17\}$ **32.** $\{1.3, 7.4\}$ **33.** $\{-0.44, 2.54\}$
34. $\{5, -9\}$ **35.** $\{3, 1\}$ **36.** $\{\,\}$

37. $\{\,\}$ **38.** $\left\{\dfrac{3}{7}\right\}$ **39.** $\left\{-\dfrac{5}{4}\right\}$ **40.** $\left\{6, \dfrac{4}{5}\right\}$

41. $\left\{-\dfrac{1}{2}\right\}$ **42.** Both expressions give the distance between 3 and -2.   **43.** $|x| > 5$ **44.** $|x| < 4$

45. $|x| < 6$ **46.** $|x| > \dfrac{2}{3}$

47. $(-\infty, -14] \cup [2, \infty)$

48. $[-11, -5]$

49. $\left(-\infty, \dfrac{1}{7}\right) \cup \left(\dfrac{1}{7}, \infty\right)$

50. $\left(-\infty, -\dfrac{1}{5}\right) \cup \left(-\dfrac{1}{5}, \infty\right)$

51. $\left[-2, -\dfrac{2}{3}\right]$

52. $\left[0, \dfrac{6}{5}\right]$

53. $(2, 22)$

54. $(-12, 0)$

55. $(-\infty, \infty)$
56. $(-\infty, \infty)$
57. $(-\infty, \infty)$
58. $(-\infty, \infty)$

59. $\{\,\}$ **60.** $\{\,\}$ **61.** If an absolute value is less than a negative number, there will be no solution.   **62.** If an absolute value is greater than a negative number, then all real numbers are solutions.   **63.** $0.17 \le p \le 0.23$ or, equivalently in interval notation, $[0.17, 0.23]$. This means that the actual percentage of viewers is estimated to be between 17% and 23% inclusive.   **64.** $3\frac{1}{8} \le L \le 3\frac{5}{8}$ or, equivalently in interval notation, $[3\frac{1}{8}, 3\frac{5}{8}]$. This means that the actual length of the screw may be between $3\frac{1}{8}$ in. and $3\frac{5}{8}$ in., inclusive.

65.

66.

67.

68.

69.

70.

71.

72.

73.

74.

75.

76.

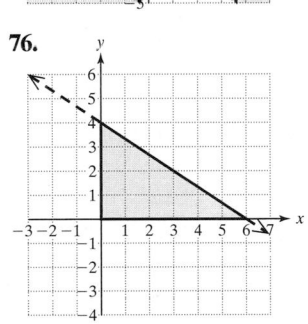

77. a. $x \geq 0, y \geq 0$ **b.** $x + y \leq 100$ **c.** $x \geq 4y$
d.

Chapter 9 Test, pp. 686–687

1. $\left[-\dfrac{1}{3}, 2\right]$ **2.** $(-\infty, -24] \cup [-15, \infty)$

3. $[-3, 0)$ **4.** $(-\infty, \infty)$ **5.** $\{\ \}$

6. a. $9 \leq x \leq 33$ **b.** $x < 9$ or $x > 33$

7. $(-5, 5)$ **8.** $(-\infty, -3) \cup (-2, 2)$ **9.** $\{\ \}$

10. $\{-11\}$ **11.** $\left[\dfrac{1}{2}, 6\right)$ **12.** $\left(-3, -\dfrac{3}{2}\right)$

13. $\{10, -22\}$ **14.** $\{-8, 2\}$ **15.** $\{\ \}$

16. $\left(-\infty, -\dfrac{1}{3}\right) \cup \left(\dfrac{17}{3}, \infty\right)$ **17.** $(-18.75, 17.25)$

18. $(-\infty, \infty)$ **19.** $|x - 15.41| \leq 0.01$

20.

21.

22.

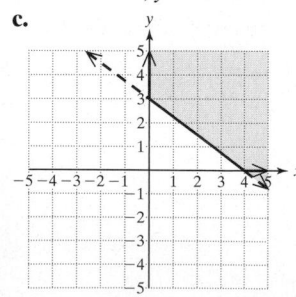

23. a. $x \geq 0, y \geq 0$ **b.** $300x + 400y \geq 1200$
c.

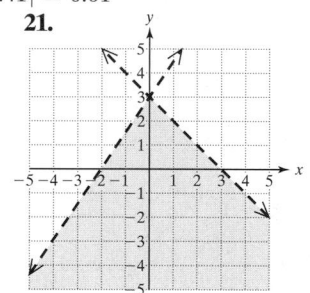

Chapters 1–9 Cumulative Review Exercises, pp. 687–689

1. $x^2 - x - 13$ **2.** $\left\{-\dfrac{3}{2}, 1\right\}$

3. a. $\{0, 6\}$ **b.** $(0, 6)$ **c.** $(-\infty, 0) \cup (6, \infty)$
4. a. $\{14, -10\}$ **b.** $(-10, 14)$ **c.** $(-\infty, -10) \cup (14, \infty)$
5.

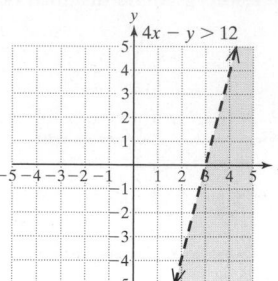

6. a. $t(1) = 9$. After one trial the rat requires 9 min to complete the maze. $t(50) = 3.24$. After 50 trials the rat requires 3.24 min to complete the maze. $t(500) = 3.02$. After 500 trials the rat requires 3.02 min to complete the maze. **b.** The limiting time is 3 min.   **c.** More than 5 trials

7. a. $\left(-\infty, -\dfrac{5}{2}\right] \cup [2, \infty)$ **b.** On these intervals the graph is on or above the x-axis.

8.

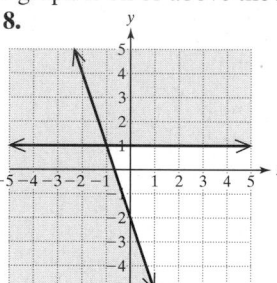

9. $-7x + 13$

10. a. Quotient: $2x^2 - 5x + 12$; remainder: $-24x + 5$

11. a. $b_1 = \dfrac{2A - hb_2}{h}$ or $b_1 = \dfrac{2A}{h} - b_2$ **b.** 10 cm

12. 75 mph   **13.** $57°, 123°$ **14.** $8000 in the 6.5% account; $5000 in the 5% account   **15.** Neither

16. a. x-intercept $(1, 0)$; no y-intercept; undefined slope   **b.** x-intercept $(8, 0)$; y-intercept $(0, 4)$; slope $-\dfrac{1}{2}$

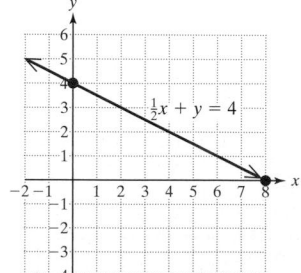

17. $y = -\dfrac{2}{3}x - \dfrac{13}{3}$ **18.** $\{(-1, 3, -2)\}$ **19.** $\dfrac{6}{x^4 y^5}$

20. Plane: 500 mph; wind: 20 mph   **21. a.** Quadratic
b. $P(0) = -2600$. The company will lose $2600 if no desks are produced.   **c.** $P(x) = 0$ for $x = 20$ and $x = 650$. The company will break even ($0 profit) when 20 desks or 650 desks are produced.   **22.** $3(x - 2)^2(x + 2)$

23. $-\dfrac{xy}{x + y}$ **24.** $-\dfrac{a + 1}{a}$ **25.** $\dfrac{2x + 5}{(x - 5)(x - 2)(x + 10)}$

Chapter 10

Chapter Opener Puzzle

I	M	A	G	I	N	A	R	Y		N	U	M	B	E	R
4	8	7	1	4	3	7	6	9		3	5	8	10	2	6

Section 10.1 Practice Exercises, pp. 699–702

3. a. $8, -8$ **b.** 8 **c.** There are two square roots for every positive number. $\sqrt{64}$ identifies the positive square root.

5. a. 9 **b.** -9 **7.** There is no real number b such that $b^2 = -36$. **9.** 7 **11.** -7 **13.** Not a real number

15. $\dfrac{8}{3}$ **17.** 0.9 **19.** -0.4 **21. a.** 8 **b.** 4

c. -8 **d.** -4 **e.** Not a real number **f.** -4

23. -3 **25.** $\dfrac{1}{2}$ **27.** 2 **29.** $-\dfrac{5}{4}$ **31.** Not a real number **33.** 10 **35.** -0.2 **37.** 0.5 **39.** $|a|$

41. a **43.** $|a|$ **45.** $|x+1|$ **47.** $|x|y^2$ **49.** $-\dfrac{x}{y}$

51. $\dfrac{2}{|x|}$ **53.** -92 **55.** 2 **57.** -923 **59.** xy^2

61. $\dfrac{a^3}{b}$ **63.** $-\dfrac{5}{q}$ **65.** $3xy^2z$ **67.** $\dfrac{hk^2}{4}$ **69.** $-\dfrac{t}{3}$

71. $2y^2$ **73.** $2p^2q^3$ **75.** 9 cm **77.** 13 ft
79. They were 5 mi apart. **81.** They are 25 mi apart.
83. a. Not a real number **b.** Not a real number

c. 0 **d.** 1 **e.** 2; Domain: $[2, \infty)$ **85. a.** -2 **b.** -1

c. 0 **d.** 1; Domain: $(-\infty, \infty)$ **87.** $\left(-\infty, \dfrac{5}{2}\right]$

89. $(-\infty, \infty)$ **91.** $[5, \infty)$ **93.** $(-\infty, \infty)$
95. $(-\infty, 1]$; b **97.** $[10, \infty)$; d **99.** $q + p^2$

101. $\dfrac{6}{\sqrt[3]{x}}$ **103.** 8 in.

Section 10.1 Graphing Calculator Exercises, p. 702

105. 8.3066 **106.** 76.1446 **107.** 3.7100
108. -0.5566 **109.** 15.6525 **110.** -6.2403
111. -0.1235 **112.** 1.0622
113.   **114.**

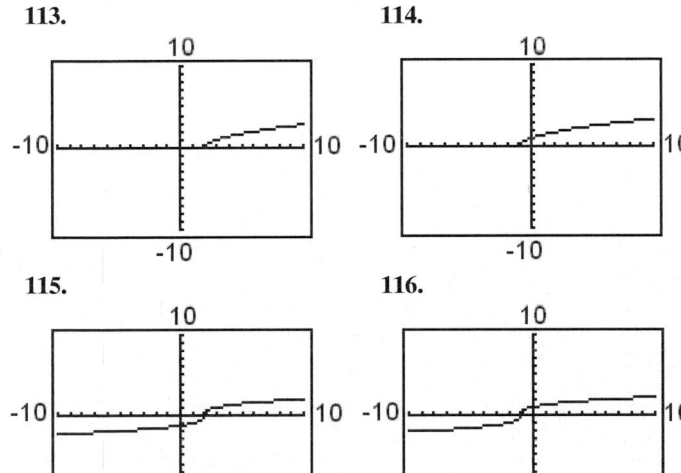

115.   **116.**

Section 10.2 Practice Exercises, pp. 707–710

3. a. 3 **b.** 27 **5.** 5 **7.** 3 **9.** 12 **11.** -12

13. Not a real number **15.** -4 **17.** $\dfrac{1}{5}$ **19.** $-\dfrac{1}{7}$

21. $a^{m/n} = \sqrt[n]{a^m}$; The numerator of the exponent represents the power of the base. The denominator of the exponent represents the index of the radical. **23. a.** 8 **b.** -8

c. Not a real number **d.** $\dfrac{1}{8}$ **e.** $-\dfrac{1}{8}$ **f.** Not a real number

25. a. 125 **b.** -125 **c.** Not a real number **d.** $\dfrac{1}{125}$

e. $-\dfrac{1}{125}$ **f.** Not a real number **27.** $\dfrac{1}{512}$ **29.** 27

31. $-\dfrac{1}{81}$ **33.** $\dfrac{27}{1000}$ **35.** Not a real number **37.** -2

39. -2 **41.** 6 **43.** 10 **45.** $\dfrac{3}{4}$ **47.** 1 **49.** $\dfrac{9}{2}$

51. $\sqrt[3]{q^2}$ **53.** $6\sqrt[4]{y^3}$ **55.** $\sqrt[3]{x^2y}$ **57.** $\dfrac{1}{\sqrt[5]{qr}}$

59. $x^{1/3}$ **61.** $10b^{1/2}$ **63.** $y^{2/3}$ **65.** $(a^2b^3)^{1/4}$

67. $\dfrac{1}{x}$ **69.** p **71.** y^2 **73.** $6^{2/5}$ **75.** $\dfrac{4}{t^{5/3}}$

77. a^7 **79.** $\dfrac{25a^4d}{c}$ **81.** $\dfrac{y^9}{x^8}$ **83.** $\dfrac{2z^3}{w}$ **85.** $5xy^2z^3$

87. $x^{13}z^{4/3}$ **89.** $\dfrac{x^3y^2}{z^5}$ **91. a.** 10.9% **b.** 8.8%

c. The account in part (a). **93.** 2.7 in. **95.** $\sqrt{y}$
97. $\sqrt[4]{z}$ **99.** $\sqrt[3]{x^2}$ **101.** $y\sqrt{x}$ **103.** $4x^4y^3$
105. $2xy^2z^2\sqrt[3]{yz^2}$ **107.** $\sqrt[6]{x}$ **109.** $\sqrt[15]{w}$ **111.** 3
113. 0.3761 **115.** 2.9240 **117.** 31.6228

Section 10.3 Practice Exercises, pp. 714–716

3. $\dfrac{p}{q^5}$ **5.** $\sqrt[7]{x^4}$ **7.** $y^{9/2}$ **9.** $x^2\sqrt{x}$ **11.** $q^2\sqrt[3]{q}$

13. $a^2b^2\sqrt{a}$ **15.** $-x^2y^3\sqrt[4]{y}$ **17.** $2\sqrt{7}$ **19.** $2\sqrt{5}$
21. $15\sqrt{2}$ **23.** $3\sqrt[3]{2}$ **25.** $5b\sqrt{ab}$ **27.** $2x^2\sqrt[3]{5x}$
29. $-2x^2z\sqrt[3]{2y}$ **31.** $2wz\sqrt[4]{5z^3}$ **33.** x **35.** p^2
37. 5 **39.** $\dfrac{1}{2}$ **41.** $\dfrac{5\sqrt[3]{2}}{3}$ **43.** $\dfrac{5\sqrt[3]{9}}{6}$ **45.** $4\sqrt{5}$

47. $-30\sqrt{3}$ **49.** $5x^2y\sqrt{y}$ **51.** $3yz\sqrt[3]{x^2z}$ **53.** $2w^2$

55. $\dfrac{1}{10y^6}$ **57.** $\dfrac{2}{b}$ **59.** $2a^7b^4c^{15}d^{11}\sqrt{2c}$

61. $3a^3b\sqrt{2b}$ **63.** $-10a^2b^2\sqrt{3ac}$ **65.** $x^2\sqrt{7xy}$

67. $3a^2b\sqrt{6}$ **69.** $2\sqrt{3}$ **71.** $\dfrac{3\sqrt{5}}{4}$

73. $\dfrac{1}{\sqrt[3]{w^6}}$ simplifies to $\dfrac{1}{w^2}$ **75.** $\sqrt{k^3}$ simplifies to $k\sqrt{k}$

77. $2\sqrt{41}$ ft **79.** $6\sqrt{5}$ m **81.** The distance is $90\sqrt{2}$ ft or approximately 127.3 ft. **83.** The path from A to B and B to C is faster.

Section 10.4 Practice Exercises, pp. 720–722

3. $-xy\sqrt[4]{x^3}$ **5.** $\dfrac{b^2}{2}$ **7.** $(x^3y)^{1/4}$ **9.** $y^{11/12}$

11. a. Not *like* radicals   **b.** *Like* radicals
c. Not *like* radicals   **13. a.** Both expressions can be simplified by using the distributive property.   **b.** Neither expression can be simplified because the terms do not contain *like* radicals or *like* terms.   **15.** $9\sqrt{5}$ **17.** $2\sqrt[3]{tw}$
19. $5\sqrt{10}$ **21.** $8\sqrt[4]{3} - \sqrt[4]{14}$ **23.** $2\sqrt{x} + 2\sqrt{y}$
25. Cannot be simplified further

27. Cannot be simplified further   **29.** $\dfrac{29}{18}z\sqrt[3]{6}$

31. $0.7x\sqrt{y}$ **33.** Simplify each radical: $3\sqrt{2} + 35\sqrt{2}$.
Then add *like* radicals: $38\sqrt{2}$ **35.** 15 **37.** $8\sqrt{3}$
39. $3\sqrt{7}$ **41.** $-\sqrt{2}$ **43.** $\sqrt[3]{3}$ **45.** $-5\sqrt{2a}$
47. $8s^2t^2\sqrt[3]{s^2}$ **49.** $6x\sqrt[3]{x}$ **51.** $14p^2\sqrt{5}$
53. $-\sqrt[3]{a^2b}$ **55.** $(5x+6)\sqrt{x}$ **57.** $(5x-6)\sqrt{2}$
59. $33d\sqrt[3]{2c}$ **61.** $2a^2b\sqrt{6a}$ **63.** $5x\sqrt[3]{2} - 6\sqrt[3]{x}$
65. False; $\sqrt{9} + \sqrt{16} \neq \sqrt{9+16}$; $7 \neq 5$ **67.** True
69. False; $\sqrt{y} + \sqrt{y} = 2\sqrt{y} \neq \sqrt{2y}$
71. $\sqrt{48} + \sqrt{12}$ simplifies to $6\sqrt{3}$
73. $5\sqrt[3]{x^6} - x^2$ simplifies to $4x^2$ **75.** The difference of the principal square root of 18 and the square of 5
77. The sum of the principal fourth root of x and the cube of y **79.** $9\sqrt{6}$ cm ≈ 22.0 cm   **81.** $x = 2\sqrt{2}$ ft
83. a. $10\sqrt{5}$ yd   **b.** 22.36 yd   **c.** $105.95

Section 10.5 Practice Exercises, pp. 727–729

1. $-2xy^2z^2\sqrt[3]{2x^2z}$ **3.** $2yz^2\sqrt{2z}$ **5.** $\dfrac{q^2}{p^{1/8}}$ **7.** $2\sqrt[3]{7}$

9. $\sqrt[3]{21}$ **11.** $2\sqrt{5}$ **13.** $4\sqrt[4]{4}$ **15.** $8\sqrt[3]{20}$
17. $-24ab\sqrt{a}$ **19.** $6\sqrt{10}$ **21.** $6x\sqrt{2}$
23. $10a^3b^2\sqrt{b}$ **25.** $-24x^2y^2\sqrt{2y}$ **27.** $6ab\sqrt[3]{2a^2b^2}$
29. $12 - 6\sqrt{3}$ **31.** $2\sqrt{3} - \sqrt{6}$ **33.** $-2x - \dfrac{7}{3}\sqrt{x}$

35. $-8 + 7\sqrt{30}$ **37.** $x - 5\sqrt{x} - 36$
39. $\sqrt[3]{y^2} - \sqrt[3]{y} - 6$ **41.** $9a - 28\sqrt{ab} + 3b$
43. $8\sqrt{p} + 3p + 5\sqrt{pq} + 16\sqrt{q} - 2q$ **45.** 15
47. $3y$ **49.** 6   **51.** 709   **53. a.** $x^2 - y^2$
b. $x^2 - 25$ **55.** $29 + 8\sqrt{13}$ **57.** $p - 2\sqrt{7p} + 7$
59. $2a - 6\sqrt{2ab} + 9b$ **61.** $3 - x^2$ **63.** 4
65. $\dfrac{4}{9}x - \dfrac{1}{4}y$ **67. a.** $3 - x$ **b.** $3 + 2\sqrt{3x} + x$

c. $3 - 2\sqrt{3x} + x$ **69.** True   **71.** False;
$(x - \sqrt{5})^2 = x^2 - 2x\sqrt{5} + 5$ **73.** False; 5 is multiplied by 3 only.   **75.** True   **77.** $6x$ **79.** $3x + 1$
81. $x + 19 - 8\sqrt{x+3}$ **83.** $2t + 10\sqrt{2t-3} + 22$
85. $12\sqrt{5}$ ft²   **87.** $18\sqrt{15}$ in.²   **89.** $\sqrt[4]{x^3}$
91. $\sqrt[15]{(2z)^8}$ **93.** $p^2\sqrt[6]{p}$ **95.** $u\sqrt[6]{u}$
97. $\sqrt[6]{x^2y}$ **99.** $\sqrt[4]{2^3 \cdot 3^2}$ or $\sqrt[4]{72}$ **101.** $\sqrt[12]{2^4 5^3 x^7 y^7}$
103. $2m\sqrt[6]{3^3 2mn^5}$ **105.** $a + b$

Chapter 10 Problem Recognition Exercises, p. 730

1. a. $2\sqrt{6}$ **b.** $2\sqrt[3]{3}$ **2. a.** $3\sqrt{6}$ **b.** $3\sqrt[3]{2}$
3. a. $10y^3\sqrt{2}$ **b.** $2y^2\sqrt[3]{25}$ **4. a.** $4z^7\sqrt{2z}$ **b.** $2z^5\sqrt[3]{4}$

5. a. $4\sqrt{5}$ **b.** $2\sqrt[3]{10}$ **c.** $2\sqrt[4]{5}$ **6. a.** $4\sqrt{3}$ **b.** $2\sqrt[3]{6}$
c. $2\sqrt[4]{3}$ **7. a.** $x^2y^3\sqrt{x}$ **b.** $xy^2\sqrt[3]{x^2}$ **c.** $xy\sqrt[4]{xy^2}$
8. a. a^5b^6 **b.** $a^3b^4\sqrt[3]{a}$ **c.** $a^2b^3\sqrt[4]{a^2}$ **9. a.** $2st^2\sqrt[3]{4s^2}$
b. $2st\sqrt[4]{2st^2}$ **c.** $2st\sqrt[5]{t}$ **10. a.** $2v^2w^6\sqrt[3]{12vw^2}$
b. $2vw^5\sqrt[4]{6v^3}$ **c.** $2vw^4\sqrt[5]{3v^2}$ **11. a.** $2\sqrt{5}$ **b.** 5
12. a. $2\sqrt{10}$ **b.** 10   **13. a.** $-3\sqrt{6}$ **b.** 60
14. a. $-7\sqrt{7}$ **b.** 210   **15. a.** $3\sqrt{2}$ **b.** 4
16. a. $3\sqrt{3}$ **b.** 6   **17. a.** $7\sqrt{2}$ **b.** 240
18. a. $-\sqrt{2}$ **b.** 60   **19. a.** $14\sqrt[3]{3}$ **b.** $48\sqrt[3]{9}$
20. a. $\sqrt[3]{2}$ **b.** $30\sqrt[3]{4}$

Section 10.6 Practice Exercises, pp. 737–740

3. $12y\sqrt{5}$ **5.** $-18y + 3\sqrt{y} + 3$ **7.** $64 - 16\sqrt{t} + t$

9. -5 **11.** $\dfrac{7x^2}{y^3}$ **13.** $\dfrac{2a\sqrt{2}}{x^3}$ **15.** $\dfrac{-2j\sqrt{2}}{k}$

17. $3b^2$ **19.** $\dfrac{1}{2b^2}$ **21.** $\dfrac{z\sqrt{3y}}{w^2}$ **23.** $\dfrac{\sqrt{5}}{\sqrt{5}}$

25. $\dfrac{\sqrt[3]{x^2}}{\sqrt[3]{x^2}}$ **27.** $\dfrac{\sqrt{3z}}{\sqrt{3z}}$ **29.** $\dfrac{\sqrt[4]{2a^2}}{\sqrt[4]{2a^2}}$ **31.** $\dfrac{\sqrt{3}}{3}$

33. $\dfrac{\sqrt{x}}{x}$ **35.** $\dfrac{3\sqrt{2y}}{y}$ **37.** $\dfrac{a\sqrt{2a}}{2}$ **39.** $\dfrac{3\sqrt{2}}{2}$

41. $\dfrac{3\sqrt[3]{4}}{2}$ **43.** $\dfrac{-6\sqrt[4]{x^3}}{x}$ **45.** $\dfrac{7\sqrt[3]{2}}{2}$ **47.** $\dfrac{\sqrt[3]{4w}}{w}$

49. $\dfrac{2\sqrt[4]{27}}{3}$ **51.** $\dfrac{\sqrt[3]{2x}}{x}$ **53.** $\dfrac{2\sqrt{6}}{21}$ **55.** $\dfrac{\sqrt{x}}{x^4}$

57. $\dfrac{\sqrt{2x}}{2x^3}$ **59.** $\sqrt{2} + \sqrt{6}$ **61.** $\sqrt{x} - 23$

63. $\dfrac{4\sqrt{2} - 12}{-7}$ or $\dfrac{-4\sqrt{2} + 12}{7}$ **65.** $4\sqrt{6} + 8$

67. $-\sqrt{21} + 2\sqrt{7}$ **69.** $\dfrac{-\sqrt{p} + \sqrt{q}}{p - q}$ **71.** $\sqrt{x} - \sqrt{5}$

73. $\dfrac{w + 11\sqrt{w} + 18}{81 - w}$ **75.** $\dfrac{4\sqrt{xy} - 3x - y}{y - x}$

77. $5 - \sqrt{10}$ **79.** $\dfrac{5 + \sqrt{21}}{4}$ **81.** $-6\sqrt{5} - 13$

83. $\dfrac{16}{\sqrt[3]{4}}$ simplifies to $8\sqrt[3]{2}$

85. $\dfrac{4}{x - \sqrt{2}}$ simplifies to $\dfrac{4x + 4\sqrt{2}}{x^2 - 2}$

87. $\dfrac{\pi\sqrt{2}}{4}$ sec ≈ 1.11 sec   **89.** $\dfrac{2\sqrt{6}}{3}$ **91.** $\dfrac{17\sqrt{15}}{15}$

93. $\dfrac{8\sqrt[3]{25}}{5}$ **95.** $\dfrac{-33}{2\sqrt{3} - 12}$ **97.** $\dfrac{a - b}{a + 2\sqrt{ab} + b}$

99. $\dfrac{3}{\sqrt{5 + 3h} + \sqrt{5}}$ **101.** $\dfrac{5}{\sqrt{4 + 5h} + 2}$

Section 10.7 Practice Exercises, pp. 747–749

3. $\dfrac{3w\sqrt{w}}{4}$ **5.** $3c\sqrt[3]{2c}$ **7.** $4x - 6$ **9.** $9p + 7$

11. $\{4\}$ **13.** $\{3\}$ **15.** $\{42\}$ **17.** $\{29\}$ **19.** $\{140\}$
21. $\{\ \}$ (The value 25 does not check.)   **23.** $\{7\}$ (The value -1 does not check.)   **25.** $\{\ \}$ (The value 3 does not check.)

27. $V = \dfrac{4\pi r^3}{3}$ **29.** $h^2 = \dfrac{r^2 - \pi^2 r^2}{\pi^2}$ or $h^2 = \dfrac{r^2}{\pi^2} - r^2$

31. $a^2 + 10a + 25$ **33.** $5a - 6\sqrt{5a} + 9$
35. $r + 22 + 10\sqrt{r - 3}$ **37.** $\{-3\}$
39. $\{\ \}$ (The value $\frac{1}{2}$ does not check.)
41. $\{2\}$ (The value 18 does not check.)   **43.** $\{9\}$
45. $\{-4\}$ **47.** $\left\{\dfrac{9}{5}\right\}$ **49.** $\{2\}$
51. $\{\ \}$ (The value 9 does not check.)
53. $\left\{-\dfrac{11}{4}\right\}$ **55.** $\{\ \}$ (The value $\frac{8}{3}$ does not check.)
57. $\{-1\}$ (The value 3 does not check.)   **59.** $\left\{\dfrac{1}{3}, -1\right\}$
61. $\{\ \}$ (The values 3 and 23 do not check.)
63. $\{6\}$ **65.** $\{2\}$ (The value 18 does not check.)
67. a. 30.25 ft   **b.** 34.5 m   **69. a.** $2 million
b. $1.2 million   **c.** 50,000 passengers   **71. a.** 12 lb
b. $i(18) - 5.1$. An 18-lb turkey will take about 5.1 hr to cook.
73. $b = \sqrt{25 - h^2}$ **75.** $a = \sqrt{k^2 - 196}$

Section 10.7 Graphing Calculator Exercises, p. 749

76. The x-coordinate of the point of intersection is the solution to the equation.   **77.** The x-coordinate of the point of intersection is the solution to the equation.

78.
79.

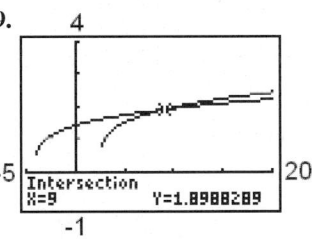

Section 10.8 Practice Exercises, pp. 757–759

3. $9 - x$ **5.** $\{-8\}$ **7.** $\left\{\dfrac{1}{25}\right\}$ **9.** $\sqrt{-1} = i$ and $-\sqrt{1} = -1$ **11.** $12i$ **13.** $i\sqrt{3}$ **15.** $2i\sqrt{5}$
17. -60 **19.** $13i\sqrt{7}$ **21.** -7 **23.** -12
25. $-3\sqrt{10}$ **27.** $i\sqrt{2}$ **29.** 3 **31.** $-i$ **33.** 1
35. i **37.** 1 **39.** $-i$ **41.** -1 **43.** $a - bi$
45. Real: -5; imaginary: 12   **47.** Real: 0; imaginary: -6
49. Real: 35; imaginary: 0   **51.** Real: $\dfrac{3}{5}$; imaginary: 1
53. $7 + 6i$ **55.** $\dfrac{3}{10} + \dfrac{3}{2}i$ **57.** $5 + 0i$
59. $-1 + 10i$ **61.** $-24 + 0i$ **63.** $18 + 6i$
65. $26 - 26i$ **67.** $-29 + 0i$ **69.** $-9 + 40i$
71. $35 + 20i$ **73.** $-20 + 48i$ **75.** $\dfrac{13}{16} + 0i$

77. $\dfrac{1}{5} - \dfrac{3}{5}i$ **79.** $\dfrac{3}{25} - \dfrac{4}{25}i$ **81.** $\dfrac{21}{29} + \dfrac{20}{29}i$
83. $-\dfrac{17}{10} - \dfrac{1}{10}i$ **85.** $-\dfrac{1}{2} - \dfrac{5}{2}i$ **87.** $\dfrac{1}{2} - \dfrac{1}{3}i$
89. $1 + 10i$ **91.** $\dfrac{1}{4} + \dfrac{1}{2}i$ **93.** $-1 + i\sqrt{2}$
95. $-2 - i\sqrt{3}$ **97.** $-\dfrac{1}{2} + \dfrac{\sqrt{2}}{2}i$ **99.** Yes   **101.** Yes

Chapter 10 Review Exercises, pp. 767–769

1. a. False; $\sqrt{0} = 0$ is not positive.   **b.** False; $\sqrt[3]{-8} = -2$
2. $\sqrt{(-3)^2} = \sqrt{9} = 3$ **3. a.** False   **b.** True
4. $\dfrac{5}{4}$ **5.** 5   **6.** 6   **7. a.** 3   **b.** 0   **c.** $\sqrt{7}$
d. $[1, \infty)$ **8. a.** 0   **b.** 1   **c.** 3   **d.** $[-5, \infty)$
9. $\dfrac{\sqrt[3]{2x}}{\sqrt[4]{2x}} + 4$ **10. a.** $|x|$ **b.** x **c.** $|x|$ **d.** $x + 1$
11. a. $2|y|$ **b.** $3y$ **c.** $|y|$ **d.** y **12.** 8 cm
13. Yes, provided the expressions are defined. For example: $x^5 \cdot x^3 = x^8$ and $x^{1/5} \cdot x^{2/5} = x^{3/5}$ **14.** n represents the root.
15. Take the reciprocal of the base and change the exponent to positive.   **16.** -5 **17.** $\dfrac{1}{2}$ **18.** 4
19. b^{10} **20.** $\dfrac{16y^{12}}{xz^9}$ **21.** $\dfrac{a^3c}{b^2}$ **22.** $x^{3/4}$
23. $(2y^2)^{1/3}$ **24.** 2.1544   **25.** 6.8173   **26.** 54.1819
27. See page 711.   **28.** $6\sqrt{3}$ **29.** $xz\sqrt[4]{xy}$
30. $-10ab^3\sqrt[3]{2b}$ **31.** $-\dfrac{2a}{b}$
32. a. The principal square root of the quotient of 2 and x
b. The cube of the sum of x and 1   **33.** 31 ft
34. they are *like* radicals.   **35.** Cannot be combined; the indices are different.   **36.** Cannot be combined; one term has a radical, but the other does not.   **37.** Can be combined: $3\sqrt[4]{3xy}$ **38.** Can be added after simplifying: $19\sqrt{2}$
39. $5\sqrt{7}$ **40.** $9\sqrt[3]{2} - 8$ **41.** $10\sqrt{2}$ **42.** $13x\sqrt[3]{2x^2}$
43. False; 5 and $3\sqrt{x}$ are not *like* radicals.
44. False; $\sqrt{y} + \sqrt{y} = 2\sqrt{y}$ (add the coefficients).
45. 6   **46.** $2\sqrt[4]{2}$ **47.** $-2\sqrt{21} + 6\sqrt{33}$
48. $-6\sqrt{15} + 15$ **49.** $4x - 9$ **50.** $y - 16$
51. $7y - 2\sqrt{21xy} + 3x$ **52.** $12w + 20\sqrt{3w} + 25$
53. $-2z - 9\sqrt{6z} - 42$ **54.** $3a + 5\sqrt{5a} - 10$
55. $u^2\sqrt[3]{u^5}$ **56.** $\sqrt[4]{4w^3}$ **57.** $\dfrac{y^2\sqrt{3y}}{5x^3}$
58. $\dfrac{-2x^2y^2\sqrt[3]{2x}}{z^3}$ **59.** $9w^2$ **60.** $\dfrac{t^4}{4}$ **61.** $\dfrac{\sqrt{14y}}{2y}$
62. $\dfrac{\sqrt{15w}}{3w}$ **63.** $\dfrac{4\sqrt[3]{3p}}{3p}$ **64.** $-\dfrac{\sqrt[3]{4x^2}}{x}$
65. $\sqrt{10} - \sqrt{15}$ **66.** $3\sqrt{5} - 3\sqrt{7}$ **67.** $\sqrt{t} + \sqrt{3}$
68. $\sqrt{w} + \sqrt{7}$ **69.** The quotient of the principal square root of 2 and the square of x
70. $\left\{\dfrac{49}{2}\right\}$ **71.** $\{31\}$ **72.** $\{-12\}$ **73.** $\{7\}$
74. $\{9\}$ **75.** $\{\ \}$ (The value -2 does not check.)

76. $\left\{\dfrac{1}{2}, 4\right\}$ **77.** $\{-2\}$ (The value 2 does not check.)

78. $6\sqrt{5}$ m ≈ 13.4 m   **79. a.** $v(20) \approx 25.3$ ft/sec. When the water depth is 20 ft, a wave travels about 25.3 ft/sec.
b. 8 ft   **80.** $a + bi$, where a and b are real numbers and $i = \sqrt{-1}$ **81.** $a + bi$, where $b \neq 0$ **82.** In each case we simplify the expression by multiplying the numerator and denominator by the conjugate of the denominator.   **83.** $4i$
84. $-i\sqrt{5}$ **85.** -15 **86.** $-2i$ **87.** -1 **88.** i
89. $-i$ **90.** 0   **91.** $-5 + 5i$ **92.** $9 + 17i$
93. $25 + 0i$ **94.** $24 - 10i$

95. $-\dfrac{17}{4} + i$; real part: $-\dfrac{17}{4}$; imaginary part: 1

96. $-2 - i$; real part: -2; imaginary part: -1

97. $\dfrac{4}{13} - \dfrac{7}{13}i$ **98.** $3 + 4i$ **99.** $-\dfrac{3}{2} + \dfrac{5}{2}i$

100. $-\dfrac{4}{17} + \dfrac{16}{17}i$ **101.** $-\dfrac{2}{3} + \dfrac{\sqrt{10}}{6}i$ **102.** $2 - 4i$

Chapter 10 Test, pp. 770–771

1. a. 6 **b.** -6 **2. a.** Real **b.** Not real **c.** Real
d. Real   **3. a.** y **b.** $|y|$ **4.** 3   **5.** $\dfrac{4}{3}$ **6.** $2\sqrt[3]{4}$

7. $a^2bc^2\sqrt{bc}$ **8.** $3x^2yz^2\sqrt{2xy}$ **9.** $4w^2\sqrt{w}$ **10.** $\dfrac{x^2}{5y}$

11. $\dfrac{3\sqrt{2}}{2}$ **12. a.** $f(-8) = 2\sqrt{3}$; $f(-6) = 2\sqrt{2}$;
$f(-4) = 2$; $f(-2) = 0$ **b.** $(-\infty, -2]$ **13.** -0.3080
14. -3 **15.** $\dfrac{20x^2y^3}{z}$ **16.** $\sqrt[6]{7y^3}$ **17.** $\sqrt[12]{10}$
18. $3\sqrt{5}$ **19.** $3\sqrt{2x} - 3\sqrt{5x}$ **20.** $40 - 10\sqrt{5x} - 3x$
21. $\dfrac{-2\sqrt[3]{x^2}}{x}$ **22.** $\dfrac{x + 6 + 5\sqrt{x}}{9 - x}$ **23. a.** $2i\sqrt{2}$ **b.** $8i$
c. $\dfrac{1}{2} + \dfrac{\sqrt{2}}{2}i$ **24.** $1 - 11i$ **25.** $30 + 16i$ **26.** -28
27. $-33 - 56i$ **28.** 104   **29.** $\dfrac{17}{25} + \dfrac{6}{25}i$
30. $-\dfrac{15}{17} + \dfrac{9}{17}i$ **31.** $r(10) \approx 1.34$; the radius of a sphere of volume 10 cubic units is approximately 1.34 units.
32. 21 ft   **33.** $\{-16\}$ **34.** $\left\{\dfrac{17}{5}\right\}$
35. $\{2\}$ (The value 42 does not check.)

Chapters 1–10 Cumulative Review Exercises, pp. 771–772

1. 54   **2.** $15x - 5y - 5$ **3.** $\{-3\}$ **4.** $(-\infty, -5)$
5. $[-9, -3)$ **6.** $\{\ \}$ **7.** $(-\infty, -3] \cup [1, \infty)$
8. $y = -2x + 5$ **9.** $x = -5$
10. $\left\{\left(\dfrac{1}{2}, \dfrac{1}{3}\right)\right\}$ **11.** $\left(2, -2, \dfrac{1}{2}\right)$ is not a solution.
12. Together it will take them $1\dfrac{7}{8}$ hr.

13. a. $f(-2) = -10$; $f(0) = -2$; $f(4) = 14$; $f\left(\dfrac{1}{2}\right) = 0$
b. $(-2, -10), (0, -2), (4, 14), \left(\dfrac{1}{2}, 0\right)$
c.

14. $a^6b^{12}c^4$ **15. a.** 1.4×10^{-4} **b.** 3.14×10^9
16. $2x^2 - x - 15$; 2nd degree   **17.** $\sqrt{15} + 3\sqrt{2} + 3$
18. $x - 4$ **19.** $-\dfrac{1}{6}$ **20.** $\dfrac{3c\sqrt[3]{2}}{d}$ **21.** $32b\sqrt{5b}$
22. $\{10\}$ **23.** $\dfrac{x - 15}{x(x + 5)(x - 5)}$ **24.** $\dfrac{-1}{(2a + 1)(a + 2)}$
25. $-14x^2 + 26x - 17$ **26.** $2\sqrt{3} + 2\sqrt{5}$
27. $\dfrac{6}{17} + \dfrac{10}{17}i$ **28.** $\left\{\dfrac{7}{6}, -\dfrac{3}{2}\right\}$
29. $(x + 3 - y)(x + 3 + y)$ **30.** $(x^2 + 2)(x^4 - 2x^2 + 4)$

Chapter 11

Chapter Opener Puzzle

Q	U	A	D	R	A	T	I	C
2	1	6	5	8	6	4	7	3

Section 11.1 Practice Exercises, pp. 780–783

3. $\{\pm 2\}$ **5.** $\{\pm\sqrt{7}\}$ **7.** $\{\pm 5i\}$ **9.** $\{-1, -5\}$
11. $\left\{\dfrac{-3 \pm \sqrt{7}}{2}\right\}$ **13.** $\{-5 \pm 3i\sqrt{2}\}$ **15.** $\left\{\pm\dfrac{\sqrt{33}}{3}\right\}$
17. $\left\{-\dfrac{4}{5} \pm \dfrac{\sqrt{3}}{5}i\right\}$ **19.** 1. Factoring and applying the zero product rule. 2. Applying the square root property. $\{\pm 6\}$
21. $n = 9$; $(x - 3)^2$ **23.** $n = 16$; $(t + 4)^2$
25. $n = \dfrac{1}{4}$; $\left(c - \dfrac{1}{2}\right)^2$ **27.** $n = \dfrac{25}{4}$; $\left(y + \dfrac{5}{2}\right)^2$
29. $n = \dfrac{1}{25}$; $\left(b + \dfrac{1}{5}\right)^2$ **31.** $n = \dfrac{1}{9}$; $\left(p - \dfrac{1}{3}\right)^2$
33. See page 777.   **35.** $\{-3, -5\}$ **37.** $\{-3 \pm i\sqrt{7}\}$
39. $\{-2 \pm i\sqrt{2}\}$ **41.** $\{5, -2\}$ **43.** $\left\{-1 \pm \dfrac{\sqrt{6}}{2}i\right\}$
45. $\left\{2 \pm \dfrac{2}{3}i\right\}$ **47.** $\left\{\dfrac{1}{5} \pm \dfrac{\sqrt{3}}{5}\right\}$ **49.** $\left\{-\dfrac{3}{4} \pm \dfrac{\sqrt{65}}{4}\right\}$
51. $\{2 \pm \sqrt{11}\}$ **53.** $\{1, -7\}$ **55. a.** $t = \dfrac{\sqrt{d}}{4}$ **b.** 8 sec
57. $r = \sqrt{\dfrac{A}{\pi}}$ or $r = \dfrac{\sqrt{A\pi}}{\pi}$ **59.** $a = \sqrt{d^2 - b^2 - c^2}$

61. $r = \sqrt{\dfrac{3V}{\pi h}}$ or $r = \dfrac{\sqrt{3V\pi h}}{\pi h}$ **63.** 4.2 ft   **65.** 7.1 in.

67. a. 4.5 thousand textbooks or 35.5 thousand textbooks
b. Profit increases to a point as more books are produced. Beyond that point, the market is "flooded," and profit decreases. There are two points at which the profit is $20,000. Producing 4.5 thousand books makes the same profit using fewer resources as producing 35.5 thousand books.

Section 11.2 Practice Exercises, pp. 794–798

3. $4 - 2\sqrt{5}$ **5.** $2 - i\sqrt{3}$
7. The form $ax^2 + bx + c = 0$ **9.** $\{-12, 1\}$
11. $\left\{\dfrac{1}{9} \pm \dfrac{2\sqrt{11}}{9}i\right\}$ **13.** $\left\{\dfrac{1}{6} \pm \dfrac{\sqrt{14}}{6}i\right\}$ **15.** $\{7, -5\}$
17. $\left\{\dfrac{-3 \pm \sqrt{41}}{2}\right\}$ **19.** $\left\{\dfrac{2}{5}\right\}$ **21.** $\{3 \pm i\sqrt{5}\}$
23. $\left\{\dfrac{1 \pm \sqrt{29}}{2}\right\}$ **25.** $\left\{\dfrac{-1 \pm \sqrt{13}}{4}\right\}$
27. $\left\{-\dfrac{2}{3} \pm \dfrac{2\sqrt{2}}{3}i\right\}$ **29.** $\left\{\dfrac{-5 \pm \sqrt{13}}{2}\right\}$
31. $\{-2, -4\}$ **33.** $\left\{\dfrac{-7 \pm \sqrt{109}}{6}\right\}$

35. a. $(x - 3)(x^2 + 3x + 9)$ **b.** $\left\{3, -\dfrac{3}{2} \pm \dfrac{3\sqrt{3}}{2}i\right\}$
37. a. $3x(x^2 - 2x + 2)$ **b.** $\{0, 1 \pm i\}$ **39.** The length of each side is 3 ft.   **41.** The legs are approximately 1.6 in. and 3.6 in.   **43.** The legs are approximately 8.2 m and 6.1 m.
45. a. Approximately 4.5 fatalities per 100 million miles driven **b.** Approximately 1 fatality per 100 million miles driven **c.** Approximately 4.2 fatalities per 100 million miles driven **d.** For drivers 26 yr old and 71 yr old
47. The times are $\dfrac{3 + \sqrt{5}}{2}$ sec ≈ 2.62 sec or $\dfrac{3 - \sqrt{5}}{2}$ sec ≈ 0.38 sec.   **49. a.** $x^2 + 2x + 1 = 0$
b. 0 **c.** 1 rational solution   **51. a.** $19m^2 - 8m + 0 - 0$
b. 64 **c.** 2 rational solutions   **53. a.** $5p^2 + 0p - 21 = 0$
b. 420 **c.** 2 irrational solutions   **55. a.** $n^2 + 3n + 4 = 0$
b. -7 **c.** 2 imaginary solutions   **57.** Discriminant: 16; two x intercepts   **59.** Discriminant: 0; one x intercept
61. Discriminant: -39; no x-intercepts
63. x-intercepts: $\left(\dfrac{5 + \sqrt{13}}{2}, 0\right), \left(\dfrac{5 - \sqrt{13}}{2}, 0\right)$;
y-intercept: $(0, 3)$ **65.** x-intercepts: none; y-intercept: $(0, -1)$
67. x-intercepts: $\left(\dfrac{-5 - \sqrt{41}}{4}, 0\right), \left(\dfrac{-5 + \sqrt{41}}{4}, 0\right)$;
y-intercept: $(0, -2)$ **69.** $\left\{-\dfrac{3}{2} \pm \dfrac{\sqrt{7}}{2}i\right\}$
71. $\left\{-\dfrac{1}{3}, 6\right\}$ **73.** $\left\{-\dfrac{5}{2}, \dfrac{1}{2}\right\}$ **75.** $\left\{-\dfrac{1}{2} \pm 2i\right\}$
77. $\left\{\dfrac{3 \pm \sqrt{7}}{2}\right\}$ **79.** $\{1 \pm 3i\sqrt{2}\}$ **81.** $\{2 \pm \sqrt{2}\}$
83. $\left\{-\dfrac{1}{8}, \dfrac{3}{4}\right\}$ **85.** $\{3, -3\}$

87. a. $\{-3 \pm \sqrt{14}\}$ **b.** $\{-3 \pm \sqrt{14}\}$ **c.** Answers will vary
89. b. $x^2 = \left(\dfrac{18 - x}{2}\right)^2 + \left(\dfrac{18 - x}{2}\right)^2$
c. $x^2 + 36x - 324 = 0$ **d.** 7.5 in., -43.5 in. **e.** 7.5 in. is appropriate; the other solution is negative.

Section 11.2 Graphing Calculator Exercises, p. 798

91.   **92.**

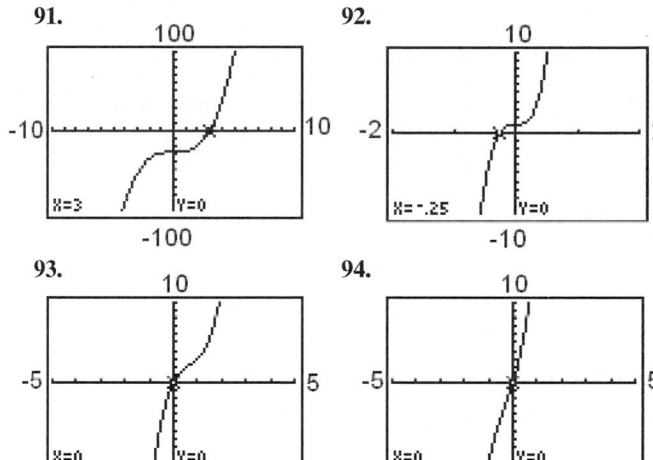

93.   **94.**

Section 11.3 Practice Exercises, pp. 802–803

1. An equation is in quadratic form if it can be written as $au^2 + bu + c = 0$ where u represents an algebraic expression.
3. $\left\{\dfrac{3}{2} \pm \dfrac{\sqrt{7}}{2}\right\}$ **5.** $\{-4\}$ **7.** $\{2 \pm \sqrt{26}\}$
9. a. $\{-4, -6\}$ **b.** $\{-4, -1, -2, -3\}$
11. $\{1 \pm i\sqrt{2}, 1 \pm \sqrt{2}\}$ **13.** $\{5, -1, 2\}$ **15.** $\{27, -8\}$
17. $\left\{-\dfrac{1}{32}, -243\right\}$ **19.** $\{4\}$ (The value 64 does not check.)
21. $\left\{\dfrac{1}{4}\right\}$ (The value 4 does not check.)
23. $\{-7\}$ **25.** $\{16\}$; yes   **27.** $\{\pm 3i, \pm\sqrt{5}\}$
29. $\left\{\pm\dfrac{\sqrt{3}}{2}, \pm i\sqrt{5}\right\}$ **31.** $\left\{\dfrac{-5 \pm \sqrt{13}}{2}\right\}$
33. $\left\{\dfrac{9 \pm \sqrt{73}}{4}\right\}$ **35.** $\{2 \pm \sqrt{3}\}$ **37.** $\{\pm 2, \pm 2i\}$
39. $\left\{-\dfrac{7}{4}, -\dfrac{3}{2}\right\}$ **41.** $\left\{\dfrac{1}{2}, -\dfrac{1}{2}, \sqrt{2}, -\sqrt{2}\right\}$
43. $\left\{2, 1, -1 \pm i\sqrt{3}, -\dfrac{1}{2} \pm \dfrac{\sqrt{3}}{2}i\right\}$ **45.** $\{5, 4\}$
47. $\{0, 2\}$ **49.** $\left\{1, \dfrac{17}{2}\right\}$ **51.** $\{64, -125\}$
53. $\{\pm\sqrt{2}, \pm 2i\}$ **55.** $\{\pm 4i, 1\}$
57. $\{4, \pm i\sqrt{5}\}$ **59.** $\left\{\dfrac{8}{3}, 2\right\}$

Section 11.3 Graphing Calculator Exercises, p. 803

61. a. $\{\pm i\sqrt{2}\}$ **b.** Two imaginary solutions; no real solutions   **c.** No x-intercepts

d.

62. a. $\{1, -1\}$ **b.** Two real solutions; no imaginary solutions   **c.** Two x-intercepts

d.

63. a. $\{0, 3, -2\}$ **b.** Three real solutions; no imaginary solutions   **c.** Three x-intercepts

d.

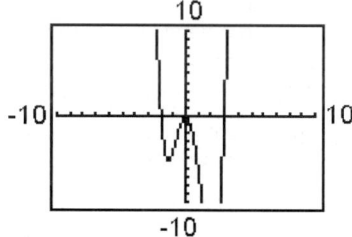

64. a. $\{\pm 1, \pm 3\}$ **b.** Four real solutions; no imaginary solutions   **c.** Four x-intercepts

d.

Chapter 11 Problem Recognition Exercises, p. 804

1. $\{-5 \pm \sqrt{22}\}$ **2.** $\{8 \pm \sqrt{59}\}$ **3.** $\left\{-\dfrac{1}{6} \pm \dfrac{\sqrt{47}}{6}i\right\}$

4. $\left\{-\dfrac{3}{8} \pm \dfrac{\sqrt{71}}{8}i\right\}$ **5. a.** Quadratic   **b.** $\{2, -7\}$

6. a. Quadratic   **b.** $\{4, 5\}$ **7. a.** Quadratic form
b. $\{-3, -1, 1, 3\}$ **8. a.** Quadratic form   **b.** $\{2, -2, i, -i\}$
9. a. Quadratic form (or radical)   **b.** $\{16\}$ (The value 1
does not check.)   **10. a.** Quadratic   **b.** $\left\{\dfrac{9 \pm \sqrt{89}}{2}\right\}$

11. a. Linear   **b.** $\{4\}$ **12. a.** Linear   **b.** $\{-1\}$
13. a. Quadratic   **b.** $\{\pm i\sqrt{2}\}$ **14. a.** Quadratic
b. $\{\pm i\sqrt{6}\}$ **15. a.** Rational   **b.** $\{2, -1\}$

16. a. Rational   **b.** $\{-2, 4\}$
17. a. Quadratic   **b.** $\{10 \pm \sqrt{101}\}$
18. a. Quadratic   **b.** $\{-9 \pm \sqrt{77}\}$
19. a. Quadratic   **b.** $\left\{\dfrac{1 \pm \sqrt{17}}{2}\right\}$
20. a. Quadratic   **b.** $\left\{\dfrac{1 \pm \sqrt{13}}{2}\right\}$
21. a. Radical   **b.** $\{3\}$ (The value -1 does not check.)
22. a. Radical   **b.** $\{6\}$ (The value -1 does not check.)
23. a. Quadratic form (or radical)   **b.** $\{-125, 27\}$
24. a. Quadratic form (or radical)   **b.** $\{-64, -1\}$

Section 11.4 Practice Exercises, pp. 813–817

3. $\{3 \pm 2i\}$ **5.** $\left\{\dfrac{5 \pm \sqrt{10}}{5}\right\}$ **7.** $\{-27, -8\}$

9. The value of k shifts the graph of $y = x^2$ vertically.

11.

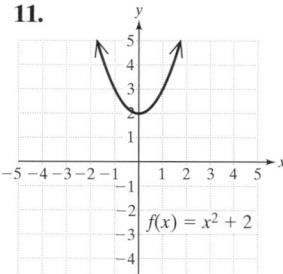

$f(x) = x^2 + 2$

13.

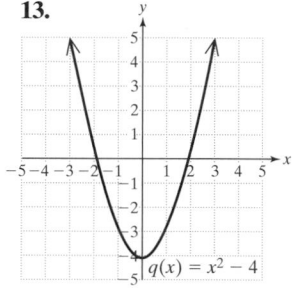

$q(x) = x^2 - 4$

15.

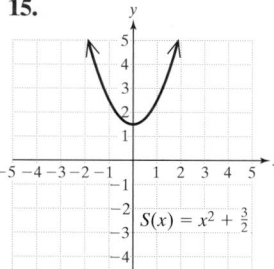

$S(x) = x^2 + \frac{3}{2}$

17.

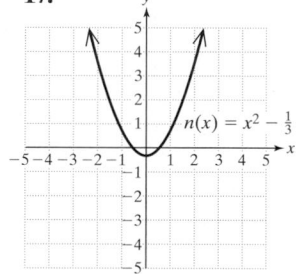

$n(x) = x^2 - \frac{1}{3}$

19.

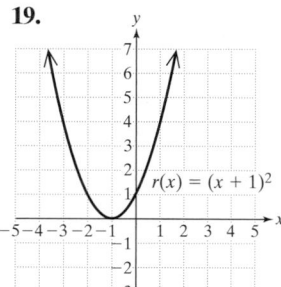

$r(x) = (x + 1)^2$

21.

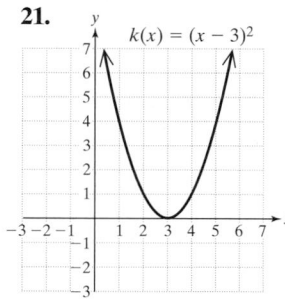

$k(x) = (x - 3)^2$

23.

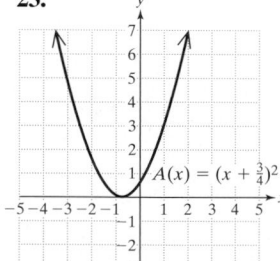

$A(x) = \left(x + \frac{3}{4}\right)^2$

25.

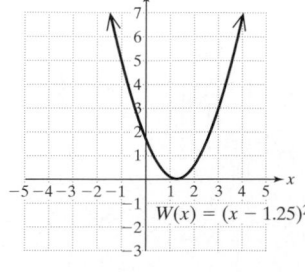

$W(x) = (x - 1.25)^2$

27. The value of *a* vertically stretches or shrinks the graph of $y = x^2$.

29.

31.

33.

35.

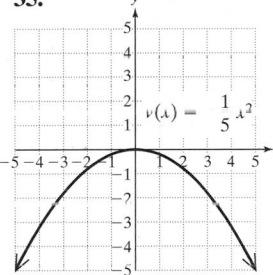

37. d   **39.** g   **41.** a   **43.** e

45.

47.

49.

51.

53.

55.

57.

59.

61.

63.

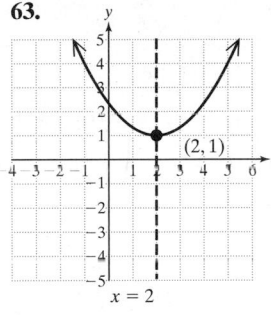

65. a. $y = x^2 + 3$ is $y = x^2$ shifted up 3 units.
b. $y = (x + 3)^2$ is $y = x^2$ shifted left 3 units.
c. $y = 3x^2$ is $y = x^2$ with a vertical stretch.
67. Vertex $(6, -9)$; minimum point; minimum value: -9
69. Vertex $(2, 5)$; maximum point; maximum value: 5
71. Vertex $(-8, 0)$; minimum point; minimum value: 0
73. Vertex $\left(0, \dfrac{21}{4}\right)$; maximum point; maximum value: $\dfrac{21}{4}$
75. Vertex $\left(7, -\dfrac{3}{2}\right)$; minimum point; minimum value: $-\dfrac{3}{2}$
77. Vertex $(0, 0)$; minimum point; minimum value: 0
79. True   **81.** False   **83. a.** $(60, 30)$ **b.** 30 ft   **c.** 70 ft
85. a. The fireworks will explode at a height of 150 ft.
b. Yes, because the ordered pair $(3, 150)$ is the vertex.

Section 11.5 Practice Exercises, pp. 824–828

1. For $f(x) = ax^2 + bx + c$, the vertex (h, k) is given by $\left(\dfrac{-b}{2a}, \dfrac{4ac - b^2}{4a}\right)$ or $\left(\dfrac{-b}{2a}, f\left(\dfrac{-b}{2a}\right)\right)$.   **3.** The graph of p is the graph of $y = x^2$ shrunk vertically by a factor of $\frac{1}{4}$.   **5.** The graph of r is the graph of $y = x^2$ shifted up 7 units.   **7.** The graph of t is the graph of $y = x^2$ shifted to the left 10 units.   **9.** $16; (x - 4)^2$ **11.** $\dfrac{49}{4}; \left(y + \dfrac{7}{2}\right)^2$
13. $\dfrac{1}{81}; \left(b + \dfrac{1}{9}\right)^2$ **15.** $\dfrac{1}{36}; \left(t - \dfrac{1}{6}\right)^2$
17. $g(x) = (x - 4)^2 - 11; (4, -11)$
19. $n(x) = 2(x + 3)^2 - 5; (-3, -5)$
21. $p(x) = -3(x - 1)^2 - 2; (1, -2)$
23. $k(x) = \left(x + \dfrac{7}{2}\right)^2 - \dfrac{89}{4}; \left(-\dfrac{7}{2}, -\dfrac{89}{4}\right)$
25. $F(x) = 5(x + 1)^2 - 4; (-1, -4)$
27. $P(x) = -2\left(x - \dfrac{1}{4}\right)^2 + \dfrac{1}{8}; \left(\dfrac{1}{4}, \dfrac{1}{8}\right)$ **29.** $(2, 3)$
31. $(-1, -2)$ **33.** $(-4, -15)$ **35.** $(-1, 2)$ **37.** $(1, 3)$

39. $\left(\dfrac{3}{2}, \dfrac{3}{4}\right)$ **41.** $(-4, -15)$ **43.** $(-1, 4)$

45. a. $(-1, -4)$ **b.** $(0, -3)$ **47. a.** $\left(\frac{1}{2}, \frac{7}{2}\right)$ **b.** $(0, 4)$

c. $(1, 0), (-3, 0)$ **c.** No x-intercepts

d.   **d.**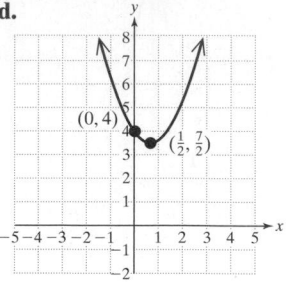

49. a. $\left(\frac{3}{2}, 0\right)$ **b.** $\left(0, -\frac{9}{4}\right)$ **51. a.** $(-1, 4)$ **b.** $(0, 3)$

c. $\left(\frac{3}{2}, 0\right)$ **c.** $(1, 0), (-3, 0)$

d.   **d.**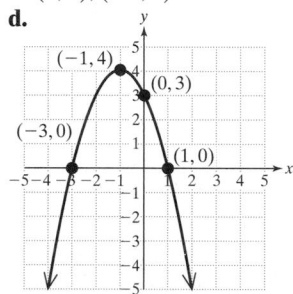

53. Mia must package 10 MP3 players.   **55. a.** 164.25 ft

b. 3.125 sec   **57. a.** 45 mph **b.** 32 mpg   **59. a.** 48 hr

b. 2 g   **61.** $a = -9, b = 5, c = 4; y = -9x^2 + 5x + 4$

63. $a = 2, b = -1, c = -5; y = 2x^2 - x - 5$

65. $a = -3, b = 4, c = 0; y = -3x^2 + 4x$

67. a. The sum of the sides must equal the total amount of fencing. **b.** $A = x(200 - 2x)$ **c.** 50 ft by 100 ft

Section 11.5 Graphing Calculator Exercises, p. 828

69.   **70.**

71.   **72.**

73.   **74.**

Chapter 11 Review Exercises, pp. 833–836

1. $\{\pm\sqrt{5}\}$ **2.** $\{\pm 2i\}$ **3.** $\{\pm 9\}$ **4.** $\left\{\pm\dfrac{\sqrt{57}}{3}i\right\}$

5. $\{2 \pm 6\sqrt{2}\}$ **6.** $\left\{\dfrac{5}{2} \pm \dfrac{3}{2}i\right\}$ **7.** $\left\{\dfrac{1 \pm \sqrt{3}}{3}\right\}$

8. $\{4 \pm \sqrt{5}\}$ **9.** $5\sqrt{3}$ in. ≈ 8.7 in.   **10.** 9 in.

11. $5\sqrt{6}$ in. ≈ 12.2 in.   **12.** $n = 64; (x + 8)^2$

13. $n = \dfrac{81}{4}; \left(x - \dfrac{9}{2}\right)^2$ **14.** $n = \dfrac{1}{16}; \left(y + \dfrac{1}{4}\right)^2$

15. $n = \dfrac{1}{25}; \left(z - \dfrac{1}{5}\right)^2$ **16.** $\{-2 \pm 3i\}$ **17.** $\{1 \pm \sqrt{6}\}$

18. $\{3 \pm 2\sqrt{3}\}$ **19.** $\{4 \pm 3i\}$ **20.** $\left\{\dfrac{1}{3}, -1\right\}$

21. $\left\{\dfrac{1}{2}, -4\right\}$ **22.** $r = \sqrt{\dfrac{V}{\pi h}}$ or $r = \dfrac{\sqrt{V\pi h}}{\pi h}$

23. $s = \sqrt{\dfrac{A}{6}}$ or $s = \dfrac{\sqrt{6A}}{6}$ **24.** See page 788.

25. Two rational solutions   **26.** Two rational solutions

27. Two irrational solutions   **28.** Two imaginary solutions

29. One rational solution   **30.** Two imaginary solutions

31. $\{2 \pm \sqrt{3}\}$ **32.** $\left\{\dfrac{5}{2} \pm \dfrac{5\sqrt{3}}{2}i\right\}$ **33.** $\left\{2, -\dfrac{5}{6}\right\}$

34. $\left\{2, \dfrac{4}{3}\right\}$ **35.** $\left\{\dfrac{4}{5}, -\dfrac{1}{5}\right\}$ **36.** $\left\{\dfrac{1}{10}, -\dfrac{1}{2}\right\}$

37. $\{2 \pm 2i\sqrt{7}\}$ **38.** $\{4 \pm \sqrt{6}\}$ **39.** $\left\{\dfrac{2 \pm \sqrt{22}}{3}\right\}$

40. $\{8, -2\}$ **41.** $\{-7 \pm \sqrt{3}\}$ **42.** $\{-1 \pm \sqrt{11}\}$

43. a. 1822 ft **b.** 115 ft/s   **44. a.** $\approx 53{,}939$ thousand

b. 2021   **45.** The dimensions are approximately 3.1 ft by 7.2 ft.   **46.** The distance between Lincoln and Omaha is approximately 50 mi.   **47.** $\{49\}$ (The value 9 does not check.)

48. $\{4, 16\}$ **49.** $\{\pm 3, \pm\sqrt{2}\}$ **50.** $\left\{\pm\dfrac{\sqrt{6}}{2}, \pm i\right\}$

51. $\{-243, 32\}$ **52.** $\{32, 1\}$ **53.** $\{3 \pm \sqrt{10}\}$

54. $\left\{\dfrac{1 \pm \sqrt{181}}{6}\right\}$ **55.** $\{\pm 3i, \pm i\sqrt{3}\}$ **56.** $\{\pm\sqrt{7}, \pm 2\}$

57.   **58.**

59.

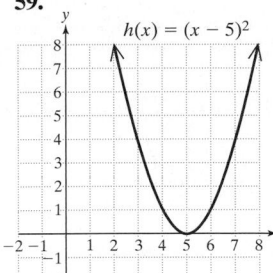

$h(x) = (x - 5)^2$

60.

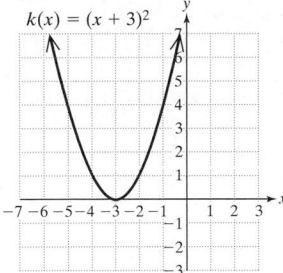

$k(x) = (x + 3)^2$

61.

$m(x) = -2x^2$

62.

$n(x) = -4x^2$

63.

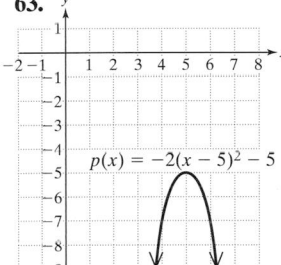

$p(x) = -2(x - 5)^2 - 5$

64.

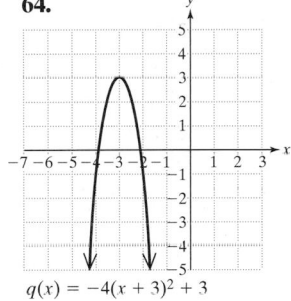

$q(x) = -4(x + 3)^2 + 3$

65. $\left(4, \dfrac{5}{3}\right)$ is the minimum point. The minimum value is $\dfrac{5}{3}$.

66. $\left(1, -\dfrac{1}{7}\right)$ is the maximum point. The maximum value is

$-\dfrac{1}{7}$. **67.** $x = -\dfrac{2}{11}$ **68.** $x = \dfrac{3}{16}$

69. $z(x) = (x - 3)^2 - 2; (3, -2)$
70. $b(x) = (x - 2)^2 - 48; (2, -48)$
71. $p(x) = -5(x + 1)^2 - 8; (-1, -8)$
72. $q(x) = -3(x + 4)^2 - 6; (-4, -6)$ **73.** $(1, -15)$

74. $(-1, 7)$ **75.** $\left(\dfrac{1}{2}, \dfrac{41}{4}\right)$ **76.** $\left(-\dfrac{1}{3}, -\dfrac{22}{3}\right)$

77. a. $(2, -3)$ **b.** $(0, 0), (4, 0)$
c.

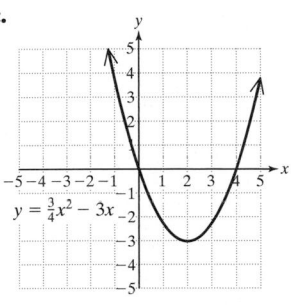

$y = \tfrac{3}{4}x^2 - 3x$

78. a. $(-2, 4)$ **b.** $(0, 0)\ (-4, 0)$
c.

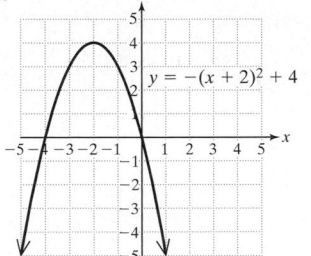

$y = -(x + 2)^2 + 4$

79. a. 3 sec **b.** 144 ft **80. a.** 150 meals **b.** $1200
81. $a = 1, b = 4, c = -1; y = x^2 + 4x - 1$
82. $a = 1, b = -1, c = 6; y = x^2 - x + 6$

Chapter 11 Test, pp. 836–837

1. $\{2, -8\}$ **2.** $\{2 \pm 2\sqrt{3}\}$ **3.** $\{-1 \pm i\}$

4. $n = \dfrac{121}{4}; \left(d + \dfrac{11}{2}\right)^2$ **5.** $\{-3 \pm 3\sqrt{3}\}$

6. $\left\{\dfrac{3}{4} \pm \dfrac{\sqrt{47}}{4}i\right\}$ **7. a.** $x^2 - 3x + 12 = 0$

b. $a = 1, b = -3, c = 12$ **c.** -39 **d.** Two imaginary
solutions **8. a.** $y^2 - 2y + 1 = 0$ **b.** $a = 1, b = -2, c = 1$
c. 0 **d.** One rational solution

9. $\left\{1, \dfrac{1}{3}\right\}$ **10.** $\left\{\dfrac{-7 \pm \sqrt{5}}{2}\right\}$ **11.** The height is

approximately 4.6 ft and the base is 6.2 ft. **12.** The radius
is approximately 12.0 ft. **13.** $\{9\}$ (The value 4 does not

check.) **14.** $\{8, -64\}$ **15.** $\left\{\dfrac{11}{3}, 6\right\}$

16. $\{\pm\sqrt{6}, \pm 3\}$ **17.** $\left\{\dfrac{5 \pm \sqrt{57}}{2}\right\}$

18. The vertex is $(3, -17)$.
19.

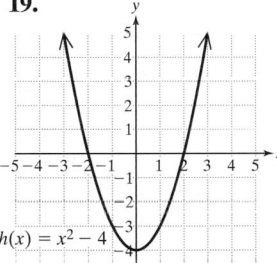

$h(x) = x^2 - 4$

20.

$f(x) = (x - 4)^2$

21.

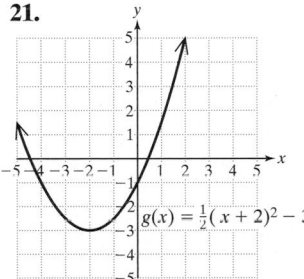

$g(x) = \tfrac{1}{2}(x + 2)^2 - 3$

22. The rocket will hit the ground 256 ft away.
23. a. 1320 million **b.** 1999 **24.** The graph of $y = x^2 - 2$ is the graph of $y = x^2$ shifted down 2 units. **25.** The graph of $y = (x + 3)^2$ is the graph of $y = x^2$ shifted 3 units to the left.
26. The graph of $y = -4x^2$ is the graph of $y = 4x^2$ opening downward instead of upward. **27. a.** $(4, 2)$
b. Downward **c.** Maximum point **d.** The maximum value is 2. **e.** $x = 4$ **28. a.** $g(x) = 2(x - 5)^2 + 1; (5, 1)$
b. $(5, 1)$ **29. a.** $f(x) = (x + 2)^2 - 16$ **b.** Vertex: $(-2, -16)$
c. x-intercepts: $(-6, 0)$ and $(2, 0)$; y-intercept: $(0, -12)$
d. The minimum value is -16 **e.** $x = -2$
30. a. 200 ft **b.** 20,000 ft^2

Chapters 1–11 Cumulative Review Exercises, pp. 838–839

1. a. $\{2, 4, 6, 8, 10, 12, 16\}$ **b.** $\{2, 8\}$ **2.** $-3x^2 - 13x + 1$
3. -16 **4.** 1.8×10^{10} **5. a.** $(x + 2)(x + 3)(x - 3)$
b. Quotient: $x^2 + 5x + 6$; remainder: 0 **6.** $x - 2$
7. $\dfrac{2\sqrt{2x}}{x}$ **8.** $8000 in 12% account; $2000 in 3% account
9. $\{(8, 7)\}$ **10. a.** 720 ft **b.** 720 ft **c.** 12 sec
11. $\{3 \pm 4i\}$ **12.** $\left\{\dfrac{-5 \pm \sqrt{33}}{4}\right\}$ **13.** $n = 25; (x + 5)^2$
14. $2(x + 5)(x^2 - 5x + 25)$
15.

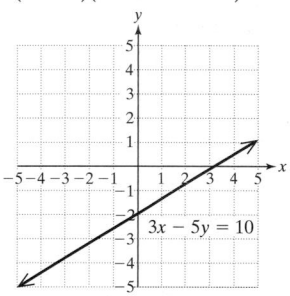

16. a. $\left(\dfrac{5}{2}, 0\right), (2, 0)$ **b.** $(0, 10)$ **17.** The domain element 3 has more than one corresponding range element.
18.

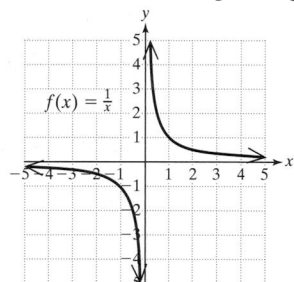

19. $y = 39$ **20. a.** Linear **b.** $(0, 300,000)$. If there are no passengers, the airport runs 300,000 flights per year.
c. $m = 0.008$ or $m = \frac{8}{1000}$. There are eight additional flights per 1000 passengers. **21. a.** $[-4, \infty)$ **b.** $(-\infty, \infty)$
22. a. $(-\infty, 2]$ **b.** $(-\infty, 4]$ **c.** 4 **d.** 3 **e.** $x = -1$
23. $\left\{\dfrac{1}{18}, \dfrac{1}{2}\right\}$ **24.** $f = \dfrac{pq}{p + q}$ **25.** $\{7\}$
26. $\dfrac{y + 1}{y - 3}$ **27. a.** $(3, 1)$ **b.** Upward **c.** $(0, 19)$
d. No x-intercept

e.

28. Vertex: $(8, -62)$ **29. a.** $\left(-\infty, -\dfrac{5}{2}\right] \cup [2, \infty)$ **b.** On these intervals, the graph is on or above the x-axis
30. $(-\infty, 3) \cup [5, \infty)$

Chapter 12

Chapter Opener Puzzle

		B 4	C 3	6	2
3	F 6	2	1	4	5
G 1	5	3	6	D 2	4
A 2	4	6	5	1	3
6	2	5	E 4	3	1
4	3	H 1	2	5	6

Top-left cell reads "5 1".

Section 12.1 Practice Exercises, pp. 848–851

3. $2x^2 + 4x + 1$ **5.** $6x^3 + x^2 + 5x - 2$
7. $18x^2 - 9x + 3$ **9.** $g^{-1} = \{(5, 3), (1, 8), (9, -3), (2, 0)\}$
11. $r^{-1} = \{(3, a), (6, b), (9, c)\}$ **13.** The function is not one-to-one. **15.** Yes **17.** No **19.** Yes
21. $h^{-1}(x) = x - 4$ **23.** $m^{-1}(x) = 3(x + 2)$
25. $p^{-1}(x) = -x + 10$ **27.** $f^{-1}(x) = \sqrt[3]{x - 1}$
29. $g^{-1}(x) = \dfrac{x^3 + 1}{2}$ **31.** $g^{-1}(x) = \sqrt{x - 9}$
33. a. 1.2192 m, 15.24 m **b.** $f^{-1}(x) = \dfrac{x}{0.3048}$ **c.** 4921.3 ft
35. False **37.** True **39.** False **41.** True **43.** $(b, 0)$
45. a. Domain $[1, \infty)$, range $[0, \infty)$ **b.** Domain $[0, \infty)$, range $[1, \infty)$ **47. a.** $[-4, 0]$ **b.** $[0, 2]$ **c.** $[0, 2]$ **d.** $[-4, 0]$

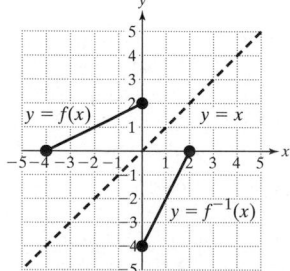

49. a. $[0, 2]$ **b.** $[0, 4]$ **c.** $[0, 4]$ **d.** $[0, 2]$

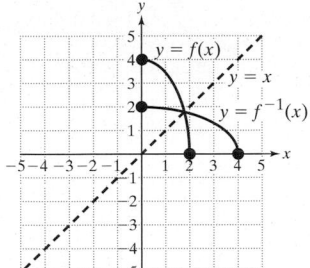

51. a. $(f \circ g)(x) = 6\left(\dfrac{x - 1}{6}\right) + 1 = x$

b. $(g \circ f)(x) = \dfrac{(6x + 1) - 1}{6} = x$

53. a. $(f \circ g)(x) = \dfrac{\sqrt[3]{8x^3}}{2} = x$ **b.** $(g \circ f)(x) = 8\left(\dfrac{\sqrt[3]{x}}{2}\right)^3 = x$

55. a. $(f \circ g)(x) = (\sqrt{x - 1})^2 + 1 = x$

b. $(g \circ f)(x) = \sqrt{(x^2 + 1) - 1} = x$

57. $q^{-1}(x) = x^2 - 4, \; x \geq 0$ **59.** $z^{-1}(x) = x^2 - 4, x \leq 0$

61. $f^{-1}(x) = \dfrac{x + 1}{1 - x}$ **63.** $t^{-1}(x) = \dfrac{x + 2}{x}$

65. $n^{-1}(x) = -\sqrt{x - 9}$

Section 12.1 Graphing Calculator Exercises, p. 851

67. $f^{-1}(x) = x^3 - 5$ **68.** $k^{-1}(x) = \sqrt[3]{x} + 4$

 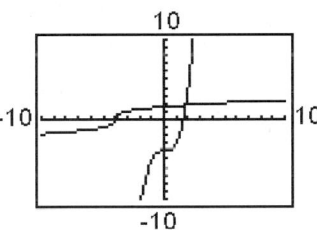

69. $g^{-1}(x) = \sqrt[3]{2x + 4}$ **70.** $m^{-1}(x) = \dfrac{x + 4}{3}$

 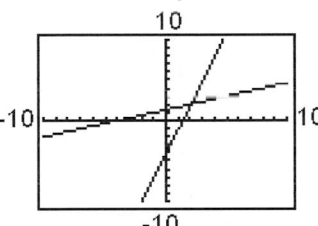

Section 12.2 Practice Exercises, pp. 857–860

3. $\{0, -2, 1, 3\}$ **5.** Yes **7.** $\{0, -2, 1, 3\}$

9. 25 **11.** $\dfrac{1}{1000}$ **13.** 6 **15.** 8 **17.** 5.8731

19. 1385.4557 **21.** 0.0063 **23.** 0.8950

25. a. $x = 2$ **b.** $x = 3$ **c.** Between 2 and 3

27. a. $x = 4$ **b.** $x = 5$ **c.** Between 4 and 5

29. $f(0) = 1, f(1) = \dfrac{1}{5}, f(2) = \dfrac{1}{25}, f(-1) = 5, f(-2) = 25$

31. $h(0) = 1, h(1) = 3, h(-1) = \dfrac{1}{3}, h(\sqrt{2}) \approx 4.73,$

$h(\pi) \approx 31.54$ **33.** If $b > 1$, the graph is increasing. If $0 < b < 1$, the graph is decreasing.

35.

37.

39.

41.

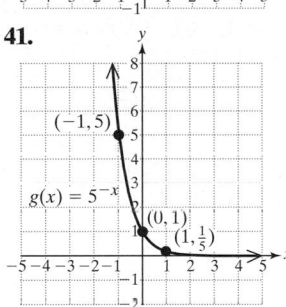

43. a. 0.25 g **b.** ≈ 0.16 g **45. a.** 758,000 **b.** 379,000

c. 144,000 **47. a.** $P(t) = 153,000,000(1.0125)^t$

b. $P(41) \approx 255,000,000$ **49. a.** $1640.67 **b.** $2691.80

c. $A(0) = 1000$. The initial amount of the investment is \$1000. $A(7) = 2000$. The amount of the investment doubles in 7 yr.

Section 12.2 Graphing Calculator Exercises, p. 860

51.

52.

53.

54.

55.

56.

57.

58.

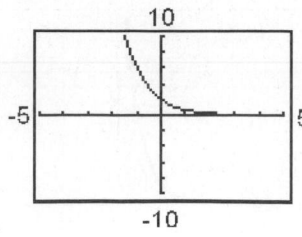

Section 12.3 Practice Exercises, pp. 869–873

3. i

5. a. $s(-2) = \dfrac{25}{4}, s(-1) = \dfrac{5}{2}, s(0) = 1, s(1) = \dfrac{2}{5}, s(2) = \dfrac{4}{25}$

b.

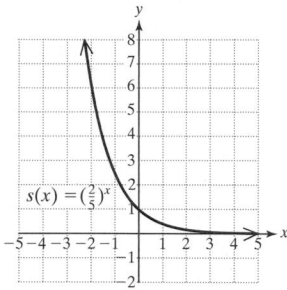

7. $g(-2) = \dfrac{1}{9}, g(-1) = \dfrac{1}{3}, g(0) = 1, g(1) = 3, g(2) = 9$

9. $b^y = x$ **11.** $5^4 = 625$ **13.** $10^{-4} = 0.0001$

15. $6^2 = 36$ **17.** $b^x = 15$ **19.** $3^x = 5$

21. $\left(\dfrac{1}{4}\right)^{10} = x$ **23.** $\log_3 81 = x$ **25.** $\log_5 25 = 2$

27. $\log_7\left(\dfrac{1}{7}\right) = -1$ **29.** $\log_b y = x$ **31.** $\log_e y = x$

33. $\log_{1/3} 9 = -2$ **35.** 2   **37.** −1   **39.** $\dfrac{1}{2}$ **41.** 0

43. 5   **45.** 1   **47.** 3   **49.** $\dfrac{1}{2}$ **51.** 1   **53.** 3

55. 6   **57.** −2   **59.** 0.7782   **61.** 0.4971

63. −1.5051   **65.** −2.2676   **67.** 5.5315

69. −7.4202   **71. a.** Slightly less than 2   **b.** Slightly more than 1   **c.** $\log 93 \approx 1.9685$, $\log 12 \approx 1.0792$

73. a. $f\left(\dfrac{1}{64}\right) = -3, f\left(\dfrac{1}{16}\right) = -2, f\left(\dfrac{1}{4}\right) = -1, f(1) = 0,$
$f(4) = 1, f(16) = 2, f(64) = 3$

b.

75. $3^y = x$

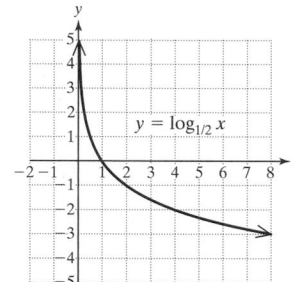

x	y
$\frac{1}{9}$	−2
$\frac{1}{3}$	−1
1	0
3	1
9	2

77. $\left(\dfrac{1}{2}\right)^y = x$

x	y
4	−2
2	−1
1	0
$\frac{1}{2}$	1
$\frac{1}{4}$	2

79. $(5, \infty)$ **81.** $(-\infty, 2)$ **83.** $\left(\dfrac{1}{3}, \infty\right)$ **85.** $(-1.2, \infty)$

87. $(-\infty, 2)$ **89.** $(-\infty, 0) \cup (0, \infty)$ **91.** ≈ 7.35

93. a.

t (months)	0	1	2	6	12	24
$S_1(t)$	91	82.0	76.7	65.6	57.6	49.1
$S_2(t)$	88	83.5	80.8	75.3	71.3	67.0

b. Group 1: 91; Group 2: 88   **c.** Method II

Section 12.3 Graphing Calculator Exercises, p. 873

95. Domain: $(-6, \infty)$; asymptote: $x = -6$

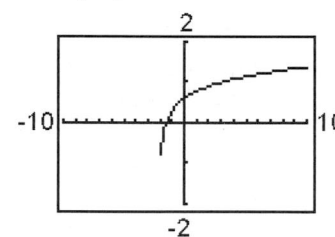

96. Domain: $(-2, \infty)$; asymptote: $x = -2$

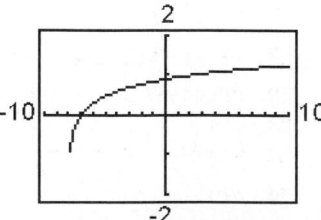

97. Domain: $(2, \infty)$; asymptote: $x = 2$

98. Domain: $(-8, \infty)$; asymptote: $x = -8$

99. Domain: $(-\infty, 2)$; asymptote: $x = 2$

100. Domain: $(-\infty, 3)$; asymptote: $x = 3$

c. They are equivalent for all x in the intersection of their domains, $(0, \infty)$.

92. a. Domain: $(-\infty, 1) \cup (1, \infty)$ **b.** Domain: $(1, \infty)$

c. They are equivalent for all x in the intersection of their domains, $(1, \infty)$.

Chapter 12 Problem Recognition Exercises, p. 874

1. e   **2.** l   **3.** j   **4.** g   **5.** c   **6.** a
7. k   **8.** b   **9.** i   **10.** h   **11.** f   **12.** d

Section 12.4 Practice Exercises, pp. 880–883

3. 4   **5.** $\dfrac{1}{6}$ **7.** 0.9031   **9.** 5.0475   **11.** a
13. c   **15.** a, b, c   **17.** 1   **19.** 4   **21.** 11   **23.** 3
25. 0   **27.** 9   **29.** 0   **31.** 3   **33.** 1   **35.** $2x$
37. 4   **39.** 0   **41.** Expressions a and c are equivalent.
43. Expressions a and c are equivalent.
45. $\log_3 x - \log_3 5$ **47.** $\log 2 + \log x$ **49.** $4\log_5 x$
51. $\log_4 a + \log_4 b - \log_4 c$
53. $\dfrac{1}{2}\log_b x + \log_b y - 3\log_b z - \log_b w$
55. $\log_2 (x + 1) - 2\log_2 y - \dfrac{1}{2}\log_2 z$
57. $\dfrac{1}{3}\log a + \dfrac{2}{3}\log b - \dfrac{1}{3}\log c$ **59.** $-5\log w$
61. $\dfrac{1}{2}\log_b a - 3 - \log_b c$ **63.** 3   **65.** $\log_3\left(\dfrac{x^2 z}{y^3}\right)$
67. $\log_3\left(\dfrac{a^2 c}{\sqrt[4]{b}}\right)$ **69.** $\log_b x^2$
71. $\log_8 (8a^5)$ or $\log_8 a^5 + 1$ **73.** $\log\left[\dfrac{(x + 6)^2 \sqrt[3]{y}}{z^5}\right]$
75. $\log_b\left(\dfrac{1}{x - 1}\right)$ **77.** 1.792   **79.** 2.485   **81.** 4.396
83. 0.916   **85.** 13.812   **87.** 16.09
89. a. $B = 10\log I - 10\log I_0$ **b.** $10\log I + 160$

Section 12.4 Graphing Calculator Exercises, p. 883

91. a. Domain: $(-\infty, 0) \cup (0, \infty)$ **b.** Domain: $(0, \infty)$

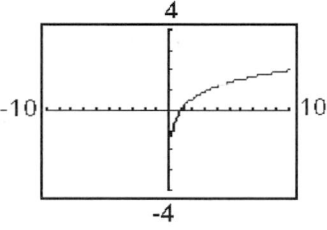

Section 12.5 Practice Exercises, pp. 891–895

3. $\log_3\left(\dfrac{a\sqrt{d}}{c^5}\right)$ **5.** $\dfrac{1}{4}\log_6 x + \dfrac{1}{2}\log_6 y - \dfrac{3}{4}\log_6 z$

7.

x	y
-4	0.05
-3	0.14
-2	0.37
-1	1
0	2.72
1	7.39

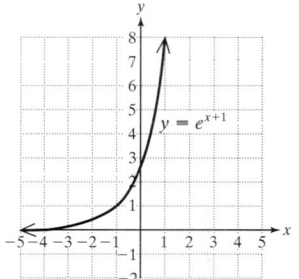

Domain: $(-\infty, \infty)$

9.

x	y
-2	2.14
-1	2.37
0	3
1	4.72
2	9.39
3	22.09

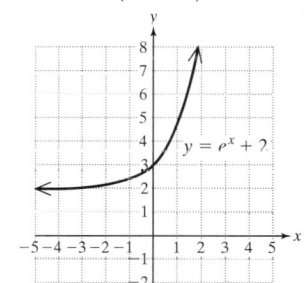

Domain: $(-\infty, \infty)$

11. a. \$12,209.97   **b.** \$13,488.50   **c.** \$14,898.46   **d.** \$16,050.09
An investment grows more rapidly at higher interest rates.
13. a. \$12,423.76   **b.** \$12,515.01   **c.** \$12,535.94   **d.** \$12,546.15
e. \$12,546.50   More money is earned at a greater number of compound periods per year.   **15. a.** \$6920.15   **b.** \$9577.70
c. \$13,255.84   **d.** \$18,346.48   **e.** \$35,143.44   More money is earned over a longer period of time.

17.

x	y
2.25	-1.39
2.50	-0.69
2.75	-0.29
3	0
4	0.69
5	1.10
6	1.39

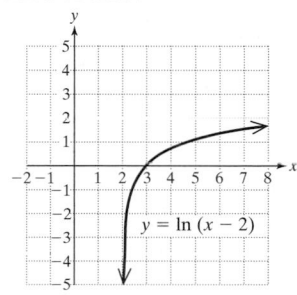

Domain: $(2, \infty)$

19.

x	y
0.25	-2.39
0.5	-1.69
0.75	-1.29
1	-1.00
2	-0.31
3	0.10
4	0.39

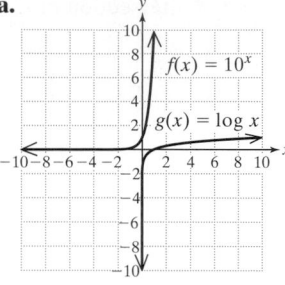

$y = \ln x - 1$

Domain: $(0, \infty)$

21. a.

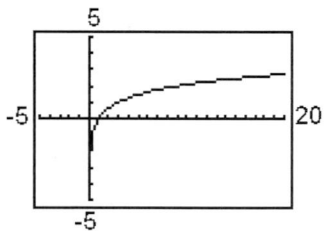

$f(x) = 10^x$

$g(x) = \log x$

b. Domain: $(-\infty, \infty)$; range: $(0, \infty)$
c. Domain: $(0, \infty)$; range: $(-\infty, \infty)$ **23.** 1   **25.** 0

27. -6 **29.** $2x + 3$ **31.** $\ln\left(p^6 \sqrt[3]{q}\right)$ **33.** $\ln\sqrt{\dfrac{x}{y^3}}$

35. $\ln\left(\dfrac{a^2}{b\sqrt[3]{c}}\right)$ **37.** $\ln\left(\dfrac{x^4}{y^3 z}\right)$ **39.** $2\ln a - 2\ln b$

41. $2\ln b + 1$ **43.** $4\ln a + \dfrac{1}{2}\ln b - \ln c$

45. $\dfrac{1}{5}\ln a + \dfrac{1}{5}\ln b - \dfrac{2}{5}\ln c$ **47. a.** 2.9570 **b.** 2.9570
c. They are the same. **49.** 2.8074 **51.** 1.5283
53. -2.1269 **55.** 0 **57.** -3.3219 **59.** -3.8124
61. a. 15.4 yr **b.** 6.9 yr **c.** 13.8 yr **63. a.** 19.8 yr
b. 13.9 yr **c.** 27.8 yr

Section 12.5 Graphing Calculator Exercises, pp. 895–896

65. a–b

c. They appear to be the same.
66. a–b

c. They appear to be the same.

67. **68.**

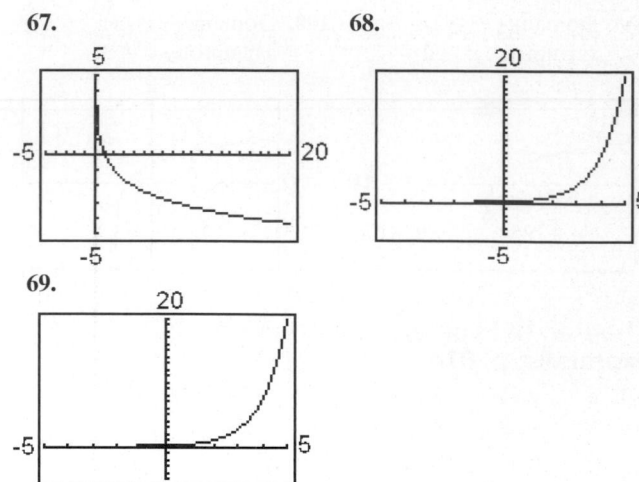

69.

Chapter 12 Problem Recognition Exercises, p. 896

	Exponential Form	Logarithmic Form
1.	$2^5 = 32$	$\log_2 32 = 5$
2.	$3^4 = 81$	$\log_3 81 = 4$
3.	$z^y = x$	$\log_z x = y$
4.	$b^c = a$	$\log_b a = c$
5.	$10^3 = 1000$	$\log 1000 = 3$
6.	$10^1 = 10$	$\log 10 = 1$
7.	$e^a = b$	$\ln b = a$
8.	$e^q = p$	$\ln p = q$
9.	$\left(\frac{1}{2}\right)^2 = \frac{1}{4}$	$\log_{1/2}\left(\frac{1}{4}\right) = 2$
10.	$\left(\frac{1}{3}\right)^{-2} = 9$	$\log_{1/3} 9 = -2$
11.	$10^{-2} = 0.01$	$\log 0.01 = -2$
12.	$10^x = 4$	$\log 4 = x$
13.	$e^0 = 1$	$\ln 1 = 0$
14.	$e^1 = e$	$\ln e = 1$
15.	$25^{1/2} = 5$	$\log_{25} 5 = \frac{1}{2}$
16.	$16^{1/4} = 2$	$\log_{16} 2 = \frac{1}{4}$
17.	$e^t = s$	$\ln s = t$
18.	$e^r = w$	$\ln w = r$
19.	$15^{-2} = \frac{1}{225}$	$\log_{15}\left(\frac{1}{225}\right) = -2$
20.	$3^{-1} = p$	$\log_3 p = -1$

Section 12.6 Practice Exercises, pp. 905–909

3. $\log_b\left[x(2x + 3)\right]$ **5.** $\log_b\left(\dfrac{x + 2}{3x - 5}\right)$ **7.** $\{9\}$

9. $\{10^{42}\}$ **11.** $\{e^{0.08}\}$ **13.** $\{10^{-9.2} - 40\}$ **15.** $\{5\}$
17. $\{10\}$ **19.** $\{25\}$ **21.** $\{59\}$ **23.** $\{1\}$ **25.** $\{0\}$

27. $\left\{-\dfrac{37}{9}\right\}$ **29.** $\{3\}$ (The value -3 does not check.)

31. $\{4\}$ **33.** $\{3\}$ **35.** $\{2\}$ **37.** $\{\ \}$ (The value -3 does not check.) **39.** $\{4\}$ **41.** $\{-6\}$

43. $\left\{\dfrac{1}{2}\right\}$ **45.** $\{2\}$ **47.** $\left\{\dfrac{11}{12}\right\}$ **49.** $\{1\}$

51. $\left\{\dfrac{4}{19}\right\}$ **53.** $\{-2, 1\}$ **55.** $\left\{\dfrac{\ln 21}{\ln 8}\right\}$

57. $\{\ln 8.1254\}$ **59.** $\{\log 0.0138\}$ **61.** $\left\{\dfrac{\ln 15}{0.07}\right\}$

63. $\left\{\dfrac{\ln 3}{1.2}\right\}$ **65.** $\left\{\dfrac{\ln 3}{\ln 5 - \ln 3}\right\}$ **67.** $\left\{\dfrac{2\ln 2}{\ln 6 - \ln 2}\right\}$

69. $\left\{\dfrac{\ln 4}{0.04}\right\}$ **71.** $\left\{3\ln\left(\dfrac{125}{6}\right)\right\}$ **73.** $\left\{\dfrac{\ln 20}{\ln 5} + 2\right\}$

75. a. ≈ 1285 million (or 1,285,000,000) people **b.** ≈ 1466.5 million (or 1,466,500,000) people **c.** The year 2049 ($t \approx 50.8$) **77. a.** 500 bacteria **b.** ≈ 660 bacteria **c.** ≈ 25 min **79.** It will take 9.9 yr for the investment to double. **81. a.** 7.8 g **b.** 18.5 days **83.** The intensity of sound of heavy traffic is $10^{-3.07}$ W/m². **85.** It will take 38.4 yr. **87. a.** 1.42 kg **b.** No **89.** $[10^5, 10^{-3}]$

91. $\left\{\dfrac{1}{27}, \dfrac{1}{9}\right\}$

Section 12.6 Graphing Calculator Exercises, p. 909

93.

94.

Chapter 12 Review Exercises, pp. 915–918

1. No **2.** Yes **3.** $\{(5, 3), (9, 2), (-1, 0), (1, 4)\}$

4. $q^{-1}(x) = \dfrac{4}{3}(x + 2)$ **5.** $f^{-1}(x) = \sqrt[3]{x} + 1$

6. $n^{-1}(x) = \dfrac{2x + 4}{x}$

7. $(f \circ g)(x) = 5\left(\dfrac{1}{5}x + \dfrac{2}{5}\right) - 2 = x + 2 - 2 = x$

$(g \circ f)(x) = \dfrac{1}{5}(5x - 2) + \dfrac{2}{5} = x - \dfrac{2}{5} + \dfrac{2}{5} = x$

8. The graphs are symmetric about the line $y = x$.

9. a. Domain: $[-1, \infty)$; range: $[0, \infty)$ **b.** Domain: $[0, \infty)$ range: $[-1, \infty)$ **10.** $p^{-1}(x) = (x - 2)^2, x \geq 2$

11. 1024 **12.** $\dfrac{1}{36} \approx 0.028$ **13.** 2 **14.** 10

15. 8.825 **16.** 16.242 **17.** 1.627 **18.** 0.681

19.

20.

21.

22.

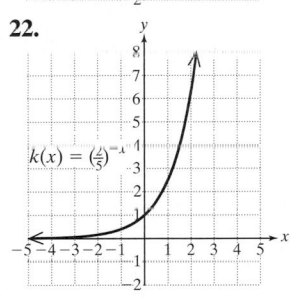

23. a. Horizontal **b.** $y = 0$ **24. a.** 15,000 mrem **b.** 3750 mrem **c.** Yes **25.** -3 **26.** 0 **27.** 1 **28.** 8 **29.** 4 **30.** 4 **31.** 5 **32.** -1

33.

34.

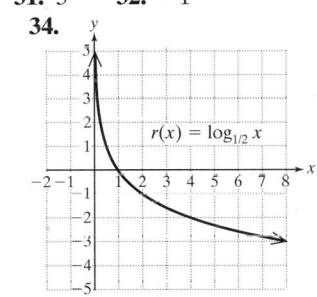

35. a. Vertical asymptote **b.** $x = 0$ **36. a.** 2.5 **b.** 9.5 **37.** 1 **38.** 6 **39.** 0 **40.** 7

41. a. $\log_b x + \log_b y$ **b.** $\log_b\left(\dfrac{x}{y}\right)$ **c.** $p \log_b x$

42. a. 1 **b.** x **c.** 0 **43.** $\log_b\left(\dfrac{\sqrt[4]{x^3 y}}{z}\right)$

44. $\log_3\left(\dfrac{\sqrt{ab}}{c^2 d^4}\right)$ **45.** $\log 5$ **46.** 0 **47.** b

48. a **49.** 148.4132 **50.** 14.0940 **51.** 32.2570 **52.** 57.2795 **53.** 1.7918 **54.** -2.1972 **55.** 1.3424 **56.** 1.3029 **57.** 3.3219 **58.** 1.9943 **59.** -0.8370 **60.** -3.6668 **61. a.** \$33,361.92 **b.** \$33,693.90 **c.** \$33,770.48 **d.** \$33,809.18 **62. a.** $S(0) = 95$; the student's score is 95 at the end of the course. **b.** $S(6) \approx 23.7$; the student's score is 23.7 after 6 months. **c.** $S(12) \approx 20.2$; the student's score is 20.2 after 1 yr. **63.** $(-\infty, \infty)$ **64.** $(-\infty, \infty)$ **65.** $(-\infty, \infty)$

66. $(0, \infty)$ **67.** $(-5, \infty)$ **68.** $(7, \infty)$ **69.** $\left(\dfrac{4}{3}, \infty\right)$

70. $(-\infty, 5)$ **71.** $\{125\}$ **72.** $\left\{\dfrac{1}{49}\right\}$ **73.** $\{216\}$

74. $\{3^{1/12}\}$ **75.** $\left\{\dfrac{1001}{2}\right\}$ **76.** $\{9\}$

77. $\{5\}$ (The value -2 does not check.)   **78.** $\left\{\dfrac{190}{321}\right\}$

79. $\{-1\}$ **80.** $\left\{\dfrac{4}{7}\right\}$ **81.** $\left\{\dfrac{\ln 21}{\ln 4}\right\}$ **82.** $\left\{\dfrac{\ln 18}{\ln 5}\right\}$

83. $\{-\ln 0.1\}$ **84.** $\left\{-\dfrac{\ln 0.06}{2}\right\}$ **85.** $\left\{\dfrac{\log 1512}{2}\right\}$

86. $\left\{\dfrac{\log 821}{3}\right\}$ **87.** $\left\{\dfrac{3\ln 2}{\ln 7 - \ln 2}\right\}$

88. $\left\{\dfrac{5\ln 14}{\ln 14 - \ln 6}\right\}$ **89. a.** $1.09\ \mu g$ **b.** $0.15\ \mu g$

c. 16.08 days   **90. a.** 150 bacteria   **b.** ≈ 185 bacteria
c. ≈ 99 min   **91. a.** $V(0) = 15{,}000$; the initial value of the
car is \$15,000.   **b.** $V(10) = 3347$; the value of the car after 10
years is \$3347.   **c.** 7.3 yr

Chapter 12 Test, pp. 918–920

1. A function is one-to-one if it passes the horizontal
line test.   **2.** b   **3.** $f^{-1}(x) = 4x - 12$
4. $g^{-1}(x) = \sqrt{x} + 1$
5.

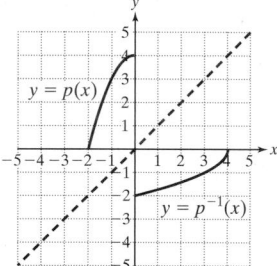

6. a. 4.6416   **b.** 32.2693   **c.** 687.2913
7.

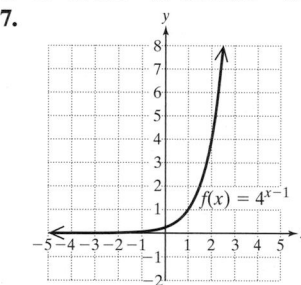

8. a. $\log_{16} 8 = \dfrac{3}{4}$ **b.** $x^5 = 31$

9.

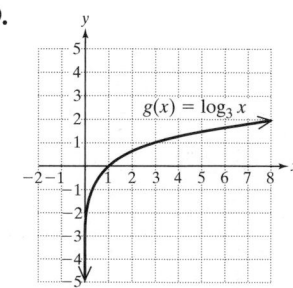

10. $\dfrac{\log_a n}{\log_a b}$ **11. a.** 1.3222   **b.** 1.8502   **c.** -2.5850
12. a. $1 + \log_3 x$ **b.** -5 **13. a.** $\log_b(\sqrt{x}y^3)$

b. $\log\left(\dfrac{1}{a^3}\right)$ or $-\log a^3$ **14. a.** 1.6487   **b.** 0.0498

c. -1.0986 **d.** 1   **15. a.** $y = \ln x$ **b.** $y = e^x$
16. a. $p(4) \approx 59.8$; 59.8% of the material is retained after
4 months.   **b.** $p(12) \approx 40.7$; 40.7% of the material is retained
after 1 yr.   **c.** $p(0) = 92$; 92% of the material is retained at
the end of the course.   **17. a.** $A(10{,}000) \approx 1300$. The
mean online enrollment for an institution of 10,000 students
is approximately 1300 students.   **b.** $A(20{,}000) \approx 5990$.
The mean online enrollment for an institution of 20,000
students is approximately 5990 students.
18. a. $P(0) = 300$; there are 300 bacteria initially.
b. 35,588 bacteria   **c.** 1,120,537 bacteria   **d.** 1,495,831
bacteria   **19.** $\{25\}$ (The value -4 does not check.)

20. $\{32\}$ **21.** $\{e^{2.4} - 7\}$ **22.** $\{-7\}$ **23.** $\left\{\dfrac{\ln 50}{\ln 4}\right\}$

24. $\left\{\dfrac{\ln 250}{2.4}\right\}$ **25.** $\left\{\dfrac{\ln 58}{\ln 2} + 3\right\}$ **26.** $\left\{\dfrac{7\ln 4}{\ln 5 - \ln 4}\right\}$

27. a. $P(2500) = 560.2$; at 2500 m the atmospheric pressure
is 560.2 mm Hg.   **b.** 760 mm Hg   **c.** 1498.8 m
28. a. \$2909.98   **b.** 9.24 yr to double

Chapters 1–12 Cumulative Review Exercises, pp. 920–922

1. $-\dfrac{5}{4}$ **2.** $-1 + \dfrac{p}{2} + \dfrac{3p^3}{4}$ **3.** Quotient:

$t^3 + 2t^2 - 9t - 18$; remainder: 0   **4.** $|x - 3|$

5. $\dfrac{2\sqrt[3]{25}}{5}$ **6.** $2\sqrt{7}$ in.   **7.** $\dfrac{4d^{1/10}}{c}$

8. $(\sqrt{15} - \sqrt{6} + \sqrt{30} - 2\sqrt{3})$ m^2 **9.** $-\dfrac{7}{29} - \dfrac{26}{29}i$

10. $\left\{6, \dfrac{3}{2}\right\}$ **11.** 4.8 L   **12.** 24 min   **13.** $\{(7, -1)\}$

14. $\left\{-\dfrac{23}{11}\right\}$ **15.** $x = \dfrac{c + d}{a - b}$ **16.** $t = \dfrac{\sqrt{2sg}}{g}$

17. $\left\{\dfrac{4 \pm \sqrt{34}}{3}\right\}$ **18.** $(7, 0), (3, 0)$
19. a. $-30t$ **b.** $-10t^2$ **c.** $2t^2 + 5t$ **20.** $\{0\}$

21. a. $x = 2$ **b.** $y = 6$ **c.** $y = \dfrac{1}{2}x + 5$

22. $40°, 80°, 60°$ **23.** $\{(-2, 3, -1)\}$

24. $\left[\dfrac{1}{2}, \infty\right)$ **25.** $f^{-1}(x) = \dfrac{1}{5}x + \dfrac{2}{15}$ **26.** 40 m^3

27. $\dfrac{-x^2 + 5x - 25}{(2x + 1)(x - 2)}$ **28.** $1 + x$ **29. a.** Yes;

$x \neq 4, x \neq -2$ **b.** $\{8\}$ **c.** $(-\infty, -2) \cup (4, 8]$

30. The numbers are $-\dfrac{3}{4}, 4$.   **31.** $\{-4\}$ (The value -9

does not check.)   **32.** $(-\infty, \infty)$
33. a. $P(6) = 2{,}000{,}000$, $P(12) = 1{,}000{,}000$, $P(18) = 500{,}000$,
$P(24) = 250{,}000$, $P(30) = 125{,}000$ **b.** 48 hr
34. a. 2   **b.** -3 **c.** 6   **d.** 3   **35. a.** 217.0723
b. 23.1407   **c.** 0.1768   **d.** 3.7293   **e.** -0.4005 **f.** 2.6047

36. $\left\{\dfrac{2}{3}\right\}$ **37.** $\{\ln 100\}$ **38.** $\{3\}$ (The value -9

does not check.)   **39.** $\log\left(\dfrac{\sqrt{z}}{x^2y^3}\right)$ **40.** $\dfrac{2}{3}\ln x - \dfrac{1}{3}\ln y$

Chapter 13

Chapter Opener Puzzle

$$\underset{5}{C}\ \underset{4}{O}\ \underset{6}{N}\ \underset{3}{I}\ \underset{5}{C}\quad \underset{1}{S}\ \underset{7}{E}\ \underset{5}{C}\ \underset{2}{T}\ \underset{3}{I}\ \underset{4}{O}\ \underset{6}{N}\ \underset{1}{S}$$

Section 13.1 Practice Exercises, pp. 929–934

3. $3\sqrt{5}$ **5.** $\sqrt{34}$ **7.** $\dfrac{\sqrt{73}}{8}$ **9.** 4   **11.** 8
13. $4\sqrt{2}$ **15.** $\sqrt{42}$ **17.** Subtract 5 and -7. This becomes $5-(-7)=12$.   **19.** $y=13, y=1$
21. $x=0, x=8$ **23.** Yes   **25.** No
27. Center $(4,-2); r=3$ **29.** Center $(-1,-1); r=1$

31. Center $(0,2); r=2$ **33.** Center $(3,0); r=2\sqrt{2}$

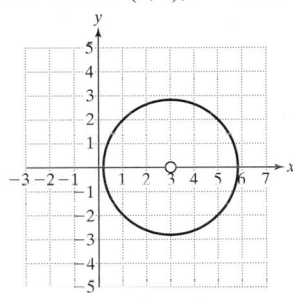

35. Center $(0,0); r=\sqrt{6}$ **37.** Center $\left(-\dfrac{4}{5},0\right); r=\dfrac{8}{5}$

39. Center $(1,3); r=6$ **41.** Center: $(0,3); r=2$

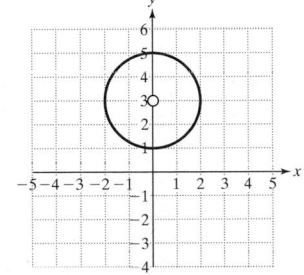

43. Center $(0,-3); r=\dfrac{4}{3}$ **45.** Center: $(-1,-2); r=3$

47. Center $(0,0); r=1$

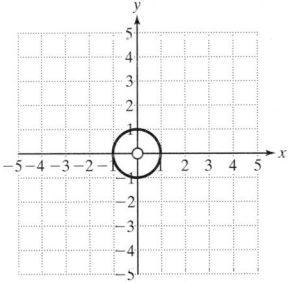

49. $x^2+y^2=4$ **51.** $x^2+(y-2)^2=4$
53. $(x+2)^2+(y-2)^2=9$ **55.** $x^2+y^2=49$
57. $(x+3)^2+(y+4)^2=36$
59. $(1,2)$ **61.** $(-1,0)$ **63.** $(-1,6)$ **65.** $(0,3)$
67. $\left(-\dfrac{1}{2},\dfrac{3}{2}\right)$ **69.** $(-0.4,-1)$ **71.** $(1,3)$
73. $(40, 7\frac{1}{2})$; they should meet 40 mi east, $7\frac{1}{2}$ mi north of the warehouse.   **75.** $x^2+(y-3)^2=4$
77. $(x-4)^2+(y-4)^2=16$

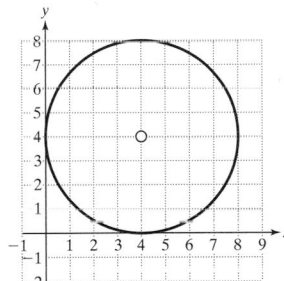

79. $(x-1)^2+(y-1)^2=29$

Section 13.1 Graphing Calculator Exercises, p. 934

81.

82.

83.

84.

85.

86.

17.

19.

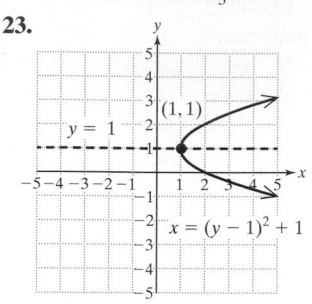

Section 13.2 Practice Exercises, pp. 941–944

3. 5

5. Center: $(0, -1)$; radius: 4

7. $\left(\dfrac{11}{2}, 1\right)$

9.

11.

13.

15.

21.

23.

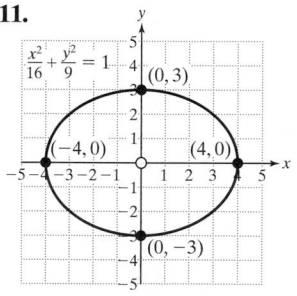

25. $(2, -1)$ **27.** $(5, -1)$ **29.** $\left(2, \dfrac{7}{4}\right)$ **31.** $\left(\dfrac{3}{2}, -\dfrac{1}{4}\right)$

33. $(10, -1)$ **35.** The maximum height of the water is 22 ft.

37. A parabola whose equation is in the form $y = a(x - h)^2 + k$ has a vertical axis of symmetry. A parabola whose equation is in the form $x = a(y - k)^2 + h$ has a horizontal axis of symmetry.

39. Vertical axis of symmetry; opens upward

41. Vertical axis of symmetry; opens downward

43. Horizontal axis of symmetry; opens right

45. Horizontal axis of symmetry; opens left

47. Vertical axis of symmetry; opens downward

49. Horizontal axis of symmetry; opens right

Section 13.3 Practice Exercises, pp. 949–953

3. Center: $(8, -6)$; radius: 10

5. Vertex: $(-3, -1)$; $x = -3$

7. $\left(x - \dfrac{1}{2}\right)^2 + \left(y - \dfrac{5}{2}\right)^2 = \dfrac{1}{4}$

9.

11.

13.

15.

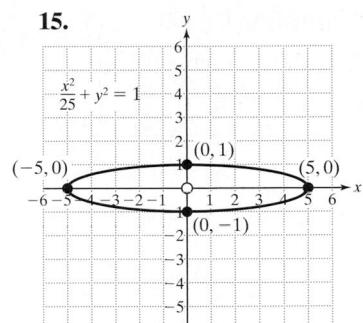

$\frac{x^2}{25} + y^2 = 1$

17. Center: $(4, 5)$ **19.** Center: $(-1, 2)$

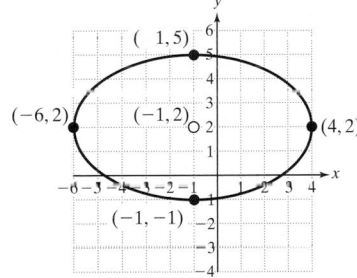

21. Center: $(2, -3)$ **23.** Center: $(0, 1)$

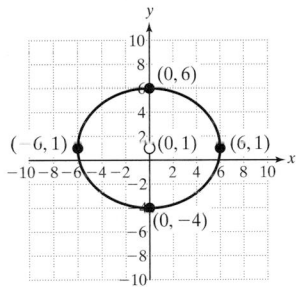

25. Vertical   **27.** Horizontal   **29.** Horizontal
31. Vertical
33.

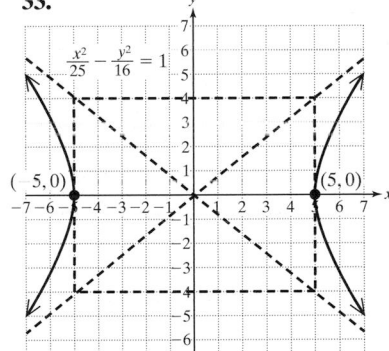

$\frac{x^2}{25} - \frac{y^2}{16} = 1$

35.

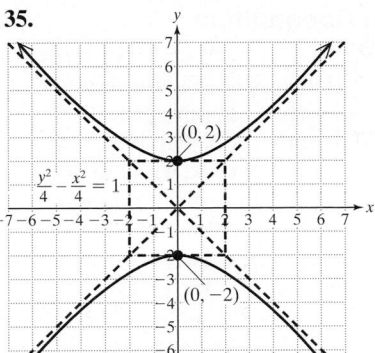

$\frac{y^2}{4} - \frac{x^2}{4} = 1$

37.

$x^2 - \frac{y^2}{36} = 1$

39.

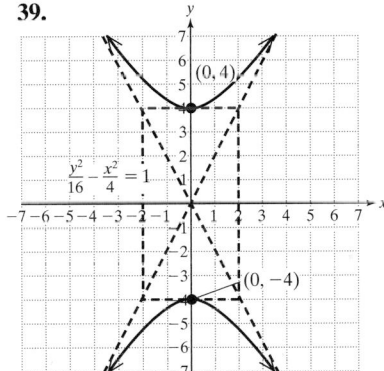

$\frac{y^2}{16} - \frac{x^2}{4} = 1$

41. Hyperbola   **43.** Ellipse
45. Ellipse   **47.** Hyperbola
49. Ellipse   **51.** Hyperbola
53. The height 10 ft from the center is approximately 49 ft.
55.

57.

Chapter 13 Problem Recognition Exercises, pp. 953–954

1. Standard equation of a circle **2.** Ellipse centered at the origin **3.** Distance between two points
4. Midpoint between two points **5.** Parabola with vertical axis of symmetry **6.** Hyperbola with horizontal transverse axis **7.** Hyperbola with vertical transverse axis
8. Parabola with horizontal axis of symmetry
9. Parabola **10.** Parabola **11.** Circle **12.** Circle
13. Hyperbola **14.** Hyperbola **15.** Circle
16. Circle **17.** Parabola **18.** Parabola **19.** Ellipse
20. Ellipse **21.** Circle **22.** Hyperbola
23. Parabola **24.** Ellipse **25.** Hyperbola
26. Circle **27.** Ellipse **28.** Parabola

Section 13.4 Practice Exercises, pp. 958–961

3. $7\sqrt{2}$ **5.** $(x + 5)^2 + (y - 3)^2 = 64$ **7.** $\left(-\dfrac{1}{2}, -\dfrac{7}{2}\right)$

9. Zero, one, or two **11.** Zero, one, or two
13. Zero, one, two, three, or four **15.** Zero, one, two, three, or four
17. $\{(-3, 0), (2, 5)\}$ **19.** $\{(0, 1), (-1, 0)\}$

  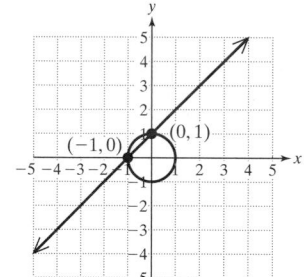

21. $\{(\sqrt{2}, 2), (-\sqrt{2}, 2)\}$

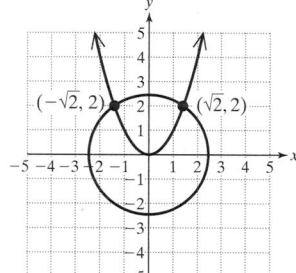

23. $\{(4, 2)\}$ **25.** $\{(0, 0)\}$ **27.** $\left\{\left(\dfrac{3}{2}, \dfrac{9}{4}\right)\right\}$

29. $\{(0, 0), (-2, -8)\}$ **31.** $\{(1, 4)\}$
33. $\{(1, 0), (-1, 0)\}$ **35.** $\{(2, 0), (-2, 0)\}$
37. $\{(3, 2), (-3, 2), (3, -2), (-3, -2)\}$
39. $\{(8, 6), (-8, -6)\}$ **41.** $\{(0, -2), (0, 2)\}$
43. $\{(2, 0), (0, 1)\}$ **45.** $\{(4, 5), (-4, -5)\}$
47. $\left\{\left(-\sqrt{2}, \dfrac{\sqrt{2}}{2}\right), \left(\sqrt{2}, -\dfrac{\sqrt{2}}{2}\right)\right\}$ **49.** 3 and 4
51. 5 and $\sqrt{7}$, -5 and $\sqrt{7}$, 5 and $-\sqrt{7}$, or -5 and $-\sqrt{7}$

Section 13.4 Graphing Calculator Exercises, p. 961

53. $\{(-3, 0), (2, 5)\}$

54. $\{(-3, -5), (2, 0)\}$

55. $\{(0, 0)\}$

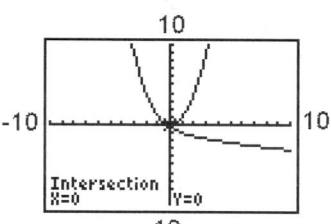

56. $\{(0, 0), (1, -1)\}$

  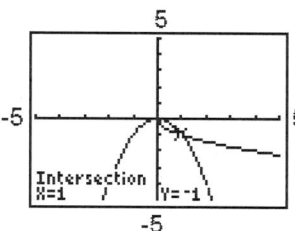

57. $\{\ \}$ **58.** $\{\ \}$

  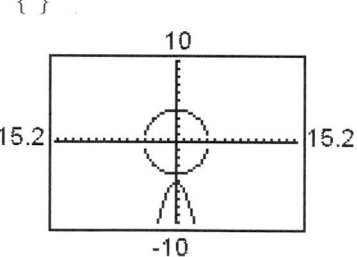

Section 13.5 Practice Exercises, pp. 964–969

1. k **3.** e **5.** i **7.** j **9.** a **11.** d
13. True **15.** False
17. a.

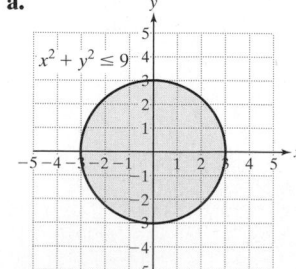

b. The set of points on and "outside" the circle $x^2 + y^2 = 9$
c. The set of points on the circle $x^2 + y^2 = 9$

19. a.

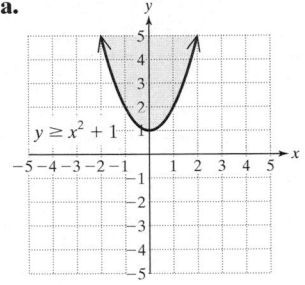

b. The parabola $y = x^2 + 1$ would be drawn as a dashed curve.

21. $(x - 3)^2 + (y + 4)^2 \leq 625$

23.

25.

27.

29.

31.

33.

35.

37.

39.

41.

43.

45.

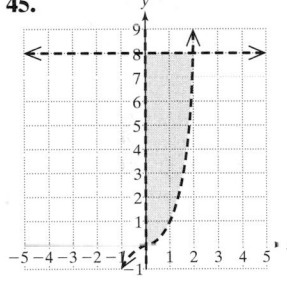

47. $\{ \ \}$

49.

51.

53.

55.

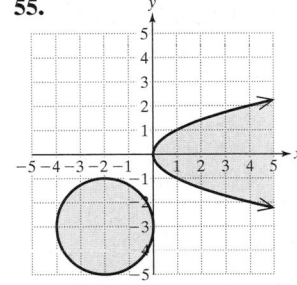

Chapter 13 Review Exercises, pp. 976–979

1. $2\sqrt{10}$ **2.** $\sqrt{89}$ **3.** $x = 5$ or $x = -1$

4. $x = -3$ **5.** Center $(12, 3); r = 4$

6. Center $(-7, 5); r = 9$ **7.** Center $(-3, -8); r = 2\sqrt{5}$

8. Center $(1, -6); r = 4\sqrt{2}$ **9. a.** $x^2 + y^2 = 64$

b. $(x - 8)^2 + (y - 8)^2 = 64$ **10.** $(x + 6)^2 + (y - 5)^2 = 10$

11. $(x + 2)^2 + (y + 8)^2 = 8$

12. $\left(x - \dfrac{1}{2}\right)^2 + (y - 2)^2 = 4$

13. $(x - 3)^2 + \left(y - \dfrac{1}{3}\right)^2 = 9$ **14.** $x^2 + y^2 = \dfrac{49}{4}$

15. $x^2 + (y - 2)^2 = 9$ **16.** $(-4, -2)$ **17.** $(-1, 8)$

18. Vertical axis of symmetry; parabola opens downward

19. Horizontal axis of symmetry; parabola opens right

20. Horizontal axis of symmetry; parabola opens left

21. Vertical axis of symmetry; parabola opens upward

22.

23.

24.

25.
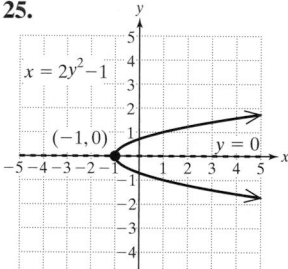

26. $y = (x - 3)^2 - 4$; vertex: $(3, -4)$; axis of symmetry: $x = 3$

27. $x = (y + 2)^2 - 2$; vertex: $(-2, -2)$; axis of symmetry: $y = -2$

28. $x = -4\left(y - \dfrac{1}{2}\right)^2 + 1$; vertex: $\left(1, \dfrac{1}{2}\right)$;

axis of symmetry: $y = \dfrac{1}{2}$

29. $y = -2\left(x + \dfrac{1}{2}\right)^2 + \dfrac{1}{2}$; vertex: $\left(-\dfrac{1}{2}, \dfrac{1}{2}\right)$;

axis of symmetry: $x = -\dfrac{1}{2}$

30.

31.

32. Center: $(5, -3)$

33. Center: $(0, 2)$
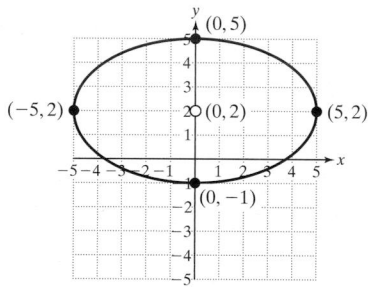

34. Horizontal   **35.** Vertical

36. Vertical   **37.** Horizontal

38.

39.
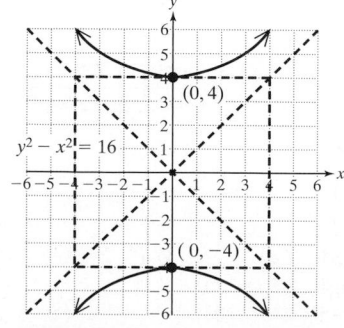

40. Hyperbola   **41.** Ellipse
42. Ellipse   **43.** Hyperbola
44. a. Line and parabola

b.

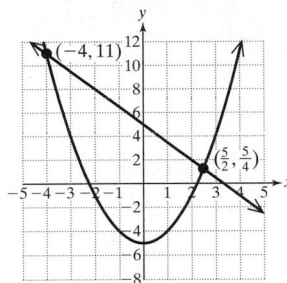

c. $\left\{\left(\dfrac{5}{2}, \dfrac{5}{4}\right), (-4, 11)\right\}$

45. a. Line and parabola

b.

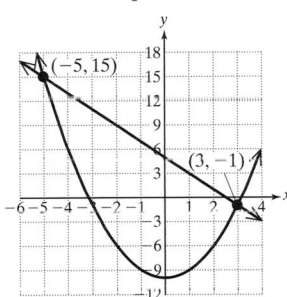

c. $\{(-5, 15), (3, -1)\}$

46. a. Circle and line

b.

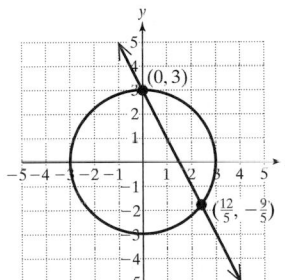

c. $\left\{(0, 3), \left(\dfrac{12}{5}, -\dfrac{9}{5}\right)\right\}$

47. a. Circle and line

b.

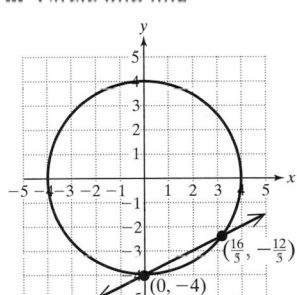

c. $\left\{(0, -4), \left(\dfrac{16}{5}, -\dfrac{12}{5}\right)\right\}$

48. $\left\{(0, -2), \left(\dfrac{16}{9}, \dfrac{14}{9}\right)\right\}$ **49.** $\left\{\left(-\dfrac{7}{5}, \dfrac{13}{5}\right), (-5, -1)\right\}$

50. $\{(8, 4), (2, -2)\}$ **51.** $\{(2, 4), (-2, 4), (\sqrt{2}, 2), (-\sqrt{2}, 2)\}$

52. $\{(3, 1), (3, -1), (-3, 1), (-3, -1)\}$

53. $\{(6, 5), (-6, 5), (6, -5), (-6, -5)\}$

54.

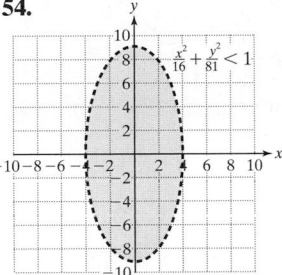

$\dfrac{x^2}{16} + \dfrac{y^2}{81} < 1$

55.

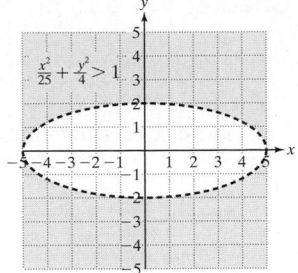

$\dfrac{x^2}{25} + \dfrac{y^2}{4} > 1$

56.

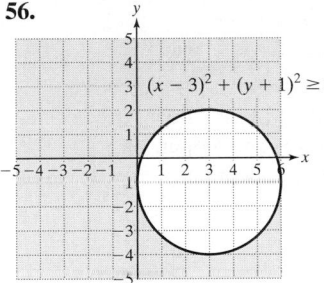

$(x - 3)^2 + (y + 1)^2 \geq 9$

57.

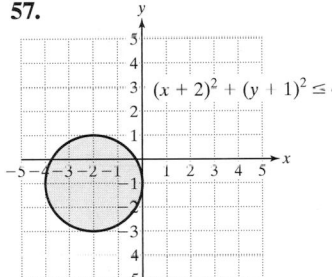

$(x + 2)^2 + (y + 1)^2 \leq 4$

58.

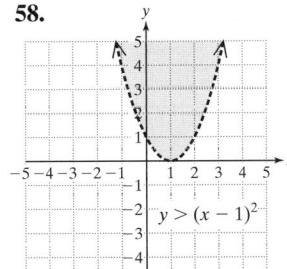

$y > (x - 1)^2$

59.

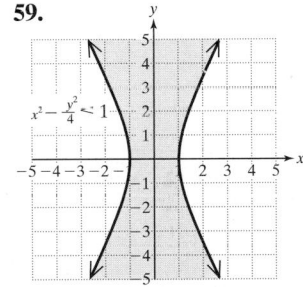

$x^2 - \dfrac{y^2}{4} < 1$

60.

61.

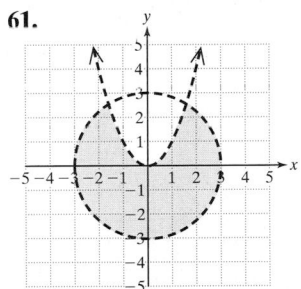

Chapter 13 Test, pp. 979–980

1. $2\sqrt{10}$ **2.** Center: $\left(\dfrac{5}{6}, -\dfrac{1}{3}\right)$; $r = \dfrac{5}{7}$

3. Center: $(0, 2)$; $r = 3$ **4. a.** $\sqrt{5}$ **b.** $x^2 + (y - 4)^2 = 5$

5. The center is the midpoint $(3.8, 1.95)$.

6.

7.

8.

9.

10.

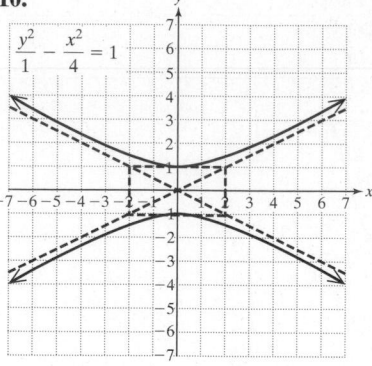

11. $\{(-3, 0), (0, 4)\}$; graph b   **12.** $\{\ \}$; graph a

13. The addition method can be used if the equations have corresponding *like* terms.   **14.** $\{(2, 0), (-2, 0)\}$

15.

16.

17.

18.

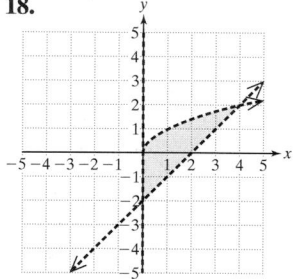

Chapters 1–13 Cumulative Review Exercises, pp. 981–982

1. $\{x \mid x \text{ is a real number}\}$

2. $\left(\dfrac{10}{3}, \infty\right)$

3. $10, 15$ **4. a.** $(-5, 0), (0, 3)$ **b.** $m = \dfrac{3}{5}$

c.

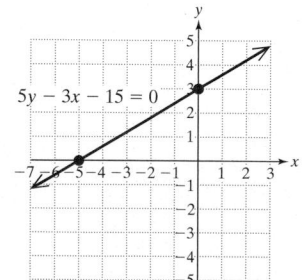

5. slope: $\frac{3}{4}$; y-intercept: $\left(0, -\frac{3}{2}\right)$ **6.** 12 dimes, 5 quarters

7. $\{(2, -3, 1)\}$ **8.** $\left\{\left(\frac{5}{2}, \frac{3}{2}\right)\right\}$ **9.** $\{ \ \}$

10. $f(0) = -12; f(-1) = -16; f(2) = -10; f(4) = -16$

11. $(-4, -2)$ **12.** $z = 32$ **13.** $(g \circ f)(x) = x + 7$;
$x \geq -1$ **14. a.** -5 **b.** $(x + 1)(x^2 + 1)$; -5
c. They are the same.   **15.** $(x + y)(x - y - 6)$

16. $x^3 - 2x^2 - 7x - 4$ **17.** $\left\{6, \frac{3}{2}\right\}$ **18.** $\frac{a - 1}{a + 2}$

19. $\frac{-x^2 - x - 4}{(x + 3)(x - 2)}$ **20.** $\{0, -1\}$ **21. a.** $\{ \ \}$

b. $\{-11\}$ **22.** $-30 + 24i$ **23.** $\frac{12}{41} + \frac{15}{41}i$

24. $2\sqrt{7}$ m   **25. a.** 17.6 ft; 39.6 ft; 70.4 ft   **b.** 8 sec

26. $\left\{-\frac{1}{5}, \frac{1}{10} \pm \frac{\sqrt{3}}{10}i\right\}$ **27.** $\{2 \pm \sqrt{11}\}$

28. $(-5, -36)$

29. a. $(-3, 0), (1, 0)$ **b.** $(0, 3)$ **c.** $(-1, 4)$

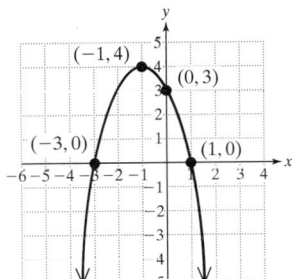

30. $(-1, 19)$ **31.** $\left(-\infty, \frac{1}{2}\right] \cup \left[\frac{9}{2}, \infty\right)$ **32.** $\log_8 32 = \frac{5}{3}$

33. $\left\{\frac{2}{3}\right\}$ **34.** $h^{-1}(x) = \sqrt[3]{x + 1}$

35. $x^2 + (y - 5)^2 = 16$

36.

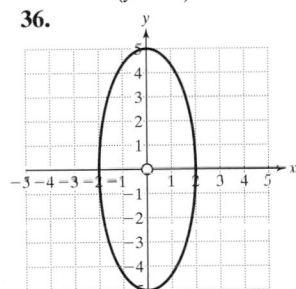

37. $\left(-\frac{1}{2}, 0\right)$ **38.** $\{(0, -4)\}$

39.

40.

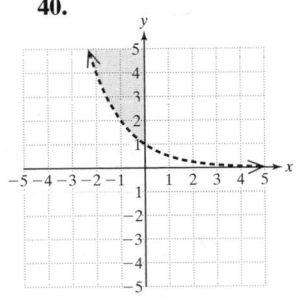

Chapter 14
Chapter Opener Puzzle

1. $13, 16, 19$ **2.** $-26, -34, -42$ **3.** $48, 96, 192$
4. $\frac{1}{9}, \frac{1}{27}, \frac{1}{81}$ **5.** $25, 36, 49$ **6.** $-324, 972, -2916$
7. x^3y^4, x^2y^5, xy^6 **8.** a^5b^4, a^4b^5, a^3b^6
9. $a^2 + 2ab + b^2$ **10.** $a^3 + 3a^2b + 3ab^2 + b^3$
11. $n + 1$

Section 14.1 Practice Exercises, pp. 989–990

3. $a^3 + 3a^2b + 3ab^2 + b^3$ **5.** $1 + 4g + 6g^2 + 4g^3 + g^4$
7. $p^7 + 7p^6q^2 + 21p^5q^4 + 35p^4q^6 + 35p^3q^8 + 21p^2q^{10} + 7pq^{12} + q^{14}$ **9.** $625 - 500u^3 + 150u^6 - 20u^9 + u^{12}$
11. 120   **13.** 1   **15.** False   **17.** True
19. $6! = 6 \cdot (5 \cdot 4 \cdot 3 \cdot 2 \cdot 1) = 6 \cdot 5!$ **21.** 1680
23. 6   **25.** 56   **27.** 1   **29.** $m^{11} + 11m^{10}n + 55m^9n^2$
31. $u^{24} - 12u^{22}v + 66u^{20}v^2$ **33.** 9 terms
35. $s^6 + 6s^5t + 15s^4t^2 + 20s^3t^3 + 15s^2t^4 + 6st^5 + t^6$
37. $b^3 - 9b^2 + 27b - 27$ **39.** $16x^4 + 32x^3y + 24x^2y^2 + 8xy^3 + y^4$ **41.** $c^{14} - 7c^{12}d + 21c^{10}d^2 - 35c^8d^3 + 35c^6d^4 - 21c^4d^5 + 7c^2d^6 - d^7$

43. $\frac{1}{32}a^5 - \frac{5}{16}a^4b + \frac{5}{4}a^3b^2 - \frac{5}{2}a^2b^3 + \frac{5}{2}ab^4 - b^5$

45. $-462m^6n^5$ **47.** $495u^{16}v^4$ **49.** g^9

Section 14.2 Practice Exercises, pp. 996–998

3. 28   **5.** $16x^4 + 32x^3z + 24x^2z^2 + 8xz^3 + z^4$

7. $4, 7, 10, 13$ **9.** $\sqrt{3}, 2, \sqrt{5}, \sqrt{6}$ **11.** $-\frac{2}{3}, \frac{3}{4}, -\frac{4}{5}, \frac{5}{6}$

13. $0, -3, 8, -15$ **15.** $0, 2, 6, 12$ **17.** $-3, 9, -27, 81$
19. When n is odd, the term is negative. When n is even, the term is positive.   **21.** $a_n = 2n$ **23.** $a_n = 2n - 1$

25. $a_n = \frac{1}{n^2}$ **27.** $a_n = (-1)^{n+1}$ **29.** $a_n = (-1)^n 2^n$

31. $a_n = \frac{3}{5^n}$ **33.** \$60, \$58.80, \$57.62, \$56.47

35. $25{,}000; 50{,}000; 100{,}000; 200{,}000; 400{,}000; 800{,}000; 1{,}600{,}000$
37. A sequence is an ordered list of terms. A series is the sum of the terms of a sequence.

39. 90   **41.** $\frac{31}{16}$ **43.** 30   **45.** 10   **47.** $\frac{73}{12}$ **49.** 38

51. -1 **53.** 55   **55.** $\sum_{n=1}^{6} n$ **57.** $\sum_{i=1}^{5} 4$ **59.** $\sum_{j=1}^{5} 4j$

61. $\sum_{k=1}^{4} (-1)^{k+1} \frac{1}{3^k}$ **63.** $\sum_{n=1}^{5} x^n$

65. $-3, 2, 7, 12, 17$ **67.** $5, 21, 85, 341, 1365$
69. $1, 1, 2, 3, 5, 8, 13, 21, 34, 55$

Section 14.3 Practice Exercises, pp. 1002–1004

3. $-1, 1, -1, 1$ **5.** -55 **7.** 2   **9.** -3

11. -2 **13.** $3, 8, 13, 18, 23$ **15.** $2, \frac{5}{2}, 3, \frac{7}{2}, 4$

17. $2, -2, -6, -10, -14$ **19.** $a_n = -5 + 5n$

21. $a_n = -2n$ **23.** $a_n = \frac{3}{2} + \frac{1}{2}n$ **25.** $a_n = 25 - 4n$

27. $a_n = -14 + 6n$ **29.** $a_6 = 17$ **31.** $a_9 = 47$

33. $a_7 = -30$ **35.** $a_{11} = -48$ **37.** 19   **39.** 22
41. 23   **43.** 11   **45.** $a_1 = -2, a_2 = -5$ **47.** 670
49. 290   **51.** -15 **53.** 95   **55.** 924   **57.** 300
59. -210 **61.** 5050   **63.** 980 seats; $14,700

Section 14.4 Practice Exercises, pp. 1009–1012

3. $a_n = 4n - 8$ **5.** 25   **7.** 2   **9.** $-\dfrac{1}{4}$ **11.** -2

13. $-3, 6, -12, 24, -48$ **15.** $6, 3, \dfrac{3}{2}, \dfrac{3}{4}, \dfrac{3}{8}$

17. $-1, -6, -36, -216, -1296$ **19.** $a_n = 3(4)^{n-1}$

21. $a_n = -5(-3)^{n-1}$ **23.** $a_n = \frac{1}{2}(4)^{n-1}$ **25.** $\dfrac{1}{64}$

27. $-\dfrac{243}{8}$ **29.** -48 **31.** -9 **33.** $\dfrac{1}{8}$ **35.** 4

37. A geometric sequence is an ordered list of numbers in which the ratio between each term and its predecessor is constant. A geometric series is the sum of the terms of such a sequence.

39. $\dfrac{1562}{125}$ **41.** $-\dfrac{11}{8}$ **43.** $\dfrac{3124}{27}$ **45.** $\dfrac{665}{243}$

47. -172 **49. a.** $1050.00, $1102.50, $1157.63, $1215.51
b. $a_{10} = $1628.89; a_{20} = $2653.30; a_{40} = 7039.99

51. $r = \dfrac{1}{6}; \dfrac{6}{5}$ **53.** $r = -\dfrac{1}{3}; -\dfrac{9}{4}$

55. $r = -\dfrac{3}{2};$ sum does not exist

57. The sum is $800 million.   **59.** The total vertical distance traveled is 28 ft.

61. a. $\dfrac{7}{10}$ **b.** $\dfrac{1}{10}$ **c.** $\dfrac{7}{9}$ **63. a.** $1,429,348
b. $1,505,828   **c.** $76,480

Chapter 14 Problem Recognition Exercises, p. 1012

1. Geometric, $r = -\dfrac{1}{2}$ **2.** Geometric, $r = -\dfrac{3}{2}$

3. Arithmetic, $d = \dfrac{1}{2}$ **4.** Arithmetic, $d = \dfrac{2}{3}$

5. Geometric, $r = 2$ **6.** Geometric, $r = 3$
7. Arithmetic, $d = -2$ **8.** Arithmetic, $d = 4$
9. Neither   **10.** Neither   **11.** Neither
12. Neither   **13.** Geometric, $r = -1$
14. Geometric, $r = -1$

Chapter 14 Review Exercises, pp. 1017–1018

1. 40,320   **2.** 120   **3.** 66   **4.** 84
5. $x^{10} + 20x^8 + 160x^6 + 640x^4 + 1280x^2 + 1024$
6. $c^4 - 12c^3d + 54c^2d^2 - 108cd^3 + 81d^4$
7. $a^{11} - 22a^{10}b + 220a^9b^2$ **8.** $1512x^{10}y^3$
9. $-15,000x^3y^{21}$ **10.** $160a^3b^3$ **11.** $1, -2, -5, -8, -11$
12. $-2, -16, -54$ **13.** $\dfrac{1}{3}, -\dfrac{1}{2}, \dfrac{3}{5}, -\dfrac{2}{3}$ **14.** $\dfrac{2}{3}, \dfrac{4}{9}, -\dfrac{8}{27}, \dfrac{16}{81}$

15. $a_n = \dfrac{n}{n+1}$ **16.** $a_n = (-1)^n \cdot \dfrac{3}{2^n}$ **17.** k **18.** 5

19. 5   **20.** -22 **21.** $\displaystyle\sum_{i=1}^{7} \dfrac{3+i}{i}$ **22.** $a_n = n^2 + \left(\dfrac{n}{2}\right)h$

23. $-12, -10.5, -9, -7.5, -6$ **24.** $\dfrac{2}{3}, 1, \dfrac{4}{3}, \dfrac{5}{3}, 2$

25. $a_n = 10n - 9$ **26.** $a_n = -14n + 20$ **27.** $a_{17} = \dfrac{9}{2}$

28. $a_{25} = -155$ **29.** 24 terms   **30.** 19 terms
31. $d = 10$ **32.** $a_n = -5n + 19$ **33.** -620
34. 92.5   **35.** 294   **36.** 5989   **37.** $r = 3$

38. $r = 1.2$ **39.** $-1, \dfrac{1}{4}, -\dfrac{1}{16}, \dfrac{1}{64}$ **40.** 10, 20, 40, 80

41. $a_n = -4(2)^{n-1}$ **42.** $a_n = 6\left(-\dfrac{1}{3}\right)^{n-1}$ **43.** $a_6 = \dfrac{128}{243}$

44. $a_4 = 270$ **45.** $a_1 = 4$ **46.** $a_1 = 1$ **47.** 1275

48. $-\dfrac{182}{3}$ **49.** 18   **50.** $\dfrac{25}{2}$

51. a. $10,700, $11,449, $12,250.43   **b.** The account is worth $12,250.43 after 3 yr.   **c.** $19,671.51

Chapter 14 Test, pp. 1018–1019

1. 1   **2.** 210   **3.** $a^4 + 4a^3b + 6a^2b^2 + 4ab^3 + b^4$
4. $81y^4 - 216y^3x^2 + 216y^2x^4 - 96yx^6 + 16x^8$

5. $-56a^3c^{15}$ **6.** $-1, -\dfrac{3}{4}, -\dfrac{3}{5}, -\dfrac{1}{2}$ **7.** 65

8. a. $8, 9.5, 11, 12.5, 14$ **b.** $a_n = 1.5n + 6.5$ **9.** $\displaystyle\sum_{n=1}^{4} x^{3n}$

10. $d = \dfrac{1}{4}$ **11.** $r = \dfrac{1}{3}$ **12. a.** $-15, -18, -21, -24$

b. $a_n = -3n - 12$ **c.** $a_{40} = -132$ **13. a.** $4, -8, 16, -32$

b. $a_n = 4(-2)^{n-1}$ **c.** -2048 **14.** $a_n = \dfrac{3}{5} \cdot \left(\dfrac{1}{2}\right)^{n-1}$

15. $a_n = -2n + 22$ **16.** 31 terms   **17.** 7 terms

18. 10,900   **19.** $\dfrac{1023}{64}$ **20.** 8   **21.** $a_1 = \dfrac{1}{27}$

22. $a_{18} = -202$ **23. a.** $1095   **b.** $1160.70
c. $5933.13   **d.** $86,568.71

Chapters 1–14 Cumulative Review Exercises, pp. 1020–1021

1. $x^2 - x - 13$ **2.** $\dfrac{20a^6}{b^{10}}$ **3.** $\dfrac{1}{16}$ **4.** $\dfrac{\sqrt{10}}{2}$

5. $\dfrac{2c+5}{2(c+4)}$ **6.** $-\dfrac{xy}{x+y}$ **7.** 4   **8.** $3xy^4\sqrt[3]{2x^2z^2}$

9. $-\dfrac{a+1}{a}$ **10.** $\dfrac{2x+5}{(x-5)(x-2)(x+10)}$ **11.** $7x^2\sqrt{2x}$

12. $x - 9y$ **13.** $2x^3 + 3x^2 + 6x + 17 + \dfrac{27}{x-2}$

14. $(2a - 7)(3a + 2)$ **15.** $3c(5c - 2)(5c + 2)$
16. $(3x + 4y^2)(9x^2 - 12xy^2 + 16y^4)$
17. $(w + 9)(w - 2)(w + 2)$ **18.** $\{4\}$ **19.** $\{0\}$

20. $\left\{\dfrac{5}{4}\right\}$ **21.** $\left\{\dfrac{2}{5} \pm \dfrac{\sqrt{3}}{5}i\right\}$ **22.** $\{4, -4, 1, -1\}$

23. $\left\{\dfrac{7}{2}, -\dfrac{3}{4}\right\}$ **24.** $\{1\}$ **25.** $\{2\}$ (The value -5 does not check.)   **26.** $\ln\left(\dfrac{x\sqrt{z}}{y^5}\right)$ **27.** 3.4929

28. $[-2, 5)$ **29.** $[-5, 0] \cup [1, \infty)$ **30.** $\{5\}$
31. $(-\infty, -4) \cup [-1, \infty)$ **32.** $(-\infty, 1) \cup (3, \infty)$

33.

34.

35.

36.
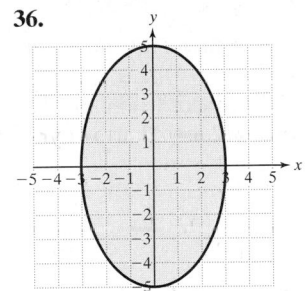

37. a. $(-1, 0), (-5, 0)$ **b.** $(0, 5)$ **c.** $(-3, -4)$
38. slope -4; y-intercept $(0, 6)$ **39.** $y = -5x + 18$
40. a. 2 **b.** undefined **c.** $x = 2$ **d.** $(-\infty, 4)$ **e.** $(-\infty, 3]$
41. $(-\infty, 5]$ **42.** $\{(3, -1)\}$ **43.** $\{(1, 2, 3)\}$
44. a. $2\sqrt{13}$ **b.** $(6, -2)$ **45.** $b_1 = \dfrac{2A - hb_2}{h}$

46. $t(9) = 4.2$; This means that it will take the rat 4.2 min if the rat has practiced 9 times.   **47.** The car is moving 75 mph.   **48.** The angles are 57° and 123°.   **49.** She invested $8000 at 6.5% and $5000 at 5%.   **50.** The plane travels 500 mph in still air. The wind speed is 50 mph.

Additional Topics Appendix

Section A.1 Practice Exercises, pp. A-6–A-10
3. 5   **5.** 6   **7.** -15.8 **9.** 5.8 hr
11. a. 397 Cal **b.** 386 Cal **c.** There is only an 11-Cal difference in the means.   **13. a.** 86.5% **b.** 81%
c. The low score of 59% decreased Zach's average by 5.5%.
15. 17   **17.** 110.5   **19.** 52.5   **21.** 3.93 deaths per 1000   **23.** 0   **25.** 51.7 million passengers   **27.** 4
29. -21 and -24 **31.** No mode   **33.** $600
35. 5.2% and 5.8%   **37.** Mean: 85.5%; median: 94.5%; The median gave Jonathan a better overall score.
39. Mean: $250; median: $256; mode: There is no mode.
41. Mean: $942,500; median: $848,500; mode: $850,000
43. 2.38   **45.** 2.77   **47.** 3.3; Elmer's GPA improved from 2.5 to 3.3.
49.

Number of Residents in Each House	Number of Houses	Product
1	3	3
2	9	18
3	10	30
4	9	36
5	6	30
Total:	37	117

The mean number of residents is approximately 3.2.

Section A.2 Practice Exercises, pp. A-21–A-27
3. 32 m   **5.** 17.2 mi   **7.** $11\frac{1}{2}$ in.   **9.** 31.4 ft
11. a, f, g   **13.** 33 cm^2 **15.** 16.81 m^2 **17.** 84 in.^{2}
19. 10.12 km^2 **21.** 13.8474 ft^2 **23.** 66 in.^{2}
25. 31.5 ft^2 **27.** c, d, h   **29.** 307.72 cm^3
31. 39 in.^{3} **33.** 113.04 cm^3 **35.** 1695.6 cm^3
37. 3052.08 in.^{3} **39.** 113.04 cm^3
41. a. $0.25/ft^2 **b.** $104   **43.** Perimeter
45. 54 ft   **47. a.** 57,600 ft^2 **b.** 19,200 pieces
49. a. 50.24 in.^{2} **b.** 113.04 in.^{2} **c.** One 12-in. pizza
51. 289.3824 cm^3 **53.** True   **55.** True   **57.** True
59. Not possible   **61.** For example: 100°, 80°
63. 45°   **65. a.** $\angle 1$ and $\angle 3$, $\angle 2$ and $\angle 4$
b. $\angle 1$ and $\angle 2$, $\angle 2$ and $\angle 3$, $\angle 3$ and $\angle 4$, $\angle 1$ and $\angle 4$
c. $m(\angle 1) = 100°$, $m(\angle 2) = 80°$, $m(\angle 3) = 100°$
67. 57°   **69.** 78°   **71.** 147°   **73.** 58°
75. 7   **77.** 1   **79.** 1   **81.** 5
83. $m(\angle a) = 45°$, $m(\angle b) = 135°$, $m(\angle c) = 45°$, $m(\angle d) = 135°$, $m(\angle e) = 45°$, $m(\angle f) = 135°$, $m(\angle g) = 45°$
85. Scalene   **87.** Isosceles   **89.** True
91. No, a 90° angle plus an angle greater than 90° would make the sum of the angles greater than 180°.   **93.** 40°
95. 37°   **97.** $m(\angle a) = 80°$, $m(\angle b) = 80°$, $m(\angle c) = 100°$, $m(\angle d) = 100°$, $m(\angle e) = 65°$, $m(\angle f) = 115°$, $m(\angle g) = 115°$, $m(\angle h) = 35°$, $m(\angle i) = 145°$, $m(\angle j) = 145°$
99. $m(\angle a) = 70°$, $m(\angle b) = 65°$, $m(\angle c) = 65°$, $m(\angle d) = 110°$, $m(\angle e) = 70°$, $m(\angle f) = 110°$, $m(\angle g) = 115°$, $m(\angle h) = 115°$, $m(\angle i) = 65°$, $m(\angle j) = 70°$, $m(\angle k) = 65°$
101. 82 ft   **103.** 36 in.^{2} **105.** 15.2464 cm^2

Section A.3 Practice Exercises, pp. A-34–A-37
3. $\left\{\left(12, \dfrac{1}{2}\right)\right\}$ **5.** $\{(1, 3, -3)\}$
7. a. 3×1 **b.** column matrix
9. a. 2×2 **b.** square matrix   **11. a.** 1×4
b. row matrix   **13. a.** 2×3 **b.** none of these
15. $\begin{bmatrix} 1 & -2 & | & -1 \\ 2 & 1 & | & -7 \end{bmatrix}$ **17.** $\begin{bmatrix} 1 & -2 & 1 & | & 5 \\ 2 & 6 & 3 & | & -2 \\ 3 & -1 & -2 & | & 1 \end{bmatrix}$
19. $4x + 3y = 6$ **21.** $x = 4, y = -1, z = 7$
      $12x + 5y = -6$
23. a. 7 **b.** -2 **25.** $\begin{bmatrix} 1 & \frac{1}{2} & | & \frac{11}{2} \\ 2 & -1 & | & 1 \end{bmatrix}$
27. $\begin{bmatrix} 1 & -4 & | & 3 \\ 5 & 2 & | & 1 \end{bmatrix}$ **29.** $\begin{bmatrix} 1 & 5 & | & 2 \\ 0 & 11 & | & 5 \end{bmatrix}$
31. a. $\begin{bmatrix} 1 & 3 & 0 & | & -1 \\ 0 & -11 & -5 & | & 10 \\ -2 & 0 & -3 & | & 10 \end{bmatrix}$ **b.** $\begin{bmatrix} 1 & 3 & 0 & | & -1 \\ 0 & -11 & -5 & | & 10 \\ 0 & 6 & -3 & | & 8 \end{bmatrix}$
33. $\{(-3, -1)\}$ **35.** $\{(-21, 9)\}$ **37.** Infinitely many solutions; $\{(x, y) \mid x + 3y = 3\}$; dependent system
39. $\{(3, -1)\}$ **41.** $\{(-10, 3)\}$ **43.** $\{ \}$; inconsistent system   **45.** $\{(1, 2, 3)\}$ **47.** $\{(1, -2, 0)\}$
49. True   **51.** True   **53.** Interchange rows 1 and 2.
55. Multiply row 1 by -3 and add to row 2. Replace row 2 with the result.

Section A.3 Graphing Calculator Exercises, p. A-37

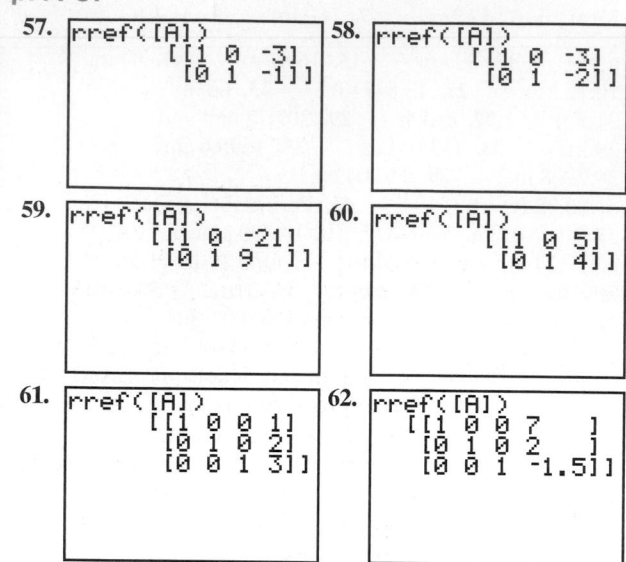

57.
```
rref([A])
    [[1 0 -3]
     [0 1 -1]]
```
58.
```
rref([A])
    [[1 0 -3]
     [0 1 -2]]
```
59.
```
rref([A])
    [[1 0 -21]
     [0 1 9  ]]
```
60.
```
rref([A])
    [[1 0 5]
     [0 1 4]]
```
61.
```
rref([A])
    [[1 0 0 1]
     [0 1 0 2]
     [0 0 1 3]]
```
62.
```
rref([A])
    [[1 0 0 7  ]
     [0 1 0 2  ]
     [0 0 1 -1.5]]
```

Section A.4 Practice Exercises, pp. A-45–A-48

3. 16   **5.** 1   **7.** 4   **9.** 6   **11.** 26   **13.** 6
15. 46   **17. a.** 30   **b.** 30   **19.** Choosing the row or column with the most zero elements simplifies the arithmetic when evaluating a determinant.
21. 12   **23.** −15   **25.** 0   **27.** $8a - 2b$
29. $4x - 3y + 6z$ **31.** 0
33. $D = 16; D_x = -63; D_y = 66$ **35.** $\{(2, -1)\}$
37. $\{(4, -1)\}$ **39.** $\left\{\left(\dfrac{23}{13}, \dfrac{9}{13}\right)\right\}$ **41.** $x = 1$
43. $z = \dfrac{1}{2}$ **45.** $y = \dfrac{16}{41}$
47. Cramer's rule does not apply when the determinant $D = 0$.
49. $\{\ \}$; inconsistent system   **51.** $\{(0, 0)\}$
53. Infinitely many solutions; $\{(x, y)\,|\,x + 5y = 3\}$; dependent system   **55.** $\{(3, 2, 1)\}$
57. $\{\ \}$; inconsistent system   **59.** $x = -19$
61. $w = 1$ **63.** 36   **65. a.** 2   **b.** −2   **c.** $x = -1$

Application Index

www

1 FV = 3000
   PV = $ 7000
   r = 8%.
   Find time.

2 PV @ 1000

   $ FV = PV $(1 + \frac{1}{n})$

   $ FV = 2500 $(1 + \frac{.7}{n})$

   FV = 1000 $(1 + 0.07)^{10}$

Subject Index

Perimeter and Circumference

Rectangle

$P = 2l + 2w$

Square

$P = 4s$

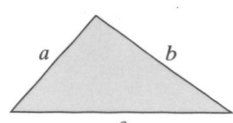

Triangle

$P = a + b + c$

Circle

Circumference: $C = 2\pi r$

Area

Rectangle

$A = lw$

Square

$A = s^2$

Parallelogram

$A = bh$

Triangle

$A = \frac{1}{2}bh$

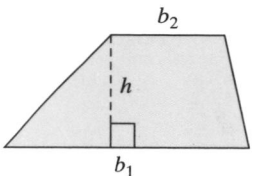

Trapezoid

$A = \frac{1}{2}(b_1 + b_2)h$

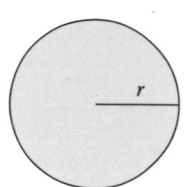

Circle

$A = \pi r^2$

Volume

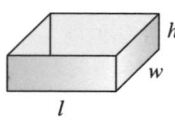

Rectangular Solid

$V = lwh$

Cube

$V = s^3$

Right Circular Cylinder

$V = \pi r^2 h$

Right Circular Cone

$V = \frac{1}{3}\pi r^2 h$

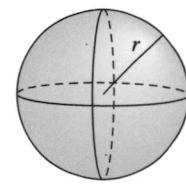

Sphere

$V = \frac{4}{3}\pi r^3$

Angles

- Two angles are **complementary** if the sum of their measures is 90°.

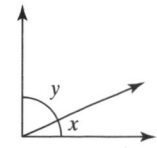

- $\angle a$ and $\angle c$ are vertical angles, and $\angle b$ and $\angle d$ are vertical angles. The measures of vertical angles are equal.

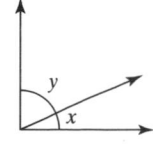

- Two angles are **supplementary** if the sum of their measures is 180°.

- The sum of the measures of the angles of a triangle is 180°.

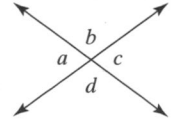

$x° + y° + z° = 180°$